Stanley Gibbons
STAMP CATALOGUE

Commonwealth & British Empire Stamps 1840–1952

(Formerly PART 1)

105th edition

Stanley Gibbons Ltd
London and Ringwood

By Appointment to Her Majesty The Queen
Stanley Gibbons Ltd, London
Philatelists

Published by **Stanley Gibbons Ltd**
Editorial, Publications Sales Offices and Distribution Centre:
Parkside, Christchurch Road, Ringwood,
Hants BH24 3SH.

ISBN: 0-85259-528-X

Item No. 2813 (03)

Text assembled by Black Bear Press Limited, Cambridge

Made and Printed in Great Britain by William Clowes Limited, Beccles, Suffolk

Preface to the 2003 Edition

THE WAY FORWARD

llectors will notice a major difference in this 3 edition of what was previously the *Part 1 talogue*.

)ue to the problems high-lighted in previous tions, it has been decided that this volume uld be limited to the stamps of the British pire and Commonwealth between 1840 and end of the reign of King George VI in 1952. know from the numerous letters received that ny collectors are now concentrating on stamps m this era, while continuing a limited number countries into the modern period.

To cater for those who require one-country ings, we have commenced a series of individual alogues, supplied punched for insertion into a neral binder and produced by modern digital thods. This series will be available with stamp strations in black/white or colour. Listings for lkland Islands (with Dependencies) and India cluding Convention States) have so far peared, with others to follow.

In addition, post-1952 Commonwealth stamps ve been specially repriced for the 2003 *Stamps the World* four-volume series. It is planned to lude miniature sheet listings in *Stamps of the orld* from the edition to be dated 2004.

We hope that these new formats will be lcomed by collectors. As our modern hnology expands it is our intention to entually offer a "bespoke service" so that lividual collectors can be provided with the untries they require, either in printed form or the Internet.

Countries in this volume have been re-arranged that they appear under the names current in 52. This means that British Guiana is used stead of Guyana, Ceylon instead of Sri Lanka d Nyasaland instead of Malawi. Those colonies nich subsequently formed parts of the larger minions are still, however, grouped together so at, for example, the Australian States precede ustralia. The only position which may be familiar is Labuan, which follows North Borneo it was part of that colony in 1952.

A complete two-page contents list appears in e Catalogue Introduction and there is a full dex at the end of the volume.

PRICES

he decision to restrict this volume to issues etween 1840–1952 has provided an opportunity review the prices of these stamps in even eater depth. There are many more alterations roughout the listings, with a number of items iced for the first time.

Trends tend to be generally upwards, although me countries and periods show more evidence this than others. Errors and varieties remain nerally popular, even for issues where there is ttle movement for the basic stamps. Good xamples of this trend can be found amongst the adge types of **Ascension** and **St. Helena** and on arious King George VI Key type issues.

The interest in the postal history aspect of amp collecting continues to grow. Prices for amps Used Abroad have risen considerably for **amaica** used in the **Cayman Islands**, **Hong Kong** sed in **China**, **India** used in the **Straits ettlements**, **Mauritius** used in the **Seychelles** and **ndia** used in **Zanzibar**.

As a general trend, price increases for King George VI issues are less spectacular than in the past, but there are exceptions such as the **Burma** 1937 overprinted series, **Cyrenaica** and the **Seychelles**. There is generally more movement in the period from the middle of Queen Victoria's reign to King George V, involving both major countries and more unusual areas.

There has been considerable work done on prices for **Australia**, much of which has been based on advice from Simon Dunkerley. Rises are particularly noticeable for **South Australia**, **Tasmania** and **Western Australia**, while those interested in the Australian territories will be pleased to learn that the **New Guinea** N.W.P.I. overprints punctured "OS", added to the listings last year, are now priced.

For **Canada**, the strong demand for issues of **Prince Edward Island** continues.

Interest in some of the West Indies islands continues to revive with **Barbados**, **British Guiana** and **Trinidad** receiving considerable attention this time.

The market in issues from Asia remains buoyant, with considerable movement for **Ceylon** after 1863, the Queen Victoria issues of **Straits Settlements** and also for both **North Borneo** and **Labuan**.

There are important changes for **Bechuanaland** and for a number of the provinces of **South Africa**.

Finally, from more often neglected areas, there is news of considerable increases for the **British Occupation of Baghdad** surcharges, and for the **Sudan** Official and Army Official stamps.

REVISIONS FOR THIS EDITION

Many more watermark varieties have been added to this edition, in particular to the listings for **Western Australia**, **Bahamas**, **Ceylon** (a new King George VI inverted), **Fiji**, **Natal** and **Trinidad**.

Further King George VI plate and cylinder flaws also appear for the first time, notably for **Aden**, **Falkland Islands**, **Fiji**, **Grenada** and **South Africa**.

The notes on forged postmarks for twentieth-century issues have also been expanded where the dates shown on the forgeries have been identified.

Australia. Much work has been undertaken on **New South Wales** following detailed comments supplied by the Australian States Study Circle. The listings from 1852 have been re-arranged and partly renumbered to provide a clearer chronological sequence.

Bahrain. Additional India stamps used in Bahrain have been included with the help of John Gillham.

Canada. A new discovery, the 2d. rose perforated 11 on yellowish paper, has been added to **Prince Edward Island**, following the research published by Alan Griffiths.

Fiji. Several previously unlisted items which featured in the recent "Evans" sale, have been added to the 1878–99 issue.

Hong Kong. The listing of King Edward VII inverted watermarks has been expanded, and the stamp booklet section completely rewritten, both from information supplied by Paul Campion. There are a number of new listings in both sections.

India. It has finally been possible to revise the shades for the 1911–22 De La Rue King George V definitives. A few values have not, so far, been dealt with, but the vast majority under India, the Convention States and elsewhere in the catalogue have had their colour description changed, amended and, in some instances, new items added. Of particular importance is the identification of a previously unlisted shade of the 1 r. in orange-brown and deep turquoise-green. Enlarged illustrations of examples showing the two processes found on the 9 p. of the 1932–36 series also appear for the first time, enabling the two stamps to be listed separately. The coverage of India inverted watermarks has been considerably expanded, with many of the new items reported by Björn Johnsson. There are also revisions to the **Jammu & Kashmir** 1866–76 stamps, based on suggestions received from Peter Röver. The **Soruth** 1932 Officials have been revised, as it is now agreed that values showing the previous Type O **3** overprint actually appeared first.

Malaya. Work on the Malaya-Borneo Exhibition stamps has been completed, with revisions for **Kelantan** and **Trengganu**, based on *Gibbons Stamp Monthly* articles by Keith Elliot.

New Zealand. Following the discovery of a genuine postally-used example from 1882, the 2s. "LAW COURTS" Postal Fiscal, deleted many years ago, has now been re-instated.

North Borneo. The overprinted Postage Dues between 1895 and 1931 have been completely rewritten based, with permission, on the monograph by Bruce Marshall, published by the Sarawak Specialist Society. The later issues in particular show many changes with the two types of overprints previously recorded in a footnote now given full listing.

Palestine. The settings and varieties of the 1st September 1920 issue, Nos. 16/29, have been revised and the varieties previously mentioned in the footnote are now included in the listing.

Omnibus Tables. These continue to appear at the end of the volume and have been revised to provide a clear guide as to which stamps are included in which issue.

Additionally there are, of course, many other corrections and new items throughout the catalogue and we are, once again, most grateful to all those collectors and dealers who have contributed.

DAVID J AGGERSBERG
Catalogue Editor

Stanley Gibbons Holdings Plc Addresses

STANLEY GIBBONS LIMITED, STANLEY GIBBONS AUCTIONS

399 Strand, London WC2R 0LX
Auction Room and Specialist Stamp Departments. Open Monday–Friday 9.30 a.m. to 5 p.m.
Shop. Open Monday–Friday 9 a.m. to 5.30 p.m. and Saturday 9.30 a.m. to 5.30 p.m.
Telephone 020 7836 8444, Fax 020 7836 7342, E-mail: enquiries @stanleygibbons.co.uk and Internet: www.stanleygibbons.com for all departments

STANLEY GIBBONS PUBLICATIONS

Parkside, Christchurch Road, Ringwood, Hants BH24 3SH.
Telephone 01425 472363 (24 hour answer phone service), Fax 01425 470247 and E-mail info@stanleygibbons.co.uk
Publications Mail Order. FREEPHONE 0800 611622. Monday–Friday 8.30 a.m. to 5 p.m.

FRASER'S

(a division of Stanley Gibbons Ltd)
399 Strand, London WC2R 0LX
Autographs, photographs, letters and documents.
Monday–Friday 9 a.m. to 5.30 p.m. and Saturday 10 a.m. to 4 p.m.
Telephone 020 7836 8444, Fax 020 7836 7342 E-mail: info@frasersautographs.co.uk and Internet: www.frasersautographs.com

STANLEY GIBBONS PUBLICATIONS OVERSEAS REPRESENTATION

Stanley Gibbons Publications are represented overseas by the following sole distributors (*), distributors (**) or licensees (***).

Australia

Lighthouse Philatelic (Aust.) Pty Ltd*
Locked Bag 5900
Botany DC
New South Wales 2019
Australia

Stanley Gibbons (Australia) Pty Ltd***
Level 6, 36 Clarence Street
Sydney N.S.W. 2000
Australia

Belgium and Luxembourg**

Davo c/o Philac
Rue du Midi 48
Bruxelles 1000
Belgium

Canada*

Lighthouse Publications (Canada) Ltd
255 Duke Street
Montreal
Quebec
Canada H3C 2M2

Denmark**

Samlerforum/Davo
Ostergade 3
DK 7470 Karup
Denmark

Finland**

Davo
c/o Kapylan Merkkiky
Pohjolankatu 1
00610 Helsinki
Finland

France*

Davo France (Casteilla)
10 Rue Leon Foucault
78184 St Quentin Yvelines Cesex
France

Hong Kong**

Po-on Stamp Service
GPO Box 2498
Hong Kong

Israel**

Capital Stamps
PO Box 3769
Jerusalem 91036
Israel

Italy*

Ernesto Marini Srl
Via Struppa 300
1-16165 Genova GE
Italy

Japan**

Japan Philatelic Co Ltd
PO Box 2
Suginami-Minami
Tokyo
Japan

Netherlands*

Davo Publications
PO Box 411
7400 AK Deventer
Netherlands

New Zealand***

Mowbray Collectables
PO Box 80
Wellington
New Zealand

Norway**

Davo Norge A/S
PO Box 738 Sentrum
N-01 05 Oslo
Norway

Singapore**

Stamp Inc Collectibles Pte Ltd
10 Ubi Crescent
#01-43 Ubi Tech Park
Singapore 408564

Sweden*

Chr Winther Sorensen AB
Box 43
S-310 Knaered
Sweden

Switzerland**

Phila Service
Burgstrasse 160
CH 4125 Riehen
Switzerland

Stanley Gibbons Stamp Catalogue Complete List of Parts

Commonwealth & British Empire 1840–1952
(Annual plus range of one-country catalogues)

2 Austria & Hungary (6th edition, 2002)
Austria, U.N. (Vienna), Hungary

3 Balkans (4th edition, 1998)
Albania, Bosnia & Herzegovina, Bulgaria, Croatia, Greece & Islands, Macedonia, Rumania, Slovenia, Yugoslavia

4 Benelux (4th edition, 1993)
Belgium & Colonies, Luxembourg, Netherlands & Colonies

5 Czechoslovakia & Poland (5th edition, 1994)
Czechoslovakia, Czech Republic, Slovakia, Poland

6 France (5th edition, 2001)
France, Colonies, Post Offices, Andorra, Monaco

7 Germany (6th edition, 2002)
Germany, States, Colonies, Post Offices

8 Italy & Switzerland (5th edition, 1997)
Italy & Colonies, Liechtenstein, San Marino, Switzerland, U.N. (Geneva), Vatican City

9 Portugal & Spain (4th edition, 1996)
Andorra, Portugal & Colonies, Spain & Colonies

10 Russia (5th edition, 1999)
Russia, Armenia, Azerbaijan, Belarus, Estonia, Georgia, Kazakhstan, Kyrgyzstan, Latvia, Lithuania, Moldova, Tajikistan, Turkmenistan, Ukraine, Uzbekistan, Mongolia

11 Scandinavia (5th edition, 2001)
Aland Islands, Denmark, Faroe Islands, Finland, Greenland, Iceland, Norway, Sweden

12 Africa since Independence A-E (2nd edition, 1983)
Algeria, Angola, Benin, Burundi, Cameroun, Cape Verde, Central African Republic, Chad, Comoro Islands, Congo, Djibouti, Equatorial Guinea, Ethiopia

13 Africa since Independence F-M (1st edition, 1981)
Gabon, Guinea, Guinea-Bissau, Ivory Coast, Liberia, Liby Malagasy Republic, Mali, Mauritania, Morocco, Mozambiqu

14 Africa since Independence N-Z (1st edition, 1981)
Niger Republic, Rwanda, St. Thomas & Prince, Senegal, Somali Sudan, Togo, Tunisia, Upper Volta, Zaire

15 Central America (2nd edition, 1984)
Costa Rica, Cuba, Dominican Republic, El Salvador, Guat- mala, Haiti, Honduras, Mexico, Nicaragua, Panama

16 Central Asia (3rd edition, 1992)
Afghanistan, Iran, Turkey

17 China (6th edition, 1998)
China, Taiwan, Tibet, Foreign P.O.'s, Hong Kong, Macao

18 Japan & Korea (4th edition, 1997)
Japan, Korean Empire, South Korea, North Korea

19 Middle East (5th edition, 1996)
Bahrain, Egypt, Iraq, Israel, Jordan, Kuwait, Lebanon, Oma Qatar, Saudi Arabia, Syria, U.A.E., Yemen

20 South America (3rd edition, 1989)
Argentina, Bolivia, Brazil, Chile, Colombia, Ecuador, Para guay, Peru, Surinam, Uruguay, Venezuela

21 South-East Asia (3rd edition, 1995)
Bhutan, Burma, Indonesia, Kampuchea, Laos, Nepal, Philip pines, Thailand, Vietnam

22 United States (5th edition, 2000)
U.S. & Possessions, Marshall Islands, Micronesia, Palau U.N. (New York, Geneva, Vienna)

GREAT BRITAIN SPECIALISED CATALOGUES

Volume 1 Queen Victoria (12th edition, 2001)
Volume 2 King Edward VII to King George VI (11th edition, 1999)
Volume 3 Queen Elizabeth II Pre-decimal Issues (10th edition, 1998)
Volume 4 Queen Elizabeth II Decimal Definitive Issues (9th edition, 2000)
Volume 5 Queen Elizabeth II Decimal Special Issues (3rd edition, 1998, with 1998–99 and 2000/1 Supplements)

THEMATIC CATALOGUES

Collect Aircraft on Stamps (out of print)
Collect Birds on Stamps (new edition in preparation)
Collect Chess on Stamps (2nd edition, 1999)
Collect Fish on Stamps (1st edition, 1999)
Collect Fungi on Stamps (2nd edition, 1997)
Collect Railways on Stamps (3rd edition, 1999)
Collect Shells on Stamps (1st edition, 1995)
Collect Ships on Stamps (3rd edition, 2001)

Stamps Added

Excluding new issues which have appeared in *Gibbons Stamp Monthly* supplements, the following are the catalogue numbers of stamps listed in this edition for the first time.

Great Britain. 84c

Aden. 28a

Australia—New South Wales. 24c/d, 26c/d, 165ab, 166a, 215ca, 222b, 224ba, 226a, 231b, O22ba, O25a, O31c

South Australia. 268a

Tasmania. 91*a*

Western Australia. 52w, 53w, 55aw, 55x, 56w/x, 57x, 58x, 60x, 68w, 75bw, 76w/x, 78w, 80w, 80y, 84w, 85w

Commonwealth of Australia. 2aw, O38a, O62, O69*b*, O125w

Papua. 89w

Bahamas. 27y, 32x, 39*b*, 98x, 143h.

Bahrain. Z5*a*, Z6*a*, Z9*a*, Z15*a*, Z17, Z25*a*, Z48*a*, Z52*a*, Z53*a*, Z55*a*, Z80*a*, Z81*a*, Z83*a*/*b*, Z87, Z95*a*, Z138, Z140, 3a

Barbados. 70w/x

Bechuanaland. 124ab

Bermuda. 56ay

British Guiana. 142a, 217x, 235w

Brunei. 11c, 37a

Burma. 16w, O2w

Canada—British Columbia and Vancouver Island. 13x

Prince Edward Island. 6*a*

Ceylon. 67aw, 124w, 132x, 309a, 382f, 387dw

Cyprus. 23c, 25c, 164a

Dominica. 56w, 57w, 60b, 126c

Falkland Islands—Dependencies. Z27*a*, Z107, Z144*a*, G1d, G2d, G3d, G4d, G6d, G6ed

Fiji. 16f, 17f, 18g, 22g, 24h, 26c, 48*a*/*b*, 50*a*, 51*ab*, 119w, 127ax, 127bw, 128b, 256a, 256ba, 256ca

Gambia. 13Bw

Gibraltar. 77ay

Grenada. 154ab, 156ab, 158ac

Hong Kong. 77aw, 90aw, 91x, 92w, 123w, SB2a/b, SB3, SB4, SB5, SB7a

British Post Offices in China. Z347, Z747, 1w

India. 154*b*, 157, 186*a*, 233*b*, 248w, 249w, 251w, 253w, 254w, 255w, 257w, 258w, 259w, 264w, 265w, 268w, 269bw, 270w, 272w, 273w, 275w, O73a, O75*b*, O78, O83*a*, O84*a*, O91*a*, O118w, O127aw, O127*b*, O129w, O130aw, O132w, O140w, O142w

Indian Expeditionary Forces. E13*b*.

Convention States—Chamba. 43*a*/*b*, 44*a*/*b*, 45*b*/*c*, 47*a*, 48*a*, 50*a*, 51*a*/*c*, 52*a*, 53*b*/*c*, 64*a*, 106w, O34*a*/*b*, O36*b*, O40*a*/*b*, O42*a*, O43*b*

Gwalior. 67/*b*, 68*a*/*b*, 70*a*/*c*, 71*a*, 73*a*, 74*a*/*b*, 75*a*, 76*b*/*c*, 88*b*, O51/*b*, O52*b*/*c*, O55*a*/*c*, O57*a*/*b*, O58*b*/*c*

Jind. 64/*b*, 65*a*/*b*, 69*a*/*b*, 73*a*, 74*a*/*b*, 76*b*, O35*b*/*c*, O36*a*/*b*, O39*a*/*b*, O42*a*, O43*b*, O49*a*

Nabha. 49/*b*, 50*a*/*b*, 52*a*/*b*, 53*a*, 55*a*, 56*a*/*b*, 58*b*/*c*, 61*b*, O39*a*/*b*, O40*a*/*b*, O42*a*/*c*, O44*a*/*b*, O46*a*

Patiala. 48/*b*, 49*a*/*b*, 52*a*/*c*, 56*a*, 58*b*, 65*a*, O35*a*, O36*a*/*b*, O39*a*/*b*, O72w

Feudatory States—Barwani. 28ac

Bhopal. O337c

Cochin. 72w.

Duttia. 21a, 22a, 30a, 31ab, 34a, 36b

Hyderabad. 35db, 43b, O8ca, O41ed, O49b

Jammu and Kashmir. 91a.

Kishangarh. 30a.

Nawanagar. 13d.

Poonch. 12a, 52a, 58a

Travancore. 29a, 32fa, 39ca, O1f

Travancore-Cochin. O13cc.

Ireland. 72aw.

Kenya, Uganda and Tanganyika. 26w, 67x, 94w, 99w, 113a

Kuwait. 1c, 11*a*, 16bw, 24w, 26w, O10*a*

Malaya—Straits Settlements. 200aw, 225bx

Federated Malay States. 11w, 47caw, 69b, 80w

Kelantan. 31a

Selangor. 18a.

Trengganu. 48b/f, 49b/f, 50b/f, 51b/f, 52 53b/f, 54b/f, 55b/f, 56b/f, 57b/f, 58c/d

Thai Occupation. TT2*a*, TT9*a*, TT13*a*, TT1

Malta. 232w

New Zealand. 149c, 184w, 216ca, 377b, 3 446cc, D2a, L1a, F4*a*

Cook Islands. 82x

North Borneo. D2b, D56, D58, D60, D74/83

Pakistan—Bahawalpur. 14a.

Palestine. 3b, 4b, 9b, 10a, 16b/d, 17b/d, 18 19b/d, 20c/d, 21d, 22a/d, 23b/d, 24b/d, 25 26b/d, 27d, 29d, 93aw

Pitcairn Islands. Z17

Rhodesia. 123b.

St. Helena. 7w, 19x

St. Lucia. 40a

St. Vincent. 111x

South Africa—Cape of Good Hope. 52w

Mafeking Siege Stamps. 21a.

Natal. 21x, 26x, 27x, 30x, 33x, 36x, 39x, 5 51x, 65x, 76x, 77x, 81x, 82x, 83x, 91x, 92x, 9 99w

Transvaal. 228g, 238a

Zululand. 7w.

South Africa. 99c, 100d, 104b

Southern Rhodesia. 8a, SB4a/b

South West Africa. O6w

Sudan. 100w

Tanganyika. 49y

Tonga. 22c, 36Bc

Trinidad and Tobago—Trinidad. 69y, 70w, 71 76y

Trinidad and Tobago. 150w

Turks and Caicos Islands. 140ab.

Virgin Islands. 42dc

Zanzibar. 7n, 201, 327a, 328a, 330a

Contents

Catalogue Numbers Altered

ıe table below is a cross-reference of those catalogue ımbers which have been altered in this edition.

ld	*New*
reat Britain	
c	84d
scension	
v	1x
ustralia—New South Wales	
[illegible]	20
[illegible]	19
c/d	24f/g
c/d	26f/g
a/b	28e/g
/92	102/6
/101	119/27
2/8	107/113
0	118
10*b*/13	114/17
14/29	88/101
73	195
90/7	196/202
98/201	191/4
2	190
10aa	*Deleted*
20h	220ca
22b	222ba
25a	*Deleted*
26a/e	226b/f
31b	231c
38/9	243/4
40/1	269/70
41a/3	327/9
44/8	238/42
49/50*b*	274/9
50*c*	276a
51/b	277/b
52	278
81/4	265/8
85/7	271/3
87*c*/*d*	280/1
27/60	330/63
25a	O25b
Tasmania	
31e	O31ea
31	*Deleted*
Western Australia	
5*b*	75*c*
Commonwealth of Australia	
49a	49b
49w	49aw
155a	*Deleted*
O69w	O69aw

Old	*New*
Bahamas	
39b	39ba
50s	52s
Bahrain	
Z17/18	Z18/19
Z80/7	Z79/86
Z129	*Deleted*
Z138	Z139
Z139	Z141
Canada—Newfoundland	
269d	278b
Dominica	
22aw	22w
Falkland Islands—Dependencies	
G6*d*/dc	G6*e*/ec
Fiji	
256a/b	256b/c
Grenada	
153a	153b
153*b*	153*a*
Hong Kong	
90a	90b
SB2	SB1a
SB3	SB2
SB4	SB3a
SB4a	*Deleted*
SB5	SB4a
India	
153	154
154	153
167/8	168/9
169	167
176	*Deleted*
181	182
182	181
185	186
186	185
233w	233aw
O74	O75
O75	O74
O76a	O78a
O83	O84
O84	O83
O127*a*/aw	O127*c*/cw

Old	*New*
Indian Convention States —Chamba	
43a	*Deleted*
46/a	45*a*/ab
O35	O34
O34	O34*c*
O37	O36*a*
O39	O38*a*
Gwalior	
67	67*d*
67b	67da
68a	68ba
70w	70aw
88w	88aw
O51/a	O51*c*/ca
Jind	
64	64*c*
68	67a
O38	O37*a*
Nabha	
49	49*c*
O39*a*	O39*c*
Patiala	
48/a	48*c*/ca
O35*a*	O35*b*
Indian Feudatory States—Bhopal	
O337c/d	O337d/e
Jammu and Kashmir	
3	6*a*
8/9	12/13
10	8
11	12*a*
12	13*a*
13	9
13*a*	11
13*c*	10
Kishangarh	
11a	11ca
17	18
18	17
Nandgaon	
4a	*Deleted*
5b/ba	*Deleted*
6a/b	*Deleted*
Ireland	
72a	72b

Old	*New*
Kenya, Uganda and Tanganyika	
SB4a	*Deleted*
SB4ab	SB4a
Kuwait	
10*a*	*Deleted*
O9*a*	*Deleted*
O10a	O10b
Malaya—Straits Settlements	
225b	225c
225w	225bw
256j/9j	*Deleted*
Federated Malay States	
47ca/*cd*	47cb/*ce*
Selangor	
70ab	*Deleted*
Japanese Occupation	
J37/40	*Deleted*
New Zealand—Aitutaki	
7c/ca	*Deleted*
North Borneo	
D2b	D2c
D3*c*/cb	D4/b
D4/e	D5/e
D5/d	D6/d
D6/a	D10c/ca
D13	D12b
D14	D19
D14a	D29
D15/d	D13/d
D16	D14a
D16a	D26
D16b	D14
D16c/d	D14b/c
D16e	D26a
D17	D15
D17a/b	D27/a
D18	D16a
D18a	D14
D19	D17a
D19a	D17
D19b	D28
D20	D18a
D20a	D18
D20b/cs	D18b/s
D20*d*	D19a
D21	D20b
D21a/ab	D20/a
D22	D21a
D22a	D21

Old	*New*
D23	*Deleted*
D23a	D22
D24/5	D23/4
D26	D25a
D26a	D25
D27	D13e
D28	*Deleted*
D28a	D30
D29/33	D32/6
D34	D50a
D34a	D50
D35	D51
D35*a*/b	D37/a
D36/42a	D38/44a
D42b	D45
D43/b	D46/9
D47	D31
D48	D54
D49/50	D52/3
D51	D55
D52	D57
D53	D59
D53*a*/6a	D61/4
D56*b*/*ba*	D65/a
D57/64	D66/73
D65	D84
D66/70	D85/9
Labuan	
D6a	D6ba
Palestine	
49a	*Deleted*
93c	93ac
100w	100x
South Africa—Natal	
SB1	SB2
SB2	SB1
Transjordan	
151	152
152	151
Trinidad and Tobago—Trinidad	
100x	100
131ab	*Deleted*
Virgin Islands	
14aa	14a
14a/b	14b/ba
21aa	21a
21a/b	21b/ba

General Philatelic Information

and Guidelines to the Scope of the Part 1 (British Commonwealth) Catalogue

The notes which follow seek to reflect current practice in compiling the Part 1 (British Commonwealth) Catalogue.

It scarcely needs emphasising that the *Stanley Gibbons Stamp Catalogue* has a very long history and that the vast quantity of information it contains has been carefully built up by successive generations through the work of countless individuals. Philately itself is never static and the Catalogue has evolved and developed during this long time-span. Thus, while these notes are important for today's criteria, they may be less precise the further back in the listings one travels. They are not intended to inaugurate some unwanted series of piecemeal alterations in a widely respected work, but it does seem to us useful that Catalogue users know as exactly as possible the policies currently in operation.

PRICES

The prices quoted in this Catalogue are the estimated selling prices of Stanley Gibbons Ltd at the time of publication. They are, *unless it is specifically stated otherwise*, for examples in fine condition for the issue concerned. Superb examples are worth more; those of a lower quality considerably less.

All prices are subject to change without prior notice and Stanley Gibbons Ltd may from time to time offer stamps below catalogue price. Individual low value stamps sold at 399, Strand are liable to an additional handling charge. Purchasers of new issues are asked to note that the prices charged for them contain an element for the service rendered and so may exceed the prices shown when the stamps are subsequently catalogued. Postage and handling charges are extra.

No guarantee is given to supply all stamps priced, since it is not possible to keep every catalogued item in stock. Commemorative issues may, at times, only be available in complete sets and not as individual values.

Quotation of prices. The prices in the left-hand column are for unused stamps and those in the right-hand column are for used.

A dagger (†) denotes that the item listed does not exist in that condition and a blank, or dash, that it exists, or may exist, but no market price is known.

Prices are expressed in pounds and pence sterling. One pound comprises 100 pence (£1 = 100p).

The method of notation is as follows: pence in numerals (e.g. 10 denotes ten pence); pound and pence, up to £100, in numerals (e.g. 4·25 denotes four pounds and twenty-five pence); prices above £100 expressed in whole pounds with the "£" sign shown.

Unused stamps. Great Britain and Commonwealth: the prices for unused stamps of Queen Victoria to King George V are for lightly hinged examples. Unused prices for King Edward VIII and King George VI issues are for unmounted mint.

Some stamps from the King George VI period are often difficult to find in unmounted mint condition. In such instances we would expect that collectors would need to pay a high proportion of the price quoted to obtain mounted mint examples. Generally speaking lightly mounted mint stamps from this reign, issued before 1945, are in considerable demand.

Used stamps. The used prices are normally for stamps postally used but may be for stamps cancelled-to-order where this practice exists.

A pen-cancellation on early issues can sometimes correctly denote postal use. Instances are individually noted in the Catalogue in explanation of the used price given.

Prices quoted for bisects on cover or on large piece are for those dated during the period officially authorised.

Stamps not sold unused to the public (e.g. some official stamps) are priced used only.

The use of "unified" designs, that is stamps inscribed for both postal and fiscal purposes, results in a number of stamps of very high face value. In some instances these may not have been primarily intended for postal purposes, but if they are so inscribed we include them. We only price such items used, however, where there is evidence of normal postal usage.

Cover prices. To assist collectors, cover prices are quoted for issues up to 1945 at the beginning of each country.

The system gives a general guide in the form of a factor by which the corresponding used price of the basic loose stamp should be multiplied when found in fine average condition on cover.

Care is needed in applying the factors and they relate to a cover which bears a single of the denomination listed; strips and blocks would need individual valuation outside the scope. If more than one denomination is present the most highly priced attracts the multiplier and the remainder are priced at the simple figure for used singles in arriving at a total.

The cover should be of non-philatelic origin, bearing the correct postal rate for the period and distance involved and cancelled with the markings normal to the offices concerned. Purely philatelic items have a cover value only slightly greater than the catalogue value for the corresponding used stamps. This applies generally to those high-value stamps used philatelically rather than in the normal course of commerce. Low-value stamps, e.g. ¼d. and ½d., are desirable when used as a single rate on cover and merit an increase in "multiplier" value.

First-day covers in the period up to 1945 are not within the scope of the system and the multiplier should not be used. As a special category of philatelic usage, with wide variations in valuation according to scarcity, they require separate treatment.

Oversized covers, difficult to accommodate on an album page, should be reckoned as worth little more than the corresponding value of the used stamps. The condition of a cover affects its value. Except for "wreck covers", serious damage or soiling reduce the value where the postal markings and stamps are ordinary ones. Conversely, visual appeal adds to the value and this can include freshness of appearance, important addresses, old-fashioned but legible hand-writing, historic town-names, etc.

The multipliers are a base on which further value would be added to take account of the cover's postal historical importance in demonstrating such things as unusual, scarce or emergency cancels, interesting routes, significant postal markings, combination usage, the development of postal rates, and so on.

For *Great Britain*, rather than multiplication factors, the cover price is shown as a third column, following the prices for unused and used stamps. It will be extended beyond King Edward VII in subsequent editions.

Minimum price. The minimum catalogue price quoted is 10p. For individual stamps prices between 10p. and 45p. are provided as a guide for catalogue users. The lowest price *charged* for individual stamps or sets purchased from Stanley Gibbons Ltd is 50p.

Set prices. Set prices are generally for one of each value, excluding shades and varieties, but including major colour changes. Where there are alternative shades, etc., the cheapest is usually included. The number of stamps in the set is always stated for clarity. The mint prices for sets containing *se-tenant* pieces are based on the prices quoted for such combinations, and not on those for the individual stamps.

Varieties. Where plate or cylinder varieties a[re] priced in a used condition the price quoted is fo[r a] fine used example with the cancellation well cl[ear] of the listed flaw.

Specimen stamps. The pricing of these items [is] explained under that heading.

Stamp booklets. Prices are for compl[ete] assembled booklets in fine condition with th[ose] issued before 1945 showing normal wear and te[ar]. Incomplete booklets and those which have be[en] "exploded" will, in general, be worth less than t[he] figure quoted.

Repricing. Collectors will be aware that t[he] market factors of supply and demand direc[tly] influence the prices quoted in this Catalogu[e]. Whatever the scarcity of a particular stamp, if the[re] is no one in the market who wishes to buy it [it] cannot be expected to achieve a high pric[e]. Conversely, the same item actively sought [by] numerous potential buyers may cause the price [to] rise.

All the prices in this Catalogue are examin[ed] during the preparation of each new edition [by] expert staff of Stanley Gibbons and repriced [as] necessary. They take many factors into accou[nt] including supply and demand, and are in clo[se] touch with the international stamp market and t[he] auction world.

Commonwealth cover prices and advice on pos[tal] history material originally provided by Edward [B.] Proud.

GUARANTEE

All stamps are guaranteed genuine originals in th[e] following terms:

If not as described, and returned by the purchase[r], we undertake to refund the price paid to us in th[e] original transaction. If any stamp is certified [as] genuine by the Expert Committee of the Roy[al] Philatelic Society, London, or by B.P.A. Experti[s]ing Ltd, the purchaser shall not be entitled to mak[e] any claim against us for any error, omission o[r] mistake in such certificate.

Consumers' statutory rights are not affected b[y] the above guarantee.

The recognised Expert Committees in thi[s] country are those of the Royal Philatelic Society, 41 Devonshire Place, London W1G 6JY, an[d] B.P.A. Expertising Ltd, P.O. Box 137, Leatherhead, Surrey KT22 0RG. They do no[t] undertake valuations under any circumstance[s] and fees are payable for their services.

THE CATALOGUE IN GENERAL

Contents. The Catalogue is confined to adhesiv[e] postage stamps, including miniature sheets. Fo[r] particular categories the rules are:

(*a*) Revenue (fiscal) stamps or telegraph stamps are listed only where they have been expressly authorised for postal duty.

(*b*) Stamps issued only precancelled ar[e] included, but normally issued stamps available additionally with precancel have no separate precancel listing unless the face value is changed.

(*c*) Stamps prepared for use but not issued hitherto accorded full listing, are nowadays foot noted with a price (where possible).

(*d*) Bisects (trisects, etc.) are only listed where such usage was officially authorised.

(*e*) Stamps issued only on first day covers or in presentation packs and not available separately are not listed but may be priced in a footnote.

(*f*) New printings are only included in this Catalogue where they show a major philatelic variety, such as a change in shade, watermark or paper. Stamps which exist with or without imprint dates are listed separately; changes in imprint dates are mentioned in footnotes.

(*g*) Official and unofficial reprints are dealt with by footnote.

(*h*) Stamps from imperforate printings of modern issues which also occur perforated are covered by footnotes, but are listed where widely available for postal use.

Exclusions. The following are excluded: (*a*) non-stal revenue or fiscal stamps; (*b*) postage stamps ed fiscally; (*c*) local carriage labels and private cal issues; (*d*) telegraph stamps; (*e*) bogus or antom stamps; (*f*) railway or airline letter fee mps, bus or road transport company labels; (*g*) -outs; (*h*) all types of non-postal labels and ıvenirs; (*i*) documentary labels for the postal rvice, e.g. registration, recorded delivery, air-ail etiquettes, etc.; (*j*) privately applied embel-hments to official issues and privately commis-ned items generally; (*k*) stamps for training stal officers.

Full listing. "Full listing" confers our recognition d implies allotting a catalogue number and herever possible) a price quotation.

In judging status for inclusion in the catalogue oad considerations are applied to stamps. They ıst be issued by a legitimate postal authority, cognised by the government concerned, and ust be adhesives valid for proper postal use in the ıss of service for which they are inscribed. amps, with the exception of such categories as stage dues and officials, must be available to the neral public, at face value, in reasonable quanti-s without any artificial restrictions being posed on their distribution.

For errors and varieties the criterion is gitimate (albeit inadvertent) sale through a ɔstal administration in the normal course of ısiness. Details of provenance are always ıportant; printers' waste and deliberately anufactured material are excluded.

Certificates. In assessing unlisted items due eight is given to Certificates from recognised xpert Committees and, where appropriate, we ill usually ask to see them.

Date of issue. Where local issue dates differ from ates of release by agencies, "date of issue" is the ocal date. Fortuitous stray usage before the fficially intended date is disregarded in listing. or ease of reference, the Catalogue displays in ıe top corner the date of issue of the first set listed n each page.

Catalogue numbers. Stamps of each country are atalogued chronologically by date of issue. Sub-idiary classes are placed at the end of the country, s separate lists, with a distinguishing letter prefix o the catalogue number, e.g. D for postage due, O or official and E for express delivery stamps.

The catalogue number appears in the extreme eft column. The boldface Type numbers in the ıext column are merely cross-references to illus-rations.

Once published in the Catalogue, numbers are hanged as little as possible; really serious renum-ering is reserved for the occasions when a omplete country or an entire issue is being ewritten. The edition first affected includes cross-eference tables of old and new numbers.

Our catalogue numbers are universally recog-nised in specifying stamps and as a hallmark of status.

Illustrations. Stamps are illustrated at three-quarters linear size. Stamps not illustrated are the same size and format as the value shown, unless otherwise indicated. Stamps issued only as minia-ture sheets have the stamp alone illustrated but sheet size is also quoted. Overprints, surcharges, watermarks and postmarks are normally actual size. Illustrations of varieties are often enlarged to show the detail. Stamp booklet covers are illustrated half-size, unless otherwise indicated.

Designers. Designers' names are quoted where known, though space precludes naming every individual concerned in the production of a set. In particular, photographers supplying material are usually named only where they also make an active contribution in the design stage; posed photo-graphs of reigning monarchs are, however, an exception to this rule.

CONTACTING THE CATALOGUE EDITOR

The editor is always interested in hearing from people who have new information which will improve or correct the Catalogue. As a general rule he must see and examine the actual stamps before they can be considered for listing; photo-graphs or photocopies are insufficient evidence.

Submissions should be made in writing to the Catalogue Editor, Stanley Gibbons Publications at the Ringwood office. The cost of return postage for items submitted is appreciated, and this should include the registration fee if required.

Where information is solicited purely for the benefit of the enquirer, the editor cannot under-take to reply if the answer is already contained in these published notes or if return postage is omitted. Written communications are greatly pre-ferred to enquiries by telephone and the editor regrets that he or his staff cannot see personal callers without a prior appointment being made. Correspondence may be subject to delay during the production period of each new edition.

The editor welcomes close contact with study circles and is interested, too, in finding reliable local correspondents who will verify and supple-ment official information in countries where this is deficient.

We regret we do not give opinions as to the genuineness of stamps, nor do we identify stamps or number them by our Catalogue.

TECHNICAL MATTERS

The meanings of the technical terms used in the catalogue will be found in our *Philatelic Terms Illustrated* (*new edition in preparation*).

References below to "more specialised" listings are to be taken to indicate, as appropiate, the Stanley Gibbons *Great Britain Specialised Catalogue* in 5 volumes or the *Great Britain Concise Catalogue*.

1. Printing

Printing errors. Errors in printing are of major interest to the Catalogue. Authenticated items meriting consideration would include: back-ground, centre or frame inverted or omitted; centre or subject transposed; error of colour; error or omission of value; double prints and impres-sions; printed both sides; and so on. Designs *tête-bêche*, whether intentionally or by accident, are listable. *Se-tenant* arrangements of stamps are recognised in the listings or footnotes. Gutter pairs (a pair of stamps separated by blank margin) are not included in this volume. Colours only partially omitted are not listed. Stamps with embossing omitted are reserved for our more specialised listings.

Printing varieties. Listing is accorded to major changes in the printing base which lead to comple-tely new types. In recess-printing this could be a design re-engraved; in photogravure or photolith-ography a screen altered in whole or in part. It can also encompass flat-bed and rotary printing if the results are readily distinguishable.

To be considered at all, varieties must be constant.

Early stamps, produced by primitive methods, were prone to numerous imperfections: the lists reflect this, recognising re-entries, retouches, broken frames, misshapen letters, and so on. Printing technology has, however, radically improved over the years, during which time photogravure and lithography have become pre-dominant. Varieties nowadays are more in the nature of flaws and these, being too specialised for this general catalogue, are almost always outside the scope. The development of our range of specialised catalogues allows us now to list those items which have philatelic significance in their appropriate volume.

In no catalogue, however, do we list such items as: dry prints, kiss prints, doctor-blade flaws, colour shifts or registration flaws (unless they lead to the complete omission of a colour from an individual stamp), lithographic ring flaws, and so on. Neither do we recognise fortuitous happenings like paper creases or confetti flaws.

Overprints (and surcharges). Overprints of different types qualify for separate listing. These include overprints in different colours; overprints from different printing processes such as litho and typo; overprints in totally different typefaces, etc. Major errors in machine-printed overprints are important and listable. They include: overprint inverted or omitted; overprint double (treble, etc.); overprint diagonal; overprint double, one inverted; pairs with one overprint omitted, e.g. from a radical shift to an adjoining stamp; error of colour; error of type fount; letters inverted or omitted, etc. If the overprint is handstamped, few of these would qualify and a distinction is drawn. We continue, however, to list pairs of stamps where one has a handstamped overprint and the other has not.

Varieties occurring in overprints will often take the form of broken letters, slight differences in spacing, rising spaces, etc. Only the most import-ant would be considered for footnote mention.

Sheet positions. If space permits we quote sheet positions of listed varieties and authenticated data is solicited for this purpose.

De La Rue plates. The Catalogue classifies the general plates used by De La Rue for printing British Colonial stamps as follows:

VICTORIAN KEY TYPE

Die I

1. The ball of decoration on the second point of the crown appears as a dark mass of lines.
2. Dark vertical shading separates the front hair from the bun.
3. The vertical line of colour outlining the front of the throat stops at the sixth line of shading on the neck.
4. The white space in the coil of the hair above the curl is roughly the shape of a pin's head.

Die II

1. There are very few lines of colour in the ball and it appears almost white.
2. A white vertical strand of hair appears in place of the dark shading.
3. The line stops at the eighth line of shading.
4. The white space is oblong, with a line of colour partially dividing it at the left end.

Plates numbered 1 and 2 are both Die I. Plates 3 and 4 are Die II.

GEORGIAN KEY TYPE

Die I

A. The second (thick) line below the name of the country is cut slanting, conforming roughly to the shape of the crown on each side.
B. The labels of solid colour bearing the words "POSTAGE" and "& REVENUE" are square at the inner top corners.
C. There is a projecting "bud" on the outer spiral of the ornament in each of the lower corners.

Die II

A. The second line is cut vertically on each side of the crown.
B. The labels curve inwards at the top.
C. There is no "bud" in this position.

Unless otherwise stated in the lists, all stamps with watermark Multiple Crown CA (w **8**) are Die I while those with watermark Multiple Crown Script CA (w **9**) are Die II. The Georgian Die II was introduced in April 1921 and was used for Plates 10 to 22 and 26 to 28. Plates 23 to 25 were made from Die I by mistake.

2. Paper

All stamps listed are deemed to be on "ordinary" paper of the wove type and white in colour; only departures from this are normally mentioned.

Types. Where classification so requires we distinguish such other types of paper as, for example, vertically and horizontally laid; wove and laid bâtonné; card(board); carton; cartridge; glazed; granite; native; pelure; porous; quadrillé; ribbed; rice; and silk thread.

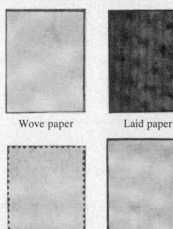

Wove paper

Laid paper

Granite paper

Quadrillé paper

Burelé band

The various makeshifts for normal paper are listed as appropriate. The varieties of double paper and joined paper are recognised. The security device of a printed burelé band on the back of a stamp, as in early Queensland, qualifies for listing.

Descriptive terms. The fact that a paper is handmade (and thus probably of uneven thickness) is mentioned where necessary. Such descriptive terms as "hard" and "soft"; "smooth" and 'rough"; "thick", "medium" and "thin" are applied where there is philatelic merit in classifying papers. We do not, for example, even in more specialised listings, classify paper thicknesses in the Wilding and Machin definitives of Great Britain. Weight standards for the paper apply to complete reels only, so that differences on individual stamps are acceptable to the printer provided the reel conforms overall.

Coloured, very white and toned papers. A coloured paper is one that is coloured right through (front and back of the stamp). In the Catalogue the colour of the paper is given in *italics,* thus:

black/*rose* = black design on rose paper.

Papers have been made specially white in recent years by, for example, a very heavy coating of chalk. We do not classify shades of whiteness of paper as distinct varieties. There does exist, however, a type of paper from early days called toned. This is off-white, often brownish or buffish, but it cannot be assigned any definite colour. A toning effect brought on by climate, incorrect storage or gum staining is disregarded here, as this was not the state of the paper when issued.

"Ordinary" and "Chalk-surfaced" papers. The availability of many postage stamps for revenue purposes made necessary some safeguard against the illegitimate re-use of stamps with removable cancellations. This was at first secured by using fugitive inks and later by printing on paper surfaced by coatings containing either chalk or china clay, both of which made it difficult to remove any form of obliteration without damaging the stamp design.

This catalogue lists these chalk-surfaced paper varieties from their introduction in 1905. Where no indication is given, the paper is "ordinary".

Our chalk-surfaced paper is specifically one which shows a black mark when touched with a silver wire. The paper used during the Second World War for high values, as in Bermuda, the Leeward Islands, etc., was thinly coated with some kind of surfacing which does not react to silver and is therefore regarded (and listed) as "ordinary". Stamps on chalk-surfaced paper can easily lose this coating through immersion in water.

Another paper introduced during the War as a substitute for chalk-surfaced is rather thick, very white and glossy and shows little or no watermark, nor does it show a black line when touched with silver. In the Bahamas high values this paper might be mistaken for the chalk-surfaced (which is thinner and poorer-looking) but for the silver test.

Some modern coated papers show little or no reaction to the silver test and, therefore, cannot be classed as chalk-surfaced.

Green and yellow papers. Issues of the First World War and immediate postwar period occur on green and yellow papers and these are given separate Catalogue listing. The original coloured papers (coloured throughout) gave way to surface-coloured papers, the stamps having "white backs"; other stamps show one colour on the front and a different one at the back. Because of the numerous variations a grouping of colours is adopted as follows:

YELLOW PAPERS

(1) The original *yellow* paper (throughout) usually bright in colour. The gum is often sparse, of harsh consistency and dull-looking. Used 1912–1920.

(2) The *white backs*. Used 1913–1914.

(3) A bright *lemon* paper. The colour must have a pronounced greenish tinge, different from the "yellow" in (1). As a rule, the gum on stamps using this lemon paper is plentiful, smooth and shiny, and the watermark shows distinctly. Care is needed with stamps printed in green on yellow paper (1) as it may appear that the paper is the lemon. Used 1914–1916.

(4) An experimental *orange-buff* paper. The colour must have a distinct brownish tinge. It is not to be confused with a muddy yellow (1) nor the misleading appearance (on the surface) of stamps printed in red on yellow paper where an engraved plate has been insufficiently wiped. Used 1918–1921.

(5) An experimental *buff* paper. This lacks the brownish tinge of (4) and the brightness of the yellow shades. The gum is shiny when compared with the matt type used on (4). Used 1919–1920.

(6) A *pale yellow* paper that has a creamy tone to the yellow. Used from 1920 onwards.

GREEN PAPERS

(7) The original "green" paper, varying considerably through shades of *blue-green* and *yellow-green*, the front and back sometimes differing. Used 1912–1916.

(8) The *white backs*. Used 1913–1914.

(9) A paper blue-green on the surface with *pale olive* back. The back must be markedly paler than the front and this and the pronounced olive tinge to the back distinguish it from (7). Used 1916–1920.

(10) Paper with a vivid green surface, commonly called *emerald-green*; it has the olive back of (9). Used 1920.

(11) Paper with *emerald-green* both back and front. Used from 1920 onwards.

3. Perforation and Rouletting

Perforation gauge. The gauge of a perforation is the number of holes in a length of 2 cm. For correct classification the size of the holes (large or small) may need to be distinguished; in a few cases the actual number of holes on each edge of the stamp needs to be quoted.

Measurement. The Gibbons *Instanta* gauge is the standard for measuring perforations. The stamp is viewed against a dark background with the transparent gauge put on top of it. Though the gauge measures to decimal accuracy, perforations read from it are generally quoted in the Catalogue to the nearest half. For example:

Just over perf 12¾ to just under 13¼ = perf 13
Perf 13¼ exactly, rounded up = perf 13½
Just over perf 13¼ to just under 13¾ = perf 13½
Perf 13¾ exactly, rounded up = perf 14

However, where classification depends on it, actual quarter-perforations are quoted.

Notation. Where no perforation is quoted for an issue it is imperforate. Perforations are usually abbreviated (and spoken) as follows, though sometimes they may be spelled out for clarity. This notation for rectangular stamps (the majority) applies to diamond shapes if "top" is read as the edge to the top right.

P 14: perforated alike on all sides (read: "perf 14").

P 14 × 15: the first figure refers to top and bottom, the second to left and right sides (read: "perf 14 by 15"). This is a compound perforation. For an upright triangular stamp the first figure refers to the two sloping sides and second to the base. In inverted triangulars the base is first and the second figure refers to the sloping sides.

14–15: perforation measuring anything between 14 and 15: the holes are irregularly spaced, thus the gauge may vary along a single line or even along a single edge of the stamp (read: "perf 14 to 15").

14 *irregular*: perforated 14 from a worn perforator, giving badly aligned holes irregularly spaced (read: "irregular perf 14").

comp(ound) 14 × 15: two gauges in use but not necessarily on opposite sides of the stamp. It could be one side in one gauge and three in the other; or two adjacent sides with the same gauge. (Read: "perf compound of 14 and 15".) For three gauges or more, abbreviated as "*P* 14, $14\frac{1}{2}$, 15 *or compound*" for example.

14, $14\frac{1}{2}$: perforated approximately $14\frac{1}{4}$ (read: "perf 14 or $14\frac{1}{2}$"). It does *not* mean two stamps, one perf 14 and the other perf $14\frac{1}{2}$. This obsolescent notation is gradually being replaced in the Catalogue.

nperf: imperforate (not perforated).

nperf × *P* 14: imperforate at top and bottom and perf 14 at sides.

14 × *imperf*: perf 14 at top and bottom and imperforate at sides.

Such headings as "*P* 13 × 14 (*vert*) and *P* 14 × 13 *ıoriz*)" indicate which perforations apply to which amp format—vertical or horizontal.

Some stamps are additionally perforated so that label or tab is detachable; others have been erforated suitably for use as two halves. Listings re normally for whole stamps, unless stated therwise.

Perf × imperf

Other terms. Perforation almost always gives ircular holes; where other shapes have been used hey are specified, e.g. square holes; lozenge perf. nterrupted perfs are brought about by the omission of pins at regular intervals. Perforations merely simulated by being printed as part of the design are of course ignored. With few exceptions, privately applied perforations are not listed.

In the nineteenth century perforations are often described as clean cut (clean, sharply incised holes), intermediate or rough (rough holes, imperfectly cut, often the result of blunt pins).

Perforation errors and varieties. Authenticated errors, where a stamp normally perforated is accidentally issued imperforate, are listed provided no traces of perforation (blind holes or indentations) remain. They must be provided as pairs, both stamps wholly imperforate, and are only priced in that form.

Stamps imperforate between stamp and sheet margin are not listed in this catalogue, but such errors on Great Britain stamps will be found in the *Great Britain Specialised Catalogue*.

Pairs described as "imperforate between" have the line of perforations between the two stamps omitted.

Imperf between (*horiz pair*): a horizontal pair of stamps with perfs all around the edges but none between the stamps.

Imperf between (*vert pair*): a vertical pair of stamps with perfs all around the edges but none between the stamps.

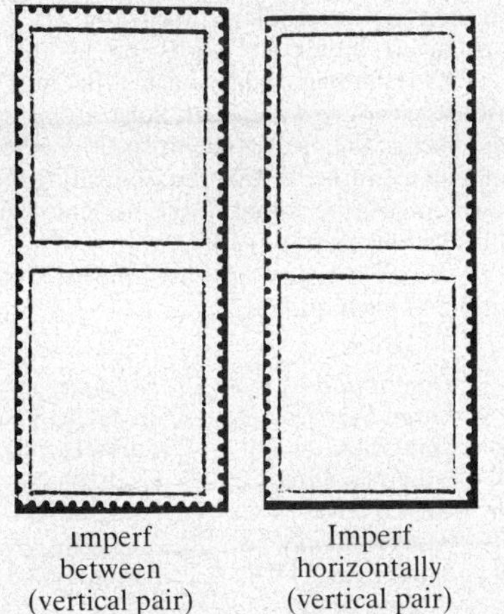

Imperf between (vertical pair) — Imperf horizontally (vertical pair)

Where several of the rows have escaped perforation the resulting varieties are listable. Thus:

Imperf vert (*horiz pair*): a horizontal pair of stamps perforated top and bottom; all three vertical directions are imperf—the two outer edges and between the stamps.

Imperf horiz (*vert pair*): a vertical pair perforated at left and right edges; all three horizontal directions are imperf—the top, bottom and between the stamps.

Straight edges. Large sheets cut up before issue to post offices can cause stamps with straight edges, i.e. imperf on one side or on two sides at right angles. They are not usually listable in this condition and are worth less than corresponding stamps properly perforated all round. This does not, however, apply to certain stamps, mainly from coils and booklets, where straight edges on various sides are the manufacturing norm affecting every stamp. The listings and notes make clear which sides are correctly imperf.

Malfunction. Varieties of double, misplaced or partial perforation caused by error or machine malfunction are not listable, neither are freaks, such as perforations placed diagonally from paper folds, nor missing holes caused by broken pins.

Centering. Well-centred stamps have designs surrounded by equal opposite margins. Where this condition affects the price the fact is stated.

Types of perforating. Where necessary for classification, perforation types are distinguished. These include:

Line perforation from one line of pins punching single rows of holes at a time.

Comb perforation from pins disposed across the sheet in comb formation, punching out holes at three sides of the stamp a row at a time.

Harrow perforation applied to a whole pane or sheet at one stroke.

Rotary perforation from toothed wheels operating across a sheet, then crosswise.

Sewing-machine perforation. The resultant condition, clean-cut or rough, is distinguished where required.

Pin-perforation is the commonly applied term for pin-roulette in which, instead of being punched out, round holes are pricked by sharp-pointed pins and no paper is removed.

Mixed perforation occurs when stamps with defective perforations are re-perforated in a different gauge.

Punctured stamps. Perforation holes can be punched into the face of the stamp. Patterns of small holes, often in the shape of initial letters, are privately applied devices against pilferage. These "perfins" are outside the scope except for Australia, Canada, Cape of Good Hope, Papua and Sudan where they were used as official stamps by the national administration. Identification devices, when officially inspired, are listed or noted; they can be shapes, or letters or words formed from holes, sometimes converting one class of stamp into another.

Rouletting. In rouletting the paper is cut, for ease of separation, but none is removed. The gauge is measured, when needed, as for perforations. Traditional French terms descriptive of the type of cut are often used and types include:

Arc roulette (*percé en arc*). Cuts are minute, spaced arcs, each roughly a semicircle.

Cross roulette (*percé en croix*). Cuts are tiny diagonal crosses.

Line roulette (*percé en ligne* or *en ligne droite*). Short straight cuts parallel to the frame of the stamp. The commonest basic roulette. Where not further described, "roulette" means this type.

Rouletted in colour or *coloured roulette* (*percé en lignes colorées* or *en lignes de couleur*). Cuts with coloured edges, arising from notched rule inked simultaneously with the printing plate.

Saw-tooth roulette (*percé en scie*). Cuts applied zigzag fashion to resemble the teeth of a saw.

Serpentine roulette (*percé en serpentin*). Cuts as sharply wavy lines.

Zigzag roulette (*percé en zigzags*). Short straight cuts at angles in alternate directions, producing sharp points on separation. U.S. usage favours "serrate(d) roulette" for this type.

Pin-roulette (originally *percé en points* and now *perforés trous d'epingle*) is commonly called pin-perforation in English.

4. Gum

All stamps listed are assumed to have gum of some kind; if they were issued without gum this is stated. Original gum (o.g.) means that which was present on the stamp as issued to the public. Deleterious climates and the presence of certain chemicals can cause gum to crack and, with early stamps, even make the paper deteriorate. Unscrupulous fakers are adept in removing it and regumming the stamp to meet the unreasoning demand often made for "full o.g." in cases where such a thing is virtually impossible.

5. Watermarks

Stamps are on unwatermarked paper except where the heading to the set says otherwise.

Detection. Watermarks are detected for Catalogue description by one of four methods: (1) holding stamps to the light; (2) laying stamps face down on a dark background; (3) adding a few drops of petroleum ether 40/60 to the stamp laid face down in a watermark tray; (4) by use of the Morley-Bright Detector, or other equipment, which work by revealing the thinning of the paper at the watermark (Note that petroleum ether is highly inflammable in use and can damage photogravure stamps.)

Listable types. Stamps occurring on both watermarked and unwatermarked papers are different types and both receive full listing.

Single watermarks (devices occurring once on every stamp) can be modified in size and shape as between different issues; the types are noted but not usually separately listed. Fortuitous absence of watermark from a single stamp or its gross displacement would not be listable.

To overcome registration difficulties the device may be repeated at close intervals (a *multiple watermark*), single stamps thus showing parts of several devices. Similarly, a large *sheet watermark* (or *all-over watermark*) covering numerous stamps can be used. We give informative notes and illustrations for them. The designs may be such that numbers of stamps in the sheet automatically lack watermark: this is not a listable variety. Multiple and all-over watermarks sometimes undergo modifications, but if the various types are difficult to distinguish from single stamps notes are given but not separate listings.

Papermakers' watermarks are noted where known but not listed separately, since most stamps in the sheet will lack them. Sheet watermarks which are nothing more than officially adopted papermakers' watermarks are, however, given normal listing.

Marginal watermarks, falling outside the pane of stamps, are ignored except where misplacement caused the adjoining row to be affected, in which case they are footnoted.

Watermark errors and varieties. Watermark errors are recognised as of major importance. They comprise stamps intended to be on unwatermarked paper but issued watermarked by mistake, or stamps printed on paper with the wrong watermark. Varieties showing letters omitted from the watermark are also included, but broken or deformed bits on the dandy roll are not listed unless they represent repairs.

Watermark positions. The diagram shows how watermark position is described in the Catalogue. Paper has a side intended for printing and watermarks are usually impressed so that they read normally when looked through from that printed side. However, since philatelists customarily detect watermarks by looking at the back of the stamp the watermark diagram also makes clear what is actually seen.

Illustrations in the Catalogue are of watermarks in normal positions (from the front of the stamps) and are actual size where possible.

Differences in watermark position are collectable as distinct varieties. This Catalogue now lists inverted, sideways inverted and reversed watermark varieties on Commonwealth stamps from the 1860s onwards *except* where the watermark position is completely haphazard.

Great Britain inverted and sideways inverted watermarks can be found in the *Great Britain Specialised Catalogue* and the *Great Britain Concise Catalogue*.

Where a watermark comes indiscriminately in various positions our policy is to cover this by a general note: we do not give separate listings because the watermark position in these circumstances has no particular philatelic importance.

AS DESCRIBED (Read through front of stamp)		AS SEEN DURING WATERMARK DETECTION (Stamp face down and back examined)
GvR	Normal	GvR (reversed)
GvR (inverted)	Inverted	GvR (inverted and reversed)
GvR (reversed)	Reversed	GvR
GvR (reversed and inverted)	Reversed and inverted	GvR (inverted)
GvR (sideways)	Sideways	GvR (sideways, reversed)
GvR (sideways inverted)	Sideways inverted	GvR (sideways inverted, reversed)

Standard types of watermark. Some watermarks have been used generally for various British possessions rather than exclusively for a single colony. To avoid repetition the Catalogue classifies 11 general types, as under, with references in the headings throughout the listings being given either in words or in the form "*W* w **9**" (meaning "watermark type w **9**"). In those cases where watermark illustrations appear in the listings themselves, the respective reference reads, for example, *W* **153**, thus indicating that the watermark will be found in the normal sequence of illustrations as (type) **153**.

The general types are as follows, with an example of each quoted.

W	*Description*	*Example*
w **1**	Large Star	St. Helena No. 1
w **2**	Small Star	Turks Is. No. 4
w **3**	Broad (pointed) Star	Grenada No. 24
w **4**	Crown (over) CC, small stamp	Antigua No. 13
w **5**	Crown (over) CC, large stamp	Antigua No. 31
w **6**	Crown (over) CA, small stamp	Antigua No. 21
w **7**	Crown CA (CA over Crown), large stamp	Sierra Leone No. 54
w **8**	Multiple Crown CA	Antigua No. 41
w **9**	Multiple Crown Script CA	Seychelles No. 158
w **9*a***	do. Error	Seychelles No. 158a
w **9*b***	do. Error	Seychelles No. 158b
w **10**	V over Crown	N.S.W. No. 327
w **11**	Crown over A	N.S.W. No. 347

CC in these watermarks is an abbreviation for "Crown Colonies" and CA for "Crown Agents". Watermarks w **1**, w **2** and w **3** are on stamps printed by Perkins, Bacon; w **4** onwards on stamps from De La Rue and other printers.

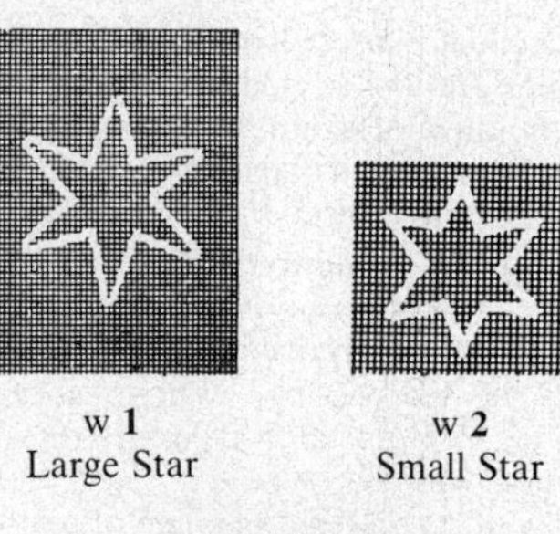

w **1**
Large Star

w **2**
Small Star

w **3**
Broad (pointed) Star

Watermark w **1**, *Large Star,* measures 15 to 16 mm across the star from point to point and about 27 mm from centre to centre vertically between stars in the sheet. It was made for long stamps like Ceylon 1857 and St. Helena 1856.

Watermark w **2**, *Small Star,* is of similar design but measures 12 to 13½ mm from point to point and 24 mm from centre to centre vertically. It was for use with ordinary-size stamps such as Grenada 1863–71.

When the Large Star watermark was used with the smaller stamps it only occasionally comes in the centre of the paper. It is frequently so misplaced as to show portions of two stars above and below and this eccentricity will very often help in determining the watermark.

Watermark w **3**, *Broad (pointed) Star,* resembles w **1** but the points are broader.

w **4**
Crown (over) CC

w **5**
Crown (over) CC

Two *Crown (over) CC* watermarks were used: w **4** was for stamps of ordinary size and w **5** for those of larger size.

w **6**
Crown (over) CA

w **7**
CA over Crown

Two watermarks of *Crown CA* type were used: w **6** being for stamps of ordinary size. The other w **7**, is properly described as *CA over Crown*. It was specially made for paper on which it was intended to print long fiscal stamps: that some were used postally accounts for the appearance of w **7** in the Catalogue. The watermark occupies twice the space of the ordinary Crown CA watermark, w **6**. Stamps of normal size printed on paper with w **7** watermark show it *sideways*; it takes a horizontal pair of stamps to show the entire watermark.

w **8**
Multiple Crown CA

w **9**
Multiple Crown Script CA

Multiple watermarks began in 1904 with w **8**, *Multiple Crown CA,* changed from 1921 to w **9**, *Multiple Crown Script CA*. On stamps of ordinary size portions of two or three watermarks appear and on the large-sized stamps a greater number can be observed. The change to letters in script character with w **9** was accompanied by a Crown of distinctly different shape.

It seems likely that there were at least two dandy rolls for each Crown Agents watermark in use at any one time with a reserve roll being employed when the normal one was withdrawn for maintenance or repair.

Both the Mult Crown CA and the Mult Script CA types exist with one or other of the letters omitted from individual impressions. It is possible that most of these occur from the reserve rolls as they have only been found on certain issues. The MCA watermark experienced such problems during the early 1920s and the Script over a longer period from the early 1940s until 1951.

During the 1920s damage must also have occurred on one of the Crowns as a substituted Crown has been found on certain issues. This is smaller than the normal and consists of an oval e joined to two upright ovals with a circle itioned between their upper ends. The upper of the Crown's base is omitted, as are the left right-hand circles at the top and also the cross r the centre circle.

Substituted Crown

w **9***a*: Error, Crown missing

w **9***b*: Error, St. Edward's Crown

The *Multiple Crown Script CA* watermark, w **9**, known with two errors recurring among the 950–52 printings of several territories. In the first crown has fallen away from the dandy-roll that npresses the watermark into the paper pulp. It ves w **9***a, Crown missing*, but this omission has een found in both "Crown only" (*illustrated*) and Crown CA" rows. The resulting faulty paper was sed for Bahamas, Johore, Seychelles and the ostage due stamps of nine colonies.

When the omission was noticed a second nishap occurred, which was to insert a wrong rown in the space, giving w **9***b*, *St. Edward's Crown*. This produced varieties in Bahamas, erlis, St. Kitts-Nevis and Singapore and the ncorrect crown likewise occurs in "Crown only" nd "Crown CA" rows.

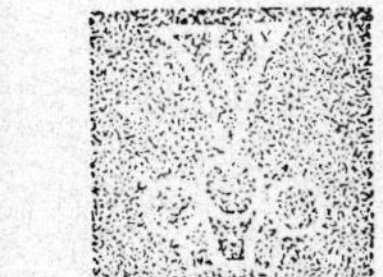

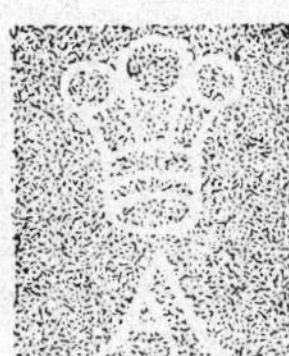

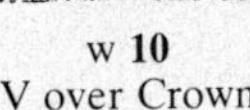

w **10** V over Crown

w **11** Crown over A

Resuming the general types, two watermarks found in issues of several Australian States are: w **10**, *V over Crown*, and w **11**, *Crown over A*.

6. Colours

Stamps in two or three colours have these named in order of appearance, from the centre moving outwards. Four colours or more are usually listed as multicoloured.

In compound colour names the second is the predominant one, thus:

orange-red = a red tending towards orange;

red-orange = an orange containing more red than usual.

Standard colours used. The 200 colours most used for stamp identification are given in the Stanley Gibbons Stamp Colour Key. The Catalogue has used the Stamp Colour Key as standard for describing new issues for some years. The names are also introduced as lists are rewritten, though exceptions are made for those early issues where traditional names have become universally established.

Determining colours. When comparing actual stamps with colour samples in the Stamp Colour Key, view in a good north daylight (or its best substitute: fluorescent "colour-matching" light). Sunshine is not recommended. Choose a solid portion of the stamp design; if available, marginal markings such as solid bars of colour or colour check dots are helpful. Shading lines in the design can be misleading as they appear lighter than solid colour. Postmarked portions of a stamp appear darker than normal. If more than one colour is present, mask off the extraneous ones as the eye tends to mix them.

Errors of colour. Major colour errors in stamps or overprints which qualify for listing are: wrong colours; one colour inverted in relation to the rest; albinos (colourless impressions), where these have Expert Committee certificates; colours completely omitted, but only on unused stamps (if found on used stamps the information is footnoted) and with good credentials, missing colours being frequently faked.

Colours only partially omitted are not recognised. Colour shifts, however spectacular, are not listed.

Shades. Shades in philately refer to variations in the intensity of a colour or the presence of differing amounts of other colours. They are particularly significant when they can be linked to specific printings. In general, shades need to be quite marked to fall within the scope of this Catalogue; it does not favour nowadays listing the often numerous shades of a stamp, but chooses a single applicable colour name which will indicate particular groups of outstanding shades. Furthermore, the listings refer to colours as issued: they may deteriorate into something different through the passage of time.

Modern colour printing by lithography is prone to marked differences of shade, even within a single run, and variations can occur within the same sheet. Such shades are not listed.

Aniline colours. An aniline colour meant originally one derived from coal-tar; it now refers more widely to colour of a particular brightness suffused on the surface of a stamp and showing through clearly on the back.

Colours of overprints and surcharges. All overprints and surcharges are in black unless stated otherwise in the heading or after the description of the stamp.

7. Specimen Stamps

Originally, stamps overprinted SPECIMEN were circulated to postmasters or kept in official records, but after the establishment of the Universal Postal Union supplies were sent to Berne for distribution to the postal administrations of member countries.

During the period 1884 to 1928 most of the stamps of British Crown Colonies required for this purpose were overprinted SPECIMEN in various shapes and sizes by their printers from typeset formes. Some locally produced provisionals were handstamped locally, as were sets prepared for presentation. From 1928 stamps were punched with holes forming the word SPECIMEN, each firm of printers using a different machine or machines. From 1948 the stamps supplied for U.P.U. distribution were no longer punctured.

Stamps of some other Commonwealth territories were overprinted or handstamped locally, while stamps of Great Britain and those overprinted for use in overseas postal agencies (mostly of the higher denominations) bore SPECIMEN overprints and handstamps applied by the Inland Revenue or the Post Office.

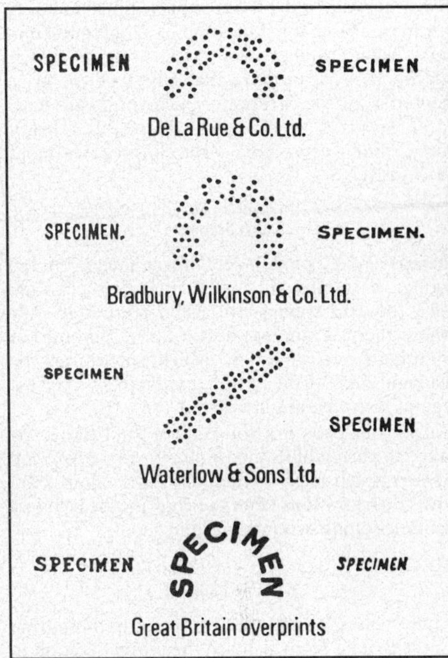

Some of the commoner types of overprints or punctures are illustrated here. Collectors are warned that dangerous forgeries of the punctured type exist.

The *Part* 1 (*British Commonwealth*) *Catalogue* records those Specimen overprints or perforations intended for distribution by the U.P.U. to member countries. In addition the Specimen overprints of Australia and its dependent territories, which were sold to collectors by the Post Office, are also included.

Various Perkins Bacon issues exist obliterated with a "CANCELLED" within an oval of bars handstamp.

Perkins Bacon "CANCELLED" Handstamp

This was applied to six examples of those issues available in 1861 which were then given to members of Sir Rowland Hill's family. Seventy-five different stamps (including four from Chile) are recorded with this handstamp although others may possibly exist. The unauthorised gift of these "CANCELLED" stamps to the Hill family was a major factor in the loss of the Agent General for the Crown Colonies (the forerunner of the Crown Agents) contracts by Perkins Bacon in the following year. Where examples of these scarce items are known to be in private hands the catalogue provides a price.

For full details of these stamps see *CANCELLED by Perkins Bacon* by Peter Jaffé (published by Spink in 1998).

All other Specimens are outside the scope of this volume.

Specimens are not quoted in Great Britain as they are fully listed in the Stanley Gibbons *Great Britain Specialised Catalogue.*

In specifying type of specimen for individual high-value stamps, "H/S" means handstamped, "Optd" is overprinted and "Perf" is punctured. Some sets occur mixed, e.g. "Optd/Perf". If unspecified, the type is apparent from the date or it is the same as for the lower values quoted as a set.

Prices. Prices for stamps up to £1 are quoted in sets; higher values are priced singly. Where specimens exist in more than one type the price quoted is for the cheapest. Specimen stamps have rarely survived even as pairs; these and strips of three, four or five are worth considerably more than singles.

8. Coil Stamps

Stamps issued only in coil form are given full listing. If stamps are issued in both sheets and coils the coil stamps are listed separately only where there is some feature (e.g. perforation or watermark sideways) by which singles can be distinguished. Coil strips containing different stamps *se-tenant* are also listed.

Coil join pairs are too random and too easily faked to permit of listing; similarly ignored are coil stamps which have accidentally suffered an extra row of perforations from the claw mechanism in a malfunctioning vending machine.

9. Stamp Booklets

Stamp booklets (with the exception of those from Great Britain for which see the current edition of the *Great Britain Concise Catalogue*) are now listed in this catalogue.

Single stamps from booklets are listed if they are distinguishable in some way (such as watermark or perforation) from similar sheet stamps.

Booklet panes are listed where they contain stamps of different denominations *se-tenant*, where stamp-size labels are included, or where such panes are otherwise identifiable. Booklet panes are placed in the listing under the lowest denomination present.

Particular perforations (straight edges) are covered by appropriate notes.

10. Miniature Sheets and Sheetlets

We distinguish between "miniature sheets" and "sheetlets" and this affects the catalogue numbering. An item in sheet form that is postally valid, containing a single stamp, pair, block or set of stamps, with wide, inscribed and/or decorative margins, is a *miniature sheet* if it is sold at post offices as an indivisable entity. As such the Catalogue allots a single **MS** number and describes what stamps make it up. The *sheetlet* o*r small sheet* differs in that the individual stamps are intended to be purchased separately for postal purposes. For sheetlets, all the component postage stamps are numbered individually and the composition explained in a footnote. Note that the definitions refer to post office sale—not how items may be subsequently offered by stamp dealers.

11. Forgeries and Fakes

Forgeries. Where space permits, notes are considered if they can give a concise description that will permit unequivocal detection of a forgery. Generalised warnings, lacking detail, are not nowadays inserted, since their value to the collector is problematic.

Fakes. Unwitting fakes are numerous, particularly "new shades" which are colour changelings brought about by exposure to sunlight, soaking in water contaminated with dyes from adherent paper, contact with oil and dirt from a pocketbook, and so on. Fraudulent operators, in addition, can offer to arrange: removal of hinge marks; repairs of thins on white or coloured papers; replacement of missing margins or perforations; reperforating in true or false gauges; removal of fiscal cancellations; rejoining of severed pairs, strips and blocks; and (a major hazard) regumming. Collectors can only be urged to purchase from reputable sources and to insist upon Expert Committee certification where there is any kind of doubt.

The Catalogue can consider footnotes about fakes where these are specific enough to assist in detection.

Abbreviations

Printers

A.B.N. Co	American Bank Note Co, New York.
B.A.B.N.	British American Bank Note Co, Ottawa
B.W.	Bradbury Wilkinson & Co, Ltd.
C.B.N.	Canadian Bank Note Co, Ottawa.
Continental B.N. Co	Continental Bank Note Co.
Courvoisier	Imprimerie Courvoisier S.A., La-Chaux-de-Fonds, Switzerland.
D.L.R.	De La Rue & Co, Ltd, London.
Enschedé	Joh. Enschedé en Zonen, Haarlem, Netherlands.
Harrison	Harrison & Sons, Ltd, London
P.B.	Perkins Bacon Ltd, London.
Waterlow	Waterlow & Sons, Ltd, London.

General Abbreviations

Alph	Alphabet
Anniv	Anniversary
Comp	Compound (perforation)
Des	Designer; designed
Diag	Diagonal; diagonally
Eng	Engraver; engraved
F.C.	Fiscal Cancellation
H/S	Handstamped
Horiz	Horizontal; horizontally
Imp, Imperf	Imperforate
Inscr	Inscribed
L	Left
Litho	Lithographed
mm	Millimetres
MS	Miniature sheet
N.Y.	New York
Opt(d)	Overprint(ed)
P or P-c	Pen-cancelled
P, Pf or Perf	Perforated
Photo	Photogravure
Pl	Plate
Pr	Pair
Ptd	Printed
Ptg	Printing
R	Right
R.	Row
Recess	Recess-printed
Roto	Rotogravure
Roul	Rouletted
S	Specimen (overprint)
Surch	Surcharge(d)
T.C.	Telegraph Cancellation
T	Type
Typo	Typographed
Un	Unused
Us	Used
Vert	Vertical; vertically
W or wmk	Watermark
Wmk s	Watermark sideways

(†)=Does not exist.

(—) (or blank price column)=Exists, or may ex but no market price is known.

/ between colours means "on" and the colc following is that of the paper on which the stamp printed.

Colours of Stamps

Bl (blue); blk (black); brn (brown); car, ca (carmine); choc (chocolate); clar (claret); em (emerald); grn (green); ind (indigo); m (magenta); mar (maroon); mult (multicoloure mve (mauve); ol (olive); orge (orange); pk (pink pur (purple); scar (scarlet); sep (sepia); tu (turquoise); ultram (ultramarine); verm (ve milion); vio (violet); yell (yellow).

Colour of Overprints and Surcharges

(B.) = blue, (Blk.) = black, (Br.) = brown, (C.) carmine, (G.) = green, (Mag.) = magenta, (Mve = mauve, (Ol.) = olive, (O.) = orange, (P.) purple, (Pk.) = pink, (R.)=red, (Sil.) = silver, (V = violet, (Vm.) or (Verm.) = vermilion, (W.) white, (Y.) = yellow.

Arabic Numerals

As in the case of European figures, the details of th Arabic numerals vary in different stamp design but they should be readily recognised with the aid this illustration.

٠	١	٢	٣	٤	٥	٦	٧	٨	٩
0	1	2	3	4	5	6	7	8	9

International Philatelic Glossary

glish	*French*	*German*	*Spanish*	*Italian*
gate	Agate	Achat	Agata	Agata
r stamp	Timbre de la poste aérienne	Flugpostmarke	Sello de correo aéreo	Francobollo per posta aerea
pple Green	Vert-pomme	Apfelgrün	Verde manzana	Verde mela
arred	Annulé par barres	Balkenentwertung	Anulado con barras	Sbarrato
sected	Timbre coupé	Halbiert	Partido en dos	Frazionato
stre	Bistre	Bister	Bistre	Bistro
stre-brown	Brun-bistre	Bisterbraun	Castaño bistre	Bruno-bistro
ack	Noir	Schwarz	Negro	Nero
ackish Brown	Brun-noir	Schwärzlichbraun	Castaño negruzco	Bruno nerastro
ackish Green	Vert foncé	Schwärzlichgrün	Verde negruzco	Verde nerastro
ackish Olive	Olive foncé	Schwärzlicholiv	Oliva negruzco	Oliva nerastro
ock of four	Bloc de quatre	Viererblock	Bloque de cuatro	Bloco di quattro
ue	Bleu	Blau	Azul	Azzurro
ue-green	Vert-bleu	Blaugrün	Verde azul	Verde azzurro
uish Violet	Violet bleuâtre	Bläulichviolett	Violeta azulado	Violetto azzurrastro
ooklet	Carnet	Heft	Cuadernillo	Libretto
right Blue	Bleu vif	Lebhaftblau	Azul vivo	Azzurro vivo
right Green	Vert vif	Lebhaftgrün	Verde vivo	Verde vivo
right Purple	Mauve vif	Lebhaftpurpur	Púrpura vivo	Porpora vivo
ronze Green	Vert-bronze	Bronzegrün	Verde bronce	Verde bronzo
rown	Brun	Braun	Castaño	Bruno
rown-lake	Carmin-brun	Braunlack	Laca castaño	Lacca bruno
rown-purple	Pourpre-brun	Braunpurpur	Púrpura castaño	Porpora bruno
rown-red	Rouge-brun	Braunrot	Rojo castaño	Rosso bruno
uff	Chamois	Sämisch	Anteado	Camoscio
ancellation	Oblitération	Entwertung	Cancelación	Annullamento
ancelled	Annulé	Gestempelt	Cancelado	Annullato
armine	Carmin	Karmin	Carmín	Carminio
armine-red	Rouge-carmin	Karminrot	Rojo carmín	Rosso carminio
entred	Centré	Zentriert	Centrado	Centrato
erise	Rouge-cerise	Kirschrot	Color de ceresa	Color Ciliegia
halk-surfaced paper	Papier couché	Kreidepapier	Papel estucado	Carta gessata
halky Blue	Bleu terne	Kreideblau	Azul turbio	Azzurro smorto
harity stamp	Timbre de bienfaisance	Wohltätigkeitsmarke	Sello de beneficenza	Francobollo di beneficenza
hestnut	Marron	Kastanienbraun	Castaño rojo	Marrone
hocolate	Chocolat	Schokolade	Chocolate	Cioccolato
innamon	Cannelle	Zimtbraun	Canela	Cannella
laret	Grenat	Weinrot	Rojo vinoso	Vinaccia
obalt	Cobalt	Kobalt	Cobalto	Cobalto
olour	Couleur	Farbe	Color	Colore
omb-perforation	Dentelure en peigne	Kammzähnung, Reihenzähnung	Dentado de peine	Dentellatura e pettine
Commemorative stamp	Timbre commémoratif	Gedenkmarke	Sello conmemorativo	Francobollo commemorativo
Crimson	Cramoisi	Karmesin	Carmesí	Cremisi
Deep Blue	Bleu foncé	Dunkelblau	Azul oscuro	Azzurro scuro
Deep Bluish Green	Vert-bleu foncé	Dunkelbläulichgrün	Verde azulado oscuro	Verde azzurro scuro
Design	Dessin	Markenbild	Diseño	Disegno
Die	Matrice	Urstempel. Type, Platte	Cuño	Conio, Matrice
Double	Double	Doppelt	Doble	Doppio
Drab	Olive terne	Trüboliv	Oliva turbio	Oliva smorto
Dull Green	Vert terne	Trübgrün	Verde turbio	Verde smorto
Dull Purple	Mauve terne	Trübpurpur	Púrpura turbio	Porpora smorto
Embossing	Impression en relief	Prägedruck	Impresión en relieve	Impressione a relievo
Emerald	Vert-eméraude	Smaragdgrün	Esmeralda	Smeraldo
Engraved	Gravé	Graviert	Grabado	Inciso
Error	Erreur	Fehler, Fehldruck	Error	Errore
Essay	Essai	Probedruck	Ensayo	Saggio
Express letter stamp	Timbre pour lettres par exprès	Eilmarke	Sello de urgencia	Francobollo per espresso
Fiscal stamp	Timbre fiscal	Stempelmarke	Sello fiscal	Francobollo fiscale
Flesh	Chair	Fleischfarben	Carne	Carnicino
Forgery	Faux, Falsification	Fälschung	Falsificación	Falso, Falsificazione
Frame	Cadre	Rahmen	Marco	Cornice
Granite paper	Papier avec fragments de fils de soie	Faserpapier	Papel con filamentos	Carto con fili di seta
Green	Vert	Grün	Verde	Verde
Greenish Blue	Bleu verdâtre	Grünlichblau	Azul verdoso	Azzurro verdastro

English	*French*	*German*	*Spanish*	*Italian*
Greenish Yellow	Jaune-vert	Grünlichgelb	Amarillo verdoso	Giallo verdastro
Grey	Gris	Grau	Gris	Grigio
Grey-blue	Bleu-gris	Graublau	Azul gris	Azzurro grigio
Grey-green	Vert gris	Graugrün	Verde gris	Verde grigio
Gum	Gomme	Gummi	Goma	Gomma
Gutter	Interpanneau	Zwischensteg	Espacio blanco entre dos grupos	Ponte
Imperforate	Non-dentelé	Geschnitten	Sin dentar	Non dentellato
Indigo	Indigo	Indigo	Azul indigo	Indaco
Inscription	Inscription	Inschrift	Inscripción	Dicitura
Inverted	Renversé	Kopfstehend	Invertido	Capovolto
Issue	Émission	Ausgabe	Emisión	Emissione
Laid	Vergé	Gestreift	Listado	Vergato
Lake	Lie de vin	Lackfarbe	Laca	Lacca
Lake-brown	Brun-carmin	Lackbraun	Castaño laca	Bruno lacca
Lavender	Bleu-lavande	Lavendel	Color de alhucema	Lavanda
Lemon	Jaune-citron	Zitrongelb	Limón	Limone
Light Blue	Bleu clair	Hellblau	Azul claro	Azzurro chiaro
Lilac	Lilas	Lila	Lila	Lilla
Line perforation	Dentelure en lignes	Linienzähnung	Dentado en linea	Dentellatura lineare
Lithography	Lithographie	Steindruck	Litografía	Litografia
Local	Timbre de poste locale	Lokalpostmarke	Emisión local	Emissione locale
Lozenge roulette	Percé en losanges	Rautenförmiger Durchstich	Picadura en rombos	Perforazione a losanghe
Magenta	Magenta	Magentarot	Magenta	Magenta
Margin	Marge	Rand	Borde	Margine
Maroon	Marron pourpré	Dunkelrotpurpur	Púrpura rojo oscuro	Marrone rossastro
Mauve	Mauve	Malvenfarbe	Malva	Malva
Multicoloured	Polychrome	Mehrfarbig	Multicolores	Policromo
Myrtle Green	Vert myrte	Myrtengrün	Verde mirto	Verde mirto
New Blue	Bleu ciel vif	Neublau	Azul nuevo	Azzurro nuovo
Newspaper stamp	Timbre pour journaux	Zeitungsmarke	Sello para periódicos	Francobollo per giornali
Obliteration	Oblitération	Abstempelung	Matasello	Annullamento
Obsolete	Hors (de) cours	Ausser Kurs	Fuera de curso	Fuori corso
Ochre	Ocre	Ocker	Ocre	Ocra
Official stamp	Timbre de service	Dienstmarke	Sello de servicio	Francobollo di servizio
Olive-brown	Brun-olive	Olivbraun	Castaño oliva	Bruno oliva
Olive-green	Vert-olive	Olivgrün	Verde oliva	Verde oliva
Olive-grey	Gris-olive	Olivgrau	Gris oliva	Grigio oliva
Olive-yellow	Jaune-olive	Olivgelb	Amarillo oliva	Giallo oliva
Orange	Orange	Orange	Naranja	Arancio
Orange-brown	Brun-orange	Orangebraun	Castaño naranja	Bruno arancio
Orange-red	Rouge-orange	Orangerot	Rojo naranja	Rosso arancio
Orange-yellow	Jaune-orange	Orangegelb	Amarillo naranja	Giallo arancio
Overprint	Surcharge	Aufdruck	Sobrecarga	Soprastampa
Pair	Paire	Paar	Pareja	Coppia
Pale	Pâle	Blass	Pálido	Pallido
Pane	Panneau	Gruppe	Grupo	Gruppo
Paper	Papier	Papier	Papel	Carta
Parcel post stamp	Timbre pour colis postaux	Paketmarke	Sello para paquete postal	Francobollo per pacchi postali
Pen-cancelled	Oblitéré à plume	Federzugentwertung	Cancelado a pluma	Annullato a penna
Percé en arc	Percé en arc	Bogenförmiger Durchstich	Picadura en forma de arco	Perforazione ad arco
Percé en scie	Percé en scie	Bogenförmiger Durchstich	Picado en sierra	Foratura a sega
Perforated	Dentelé	Gezähnt	Dentado	Dentellato
Perforation	Dentelure	Zähnung	Dentar	Dentellatura
Photogravure	Photogravure, Heliogravure	Rastertiefdruck	Fotograbado	Rotocalco
Pin perforation	Percé en points	In Punkten durchstochen	Horadado con alfileres	Perforato a punti
Plate	Planche	Platte	Plancha	Lastra, Tavola
Plum	Prune	Pflaumenfarbe	Color de ciruela	Prugna
Postage Due stamp	Timbre-taxe	Portomarke	Sello de tasa	Segnatasse
Postage stamp	Timbre-poste	Briefmarke, Freimarke, Postmarke	Sello de correos	Francobollo postale
Postal fiscal stamp	Timbre fiscal-postal	Stempelmarke als Postmarke verwendet	Sello fiscal-postal	Fiscale postale
Postmark	Oblitération postale	Poststempel	Matasello	Bollo
Printing	Impression, Tirage	Druck	Impresión	Stampa, Tiratura
Proof	Épreuve	Druckprobe	Prueba de impresión	Prova
Provisionals	Timbres provisoires	Provisorische Marken, Provisorien	Provisionales	Provvisori

lish	*French*	*German*	*Spanish*	*Italian*
ssian Blue	Bleu de Prusse	Preussischblau	Azul de Prusia	Azzurro di Prussia
ple	Pourpre	Purpur	Púrpura	Porpora
ple-brown	Brun-pourpre	Purpurbraun	Castaño púrpura	Bruno porpora
cess-printing	Impression en taille douce	Tiefdruck	Grabado	Incisione
d	Rouge	Rot	Rojo	Rosso
d-brown	Brun-rouge	Rotbraun	Castaño rojizo	Bruno rosso
ddish Lilac	Lilas rougeâtre	Rötlichlila	Lila rojizo	Lilla rossastro
ddish Purple	Pourpre-rouge	Rötlichpurpur	Púrpura rojizo	Porpora rossastro
ddish Violet	Violet rougeâtre	Rötlichviolett	Violeta rojizo	Violetto rossastro
d-orange	Orange rougeâtre	Rotorange	Naranja rojizo	Arancio rosso
gistration stamp	Timbre pour lettre chargée (recommandée)	Einschreibemarke	Sello de certificado	Francobollo per lettere raccomandate
print	Réimpression	Neudruck	Reimpresión	Ristampa
versed	Retourné	Umgekehrt	Invertido	Rovesciato
se	Rose	Rosa	Rosa	Rosa
se-red	Rouge rosé	Rosarot	Rojo rosado	Rosso rosa
sine	Rose vif	Lebhaftrosa	Rosa vivo	Rosa vivo
ulette	Percage	Durchstich	Picadura	Foratura
uletted	Percé	Durchstochen	Picado	Forato
yal Blue	Bleu-roi	Königblau	Azul real	Azzurro reale
ge Green	Vert-sauge	Salbeigrün	Verde salvia	Verde salvia
lmon	Saumon	Lachs	Salmón	Salmone
arlet	Écarlate	Scharlach	Escarlata	Scarlatto
pia	Sépia	Sepia	Sepia	Seppia
rpentine roulette	Percé en serpentin	Schlangenliniger Durchstich	Picado a serpentina	Perforazione a serpentina
ade	Nuance	Tönung	Tono	Gradazione de colore
eet	Feuille	Bogen	Hoja	Foglio
ate	Ardoise	Schiefer	Pizarra	Ardesia
ate-blue	Bleu-ardoise	Schieferblau	Azul pizarra	Azzurro ardesia
ate-green	Vert-ardoise	Schiefergrün	Verde pizarra	Verde ardesia
ate-lilac	Lilas-gris	Schieferlila	Lila pizarra	Lilla ardesia
ate-purple	Mauve-gris	Schieferpurpur	Púrpura pizarra	Porpora ardesia
ate-violet	Violet-gris	Schieferviolett	Violeta pizarra	Violetto ardesia
pecial delivery stamp	Timbre pour exprès	Eilmarke	Sello de urgencia	Francobollo per espressi
pecimen	Spécimen	Muster	Muestra	Saggio
teel Blue	Bleu acier	Stahlblau	Azul acero	Azzurro acciaio
trip	Bande	Streifen	Tira	Striscia
urcharge	Surcharge	Aufdruck	Sobrecarga	Soprastampa
ête-bêche	Tête-bêche	Kehrdruck	Tête-bêche	Tête-bêche
inted paper	Papier teinté	Getöntes Papier	Papel coloreado	Carta tinta
oo-late stamp	Timbre pour lettres en retard	Verspätungsmarke	Sello para cartas retardadas	Francobollo per le lettere in ritardo
urquoise-blue	Bleu-turquoise	Türkisblau	Azul turquesa	Azzurro turchese
urquoise-green	Vert-turquoise	Türkisgrün	Verde turquesa	Verde turchese
ypography	Typographie	Buchdruck	Tipografia	Tipografia
ltramarine	Outremer	Ultramarin	Ultramar	Oltremare
nused	Neuf	Ungebraucht	Nuevo	Nuovo
Used	Oblitéré, Usé	Gebraucht	Usado	Usato
Venetian Red	Rouge-brun terne	Venezianischrot	Rojo veneciano	Rosso veneziano
Vermilion	Vermillon	Zinnober	Cinabrio	Vermiglione
Violet	Violet	Violett	Violeta	Violetto
Violet-blue	Bleu-violet	Violettblau	Azul violeta	Azzurro violetto
Watermark	Filigrane	Wasserzeichen	Filigrana	Filigrana
Watermark sideways	Filigrane couché	Wasserzeichen liegend	Filigrana acostado	Filigrana coricata
Wove paper	Papier ordinaire, Papier uni	Einfaches Papier	Papel avitelado	Carta unita
Yellow	Jaune	Gelb	Amarillo	Giallo
Yellow-brown	Brun-jaune	Gelbbraun	Castaño amarillo	Bruno giallo
Yellow-green	Vert-jaune	Gelbgrün	Verde amarillo	Verde giallo
Yellow-olive	Olive jaunâtre	Gelboliv	Oliva amarillo	Oliva giallastro
Yellow-orange	Orange jaunâtre	Gelborange	Naranja amarillo	Arancio giallastro
Zig-zag roulette	Percé en zigzag	Sägezahnartiger Durchstich	Picado en zigzag	Perforazione a zigzag

Specialist Philatelic Societies

Requests for inclusion on this page should · sent to the Catalogue Editor.

reat Britain Philatelic Society
embership Secretary—Mr. A. G. Lajer
ne Old Post Office, Hurst,
erks RG10 0TR

reat Britain Decimal Stamp Book Study rcle
embership Secretary—Mr. A. J. Wilkins,
Buttermere Close, Brierley Hill,
'est Midlands DY5 3SD

reat Britain Collectors' Club
ecretary—Mr. Parker A. Bailey Jr,
Greenwood Road, Merrimack,
H03054, U.S.A.

hannel Islands Specialists Society
embership Secretary—Mr. R. Osborne,
Overlord Close, Broxbourne, Herts
N10 7TG

---

scension Study Circle
ecretary—Dr. R. C. F. Baker
reys, Tower Road, Whitstable, Kent
T5 2ER

ustralian States Study Circle
oyal Sydney Philatelic Club
onorary Secretary—Mr. B. Palmer
.P.O. Box 1751, Sydney, N.S.W. 1043,
ustralia

ritish Society of Australian Philately
ecretary—Mr. A. J. Griffiths
/o The British Philatelic Centre,
07 Charterhouse Street,
ondon EC1M 6PT

ociety of Australasian Specialists/Oceania
ecretary—Mr. S. Leven
.O. Box 24764, San Jose, CA 95154-4764,
U.S.A.

Bechuanalands and Botswana Society
Membership Secretary—Mr. N. Midwood
9 Porlock Lane, Furzton, Milton Keynes
MK4 1JY

Bermuda Collectors Society
Secretary—Mr. T. J. McMahon
P.O. Box 1949, Stuart, FL 34995, U.S.A.

British Caribbean Philatelic Study Group
Overseas Director—Mr. D. N. Druett
Pennymead Auctions, 1 Brewerton Street,
Knaresborough, North Yorkshire HG5 8AZ

British West Indies Study Circle
Membership Secretary—Mr. P. G. Boulton
84 Tangier Road, Richmond, Surrey
TW10 5DN

Burma Philatelic Study Circle
Secretary—Mr. A. Meech
7208-91 Avenue, Edmonton, Alberta,
Canada T6B 0R8

Ceylon Study Circle
Secretary—Mr. R.W.P. Frost
42 Lonsdale Road, Cannington, Bridgwater,
Somerset TA5 2JS

Cyprus Study Circle
Membership Secretary— Mr. J. Wigmore,
19 Riversmeet, Appledore, Bideford,
North Devon EX39 1RE

East Africa Study Circle
Hon. Secretary—Mr. K. Hewitt
16 Ashleigh Road,
Solihull, B91 1AE

Falklands Islands Study Group
Membership Secretary—Mr. D. W. A. Jeffery
38 Bradstock Road, Stoneleigh, Epsom,
Surrey KT17 2LH

Hong Kong Study Circle
Membership Secretary—Mr. P. V. Ball
37 Hart Court, Newcastle-under-Lyme,
Staffordshire ST5 2AL

Indian Ocean Study Circle
Secretary—Mr. K. B. Fitton
50 Firlands, Weybridge, Surrey KT13 0HR

India Study Circle
Secretary—Mr. C. Haines
134a North View Road, London N8 7LP

Irish Philatelic Circle
General Secretary—Mr. F. McDonald
63 Rafters Road
Drimnagh, Dublin 12, Ireland

King George V Silver Jubilee Study Circle
Secretary—Mr. N. Levinge
80 Towcester Road, Northampton
NN4 8LQ

King George VI Collectors Society
Secretary—Mr. F. R. Lockyer, OBE
98 Albany, Manor Road, Bournemouth,
Dorset BH1 3EW

Kiribati and Tuvalu Philatelic Society
Honorary Secretary—Mr. M. J. Shaw
88 Stoneleigh Avenue, Worcester Park,
Surrey KT4 8XY

Malaya Study Group
Secretary—Mr. J. Robertson
12 Lisa Court, Downsland Road,
Basingstoke, Hampshire RG21 8TU

Malta Study Circle
Hon Secretary—Mr. D. Crookes
9a Church Street
Durham DH1 3DG

New Zealand Society of Great Britain
General Secretary—Mr. K. C. Collins
13 Briton Crescent, Sanderstead,
Surrey CR2 0JN.

Orange Free State Study Circle
Secretary—Mr. J. R. Stroud
28 Oxford Street, Burnham-on-Sea,
Somerset TA8 1LQ

Pacific Islands Study Circle
Honorary Secretary—Mr. J. D. Ray
24 Woodvale Avenue, London SE25 4AE

Papuan Philatelic Society
Secretary—Mr. D. C. Ashton
71, Lowerside, Ham, Plymouth, Devon
PL2 2HU

Pitcairn Islands Study Group (U.K.)
Honorary Secretary—Mr. D. Sleep
6 Palace Gardens, 100 Court Road, Eltham,
London SE9 5NS

Rhodesian Study Circle
Secretary—Mr. R. G. Barnett
2 Cox Ley, Hatfield Heath,
Bishop's Stortford, CM22 7ER

St. Helena, Ascension and Tristan da Cunha Philatelic Society
Secretary—Mr. J. Havill
205 N. Murray Blvd., #221, Colorado
Springs, CO 80916, U.S.A.

Sarawak Specialists Society (also Brunei, North Borneo and Labuan)
Secretary—Dr. J. Higgins
31 Grimston Road, Kings Lynn,
Norfolk PE30 3HT

South African Collectors' Society
General Secretary—Mr. R. Ross
28 Duddon Drive, Barrow-in-Furness,
Cumbria LA14 3TW

Philatelic Society of Sri Lanka
Secretary—Mr. H. Goonawardena, J.P.
44A Hena Road, Mt. Lavinia 10370,
Sri Lanka.

Sudan Study Group
Secretary—Mr. N. D. Collier
34 Padleys Lane, Burton Joyce,
Nottingham NG14 5BZ

Transvaal Study Circle
Secretary—Mr. J. Woolgar
132 Dale Street, Chatham, Kent ME4 6QH

West Africa Study Circle
Secretary—Mr. J. Powell
23 Brook Street, Edlesborough, Dunstable,
Bedfordshire LU6 2JG

Select Bibliography

The literature on British Commonwealth stamps is vast, but works are often difficult to obtain once they are out of print. The selection of books below has been made on the basis of authority together with availability to the general reader, either as new or secondhand. Very specialised studies, and those covering aspects of postal history to which there are no references in the catalogue, have been excluded.

The following abbreviations are used to denote publishers:
CRL–Christie's Robson Lowe; HH–Harry Hayes; PB–Proud Bailey Co. Ltd. and Postal History Publications Co.; PC–Philip Cockrill; RPSL–Royal Philatelic Society, London; SG–Stanley Gibbons Ltd.

Where no publisher is quoted, the book is published by its author.

GENERAL. *Encyclopaedia of British Empire Postage Stamps.* Vols 1–6. Edited Robson Lowe. (CRL, 1951–1991)

Specimen Stamps of the Crown Colonies 1857–1948. Marcus Samuel. (RPSL, 1976 and 1984 Supplement)

Cancelled by Perkins Bacon. P. Jaffé. (Spink & Son Ltd, 1998)

U.P.U. Specimen Stamps. J. Bendon. (1988)

King George V Key Plates of the Imperium Postage and Revenue Design. P. Fernbank. (West Africa Study Circle, 1997)

Silver Jubilee of King George V Stamps Handbook. A.J. Ainscough. (Ainweel Developments, 1985)

The Commemorative Stamps of the British Commonwealth. H.D.S. Haverbeck. (Faber, 1955)

The Printings of King George VI Colonial Stamps. W.J.W. Potter & Lt-Col R.C.M. Shelton. (1952 and later facsimile edition)

King George VI Large Key Type Stamps of Bermuda, Leeward Islands, Nyasaland. R.W. Dickgiesser and E.P. Yendall. (Triad Publications, 1985)

Madame Joseph Forged Postmarks. D. Worboys (RPSL, 1994)

G.B. Used Abroad: Cancellations and Postal Markings. J. Parmenter. (The Postal History Society, 1993)

GREAT BRITAIN. For extensive bibliographies see *G.B. Specialised Catalogues. Vols 1-5.*

Stamps and Postal History of the Channel Islands. W. Newport. (Heineman, 1972)

ADEN. *The Postal History of British Aden 1839–67.* Major R.W. Pratt. (PB, 1985)

ASCENSION. *Ascension. The Stamps and Postal History.* J.H. Attwood. (CRL, 1981)

AUSTRALIA. *The Postal History of New South Wales 1788–1901.* Edited J.S. White (Philatelic Assoc of New South Wales, 1988)

South Australia. The Long Stamps 1902–12. J.R.W. Purves. (Royal Philatelic Society of Victoria, 1978)

The Departmental Stamps of South Australia. A.R. Butler. (RPSL, 1978)

A Priced Listing of the Departmental Stamps of South Australia. A.D. Presgrave (2nd edition, 1999)

Stamps and Postal History of Tasmania. W.E. Tinsley. (RPSL, 1986)

The Pictorial Stamps of Tasmania 1899–1912. K.E. Lancaster. (Royal Philatelic Society of Victoria, 1986)

The Stamps of Victoria. G. Kellow. B. & K. Philatelic Publishing, 1990)

Western Australia. The Stamps and Postal History. Ed. M. Hamilton and B. Pope. (W. Australian Study Group, 1979)

Postage Stamps and Postal History of Western Australia. Vols 1–3. M. Juhl. (1981–83)

The Chapman Collection of Australian Commonwealth Stamps. R. Chapman. (Royal Philatelic Society of Victoria, 1999)

The Postal History of British New Guinea and Papua 1885–1942. R. Lee. (CRL, 1983)

Norfolk Island. A Postal and Philatelic History, 1788–1969. P. Collas & R. Breckon. (B.& K. Philatelic Publishing, 1997)

BAHAMAS. *The Postage Stamps and Postal History of the Bahamas.* H.G.D. Gisburn. (SG, 1950 and later facsimile edition)

BARBADOS. *The Stamps of Barbados.* E.A. Bayley. (1989)

Advanced Barbados Philately. H.F. Deakin. (B.W.I. Study Circle, 1997)

BASUTOLAND. *The Cancellations and Postal Markings of Basutoland/Lesotho Post Offices.* A.H. Scott. (Collectors Mail Auctions (Pty) Ltd, 1980)

BATUM. *British Occupation of Batum.* P.T. Ashford. (1989)

BECHUANALAND. *The Postage Stamps, Postal Stationery and Postmarks of the Bechuanalands.* H.R. Holmes. (RPSL, 1971)

BERMUDA. *The Postal History and Stamps of Bermuda.* M.H. Ludington (Quarterman Publications Inc., 1978)

The King George V High-value Stamps of Bermuda, 1917–1938. M. Glazer. (Calaby Publishers, 1994)

BRITISH GUIANA. *The Postage Stamps and Postal History of British Guiana.* W.A. Townsend and F.G. Howe. (RPSL, 1970)

BRITISH HONDURAS. *The Postal History of British Honduras.* Edward B. Proud. (PB, 1999)

BRITISH OCCUPATION OF GERMAN COLONIES. *G.R.I.* R.M. Gibbs. (CRL, 1989)

BRITISH POSTAL AGENCIES IN EASTERN ARABIA. *The Postal Agencies in Eastern Arabia and the Gulf.* N. Donaldson (HH, 1975) and Supplement (Bridger & Kay Guernsey Ltd, 1994)

BRITISH SOLOMON ISLANDS. *British Solomon Islands Protectorate. Its Postage Stamps and Postal History.* H.G.D. Gisburn. (T. Sanders (Philatelist) Ltd, 1956)

BRITISH WEST AFRICA. *The Postal History and Handstamps of British West Africa.* C. McCaig. (CRL, 1978)

BURMA. *Burma Postal History.* G. Davis and D. Martin. (CRL, 1971 and 1987 Supplement).

CAMEROONS. *The Postal Arrangements of the Anglo-French Cameroons Expeditionary Force 1914–16.* R.J. Maddocks. (1996)

CANADA. *The Postage Stamps and Postal History of Newfoundland.* W.S. Boggs. (Quarterman Publications Inc., 1975)

Stamps of British North America. F. Jarrett. (Quarterman Publications Inc., 1975)

The Postage Stamps and Postal History of Canac W.S. Boggs. (Quarterman Publications In 1974)

The First Decimal Issue of Canada 1859–(G. Whitworth. (RPSL, 1966)

The Five Cents Beaver Stamp of Canac G. Whitworth. (RPSL, 1985)

The Edward VII Issue of Canada. G.C. Marl (National Postal Museum, Canada, 1975)

The Admiral Issue of Canada. G.C. Marl (American Philatelic Society, 1982)

CYPRUS. *Cyprus 1353–1986.* W. Castle. (CR 3rd edition, 1987)

DOMINICA. *Dominica Postal History, Stam and Postal Stationery to 1935.* E.V. To (B.W.I. Study Circle, 1994)

EGYPT. *Egypt Stamps & Postal History.* P.A. Smith. (James Bendon, 1999)

FALKLAND ISLANDS. *The Postage Stamps the Falkland Islands and Dependencies.* B.S.I Grant. (SG, 1952 and later facsimile edition)

The Falkland Islands Philatelic Digest. Nos. 1 & M. Barton and R. Spafford. (HH, 1975 & 197

The De La Rue Definitives of the Falkland Islan 1901–29. J.P. Bunt. (1986 and 19 Supplement)

The War Stamp Overprints of the Falkland Islan 1918–20. J.P. Bunt. (1981)

The Falkland Islands. Printings of the Pictor Issue of 1938–49. C.E. Glass. (CRL, 1979)

FIJI. *Fiji Philatelics.* D.W.F. Alford. (Paci Islands Study Circle, 1994)

The Postal History of Fiji 1911–1952. J.(Rodger. (Pacific Islands Study Circle, 1991).

GAMBIA. *The Stamps and Postal History of t Gambia.* Edited J.O. Andrew. (CRL, 1985)

The Postal History of the Gambia. E.B. Prou (PB, 1994)

GIBRALTAR. *Posted in Gibraltar.* W. Hin Haycock. (CRL, 1978 and 1983 Supplement)

Gibraltar. The Postal History and Postage Stamp Vol 1 (to 1885). G. Osborn. (Gibraltar Stud Circle, 1995)

The Postal History of Gibraltar. R.J.M. Garcia (E.B. Proud. (PB, 1998)

GOLD COAST. *The Postal History of the Gol Coast.* E.B. Proud (PB, 1995)

The Postal Services of the Gold Coast, 1901–195 Edited by M. Ensor. (West Africa Study Circle 1998)

HONG KONG. *The Philatelic History of Hon Kong. Vol 1.* (Hong Kong Study Circle, 1984)

Hong Kong Postage Stamps of the Queen Victori Period. R.N. Gurevitch (1993)

Hong Kong. The 1898 10c. on 30c. Provisiona Issue. A.M. Chu. (1998)

British Post Offices in the Far East. E.B. Proud (PB, 1991)

Cancellations of the Treaty Ports of Hong Kong H. Schoenfeld. (1988)

The Crown Colony of Wei Hai Wei. M. Goldsmit and C.W. Goodwyn. (RPSL, 1985)

INDIA. *C.E.F. The China Expeditionary Force 1900–1923.* D.S. Virk, J.C. Hume, D. Lang. G. Sattin. (Philatelic Congress of India, 1992)

India Used Abroad. V.S. Dastur. (Mysore Philatelics, 1982)

A Handbook on Gwalior Postal History and Stamps. V.K. Gupta. (1980)

The Stamps of Jammu & Kashmir. F. Staal. (The Collectors Club, 1983)

rath Stamps and Postal History. R.A. Malaviya. (Ravi Prakashan, 1999)

:AQ. *The Postal History of Iraq*. P.C. Pearson and E.B. Proud. (PB, 1996)

ELAND. *Irish Stamp Booklets 1931–1991*. C.I. Dulin (1998)

AMAICA. *Encyclopaedia of Jamaican Philately. Vol 1*. D. Sutcliffe & S. Jarvis (1997); *Vol 6*. S. Jarvis (2001) (B.W.I. Study Circle)

ENYA. *British East Africa. The Stamps and Postal Stationery*. J. Minns. (RPSL, 1982 and 1990 Supplement)

ie Postal History of Kenya. E.B. Proud (PB, 1992)

EEWARD ISLANDS. *The Leeward Islands—Notes for Philatelists*. M.N. Oliver (B.W.I. Study Circle, 2000)

ALAYA. *The Postal History of British Malaya. Vols 1–3*. E.B. Proud. (PB, 1982–84)

ie Postage Stamps of Federated Malay States. W.A. Reeves. (Malaya Study Group, 1978)

edah and Perlis. D.R.M. Holley. (Malaya Study Group, 1995)

elantan. Its Stamps and Postal History. W.A. Reeves and B.E. Dexter. (Malaya Study Group, 1992)

he Postal History of the Occupation of Malaya and British Borneo 1941–1945. E.B. Proud and M.D. Rowell. (PB, 1992)

ALTA. *Malta. The Postal History and Postage Stamps*. Edited R.E. Martin. (CRL, 1980 and 1985 Supplement)

AURITIUS. *The Postal History and Stamps of Mauritius*. P. Ibbotson (RPSL, 1991) revisions and additions Supplement (Indian Ocean Study Circle, 1995)

IONTSERRAT. *Montserrat to 1965*. L.E. Britnor (B.W.I. Study Circle, 2nd edition, 1998)

IOROCCO AGENCIES. *British Post Offices and Agencies in Morocco 1857–1907 and Local Posts 1891–1914*. R.K. Clough. (Gibraltar Study Circle, 1984)

IEW ZEALAND. *The Postage Stamps of New Zealand. Vols I–VII*. (Royal Philatelic Society of New Zealand, 1939–98)

The Early Cook Islands Post Office. A.R. Burge. (Hawthorn Press, 1978)

The Postal History and Postage Stamps of the Tokelau/Union Islands. A.H. Burgess. (Pacific Islands Study Circle, 2nd edition, 1998)

A Postal History of the Samoan Islands (Parts I and II). Edited R. Burge. (Royal Philatelic Society of New Zealand, 1987–89)

NIGERIA. *The Stamps and Postal History of the Niger Territories and the Niger Coast Protectorate*. M.P. Nicholson. (PC, 1982)

The Local Bisects and Surcharges of the Oil Rivers and Niger Coast 1893–94. M.P. Nicholson. (PC, 1982)

The Stamps and Postal History of Southern Nigeria. M.P. Nicholson. (PC, 1982)

The Postal Services of the British Nigeria Region. J. Ince and J. Sacher. (RPSL, 1992)

The Postal History of Nigeria. E.B. Proud. (PB, 1995)

NORTH BORNEO. *A Concise Guide to the Queen Issues of Labuan*. R. Price. (Sarawak Specialists Society, 1991)

The Stamps and Postal History of North Borneo. Parts 1–3. L.H. Shipman and P.K. Cassells. (Sarawak Specialists Society, 1976–88)

NYASALAND. *The Postal History of Nyasaland*. E.B. Proud. (PB, 1997)

PITCAIRN ISLANDS. *Pitcairn Islands Philately*. D.E. Hume. (2nd edition, 1999)

RHODESIA. *Mashonaland. A Postal History 1890–96*. Dr. A. R. Drysdall and D. Collis (CRL, 1990)

Rhodesia. A Postal History. R.C. Smith. (1967 and 1970 Supplement)

ST. HELENA. *St. Helena, Postal History and Stamps*. E. Hibbert. (CRL, 1979)

ST. KITTS-NEVIS. *A Study of the King George VI Stamps of St. Kitts-Nevis*. P.L. Baldwin. (Murray Payne Ltd. 2nd edition 1997)

The Philately of Nevis. F. Borromeo (British West Indies Study Circle, 2001)

SARAWAK. *The Stamps and Postal History of Sarawak*. W.A. Forrester-Wood. (Sarawak Specialists Society, 1959 and 1970 Supplement)

Sarawak: The Issues of 1871 and 1875. W. Batty-Smith and W. Watterson

SIERRA LEONE. *The Postal Service of Sierra Leone*. P.O. Beale. (RPSL, 1988)

The Postal History of Sierra Leone. E.B. Proud. (PB, 1994)

Sierra Leone King George VI Definitive Stamps. F. Walton (West Africa Study Circle, 2001)

SOUTH AFRICA. *Postmarks of the Cape of Good Hope*. R. Goldblatt. (Reijger Publishers (Pty) Ltd., 1984)

Stamps of the Orange Free State. Parts 1–3. G.D. Buckley & W.B. Marriott. (O.F.S. Study Circle, 1967–80)

Transvaal Philately. Edited I.B. Mathews. (Reijger Publishers (Pty) Ltd, 1986)

Transvaal. The Provisional Issues of the First British Occupation. Dr. A.R. Drysdall. (James Bendon, 1994)

The Wherewithal of Wolmaransstad. H. Birkhead and J. Groenewald (Philatelic Foundation of Southern Africa, 1999)

SOUTH WEST AFRICA. *The Overprinted Stamps of South West Africa to 1930*. N. Becker. (Philatelic Holdings (Pty) Ltd, 1990)

SUDAN. *Sudan. The Stamps and Postal Stationery of 1867 to 1970*. E.C.W. Stagg. (HH, 1977)

TANGANYIKA. *The Postal History of Tanganyika. 1915-1961*. E.B. Proud. (PB, 1989)

TOGO. *Togo–The Postal History of the Anglo-French Occupation 1914-22*. J. Martin and F. Walton. (West Africa S.C., 1995)

TRANSJORDAN. *The Stamps of Jordan 1920–1965*. A.H. Najjar. (Sahara Publications Ltd, 1998)

TRINIDAD AND TOBAGO. *The Postal History of Trinidad and Tobago*. J.C. Aleong and E.B. Proud. (PB, 1997)

TRISTAN DA CUNHA. *The History and Postal History of Tristan da Cunha*. G. Crabb. (1980)

TURKS AND CAICOS ISLANDS. *Turks Islands and Caicos Islands to 1950*. J.J. Challis. (Roses Caribbean Philatelic Society, 1983)

UGANDA. *The Postal History of Uganda and Zanzibar*. E.B. Proud (PB, 1993)

STANLEY GIBBONS STAMP CATALOGUE

COMMONWEALTH & BRITISH EMPIRE

1840–1952

(formerly Part 1)

105th EDITION—2003

Great Britain

'AMPS ON COVER. Prices are quoted, as a third price umn, for those Victorian and Edwardian issues usually found ed on cover. In general these prices refer to the cheapest rsion of each basic stamp with other shades, plates or varieties, gether with unusual frankings and postmarks, being worth ore.

NITED KINGDOM OF GREAT BRITAIN AND IRELAND

QUEEN VICTORIA

20 June 1837—22 January 1901

IULREADY ENVELOPES AND LETTER SHEETS, so called n the name of the designer, William Mulready, were issued currently with the first British adhesive stamps.

1d. black

Envelopes: £250 *unused*; £300 *used*.
Letter Sheets: £225 *unused*; £275 *used*.

2d. blue

Envelopes: £325 *unused*; £850 *used*.
Letter Sheets: £300 *unused*; £800 *used*.

LINE-ENGRAVED ISSUES

GENERAL NOTES

Brief notes on some aspects of the line-engraved stamps follow, for further information and a full specialist treatment of these es collectors are recommended to consult Volume 1 of the Stanley bons *Great Britain Specialised Catalogue*.

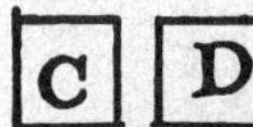

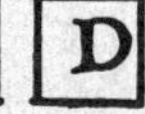

Alphabet I

Alphabet II

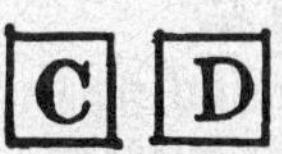

Alphabet III

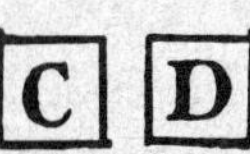

Alphabet IV

Typical Corner Letters of the four Alphabets

Alphabets. Four different styles were used for the corner letters stamps prior to the issue with letters in all four corners, these ing known to collectors as:

Alphabet I. Used for all plates made from 1840 to the end of 1851. etters small.

Alphabet II. Plates from 1852 to mid-1855. Letters larger, avier and broader.

Alphabet III. Plates from mid-1855 to end of period. Letters tall d more slender.

Alphabet IV. 1861. 1d. Die II, Plates 50 and 51 only. Letters were and-engraved instead of being punched on the plate. They are erefore inconsistent in shape and size but generally larger and itstanding.

While the general descriptions and the illustrations of typical letters ven above may be of some assistance, only long experience and blished aids can enable every stamp to be allocated to its particular lphabet without hesitation, as certain letters in each are similar to ose in one of the others.

Blue Paper. The blueing of the paper of the earlier issues is elieved to be due to the presence of prussiate of potash in the printing k, or in the paper, which, under certain conditions, tended to colour e paper when the sheets were damped for printing. An alternative rm is bleuté paper.

Corner Letters. The corner letters on the early British stamps ere intended as a safeguard against forgery, each stamp in the sheet aving a different combination of letters. Taking the first 1d. stamp, printed in 20 horizontal rows of 12, as an example, the lettering is as follows:

Row 1. A A, A B, A C, etc. to A L.

Row 2. B A, B B, B C, etc. to B L.

and so on to

Row 20. T A, T B, T C, etc. to T L.

On the stamps with four corner letters, those in the upper corners are in the reverse positions to those in the lower corners. Thus in a sheet of 240 (12 × 20) the sequence is:

Row 1. AA/AA BA/AB CA/AC etc. to LA/AL

Row 2. AB/BA BB/BB CB/BC etc. to LB/BL

and so on to

Row 20. AT/TA BT/TB CT/TC etc. to LT/TL

Placing letters in all four corners was not only an added precaution against forgery but was meant to deter unmarked parts of used stamps being pieced together and passed off as an unused whole.

Dies. The first die of the 1d. was used for making the original die of the 2d., both the No Lines and White Lines issues. In 1855 the 1d. Die I was amended by retouching the head and deepening the lines on a transferred impression of the original. This later version, known to collectors as Die II, was used for making the dies for the 1d. and 2d. with letters in all four corners and also for the 1½d.

The two dies are illustrated above No. 17 in the catalogue.

Double letter

Guide line in corner

Guide line through value

Double Corner Letters. These are due to the workman placing his letter-punch in the wrong position at the first attempt, when lettering the plate, and then correcting the mistake; or to a slight shifting of the punch when struck. If a wrong letter was struck in the first instance, traces of a wrong letter may appear in a corner in addition to the correct one. A typical example is illustrated.

Guide Lines and Dots. When laying down the impressions of the design on the early plates, fine vertical and horizontal guide lines were marked on the plates to assist the operative. These were usually removed from the gutter margins, but could not be removed from the stamp impressions without damage to the plate, so that in such cases they appear on the printed stamps, sometimes in the corners, sometimes through "POSTAGE" or the value. Typical examples are illustrated.

Guide dots or cuts were similarly made to indicate the spacing of the guide lines. These too sometimes appear on the stamps.

Ivory Head

"Ivory Head." The so-called "ivory head" variety is one in which the Queen's Head shows white on the back of the stamp. It arises from the comparative absence of ink in the head portion of the design, with consequent absence of blueing. (*See* "Blued Paper" note above.)

Line-engraving. In this context "line-engraved" is synonymous with recess-printing, in which the engraver cuts recesses in a plate and printing (the coloured areas) is from these recesses. "Line-engraved" is the traditional philatelic description for these stamps; other equivalent terms found are "engraving in *taille-douce*" (French) or "in *intaglio*" (Italian).

Plates. Until the introduction of the stamps with letters in all four corners, the number of the plate was not indicated in the design of the stamp, but was printed on the sheet margin. By long study of identifiable blocks and the minor variations in the design, coupled with the position of the corner letters, philatelists are now able to allot many of these stamps to their respective plates. Specialist collectors often endeavour to obtain examples of a given stamp printed from its different plates and our catalogue accordingly reflects this depth of detail.

Maltese Cross Type of Town postmark

Type of Penny Post cancellation

Example of 1844 type postmark

Postmarks. The so-called "Maltese Cross" design was the first employed for obliterating British postage stamps and was in use from 1840 to 1844. Being hand-cut, the obliterating stamps varied greatly in detail and some distinctive types can be allotted to particular towns or offices. Local types, such as those used at Manchester, Norwich, Leeds, etc., are keenly sought. A red ink was first employed, but was superseded by black, after some earlier experiments, in February 1841. Maltese Cross obliterations in other colours are rare.

Obliterations of this type, numbered 1 to 12 in the centre, were used at the London Chief Office in 1843 and 1844.

Some straight-line cancellations were in use in 1840 at the Penny Post receiving offices, normally applied on the envelope, the adhesives then being obliterated at the Head Office. They are nevertheless known, with or without Maltese Cross, on the early postage stamps.

In 1842 some offices in S.W. England used dated postmarks in place of the Maltese Cross, usually on the back of the letter since they were not originally intended as obliterators. These town postmarks have likewise been found on adhesives.

In 1844 the Maltese Cross design was superseded by numbered obliterators of varied type, one of which is illustrated. They are naturally comparatively scarce on the first 1d. and 2d. stamps. Like the Maltese Cross they are found in various colours, some of which are rare.

Re-entry

"Union Jack" re-entry

Re-entries. Re-entries on the plate show as a doubling of part of the design of the stamp generally at top or bottom. Many re-entries are very slight while others are most marked. A typical one is illustrated.

The "*Union Jack*" *re-entry*, so called owing to the effect of the re-entry on the appearance of the corner stars (*see illustration*) occurs on stamp L K of Plate 75 of the 1d. red, Die I.

T A (T L) M A (M L)
Varieties of Large Crown Watermark

I Two states of Large Crown Watermark II

'atermarks. Two watermark varieties, as illustrated, consisting of wns of entirely different shape, are found in sheets of the Large own paper and fall on stamps lettered M A and T A (or M L and T L n the paper is printed on the wrong side). Both varieties are found ne 1d. rose-red of 1857, while the M A (M L) variety comes also on e plates of the 1d. of 1864 (Nos. 43, 44) up to about Plate 96. On 2d. the T A (T L) variety is known on plates 8 and 9, and the M A L) on later prints of plate 9. These varieties may exist inverted, or rted reversed on stamps lettered A A and A L and H A and H L, some are known.

n 1861 a minor alteration was made in the Large Crown watermark he removal of the two vertical strokes, representing *fleurs-de-lis*, ch projected upwards from the uppermost of the three horizontal ves at the base of the Crown. Hence two states are distinguishable, llustrated.

NDITION—IMPERFORATE LINE-ENGRAVED ISSUES

he prices quoted for the 1840 and 1841 imperforate Line-raved issues are for "fine" examples. As condition is most ortant in assessing the value of a stamp, the following definitions assist collectors in the evaluation of individual examples.

'our main factors are relevant when considering quality.

a) **Impression.** This should be clean and the surface free of any bing or unnatural blurring which would detract from the earance.

b) **Margins.** This is perhaps the most difficult factor to evaluate. mps described as "fine", the standard adopted in this catalogue for cing purposes, should have margins of the recognised width, ined as approximately one half of the distance between two oining unsevered stamps. Stamps described as "very fine" or perb" should have margins which are proportionately larger than se of a "fine" stamp. Examples with close margins should not, nerally, be classified as "fine".

c) **Cancellation.** On a "fine" stamp this should be reasonably clear d not noticeably smudged. A stamp described as "superb" should ve a neat cancellation, preferably centrally placed or to the right.

d) **Appearance.** Stamps, at the prices quoted, should always be hout any tears, creases, bends or thins and should not be toned on her the front or back. Stamps with such defects are worth only a oportion of the catalogue price.

Good

Fine

Very Fine

Superb

The above actual size illustrations of 1840 1d. blacks show the arious grades of quality. When comparing these illustrations it hould be assumed that they are all from the same plate and that they re free of any hidden defects.

PRINTERS. Nos. 1/53*a* were recess-printed by Perkins, Bacon & Petch, known from 1852 as Perkins, Bacon & Co.

1

1*a*

2 Small Crown

(Eng Charles and Frederick Heath)

1840 (6 May). *Letters in lower corners. Wmk Small Crown. W* **2**. *Imperf.*

No.	*Type*		*Un*	*Used*	*Used on cover*
1	**1**	1d. intense black	£4250	£275	
2		1d. black	£3500	£200	£325
3		1d. grey-black (worn plate) ..	£3500	£275	
4	**1*a***	2d. deep full blue	£9000	£550	
5		2d. blue	£7500	£425	£950
6		2d. pale blue	£9000	£450	

The 1d. stamp in black was printed from Plates 1 to 11. Plate 1 exists in two states (known to collectors as 1*a* and 1*b*), the latter being the result of extensive repairs.

Repairs were also made to Plates 2, 5, 6, 8, 9, 10 and 11, and certain impressions exist in two or more states.

The so-called "Royal reprint" of the 1d. black was made in 1864, from Plate 66, Die II, on paper with Large Crown watermark, inverted. A printing was also made in carmine, on paper with the same watermark, normal.

For 1d. black with "VR" in upper corners *see* No. V1 under Official Stamps.

The 2d. stamps were printed from Plates 1 and 2.

Plates of 1d. black

Plate	*Un*	*Used*
1*a*	£5000	£225
1*b*	£3500	£200
2	£3500	£200
3	£4000	£250
4	£3500	£225
5	£3500	£200
6	£3500	£200
7	£3750	£225
8	£4000	£275
9	£4750	£325
10	£6000	£450
11	£5000	£2250

Varieties of 1d. black

		Un	*Used*
a.	On *bleuté* paper (Plates 1 to 8) .. *from*	—	£275
b.	Double letter in corner .. *from*	£3750	£250
bb.	Re-entry	£3750	£275
bc.	"PB" re-entry (Plate 5, 3rd state)	—	£4250
cc.	Large letters in each corner (E J, I L, J C and P A) (Plate 1*b*) .. .. .. *from*	£3750	£375
c.	Guide line in corner	£3750	£225
d.	,, ,, through value	£3750	£250
e.	Watermark inverted	£5000	£600
g.	Obliterated by Maltese Cross		
	In red	—	£225
	In black	—	£200
	In blue	—	£2750
	In magenta	—	£1100
	In yellow	—	—
h.	Obliterated by Maltese Cross with number in centre .. *from*		
	No. 1	—	£3250
	No. 2	—	£2250
	No. 3	—	£2250
	No. 4	—	£2250
	No. 5	—	£2250
	No. 6	—	£2250
	No. 7	—	£2250
	No. 8	—	£2250
	No. 9	—	£2250
	No. 10	—	£2250
	No. 11	—	—
	No. 12	—	£2250
i.	Obliterated "Penny Post" in black .. *from*	—	£1750
j.	Obliterated by town postmark (without Maltese Cross)		
	In black *from*	—	£1750
	In yellow *from*	—	£8000
	In red *from*	—	£1750
k.	Obliterated by 1844 type postmark in black *from*	—	£550

Plates of 2d. blue

Plate		*Un*	*Used*
1	*Shades from*	£7500	£425
2	*Shades from*	£8500	£475

Varieties of 2d. blue

		Un	*Used*
a.	Double letter in corner	—	£525
aa.	Re-entry	—	£575
b.	Guide line in corner	—	£475
c.	Guide line through value	—	£475
d.	Watermark inverted .. *from*	£14000	£2500
e.	Obliterated by Maltese Cross		
	In red	—	£475
	In black	—	£425
	In blue	—	£3750
	In magenta	—	£3250
f.	Obliterated by Maltese Cross with number in centre .. .. .. *from*		
	No. 1	—	£3250
	No. 2	—	£3250
	No. 3	—	£3500
	No. 4	—	£3250
	No. 5	—	£3250
	No. 6	—	£3500
	No. 7	—	£3250
	No. 8	—	£3250
	No. 9	—	£3750
	No. 10	—	£3500
	No. 11	—	£3500
	No. 12	—	£3500
g.	Obliterated "Penny Post" in black .. *from*	—	£2000
h.	Obliterated by town postmark (without Maltese Cross) in black .. *from*	—	£1900
i.	Obliterated by 1844 type postmark		
	In black *from*	—	£1100
	In blue *from*	—	£3250

1841 (10 Feb). *Printed from "black" plates. Wmk W* **2**. *Paper more or less blued. Imperf.*

No.	*Type*		*Un*	*Used*	*Used on cover*
7	**1**	1d. red-brown (*shades*)	£650	75·00	£140
		a. "PB" re-entry (Plate 5, 3rd state)	—	£1300	

The first printings of the 1d. in red-brown were made from Plates 1*b*, 2, 5 and 8 to 11 used for the 1d. black.

1d. red-brown from "black" plates

Plate	*Un*	*Used*
1*b*	£3500	£225
2	£2250	£190
5	£750	£110
8	£650	75·00
9	£650	75·00
10	£650	75·00
11	£650	75·00

1841 (late Feb). *Plate* 12 *onwards. Wmk W* **2**. *Paper more or less blued. Imperf.*

			Un	*Used*	*Used on cover*
8	**1**	1d. red-brown	£180	15·00	25·00
8*a*		1d. red-brown on very blue paper	£200	15·00	
9		1d. pale red-brown (worn plates)	£275	25·00	
10		1d. deep red-brown	£275	30·00	
11		1d. lake-red	£1000	£375	
12		1d. orange-brown ..	£425	£100	

Error. No letter "A" in right lower corner (*Stamp* B(A), *Plate* 77)

12*a*	**1**	1d. red-brown	—	£6000

The error "No letter A in right corner" was due to the omission to insert this letter on stamp B A of Plate 77. The error was discovered some months after the plate was registered and was then corrected.

There are innumerable variations in the colour and shade of the 1d. "red" and those given in the above list represent colour groups each covering a wide range.

Varieties of 1d. red-brown, etc.

		Un	*Used*
b.	Re-entry .. .. *from*	—	40·00
c.	Double letter in corner .. *from*	—	25·00
d.	Double Star (Plate 75) "Union Jack" re-entry	£8000	£850
e.	Guide line in corner	—	18·00
f.	Guide line through value	—	22·00
g.	Thick outer frame to stamp	—	22·00
h.	Ivory head	£210	22·00
i.	Watermark inverted	£550	£175
j.	Left corner letter "S" inverted (Plates 78, 105, 107) .. .. *from*	—	90·00
k.	P converted to R (Plates 30/1, 33, 83, 86) *from*	—	60·00
l.	Obliterated by Maltese Cross		
	In red	—	£1500
	In black	—	25·00
	In blue	—	£250
m.	Obliterated by Maltese Cross with number in centre		
	No. 1	—	60·00
	No. 2	—	60·00
	No. 3	—	80·00
	No. 4	—	£190
	No. 5	—	60·00
	No. 6	—	50·00
	No. 7	—	45·00
	No. 8	—	45·00
	No. 9	—	60·00
	No. 10	—	80·00
	No. 11	—	90·00
	No. 12	—	£125
n.	Obliterated "Penny Post" in black	—	£275
o.	Obliterated by town postmark (without Maltese Cross)		
	In black *from*	—	£200
	In blue *from*	—	£375
	In green *from*	—	£600
	In yellow *from*	—	—
	In red *from*	—	£2500
p.	Obliterated by 1844 type postmark		
	In blue *from*	—	90·00
	In red *from*	—	£1500
	In green *from*	—	£350
	In violet *from*	—	£900
	In black *from*	—	15·00

Stamps with thick outer frame to the design are from plates on which the frame-lines have been strengthened or recut, particularly Plates 76 and 90.

For "Union Jack" re-entry *see* General Notes to Line-engraved Issues.

In "P converted to R" the corner letter "R" is formed from the "P", the distinctive long tail having been hand-cut.

KEY TO LINE-ENGRAVED ISSUES

	Description	*Date*	*Wmk*	*Perf*	*Die*	*Alpha-bet*
	THE IMPERFORATE ISSUES					
	1d. black	6.5.40	SC	Imp	I	I
	2d. no lines	8.5.40	SC	Imp	I	I
	PAPER MORE OR LESS BLUED					
	1d. red-brown	Feb 1841	SC	Imp	I	I
	1d. red-brown	Feb 1841	SC	Imp	I	I
	1d. red-brown	6.2.52	SC	Imp	I	II
	2d. white lines	13.3.41	SC	Imp	I	I
	THE PERFORATED ISSUES					
	ONE PENNY VALUE					
	1d. red-brown	1848	SC	Roul	I	I
	1d. red-brown	1850	SC	16	I	I
	1d. red-brown	1853	SC	16	I	II
3	1d. red-brown	Feb 1854	SC	16	I	II
	1d. red-brown	Jan 1855	SC	14	I	II
	1d. red-brown	28.2.55	SC	14	II	II
	1d. red-brown	1.3.55	SC	16	II	II
	1d. red-brown	15.5.55	LC	16	II	II
3	1d. red-brown	Aug 1855	LC	14	II	III
	NEW COLOURS ON WHITE PAPER					
1	1d. rose-red	Nov 1856	LC	14	II	III
	1d. rose-red	26.12.57	LC	16	II	III
	1d. rose-red	1861	LC	14	II	IV
	TWO PENCE VALUE					
20	2d. blue	1.3.54	SC	16	I	I
	2d. blue	22.2.55	SC	14	I	I
	2d. blue	5.7.55	SC	14	I	II
	2d. blue	18.8.55	SC	16	I	II
	2d. blue	20.7.55	LC	16	I	II
	2d. blue	20.7.55	LC	14	I	II
	2d. blue	2.7.57	LC	14	I	III
	2d. blue	1.2.58	LC	16	I	III
	LETTERS IN ALL FOUR CORNERS					
	½d. rose-red	1.10.70	W **9**	14	—	
	1d. rose-red	1.4.64	LC	14	II	
	1½d. rosy mauve	1860	LC	14	II	
3	1½d. rose-red	1.10.70	LC	14	II	
	2d. blue	July 1858	LC	14	II	
7	2d. thinner lines	7.7.69	LC	14	II	

Watermarks: SC = Small Crown, T **2**.
LC = Large Crown, T **4**.
Dies: *See* notes above No. 17 in the catalogue.
Alphabets: *See* General Notes to this section.

3 White lines added

1 (13 Mar)–51. *White lines added. Wmk W* **2**. *Paper more or less blued. Imperf.*

			Un	*Used*	*Used on cover*
	3	2d. pale blue	£1800	70·00	
		2d. blue	£1500	60·00	£225
		2d. deep full blue ..	£2000	80·00	
aa		2d. violet-blue (1851) ..	£8000	£650	

The 2d. stamp with white lines was printed from Plates 3 and 4. No. 15*aa* came from Plate 4 and the price quoted is for examples on thicker, lavender tinted paper.

Plates of 2d. blue

Plate		*Un*	*Used*
3	*Shades from*	£1500	70·00
4	*Shades from*	£1750	60·00

Varieties of 2d. blue

		Un	*Used*
Guide line in corner		—	75·00
,, ,, through value		£1800	75·00
Double letter in corner		—	80·00
Re-entry		£2100	90·00
Ivory head		£1900	70·00
Watermark inverted		£3000	£350
Obliterated by Maltese Cross			
	In red	—	£7000
	In black	—	£100
	In blue	—	£1900
Obliterated by Maltese Cross with number in centre			
	No. 1	—	£250
	No. 2	—	£250
	No. 3	—	£250
	No. 4	—	£240
	No. 5	—	£350
	No. 6	—	£250
	No. 7	—	£475
	No. 8	—	£375
	No. 9	—	£475
	No. 10	—	£525
	No. 11	—	£350
	No. 12	—	£200
Obliterated by town postmark (without Maltese Cross)			
	In black *from*	—	£600
	In blue *from*	—	£1000

h. Obliterated by 1844 type postmark			
	In black *from*	—	60·00
	In blue *from*	—	£425
	In red *from*	—	£7000
	In green *from*	—	£1200

1841 (April). *Trial printing (unissued) on Dickinson silk-thread paper. No wmk. Imperf.*

16 **1** 1d. red-brown (Plate 11) £2750

Eight sheets were printed on this paper, six being gummed, two ungummed, but we have only seen examples without gum.

1848. *Wmk Small Crown, W* **2**. *Rouletted approx* 11½ *by Henry Archer.*

16*a* **1** 1d. red-brown (Plates 70, 71) £4750

1850. *Wmk Small Crown, W* **2**. *P* 16 *by Henry Archer.*

16*b* **1** 1d. red-brown (Alph 1) (from Plates 90–101) .. .. .. *from* £750 £275

Stamp on cover, dated prior to February 1854 (*price* £375); dated during or after February 1854 (*price* £275).

1853. *Government Trial Perforation. Wmk Small Crown. W* **2**.

16*c* **1** 1d. red-brown (*p* 16) (Alph II) (*on cover*) † £5750

SEPARATION TRIALS. Although the various trials of machines for rouletting and perforating were unofficial, Archer had the consent of the authorities in making his experiments, and sheets so experimented upon were afterwards used by the Post Office.

As Archer ended his experiments in 1850 and plates with corner letters Alphabet II did not come into issue until 1852, perforated stamps with corner letters of Alphabet I may safely be assumed to be Archer productions, if genuine.

The Government trial perforation is believed to have been done on Archer's machines after they had been purchased in 1853. As Alphabet II was by that time in use, the trials can only be distinguished from the perforated stamps listed below by being dated prior to 24 February 1854, the date when the perforated stamps were officially issued.

Die I Alphabet I, stamps from plates 74 and 113 perforated 14 have been recorded for many years, but it is now generally recognised that the type of comb machine used, producing one extension hole in the side margins, cannot be contemporary with other trials of this period.

Die I

Die II

4 Large Crown

Die I: The features of the portrait are lightly shaded and consequently lack emphasis.

Die II (Die I retouched): The lines of the features have been deepened and appear stronger.

The eye is deeply shaded and made more lifelike. The nostril and lips are more clearly defined, the latter appearing much thicker. A strong downward stroke of colour marks the corner of the mouth. There is a deep indentation of colour between lower lip and chin. The band running from the back of the ear to the chignon has a bolder horizontal line below it than in Die I.

The original die (Die I) was used to provide roller dies for the laying down of all the line-engraved stamps from 1840 to 1855. In that year a new master die was laid down (by means of a Die I roller die) and the impression was retouched by hand engraving by William Humphrys. This retouched die, always known to philatelists as Die II, was from that time used for preparing all new roller dies.

One Penny. The numbering of the 1d. plates recommenced at 1 on the introduction of Die II. Plates 1 to 21 were Alphabet II from which a scarce plum shade exists. Corner letters of Alphabet III appear on Plate 22 and onwards.

As an experiment, the corner letters were engraved by hand on Plates 50 and 51 in 1856, instead of being punched (Alphabet IV), but punching was again resorted to from Plate 52 onwards. Plates 50 and 51 were not put into use until 1861.

Two Pence. Unlike the 1d. the old sequence of plate numbers continued. Plates 3 and 4 of the 2d. had corner letters of Alphabet I, Plate 5 Alphabet II and Plate 6 Alphabet III. In Plate 6 the white lines are thinner than before.

1854–57. *Paper more or less blued. (a) Wmk Small Crown, W* **2**. *P* 16.

			Un	★ *Used*	*Used on cover*
17	**1**	1d. red-brown (Die I) (24.2.54)	£190	18·00	40·00
		a. Imperf three sides (horiz pair)	†	—	
18		1d. yellow brown (Die I) ..	£275	30·00	
19	**3**	2d. deep blue (Plate 4) (12.3.54)	£1800	85·00	£130
		a. Imperf three sides (horiz pair)	†	—	
20		2d. pale blue (Plate 4)	£1900	90·00	
20*a*		2d. blue (Plate 5) (18.8.55) ..	£4000	£250	£400
21	**1**	1d. red-brown (Die II) (22.2.55)	£275	50·00	90·00
		a. Imperf			
		(b) Wmk Small Crown, W **2**. *P* 14			
22	**1**	1d. red-brown (Die I) (1.55) ..	£450	60·00	£110
23	**3**	2d. blue (Plate 4) (22.2.55) ..	£2500	£180	£275
23*a*		2d. blue (Plate 5) (5.7.55) ..	£2250	£180	£275
		b. Imperf (Plate 5)			
24	**1**	1d. red-brown (Die II) (27.2.55)	£350	45·00	75·00
24*a*		1d. deep red-brown (very blue paper) (Die II)	£425	60·00	
25		1d. orange-brown (Die II) ..	£850	£110	
		(c) Wmk Large Crown, W **4**. *P* 16			
26	**1**	1d. red-brown (Die II) (15.5.55)	£700	80·00	£150
		a. Imperf (Plate 7)			
27	**3**	2d. blue (Plate 5) (20.7.55) ..	£3500	£250	£400
		a. Imperf	—	£2750	
		(d) Wmk Large Crown, W **4**. *P* 14			
29	**1**	1d. red-brown (Die II) (6.55) ..	£180	10·00	30·00
		a. Imperf (*shades*) (Plates 22, 24, 25, 32, 43)	£1300	£1000	
30		1d. brick-red (Die II)	£250	35·00	
31	**1**	1d. plum (Die II) (2.56)	£1200	£350	
32		1d. brown-rose (Die II)	£250	35·00	
33		1d. orange-brown (Die II) (3.57)	£375	40·00	
34	**3**	2d. blue (Plate 5) (20.7.55) ..	£1500	50·00	£130
35		2d. blue (Plate 6) (2.7.57) ..	£1600	50·00	£130
		a. Imperf	—	£4000	
		b. Imperf horiz (vert pair) ..	†	—	
★17/35a		**For well-centred, lightly used** ..		+125%	

1856–58. *Wmk Large Crown, W* **4**. *Paper no longer blued.*

		(a) P 16.			
36	**1**	1d. rose-red (Die II) (26.12.57) ..	£900	50·00	£130
36*a*	**3**	2d. blue (Plate 6) (1.2.58) ..	£3750	£200	£325
		(b) Die II. P 14			
37	**1**	1d. red-brown (11.56)	£375	£100	£225
38		1d. pale red (9.4.57)	75·00	15·00	
		a. Imperf	£700	£550	
39		1d. pale rose (3.57)	75·00	25·00	
40		1d. rose-red (9.57)	40·00	9·00	20·00
		a. Imperf	£700	£600	
		b. Imperf vert (horiz pair) ..	†	—	
41		1d. deep rose-red (7.57) ..	90·00	12·00	

1861. *Letters engraved on plate instead of punched (Alphabet IV).*

42	**1**	1d. rose-red (Die II) (Plates 50 and 51)	£190	30·00	50·00
		a. Imperf	—	£2100	
★36/42a		**For well-centred, lightly used** ..		+125%	

In both values, varieties may be found as described in the preceding issues—ivory heads, inverted watermarks, re-entries, and double letters in corners.

The change of perforation from 16 to 14 was decided upon late in 1854 since the closer holes of the former gauge tended to cause the sheets of stamps to break up when handled, but for a time both gauges were in concurrent use. Owing to faulty alignment of the impressions on the plates and to shrinkage of the paper when damped, badly perforated stamps are plentiful in the line-engraved issues.

5

6

Showing position of the plate number on the 1d. and 2d. values. (Plate 170 shown)

1858–79. *Letters in all four corners. Wmk Large Crown, W* **4**. *Die* II *(1d. and 2d.). P* 14.

			Un	★ *Used*	*Used on cover*
43	**5**	1d. rose-red (1.4.64)	15·00	2·00	6·00
44		1d. lake-red	15·00	2·00	
		a. Imperf .. .. *from*	£1100	£900	
★43/4a		**For well-centred, lightly used** ..		+125%	

Plate	*Un*	*Used*	*Plate*	*Un*	*Used*
71	35·00	3·00	133	£110	9·00
72	40·00	4·00	134	15·00	2·00
73	40·00	3·00	135	95·00	26·00
74	40·00	2·00	136	90·00	20·00
76	35·00	2·00	137	28·00	2·25
77	£100000	£80000	138	18·00	2·00
78	90·00	2·00	139	60·00	16·00
79	30·00	2·00	140	18·00	2·00
80	45·00	2·00	141	£110	9·00
81	45·00	2·25	142	70·00	24·00
82	90·00	4·00	143	60·00	15·00
83	£110	7·00	144	95·00	20·00
84	60·00	2·25	145	30·00	2·25
85	40·00	2·25	146	40·00	6·00
86	50·00	4·00	147	50·00	3·00
87	30·00	2·00	148	40·00	3·00
88	£130	8·00	149	40·00	6·00
89	40·00	2·00	150	15·00	2·00
90	40·00	2·00	151	60·00	9·00
91	55·00	6·00	152	60·00	5·50
92	35·00	2·00	153	£100	9·00
93	50·00	2·00	154	50·00	2·00
94	45·00	5·00	155	50·00	2·25
95	40·00	2·00	156	45·00	2·00
96	45·00	2·00	157	50·00	2·00
97	40·00	3·50	158	30·00	2·00
98	50·00	6·00	159	30·00	2·00
99	55·00	5·00	160	30·00	2·00
100	60·00	2·25	161	60·00	7·00
101	60·00	9·00	162	50·00	7·00
102	45·00	2·00	163	50·00	3·00
103	50·00	3·50	164	50·00	3·00
104	75·00	5·00	165	45·00	2·00
105	90·00	7·00	166	45·00	6·00
106	55·00	2·00	167	45·00	2·00
107	60·00	7·00	168	50·00	8·00
108	80·00	2·25	169	60·00	7·00
109	85·00	3·50	170	35·00	2·00
110	60·00	9·00	171	15·00	2·00
111	50·00	2·25	172	30·00	2·00
112	70·00	2·25	173	70·00	9·00
113	50·00	12·00	174	30·00	2·00
114	£250	12·00	175	60·00	3·50
115	90·00	2·25	176	60·00	2·25
116	75·00	9·00	177	40·00	2·00
117	45·00	2·00	178	60·00	3·50
118	50·00	2·00	179	50·00	2·25
119	45·00	2·00	180	60·00	5·00
120	15·00	2·00	181	45·00	2·00
121	40·00	9·50	182	90·00	5·00
122	15·00	2·00	183	55·00	3·00
123	40·00	2·00	184	30·00	2·25
124	28·00	2·00	185	50·00	3·00
125	40·00	2·00	186	65·00	2·25
127	55·00	2·25	187	50·00	2·00
129	40·00	8·00	188	70·00	10·00
130	55·00	2·25	189	70·00	7·00
131	65·00	16·00	190	50·00	6·00
132	£130	22·00	191	30·00	7·00

Plate	*Un*	*Used*	*Plate*	*Un*	*Used*
192	50·00	2·00	209	50·00	9·00
193	30·00	2·00	210	65·00	12·00
194	50·00	8·00	211	70·00	20·00
195	50·00	8·00	212	60·00	11·00
196	50·00	5·00	213	60·00	11·00
197	55·00	9·00	214	65·00	18·00
198	40·00	6·00	215	65·00	18·00
199	55·00	6·00	216	70·00	18·00
200	60·00	2·00	217	70·00	7·00
201	30·00	5·00	218	65·00	8·00
202	60·00	8·00	219	90·00	70·00
203	30·00	16·00	220	40·00	7·00
204	55·00	2·25	221	70·00	16·00
205	55·00	3·00	222	80·00	40·00
206	55·00	9·00	223	90·00	60·00
207	60·00	9·00	224	£100	50·00
208	55·00	16·00	225	£1250	£400

Error. Imperf. Issued at Cardiff (Plate 116)

		Un	*Used*
44*b* **5**	1d. rose-red (18.1.70)	£2250	£1500

The following plate numbers are also known imperf and used (No. 44a); 72, 79, 80, 81, 82, 83, 84, 85, 86, 87, 88, 90, 91, 92, 93, 96, 97, 98, 100, 101, 102, 103, 104, 105, 107, 108, 109, 112, 113, 114, 116, 117, 120, 121, 122, 136, 137, 142, 146, 148, 158, 162, 164, 166, 171, 174, 191 and 202.

The numbering of this series of 1d. red plates follows after that of the previous 1d. stamp, last printed from Plate 68.

Plates 69, 70, 75, 126 and 128 were prepared for this issue but rejected owing to defects, and stamps from these plates do not exist, so that specimens which appear to be from these plates (like many of those which optimistic collectors believe to be from Plate 77) bear other plate numbers. Owing to faulty engraving or printing it is not always easy to identify the plate number. Plate 77 was also rejected but some stamps printed from it were used. One specimen is in the Tapling Collection and six or seven others are known. Plates 226 to 228 were made but not used.

Specimens from most of the plates are known with inverted watermark. The variety of watermark described in the General Notes to this section occurs on stamp M A (or M L) on plates up to about 96 (*Prices from £110 used*).

Re-entries in this issue are few, the best being on stamps M K and T K of Plate 71 and on S L and T L, Plate 83.

			Un	*Used*	★ *Used on cover*
45	**6**	2d. blue (thick lines) (7.58)	£225	10·00	22·00
		a. Imperf (Plate 9)	—	£3750	
		Plate			
		7	£650	45·00	
		8	£600	32·00	
		9	£225	10·00	
		12	£1000	£110	
46		2d. blue (thin lines) (1.7.69)	£250	20·00	30·00
47		2d. deep blue (thin lines)	£250	20·00	
		a. Imperf (Plate 13)	£2750		
		Plate			
		13	£250	20·00	
		14	£300	25·00	
		15	£275	25·00	

★45/7 **For well-centred, lightly used** .. +125%

Plates 10 and 11 of the 2d. were prepared but rejected. Plates 13 to 15 were laid down from a new roller impression on which the white lines were thinner.

There are some marked re-entries and repairs, particularly on Plates 7, 8, 9 and 12.

Stamps with inverted watermark may be found and also the T A (T L) and M A (M L) watermark varieties (*see* General Notes to this section).

Though the paper is normally white, some printings showed blueing and stamps showing the "ivory head" may therefore be found.

7

Showing the plate number (9)

9

1870 (1 Oct). *Wmk W* **9**, *extending over three stamps. P* 14.

			Un	*Used*	★ *Used on cover*
48	**7**	½d. rose-red	75·00	15·00	50·00
49		½d. rose	75·00	15·00	
		a. Imperf (Plates 1, 4, 5, 6, 8, 14) .. *from*	£1100	£700	
		Plate			
		1	£150	70·00	
		3	£125	35·00	
		4	£110	25·00	
		5	75·00	15·00	
		6	80·00	15·00	
		8	£190	90·00	
		9	£2500	£450	
		10	90·00	15·00	
		11	80·00	15·00	
		12	80·00	15·00	
		13	80·00	15·00	
		14	80·00	15·00	
		15	£125	35·00	
		19	£140	50·00	
		20	£160	70·00	

★49/9a **For well-centred, lightly used** .. +200%

The ½d. was printed in sheets of 480 (24 × 20) so that the check letters run from AA XT to AA TX

Plates 2, 7, 16, 17 and 18 were not completed while Plates 21 and 22, though made, were not used.

Owing to the method of perforating, the outer side of stamps in either the A or X row (i e the left or right side of the sheet) is imperf.

Stamps may be found with watermark inverted or reversed, or without watermark, the latter due to misplacement of the paper when printing.

8

Position of plate Number

1870 (1 Oct). *Wmk W* **4.** *P* 14.

			Un	*Used*	★ *Used on cover*
51	**8**	1½d. rose-red	£250	45·00	£200
52		1½d. lake-red	£250	40·00	
		a. Imperf (Plates 1 and 3) *from*	£2500	†	
		Plate			
		(1)	£450	65·00	
		3	£250	40·00	

Error of lettering. OP-PC *for* CP-PC (*Plate* 1)

53	**8**	1½d. rose-red	£5500	£800

Prepared for use in 1860 but not issued; blued paper.

53*a*	**8**	1½d. rosy mauve (Plate 1)	£2750
		b. Error of lettering, OP-PC for CP-PC	

★51/3 **For well-centred, lightly used** .. +125%

Owing to a proposed change in the postal rates, 1½d. stamps were first printed in 1860, in rosy mauve, No. 53*a*, but the change was not approved and the greater part of the stock was destroyed, although three or four postally used examples have been recorded.

In 1870 a 1½d. stamp was required and was issued in rose-red.

Plate 1 did not have the plate number in the design of the stamps, but on stamps from Plate 3 the number will be found in the frame as shown above.

Plate 2 was defective and was not used.

The error of lettering OP-PC on Plate 1 was apparently not noticed by the printers, and therefore not corrected.

EMBOSSED ISSUES

Volume 1 of the Stanley Gibbons *Great Britain Specialised Catalogue* gives further detailed information on the embossed issues.

PRICES. The prices quoted are for cut-square stamps with average to fine embossing. Stamps with exceptionally clear embossing are worth more.

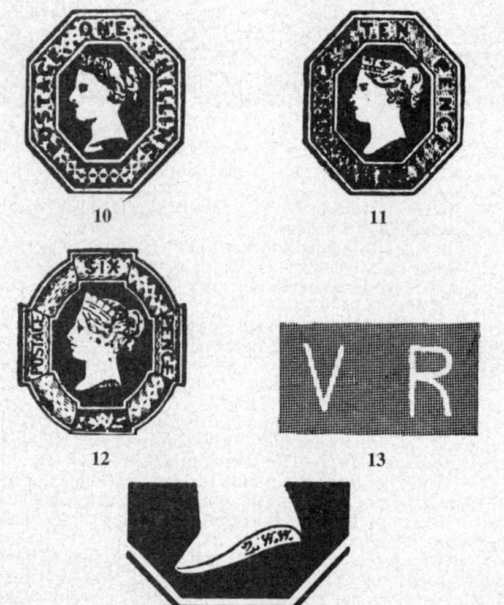

10 11 12 13

Position of die number

(Primary die engraved at the Royal Mint by William Wyon. Stamps printed at Somerset House)

1847–54. *Imperf.* (For paper and wmk see footnote.)

			Un	*Used*	*Used on cover*
54	**10**	1s. pale green (11.9.47)	£5000	£500	£600
55		1s. green	£5000	£550	
56		1s. deep green	£5500	£550	
		Die 1 (1847)	£5000	£500	
		Die 2 (1854)	£5500	£575	
57	**11**	10d. brown (6.11.48)	£3750	£725	£1300
		Die 1 (1848)	£4000	£775	
		Die 2 (1850)	£3750	£725	
		Die 3 (1853)	£3750	£725	
		Die 4 (1854)	£4000	£725	
		Die 5	£32000		
58	**12**	6d. mauve (1.3.54)	£4250	£575	
59		6d. dull lilac	£4250	£550	£650
60		6d. purple	£4250	£550	
61		6d. violet	£5500	£1500	

The 1s. and 10d. are on "Dickinson" paper with "silk" threads (actually a pale blue twisted cotton yarn). The 6d. is on paper watermarked V R in single-lined letters, W **13**, which may be found in four ways—upright, inverted, upright reversed, and inverted reversed, upright reversed being the most common.

The die numbers are indicated on the base of the bust. Only Die 1 (1 WW) of the 6d. was used for the adhesive stamps. The 10d. is from Die 1 (W.W.1 on stamps), and Dies 2 to 5 (2 W.W., 3 W.W., 4 W.W. and 5 W.W.) but the number and letters on stamps from Die 1 are seldom clear and many specimens are known without any trace of them. Because of this the stamp we previously listed as "No die number" has been deleted. That they are from Die 1 is proved by the existence of blocks showing stamps with and without the die number The 1s. is from Dies 1 and 2 (W.W.1, W.W.2).

The normal arrangement of the "silk" threads in the paper was in pairs running down each vertical row of the sheet, the space bet the threads of each pair being approximately 5 mm and be pairs of threads 20 mm. Varieties due to misplacement of the in printing show a single thread on the first stamp from the margin and two threads 20 mm apart on the other stamps of the Faulty manufacture is the cause of stamps with a single thread middle.

Through bad spacing of the impressions, which were handst all values may be found with two impressions more or overlapping. Owing to the small margin allowed for variatic spacing, specimens with good margins on all sides are not comm

Double impressions are known of all values.

Later printings of the 6d. had the gum tinted green to enabl printer to distinguish the gummed side of the paper.

SURFACE-PRINTED ISSUES

GENERAL NOTES

Volume 1 of the Stanley Gibbons *Great Britain Specia Catalogue* gives further detailed information on the surface-pri issues.

"Abnormals". The majority of the great rarities in the sur printed group of issues are the so-called "abnormals", w existence is due to the practice of printing six sheets from every as soon as made, one of which was kept for record purpose Somerset House, while the others were perforated and usually iss If such plates were not used for general production or if, before came into full use, a change of watermark or colour took place six sheets originally printed would differ from the main issue in p colour or watermark and, if issued, would be extremely rare.

The abnormal stamps of this class listed in this Catalogue distinguished, where not priced, by an asterisk (*), are:

No.	
78	3d. Plate 3 (with white dots)
152	4d. vermilion, Plate 16
153	4d. sage-green, Plate 17
109	6d. mauve, Plate 10
124/*a*	6d. chestnut and 6d. pale chestnut, Plate 12
145	6d. pale buff, Plate 13
88	9d. Plate 3 (hair lines)
98	9d. Plate 5 (*see* footnote to No. 98)
113	10d. Plate 2
91	1s. Plate 3 ("Plate 2")
148/50	1s. green, Plate 14
120	2s. blue, Plate 3

Those which may have been issued, but of which no specimens known, are 2½d. wmk Anchor, Plates 4 and 5; 3d. wmk Emble Plate 5; 3d. wmk Spray, Plate 21; 6d. grey, wmk Spray, Plate 18; orange, Plate 2; 1s. wmk Emblems, Plate 5. 5s. wmk Maltese Cr Plate 4.

The 10d. Plate 1, wmk Emblems (No. 99), is sometimes recko among the abnormals, but was an error, due to the use of the wr paper.

Corner Letters. With the exception of the 4d., 6d. and 1s. of 18 57, the ½d., 1½d., 2d. and 5d. of 1880, the 1d. lilac of 1881 and the (which had letters in lower corners only, and in the reverse orde the normal), all the surface-printed stamps issued prior to 1887 h letters in all four corners, as in the later line-engraved stamps. arrangement is the same, the letters running in sequence right acr and down the sheets, whether these were divided into panes or n The corner letters existing naturally depend on the number of stam in the sheet and their arrangement.

Imprimaturs and Imperforate Stamps. The Post Office retained their records (now in the National Postal Museum) one imperfor sheet from each plate, known as the Imprimatur (or officia approved) sheet. Some stamps were removed from time to time presentation purposes and have come on to the market, but the imperforates are not listed as they were not issued. Full details c be found in Volume I of the *Great Britain Specialised Catalogue.*

However, other imperforate stamps are known to have been issu and these are listed where it has been possible to prove that they not come from the Imprimatur sheets. It is therefore advisable purchase these only when acccompanied by an Expert Committ certificate of genuineness.

Plate Numbers. All stamps from No. 75 to No. 163 bear in the designs either the plate number or, in one or two earlier instanc some other indication by which one plate can be distinguished fr another. With the aid of these and of the corner letters it is th possible to "reconstruct" a sheet of stamps from any plate of a issue or denomination.

Surface-printing. In this context the traditional designati "surface-printing" is synonymous with typo(graphy)—a philatel term—or letterpress—the printers' term—as meaning printing fro (the surface of) raised type. It is also called relief-printing, as t image is in relief (in French, *en épargne*), unwanted parts of t design having been cut away. Duplicate impressions can electrotyped or stereotyped from an original die, the resulting *clich* being locked together to form the printing plate.

Wing Margins. As the vertical gutters (spaces) between the pane into which sheets of stamps of most values were divided until t introduction of the Imperial Crown watermark, were perforat through the centre with a single row of holes, instead of each vertic row of stamps on the inner side of the panes having its own line perforation as is now usual, a proportion of the stamps in each she have what is called a "wing margin" about 5 mm wide on one other side.

The stamps with "wing margins" are the watermark Emblems an Spray of Rose series (3d. 6d. 9d. 10d. 1s. and 2s.) with letters D, E, or I in S.E. corner, and the watermark Garter series (4d. and 8d with letters F or G in S.E. corner. Knowledge of this lettering wi enable collectors to guard against stamps with wing margin cut dow and re-perforated, but note that wing margin stamps of Nos. 62 to 7 are also to be found re-perforated.

PRINTERS. The issues of Queen Victoria, Nos. 62/214, were typo b Thomas De La Rue & Co.

PERFORATIONS. All the surface-printed issues of Queen Victori are Perf 14, with the exception of Nos. 126/9.

ALTERED CATALOGUE NUMBERS

Any Catalogue numbers altered from the las edition are shown as a list in the introductory pages.

KEY TO SURFACE-PRINTED ISSUES 1855–83

…. Nos.	Description	Watermark	Date of Issue
	NO CORNER LETTERS		
	4d. carmine	Small Garter	31.7.55
…5	4d. carmine	Medium Garter	25.2.56
…a	4d. carmine	Large Garter	Jan 1857
…70	6d. lilac	Emblems	21.10.56
…3	1s. green	Emblems	1.11.56
	SMALL WHITE CORNER LETTERS		
…7	3d. carmine	Emblems	1.5.62
	3d. carmine (dots)	Emblems	Aug 1862
…82	4d. red	Large Garter	15.1.62
…5	6d. lilac	Emblems	1.12.62
…8	9d. bistre	Emblems	15.1.62
…91	1s. green	Emblems	1.12.62
	LARGE WHITE CORNER LETTERS		
	3d. rose	Emblems	1.3.65
…/3	3d. rose	Spray	July 1867
…4	4d. vermilion	Large Garter	4.7.65
…7	6d. lilac	Emblems	7.3.65
…/7	6d. lilac	Spray	21.6.67
…/9	6d. lilac	Spray	8.3.69
…/4	6d. chestnut	Spray	12.4.72
…	6d. grey	Spray	24.4.73
	9d. straw	Emblems	30.10.65
…/11	9d. straw	Spray	3.10.67
	10d. brown	Emblems	11.11.67
…/14	10d. brown	Spray	1.7.67
	1s. green	Emblems	19.1.65
…/17	1s. green	Spray	13.7.67
…/20*b*	2s. blue	Spray	1.7.67
…	2s. brown	Spray	27.2.80
…/7	5s. rose	Cross	1.7.67
…8	10s. grey	Cross	26.9.78
…9	£1 brown-lilac	Cross	26.9.78
…, 134	5s. rose	Anchor	25.11.82
…, 135	10s. grey-green	Anchor	Feb 1883
…, 136	£1 brown-lilac	Anchor	Dec 1882
…, 137	£5 orange	Anchor	21.3.82
	LARGE COLOURED CORNER LETTERS		
…5	1d. Venetian red	Crown	1.1.80
…/9	2½d. rosy mauve	Anchor	1.7.75
…	2½d. rosy mauve	Orb	1.5.76
…2	2½d. blue	Orb	5.2.80
…7	2½d. blue	Crown	23.3.81
…/4	3d. rose	Spray	5.7.73
…8	3d. rose	Crown	Jan 1881
…9	3d. on 3d. lilac	Crown	1.1.83
…2	4d. vermilion	Large Garter	1.3.76
…3	4d. sage-green	Large Garter	12.3.77
…4	4d. brown	Large Garter	15.8.80
…0	4d. brown	Crown	9.12.80
…5	6d. buff	Spray	15.3.73
…/7	6d. grey	Spray	20.3.74
…1	6d. grey	Crown	1.1.81
…2	6d. on 6d. lilac	Crown	1.1.83
…*a*	8d. purple-brown	Large Garter	July 1876
…6	8d. orange	Large Garter	11.9.76
…/50	1s. green	Spray	1.9.73
…1	1s. brown	Spray	14.10.80
…3	1s. brown	Crown	24.5.81

Watermarks:		
	Anchor	W **40, 47**
	Cross	W **39**
	Crown	W **49**
	Emblems	W **20**
	Large Garter	W **17**
	Medium Garter	W **16**
	Orb	W **48**
	Small Garter	W **15**
	Spray	W **33**

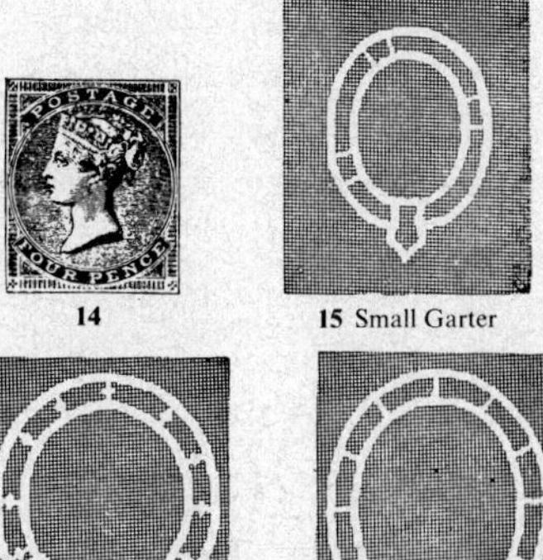

14   15 Small Garter

16 Medium Garter   17 Large Garter

…855–57. *No corner letters.*

…) *Wmk Small Garter, W* **15.** *Highly glazed, deeply blued paper* (31 July 1855)

			Un	★ Used	Used on cover
…2	**14**	4d. carmine (*shades*)	£3250	£325	£500
		a. Paper slightly blued ..	£3500	£325	
		b. White paper	£4750	£600	

(*b*) *Wmk Medium Garter, W* **16**

(i) *Thick, blued highly glazed paper* (25 February 1856)

63	**14**	4d. carmine (*shades*)	£4000	£375	£500
		a. White paper	£3250		

(ii) *Ordinary thin white paper* (September 1856)

64	**14**	4d. pale carmine	£2750	£300	£375
		a. Stamp printed double ..	†	—	

(iii) *Ordinary white paper, specially prepared ink* (1 November 1856)

65	**14**	4d. rose *or* deep rose	£3000	£325	£425

(*c*) *Wmk Large Garter, W* **17.** *Ordinary white paper* (January 1857)

66	**14**	4d. rose-carmine	£1100	90·00	£150
		a. Rose	£1000	90·00	
		b. Thick glazed paper	£2250	£200	
★62/6b		**For well-centred, lightly used** ..	**+125%**		

18   19   **20** Emblems wmk (normal)

20*a* Wmk error, three roses and shamrock

20*b* Wmk error, three roses and thistle

(*d*) *Wmk Emblems, W* **20**

			Un	★ Used	Used on cover
69	**18**	6d. deep lilac (21.10.56) ..	£750	£110	
70		6d. pale lilac	£675	80·00	£140
		a. Azure paper	£3250	£450	
		b. Thick paper	£1100	£250	
		c. Error. Wmk W **20*a***			
71	**19**	1s. deep green (1.11.56) ..	£2000	£275	
72		1s. green	£1000	£225	£300
73		1s. pale green	£1000	£225	
		a. Azure paper	—	£800	
		b. Thick paper	—	£275	
		c. Imperf	†	—	
★69/73b		**For well-centred, lightly used** ..	**+125%**		

21

22

23

24

25 Plate 2

A. White dots added

B. Hair lines

1862–64. *A small uncoloured letter in each corner, the 4d. wmk Large Garter. W* **17**, *the others Emblems, W* **20**.

			Un	★ Used	Used on cover
75	**21**	3d. deep carmine-rose (Plate 2) (1.5.62)	£1900	£275	
76		3d. bright carmine-rose	£1000	£225	£400
77		3d. pale carmine-rose	£1000	£225	
		b. Thick paper	—	£300	
78		3d. rose (with white dots, Type A, Plate 3) (8.62)	£15000	£3250	
		a. Imperf (Plate 3)	£2750		
79	**22**	4d. bright red (Plate 3) (15.1.62)	£1200	£100	
80		4d. pale red	£1000	80·00	£150
81		4d. bright red (Hair lines, Type B, Plate 4) (16.10.63)	£1000	80·00	
82		4d. pale red (Hair lines, Type B, Plate 4)	£900	70·00	£180
		a. Imperf (Plate 4)	£2250		
83	**23**	6d. deep lilac (Plate 3) (1.12.62)	£1200	£100	
84	**23**	6d. lilac	£1100	80·00	£150
		a. Azure paper	—	£700	
		b. Thick paper	—	£200	
		c. Error. Shamrock missing from wmk (stamp TF)			
		d. Error. Wmk W **20*b*** (stamp TF)			
85		6d. lilac (Hair lines, Plate 4) (20.4.64)	£1600	£160	£250
		a. Imperf	£1750		
		c. Thick paper	£2000	£200	
		d. Error. Wmk W **20*b*** (stamp TF)			
86	**24**	9d. bistre (Plate 2) (15.1.62) ..	£2500	£275	£350
87		9d. straw	£2500	£250	
		a. On azure paper			
		b. Thick paper	£3000	£350	
		c. Error. Watermark W **20*b*** (stamp TF)	†	—	
88		9d. bistre (Hair lines, Plate 3) (5.62)	£8000	£3250	
89	**25**	1s. deep green (Plate No. 1 = Plate 2) (1.12.62)	£1500	£250	
90		1s. green (Plate No. 1 = Plate 2)	£1300	£140	£225
		a. "K" in lower left corner in white circle (stamp KD) ..	£4750	£650	
		aa. "K" normal (stamp KD) ..	—	£900	
		b. On azure paper			
		c. Thick paper	—	£250	
		ca. Thick paper, "K" in circle as No. 90a	—	£1300	
91		1s. deep green (Plate No. 2 = Plate 3)	£15000		
		a. Imperf	£2000		
★75/91		**For well-centred, lightly used** ..	**+125%**		

The 3d. as Type **21**, but with network background in the spandrels which is found overprinted SPECIMEN, was never issued.

The plates of this issue may be distinguished as follows:

3d. Plate 2. No white dots.
Plate 3. White dots as Illustration A.
4d. Plate 3. No hair lines. Roman I next to lower corner letters.
Plate 4. Hair lines in corners. (Illustration B.). Roman II.
6d. Plate 3. No hair lines.
Plate 4. Hair lines in corners.
9d. Plate 2. No hair lines.
Plate 3. Hair lines in corners. Beware of faked lines.
1s. Plate 2. Numbered 1 on stamps.
Plate 3. Numbered 2 on stamps and with hair lines.

The 9d. on azure paper (No. 87a) is very rare, only one confirmed example being known.

The variety "K" in circle, No. 90a, is believed to be due to a damaged letter having been cut out and replaced. It is probable that the punch was driven in too deeply, causing the flange to penetrate the surface, producing an indentation showing as an uncoloured circle.

The watermark variety "three roses and a shamrock" illustrated in W **20*a*** was evidently due to the substitution of an extra rose for the thistle in a faulty watermark bit. It is found on stamp TA of Plate 4 of the 3d., Plates 1 (No. 70c), 3, 5 and 6 of the 6d., Plate 4 of the 9d. and Plate 4 of the 1s.

Similar problems occurred on stamp TF of the 6d. and 9d. Here the shamrock emblem became detached and a used example of the 6d. (No. 84) is known showing it omitted. It was replaced by a third rose (W **20*b***) and this variety exists on the 6d. (Nos. 84/5 and 97) and 9d. (Nos. 87 and 98).

26   27

28 (with hyphen)   28*a* (without hyphen)

29

30

31

1865–67. *Large uncoloured corner letters. Wmk Large Garter* (4*d.*); *others Emblems.*

			Un	★ Used	Used on cover
92	**26**	3d. rose (Plate 4) (1.3.65) ..	£750	90·00	£175
		a. Error. Wmk W **20*a*** ..	£1700	£450	
		b. Thick paper	£900	£125	
93	**27**	4d. dull vermilion (4.7.65) ..	£400	50·00	
94		4d. vermilion	£375	50·00	£110
		a. Imperf (Plates 11, 12) ..	£750		
		Plate			
		7 (1865)	£450	80·00	
		8 (1866)	£400	50·00	
		9 (1867)	£400	50·00	
		10 (1868)	£500	90·00	
		11 (1869)	£400	50·00	
		12 (1870)	£375	50·00	
		13 (1872)	£400	50·00	
		14 (1873)	£450	80·00	
96	**28**	6d. deep lilac (with hyphen) (7.3.65)	£600	90·00	

No.	Type	Description	Un	Used	Used on cover
	28	6d. lilac (with hyphen) ..	£500	70·00	£110
		a. Thick paper	£600	£100	
		b. Stamp doubly printed (Pl 6)	—	£7000	
		c. Error. Wmk W **20***a* (Pl 5, 6) .. .. .. *from*	—	£500	
		d. Error. Wmk W **20***b* (Plate 5)			
		Plate			
		5 (1865)	£500	70·00	
		6 (1867)	£1500	£130	
	29	9d. straw (Plate 4) (30.10.65) ..	£1500	£350	£450
		a. Thick paper	£1800	£500	
		b. Error. Wmk W **20***a* ..	—	£600	
		c. Error. Wmk W **20***b* (stamp T F)			
	30	10d. red-brown (Pl 1) (11.11.67)	†	£15000	
	31	1s. green (Plate 4) (19.1.65) ..	£1100	£150	£200
		a. Error. Wmk W **20***a* ..	—	£500	
		b. Thick paper	£1200	£240	
		c. Imperf between (vert pair)	—	£5000	
/101c		**For well-centred, lightly used** ..		+100%	

om mid-1866 to about the end of 1871 4d. stamps of this issue ared generally with watermark inverted.

nused examples of No. 98 from Plate 5 exist, but this was never o press and all evidence points to such stamps originating from rtion of the Imprimatur sheet which was perforated by De La in 1887 for insertion in albums to be presented to members of Stamp Committee (*Price* £14000 *un*).

ne 10d. stamps, No. 99, were printed in *error* on paper rmarked "Emblems" instead of on "Spray of Rose".

32

33 Spray of Rose

34

–80. *Wmk Spray of Rose, W* **33**.

No.	Type	Description	Un	★ Used	Used on cover
	26	3d. deep rose (12.7.67) ..	£325	50·00	
		3d. rose	£325	40·00	70·00
		a. Imperf (Plates 5, 6, 8) *from*	£1100		
		Plate			
		4 (1867)	£650	£150	
		5 (1868)	£325	40·00	
		6 (1870)	£350	40·00	
		7 (1871)	£425	45·00	
		8 (1872)	£400	45·00	
		9 (1872)	£400	50·00	
		10 (1873)	£425	90·00	
	28	6d. lilac (with hyphen) (Plate 6) (21.6.67)	£725	75·00	£140
		a. Imperf			
		6d. deep lilac (with hyphen) (Plate 6)	£725	75·00	
		6d. purple (with hyphen) (Pl 6)	£725	£100	
		6d. bright violet (with hyphen) (Plate 6) (22.7.68) ..	£725	£800	
	28*a*	6d. dull violet (without hyphen) (Plate 8) (8.3.69) ..	£500	65·00	
		6d. mauve (without hyphen)	£450	65·00	90·00
		a. Imperf (Plate Nos. 8 and 9)	£1500	£1200	
		Plate			
		8 (1869, mauve) ..	£450	65·00	
		9 (1870, mauve) ..	£450	65·00	
		10 (1869, mauve) ..	*	£15000	
	29	9d. straw (Plate No. 4) (3.10.67)	£1000	£190	£275
		9d. pale straw (Plate No. 4) ..	£800	£190	
		a. Imperf (Plate 4)	£3500		
	30	10d. red-brown (1.7.67) ..	£1700	£250	£450
		10d. pale red-brown	£1700	£275	
		10d. deep red-brown	£2000	£300	
		a. Imperf (Plate 1)	£3500		
		Plate			
		1 (1867)	£1700	£250	
		2 (1867)	£15000	£3500	
5	**31**	1s. deep green (13.7.67) ..	£650	35·00	
7		1s. green	£550	30·00	50·00
		a. Imperf between (horiz pair) (Plate 7)			
		b. Imperf (Plate 4) ..	£1700	£900	
		Plate			
		4 (1867)	£550	32·00	
		5 (1871)	£600	30·00	
		6 (1871)	£750	30·00	
		7 (1873)	£750	60·00	
8	**32**	2s. dull blue (1.7.67) ..	£1600	£125	£450
9		2s. deep blue	£1600	£125	
		a. Imperf (Plate 1)	£4000		
0		2s. pale blue	£2250	£180	
		aa. Imperf (Plate 1)	£3500		
0*a*		2s. cobalt	£7500	£1500	
0*b*		2s. milky blue	£5000	£700	
		Plate			
		1 (1867)	£1600	£125	
		3 (1868)	*	£6000	
1		2s. brown (Plate No. 1) (27.2.80)	£9000	£1900	
		a. Imperf	£6500		
		b. No watermark	†	—	
102/21		**For well-centred, lightly used** ..		+75%	

Examples of the 1s. from Plates 5 and 6 *without* watermark are stal forgeries used at the Stock Exchange Post Office in the early 70's.

72–73. *Uncoloured letters in corners. Wmk Sprav, W* **33**.

No.	Type	Description	Un	★ Used	Used on cover
2	**34**	6d. deep chestnut (Plate 11) (12.4.72)	£575	50·00	90·00
2*a*		6d. chestnut (Plate 11) (22.5.72)	£500	45·00	
2*b*		6d. pale chestnut (Plate 11) (1872)	£500	45·00	
3		6d. pale buff (19.10.72) ..	£550	70·00	£190
		Plate			
		11 (1872, pale buff) ..	£550	70·00	
		12 (1872, pale buff) ..	£1500	£200	
124	**34**	6d. chestnut (Plate 12) (1872) ..	*	£2500	
124*a*		6d. pale chestnut (Plate 12) (1872)	*	£2500	
125		6d. grey (Plate 12) (24.4.73) ..	£1000	£190	£240
		a. Imperf	£2000		
★122/5		**For well-centred, lightly used** ..		+50%	

35

36

37

38

39 Maltese Cross

40 Large Anchor

1867–83. *Uncoloured letters in corners.*

(*a*) *Wmk Maltese Cross, W* **39**. *P* 15½ × 15

No.	Type	Description	Un	★ Used
126	**35**	5s. rose (1.7.67)	£4000	£400
127		5s. pale rose	£4000	£400
		a. Imperf (Plate 1)	£5500	
		Plate		
		1 (1867)	£4000	£400
		2 (1874)	£5250	£525
128	**36**	10s. greenish grey (Plate 1) (26.9.78) ..	£28000	£1400
129	**37**	£1 brown-lilac (Plate 1) (26.9.78) ..	£32000	£2000
		(*b*) *Wmk Anchor, W* **40**. *P* 14. (i) *Blued paper*		
130	**35**	5s. rose (Plate 4) (25.11.82)	£8000	£1800
131	**36**	10s. grey-green (Plate 1) (2.83)	£35000	£2500
132	**37**	£1 brown-lilac (Plate 1) (12.82) ..	£42000	£4500
133	**38**	£5 orange (Plate 1) (21.3.82)	£25000	£5750
		(ii) *White paper*		
134	**35**	5s. rose (Plate 4)	£8000	£1800
135	**36**	10s. greenish grey (Plate 1)	£35000	£2200
136	**37**	£1 brown-lilac (Plate 1)	£45000	£3250
137	**38**	£5 orange (Plate 1)	£6500	£2500
★126/37		**For well-centred, lightly used**		+75%

41

42

43

44

45

46

47 Small Anchor

48 Orb

1873–80. *Large coloured letters in the corners.*

(*a*) *Wmk Anchor, W* **47**

No.	Type	Description	Un	★ Used	Used on cover
138	**41**	2½d. rosy mauve (*blued paper*) (1.7.75)	£575	90·00	
		a. Imperf			
		Plate			
		1 (*blued paper*) (1875) ..	£575	90·00	
		2 (*blued paper*) (1875) ..	£3750	£800	
		3 (*blued paper*) (1875) ..	—	£3000	
139		2½d. rosy mauve (*white paper*)	£400	75·00	£125
		Plate			
		1 (*white paper*) (1875) ..	£400	75·00	
		2 (*white paper*) (1875) ..	£400	75·00	
		3 (*white paper*) (1875) ..	£650	£110	
		Error of Lettering L H—F L for L H—H L (*Plate* 2)			
140	**41**	2½d. rosy mauve	£10000	£1200	
		(*b*) *Wmk Orb, W* **48**			
141	**41**	2½d. rosy mauve (1.5.76) ..	£350	40·00	70·00
		Plate			
		3 (1876)	£675	80·00	
		4 (1876)	£350	40·00	
		5 (1876)	£350	40·00	
		6 (1876)	£350	40·00	
		7 (1877)	£350	40·00	
		8 (1877)	£350	40·00	
		9 (1877)	£350	40·00	
		10 (1878)	£375	50·00	
		11 (1878)	£350	40·00	
		12 (1878)	£350	40·00	
		13 (1878)	£350	40·00	
		14 (1879)	£350	40·00	
		15 (1879)	£350	40·00	
		16 (1879)	£350	40·00	
		17 (1880)	£1000	£200	
142		2½d. blue (5.2.80)	£275	30·00	40·00
		Plate			
		17 (1880)	£350	50·00	
		18 (1880)	£325	35·00	
		19 (1880)	£275	30·00	
		20 (1880)	£325	35·00	
		(*c*) *Wmk Spray, W* **33**			
143	**42**	3d. rose (5.7.73)	£275	35·00	50·00
144		3d. pale rose	£275	35·00	
		Plate			
		11 (1873)	£275	35·00	
		12 (1873)	£325	35·00	
		14 (1874)	£350	35·00	
		15 (1874)	£275	35·00	
		16 (1875)	£275	35·00	
		17 (1875)	£325	35·00	
		18 (1875)	£325	35·00	
		19 (1876)	£275	35·00	
		20 (1879)	£375	60·00	
145	**43**	6d. pale buff (Plate 13) (15.3.73)	*	£9000	
146		6d. deep grey (20.3.74) ..	£350	50·00	80·00
147		6d. grey	£350	50·00	
		Plate			
		13 (1874)	£350	50·00	
		14 (1875)	£350	50·00	
		15 (1876)	£350	50·00	
		16 (1878)	£350	50·00	
		17 (1880)	£500	£100	
148	**44**	1s. deep green (1.9.73) ..	£475	75·00	
150		1s. green	£400	60·00	85·00
		Plate			
		8 (1873)	£475	75·00	
		9 (1874)	£475	75·00	
		10 (1874)	£475	80·00	
		11 (1875)	£475	80·00	
		12 (1875)	£400	60·00	
		13 (1876)	£400	60·00	
		14 (—)	*	£16000	
151		1s. orange-brown (Plate 13) (14.10.80)	£2250	£400	£550
		(*d*) *Wmk Large Garter, W* **17**			
152	**45**	4d. vermilion (1.3.76)	£1200	£325	£475
		Plate			
		15 (1876)	£1200	£325	
		16 (1877)	*	£14000	
153		4d. sage-green (12.3.77) ..	£550	£180	£275
		Plate			
		15 (1877)	£625	£200	
		16 (1877)	£550	£180	
		17 (1877)	*	£10000	
154		4d. grey-brown (Plate 17) (15.8.80)	£1100	£300	£400
		a. Imperf	£3000		
156	**46**	8d. orange (Plate 1) (11.9.76) ..	£800	£250	£275
★138/56		**For well-centred, lightly used** ..		+100%	

1876 (July). *Prepared for use but not issued.*

No.	Type	Description	Un
156*a*	**46**	8d. purple-brown (Plate 1) ..	£4500

49 Imperial Crown

3d ..

(50)

1880–83. *Wmk Imperial Crown, W* **49**.

			Un	Used	★ Used on cover
157	**41**	2½d. blue (23.3.81)	£275	25·00	40·00
		Plate			
		21 (1881)	£325	30·00	
		22 (1881)	£275	25·00	
		23 (1881)	£275	25·00	
158	**42**	3d. rose (3.81)	£325	60·00	£100
		Plate			
		20 (1881)	£425	£110	
		21 (1881)	£325	60·00	
159	**50**	3d. on 3d. lilac (C.) (Plate 21) (1.1.83)	£325	£110	£325
160	**45**	4d. grey-brown (8.12.80) ..	£275	45·00	£110
		Plate			
		17 (1880)	£275	45·00	
		18 (1882)	£275	45·00	
161	**43**	6d. grey (1.1.81)	£250	50·00	80·00
		Plate			
		17 (1881)	£275	50·00	
		18 (1882)	£250	50·00	
162	**50**	6d. on 6d. lilac (C.) (Plate 18) (1.1.83)	£350	£110	£300
		a. Slanting dots (various) *from*	£375	£125	
		b. Opt double	—	£8000	
163	**44**	1s. orange-brown (24.5.81) ..	£350	£100	£200
		Plate			
		13 (1881)	£400	£100	
		14 (1881)	£350	£100	
★157/63		**For well-centred, lightly used** ..		+75%	

The 1s. Plate 14 (line perf 14) exists in purple, but was not issued in this shade (*Price* £4500 *unused*). Examples were included in a few of the Souvenir Albums prepared for members of the "Stamp Committee of 1884".

52

53

54

55

56

1880–81. *Wmk Imperial Crown, W* **49**.

			Un	Used	★ Used on cover
164	**52**	½d. deep green (14.10.80) ..	40·00	10·00	20·00
		a. Imperf	£900		
		b. No watermark	£4000		
165		½d. pale green	40·00	15·00	
166	**53**	1d. Venetian red (1.1.80) ..	15·00	10·00	18·00
		a. Imperf	£900		
167	**54**	1½d. Venetian red (14.10.80) ..	£140	35·00	£110
168	**55**	2d. pale rose (8.12.80) ..	£175	70·00	£110
168*a*		2d. deep rose	£175	70·00	
169	**56**	5d. indigo (15.3.81)	£475	90·00	£175
		a. Imperf	£2000	£1500	
★164/9		**For well-centred, lightly used** ..		+75%	

Two used examples of the 1d. value have been reported on the Orb (fiscal) watermark.

Die I

57

Die II

1881. *Wmk Imperial Crown, W* **49**. (*a*) 14 *dots in each corner, Die* I (12 July).

			Un	Used	★ Used on cover
170	**57**	1d. lilac	£125	25·00	35·00
171		1d. pale lilac	£125	25·00	

(*b*) 16 *dots in each corner, Die* II (13 December)

			Un	Used	★ Used on cover
172	**57**	1d. lilac	2·50	2·00	3·00
172*a*		1d. bluish lilac	£250	70·00	
173		1d. deep purple	2·50	2·00	
		a. Printed both sides	£600	†	
		b. Frame broken at bottom ..	£575	£275	
		c. Printed on gummed side ..	£575	†	
		d. Imperf three sides (pair) ..	£3000	†	
		e. Printed both sides but impression on back inverted	£650	†	
		f. No watermark	£1000	†	
		g. Blued paper	£2500		
174		1d. mauve	2·50	1·50	
		a. Imperf (pair)	£1300		
★170/4		**For well-centred, lightly used** ..		+50%	

1d. stamps with the words "PEARS SOAP" printed on the back in *orange, blue* or *mauve* price *from* £425, *unused*.

The variety "frame broken at bottom" (No. 173b) shows a white space just inside the bottom frame-line from between the "N" and "E" of "ONE" to below the first "N" of "PENNY", breaking the pearls and cutting into the lower part of the oval below "PEN".

KEY TO SURFACE-PRINTED ISSUES 1880–1900

S.G. Nos.	Description	Date of Issue
164/5	½d. green	14.10.80
187	½d. slate-blue	1.4.84
197/*e*	½d. vermilion	1.1.87
213	½d. blue-green	17.4.1900
166	1d. Venetian red	1.1.80
170/1	1d. lilac, Die I	12.7.81
172/4	1d. lilac, Die II	12.12.81
167	1½d. Venetian red	14.10.80
188	1½d. lilac	1.4.84
198	1½d. purple and green	1.1.87
168/*a*	2d. rose	8.12.80
189	2d. lilac	1.4.84
199/200	2d. green and red	1.1.87
190	2½d. lilac	1.4.84
201	2½d. purple on blue paper	1.1.87
191	3d. lilac	1.4.84
202/4	3d. purple on yellow paper	1.1.87
192	4d. dull green	1.4.84
205/*a*	4d. green and brown	1.1.87
206	4½d. green and carmine	15.9.92
169	5d. indigo	15.3.81
193	5d. dull green	1.4.84
207	5d. purple and blue, Die I	1.1.87
207*a*	5d. purple and blue, Die II	1888
194	6d. dull green	1.4.84
208/*a*	6d. purple on rose-red paper	1.1.87
195	9d. dull green	1.8.83
209	9d. purple and blue	1.1.87
210/*b*	10d. purple and carmine	24.2.90
196	1s. dull green	1.4.84
211	1s. green	1.1.87
214	1s. green and carmine	11.7.1900
175	2s. 6d. lilac on blued paper	2.7.83
178/9	2s. 6d. lilac	1884
176	5s. rose on blued paper	1.4.84
180/1	5s. rose	1884
177/*a*	10s. ultramarine on blued paper ..	1.4.84
182/3*a*	10s. ultramarine	1884
185	£1 brown-lilac, wmk Crowns	1.4.84
186	£1 brown-lilac, wmk Orbs	2.88
212	£1 green	28.1.91

Note that the £5 value used with the above series is listed as Nos. 133 and 137.

58

59

60

1883–84. *Coloured letters in the corners. Wmk Anchor, W* **40**.

(*a*) *Blued paper*

			Un	★ Used
175	**58**	2s. 6d. lilac (2.7.83)	£3000	£800
176	**59**	5s. rose (1.4.84)	£5000	£1700
177	**60**	10s. ultramarine (1.4.84)	£18000	£4500
177*a*		10s. cobalt (5.84)	£25000	£7500

(*b*) *White paper*

			Un	★ Used
178	**58**	2s. 6d. lilac	£350	£110
179		2s. 6d. deep lilac	£350	£110
		a. Error. On blued paper ..	£3000	£800
180	**59**	5s. rose	£550	£140
181		5s. crimson	£550	£140
182	**60**	10s. cobalt	£18000	£5000
183		10s. ultramarine	£1250	£375
183*a*		10s. pale ultramarine	£1250	£375
★175/83*a*		**For well-centred, lightly used**		+50%

For No. 180 perf 12 *see* second note below No. 196.

61

Broken frames, Plate 2

1884 (1 April). *Wmk Three Imperial Crowns, W* **49**.

			Un	
185	**61**	£1 brown-lilac	£18000	£
		a. Frame broken	£23000	£

1888 (Feb). *Wmk Three Orbs. W* **48**.

186	**61**	£1 brown-lilac	£35000	£
		a. Frame broken	£40000	£
★185/6a		**For well-centred, lightly used**		+

The broken-frame varieties, Nos. 185a and 186a, are on Pl stamps JC and TA, as illustrated. *See also* No. 212a.

62

63

64

65

66

1883 (1 Aug) (*9d.*) *or* **1884** (1 April) (*others*). *Wmk Imperial Cr W* **49** (*sideways on horiz designs*).

			Un	Used	★ Used co
187	**52**	½d. slate-blue	20·00	7·00	12
		a. Imperf	£750		
188	**62**	1½d. lilac	85·00	35·00	£
		a. Imperf	£750		
189	**63**	2d. lilac	£140	65·00	£
		a. Imperf	£850		
190	**64**	2½d. lilac	70·00	12·00	24
		a. Imperf	£850		
191	**65**	3d. lilac	£175	85·00	£
		a. Imperf	£850		
192	**66**	4d. dull green	£400	£175	£
		a. Imperf	£900		
193	**62**	5d. dull green	£400	£175	£2
		a. Imperf	£900		
194	**63**	6d. dull green	£425	£200	£2
		a. Imperf	£900		
195	**64**	9d. dull green (1.8.83) ..	£750	£375	£1
196	**65**	1s. dull green	£550	£200	£
		a. Imperf	£2000		
★187/96		**For well-centred, lightly used** ..		+100%	

The above prices are for stamps in the true dull green colo Stamps which have been soaked, causing the colour to run, virtually worthless.

Stamps of the above set and No. 180 are also found perf 12; the are official perforations, but were never issued. A second variety the 5d. is known with a line instead of a stop under the "d" in t value; this was never issued and is therefore only known *unus* (*Price* £7500).

71

72

73

74

75

76

77

78

79

80

81

82

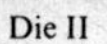

Die I — Die II

Die I: Square dots to right of "d".
Die II: Thin vertical lines to right of "d".

7 (1 Jan)–**1892.** *"Jubilee" issue. New types. The bicoloured stamps ave the value tablets, or the frames including the value tablets, in the econd colour. Wmk Imperial Crown, W* **49** (*Three Crowns on* £1).

No.	Type	Description	*Un*	★ *Used*	*Used on cover*
	71	½d. vermilion	1·50	1·00	6·00
		a. Printed on gummed side ..	£1000	†	
		b. Printed both sides ..			
		c. Doubly printed	£8000		
		d. Imperf	£1600		
e		½d. orange-vermilion	1·50	1·00	
	72	1½d. dull purple and pale green	15·00	7·00	22·00
		a. Purple part of design double	—	£5000	
	73	2d. green and scarlet ..	£350	£200	
		2d. grey-green and carmine ..	28·00	12·00	24·00
	74	2½d. purple/*blue*	22·00	3·00	6·00
		a. Printed on gummed side ..	£3250	†	
		b. Imperf three sides ..	£2750		
		c. Imperf	£3000		
	75	3d. purple/*yellow*	22·00	3·25	24·00
		a. Imperf	£4000		
		3d. deep purple/*yellow* ..	22·00	3·25	
		3d. purple/*orange* (1890) ..	£425		
	76	4d. green and purple-brown ..	30·00	13·00	30·00
		aa. Imperf			
5a		4d. green and deep brown ..	30·00	13·00	
	77	4½d. green and carmine (15.9.92)	10·00	40·00	65·00
5a		4½d. green & deep brt carmine	£475	£350	
	78	5d. dull purple and blue (Die I)	£475	50·00	95·00
7a		5d. dull pur & bl (Die II) (1888)	35·00	11·00	32·00
	79	6d. purple/*rose-red*	30·00	10·00	28·00
8a		6d. deep purple/*rose-red* ..	30·00	11·00	
	80	9d. dull purple and blue ..	60·00	40·00	90·00
	81	10d. dull purple and carmine (*shades*) (24.2.90) ..	45·00	38·00	£110
		aa. Imperf	£4750		
0a		10d. dull purple & dp dull carm	£400	£200	
0b		10d. dull purple and scarlet ..	60·00	45·00	
	82	1s. dull green	£200	60·00	£125
	61	£1 green (28.1.91)	£2500	£450	
		a. Frame broken	£5250	£1250	
197/212a		**For well-centred, lightly used** ..		+50%	

The broken-frame varieties, No. 212a, are on Plate 2 stamps JC or , as illustrated above No. 185.

½d. stamps with "PEARS SOAP" printed on the back in *orange, e* or *mauve*, price *from* £400 each.

No used price is quoted for No. 204 as it is not possible to thenticate the paper colour on stamps in used condition.

00. *Colours changed. Wmk Imperial Crown, W* **49**.

No.	Type	Description	*Un*	★ *Used*	*Used on cover*
3	**71**	½d. blue-green (17.4)	1·75	2·00	6·00
		a. Printed on gummed side	—	†	
		b. Imperf	£2500		
4	**82**	1s. green and carmine (11.7)	50·00	£125	£375
7/214		.. .. .. *Set of* 14	£500	£325	
213/14		**For well-centred, lightly used** ..		+50%	

The ½d., No. 213, in bright blue, is a colour changeling caused by constituent of the ink used for some months in 1900.

KING EDWARD VII
22 January 1901–6 May 1910

RINTINGS. Distinguishing De La Rue printings from the ovisional printings of the same values made by Harrison & Sons td. or at Somerset House may prove difficult in some cases. For very ll guidance Volume 2 of the Stanley Gibbons *Great Britain pecialised Catalogue* should prove helpful.

Note that stamps perforated 15 × 14 must be Harrison; the 2½d., . and 4d. in this perforation are useful reference material, their ades and appearance in most cases matching the Harrison perf 14 intings.

Except for the 6d. value, all stamps on chalk-surfaced paper were inted by De La Rue.

Of the stamps on ordinary paper, the De La Rue impressions are sually clearer and of a higher finish than those of the other printers. he shades are markedly different except in some printings of the ., 6d. and 7d. and in the 5s., 10s. and £1.

Used stamps in good, clean, unrubbed condition and with dated ostmarks can form the basis of a useful reference collection, the ates often assisting in the assignment to the printers.

USED STAMPS. For well-centred, lightly used examples of King Edward VII stamps, add the following percentages to the used prices quoted below:

De La Rue printings (Nos. 215/66)—3d. values +35%, 4d. orange +100%, 6d. +75%, 7d. and 1s. +25%, all other values +50%.
Harrison printings (Nos. 267/86)—all values and perforations +75%
Somerset House printings (Nos. 287/320)—1s. values +25%, all other values +50%.

83

84

85

86

87

88

89

90

91

92 — 93

94

95

96

97

(Des E. Fuchs)

1902 (1 Jan)–**10**. *Printed by De La Rue & Co. Wmk Imperial Crown* (½*d. to* 1*s.*); *Anchor* (2*s.* 6*d. to* 10*s.*); *Three Crowns* (£1). *Ordinary paper. P* 14.

No.	Type	Description	*Un*	*Used*	*Used on cover*
215	**83**	½d. dull blue-green (1.1.02) ..	2·00	1·50	2·50
216		½d. blue-green	2·00	1·50	
217		½d. pale yellowish grn (26.11.04)	2·00	1·50	2·50
218		½d. yellowish green	2·00	1·50	
		a. Booklet pane. Five stamps plus St. Andrew's Cross label (6.06)	£300		
		b. Doubly printed (bottom row on one pane) (Control H9)	£15000		
219		1d. scarlet (1.1.02)	2·00	1·50	2·50
220		1d. bright scarlet	2·00	1·50	
		a. Imperf (pair)	£10000		
221	**84**	1½d. dull purple & grn (21.3.02)	35·00	18·00	
222		1½d. slate-purple and green ..	38·00	18·00	28·00
223		1½d. pale dull pur & grn (*chalk-surfaced paper*) (8.05) ..	40·00	18·00	
224		1½d. slate-purple & bluish green (*chalk-surfaced paper*) ..	40·00	15·00	
225	**85**	2d. yellowish green & carmine-red (25.3.02)	45·00	18·00	30·00
226		2d. grey-grn & carm-red (1904)	45·00	20·00	
227		2d. pale grey-green & carm-red (*chalk-surfaced paper*) (4.06)	40·00	24·00	
228		2d. pale grey-grn & scar (*chalk-surfaced paper*) (1909) ..	40·00	24·00	
229		2d. dull blue-grn & carm (*chalk-surfaced paper*) (1907) ..	70·00	45·00	
230	**86**	2½d. ultramarine (1.1.02) ..	20·00	10·00	20·00
231		2½d. pale ultramarine ..	20·00	10·00	
232	**87**	3d. dull pur/*orge-yell* (20.3.02)	40·00	12·00	30·00
		a. Chalk-surfaced paper (3.06)	£150	70·00	
232*b*		3d. deep purple/*orange-yellow*	40·00	12·00	
232*c*		3d. pale reddish pur/*orge-yell* (*chalk-surfaced paper*) (3.06)	£150	60·00	
233		3d. dull reddish pur/*yell* (*lemon back*) (*chalk-surfaced paper*)	£150	75·00	
233*b*		3d. pale purple/*lemon* (*chalk-surfaced paper*)	35·00	15·00	
234		3d. pur/*lemon* (*chalk-surfaced paper*)	35·00	15·00	
235	**88**	4d. green & grey-brn (27.3.02)	50·00	30·00	
236		4d. green and chocolate-brown	50·00	30·00	
		a. Chalk-surfaced paper (1.06)	40·00	18·00	40·00
238		4d. dp green & choc-brn (*chalk-surfaced paper*) (1.06) ..	40·00	18·00	
239		4d. brown-orange (1.11.09) ..	£150	£130	
240		4d. pale orange (12.09) ..	20·00	15·00	35·00
241		4d. orange-red (12.09) ..	20·00	15·00	
242	**89**	5d. dull pur & ultram (14.5.02)	55·00	20·00	50·00
		a. Chalk-surfaced paper (5.06)	50·00	20·00	
244		5d. slate-pur & ultram (*chalk-surfaced paper*) (5.06) ..	50·00	20·00	
245	**83**	6d. pale dull purple (1.1.02) ..	35·00	18·00	45·00
		a. Chalk-surfaced paper (1.06)	35·00	18·00	
246		6d. slate-purple	35·00	18·00	
248		6d. dull purple (*chalk-surfaced paper*) (1.06)	35·00	18·00	
249	**90**	7d. grey-black (4.5.10) ..	10·00	18·00	£175
249*a*		7d. deep grey-black ..	£100	£100	
250	**91**	9d. dull pur & ultram (7.4.02)	80·00	60·00	£175
		a. Chalk-surfaced paper (6.05)	80·00	60·00	
251		9d. slate-purple & ultramarine	80·00	60·00	
		a. Chalk-surfaced paper (6.05)	80·00	60·00	
254	**92**	10d. dull purple & carm (3.7.02)	80·00	60·00	£190
		a. No cross on crown ..	£275	£160	
		b. Chalk-surfaced paper (9.06)	80·00	60·00	
255		10d. slate-purple & carm (*chalk-surfaced paper*) (9.06) ..	80·00	60·00	
		a. No cross on crown ..	£250	£160	
256		10d. dull purple & scarlet (*chalk-surfaced paper*) (9.10) ..	80·00	60·00	
		a. No cross on crown ..	£225	£150	
257	**93**	1s. dull green & carm (24.3.02)	80·00	35·00	£120
		a. Chalk-surfaced paper (9.05)	80·00	35·00	
259		1s. dull green & scarlet (*chalk-surfaced paper*) (9.10) ..	80·00	50·00	
260	**94**	2s. 6d. lilac (5.4.02) ..	£180	75·00	£600
261		2s. 6d. pale dull purple (*chalk-surfaced paper*) (7.10.05)	£200	£130	
262		2s. 6d. dull pur (*chalk-surfaced paper*)	£200	£130	
263	**95**	5s. bright carmine (5.4.02)	£210	£130	£700
264		5s. deep bright carmine ..	£210	£130	
265	**96**	10s. ultramarine (5.4.02) ..	£550	£325	
266	**97**	£1 dull blue-green (16.6.02)	£1300	£500	

97*a*

1910 (May). *Prepared for use by De La Rue but not issued. Wmk Imperial Crown, W* **49**. *P* 14.

266*a* **97*a*** 2d. Tyrian plum £20000

One example of this stamp is known used, but it was never issued to the public.

1911. *Printed by Harrison & Sons. Ordinary paper. Wmk Imperial Crown.* (*a*) *P* 14.

No.	Type	Description	*Un*	*Used*	*Used on cover*
267	**83**	½d. dull yellow-green (3.5.11)	2·50	1·50	4·00
268		½d. dull green	2·75	1·50	
269		½d. deep dull green	11·00	4·00	
270		½d. pale bluish green ..	40·00	40·00	
		a. Booklet pane. Five stamps plus St. Andrew's Cross label	£350		
		b. Wmk sideways	—	£13000	
		c. Imperf (pair)	£15000	†	
271		½d. brt green (fine impression) (6.11)	£225	£140	
272		1d. rose-red (3.5.11)	8·00	12·00	15·00
		a. No wmk	40·00	40·00	
273		1d. deep rose-red	8·00	12·00	
274		1d. rose-carmine	55·00	30·00	
275		1d. aniline pink (5.11) ..	£375	£200	
275*a*		1d. aniline rose	£180	£140	
276	**86**	2½d. bright blue (10.7.11) ..	45·00	30·00	40·00
277	**87**	3d. purple/*lemon* (12.9.11) ..	65·00	£150	£500
277*a*		3d. grey/*lemon*	£3000		
278	**88**	4d. bright orange (12.7.11) ..	65·00	50·00	£175
		(*b*) *P* 15×14			
279	**83**	½d. dull green (30.10.11) ..	40·00	45·00	£100
279*a*		½d. deep dull green	40·00	45·00	
280		1d. rose-red (4.10.11) ..	38·00	25·00	
281		1d. rose-carmine	15·00	15·00	30·00
282		1d. pale rose-carmine ..	22·00	15·00	
283	**86**	2½d. bright blue (14.10.11) ..	22·00	15·00	30·00
284		2½d. dull blue	22·00	15·00	
285	**87**	3d. purple/*lemon* (22.9.11) ..	40·00	15·00	40·00
285*a*		3d. grey/*lemon*	£2250		
286	**88**	4d. bright orange (11.11.11) ..	30·00	15·00	65·00
279/86		.. .. .. *Set of* 5	£130	80·00	

1911–13. *Printed at Somerset House. Ordinary paper. Wmk as* 1902–10. *P* 14.

No.	Type	Description	*Un*	*Used*	*Used on cover*
287	**84**	1½d. reddish purple and bright green (13.7.11)	40·00	35·00	
288		1½d. dull purple and green ..	25·00	28·00	50·00
289		1½d. slate-purple & grn (9.12)	28·00	28·00	
290	**85**	2d. dp dull grn & red (8.8.11)	25·00	20·00	40·00
291		2d. deep dull green & carmine	25·00	20·00	
292		2d. grey-green & bright carmine (carmine shows clearly on back) (11.3.12)	25·00	25·00	
293	**89**	5d. dull reddish purple and bright blue (7.8.11) ..	30·00	20·00	65·00
294		5d. deep dull reddish purple and bright blue	28·00	20·00	
295	**83**	6d. royal purple (31.10.11) ..	45·00	70·00	
296		6d. bright magenta (*chalk-surfaced paper*) (31.10.11)	£2750		
297		6d. dull purple	30·00	20·00	70·00
298		6d. reddish purple (11.11) ..	30·00	25·00	
		a. No cross on crown (*various shades*)	£275		
299		6d. very dp reddish pur (11.11)	40·00	40·00	
300		6d. dark purple (3.12) ..	30·00	35·00	
301		6d. dull purple ("Dickinson" coated paper*) (3.13) ..	£140	£140	
303		6d. deep plum (7.13) ..	28·00	70·00	
		a. No cross on crown ..	£300		
305	**90**	7d. slate-grey (1.8.12) ..	15·00	22·00	£120
306	**91**	9d. reddish purple and light blue (24.7.11)	80·00	75·00	

306*a*	**91**	9d. deep dull reddish purple & deep bright blue (9.11)	80·00	75·00	
307		9d. dull reddish purple & blue (10.11)	60·00	60·00	£140
307*a*		9d. deep plum and blue (7.13)	60·00	60·00	
308		9d. slate-pur & cobalt-bl (3.12)	95·00	85·00	
309	**92**	10d. dull purple & scar (9.10.11)	80·00	75·00	
310		10d. dull reddish pur & aniline pink	£250	£225	
311		10d. dull reddish purple & carm (5.12)	60·00	60·00	£175
		a. No cross on crown ..	£550		
312	**93**	1s. dark green & scar (13.7.11)	90·00	60·00	
313		1s. dp green & scar (9.10.11)	60·00	35·00	
314		1s. green & carmine (15.4.12)	50·00	35·00	£125
315	**94**	2s. 6d. dull greyish purple (15.9.11)	£400	£250	
316		2s. 6d. dull reddish purple ..	£190	£125	£750
317		2s. 6d. dark purple	£190	£125	
318	**95**	5s. carmine (29.2.12) ..	£225	£125	£625
319	**96**	10s. blue (14.1.12)	£500	£400	
320	**97**	£1 deep green (3.9.11) ..	£1300	£550	

*No. 301 was on an experimental coated paper which does not respond to the silver test.

KING GEORGE V
6 May 1910–20 January 1936

Further detailed information on the issues of King George V will be found in Volume 2 of the Stanley Gibbons *Great Britain Specialised Catalogue*.

PRINTERS. Types **98** to **102** were typographed by Harrison & Sons Ltd, with the exception of certain preliminary printings made at Somerset House and distinguishable by the controls "A.11", B.11" or "B.12" (the Harrison printings do not have a full stop after the letter). The booklet stamps, Nos. 334/7, and 344/5 were printed by Harrisons only.

WATERMARK VARIETIES. Many British stamps to 1967 exist without watermark owing to misplacement of the paper, and with either inverted, reversed, or inverted and reversed watermarks. A proportion of the low-value stamps issued in booklets have the watermark inverted in the normal course of printing.

Low values with *watermark sideways* are normally from stamp rolls used in machines with sideways delivery or, from June 1940, certain booklets.

STAMPS WITHOUT WATERMARK. Stamps found without watermark, due to misplacement of the sheet in relation to the dandy roll, are not listed here, but will be found in the *Great Britain Specialised Catalogue*.

The 1½d. and 5d. 1912–22, and 2d. and 2½d., 1924–26, listed here, are from *whole* sheets completely without watermark.

98

99

For type differences with T **101/2** *see* notes below the latter.

Die A

Die B

Dies of Halfpenny

Die A. The three upper scales on the body of the right hand dolphin form a triangle; the centre jewel of the cross inside the crown is suggested by a comma.

Die B. The three upper scales are incomplete; the centre jewel is suggested by a crescent.

Die A

Die B

Dies of One Penny

Die A. The second line of shading on the ribbon to the right of the crown extends right across the wreath; the line nearest to the crown on the right hand ribbon shows as a short line at the bottom of the ribbon.

Die B. The second line of shading is broken in the middle; the first line is little more than a dot.

(Des Bertram Mackennal and G. W. Eve. Head from photograph by W. & D. Downey. Die eng J. A. C. Harrison)

1911–12. *Wmk Imperial Crown, W* **49**. *P* 15 × 14.

			Un	*Used*
321	**98**	½d. pale green (Die A) (22.6.11) ..	5·00	4·00
322		½d. green (Die A) (22.6.11)	5·00	4·00
		a. Error. Perf 14 (8.11)	£9500	£400
323		½d. bluish green (Die A)	£300	£180
324		½d. yellow-green (Die B)	8·00	1·50
325		½d. bright green (Die B)	4·50	1·50
		a. Wmk sideways	—	£3000
326		½d. bluish green (Die B)	£160	£100
327	**99**	1d. carmine-red (Die A) (22.6.11) ..	4·50	2·50
		c. Wmk sideways	†	—
328		1d. pale carmine (Die A) (22.6.11) ..	14·00	3·00
		a. No cross on crown	£325	£200
329		1d. carmine (Die B)	7·00	3·00
330		1d. pale carmine (Die B)	10·00	4·00
		a. No cross on crown	£425	£300
331		1d. rose-pink (Die B)	£100	40·00
332		1d. scarlet (Die B) (6.12)	22·00	18·00
333		1d. aniline scarlet (Die B)	£150	90·00

For note on the aniline scarlet No. 333 see below No. 343.

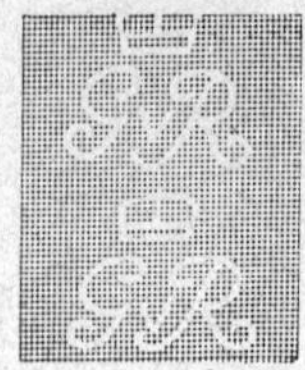
100 Simple Cypher

1912 (Aug). *Booklet stamps. Wmk Royal Cypher ("Simple"), W* **100**. *P* 15 × 14.

334	**98**	½d. pale green (Die B)	40·00	40·00
335		½d. green (Die B)	40·00	40·00
336	**99**	1d. scarlet (Die B)	30·00	30·00
337		1d. bright scarlet (Die B)	30·00	30·00

101

102

103 Multiple Cypher

Type differences

½d. In T **98** the ornament above "P" of "HALFPENNY" has two thin lines of colour and the beard is undefined. In T **101** the ornament has one thick line and the beard is well defined.

1d. In T **99** the body of the lion is unshaded and in T **102** it is shaded.

1912 (1 Jan). *Wmk Imperial Crown, W* **49**. *P* 15 × 14.

338	**101**	½d. deep green	15·00	8·00
339		½d. green	15·00	8·00
340		½d. yellow-green	15·00	8·00
		a. No cross on crown	70·00	30·00
341	**102**	1d. bright scarlet	5·00	2·00
		a. No cross on crown	60·00	30·00
		b. Printed double, one albino ..	£160	
342		1d. scarlet	5·00	2·00
343		1d. aniline scarlet*	£150	90·00
		a. No cross on crown	£750	

* Our prices for the aniline scarlet 1d. stamps, Nos. 333 and 343, are for specimens in which the colour is suffused on the surface of the stamp and shows through clearly on the back. Specimens without these characteristics but which show "aniline" reactions under the quartz lamp are relatively common.

1912 (Aug). *Wmk Royal Cypher ("Simple"), W* **100**. *P* 15 × 14.

344	**101**	½d. green	7·00	3·00
		a. No cross on crown	80·00	30·00
345	**102**	1d. scarlet	8·00	3·00
		a. No cross on crown	80·00	28·00

1912 (Sept–Oct). *Wmk Royal Cypher ("Multiple"), W* **103**. *P* 15 × 14.

346	**101**	½d. green (Oct)	12·00	8·00
		a. No cross on crown	80·00	50·00
		b. Imperf	£110	
		c. Wmk sideways	†	£1300
		d. Printed on gummed side	—	†
347		½d. yellow-green	15·00	8·00
348		½d. pale green	15·00	8·00
349	**102**	1d. bright scarlet	15·00	8·00
350		1d. scarlet	15·00	8·00
		a. No cross on crown	90·00	28·00
		b. Imperf	85·00	
		c. Wmk sideways	90·00	90·00
		d. Wmk sideways. No cross on crown	£600	

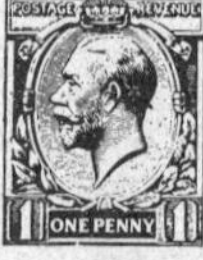

104

105

106

No. 357ab

No. 357ac

No. 357a

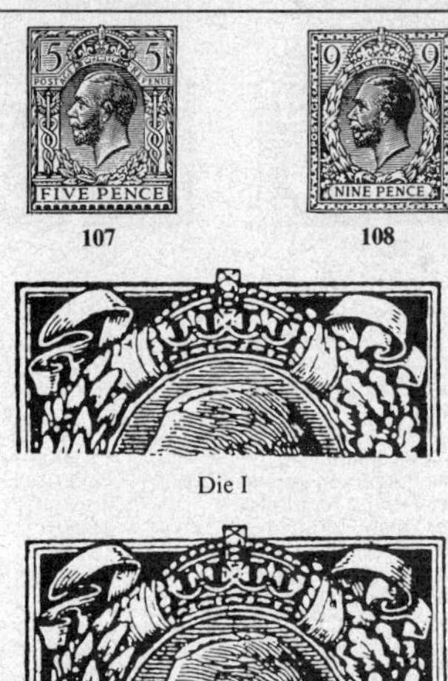

107 108

Die I

Die II

Dies of 2d.

Die I.— Inner frame-line at top and sides close to solid of backgrou[n] *Four* complete lines of shading between top of head and o[val] frame-line. These four lines do *not* extend to the oval its[elf]. White line round "TWOPENCE" thin.

Die II.— Inner frame-line farther from solid of background. *Th[ree]* lines between top of head and extending to the oval. Wh[ite] line round "TWOPENCE" thicker.

(Des Bertram Mackennal (heads) and G. W. Eve (frames). Coina[ge] head (½, 1½, 2, 3 and 4d.); large medal head (1d., 2½d.); intermedia[te] medal head (5d. to 1s.); small medal head used for fiscal stamp[s]. Dies eng J. A. C. Harrison)

(Typo by Harrison & Sons Ltd., except the 6d. printed by t[he] Stamping Department of the Board of Inland Revenue, Somers[et] House. The latter also made printings of the following which c[an] only be distinguished by the controls: ½d. B.13; 1½d. A.12; 2[d.] C.13; 2½d. A.12; 3d. A.12, B.13, C.13; 4d. B.13; 5d. B.13; 7[d.] C.13; 8d. C.13; 9d. agate B.13; 10d. C.13; 1s. C.13)

1912–24. *Wmk Royal Cypher, W* **100**. *Chalk-surfaced paper* (6d. *P* 15×14.

351	**105**	½d. green (1.13)	1·00	1·
		a. Partial double print (half of bottom row from Control G15)	£15000	
		b. Gummed both sides		
352		½d. bright green	1·00	1·
353		½d. deep green	4·00	2·
354		½d. yellow-green	5·00	3·
355		½d. very yellow (Cyprus) green (1914)	£2500	
356		½d. blue-green	40·00	25·
357	**104**	1d. bright scarlet (8.10.12)	1·00	1·
		a. "Q" for "O" (R.1/4) (Control E14)	£150	£1
		ab. "Q" for "O" (R.4/11) (Control T22)	£350	£1
		ac. Reversed "Q" for "O" (R.15/9) (Control T22)	£300	£2
		ad. Inverted "Q" for "O" (R.20/3) ..	£375	£2
		b. *Tête-bêche* (pair)	£50000	
358		1d. vermilion	5·00	2·
359		1d. pale rose-red	15·00	2·
360		1d. carmine-red	11·00	5·
361		1d. scarlet-vermilion	£110	40·
		a. Printed on back†	£225	
362	**105**	1½d. red-brown (15.10.12)	4·00	1·
		a. "PENCF" (R.15/12)	£180	£1
		b. Booklet pane. Four stamps plus two printed labels (2.24)	£350	
363		1½d. chocolate-brown	5·00	2·
		a. Without wmk	£160	£1
364		1½d. chestnut	5·00	1·
		a. "PENCF" (R.15/12)	£100	80·
365		1½d. yellow-brown	20·00	16·
366	**106**	2d. orange-yellow (Die I) (20.8.12) ..	7·00	3·
367		2d. reddish orange (Die I) (11.13) ..	6·00	3·
368		2d. orange (Die I)	6·00	3·
369		2d. bright orange (Die I)	5·00	3·
370		2d. orange (Die II) (9.21)	5·00	3·
371	**104**	2½d. cobalt-blue (18.10.12)	12·00	4·
371*a*		2½d. bright blue (1914)	12·00	4·
372		2½d. blue	12·00	4·
373		2½d. indigo-blue* (1920)	£1200	£7
373*a*		2½d. dull Prussian blue* (1921) ..	£550	£4
374	**106**	3d. dull reddish violet (9.10.12) ..	12·00	2·
375		3d. violet	7·00	3·
376		3d. bluish violet (11.13)	7·00	2·
377		3d. pale violet	7·00	2·
378		4d. deep grey-green (15.1.13) ..	35·00	10·
379		4d. grey-green	15·00	2·
380		4d. pale grey-green	25·00	5·
381	**107**	5d. brown (30.6.13)	15·00	5·
382		5d. yellow-brown	15·00	5·
		a. Without wmk	£500	
383		5d. bistre-brown	£100	50·0
384		6d. dull purple (1.8.13)	25·00	10·0
385		6d. reddish purple (8.13)	15·00	7·0
		a. Perf 14 (9.20)	90·00	£11
386		6d. deep reddish purple	20·00	5·0
387		7d. olive (8.13)	20·00	10·00
388		7d. bronze-green (1915)	60·00	25·00
389		7d. sage-green (1917)	60·00	15·00
390		8d. black/*yellow* (1.8.13)	32·00	11·00
391		8d. black/*yellow-buff* (*granite*) (5.17)	40·00	15·00
392	**108**	9d. agate (30.6.13)	20·00	6·00
		a. Printed double, one albino ..		
393		9d. deep agate	25·00	6·00
393*a*		9d. olive-green (9.22)	£100	30·00
393*b*		9d. pale olive-green	£100	40·00
394		10d. turquoise-blue (1.8.13)	22·00	20·00
394*a*		10d. deep turquoise-blue	70·00	25·00

108	1s. bistre (1.8.13)		20·00	4·00
	1s. bistre-brown		35·00	12·00
'95		*Set of* 15	£250	£100

nperf stamps of this issue exist but may be war-time colour trials.
The impression of No. 361a is set sideways and is very pale.
No. 373 comes from Control O 20 and also exists on toned paper.
373*a* comes from Control R 21 and also exists on toned paper, both are unlike the rare Prussian blue shade of the 1935 2½d. lee issue.
ee also Nos. 418/29.
or the 2d., T **106** bisected, see note under Guernsey, War upation Issues.

3 (Aug). *Wmk Royal Cypher* ("*Multiple*"). *W* **103**. *P* 15×14.

105	½d. bright green		£150	£180
	a. Wmk sideways		†	£18000
104	1d. dull scarlet		£225	£225

oth these stamps were originally issued in rolls only. sequently sheets were found, so that horizontal pairs and blocks known but are of considerable rarity.

109

A

110 Single Cypher

Major Re-entries on 2s. 6d.

Nos. 400a and 408a

No. 415b

(Des Bertram Mackennal. Dies eng J. A. C. Harrison. Recess)

'igh values, so-called "Sea Horses" design: T **109**. *Background around portrait consists of horizontal lines, Type* A. *Wmk Single Cypher, W* **110.** *P* 11 × 12.

913 (30 June–Aug). *Printed by Waterlow Bros & Layton.*

99	2s. 6d. deep sepia-brown	£200	£125
00	2s. 6d. sepia-brown	£200	£125
	a. Re-entry (R. 2/1)	£800	£525
)1	5s. rose-carmine	£300	£250
)2	10s. indigo-blue (1 Aug)	£450	£350
)3	£1 green (1 Aug)	£1300	£800
)4	£1 dull blue-green (1 Aug)	£1300	£850
★399/404	**For well-centred, lightly used**		+35%

915 (Oct–Dec). *Printed by De La Rue & Co.*

)5	2s. 6d. deep yellow-brown (Nov)	£200	£175
06	2s. 6d. yellow-brown	£200	£175
07	2s. 6d. pale brown (worn plate)	£200	£175
)8	2s. 6d. sepia (seal-brown)	£200	£175
	a. Re-entry (R. 2/1)	£750	£500
)9	5s. bright carmine	£325	£275
10	5s. pale carmine (worn plate)	£400	£260
11	10s. deep blue (Dec)	£1400	£800
12	10s. blue	£1100	£650
13	10s. pale blue	£1100	£650
★405/13	**For well-centred, lightly used**		+ 45%

918 (Dec)–**19**. *Printed by Bradbury, Wilkinson & Co, Ltd.*

13*a*	2s. 6d. olive-brown	90·00	60·00
14	2s. 6d. chocolate-brown	£100	60·00
15	2s. 6d. reddish brown	£110	60·00
15*a*	2s. 6d. pale brown	£100	60·00
	b. Major re-entry (R.1/2)	£525	£325
16	5s. rose-red (1.19)	£225	90·00
17	10s. dull grey-blue (1.19)	£300	£140
399/417	*Set of* 4	£1700	£950
★413*a*/17	**For well-centred, lightly used**		+35%

)ISTINGUISHING PRINTINGS. Note that the £1 value was only ›rinted by Waterlow.

Waterlow and De La Rue stamps measure exactly 22 mm vertically. In the De La Rue printings the gum is usually patchy and yellowish, and the colour of the stamp, particularly in the 5s. tends to show through the back. The holes of the perforation are smaller than those of the other two printers, but there is a thick perforation tooth at the top of each vertical side.

In the Bradbury Wilkinson printings the height of the stamp is 22¾ or 23 mm. On most of the 22¾ mm high stamps a minute coloured guide dot appears in the margin just above the middle of the upper frame-line.

For (1934) re-engraved Waterlow printings *see* Nos. 450/2.

UNITED KINGDOM OF GREAT BRITAIN AND NORTHERN IRELAND

111 Block Cypher **111*a***

The watermark Type **111*a***, as compared with Type **111**, differs as follows: Closer spacing of horizontal rows (12½ mm instead of 14½ mm). Letters shorter and rounder. Watermark thicker.

(Typo by Waterlow & Sons, Ltd (all values except 6d.) and later, 1934–35, by Harrison & Sons, Ltd (all values). Until 1934 the 6d. was printed at Somerset House where a printing of the 1½d. was also made in 1926 (identifiable only by control E.26). Printings by Harrisons in 1934–35 can be identified, when in mint condition, by the fact that the gum shows a streaky appearance vertically, the Waterlow gum being uniformly applied, but Harrisons also used up the balance of the Waterlow "smooth gum" paper)

1924 (Feb)–**26**. *Wmk Block Cypher, W* **111**. *P* 15×14.

418	**105**	½d. green	1·00	1·00
		a. Wmk sideways (5.24)	6·00	3·25
		b. Doubly printed	£7500	†
419	**104**	1d. scarlet	1·00	1·00
		a. Wmk sideways	15·00	15·00
		b. Experimental paper, W **111*a*** (10.24)	22·00	
		c. Partial double print, one inverted	£5500	
		d. Inverted "Q" for "O" (R. 20/3)	£350	
420	**105**	1½d. red-brown	1·00	1·00
		a. *Tête-bêche* (pair)	£350	£600
		b. Wmk sideways (8.24)	7·00	3·50
		c. Printed on the gummed side ..	£350	†
		d. Booklet pane. Four stamps plus two printed labels (3.24) ..	£100	
		e. Ditto. Wmk sideways	£3250	
		f. Experimental paper, W **111*a*** (10.24)	60·00	70·00
		g. Double impression	£8500	†
421	**106**	2d. orange (Die II) (7.24)	2·50	2·50
		a. No wmk	£525	
		b. Wmk sideways (7.26)	70·00	80·00
		c. Partial double print	£13000	†
422	**104**	2½d. blue (10.24)	5·00	3·00
		a. No wmk	£800	
		b. Wmk sideways	†	£4500
423	**106**	3d. violet (10.24)	10·00	2·50
424		4d. grey-green (11.24)	12·00	2·50
		a. Printed on the gummed side ..	£1500	†
425	**107**	5d. brown (11.24)	20·00	3·00
426		6d. reddish purple (*chalk-surfaced paper*) (9.24)	12·00	2·50
426*a*		6d. purple (6.26)	3·00	1·50
427	**108**	9d. olive-green (12.24)	12·00	3·50
428		10d. turquoise-blue (11.24)	35·00	40·00
429		1s. bistre-brown (10.24)	22·00	3·00
418/29		.. .. *Set of* 12	£110	60·00

There are numerous shades in this issue.

The 6d. on both chalk-surfaced and ordinary papers was printed by both Somerset House and Harrisons. The Harrisons printings have streaky gum, differ slightly in shade, and that on chalk-surfaced paper is printed in a highly fugitive ink. The prices quoted are for the commonest (Harrison) printing in each case.

The dandy roll to produce watermark Type **111*a*** was provided by Somerset House in connection with experiments in paper composition undertaken during 1924–25. These resulted in a change from rag only paper to that made from a mixture including esparto and sulphite.

112

(Des H. Nelson. Eng J. A. C. Harrison. Recess Waterlow)

1924–25. *British Empire Exhibition. W* **111.** *P* 14.

(*a*) *Dated* "1924" (23.4.24)

430	**112**	1d. scarlet	10·00	11·00
431		1½d. brown	15·00	15·00

(*b*) *Dated* "1925" (9.5.25)

432	**112**	1d. scarlet	15·00	25·00
433		1½d. brown	40·00	65·00

113

114

115

116 St. George and the Dragon

117

(Des J. Farleigh (T **113** and **115**), E. Linzell (T **114**) and H. Nelson (T **116**). Eng C. G. Lewis (T **113**), T. E. Storey (T **115**), both at the Royal Mint; J. A. C. Harrison, of Waterlow (T **114** and **116**). Typo by Waterlow from plates made at the Royal Mint, except T **116**, recess by Bradbury, Wilkinson from die and plate of their own manufacture)

1929 (10 May). *Ninth U.P.U. Congress, London.*

(*a*) *W* **111.** *P* 15 × 14

434	**113**	½d. green	2·25	2·25
		a. Wmk sideways	30·00	35·00
435	**114**	1d. scarlet	2·25	2·25
		a. Wmk sideways	50·00	50·00
436		1½d. purple-brown	2·25	1·75
		a. Wmk sideways	30·00	25·00
		b. Booklet pane. Four stamps plus two printed labels	£170	
437	**115**	2½d. blue	10·00	10·00

(*b*) *W* **117.** *P* 12

438	**116**	£1 black	£750	£550
434/7		.. .. .. *Set of* 4 (*to* 2½*d.*)	15·00	14·50

PRINTERS. All subsequent issues were printed in photogravure by Harrison and Sons Ltd *except where otherwise stated.*

118

119

120

121 **122**

1934–36. *W* **111.** *P* 15 × 14.

439	**118**	½d. green (19.11.34)	50	50
		a. Wmk sideways	7·00	3·50
		b. Imperf three sides	£1500	
440	**119**	1d. scarlet (24.9.34)	50	50
		a. Imperf (pair)	£1250	
		b. Printed on the gummed side ..	£450	†
		c. Wmk sideways	12·00	6·00
		d. Double impression	†	£12500
		e. Imperf between (pair)	£2000	
		f. Imperf three sides (pair)	£1500	
441	**118**	1½d. red-brown (20.8.34)	50	50
		a. Imperf (pair)	£325	
		b. Imperf three sides (lower stamp in vert pair)	£800	
		c. Imperf between (horiz pair) ..		
		d. Wmk sideways	6·00	4·00
		e. Booklet pane. Four stamps plus two printed labels (1.35)	60·00	
442	**120**	2d. orange (21.1.35)	75	75
		a. Imperf (pair)	£1750	
		b. Wmk sideways	90·00	60·00
443	**119**	2½d. ultramarine (18.3.35)	1·50	1·25
444	**120**	3d. violet (18.3.35)	1·50	1·25
445		4d. deep grey-green (2.12.35) ..	2·00	1·25
446	**121**	5d. yellow-brown (17.2.36)	6·00	2·75
447	**122**	9d. deep olive-green (2.12.35) ..	12·00	2·25
448		10d. turquoise-blue (24.2.36)	15·00	10·00
449		1s. bistre-brown (24.2.36)	15·00	1·25
		a. Double impression	—	†
439/49		.. .. *Set of* 11	48·00	18·00

Owing to the need for wider space for the perforations the size of the designs of the ½d. and 2d. were once, and the 1d. and 1½d. twice reduced from that of the first printings.

There are also numerous minor variations, due to the photographic element in the process.

The ½d. imperf three sides, No. 439b, is known in a block of four, from a sheet, in which the bottom pair is imperf at top and sides.

For No. 442 bisected, see Guernsey, War Occupation Issues.

B

123

(Eng J. A. C. Harrison. Recess Waterlow)

1934 (16 Oct). *T* **109** (*re-engraved*). *Background around portrait consists of horizontal and diagonal lines. Type* B. *W* **110**. *P* 11×12.

450	**109**	2s. 6d. chocolate-brown	65·00	35·00
451		5s. bright rose-red	£150	80·00
452		10s. indigo	£325	75·00
450/2		.. .. *Set of* 3	£475	£180

There are numerous other minor differences in the design of this issue.

(Des B. Freedman)

1935 (7 May). *Silver Jubilee. W* **111.** *P* 15 × 14.

453	**123**	½d. green	75	50
454		1d. scarlet	1·25	1·50
455		1½d. red-brown	75	50
456		2½d. blue	4·50	5·50
456*a*		2½d. Prussian blue	£5000	£5000
453/6		.. .. *Set of* 4	6·00	7·00

The 1½d. and 2½d. values differ from T **123** in the emblem in the panel at right.

Four sheets of No. 456*a*, printed in the wrong shade, were issued in error by the Post Office Stores Department on 25 June 1935. It is known that three of the sheets were sold from the sub-office at 134 Fore Street, Upper Edmonton, London, between that date and 4 July.

KING EDWARD VIII
20 January–10 December 1936

Further detailed information on the stamps of King Edward VIII will be found in Volume 2 of the Stanley Gibbons *Great Britain Specialised Catalogue*.

124

125

(Des H. Brown, adapted Harrison using a photo by Hugh Cecil)

1936. *W* **125**. *P* 15×14.

457	**124**	½d. green (1.9.36)	30	30
		a. Double impression		
458		1d. scarlet (14.9.36)	60	50
459		1½d. red-brown (1.9.36)	30	30
		a. Booklet pane. Four stamps plus two printed labels (10.36)	60·00	
460		2½d. bright blue (1.9.36)	30	85
457/60		.. .. *Set of* 4	1·25	1·75

KING GEORGE VI
11 December 1936–6 February 1952

Further detailed information on the stamps of King George VI will be found in Volume 2 of the Stanley Gibbons *Great Britain Specialised Catalogue*.

126 King George VI and Queen Elizabeth

(Des E. Dulac)

1937 (13 May). *Coronation. W* **127.** *P* 15 × 14.

461	**126**	1½d. maroon	30	30

127

128

129

130

King George VI and National Emblems

(Des T **128/9,** E. Dulac (head) and E. Gill (frames). T **130,** E. Dulac (whole stamp))

1937–47. *W* **127.** *P* 15 × 14.

462	**128**	½d. green (10.5.37)	30	25
		a. Wmk sideways (1.38)	50	50
		ab. Booklet pane of 4 (6.40) ..	38·00	
463		1d. scarlet (10.5.37)	30	25
		a. Wmk sideways (2.38)	20·00	9·00
		ab. Booklet pane of 4 (6.40) ..	95·00	
464		1½d. red-brown (30.7.37)	20	25
		a. Wmk sideways (2.38)	1·00	1·25
		b. Booklet pane. Four stamps plus two printed labels (8.37) ..	55·00	
		c. Imperf three sides (pair) ..		
465		2d. orange (31.1.38)	75	50
		a. Wmk sideways (2.38)	70·00	38·00
		b. Bisected (on cover)	†	35·00
466		2½d. ultramarine (10.5.37)	30	25
		a. Wmk sideways (6.40)	65·00	20·00
		b. *Tête-bêche* (horiz pair)		
467		3d. violet (31.1.38)	3·75	1·00
468	**129**	4d. grey-green (21.11.38)	60	75
		a. Imperf (pair)	£2500	
		b. Imperf three sides (horiz pair) ..	£3000	
469		5d. brown (21.11.38)	2·50	85
		a. Imperf (pair)	£3000	
		b. Imperf three sides (horiz pair) ..	£2500	
470		6d. purple (30.1.39)	1·25	60
471	**130**	7d. emerald-green (27.2.39) ..	4·25	60
		a. Imperf three sides (horiz pair) ..	£2500	
472		8d. bright carmine (27.2.39) ..	3·75	80
473		9d. deep olive-green (1.5.39) ..	5·50	80
474		10d. turquoise-blue (1.5.39)	5·75	80
		aa. Imperf (pair)	£3750	
474*a*		11d. plum (29.12.47)	2·00	2·75
475		1s. bistre-brown (1.5.39)	6·00	75
462/75		.. .. *Set of* 15	32·00	10·00

For later printings of the lower values in apparently lighter shades and different colours, see Nos. 485/90 and 503/8.

No. 465b was authorised for use in Guernsey. See notes on War Occupation Issues.

Nos. 468b and 469b are perforated at foot only and each occurs in the same sheet as Nos. 468a and 469a.

No. 471a is also perforated at foot only, but occurs on the top row of a sheet.

131 King George VI

132 King George VI

133

(Des E. Dulac (T **131**) and Hon. G. R. Bellew (T **132**). Eng J. A. C. Harrison. Recess Waterlow)

1939–48. *W* **133.** *P* 14.

476	**131**	2s. 6d. brown (4.9.39)	35·00	6·00
476*a*		2s. 6d. yellow-green (9.3.42)	4·50	1·50
477		5s. red (21.8.39)	9·00	2·00
478	**132**	10s. dark blue (30.10.39)	£225	20·00
478*a*		10s. ultramarine (30.11.42)	20·00	5·00
478*b*		£1 brown (1.10.48)	7·00	26·00
476/8*b*		.. .. *Set of* 6	£275	55·00

134 Queen Victoria and King George VI.

(Des H. L. Palmer)

1940 (6 May). *Centenary of First Adhesive Postage Stamps. W* **127.** *P* 14½ × 14.

479	**134**	½d. green	30	30
480		1d. scarlet	1·00	40
481		1½d. red-brown	50	75
482		2d. orange	50	40
		a. Bisected (on cover)	†	25·00
483		2½d. ultramarine	2·25	50
484		3d. violet	3·00	3·50
479/84		.. .. *Set of* 6	6·50	5·25

No. 482a was authorised for use in Guernsey. See notes on War Occupation Issues.

1941–42. *Head as Nos.* 462/7, *but lighter background. W* **127.** *P* 15 × 14.

485	**128**	½d. pale green (1.9.41)	30	30
		a. *Tête-bêche* (horiz pair)	£4000	
		b. Imperf (pair)	£2500	
486		1d. pale scarlet (11.8.41)	30	30
		a. Wmk sideways (10.42)	4·00	4·50
		b. Imperf (pair)	£3250	
		c. Imperf three sides (horiz pair) ..	£3250	
487	**128**	1½d. pale red-brown (28.9.42) ..	50	
488		2d. pale orange (6.10.41)	50	
		a. Wmk sideways (6.42)	28·00	19
		b. *Tête-bêche* (horiz pair)	£3500	
		c. Imperf (pair)	£2500	
		d. Imperf pane*	£5000	
489		2½d. light ultramarine (21.7.41) ..	30	
		a. Wmk sideways (8.42)	15·00	12
		b. *Tête-bêche* (horiz pair)	£3500	
		c. Imperf (pair)	£3000	
		d. Imperf pane*	£4500	
		e. Imperf three sides (horiz pair) ..	£4000	
490		3d. pale violet (3.11.41)	2·00	1
485/90		.. .. *Set of* 6	3·50	2

The *tête-bêche* varieties are from defectively made-up sta booklets.

Nos. 486c and 489e are perforated at foot only and occur in same sheets as Nos. 486b and 489c.

*BOOKLET ERRORS. Those listed as "imperf panes" sh one row of perforations either at the top or at the bottom of pane of 6.

WATERMARK VARIETIES. Please note that *inverted waterma* are outside the scope of this listing but are fully listed in the *Gr Britain Specialised* and *Great Britain Concise* Catalogues. See a the notes about watermarks at the beginning of the King George section.

135

136 Symbols of Peace and Reconstruction

(Des H. L. Palmer (T **135**) and R. Stone (T **136**))

1946 (11 June). *Victory. W* **127.** *P* 15 × 14.

491	**135**	2½d. ultramarine	20	
492	**136**	3d. violet	20	

137

138 King George VI and Queen Elizabeth

(Des G. Knipe and Joan Hassall from photographs by Doroth Wilding)

1948 (26 Apr). *Royal Silver Wedding. W* **127.** *P* 15 × 14 (2½*d.*) 14 × 15 (£1).

493	**137**	2½d. ultramarine	35	2
494	**138**	£1 blue	38·00	38·0

1948 (10 May). Stamps of 1d. and 2½d. showing seaweed-gatherin were on sale at eight Head Post Offices in Great Britain, but wer primarily for use in the Channel Islands and are listed there (se after Great Britain Postal Fiscals).

139 Globe and Laurel Wreath

140 "Speed"

141 Olympic Symbol

142 Winged Victory

s P. Metcalfe (T **139**), A. Games (T **140**), S. D. Scott (T **141**) and E. Dulac (T **142**))

3 (29 July). *Olympic Games. W* **127.** *P* 15 × 14.

139	2½d.	ultramarine	35	10
140	3d.	violet	35	55
141	6d.	bright purple	75	40
142	1s.	brown	1·40	1·60
/8 ..		.. .. *Set of* 4	2·50	2·40

143 Two Hemispheres

144 U.P.U. Monument, Berne

145 Goddess Concordia, Globe and Points of Compass

146 Posthorn and Globe

es Mary Adshead (T **143**), P. Metcalfe (T **144**), H. Fleury (T **145**) and Hon. G. R. Bellew (T **146**))

9 (10 Oct). *75th Anniv of Universal Postal Union. W* **127.** P 15 × 14.

143	2½d.	ultramarine	15	10
) **144**	3d.	violet	15	50
145	6d.	bright purple	25	50
146	1s.	brown	60	1·25
)/502..		.. .. *Set of* 4	1·00	2·10

50–52. 4*d. as Nos.* 468 *and others as Nos.* 485/9, *but colours changed. W* **127.** *P* 15×14.

3 **128**	½d.	pale orange (3.5.51)	30	30
		a. Imperf (pair)		
		b. *Tête-bêche* (horiz pair)	£3500	
		c. Imperf pane*	£4500	
4	1d.	light ultramarine (3.5.51)	30	30
		a. Wmk sideways (5.51)	1·10	1·25
		b. Imperf (pair)	£2250	
		c. Imperf three sides (horiz pair) ..	£1750	
		d. Booklet pane. Three stamps plus three printed labels (3.52) ..	18·00	
		e. Ditto. Partial *tête-bêche* pane ..	£3000	
5	1½d.	pale green (3.5.51)	65	60
		a. Wmk sideways (9.51)	3·25	5·00
6	2d.	pale red-brown (3.5.51)	75	40
		a. Wmk sideways (5.51)	1·75	2·00
		b. *Tête-bêche* (horiz pair)	£3500	
		c. Imperf three sides (horiz pair) ..	£1750	
7	2½d.	pale scarlet (3.5.51)	60	40
		a. Wmk sideways (5.51)	1·75	1·75
		b. *Tête-bêche* (horiz pair)		
8 **129**	4d.	light ultramarine (2.10.50) ..	2·00	1·75
		a. Double impression	†	£5000
3/8 ..		.. .. .. *Set of* 6	4·00	3·25

No. 504c is perforated at foot only and occurs in the same sheet No. 504b.

No. 506c is also perforated at foot only.

*BOOKLET ERRORS. Those listed as "imperf panes" show one w of perforations either at the top or at the bottom of the pane of

147 H.M.S. *Victory*

148 White Cliffs of Dover

149 St. George and the Dragon

150 Royal Coat of Arms

(Des Mary Adshead (T **147/8**), P. Metcalfe (T **149/50**). Recess Waterlow)

1951 (3 May). *W* **133.** *P* 11 × 12.

509	**147**	2s. 6d. yellow-green		2·00	1·00
510	**148**	5s. red		40·00	1·50
511	**149**	10s. ultramarine		10·00	8·50
512	**150**	£1 brown		48·00	20·00
509/12 ..		.. .. *Set of* 4		85·00	25·00

151 "Commerce and Prosperity"

152 Festival Symbol

(Des E. Dulac (T **151**), A. Games (T **152**))

1951 (3 May). *Festival of Britain. W* **127.** *P* 15 × 14.

513	**151**	2½d. scarlet	15	20
514	**152**	4d. ultramarine	30	65

STAMP BOOKLETS

For a full listing of Great Britain stamp booklets see the *Great Britain Concise Catalogue* published each Spring.

POSTAGE DUE STAMPS

PERFORATIONS. All postage due stamps to No. D39 are perf 14×15.

D 1

D 2

(Des G. Eve. Typo Somerset House (early trial printings of ½d., 1d., 2d., and 5d.; all printings of 1s.) or Harrison (later printings of all values except 1s.)).

1914 (20 Apr)–**22.** *W* **100** (*Simple Cypher*) *sideways.*

D1	**D 1**	½d. emerald	50	25
D2		1d. carmine	50	25
		a. Pale carmine	75	50
D3		1½d. chestnut (1922)	48·00	20·00
D4		2d. agate	50	25
D5		3d. violet (1918)	5·00	75
		a. Bluish violet	6·00	2·75
D6		4d. dull grey-green (12.20)	18·00	5·00
D7		5d. brownish cinnamon	6·00	3·50
D8		1s. bright blue (1915)	40·00	4·75
		a. Deep bright blue	40·00	5·00
D1/8		.. .. *Set of* 8	£110	32·00

The 1d. is known bisected from various offices between 1914 and 1924, the 2d. bisected for use as a 1d. between 1918 and 1923, the 3d. bisected for use as a 1½d. in 1922 at Warminster and trisected for use as a 1d. in 1921 at Malvern.

1924. *As* 1914–22, *but on thick chalk-surfaced paper.*

D9	**D 1**	1d. carmine	2·25	3·50

(Typo Waterlow and (from 1934) Harrison)

1924–31. *W* **111** (*Block Cypher*) *sideways.*

D10	**D 1**	½d. emerald (6.25)	1·25	75
D11		1d. carmine (4.25)	60	25
D12		1½d. chestnut (10.24)	45·00	18·00
D13		2d. agate (7.24)	1·00	25
D14		3d. dull violet (10.24)	1·50	25
		a. Printed on gummed side ..	75·00	†
		b. Experimental paper W **111***a* ..	38·00	35·00
D15		4d. dull grey-green (10.24)	15·00	3·00
D16		5d. brownish cinnamon (1.31) ..	32·00	28·00
D17		1s. deep blue (9.24)	10·00	1·00
D18	**D 2**	2s. 6d. purple/*yellow* (5.24)	45·00	2·00
D10/18		.. .. *Set of* 9	£140	48·00

The 1d. is known bisected from various offices between 1925 and 1932 and the 2d. exists bisected to make up the 2½d. rate at Perranwell Station, Cornwall, in 1932.

1936–37. *W* **125** (E 8 R) *sideways.*

D19	**D 1**	½d. emerald (6.37)	7·50	8·00
D20		1d. carmine (5.37)	1·50	2·00
D21		2d. agate (5.37)	7·00	11·00
D22		3d. dull violet (3.37)	1·50	2·25
D23		4d. dull grey-green (12.36)	23·00	35·00
D24		5d. brownish cinnamon (11.36) ..	55·00	25·00
		a. Yellow-brown (1937)	16·00	23·00
D25		1s. deep blue (12.36)	11·00	9·00
D26	**D 2**	2s. 6d. purple/*yellow* (5.37)	£275	9·00
D19/26		.. .. .. *Set of* 8 (*cheapest*)	£300	90·00

The 1d. is known bisected at Solihull in 1937.

1937–38. *W* **127** (G VI R) *sideways.*

D27	**D 1**	½d. emerald (5.38)	9·00	5·00
D28		1d. carmine (5.38)	3·00	75
D29		2d. agate (5.38)	2·50	75
D30		3d. violet (12.37)	12·00	1·00
D31		4d. dull grey-green (9.37)	75·00	13·00
D32		5d. yellow-brown (11.38)	14·00	75
D33		1s. deep blue (10.37)	75·00	2·00
D34	**D 2**	2s. 6d. purple/*yellow* (9.38)	75·00	2·50
D27/34		.. .. *Set of* 8	£250	23·00

The 2d. is known bisected at various offices between 1951 and 1954.

DATES OF ISSUE. The dates for Nos. D35/9 are those on which stamps were first issued by the Supplies Department to postmasters.

1951–52. *Colours changed and new value* (1½*d.*). *W* **127** (G VI R) *sideways.*

D35	**D 1**	½d. orange (18.9.51)	1·00	3·00
D36		1d. violet-blue (6.6.51)	1·50	1·50
D37		1½d. green (11.2.52)	1·75	3·00
D38		4d. blue (14.8.51)	32·00	12·00
D39		1s. ochre (6.12.51)	38·00	14·00
D35/9		.. .. *Set of* 5	65·00	30·00

The 1d. is known bisected at Capel, Dorking in 1952 and at Camberley in 1954.

PRICES OF SETS

Set prices are given for many issues, generally those containing three stamps or more. Definitive sets include one of each value or major colour change, but do not cover different perforations, die types or minor shades. Where a choice is possible the set prices are based on the cheapest versions of the stamps included in the listings.

OFFICIAL STAMPS

In 1840 the 1d. black (Type 1), with "V R" in the upper corners, was prepared for official use, but never issued for postal purposes. Obliterated specimens are those which were used for experimental trials of obliterating inks, or those that passed through the post by oversight.

V 1

1840. *Prepared for use but not issued; "V" "R" in upper corners. Imperf.*

			Un	Used	Used on cover
V1	V 1	1d. black	£7000	£12000	

The following Official stamps would be more correctly termed Departmental stamps as they were exclusively for the use of certain government departments. Until 1882 official mail used ordinary postage stamps purchased at post offices, the cash being refunded once a quarter. Later the government departments obtained Official stamps by requisition.

Official stamps were on sale to the public for a short time at Somerset House but they were not sold from post offices. The system of only supplying the Government departments was open to abuse so that all Official stamps were withdrawn on 13 May 1904.

OVERPRINTS, PERFORATIONS, WATERMARKS. All Official stamps were overprinted by Thomas De La Rue & Co. and are perf 14. They are on Crown watermarked paper unless otherwise stated.

INLAND REVENUE

These stamps were used by revenue officials in the provinces, mail to and from Head Office passing without a stamp. The London Office used these stamps only for foreign mail.

I.R.

OFFICIAL

(O 1)

I. R.

OFFICIAL

(O 2)

Optd with Types O 1 (*½d. to 1s.*) *or* O 2 (*others*)

1882–1901. *Stamps of Queen Victoria.* (*a*) *Issues of* 1880–81.

		Un	Used	★ Used on cover
O 1	½d. deep green (1.11.82)	50·00	20·00	60·00
O 2	½d. pale green	50·00	20·00	
O 3	1d. lilac (Die II) (1.10.82)	4·00	2·00	20·00
	a. Optd in blue-black	£100	50·00	
	b. "OFFICIAL" omitted	—	£4000	
O 4	6d. grey (Plate 18) (3.11.82)	£190	50·00	

No. O3 with the lines of the overprint transposed is an essay.

(*b*) *Issues of* 1884–88

		Un	Used	Used on cover
O 5	½d. slate-blue (8.5.85)	50·00	22·00	90·00
O 6	2½d. lilac (12.3.85)	£160	55·00	£675
O 7	1s. dull green (12.3.85)	£2750	£575	
O 8	5s. rose (*blued paper*) (wmk Anchor) (12.3.85)	£3000	£900	
O 9	5s. rose (wmk Anchor) (3.90)	£1600	£475	
	a. Raised stop after "R"	£1800	£500	
	b. Optd in blue-black	£2400	£500	
O 9*c*	10s. cobalt (*blued paper*) (wmk Anchor) (12.3.85)	£5750	£1000	
O 9*d*	10s. ultramarine (*blued paper*) (wmk Anchor) (12.3.85)	£5750	£1900	
O10	10s. ultram (wmk Anchor) (3.90)	£3250	£650	
	a. Raised stop after "R"	£3750	£700	
	b. Optd in blue-black	£4000	£900	
O11	£1 brown-lilac (wmk Crowns) (12.3.85)	£24000		
	a. Frame broken	£29000		
O12	£1 brown-lilac (wmk Orbs) (3.90)	£32000		
	a. Frame broken	£35000		

(*c*) *Issues of* 1887–92

		Un	Used	Used on cover
O13	½d. vermilion (15.5.88)	2·50	1·50	30·00
	a. Without "I.R."	£2500		
	b. Imperf	£1700		
	c. Opt double (imperf)	£2000		
O14	2½d. purple/*blue* (2.92)	70·00	6·00	£225
O15	1s. dull green (9.89)	£240	£100	£1300
O16	£1 green (6.92)	£4000	£600	
	a. No stop after "R"	—	£1000	
	b. Frame broken	£6500	£1200	

Nos. O3, O13, O15 and O16 may be found with two varieties of overprint, namely, 1882 printings, *thin* letters, and 1894 printings, *thicker* letters.

(*d*) *Issues of* 1887 *and* 1900

		Un	Used	Used on cover
O17	½d. blue-green (4.01)	6·00	4·50	£110
O18	6d. purple/*rose-red* (1.7.01)	£175	45·00	
O19	1s. green and carmine (12.01)	£850	£350	
★O1/19	**For well-centred, lightly used**		+35%	

1902–04. *Stamps of King Edward VII. Ordinary paper.*

		Un	Used	Used on cover
O20	½d. blue-green (4.2.02)	22·00	3·00	£110
O21	1d. scarlet (4.2.02)	15·00	2·00	75·00
O22	2½d. ultramarine (19.2.02)	£475	£100	
O23	6d. pale dull purple (14.3.04)	£90000	£70000	
O24	1s. dull green & carmine (29.4.02)	£600	£150	
O25	5s. bright carmine (29.4.02)	£4750	£2000	
	a. Raised stop after "R"	£5250	£2200	
O26	10s. ultramarine (29.4.02)	£17000	£10000	
	a. Raised stop after "R"	£20000	£13000	
O27	£1 dull blue-green (29.4.02)	£14000	£8000	

OFFICE OF WORKS

These were issued to Head and Branch (local) offices in London and to Branch (local) offices at Birmingham, Bristol, Edinburgh, Glasgow, Leeds, Liverpool, Manchester and Southampton. The overprints on stamps of value 2d. and upwards were created later in 1902, the 2d. for registration fees and the rest for overseas mail.

O.W.

OFFICIAL

(O 3)

Optd with Type O 3

1896 (24 Mar)–**02.** *Stamps of Queen Victoria.*

		Un	Used	Used on cover
O31	½d. vermilion	£110	60·00	£275
O32	½d. blue-green (2.02)	£190	95·00	
O33	1d. lilac (Die II)	£190	60·00	£300
O34	5d. dull purple and blue (II) (29.4.02)	£900	£210	
O35	10d. dull purple and carmine (28.5.02)	£1500	£300	

1902 (11 Feb)–**03.** *Stamps of King Edward VII. Ordinary paper.*

		Un	Used	Used on cover
O36	½d. blue-green (2.02)	£425	£110	£1000
O37	1d. scarlet	£425	£110	£225
O38	2d. yellowish green & carmine-red (27.4.02)	£800	£250	£1300
O39	2½d. ultramarine (29.4.02)	£850	£300	
O40	10d. dull purple & carmine (28.5.03)	£6000	£2400	
★O31/40	**For well-centred, lightly used**		+25%	

ARMY

Letters to and from the War Office in London passed without postage. The overprinted stamps were distributed to District and Station Paymasters nationwide, including Cox and Co., the Army Agents, who were paymasters to the Household Division.

ARMY

OFFICIAL

(O 4)

ARMY

OFFICIAL

(O 5)

ARMY

OFFICIAL

(O 6)

1896 (1 Sept)–**01.** *Stamps of Queen Victoria optd with Type* O 4 (*½d., 1d.*) *or* O 5 (*2½d., 6d.*).

		Un	Used	Used on cover
O41	½d. vermilion	2·50	1·50	28·00
	a. "OFFICIAI" (R. 13/7)	60·00	30·00	
	b. Lines of opt transposed	£1250		
O42	½d. blue-green (6.00)	2·50	4·50	
O43	1d. lilac (Die II)	2·50	1·50	45·00
	a. "OFFICIAI" (R. 13/7)	60·00	25·00	
O44	2½d. purple/*blue*	6·00	3·50	£325
O45	6d. purple/*rose-red* (20.9.01)	18·00	20·00	£700

Nos. O41a and O43a occur on sheets overprinted by Forme 1.

1902–03. *Stamps of King Edward VII optd with Type* O 4 (*Nos.* O48/50) *or Type* O 6 (*No.* O52). *Ordinary paper.*

		Un	Used	Used on cover
O48	½d. blue-green (11.2.02)	3·00	1·50	75·00
O49	1d. scarlet (11.2.02)	3·00	1·50	75·00
	a. "ARMY" omitted	†	—	
O50	6d. pale dull purple (23.8.02)	80·00	35·00	
O52	6d. pale dull purple (12.03)	£1000	£350	

GOVERNMENT PARCELS

These stamps were issued to all departments, including the Head Office, for use on parcels weighing over 3 lb. Below this weight government parcels were sent by letter post to avoid the 55% of the postage paid from accruing to the railway companies, as laid down by parcel-post regulations. Most government parcels stamps suffered heavy postmarks in use.

GOVT

PARCELS

(O 7)

Optd as Type O 7

1883 (1 Aug)–**86.** *Stamps of Queen Victoria.*

		Un	★ Used
O61	1½d. lilac (1.5.86)	£125	30·00
	a. No dot under "T"	£190	32·00
	b. Dot to left of "T"	£150	32·00
O62	6d. dull green (1.5.86)	£825	£300
O63	9d. dull green	£675	£190
O64	1s. orange-brown (wmk Crown, Pl 13)	£450	80·00
	a. No dot under "T"	£600	90·00
	b. Dot to left of "T"	£600	90·00
O64*c*	1s. orange-brown (Pl 14)	£775	£125
	ca. No dot under "T"	£900	£110
	cb. Dot to left of "T"		

1887–90. *Stamps of Queen Victoria.*

		Un	Used
O65	1½d. dull purple and pale green (29.10.87)	25·00	3·00
	a. No dot under "T"	40·00	7·00
	b. Dot to right of "T"	40·00	6·00
	c. Dot to left of "T"	40·00	6·00
O66	6d. purple/*rose-red* (19.12.87)	60·00	12·00
	a. No dot under "T"	90·00	14·00
	b. Dot to right of "T"	90·00	14·00
	c. Dot to left of "T"	90·00	12·00
O67	9d. dull purple and blue (21.8.88)	70·00	16·00
O68	1s. dull green (25.3.90)	£150	8
	a. No dot under "T"	£200	8
	b. Dot to right of "T"	£200	8
	c. Dot to left of "T"	£225	9
	d. Optd in blue-black		

1891–1900. *Stamps of Queen Victoria.*

		Un	Used
O69	1d. lilac (Die II) (18.6.97)	30·00	9
	a. No dot under "T"	45·00	21
	b. Dot to left of "T"	45·00	21
	c. Opt inverted	£1500	£
	d. Ditto. Dot to left of "T"	£1750	£1
O70	2d. grey-green and carmine (24.10.91)	50·00	8
	a. No dot under "T"	80·00	10
	b. Dot to left of "T"	80·00	10
O71	4½d. green and carmine (29.9.92)	£125	80
	b. Dot to right of "T"		
O72	1s. green and carmine (11.00)	£175	55
	a. Opt inverted	†	£4
★O61/72	**For well-centred lightly used**		+10

The "no dot under T" variety occurred on R.12/3 and 20/2. T "dot to left of T" comes four times in the sheet on R.2/7, 6/7, and 12/9. The best example of the "dot to right of T" is on R.20 All three varieties were corrected around 1897.

1902. *Stamps of King Edward VII. Ordinary paper.*

		Un	Used
O74	1d. scarlet (30.10.02)	17·00	6
O75	2d. yellowish green & carmine-red (29.4.02)	70·00	18
O76	6d. pale dull purple (19.2.02)	£110	18
	a. Opt double, one albino	£7500	
O77	9d. dull purple and ultramarine (28.8.02)	£250	60
O78	1s. dull green and carmine (17.12.02)	£375	90

BOARD OF EDUCATION

BOARD

OF

EDUCATION

(O 8)

Optd with Type O 8

1902 (19 Feb). *Stamps of Queen Victoria.*

		Un	Used	Used Co
O81	5d. dull purple and blue (II)	£600	£140	
O82	1s. green and carmine	£1200	£600	

1902 (19 Feb)–**04.** *Stamps of King Edward VII. Ordinary paper*

		Un	Used	Used Co
O83	½d. blue-green	90·00	30·00	£3
O84	1d. scarlet	90·00	30·00	£3
O85	2½d. ultramarine	£600	70·00	
O86	5d. dull purple & ultram (6.2.04)	£2400	£1100	
O87	1s. dull green & carmine (23.12.02)	£45000		

ROYAL HOUSEHOLD

R.H.

OFFICIAL

(O 9)

1902. *Stamps of King Edward VII optd with Type* O 9. *Ordina paper.*

		Un	Used	Used Co
O91	½d. blue-green (29.4.02)	£170	£110	£6
O92	1d. scarlet (19.2.02)	£150	£100	£5

ADMIRALTY

ADMIRALTY

OFFICIAL

(O 10)

ADMIRALTY

OFFICIAL

(O 11)
(with different "M")

1903 (1 Apr). *Stamps of King Edward VII optd with Type* O 1(*Ordinary paper.*

		Un	Used	Used Co
O101	½d. blue-green	12·00	10·00	
O102	1d. scarlet	7·00	4·00	£22
O103	1½d. dull purple and green	70·00	55·00	
O104	2d. yellowish green & carmine-red	£140	70·00	
O105	2½d. ultramarine	£150	55·00	
O106	3d. purple/*yellow*	£140	55·00	

1903–04. *Stamps of King Edward VII optd with Type* O 11 *Ordinary paper.*

		Un	Used	Used Co
O107	½d. blue-green (9.03)	12·00	7·00	£32
O108	1d. scarlet (12.03)	11·00	6·00	65·0
O109	1½d. dull purple and green (2.04)	£300	£200	
O110	2d. yellowish green and carmine-red (3.04)	£475	£225	
O111	2½d. ultramarine (3.04)	£575	£325	
O112	3d. dull purple/*orange-yell* (12.03)	£400	£100	

Stamps of various issues perforated with a Crown and initial ("H.M.O.W.", "O.W.", "B.T." or "S.O.") or with initials onl ("H.M.S.O." or "D.S.I.R.") have also been used for official purposes but these are outside the scope of the catalogue.

POSTAL FISCAL STAMPS

PRICES. Prices in the used column are for stamps with genuin postal cancellations dated from the time when they were authorise for use as postage stamps. Beware of stamps with fiscal cancellation removed and fraudulent postmarks applied.

…LIDITY. The 1d. Surface-printed stamps were authorised for …al use from 1 June 1881 and at the same time the 1d. postage …, No. 166, was declared valid for fiscal purposes. The 3d. and …values, together with the Embossed issues were declared valid …postal purposes by another Act effective from 1 January 1883.

SURFACE-PRINTED ISSUES

(Typo Thomas De La Rue & Co)

F 1
Rectangular Buckle

F 2

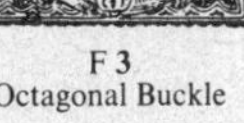

F 3
Octagonal Buckle

F 4

F 5
Double-lined Anchor

F 6
Single-lined Anchor

…3–57. *P* 15½ × 15. (*a*) *Wmk* F **5** (*inverted*) (1853–55).

			Un	*Used*	*Used on cover*
F **1**	1d.	light blue (10.10.53) ..	25·00	30·00	£120
F **2**	1d.	ochre (10.53)	75·00	90·00	£350
		a. *Tête-bêche* (in block of four)	£10000		
F **3**	1d.	pale turquoise-blue (12.53)	20·00	30·00	£180
	1d.	light blue/*blue* (12.53) ..	50·00	50·00	£300
F **4**	1d.	reddish lilac/*blue glazed paper* (25.3.55)	75·00	80·00	£250

Only one example is known of No. F2a outside the National Postal …useum and the Royal Collection.

(*b*) *Wmk* F **6** (1856–57)

F **4**	1d.	reddish lilac (*shades*) ..	7·00	5·00	£100
	1d.	reddish lilac/*bluish* (*shades*) (1857)	7·00	5·00	£100

INLAND REVENUE

(F 7)

…60 (3 Apr). *No.* F7 *optd with Type* F **7**, *in red.*

…8	F **4**	1d.	dull reddish lilac/*blue* ..	£500	£425	£750

…LUE PAPER. In the following issues we no longer distinguish …tween bluish and white paper. There is a range of papers from …hite or greyish to bluish.

F **8**

F **9**

F **10**

…60–67. *Bluish to white paper. P* 15½ × 15. (*a*) *Wmk* F **6** (1860).

…9	F **8**	1d.	reddish lilac (May) ..	8·00	8·00	95·00
…10	F **9**	3d.	reddish lilac (June) ..	£250	£150	£300
…11	F **10**	6d.	reddish lilac (Oct) ..	£120	£100	£250

(*b*) *W* **40**. (*Anchor* 16 *mm high*) (1864)

F12	F **8**	1d.	pale reddish lilac (Nov)	7·00	7·00	95·00
F13	F **9**	3d.	pale reddish lilac ..	£150	£100	£300
F14	F **10**	6d.	pale reddish lilac ..	£120	£100	£250

(*c*) *W* **40** (*Anchor* 18 *mm high*) (1867)

F15	F **8**	1d.	reddish lilac	13·00	13·00	£150
F16	F **9**	3d.	reddish lilac	70·00	65·00	£250
F17	F **10**	6d.	reddish lilac	60·00	50·00	£170

For stamps perf 14, see Nos. F24/7.

F **11**

F **12**

Four Dies of Type F 12

Die 1. Corner ornaments small and either joined or broken; heavy shading under chin

Die 2. Ornaments small and always broken; clear line of shading under chin

Die 3. Ornaments larger and joined; line of shading under chin extended half way down neck

Die 4. Ornaments much larger; straight line of shading continued to bottom of neck

1867–81. *White to bluish paper. P* 14. (*a*) *W* **47** (*Small Anchor*).

F18	F **11**	1d.	purple (1.9.67)	12·00	12·00	80·00
F19	F **12**	1d.	purple (Die 1) (6.68) ..	3·50	4·00	80·00
F20		1d.	purple (Die 2) (6.76) ..	15·00	10·00	£180
F21		1d.	purple (Die 3) (3.77) ..	6·00	6·00	£100
F22		1d.	purple (Die 4) (7.78) ..	4·00	4·00	65·00

(*b*) *W* **48** (*Orb*)

F23	F **12**	1d.	purple (Die 4) (1.81) ..	3·00	1·50	40·00

1881. *White to bluish paper. P* 14.

(*a*) *W* **40** (*Anchor* 18 *mm high*) (Jan)

F24	F **9**	3d.	reddish lilac	£400	£225	£450
F25	F **10**	6d.	reddish lilac	£220	£100	£250

(*b*) *W* **40** (*Anchor* 20 *mm high*) (May)

F26	F **9**	3d.	reddish lilac	£350	£200	£400
F27	F **10**	6d.	reddish lilac	£200	£100	£250

ISSUES EMBOSSED IN COLOUR

(Made at Somerset House)

The embossed stamps were struck from dies not appropriated to any special purpose on paper which had the words "INLAND REVENUE" previously printed, and thus became available for payment of any duties for which no special stamps had been provided.

The die letters are included in the embossed designs and holes were drilled for the insertion of plugs showing figures indicating dates of striking.

F 13

F 14

INLAND REVENUE

(F 15)

INLAND REVENUE

(F 16)

1860 (3 Apr)–**71.** *Types* F **13/14** *and similar types embossed on bluish paper. Underprint Type* F **15.** *No wmk. Imperf.*

			Un	*Used*
F28	2d.	pink (Die A) (1.1.71)	£400	
F29	3d.	pink (Die C)	£100	
		a. *Tête-bêche* (vert pair)	£800	
F30	3d.	pink (Die D)	£400	
F31	6d.	pink (Die T)		
F32	6d.	pink (Die U)	£200	
		a. *Tête-bêche* (vert pair)		
F33	9d.	pink (Die C) (1.1.71)	£500	
F34	1s.	pink (Die E) (28.6.61)	£400	
		a. *Tête-bêche* (vert pair)		
F35	1s.	pink (Die F) (28.6.61)	£150	
		a. *Tête-bêche* (vert pair)	£600	
F36	2s.	pink (Die K) (6.8.61)	£400	
F37	2s. 6d.	pink (Die N) (28.6.61) ..		
F38	2s. 6d.	pink (Die O) (28.6.61)	£200	

1871 (Aug). *As last but perf* 12½.

F39	2d.	pink (Die A)	£250	
F42	9d.	pink (Die C)	£600	
F43	1s.	pink (Die E)	£400	
F44	1s.	pink (Die F)	£350	
F45	2s. 6d.	pink (Die O)	£200	

1874 (Nov). *Types as before embossed on white paper. Underprint Type* F **16**, *in green. W* **47** (*Small Anchor*). *P* 12½.

F46	2d.	pink (Die A)		
F47	9d.	pink (Die C)		
F48	1s.	pink (Die F)	£300	
F49	2s. 6d.	pink (Die O)		

It is possible that the 2d., 9d. and 2s. 6d. may not exist with the thin underprint, Type F **16**, in this shade.

1875 (Nov)–**80.** *As last but colour changed and on white or bluish paper.*

F50	2d.	vermilion (Die A) (1880)	£300	
F51	9d.	vermilion (Die C) (1876)	£400	
F52	1s.	vermilion (Die E)	£250	
F53	1s.	vermilion (Die F)	£500	
F54	2s. 6d.	vermilion (Die O) (1878)	£250	

1882 (Oct). *As last but W* **48** (*Orbs*).

F55	2d.	vermilion (Die A)		
F56	9d.	vermilion (Die C)		
F57	1s.	vermilion (Die E)		
F58	2s. 6d.	vermilion (Die O)	£500	£400

Although specimen overprints of Nos. F55/7 are known there is some doubt if these values were issued.

The sale of Inland Revenue stamps up to the 2s. value ceased from 30 December 1882 and stocks were called in and destroyed. The 2s. 6d. value remained on sale until 2 July 1883 when it was replaced by the 2s. 6d. "Postage & Revenue" stamp. Inland Revenue stamps still in the hands of the public continued to be accepted for revenue and postal purposes.

TELEGRAPH STAMPS. A priced listing of the Post Office telegraph stamps appears in Volume 1 of the Stanley Gibbons *Great Britain Specialised Catalogue*. The last listing for the private telegraph companies in the Part 1 Catalogue was in the 1940 edition and for military telegraphs the 1941 edition.

CHANNEL ISLANDS

GENERAL ISSUE

C **1** Gathering Vraic

C **2** Islanders gathering Vraic

(Des J. R. R. Stobie (1d.) or from drawing by E. Blampied (2½d.). Photo Harrison)

1948 (10 May). *Third Anniv of Liberation. W* **127** *of Great Britain. P* 15 × 14.

C1	C **1**	1d. scarlet	25	30
C2	C **2**	2½d. ultramarine	25	30

Supplies of these stamps were also available from eight head post offices on the mainland of Great Britain.

GUERNSEY

WAR OCCUPATION ISSUES

Stamps issued under British authority during the German Occupation

BISECTS. On 24 December 1940 authority was given, by Post Office notice, that prepayment of penny postage could be effected by using half a British 2d. stamp, diagonally bisected. Such stamps were first used on 27 December 1940.

The 2d. stamps generally available were those of the Postal Centenary issue, 1940 (S.G. 482) and the first colour of the King George VI issue (S.G. 465). These are listed under Nos. 482a and 465b. A number of the 2d. King George V, 1912–22, and of the King George V photogravure stamp (S.G. 442) which were in the hands of philatelists, were also bisected and used.

1

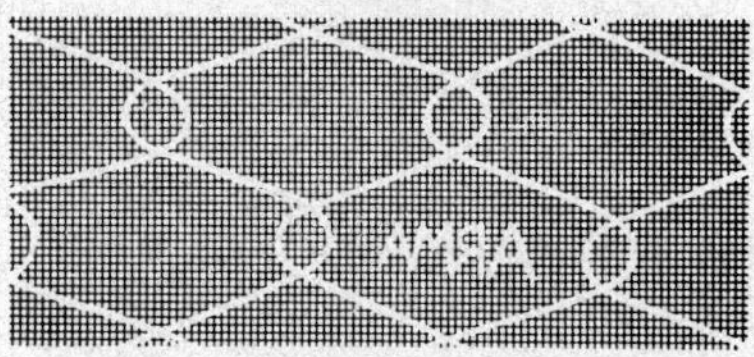

1*a* Loops (*half actual size*)

(Des E. W. Vaudin. Typo Guernsey Press Co Ltd)

1941–44. *Rouletted. (a) White paper. No wmk.*

1	**1**	½d. light green (7.4.41)	3·00	1·50
		a. Emerald-green (6.41)	3·50	1·50
		b. Bluish green (11.41)	30·00	13·00
		c. Bright green (2.42)	18·00	9·00
		d. Dull green (9.42)	2·50	1·50
		e. Olive-green (2.43)	25·00	10·00
		f. Pale yellowish green (7.43 and later) (*shades*)	3·00	1·50
		g. Imperf (pair)	£200	
		h. Imperf between (horiz pair)	£700	
		i. Imperf between (vert pair)	£800	
2		1d. scarlet (18.2.41)	2·00	75
		a. Pale vermilion (7.43) (etc.)	2·50	75
		b. Carmine (1943)	2·00	75
		c. Imperf (pair)	£150	75·00
		d. Imperf between (horiz pair)	£700	
		da. Imperf vert (centre stamp of horiz strip of 3)		
		e. Imperf between (vert pair)	£800	
		f. Printed double (scarlet shade)	£100	
3		2½d. ultramarine (12.4.44)	3·25	5·00
		a. Pale ultramarine (7.44)	3·25	5·00
		b. Imperf (pair)	£500	
		c. Imperf between (horiz pair)	£1000	

(b) Bluish French bank-note paper. W **1***a (sideways)*

4	**1**	½d. bright green (11.3.42)	21·00	18·00
5		1d. scarlet (9.4.42)	10·00	16·00

The dates given for the shades of Nos. 1/3 are the months in which they were printed as indicated on the printer's imprints. Others are issue dates.

JERSEY

WAR OCCUPATION ISSUES

Stamps issued under British authority during the German Occupation

1

(Des Major N. V. L. Rybot. Typo *Jersey Evening Post*, St. Helier)

1941–43. *White paper (thin to thick). No wmk. P* 11.

1	**1**	½d. bright green (29.1.42)	4·50	3·25
		a. Imperf between (vert pair)	£800	
		b. Imperf between (horiz pair)	£700	
		c. Imperf (pair)	£250	
		d. On greyish paper (1.43)	5·50	5·50
2		1d. scarlet (1.4.41)	4·25	2·00
		a. Imperf between (vert pair)	£800	
		b. Imperf between (horiz pair)	£700	
		c. Imperf (pair)	£275	
		d. On chalk-surfaced paper	42·00	38·00
		e. On greyish paper (1.43)	5·50	5·75

2 Old Jersey Farm

3 Portelet Bay

4 Corbière Lighthouse

5 Elizabeth Castle

6 Mont Orgueil Castle

7 Gathering Vraic (seaweed)

(Des E. Blampied. Eng H. Cortot. Typo French Govt Works, Paris)

1943–44. *No wmk. P* 13½.

3	**2**	½d. green (1 June)	7·00	5·50
		a. Rough, grey paper (6.10.43)	7·50	5·50
4	**3**	1d. scarlet (1 June)	2·00	75
		a. On newsprint (28.2.44)	2·50	75
5	**4**	1½d. brown (8 June)	3·25	3·00
6	**5**	2d. orange-yellow (8 June)	4·75	3·25
7	**6**	2½d. blue (29 June)	2·00	1·00
		a. On newsprint (25.2.44)	1·10	1·00
		ba. Thin paper*	£225	
8	**7**	3d. violet (29 June)	1·25	2·75
3/8		*Set of* 6	17·00	14·50

*On No. 7ba the design shows clearly through the back of the stamp.

British Post Offices Abroad

'he origins of the network of Post Offices, Postal Agencies and ·ket Agents can be recognised from the 18th century, but the ·em did not become established until the expansion of trade, ›wing the end of the Napoleonic Wars in 1815.

Iany offices were provided in newly acquired dependent terri- es, and were then, eventually, transferred from the control of the tish Post Office to the evolving local administrations.

'hose in foreign countries, nearly always based on existing British ısular appointments, were mostly connected to the network of tish Packet lines which had been re-established in 1814. They ded to survive until the country in which they were situated ablished its own efficient postal service or joined the U.P.U. The n "Post Office Agent" was employed by the British G.P.O. and acket Agent" by the shipping lines to describe similar functions.

Listed in this section are the Crowned-circle handstamps and G.B. mps used in the Post Offices and Agencies situated in foreign ıntries. Those for the territories within the scope of this alogue will be found under the following headings:

Prices. Catalogue prices quoted in this section, and throughout the volume, covering Crowned-circle handstamps and stamps of Great Britain used abroad are for fine used examples with the cancellation or handstamp clearly legible. Poor impressions of the cancellations and handstamps are worth much less than the prices quoted.

CROWNED-CIRCLE HANDSTAMPS

Following the introduction, in 1840, of adhesive stamps in Great Britain there was considerable pressure from a number of the dependent territories for the British Post Office to provide something similar for their use.

Such suggestions were resisted, however, because of supposed operational problems, but the decision was taken, in connection with an expansion of the Packet Service, to issue a uniform series of handstamps and date stamps to the offices abroad, both in the dependent territories and in foreign countries.

Under the regulations circulated in December 1841, letters and packets forwarded through these offices to the United Kingdom or any of its territories were to be sent unpaid, the postage being collected on delivery. Where this was not possible, for example from a British colony to a foreign country or between two foreign ports, then a *crowned-circle handstamp* was to be applied with the postage, paid in advance, noted alongside in manuscript.

Examples of these handstamps were supplied over twenty years from 1842, but many continued to fulfil other functions long after the introduction of adhesive stamps in the colony concerned.

Our listings cover the use of these handstamps for their initial purpose and the prices quoted are for examples used on cover during the pre-adhesive period.

In most instances the dates quoted are those on which the handstamp appears in the G.P.O. Record Books, but it seems to have been normal for the handstamps to be sent to the office concerned immediately following this registration.

Many of the handstamps were individually cut by hand, so that each has its own characteristics, but for the purposes of the listing they have been grouped into nine Types as shown in the adjacent column. No attempt has been made to identify them by anything but the most major differences, so that minor differences in size and in the type of the crown have been ignored.

DOUBLE CIRCLE

CC 1

CC 1a

Curved "PAID"

CC 1b

CC 1c

Curved "PAID"

CC 2

Straight "PAID"

SINGLE CIRCLE

CC 3

CC 4

Straight "PAID"

CC 5

Curved "PAID"

CC 6

Straight "PAID"

CC 7

Curved "PAID"

GREAT BRITAIN STAMPS USED ABROAD

Prices quoted are for single stamps not on cover unless otherwise stated. Stamps on cover are worth considerably more in most cases.

In many instances obliterators allocated to post offices abroad were, at a later date re-allocated to offices at home. Postmarks on issues later than those included in our lists can therefore safely be regarded as *not* having been "used abroad".

INDEX

ALTERED CATALOGUE NUMBERS

Any Catalogue numbers altered from the last edition are shown as a list in the introductory pages.

TYPES OF OBLITERATOR FOR GREAT BRITAIN STAMPS USED ABROAD

HORIZONTAL OVAL

(1)

(2)

(3)

(4)

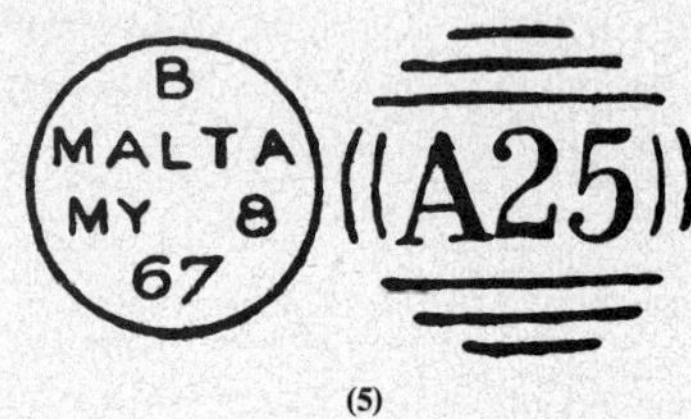

(5)

(6)

(7)

VERTICAL OVAL

(8)

(9)

(10)

(11)

(12)

(13)

(14)

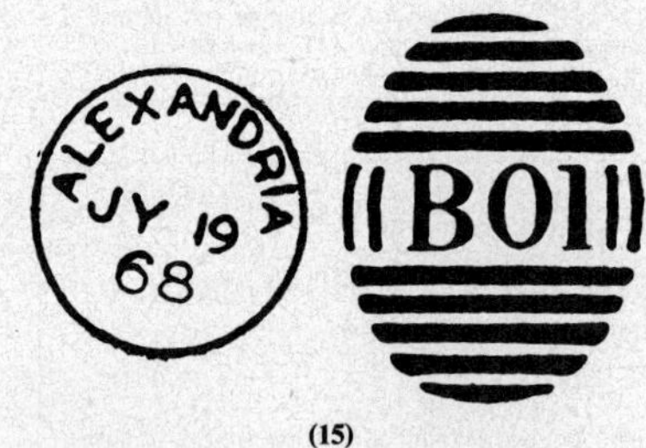

(15)

CIRCULAR DATE STAMPS

(16)

(17)

(18)

(19)

(20)

ARGENTINE REPUBLIC

BUENOS AYRES

he first regular monthly British mail packet service was oduced in 1824, replacing a private arrangement which had iously existed for some years.

reat Britain stamps were used from 1860 until the office closed ne end of June 1873. Until 1878 the British Consul continued to stamps which were used in combination with an Argentine value paying the internal rate. The British stamps on such covers were celled on arrival in England.

CROWNED-CIRCLE HANDSTAMPS

1	CC **7**	BUENOS AYRES (Black or R.) (5.1.1851) *Price on cover*	£700

mps of GREAT BRITAIN *cancelled* "B 32" *as in Types* **2, 12** *or* **3.**

0 *to* **1873.**

No.	Stamp		Price
	1d. rose-red (1857)		
2	1d. rose-red (1864)	*From*	30·00
	Plate Nos. 71, 72, 73, 74, 76, 78, 79, 80, 81, 82, 85, 87, 89, 90, 91, 92, 93, 94, 95, 96, 97, 99, 101, 103, 104, 107, 108, 110, 112, 113, 114, 117, 118, 119, 120, 121, 123, 125, 127, 129, 130, 131, 135, 136, 138, 139, 140, 142, 143, 145, 147, 149, 150, 151, 155, 159, 163, 164, 166, 169, 172.		
3	2d. blue (1858–69)	*From*	35·00
	Plate Nos. 8, 9, 12, 13, 14.		
4	3d. carmine-rose (1862)		£225
5	3d. rose (1865) (Plate No. 4)		80·00
6	3d. rose (1867–73)	*From*	40·00
	Plate Nos. 4, 5, 6, 7, 8, 9, 10.		
7	4d. rose (1857)		90·00
8	4d. red (1862) (Plate Nos. 3, 4)		80·00
9	4d. vermilion (1865–73)	*From*	45·00
	Plate Nos. 7, 8, 9, 10, 11, 12, 13.		
0	6d. lilac (1856)		80·00
1	6d. lilac (1862) (Plate Nos. 3, 4)		
2	6d. lilac (1865–67) (Plate Nos. 5, 6)	*From*	70·00
3	6d. lilac (1867) (Plate No. 6)		80·00
4	6d. violet (1867–70) (Plate Nos. 6, 8, 9)	*From*	65·00
5	6d. buff (1872) (Plate No. 11)		75·00
6	6d. chestnut (1872) (Plate No. 11)		40·00
7	9d. bistre (1862)		£275
8	9d. straw (1862)		£250
9	9d. straw (1865)		£425
20	9d. straw (1867)		£275
1	10d. red-brown (1867)		£275
2	1s. green (1856)		£250
3	1s. green (1862)		£150
4	1s. green (1865) (Plate No. 4)		£140
5	1s. green (1867–73) (Plate Nos. 4, 5, 6, 7)	*From*	35·00
6	1s. green (1873–77) (Plate No. 8)		
7	2s. blue (1867)		£130
8	5s. rose (1867) (Plate No. 1)		£400

A "B 32" obliteration was later used by Mauritius on its own mps.

AZORES

ST. MICHAELS (SAN MIGUEL)

A British Postal Agency existed at Ponta Delgada, the chief port the island, to operate with the services of the Royal Mail Steam acket Company.

CROWNED-CIRCLE HANDSTAMPS

C1 CC **1b** ST. MICHAELS (27.5.1842)

BOLIVIA

COBIJA

It is believed that the British Postal Agency opened in 1862. The amps of Great Britain were used between 1865 and 1878. They an be found used in combination with Bolivia adhesive stamps aying the local postage. The Agency closed in 1881, the town aving been occupied by Chile in 1879.

CROWNED-CIRCLE HANDSTAMPS

C1 CC **4** COBIJA (29.3.1862)

tamps of GREAT BRITAIN *cancelled* "C 39" *as Types* **4, 8** *or* **12.**

865 *to* **1878.**

No.	Stamp		Price
1	1d. rose-red (Plate Nos. 93, 95)		
2	2d. blue (1858–69) (Plate No. 14)		
3	3d. rose (1867–73) (Plate No. 6)		
4	3d. rose (1873–76) (Plate Nos. 16, 19)		
5	4d. sage-green (1877) (Plate No. 15)		£400
6	6d. violet (1867–70) (Plate No. 9)		£375
7	6d. buff (1872) (Plate No. 11)		
8	6d. grey (1874–76) (Plate Nos. 13, 14, 15, 16)		
9	1s. green (1867–73) (Plate Nos. 4, 5)		£300
Z10	1s. green (1873–77) (Plate Nos. 10, 11, 12, 13)		
Z11	2s. blue (1867)		£300
Z12	5s. rose (1867–74) (Plate No. 2)		£500

BRAZIL

The first packets ran to Brazil in 1808 when the Portuguese royal amily went into exile at Rio de Janeiro. The Agencies at Bahia and Pernambuco did not open until 1851. All three agencies used the tamps of Great Britain from 1866 and these can be found used in ombination with Brazil adhesive stamps paying the local postage. The agencies closed on 30 June 1874.

BAHIA

CROWNED-CIRCLE HANDSTAMPS

CC1	CC **7**	BAHIA (Black, G. *or* R.) (6.1.1851) *Price on cover*	£2500

tamps of GREAT BRITAIN *cancelled* "C 81" *as Type* **12.**

1866 *to* **1874.**

No.	Stamp		Price
Z 1	1d. rose-red (1864–79)	*From*	35·00
	Plate Nos. 90, 93, 96, 108, 113, 117, 135, 140, 147, 155.		
Z 2	1½d. lake-red (1870–74) (Plate No. 3)		£100
Z 3	2d. blue (1858–69) (Plate Nos. 9, 12, 13, 14)		60·00
Z 4	3d. rose (1865) (Plate No. 4)		
Z 5	3d. rose (1867–73) (Plate Nos. 4, 6, 8, 9, 10)		50·00
Z 6	3d. rose (1873–79) (Plate No. 11)		
Z 7	4d. vermilion (1865–73)	*From*	45·00
	Plate Nos. 8, 9, 10, 11, 12, 13.		
Z 8	6d. lilac (1865–67) (Plate No. 5)		
Z 9	6d. lilac (1867) (Plate No. 6)		80·00
Z10	6d. violet (1867–70) (Plate Nos. 6, 8, 9)	*From*	65·00
Z11	6d. buff (1872–73) (Plate Nos. 11, 12)	*From*	90·00
Z12	6d. chestnut (1872) (Plate No. 11)		
Z13	6d. grey (1873) (Plate No. 12)		
Z14	6d. grey (1874–76) (Plate No. 13)		
Z15	9d. straw (1865)		£375
Z16	9d. straw (1867)		£225
Z17	1s. green (1865) (Plate No. 4)		£150
Z18	1s. green (1867–73) (Plate Nos. 4, 5, 6, 7)	*From*	45·00
Z19	1s. green (1873–77) (Plate Nos. 8, 9)		75·00
Z20	2s. blue (1867)		£225
Z21	5s. rose (1867) (Plate No. 1)		£400

PERNAMBUCO

CROWNED-CIRCLE HANDSTAMPS

CC2	CC **7**	PERNAMBUCO (Black *or* R.) (6.1.1851) *Price on cover*	£2500

Stamps of GREAT BRITAIN *cancelled* "C 82" *as Type* **12** *or with circular date stamp as Type* **16**.

1866 *to* **1874.**

No.	Stamp		Price
Z22	1d. rose-red (1864–79)	*From*	35·00
	Plate Nos. 85, 108, 111, 130, 131, 132, 149, 157, 159, 160, 187		
Z23	2d. blue (1858–69) (Plate Nos. 9, 12, 13, 14)	*From*	50·00
Z23*a*	3d. rose (1865) (Plate No. 4)		80·00
Z24	3d. rose (1867–73) (Plate Nos. 4, 5, 6, 7, 10)		50·00
Z25	3d. rose (1873–77) (Plate No. 11)		
Z26	4d. vermilion (1865–73)	*From*	45·00
	Plate Nos. 9, 10, 11, 12, 13, 14.		
Z27	6d. lilac (1865–67) (Plate Nos. 5, 6)		
Z28	6d. lilac (1867) (Plate No. 6)		70·00
Z29	6d. violet (1867–70) (Plate Nos. 8, 9)	*From*	65·00
Z30	6d. buff (1872–73) (Plate Nos. 11, 12)	*From*	70·00
Z31	6d. chestnut (1872) (Plate No. 11)		50·00
Z32	6d. grey (1873) (Plate No. 12)		
Z33	9d. straw (1865)		£375
Z34	9d. straw (1867)		£200
Z35	10d. red-brown (1867)		£275
Z36	1s. green (1865) (Plate No. 4)		£150
Z37	1s. green (1867–73) (Plate Nos. 4, 5, 6, 7)	*From*	45·00
Z38	2s. blue (1867)		£225
Z39	5s. rose (1867–74) (Plate Nos. 1, 2)	*From*	£425

RIO DE JANEIRO

CROWNED-CIRCLE HANDSTAMPS

CC3	CC **7**	RIO DE JANEIRO (Black, B., G. *or* R.) (6.1.1851) *Price on cover*	£450

Stamps of GREAT BRITAIN *cancelled* "C 83" *as Type* **12.**

1866 *to* **1874.**

No.	Stamp		Price
Z40	1d. rose-red (1857)		38·00
Z41	1d. rose-red (1864–79)	*From*	30·00
	Plate Nos. 71, 76, 80, 82, 86, 94, 103, 113, 117, 119, 123, 130, 132, 134, 135, 146, 148, 159, 161, 166, 185, 200, 204.		
Z42	2d. blue (1858–69) (Plate Nos. 9, 12, 13, 14)	*From*	30·00
Z43	3d. rose (1867–73) (Plate Nos. 4, 5, 6, 7, 8)	*From*	40·00
Z44	3d. rose (1873–77) (Plate No. 11)		
Z45	4d. vermilion (1865–73)	*From*	45·00
	Plate Nos. 8, 9, 10, 11, 12, 13, 14.		
Z46	6d. lilac (1865–67) (Plate No. 5)		
Z47	6d. lilac (1867) (Plate No. 6)		70·00
Z48	6d. violet (1867–70) (Plate Nos. 6, 8, 9)	*From*	65·00
Z49	6d. buff (1872) (Plate No. 11)		70·00
Z50	6d. chestnut (1872) (Plate No. 11)		40·00
Z51	6d. grey (1873) (Plate No. 12)		
Z52	9d. straw (1865)		£350
Z53	9d. straw (1867)		£180
Z54	10d. red-brown (1867)		£250
Z55	1s. green (1865) (Plate No. 4)		£130
Z56	1s. green (1867–73) (Plate Nos. 4, 5, 6, 7)	*From*	35·00
Z57	1s. green (1873–77) (Plate Nos. 8, 9)		65·00
Z58	2s. blue (1867)		£120
Z59	5s. rose (1867–74) (Plate Nos. 1, 2)	*From*	£375

CAPE VERDE ISLANDS

The British Packet Agency at St. Vincent opened in 1851 as part of the revised service to South America. The agency was closed by 1860.

CROWNED-CIRCLE HANDSTAMPS

CC1 CC **6** ST. VINCENT C.DE.V. (6.1.1851)

CHILE

The British Postal Agency at Valparaiso opened on 7 May 1846, to be followed by further offices at Caldera (1858) and Coquimbo (1863). The stamps of Great Britain were introduced in 1865 and can be found used in combination with Chile adhesives paying the local postage. All three offices closed on 31 March 1881 when Chile joined the U.P.U.

CALDERA

Stamps of GREAT BRITAIN *cancelled* "C 37" *as in Type* **4.**

1865 *to* **1881**.

No.	Stamp		Price
Z 1	1d. rose-red (1864–79)	*From*	40·00
	Plate Nos. 71, 72, 88, 90, 95, 160, 195.		
Z 2	1½d. lake-red (1870–74) (Plate No. 3)		
Z 3	2d. blue (1858–69) (Plate No. 9)		45·00
Z 4	3d. rose (1865) (Plate No. 4)		80·00
Z 5	3d. rose (1867–73) (Plate Nos. 5, 7)		
Z 6	3d. rose (1873–76)	*From*	45·00
	Plate Nos. 11, 12, 16, 17, 18, 19.		
Z 7	4d. red (1862) (Plate No. 4)		
Z 8	4d. vermilion (1865–73)	*From*	45·00
	Plate Nos. 8, 11, 12, 13, 14.		
Z 9	4d. sage-green (1877) (Plate No. 16)		
Z10	6d. lilac (1862) (Plate No. 4)		90·00
Z11	6d. lilac (1865–67) (Plate Nos. 5, 6)		
Z12	6d. violet (1867–70) (Plate Nos. 6, 8, 9)	*From*	80·00
Z13	6d. buff (1872) (Plate No. 11)		
Z14	6d. chestnut (1872) (Plate No. 11)		
Z15	6d. grey (1873) (Plate No. 12)		
Z16	6d. grey (1874–80)	*From*	45·00
	Plate Nos. 13, 14, 15, 16, 17.		
Z17	8d. orange (1876)		£325
Z18	9d. straw (1867)		£225
Z19	10d. red-brown (1867)		£250
Z20	1s. green (1865) (Plate No. 4)		
Z21	1s. green (1867–73) (Plate Nos. 4, 5, 6)	*From*	45·00
Z22	1s. green (1873–77)	*From*	70·00
	Plate Nos. 8, 10, 11, 12, 13.		
Z23	2s. blue (1867)		£200
Z23*a*	2s. cobalt (1867)		
Z24	2s. brown (1880)		£1700
Z25	5s. rose (1867–74) (Plate No. 2)		£425

COQUIMBO

Stamps of GREAT BRITAIN *cancelled* "C 40" *as in Type* **4** *or with circular date stamp as Type* **16**.

1865 *to* **1881.**

No.	Stamp		Price
Z26	½d. rose-red (1870–79) (Plate No. 14)		
Z27	1d. rose-red (1857)		
Z28	1d. rose-red (1864–79) (Plate Nos. 85, 204)		
Z29	2d. blue (1858–69) (Plate Nos. 9, 14)		
Z30	3d. rose (1865)		
Z31	3d. rose (1872) (Plate No. 8)		
Z32	3d. rose (1873-76) (Plate Nos. 18, 19)	*From*	45·00
Z33	4d. red (1863) (Plate No. 4) (*Hair lines*)		
Z34	4d. vermilion (1865-73) (Plate Nos. 12,14)		50·00
Z35	4d. sage-green (1877) (Plate Nos. 15, 16)	*From*	£180
Z36	6d. lilac (1862) (Plate Nos. 3, 4)	*From*	75·00
Z37	6d. lilac (1865–67) (Plate No. 5)		
Z38	6d. lilac (1867) (Plate No. 6)		70·00
Z39	6d. violet (1867–70) (Plate Nos. 6, 8, 9)	*From*	65·00
Z40	6d. buff (1872–73) (Plate Nos. 11, 12)	*From*	70·00
Z41	6d. chestnut (1872) (Plate No. 11)		
Z42	6d. grey (1873) (Plate No. 12)		£190
Z43	6d. grey (1874–76) (Plate Nos. 13, 14, 15, 16)	*From*	45·00
Z44	8d. orange (1876)		
Z45	9d. straw (1862)		£275
Z46	9d. straw (1867)		£200
Z47	10d. red-brown (1867)		
Z48	1s. green (1865) (Plate No. 4)		£150
Z49	1s. green (1867–73) (Plate Nos. 4, 5, 6)		45·00
Z50	1s. green (1873–77)	*From*	65·00
	Plate Nos. 8, 10, 11, 12, 13.		
Z51	2s. blue (1867)		£130
Z51*a*	2s. cobalt (1867)		
Z52	2s. brown (1880)		£1700
Z53	5s. rose (1867–74) (Plate Nos. 1, 2)	*From*	£425

VALPARAISO

CROWNED-CIRCLE HANDSTAMPS

CC1	CC **1**	VALPARAISO (R.) (*without stop*) (13.1.1846) *Price on cover*	£350
CC2		VALPARAISO. (R.) (*with stop*) (16.7.1846) *Price on cover*	£400

Stamps of GREAT BRITAIN *cancelled* "C 30", *as in Types* **12** *and* **14** (*without* "PAID" *before* 1870) *or with circular date stamp as Type* **16**.

1865 *to* **1881.**

No.	Stamp		Price
Z54	½d. rose-red (1870–79)	*From*	60·00
	Plate Nos. 6, 11, 12, 13, 14.		
Z55	1d. rose-red (1864–79)	*From*	30·00
	Plate Nos. 80, 84, 85, 89, 91, 101, 106, 113, 116, 122, 123, 138, 140, 141, 146, 148, 149, 152, 157, 158, 162, 167, 175, 178, 181, 185, 186, 187, 189, 190, 195, 197, 198, 199, 200, 201, 207, 209, 210, 211, 212, 213, 214, 215, 217.		
Z56	1½d. lake-red (1870–74) (Plate Nos. 1, 3)	*From*	60·00
Z57	2d. blue (1858–69) (Plate Nos. 9, 13, 14, 15)		40·00
Z58	2½d. rosy mauve (1875), white paper (Plate No. 2)		£100
Z59	2½d. rosy mauve (1876) (Plate Nos. 4, 8)		75·00
Z60	3d. carmine-rose (1862)		
Z61	3d. rose (1865) (Plate No. 4)		
Z62	3d. rose (1867–73)	*From*	45·00
	Plate Nos. 5, 6, 7, 8, 9, 10.		
Z63	3d. rose (1873–76)	*From*	35·00
	Plate Nos. 11, 12, 14, 16, 17, 18, 19.		
Z63*a*	4d. red (1862) (Plate No. 4)		
Z63*b*	4d. red (1863) (Plate No. 4) (*Hair lines*)		
Z64	4d. vermilion (1865–73)	*From*	45·00
	Plate Nos. 9, 10, 11, 12, 13, 14.		
Z65	4d. vermilion (1876) (Plate No. 15)		£275
Z66	4d. sage-green (1877) (Plate Nos. 15, 16)	*From*	£180
Z67	4d. grey-brown (1880) *wmk* Large Garter		
	Plate No. 17.		
Z68	6d. lilac (1862) (Plate Nos. 3, 4)	*From*	75·00
Z69	6d. lilac (1865) (Plate Nos. 5, 6)		
Z70	6d. lilac (1867) (Plate No. 6)		
Z71	6d. violet (1867–70) (Plate Nos. 6, 8, 9)	*From*	65·00
Z72	6d. buff (1872–73) (Plate Nos. 11, 12)	*From*	70·00
Z73	6d. chestnut (1872) (Plate No. 11)		40·00
Z74	6d. grey (1873) (Plate No. 12)		£190
Z75	6d. grey (1874–80)	*From*	40·00
	Plate Nos. 13, 14, 15, 16, 17.		
Z76	6d. grey (1881) (Plate No. 17)		
Z77	8d. orange (1876)		£250
Z78	9d. straw (1862)		
Z79	9d. straw (1865)		
Z80	9d. straw (1867)		£180
Z81	10d. red-brown (1867)		£250
Z82	1s. green (1865) (Plate No. 4)		
Z83	1s. green (1867–73) (Plate Nos. 4, 5, 6, 7)	*From*	35·00
Z84	1s. green (1873–77)	*From*	60·00
	Plate Nos. 8, 9, 10, 11, 12, 13.		
Z85	1s. orange-brown (1880) (Plate No. 13)		£350
Z86	2s. blue (1867)		£110
Z86*a*	2s. cobalt (1867)		£1400
Z87	2s. brown (1880)		£1700
Z88	5s. rose (1867–74) (Plate Nos. 1, 2)	*From*	£350
Z89	10s. grey-green (1878) (*wmk* Cross)		£2000
Z90	£1 brown-lilac (1878) (*wmk* Cross)		£3000

1880.

No.	Stamp		Price
Z91	1d. Venetian red		
Z92	1½d. Venetian red		

COLOMBIA

The system of British Postal Agencies in the area was inaugurated by the opening of the Carthagena office in 1825. In 1842 agencies at Chagres, Panama and Santa Martha were added to the system. A further office opened at Colon in 1852, this port also being known as Aspinwall. During 1872 the system was further enlarged by an office at Savanilla, although this agency was later, 1878, transferred to Barranquilla.

Stamps of Great Britain were supplied to Carthagena, Panama and Santa Martha in 1865, Colon in 1870 and Savanilla in 1872. Combination covers with Colombia stamps paying the local postage are known from Santa Martha and Savanilla as are similar covers from Panama showing Costa Rica and El Salvador stamps.

All offices, except Chagres which had ceased to operate in 1855, closed for public business on 30 June 1881. Colon and Panama continued to exist as transit offices to deal with the mail across the isthmus. Both finally closed on 31 March 1921.

CARTHAGENA

CROWNED-CIRCLE HANDSTAMPS

CC1 CC **1b** CARTHAGENA (R.) (15.1.1841)
CC2 CC **1** CARTHAGENA (1.7.1846) *Price on cover* £900

Stamps of GREAT BRITAIN *cancelled* "C 56" *as in Type* **4**.

1865 *to* **1881.**
Z 1 ½d. rose-red (1870–79) (Plate No. 10)
Z 2 1d. rose-red (1864–79) *From* 45·00
Plate Nos. 78, 87, 100, 111, 113, 117, 119, 125, 172, 189, 217.
Z 3 2d. blue (1858–69) (Plate Nos. 9, 14) *From* 45·00
Z 4 3d. rose (1865) (Plate No. 4)
Z 5 3d. rose (1865–68) (Plate Nos. 4, 5)
Z 6 3d. rose (1873–79) (Plate Nos. 12, 17, 18) *From* 50·00
Z 7 4d. vermilion (1865–73) *From* 50·00
Plate Nos. 7, 8, 9, 10, 11, 12, 13, 14.
Z 8 4d. vermilion (1876) (Plate No. 15) £275
Z 9 4d. sage-green (1877) (Plate Nos. 15, 16) *From* £180
Z10 6d. lilac (1865–67) (Plate Nos. 5, 6)
Z11 6d. violet (1867–70) (Plate Nos. 6, 8) *From* 70·00
Z12 6d. grey (1873) (Plate No. 12) £190
Z13 6d. grey (1874–76) (Plate Nos. 13, 14, 15, 16) *From* 45·00
Z14 8d. orange (1876) £275
Z15 9d. straw (1865)
Z16 1s. green (1865)
Z17 1s. green (1867–73) (Plate Nos. 4, 5, 7) *From* 50·00
Z18 1s. green (1873–77) *From* 60·00
Plate Nos. 8, 9, 10, 11, 12, 13
Z19 1s. orange-brown (1880)
Z20 2s. blue (1867) £200
Z21 5s. rose (1867) (Plate No. 1) £450

Cancelled "C 65" (*incorrect handstamp, supplied in error*) *as T* **12**.

1866 *to* **1881.**
Z22 ½d. rose-red (1870–79) (Plate No. 10)
Z23 1d. rose-red (1864–79) (Plate Nos. 100, 106, 111, 123) *From* 60·00
Z23*a* 1½d. lake-red (1870) (Plate No. 3)
Z24 2d. blue (1858–69) (Plate No. 9) 60·00
Z25 2d. rose (1880)
Z26 2½d. blue (1880) (Plate No. 19)
Z27 3d. rose (1867–73) (Plate No. 9)
Z28 3d. rose (1873–79) (Plate Nos. 14, 17, 19, 20)
Z29 4d. vermilion (1865–73) *From* 50·00
Plate Nos. 7, 8, 9, 11, 12, 13, 14.
Z30 4d. vermilion (1876) (Plate No. 15) £275
Z31 4d. sage-green (1877) (Plate Nos. 15, 16) *From* £180
Z32 6d. violet (1867–70) (Plate Nos. 6, 8) 80·00
Z33 6d. pale buff (1872) (Plate No. 11)
Z34 6d. grey (1873) (Plate No. 12) £190
Z35 6d. grey (1874–80) (Plate Nos. 13, 15, 16, 17) 45·00
Z36 8d. orange (1876) £325
Z37 9d. straw (1865) £350
Z38 1s. green (1865) (Plate No. 4) £100
Z39 1s. green (1867) (Plate Nos. 4, 5, 6, 7) *From* 50·00
Z40 1s. green (1873–77) (Plate Nos. 8, 11, 12, 13) *From* 60·00
Z41 1s. orange-brown (1880)
Z42 2s. blue (1867) £350
Z43 2s. brown (1880) £2000
Z44 5s. rose (1867) (Plate Nos. 1, 2) *From* £475

CHAGRES

CROWNED-CIRCLE HANDSTAMPS

CC3 CC **1** CHAGRES (16.9.1846)

COLON

CROWNED-CIRCLE HANDSTAMPS

CC4 CC **5** COLON (R.) (21.6.1854) *Price on cover* £4250

Stamps of GREAT BRITAIN *cancelled* "E 88" *as in Type* **12** *or with two types of circular date stamp as Type* **16**, *one with* "COLON" *straight*.

1870 *to* **1881.**
Z45 1d. rose-red (1864–79) *From* 40·00
Plate Nos. 107, 121, 122, 123, 125, 127, 130, 131, 133, 136, 138, 142, 150, 151, 152, 153, 155, 156, 157, 158, 160, 169, 170, 171, 174, 176, 178, 179, 184, 187, 188, 194, 195, 201, 209, 213, 214, 217.
Z46 1d. Venetian red (1880)
Z47 1½d. lake-red (1870–74) (Plate No. 3) 90·00
Z48 2d. blue (1858–69) (Plate Nos. 14, 15) 40·00
Z49 2d. pale rose (1880)
Z50 3d. rose (1867–73) (Plate Nos. 6, 9)
Z51 3d. rose (1873–76) *From* 45·00
Plate Nos. 11, 12, 16, 18, 19, 20.
Z52 4d. vermilion (1865–73) *From* 45·00
Plate Nos. 10, 11, 12, 13, 14.
Z53 4d. vermilion (1876) (Plate No. 15)
Z54 4d. sage-green (1877) (Plate Nos. 15, 16) *From* £180
Z55 4d. grey-brown (1880) *wmk* Large Garter £300
Plate No. 17.
Z56 4d. grey-brown (1880) *wmk* Crown (Plate No. 17)
Z57 6d. violet (1867–70) (Plate Nos. 6, 8, 9)
Z58 6d. buff (1872) (Plate No. 11)
Z59 6d. chestnut (1872) (Plate No. 11) 60·00
Z60 6d. grey (1873) (Plate No. 12)
Z61 6d. grey (1874–80) *From* 45·00
Plate Nos. 13, 14, 15, 16, 17.
Z62 8d. orange (1876)
Z63 9d. straw (1867) £180
Z63*a* 10d. red-brown (1867)
Z64 1s. green (1867–73) (Plate Nos. 4, 5, 6, 7) *From* 40·00
Z65 1s. green (1873–77) *From* 55·00
Plate Nos. 8, 9, 10, 11, 12, 13.
Z66 1s. orange-brown (1880) (Plate 13) £350
Z67 1s. orange-brown (1881) (Plate 13) £125
Z68 2s. blue (1867) £140
Z69 2s. brown (1880) £1700
Z70 5s. rose (1867) (Plate Nos. 1, 2) *From* £400

PANAMA

CROWNED-CIRCLE HANDSTAMPS

CC5 CC **1** PANAMA (R.) (24.8.1846) *Price on cover* £1700

Stamps of GREAT BRITAIN *cancelled* "C 35" *as in Type* **4**, **11** *or as* **14** *with* "PANAMA" *straight*.

1865 *to* **1881.**
Z 71 ½d. rose-red (1870–79) *From* 45·00
Plate Nos. 10, 11, 12, 13, 14, 15, 19
Z 72 1d. rose-red (1864–79) *From* 30·00
Plate Nos. 71, 72, 76, 81, 85, 87, 88, 89, 93, 95, 96, 101, 104, 114, 122, 124, 130, 138, 139, 142, 159, 168, 171, 172, 174, 177, 179, 180, 184, 185, 187, 189, 191, 192, 193, 196, 197, 200, 203, 204, 205, 207, 208, 209, 210, 211, 213, 214, 215, 218, 224
Z 73 1½d. lake-red (1870–74) (Plate No. 3) 60·00
Z 74 2d. blue (1858–69) *From* 35·00
Plate Nos. 9, 12, 13, 14, 15.
Z 75 2½d. rosy mauve (1875) (Plate No. 1)
Z 76 2½d. rosy mauve (1876–80) (Plate Nos. 4, 12, 16)
Z 77 2½d. blue (1880) (Plate No. 19)
Z 78 2½d. blue (1881) (Plate Nos. 22, 23)
Z 79 3d. carmine-rose (1862) £225
Z 80 3d. rose (1865) (Plate No. 4)
Z 81 3d. rose (1867–73) *From* 45·00
Plate Nos. 4, 5, 6, 7, 8, 9.
Z 82 3d. rose (1873–76) *From* 35·00
Plate Nos. 12, 14, 15, 16, 17, 18, 19, 20.
Z 83 3d. rose (1881) (Plate Nos. 20, 21)
Z 84 4d. red (1863) (Plate No. 4) (*Hair lines*) 85·00
Z 85 4d. vermilion (1865–73) *From* 45·00
Plate Nos. 7, 8, 9, 10, 11, 12, 13, 14.
Z 86 4d. vermilion (1876) (Plate No. 15) £275
Z 87 4d. sage-green (1877) (Plate Nos. 15, 16) *From* £180
Z 88 4d. grey-brown (1880) *wmk* Crown *From* 50·00
Plate Nos. 17, 18.
Z 89 6d. lilac (1862) (Plate Nos. 3, 4) *From* 75·00
Z 90 6d. lilac (1865–67) (Plate Nos. 5, 6) *From* 70·00
Z 91 6d. lilac (1867) (Plate No. 6)
Z 92 6d. violet (1867–70) (Plate Nos. 6, 8, 9) 65·00
Z 93 6d. buff (1872–73) (Plate Nos. 11, 12) *From* 70·00
Z 94 6d. chestnut (Plate No. 11) 45·00
Z 95 6d. grey (1873) (Plate No. 12) £190
Z 96 6d. grey (1874–80) *From* 45·00
Plate Nos. 13, 14, 15, 16, 17.
Z 97 6d. grey (1881) (Plate No. 17) 65·00
Z 98 8d. orange (1876) £225
Z 99 9d. straw (1862) £250
Z100 9d. straw (1867) £225
Z101 10d. red-brown (1867) £250
Z102 1s. green (1865) (Plate No. 4) £130
Z103 1s. green (1867–73) (Plate Nos. 4, 5, 6, 7) *From* 40·00
Z104 1s. green (1873–77) *From* 55·00
Plate Nos. 8, 9, 10, 11, 12, 13.
Z105 1s. orange-brown (1880) (Plate No. 13) £350
Z106 1s. orange-brown (1881) (Plate No. 13) £100
Z107 2s. blue (1867) £120
Z108 2s. brown (1880) £1700
Z109 5s. rose (1867–74) (Plate Nos. 1, 2) *From* £400

1880.
Z110 1d. Venetian red 40·00
Z111 2d. rose 90·00
Z112 5d. indigo £140

Later stamps cancelled "C 35" are believed to originate from sailors' letters or other forms of maritime mail.

SANTA MARTHA

CROWNED-CIRCLE HANDSTAMPS

CC6 CC **1b** SANTA MARTHA (R.) (15.12.1841) *Price on cover* £1700

Stamps of GREAT BRITAIN *cancelled* "C 62" *as in Type* **4**.

1865 *to* **1881.**
Z113 ½d. rose-red (1870–79) (Plate No. 6) 80·00
Z114 1d. rose-red (1864–79) (Plate No. 106) 55·00
Z115 2d. blue (1858–69) (Plate Nos. 9, 13) 80·00
Z116 4d. vermilion (1865–73) *From* 50·00
Plate Nos. 7, 8, 9, 11, 12, 13, 14.
Z117 4d. sage-green (1877) (Plate No. 15) £180
Z118 4d. grey-brown (1880) *wmk* Large Garter £300
Plate No. 17.
Z119 4d. grey-brown (1880) *wmk* Crown (Plate No. 17) 70·00
Z120 6d. lilac (1865–67) (Plate No. 5) 80·00
Z121 6d. grey (1873) (Plate No. 12)
Z122 6d. grey (1874–76) (Plate No. 14)
Z123 8d. orange (1876) £275
Z123*a* 9d. bistre (1862)
Z124 1s. green (1865) (Plate No. 4) £150
Z125 1s. green (1867–73) (Plate Nos. 5, 7) *From* 60·00
Z126 1s. green (1873–77) (Plate No. 8)
Z127 2s. blue (1867) £275
Z128 5s. rose (1867) (Plate No. 2) £475

SAVANILLA (BARRANQUILLA)

Stamps of GREAT BRITAIN *cancelled* "F 69" *as in Type* **12**.

1872 *to* **1881.**
Z129 ½d. rose-red (1870–79) (Plate No. 6) 80·00
Z130 1d. rose-red (1864–79) (Plate Nos. 122, 171) 55·00
Z131 1½d. lake-red (1870–74) (Plate No. 3) £100
Z132 3d. rose (1867–73) (Plate No. 7)
Z133 3d. rose (1873–76) (Plate No. 20) 90·00
Z134 3d. rose (1881) (Plate No. 20) 90·00
Z135 4d. verm (1865–73) (Plate Nos. 12, 13, 14) *From* 50·00
Z136 4d. vermilion (1876) (Plate No. 15) £
Z137 4d. sage-green (1877) (Plate Nos. 15, 16) *From* £
Z138 4d. grey-brown (1880) *wmk* Large Garter £
Plate No. 17.
Z139 4d. grey-brown (1880) *wmk* Crown (Plate No. 17) 60
Z140 6d. buff (1872) (Plate No. 11)
Z141 6d. grey (1878) (Plate Nos. 16, 17) *From* 70
Z142 8d. orange (1876) £
Z143 1s. green (1867–73) (Plate Nos. 5, 7) 50
Z144 1s. green (1873–77) (Plate Nos. 8, 11, 12, 13) 70
Z145 1s. orange-brown (1880) £
Z146 2s. blue (1867) £
Z147 5s. rose (1867–74) (Plate No. 2) £

CUBA

The British Postal Agency at Havana opened in 1762, the isl[and] then being part of the Spanish Empire. A further office, at St. J[ago] de Cuba, was added in 1841.

Great Britain stamps were supplied to Havana in 1865 and to [St.] Jago de Cuba in 1866. They continued in use until the offices clo[sed] on 30 May 1877.

HAVANA

CROWNED-CIRCLE HANDSTAMPS

CC1 CC **1b** HAVANA (13.11.1841) *Price on cover* £9
CC2 CC **1c** HAVANA (1848) *Price on cover* £9
CC3 CC **2** HAVANA (14.7.1848) *Price on cover* £7

Stamps of GREAT BRITAIN *cancelled* "C 58" *as in Type* **4**, *or Type* **14** *but with* "HAVANA" *straight*.

1865 *to* **1877.**
Z 1 ½d. rose-red (1870) (Plate Nos. 6, 12) 60·
Z 2 1d. rose-red (1864–79) 50·
Plate Nos. 86, 90, 93, 115, 120, 123, 144, 146, 171, 174, 208.
Z 3 2d. blue (1858–69) (Plate Nos. 9, 14, 15) 50·
Z 4 3d. rose (1867–73) (Plate No. 4) £1
Z 5 3d. rose (1873–76) (Plate Nos. 18, 19)
Z 6 4d. vermilion (1865–73) *From* 50·
Plate Nos. 7, 8, 10, 11, 12, 13, 14.
Z 7 4d. vermilion (1876) (Plate No. 15) £2
Z 8 6d. lilac (1865) (with hyphen) (Plate No. 5)
Z 9 6d. grey (1874–76) (Plate No. 15)
Z10 8d. orange (1876)
Z11 9d. straw (1867) £2
Z12 10d. red-brown (1867) £2
Z13 1s. green (1865) (Plate No. 4) £1
Z14 1s. green (1867–73) (Plate Nos. 4, 5, 7) *From* 45·
Z15 1s. green (1873–77) (Plate Nos. 10, 12, 13) *From* 60·
Z16 2s. blue (1867) £17
Z17 5s. rose (1867–74) (Plate Nos. 1, 2) *From* £42

ST. JAGO DE CUBA

CROWNED-CIRCLE HANDSTAMPS

CC4 CC **1b** ST. JAGO-DE-CUBA (R.) (15.12.1841) *Price on cover* £550

Stamps of GREAT BRITAIN *cancelled* "C 88" *as Type* **12**.

1866 *to* **1877.**
Z18 ½d. rose-red (1870–79) (Plate Nos. 4, 6, 14)
Z19 1d. rose-red (1864–79) *From* 90·0
Plate Nos. 100, 105, 106, 109, 111, 120, 123, 138, 144, 146, 147, 148, 171, 208.
Z20 1½d. lake-red (1870–74) (Plate No. 3)
Z21 2d. blue (1858–69) (Plate Nos. 9, 12, 13, 14)
Z22 3d. rose (1867) (Plate No. 5)
Z23 4d. vermilion (1865–73) *From* £10
Plate Nos. 9, 10, 11, 12, 13, 14.
Z24 4d. vermilion (1876) (Plate No. 15) £35
Z25 6d. violet (1867–70) (Plate Nos. 6, 8, 9) *From* £25
Z26 6d. buff (Plate No. 11)
Z27 9d. straw (1865)
Z27*a* 9d. straw (1867)
Z28 10d. red-brown (1867) £40
Z29 1s. green (1867–73) (Plate Nos. 4, 5, 6) *From* £25
Z30 1s. green (1873–77) (Plate Nos. 9, 10, 12, 13)
Z31 2s. blue (1867)
Z32 5s. rose (1867) (Plate 1)

DANISH WEST INDIES

ST. THOMAS

The British Postal Agency at St. Thomas opened in January 180[9] and by 1825 was the office around which many of the packet routes were organised.

Great Britain stamps were introduced on 3 July 1865 and can be found used in combination with Danish West Indies adhesives paying the local postage.

Following a hurricane in October 1867 the main British packet office was moved to Colon in Colombia.

The British Post Office at St. Thomas closed to the public on [1] September 1877, but continued to operate as a transit office for a further two years.

CROWNED-CIRCLE HANDSTAMPS

CC1 CC **1** ST. THOMAS (R.) (20.2.49) *Price on cover* £450
CC2 CC **6** ST. THOMAS (R.) (1.5.1855) *Price on cover* £1500

Stamps of GREAT BRITAIN *cancelled* "C 51" *as in Types* **4**, **12** *or* **14**.

1865 *to* **1879.**
Z 1 ½d. rose-red (1870–79) 35·00
Plate Nos. 5, 6, 8, 10, 11, 12.
Z 2 1d. rose-red (1857)
Z 3 1d. rose-red (1864–79) *From* 25·00
Plate Nos. 71, 72, 79, 81, 84, 85, 86, 87, 88, 89, 90, 93, 94, 95, 96, 97, 98, 99, 100, 101, 102, 105, 106, 107, 108, 109, 110, 111, 112, 113, 114, 116, 117, 118, 119, 120, 121, 122, 123, 124, 125, 127, 129, 130, 131, 133, 134, 136, 137, 138, 139, 140, 141, 142, 144, 145, 146, 147, 148, 149, 150, 151, 152, 154, 155, 156, 157, 158, 159, 160, 161, 162, 163, 164, 165, 166, 167, 169, 170, 171, 172, 173, 174, 175, 176, 177, 178, 179, 180, 181, 182, 184, 185, 186, 187, 189, 190, 197.

	1½d.	lake-red (1870–74) (Plate Nos. 1, 3)	60·00
	2d.	blue (1858–69) *From* Plate Nos. 9, 12, 13, 14, 15.	30·00
	3d.	rose (1865) (Plate No. 4)	80·00
	3d.	rose (1867–73) *From* Plate Nos. 4, 5, 6, 7, 8, 9, 10.	40·00
	3d.	rose (1873–76) *From* Plate Nos. 11, 12, 14, 15, 16, 17, 18, 19.	30·00
	4d.	red (1862) (Plate Nos. 3, 4)	70·00
	4d.	vermilion (1865–73) *From* Plate Nos. 7, 8, 9, 10, 11, 12, 13, 14.	45·00
	4d.	vermilion (1876) (Plate No. 15)	£275
	4d.	sage-green (1877) (Plate Nos. 15, 16) *From*	£180
	6d.	lilac (1864) (Plate No. 4)	£140
	6d.	lilac (1865–67) (Plate Nos. 5, 6) *From*	70·00
	6d.	lilac (1867) (Plate No. 6)	70·00
	6d.	violet (1867–70) (Plate Nos. 6, 8, 9) *From*	65·00
	6d.	buff (1872–73) (Plate Nos. 11, 12) *From*	70·00
	6d.	chestnut (1872) (Plate No. 11)	40·00
	6d.	grey (1873) (Plate No. 12)	£190
	6d.	grey (1874–76) (Plate Nos. 13, 14, 15, 16) *From*	40·00
	8d.	orange (1876)	£250
	9d.	straw (1862)	£225
	9d.	bistre (1862)	£250
	9d.	straw (1865)	£350
	9d.	straw (1867)	£180
	10d.	red-brown (1867)	£250
	1s.	green (1865) (Plate No. 4)	£130
	1s.	green (1867–73) (Plate Nos. 4, 5, 6, 7) *From*	30·00
	1s.	green (1873–77) *From* Plate Nos, 8, 9, 10, 11, 12, 13.	55·00
	2s.	blue (1867)	£120
	5s.	rose (1867–74) (Plate Nos. 1, 2) *From*	£400

DOMINICAN REPUBLIC

ritish Postal Agencies may have existed in the area before 1867, it is only from that year that details can be found concerning ces at Porto Plata and St. Domingo. Both were closed in 1871, re-opened in 1876.

lthough postmarks were supplied in 1866 it seems likely that at Britain stamps were not sent until the offices re-opened in 6.

overs exist showing Great Britain stamps used in combination h those of Dominican Republic with the latter paying the local tage. Both agencies finally closed in 1881.

PORTO PLATA

mps of GREAT BRITAIN *cancelled* "C 86" *or circular date stamp s in Types* **8** *or* **17**.

6 *to* **1881**

	½d.	rose-red (1870–79) (Plate Nos. 10, 12, 14) *From*	70·00
2	1d.	rose-red (1864–79) *From* Plate Nos. 123, 130, 136, 146, 151, 178, 199, 200, 205, 217.	55·00
3	1½d.	lake-red (1870–74) (Plate No. 3)	£100
4	2d.	blue (1858–69) (Plate Nos. 14, 15)	60·00
5	2½d.	rosy mauve (1876–79) (Plate Nos. 13, 14) *From*	£140
6	3d.	rose (1873–76) (Plate No. 18)	80·00
7	4d.	vermilion (1873) (Plate No. 14)	80·00
8	4d.	vermilion (1876) (Plate No. 15)	£300
9	4d.	sage-green (1877) (Plate No. 15)	£200
0	6d.	violet (1867–70) (Plate No. 8)	
1	6d.	grey (1874–76) (Plate No. 15)	70·00
2	8d.	orange (1876)	£275
3	1s.	green (1867–73) (Plate Nos. 4, 7) *From*	50·00
4	1s.	green (1873–77) (Plate Nos. 11, 12, 13) *From*	60·00
5	2s.	blue (1867)	£200
5*a*	5s.	rose (1867–83) (Plate No. 2)	

ST. DOMINGO

amps of GREAT BRITAIN *cancelled* "C 87" *or circular date stamp as in Types* **12** *or* **16**.

76 *to* **1881**

6	½d.	rose-red (1870–79) *From* Plate Nos. 5, 6, 8, 10, 11, 13.	80·00
7	1d.	rose-red (1864–79) *From* Plate Nos. 146, 154, 171, 173, 174, 176, 178, 186, 190, 197, 220.	60·00
18	1½d.	lake-red (1870–74) (Plate No. 3)	£100
19	2d.	blue (1858–69) (Plate Nos. 13, 14)	80·00
20	3d.	rose (1873–76) (Plate No. 18)	
21	4d.	vermilion (1865–73) *From* Plate Nos. 11, 12, 14.	80·00
22	4d.	vermilion (1876) (Plate No. 15)	£300
23	4d.	sage-green (1877) (Plate No. 15)	£200
24	6d.	grey (1874–76) (Plate No. 15)	
25	9d.	straw (1867)	
26	1s.	green (1867) (Plate No. 4)	
27	1s.	green (1873–77) *From* Plate Nos. 10, 11, 12, 13.	80·00
28	2s.	blue (1867)	

ECUADOR

GUAYAQUIL

The first British Postal Agent in Guayaquil was appointed in 848.

Great Britain stamps were supplied in 1865 and continued to be sed until the agency closed on 30 June 1880. They can be found sed in combination with stamps of Ecuador with the latter paying e local postage.

tamps of GREAT BRITAIN *cancelled* "C 41" *as Type* **4**.

865 *to* **1880**.

Z 1	½d.	rose-red (1870–79) (Plate Nos. 5, 6)	55·00
Z 2	1d.	rose-red (1857)	
Z 3	1d.	rose-red (1864–79) *From* Plate Nos. 74, 78, 85, 92, 94, 105, 110, 115, 133, 140, 145, 166, 174, 180, 216.	40·00
Z 4	1½d.	lake-red (1870–74) (Plate No. 3)	80·00
Z 5	2d.	blue (1858–69) (Plate Nos. 9, 13, 14) *From*	40·00
Z 6	3d.	carmine-rose (1862)	£225
Z 7	3d.	rose (1865) (Plate No. 4)	90·00
Z 8	3d.	rose (1867–73) (Plate Nos. 6, 7, 9, 10) *From*	45·00
Z 9	3d.	rose (1873–76) *From* Plate Nos. 11, 12, 15, 16, 17, 18, 19, 20.	45·00
Z10	4d.	red (1862) (Plate Nos. 3, 4)	90·00
Z11	4d.	vermilion (1865–73) *From* Plate Nos. 7, 8, 9, 10, 11, 12, 13, 14.	45·00
Z12	4d.	vermilion (1876) (Plate No. 15)	£275
Z13	4d.	sage-green (1877) (Plate Nos. 15, 16) *From*	£180
Z14	6d.	lilac (1864) (Plate No. 4)	£140
Z15	6d.	lilac (1865–67) (Plate Nos. 5, 6) *From*	70·00
Z16	6d.	lilac (1867) (Plate No. 6)	
Z17	6d.	violet (1867–70) (Plate Nos. 6, 8, 9) *From*	65·00
Z18	6d.	buff (1872–73) (Plate Nos. 11, 12) *From*	75·00
Z19	6d.	chestnut (1872) (Plate No. 11)	
Z20	6d.	grey (1873) (Plate No. 12)	
Z21	6d.	grey (1874–76) (Plate Nos. 13, 14, 15, 16) *From*	45·00
Z22	8d.	orange (1876)	£250
Z23	9d.	straw (1862)	£225
Z24	9d.	straw (1867)	£180
Z25	10d.	red-brown (1867)	£250
Z26	1s.	green (1865) (Plate No. 4)	£150
Z27	1s.	green (1867–73) (Plate Nos. 4, 5, 6, 7) *From*	40·00
Z28	1s.	green (1873–77) *From* Plate Nos. 8, 9, 10, 11, 12, 13.	70·00
Z29	2s.	blue (1867)	£140
Z30	2s.	brown (1880)	£2000
Z31	5s.	rose (1867–74) (Plate Nos. 1, 2) *From*	£400

FERNANDO PO

The British government leased naval facilities on this Spanish island from 1827 until 1834. A British Consul was appointed in 1849 and a postal agency was opened on 1 April 1858.

The use of Great Britain stamps was authorised in 1858, but a cancellation was not supplied until 1874. The office remained open until 1877.

CROWNED-CIRCLE HANDSTAMPS

CC1 CC **4** FERNANDO-PO (R.) (19.2.1859) *Price on cover* £5000

Stamps of GREAT BRITAIN *cancelled* "247" *as Type* **9**.

1874 *to* **1877**.

Z1	4d.	vermilion (1865–72) (Plate Nos. 13, 14)	
Z2	4d.	vermilion (1876) (Plate No. 15)	
Z3	6d.	grey (1874–76) (Plate Nos. 13, 14, 15, 16)	

GUADELOUPE

A British Packet Agency was established on Guadeloupe on 1 October 1848 and continued to function until 1874.

No. CC1 is often found used in conjunction with French Colonies (General Issues) adhesive stamps.

A similar packet agency existed on Martinique from 1 October 1848 until 1879, but no crowned-circle handstamp was issued for it.

CROWNED-CIRCLE HANDSTAMPS

CC1 CC **1** GUADALOUPE (R., B. or Black) (9.3.1849) *Price on cover* £1800

HAITI

The original British Postal Agencies in Haiti date from 1830 when it is known a Packet Agency was established at Jacmel. An office at Port-au-Prince followed in 1842, both these agencies remaining in operation until 30 June 1881.

During this period short-lived agencies also operated in the following Haitian towns: Aux Cayes (1848 to 1863), Cap Haitien (1842 to 1863), Gonaives (1849 to 1857) and St. Marc (1854 to 1861). A further agency may have operated at Le Mole around the year 1841.

Great Britain stamps were supplied to Jacmel in 1865 and to Port-au-Prince in 1869.

CAP HAITIEN

CROWNED-CIRCLE HANDSTAMPS

CC1 CC **1b** CAPE-HAITIEN (R.) (31.12.1841)

JACMEL

CROWNED-CIRCLE HANDSTAMPS

CC2 CC **1b** JACMEL (R.) (29.6.1843) *Price on cover* £800

Stamps of GREAT BRITAIN *cancelled* "C 59" *as Type* **4** *or with circular date stamp as Type* **16**, *but with* "JACMEL" *straight*.

1865 *to* **1881**.

Z 1	½d.	rose-red (1870–79) *From* Plate Nos. 4, 5, 6, 10, 11, 12, 14, 15.	55·00
Z 2	1d.	rose-red (1864–79) *From* Plate Nos. 74, 81, 84, 87, 95, 106, 107, 109, 122, 136, 137, 139, 148, 150, 151, 152, 156, 157, 159, 160, 162, 164, 166, 167, 170, 171, 179, 181, 183, 184, 186, 187, 189, 192, 194, 198, 200, 204, 206, 215, 219.	40·00
Z 3	1½d.	lake-red (1870–74) (Plate No. 3)	60·00
Z 4	2d.	blue (1858–69) (Plate Nos. 9, 13, 14, 15)	40·00
Z 5	2½d.	rosy mauve (1876) (Plate No. 4)	
Z 6	3d.	rose (1867–73) (Plate Nos. 5, 6, 7, 8, 9, 10) *From*	45·00
Z 7	3d.	rose (1873–76) Plate Nos. 11, 12, 14, 16, 17, 18, 19.	45·00
Z 8	4d.	red (1863) (Plate No. 4) (*Hair lines*)	90·00
Z 9	4d.	vermilion (1865–73) *From* Plate Nos. 7, 8, 9, 10, 11, 12, 13, 14.	45·00
Z10	4d.	vermilion (1876) (Plate No. 15)	£275
Z11	4d.	sage-green (1877) (Plate Nos. 15, 16) *From*	£180
Z12	4d.	grey-brown (1880) *wmk* Large Garter Plate No. 17.	£300
Z13	4d.	grey-brown (1880) *wmk* Crown (Plate No. 17)	50·00
Z14	6d.	lilac (1867) (Plate Nos. 5, 6)	75·00
Z15	6d.	violet (1867–70) (Plate Nos. 8, 9)	70·00
Z16	6d.	buff (1872–73) (Plate Nos. 11, 12) *From*	75·00
Z17	6d.	chestnut (1872) (Plate No. 11)	
Z18	6d.	grey (1873) (Plate No. 12)	
Z19	6d.	grey (1874–76) *From* Plate Nos. 13, 14, 15, 16, 17.	50·00
Z20	8d.	orange (1876)	£275
Z21	9d.	straw (1862)	£225
Z22	9d.	straw (1867)	£180
Z23	10d.	red-brown (1867)	£250
Z24	1s.	green (1865) (Plate No. 4)	£130
Z25	1s.	green (1867–73) (Plate Nos. 4, 5, 6, 7) *From*	40·00
Z26	1s.	green (1873–77) *From* Plate Nos. 8, 9, 10, 11, 12, 13.	60·00
Z27	1s.	orange-brown (1880) (Plate No. 13)	£350
Z28	2s.	blue (1867)	£120
Z29	2s.	brown (1880)	£2000
Z30	5s.	rose (1867–74) (Plate Nos. 1, 2) *From*	£400

1880.

Z31	½d.	green (1880)	40·00
Z32	1d.	Venetian red	40·00
Z33	1½d.	Venetian red	60·00
Z34	2d.	rose	90·00

PORT-AU-PRINCE

CROWNED-CIRCLE HANDSTAMPS

CC3 CC **1b** PORT-AU-PRINCE (R.) (29.6.1843) *Price on cover* £2000

Stamps of GREAT BRITAIN *cancelled* "E 53" *as in Types* **8**, **12** *or* **16**.

1869 *to* **1881**.

Z35	½d.	rose-red (1870-79) *From* Plate Nos. 5, 6, 10, 11, 12, 13, 14.	55·00
Z36	1d.	rose-red (1864–79) *From* Plate Nos. 87, 134, 154, 159, 167, 171, 173, 174, 177, 183, 187, 189, 193, 199, 200, 201, 202, 206, 209, 210, 218, 219.	40·00
Z37	1½d.	lake-red (1870–74) (Plate No. 3)	75·00
Z38	2d.	blue (1858–69) (Plate Nos. 9, 14, 15)	45·00
Z40	2½d.	rosy mauve (1876–79) (Plate Nos. 3, 9) *From*	80·00
Z41	3d.	rose (1867–73) (Plate Nos. 6, 7)	
Z42	3d.	rose (1873–79) (Plate Nos. 17, 18, 20) *From*	45·00
Z43	4d.	vermilion (1865–73) *From* Plate Nos. 11, 12, 13, 14.	45·00
Z44	4d.	vermilion (1876) (Plate No. 15)	£275
Z45	4d.	sage-green (1877) (Plate Nos. 15, 16) *From*	£180
Z46	4d.	grey-brown (1880) *wmk* Large Garter Plate No. 17.	£300
Z47	4d.	grey-brown (1880) *wmk* Crown (Plate No. 17)	50·00
Z48	6d.	grey (1874–76) (Plate Nos. 15, 16)	
Z49	8d.	orange (1876)	£225
Z50	1s.	green (1867–73) (Plate Nos. 4, 5, 6, 7) *From*	40·00
Z51	1s.	green (1873–77) *From* Plate Nos. 8, 9, 10, 11, 12, 13	60·00
Z52	1s.	orange-brown (1880) (Plate No. 13)	£350
Z53	1s.	orange-brown (1881) (Plate No. 13)	£110
Z54	2s.	blue (1867)	£120
Z55	2s.	brown (1880)	£2000
Z56	5s.	rose (1867–74) (Plate Nos. 1, 2) *From*	£400
Z57	10s.	greenish grey (1878)	£2500

1880.

Z58	½d.	green	40·00
Z59	1d.	Venetian red	40·00
Z60	1½d.	Venetian red	55·00
Z61	2d.	rose	90·00

MACAO

A British Consular Post Office opened in 1841. It had been preceded by the Macao Boat Office, possibly a private venture, which operated in the 1830s. The office closed when the consulate closed on 30 September 1845, but was back in operation by 1854.

The Agency continued to function, in conjunction with the Hong Kong Post Office, until 28 February 1884 when Portugal joined the U.P.U.

CROWNED-CIRCLE HANDSTAMPS

Z 2

CC1 – PAID AT MACAO (crowned-oval 20 mm wide) (R.) (1844) *Price on cover* £20000

CC2 Z **2** Crown and Macao (1881)

No. CC2 with the Crown removed was used by the Portuguese post office in Macao as a cancellation until 1890.

A locally-cut mark, as Type CC **2**, inscribed "PAGO EM MACAO" is known on covers between 1870 and 1877. It was probably used by the Portuguese postmaster to send letters via the British Post Office (*Price* £10000).

MADEIRA

The British Packet Agency on this Portuguese island was opened in 1767 and was of increased importance from 1808 following the exile of the Portuguese royal family to Brazil. The South American packets ceased to call in 1858. It appears to have closed sometime around 1860.

CROWN-CIRCLE HANDSTAMPS

CC1 CC **1b** MADEIRA (R.) (28.2.1842) *Price on cover* £16000

MEXICO

The British Postal Agency at Vera Cruz opened in 1825, following the introduction of the Mexican Packet service. No handstamps were supplied, however, until 1842, when a similar agency at Tampico was set up.

Great Britain stamps were used at Tampico from 1867, but, apparently, were never sent to the Vera Cruz office. Combination covers exist showing the local postage paid by Mexican adhesives. The Agency at Vera Cruz closed in 1874 and that at Tampico in 1876.

TAMPICO

CROWNED-CIRCLE HANDSTAMPS

CC1 CC **1b** TAMPICO (R.) (13.11.1841) . . *Price on cover* £1600

No. CC1 may be found on cover, used in conjunction with Mexico adhesive stamps.

Stamps of GREAT BRITAIN *cancelled* "C 63" *as Type* **4**.

1867 *to* **1876**.
Z 1 1d. rose-red (1864–79) . . . . . . *From* 90·00
Plate Nos. 81, 89, 103, 117, 139, 147.
Z 2 2d. blue (1858–69) (Plate Nos. 9, 14) £120
Z 3 4d. vermilion (1865–73) . . . . . . *From* 60·00
Plate Nos. 7, 8, 10, 11, 12, 13, 14.
Z 4 1s. green (1867–73) (Plate Nos. 4, 5, 7, 8) . . . . 85·00
Z 5 2s. blue (1867) £350

VERA CRUZ

CROWNED-CIRCLE HANDSTAMPS

CC2 CC **1b** VERA CRUZ (R.) (13.11.1841) *Price on cover* £1600
CC3 VERA CRUZ (Black) (*circa* 1845)
Price on cover £800

No. CC3 can also be found used in conjunction with Mexico adhesive stamps.

NICARAGUA

GREYTOWN

British involvement on the Mosquito Coast of Nicaragua dates from 1655 when contacts were first made with the indigenous Misquito Indians. A formal alliance was signed in 1740 and the area was considered as a British dependency until the Spanish authorities negotiated a withdrawal in 1786.

The Misquitos remained under British protection, however, and, following the revolutionary period in the Spanish dominions, this eventually led to the appropriation, by the Misquitos with British backing, of the town of San Juan del Norte, later renamed Greytown.

The port was included in the Royal West Indian Mail Steam Packet Company's mail network from January 1842, forming part of the Jamaica District. This arrangement only lasted until September of that year, however, although packets were once again calling at Greytown by November 1844. Following the discovery of gold in California the office increased in importance, owing to the overland traffic, although the first distinctive postmark is not recorded in use until February 1856.

A subsidiary agency, without its own postmark, operated at Bluefields from 1857 to 1863.

The British Protectorate over the Misquitos ended in 1860, but the British Post Office at Greytown continued to operate, being supplied with Great Britain stamps in 1865. These are occasionally found used in combination with Nicaragua issues, which had only internal validity.

The British Post Office at Greytown closed on 1 May 1882 when the Republic of Nicaragua joined the U.P.U.

CROWNED-CIRCLE HANDSTAMPS

Z 1

CC1 Z **1** GREYTOWN (R.) (14.4.1859) . . . .

Z 2 Z 4

Z 3

Stamps of GREAT BRITAIN *cancelled* "C 57" *as in Types* Z **2** (*issued* 1865), Z **3** (*issued* 1875), *or with circular postmark as Type* Z **4** (*issued* 1864).

1865 *to* **1882**.
Z 1 ½d. rose-red (1870–79) (Plate Nos. 5, 10, 11) . . 75·00
Z 2 1d. rose-red (1864–79) (Plate Nos. 180, 197, 210) . . 40·00
Z 3 1½d. lake-red (1870) (Plate No. 3) . . . . 70·00
Z 4 2d. blue (1858–69) (Plate Nos. 9, 14, 15) . .
Z 5 3d. rose (1873–76) (Plate Nos. 17, 18, 19, 20) . . 50·00
Z 6 3d. rose (1881) (Plate No. 20) . . . . . .
Z 7 4d. vermilion (1865–73) . . . . . . *From* 50·00
Plate Nos. 8, 10, 11, 12, 13, 14.
Z 8 4d. vermilion (1876) (Plate No. 15) £275
Z 9 4d. sage-green (1877) (Plate Nos. 15, 16) *From* £180
Z10 4d. grey-brown (1880) *wmk* Large Garter . . £300
Plate No. 17.
Z11 4d. grey-brown (1880) *wmk* Crown (Plate No. 17)
Z12 6d. grey (1874–76) (Plate Nos. 14, 15, 16) . . 85·00
Z13 8d. orange (1876) £250
Z14 1s. green (1865) (Plate No. 4) . . . .
Z15 1s. green (1867–73) (Plate Nos. 6, 7) . . . .
Z16 1s. green (1873–77) . . . . . . *From* 60·00
Plate Nos. 8, 10, 12, 13.
Z17 1s. orange-brown (1880) (Plate No. 13) £350
Z18 1s. orange-brown (1881) (Plate No. 13) £100
Z19 2s. blue (1867) £150
Z20 2s. brown (1880) £2000
Z21 5s. rose (1867–74) (Plate Nos. 1, 2) . . *From* £400
Z22 5s. rose (1882) (Plate No. 4), blue *paper* . . £1400
Z23 10s. greenish grey (1878) £1800

1880.
Z24 1d. Venetian red . . . .
Z25 1½d. Venetian red . . . . 50·00

PERU

British Agencies in Peru date from 1846 when offices were established at Arica and Callao. The network was later expanded to include agencies at Paita (1848), Pisco (1868) and Iquique and Islay (both 1869). This last office was transferred to Mollendo in 1877.

It is believed that a further agency existed at Pisagua, but no details exist.

Great Britain stamps were supplied from 1865 and are often found in combination with Peru adhesives which paid the local postal tax.

The Postal Agency at Pisco closed in 1870 and the remainder in 1879, the towns of Arica, Iquique and Pisagua passing to Chile by treaty in 1883.

ARICA

CROWNED-CIRCLE HANDSTAMPS

CC1 CC **1** ARICA (Black or R.) (5.11.1850)
Price on cover £3750

Stamps of Great Britain cancelled "C 36" *as Types* **4**, **12** *and* **14** (*with* "ARICA" *straight*) *or with circular date stamp as Type* **16**, *but with* "ARICA" *straight*.

1865 *to* **1879**.
Z 1 ½d. rose-red (1870–79) . . . . . . *From* 70·00
Plate Nos. 5, 6, 10, 11, 13.
Z 2 1d. rose-red (1864–79) . . . . . . *From* 50·00
Plate Nos. 102, 139, 140, 163, 167.
Z 3 1½d. lake-red (1870–74) (Plate No. 3) . . . .
Z 4 2d. blue (1858–69) (Plate No. 14) . . . . 70·00
Z 5 3d. rose (1867–73) (Plate Nos. 5, 9) . . . .
Z 6 3d. rose (1873–76) . . . . . . *From* 45·00
Plate Nos. 11, 12, 17, 18, 19.
Z 7 4d. vermilion (1865–73) . . . . . . *From* 45·00
Plate Nos. 10, 11, 12, 13, 14.
Z 8 4d. vermilion (1876) (Plate No. 15) . . . .
Z 9 4d. sage-green (1877) (Plate Nos. 15, 16) £180
Z10 6d. lilac (1862) (Plate Nos. 3, 4) . . . .
Z11 6d. lilac (1865–67) (Plate No. 5) . . . .
Z12 6d. violet (1867–70) (Plate Nos. 6, 8, 9) . . *From* 75·00
Z13 6d. buff (1872) (Plate No. 11) . . . . 90·00
Z14 6d. chestnut (1872) (Plate No. 11) . . . .
Z15 6d. grey (1873) (Plate No. 12) £190
Z16 6d. grey (1874–76) (Plate Nos. 13, 14, 15, 16) *From* 45·00
Z17 8d. orange (1876) . . . .
Z18 9d. straw (1862) . . . .
Z19 9d. straw (1865) . . . .
Z20 9d. straw (1867) £180
Z21 10d. red-brown (1867) . . . .
Z22 1s. green (1862) . . . .
Z23 1s. green (1865) . . . .
Z24 1s. green (1867–73) (Plate Nos. 4, 5, 6, 7) . . *From* 45·00
Z25 1s. green (1873–77) . . . . . . *From* 60·00
Plate Nos. 8, 9, 10, 11, 12, 13.
Z26 2s. blue (1867) £150
Z27 5s. rose (1867–74) (Plate Nos. 1, 2) . . *From* £400

CALLAO

CROWNED-CIRCLE HANDSTAMPS

CC2 CC **1** CALLAO (R.) (13.1.1846) . . *Price on cover* £600

A second version of No. CC 2, showing "PAID" more curved, was supplied in July 1847.

No. CC2 can be found used on covers from 1865 showing the local postage paid by a Peru adhesive.

Stamps of GREAT BRITAIN *cancelled* "C 38" *as in Types* **4**, **12** *and* **14** (*with* "CALLAO" *straight*) *or with circular date stamp as Type* **5**.

1865 *to* **1879**.
Z28 ½d. rose-red (1870–79) . . . . . . *From* 40·00
Plate Nos. 5, 6, 10, 11, 12, 13, 14.
Z29 1d. rose-red (1864–79) . . . . . . *From* 30·00
Plate Nos. 74, 88, 89, 93, 94, 97, 108, 123, 127, 128, 130, 134, 137, 139, 140, 141, 143, 144, 145, 146, 148, 149, 156, 157, 160, 163, 167, 171, 172, 173, 175, 176, 180, 181, 182, 183, 185, 187, 190, 193, 195, 198, 199, 200, 201, 204, 206, 209, 210, 212, 213, 215.
Z30 1½d. lake-red (1870–74) (Plate No. 3) . . . .
Z31 2d. blue (1858–69) . . . . . . *From* 30·00
Plate Nos. 9, 12, 13, 14, 15.
Z32 3d. carmine-rose (1862) . . . . . .
Z33 3d. rose (1865) (Plate No. 4) . . . . . . 80·00
Z34 3d. rose (1867–73) . . . . . . *From* 40·00
Plate Nos. 5, 6, 7, 8, 9, 10.
Z35 3d. rose (1873–76) . . . . . . *From* 40·00
Plate Nos. 11, 12, 14, 15, 16, 17, 18, 19.
Z36 4d. red (1862) (Plate Nos. 3, 4) . . . .
Z37 4d. vermilion (1865–73) . . . . . . *From* 35·00
Plate Nos. 8, 10, 11, 12, 13, 14.
Z38 4d. vermilion (1876) (Plate No. 15) £275
Z39 4d. sage-green (1877) (Plate Nos. 15, 16) £180
Z40 6d. lilac (1862) (Plate Nos. 3, 4) . . . .
Z40*a* 6d. lilac (1865) (Plate No. 5) . . . .
Z41 6d. lilac (1867) . . . .
Z42 6d. violet (1867–70) (Plate Nos. 6, 8, 9) . . *From* 65
Z43 6d. buff (1872–73) (Plate Nos. 11, 12) . . *From* 65
Z44 6d. chestnut (1872) (Plate No. 11) 45
Z45 6d. grey (1873) (Plate No. 12) . . . . £
Z46 6d. grey (1874–80) (Plate Nos. 13, 14, 15, 16) *From* 45
Z47 8d. orange (1876) . . . . £
Z48 9d. straw (1862) . . . .
Z49 9d. straw (1865) . . . . £
Z50 9d. straw (1867) . . . . £
Z51 10d. red-brown (1867) . . . . £
Z52 1s. green (1865) . . . .
Z53 1s. green (1867–73) (Plate Nos. 4, 5, 6, 7) . . *From* 35
Z54 1s. green (1873–77) . . . . . . *From* 50
Plate Nos. 8, 9, 10, 11, 12, 13.
Z55 2s. blue (1867) £1
Z56 5s. rose (1867–74) (Plate Nos. 1, 2) . . *From* £4

IQUIQUE

Stamps of GREAT BRITAIN *cancelled* "D 87" *as Type* **12**.

1865 *to* **1879.**
Z57 ½d. rose-red (1870–79) (Plate Nos. 5, 6, 13, 14) . . 70
Z58 1d. rose-red (1864–79) 45
Plate Nos. 76, 179, 185, 205.
Z59 2d. blue (1858–69) (Plate Nos. 9, 12, 13, 14) . . 45
Z60 3d. rose (1867–73) (Plate Nos. 5, 6, 7, 8, 9) *From* 55
Z61 3d. rose (1873–76) (Plate Nos. 12, 18, 19) . . 70
Z62 4d. vermilion (1865–73) . . . . . . *From* 60
Plate Nos. 12, 13, 14.
Z63 4d. vermilion (1876) (Plate No. 15) £2
Z64 4d. sage-green (1877) (Plate Nos. 15, 16) *From* £1
Z65 6d. mauve (1869) (Plate Nos. 8, 9) . . . .
Z66 6d. buff (1872–73) (Plate Nos. 11, 12) . . *From* £1
Z67 6d. chestnut (1872) (Plate No. 11) . . . .
Z68 6d. grey (1873) (Plate No. 12) £1
Z69 6d. grey (1874–76) (Plate Nos. 13, 14, 15, 16) . . 75·
Z70 8d. orange (1876) £3
Z71 9d. straw (1867) £1
Z72 10d. red-brown (1867) . . . .
Z73 1s. green (1867–73) (Plate Nos. 4, 6, 7) . . *From* 55·
Z74 1s. green (1873–77) . . . . . . *From* 75·
Plate Nos. 8, 9, 10, 11, 12, 13.
Z75 2s. blue (1867) . . . .

ISLAY (*later* MOLLENDO)

CROWNED-CIRCLE HANDSTAMPS

CC4 CC **1** ISLAY (Black or R.) (23.10.1850) *Price on cover* £45

Stamps of GREAT BRITAIN *cancelled* "C 42" *as Type* **4** *or w circular date stamp as Type* **16**.

1865 *to* **1879**.
Z76 1d. rose-red (1864–79) . . . . . . *From* 45·
Plate Nos. 78, 84, 87, 88, 96, 103, 125, 134.
Z77 1½d. lake-red (1870–74) (Plate No. 3) . . . .
Z78 2d. blue (1858–69) (Plate Nos. 9, 13, 15) . . . . 45·
Z79 3d. carmine-rose (1862) . . . . . .
Z80 3d. rose (1865) . . . . 80·
Z81 3d. rose (1867–73) (Plate Nos. 4, 5, 6, 10) . . *From* 55·
Z82 4d. red (1862) (Plate Nos. 3, 4) . . . . . . 90·
Z83 4d. vermilion (1867–73) . . . . . . *From* 55·
Plate Nos. 9, 10, 11, 12, 13.
Z84 4d. vermilion (1876) (Plate No. 15) . . . .
Z85 4d. sage-green (1877) (Plate Nos. 15, 16) . . *From* £1
Z86 6d. lilac (1862) (Plate Nos. 3, 4) . . . . *From* 80·
Z87 6d. lilac (1865) (Plate No. 5) . . . . . . 75·
Z88 6d. violet (1867–70) (Plate Nos. 6, 8, 9) . . *From* 75·
Z89 6d. buff (1873) (Plate No. 12) . . . .
Z90 6d. grey (1873) (Plate No. 12) . . . .
Z91 6d. grey (1874–76) (Plate Nos. 13, 14, 15, 16) *From* 60·
Z92 9d. straw (1865) £3
Z93 9d. straw (1867) £1
Z94 10d. red-brown (1867) £2
Z95 1s. green (1865) (Plate No. 4) . . . .
Z96 1s. green (1867–73) (Plate Nos. 4, 5, 6, 7) . . *From* 55·
Z97 1s. green (1873–77) (Plate Nos. 8, 10, 12, 13) *From* 75·
Z98 2s. blue (1867) . . . .
Z99 5s. rose (1867) (Plate No. 1) . . . .

PAITA

CROWNED-CIRCLE HANDSTAMPS

CC5 CC **1** PAITA (Black *or* R.) (5.11.1850)
Price on cover £450

Stamps of GREAT BRITAIN *cancelled* "C 43" *as Type* **4** *or with circular date stamp as Type* **16** *showing* "PAYTA" *straight*.

1865 *to* **1879**.
Z100 1d. rose-red (1864–79) (Plate Nos. 127, 147) . .
Z101 2d. blue (1858–69) (Plate Nos. 9, 14) . . . .
Z102 3d. rose (1867–73) (Plate Nos. 5, 6) . . . . 55·00
Z103 3d. rose (1876) (Plate Nos. 17, 18, 19) . . . . 55·00
Z104 4d. vermilion (1865–73) . . . . . . *From* 55·00
Plate Nos. 10, 11, 12, 13, 14.
Z105 4d. sage-green (1877) (Plate No. 15) . . . .
Z106 6d. lilac (1862) (Plate No. 3) . . . . 85·00
Z107 6d. lilac (1865–67) (Plate Nos. 5, 6) . . *From* 80·00
Z108 6d. violet (1867–70) (Plate Nos. 6, 8, 9) . . *From* 75·00
Z109 6d. buff (1872–73) (Plate Nos. 11, 12) . . *From* 80·00
Z110 6d. chestnut (Plate No. 11) . . . . . . 60·00
Z111 6d. grey (1873) . . . .
Z112 6d. grey (1874–76) (Plate Nos. 13, 14, 15) . .
Z113 9d. straw (1862) . . . .
Z114 10d. red-brown (1867) £275
Z115 1s. green (1865) (Plate No. 4) . . . .
Z116 1s. green (1867–73) (Plate No. 4) . . . . 60·00
Z117 1s. green (1873–77) (Plate Nos. 8, 9, 10, 13) . . 75·00
Z118 2s. blue (1867) £200
Z119 5s. rose (1867) (Plate No. 1) £500

PISAGUA(?)

Stamp of GREAT BRITAIN *cancelled* "D 65" *as Type* **12**.

Z120 2s. blue (1867) . . . .

PISCO AND CHINCHA ISLANDS

Stamps of GREAT BRITAIN *cancelled* "D 74" *as Type* **12**.

1865 *to* **1870**.
Z121 2d. blue (1858–69) (Plate No. 9) . . . .
Z122 4d. vermilion (1865–73) (Plate Nos. 10, 12) . . £450
Z123 6d. violet (1868) (Plate No. 6) £1000
Z124 1s. green (1867) (Plate No. 4) . . . .
Z125 2s. blue (1867) £900

PORTO RICO

British Postal Agency operated at San Juan from 1844. On 24 ober 1872 further offices were opened at Aguadilla, Arroyo, yaguez and Ponce, with Naguabo added three years later. reat Britain stamps were used from 1865 to 1877, but few letters ear to have used the San Juan postal agency between 1866 and 3 due to various natural disasters and the hostile attitude of the l authorities. All the British Agencies closed on 1 May 1877.

AGUADILLA

mps of GREAT BRITAIN *cancelled* "F 84" *as Type* **8.**

3 *to* **1877**.
½d. rose-red (1870) (Plate No. 6) .. .. .. 80·00
1d. rose-red (1864–79) .. .. 45·00
Plate Nos. 119, 122, 139, 149, 156, 160.
2d. blue (1858–69) (Plate No. 14) .. .. ..
3d. rose (1867–73) (Plate Nos. 7, 8, 9) .. ..
3d. rose (1873–76) (Plate No. 12) .. .. ..
4d. vermilion (1865–73) (Plate Nos. 12, 13, 14) *From* 60·00
4d. vermilion (1876) (Plate No. 15) £275
7a 6d. pale buff (1872–73) (Plate No. 11) .. ..
6d. grey (1874–76) (Plate Nos. 13, 14) .. ..
9d. straw (1867) £300
10d. red-brown (1867) £250
1s. green (1867–73) (Plate Nos. 4, 5, 6, 7) .. *From* 50·00
1s. green (1873–77) .. .. *From* 60·00
Plate Nos. 8, 9, 10, 11, 12.
2s. blue (1867) £225

ARROYO

mps of GREAT BRITAIN *cancelled* "F 83" *as Type* **8** *or with ircular date stamps as Types* **17** *and* **18**.

73 *to* **1877.**
4 ½d. rose-red (1870) (Plate No. 5) .. .. 55·00
5 1d. rose-red (1864–79) .. .. 50·00
Plate Nos. 149, 150, 151, 156, 164, 174, 175.
6 1½d. lake-red (1870) (Plate Nos. 1, 3) .. ..
7 2d. blue (1858–69) (Plate No. 14) .. ..
8 3d. rose (1867–73) (Plate Nos. 5, 7, 10) .. *From* 55·00
9 3d. rose (1873–76) .. .. .. *From* 60·00
Plate Nos. 11, 12, 14, 16, 18
0 4d. verm (1865–73) (Plate Nos. 12, 13, 14) *From* 50·00
1 4d. vermilion (1876) (Plate No. 15) £275
2 6d. chestnut (1872) (Plate No. 11) .. .. 60·00
3 6d. pale buff (1872) (Plate No. 11) .. .. 75·00
3a 6d. grey (1873) (Plate No. 12) .. .. ..
4 6d. grey (1874–76) (Plate Nos. 13, 14, 15) .. 55·00
5 9d. straw (1867) £225
6 10d. red-brown (1867) £250
7 1s. green (1865) (Plate No. 4) .. .. ..
8 1s. green (1867–73) (Plate Nos. 4, 5, 6, 7) *From* 50·00
9 1s. green (1873–77) .. .. .. *From* 60·00
Plate Nos. 8, 9, 10, 11, 12, 13.
0 2s. blue (1867) £200
1 5s. rose (1867–74) (Plate No. 2) .. ..

MAYAGUEZ

amps of GREAT BRITAIN *cancelled* "F 85" *as Type* **8**.

73 *to* **1877.**
32 ½d. rose-red (1870) .. .. .. *From* 45·00
Plate Nos. 4, 5, 6, 8, 10, 11.
33 1d. rose-red (1864–79) .. .. .. *From* 30·00
Plate Nos. 76, 120, 121, 122, 124, 134, 137, 140, 146, 149, 150, 151, 154, 155, 156, 157, 160, 167, 170, 171, 174, 175, 176, 178, 180, 182, 185, 186, 189.
34 1½d. lake-red (1870–74) (Plate Nos. 1, 3) .. .. 40·00
35 2d. blue (1858–69) (Plate Nos. 13, 14, 15) .. 40·00
36 3d. rose (1867–73) (Plate Nos. 7, 8, 9, 10) *From* 45·00
37 3d. rose (1873–76) .. .. .. *From* 40·00
Plate Nos. 11, 12, 14, 15, 16, 17, 18, 19.
38 4d. verm (1865–73) (Plate Nos. 11, 12, 13, 14) *From* 45·00
39 4d. vermilion (1876) (Plate No. 15) £275
40 4d. sage-green (1877) (Plate No. 15) .. ..
41 6d. mauve (1870) (Plate No. 9) .. .. ..
42 6d. buff (1872) (Plate No. 11) .. .. .. 75·00
43 6d. chestnut (1872) (Plate No. 11) .. .. 65·00
44 6d. grey (1873) (Plate No. 12) .. .. ..
45 6d. grey (1874–80) (Plate Nos. 13, 14, 15, 16) *From* 45·00
46 8d. orange (1876) £250
47 9d. straw (1867) £180
48 10d. red-brown (1867) £250
49 1s. green (1867–73) (Plate Nos. 4, 5, 6, 7) *From* 35·00
50 1s. green (1873–77) .. .. .. *From* 50·00
Plate Nos. 8, 9, 10, 11, 12.
51 2s. blue (1867) £160
52 5s. rose (1867–74) (Plate Nos. 1, 2) .. ..

NAGUABO

tamps of GREAT BRITAIN *cancelled* "582" *as Type* **9**.

875 *to* **1877**.
Z53 ½d. rose-red (1870–79) (Plate Nos. 5, 12, 14) ..
Z54 1d. rose-red (1864–79) (Plate Nos. 150, 159, 165) £275
Z55 3d. rose (1873–76) (Plate Nos. 17, 18) £450
Z56 4d. vermilion (1872–73) (Plate Nos. 13, 14) *From* £425
Z57 4d. vermilion (1876) (Plate No. 15) .. ..
Z58 6d. grey (1874–76) (Plate Nos. 14, 15) .. ..
Z59 9d. straw (1867) .. ..
Z60 10d. red-brown (1867) £800
Z61 1s. green (1873–77) (Plate Nos. 11, 12) .. ..
Z62 2s. dull blue (1867) (Plate No. 1) £600

PONCE

Stamps of GREAT BRITAIN *cancelled* "F 88" *as Type* **8**.

1873 *to* **1877**.
Z63 ½d. rose-red (1870) (Plate Nos. 5, 10, 12) .. .. 50·00
Z64 1d. rose-red (1864–79) .. .. .. *From* 35·00
Plate Nos. 120, 121, 122, 123, 124, 146, 148, 154, 156, 157, 158, 160, 167, 171, 174, 175, 179, 186, 187.
Z65 1½d. lake-red (1870–74) (Plate No. 3) £100
Z66 2d. blue (1858–69) (Plate Nos. 13, 14) .. .. 45·00
Z67 3d. rose (1867–73) (Plate Nos. 7, 8, 9) .. ..
Z68 3d. rose (1873–76) (Plate Nos. 12, 16, 17, 18, 19) .. 45·00
Z69 4d. vermilion (1865–73) .. .. .. *From* 50·00
Plate Nos. 8, 9, 12, 13, 14.
Z70 4d. vermilion (1876) (Plate No. 15) £275
Z71 4d. sage-green (1877) (Plate Nos. 15, 16) .. *From* £180
Z72 6d. buff (1872–73) (Plate Nos. 11, 12) .. *From* 70·00
Z73 6d. chestnut (1872) (Plate No. 11) .. .. .. 55·00
Z74 6d. grey (1873) (Plate No. 12) .. .. ..
Z75 6d. grey (1874–76) (Plate Nos. 13, 14, 15) .. *From* 45·00
Z76 9d. straw (1867) £200
Z77 10d. red-brown (1867) £250
Z78 1s. green (1867–73) (Plate Nos. 4, 6, 7) .. .. 35·00
Z79 1s. green (1873–77) .. .. *From* 50·00
Plate Nos. 8, 9, 10, 11, 12, 13.
Z80 2s. blue (1867) .. ..
Z81 5s. rose (1867–74) (Plate Nos. 1, 2) .. *From* £350

SAN JUAN

CROWNED-CIRCLE HANDSTAMPS

CC1 CC **1** SAN JUAN PORTO RICO (R. *or* Black) (25.5.1844) .. .. .. *Price on cover* £600

No. CC1 may be found on cover, used in conjunction with Spanish colonial adhesive stamps paying the local postage.

Stamps of GREAT BRITAIN *cancelled* "C 61" *as in Types* **4**, **8**, **12** *or* **14** (*without* "PAID").

1865 *to* **1877**.
Z 82 ½d. rose-red (1870) (Plate Nos. 5, 10, 15) .. *From* 40·00
Z 83 1d. rose-red (1857) .. ..
Z 84 1d. rose-red (1864–79) .. .. .. *From* 30·00
Plate Nos. 73, 74, 81, 84, 90, 94, 100, 101, 102, 107, 117, 122, 124, 125, 127, 130, 137, 138, 139, 140, 145, 146, 149, 153, 156, 159, 160, 162, 163, 169, 171, 172, 173, 174, 175, 179, 180, 182, 186.
Z 85 1½d. lake-red (1870–74) (Plate Nos. 1, 3) .. *From* 60·00
Z 86 2d. blue (1858–69) (Plate Nos. 9, 13, 14) .. *From* 30·00
Z 87 3d. rose (1865) (Plate No. 4) .. .. .. 80·00
Z 88 3d. rose (1867–73) .. .. *From* 40·00
Plate Nos. 5, 6, 7, 8, 9, 10.
Z 89 3d. rose (1873–76) .. .. *From* 35·00
Plate Nos. 11, 12, 14, 15, 16, 17, 18.
Z 90 4d. vermilion (1865–73) .. .. .. *From* 45·00
Plate Nos. 7, 8, 9, 10, 11, 12, 13, 14.
Z 91 4d. vermilion (1876) (Plate No. 15) £275
Z 92 6d. lilac (1865–67) (Plate Nos. 5, 6) .. *From* 70·00
Z 93 6d. lilac (1867) (Plate No. 6) .. .. .. 70·00
Z 94 6d. violet (1867–70) (Plate Nos. 6, 8, 9) .. *From* 65·00
Z 95 6d. buff (1872–73) (Plate Nos. 11, 12) .. *From* 70·00
Z 96 6d. chestnut (1872) (Plate No. 11) .. .. .. 40·00
Z 97 6d. grey (1873) (Plate No. 12) .. .. ..
Z 98 6d. grey (1874–76) (Plate Nos. 13, 14, 15) .. *From* 40·00
Z 99 9d. straw (1862) £225
Z100 9d. straw (1865) £350
Z101 9d. straw (1867) £180
Z102 10d. red-brown (1867) £250
Z103 1s. green (1865) (Plate No. 4) £130
Z104 1s. green (1867–73) (Plate Nos. 4, 5, 6, 7) .. *From* 35·00
Z105 1s. green (1873–77) .. .. *From* 50·00
Plate Nos. 8, 9, 10, 11, 12, 13.
Z106 2s. blue (1867) £110
Z107 5s. rose (1867) (Plate Nos. 1, 2) .. .. *From* £400

RUSSIA

ARMY FIELD OFFICES IN THE CRIMEA

1854 *to* **1857.**

Crown between Stars
Z 1 1d. red-brown (1841), *imperf* £550
Z 2 1d. red-brown (1854), Die I, *wmk* Small Crown, *perf* 16 .. ..
Z 3 1d. red-brown (1855), Die II, *wmk* Small Crown, *perf* 16 .. .. £150
Z 4 1d. red-brown, Die I, *wmk* Small Crown, *perf* 14 ..
Z 5 1d. red-brown (1855), Die II, Small Crown, *perf* 14
Z 6 2d. blue (1841) *imperf* £900
Z 7 2d. blue, Small Crown (1854), *perf* 16 (Plate No. 4)
Z 8 1s. green (1847), embossed £1400

Star between Cyphers
Z 9 1d. red-brown (1841), *imperf* .. .. ..
Z10 1d. red-brown (1854), Die I, *wmk* Small Crown, *perf* 16 .. .. 70·00
Z11 1d. red-brown (1855), Die II, *wmk* Small Crown, *perf* 16 .. .. 70·00
Z12 1d. red-brown (1855), Die I, *wmk* Small Crown, *perf* 14 .. .. 70·00
Z13 1d. red-brown (1855), Die II, *wmk* Small Crown, *perf* 14 .. .. 70·00
Z14 1d. red-brown (1855), Die II, *wmk* Large Crown, *perf* 16 .. .. 90·00
Z15 1d. red-brown (1855), Die II, *wmk* Large Crown, *perf* 14 .. .. 42·00
Z16 2d. blue (1841), *imperf* £1000
Z17 2d. blue (1854) *wmk* Small Crown, *perf* 16 *From* £130
Plate Nos. 4, 5.
Z18 2d. blue (1855) *wmk* Small Crown, *perf* 14 .. £175
Plate No. 4.
Z19 2d. blue (1855), *wmk* Large Crown, *perf* 16 .. £200
Plate No. 5.
Z20 2d. blue (1855), *wmk* Large Crown, *perf* 14 .. £120
Plate No. 5.
Z21 4d. rose (1857) £800
Z22 6d. violet (1854), embossed £1100
Z23 1s. green (1847), embossed £1100

SPAIN

Little is known about the operation of British Packet Agencies in Spain, other than the dates recorded for the various postal markings in the G.P.O. Proof Books. The Agency at Corunna is said to date from the late 17th century when the Spanish packets for South America were based there. No. CC1 was probably issued in connection with the inauguration of the P & O service to Spain in 1843. The Spanish port of call was changed to Vigo in 1846 and the office at Corunna was then closed. Teneriffe became a port-of-call for the South American packets in 1817 and this arrangement continued until 1858.

CORUNNA

CROWNED-CIRCLE HANDSTAMPS

CC1 CC **1b** CORUNNA (28.2.1842) .. .. ..

Although recorded in the G.P.O. Proof Books no example of No. CC1 on cover is known.

TENERIFFE (CANARY ISLANDS)

CROWNED-CIRCLE HANDSTAMPS

CC2 CC **7** TENERIFFE (6.1.1851) .. *Price on cover* £3500
CC3 CC **4** TENERIFFE (23.10.1857) .. *Price on cover* £3500

No. CC2/3 can be found used on covers from Spain to South America with the rate from Spain to Teneriffe paid in Spanish adhesive stamps.

UNITED STATES OF AMERICA

The network of British Packet Agencies, to operate the trans-Atlantic Packet system, was re-established in 1814 after the War of 1812.

The New York Agency opened in that year to be followed by further offices at Boston, Charleston (South Carolina), New Orleans, Savannah (Georgia) (all in 1842), Mobile (Alabama) (1848) and San Francisco (1860). Of these agencies Charleston and Savannah closed the same year (1842) as did New Orleans, although the latter was re-activated from 1848 to 1850. Mobile closed 1850, Boston in 1865, New York in 1882 and San Francisco, for which no postal markings have been recorded, in 1883.

Although recorded in the G.P.O. Proof Books no actual examples of the Crowned-circle handstamps for Charleston, Mobile, New Orleans and Savannah are known on cover.

The G.P.O. proof books record, in error, a Crowned-circle handstamp for St. Michaels, Maryland. This handstamp was intended for the agency on San Miguel in the Azores.

CHARLESTON

CROWNED-CIRCLE HANDSTAMPS

CC1 CC **1b** CHARLESTON (15.12.1841) .. ..

MOBILE

CROWNED-CIRCLE HANDSTAMPS

CC2 CC **1b** MOBILE (15.12.1841) .. .. ..

NEW ORLEANS

CROWNED-CIRCLE HANDSTAMPS

CC3 CC **1b** NEW ORLEANS (15.12.1841) .. ..
CC4 CC **1** NEW ORLEANS (27.4.1848) .. ..

NEW YORK

CROWNED-CIRCLE HANDSTAMPS

CC5 CC **1b** NEW YORK (R.) (15.12.1841) *Price on cover* £25000

SAVANNAH

CROWNED-CIRCLE HANDSTAMPS

CC6 CC **1b** SAVANNAH (15.12.1841) .. ..

URUGUAY

MONTEVIDEO

British packets commenced calling at Montevideo in 1824 on passage to and from Buenos Aires.

Great Britain stamps were in use from 1864. Combination covers exist with the local postage paid by Uruguay adhesive stamps. The agency was closed on 31 July 1873.

CROWNED-CIRCLE HANDSTAMPS

CC1 CC **5** MONTEVIDEO (Black *or* R.) (6.1.1851) *Price on cover* £900

Stamps of GREAT BRITAIN *cancelled* "C 28" *as in Type* **4**.

1864 *to* **1873**.
Z 1 1d. rose-red (1864) .. .. 50·00
Plate Nos. 73, 92, 93, 94, 119, 148, 154, 157, 171.
Z 2 2d. blue (1858–69) (Plate Nos. 9, 13) .. .. 50·00
Z 3 3d. rose (1865) (Plate No. 4) .. .. ..
Z 4 3d. rose (1867–71) (Plate Nos. 4, 5, 7) .. *From* 45·00
Z 6 4d. rose (1857) .. ..
Z 7 4d. red (1862) (Plate No. 4) .. ..
Z 8 4d. vermilion (1865–70) .. .. .. *From* 45·00
Plate Nos. 7, 8, 9, 10, 11, 12.
Z 9 6d. lilac (1856) .. ..
Z10 6d. lilac (1862) (Plate No. 4) .. .. ..
Z11 6d. lilac (1865–67) (Plate Nos. 5, 6) .. *From* 80·00
Z12 6d. lilac (1867) (Plate No. 6) .. .. ..
Z13 6d. violet (1867–70) (Plate Nos. 8, 9) .. *From* 75·00
Z14 6d. buff (1872) .. ..
Z15 6d. chestnut (1872) .. ..
Z16 9d. straw (1862) .. ..
Z17 9d. straw (1865) .. ..
Z18 9d. straw (1867) £190
Z19 10d. red-brown (1867) £250
Z20 1s. green (1862) £150
Z21 1s. green (1865) (Plate No. 4) £130
Z22 1s. green (1867–73) (Plate Nos. 4, 5) .. *From* 45·00
Z23 2s. blue (1867) £130
Z24 5s. rose (1867) (Plate No. 1) £400

VENEZUELA

British Postal Agencies were initially opened at La Guayra and Porto Cabello on 1 January 1842. Further offices were added at Maracaibo in 1842 and Ciudad Bolivar during January 1868. Porto Cabello closed in 1858 and Maracaibo was also short-lived. The remaining offices closed at the end of 1879 when Venezuela joined the U.P.U.

Great Britain stamps were used at La Guayra from 1865 and at Ciudad Bolivar from its establishment in 1868. They can be found used in combination with Venezuela adhesives paying the local postage.

CIUDAD BOLIVAR

Stamps of GREAT BRITAIN *cancelled* "D 22" *as Type* **12**, *or circular date stamps as Types* **16** *or* **17**.

1868 *to* **1879.**

Z 1 1d. rose-red (1864–79) (Plate No. 133) £120
Z 2 2d. blue (1858–69) (Plate No. 13) .. ..
Z 3 3d. rose (1867–73) (Plate No. 5) .. ..
Z 4 3d. rose (1873–79) (Plate No. 11) £130
Z 5 4d. verm (1865–73) (Plate Nos. 9, 11, 12, 14) *From* 80·00
Z 6 4d. sage-green (1877) (Plate Nos. 15, 16) .. *From* £225
Z 7 4d. grey-brown (1880) *wmk* Crown (Plate No. 17)
Z 8 9d. straw (1867) .. ..
Z 9 10d. red-brown (1867) .. ..
Z10 1s. green (1867–73) (Plate Nos. 4, 5, 7) .. *From* £125
Z11 1s. green (1873–77) (Plate Nos. 10, 12, 13) *From* £110
Z12 2s. blue (1867) £325
Z13 5s. rose (1867–74) (Plate Nos. 1, 2) .. *From* £500

LA GUAYRA

CROWNED-CIRCLE HANDSTAMPS

CC1 CC **1b** LA GUAYRA (R.) (15.12.1841) *Price on cover* £1200

Stamps of GREAT BRITAIN *cancelled* "C 60" *as Type* **4**, *circular date stamp as Types* **16** *and* **17** *or with No.* CC1.

1865 *to* **1880**.

Z14 ½d. rose-red (1870) (Plate No. 6) .. .. ..
Z15 1d. rose-red (1864–79) .. .. .. *From* 50·00
Plate Nos. 81, 92, 96, 98, 111, 113, 115, 131, 138, 144, 145, 154, 177, 178, 180, 196.
Z16 1½d. lake-red (1870–74) (Plate No. 3) .. ..
Z17 2d. blue (1858–69) (Plate Nos. 13, 14) .. .. 50·00
Z18 3d. rose (1873–76) .. .. .. *From* 55·00
Plate Nos. 14, 15, 17, 18, 19.
Z19 4d. vermilion (1865–73) .. .. .. *From* 50·00
Plate Nos. 7, 9, 11, 12, 13, 14.
Z20 4d. vermilion (1876) (Plate No. 15) £275
Z21 4d. sage-green (1877) (Plate Nos. 15, 16) .. *From* £180
Z22 6d. lilac (1865) (Plate No. 5) .. ..
Z23 6d. violet (1867–70) (Plate Nos. 6, 8) .. ..
Z24 6d. buff (1872–73) (Plate Nos. 11, 12) .. *From* 90·00
Z25 6d. grey (1873) (Plate No. 12) £190
Z26 6d. grey (1874–76) (Plate Nos. 13, 14, 15, 16) .. 45·00
Z27 8d. orange (1876) £275
Z28 9d. straw (1862) .. ..
Z29 9d. straw (1867) .. ..
Z30 10d. red-brown (1867) .. ..
Z31 1s. green (1865) (Plate No. 4) £130
Z32 1s. green (1867–73) (Plate Nos. 4, 7) .. ..
Z33 1s. green (1873–77) .. .. .. *From* 50·00
Plate Nos. 8, 9, 10, 11, 12, 13.
Z34 2s. blue (1867) £200
Z35 5s. rose (1867–74) (Plate No. 1, 2) .. .. *From* £400

MARACAIBO

CROWNED-CIRCLE HANDSTAMPS

CC2 CC **1b** MARACAIBO (31.12.1841) .. ..
No examples of No. CC2 on cover have been recorded.

PORTO CABELLO

CROWNED-CIRCLE HANDSTAMPS

CC3 CC **1b** PORTO-CABELLO (R.) (15.12.1841)
Price on cover £3000

MAIL BOAT OBLITERATIONS

The following cancellations were supplied to G.P.O. sorters operating on ships holding mail contracts from the British Post Office. They were for use on mail posted on board, but most examples occur on letters from soldiers and sailors serving overseas which were forwarded to the mailboats without postmarks.

P. & O. MEDITERRANEAN AND FAR EAST MAILBOATS

The first such cancellation, "A 17" as Type **2**, was issued to the Southampton–Alexandria packet in April 1858, but no examples have been recorded.

The G.P.O. Proof Book also records "B 16", in Type **2**, as being issued for marine sorting in November 1859, but this postmark was subsequently used by the Plymouth and Bristol Sorting Carriage.

Sorting on board P. & O. packets ceased in June 1870 and many of the cancellation numbers were subsequently reallocated using Types **9**, **11** or **12**.

Stamps of GREAT BRITAIN *cancelled* "A 80" *as Type* **2**.

1859 (Mar) *to* **1870.**

Z1 1d. rose-red (1857), Die II, *wmk* Large Crown, *perf* 14 .. .. 35·00
Z2 6d. lilac (1856) £125

Stamps of GREAT BRITAIN *cancelled* "A 81" *as Type* **2**.

1859 (Mar) *to* **1870.**

Z 3 1d. rose-red (1857), Die II, *wmk* Large Crown, *perf* 14 .. .. 35·00
Z 4 1d. rose-red (1864–79) .. .. .. *From* 30·00
Plate Nos. 84, 85, 86, 91, 97
Z 5 2d. blue (1858–69) (Plate No. 9) .. .. 40·00
Z 6 4d. red (1862) (Plate No. 4) £100
Z 7 4d. vermilion (1865–73) (Plate No. 8) .. .. 50·00
Z 8 6d. lilac (1856) £125
Z 9 6d. lilac (1862) (Plate No. 3) £100
Z10 6d. lilac (1865–67) .. .. .. *From* 85·00
Plate Nos. 5, 6.
Z11 6d. lilac (1867) (Plate No. 6) .. .. .. 80·00
Z12 6d. violet (1867–70) .. .. .. *From* 65·00
Plate Nos. 6, 8.
Z13 10d. red-brown (1867) £400
Z14 1s. green (1856) £225

Stamps of GREAT BRITAIN *cancelled* "A 82" *as Type* **2**.

1859 (Mar) *to* **1870.**

Z15 1d. rose-red (1857), Die II, *wmk* Large Crown, *perf* 14 .. .. 40·00
Z16 2d. blue (1858) (Plate No. 7) .. .. .. 45·00
Z17 4d. rose (1856) £180
Z18 6d. lilac (1856) £160
Z19 6d. lilac (1865–67) .. .. .. *From* £110
Plate Nos. 5, 6.
Z20 6d. lilac (1867) (Plate No. 6) .. .. .. 90·00

Stamps of GREAT BRITAIN *cancelled* "A 83" *as Type* **2**.

1859 (Apr) *to* **1870.**

Z21 1d. rose-red (1857), Die II, *wmk* Large Crown, *perf* 14 .. .. 35·00
Z22 1d. rose-red (1864–79) .. .. .. *From* 30·00
Plate Nos. 73, 74, 84, 91, 109.
Z23 3d. carmine-rose (1862) £225
Z24 4d. rose (1857) £160
Z25 4d. red (1862) .. .. 90·00
Z26 4d. vermilion (1865–73) .. .. .. *From* 50·00
Plate Nos. 9, 10.
Z27 6d. lilac (1856) £125
Z28 6d. lilac (1862) £100
Z29 6d. lilac (1865–67) .. .. .. *From* 85·00
Plate Nos. 5, 6.
Z30 6d. violet (1867–70) .. .. .. *From* 65·00
Plate Nos. 6, 8.
Z31 10d. red-brown (1867) £400
Z32 1s. green (1862) £225

Stamps of GREAT BRITAIN *cancelled* "A 84" *as Type* **2**.

1859 (Apr) *to* **1870.**

Z33 1d. rose-red (1857). Die II, *wmk* Large Crown, *perf* 14 .. .. 90·00

Stamps of GREAT BRITAIN *cancelled* "A 85" *as Type* **2**.

1859 (Apr) *to* **1870.**

Z34 1d. rose-red (1857), Die II, *wmk* Large Crown, *perf* 14 .. .. 35·00
Z35 1d. rose-red (1864–79) .. .. .. *From* 30·00
Plate Nos. 79, 97, 103.
Z36 3d. carmine-rose (1862) £225
Z37 4d. red (1862) .. .. 90·00
Z38 6d. lilac (1856) £125
Z39 6d. lilac (1862) .. .. .. *From* £100
Plate Nos. 3, 4.
Z40 6d. lilac (1865–67) (Plate No. 5) .. .. 85·00
Z41 6d. lilac (1867) (Plate No. 6) .. .. .. 70·00
Z42 1s. green (1862) £250

Stamps of GREAT BRITAIN *cancelled* "A 86" *as Type* **2**.

1859 (Apr) *to* **1870.**

Z43 1d. rose-red (1857), Die II, *wmk* Large Crown, *perf* 14 .. .. 35·00
Z44 1d. rose-red (1864–79) .. .. .. *From* 30·00
Plate Nos. 73, 84, 94, 97, 114, 118.
Z45 3d. rose (1865) £200
Z46 3d. rose (1867–73) .. .. .. *From* 65·00
Plate Nos. 4, 5.
Z47 4d. rose (1857) £160
Z48 4d. red (1862) (Plate No. 4) .. .. .. 90·00
Z49 4d. vermilion (1865–73) (Plate No. 10) .. .. 70·00
Z50 6d. lilac (1856) £125
Z51 6d. lilac (1862) .. .. .. *From* £100
Plate Nos. 3, 4.
Z52 6d. lilac (1865–67) .. .. .. *From* 85·00
Plate Nos. 5, 6.
Z53 6d. lilac (1867) .. .. .. *From* 65·00
Plate Nos. 6, 8.
Z54 10d. red-brown (1867) £375
Z55 1s. green (1862) £225

Stamps of GREAT BRITAIN *cancelled* "A 87" *as Type* **2**.

1859 (Apr) *to* **1870.**

Z56 1d. rose-red (1857), Die II, *wmk* Large Crown, *perf* 14 .. .. 45·00
Z57 4d. rose (1856) £200
Z58 6d. lilac (1867) (Plate No. 6) £100

Stamps of GREAT BRITAIN *cancelled* "A 88" *as Type* **2**.

1859 (Apr) *to* **1870.**

Z59 1d. rose-red (1857), Die II, *wmk* Large Crown, *perf* 14 .. .. 35·00
Z60 1d. rose-red (1864–79) .. .. .. *From* 30·00
Plate Nos. 74, 80, 85.
Z61 4d. rose (1857) £175
Z62 4d. red (1862) £100
Z63 4d. vermilion (1865–73) (Plate No. 8) .. .. 50·00
Z64 6d. lilac (1856) .. ..
Z65 6d. lilac (1862) (Plate No. 4) £125
Z66 6d. lilac (1865–67) (Plate No. 5) £100
Z67 6d. lilac (1867) (Plate No. 6) .. .. .. 85·00
Z68 6d. violet (1867–70) (Plate No. 8) .. .. 65·00
Z69 10d. red-brown (1867) £425
Z70 1s. green (1856) £250

Stamps of GREAT BRITAIN *cancelled* "A 89" *as Type* **2**.

1859 (Apr) *to* **1870.**

Z71 1d. rose-red (1857), Die II, *wmk* Large Crown, *perf* 14 90
Z72 6d. lilac (1856) .. .. £

Stamps of GREAT BRITAIN *cancelled* "A 90" *as Type* **2**.

1859 (June) *to* **1870.**

Z73 1d. rose-red (1857), Die II, *wmk* Large Crown, *perf* 14 .. .. 55·
Z74 4d. rose (1856) .. ..
Z75 6d. lilac (1856) £2
Z76 6d. lilac (1865–67) .. .. .. *From* £1
Plate Nos. 5, 6.
Z77 9d. straw (1867) .. ..

Stamps of GREAT BRITAIN *cancelled* "A 99" *as Type* **2**.

1859 (June) *to* **1870.**

Z78 1d. rose-red (1857), Die II, *wmk* Large Crown, *perf* 14 35
Z79 1d. rose-red (1864–79) .. .. .. *From* 30
Plate Nos. 93, 97, 99, 118. £1
Z80 4d. rose (1857) .. ..
Z81 4d. red (1862) .. .. 90·
Z82 4d. vermilion (1865–73) (Plate No. 11) .. .. 50·
Z83 6d. lilac (1856) .. ..
Z84 6d. lilac (1862) £1
Z85 6d. lilac (1865–67) .. .. .. *From* £1
Plate Nos. 5, 6.
Z86 10d. red-brown (1867) £4

Stamps of GREAT BRITAIN *cancelled* "B 03" *as Type* **2**.

1859 (Aug) *to* **1870.**

Z87 1d. rose-red (1857), Die II, *wmk* Large Crown, *perf* 14 .. .. 45·
Z88 1d. rose-red (1864–79) .. .. .. *From* 35·
Plate Nos. 109, 116.
Z89 3d. rose (1865) (Plate No. 4) .. .. .. 80·
Z90 6d. lilac (1856) £1
Z91 6d. lilac (1867) (Plate No. 6) £1
Z92 6d. violet (1867–70) .. .. .. *From* 80·
Plate Nos. 6, 8.
Z93 10d. red-brown (1867) £4

Stamps of GREAT BRITAIN *cancelled* "B 12" *as Type* **2**.

1859 (Oct) *to* **1870.**

Z 94 1d. rose-red (1857), Die II, *wmk* Large Crown, *perf* 14 .. .. 45·
Z 95 1d. rose-red (1864–79) (Plate No. 94) .. .. 35·
Z 96 3d. rose (1865) (Plate No. 4) .. .. .. 80·
Z 97 4d. red (1862) £10
Z 98 4d. vermilion (1865–73) (Plate No. 8) .. .. 65·
Z 99 6d. lilac (1856) .. ..
Z100 6d. lilac (1862) £14
Z101 6d. lilac (1865–67) .. .. .. *From* £1
Plate Nos. 5, 6.
Z102 6d. violet (1867–70) (Plate No. 8) .. .. 75·0

Stamps of GREAT BRITAIN *cancelled* "B 56" *as Type* **2**.

1861 (July) *to* **1870.**

Z103 1d. rose-red (1864–70) (Plate No. 84) .. .. 35·0
Z104 2d. blue (1858–69) (Plate No. 9) .. .. 50·0
Z105 4d. red (1862) (Plate No. 4) £10
Z106 4d. vermilion (1865–73) .. .. 55·0
Plate Nos. 7, 8.
Z107 6d. lilac (1862) .. .. .. *From* £12
Plate Nos. 3, 4.
Z108 6d. lilac (1865–67) .. .. .. *From* £10
Plate Nos. 5, 6.
Z109 6d. violet (1867–70) .. .. .. *From* 80·00
Plate Nos. 6, 8.

Stamps of GREAT BRITAIN *cancelled* "B 57" *as Type* **2**.

1861 (July) *to* **1870.**

Z110 1d. rose-red (1857). Die II. *wmk* Large Crown, *perf* 14 .. .. 40·00
Z111 1d. rose-red (1864–79) (Plate No. 81) .. .. 35·00
Z112 2d. blue (1858–69) (Plate No. 9) .. .. 50·00
Z113 4d. red (1862) £100
Z114 4d. vermilion (1865–73) .. .. 55·00
Plate Nos. 7, 8.
Z115 6d. lilac (1865–67) .. .. .. *From* £100
Plate Nos. 5, 6.

Stamps of GREAT BRITAIN *cancelled* "C 79" *as Type* **12**.

1866 (June) *to* **1870.**

Z116 6d. violet (1867–70) .. .. .. *From* 75·00
Plate Nos. 6, 8.
Z117 10d. red-brown (1867) £375

CUNARD LINE ATLANTIC MAILBOATS

These were all issued in June 1859. No examples are known used after August 1868. "B 61" is recorded as being issued in March 1862, but no examples are known. Cancellation numbers were subsequently reallocated to offices in Great Britain or, in the case of "A 91", the British Virgin Islands.

Stamps of GREAT BRITAIN *cancelled* "A 91" *as Type* **2**.

1859 (June) *to* **1868.**

Z130 1d. rose-red (1857), Die II, *wmk* Large Crown, *perf* 14 .. .. 60·00
Z131 1d. rose-red (1864–79) (Plate No. 121) .. .. 50·00
Z132 2d. blue (1855), *wmk* Small Crown, *perf* 14 ..

2d. blue (1858–69) .. .. 75·00
Plate Nos. 8, 9.
4d. rose (1857) £200
4d. red (1862) £110
6d. lilac (1856) £150
6d. lilac (1862) £125
6d. lilac (1865–67) £100
9d. straw (1862) .. ..
1s. green (1856) £275

...ps of GREAT BRITAIN *cancelled* "A 92" *as Type* **2**.

... (June) *to* **1868.**
1d. rose-red (1857), Die II, *wmk* Large Crown, *perf* 14 .. .. 60·00
2 1d. rose-red (1864–79) .. .. .. *From* 50·00
Plate Nos. 93, 97.
3 6d. lilac (1856) £150
4 6d. lilac (1862) (Plate No. 3) £125
5 6d. lilac (1865–67) .. .. .. *From* £100
Plate Nos. 5, 6.

...ps of GREAT BRITAIN *cancelled* "A 93" *as Type* **2**.

... (June) *to* **1868.**
6 1d. rose-red (1857), Die II, *wmk* Large Crown, *perf* 14 .. .. 60·00
7 1d. rose-red (1864–79) (Plate No. 85) .. .. 50·00
8 6d. lilac (1856) £150
9 6d. lilac (1865–67) (Plate No. 6) £130
0 10d. red-brown (1867) £425

...ps of GREAT BRITAIN *cancelled* "A 94" *as Type* **2**.

9 (June) *to* **1868.**
1 1d. rose-red (1857), Die II, *wmk* Large Crown, *perf* 14 .. .. 75·00

Z152 1d. rose-red (1864–79) .. .. .. *From* 60·00
Plate Nos. 74, 97.
Z153 4d. vermilion (1865–73) (Plate No. 7) .. .. 85·00
Z154 6d. lilac (1856) £160
Z155 6d. lilac (1862) £140
Z156 6d. lilac (1865–67) .. .. .. *From* £120
Plate Nos. 5, 6.

Stamps of GREAT BRITAIN *cancelled* "A 95" *as Type* **2**.

1859 (June) *to* **1868.**
Z157 1d. rose-red (1857), Die II, *wmk* Large Crown, *perf* 14 .. .. 55·00
Z158 1d. rose-red (1864–79) .. .. .. *From* 45·00
Plate Nos. 72, 89, 97.
Z159 3d. rose (1867–73) (Plate No. 5) .. .. 75·00
Z160 4d. red (1862) £110
Z161 4d. vermilion (1865–73) (Plate No. 8) .. .. 60·00
Z162 6d. lilac (1862) £150
Z163 6d. lilac (1865–67) (Plate No. 5) £125
Z164 6d. lilac (1867) (Plate No. 6) £110
Z165 1s. green (1856) £225

Stamps of GREAT BRITAIN *cancelled* "A 96" *as Type* **2**.

1859 (June) *to* **1868.**
Z166 1d. rose-red (1857), Die II, *wmk* Large Crown, *perf* 14 .. .. 60·00
Z167 4d. vermilion (1865–73) (Plate No. 7) .. .. 80·00
Z168 6d. lilac (1856) £150
Z169 1s. green (1856) £250

Stamps of GREAT BRITAIN *cancelled* "A 97" *as Type* **2**.

1859 (June) *to* **1868.**
Z170 1d. rose-red (1857), Die II, *wmk* Large Crown, *perf* 14 .. .. 60·00
Z171 1d. rose-red (1864–79) (Plate No. 71) .. .. 50·00
Z172 4d. red (1862) (Plate No. 3) £120

Stamps of GREAT BRITAIN *cancelled* "A 98" *as Type* **2**.

1859 (June) *to* **1868.**
Z173 1d. rose-red (1857), Die II, *wmk* Large Crown, *perf* 14 .. .. 60·00
Z174 4d. red (1862) £120
Z175 6d. lilac (1856) £160
Z176 6d. lilac (1862) (Plate No. 4) £140
Z177 6d. lilac (1865–67) .. .. .. *From* £100
Plate Nos. 5, 6.

ALLAN LINE ATLANTIC MAILBOATS

British G.P.O. sorters worked on these Canadian ships between November 1859 and April 1860. Cancellations as Type **2** numbered "B 17", "B 18", "B 27", "B 28", B 29" and "B 30" were issued to them, but have not been reported used on Great Britain stamps during this period. All were subsequently reallocated to British post offices.

SPANISH WEST INDIES MAILBOATS

"D 26" was supplied for use by British mail clerks employed on ships of the Herrara Line operating between St. Thomas (Danish West Indies), Cuba, Dominican Republic and Porto Rico.

Stamps of GREAT BRITAIN *cancelled* "D 26" *as Type* **12**.

1868 *to* **1871**.
Z190 1d. rose-red (1864–79) .. ..
Plate Nos. 98, 125.
Z191 4d. vermilion (1865–73) £600
Plate Nos. 9, 10, 11.
Z192 6d. violet (1867–70) (Plate No. 8) .. ..
Z193 1s. green (1867) (Plate No. 4) .. .. ..

Aitutaki

see after New Zealand

Aitutaki *see after* New Zealand

Aden

e first post office in Aden opened during January 1839, situ- in what became known as the Crater district. No stamps were ally available, but, after the office was placed under the bay Postal Circle, stocks of the 1854 ½ a. and 1 a. stamps placed on sale in Aden from 10 October 1854. Supplies of 2 a. and 4 a. values did not arrive until December. Most an issues from the 1854 lithographs up to 1935 Silver lee set can be found with Aden postmarks.

aring January 1858 a further office, Aden Steamer Point, opened in the harbour area and much of the business was sferred to it by 1869. The original Aden post office, in er, was renamed Aden Cantonment, later to be changed n to Aden Camp.

e first cancellation used with the Indian stamps was a plain ond of dots. This type was also used elsewhere so that bution to Aden is only possible when on cover. Aden was gned "124" in the Indian postal number system and this ed the main feature of marks from 1855, either on its own part of a duplex.

1858 "124" Cancellation

1870 Aden Duplex

1872 Aden Steamer Point Duplex

Both post offices used this number until 1871 when Aden ntonment was assigned "125", only to have this swiftly amended '124A" in the same year.

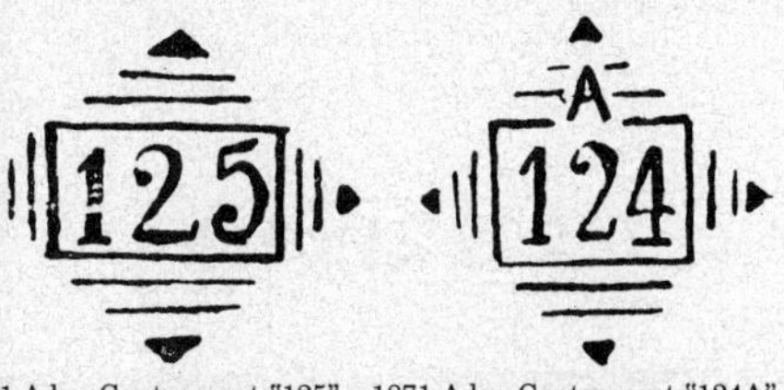

71 Aden Cantonment "125" Cancellation   1871 Aden Cantonment "124A" Cancellation

Cancellations inscribed "Aden Steamer Point" disappear after 74 and this office was then known simply as Aden. Following is change the office was given number "B-22" under the revised dian P.O. scheme and this number appears as a major part of the ncellations from 1875 to 1886, either on its own or as part of a plex, Aden Camp, the alternative name for the Cantonment fice, became "B-22/1".

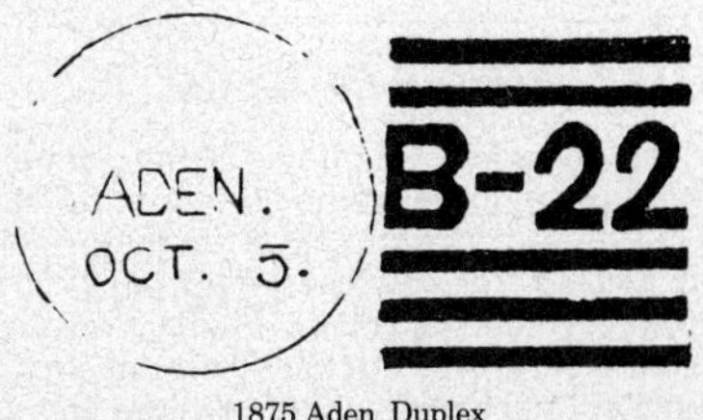

1875 Aden Duplex

Squared-circle types for Aden and Aden Cantonment were introduced in 1884 and 1888 to be in turn replaced by standard Indian double and single circle from 1895 onwards.

A number of other post offices were opened between 1891 and 1937:

Dthali (*opened* 1903, *initially using* "EXPERIMENTAL P.O. B-84" *postmark*; *closed* 1907)
Kamaran (*opened c* 1915, *but no civilian postmarks known before* 1925)
Khormaksar (*opened* 1892; *closed* 1915; *reopened* 1925)
Maalla (*opened* 1923; *closed* 1931)
Nobat-Dakim (*opened* 1904, *initially using* "EXPERIMENTAL P.O. B-84" *postmark*; *closed* 1905)
Perim (*opened* 1915; *closed* 1936)
Sheikh Othman (*opened* 1891; *closed* 1915; *reopened* 1922; *closed* 1937)

PRICES FOR STAMPS ON COVER TO 1945
Nos. 1/15 *from* × 6
Nos. 16/27 *from* × 3

(Currency. 12 pies = 1 anna; 16 annas = 1 rupee)

1 Dhow

3 Aidrus Mosque, Crater

(Recess D.L.R.)

1937 (1 Apr). *Wmk Mult Script CA sideways. P* 13 × 12.

No.	Type	Description	Unused	Used
1	1	½ a. yellow-green	3·75	1·50
2		9 p. deep green	3·75	1·75
3		1 a. sepia	3·75	70
4		2 a. scarlet	3·75	2·00
5		2½ a. bright blue	3·75	80
6		3 a. carmine	9·00	6·50
7		3½ a. grey-blue	7·50	2·50
8		8 a. pale purple	22·00	5·50
9		1 r. brown	32·00	6·00
10		2 r. yellow	48·00	16·00
11		5 r. deep purple	90·00	65·00
12		10 r. olive-green	£275	£325
1/12		*Set of* 12	£450	£375
1s/12s		Perf "Specimen" *Set of* 12	£325	

1937 (12 May). *Coronation. As Nos. 95/7 of Antigua, but ptd by D.L.R. P* 14.

No.	Description	Unused	Used
13	1 a. sepia	65	80
14	2½ a. light blue	75	1·40
15	3½ a. grey-blue	1·00	2·50
13/15	*Set of* 3	2·25	4·25
13s/15s	Perf "Specimen" *Set of* 3	70·00	

(Recess Waterlow)

1939 (19 Jan)–**48**. *Horiz designs as T* **3**. *Wmk Mult Script CA. P* 12½.

No.	Description	Unused	Used
16	½ a. yellowish green	50	60
	a. Bluish green (13.9.48)	2·25	3·75
17	¾ a. red-brown	1·25	1·25
18	1 a. pale blue	20	40
19	1½ a. scarlet	55	60
20	2 a. sepia	20	25
21	2½ a. deep ultramarine	40	30
22	3 a. sepia and carmine	60	25
23	8 a. red-orange	55	40
23*a*	14 a. sepia and light blue (15.1.45)	2·50	1·00
24	1 r. emerald-green	2·25	2·00
25	2 r. deep blue and magenta	4·75	2·25
26	5 r. red-brown and olive-green	11·00	8·00
27	10 r. sepia and violet	30·00	11·00
16/27	*Set of* 13	48·00	25·00
16s/27s	Perf "Specimen" *Set of* 13	£180	

Designs:—½ a., 2 a., Type **3**; ¾ a., 5 r. Adenese Camel Corps; 1 a., 2 r. The Harbour; 1½ a., 1 r. Adenese Dhow; 2½ a., 8 a. Mukalla; 3 a., 14 a., 10 r. "Capture of Aden, 1839" (Capt. Rundle).

Accent over "D" (R. 7/1, later corrected)

1946 (15 Oct). *Victory. As Nos. 110/11 of Antigua.*

No.	Description	Unused	Used
28	1½ a. carmine	15	1·00
	a. Accent over "D"	20·00	
29	2½ a. blue	15	30
	w. Wmk inverted	£450	
28s/9s	Perf "Specimen" *Set of* 2	50·00	

1949 (7 Jan). *Royal Silver Wedding. As Nos. 112/13 of Antigua.*

No.	Description	Unused	Used
30	1½ a. scarlet (*p* 14×15)	40	1·00
31	10 r. mauve (*p* 11½×11)	27·00	32·00

1949 (10 Oct). *75th Anniv of U.P.U. As Nos. 114/17 of Antigua, surch with new values by Waterlow.*

No.	Description	Unused	Used
32	2½ a. on 20 c. ultramarine	50	1·50
33	3 a. on 30 c. carmine-red	1·75	1·50
34	8 a. on 50 c. orange	1·10	1·50
35	1 r. on 1 s. blue	1·60	2·75
32/5	*Set of* 4	4·50	6·50

(New Currency. 100 cents = 1 shilling)

5 CENTS
(12)

1951 (1 Oct). *Nos. 18 and 20/7 surch with new values, in cents or shillings, as T* **12**, *or in one line between bars* (30 c.) *by Waterlow.*

No.	Description	Unused	Used
36	5 c. on 1 a. pale blue	15	40
37	10 c. on 2 a. sepia	15	45
38	15 c. on 2½ a. deep ultramarine	20	1·25
	a. Surch double	£700	
39	20 c. on 3 a. sepia and carmine	30	40
40	30 c. on 8 a. red-orange (R.)	30	65
41	50 c. on 8 a. red-orange	30	35
42	70 c. on 14 a. sepia and light blue	2·00	1·50
43	1 s. on 1 r. emerald-green	35	30
44	2 s. on 2 r. deep blue and magenta	7·50	2·75
	a. Surch albino	£425	
45	5 s. on 5 r. red-brown and olive-green	16·00	9·50
46	10 s. on 10 r. sepia and violet	24·00	11·00
36/46	*Set of* 11	45·00	25·00

ADEN PROTECTORATE STATES

KATHIRI STATE OF SEIYUN

The stamps of ADEN were used in Kathiri State of Seiyun from 22 May 1937 until 1942. A further office was opened at Tarim on 11 December 1940.

PRICES FOR STAMPS ON COVER TO 1945
Nos. 1/11 *from* × 10

1 Sultan of Seiyun

2 Seiyun

(Recess D.L.R.)

1942 (July–Oct). *Designs as T* **1/2**. *Wmk Mult Script CA. T* **1**, *perf* 14; *others, perf* 12 × 13 (*vert*) *or* 13 × 12 (*horiz*).

No.	Description	Unused	Used
1	½ a. blue-green	20	50
2	¾ a. brown	40	80
3	1 a. blue	70	50
4	1½ a. carmine	70	70
5	2 a. sepia	40	70
6	2½ a. blue	1·25	1·00
7	3 a. sepia and carmine	1·75	2·00
8	8 a. red	1·25	50
9	1 r. green	3·50	1·50
10	2 r. blue and purple	7·00	10·00
11	5 r. brown and green	22·00	16·00
1/11	*Set of* 11	35·00	30·00
1s/11s	Perf "Specimen" *Set of* 11	£140	

Designs:—½ to 1 a. Type **1**. *Vert as T* **2**—2 a. Tarim; 2½ a. Mosque, Seiyun; 1 r. South Gate, Tarim; 5 r. Mosque entrance, Tarim. *Horiz as T* **2**—3 a. Fortress, Tarim; 8 a. Mosque, Seiyun; 2 r. A Kathiri house.

VICTORY
ISSUE
8TH JUNE 1946
(10)

1946 (15 Oct). *Victory. No. 4 optd with T* **10**, *and No. 6 optd similarly but in four lines, by De La Rue.*

No.	Description	Unused	Used
12	1½ a. carmine	10	65
13	2½ a. blue (R.)	10	10
	a. Opt inverted	£450	
12s/13s	Perf "Specimen" *Set of* 2	55·00	

No. 13 is known with overprint double but the second impression is almost coincident with the first.

1949 (17 Jan). *Royal Silver Wedding. As Nos. 112/13 of Antigua.*

No.	Description	Unused	Used
14	1½ a. scarlet	30	2·00
15	5 r. green	14·00	9·00

1949 (10 Oct). *75th Anniv of U.P.U. As Nos. 114/17 of Antigua, surch with new values by Waterlow.*

No.	Description	Unused	Used
16	2½ a. on 20 c. ultramarine	15	50
17	3 a. on 30 c. carmine-red	1·00	65
18	8 a. on 50 c. orange	25	75
19	1 r. on 1 s. blue	30	90
16/19	*Set of* 4	1·50	2·50

5 CTS (11)   **50 CENTS** (12)   **5/-** (13)

1951 (1 Oct). *Currency changed. Nos. 3 and 5/11 surch as T* **11** (5 c.), **12** (10 c. ("CTS"), 15 c. ("CTS"), 20 c. and 50 c.) *or* **13** (1s. to 5s.), *by Waterlow.*

No.	Description	Unused	Used
20	5 c. on 1 a. blue (R.)	15	50
21	10 c. on 2 a. sepia	30	50
22	15 c. on 2½ a. blue	15	65

23 20 c. on 3 a. sepia and carmine .. .. 20 1·25
24 50 c. on 8 a. red 20 50
25 1 s. on 1 r. green .. .. 30 1·50
26 2 s. on 2 r. blue and purple .. .. .. 3·00 18·00
27 5 s. on 5 r. brown and green .. .. .. 18·00 32·00
20/27 .. .. *Set of* 8 20·00 50·00

QU'AITI STATE IN HADHRAMAUT

The stamps of ADEN were used in Qu'aiti State in Hadhramaut from 22 April 1937 until 1942. The main post office was at Mukalla. Other offices existed at Du'an (*opened* 1940), Gheil Ba Wazir (*opened* 1942), Haura (*opened* 1940), Shibam (*opened* 1940) and Shihr (*opened* 1939).

PRICES FOR STAMPS ON COVER TO 1945
Nos. 1/11 *from* × 6

I. ISSUES INSCR "SHIHR AND MUKALLA"

1 Sultan of Shihr and Mukalla

2 Mukalla Harbour

VICTORY
ISSUE
8TH JUNE
1946
(10)

(Recess D.L.R.)

1942 (July)–**46**. *Wmk Mult Script CA. Designs as* T **1** (½ *to* 1 *a.*) *or* T **2** (*others*). *P* 14 (½ *to* 1 *a.*), 12 × 13 (1½, 2, 3 *a. and* 1 *r.*) *or* 13 × 12 (*others*).
1 ½ a. blue-green 60 40
a. Olive-green (12.46) .. .. .. 24·00 35·00
2 ¾ a. brown .. .. 1·00 30
3 1 a. blue .. .. 1·00 1·00
4 1½ a. carmine .. .. 1·25 50
5 2 a. sepia .. .. 1·50 1·75
6 2½ a. blue 50 30
7 3 a. sepia and carmine 80 75
8 8 a. red 50 40
9 1 r. green .. .. 3·50 2·50
a. "A" of "CA" missing from wmk .. † —
10 2 r. blue and purple .. .. .. 11·00 8·00
11 5 r. brown and green .. .. .. 14·00 11·00
1/11 .. .. *Set of* 11 32·00 24·00
1s/11s Perf "Specimen" .. .. *Set of* 11 £140

Designs: *Vert*—2 a. Gateway of Shihr; 3 a. Outpost of Mukalla; 1 r. Du'an. *Horiz*—2½ a. Shibam; 8 a. 'Einat; 2 r. Mosque in Hureidha; 5 r. Meshhed.

1946 (15 Oct). *Victory. No.* 4 *optd. with* T **10** *and No.* 6 *optd similarly, but in three lines, by De La Rue.*
12 1½ a. carmine 10 65
13 2½ a. blue (R.) 10 10
12s/13s Perf "Specimen" .. .. *Set of* 2 55·00

1949 (17 Jan). *Royal Silver Wedding. As Nos.* 112/13 *of Antigua.*
14 1½ a. scarlet .. .. 50 3·00
15 5 r. green .. .. 15·00 9·00

1949 (10 Oct). *75th Anniv of U.P.U. As Nos.* 114/17 *of Antigua, surch with new values by Waterlow.*
16 2½ a. on 20 c. ultramarine 15 20
17 3 a. on 30 c. carmine-red .. .. 1·10 50
18 8 a. on 50 c. orange 25 60
19 1 r. on 1s. blue 30 50
a. Surch omitted £1400
16/19 .. .. *Set of* 4 1·60 1·60

1951 (1 Oct). *Currency changed. Surch with new values in cents or shillings as* T **11** (5 *c.*), **12** (10 *c.* ("CTS"), 15 *c.*, 20 *c. and* 50 *c.*) *or* **13** (1 *s. to* 5 *s.*) *of Seiyun, by Waterlow.*
20 5 c. on 1 a. blue (R.) 15 15
21 10 c. on 2 a. sepia 15 15
22 15 c. on 2½ a. blue 15 15
23 20 c. on 3 a. sepia and carmine 30 50
a. Surch double, one albino £190
24 50 c. on 8 a. red 30 90
25 1 s. on 1 r. green .. .. .. 1·50 30
26 2 s. on 2 r. blue and purple .. .. 7·00 12·00
27 5 s. on 5 r. brown and green .. .. 10·00 16·00
20/27 .. .. *Set of* 8 17·00 27·00

Antigua

It is believed that the first postmaster for Antigua was appointed under Edward Dummer's scheme in 1706. After the failure of his service control of the overseas mails passed to the British G.P.O. Mail services before 1850 were somewhat haphazard, until St. John's was made a branch office of the British G.P.O. in 1850. A second office, at English Harbour, opened in 1857.

The stamps of Great Britain were used between May 1858 and the end of April 1860, when the island postal service became the responsibility of the local colonial authorities. In the interim period, between the take-over and the appearance of Antiguan stamps, the crowned-circle handstamps were again utilised and No. CC1 can be found used as late as 1869.

For illustrations of the handstamp and postmark types see BRITISH POST OFFICES ABROAD notes, following GREAT BRITAIN.

ST. JOHN'S

CROWNED-CIRCLE HANDSTAMPS

CC1 CC 1 ANTIGUA (St. John's) (9.3.1850) (R.)
Price on cover £600

Stamps of GREAT BRITAIN *cancelled* "A 02" *as Type* **2**.

1858 *to* **1860**.
Z1 1d. rose-red (1857), *perf* 14 .. .. £500
Z2 2d. blue (1855), *perf* 14 (Plate No. 6) £900
Z3 2d. blue (1858) (Plate Nos. 7, 8, 9) £600
Z4 4d. rose (1857) £500
Z5 6d. lilac (1856) £160
Z6 1s. green (1856) £1700

ENGLISH HARBOUR

CROWNED-CIRCLE HANDSTAMPS

CC2 CC 3 ENGLISH HARBOR (10.12.1857)
Price on cover £4750

Stamps of GREAT BRITAIN *cancelled* "A 18" *as Type* **2**.

1858 to **1860**.
Z7 2d. blue (1858) (Plate No. 7) £5000
Z8 4d. rose (1857) £5000
Z9 6d. lilac £2000
Z10 1s. green (1856) .. ..

PRICES FOR STAMPS ON COVER TO 1945

No. 1	*from* × 8
Nos. 2/4	†
Nos. 5/10	*from* × 15
Nos 13/14	*from* × 20
No. 15	*from* × 50
Nos. 16/18	*from* × 30
Nos. 19/23	*from* × 12
No. 24	*from* × 40
Nos. 25/30	*from* × 10
Nos. 31/51	*from* × 4
Nos. 52/4	*from* × 10
Nos. 55/61	*from* × 4
Nos. 62/80	*from* × 3
Nos. 81/90	*from* × 4
Nos. 91/4	*from* × 5
Nos. 95/7	*from* × 4
Nos. 98/109	*from* × 3

CROWN COLONY

1

3 (Die I)

(Eng C. Jeens after drawing by Edward Corbould. Recess P.B.)

1862 (Aug). *No wmk.* (*a*) *Rough perf* 14 *to* 16.
1 1 6d. blue-green £800 £500

(*b*) *P* 11 *to* 12½
2 1 6d. blue-green £5000

(*c*) *P* 14 *to* 16 × 11 *to* 12½
3 1 6d. blue-green £2750

(*d*) *P* 14 *to* 16 *compound with* 11 *to* 12½
4 1 6d. blue-green £3000

Nos. 2/4 may be trial perforations. They are not known used.

1863 (Jan)–**67**. *Wmk Small Star. W* w **2** (*sideways on* 6*d.*). *Rough perf* 14 *to* 16.
5 1 1d. rosy mauve .. .. £130 48·00
6 1d. dull rose (1864) .. .. £100 35·00
a. Imperf between (vert pair) £17000
7 1d. vermilion (1867) .. .. £160 22·00
a. Imperf between (horiz pair) £17000
b. Wmk sideways .. .. £200 38·00
8 6d. green (*shades*) .. .. £450 22·00
a. Wmk upright .. .. — 85·00
9 6d. dark green .. .. £475 22·00
10 6d. yellow-green .. .. £3000 75·00

Caution is needed in buying No. 10 as some of the shades of No. 8 verge on yellow-green.

The 1d. rosy mauve exists showing trial perforations of 11 to 12½ and 14 to 16.

(Recess D.L.R. from P.B. plates)

1872. *Wmk Crown CC. P* 12½.
13 1 1d. lake £130 1
w. Wmk inverted .. .. ..
x. Wmk reversed £130 1
y. Wmk inverted and reversed .. ..
14 1d. scarlet £160 1
w. Wmk inverted £200 5
x. Wmk reversed .. .. ..
15 6d. blue-green £500
w. Wmk inverted .. .. .. — 6
x. Wmk reversed £500 1
y. Wmk inverted and reversed .. ..

1876. *Wmk Crown CC. P* 14.
16 1 1d. lake £130
a. Bisected (½d.) (1883) (on cover) .. † £3
x. Wmk reversed .. .. ..
17 1d. lake-rose £130
w. Wmk inverted £170 60
x. Wmk reversed .. .. ..
y. Wmk inverted and reversed .. ..
18 6d. blue-green £325 13
w. Wmk inverted .. .. .. † 80
x. Wmk reversed £325 14
y. Wmk inverted and reversed .. .. — 55

(Recess (T **1**); typo (T **3**) De La Rue & Co)

1879. *Wmk Crown CC. P* 14.
19 3 2½d. red-brown £600 £1
a. Large "2" in "2½" with slanting foot £8000 £2
20 4d. blue £250 14

Top left triangle detached
(Pl 2 R. 3/3 of right pane)

1882. *Wmk Crown CA. P* 14.
21 3 ½d. dull green .. .. 2·50 12·
a. Top left triangle detached £160
22 2½d. red-brown .. .. £160 55·
a. Large "2" in "2½" with slanting foot £2750 £11
23 4d. blue .. .. £275 15·
a. Top left triangle detached .. .. — £4

1884. *Wmk Crown CA. P* 12.
24 1 1d. carmine-red .. .. 50·00 15·
w. Wmk inverted .. .. ..
y. Wmk inverted and reversed .. ..

The 1d. scarlet is a colour changeling.

1884–86. *Wmk Crown CA. P* 14.
25 1 1d. carmine-red .. .. .. 1·75 2·
x. Wmk reversed .. .. .. — 20·
y. Wmk inverted and reversed ..
26 1d. rose .. .. 55·00 12·
27 3 2½d. ultramarine (1886) .. .. 6·00 11·
a. Large "2" in "2½" with slanting foot £160 £25
b. Top left triangle detached £325
s. Optd "Specimen" .. .. .. 45·00
28 4d. chestnut (1886) .. .. .. 2·00 2·
a. Top left triangle detached £160
s. Optd "Specimen" .. .. .. 45·00
29 1 6d. deep green .. .. 60·00 £12
30 3 1s. mauve (1886) £160 £13
a. Top left triangle detached £900
s. Optd "Specimen" .. .. .. 70·00

Nos. 25 and 26 postmarked "A 12" in place of "A 02" were used i St. Christopher.

2½ 2½ 2½
A B C

The variety "Large '2' in '2½' with slanting foot" occurs on th first stamp of the seventh row in both left (A) and right (B) panes (i which positions the "NN" of "PENNY" have three vertical stroke shortened) and on the first stamp of the third row of the right-han pane (C). The "2" varies slightly in each position.

From 31 October 1890 until July 1903 Leeward Islands general issues were used. Subsequently both general issues and the following separate issues were in concurrent use until July 1956, when the general Leewards Island stamps were withdrawn.

PRICES OF SETS

Set prices are given for many issues, generally those containing three stamps or more. Definitive sets include one of each value or major colour change, but do not cover different perforations, die types or minor shades. Where a choice is possible the set prices are based on the cheapest versions of the stamps included in the listings.

4 5

(Typo D.L.R.)

(July)–09. *Wmk Crown CC. Ordinary paper. P 14.*
4 ½d. grey-black and grey-green . . . . 3·75 6·50
1d. grey-black and rose-red . . . . 6·50 1·25
a. Bluish paper (1909) . . . . 95·00 95·00
2d. dull purple and brown . . . . 7·50 24·00
2½d. grey-black and blue . . . . 9·00 15·00
a. Chalk-surfaced paper (1907) . . 22·00 50·00
3d. grey-green and orange-brown . . 11·00 20·00
6d. purple and black . . . . . . 32·00 48·00
w. Wmk inverted £110
1s. blue and dull purple . . . . 45·00 55·00
a. Chalk-surfaced paper (1907) . . 50·00 95·00
2s. grey-green and pale violet . . . . 75·00 90·00
2s. 6d. grey-black and purple . . . . 18·00 55·00
5 5s. grey-green and violet . . . . 70·00 95·00
a. Chalk-surfaced paper (1907) . . 90·00 £120
. . . . *Set of* 10 £250 £350
0s Optd "Specimen" . . *Set of* 10 £150

–17. *Wmk Mult Crown CA. Chalk-surfaced paper (2d., . to 2s.). P 14.*
4 ½d. green . . . . 2·75 4·50
s. Optd "Specimen" . . . . 18·00
w. Wmk inverted . . . . . .
½d. blue-green (1917) . . . . . . 3·75 6·50
1d. red (1909) . . . . 6·00 2·25
s. Optd "Specimen" . . . . 30·00
1d. scarlet (5.8.15) . . . . . . 7·00 3·25
2d. dull purple and brown (1912) . . 4·75 28·00
2½d. ultramarine . . . . . . 12·00 15·00
a. Blue . . . . 17·00 21·00
s. Optd "Specimen" . . . . 25·00
3d. grey-green and orange-brown (1912) 6·50 19·00
6d. purple and black (1911) . . . . 7·50 40·00
1s. blue and dull purple . . . . 15·00 70·00
2s. grey-green and violet (1912) . . 75·00 85·00
0 . . . . *Set of* 8 £110 £225

3. *As T 5, but portrait of King George V. Wmk Mult Crown A. Chalk-surfaced paper. P 14.*
5s. grey-green and violet . . . . . . 70·00 £110
s. Optd "Specimen" . . . . . . 60·00

WAR STAMP

(7)

8

6 (Sept)–17. *No. 41 optd in London with T 7.*
4 ½d. green (Bk.) . . . . 1·25 2·50
½d. green (R.) (1.10.17) . . . . . . 1·50 2·50

8 (July). *Optd with T 7. Wmk Mult Crown CA. P 14.*
4 1½d. orange . . . . 1·00 1·25
/4s Optd "Specimen" . . *Set of* 3 70·00

(Typo D.L.R.)

1–29. *P 14. (a) Wmk Mult Crown CA. Chalk-surfaced aper.*
8 3d. purple/*pale yellow* . . . . 4·50 11·00
4d. grey-black and red/*pale yellow* (1922) 2·25 5·50
1s. black/*emerald* . . . . . . 4·25 9·00
y. Wmk inverted and reversed . . £190
2s. purple and blue/*blue* . . . . 13·00 19·00
2s. 6d. black and red/*blue* . . . . 17·00 50·00
5s. green and red/*pale yellow* (1922) . . 8·50 50·00
£1 purple and black/*red* (1922) £170 £275
61 . . . . *Set of* 7 £190 £375
/61s Optd "Specimen" . . *Set of* 7 £170

b) Wmk Mult Script CA. Chalk-surfaced paper (3d. to 4s.).
8 ½d. dull green . . . . 2·25 50
1d. carmine-red . . . . 2·00 50
1d. bright violet (1923) . . . . . . 3·50 1·50
a. Mauve . . . . 10·00 7·00
1d. bright scarlet (1929) . . . . 16·00 3·25
1½d. dull orange (1922) . . . . . . 3·00 7·00
1½d. carmine-red (1926) . . . . . . 4·25 1·75
1½d. pale red-brown (1929) . . . . 3·00 60
2d. grey (1922) . . . . 2·50 75
a. Wmk sideways . . . . . .
2½d. bright blue (1922) . . . . . . 6·50 17·00
2½d. orange-yellow (1923) . . . . 2·50 17·00
2½d. ultramarine (1927) . . . . . . 4·25 5·50
3d. purple/*pale yellow* (1925) . . . . 4·50 8·50
6d. dull and bright purple (1922) . . 3·25 6·50
1s. black/*emerald* (1929) . . . . 6·00 8·00
2s. purple and blue/*blue* (1927) . . 10·00 55·00
2s. 6d. black and red/*blue* (1927) . . 24·00 28·00
3s. green and violet (1922) . . . . 28·00 90·00
4s. grey-black and red (1922) . . . . 48·00 65·00
/80 . . . . *Set of* 16 £130 £275
s/80s Optd or Perf (Nos. 65, 69, 76) "Specimen" *Set of* 18 £325

9 Old Dockyard, English Harbour

10 Government House, St. John's

(Des Mrs. J. Goodwin (5s.), Waterlow (others). Recess Waterlow)

1932 (27 Jan). *Tercentenary. T* **9/10** *and similar designs. Wmk Mult Script CA. P 12½.*
81 **9** ½d. green . . . . 2·75 7·00
82 1d. scarlet . . . . 3·25 6·50
83 1½d. brown . . . . 3·25 4·75
84 **10** 2d. grey . . . . 4·25 17·00
85 2½d. deep blue . . . . . . 4·25 8·50
86 3d. orange . . . . 4·25 12·00
87 – 6d. violet . . . . 15·00 12·00
88 – 1s. olive-green . . . . . . 19·00 27·00
89 – 2s. 6d. claret . . . . . . 40·00 55·00
90 – 5s. black and chocolate . . . . 85·00 £110
81/90 . . . . . . *Set of* 10 £160 £225
81s/90s Perf "Specimen" . . *Set of* 10 £200

Designs: *Horiz*—6d., 1s., 2s. 6d. Nelson's *Victory. Vert*—5s. Sir Thomas Warner's *Concepcion*.

Examples of all values are known showing a forged St. Johns postmark dated "MY 18 1932".

13 Windsor Castle

(Des H. Fleury. Recess D.L.R.)

1935 (6 May). *Silver Jubilee. Wmk Mult Script CA. P 13½ × 14.*
91 **13** 1d. deep blue and carmine . . . . 2·00 2·50
f. Diagonal line by turret . . . . 55·00
92 1½d. ultramarine and grey . . . . 2·75 55
93 2½d. brown and deep blue . . . . 6·50 1·25
g. Dot to left of chapel £140
94 1s. slate and purple . . . . 8·50 12·00
h. Dot by flagstaff £180
91/4 . . . . . . *Set of* 4 18·00 14·00
91s/4s Perf "Specimen" . . *Set of* 4 70·00

For illustrations of plate varieties see Omnibus section following Zanzibar.

14 King George VI and Queen Elizabeth

(Des D.L.R.. Recess B.W.)

1937 (12 May). *Coronation. Wmk Mult Script CA. P 11×11½.*
95 **14** 1d. carmine . . . . 50 1·00
96 1½d. yellow-brown . . . . . . 60 1·00
97 2½d. blue . . . . 1·25 1·75
95/7 . . . . . . *Set of* 3 2·10 3·25
95s/7s Perf "Specimen" . . *Set of* 3 50·00

15 English Harbour

16 Nelson's Dockyard

(Recess Waterlow)

1938 (15 Nov)–**51**. *T* **15, 16** *and similar designs. Wmk Mult Script CA. P 12½.*
98 **15** ½d. green . . . . 40 1·25
99 **16** 1d. scarlet . . . . 2·75 2·00
a. Red (8.42 and 11.47) . . . . 4·00 2·50
100 1½d. chocolate-brown . . . . 6·00 1·00
a. Dull reddish brown (12.43) . . 2·25 1·75
b. Lake-brown (7.49) . . . . 28·00 13·00
101 **15** 2d. grey 50 50
a. Slate-grey (6.51) . . . . 7·50 5·00
102 **16** 2½d. deep ultramarine 80 80
103 – 3d. orange . . . . 75 1·00
104 – 6d. violet . . . . 2·75 1·25
105 – 1s. black and brown . . . . 3·25 1·50
a. Black and red-brown (7.49) . . 32·00 11·00
ab. Frame ptd double, once albino . . £3250
106 – 2s. 6d. brown-purple . . . . 45·00 9·00
a. Maroon (8.42) . . . . 22·00 9·00
107 – 5s. olive-green . . . . . . 14·00 7·50
108 **16** 10s. magenta (1.4.48) . . . . 16·00 26·00
109 – £1 slate-green (1.4.48) . . . . 25·00 38·00
98/109 . . . . . . *Set of* 12 75·00 80·00
98s/109s Perf "Specimen" . . *Set of* 12 £180

Designs: *Horiz*—3d., 2s. 6d., £1 Fort James. *Vert*—6d., 1s., 5s. St. John's Harbour.

17 Houses of Parliament, London

(Des and recess D.L.R.)

1946 (1 Nov). *Victory. Wmk Mult Script CA. P 13½×14.*
110 **17** 1½d. brown 20 10
111 3d. red-orange 20 30
110s/11s Perf "Specimen" . . *Set of* 2 50·00

18 **19**
King George VI and Queen Elizabeth

(Des and photo Waterlow (T **18**). Design recess; name typo B.W. (T **19**))

1949 (3 Jan). *Royal Silver Wedding. Wmk Mult Script CA.*
112 **18** 2½d. ultramarine (*p* 14×15) . . . . 40 1·50
113 **19** 5s. grey-olive (*p* 11½×11) . . . . 8·50 7·00

20 Hermes, Globe and Forms of Transport

21 Hemispheres, Jet-powered Vickers Viking Airliner and Steamer

22 Hermes and Globe

23 U.P.U. Monument

(Recess Waterlow (T **20, 23**). Designs recess, name typo B.W. (T **21/2**))

1949 (10 Oct). *75th Anniv of Universal Postal Union. Wmk Mult Script CA.*
114 **20** 2½d. ultramarine (*p* 13½–14) 40 50
115 **21** 3d. orange (*p* 11 × 11½) . . . . 1·50 2·00
116 **22** 6d. purple (*p* 11 × 11½) . . . . 45 1·25
117 **23** 1s. red-brown (*p* 13½–14) 45 75
114/17 . . . . . . *Set of* 4 2·50 4·00

(New Currency. 100 cents = 1 West Indian, later Eastern Caribbean, dollar)

24 Arms of University

25 Princess Alice

(Recess Waterlow)

1951 (16 Feb). *Inauguration of B.W.I. University College. Wmk Mult Script CA. P 14×14½.*
118 **24** 3 c. black and brown 45 50
119 **25** 12 c. black and violet 65 80

BARBUDA

DEPENDENCY OF ANTIGUA

PRICES FOR STAMPS ON COVER TO 1945
Nos. 1/11 *from* × 5

BARBUDA

(1)

1922 (13 July). *Stamps of Leeward Islands optd with T* **1**. *All Die II. Chalk-surfaced paper (3d. to 5s.).*

(a) Wmk Mult Script CA

1	**11**	½d. deep green	1·50	8·50
2		1d. bright scarlet	1·25	8·50
		x. Wmk reversed	£500	
3	**10**	2d. slate-grey	1·50	7·00
		x. Wmk reversed	55·00	
4	**11**	2½d. bright blue	1·25	7·50
		w. Wmk inverted	25·00	75·00
5		6d. dull and bright purple	2·00	18·00
6	**10**	2s. purple and blue/*blue*	14·00	48·00
7		3s. bright green and violet	32·00	75·00
8		4s. black and red (R.)	40·00	75·00

(b) Wmk Mult Crown CA

9	**10**	3d. purple/*pale yellow*	1·75	12·00
10	**12**	1s. black/*emerald* (R.)	1·50	8·00
11		5s. green and red/*pale yellow*	65·00	£130
1/11		*Set of* 11	£130	£325
1s/11s Optd "Specimen"		*Set of* 11	£225	

Examples of all values are known showing a forged Barbuda postmark of "JU 1 23".

Stocks of the overprinted stamps were exhausted by October 1925 and issues of Antigua were then used in Barbuda until 1968.

Ascension

DEPENDENCY OF ST. HELENA

Ascension, first occupied in 1815, was retained as a Royal Navy establishment from 1816 until 20 October 1922 when it became a dependency of St. Helena by Letters Patent.

Under Post Office regulations of 1850 (ratings) and 1854 (officers) mail from men of the Royal Navy serving abroad had the postage prepaid in Great Britain stamps, supplies of which were issued to each ship. Great Britain stamps used on Ascension before 1860 may have been provided by the naval officer in charge of the postal service.

The British G.P.O. assumed responsibility for such matters in 1860, but failed to send any stamps to the island until January 1867.

Until about 1880 naval mail, which made up most early correspondence, did not have the stamps cancelled until arrival in England. The prices quoted for Nos. Z1/3 and Z6 are for examples on cover showing the Great Britain stamps cancelled on arrival and an Ascension postmark struck elsewhere on the front of the envelope.

The use of British stamps ceased in December 1922.

The following postmarks were used on Great Britain stamps from Ascension:

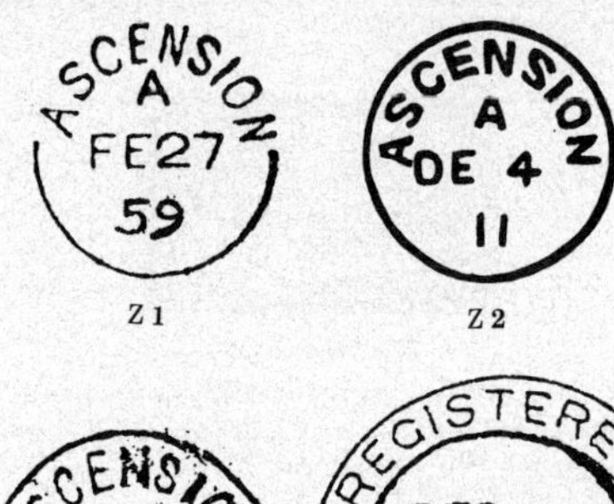

Z 1 Z 2

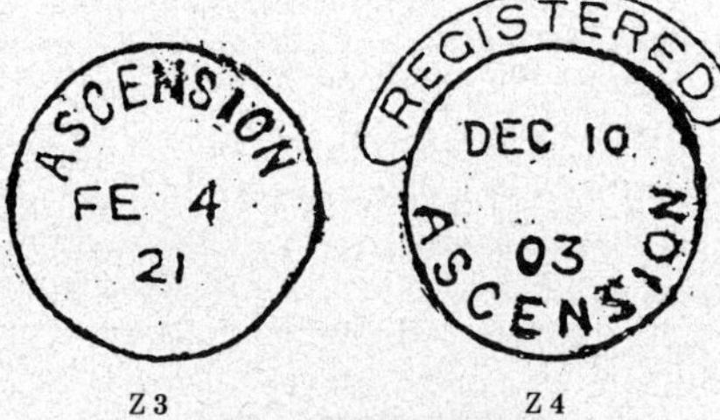

Z 3 Z 4

Z 5

Postmark Type	*Approx Period of Use*	*Diameter*	*Index Letter*
Z 1	1862	20 mm	A
Z 2	1864–1872	20 mm	A
	1872–1878	21½ mm	A
	1879–1889	19½ mm	A
	1891–1894	21½ mm	C
	1894–1902	22 mm	A
	1903–1907	20½ mm	A
	1908–1920	21 mm	A or none
	1909–1920	23 mm	C sideways (1909), none (1910–11), B (1911–20)
Z 3	1920–1922	24 mm	none
Z 4	1897–1903 Registered	23 mm	none
Z 5	1900–1902 Registered	28 mm	C
	1903–1904 Registered	29 mm	A

Postmark Type Z **1** appears in the G.P.O. proof book for 1858, but the first recorded use is 3 November 1862.

Forged postmarks exist. Those found most frequently are genuine postmarks of the post-1922 period with earlier date slugs fraudulently inserted, namely a 20 mm postmark as Type Z **2** (because of the shape of the "O" in "ASCENSION" this is often known as the Square O postmark) and a 24 mm postmark as Type Z **3** but with the index letter A.

Stamps of GREAT BRITAIN *cancelled with Types* Z **2/5**. *Prices quoted for Nos.* Z 1/6 *are for complete covers.*

Line-engraved issues.

Z 1 1d. red-brown (1855) .. £3750
Z 2 1d. rose-red (1864–79) .. *From* £1700
Plate Nos. 71, 74, 76, 78, 83, 85, 96, 100, 102, 103, 104, 122, 134, 168, 154, 155, 157, 160, 168, 178

Surface-printed issues (1856–1883).

Z 2*a* 6d. lilac (1856)
Z 3 6d. lilac (1865) (Plate No. 5) .. £3750
Z 4 1s. green (1865) (Plate No. 4)
Z 5 1s. green (1867) (Plate No. 7)
Z 6 6d. grey (1874) (Plate Nos. 15, 16) .. £3000
Z 6*a* 6d. on 6d. lilac (1883)
Z 7 1d. lilac (1881) (16 dots) .. 38·00

1887–92.

Z 8 ½d. vermilion .. 5
Z 9 1½d. purple and green
Z10 2d. green and carmine
Z11 2½d. purple/*blue* .. 5
Z12 3d. purple/*yellow*
Z13 4d. green and brown
Z14 4½d. green and carmine
Z15 5d. dull purple and blue
Z16 6d. purple/*rose-red*
Z17 9d. purple and blue
Z17*a* 10d. dull purple and carmine
Z18 1s. green

1900.

Z19 ½d. blue-green .. 5
Z20 1s. green and carmine

King Edward VII issues (1902–1911).

Z21 ½d. green .. 3
Z22 1d. red .. 1
Z23 1½d. purple and green .. £
Z24 2d. green and carmine .. 8
Z25 2½d. blue .. 8
Z26 3d. purple/*yellow* .. £
Z27 4d. green and brown .. £
Z28 4d. orange (1909) .. £
Z29 5d. purple and ultramarine .. £
Z30 6d. purple .. £
Z31 7d. grey-black (1910) .. £
Z32 9d. purple and ultramarine (1910) .. £
Z32*a* 10d. dull purple and scarlet .. £
Z33 1s. green and carmine .. 8
Z33*a* 2s. 6d. dull reddish purple (1911) .. £
Z34 5s. carmine .. £
Z35 10s. ultramarine .. £1
Z35*a* £1 green .. £2

1911–12. *T* **98/9** *of Great Britain.*

Z36 ½d. green (Die A) .. 7
Z37 ½d. yellow-green (Die B) .. 3
Z38 1d. scarlet (Die B) .. 4

1912. *T* **101/2** *of Great Britain.*

Z38*a* ½d. green .. 45
Z38*b* 1d. scarlet .. 45

1912–22.

Z39 ½d. green (1913) .. 32
Z40 1d. scarlet .. 1
Z41 1½d. red-brown .. 45
Z42 2d. orange (Die I) .. 40
Z42*a* 2d. orange (Die II) (1921) .. £
Z43 2½d. blue .. 50
Z44 3d. violet .. 70
Z45 4d. grey-green (1913) .. 90
Z46 5d. brown (1913) .. 90
Z47 6d. purple (1913) .. 80
Z47*a* 7d. green (1913) .. £
Z47*b* 8d. black/*yellow* (1913) .. £
Z48 9d. agate (1913) .. £
Z49 9d. olive-green (1922) .. £
Z50 10d. turquoise-blue (1913) .. £
Z51 1s. bistre (1913) .. £
Z52 2s. 6d. brown (1918) .. £
Z53 5s. rose-red (1919) .. £1

Supplies of some values do not appear to have been sent to the island and known examples originate from maritime or, in the case of high values, philatelic mail.

PRICES FOR STAMPS ON COVER TO 1945
Nos. 1/34 *from* × 5
Nos. 35/7 *from* × 10
Nos. 38/47 *from* × 6

ASCENSION

(1)

Line through "P" of "POSTAGE" (R. 3/6)

1922 (2 Nov). *Stamps of St. Helena, showing Government House or the Wharf, optd with T* **1** *by D.L.R.*

(a) Wmk Mult Script CA

1	½d. black and green	4·50	15·
	x. Wmk reversed	£450	
2	1d. green	4·50	14·
3	1½d. rose-scarlet	15·00	48·
4	2d. black and grey	15·00	13·
	a. Line through "P" of "POSTAGE"	£200	£2
5	3d. bright blue	13·00	17·
6	8d. black and dull purple	26·00	48·
7	2s. black and blue/*blue*	85·00	£1
8	3s. black and violet	£120	£1

(b) Wmk Mult Crown CA

9	1s. black/*green* (R.)	28·00	48·
1/9	*Set of* 9	£275	£4
1s/9s	*Set of* 9	£600	

Nos. 1, 4 and 6/8 are on special printings which were n issued without overprint.

Examples of all values are known showing a forged Ascensio postmark dated "MY 24 23".

PLATE FLAWS ON THE 1924–33 ISSUE. Many consta plate varieties exist on both the vignette and duty plates of th issue.

The three major varieties are illustrated and listed below.

This issue utilised the same vignette plate as the St. Heler 1922–36 set so that these flaws occur there also.

2 Badge of St. Helena

Broken mainmast. Occurs on R.2/1 of all values.

flag. Occurs on R.4/6 of all values except the 5d. Retouched on sheets of ½d. and 1d. printed after 1927.

Cleft rock. Occurs on R.5/1 of all values.

Broken scroll. Occurs on R. 1/4 of 1½d. only

(Typo D.L.R.)

4 (20 Aug)–**33**. *Wmk Mult Script CA. Chalk-surfaced aper. P* 14.

No.	Type	Description	Unused	Used
	2	½d. grey-black and black	3·50	13·00
		a. Broken mainmast	65·00	£110
		b. Torn flag	90·00	£140
		c. Cleft rock	55·00	£100
		1d. grey-black and deep blue-green	5·50	7·50
		a. Broken mainmast	75·00	£100
		b. Torn flag	90·00	£120
		c. Cleft rock	65·00	90·00
d		1d. grey-black & brt blue-green (1933)	85·00	£400
		da. Broken mainmast	£375	
		dc. Cleft rock	£350	
		1½d. rose-red	7·50	26·00
		a. Broken mainmast	80·00	£140
		b. Torn flag	80·00	£140
		c. Cleft rock	65·00	£120
		d. Broken scroll	90·00	£150
		2d. grey-black and grey	13·00	7·00
		a. Broken mainmast	95·00	£100
		b. Torn flag	£110	£120
		c. Cleft rock	85·00	90·00
		3d. blue	8·00	13·00
		a. Broken mainmast	85·00	£110
		b. Torn flag	85·00	£110
		c. Cleft rock	70·00	£100
		4d. grey-black and black/*yellow*	48·00	80·00
		a. Broken mainmast	£200	£300
		b. Torn flag	£200	£300
		c. Cleft rock	£170	£250
d		5d. purple and olive-green (8.27)	10·00	20·00
		da. Broken mainmast	£130	£190
		dc. Cleft rock	£110	£160
		6d. grey-black and bright purple	48·00	90·00
		a. Broken mainmast	£250	£350
		b. Torn flag	£250	£350
		c. Cleft rock	£200	£300
17	**2**	8d. grey-black and bright violet	15·00	42·00
		a. Broken mainmast	£130	£200
		b. Torn flag	£130	£200
		c. Cleft rock	£100	£170
18		1s. grey-black and brown	20·00	50·00
		a. Broken mainmast	£160	£225
		b. Torn flag	£160	£225
		c. Cleft rock	£140	£200
19		2s. grey-black and blue/*blue*	55·00	85·00
		a. Broken mainmast	£275	£375
		b. Torn flag	£275	£375
		c. Cleft rock	£225	£325
20		3s. grey-black and black/*blue*	80·00	90·00
		a. Broken mainmast	£400	£475
		b. Torn flag	£400	£475
		c. Cleft rock	£350	£425
10/20		*Set of* 12	£275	£450
10s/20s Optd "Specimen"		*Set of* 12	£500	

3 Georgetown

4 Ascension Island

(Des and recess D.L.R.)

1934 (2 July). *T* **3/4** *and similar designs. Wmk Mult Script CA. P* 14.

No.	Type	Description	Unused	Used
21	**3**	½d. black and violet	90	80
22	**4**	1d. black and emerald	1·75	1·25
23	–	1½d. black and scarlet	1·75	2·25
24	**4**	2d. black and orange	1·75	2·50
25	–	3d. black and ultramarine	1·75	1·50
26	–	5d. black and blue	2·25	3·25
27	**4**	8d. black and sepia	4·25	4·75
28	–	1s. black and carmine	18·00	6·50
29	**4**	2s. 6d. black and bright purple	45·00	32·00
30	–	5s. black and brown	45·00	55·00
21/30		*Set of* 10	£110	£100
21s/30s Perf "Specimen"		*Set of* 10	£275	

Designs: *Horiz*—1½d. The Pier; 3d. Long Beach; 5d. Three Sisters; 1s. Sooty Tern and Wideawake Fair; 5s. Green Mountain.

1935 (6 May). *Silver Jubilee. As Nos.* 91/4 *of Antigua, but ptd by Waterlow. P* 11 × 12.

No.	Description	Unused	Used
31	1½d. deep blue and scarlet	3·50	7·00
	l. Kite and horizontal log	£120	
32	2d. ultramarine and grey	11·00	23·00
	l. Kite and horizontal log	£250	
33	5d. green and indigo	17·00	24·00
	k. Kite and vertical log	£200	
	l. Kite and horizontal log	£325	
34	1s. slate and purple	23·00	27·00
	l. Kite and horizontal log	£375	
31/4	*Set of* 4	48·00	70·00
31s/4s Perf "Specimen"	*Set of* 4	£170	

For illustrations of plate varieties see Omnibus section following Zanzibar.

1937 (19 May). *Coronation. As Nos.* 95/7 *of Antigua, but printed by D.L.R. P* 14.

No.	Description	Unused	Used
35	1d. green	50	80
36	2d. orange	1·00	40
37	3d. bright blue	1·00	50
35/7	*Set of* 3	2·25	1·50
35s/7s Perf "Specimen"	*Set of* 3	£140	

10 The Pier

Long centre bar to "E" in "GEORGETOWN" (R. 2/3)

"Davit" flaw (R. 5/1) (all ptgs of 1½d. and 2s. 6d.)

(Recess D.L.R.)

1938 (12 May)–**53.** *Horiz designs as King George V issue, but modified and with portrait of King George VI as in T* **10**. *Wmk Mult Script CA. P* 13½.

No.	Type	Description	Unused	Used
38	**3**	½d. black and violet	3·50	1·25
		a. Long centre bar to E	£130	
		b. Perf 13. *Black and bluish violet* (17.5.44)	70	1·75
		ba. Long centre bar to E	55·00	
39	–	1d. black and green	40·00	8·00
39*a*	–	1d. black and yellow-orange (8.7.40)	14·00	9·00
		b. Perf 13 (5.42)	45	60
		c. Perf 14 (17.2.49)	70	16·00
39*d*	–	1d. black and green, *p* 13 (1.6.49)	60	50
40	**10**	1½d. black and vermilion	4·50	1·40
		a. Davit flaw	£200	
		b. Perf 13 (17.5.44)	85	80
		ba. Davit flaw	95·00	
		c. Perf 14 (17.2.49)	1·75	13·00
		ca. Davit flaw	£130	
40*d*		1½d. black and rose-carmine, *p* 14 (1.6.49)	55	80
		da. Davit flaw	90·00	
		db. *Black and carmine*	7·00	5·00
		dba. Davit flaw	£250	
		e. Perf 13 (25.2.53)	45	6·50
		ea. Davit flaw	85·00	
41	–	2d. black and red-orange	4·00	1·00
		a. Perf 13 (17.5.44)	80	40
		b. Perf 14 (17.2.49)	1·75	35·00
41*c*	–	2d. black and scarlet, *p* 14 (1.6.49)	1·00	85
42	–	3d. black and ultramarine	£100	27·00
42*a*	–	3d. black and grey (8.7.40)	18·00	90
		b. Perf 13 (17.5.44)	70	80
42*c*	–	4d. black and ultramarine (8.7.40)	16·00	3·25
		d. Perf 13 (17.5.44)	4·50	3·00
43	–	6d. black and blue	9·00	1·50
		a. Perf 13 (17.5.44)	9·00	5·00
44	**3**	1s. black and sepia	17·00	1·90
		a. Perf 13 (17.5.44)	4·75	2·00
45	**10**	2s. 6d. black and deep carmine	42·00	9·50
		a. Frame printed double, once albino	£3000	
		b. Davit flaw	£700	£300
		c. Perf 13 (17.5.44)	27·00	32·00
		ca. Davit flaw	£600	
46	–	5s. black and yellow-brown	95·00	8·50
		a. Perf 13 (17.5.44)	38·00	27·00
47	–	10s. black and bright purple	£110	42·00
		a. Perf 13 (17.5.44)	42·00	55·00
38/47a		*Set of* 16	£250	90·00
38s/47s Perf "Specimen"		*Set of* 13	£500	

Designs: *Horiz*—1d. (Nos. 39/c), 2d., 4d. Green Mountain; 1d. (No. 39*d*), 6d., 10s. Three Sisters; 3d., 5s. Long Beach.

1946 (21 Oct). *Victory. As Nos.* 110/11 *of Antigua.*

No.	Description	Unused	Used
48	2d. red-orange	40	50
49	4d. blue	40	30
48s/9s Perf "Specimen"	*Set of* 2	£150	

1948 (20 Oct). *Royal Silver Wedding. As Nos.* 112/13 *of Antigua.*

No.	Description	Unused	Used
50	3d. black	50	30
51	10s. bright purple	45·00	40·00

1949 (10 Oct). *75th Anniv of Universal Postal Union. As Nos.* 114/17 *of Antigua.*

No.	Description	Unused	Used
52	3d. carmine	1·00	1·25
53	4d. deep blue	3·50	1·25
54	6d. olive	2·00	2·75
55	1s. blue-black	2·00	1·50
52/5	*Set of* 4	7·50	6·00

Australia

The Australian colonies of New South Wales, Queensland, South Australia, Tasmania, Victoria and Western Australia produced their own issues before federation in 1901. Stamps inscribed for the individual states continued in use after federation until the end of December 1912.

INVERTED WATERMARKS. The stamp printers in the various Australian colonies paid little attention to the position of the watermark in the sheets they produced so that some entire printings had the watermark inverted, some 50% upright and 50% inverted while on others the inverted watermarks were restricted to odd sheets. In such circumstances it is impossible to provide adequate prices for such items so only those inverted watermarks occurring on stamps printed in Great Britain are included in the following listings.

NEW SOUTH WALES

PRICES FOR STAMPS ON COVER

Nos. 1/83	*from* × 2
Nos. 84/7	*from* × 3
No. 88	—
Nos. 89/96	*from* × 2
Nos. 97/8	—
Nos. 99/101	*from* × 2
Nos. 102/13	*from* × 3
No. 114	*from* × 10
Nos. 115/17	*from* × 2
Nos. 118/27	*from* × 3
Nos. 131/53	*from* × 2
Nos. 154/70	*from* × 3
Nos. 171/81	—
Nos. 186/202	*from* × 2
Nos. 203/6	*from* × 10
Nos. 207/21	*from* × 5
Nos. 222/37	*from* × 6
Nos. 238/42	—
Nos. 243/4	*from* × 6
Nos. 253/64	*from* × 10
Nos. 265/8	*from* × 15
Nos. 269/70	*from* × 2
Nos. 271/3	*from* × 10
Nos. 280/1	*from* × 2
Nos. 288/97	*from* × 10
Nos. 298/312	*from* × 12
Nos. 313/31	*from* × 10
No. 332	—
Nos. 333/49	*from* × 12
No. 350	—
Nos. 351/63	*from* × 12
No. O1	—
Nos. O2/12	*from* × 4
Nos. O13/18	—
Nos. O19/34	*from* × 20
Nos. O35/8	—
Nos. O39/47	*from* × 40
Nos. O48/53	—
Nos. O54/8	*from* × 20
No. O59	—
Nos. D1/7	*from* × 50
Nos. D8/10	—
Nos. D11/15	*from* × 50

EMBOSSED LETTER SHEETS AND ENVELOPES. From 1 November 1838 the Sydney G.P.O. supplied letter sheets pre-stamped with an albino embossing, as illustrated, at 1½d. each or 1s. 3d. per dozen. From January 1841 the price was reduced to 1s. per dozen. The public were also able to present their own stationery for embossing. The circular design measures approximately 29 mm in diameter, and examples are known on laid or wove paper of varying colours. Embossing continued until 1 May 1852 after which the Post Office refused to carry mail which was not franked with postage stamps. The die was used for reprints in 1870 and 1898 before it was destroyed later the same year.

PRINTERS. The early issues of New South Wales were printed on a press supervised by the Inspector of Stamps. On 1 January 1857 this responsibility passed to the Government printer who produced all subsequent issues, *unless otherwise stated.*

SPECIMEN OVERPRINTS. Those listed are from U.P.U. distributions between 1892 and 1903. Further "Specimen" overprints exist, but these were used for other purposes. From 1891 examples of some of these Specimens, together with cancelled stamps, were sold to collectors by the N.S.W. Post Office.

NEW SOUTH WALES USED IN NEW CALEDONIA. From October 1859 mail for Europe from New Caledonia was routed via Sydney and franked with New South Wales stamps in combination with local issues. Such N.S.W. stamps were cancelled on arrival in Sydney.

1

2

(Eng Robert Clayton, Sydney)

1850 (1 Jan). *T* **1.** *Plate I. No clouds.* (*a*) *Soft yellowish paper.*

1 1d. crimson-lake .. £4250 £450
2 1d. carmine .. £4000 £400
3 1d. reddish rose .. £3750 £375
4 1d. brownish red .. £4000 £400

(*b*) *Hard bluish paper*

5 1d. pale red .. £3750 £375
6 1d. dull lake .. £4000 £400

1850 (Aug). *T* **2.** *Plate I, re-engraved by H. C. Jervis, commonly termed Plate II. With clouds.* (*a*) *Hard toned white to yellowish paper.*

7 1d. vermilion .. £2500 £300
8 1d. dull carmine .. £2500 £300
a. No trees on hill (R.2/2) .. £4500 £475
b. Hill unshaded (R.2/3) .. £4500 £475
c. Without clouds (R.3/5) .. £4500 £475

(*b*) *Hard greyish or bluish paper*

9 1d. crimson-lake .. £2500 £300
10 1d. gooseberry-red .. £3000 £475
11 1d. dull carmine .. £2250 £275
12 1d. brownish red .. £2250 £275
a. No trees on hill (R.2/2) .. £4500 £475
b. Hill unshaded (R.2/3) .. £4500 £475
c. Without clouds (R.3/5) .. £4500 £475

(*c*) *Laid paper*

13 1d. carmine .. £4000 £475
14 1d. vermilion .. £4500 £450
a. No trees on hill (R.2/2) .. — £800
b. Hill unshaded (R.2/3) .. — £800
c. Without clouds (R.3/5) .. — £800

The varieties quoted with the letters "a", "b", "c" of course exist in each shade; the prices quoted are for the commonest shade, and the same applies to the following portions of this list.

Nos. 1/14 were printed in sheets of 25 (5×5).

LAID PAPER. Nos. 13/14, 34/5, 38 and 43*d*/*e* can be found showing parts of the papermaker's watermark (T. H. SAUNDERS 1847 in double-lined capitals and the figure of Britannia seated in an oval beneath a crown).

3

4

A (Pl I)

Illustrations A, B, C, and D are sketches of the lower part of the inner circular frame, showing the characteristic variations of each plate.

(Eng John Carmichael)

1850 (1 Jan). *Plate I. Vertical-lined background. T* **3.**

(*a*) *Early impressions, full details of clouds, etc.*

15 2d. greyish blue .. £4500 £400
16 2d. deep blue .. — £450
a. Double lines on bale (R.2/7) .. — £650

(*b*) *Intermediate impressions*

16*b* 2d. greyish blue .. £3000 £275
16*c* 2d. deep blue .. £3250 £325

(*c*) *Later impressions, clouds, etc., mostly gone, T* **4**

17 2d. greyish blue .. £2250 £150
18 2d. dull blue .. £1800 £140

(*d*) *Stamps in the lower row partially retouched* (end Jan)

19 2d. greyish blue .. £2750 £225
20 2d. dull blue .. £3000 £275

5

B (Pl II)

C (Pl III)

(Plate entirely re-engraved by H. C. Jervis)

1850 (Apr). *T* **5.** *Plate II. Horizontal-lined background. Bale on left side supporting the seated figure, dated. Dot in centre of the star in each corner.* (*a*) *Early impressions.*

21 2d. indigo .. £3500 £275
22 2d. lilac-blue .. — £1000
23 2d. grey-blue .. £3500 £225
24 2d. bright blue .. £3500 £225
a. Fan as in Pl III, but with shading outside (R. 1/1) .. — £375
b. Fan as in Pl III, but without shading, and inner circle intersects the fan (R. 1/2) .. — £375
c. Fan as B, but inner circle intersects fan (R. 1/3) .. — £375
d. No whip and inner circle intersects fan (R. 1/4) .. — £375
e. No whip (R. 1/8, 2/8) .. — £300
f. Pick and shovel omitted (R. 1/10) .. — £375
g. "CREVIT" omitted (R. 2/1) .. — £600

(*b*) *Worn impressions*

25 2d. dull blue .. £1800 £130
26 2d. Prussian blue .. £1900
a. Fan as in Pl III, but with shading outside (R. 1/1) .. —
b. Fan as in Pl III, but without shading, and inner circle intersects the fan (R. 1/2) .. —
c. Fan as B, but inner circle intersects fan (R. 1/3) .. —
d. No whip and inner circle intersects fan (R. 1/4) .. —
e. No whip (R. 1/8, 2/8) .. £2500
f. Pick and shovel omitted (R. 1/10) .. —
g. "CREVIT" omitted (R. 2/1) .. —

(*c*) *Bottom row retouched with dots and dashes in lower spandrels* (*from* July)

27 2d. Prussian blue .. £2750
28 2d. dull blue .. £2500
e. No whip (R. 2/8) .. —
g. "CREVIT" omitted (R. 2/1) .. —

(Plate re-engraved a second time by H.C. Jervis)

1850 (Sept). *Plate III. Bale not dated and single-lined, ex on No.* 30c *which is doubled-lined. No dots in stars.*

29 2d. ultramarine .. £2250
30 2d. deep blue .. £2250
a. No whip (R.2/3, 2/7) .. —
b. Fan with 6 segments (R. 2/8) .. —
c. Double lines on bale (R. 1/7, 1/10, 1/12) .. —

(Plate re-engraved a third time by H. C. Jervis)

1851 (Jan). *Plate IV. Double-lined bale, and circle in centre of star.* (*a*) *Hard bluish grey wove paper.*

31 2d. ultramarine .. £2750
32 2d. Prussian blue .. £2250
33 2d. bright blue .. £2500
a. Hill not shaded (R.1/12) .. —
b. Fan with 6 segments (R.2/8) .. —
c. No clouds (R.2/10) .. —
d. Retouch (R.2/1) .. —
e. No waves (R.1/9, 2/5) .. —

(*b*) *Stout yellowish vertically laid paper*

34 2d. ultramarine .. £3000
35 2d. Prussian blue .. £3250
a. Hill not shaded (R.1/12) .. —
b. Fan with 6 segments (R.2/8) .. —
c. No clouds (R.2/10) .. —
d. Retouch (R.2/1) .. —
e. No waves (R.1/9, 2/5) .. —
f. "PENOE" (R.1/10, 2/12) .. —

The retouch, Nos. 33d and 35d., occurs outside the left mar line on R.2/1.

6

D (Pl V)

7

(Plate re-engraved a fourth time by H. C. Jervis)

1851 (Apr). *T* **6.** *Plate V. Pearl in fan.* (*a*) *Hard greyish wove pap*

36 2d. ultramarine .. £2500
37 2d. dull blue .. £2500
a. Pick and shovel omitted (R.2/5) .. —
b. Fan with 6 segments (R.2/8) .. —

(*b*) *Stout yellowish vertically laid paper*

38 2d. dull ultramarine .. £3750
a. Pick and shovel omitted (R.2/5) .. —
b. Fan with 6 segments (R.2/8) .. —

Nos. 15/38 were printed in sheets of 24 (12×2), although existence of an inter-panneau *tête-bêche* pair from Plate indicates that the printer applied two impressions of the plate each sheet of paper. The two panes were normally separat before issue. The original plate I was re-cut four times to fo Plates II to V. An interesting variety occurs on R.1/9-11 and in all five plates. It consists of ten loops of the engine-turning each side of the design instead of the normal nine loops.

(Eng H. C. Jervis)

1850. *T* **7.** (*a*) *Soft yellowish wove paper.*

39 3d. yellow-green .. £3000
40 3d. myrtle-green .. £10000
41 3d. emerald-green .. £3500
a. No whip (R.4/3–4) .. —
b. "SIGIIIUM" for "SIGILLUM" (R.5/3) .. —

(*b*) *Bluish to grey wove paper*

42 3d. yellow-green .. £2500
43 3d. emerald-green .. £3000
b. No whip (R.4/3–4) .. —
c. "SIGIIIUM" for "SIGILLUM" (R.5/3) .. —

(*c*) *Yellowish to bluish laid paper*

43*d* 3d. bright green .. £5500
43*e* 3d. yellowish green .. £5000
f. No whip (R.4/3–4) .. —
g. "SIGIIIUM" for "SIGILLUM" (R.5/3) .. —

Nos. 39/43*e* were printed in sheets of 25 (5×5).

A used example of No. 42 is known printed double, one albin

8

9

(Des A. W. Manning from sketch by W. T. Levine; eng on steel John Carmichael, Sydney)

1851 (18 Dec)–**52.** *Imperf.* (*a*) *Thick yellowish paper*

44 **8** 1d. carmine .. £1800
a. No leaves right of "SOUTH" (R.1/7, 3/1) .. —
b. Two leaves right of "SOUTH" (R.2/5) .. —
c. "WALE" (R.1/9) .. —

(*b*) *Bluish medium wove paper* (1852)
1d. carmine £1000 £120
1d. scarlet £1000 £120
1d. vermilion £900 £100
1d. brick-red £900 £100
a. No leaves right of "SOUTH" (R.1/7, 3/1) — £225
b. Two leaves right of "SOUTH" (R.2/5) — £300
c. "WALE" (R.1/9) — £300

(*c*) *Thick vertically laid bluish paper* (1852?)
1d. orange-brown £3000 £350
1d. claret £3000 £375
a. No leaves right of "SOUTH" (R.1/7, 3/1) — £600
b. Two leaves right of "SOUTH" ((R.2/5) — £700
c. "WALE" (R.1/9) — £700

ɔs. 44/50 were printed in sheets of 50 (10×5).

ıg John Carmichael (Nos. 51/9), H. C. Jervis (Nos. 60/4))

(24 July)–**55.** *Imperf.* (*a*) *Plate I.* (i) *Thick yellowish wove* ɔer
2d. ultramarine £850 80·00

(ii) *Fine impressions, blue to greyish medium paper*
2d. ultramarine £750 30·00
2d. chalky blue £650 30·00
2d. dark blue £650 30·00
2d. greyish blue £650 30·00

(iii) *Worn plate, blue to greyish medium paper*
2d. ultramarine £450 30·00
2d. Prussian blue £450 30·00

(iv) *Worn plate, blue wove medium paper*
2d. ultramarine £350 30·00
2d. Prussian blue £325 30·00

(*b*) *Plate II. Stars in corners* (Oct 1853)

(i) *Bluish medium to thick wove paper*
2d. deep ultramarine £1000 £110
2d. indigo £1100 90·00
a. "WAEES" (R. 3/3) — £375

(ii) *Worn plate, hard blue wove paper*
2d. deep Prussian blue £1000 £100
a. "WAEES" (R. 3/3) — £375

Plate III, being Plate I (*T* **8**) *re-engraved by H. C. Jervis. Background of crossed lines* (Sept 1855)

(i) *Medium bluish wove paper*
– 2d. Prussian blue £475 55·00
a. "WALES" partly covered with wavy lines (R. 1/3) — £190

(ii) *Stout white wove paper*
– 2d. Prussian blue £475 55·00
a. "WALES" partly covered with wavy lines (R. 1/3) — £190

ɔs. 51/64 were printed in sheets of 50 (10×5).

(Eng John Carmichael)

2 (3 Dec). *Imperf.* (*a*) *Medium greyish blue wove paper*
8 3d. deep green £1600 £200
3d. green £1300 £140
3d. dull yellow-green £1200 £100
a. "WAEES" with centre bar of first "E" missing (R.4/7) — £350

(*b*) *Thick blue wove paper*
8 3d. emerald-green £1600 £200
3d. blue-green £1600 £200
a. "WAEES" with centre bar of first "E" missing (R.4/7) — £550

Ios. 65/71 were printed in sheets of 50 (10×5).

52 (Apr)–**53.** *Imperf.* (*a*) *Plate I*

(i) *Medium white wove paper*
8 6d. vandyke-brown — £900
a. "WALLS" (R. 2/3) — £1600

(ii) *Medium bluish grey wove paper*
8 6d. vandyke-brown £1700 £250
6d. yellow-brown £1800 £275
6d. chocolate-brown £1700 £250
6d. grey-brown £1600 £250
a. "WALLS" (R. 2/3) — £600

(*b*) *Plate I re-engraved by H. C. Jervis. Coarse background* (June 1853)
– 6d. brown £1800 £300
– 6d. grey-brown £1700 £300

Examples of the 6d. in vandyke-brown on thick yellowish ɔer are proofs.

Nos. 72/6 and 77/8 were printed in sheets of 25 (5×5).

(Eng H. C. Jervis)

53 (May). *Medium bluish paper. Imperf.*
8d. dull yellow £3500 £600
8d. orange-yellow £3500 £600
8d. orange £3750 £650
a. No bow at back of head (R.1/9) — £1300
b. No leaves right of "SOUTH" (R.3/1) — £1300
c. No lines in spandrel (R.2/2, 3/2, 4/2) — £800

Nos. 79/81 were issued in sheets of 50 (10×5).

10

OTE. All watermarked stamps from No. 82 to No. 172 have ɔuble-lined figures, as T **10**.

1854 (Jan–Mar). *Wmk "1", "2", or "3" as T* **10**, *to match face value. Yellowish wove paper. Imperf.*
82 **8** 1d. red-orange (Feb) £170 18·00
83 1d. orange-vermilion £170 18·00
a. No leaves right of "SOUTH" (R. 1/7, 3/1) £350 85·00
b. Two leaves right of "SOUTH" (R. 2/5) £475 £120
c. "WALE" (R. 1/9) £475 £120
84 – 2d. ultramarine (Pl III) (Jan) £110 11·00
85 – 2d. Prussian blue (Pl III) £110 11·00
86 – 2d. chalky blue (Pl III) £110 8·50
a. "WALES" partly covered by wavy lines (R. 1/3) £425 50·00
87 **8** 3d. yellow-green (Mar) £200 28·00
a. "WAEES" with centre bar of first "E" missing (R. 4/7) — £120
b. Error. Wmk "2" £3000 £1500

Nos. 82/7 were printed in sheets of 50 (10×5).

11 12 13 14

(6d. and 1s. des E. H. Corbould after sketches by T. W. Levinge. Printed by New South Wales Govt Ptg Dept from Perkins Bacon plates)

1854 (1 Feb)–**59.** *Wmk "5", "6",* **8** *or "12" to match face value. Imperf.*
88 **11** 5d. dull green (1.12.55) £1000 £600
89 **12** 6d. deep slate £500 35·00
a. Wmk sideways † £750
90 6d. greenish grey £400 35·00
91 6d. slate-green £400 35·00
a. Printed both sides
92 6d. bluish grey £450 55·00
93 6d. fawn £500 95·00
a. Wmk "8" (15.8.59) £1600 £110
94 6d. grey £450 55·00
95 6d. olive-grey £450 35·00
96 6d. greyish brown £450 35·00
a. Wmk "8" (15.8.59) £1600 £110
ab. Wmk sideways — £350
97 **13** 8d. golden yellow (1.12.55) £4000 £900
98 8d. dull yellow-orange £3500 £850
99 **14** 1s. rosy vermilion (2.54) £750 70·00
a. Wmk "8" (20.6.57) £2000 £180
100 1s. pale red £750 70·00
101 1s. brownish red £800 80·00

Nos. 93a, 96a and 99a come from printings made when supplies of the correct numeral watermarks were unavailable.

Plate proofs of the 6d. in red-brown and of the 1s. in deep blue on unwatermarked paper exist handstamped "CANCELLED" in oval of bars (see note on Perkins Bacon "CANCELLED" in Catalogue introduction) (*Price* £4250 *each*).

For further examples of Types **11/14** on different watermarks see Nos. 141/53, 160/70, 215, 218, 231/3, 236 and 329.

15

16

(Eng John Carmichael)

1856 (1 Jan)–**59.** *For Registered Letters. No wmk. Imperf.*

(*a*) *Soft medium yellowish paper*
102 **15** (6d.) vermilion and Prussian blue £750 £160
a. Frame printed on back £2750 £2000
103 (6d.) salmon and indigo £750 £180
104 (6d.) orange and Prussian blue £750 £225
105 (6d.) orange and indigo £750 £190

(*b*) *Hard medium bluish wove paper, with manufacturer's wmk in sans-serif, double-lined capitals across sheet and only showing portions of letters on a few stamps in a sheet*
106 **15** (6d.) orange and Prussian blue (4.59) £900 £170

For further examples of Type **15** on different watermarks see Nos. 119/27.

(Printed by New South Wales Govt Ptg Dept from plates engraved by Perkins, Bacon & Co)

1856 (7 Jan)–**60.** *Wmk "1", "2" or "3" to match face value. Imperf.* (*a*) *Recess*
107 **16** 1d. orange-vermilion (6.4.56) £150 22·00
a. Error. Wmk "2"
108 1d. carmine-vermilion £150 22·00
109 1d. orange-red £150 22·00
a. Printed on both sides £1400 £1400
110 2d. deep turquoise-blue (Pl I) £140 9·00
111 2d. ultramarine (Pl I) £130 9·00
112 2d. blue (Pl I) £130 9·00
a. Major retouch (1858) £1800 £450
b. Error. Wmk "1" — £4000
c. Wmk "5" (3.57) £450 60·00
d. Error. Wmk "8"
113 **16** 2d. pale blue (Pl I) £130 9·00
114 2d. blue (Pl II) (1.60) £500 50·00
115 3d. yellow-green (10.10.56) £800 80·00
116 3d. bluish green £850 85·00
117 3d. dull green £850 85·00
a. Error, Wmk "2" — £3000

(*b*) *Lithographic transfer of Plate I*
118 **16** 2d. pale blue (3.8.59) — £750
a. Retouched — £2500

For further examples of Type **16** on different watermarks see Nos. 131/40, 154/8, 171/2, 211/12, 226/8 and 327/8.

Two plates were used for the 2d. The 2d. Plate I was retouched, on a total of ten positions, several times as No. 112a. Stamps from Plate II are wider apart and are more regularly spaced. There is also a white patch between "A" of "WALES" and the back of the Queen's head.

On the 3d. the value is in block letters on a white background.

No. 112c comes from a printing made when supplies of the "2" paper were unavailable. Of the errors there are only two known of both Nos. 112b and 112d, all used. One example of each is in the Royal Collection.

The 1d. exists privately rouletted 10, a used pair of which is known postmarked 15 May 1861.

No. 114 was mainly used at post offices in Queensland.

STAMPS WITH STRAIGHT EDGES. Stamps between Nos. 119 and 243 can be found with one or two sides imperforate. These come from the outside rows which were not perforated between the stamps and the sheet margins.

1860 (Feb)–**63.** *For Registered Letters.* (*a*) *P* 12. (i) *Hard medium bluish wove paper with manufacturer's wmk in sans-serif, double-lined capitals across sheet, showing portions of letters on a few stamps.*
119 **15** (6d.) orange and Prussian blue £375 50·00
120 (6d.) orange and indigo £350 55·00

(ii) *Coarse, yellowish wove paper with manufacturer's wmk in Roman capitals* (Feb 1860)
121 **15** (6d.) rose-red and Prussian blue £275 38·00
122 (6d.) rose-red and indigo £350 85·00
123 (6d.) salmon and indigo

(*b*) *P* 13. (i) *Coarse, yellowish wove paper with manufacturer's wmk in Roman capitals* (1862)
124 **15** (6d.) rose-red and Prussian blue £275 55·00

(ii) *Yellowish wove paper. Wmk "6"* (May 1863)
125 **15** (6d.) rose-red and Prussian blue £100 18·00
126 (6d.) rose-red and indigo £160 25·00
127 (6d.) rose-red and pale blue 80·00 16·00
a. Double impression of frame — £500

1860 (14 Feb)–**72.** *Wmk double-lined figure of value.* (*a*) *P* 12
131 **16** 1d. orange-red £170 16·00
a. Imperf between (pair)
b. Double impression
132 1d. scarlet £100 16·00
133 2d. pale blue (Pl I) £500 £140
a. Retouched — £1300
134 2d. greenish blue (Pl II) 90·00 10·00
136 2d. Prussian blue (Pl II) 90·00 11·00
a. Error. Wmk "1" — £2750
b. Retouched (*shades*) — £400
137 2d. Prussian blue (Pl I) (3.61) £110 12·00
138 2d. dull blue (Pl I) £100 11·00
139 3d. yellow-green (1860) £1000 55·00
140 3d. blue-green £550 42·00
141 **11** 5d. dull green (1863) £150 48·00
142 5d. yellowish green (1863) £150 48·00
143 **12** 6d. grey-brown £275 45·00
144 6d. olive-brown £275 55·00
145 6d. greenish grey £350 45·00
146 6d. fawn £325 65·00
147 6d. mauve £300 35·00
148 6d. violet £275 16·00
a. Imperf between (pair)
149 **13** 8d. lemon-yellow — £1400
150 8d. orange £2250 £650
151 8d. red-orange £2250 £650
152 **14** 1s. brownish red £450 48·00
153 1s. rose-carmine £450 48·00
a. Imperf between (pair)

(*b*) *P* 13
154 **16** 1d. scarlet (1862) 65·00 9·00
155 1d. dull red 65·00 9·00
156 3d. blue-green (12.62) 48·00 11·00
157 3d. yellow-green 55·00 8·50
a. Wmk "6" (7.72) £100 12·00
158 3d. dull green 55·00 8·00
a. Wmk "6" (7.72) £100 15·00
160 **11** 5d. bluish green (12.63) 50·00 17·00
161 5d. bright yellow-green (8.65) 85·00 35·00
162 5d. sea-green (1866) 50·00 20·00
162*a* 5d. dark bluish green (11.70) 38·00 20·00
163 **12** 6d. reddish purple (Pl I) (7.62) 90·00 6·00
164 6d. mauve 90·00 6·00
165 6d. purple (Pl II) (1864) 60·00 4·75
a. Wmk "5" (7.66) £350 25·00
ab. Wmk "5" sideways † £1000
b. Wmk "12" (12.66 and 1868) £275 20·00
166 6d. violet 60·00 6·50
a. Wmk "5" (7.66) — 30·00
167 6d. aniline mauve £900 £120
167*a* **13** 8d. red-orange (1862) £150 55·00
167*b* 8d. yellow-orange £170 40·00
167*c* 8d. bright yellow £150 40·00
168 **14** 1s. rose-carmine (1862) 90·00 7·50
169 1s. carmine 85·00 8·00
170 1s. crimson-lake 80·00 8·00

(*c*) *Perf compound* 12×13
171 **16** 1d. scarlet (1862) — £1700
172 2d. dull blue (1.62) £2000 £180

No. 133 was made by perforating a small remaining stock of No. 113. Nos. 137/8 were printed from the original plate after its return from London, where it had been repaired.

Nos. 157a, 158a and 165a/b come from printings made when supplies of paper with the correct face value were unavailable.

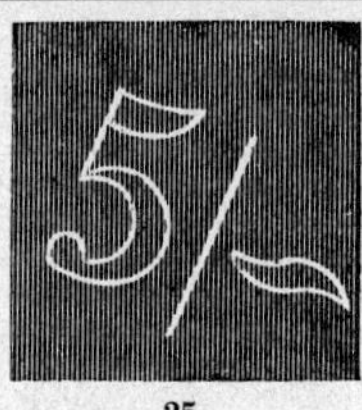

24 25

(Des E. H. Corbould, R.I.)

1861–88. *W* **25.** *Various perfs.*

No.	Type	Description	Unused	Used
174	**24**	5s. dull violet, *p* 12 (1861)	£1000	£325
		a. Perf 13 (1861)	£170	29·00
175		5s. royal purple, *p* 13 (1872)	£300	48·00
176		5s. deep rose-lilac, *p* 13 (1875)	£100	29·00
177		5s. deep purple, *p* 13 (1880)	£160	42·00
		a. Perf 10 (1882)	£160	48·00
178		5s. rose-lilac, *p* 10 (1883)	£120	42·00
179		5s. purple, *p* 12 (1885)	—	48·00
		a. Perf 10 × 12 (1885)	—	£130
180		5s. reddish purple, *p* 10 (1886)	£120	42·00
		a. Perf 12 × 10 (1887)	£250	48·00
181		5s. rose-lilac, *p* 11 (1888)	—	£130

This value was replaced by Nos. 261, etc. in 1888 but reissued in 1897, *see* Nos. 297*c*/*e*.

26 27 28

(Printed by De La Rue & Co, Ltd, London and perf at Somerset House, London)

1862–65. *Surfaced paper. P* 14. (i) *W* **27**

No.	Type	Description	Unused	Used
186	**26**	1d. dull red (Pl I) (1.4.64)	90·00	40·00
		(ii) *No wmk*		
187	**26**	1d. dull red (Pl II) (1.65)	75·00	35·00
188	**28**	2d. pale blue (25.3.62)	80·00	38·00

(Printed from the De La Rue plates in the Colony)

1862 (12 Apr–Sept). *Wmk double-lined* "**2**" (*No.* 189) *or* "**5**" (*No.* 190). *P* 13.

No.	Type	Description	Unused	Used
189	**28**	2d. blue	55·00	7·50
		a. Perf 12	£130	32·00
		b. Perf 12×13	£400	
190		2d. dull blue (9.62)	60·00	10·00

29

1863–69. *W* **29.** *P* 13.

No.	Type	Description	Unused	Used
191	**26**	1d. pale red (3.69)	95·00	14·00
192	**28**	2d. pale blue (4.63)	13·00	70
		a. Perf 12		
193		2d. cobalt-blue	13·00	70
194		2d. Prussian blue	24·00	3·75

1864–65. *W* **27.** *P* 13.

No.	Type	Description	Unused	Used
195	**16**	1d. pale red (6.64)	42·00	15·00
196	**26**	1d. dark red-brown (Pl I)	95·00	17·00
197		1d. brownish red (Pl II)	23·00	2·00
		a. Imperf between (horiz pair)	†	£550
198		1d. brick-red (Pl II)	23·00	2·00
		a. Highly surfaced paper (1865)	£200	
199	**28**	2d. pale blue	£130	3·75

Plates I and II were made from the same die; they can only be distinguished by the colour or by the marginal inscription.

1865–66. *Thin wove paper. No wmk. P* 13.

No.	Type	Description	Unused	Used
200	**26**	1d. brick-red	£100	18·00
201		1d. brownish red	£100	18·00
202	**28**	2d. pale blue (11.65)	60·00	3·25

32 34

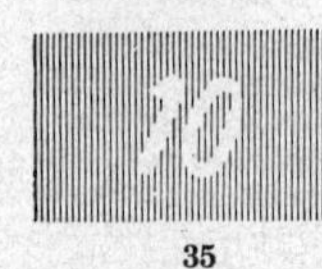

33 35

1867 (Sept)–**93.** *W* **33** *and* **35.**

No.	Type	Description	Unused	Used
203	**32**	4d. red-brown, *p* 13	48·00	3·50
204		4d. pale red-brown, *p* 13	48·00	3·50
205	**34**	10d. lilac, *p* 13	13·00	3·50
		a. Imperf between (horiz pair)	£550	
		s. Optd "Specimen"	25·00	
206		10d. lilac, *p* 11 (1893)	13·00	3·50
		a. Perf 10	15·00	4·75
		b. Perf 10×11 or 11×10	20·00	7·50
		c. Perf 12×11	£110	15·00

36 37 38

NINEPENCE

(39)

From 1871 to 1903 the 9d. is formed from the 10d. by a *black* surch. (T **39**), 15 mm long on Nos. 219 to 220h, and 13½ mm long on subsequent issues.

1871–1902. *W* **36.**

No.	Type	Description	Unused	Used
207	**26**	1d. dull red, *p* 13 (8.71)	7·00	50
		a. Imperf vert (horiz pair)	†	£650
208		1d. salmon, *p* 13 (1878)	7·00	50
		a. Perf 10 (6.80)	£250	30·00
		b. Perf 10×13 (6.80)	50·00	5·00
		ba. Perf 13×10	18·00	50
		c. *Scarlet.* Perf 10 (4.82)	—	£180
209	**28**	2d. Prussian-blue, *p* 13 (11.71)	8·50	50
		a. Perf 11×12, comb (11.84)	£250	40·00
		b. Imperf between (vert pair)	†	—
210		2d. pale blue, *p* 13 (1876)	8·50	50
		a. Perf 10 (6.80)	£250	22·00
		b. Perf 10×13 (6.80)	£100	15·00
		ba. Perf 13×10	8·50	50
		c. Surfaced paper. Perf 13		
211	**16**	3d. yellow-green, *p* 13 (3.74)	20·00	2·75
		a. Perf 10 (6.80)	65·00	6·00
		b. Perf 11 (1902)	£150	£100
		c. Perf 12 (5.85)	—	£150
		d. Perf 10×12 or 12×10 (5.85)	£150	32·00
		e. Perf 11×12 (1902)	£120	32·00
212		3d. bright green, *p* 10 (6.80)	£120	12·00
		a. Perf 13×10 (6.80)	£110	16·00
		b. Perf 13		
213	**32**	4d. pale red-brown, *p* 13 (8.77)	60·00	7·00
214		4d. red-brown, *p* 13	60·00	7·00
		a. Perf 10 (6.80)	£180	50·00
		b. Perf 10×13 (6.80)	£100	20·00
		ba. Perf 13×10	75·00	4·25
215	**11**	5d. bluish green, *p* 10 (8.84)	17·00	10·00
		a. Perf 12 (5.85)	£250	£100
		b. Perf 10×13 or 13×10		
		c. Perf 10×12 (5.85)	£120	42·00
		ca. Perf 12×10	30·00	12·00
216	**37**	6d. bright mauve, *p* 13 (1.1.72)	45·00	1·25
		a. Imperf between (horiz pair)	†	£600
217		6d. pale lilac, *p* 13 (1878)	48·00	1·25
		a. Perf 10 (6.80)	£180	12·00
		b. Perf 10×13 (6.80)	80·00	15·00
		ba. Perf 13×10	55·00	1·25
		c. Imperf between (horiz pair). Perf 13×10	†	£600
218	**13**	8d. yellow, *p* 13 (3.77)	£110	17·00
		a. Perf 10 (6.80)	£275	26·00
		b. Perf 13×10 (6.80)	£180	24·00
219	**34**	9d. on 10d. pale red-brown, *p* 13 (8.71)	24·00	4·50
220		9d. on 10d. red-brown, *p* 13 (1878)	24·00	6·00
		a. Perf 10 (6.80)	12·00	4·75
		b. Perf 12 (5.85)	12·00	4·75
		c. Perf 11 (12.85)	29·00	7·00
		ca. Surch in both black and blue (12.85)	£110	
		d. Perf 12×10 (5.85)	£250	£160
		e. Perf 10×11 or 11×10 (12.85)	48·00	10·00
		f. Perf 12×11 (12.85)	14·00	5·00
		g. Perf 12×11, comb (1.84)	14·00	5·50
		gs. Optd "Specimen"	25·00	
221	**38**	1s. black, *p* 13 (1.4.76)	80·00	3·25
		a. Perf 10 (6.80)	£200	12·00
		b. Perf 10×13 (6.80)	£240	17·00
		ba. Perf 13×10	£170	6·00
		c. Perf 11		
		d. Imperf between (vert pair)	†	£750

Collectors should note that the classification of perforations is that adopted by the Royal Philatelic Society, London. "Perf 12" denotes the perforation formerly called "11½, 12" and "perf 13" that formerly called "12½, 13".

BISECTS. Between 1887 and 1913 various 1d. and 2d. stamps can be found vertically or diagonally bisected. This was unauthorised.

40

1882 (Apr)–**97.** *W* **40.**

No.	Type	Description	Unused	Used
222	**26**	1d. salmon, *p* 10	14·00	
		a. Perf 13		
		b. Perf 10×13		
		ba. Perf 13×10	35·00	
223		1d. orange *to* scarlet, *p* 13	£800	£
		a. Perf 10	8·00	
		ab. Imperf between (horiz pair)		
		b. Perf 10×13	£120	6
		c. Perf 10×12 or 12×10 (4.85)	£250	65
		d. Perf 11×10 (12.85)	£450	£
		e. Perf 12×11 (12.85)	—	£
		f. Perf 11×12, comb (1.84)	5·50	
		h. Perf 11 (12.85)	—	£
224	**28**	2d. pale blue, *p* 13	£450	90
		a. Perf 10	17·00	
		b. Perf 10×13	65·00	2
		ba. Perf 13×10		
225		2d. Prussian blue, *p* 10	25·00	
		b. Perf 12 (4.85)	—	£
		c. Perf 11 (12.85)	—	£
		d. Perf 12×11 (12.85)	£400	£
		e. Perf 10×12 (4.85)	£225	65
		ea. Perf 12×10	£400	£
		f. Perf 10×11 or 11×10 (12.85)	£450	£
		g. Perf 11×12, comb (1.84)	12·00	
		ga. Printed double	†	£
226	**16**	3d. yellow-green, *p* 10 (1886)	7·50	
		a. Double impression	†	
		b. Wmk sideways		
		bs. Optd "Specimen"	25·00	
		c. Perf 10×12	£160	32
		ca. Perf 12×10	£120	15
		d. Perf 11	5·50	1
		da. Imperf vert (horiz pair)	£170	
		e. Perf 11×12 or 12×11	5·50	
		f. Perf 12	9·00	1
		g. Imperf (pair)	£130	
227		3d. bluish green, *p* 10	6·00	
		a. Wmk sideways	50·00	10
		b. Perf 11	6·00	1
		c. Perf 10×11	15·00	1
		ca. Perf 11×10	£100	32
		d. Perf 11×12 or 12×11	5·50	1
		e. Perf 10×12 or 12×10	30·00	3
228		3d. emerald-green, *p* 10 (1893)	55·00	7
		a. Wmk sideways	—	15
		b. Perf 10×11	55·00	3
		ba. Perf 11×10	£120	35
		c. Perf 10×12	50·00	3
		ca. Perf 12×10	75·00	5
		d. Perf 12×11	—	10
229	**32**	4d. red-brown, *p* 10	48·00	3
		a. Perf 10×12 (4.85)	—	£1
		b. Perf 11×12, comb (1.84)	50·00	1
230		4d. dark brown, *p* 10	48·00	3
		a. Perf 12 (4.85)	£250	£1
		b. Perf 10×12 (4.85)	£200	60
		ba. Perf 12×10	£300	£1
		c. Perf 11×12, comb (1.84)	30·00	1
231	**11**	5d. dull green, *p* 10 (1890)	15·00	1
		as. Optd. "Specimen"	25·00	
		b. Perf 11×10	50·00	
		c. Perf 12×10 (4.85)	80·00	3
232		5d. bright green, *p* 10	40·00	4
		b. Perf 10×11 (12.85)	48·00	4
		ba. Perf 11×10	50·00	6
		c. Perf 10×12 (4.85)	£150	30
		ca. Perf 12×10	£100	70
233		5d. blue-green, *p* 10	9·50	
		a. Perf 12 (4.85)	13·00	
		ab. Wmk sideways	50·00	
		b. Perf 11 (12.85)	9·00	
		c. Perf 10×11 (12.85)	29·00	1
		d. Perf 11×12 or 12×11 (12.85)	7·50	
		da. Wmk sideways (*p* 11×12)	—	20
		e. Imperf (pair)	£200	
234	**37**	6d. pale lilac, *p* 10	45·00	1
		a. Perf 10×13 or 13×10	—	£3
		b. Perf 10×12 or 12×10 (4.85)	48·00	1
235		6d. mauve, *p* 10	45·00	1
		a. Perf 12 (4.85)	80·00	10
		b. Perf 11 (12.85)	80·00	8
		c. Perf 10×12 (4.85)	50·00	8
		ca. Perf 12×10	45·00	2
		cb. Imperf between (horiz pair)	†	£5
		d. Perf 11×12 (12.85)	80·00	12
		da. Perf 12×11	45·00	1
		e. Perf 11×10 (12.85)	55·00	2
236	**13**	8d. yellow, *p* 10 (1883)	£100	15
		a. Perf 12 (4.85)	£170	27
		b. Perf 11 (12.85)	£100	19
		c. Perf 10×12 (4.85)	£130	35
		ca. Perf 12×10	£100	28
236*d*	**34**	9d. on 10d. red-brn, *p* 11×12 (28.2.97)	8·00	5
		das. Optd "Specimen"	25·00	
		db. Perf 12	11·00	7
		dc. Perf 11	11·00	8
		dca. Surch double	£140	£1
236*e*		10d. violet, *p* 11×12 (1897)	12·00	4
		eas. Optd "Specimen"	25·00	
		eb. Perf 12×11½	12·00	4
		ec. Perf 12	15·00	5
		ed. Perf 11	20·00	7
237	**38**	1s. black, *p* 10	65·00	2
		a. Perf 11 (12.85)	£200	9
		b. Perf 10×12	—	£25
		c. Perf 10×13		
		ca. Perf 13×10	£200	21
		d. Perf 11×12, comb (1.84)	65·00	2

41

42

-86. *W* **41** (*sideways*). (i) *Optd* "POSTAGE", *in black.*

42 5s. lilac and green, *p* 13 (15.10.85) ..
a. Perf 10 .. ..
b. Perf 12×10 .. .. .. £325 80·00
10s. lilac and claret, *p* 13 (17.5.86) ..
a. Perf 12 .. .. £500 £160
£1 lilac and claret, *p* 13 (17.5.86) .. — £2250
a. Perf 12 .. .. £2250

(ii) *Overprinted in blue*

42 10s. mauve and claret, *p* 10 .. .. £650 £180
as. Optd "Specimen" .. .. .. 60·00
b. Perf 12 .. .. £190 65·00
c. Perf 12×11 .. .. ..
£1 rose-lilac and claret, *p* 12×10 .. £2500 £1200

-87. *W* **41**.

26 1d. scarlet, *p* 10 (12.86) .. .. 13·00 4·50
a. Perf 11×12, comb .. .. .. 4·50 1·75
28 2d. deep blue, *p* 10 (12.87) .. .. 40·00 6·00
a. Perf 11×12, comb .. .. .. 13·00 1·75
b. Imperf .. ..

View of Sydney

46 Emu

47 Captain Cook

Queen Victoria Arms of Colony **49** Superb Lyrebird **50** Eastern Grey Kangaroo

51 Map of Australia **52** Capt. Arthur Phillip, first Governor and Lord Carrington, Governor in 1888

s M. Tannenberg (1d., 6d.), Miss Devine (2d., 8d.), H. arraclough (4d.), Govt Ptg Office (1s.), C. Turner (5s.), Mrs. F. toddard (20s.). Eng W. Bell).

8 (1 May)–**89.** *Centenary of New South Wales.* (*a*) *W* **40**. 11×12.

45 1d. lilac (9.7.88) .. .. 4·00 20
a. Perf 12×11½ .. .. .. 17·00 90
b. Perf 12 .. .. 5·50 20
c. Imperf (pair) .. ..
d. Mauve .. .. 4·00 20
da. Imperf between (pair) .. ..
db. Perf 12×11½ .. .. .. 6·50 40
dc. Perf 12 .. .. 6·00 40
46 2d. Prussian blue (1.9.88) .. .. 6·00 20
a. Imperf (pair) £100
b. Imperf between (pair) £400
c. Perf 12×11½ .. .. .. 10·00 20
d. Perf 12 .. .. 8·50 20
e. Chalky blue .. .. .. 6·00 20
ea. Perf 12×11½ .. .. ..
eb. Perf 12 .. .. 8·00 40
47 4d. purple-brown (8.10.88) .. .. 11·00 3·00
a. Perf 12×11½ .. .. .. 30·00 7·50
b. Perf 12 .. .. 26·00 3·25
c. Perf 11 .. .. £300 90·00
d. Red-brown .. .. .. 10·00 3·00
da. Perf 12×11½ .. .. .. 13·00 2·75
db. Perf 12 .. .. 13·00 2·75
e. Orange-brown, p 12×11½ .. .. 15·00 3·00
f. Yellow-brown, p 12×11½ .. .. 14·00 3·25
48 6d. carmine (26.11.88) .. .. 21·00 3·50
a. Perf 12×11½ .. .. .. 25·00 4·00
b. Perf 12 .. .. 21·00 8·50
49 8d. lilac-rose (17.1.89) .. .. 17·00 2·75
a. Perf 12×11½ .. .. .. 40·00 11·00
b. Perf 12 .. .. 17·00 3·00
c. Magenta .. .. 75·00 9·50
ca. Perf 12×11½ .. .. .. 17·00 2·75
cb. Perf 12 .. .. 17·00 3·25
50 1s. maroon (21.2.89) .. .. .. 21·00 1·25
a. Perf 12×11½ .. .. .. 23·00 1·25
b. Perf 12 .. .. 25·00 1·25
c. Violet-brown .. .. .. 21·00 1·25
ca. Imperf (pair) £550
cb. Perf 12×11½ .. .. .. 42·00 1·75
cc. Perf 12 .. .. 42·00 1·25
3s/8s Optd "Specimen" .. *Set of* 6 £150

(*b*) *W* **41**. *P* 11×12

259 **45** 1d. lilac (1888) .. .. 16·00
a. Mauve .. .. 14·00 1·25
260 **46** 2d. Prussian blue (1888) .. .. 50·00 3·00

(*c*) *W* **25** (*sideways on 5s.*). *P* 10

261 **51** 5s. deep purple (13.3.89) .. .. £180 48·00
a. Deep violet .. .. .. £180 48·00
262 **52** 20s. cobalt-blue (27.4.88) £225 £110

Nos. 255c and 261/2 are line perforated, the remainder are comb.

A postal forgery exists of the 2d. on unwatermarked paper and perforated 11.

53

54

1890. *W* **53** (*5s.*) *or* **54** (*20s.*). *P* 10.

263 **51** 5s. lilac .. .. £130 27·00
a. Perf 11 .. .. £180 38·00
ab. Imperf between (horiz pair) ..
b. Perf 12 .. .. £250 42·00
c. Perf 10×11 or 11×10 .. .. £170 27·00
d. Mauve .. .. £170 27·00
da. Perf 11 .. .. £170 38·00
264 **52** 20s. cobalt-blue £300 £130
a. Perf 11 .. .. £225 75·00
b. Perf 11×10 .. ..
c. Ultramarine, p 11 .. .. .. £180 75·00
ca. Perf 12 .. .. £225 £130
cb. Perf 11×12 or 12×11 .. .. £160 75·00
263s/4s Optd "Specimen" .. *Set of* 2 £180

55 Allegorical figure of Australia

Halfpenny

(56)

SEVEN-PENCE
HALFPENNY

(57)

1890 (22 Dec). *W* **40**.

265 **55** 2½d. ultramarine, *p* 11×12 *comb* .. 3·00 50
as. Optd "Specimen" .. .. .. 25·00
b. Perf 12×11½, comb .. .. 45·00
c. Perf 12, comb .. .. .. 7·50 50

1891 (5 Jan). *Surch as T* **56** *and* **57**. *W* **40**.

266 **26** ½d. on 1d. grey, *p* 11×12 *comb* .. 3·00 3·50
a. Surch omitted .. .. ..
b. Surch double £225
267 **37** 7½d. on 6d. brown, *p* 10 .. .. 5·50 3·00
a. Perf 11 .. .. 5·00 2·75
b. Perf 12 .. .. 6·50 3·25
c. Perf 11×12 or 12×11 .. .. 5·50 3·25
d. Perf 10×12 .. .. .. 6·00 3·25
268 **38** 12½d. on 1s. red, *p* 10 .. .. .. 12·00 9·00
a. "HALFPENCE" omitted ..
b. Perf 11 .. .. 13·00 9·00
c. Perf 11×12, comb .. .. 12·00 8·50
d. Perf 12×11½, comb .. .. 11·00 8·50
e. Perf 12, comb .. .. .. 15·00 8·50
266/8s Optd "Specimen" .. .. *Set of* 3 70·00

1891 (July). *Wmk* "10" *as W* **35**. *P* 10.

269 **16** 3d. green .. .. 12·00 80·00
270 3d. dark green .. .. 5·00 17·00

58

Type I. Narrow "H" in "HALF"

1892 (21 Mar)–**99.** *Type I. W* **40**.

271 **58** ½d. grey, *p* 10 .. .. 22·00 1·00
a. Perf 11 .. .. 65·00 5·50
b. Perf 10×12 or 12×10 .. .. 60·00 8·00
c. Perf 11×12 .. .. .. 2·25 20
cs. Optd "Specimen" .. .. .. 20·00
d. Perf 12 .. .. 2·50 20
272 ½d. slate, *p* 11×12 (1897) .. .. 2·25 20
a. Perf 12×11½ .. .. .. 2·25 20
b. Perf 12 .. .. 2·50 20
c. Imperf between (horiz pair). Perf 11×12 .. .. £400
273 ½d. bluish green, *p* 11×12 (1.99) .. 3·00 20
a. Perf 12×11½ .. .. .. 2·00 20
b. Perf 12 .. .. 2·50 20

The perforations 11×12, 12×11½, 12, are from comb machines.

The die for Type **58** was constructed from an electro taken from the die of the De La Rue 1d., Type **26**, with "ONE" replaced by "HALF" and two "½" plugs added to the bottom corners. These alterations proved to be less hard-wearing than the remainder of the die and defects were visible by the 1905 plate of No. 333. It seems likely that repairs were undertaken before printing from the next plate in late 1907 which produced stamps as Type II.

59

1894–1904. *Optd* "POSTAGE" *in blue. W* **59** (*sideways*).

274 **42** 10s. mauve and claret, *p* 10 .. .. £275 £120
275 10s. violet and mauve, *p* 12 .. .. £160 42·00
a. Perf 11 .. .. £250 85·00
b. Perf 12×11 .. .. .. £180 50·00
276 10s. violet and aniline crimson, *p* 12×11 £170 48·00
a. Chalk-surfaced paper (1903) ..
b. Perf 12 .. .. £250 80·00
277 10s. violet and rosine (*chalk-surfaced paper*), *p* 14 (1904) .. .. .. £170 75·00
a. Perf 11 .. .. £225 85·00
b. Perf 12×11 .. .. .. £170 45·00
278 10s. violet and claret (*chalk-surfaced paper*), *p* 12×11 (1904) .. .. £225 85·00
279 £1 violet and claret, *p* 12×11 .. ..

60

61

(Des C. Turner. Litho Govt Printing Office, Sydney)

1897. *Diamond Jubilee and Hospital Charity. T* **60/1**. *W* **40**. *P* 12×11 (*1d.*) *or* 11 (*2½d.*).

280 **60** 1d. (1s.) green and brown (22.6) .. 40·00 40·00
281 **61** 2½d. (2s. 6d.), gold, carmine & blue (28.6) £160 £160
280s/1s Optd "Specimen" .. *Set of* 2 £200

These stamps, sold at 1s. and 2s. 6d. respectively, paid postage of 1d. and 2½d. only, the difference being given to a Consumptives' Home.

62

63

64

Dies of the 1d.

Die I

Die II

1d. Die I. The first pearl on the crown on the left side is merged into the arch, the shading under the fleur-de-lis is indistinct, the "S" of "WALES" is open.

Die II. The first pearl is circular, the vertical shading under the fleur-de-lis clear, the "S" of "WALES" not so open.

Dies of the 2½d.

Die I

Die II

2½d. Die I. There are 12 radiating lines in the star on the Queen's breast.

Die II. There are 16 radiating lines in the star and the eye is nearly full of colour.

(Des D. Souter (2d., 2½d.). Eng W. Amor)

1897 (22 June)–**99.** *W* **40** (*sideways on* 2½*d.*). *P* 12×11 (2½*d.*) *or* 11×12 (*others*).
288 **62** 1d. carmine (Die I) .. .. .. 2·25 10
a. Perf 12×11½ .. .. .. 2·50 10
s. Optd "Specimen" .. .. .. 18·00
289 1d. scarlet (Die I) .. .. .. 2·25 10
a. Perf 12×11½ .. .. .. 4·75 40
b. Perf 12 .. .. .. 4·75 50
ba. Imperf horiz (vert pair) £225
290 1d. rose-carmine (Die II) (11.97) .. 2·25 10
a. Perf 12×11½ .. .. .. 2·00 10
b. Perf 12 .. .. .. 2·00 10
c. Imperf between (pair) £400
291 1d. salmon-red (Die II) (*p* 12×11½) .. 2·00 10
a. Perf 12 .. .. .. 3·75 40
292 **63** 2d. deep dull blue .. .. .. 3·00 10
a. Perf 12×11½ .. .. .. 3·00 10
b. Perf 12 .. .. .. 6·00 10
s. Optd "Specimen" .. .. .. 18·00
293 2d. cobalt-blue .. .. .. 4·25 10
a. Perf 12×11½ .. .. .. 3·50 10
b. Perf 12 .. .. .. 4·25 10
294 2d. ultramarine (1.12.97) .. .. 3·50 10
a. Perf 12×11½ .. .. .. 2·75 10
b. Perf 12 .. .. .. 2·75 10
c. Imperf between (pair) .. ..
s. Optd "Specimen" .. .. .. 20·00
295 **64** 2½d. purple (Die I) .. .. .. 8·00 1·50
a. Perf 11½×12 .. .. .. 9·50 1·00
b. Perf 11 .. .. .. 9·50 2·25
s. Optd "Specimen" .. .. .. 18·00
296 2½d. deep violet (Die II) (11.97) .. 7·00 1·00
a. Perf 11½×12 .. .. .. 9·50 1·25
b. Perf 12 .. .. .. 6·00 1·25
297 2½d. Prussian blue (17.1.99) .. .. 6·50 1·50
a. Perf 11½×12 .. .. .. 4·25 1·25
b. Perf 12 .. .. .. 3·50 1·25

The perforations 11×12, 12×11½ and 12 are from comb machines, the perforation 11 is from a single-line machine.

From 1 January 1898 the above were the only valid stamps for these face values.

1897. *Reissue of T* **24**. *W* **25**. *P* 11.
297*c* 5s. reddish purple (*shades*) .. .. 38·00 13·00
ca. Imperf between (horiz pair) £2750
d. Perf 12 .. .. .. 48·00 21·00
e. Perf 11×12 or 12×11 .. .. 40·00 19·00

1898–99. *W* **40**. *P* 11×12.
297*f* **48** 6d. emerald-green .. .. .. 30·00 10·00
fa. Perf 12×11½ .. .. .. 22·00 9·00
fb. Perf 12 .. .. .. 22·00 9·00
fs. Optd "Specimen" .. .. .. 20·00
297*g* 6d. orange-yellow (1899) .. .. 15·00 3·75
ga. Perf 12×11½ .. .. .. 14·00 3·25
gb. Perf 12 .. .. .. 24·00 5·00
gc. Yellow, p 12×11½ .. .. .. 15·00 2·00

1899 (Oct). *W* **40** (*sideways on* 2½*d.*). *Chalk-surfaced paper. P* 12×11½ *or* 11½×12 (2½*d.*), *comb.*
298 **58** ½d. blue-green (Type I) .. .. 1·00 10
a. Imperf (pair) .. .. .. 65·00 75·00
299 **62** 1d. carmine (Die II) .. .. .. 2·00 10
a. Imperf horiz (vert pair) £200
300 1d. scarlet (Die II) .. .. .. 1·25 10
301 1d. salmon-red (Die II) .. .. 2·25 10
a. Imperf (pair) .. .. .. 65·00 75·00
302 **63** 2d. cobalt-blue .. .. .. 2·00 10
a. Imperf (pair) .. .. .. 65·00
303 **64** 2½d. Prussian blue (Die II) .. .. 3·25 70
a. Imperf (pair) .. .. .. 85·00
303*b* **47** 4d. red-brown .. .. .. 11·00 4·25
c. Imperf (pair) £225
304 4d. orange-brown .. .. .. 10·00 4·25
305 **48** 6d. deep orange .. .. .. 12·00 1·75
a. Imperf (pair) £150
306 6d. orange-yellow .. .. .. 11·00 1·75
307 6d. emerald-green .. .. .. 75·00 22·00
a. Imperf (pair) £190
308 **49** 8d. magenta .. .. .. 20·00 3·25
309 **34** 9d. on 10d. dull brown .. .. 8·00 4·75
a. Surcharge double .. .. 90·00 £110
b. Without surcharge .. .. 80·00
310 10d. violet .. .. .. 13·00 4·25
311 **50** 1s. maroon .. .. .. 23·00 1·25
312 1s. purple-brown .. .. .. 23·00 1·75
a. Imperf (pair) £190

65
The spacing between the Crown and "NSW" is 1 mm in T **65** as against 2 mm in T **40**

66 Superb Lyrebird

67

1902–03. *W* **65** (*sideways on* 2½*d.*). *Chalk-surfaced paper. P* 12×11½ *or* 11½×12 (2½*d.*), *comb.*
313 **58** ½d. blue-green (Type I) .. .. 4·00 30
a. Perf 12×11 .. .. .. 4·00
314 **62** 1d. carmine (Die II) .. .. .. 2·50 20
315 **63** 2d. cobalt-blue .. .. .. 3·00 20
316 **64** 2½d. dark blue (Die II) .. .. 5·50 20
317 **47** 4d. orange-brown .. .. .. 25·00 6·00
318 **48** 6d. yellow-orange .. .. .. 18·00 2·00
319 6d. orange .. .. .. 18·00 2·00
320 6d. orange-buff .. .. .. 25·00 2·00
321 **49** 8d. magenta .. .. .. 20·00 3·00
322 **34** 9d. on 10d. brownish orange .. .. 9·00 3·50
323 10d. violet .. .. .. 18·00 4·00
324 **50** 1s. maroon .. .. .. 24·00 1·00
325 1s. purple-brown .. .. .. 26·00 1·00
326 **66** 2s. 6d. green (1903) .. .. .. 42·00 18·00
s. Optd "Specimen" .. .. .. 35·00

1903–08. *W* **65**.
327 **16** 3d. yellow-green, *p* 11 .. .. 7·50 90
b. Perf 12 .. .. .. 6·50 90
ba. Imperf between (horiz pair) ..
c. Perf 11×12 or 12×11 .. .. 6·50 90
328 3d. dull green, *p* 12 .. .. 22·00 2·00
a. Perf 11×12 or 12×11 .. .. 8·50 1·25
b. Perf 11 .. .. ..
329 **11** 5d. dark blue-green, *p* 11×12 *or* 12×11 6·50 1·00
a. Wmk sideways .. .. 18·00 5·50
b. Perf 11 .. .. .. 15·00 1·00
ba. Wmk sideways .. ..
c. Perf 12 .. .. .. 23·00 3·50
ca. Wmk sideways .. .. 35·00 11·00
d. Imperf (pair) £130

(Typo Victoria Govt Printer, Melbourne)

1903 (18 July). *Wmk double-lined V over Crown. W* w **10**.
330 **67** 9d. brown & ultram, *p* 12¼×12½, *comb* 12·00 2·25
s. Optd "Specimen" .. .. 27·00
331 9d. brown & dp blue, *p* 12¼×12½, *comb* 12·00 2·25
332 9d. brown and blue, *p* 11 .. .. £475 £300

Type II. Broad "H" in "HALF"

68

1905 (Oct)–**10.** *W* **68** (*sideways on* 2½*d.*). *Chalk-surfaced paper. P* 12×11½ *or* 11½×12 (2½*d.*) *comb, unless otherwise stated.*
333 **58** ½d. blue-green (Type I) .. .. 2·50 20
a. Perf 11½×11 .. ..
b. Type II (1908) .. .. 2·25 20
ba. Perf 11½×11 .. .. 2·25
334 **62** 1d. rose-carmine (Die II) .. .. 1·75 10
a. Double impression £225
b. Perf 11½×11 .. .. 2·00
335 **63** 2d. deep ultramarine .. .. 2·00 10
b. Perf 11½×11 .. .. 2·25
336 2d. milky blue (1910) .. .. 1·75 10
da. Perf 11 .. .. .. 48·00
db. Perf 11½×11 .. ..
337 **64** 2½d. Prussian blue (Die II) .. .. 3·50 1·50
338 **47** 4d. orange-brown .. .. 9·50 3·50
339 4d. red-brown .. .. .. 11·00 3·50
340 **48** 6d. dull yellow .. .. 13·00 2·00
a. Perf 11½×11 .. .. 22·00
341 6d. orange-yellow .. .. 13·00 2·00
a. Perf 11×11½ .. .. 28·00
342 6d. deep orange .. .. 11·00 2·00
a. Perf 11 .. .. .. £160
343 6d. orange-buff .. .. 11·00 2·00
a. Perf 11½×11 .. .. 19·00 3·00
344 **49** 8d. magenta .. .. .. 21·00 4·00
345 8d. lilac-rose .. .. .. 21·00 4·50
346 **34** 10d. violet .. .. .. 14·00 4·00
a. Perf 11½×11 .. .. 13·00 3·75
b. Perf 11 .. .. .. 13·00 3·75
347 **50** 1s. maroon .. .. .. 20·00 1·75
348 1s. purple-brown (1908) .. .. 23·00 1·75
349 **66** 2s. 6d. blue-green .. .. 45·00 20·00
a. Perf 11½×11 .. .. 29·00 18·00
b. Perf 11 .. .. .. 32·00 22·00

69

1905 (Dec). *W* **69**. *Chalk-surfaced paper. P* 11.
350 **52** 20s. cobalt-blue .. .. .. £160 65·00
a. Perf 12 .. .. .. £180 75·00
b. Perf 11×12 or 12×11 .. .. £150 60·00

(Typo Victoria Govt Printer, Melbourne)

1906 (Sept). *Wmk double-lined "A" and Crown, W* w **11**. *P* 12×12½, *comb.*
351 **67** 9d. brown and ultramarine .. .. 8·50 1·60
a. Perf 11 .. .. .. 55·00 42·00
352 9d. yellow-brown and ultramarine .. 8·50 1·50

1907 (July). *W* w **11** (*sideways on* 2½*d.*). *P* 12×11½ *or* 11½×12 (2½*d.*), *comb, unless otherwise stated.*
353 **58** ½d. blue-green (Type I) .. .. 4·00 50
354 **62** 1d. dull rose (Die II) .. .. 5·00 50
355 **63** 2d. cobalt-blue .. .. .. 5·00 60
356 **64** 2½d. Prussian blue (Die II) .. .. 42·00
357 **47** 4d. orange-brown .. .. 12·00 6·50
358 **48** 6d. orange-buff .. .. 28·00 8·50
359 6d. dull yellow .. .. .. 26·00 8·50
360 **49** 8d. magenta .. .. .. 18·00 8·50
361 **34** 10d. violet, *p* 11 .. .. 22·00 24·00
362 **50** 1s. purple-brown .. .. 29·00 5·00
a. Perf 11 .. .. ..
363 **66** 2s. 6d. blue-green .. .. 48·00 26·00

STAMP BOOKLETS

There are very few surviving examples of Nos. SB1/4. Lis are provided for those believed to have been issued with p quoted for those known to still exist.

1904 (May)–**09.** *Black on red cover with map of Australi front and picture of one of six different State G.P.O's on Stapled.*
SB1 £1 booklet containing two hundred and forty 1d. in four blocks of 30 and two blocks of 60 ..
a. Red on pink cover (1909) .. .. ..
b. Blue on pink cover .. ..

1904 (May). *Black on grey cover as No.* SB1. *Stapled.*
SB2 £1 booklet containing one hundred and twenty 2d. in four blocks of 30 .. ..

1910 (May). *Black on cream cover inscribed* "COMM WEALTH OF AUSTRALIA/POSTMASTER-GENER DEPARTMENT". *Stapled.*
SB3 2s. booklet containing eleven ½d. (No. 333), either in block of 6 plus block of 5 or block of 11, and eighteen 1d. (No. 334), either in three blocks of 6 or block of 6 plus block of 12 .. .. £2

Unsold stock of No. SB3 was uprated with one additional in May 1911.

1911 (Aug). *Red on pink cover as No.* SB3. *Stapled.*
SB4 2s. booklet containing twelve ½d. (No. 333), either in two blocks of 6 or block of 12, and eighteen 1d. (No. 334) either in three blocks of 6 or 1 block of 6 plus block of 12 .. .. £1

OFFICIAL STAMPS

O S (O 1) **O S** (O 2) **O** (O 3)

The space between the letters is normally 7 mm as illustra except on the 5d. and 8d. (11–11½ mm), 5s. (12 mm) and 20s. mm). Later printings of the 3d., W 40, are 5½ mm, and these listed. Varieties in the settings are known on the 1d. (8 and mm), 2d. (8½ mm) and 3d. (9 mm).

Varieties of Type O 1 exist with "O" sideways.

Nos. O1/35 *overprinted with Type* O 1

1879. *Wmk double-lined* "**6**". *P* 13.
O1 **16** 3d. dull green .. .. — £

1879 (Oct)–**85.** *W* **36**. *P* 13.
O 2 **26** 1d. salmon .. .. 14·00 2
a. Perf 10 (5.81) .. .. .. £180 3(
b. Perf 13×10 (1881) .. .. 27·00 4
O 3 **28** 2d. blue .. .. 18·00 2
a. Perf 10 (7.81) £225 32
b. Perf 10×13 (1881) .. .. 45·00 22
ba. Perf 13×10 .. .. .. 27·00 3
d. Perf 11×12 (11.84?) .. .. — £
O 4 **16** 3d. dull green (R.) (12.79) .. .. £450 £
O 5 3d. dull green (3.80) £250 50
a. Perf 10 (1881) £150 45
b. Yellow-green. Perf 10 (10.81) .. £150 27
ba. Perf 13×10 (1881) £150 27
bb. Perf 12 (4.85) £200 50
bc. Perf 10×12 or 12×10 (4.85) .. £200 50
O 6 **32** 4d. red-brown £170 8
a. Perf 10 (1881) .. .. .. — £
b. Perf 10×13 (1881) £225 90
ba. Perf 13×10 .. .. .. £160 12
O 7 **11** 5d. green, *p* 10 (8.84) .. .. 18·00 15
O 8 **37** 6d. pale lilac £225 6
a. Perf 10 (1881) £350 42
b. Perf 13×10 (1881) £170 42
O 9 **13** 8d. yellow (R.) (12.79) .. .. — £2
O10 8d. yellow (1880) .. .. .. — 18
a. Perf 10 (1881) £300 75
O11 **34** 9d. on 10d. brown, *p* 10 (30.5.80) .. £425
s. Optd "Specimen" .. .. .. 60·00
O12 **38** 1s. black (R.) £250 8
a. Perf 10 (1881) .. .. .. — 17
b. Perf 10×13 (1881) .. .. — 26
ba. Perf 13×10 .. .. .. — 10

Other stamps are known with red overprint but their status is doubt.

1880–88. *W* **25**. (*a*) *P* 13.
O13 **24** 5s. deep purple (15.2.80) .. .. £425 90·
a. Royal purple .. .. .. — £3
b. Deep rose-lilac .. .. .. £425 90·

(*b*) *P* 10
O14 **24** 5s. deep purple (9.82) £425 £1
a. Opt double .. .. .. † £15
b. Rose-lilac (1883) £300 £1

(*c*) *P* 10 × 12
O15 **24** 5s. purple (10.86) .. .. ..

(*d*) *P* 12 × 10
O16 **24** 5s. reddish purple (1886) £425 £1

(*e*) *P* 12
O17 **24** 5s. purple .. .. † £5

(*f*) *P* 11
O18 **24** 5s. rose-lilac (1888) .. .. .. £170 80·

1880 (31 May). *W* **35**. *P* 13.
O18*a* **34** 10d. lilac £150 £1
ab. Perf 10 and 11, compound .. £225 £2
ac. Perf 10 .. .. £225
aca. Opt double, one albino .. ..
as. Optd "Specimen" .. .. .. 60·00

-85. W 40. P 10.
26 1d. salmon . . 13·00 2·50
a. Perf 13×10 . . — £130
1d. orange *to* scarlet . . 9·50 1·75
a. Perf 10×13 . . — £130
b. Perf 11×12, comb (1.84) . . 8·00 1·40
c. Perf 10×12 or 12×10 (4.85) . . — £110
d. Perf 12×11 (12.85) . .
28 2d. blue . . 8·00 1·00
a. Perf 10×13 or 13×10 . . £190 75·00
c. Perf 11×12, comb (1.84) . . 7·50 1·00
ca. Opt double . . — £150
e. Perf 12×11 (12.85) . .
16 3d. yellow-green (7 *mm*) . . 7·50 3·50
a. Perf 12 (4.85) . . £120 80·00
b. Perf 12×10 (4.85) . .
ba. Opt double . . † £450
c. Perf 12×11 . .
3d. bluish green (7 *mm*) . . 7·50 3·50
a. Perf 12 (4.85) . . £120 80·00
b. Perf 12×10 (4.85) . .
c. Perf 10×11 (12.85) . .
3d. yellow-green (5½ *mm*) . . 8·00 3·50
a. Wmk sideways . . 35·00 20·00
as. Optd "Specimen" . . 35·00
b. Perf 10×12 or 12×10 (4.85) . . 7·50 3·50
c. Perf 10×11 or 11×10 (12.85) . .
3d. bluish green (5½ *mm*) . . 7·00 3·75
a. Wmk sideways . .
b. Perf 10×12 or 12×10 (4.85) . . 6·00 3·75
c. Perf 10×11 or 11×10 (12.85) . . 5·00 3·50
32 4d. red-brown . . 30·00 4·00
a. Perf 11×12, comb (1.84) . . 12·00 3·25
b. Perf 10×12 (4.85) . . — 70·00
4d. dark brown . . 15·00 3·25
a. Perf 11×12, comb (1.84) . . 12·00 3·25
b. Perf 12 (4.85) . . £200 £150
c. Perf 10×12 (4.85) . . £200 90·00
11 5d. dull green . . 13·00 14·00
a. Perf 12×10 (4.85) . .
s. Optd "Specimen" . . 35·00
5d. blue-green . . 14·00 15·00
a. Perf 12 (4.85) . . £100
b. Perf 10×11 . . 14·00 15·00
37 6d. pale lilac . . 20·00 5·50
a. Perf 11 (12.85) . . 22·00 5·00
6d. mauve . . 20·00 5·50
a. Perf 12 (4.85) . . — 45·00
b. Perf 10×12 or 12×10 (4.85) . . 20·00 5·00
d. Perf 11×10 (12.85) . . 20·00 5·50
e. Perf 11×12 . .
ea. Perf 12×11 (12.85) . . 55·00 15·00
13 8d. yellow . . 22·00 11·00
a. Perf 12 (4.85) . . £130 38·00
b. Perf 10×12 or 12×10 (4.85) . . 22·00 10·00
d. Perf 11 (12.85) . . 22·00 12·00
da. Opt double . .
db. Opt treble . . † —
38 1s. black (R.) . . 25·00 7·00
a. Perf 10×13 . . — 55·00
b. Perf 11×12, comb (1.84) . . 25·00 7·00
ba. Opt double . . — £200

6–87. W 41. P 10.
26 1d. scarlet . . 35·00 4·25
28 2d. deep blue . .
a. Perf 11×12, comb . .

7–90. *Nos. 241/2 optd in black.* (a) *With Type* O 1.
42 10s. mauve and claret, *p* 12 (1890) . . — £1400

(b) *With Type* O 2 (30 April 1889)

42 10s. mauve and claret . . £1200 £600
as. Optd "Specimen" . . 80·00
b. Perf 10 . . £2250 £1300

(c) *With Type* O 3 (7 Jan 1887)

42 £1 mauve and claret, *p* 12×10 . . £5500 £3500

Only nine examples of No. O38 are recorded, three of which mint. One of the used stamps, in the Royal Collection, shows erprint Type O 3 double.

88 (17 July)–90. *Optd as Type* O 1. (a) W 40. P 11×12.
9 45 1d. lilac . . 2·25 30
a. Perf 12 . . 2·25 30
b. Mauve . . 2·25 30
ba. Perf 12 . . 2·25 30
0 46 2d. Prussian blue (15.10.88) . . 4·25 30
a. Perf 12 . . 4·25 30
1 47 4d. purple-brown (10.10.89) . . 11·00 3·25
a. Perf 12 . . 14·00 3·50
b. Perf 11 . .
c. Red-brown . . 11·00 3·25
ca. Opt double . . † —
cb. Perf 12 . . 14·00 3·50
2 48 6d. carmine (16.1.89) . . 8·50 4·50
a. Perf 12 . . 12·00 4·50
3 49 8d. lilac-rose (1890) . . 20·00 10·00
a. Perf 12 . . 24·00 13·00
4 50 1s. maroon (9.1.90) . . 18·00 3·50
a. Perf 12 . . 18·00 3·50
b. Purple-brown . . 18·00 3·50
ba. Opt double . .
bb. Perf 12 . . 18·00 3·50
39s/44s Optd "Specimen" . . *Set of* 6 £200

(b) W 41. P 11×12 (1889)

45 45 1d. mauve . .
46 46 2d. blue . .

(c) W 25. P 10

47 51 5s. deep purple (R.) (9.1.90) . . £600 £500
48 52 20s. cobalt-blue (10.3.90) . . £1600 £800

390 (15 Feb)–91. *Optd as Type* O 1. W 53 (5s.) *or* 54 (20s.). P 10.
49 51 5s. lilac . . £300 £120
a. Mauve . . £160 70·00
b. Dull lilac, p 12 . . £450 £130
50 52 20s. cobalt-blue (3.91) . . £1600 £600
49s/50s Optd "Specimen" . . *Set of* 2 £200

1891 (Jan). *Optd as Type* O 1. W 40.

(a) *On No.* 265. P 11×12

O54 55 2½d. ultramarine . . 8·00 6·00

(b) *On Nos.* 266/8

O55 26 ½d. on 1d. grey, *p* 11×12 . . 55·00 50·00
O56 37 7½d. on 6d. brown, *p* 10 . . 35·00 35·00
O57 38 12½d. on 1s. red, *p* 11×12 . . 60·00 65·00
O54s/7s Optd "Specimen" . . *Set of* 4 £140

1892 (May). *No.* 271 *optd as Type* O 1. P 10.
O58 58 ½d. grey . . 8·50 14·00
a. Perf 11×12 . . 6·00 10·00
as. Optd "Specimen" . . 30·00
b. Perf 12 . . 7·50 10·00
c. Perf 12×11½ . . 13·00 12·00

Official stamps were withdrawn from the government departments on 31 December 1894.

POSTAGE DUE STAMPS

D 1

(Dies eng by A. Collingridge. Typo Govt Printing Office, Sydney)

1891 (1 Jan)–**92**. W 40. P 10.
D 1 D 1 ½d. green (21.1.92) . . 3·50 2·75
D 2 1d. green . . 7·00 1·00
a. Perf 11 . . 6·00 1·00
b. Perf 12 . . 16·00 2·75
c. Perf 12 × 10 . . 20·00 2·00
d. Perf 10 × 11 . . 9·50 1·50
e. Perf 11 × 12 or 12 × 11 . . 6·50 1·00
D 3 2d. green . . 10·00 1·50
a. Perf 11 . . 10·00 1·50
b. Perf 12 . . — 9·00
c. Perf 12×10 . . 18·00 3·25
d. Perf 10×11 . . 11·00 1·75
e. Perf 11×12 or 12×11 . . 10·00 1·25
f. Wmk sideways . . 17·00 7·00
D 4 3d. green . . 17·00 3·75
a. Perf 10 × 11 . . 17·00 3·75
D 5 4d. green . . 12·00 1·40
a. Perf 11 . . 13·00 1·40
b. Perf 10 × 11 . . 12·00 1·40
D 6 6d. green . . 21·00 4·25
D 7 8d. green . . 65·00 12·00
D 8 5s. green . . £120 40·00
a. Perf 11 . . £225 75·00
b. Perf 11 × 12 . . — £250
D 9 10s. green (early 1891) . . £250 55·00
a. Perf 12 × 10 . . £200 £110
D10 20s. green (early 1891) . . £375 90·00
a. Perf 12 . . £350
b. Perf 12 × 10 . . £225 £140
D1s/10s Optd "Specimen" . . *Set of* 10 £180

Used prices for 10s. and 20s. are for cancelled-to-order stamps. Postally used examples are rare.

1900. W 40. *Chalk-surfaced paper.* P 11.
D11 D 1 ½d. emerald-green . .
D12 1d. emerald-green . . 7·50 2·50
a. Perf 12 . . 18·00 6·00
b. Perf 11×12 or 12×11 . . 7·50 1·75
D13 2d. emerald-green . . 9·50 3·25
a. Perf 12 . . — 27·00
b. Perf 11×12 or 12×11 . . 8·50 3·00
D14 3d. emerald-green, *p* 11×12 *or* 12×11 24·00 7·00
D15 4d. emerald-green (7.00) . . 15·00 3·50

New South Wales became part of the Commonwealth of Australia on 1 January 1901.

QUEENSLAND

The area which later became Queensland was previously part of New South Wales known as the Moreton Bay District. The first post office, at Brisbane, was opened in 1834 and the use of New South Wales stamps from the District became compulsory from 1 May 1854.

Queensland was proclaimed a separate colony on 10 December 1859, but continued to use New South Wales issues until 1 November 1860.

Post Offices opened in the Moreton Bay District before 10 December 1859, and using New South Wales stamps, were

Office	*Opened*	*Numeral Cancellation*
Brisbane	1834	95
Burnett's Inn (*became* Goodes Inn)	1850	108
Callandoon	1850	74
Condamine	1856	151
Dalby	1854	133
Drayton	1846	85
Gayndah	1850	86
Gladstone	1854	131
Goode's Inn	1858	108
Ipswich	1846	87
Maryborough	1849	96
Rockhampton	1858	201
Surat	1852	110
Taroom	1856	152
Toowoomba	1858	214
Warwick	1848	81

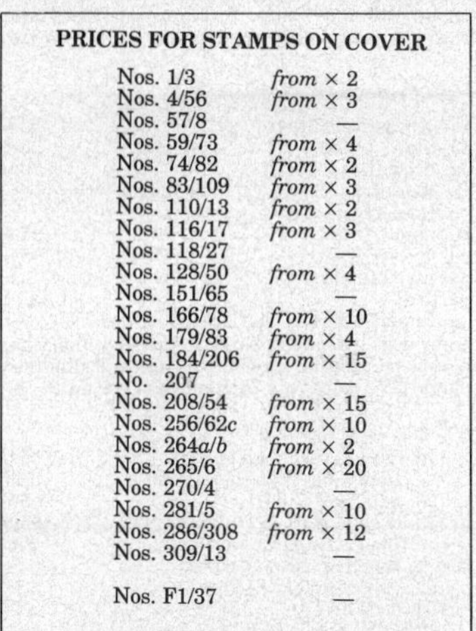

PRICES FOR STAMPS ON COVER

Nos. 1/3	*from* × 2
Nos. 4/56	*from* × 3
Nos. 57/8	—
Nos. 59/73	*from* × 4
Nos. 74/82	*from* × 2
Nos. 83/109	*from* × 3
Nos. 110/13	*from* × 2
Nos. 116/17	*from* × 3
Nos. 118/27	—
Nos. 128/50	*from* × 4
Nos. 151/65	—
Nos. 166/78	*from* × 10
Nos. 179/83	*from* × 4
Nos. 184/206	*from* × 15
No. 207	—
Nos. 208/54	*from* × 15
Nos. 256/62*c*	*from* × 10
Nos. 264*a*/*b*	*from* × 2
Nos. 265/6	*from* × 20
Nos. 270/4	—
Nos. 281/5	*from* × 10
Nos. 286/308	*from* × 12
Nos. 309/13	—
Nos. F1/37	—

PERKINS BACON "CANCELLED". For notes on these handstamps, showing "CANCELLED" between horizontal bars forming an oval, see Catalogue Introduction.

1

2 Large Star

3 Small Star

(Dies eng W. Humphrys. Recess P.B.)

1860 (1 Nov–15 Nov). W 2. (a) *Imperf.*
1 1 1d. carmine-rose . . £2750 £800
2 2d. blue . . £5500 £1500
3 6d. green . . £4000 £800

(b) *Clean-cut perf* 14–15½

4 1 1d. carmine-rose . . £1300 £250
5 2d. blue . . £500 £100
a. Imperf between (horiz pair) . . † —
6 6d. green (15 Nov) . . £550 65·00

1860–61. W 3. (a) *Clean-cut perf* 14–15½
7 1 2d. blue . . £500 £100
a. Imperf between (horiz pair) . . † £1100
8 3d. brown (15.4.61) . . £300 65·00
a. Re-entry . . — £200
b. Retouch (R. 2/8) . . — £200
9 6d. green . . £600 65·00
10 1s. violet (15.11.60) (H/S "CANCELLED" in oval £3750) . . £550 85·00
11 "REGISTERED" (6d.) olive-yellow (1.61) (H/S "CANCELLED" in oval £3750) £375 80·00
a. Imperf between (pair) . . £2750

(b) *Clean-cut perf* 14 *at Somerset House* (7.61)

12 1 1d. carmine-rose (H/S "CANCELLED" in oval £3000) . . £130 42·00
13 2d. blue (H/S "CANCELLED" in oval £3000) . . £325 55·00

(c) *Rough perf* 14–15½ (9.61)

14 1 1d. carmine-rose . . 75·00 32·00
15 2d. blue . . £110 28·00
a. Imperf between (horiz pair) . . £1800
16 3d. brown . . 50·00 32·00
a. Imperf vert (horiz pair) . . £1800
b. Re-entry . . £200 £110
c. Retouch (R. 2/8) . . — £110
17 6d. deep green (H/S "CANCELLED" in oval £3750) . . £130 27·00
18 6d. yellow-green . . £225 27·00
19 1s. violet . . £375 80·00
20 "REGISTERED" (6d.) orange-yellow . . 55·00 38·00

The perforation of No. 8 is that known as "intermediate between clean-cut and rough".

The 3d. re-entry which occurs on one stamp in the second row, shows doubling of the left-hand arabesque and the retouch has redrawn spandrel dots under "EN" of "PENCE", a single dot in the centre of the circle under "E" and the bottom outer frame liner closer to the spandrel's frame line.

(Printed and perforated by Thomas Ham, Brisbane)

1862–67. *Thick toned paper. No wmk.* (a) P 13 (1862–63).
21 1 1d. Indian red (16.12.62) . . £275 60·00
22 1d. orange-vermilion (2.63) . . 65·00 12·00
a. Imperf (pair) . . — £600
b. Imperf between (horiz pair) . . † —
23 2d. pale blue (16.12.62) . . 90·00 27·00
24 2d. blue . . 45·00 9·00
a. Imperf (pair) . . — £600
b. Imperf between (horiz pair) . . † £950
c. Imperf between (vert pair) . . £1300
25 3d. brown . . 65·00 32·00
a. Re-entry . . — £110
b. Retouch (R. 2/8) . . — £110
26 6d. apple-green (17.4.63) . . 95·00 15·00
27 6d. yellow-green . . 85·00 12·00
a. Imperf between (horiz pair) . . † £1100
28 6d. pale bluish green . . £150 27·00
a. Imperf (pair) . . — £600
29 1s. grey (14.7.63) . . £150 22·00
a. Imperf between (horiz pair) . . † £1200
b. Imperf between (vert pair) . . † —
s. Handstamped "Specimen" . . 40·00

The top or bottom row of perforation was sometimes omitted from the sheet, resulting in stamps perforated on three sides only.

(*b*) *P* 12½×13 (1863–67)

30 1 1d. orange-vermilion .. .. 65·00 27·00
31 2d. blue .. .. 55·00 20·00
32 3d. brown .. .. 70·00 25·00
a. Re-entry .. .. — 95·00
b. Retouch (R. 2/8) .. .. .. — 95·00
33 6d. apple-green .. .. 95·00 30·00
34 6d. yellow-green .. .. 95·00 30·00
34*a* 6d. pale bluish green .. .. ..
35 1s. grey .. .. £190 35·00
a. Imperf between (horiz pair) .. ..

The previously listed stamps perforated 13 round holes come from the same perforating machine as Nos. 21/9 after the pins had been replaced. The holes vary from rough to clean-cut.

1864–65. *W* **3**. (*a*) *P* 13.
44 1 1d. orange-vermilion (1.65) .. .. 65·00 22·00
a. Imperf between (horiz pair) £475
45 2d. pale blue (1.65) .. .. .. 65·00 16·00
46 2d. deep blue .. .. 65·00 16·00
a. Imperf between (vert pair) £950
b. Bisected (1d.) (on cover) .. .. † £2000
47 6d. yellow-green (1.65) .. .. .. £120 22·00
48 6d. deep green .. .. £140 22·00
49 "REGISTERED" (6d.) orge-yell (21.6.64) 85·00 35·00
a. Double printed £800
b. Imperf .. ..

(*b*) *P* 12½ × 13

50 1 1d. orange-vermilion .. .. .. 95·00 45·00
50*a* 2d. deep blue .. .. £120 45·00

1866 (24 Jan). *Wmk* "QUEENSLAND/POSTAGE—POSTAGE/STAMPS—STAMPS" *in three lines in script capitals with double wavy lines above and below the wmk and single wavy lines with projecting sprays between each line of words. There are ornaments ("fleurons") between* "POSTAGE" "POSTAGE" *and between* "STAMPS" "STAMPS". *Single stamps only show a portion of one or two letters of this wmk.* (*a*) *P* 13.
51 1 1d. orange-vermilion .. .. .. £130 27·00
52 2d. blue .. .. 50·00 17·00

(*b*) *P* 12½ × 13

52*a* 1 1d. orange-vermilion .. .. .. £160 42·00
52*b* 2d. blue .. .. £160 42·00

1866 (24 Sept). *Lithographed on thick paper. No wmk. P* 13.
53 1 4d. slate .. .. £180 23·00
a. Re-entry .. .. — 95·00
b. Retouch (R. 2/8) .. .. .. — 95·00
s. Handstamped "Specimen" .. .. 40·00
55 4d. lilac .. .. £130 18·00
a. Re-entry .. .. — 80·00
b. Retouch (R. 2/8) .. .. .. — 80·00
56 4d. reddish lilac .. .. £130 18·00
a. Re-entry .. .. — 80·00
b. Retouch (R. 2/8) .. .. .. — 80·00
57 5s. bright rose .. .. £350 95·00
s. Handstamped "Specimen" .. .. 50·00
58 5s. pale rose .. .. £275 70·00
a. Imperf between (vert pair) .. .. † £1100

The 4d. is from a transfer taken from the 3d. plate and the 5s. was taken from the 1s. plate, the final "s" being added. The alteration in the values was made by hand on the stone, and there are many varieties, such as tall and short letters in "FOUR PENCE", some of the letters of "FOUR" smudged out, and differences in the position of the two words.

4

1868–74. *Wmk small truncated Star, W* **4** *on each stamp, and the word* "QUEENSLAND" *in single-lined Roman capitals four times in each sheet.* (*a*) *P* 13.
59 1 1d. orange-vermilion (18.1.71) .. .. 45·00 4·50
60 2d. pale blue .. .. 45·00 4·50
61 2d. blue (3.4.68) .. .. 40·00 2·75
62 2d. bright blue .. .. 50·00 2·75
63 2d. greenish blue .. .. 85·00 2·50
64 2d. dark blue .. .. 45·00 2·50
a. Imperf .. ..
65 3d. olive-green (27.2.71) .. .. 85·00 6·00
a. Re-entry .. .. — 35·00
b. Retouch (R. 2/8) .. .. .. — 35·00
66 3d. greenish grey .. .. .. £100 5·50
a. Re-entry .. .. — 32·00
b. Retouch (R. 2/8) .. .. .. — 32·00
67 3d. brown .. .. 80·00 5·50
a. Re-entry .. .. — 32·00
b. Retouch (R. 2/8) .. .. .. — 32·00
68 6d. yellow-green (10.11.71) .. .. £140 7·00
69 6d. green .. .. £130 10·00
70 6d. deep green .. .. £170 17·00
71 1s. greenish grey (13.11.72) .. .. £375 40·00
72 1s. brownish grey .. .. .. £375 40·00
73 1s. mauve (19.2.74) .. .. .. £225 22·00
59s/73s H/S "Specimen" .. *Set of* 5 £180

(*b*) *P* 12 (about Feb 1874)

74 1 1d. orange-vermilion .. .. .. £275 24·00
75 2d. blue .. .. £600 38·00
76 3d. greenish grey .. .. .. — £160
a. Re-entry .. ..
b. Retouch (R. 2.8) .. .. ..
77 3d. brown £350 £160
a. Re-entry .. ..
b. Retouch (R. 2/8) .. .. ..
78 6d. green .. .. £850 40·00
79 1s. mauve .. .. £400 42·00

(*c*) *P* 13 × 12

80 1 1d. orange-vermilion .. .. .. — £170
81 2d. blue .. .. £850 40·00
82 3d. greenish grey .. .. .. — £275

Reprints were made in 1895 of all five values on the paper of the regular issue, and perforated 13; the colours are:—1d. orange and orange-brown, 2d. dull blue and bright blue, 3d. deep brown, 6d. yellow-green, 1s. red-violet and dull violet. The "Registered" was also reprinted with these on the same paper, but perforated 12. One sheet of the 2d. reprint is known to have had the perforations missing between the fourth and fifth vertical rows.

5

6

(4d., litho. Other values recess)

1868–78. *Wmk Crown and Q, W* **5**. (*a*) *P* 13 (1868–75).
83 1 1d. orange-vermilion (10.11.68) .. .. 55·00 4·50
a. Imperf (pair) £200
84 1d. pale rose-red (4.11.74) .. .. 55·00 8·50
85 1d. deep rose-red .. .. .. 95·00 9·00
86 2d. pale blue (4.11.74) .. .. .. 50·00 1·75
87 2d. deep blue (20.11.68) .. .. .. 40·00 4·50
a. Imperf (pair) £300
b. Imperf between (vert pair) .. .. † —
88 3d. brown (11.6.75) .. .. .. 75·00 12·00
a. Re-entry .. .. — 55·00
b. Retouch (R. 2/8) .. .. .. — 55·00
89 4d. yellow (1.1.75) .. .. .. £800 50·00
s. Handstamped "Specimen" .. .. 65·00
90 6d. deep green (9.4.69) .. .. .. £120 9·00
91 6d. yellow-green .. .. .. £100 6·50
92 6d. pale apple-green (1.1.75) .. .. £130 9·00
a. Imperf (pair) £300
93 1s. mauve .. .. £190 35·00

(*b*) *P* 12 (1876–78)

94 1 1d. deep orange-vermilion .. .. 38·00 5·00
95 1d. pale orange-vermilion .. .. 40·00 5·00
a. Imperf between (vert pair) .. .. † —
96 1d. rose-red .. .. 48·00 10·00
97 1d. flesh .. .. 65·00 10·00
98 2d. pale blue .. .. 85·00 15·00
99 2d. bright blue .. .. 30·00 1·00
100 2d. deep blue .. .. 32·00 1·50
101 3d. brown .. .. 65·00 9·00
a. Re-entry .. .. — 45·00
b. Retouch (R. 2/8) .. .. .. — 45·00
102 4d. yellow .. .. £650 25·00
103 4d. buff .. .. £650 23·00
104 6d. deep green .. .. £140 7·50
105 6d. green .. .. £130 4·25
106 6d. yellow-green .. .. £140 4·50
107 6d. apple-green .. .. £150 7·00
108 1s. mauve .. .. 48·00 9·00
109 1s. purple .. .. £140 5·00
a. Imperf between (vert pair) .. .. † —

(*c*) *P* 13 × 12 *or* 12 × 13

110 1 1d. orange-vermilion .. .. .. — £150
110*a* 1d. rose-red .. ..
111 2d. deep blue £1100 £250
112 4d. yellow .. .. — £300
113 6d. deep green .. .. — £300

(*d*) *P* 12½ × 13

114 1 1d. orange-vermilion .. .. .. — £350
115 2d. deep blue .. .. — £350
115*a* 6d. yellow-green .. ..

(*e*) *P* 12½

115*b* 1 2d. deep blue .. ..

Reprints exist from 1895 of the 1d., 2d., 3d., 6d. and 1s. on thicker paper, Wmk *W* **6**, and in different shades from the originals.

1879. *No wmk. P* 12.
116 1 6d. pale emerald-green .. .. .. £180 26·00
a. Imperf between (horiz pair) .. .. † £650
117 1s. mauve (*fiscal-cancel* £5) .. .. £110 55·00

No. 117 has a very indistinct lilac *burelé* band at back.

Nos. 116/17 can be found showing portions of a papermaker's watermark, either T. H. Saunders & Co or A. Pirie & Sons.

1881. *Lithographed from transfers from the* 1s. *die. Wmk Crown and Q, W* **6**. *P* 12.
118 1 2s. pale blue (6 Apr) .. .. .. 75·00 25·00
119 2s. blue (*fiscal-cancel* £4) .. .. 75·00 25·00
a. Imperf vert (horiz pair) .. ..
120 2s. deep blue (*fiscal-cancel* £4) .. .. 85·00 25·00
121 2s. 6d. dull scarlet (28 Aug) .. .. £120 50·00
122 2s. 6d. bright scarlet (*fiscal-cancel* £4) £140 50·00
123 5s. pale yellow-ochre (28 Aug) .. .. £160 75·00
124 5s. yellow-ochre (*fiscal-cancel* £5) .. £160 75·00
125 10s. reddish brown (Mar) £350 £130
a. Imperf £375
126 10s. bistre-brown £350 £130
127 20s. rose (*fiscal-cancel* £7) £700 £140

Of the 2s. and 20s. stamps there are five types of each, and of the other values ten types of each.

Beware of fiscally used copies that have been cleaned and provided with forged postmarks.

7

Die I

Die II

Dies I and II often occur in the same sheet.

Die I. The white horizontal inner line of the triangle in the u right-hand corner merges into the outer white line of the above the "L".

Die II. The same line is short and does not touch the inner ova

1879–80. *Typo. P* 12. (*a*) *Wmk Crown and Q, W* **5**.
128 7 1d. reddish brown (Die I) (15.5.79) .. 70·00 1
a. Die II £100 1
ab. "QOEENSLAND" £850
129 1d. orange-brown (Die I) £100 1
130 2d. blue (Die I) (10.4.79) .. .. 60·00 1
a. "PENGE" (R. 12/6) £650
b. "QUEENSbAND" (R. 5/6) .. .. —
c. "QU" joined .. .. —
131 4d. orange-yellow (6.6.79) £375 4

(*b*) *No wmk, with lilac burelé band on back*
132 7 1d. reddish brown (Die I) (21.10.79) .. £300 4
a. Die II £325 7
ab. "QOEENSLAND" .. .. .. — £1
133 2d. blue (Die I) (21.10.79) £375 2
a. "PENGE" (R. 12/6) £3250
b. "QUEENSbAND" (R. 5/6) .. ..

(*c*) *Wmk Crown and Q, W* **6**
134 7 1d. reddish brown (Die I) (31.10.79) .. 38·00
a. Imperf between (pair) .. .. †
b. Die II .. .. 50·00
ba. "QOEENSLAND" £200 4
bb. Imperf between (pair) .. .. †
135 1d. dull orange (Die I) .. .. .. 22·00
a. Die II .. .. 25·00
ab. "QOEENSLAND" .. .. .. 60·00 2
136 1d. scarlet (Die I) (7.3.81) .. .. 17·00
a. Die II .. .. 19·00
ab. "QOEENSLAND" .. .. .. 80·00 24
137 2d. blue (Die I) (10.4.79) .. .. 30·00
a. "PENGE" £120 4
b. "QUEENSbAND" £120 4
c. Die II .. .. 35·00
138 2d. grey-blue (Die I) .. .. .. 30·00
a. "PENGE" £120 40
b. "QUEENSbAND" £120 40
c. Die II .. .. 35·00
139 2d. bright blue (Die I) .. .. .. 35·00
a. "PENGE" £130 40
b. "QUEENSbAND" £130 40
c. Imperf between (pair) £500
d. Die II .. .. 38·00
140 2d. deep blue (Die I) .. .. .. 38·00 1
a. "PENGE" £140 40
b. "QUEENSbAND" £140 40
c. Die II .. .. 30·00 4
141 4d. orange-yellow £130 10
a. Imperf between (pair) .. ..
142 6d. deep green .. .. 70·00 4
a. Imperf between (pair) .. ..
143 6d. yellow-green .. .. .. 75·00 4
144 1s. deep violet (3.80) .. .. .. 65·00 5
145 1s. pale lilac .. .. 55·00 6

The variety "QO" is No. 48 in the first arrangement, and No in a later arrangement on the sheets.

All these values have been seen imperf and unused, but we h no evidence that any of them were used in this condition.

The above were printed in sheets of 120, from plates made u 30 groups of four electrotypes. There are four different types in e group, and two such groups of four are known of the 1d. and thus giving eight varieties of these two values. There was sc resetting of the first plate of the 1d., and there are several plate the 2d.; the value in the first plate of the latter value is in thin letters, and in the last plate three types in each group of four h the "TW" of "TWO" joined, the letters of "PENCE" are larger a therefore much closer together, and in one type the "O" of "TW is oval, that letter being circular in the other types.

(8)

9

10

1880 (21 Feb). *Surch with T* **8**.
151 7 ½d. on 1d. (No. 134) (Die I) £190 £1
a. Die II £475 £3
ab. "QOEENSLAND" £1000 £7

Examples with "Half-penny" reading downwards are forg surcharges.

(Eng H. Bourne. Recess Govt Printing Office, Brisbane fro plates made by B.W.)

1882 (13 Apr)–**95.** *P* 12. (*a*) *W* **5** (*twice sideways*). *Thin pap*
152 9 2s. bright blue (14.4.82) .. .. 70·00 25·
153 2s. 6d. vermilion (12.7.82) .. .. 65·00 20·
154 5s. rose .. .. 60·00 22·
155 10s. brown (12.7.82) .. .. .. £120 40·
156 £1 deep green (30.5.83) £275 £1
a. Re-entry (R.1/2) .. .. .. — £1
b. Retouch (R.6/4) .. .. .. — £1
152s/6s (*ex* 2s. 6d.) H/S "Specimen" *Set of* 4 £160

(*b*) *W* **10**. *Thick paper* (10.11.86)
157 9 2s. bright blue .. .. 80·00 30·
158 2s. 6d. vermilion .. .. .. 40·00 22·
159 5s. rose .. .. 38·00 30·

10s. brown £100 45·00
£1 deep green £180 60·00
a. Re-entry (R.1/2) — £100
b. Retouch (R.6/4) — £100

(*c*) *W* **6** (*twice sideways*). *Thin paper* (1895)
2s. 6d. vermilion 42·00 30·00
5s. rose 48·00 20·00
10s. brown £225 60·00
£1 deep green £190 75·00
a. Re-entry (R.1/2) — £110
b. Retouch (R.6/4) — £110

re-entry on the £1 shows as a double bottom frame line e retouch occurs alongside the bottom right numeral. also Nos. 270/1, 272/4 and 309/12.

11

12

12 the shading lines do not extend entirely across, as in T **11**, eaving a white line down the front of the throat and point of st.

(1 Aug)–**91.** *W* **6.** (*a*) *P* 12.
11 1d. pale vermilion-red (23.11.82) 4·00 40
a. Double impression
1d. deep vermilion-red 4·00 40
2d. blue 6·00 40
a. Imperf between (horiz pair)
4d. pale yellow (18.4.83) 14·00 2·25
a. "PENGE" for "PENCE" (R. 8/1) £140 45·00
b. "EN" joined in "PENCE" (R. 4/6) 95·00 30·00
c. Imperf (11.91)
6d. green (6.11.82) 10·00 1·25
1s. violet (6.2.83) 22·00 2·50
1s. lilac 11·00 2·25
1s. deep mauve 11·00 2·00
1s. pale mauve 12·00 2·00
a. Imperf † —

(*b*) *P* 9½×12 (1884)
11 1d. pale red 75·00 28·00
2d. blue £250 45·00
1s. mauve £130 35·00

above were printed from plates made up of groups of four otypes as previously. In the 1d. the words of value are ed by a full stop. There are four types of the 4d., 6d., and 1s., types of the 1d., and twelve types of the 2d.
. 169c is from a sheet used at Roma post office and comes lled with the "46" numeral postmark.

(5 May)–**89.** *W* **6.** (*a*) *P* 12.
12 1d. vermilion-red 3·50 40
2d. blue 6·50 40
a. Oval white flaw on Queen's head behind diadem (R. 12/5) 25·00 7·50
2s. deep brown (12.3.89) 70·00 38·00
2s. pale brown 60·00 28·00

(*b*) *P* 9½×12
12 2d. blue £225 45·00

ese are from new plates; four types of each value grouped as e. The 1d. is without stop. In all values No. 2 in each group of has the "L" and "A" of "QUEENSLAND" joined at the foot, and of the 2d. has "P" of word "PENCE" with a long downstroke. e 2d. is known bisected and used as a 1d. value.

13

14

–**94.** *W* **6** (*sideways on* ½*d.*). *P* 12½, 13 (*comb machine*).
13 ½d. pale green 4·00 1·25
½d. deep green 3·50 1·25
½d. deep blue-green 3·50 1·25
12 1d. vermilion-red 2·75 20
a. Imperf 38·00 38·00
b. Oval broken by tip of bust (R.10/3) 22·00 5·00
c. Double impression † £225
2d. blue (old plate) 4·75 20
2d. pale blue (old plate) 4·75 20
2d. pale blue (retouched plate) 4·50 40
a. "FWO" for "TWO" (R.8/7) — 22·00
14 2½d. carmine 10·00 1·25
12 3d. brown 8·50 2·25
11 4d. yellow 13·00 2·00
a. "PENGE" for "PENCE" (R.8/1) 65·00 22·00
b. "EN" joined in "PENCE" (R.4/6) 48·00 16·00
4d. orange 17·00 2·00
a. "PENGE" for "PENCE" (R.8/1) 75·00 22·00
b. "EN" joined in "PENCE" (R.4/6) 55·00 16·00
4d. lemon 20·00 2·25
a. "PENGE" for "PENCE" (R.8/1) 85·00 28·00
b. "EN" joined in "PENCE" (R.4/6) 65·00 20·00
6d. green 10·00 1·50
12 2s. red-brown 40·00 16·00
2s. pale brown 48·00 18·00

his issue is perforated by a new vertical comb machine, gauging ut 12¾ × 12¾. The 3d. is from a plate similar to those of the issue, No. 2 in each group of four types having "L" and "A" ed at the foot. The ½d. and 2½d. are likewise in groups of four s, but the differences are very minute. In the retouched plate of 2d. the letters "L" and "A" no longer touch in No. 2 of each group the "P" in No. 3 is normal.

1895. A. *Thick paper. W* **10.** (*a*) *P* 12½, 13.
202 **12** 1d. vermilion-red (16.1.95) 3·25 20
a. Oval broken by tip of bust (R. 10/3) 27·00 5·00
203 1d. red-orange 3·25 20
a. Oval broken by tip of bust (R. 10/3) 27·00 5·00
204 2d. blue (retouched plate) (16.1.95) 3·75 30
a. "FWO" for "TWO" (R. 8/7) 60·00 22·00

(*b*) *P* 12
205 **11** 1s. mauve (8.95) 13·00 4·00

B. *Unwmkd paper; with blue burelé band at back. P* 12½, 13
206 **12** 1d. vermilion-red (19.2.95) 2·25 20
a. Oval broken by tip of bust (R. 10/3) 20·00 5·00
b. "PE" of "PENNY" omitted (R. 1/2) £130 80·00
206*c* 1d. red-orange 2·25 20

C. *Thin paper. Crown and Q faintly impressed. P* 12½, 13
207 **12** 2d. blue (retouched plate) (6.95) 11·00
a. "FWO" for "TWO" (R. 8/7) 90·00

15

16

17

18

1895–96. A. *W* **6** (*sideways on* ½*d.*). (*a*) *P* 12½, 13.
208 **15** ½d. green (11.5.95) 1·40 75
a. Double impression
209 ½d. deep green 1·40 75
a. Printed both sides 85·00
210 **16** 1d. orange-red (28.2.95) 3·25 20
211 1d. pale red 3·50 20
212 2d. blue (19.6.95) 7·50 35
213 **17** 2½d. carmine (8.95) 12·00 3·75
214 2½d. rose 13·00 3·75
215 **18** 5d. purple-brown (10.95) 16·00 3·75

(*b*) *P* 12
217 **16** 1d. red (8.95) 38·00 13·00
218 2d. blue (8.95) 38·00 17·00

B. *Thick paper. W* **10** (*sideways*) (*part only on each stamp*).

(*a*) *P* 12½, 13
219 **15** ½d. green (6.8.95) 2·75 1·25
220 ½d. deep green 2·75 1·25

(*b*) *P* 12
221 **15** ½d. green 15·00
222 ½d. deep green 15·00

C. *No wmk; with blue burelé band at back.* (*a*) *P* 12½, 13
223 **15** ½d. green (1.8.95) 3·50 1·50
a. Without *burelé* band 40·00
224 ½d. deep green 3·50

(*b*) *P* 12
225 **15** ½d. green 18·00
a. Without *burelé* band 75·00

Nos. 223a and 225a are from the margins of the sheet.

D. *Thin paper, with Crown and Q faintly impressed. P* 12½, 13
227 **15** ½d. green 1·75 1·75
228 **16** 1d. orange-red 3·25 1·00

19

1896. *W* **6.** *P* 12½, 13.
229 **19** 1d. vermilion 10·00 50

Used examples of a 6d. green as Type **19** (figures in lower corners only) are known, mostly with readable 1902 postmark dates. It is believed that this 6d. was prepared, but not officially issued (*Price* £2500 *used*).

20 21 22

23

24

25

Die I

Die II

Two Dies of 4d.:

Die I. Serif of horizontal bar on lower right 4d. is clear of vertical frame line.
Die II. Serif joins vertical frame line.

1897–1908. *Figures in all corners. W* **6** (*sideways on* ½*d.*). *P* 12½, 13.
231 **20** ½d. deep green 3·75 4·25
a. Perf 12 — £100
232 **21** 1d. orange-vermilion 2·00 15
233 1d. vermilion 2·00 15
a. Perf 12 (1903) 3·25 70
234 2d. blue 2·25 15
a. Cracked plate 60·00 20·00
b. Perf 12 (1903) — 5·00
235 2d. deep blue 2·25 15
a. Cracked plate 60·00 20·00
236 **22** 2½d. rose (10.98) 17·00 17·00
237 2½d. purple/*blue* (20.1.99) 9·50 1·50
238 2½d. brown-purple/*blue* 9·50 1·50
239 2½d. slate/*blue* (5.08) 12·00 3·00
240 **21** 3d. brown (10.98) 10·00 1·50
241 3d. deep brown 8·00 1·50
242 3d. reddish brown (1906) 8·00 1·50
243 3d. grey-brown (1907) 12·00 1·50
244 4d. yellow (Die I) (10.98) 8·00 1·50
a. Die II 20·00 2·50
245 4d. yellow-buff (Die I) 8·00 1·50
a. Die II 18·00 2·50
246 **23** 5d. purple-brown 8·00 1·50
247 5d. dull brown (1906) 9·00 2·25
248 5d. black-brown (1907) 10·00 2·50
249 **21** 6d. green (1.4.98) 7·50 1·75
250 6d. yellow-green 6·50 1·75
251 **24** 1s. pale mauve (1.7.99) 13·00 1·75
252 1s. dull mauve 13·00 1·75
253 1s. bright mauve 15·00 2·50
254 **25** 2s. turquoise-green 30·00 17·00

The 1d. perf 12×9½ was not an authorised issue.
The cracked plate variety on the 2d. developed during 1901 and shows as a white break on the Queen's head and neck. The electro was later replaced.

1897–8. *W* **6** (*a*) *Zigzag roulette in black.* (*b*) *The same but plain.* (*c*) *Roulette* (*a*) *and also* (*b*). (*d*) *Roulette* (*b*) *and perf* 12½, 13. (*e*) *Roulette* (*a*) *and perf* 12½, 13. (*f*) *Compound of* (*a*), (*b*), *and perf* 12½, 13.
256 **21** 1d. vermilion (*a*) 11·00 8·00
257 1d. vermilion (*b*) 4·50 3·50
258 1d. vermilion (*c*) 11·00 14·00
259 1d. vermilion (*d*) 7·00 5·00
260 1d. vermilion (*e*) 65·00 80·00
261 1d. vermilion (*f*) 85·00 85·00

26

27

(Des M. Kellar)

1899–1906. *W* **6.** *P* 12½, 13.
262 **26** ½d. deep green 2·50 1·00
a. Grey-green 2·25 1·00
b. Green (*p* 12) (1903) 2·75 1·00
c. Pale green (1906) 2·25 1·00

Stamps of T **26** without wmk, are proofs.

(Des F. Elliott)

1900 (19 June). *Charity. T* **27** *and horiz design showing Queen Victoria in medallion inscr* "PATRIOTIC FUND 1900". *W* **6.** *P* 12.
264*a* 1d. (6d.) claret £120 £110
264*b* 2d. (1s.) violet £300 £275

These stamps, sold at 6d. and 1s. respectively, paid postage of 1d. and 2d. only, the difference being contributed to a Patriotic Fund.

28

QUEENSLAND
A

QUEENSLAND
B

TWO TYPES OF "QUEENSLAND". Three different duty plates, each 120 (12×10), were produced for Type **28**. The first contained country inscriptions as Type A and was only used for No. 265. The second duty plate used for Nos. 265/6 and 282/4 contained 117 examples as Type A and 3 as Type B occurring on R. 1/6, R. 2/6 and R. 3/6. The third plate, used for Nos. 266, 283 and 285, had all inscriptions as Type B.

(Typo Victoria Govt Printer, Melbourne)

1903 (4 July)–**05.** *W w* **10.** *P* 12½.
265 **28** 9d. brown and ultramarine (A) .. .. 16·00 2·75
266 9d. brown and ultramarine (B) (1905) .. 16·00 2·75

1903 (Oct). *As Nos.* 162 *and* 165. *W* **6** (*twice sideways*). *P* 12½, 13 (*irregular line*).
270 **9** 2s. 6d. vermilion .. .. 60·00 32·00
271 £1 deep green £950 £500
a. Re-entry (R.1/2) .. .. .. — £750
b. Retouch (R.6/4) .. .. .. — £750

(Litho Govt Ptg Office, Brisbane, from transfers of the recess plates)

1905 (Nov)–**06.** *W* **6** (*twice sideways*).
(*a*) *P* 12½, 13 (*irregular line*)
272 **9** £1 deep green £400 £100
a. Re-entry (R.1/2) .. .. .. — £160
b. Retouch (R.6/4) .. .. .. — £160
(*b*) *P* 12
273 **9** 5s. rose (7.06) .. .. 80·00 65·00
274 £1 deep green (7.06) .. .. .. £250 90·00
a. Re-entry (R.1/2) £375 £150
b. Retouch (R.6/4) £375 £150

30

32

Redrawn types of T **21**

T **30**. The head is redrawn, the top of the crown is higher and touches the frame, as do also the back of the chignon and the point of the bust. The forehead is filled in with lines of shading, and the figures in the corners appear to have been redrawn also.

T **32**. The forehead is plain (white instead of shaded), and though the top of the crown is made higher, it does not touch the frame; but the point of the bust and the chignon still touch The figure in the right lower corner does not touch the line below, and has not the battered appearance of that in the first redrawn type. The stamps are very clearly printed, the lines of shading being distinct.

1906 (Sept). *W* **6**. *P* 12½, 13 (*comb*).
281 **30** 2d. dull blue (*shades*) .. .. .. 8·00 3·00

(Typo Victoria Govt Printer, Melbourne)

1906 (Sept)–**10.** *Wmk Crown and double-lined A, W w* **11**.
(*a*) *P* 12 × 12½.
282 **28** 9d. brown and ultramarine (A) .. 30·00 3·50
283 9d. brown and ultramarine (B) .. 13·00 3·25
283*a* 9d. pale brown and blue (A) .. .. 30·00 4·00
284 9d. pale brown and blue (B) .. .. 13·00 3·50
(*b*) *P* 11 (1910)
285 **28** 9d. brown and blue (B) .. .. .. — £200

33

1907–11. *W* **33**. (*a*) *P* 12½, 13 (*comb*).
286 **26** ½d. deep green .. .. 1·75 1·75
287 ½d. deep blue-green .. .. 1·75 1·75
288 **21** 1d. vermilion .. .. 2·25 30
a. Imperf (pair) £190
289 **30** 2d. dull blue .. .. 4·00 35
289*a* 2d. bright blue (3.08) .. .. .. 13·00 4·50
290 **32** 2d. bright blue (4.08) .. .. .. 3·25 30
291 **21** 3d. pale brown (8.08) .. .. .. 12·00 1·50
292 3d. bistre-brown .. .. 12·00 1·60
293 4d. yellow (Die I) .. .. .. 11·00 2·25
a. Die II .. .. 26·00 3·75
294 4d. grey-black (Die I) (4.09) .. .. 14·00 2·75
a. Die II .. .. 32·00 5·50
295 **23** 5d. dull brown .. .. 9·00 4·00
295*a* 5d. sepia (12.09) .. .. 14·00 4·50
296 **21** 6d. yellow-green .. .. 10·00 3·25
297 6d. bright green .. .. 11·00 3·50
298 **24** 1s. violet (1908) .. .. 12·00 2·25
299 1s. bright mauve .. .. 13·00 2·25
300 **25** 2s. turquoise-green (8.08) .. .. 30·00 13·00

Stamps of this issue also exist with the irregular line perforation 12½, 13. This was used when the comb perforation was under repair.

(*b*) *P* 13 × 11 *to* 12½ (May 1911)
301 **26** ½d. deep green .. .. 5·00 3·50
302 **21** 1d. vermilion .. .. 6·00 1·50
303 **32** 2d. blue .. .. 7·50 3·50
304 **21** 3d. bistre-brown .. .. 13·00 6·50
305 4d. grey-black .. .. 35·00 20·00
306 **23** 5d. dull brown .. .. 20·00 20·00
307 **21** 6d. yellow-green .. .. 20·00 20·00
308 **23** 1s. violet .. .. 35·00 22·00

The perforation (*b*) is from a machine introduced to help cope with the demands caused by the introduction of penny postage. The three rows at top (or bottom) of the sheet show varieties gauging 13 × 11½, 13 × 11, and 13 × 12 respectively, these are obtainable in strips of three showing the three variations.

(Litho Govt Ptg Office, Brisbane)

1907 (Oct)–**12.** *W* **33** (*twice sideways*). *P* 12½, 13 (*irregular line*).
309 **9** 2s. 6d. vermilion .. .. 42·00 32·00
a. Dull orange (1910) .. .. .. 60·00 55·00
b. Reddish orange (1912) £160 £190
310 5s. rose (12.07) .. .. 55·00 35·00
a. Deep rose (1910) .. .. .. 65·00 50·00
b. Carmine-red (1912) £160 £225
311 10s. blackish brown .. .. £100 50·00
a. Sepia (1912) £300
312 £1 bluish green .. .. £190 85·00
a. Re-entry (R. 1/2) .. .. .. — £140
b. Retouch (R. 6/4) .. .. .. — £140
c. Deep bluish green (1910) £400 £250
ca. Re-entry (R. 1/2) .. .. .. — £350
cb. Retouch (R. 6/4) .. .. .. — £350
d. Yellow-green (1912) £850
da. Re-entry (R. 1/2) .. .. ..
db. Retouch (R. 6/4) .. .. ..

The 1912 printings are on thinner, whiter paper.

The lithographic stone used for Nos. 272/4 and 309/12 took the full sheet of 30 so the varieties on the £1 recess-printed version also appear on the stamps printed by lithography.

1911. *W* **33**. *Perf irregular compound,* 10½ *to* 12½.
313 **21** 1d. vermilion £350 £190

This was from another converted machine, formerly used for perforating Railway stamps. The perforation was very unsatisfactory and only one or two sheets were sold.

STAMP BOOKLETS

There are very few surviving examples of Nos. SB1/4. Listings are provided for those believed to have been issued with prices quoted for those known to still exist.

1904 (1 Jan)–**09.** *Black on red cover as No.* SB1 *of New South Wales. Stapled.*
SB1 £1 booklet containing two hundred and forty 1d. in four blocks of 30 and two blocks of 60 ..
a. Red on pink cover (1909) .. ..
b. Blue on pink cover £6000

1904 (1 Jan). *Black on grey cover as No.* SB1. *Stapled.*
SB2 £1 booklet containing one hundred and twenty 2d. in four blocks of 30 .. ..

1910 (May). *Black on cream cover as No.* SB3 *of New South Wales. Stapled.*
SB3 2s. booklet containing eleven ½d. (No. 301), either in block of 6 plus block of 5 or block of 11, and eighteen 1d. (No. 302), either in three blocks of 6 or block of 6 plus block of 12 .. ..

Unsold stock of No. SB3 was uprated with one additional ½d. in May 1911.

1911 (Aug). *Red on pink cover as No.* SB3. *Stapled.*
SB4 2s. booklet containing twelve ½d. (No. 301), either in two blocks of 6 or block of 12, and eighteen 1d. (No. 302), either in three blocks of 6 or block of 6 plus block of 12 .. .. .. £1700
a. Red on white £1700

POSTAL FISCALS

Authorised for use from 1 January 1880 until 1 July 1892

CANCELLATIONS. Beware of stamps which have had pen-cancellations cleaned off and then had faked postmarks applied. Used prices quoted are for postally used examples between the above dates.

F 1

F 2

1866–68. A. *No wmk. P* 13.
F 1 **F 1** 1d. blue .. .. 35·00 9·00
F 2 6d. deep violet .. .. 40·00 40·00
F 3 1s. blue-green .. .. 48·00 22·00
F 4 2s. brown .. .. £100 65·00
F 5 2s. 6d. dull red .. .. £100 55·00
F 6 5s. yellow .. .. £225 75·00
F 6*a* 6s. light brown £550
F 7 10s. green £350 £130
F 8 20s. rose £500 £200

B. *Wmk* F **2**. *P* 13
F 9 **F 1** 1d. blue .. .. 20·00 22·00
F10 6d. deep violet .. .. 40·00 40·00
F11 6d. blue .. .. 90·00 65·00
F12 1s. blue-green .. .. 48·00 35·00
F13 2s. brown .. .. £100 48·00
F13*a* 5s. yellow .. .. £225 80·00
F14 10s. green £375 £130
F15 20s. rose £500 £200

COVER PRICES

Cover factors are quoted at the beginning of each country for most issues to 1945. An explanation of the system can be found on page x. The factors quoted do not, however, apply to philatelic covers.

F 3

F 3*a*

1871–2. *P* 12 *or* 13. A. *Wmk Large Crown and Q, Wmk*
F16 **F 3** 1d. mauve .. .. 14·00
F17 6d. red-brown .. .. 35·00
F18 1s. green .. .. 42·00
F19 2s. blue .. .. 60·00
F20 2s. 6d. brick-red .. .. .. 85·00
F21 5s. orange-brown £120
F22 10s. brown £250
F23 20s. rose £425

B. *No wmk. Blue burelé band at back*
F24 **F 3** 1d. mauve .. .. 18·00
F25 6d. red-brown .. .. 35·00
F26 6d. mauve .. .. 80·00
F27 1s. green .. .. 42·00
F28 2s. blue .. .. 70·00
F29 2s. 6d. vermilion £110
F30 5s. yellow-brown £140
F31 10s. brown £275
F32 20s. rose £425

F 4

F 5

1878–9. A. *No wmk. Lilac burelé band at back. P* 12.
F33 **F 4** 1d. violet .. .. 55·00

B. *Wmk Crown and Q, W* **5**. *P* 12
F34 **F 4** 1d. violet .. .. 22·00

Stamps as Type F **5** were not issued until 1 July 1892. The e ence of postal cancellations on such issues was unauthorised.

Queensland became part of the Commonwealth of Aust on 1 January 1901.

SOUTH AUSTRALIA

PRICES FOR STAMPS ON COVER

Nos. 1/3	*from* × 3
No. 4	†
Nos. 5/12	*from* × 2
Nos. 13/18	*from* × 3
Nos. 19/43	*from* × 4
Nos. 44/9*b*	—
Nos. 50/110	*from* × 3
No. 111	—
Nos. 112/34	*from* × 6
Nos. 135/45	*from* × 3
Nos. 146/66	*from* × 5
Nos. 167/70*a*	*from* × 10
Nos. 171/2*a*	—
Nos. 173/94*a*	*from* × 12
Nos. 195/208	—
Nos. 229/31	*from* × 12
No. 232	—
Nos. 233/42	*from* × 12
Nos. 268/75	*from* × 30
Nos. 276/9	—
Nos. 280/8	*from* × 30
Nos. 289/92	—
Nos. 293/304	*from* × 15
No. 305	—
Nos. O1/13	—
Nos. O14/36	*from* × 20
Nos. O37/42	*from* × 5
Nos. O43/4	*from* × 50
Nos. O45/7	—
Nos. O48/52	*from* × 30
No. O53	—
Nos. O54/85	*from* × 50
Nos. O86/7	—

SPECIMEN OVERPRINTS. Those listed are from U.P distributions between 1889 and 1895. Further "Specim overprints exist, but these were used for other purposes.

KINS BACON "CANCELLED". For notes on these tamps, showing "CANCELLED" between horizontal bars ng an oval, see Catalogue Introduction.

1

2 Large Star

(Eng Wm Humphrys. Recess P.B.)

(26 Oct–1 Nov). *Printed in London.* W **2**. *Imperf.*

No.	Type	Description	Unused	Used
		1d. dark green (H/S "CANCELLED" in oval £4250)	£3000	£425
		2d. rose-carmine (*shades*) (1 Nov) (H/S "CANCELLED" in oval £3250)	£550	80·00
		6d. deep blue (H/S "CANCELLED" in oval £3250)	£2000	£160

Prepared and sent to the Colony, but not issued

1s. vio (II/S "CANCELLED" in oval £5500) £4750

printing of 500,000 of these 1s. stamps was delivered, but, e colour was liable to be confused with that of the 6d. p, this stock was destroyed on 5 June 1857. It is believed surviving examples of No. 4 come from Perkins, Bacon inders which came onto the market in the late 1890s.

oofs of the 1d. and 6d. without wmk exist, and these are l with forged star watermarks added, and are sometimes ed as originals.

r reprints of the above and later issues, see note after No.

-58. *Printed by Printer of Stamps, Adelaide, from rkins, Bacon plates.* W **2**. *Imperf.*

No.	Type	Description	Unused	Used
	1	1d. deep yellow-green (15.6.58)	£5000	£450
		1d. yellow-green (11.10.58)	£4000	£550
		2d. orange-red (23.4.56)	£1500	80·00
		2d. blood-red (14.11.56)	£1300	60·00
		a. Printed on both sides	†	£850
		2d. red (*shades*) (29.10.57)	£650	40·00
		a. Printed on both sides	†	£650
		6d. slate-blue (7.57)	£2250	£160
		1s. red-orange (8.7.57)	—	£475
		1s. orange (11.6.58)	£4000	£375

-59. W **2**. *Rouletted. (This first rouletted issue has the same lours as the local imperf issue).*

No.	Type	Description	Unused	Used
	1	1d. yellow-green (8.1.59)	£500	50·00
		1d. light yellow-green (18.3.59)	£500	55·00
		a. Imperf between (pair)		
		2d. red (17.2.59)	£120	20·00
		a. Printed on both sides	†	£650
		6d. slate-blue (12.12.58)	£400	28·00
		1s. orange (18.3.59)	£850	40·00
		a. Printed on both sides	†	£1100

3

4

(5)

-69. *Second rouletted issue, printed (with the exception of o. 24) in colours only found rouletted or perforated. Surch ith T* **5** *(Nos. 35/7).* W **2**.

No.	Type	Description	Unused	Used
	1	1d. bright yellow-green (22.4.61)	45·00	27·00
		1d. dull blue-green (17.12.63)	42·00	25·00
		1d. sage-green	55·00	30·00
		1d. pale sage-green (27.5.65)	45·00	
		1d. deep green (1864)	£225	65·00
		1d. deep yellow-green (1869)	90·00	
		2d. pale red	65·00	4·00
		b. Printed on both sides	†	£400
		2d. pale vermilion (3.2.63)	50·00	4·00
		2d. bright vermilion (19.8.64)	48·00	3·00
		a. Imperf between (horiz pair)	£750	£325
	3	4d. dull violet (24.1.67)	60·00	18·00
	1	6d. violet-blue (19.3.60)	£150	7·00
		6d. greenish blue (11.2.63)	70·00	4·00
		6d. dull ultramarine (25.4.64)	65·00	4·00
		a. Imperf between (horiz pair)	†	£325
		6d. violet-ultramarine (11.4.68)	£150	6·00
		6d. dull blue (26.8.65)	£100	6·50
		a. Imperf between (pair)	†	£650
		6d. Prussian blue (7.9.69)	£550	50·00
		6d. indigo	—	55·00
	4	9d. grey-lilac (24.12.60)	55·00	9·00
		a. Imperf between (horiz pair)	†	£1100
		10d. on 9d. orange-red (B.) (20.7.66)	£200	30·00
		10d. on 9d. yellow (B.) (29.7.67)	£225	25·00
		10d. on 9d. yellow (Blk.) (14.8.69)	£1200	35·00
		a. Surch inverted at the top	†	£2750
		b. Printed on both sides	†	£850
		c. Roul × perf 10	†	—
	1	1s. yellow (25.10.61)	£450	28·00
		a. Imperf between (vert pair)	†	£1200
		1s. grey-brown (10.4.63)	£160	17·00
		1s. dark grey-brown (26.5.63)	£140	17·00
		1s. chestnut (25.8.63)	£150	11·00
		1s. lake-brown (27.3.65)	£110	12·00
		a. Imperf between (horiz pair)	†	£425
	3	2s. rose-carmine (24.1.67)	£170	26·00
		a. Imperf between (vert pair)	†	£800

68–71. *Remainders of old stock subsequently perforated by the 11½–12½ machine.*

(*a*) *Imperf stamps. P 11½–12½*

No.	Type	Description	Unused	Used
	1	2d. pale vermilion (Feb 1868)	—	£900
		2d. vermilion (18.3.68)	—	£1000

(*b*) *Rouletted stamps. P 11½–12½*

No.	Type	Description	Unused	Used
46	1	1d. bright green (9.11.69)	—	£450
47		2d. pale vermilion (15.8.68)	£1500	£400
48		6d. Prussian blue (8.11.69)	—	£200
		aa. Horiz pair perf all round, roul between		
48*a*		6d. indigo	—	£300
49	4	9d. grey-lilac (29.3.71)	£1500	£160
		a. Perf × roulette	—	£180
49*b*	1	1s. lake-brown (23.5.70)		

1867–70. W **2**. *P 11½–12½ × roulette.*

No.	Type	Description	Unused	Used
50	1	1d. pale bright green (2.11.67)	£150	21·00
51		1d. bright green (1868)	£130	21·00
52		1d. grey-green (26.1.70)	£150	23·00
		a. Imperf between (horiz pair)		
53		1d. blue-green (29.11.67)	£190	35·00
54	3	4d. dull violet (July 1868)	£1500	£140
55		4d. dull purple (1869)	—	95·00
56	1	6d. bright pale blue (29.5.67)	£450	19·00
57		6d. Prussian blue (30.7.67)	£400	19·00
		a. Printed on both sides		
58		6d. indigo (1.8.69)	£500	25·00
59	4	10d. on 9d. yellow (B.) (2.2.69)	£650	35·00
		a. Printed on both sides	—	£600
60	1	1s. chestnut (April 1868)	£250	16·00
61		1s. lake-brown (3.3.69)	£250	16·00

NOTE. The stamps perf 11½, 12½, or compound of the two, are here combined in one list, as both perforations are on the one machine, and all the varieties *may* be found in each sheet of stamps. This method of classifying the perforations by the machines is by far the most simple and convenient.

3-PENCE

(6)

7 (=Victoria W **19**)

1868–79. *Surch with T* **6** *(Nos. 66/8).* W **2**. *P 11½–12½.*

No.	Type	Description	Unused	Used
62	1	1d. pale bright green (8.2.68)	£150	24·00
63		1d. grey-green (18.2.68)	£120	45·00
64		1d. dark green (20.3.68)	60·00	20·00
		a. Printed on both sides		
65		1d. deep yellow-green (28.6.72)	55·00	20·00
		a. Imperf between (horiz pair)	†	£500
66	3	3d. on 4d. Prussian blue (Blk.) (7.2.71)	—	£750
67		3d. on 4d. sky-blue (Blk.) (12.8.70)	£275	11·00
		a. Imperf		
		b. Rouletted	—	£550
68		3d. on 4d. deep ultramarine (Blk.) (9.72)	75·00	9·00
		a. Surch double	†	£3500
		b. Additional surch on back	†	£2750
		c. Surch omitted	£16000	£9000
70		4d. dull purple (1.2.68)	65·00	15·00
		a. Imperf between (horiz pair)	†	—
71		4d. dull violet (1868)	60·00	8·00
72	1	6d. bright pale blue (23.2.68)	£300	11·00
73		6d. Prussian blue (29.9.69)	90·00	6·50
		a. Perf 11½×imperf (horiz pair)	†	£500
74		6d. indigo (1869)	£120	17·00
75	4	9d. claret (7.72)	£100	8·00
76		9d. bright mauve (1.11.72)	£100	8·00
		a. Printed on both sides	†	£350
77		9d. red-purple (15.1.74)	65·00	8·00
78		10d. on 9d. yellow (B.) (15.8.68)	£1000	30·00
		a. Wmk Crown and S A (W **10**) (1868)	—	£750
79		10d. on 9d. yellow (Blk.) (13.9.69)	£225	35·00
80	1	1s. lake-brown (9.68)	£150	11·00
81		1s. chestnut (8.10.72)	£120	17·00
82		1s. dark red-brown	90·00	11·00
83		1s. red-brown (6.1.69)	£100	11·00
84	3	2s. pale rose-pink (10.10.69)	£950	£150
85		2s. deep rose-pink (8.69)	—	£100
86		2s. crimson-carmine (16.10.69)	80·00	18·00
87		2s. carmine (1869)	70·00	11·00
		a. Printed on both sides	†	£325

No. 68c comes from two sheets on which, it is believed, some stamps showed the surcharge omitted and others the surcharge double. One of the used examples of No. 68c is known postmarked in 1875 and many of the others in 1879.

No. 78a was a trial printing made to test the perforating machine on the new D.L.R. paper.

1870–71. W **2**. *P* 10.

No.	Type	Description	Unused	Used
88	1	1d. grey-green (6.70)	£120	15·00
89		1d. pale bright green (9.8.70)	£120	15·00
90		1d. bright green (1871)	£100	15·00
91	3	3d. on 4d. dull ultramarine (R.) (6.8.70)	£425	75·00
92		3d. on 4d. pale ultram (Blk.) (14.2.71)	£275	18·00
93		3d. on 4d. ultramarine (Blk.) (14.8.71)	£110	20·00
93*a*		3d. on 4d. Prussian blue (Blk.) (16.12.71)		
94		4d. dull lilac (1870)	£110	10·00
95		4d. dull purple (1871)	£100	10·00
96	1	6d. bright blue (19.6.70)	£180	17·00
97		6d. indigo (11.10.71)	£250	16·00
98		1s. chestnut (4.1.71)	£150	23·00

1870–73. W **2**. *P 10 × 11½–12½, 11½–12½ × 10, or compound.*

No.	Type	Description	Unused	Used
99	1	1d. pale bright green (11.10.70)	£140	14·00
		a. Printed on both sides		
100		1d. grey-green	£130	15·00
101		1d. deep green (19.6.71)	75·00	10·00
102	3	3d. on 4d. pale ultram (Blk.) (9.11.70)	£200	45·00
103		4d. dull lilac (11.5.72)	—	20·00
104		4d. slate-lilac (5.3.73)	£120	18·00
105	1	6d. Prussian blue (2.3.70)	£140	8·00
106		6d. bright Prussian blue (26.10.70)	£150	10·00
107	4	10d. on 9d. yellow (Blk.) (1.70)	£130	25·00
108	1	1s. chestnut (17.6.71)	£200	40·00
109	3	2s. rose-pink (24.4.71)	—	£180
110		2s. carmine (2.3.72)	£130	30·00

1871 (17 July). W **7**. *P* 10.

No.	Type	Description	Unused	Used
111	3	4d. dull lilac	£1500	£200
		a. Printed on both sides	†	—

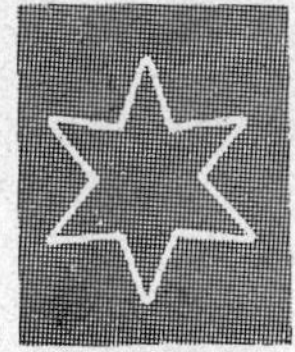

8 Broad Star

8 PENCE

(9)

1876–1900. W **8**. *Surch with T* **9** *(Nos. 118/21). (a) P 11½–12½.*

No.	Type	Description	Unused	Used
112	3	3d. on 4d. ultramarine (1.6.79)	75·00	18·00
		a. Surch double	†	£1100
113		4d. violet-slate (15.3.79)	£100	12·00
114		4d. plum (16.4.80)	55·00	6·50
115		4d. deep mauve (8.6.82)	55·00	5·50
116	1	6d. indigo (2.12.76)	£100	4·50
		a. Imperf between (horiz pair)	†	—
117		6d. Prussian blue (7.78)	65·00	4·00
118	4	8d. on 9d. brown-orange (7.76)	75·00	7·00
119		8d. on 9d. burnt umber (1880)	80·00	7·00
120		8d. on 9d. brown (9.3.80)	80·00	7·00
		a. Imperf between (vert pair)	£500	
121		8d. on 9d. grey-brown (10.5.81)	65·00	7·00
		a. Surch double	—	£400
122		9d. purple (9.3.80)	50·00	7·00
		a. Printed on both sides	—	£250
123		9d. rose-lilac (21.8.80)	16·00	3·25
124		9d. rose-lilac (*large holes*) (26.5.00)	10·00	3·50
125	1	1s. red-brown (3.11.77)	50·00	2·75
		a. Imperf between (horiz pair)	†	£325
126		1s. reddish lake-brown (1880)	48·00	3·00
127		1s. lake-brown (9.1.83)	55·00	2·75
		a. Printed double		
128		1s. Vandyke brown (1891)	65·00	8·00
129		1s. dull brown (1891)	42·00	2·75
130		1s. chocolate (*large holes*) (6.5.97)	25·00	3·00
		a. Imperf vert (horiz pair)	£200	
131		1s. sepia (*large holes*) (22.5.00)	25·00	3·00
		a. Imperf between (vert pair)	£180	
132	3	2s. carmine (15.2.77)	38·00	5·00
		a. Imperf between (horiz pair)	†	£500
		b. Imperf (pair)		
133		2s. rose-carmine (1885)	42·00	6·50
134		2s. rose-carmine (*large holes*) (6.12.98)	30·00	6·50

The perforation with larger, clean-cut holes resulted from the fitting of new pins to the machine.

(*b*) *P* 10

No.	Type	Description	Unused	Used
135	1	6d. Prussian blue (11.11.79)	£100	14·00
136		6d. bright blue (1879)	£120	14·00
136*a*		1s. reddish lake-brown	£275	

(*c*) *P 10 × 11½–12½, 11½–12½ × 10, or compound*

No.	Type	Description	Unused	Used
137	3	4d. violet-slate (21.5.79)	£110	13·00
138		4d. dull purple (4.10.79)	45·00	2·75
139	1	6d. Prussian blue (29.12.77)	60·00	2·50
140		6d. bright blue	80·00	5·50
141		6d. bright ultramarine	50·00	2·00
142		1s. reddish lake-brown (9.2.85)	85·00	9·00
143		1s. dull brown (29.6.86)	£110	10·00
144	3	2s. carmine (27.12.77)	55·00	5·50
145		2s. rose-carmine (1887)	50·00	5·00
		a. Imperf between (horiz pair)	†	£475

10

11

12

1901–2. *Wmk Crown SA (wide),* W **10**. *P 11½–12½ (large holes).*

No.	Type	Description	Unused	Used
146	4	9d. claret (1.2.02)	15·00	15·00
147	1	1s. dark brown (12.6.01)	22·00	11·00
148		1s. dark reddish brown (1902)	24·00	12·00
		a. Imperf between (vert pair)		
149		1s. red-brown (aniline) (18.7.02)	22·00	13·00
150	3	2s. crimson (29.8.01)	29·00	14·00
151		2s. carmine	24·00	10·00

(Plates and electrotypes by D.L.R. Printed in Adelaide)

1868–76. W **10**. (*a*) *Rouletted.*

No.	Type	Description	Unused	Used
152	12	2d. deep brick-red (8.68)	60·00	3·25
153		2d. pale orange-red (5.10.68)	55·00	2·75
		a. Printed on both sides	†	£250
		b. Imperf between (horiz pair)	†	£325

(*b*) *P 11½–12½*

No.	Type	Description	Unused	Used
154	11	1d. blue-green (10.1.75)	75·00	13·00
155	12	2d. pale orange-red (5.5.69)	£850	£190

(*c*) *P 11½–12½ × roulette*

No.	Type	Description	Unused	Used
156	12	2d. pale orange-red (20.8.69)	—	£130

(*d*) *P 10 × roulette*

No.	Type	Description	Unused	Used
157	12	2d. pale orange-red (7.5.70)	£225	27·00

(*e*) *P* 10

No.	Type	Description	Unused	Used
158	11	1d. blue-green (4.75)	30·00	4·50
159	12	2d. brick-red (4.70)	15·00	80
160		2d. orange-red (1.7.70)	11·00	70
		a. Printed on both sides	†	£200

(*f*) *P 10 × 11½–12½, 11½–12½ × 10, or compound*

No.	Type	Description	Unused	Used
161	11	1d. blue-green (27.8.75)	60·00	17·00
162	12	2d. brick-red (19.1.71)	£425	8·00
163		2d. orange-red (3.2.71)	£110	10·00
		a. Imperf (8.76)	£750	

1869. *Wmk Large Star, W* **2**. *(a) Rouletted.*
164 **12** 2d. orange-red (13.3.69) .. .. 60·00 13·00

(b) P 11½–12½ × roulette
165 **12** 2d. orange-red (1.8.69) .. .. .. — 90·00

(c) P 11½–12½
165*a* **12** 2d. orange-red (7.69) .. .. .. — £800

1871 (15 July). *Wmk V and Crown, W* **7**. *P* 10.
166 **12** 2d. brick-red .. .. 60·00 16·00

13

HALF-

PENNY

(14)

1876–1904. *Wmk Crown SA (close), W* **13**. *(a) P* 10 (1876–85)
167 **11** 1d. blue-green (9.2.76) .. .. 9·00 30
a. *Yellowish green* (11.78) .. .. 11·00 30
b. *Deep green* (11.79) .. .. 11·00 30
ba. Imperf between (horiz pair)
bb. Printed double .. .. .. † —
168 **12** 2d. orange-red (8.76) .. .. 10·00 30
a. *Dull brick-red* (21.5.77) .. .. 10·00 30
b. *Blood-red* (31.10.79) .. .. £200 3·00
c. *Pale red* (4.85) .. .. 10·00 30

(b) P 10×11½–12½, 11½–12½×10 or compound (1877–80)
169 **11** 1d. deep green (11.2.80) .. .. 27·00 3·00
a. *Blue-green* (2.3.80) .. .. 15·00 2·50
170 **12** 2d. orange-red (4.9.77) .. .. £120 3·50
a. *Dull brick-red* (6.80) .. .. £120 3·50

(c) P 11½–12½ (1877–84)
171 **11** 1d. blue-green (2.84) .. .. — £120
172 **12** 2d. orange-red (14.9.77) .. .. — £120
a. *Blood-red* (1.4.80) .. .. — £120

(d) P 15 (1893)
173 **11** 1d. green (8.5.93) .. .. 7·00 60
174 **12** 2d. pale orange (9.2.93) .. .. 10·00 40
a. *Orange-red* .. .. 9·50 40
b. Imperf between (vert pair) .. £200

(e) P 13 (1895–1903)
175 **11** 1d. pale green (11.1.95) .. .. 6·50 20
a. *Green* .. .. 6·50 20
b. Imperf between (vert pair) ..
176 1d. rosine (8.8.99) .. .. 3·50 20
a. *Scarlet* (23.12.03) .. .. 3·75 20
b. *Deep red* .. .. 3·50 20
177 **12** 2d. pale orange (19.1.95) .. .. 4·25 10
a. *Orange-red* (9.5.95) .. .. 6·00 10
178 2d. bright violet (10.10.99) .. .. 3·25 10

(f) P 12×11½ (comb) (1904)
179 **11** 1d. rosine (2.2.04) .. .. 7·00 20
a. *Scarlet* (25.7.04) .. .. 5·50 20
180 **12** 2d. bright violet (11.10.04) .. .. 4·75 20

Examples of the 1d. pale green with thicker lettering come from a worn plate.

1882 (1 Jan). *No.* 167 *surch with T* **14**.
181 **11** ½d. on 1d. blue-green .. .. 11·00 5·00

15

16

17

18

1883–99. *W* **13** *(sideways on ½d.). (a) P* 10 (1883–95)
182 **15** ½d. chocolate (1.3.83) .. .. 3·75 75
a. Imperf between (horiz pair) ..
b. *Red-brown* (4.4.89) .. .. 3·50 70
c. *Brown* (1895) .. .. 3·50 70
183 **16** 3d. sage-green (12.86) .. .. 11·00 1·50
a. *Olive-green* (6.6.90) .. .. 9·50 1·75
b. *Deep green* (12.4.93) .. .. 7·00 1·50
s. Optd "Specimen" .. .. 27·00
184 **17** 4d. pale violet (3.90) .. .. 11·00 1·75
a. *Aniline violet* (3.1.93) .. .. 12·00 2·00
s. Optd "Specimen" .. .. 32·00
185 **18** 6d. pale blue (4.87) .. .. 9·00 1·75
a. *Blue* (5.5.87) .. .. 11·00 70
s. Optd "Specimen" .. .. 27·00

(b) P 10×11½–12½, 11½–12½×10 or compound (1891)
186 **15** ½d. red-brown (25.9.91) .. .. 6·50 2·75
a. Imperf between (horiz pair) .. 95·00

(c) P 11½–12½ (1890)
187 **15** ½d. red-brown (12.10.90) .. .. 9·00 1·75

(d) P 15 (1893–94)
188 **15** ½d. pale brown (1.93) .. .. 3·75 90
a. *Deep brown* .. .. 3·75 90
b. Imperf between (horiz pair) .. 95·00
c. Perf 12½ between (pair) .. £130 32·00
189 **17** 4d. purple (1.1.94) .. .. 17·00 2·50
a. *Slate-violet* .. .. 17·00 2·25
190 **18** 6d. blue (20.11.93) .. .. 28·00 3·50

(e) P 13 (1895–99)
191 **15** ½d. pale brown (9.95) .. .. 2·75 30
a. *Deep brown* (19.3.97) .. .. 3·25 30
192 **16** 3d. pale olive-green (26.7.97) .. 7·00 1·40
a. *Deep olive-green* (27.11.99) .. 5·00 1·40
193 **17** 4d. violet (21.1.96) .. .. 6·00 50
194 **18** 6d. pale blue (3.96) .. .. 7·00 1·00
a. *Blue* .. .. 7·00 1·00

REPRINTS. In 1884, and in later years, reprints on paper wmkd Crown SA, W **10**, were made of Nos. 1, 2, 3, 4, 12, 13, 14, 15, 19, 24, 27, 28, 32, 33, 34, 35, 36, 37, 38, 40, 43, 44, 49*a*, 53, 65, 67, 67 with surcharge in red, 70, 71, 72, 73, 78, 79, 81, 83, 86, 90, 118, 119, 120, 121, 122, 155, 158, 159, 164, 181, 182. They are overprinted "REPRINT".

In 1889 examples of the reprints for Nos. 1/3, 12, 15, 19, 27, 32/8, 44, 67, 67 surcharged in red, 70/1, 73, 83, 86, 118, 121/2, 158/9, 164 and 181/2, together with No. 141 overprinted "Specimen", were supplied to the U.P.U. for distribution.

19

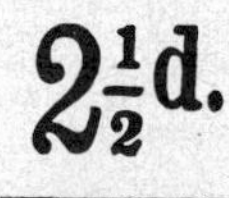

(20)

(21)

(Plates and electrotypes by D.L.R. Printed in Adelaide)

1886 (20 Dec)–**96.** *T* **19** *(inscr "POSTAGE & REVENUE"). W* **13**. *Parts of two or more wmks, on each stamp, sometimes sideways. P* 10.
195 2s. 6d. mauve .. .. 35·00 8·00
a. Perf 11½–12½. *Dull violet* .. 30·00 6·00
bb. *Bright aniline violet* .. 32·00 7·50
196 5s. rose-pink .. .. 50·00 13·00
a. Perf 11½–12½ .. .. 40·00 13·00
ab. *Rose-carmine* .. .. 40·00 15·00
197 10s. green .. .. .. £110 40·00
a. Perf 11½–12½ .. .. 90·00 38·00
198 15s. brownish yellow £300 £250
a. Perf 11½–12½ £325 £130
199 £1 blue £225 £100
a. Perf 11½–12½ .. .. £180 90·00
200 £2 Venetian red £700 £275
a. Perf 11½–12½ £700 £275
201 50s. dull pink £1000 £350
a. Perf 11½–12½ £1000 £350
202 £3 sage green £1100 £350
a. Perf 11½–12½ £1100 £350
203 £4 lemon £2000
a. Perf 11½–12½ £1800 £550
204 £5 grey £1900
a. Perf 11½–12½ £2000
205 £5 brown (*p* 11½–12½) (1896) .. £1800 £650
206 £10 bronze £2750 £750
a. Perf 11½–12½ £2250 £750
207 £15 silver £5500
a. Perf 11½–12½ £5500 £1000
208 £20 claret £7000
a. Perf 11½–12½ £7000 £1400
195s/208s Optd "Specimen" .. *Set of* 14 £500

Variations exist in the length of the words and shape of the letters of the value inscription.

The 2s. 6d. dull violet, 5s. rose-pink, 10s., £1 and £5 brown exist perf 11½–12½ with either large or small holes; the 2s. 6d. aniline, 5s. rose-carmine, 15s., £2 and 50s. with large holes only and the remainder only with small holes.

Stamps perforated 11½–12½ small holes, are, generally speaking, rather rarer than those with the 1895 (large holes) gauge.

Stamps perf 10 were issued on 20 Dec 1886. Stamps perf 11½–12½ (small holes) are known with earliest dates covering the period from June 1890 to Feb 1896. Earliest dates of stamps with large holes range from July 1896 to May 1902.

1891 (1 Jan)–**93.** *T* **17**/**18** *surch with T* **20**/**1**. *W* **13**. *(a) P* 10
229 **17** 2½d. on 4d. pale green (Br.) .. .. 7·50 2·50
a. Fraction bar omitted .. .. 95·00 75·00
b. *Deep green* .. .. 8·00 1·75
ba. Fraction bar omitted .. .. 95·00 70·00
bb. "2" and "½" closer together .. 23·00 18·00
bc. Imperf between (horiz pair) ..
bd. Imperf between (vert pair) .. — £450
s. Optd "Specimen" .. .. 27·00
230 **18** 5d. on 6d. pale brown (C.) .. .. 16·00 4·50
a. *Deep brown* .. .. 16·00 4·25
b. No stop after "5D" £160
s. Optd "Specimen" .. .. 27·00

(b) P 10×11½–12½ or 11½–12½×10
231 **17** 2½d. on 4d. pale green (Br.) .. .. 18·00 3·25
a. *Deep green* .. .. 18·00 3·25

(c) P 11½–12½
232 **17** 2½d. on 4d. deep green .. .. 28·00 45·00

(d) P 15
233 **17** 2½d. on 4d. green (14.10.93) .. .. 17·00 2·75
a. Fraction bar omitted .. ..
b. "2" and "½d." closer together .. 50·00 22·00

22 Red Kangaroo

23

24 G.P.O., Adelaide

(Des M. Tannenberg, plates by D.L.R.)

1894 (1 Mar)–**1906.** *W* **13**. *(a) P* 15
234 **22** 2½d. violet-blue .. .. 18·00
235 **23** 5d. brown-purple .. .. 20·00
234s/5s Optd "Specimen" .. *Set of* 2 55·00

(b) P 13
236 **22** 2½d. violet-blue (11.2.95) .. .. 16·00
237 2½d. indigo (25.3.98) .. .. 4·50
238 **23** 5d. brown-purple (1.96) .. .. 6·50
a. *Purple* .. .. 6·50

(c) P 12×11½ (comb)
239 **22** 2½d. indigo (4.7.06) .. .. 7·50
240 **23** 5d. dull purple (1.05) .. .. 10·00

(Typo D.L.R.)

1899 (27 Dec)–**1905.** *W* **13**. *(a) P* 13
241 **24** ½d. yellow-green .. .. 1·50

(b) P 12×11½ (comb)
242 **24** ½d. yellow-green (7.05) .. .. 2·00

25

Measurements indicate the length of the value inscriptio the bottom label. Dates are of the earliest known postmarks

1902–04. *As T* **19**, *but top tablet as T* **25** (*thin* "POSTAG
W **13**. *(a) P* 11½–12½.
268 3d. olive-green (18½ mm) (1.8.02) .. 5·00
a. Wmk sideways .. .. † £1
269 4d. red-orange (17 mm) (29.11.02) .. 7·00
270 6d. blue-green (16–16½ mm) (29.11.02) .. 6·00
271 8d. ultramarine (19 mm) (25.4.02) .. 7·50
272 8d. ultramarine (16½ mm) (22.3.04) .. 7·50
a. "EIGNT" (R. 2/9) £850 £1
273 9d. rosy lake (19.9.02) .. .. 8·00
a. Imperf between (vert pair) .. £400
b. Imperf between (horiz pair) ..
274 10d. dull yellow (29.11.02) .. .. 12·00
275 1s. brown (18.8.02) .. .. 13·00
a. Imperf between (horiz pair) ..
b. Imperf between (vert pair) .. £550
c. "POSTAGE" and value in red-brown £500 £
276 2s. 6d. pale violet (19.9.02) .. .. 32·00 15
a. *Bright violet* (2.2.03) .. .. 22·00 10
277 5s. rose (17.10.02) .. .. 55·00 40
278 10s. green (1.11.02) £100 60
279 £1 blue (1.11.02) £225 £1

(b) P 12
280 3d. olive-green (20 mm) (15.4.04) .. 9·00
a. "POSTAGE" omitted; value below "AUSTRALIA" £550
281 4d. orange-red (17½–18 mm) (18.2.03) .. 8·00
282 6d. blue-green (15 mm) (14.11.03) .. 16·00
283 9d. rosy lake (2.12.03) .. .. 45·00

PRINTER. Stamp printing in Adelaide ceased in 1909 wh the Printer of Stamps, J. B. Cooke, was appointed head of Commonwealth Stamp Printing Branch in Melbourne, Fr 9 March 1909 further printings of current South Austra stamps were made in Melbourne.

26

V

X

In Type X the letters in the bottom line are slightly larger th in Type V, especially the "A", "S" and "P".

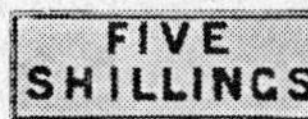

Y

Z

In Type Z the letters "S" and "G" are more open than in Type Nos. 196/*a* and 277 are similar to Type Y with all letters th and regular and the last "S" has the top curve rounded instead being slightly flattened.

1904–11. *As T* **19**, *but top tablet as T* **26** (*thick* "POSTAGE
W **13**. *P* 12.
284 6d. blue-green (27.4.04) .. .. 10·00 3
a. Imperf between (vert pair) .. £750
285 8d. bright ultramarine (4.7.05) .. 9·00 5·
a. Value closer (15¼ mm) .. 22·00
b. *Dull ultramarine* (2.4.08) .. 15·00 4·
ba. Ditto. Value closer (15¼ mm) .. 35·00
286 9d. rosy lake (17–17¼ mm) (18.7.04) .. 10·00 4·
a. Value 16½–16¾ mm (2.06) .. 25·00 6·
b. *Brown-lake*. Perf 12½ small holes (6.6.11) 13·00
287 10d. dull yellow (8.07) .. .. 14·00 10·
a. Imperf between (horiz pair) .. £475 £4
b. Imperf between (vert pair) .. £450
288 1s. brown (12.4.04) .. .. 15·00 2·
a. Imperf between (vert pair) .. £325
b. Imperf between (horiz pair) .. £400
289 2s. 6d. bright violet (V.) (14.7.05) .. 48·00 12·
a. *Dull violet* (X) (8.06) .. .. 48·00 12·
290 5s. rose-scarlet (Y) (8.04) .. .. 45·00 27·
a. *Scarlet* (Z) (8.06) .. .. 42·00 27·
b. *Pale rose*. Perf 12½ (small holes) (Z) (7.10) 60·00 32·
291 10s. green (26.8.08) £100 £1
292 £1 blue (29.12.04) £170 £1
a. Perf 12½ (small holes) (7.10) .. £140 £1

The "value closer" variety on the 8d. occurs six times in the she of 60. The value normally measures 16½ mm but in the variety is 15¼ mm.

The 9d., 5s. and £1, perf 12½ (small holes), are late printin made in 1910–11 to use up the Crown SA paper.

No. 286*b* has the value as Type C of the 9d. on Crown over paper.

27

11. *W* **27.** *P* 12 × 11½ (*new comb machine*).

4	½d. pale green (4.07)	4·00	65
	a. Yellow-green	4·00	65
1	1d. rosine (2.12.05)	3·75	10
	a. Scarlet (4.11)	3·50	80
2	2d. bright violet (2.2.06)	6·00	10
	aa. Imperf three sides (horiz pair)		
	a. Mauve (4.08)	3·75	10
2	2½d. indigo-blue (14.9.10)	9·00	4·00
3	5d. brown-purple (11.3.08)	12·00	3·00

295aa is perforated at foot.

ee types of the 9d., perf 12½, distinguishable by the distance en "NINE" and "PENCE".
)istance 1¾ mm. B. Distance 2¼ mm. C. Distance 2½ mm.

-12. *T* **19** ("POSTAGE" *thick as T* **26**). *W* **27.** *P* 12 *or* 12½ *all holes*).

3d. sage-green (19 mm) (26.6.06)	7·00	2·25
a. Imperf between (horiz pair)	†	£750
b. Perf 12½. *Sage-green* (17 mm) (9.12.09)	6·00	2·25
c. Perf 12½. *Deep olive* (20 mm) (7.10)	32·00	8·00
d. Perf 12½. *Yellow-olive* (14 mm) (16.12.11)	12·00	8·00
da. Perf 12½. *Bright olive-green* (19–19¾ mm) (5.12)	12·00	9·50
e. Perf 11 (17 mm) (10.7.11)	£500	£350
4d. orange-red (10.9.06)	10·00	2·00
a. Orange	10·00	2·00
b. Perf 12½. *Orange* (27.10.09)	9·00	3·00
6d. blue-green (1.9.06)	8·00	2·25
a. Perf 12½ (21.4.10)	7·50	3·00
ab. Perf 12½. Imperf between (vert pair)	£475	£425
8d. bright ultramarine (*p* 12½) (8.09)	10·00	8·50
a. Value closer (8.09)	40·00	30·00
9d. brown-lake (3.2.06)	10·00	2·25
a. Imperf between (vert pair)	£400	
aa. Imperf between (horiz pair)	£400	
b. Deep lake (9.5.08)	40·00	6·00
c. Perf 12½. *Lake* (A) (5.9.09)	11·00	3·75
d. Perf 12½. *Lake* (B) (7.09)	17·00	3·75
e. Perf 12½. *Brown-lake* (C)	18·00	6·50
ea. Perf 12½. *Deep lake.* Thin paper (C)	18·00	5·00
f. Perf 11 (1909)	—	£450
1s. brown (30.5.06)	12·00	3·75
a. Imperf between (horiz pair)	£400	
b. Perf 12½ (10.3.10)	10·00	4·00
2s. 6d. bright violet (X) (10.6.09)	42·00	8·00
a. Perf 12½. *Pale violet* (X) (6.10)	42·00	11·00
ab. Perf 12½. *Deep purple* (X) (5.11.12)	45·00	25·00
5s. bright rose (*p* 12½) (Z) (24.4.11)	60·00	

e "value closer" variety of the 8d. occurred 11 times in the of 60 in the later printing only. On No. 301 the value meas- 16½ mm while on No. 301a it is 15¼ mm.

e 1s. brown, perf compound of 11½ and 12½, formerly l is now omitted, as it must have been perforated by the 12 ıine, which in places varied from 11½ to 13. The 4d. has been reported with a similar perforation.

STAMP BOOKLETS

ıere are very few surviving examples of Nos. SB1/4. Listings provided for those believed to have been issued with prices ed for those known to still exist.

4 (1 Jan)–**09.** *Black on red cover as No.* SB1 *of New South ales. Stapled.*
£1 booklet containing two hundred and forty 1d. in four blocks of 30 and two blocks of 60 . .
a. Red on pink cover (1909) . .
b. Blue on pink cover . . £6500

4 (1 Jan). *Black on grey cover as No.* SB1. *Stapled.*
£1 booklet containing one hundred and twenty 2d. in four blocks of 30 . .

) (May). *Black on cream cover as No.* SB3 *of New South ales. Stapled.*
2s. booklet containing eleven ½d. (No. 262A), either in block of 6 plus block of 5 or block of 11, and eighteen 1d. (No. 264A), either in three blocks of 6 or block of 6 plus block of 12 . .

nsold stock of No. SB3 was uprated with one additional ½d. ay 1911.

1 (Aug). *Red on pink cover as No.* SB3. *Stapled.*
2s. booklet containing twelve ½d. (No. 262A), either in two blocks of 6 or block of 12, and eighteen 1d. (No. 264A), either in three blocks of 6 or block of 6 plus block of 12 . . £3000

OFFICIAL STAMPS

A. Departmentals

ollowing suspected abuses involving stamps supplied for official it was decided by the South Australian authorities that such plies were to be overprinted with a letter, or letters, indicating department of the administration to which the stamps had been oiced.

he system was introduced on 1 April 1868 using overprints ck in red. Later in the same year the colour of the overprints amended to blue, and, during the latter months of 1869, to ck.

n 1874 the Postmaster-General recommended that this somet cumbersome system be replaced by a general series of "O.S." rprints with the result that the separate accounting for the artmentals ceased on 30 June of that year. Existing stocks tinued to be used, however, and it is believed that much of the residue was passed to the Government Printer to pay postage on copies of the *Government Gazette*.

We are now able to provide a check list of these most interesting issues based on the definitive work, *The Departmental Stamps of South Australia* by A. R. Butler, FRPSL, RDP, published by the Royal Philatelic Society, London in 1978.

No attempt has been made to assign the various overprints to the catalogue numbers of the basic stamps, but each is clearly identified by both watermark and perforation. The colours are similar to those of the contemporary postage stamps, but there can be shade variations. Errors of overprint are recorded in footnotes, but not errors occurring on the basic stamps used.

Most departmental overprints are considered to be scarce to rare in used condition, with unused examples, used multiples and covers being regarded as considerable rarities.

Forgeries of a few items do exist, but most can be readily identified by comparison with genuine examples. A number of forged overprints on stamps not used for the genuine issues also occur.

A. (Architect)

Optd in red with stop. *W* **2.** 2d. (*roul*), 4d. (*p* 11½–12½), 6d. (*roul*), 1s. (*roul*)
Optd in red without stop. *W* **2.** *Roul.* 1d., 2d., 6d., 1s.
Optd in black. (*a*) *W* **2**. 4d. (*p* 10×11½–12½), 6d. (*p* 11½–12½), 2s. (*roul*)
(*b*) *W* **10**. 2d. D.L.R. (*roul*), 2d. D.L.R. (*p* 10)

A.G. (Attorney–General)

Optd in red. *W* **2.** *Roul.* 1d., 2d., 6d., 1s.
Optd in blue. (*a*) *W* **2.** *Roul.* 6d.
(*b*) *W* **10.** *Roul.* 2d. D.L.R
Optd in black. (*a*) *W* **2**. 1d. (*p* 11½–12½×*roul*), 4d. (*p* 11½–12½), 4d. (*p* 10), 6d. (*p* 11½–12½×*roul*), 6d. (*p* 11½–12½), 1s. (*p* 11½–12½×*roul*), 1s. (*p* 11½–12½), 1s. (*p* 10)
(*b*) *W* **10**. 2d. D.L.R. (*roul*), 2d. D.L.R. (*p* 10)

A.O. (Audit Office)

Optd in red. *W* **2.** 2d. (*roul*), 4d. (*p* 11½–12½), 6d. (*roul*)
Optd in blue. (*a*) *W* **2.** *P* 11½–12½. 1d., 6d.
(*b*) *W* **10.** *Roul.* 2d. D.L.R.
Optd in black. (*a*) *W* **2**. 1d. (*p* 11½–12½), 1d. (*p* 10), 2d. D.L.R. (*roul*), 4d. (*p* 11½–12½), 4d. (*p* 10), 4d. (*p* 10×11½–12½), 6d. (*roul*), 6d. (*p* 11½–12½), 1s. (*p* 11½–12½), 1s. (*p* 11½–12½×*roul*)
(*b*) *W* **7**. *P* 10. 4d.
(*c*) *W* **10**. 2d. D.L.R. (*roul*), 2d. D.L.R. (*p* 10)

B.D. (Barracks Department)

Optd in red. *W* **2.** *Roul.* 2d., 6d., 1s.

B.G. (Botanic Garden)

Optd in black. (*a*) *W* **2**. 1d. (*p* 11½–12½×*roul*), 1d. (*p* 11½–12½), 1d. (*p* 10×11½–12½), 2d. D.L.R. (*roul*), 6d. (*roul*), 6d. (*p* 11½–12½×*roul*), 6d. (*p* 11½–12½), 1s. (*p* 11½–12½×*roul*), 1s. (*p* 11½–12½), 1s. (*p* 10), 1s. (*p* 10×11½–12½)
(*b*) *W* **7**. *P* 10, 2d. D.L.R.
(*c*) *W* **10**. 2d. D.L.R. (*roul*), 2d. D.L.R. (*p* 10)
The 6d. (*W* **2**. *Roul*) is known without stamp after "B".

B.M. (Bench of Magistrates)

Optd in red. *W* **2.** *Roul.* 2d.
Optd in black. *W* **10.** *Roul.* 2d. D.L.R.

C. (Customs)

Optd in red. *W* **2.** 1d. (*roul*), 2d. (*roul*), 4d. (*p* 11½–12½), 6d. (*roul*), 1s. (*roul*)
Optd in blue. (*a*) *W* **2.** *Roul.* 1d., 4d., 6d., 1s., 2s.
(*b*) *W* **10.** *Roul.* 2d. D.L.R.
Optd in black. (*a*) *W* **2**. 1d. (*roul*), 1d. (*p* 10), 1d. (*p* 10×11½–12½), 4d. (*p* 11½–12½), 4d. (*p* 10), 4d. (*p* 10×11½–12½), 6d. (*roul*), 6d. (*p* 11½–12½), 6d. (*p* 10), 1s. (*p* 11½–12½×*roul*), 1s. (*p* 11½–12½), 2s. (*roul*)
(*b*) *W* **7**. *P* 10. 2d. D.L.R.
(*c*) *W* **10**. 2d. D.L.R. (*roul*), 2d. D.L.R. (*p* 10×*roul*), 2d. D.L.R. (*p* 10), 2d. D.L.R. (*p* 10×11½–12½)
The 2d. (*W* **10**. *Roul*) with black overprint is known showing the error "G" for "C".

C.D. (Convict Department)

Optd in red. *W* **2**. 2d. (*roul*), 4d. (*p* 11½–12½), 6d. (*roul*), 1s. (*roul*)
Optd in black. (*a*) *W* **2**. 1d. (*p* 11½–12½×*roul*), 2d. D.L.R. (*roul*), 4d. (*p* 11½–12½), 6d. (*roul*), 6d. (*p* 11½–12½×*roul*), 1s. (*p* 11½–12½×*roul*)
(*b*) *W* **10**. 2d. D.L.R. (*roul*), 2d. D.L.R. (*p* 11½–12½), 2d. D.L.R. (*p* 11½–12½×*roul*)

C.L. (Crown Lands)

Optd in red. *W* **2.** 2d. (*roul*), 4d. (*p* 11½–12½), 6d. (*roul*), 1s. (*roul*)
Optd in blue. (*a*) *W* **2.** *Roul.* 4d., 6d.
(*b*) *W* **10.** *Roul.* 2d. D.L.R.
Optd in black. (*a*) *W* **2**. 2d. D.L.R. (*roul*), 4d. (*p* 11½–12½), 4d. (*p* 10), 4d. (*p* 10×11½–12½), 6d. (*roul*), 6d. (*p* 11½–12½), 1s. (*p* 11½–12½×*roul*), 2s. (*roul*), 2s. (*p* 11½–12½)
(*b*) *W* **7**. *P* 10. 2d. D.L.R., 4d.
(*c*) *W* **10**. 2d. D.L.R. (*roul*), 2d. D.L.R. (*p* 10), 2d. D.L.R. (*p* 10×11½–12½)
The 2s. (*W* **2**. *P* 11½–12½) with black overprint is known showing the stop omitted after "L".

C.O. (Commissariat Office)

Optd in red. *W* **2**. (*roul*), 4d. (*p* 11½–12½), 6d. (*roul*), 1s. (*roul*)
Optd in black. (*a*) *W* **2**. 4d. (*p* 10), 4d. (*p* 10×11½–12½), 6d. (*p* 11½–12½), 1s. (*p* 11½–12½), 2s. (*roul*), 2s. (*p* 11½–12½)
(*b*) *W* **10**. 2d. D.L.R. (*roul*), 2d. D.L.R. (*p* 10)
The 6d. (*W* **2**. *Roul*) with red overprint is known showing the error "O" for "C", and the 2s. (*W* **2**. *P* 11½–12½) with black overprint with the stop omitted after "O".

C.P. (Commissioner of Police)

Optd in red. *W* **2**. 2d. (*roul*), 4d. (*p* 11½–12½), 6d. (*roul*)

C.S. (Chief Secretary)

Optd in red. *W* **2.** 2d. (*roul*), 4d. (*p* 11½–12½), 6d. (*roul*), 1s. (*roul*)
Optd in blue. (*a*) *W* **2.** *Roul.* 4d., 6d.
(*b*) *W* **10.** *Roul.* 2d. D.L.R.
Optd in black. (*a*) *W* **2.** 2d. D.L.R. (*roul*), 4d. (*roul*), 4d. (*p* 11½–12½ × *roul*), 4d. (*p* 11½–12½), 4d. (*p* 10), 4d. (*p* 10 × 11½–12½), 6d. (*p* 11½–12½ × *roul*), 6d. (*p* 11½–12½), 6d. (*p* 10), 6d. (*p* 10 × 11½–12½), 1s. (*p* 11½–12½ × *roul*), 1s. (*p* 11½–12½), 1s. (*p* 10), 1s. (*p* 10 × 11½–12½), 2s. (*p* 10 × 11½–12½)
(*b*) *W* **7**. *P* 10. 2d.
(*c*) *W* **10**. 2d. D.L.R. (*roul*), 2d. D.L.R. (*p* 10)
The 6d. and 1s. (*W* **2**. *Roul*) with red overprint are known showing the error "G" for "C".

C.Sgn. (Colonial Surgeon)

Optd in red. W **2**. 2d. (*roul*), 4d. (*p* 11½–12½), 6d. (*roul*)
Optd in black. (*a*) *W* **2**. 2d. D.L.R. (*roul*), 4d. (*p* 10), 4d. (*p* 10×11½–12½), 6d. (*roul*), 6d. (*p* 11½–12½×*roul*) 6d. (*p* 11½–12½)
(*b*) *W* **10**. 2d. D.L.R. (*roul*), 2d. D.L.R. (*p* 11½–12½×*roul*), 2d. (*p* 10×*roul*), 2d. D.L.R. (*p* 10)
Two types of overprint exist on the 2d. D.L.R., the second type having block capitals instead of the serifed type used for the other values.

D.B. (Destitute Board)

Optd in red. *W* **2**. 1d. (*roul*), 2d. (*roul*), 4d. (*p* 11½–12½), 6d. (*roul*), 1s. (*roul*)
Optd in blue. (*a*) *W* **2**. 2d. D.L.R. (*roul*), 4d. (*p* 11½–12½), 6d. (*roul*)
(*b*) *W* **10**. Roul. 2d. D.L.R.
Optd in black. (*a*) *W* **2**. 1d. (*p* 11½–12½), 4d. (*p* 11½–12½), 4d. (*p* 10), 6d. (*p* 10×11½–12½), 1s. (*p* 10)
(*b*) *W* **10**. 2d. D.L.R. (*roul*), 2d. D.L.R. (*p* 11½–12½), 2d. D.L.R. (*p* 10), 2d. D.L.R. (*p* 10×11½–12½)
The 2d. D.L.R. (*W* **10.** *P* 10) with black overprint is known showing the stop omitted after "D".

D.R. (Deeds Registration)

Optd in red. *W* **2.** *Roul*, 2d., 6d.

E. (Engineer)

Optd in red. *W* **2.** 2d. (*roul*), 4d. (*p* 11½–12½), 6d. (*roul*), 1s. (*roul*)
Optd in blue. (*a*) *W* **2.** *Roul.* 1s.
(*b*) *W* **10.** *Roul.* 2d. D.L.R.
Optd in black. (*a*) *W* **2**. 4d. (*p* 11½–12½), 4d. (*p* 10), 4d. (*p* 10×11½–12½), 6d. (*p* 11½–12½), 1s. (*p* 11½–12½×*roul*), 1s. (*p* 11½–12½), 1s. (*p* 10×11½–12½)
(*b*) *W* **7**. *P* 10. 4d.
(*c*) *W* **10**. *P* 10. 2d. D.L.R.

E.B. (Education Board)

Optd in red. *W* **2.** 2d. (*roul*), 4d. (*p* 11½–12½), 6d. (*roul*)
Optd in blue. (*a*) *W* **2.** *Roul.* 4d., 6d.
(*b*) *W* **10.** *Roul.* 2d. D.L.R.
Optd in black. (*a*) *W* **2**. 2d. D.L.R. (*roul*), 4d (*roul*), 4d. (*p* 11½–12½), 4d. (*p* 10), 6d. (*p* 11½–12½×*roul*), 6d. (*p* 11½×12½)
(*b*) *W* **7**. *P* 10. 2d. D.L.R.
(*c*) *W* **10**. 2d. D.L.R. (*roul*), 2d. D.L.R. (*p* 10), 2d. D.L.R. (*p* 10×11½–12½)

G.F. (Gold Fields)

Optd in black. (*a*) *W* **2.** *Roul.* 6d.
(*b*) *W* **10.** 2d. D.L.R. (*p* 10 × *roul*), 2d. D.L.R. (*p* 10)

G.P. (Government Printer)

Optd in red. *W* **2.** *Roul.* 1d., 2d., 6d., 1s.
Optd in blue. (*a*) *W* **2.** *Roul.* 1d., 6d., 1s., 2s.
(*b*) *W* **10.** *Roul.* 2d. D.L.R.
Optd in black. (*a*) *W* **2**. 1d. (*roul*), 1d. (*p* 11½–12½×*roul*), 1d. (*p* 11½–12½), 1d. (*p* 10), 1d. (*p* 10×11½–12½), 6d. (*p* 11½–12½×*roul*), 1s. (*p* 10×11½–12½), 2s. (*roul*), 2s. (*p* 11½–12½), 2s. (*p* 10×11½–12½)
(*b*) *W* **10**. 2d. D.L.R. (*roul*), 2d. D.L.R. (*p* 10)
The 1d. and 1s. (*W* **2**. *Roul*) with red overprint are known showing "C.P." instead of "G.P.".

G.S. (Government Storekeeper)

Optd in red. *W* **2**. *Roul.* 2d.

G.T. (Goolwa Tramway)

Optd in red. *W* **2.** 1d. (*roul*), 2d. (*roul*), 4d. (*p* 11½–12½), 6d. (*roul*), 1s. (*roul*)
Optd in black. (*a*) *W* **2**. 2d. D.L.R. (*roul*), 4d. (*p* 11½–12½)
(*b*) *W* **10**. *Roul.* 2d. D.L.R.
The 2d. and 6d. (both *W* **2**. *Roul*) with red overprint are known showing the stop omitted after "T". The 6d. and 1s. (*W* **2**. *Roul*) with red overprint are known showing "C.T." instead of "G.T.".

H. (Hospitals)

Optd in black. (*a*) *W* **2**. *P* 10×11½–12½. 4d.
(*b*) *W* **7**. *P* 10. 2d. D.L.R.
(*c*) *W* **10**. 2d. D.L.R. (*p* 10), 2d. D.L.R. (*p* 10×11½–12½)

H.A. (House of Assembly)

Optd in red. *W* **2.** 1d. (*roul*), 2d. (*roul*), 4d. (*p* 11½–12½), 6d. (*roul*), 1s. (*roul*)
Optd in black. (*a*) *W* **2.** 1d. (*p* 11½–12½), 1d. (*p* 10), 1d. (*p* 10 × 11½–12½), 4d. (*p* 11½–12½), 4d. (*p* 10), 6d. (*roul*), 6d. (*p* 11½–12½), 1s. (*p* 11½–12½ × *roul*), 1s. (*p* 11½–12½)
(*b*) *W* **10.** 2d. D.L.R. (*roul*), 2d. D.L.R. (*p* 10)

I.A. (Immigration Agent)

Optd in red. *W* **2.** 1d. (*roul*), 2d. (*roul*), 4d. (*p* 11½–12½), 6d. (*roul*)

I.E. (Intestate Estates)

Optd in black. *W* **10**. *P* 10. 2d. D.L.R.

I.S. (Inspector of Sheep)

Optd in red. *W* **2.** *Roul.* 2d., 6d.
Optd in blue. *W* **2.** *P* 11½–12½. 6d.
Optd in black. (*a*) *W* **2.** 2d. D.L.R. (*roul*), 6d. (*p* 11½–12½ × *roul*)
(*b*) *W* **10.** 2d. D.L.R. (*roul*), 2d. D.L.R. (*p* 10)

L.A. (Lunatic Asylum)

Optd in red. *W* **2.** 1d. (*roul*), 2d. (*roul*), 4d. (*p* 11½–12½), 6d. (*roul*), 1s. (*roul*)
Optd in black. (*a*) *W* **2.** 4d. (*p* 11½–12½), 4d. (*p* 10), 4d. (*p* 10×11½–12½), 6d. (*p* 11½–12½), 1s. (*p* 11½–12½), 2s. (*roul*)
(*b*) *W* **10.** 2d. D.L.R. (*roul*), 2d. D.L.R. (*p* 10)

L.C. (Legislative Council)

Optd in red. *W* **2.** *Roul.* 2d., 6d.
Optd in black. (*a*) *W* **2.** *Roul.* 6d.
(*b*) *W* **10.** 2d. D.L.R. (*roul*), 2d. D.L.R. (*p* 10 × *roul*)
The 2d. and 6d. (both *W* **2.** *Roul*) with red overprint are known showing the stop omitted after "C".

L.L. (Legislative Librarian)

Optd in red. *W* **2.** 2d. (*roul*), 4d. (*p* 11½–12½), 6d. (*roul*)
Optd in black. (*a*) *W* **2.** *P* 11½–12½. 6d.
(*b*) *W* **10.** *P* 10. 2d. D.L.R.
The 2d. and 6d. (both *W* **2.** *Roul*) with red overprint are known showing the stop omitted from between the two letters.

L.T. (Land Titles)

Optd in red. *W* **2.** 2d. (*roul*), 4d. (*p* 11½–12½), 6d. (*roul*), 1s. (*roul*)
Optd in blue. *W* **10.** *Roul.* 2d. D.L.R.
Optd in black. (*a*) *W* **2.** 4d. (*p* 11½–12½), 4d. (*p* 10), 4d. (*p* 10 × 11½–12½), 6d. (*p* 11½–12½ × *roul*), 6d. (*p* 11½–12½), 6d. (*p* 10), 6d. (*p* 10 × 11½–12½)
(*b*) *W* **7.** *P* 10. 2d. D.L.R.
(*c*) *W* **10.** 2d. D.L.R. (*roul*), 2d. D.L.R. (*p* 10)
The 2d. and 6d. (both *W* **2.** *Roul*) with red overprint are known showing the stop omitted after "T".

M. (Military)

Optd in red. *W* **2.** *Roul.* 2d., 6d., 1s.
Optd in black. *W* **2.** 6d. (*p* 11½–12½ × *roul*), 1s. (*p* 11½–12½ × *roul*), 2s. (*roul*)

M.B. (Marine Board)

Optd in red. *W* **2.** 1d. (*roul*), 2d. (*roul*), 4d. (*roul*), 4d. (*p* 11½–12½), 6d. (*roul*), 1s. (*roul*)
Optd in black. (*a*) *W* **2.** 1d. (*roul*), 1d. (*p* 11½–12½), 2d. D.L.R. (*roul*), 4d. (*p* 11½–12½ × *roul*), 4d. (*p* 11½–12½), 4d. (*p* 10), 4d. (*p* 10 × 11½–12½), 6d. (*roul*), 6d. (*p* 11½–12½), 6d. (*p* 10), 6d. (*p* 10 × 11½–12½), 1s. (*p* 11½–12½ × *roul*), 1s. (*p* 11½–12½), 1s. (*p* 10), 1s. (*p* 10 × 11½–12½)
(*b*) *W* **7.** *P* 10. 4d.
(*c*) *W* **10.** *Roul.* 2d. D.L.R.

M.R. (Manager of Railways)

Optd in red. *W* **2.** *Roul.* 2d., 6d.
Optd in black. (*a*) *W* **2.** 1d. (*p* 11½–12½), 1d. (*p* 10), 2d. D.L.R. (*roul*), 4d. (*roul*), 4d. (*p* 11½–12½), 6d. (*p* 11½–12½×*roul*), 1s. (*p* 11½–12½×*roul*), 2s. (*p* 11½–12½), 2s. (*p* 10×11½–12½)
(*b*) *W* **10.** 2d. D.L.R. (*roul*), 2d. D.L.R. (*p* 10), 2d. D.L.R. (*p* 10×11½–12½)

M.R.G. (Main Roads Gambierton)

Optd in red without stops. *W* **2.** *Roul.* 2d., 6d.
Optd in blue without stops. *W* **10.** *Roul.* 2d. D.L.R.
Optd in black without stops. *W* **10.** 2d. D.L.R. (*roul*), 2d. D.L.R. (*p* 10)
Optd in black with stops. *W* **10.** 2d. D.L.R. (*roul*), 2d. D.L.R. (*p* 10)
The 2d. D.L.R. (*W* **10.** *P* 10) with black overprint is known showing the stops omitted after "M" and "R".

N.T. (Northern Territory)

Optd in black. (*a*) *W* **2.** *P* 11½–12½. 1d., 3d. on 4d., 6d., 1s.
(*b*) *W* **10.** 2d. D.L.R. (*roul*), 2d. D.L.R. (*p* 10)

O.A. (Official Assignee)

Optd in red. *W* **2.** 2d. (*roul*), 4d. (*p* 11½–12½)
Optd in blue. *W* **10.** *Roul.* 2d. D.L.R.
Optd in black. (*a*) *W* **2.** *P* 10. 4d.
(*b*) *W* **7.** *P* 10. 2d. D.L.R.
(*c*) *W* **10.** 2d. D.L.R. (*roul*), 2d. D.L.R. (*p* 10×*roul*), 2d. D.L.R. (*p* 10)

P. (Police)

Optd in blue. (*a*) *W* **2.** *Roul.* 6d.
(*b*) *W* **10.** *Roul.* 2d. D.L.R.
Optd in black. (*a*) *W* **2.** 6d. (*p* 11½–12½ × *roul*), 6d. (*p* 11½–12½), 6d. (*p* 10)
(*b*) *W* **7.** *P* 10. 2d. D.L.R.
(*c*) *W* **10.** 2d. D.L.R. (*roul*), 2d. D.L.R. (*p* 11½–12½), 2d. D.L.R. (*p* 11½–12½ × *roul*), 2d. D.L.R. (*p* 10 × *roul*), 2d. D.L.R. (*p* 10), 2d. D.L.R. (*p* 10 × 11½–12½)

P.A. (Protector of Aborigines)

Optd in red. *W* **2.** *Roul.* 2d., 6d.
Optd in black. (*a*) *W* **2.** *Roul.* 2d. D.L.R., 6d.
(*b*) *W* **10.** 2d. D.L.R. (*roul*), 2d. D.L.R. (*p* 10)

P.O. (Post Office)

Optd in red. *W* **2.** *Roul.* 1d., 2d., 6d., 1s.
Optd in blue. (*a*) *W* **2.** *Roul.* 2d.
(*b*) *W* **10.** *Roul.* 2d. D.L.R.
Optd in black. (*a*) *W* **2.** 1d. (*p* 10×11½–12½), 2d. D.L.R. (*roul*), 2d. D.L.R. (*p* 11½–12½×*roul*), 4d. (*p* 11½–12½), 6d. (*roul*), 6d. (*p* 11½×12½), 1s. (*p* 11½–12½×*roul*), 1s. (*p* 11½–12½), 1s. (*p* 11½–12½), 1s. (*p* 10), 1s. (*p* 10×11½–12½)
(*b*) *W* **10.** 2d. D.L.R. (*roul*), 2d. (*p* 11½–12½×*roul*), 2d. D.L.R. (*p* 10×*roul*), 2d. D.L.R. (*p* 10)
The 4d. (*W* **2.** *P* 11½–12½) with black overprint is known showing the stop omitted after "O".

P.S. (Private Secretary)

Optd in red. *W* **2.** 1d. (*roul*), 2d. (*roul*), 4d. (*p* 11½–12½), 6d. (*roul*), 1s. (*roul*)
Optd in black. (*a*) *W* **2.** 1d. (*p* 11½–12½×*roul*), 1d. (*p* 11½–12½), 1d. (*p* 10), 2d. (*roul*), 3d. (*in black*) on 4d. (*p* 11½–12½), 3d. (*in red*) on 4d. (*p* 10), 3d. (*in black*) on 4d. (*p* 10), 4d. (*p* 11½–12½), 4d. (*p* 10), 4d. (*p* 10×11½–12½), 6d. (*roul*), 6d. (*p* 11½–12½×*roul*), 6d. (*p* 11½–12½), 6d. (*p* 10), 9d. (*roul*), 9d. (*p* 11½–12½), 10d. on 9d. (*p* 10), 10d. on 9d. (*p* 10×11½–12½), 1s. (*p* 11½–12½×*roul*)
(*b*) *W* **7.** *P* 10. 2d. D.L.R.
(*c*) *W* **10.** 2d. D.L.R. (*roul*), 2d. D.L.R. (*p* 10)

P.W. (Public Works)

Optd in red without stop after "W". *W* **2.** *Roul.* 2d., 6d., 1s.
Optd in black. (*a*) *W* **2.** 2d. D.L.R. (*roul*), 4d. (*p* 10), 6d. (*roul*), 6d. (*p* 11½–12½), 1s. (*p* 11½–12½ × *roul*)
(*b*) *W* **10.** 2d. D.L.R. (*roul*), 2d. D.L.R. (*p* 10)

R.B. (Road Board)

Optd in red. *W* **2.** 1d. (*roul*), 2d. (*roul*), 4d. (*p* 11½–12½), 6d. (*roul*), 1s. (*roul*)
Optd in blue without stops. *W* **10.** *Roul.* 2d. D.L.R.
Optd in black. (*a*) *W* **2.** 1d. (*p* 11½–12½×*roul*), 1d. (*p* 10), 4d. (*roul*), 4d. (*p* 10), 6d. (*p* 10), 2s. (*roul*)
(*b*) *W* **7.** *P* 10. 2d. D.L.R.
(*c*) *W* **10.** 2d. D.L.R. (*roul*), 2d. (D.L.R.) (*p* 10×*roul*), 2d. D.L.R. (*p* 10)
The 6d. (*W* **2.** *Roul*) with red overprint is known showing the stop omitted after "B".

R.G. (Registrar-General)

Optd in red. *W* **2.** *Roul.* 2d., 6d., 1s.
Optd in blue. (*a*) *W* **2.** *P* 11½–12½ × *roul.* 6d.
(*b*) *W* **10.** 2d. D.L.R. (*roul*), 2d. D.L.R. (*p* 11½–12½ × *roul*)
Optd in black. (*a*) *W* **2.** 2d. D.L.R. (*roul*), 6d. (*p* 10), 6d. (*p* 10 × 11½–12½), 1s. (*p* 11½–12½ × *roul*), 1s. (*p* 10)
(*b*) *W* **7.** *P* 10. 2d. D.L.R.
(*c*) *W* **10.** 2d. D.L.R. (*roul*), 2d. D.L.R. (*p* 10 × *roul*), 2d. D.L.R. (*p* 10), 2d. D.L.R. (*p* 10 × 11½–12½)
The 2d. (*W* **2.** *Roul*) with red overprint is known showing "C" for "G".

S. (Sheriff)

Optd in red. W **2.** *Roul.* 2d., 6d.
Optd in blue. W **10.** *Roul.* 2d. D.L.R.
Optd in black. (*a*) *W* **2.** 6d. (*roul*), 6d. (*p* 11½–12½×*roul*), 6d. (*p* 11½–12½), 6d. (*p* 10)
(*b*) *W* **10.** 2d. D.L.R. (*roul*), 2d. D.L.R. (*p* 10×*roul*), 2d. D.L.R. (*p* 10)

S.C. (Supreme Court)

Optd in red. *W* **2.** *Roul.* 2d., 6d.
Optd in black. *W* **10.** *P* 10. 2d. D.L.R.

S.G. (Surveyor-General)

Optd in red. *W* **2.** 2d. (*roul*), 4d. (*p* 11½–12½), 6d. (*roul*)
Optd in blue. (*a*) *W* **2.** *Roul.* 4d.
(*b*) *W* **10.** *Roul.* 2d. D.L.R.
Optd in black. (*a*) *W* **2.** 2d. D.L.R. (*roul*), 4d. (*p* 11½–12½), 4d. (*p* 10), 4d. (*p* 10 × 11½–12½), 6d. (*p* 11½–12½ × *roul*), 6d. (*p* 11½–12½), 6d. (*p* 10), 6d. (*p* 10 × 11½–12½)
(*b*) *W* **7.** *P* 10. 2d. D.L.R.
(*c*) *W* **10.** 2d. D.L.R. (*roul*), 2d. D.L.R. (*p* 11½–12½), 2d. D.L.R. (*p* 10×*roul*), 2d. D.L.R. (*p* 10)
The 2d. (*W* **7** and *W* **10.** *P* 10) with black overprint are known showing "C" for "G".

S.M. (Stipendiary Magistrate)

Optd in red. *W* **2.** *Roul.* 1d., 2d., 4d., 6d., 1s.
Optd in blue. (*a*) *W* **2.** *Roul.* 2d., 4d., 6d.
(*b*) *W* **10.** *Roul.* 2d. D.L.R.
Optd in black. (*a*) *W* **2.** 1d. (*p* 11½–12½), 1d. (*p* 10), 2d. D.L.R. (*roul*), 4d. (*roul*), 4d. (*p* 11½–12½ × *roul*), 4d. (*p* 11½–12½), 4d. (*p* 10), 4d. (*p* 10 × 11½–12½), 6d. (*p* 11½–12½ × *roul*), 6d. (*p* 11½–12½), 6d. (*p* 10), 6d. (*p* 10 × 11½–12½), 1s. (*p* 11½–12½ × *roul*)
(*b*) *W* **7.** *P* 10. 2d. D.L.R.
(*c*) *W* **10.** 2d. D.L.R. (*roul*), 2d. D.L.R. (*p* 11½–12½), 2d. D.L.R. (*p* 10×*roul*), 2d. D.L.R. (*p* 10), 2d. D.L.R. (*p* 10×11½–12½)
The 2d. and 4d. (both *W* **2.** *Roul*) with red overprint are known showing the stop omitted after "M".

S.T. (Superintendent of Telegraphs)

Optd in red. *W* **2.** *Roul.* 2d., 6d.
Optd in blue. *W* **10.** *Roul.* 2d. D.L.R.
Optd in black. (*a*) *W* **2.** *Roul.* 2d. D.L.R., 6d.
(*b*) *W* **7.** *P* 10. 2d. D.L.R.
(*c*) *W* **10.** 2d. D.L.R. (*roul*), 2d. D.L.R. (*p* 10×*roul*), 2d. D.L.R. (*p* 10)
The 2d. and 6d. (both *W* **2.** *Roul*) with red overprint are known showing the stop omitted after "T".

T. (Treasury)

Optd in red. *W* **2.** 1d. (*roul*), 2d. (*roul*), 4d. (*p* 11½–12½ × *roul*), 6d. (*roul*), 1s. (*roul*)
Optd in blue. (*a*) *W* **2.** *Roul.* 1d. 4d., 6d.
(*b*) *W* **10.** *Roul.* 2d. D.L.R.
Optd in black. (*a*) *W* **2.** 1d. (*p* 10), 2d. D.L.R. (*roul*), 4d. (*roul*), 4d. (*p* 11½–12½), 4d. (*p* 10), 6d. (*roul*), 6d. (*p* 11½–12½), 1s. (*p* 11½–12½×*roul*), 1s. (*p* 10×11½–12½), 2s. (*roul*), 2s. (*p* 11½–12½), 2s. (*p* 10×11½–12½)
(*b*) *W* **7.** *P* 10. 2d. D.L.R.
(*c*) *W* **10.** 2d. D.L.R. (*roul*), 2d. D.L.R. (*p* 10)

T.R. (Titles Registration)

Optd in black. (*a*) *W* **2.** 4d. (*p* 11½–12½), 4d. (*p* 10×11½–12½), 6d. (*p* 11½–12½), 1s. (*p* 11½–12½)
(*b*) *W* **10.** *P* 10. 2d. D.L.R.

V. (Volunteers)

Optd in black. (*a*) *W* **2.** 4d. (*p* 10×11½–12½), 6d. (*p* 11½–12½), 1s. (*p* 11½–12½)
(*b*) *W* **10.** *P* 10. 2d. D.L.R.
(*c*) *W* **10.** 2d. D.L.R. (*roul*), 2d. D.L.R. (*p* 10 × *roul*), 2d. D.L.R. (*p* 10)
The 2d. (*W* **10.** *P* 10 × *roul*) overprinted in black is only known showing the stop omitted after "V".

VA. (Valuator of Runs)

Optd in black without stop after "V". (*a*) *W* **2.** *Roul.* 4d.
(*b*) *W* **10.** *P* 10. 2d. D.L.R.

VN. (Vaccination)

Optd in black without stop after "V". W **2.** 4d. (*p* 10), 4d. (*p* 10×11½–12½)

W. (Waterworks)

Optd in red. *W* **2.** *Roul.* 2d.
Optd in black. *W* **10.** 2d. D.L.R. (*roul*), 2d. D.L.R. (*p* 10)
The 2d. (*W* **2.** *Roul*) with red overprint is known showing the stop omitted after "W".

B. General

O.S. (O **1**)   O.S. (O **2**)

1874–77. *Optd with Type* O **1.** *W* **2.** (*a*) *P* 10.

No.	Type	Description	Unused	Used
O 1	**3**	4d. dull purple (18.2.74)	£1100	
		(*b*) *P* 11½–12½ × 10.		
O 2	**1**	1d. green (2.1.74)	—	
O 3	**3**	4d. dull violet (12.2.75)	60·00	
O 4	**1**	6d. Prussian blue (20.10.75)	70·00	
O 4*a*	**3**	2s. rose-pink		
O 5		2s. carmine (3.12.76)	—	
		(*c*) *P* 11½–12½		
O 6	**1**	1d. deep yellow green (30.1.74)	£1100	
		a. Printed on both sides	—	
O 7	**3**	3d. on 4d. ultramarine (26.6.77)	£1700	
		a. No stop after "S"	—	
O 8		4d. dull violet (13.7.74)	50·00	
		a. No stop after "S"	—	
O 9	**1**	6d. bright blue (31.8.75)	80·00	
		a. "O.S." double	—	
O10		6d. Prussian blue (27.3.74)	70·00	
		a. No stop after "S"	—	
O11	**4**	9d. red-purple (22.3.76)	£950	
		a. No stop after "S"	£1400	
O12	**1**	1s. red-brown (5.8.74)	70·00	
		a. "O.S." double	—	
		b. No stop after "S"	£140	
O13	**3**	2s. crimson-carmine (13.7.75)	£110	
		a. No stop after "S"	—	
		b. No stops	—	
		c. Stops at top of letters		

1876–85. *Optd with Type* O **1.** *W* **8.** (*a*) *P* 10.

No.	Type	Description	Unused	Used
O14	**1**	6d. bright blue (1879)	75·00	
		(*b*) *P* 10 × 11½–12½, 11½–12½ × 10, *or compound*		
O15	**3**	4d. violet-slate (24.1.78)	70·00	
O16		4d. plum (29.11.81)	38·00	
O17		4d. deep mauve	32·00	
		a. No stop after "S"	£110	
		b. No stop after "O"		
		c. "O.S." double		
		d. "O.S." inverted	—	
O18	**1**	6d. bright blue (1877)	55·00	
		a. "O.S." inverted		
		b. No stop after "O"		
O19		6d. bright ultramarine (27.3.85)	50·00	
		a. "O.S." inverted		
		b. "O.S." double		
		c. "O.S." double, one inverted	—	
		d. No stop after "S"	—	
		e. No stops after "O" & "S"		
O20		1s. red-brown (27.3.83)	45·00	
		a. "O.S." inverted		
		b. No stop after "O"		
		c. No stop after "S"	—	
O21	**3**	2s. carmine (16.3.81)	90·00	
		a. "O.S." inverted	—	
		b. No stop after "S"	—	
		(*c*) *P* 11½–12½		
O22	**3**	3d. on 4d. ultramarine	£1800	
O23		4d. violet-slate (14.3.76)	£140	
O24		4d. deep mauve (19.8.79)	50·00	
		a. "O.S." inverted		
		b. "O.S." double, one inverted		
		c. No stop after "S"	—	
O25	**1**	6d. Prussian blue (6.77)	55·00	
		a. "O.S." double	—	
		b. "O.S." inverted		
O26	**4**	8d. on 9d. brown (9.11.76)	£1200	
		a. "O.S." double	£1800	
		b. "O" only	—	
O26*c*		9d. purple	£2500	
O27	**1**	1s. red-brown (12.2.78)	35·00	
		a. "O.S." inverted	£200	95
		b. No stop after "S"	£170	42
O28		1s. lake-brown (8.11.83)	35·00	
O29	**3**	2s. rose-carmine (12.8.85)	90·00	
		a. "O.S." double	—	85
		b. "O.S." inverted	—	90
		c. No stop after "S"	—	40

1891–1903. *Optd with Type* O **2.** (*a*) *W* **8.** *P* 11½–12½.

No.	Type	Description	Unused	Used
O30	**1**	1s. lake-brown (18.4.91)	40·00	10
O31		1s. Vandyke brown	50·00	7
O32		1s. dull brown (2.7.96)	35·00	5
		a. No stop after "S"	—	55
O33		1s. sepia (*large holes*) (4.1.02)	28·00	5
		a. "O.S." double		
		b. No stop after "S"		
O34	**3**	2s. carmine (26.6.00)	80·00	13
		a. No stop after "S"		
		(*b*) *W* **8.** *P* 10 × 11½–12½		
O35	**3**	2s. rose-carmine (9.11.95)	65·00	10
		a. No stop after "S"	£120	
		b. "O.S." double		
		(*c*) *W* **10.** *P* 11½–12½		
O36	**1**	1s. dull brown (1902)	45·00	10·

'6. *Optd with Type* O **1**. *W* **10**. (*a*) *P* 10.
11 1d. blue-green (30.9.75) .. .. 80·00 18·00
a. "O.S." inverted .. .. ..
b. No stop after "S" .. .. ..
12 2d. orange-red (18.2.74) .. .. 16·00 1·50
a. No stop after "S" .. .. .. — 22·00
b. "O.S." double .. .. ..

(*b*) *P* 10 × 11½–12½, 11½–12½ × 10, *or compound*
11 1d. blue-green (16.9.75) .. ..
a. No stop after "S" .. .. ..
12 2d. orange-red (27.9.76) .. .. — 8·00

(*c*) *P* 11½–12½
11 1d. blue-green (13.8.75) .. .. — 20·00
a. "O.S." inverted .. .. ..
b. No stop after "S" .. .. ..
12 2d. orange-red (20.5.74) .. .. — 85·00

80. *Optd with Type* O **1**. *W* **13**. (*a*) *P* 10
11 1d. blue-green (2.10.76) .. .. 11·00 1·00
a. "O.S." inverted .. .. .. — 38·00
b. "O.S." double .. .. .. 50·00 32·00
c. "O.S." double, one inverted ..
d. No stops .. .. — 22·00
e. No stop after "O" .. .. ..
f. No stop after "S" .. .. .. — 11·00
g. *Deep green* .. .. .. 13·00 1·00
ga. "O.S." double .. .. .. — 35·00
12 2d. orange-red (21.9.77) .. .. 7·50 80
a. "O.S." inverted .. .. .. — 18·00
b. "O.S." double .. .. .. 60·00 30·00
c. "O.S." double, one inverted ..
d. "O.S." double, both inverted .. — 90·00
e. No stops .. .. — 45·00
f. No stop after "O" .. .. .. — 15·00
g. No stop after "S" .. .. ..
h. *Dull brick-red* .. .. .. 30·00 80

(*b*) *P* 10×11½–12½, 11½–12½×10 *or compound*
11 1d. deep green (14.8.80) .. .. — 24·00
a. "O.S." double .. .. ..
12 2d. orange-red (6.4.78) .. .. 50·00 8·00
a. "O.S." inverted .. .. .. — 90·00
b. No stop after "S" .. .. .. — 45·00

(*c*) *P* 11½–12½
12 2d. orange-red (15.7.80) .. .. — 65·00

(20 Feb). *No.* 181 *optd with Type* O **1**.
11 ½d. on 1d. blue-green .. .. 60·00 14·00
a. "O.S." inverted .. .. ..

(15 Nov)–**91.** *Nos.* 184 *and* 185*a optd with Type* O **1**.
0.
17 4d. pale violet (24.1.91) .. .. 55·00 5·00
18 6d. blue .. .. 19·00 1·25
a. "O.S." double .. .. ..
b. No stop after "S" .. .. ..

. *Nos.* 229*b and* 231*a*/2 *optd with Type* O **1**. (*a*) *P* 10
17 2½d. on 4d. deep green (Br.) (1 Aug) 55·00 8·50
a. "2" and "½" closer together — 42·00
b. "O.S." inverted .. .. ..
c. "O.S." double .. .. ..
d. "O.S." omitted (in vert pair with normal) .. .. ..
e. No stop after "S" .. ..

(*b*) *P* 10×11½–12½ *or* 11½–12½×10
17 2½d. on 4d. deep green (Br.) (1 Oct) .. 60·00 12·00

(*c*) *P* 11½–12½
17 2½d. on 4d. deep green (Br.) (1 June) £110 55·00

–**96.** *Optd with Type* O **2**. *W* **13**. (*a*) *P* 10
11 1d. deep green (22.4.91) .. .. 15·00 2·00
a. "O.S." double .. .. .. 50·00 30·00
b. "O.S." double, one inverted ..
c. No stop after "S" .. .. .. 35·00 10·00
d. Blackish blue opt .. .. .. £200 4·00
12 2d. orange-red (22.4.91) .. .. 15·00 1·25
a. "O.S." double .. .. ..
b. "O.S." double, both inverted ..
c. No stop after "S" .. .. .. — 10·00

(*b*) *P* 15
11 1d. green (8.9.94) .. .. .. 10·00 1·25
a. "O.S." double .. .. ..
b. No stop after "S" .. .. ..
12 2d. orange-red (16.6.94) .. .. 9·50 50
a. "O.S." double .. .. .. — 23·00
b. "O.S." inverted .. .. .. — 17·00

(*c*) *P* 13
11 1d. green (20.5.95) .. .. .. 17·00 60
a. No stop after "S" .. .. .. 55·00 10·00
12 2d. orange-red (11.2.96) .. .. 17·00 50
a. "O.S." double .. .. .. 80·00
b. No stop after "S" .. .. .. 50·00 10·00

1–**99.** *Optd with Type* O **2**. *W* **13** (*sideways on* ½*d.*). (*a*) *P* 10
15 ½d. brown (2.5.94) .. .. .. 14·00 4·50
a. No stop after "S" .. .. .. 40·00 25·00
17 4d. pale violet (13.2.91) .. .. 50·00 3·50
a. "O.S." double .. .. ..
b. "S." omitted .. .. .. — 55·00
c. No stop after "S" .. .. ..
d. *Aniline violet* (31.8.93) .. .. 50·00 3·50
da. "O.S." double .. .. ..
dc. No stop after "S" .. .. ..
18 6d. blue (4.4.93) .. .. .. 18·00 2·50
a. No stop after "S" .. .. ..
b. Blackish blue opt .. .. ..

(*b*) *P* 10×11½–12½
15 ½d. brown (26.3.95) .. .. 12·00 6·00

(*c*) *P* 11½–12½
15 ½d. red-brown (13.6.91) .. .. 32·00 9·00

(*d*) *P* 15
O65 15 ½d. pale brown (8.6.95) .. .. 22·00 7·00
O66 17 4d. slate-violet (4.4.95) .. .. 55·00 4·50
a. "O.S." double .. .. .. £160 32·00
O67 18 6d. blue (20.9.93) .. .. .. 25·00 3·00

(*e*) *P* 13
O68 15 ½d. deep brown (17.5.98) .. .. 13·00 6·00
a. Opt triple, twice sideways .. £160
O69 17 4d. violet (12.96) .. .. .. 55·00 3·00
a. "O.S." double .. .. .. £130 32·00
b. No stop after "S" .. .. .. £130 24·00
O70 18 6d. blue (13.9.99) .. .. .. 25·00 2·00
a. No stop after "S" .. .. .. 80·00 55·00

1891–95. *Nos.* 229*b*, 230*a and* 231*a optd with Type* O **2**. (*a*) *P* 10
O71 17 2½d. on 4d. deep green (Br.) (18.8.94) 35·00 10·00
a. Fraction bar omitted .. ..
b. "2" and "½" closer together .. 85·00 30·00
c. "O.S." inverted £140
d. No stop after "S" .. .. .. — 38·00
O72 18 5d. on 6d. deep brown (C.) (2.12.91) 42·00 15·00
a. No stop after "5D" £180
b. No stop after "S" .. .. £100 40·00

(*b*) *P* 10×11½–12½
O73 17 2½d. on 4d. deep green (Br.) (17.9.95) — 50·00
a. "O.S." double .. .. ..

1897–1901. *Nos.* 235/6 *and* 238*a optd with Type* O **2**. (*a*) *P* 15
O74 23 5d. brown-purple (29.3.01) .. .. 60·00 10·00

(*b*) *P* 13
O75 22 2½d. violet-blue (5.7.97) .. .. 48·00 7·00
a. No stop after "S" .. .. .. — 30·00
O76 23 5d. purple (29.9.01) .. .. .. 60·00 11·00
a. No stop after "S" .. .. ..

O. S.

(O 3)

1899–1901. *Optd with Type* O **3**. *W* **13**. *P* 13.
O80 24 ½d. yellow-green (12.2.00) .. .. 12·00 6·00
a. "O.S." inverted .. .. .. 50·00
b. No stop after "S" .. .. .. 35·00
O81 11 1d. rosine (22.9.99) .. .. .. 12·00 1·60
a. "O.S." inverted .. .. .. 45·00 32·00
b. "O.S." double .. .. ..
c. No stop after "S" .. .. .. 40·00 16·00
O82 12 2d. bright violet (1.6.00) .. .. 12·00 80
a. "O.S." inverted .. .. .. 40·00 22·00
b. "O.S." double .. .. ..
c. No stop after "S" .. .. .. 30·00
O83 22 2½d. indigo (2.10.01) .. .. .. 55·00 18·00
a. "O.S." inverted .. .. .. — 60·00
b. No stop after "S" £150
O84 17 4d. violet (18.11.00) .. .. .. 50·00 4·00
a. "O.S." inverted £170
b. No stop after "S" £130
O85 18 6d. blue (8.10.00) .. .. .. 18·00 4·00
a. No stop after "S" .. .. .. 55·00

1891 (May). *Optd as Type* O **3** *but wider. W* **13**. *P* 10.
O86 19 2s. 6d. pale violet £2750 £2000
O87 5s. pale rose £2750 £2000
Only one sheet (60) of each of these stamps was printed.

The use of stamps overprinted "O S" was made invalid by the Posts and Telegraph Act of 1 November 1902.

South Australia became part of the Commonwealth of Australia on 1 January 1901.

TASMANIA

PRICES FOR STAMPS ON COVER

Nos. 1/4	*from* × 6
Nos. 5/12	*from* × 5
Nos. 14/24	*from* × 3
Nos. 25/56	*from* × 5
Nos. 57/77	*from* × 6
Nos. 78/9	—
Nos. 80/90	*from* × 3
No. 91	—
Nos. 92/109	*from* × 3
No. 110	—
Nos. 111/23	*from* × 3
Nos. 124/6	—
Nos. 127/34	*from* × 5
Nos. 135/55	*from* × 4
Nos. 156/8	*from* × 20
Nos. 159/66	*from* × 10
Nos. 167/9	*from* × 15
Nos. 170/4	*from* × 6
Nos. 216/22	*from* × 15
Nos. 223/5	—
Nos. 226/7	*from* × 15
Nos. 229/36	*from* × 20
Nos. 237/57	*from* × 10
No. 258	—
Nos. 259/62	*from* × 10
Nos. F1/25	—
Nos. F26/9	*from* × 15
Nos. F30/9	—

SPECIMEN OVERPRINTS. Those listed are from U.P.U. distributions between 1892 and 1904. Further "Specimen" overprints exist, but these were used for other purposes.

1

2

3

(Eng C. W. Coard. Recess H. and C. Best at the *Courier* newspaper, Hobart)

1853 (1 Nov). *No wmk. Imperf. Twenty-four varieties in four rows of six each.*

(*a*) *Medium soft yellowish paper with all lines clear and distinct*
1 1 1d. pale blue £3500 £900
2 1d. blue £3500 £900

(*b*) *Thin hard white paper with lines of the engraving blurred and worn*
3 1 1d. pale blue £3250 £800
4 1d. blue £3250 £800

1853–55. *No wmk. Imperf. In each plate there are twenty-four varieties in four rows of six each.*

(*a*) *Plate I. Finely engraved. All lines in network and background thin, clear, and well defined.* (1853)

(i) *First state of the plate, brilliant colours*
5 2 4d. bright red-orange £2750 £700
a. Double impression .. ..
6 4d. bright brownish orange .. .. — £850

(ii) *Second state of plate, with blurred lines and worn condition of the central background*
7 2 4d. red-orange £2250 £425
8 4d. orange £2000 £400
9 4d. pale orange .. .. — £400

(*b*) *Plate II. Coarse engraving, lines in network and background thicker and blurred* (1855)
10 2 4d. orange £2000 £400
a. Double print, one albino
11 4d. dull orange £2000 £350
12 4d. yellowish orange £2000 £350

In the 4d. Plate I, the outer frame-line is thin all round. In Plate II it is, by comparison with other parts, thicker in the lower left angle.

The 4d. is known on vertically laid paper from proof sheets. Examples from Plate I have the lines close together and those from Plate II wide apart (*Price* £5000 *unused*).

In 1879 reprints were made of the 1d. in blue and the 4d., Plate I, in brownish yellow, on thin, tough, white wove paper, and perforated 11½. In 1887, a reprint from the other plate of the 4d. was made in reddish brown and in black, and in 1889 of the 1d. in blue and in black, and of the 4d. (both plates) in yellow and in black on white card, imperforate. As these three plates were defaced after the stamps had been superseded, all these reprints show two, or three thick strokes across the Queen's head.

All three plates were destroyed in July 1950.

PERKINS BACON "CANCELLED". For notes on these handstamps, showing "CANCELLED" between horizontal bars forming an oval, see Catalogue Introduction.

(Eng W. Humphrys, after water-colour sketch by E. Corbould. Recess P.B.)

1855 (17 Aug–16 Sept). *Wmk Large Star, W* w **1**. *Imperf.*
14 3 1d. carmine (16.9) (H/S "CANCELLED" in oval £4750) £4250 £750
15 2d. deep green (16.9) £1800 £500
16 2d. green (16.9) (H/S "CANCELLED" in oval £4750) £1800 £450
17 4d. deep blue .. .. £1200 90·00
18 4d. bl (H/S "CANCELLED" in oval £3500) £1200 £100

Proofs of the 1d. and 4d. on thick paper, *without watermark*, are sometimes offered as the issued stamps.

The 6d. dull lilac on this watermark was prepared, but not issued. Examples exist from a creased proof sheet (*Price* £700 *unused*).

(Recess H. and C. Best, Hobart, from P.B. plates)

1856 (Apr)–**57.** *No wmk. Imperf.* (*a*) *Thin white paper.*
19 3 1d. pale brick-red (4.56) £4500 £550
20 2d. dull emerald-green (1.57) £5500 £800
21 4d. deep blue (5.57) £650 £100
22 4d. blue (5.57) £550 £100
23 4d. pale blue (5.57) .. .. .. — £140

(*b*) *Pelure paper*
24 3 1d. deep red-brown (11.56) £3250 £650

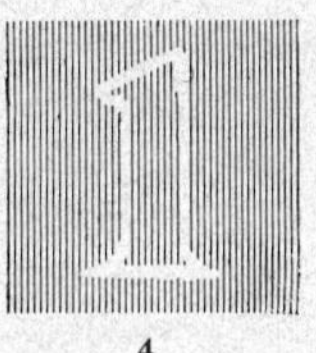

4

7

8

(Recess H. Best (August 1857–May 1859), J. Davies (August 1859–March 1862), J. Birchall (March 1863), M. Hood (October 1863–April 1864), Govt Printer (from July 1864), all from P.B. plates)

1857 (Aug)–**69.** *Wmk double-lined numerals "1", "2" or "4" as W* **4** *on appropriate value. Imperf.*
25 3 1d. deep red-brown .. .. .. £425 27·00
26 1d. pale red-brown .. .. .. £300 20·00
27 1d. brick-red (1863) .. .. .. £150 18·00
28 1d. dull vermilion (1865).. .. .. 85·00 18·00
29 1d. carmine (1867) .. .. .. 90·00 18·00
a. Double print .. .. — £130
b. Error. Wmkd "2" (1869) .. ..
30 2d. dull emerald-green .. .. .. — 80·00
31 2d. green .. .. — 38·00
a. Double print .. .. — £160

32 **3** 2d. yellow-green £275 75·00
33 2d. deep green (1858) £225 45·00
34 2d. slate-green (1860) £160 60·00
35 4d. deep blue — 75·00
a. Double print — £160
36 4d. pale blue £120 15·00
37 4d. blue £120 19·00
a. Double print — £160
38 4d. bright blue £120 19·00
a. Printed on both sides † —
b. Double print — £130
39 4d. cobalt-blue — 70·00

Printings before July 1864 were all carried out at the *Courier* printing works which changed hands several times during this period.

CANCELLATIONS. Beware of early Tasmanian stamps with pen-cancellations cleaned off and faked postmarks applied.

(Recess P.B.)

1858 (Jan). *Wmk double-lined numerals "6" or "12" as* **W 4**. *Imperf.*
40 **7** 6d. dull lilac (H/S "CANCELLED" in oval £4750) £600 75·00
41 **8** 1s. verm (*shades*) (H/S "CANCELLED" in oval £3750) £500 70·00

(Recess J. Davies (March 1860), J. Birchall (April 1863), Govt Printer (from February 1865), all from P.B. plates)

1860 (Mar)–**67**. *Wmk double-lined "6" as* **W 4**. *Imperf.*
44 **7** 6d. dull slate-grey £275 55·00
45 6d. grey — 60·00
46 6d. grey-violet (4.63) £170 55·00
a. Double print — £225
47 6d. dull cobalt (2.65) £425 90·00
48 6d. slate-violet (2.65) £300 48·00
49 6d. reddish mauve (4.67) £650 £150

In 1871 reprints were made of the 6d. (in mauve) and the 1s. on white wove paper, and perforated 11½. They are found with or without "REPRINT". In 1889 they were again reprinted on white card, imperforate. These later impressions are also found overprinted "REPRINT" and perforated 11½.

PERFORATED ISSUES. From 1 October 1857 the Tasmania Post Office only supplied purchasers requiring five or more complete sheets of stamps. The public obtained their requirements, at face value, from licensed stamp vendors, who obtained their stocks at a discount from the Post Office.

From 1863 onwards a number of the stamp vendors applied their own roulettes or perforations. The Hobart firm of J. Walch & Sons achieved this so successfully that they were given an official contract in July 1869 to perforate sheets for the Post Office. The Government did not obtain a perforating machine until late in 1871.

1863–71. *Double-lined numeral watermarks. Various unofficial roulettes and perforations.*

(*a*) *By. J. Walch & Sons, Hobart*

(i) *Roulette about* 8, *often imperf × roul* (1863–68)
50 **3** 1d. brick-red — £160
51 1d. carmine £325 £110
52 2d. yellow-green — £425
53 2d. slate-green
54 4d. pale blue — £150
55 **7** 6d. dull lilac — £180
56 **8** 1s. vermilion — £550

(ii) *P* 10 (1864–69)
57 **3** 1d. brick-red 60·00 24·00
58 1d. dull vermilion 60·00 24·00
a. Double print † —
59 1d. carmine 50·00 22·00
60 2d. yellow-green £300 85·00
61 2d. slate-green £350 £150
62 4d. pale blue £110 12·00
63 4d. blue £110 12·00
a. Double print — £120
64 **7** 6d. grey-violet £180 16·00
65 6d. dull cobalt £275 65·00
66 6d. slate-violet — 22·00
67 6d. reddish mauve £375 75·00
68 **8** 1s. vermilion £120 22·00
a. Imperf vert (horiz pair)

(iii) *P* 12 (1865–71—*from July* 1869 *under contract to the Post Office*)
69 **3** 1d. dull vermilion 55·00
a. Double print † —
70 1d. carmine 45·00 9·00
a. Error. Wmkd "2" (*pen cancel* £75) — £1000
71 2d. yellow-green £140 45·00
72 4d. deep blue 85·00 14·00
73 4d. blue 85·00 16·00
74 4d. cobalt-blue — 35·00
75 **7** 6d. slate-violet £150 22·00
a. Imperf between (vert pair)
76 6d. reddish mauve 80·00 35·00
a. Imperf between (vert or horiz pair)
77 **8** 1s. vermilion £130 32·00
a. Double print — £160
b. Imperf between (horiz pair)

(iv) *Perf compound* 10 × 12 (1865–69)
78 **3** 1d. carmine £1400
79 4d. blue — £950

(*b*) *P* 12½ *by R. Harris, Launceston* (1864–68)
80 **3** 1d. brick-red 65·00 28·00
81 1d. dull vermilion 60·00 22·00
82 1d. carmine 35·00 9·50
83 2d. yellow-green £300 95·00
84 2d. slate-green £275 £130
85 4d. blue £160 42·00
86 4d. bright blue £160 42·00
87 **7** 6d. dull cobalt £325 85·00
88 6d. slate-violet £225 48·00
89 6d. reddish mauve £400 £110
90 **8** 1s. vermilion £275 90·00

(*c*) *Imperf×oblique roulette* 11½ *at Oatlands* (1866)
91 **3** 4d. blue — £400
91*a* **7** 6d. dull cobalt

(*d*) *Oblique roulette* 10–10½, *possibly at Deloraine* (1867)
92 **3** 1d. brick-red — £350
93 1d. carmine £950 £300
94 2d. yellow-green — £450
95 4d. bright blue — £400
96 **7** 6d. grey-violet — £650

(*e*) *Oblique roulette* 14–15, *probably at Cleveland* (1867–69)
97 **3** 1d. brick-red — £400
98 1d. dull vermilion — £400
99 1d. carmine — £400
100 2d. yellow-green — £450
101 4d. pale blue — £350
102 **7** 6d. grey-violet — £600
103 **8** 1s. vermilion — £750

(*f*) *Pin-perf* 5½ *to* 9½ *at Longford* (1867)
104 **3** 1d. carmine £325 80·00
105 2d. yellow-green
106 4d. bright blue — £170
107 **7** 6d. grey-violet — £160
108 6d. reddish mauve — £450
109 **8** 1s. vermilion

(*g*) *Pin-perf* 12 *at Oatlands* (1867)
110 **3** 4d. blue

(*h*) *Pin-perf* 13½ *to* 14½ (1867)
111 **3** 1d. brick-red — £200
112 1d. dull vermilion — £200
113 1d. carmine
114 2d. yellow-green — £300
115 4d. pale blue — £170
116 **7** 6d. grey-violet — £400
117 **8** 1s. vermilion

(*j*) *Serrated perf* 19 *at Hobart* (1868–69)
118 **3** 1d. carmine (*pen-cancel* £9) £250 £110
119 2d. yellow-green — £225
120 4d. deep blue £600 £100
121 4d. cobalt-blue — £100
122 **7** 6d. slate-violet — £400
123 **8** 1s. vermilion

(*k*) *Roul* 4½, *possibly at Macquarie River* (1868)
124 **3** 4d. blue
125 **7** 6d. reddish mauve
126 **8** 1s. vermilion

An example of the 1d. carmine is known perforated 10 on three sides and serrated 19 on the fourth.

For stamps perforated 11½ or 12 by the Post Office see Nos. 134*a*/43.

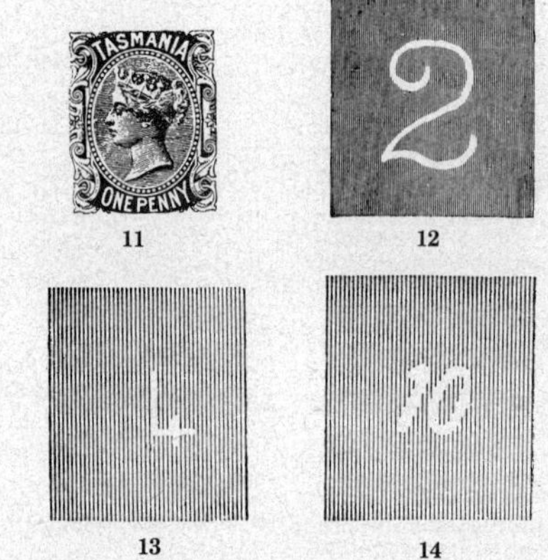

11 12 13 14

(Typo Govt Printer, Hobart, from plates made by D.L.R.)

1870 (1 Nov)–**71**. *Wmk single-lined numerals* **W 12** (*2d.*), **13** (*1d., 4d.*) *or* **14** (*1d., 10d.*). (*a*) *P* 12 *by J. Walch & Sons.*
127 **11** 1d. rose-red (*wmk* "10") 35·00 9·00
a. Imperf (pair) £325 £325
b. Deep rose-red 50·00 7·00
128 1d. rose-red (*wmk* "4") (3.71) 50·00 11·00
a. Imperf (pair) — £275
129 2d. yellow-green 60·00 5·50
a. Imperf (pair)
b. Blue-green 65·00 5·50
130 4d. blue £700 £400
131 10d. black 23·00 21·00
a. Imperf (pair) £190

(*b*) *P* 11½ *by the Post Office* (1871)
132 **11** 1d. rose-red (*wmk* "10") £900
133 2d. yellow-green £100 7·00
a. Blue-green 55·00 4·00
ab. Double print
134 10d. black 26·00 21·00

The above were printed on paper obtained from New South Wales.

See also Nos. 144/55, 156/8, 159/66, 170/4, 226/7, 242 and 255/6.

(Recess P.B.)

1871. *Wmk double-lined numeral "12". P 11½ by the Post Office.*
134*a* **7** 1s. vermilion

(Recess Govt Printer, Hobart)

1871–91. *Double-lined numeral watermarks as* **W 4**. *Perforated by the Post Office.* (*a*) *P* 11½.
135 **7** 6d. dull lilac 85·00 20·00
136 6d. lilac 80·00 20·00
a. Imperf between (pair) — £500
137 6d. deep slate-lilac (3.75) 80·00 20·00
a. Imperf (pair) — £475
138 6d. bright violet (5.78) 80·00 30·00
a. Double print — £120
b. Imperf between (horiz pair) £800
139 6d. dull reddish lilac (10.79) 75·00 38·00
140 **8** 1s. brown-red (1.73) 95·00
a. Imperf between (horiz pair)
141 1s. orange-red (3.75) 85·00
141*a* 1s. orange (5.78)

(*b*) *P* 12
142 **7** 6d. reddish purple (1884) 85·00
a. Imperf between (horiz pair) £475
143 6d. dull claret (7.91) 25·00

The perforation machine used on Nos. 142/3 was previ[ously] owned by J. Walch and Sons and passed to the ownership [of the] Government in 1884. It may have been used to perforat[e left]over sheets of previous printings.

15 16

(Typo Govt Printer, Hobart, from plates made by D.L.R.)

1871 (25 Mar)–**78**. **W 15**. (*a*) *P* 11½.
144 **11** 1d. rose (5.71) 5·50
a. Imperf (pair) (*pen cancel* £35)
b. Bright rose 5·50
c. Carmine 7·00
d. Pink 7·50
e. Vermilion (4.75) £225
145 2d. deep green (11.72) 22·00
a. Blue-green 27·00
b. Yellow-green (12.75) £130
146 3d. pale red-brown 42·00
a. Imperf (pair) £190
b. Deep red-brown 42·00
ba. Imperf between (pair)
c. Purple-brown (1.78) 42·00
ca. Imperf (pair) —
d. Brownish purple 42·00
147 4d. pale yellow (8.8.76) 50·00
a. Ochre (7.78) 55·00
b. Buff 45·00
148 9d. blue (2.10.71) 16·00
a. Imperf (pair) £180
b. Double print
149 5s. purple (*pen cancel* £3.75) £160 5
a. Imperf (pair)
b. Mauve £140 5

(*b*) *P* 12
150 **11** 1d. rose 70·00
a. Carmine 75·00
151 2d. green £475
a. Imperf (pair) —
152 3d. red-brown 70·00 1
a. Deep red-brown 70·00 1
153 4d. buff £225 1
154 9d. pale blue 28·00
155 5s. purple £300
a. Mauve £200

(Typo D.L.R.)

1878 (28 Oct). **W 16**. *P* 14.
156 **11** 1d. carmine 2·75
a. Rose-carmine 2·75
b. Scarlet 2·75
157 2d. pale green 3·75
a. Green 3·75
158 8d. dull purple-brown 14·00

(Typo Govt Printer, Hobart (some printings of 1d. in 1891 [by] *Mercury* Press) from plates made by Victoria Govt Prin[ter,] Melbourne (½d.) or D.L.R. (others))

1880 (Apr)–**91**. **W 16** (*sideways on 1d.*). (*a*) *P* 11½.
159 **11** ½d. orange (8.3.89) 2·75
a. Deep orange 2·75
160 1d. dull red (14.2.89) 5·00
a. Vermilion-red 5·00
161 3d. red-brown 13·00
a. Imperf (pair) £150
162 4d. deep yellow (1.83) 32·00
a. Chrome-yellow 32·00
b. Olive-yellow £100
c. Buff 28·00

(*b*) *P* 12
163 **11** ½d. orange 2·00 3
a. Deep orange 1·90 3
ab. Wmk sideways
164 1d. pink (1891) 18·00 3
a. Imperf (pair) £130
b. Rosine 9·50 1
c. Dull rosine 12·00 3
ca. Imperf (pair) £120
165 3d. red-brown 8·00 3
a. Imperf between (horiz pair) £550
166 4d. deep yellow 60·00
a. Chrome-yellow 75·00 13
ab. Printed both sides £350

SPECIMEN AND PRESENTATION REPRINTS OF TY[PE] 11. In 1871 the 1d., 2d., 3d., 4d. blue, 9d., 10d. and 5s. w[ere] reprinted on soft white wove paper to be followed, in 1879, by [the] 4d. yellow and 8d. on rough white wove. Both these reprinti[ngs] were perforated 11½. In 1886 it was decided to overpr[int] remaining stocks with the word "REPRINT".

In 1889 Tasmania commenced sending sample stamps to [the] U.P.U. in Berne and a further printing of the 4d. blue was ma[de] imperforate, on white card. This, together with the 5s. in mau[ve] on white card, both perforated 11½ and overprinted "RE[PRINT]", were included in presentation sets supplied to memb[ers] of the states' legislatures in 1901.

lfpenny

(17)

d. $2\frac{1}{2}$

(18) (2¼ mm between "d", and "2")

d. $2\frac{1}{2}$

(19) (3½ mm between "d" and "2")

(1 Jan). *No. 156b surch locally with T* **17**.
11 ½d. on 1d. scarlet .. .. .. 9·00 12·00
a. "al" in "Half" printed sideways (R. 1/2) £700 £500
. 167a occurred in a second printing and was later corrected.
reprint on white card, perforated 11½ or imperforate, printed "REPRINT" was produced in 1901.

(1 Jan–June). *Surch locally*. *W* **16**. (a) *With T* **18**. *P* 11½.
11 2½d. on 9d. pale blue .. .. .. 9·00 4·00
a. Surch double, one inverted .. £275 £300
b. Deep blue (May) .. .. 9·00 4·50
(b) *With T* **19**. *P* 12
11 2½d. on 9d. pale blue (June) ..
a. Blue surch.. .. .. 5·00 3·25
reprint, using a third setting, perforated 11½ and overed "REPRINT" was produced in 1901.

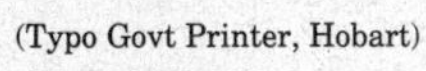

(Typo Govt Printer, Hobart)

. (Apr–Aug). *W* **15**. (a) *P* 11½.
11 ½d. orange .. .. 26·00 10·00
a. Brown-orange .. .. 21·00 9·50
1d. rosine .. .. 15·00 5·00
(b) *P* 12
11 ½d. orange .. .. 19·00 14·00
a. Imperf (pair) .. .. 90·00
1d. dull rosine .. .. 21·00 11·00
a. Rosine .. .. 35·00 15·00
4d. bistre (Aug).. .. .. .. 16·00 9·00

20

21

21*a*

(Typo D.L.R.)

2 (12 Feb)–**99**. *W* **16**. *P* 14.
20 ½d. orange and mauve (11.92) .. 1·25 60
21 2½d. purple .. .. 2·50 1·00
20 5d. pale blue and brown .. .. 4·75 1·75
6d. violet and black (11.92) .. .. 6·50 2·25
21a 10d. purple-lake & deep green (30.1.99) 9·00 8·50
20 1s. rose and green (11.92) .. .. 6·50 2·00
2s. 6d. brown and blue (11.92) .. 22·00 11·00
5s. lilac and red (3.2.97) .. .. 42·00 18·00
10s. mauve and brown (11.92) .. 80·00 55·00
£1 green and yellow (2.97) £250 £190
/25 .. .. *Set of* 10 £375 £250
s/25s Optd "Specimen" .. *Set of* 10 £275
ee also Nos. 243 and 257/8.

(Typo Govt Printer, Hobart)

6. *W* **16**. *P* 12.
11 4d. pale bistre .. .. 12·00 6·00
9d. pale blue .. .. 8·00 2·50
a. Blue.. .. .. 8·50 3·25

22 Lake Marion

23 Mount Wellington

24 Hobart

25 Tasman's Arch

26 Spring River, Port Davey

27 Russell Falls

28 Mount Gould, Lake St. Clair

29 Dilston Falls

30

(Eng. L. Phillips. Recess D.L.R.)

1899 (Dec)–**1900**. *W* **30**. *P* 14.
229 **22** ½d. deep green (31.3.00) .. .. 8·00 4·75
230 **23** 1d. bright lake (13.12.99)* .. .. 5·00 1·00
231 **24** 2d. deep violet (15.12.99)* .. .. 12·00 1·25
232 **25** 2½d. indigo (1900) .. .. .. 12·00 3·75
233 **26** 3d. sepia (1900) .. .. .. 9·00 3·75
234 **27** 4d. deep orange-buff (1900) .. .. 16·00 4·25
235 **28** 5d. bright blue (31.3.00) .. .. 18·00 9·00
236 **29** 6d. lake (31.3.00) .. .. .. 22·00 14·00
229/36 .. .. *Set of* 8 90·00 38·00
229s/36s Optd "Specimen" .. *Set of* 8 £275
*Earliest known postmark dates.
See also Nos. 237/9, 240/1, 245/8, 249/54, 259 and 261/2.

DIFFERENCES BETWEEN LITHOGRAPHED AND TYPOGRAPHED PRINTINGS OF TYPES 22/9

Lithographed	Typographed
General appearance fine.	*Comparatively crude and coarse appearance.*
½d. All "V over Crown" wmk.	All "Crown over A" wmk.
1d. The shading on the path on the right bank of the river consists of very fine dots. In printings from worn stones the dots hardly show.	The shading on the path is coarser, consisting of large dots and small patches of colour.
The shading on the white mountain is fine (or almost absent in many stamps).	The shading on the mountain is coarse, and clearly defined.
2d. Three rows of windows in large building on shore, at extreme left, against inner frame.	Two rows of windows.
3d. Clouds very white.	Clouds dark.
Stars in corner ornaments have long points.	Stars have short points.
Shading of corner ornaments is defined by a coloured outer line.	Shading of ornaments terminates against white background.
4d. Lithographed only.	—
6d. No coloured dots at base of waterfall.	Coloured dots at base of waterfall.
Outer frame of value tablets is formed by outer line of design.	Thick line of colour between value tablets and outer line.
	Small break in inner frame below second "A" of "TASMANIA".

(Litho, using transfers from D.L.R. plates, Victoria Government Printing Office, Melbourne)

1902 (Jan)–**04**. *Wmk V over Crown, W w* **10** (*sideways on* ½*d., 2d.*). *P* 12½.
237 **22** ½d. green (2.03) .. .. .. 2·25 1·25
a. Wmk upright .. .. ..
b. Perf 11 .. .. 4·25 4·00
c. Perf comp of 12½ and 11 .. .. 60·00 38·00
d. Perf comp of 12½ and 12 .. ..
s. Optd "Specimen" .. .. .. 48·00
238 **23** 1d. carmine-red .. .. .. 6·50 1·00
239 **24** 2d. deep reddish violet .. .. 5·00 50
a. Perf 11 .. .. 5·00 2·75
b. Perf comp of 12½ and 11 .. .. 65·00 38·00
c. Wmk upright (2.04) .. .. — 8·00
d. Deep rose-lilac (4.05) .. .. 10·00 20
da. Perf 11 .. .. 8·00 1·25
db. Perf comp of 12½ and 11 .. ..
s. Optd "Specimen" .. .. .. 48·00
As the V and Crown paper was originally prepared for stamps of smaller size, portions of two or more watermarks appear on each stamp.
We only list the main groups of shades in this and the following issues. There are variations of shade in all values, particularly in the 2d. where there is a wide range, also in the 1d. in some issues.

(Typo, using electrotyped plates, Victoria Govt Ptg Office, Melbourne)

1902 (Oct)–**04**. *Wmk V over Crown, W w* **10**. *P* 12½.
240 **23** 1d. pale red (*wmk sideways*) .. .. 9·50 1·00
a. Perf 11 .. .. 25·00 1·75
b. Perf comp of 12½ and 11 .. .. £160 40·00
c. Wmk upright (1.03) .. .. 23·00 5·50
ca. Perf 11 .. .. 30·00 6·50
d. Rose-red (*wmk upright*) (4.03) .. 5·50 1·50
da. Perf 11 .. .. 16·00 1·50
db. Perf comp of 12½ and 11 .. .. £160 40·00
ds. Optd "Specimen" .. .. .. 48·00
241 **23** 1d. scarlet (*wmk upright*) (9.03) .. 4·00 75
a. Perf 11 .. .. 6·00 1·00
b. Perf comp of 12½ and 11 .. ..
c. Rose-scarlet (1904) .. .. 3·50 80
ca. Perf 11 .. .. 4·00 1·00
cb. Perf comp of 12½ and 11 .. .. 60·00 17·00
The 1d. scarlet of September 1903 was from new electrotyped plates which show less intense shading.

(Typo Victoria Govt Ptg Office, Melbourne)

1903 (Apr–Dec). *Wmk V over Crown, W w* **10**. *P* 12½.
242 **11** 9d. blue (Apr) .. .. 8·00 3·25
a. Perf 11 .. .. 8·00 6·00
b. Perf comp of 12½ and 11 .. .. — £400
c. Wmk sideways .. .. .. 55·00 20·00
d. Pale blue .. .. 10·00 4·50
e. Bright blue .. .. 10·00 5·00
f. Ultramarine £350
g. Indigo £130
243 **20** 1s. rose and green (Dec) .. .. 13·00 3·75
a. Perf 11 .. .. 32·00
242s/3s Optd "Specimen" .. *Set of* 2 £110

$1\frac{1}{2}$d.

(31)

ONE PENNY

(32)

1904 (29 Dec). *No. 218 surch with T* **31**.
244 **20** 1½d. on 5d. pale blue and brown .. 1·25 60
s. Optd "Specimen" .. .. 30·00
Stamps with inverted surcharge or without surcharge *se-tenant* with stamps with normal surcharge were obtained irregularly and were not issued for postal use.

PRINTER. The Victoria Govt Ptg Office became the Commonwealth Stamp Printing Branch in March 1909.

(Litho, using transfers from D.L.R. plates, Victoria Govt Ptg Office, Melbourne)

1905 (Sept)–**12**. *Wmk Crown over A, W w* **11** (*sideways on horiz stamps*). *P* 12½.
245 **24** 2d. deep purple .. .. .. 4·50 15
a. Perf 11 .. .. 15·00 40
b. Perf comp of 12½ and 11 .. .. 17·00 3·25
c. Perf comp of 12½ and 12 .. .. — 50·00
d. Perf comp of 11 and 12 .. .. £100
e. Slate-lilac (1906) .. .. .. 5·00
ea. Perf 11 .. .. 20·00 30
eb. Perf comp of 12½ and 11 .. ..
ed. Perf comp of 11 and 12 .. ..
f. Reddish lilac (1907) .. .. 13·00 1·00
fa. Perf 11 .. ..
fb. Perf comp of 12½ and 11 .. ..
246 **26** 3d. brown (5.06) .. .. .. 8·50 3·00
a. Perf 11 .. .. 14·00 6·50
b. Perf comp of 12½ and 11 .. .. 70·00
247 **27** 4d. pale yellow-brown (3.07) .. .. 12·00 3·50
a. Perf 11 .. .. 20·00 5·00
b. Orange-buff (5.09) .. .. .. 16·00 3·50
ba. Perf 11 .. .. 20·00 10·00
bb. Perf comp of 12½ and 11 .. .. £160
c. Brown-ochre (*wmk sideways*). Perf 11 (6.11) .. .. 24·00 30·00
d. Orange-yellow (3.12) .. .. 15·00 16·00
da. Perf 11 .. .. 30·00 26·00
db. Perf comp of 12½ and 11 .. .. £160
248 **29** 6d. lake (7.08) .. .. .. 38·00 4·75
a. Perf 11 .. .. 48·00 5·00
b. Perf comp of 12½ and 11 .. .. £150 £160
Stamps with perf compound of 12½ and 12 or 11 and 12 are found on sheets which were sent from Melbourne incompletely perforated along the outside edge of the pane or sheet. The missing perforations were applied in Hobart using a line machine measuring 12 (11.8 is the exact gauge). This perforation can only occur on one side of a stamp.

(Typo, using electrotyped plates, Victoria Govt Ptg Office, Melbourne)

1905 (Aug)–**11**. *Wmk Crown over A, W w* **11** (*sideways on horiz designs*). *P* 12½.
249 **22** ½d. yellow-green (10.12.08) .. .. 1·25 20
a. Perf 11 .. .. 1·25 20
b. Perf comp of 12½ and 11 .. .. 30·00 10·00
c. Perf comp of 11 and 12 .. .. 75·00
d. Wmk upright (1909) .. .. 7·00 2·25
da. Perf 11 .. ..
250 **23** 1d. rose-red .. .. 1·50 10
a. Perf 11 .. .. 3·50 10
b. Perf comp of 12½ and 11 .. .. 4·25 2·25
c. Perf comp of 12½ and 12 .. .. 50·00 7·00
d. Perf comp of 11 and 12 .. .. 55·00 24·00
e. Wmk sideways (1908) .. .. 7·00 1·25
ea. Perf 11 .. .. — 1·50
f. Imperf (pair) £180
250*g* 1d. carmine-red (3.10) .. .. 4·00 1·00
ga. Perf 11 .. .. 6·00 1·25
gb. Perf comp of 12½ and 11 .. .. 8·00 4·25
gc. Perf comp of 12½ and 12 .. .. 50·00
gd. Perf comp of 11 and 12 .. .. 55·00
ge. Imperf (pair) £180
h. Carmine-vermilion (1911) .. .. 9·00 3·00
ha. Perf 11 .. .. 12·00 3·25
hb. Perf comp of 12½ and 11 .. ..
hc. Perf comp of 12½ and 12 .. ..
hd. Perf comp of 11 and 12 .. ..
251 **24** 2d. plum (8.07) .. .. .. 6·50 10
a. Wmk upright .. .. .. 11·00 1·75
b. Perf 11 .. .. 2·50 10
ba. Wmk upright (12.07) .. .. 11·00 1·75
c. Perf comp of 12½ and 11 .. .. 20·00 7·00
d. Perf comp of 12½ and 12 .. .. £130 55·00
e. Perf comp of 11 and 12 .. .. 80·00 42·00
f. Bright reddish violet (1910) .. 4·00 1·50
fa. Perf 11 .. .. 4·00 1·00
fb. Perf comp of 12½ and 11 .. ..

253 **26** 3d. brown (3.09) .. .. 7·00 3·50
a. Wmk upright .. ..
b. Perf 11 .. .. 13·00 4·00
c. Perf comp of 12½ and 11 .. £140
254 **29** 6d. carmine-lake (12.10) .. .. .. 16·00 22·00
a. Perf 11 .. .. 20·00 28·00
b. Perf comp of 12½ and 11 .. £180
c. *Dull carmine-red* (3.11) .. .. 22·00 26·00
ca. Wmk upright .. .. .. 28·00
cb. Perf 11 .. .. 25·00 30·00
cc. Perf comp of 12½ and 11 .. £150

The note after No. 248 re perfs compound with perf 12 also applies here.

Nos. 250/f were printed from the same plates as Nos. 241/cb. Nos. 250*g*/hd are from a further pair of new plates and the images are sharper.

(Typo Victoria Govt Printing Office, Melbourne)

1906–13. *Wmk Crown over A, W* w **11**. *P* 12½.
255 **11** 8d. purple-brown (1907) .. .. 17·00 5·50
a. Perf 11 .. .. 15·00 4·00
256 9d. blue (1907) .. .. 7·00 3·25
a. Perf 11 .. .. 7·00 3·25
b. Perf comp of 12½ and 11 (1909) .. 55·00
c. Perf comp of 12½ and 12 (1909) .. £130
d. Perf comp of 11 and 12 .. .. £225
257 **20** 1s. rose and green (1907) .. .. 13·00 3·50
a. Perf 11 (1907) .. .. .. 20·00 10·00
b. Perf comp of 12½ and 11 .. .. 22·00
c. Perf comp of 12½ and 12 .. .. 75·00
258 10s. mauve and brown (1906) £120 £120
a. Perf 11 .. .. £200
b. Perf comp of 12½ and 12 .. .. £250

The note after No. 248 *re* perfs compound with perf 12, also applies here.

(Typo, using stereotyped plates, Commonwealth Stamp Ptg Branch, Melbourne)

1911 (Jan). *Wmk Crown over A, W* w **11** (*sideways*). *P* 12½.
259 **24** 2d. bright violet .. .. .. 6·00 2·50
a. Wmk upright .. .. .. 18·00 3·50
b. Perf 11 .. .. 6·00 2·50
c. Perf comp of 12½ and 11 .. .. 60·00 17·00
d. Perf comp of 12½ and 12 .. .. £170

Stamps from this stereotyped plate differ from No. 251 in the width of the design (33 to 33¾ mm, against just over 32 mm), in the taller, bolder letters of "TASMANIA", in the slope of the mountain in the left background, which is clearly outlined in white, and in the outer vertical frame-line at left, which appears "wavy". Compare Nos. 260, etc, which are always from this plate.

1912 (Oct) *No.* 259 *surch with T* **32**. *P* 12½.
260 **24** 1d. on 2d. bright violet (R.) 90 60
a. Perf 11 .. .. 1·50 60
b. Perf comp of 12½ and 11 .. .. £100 £100

(Typo, using electrotyped plates, Commonwealth Stamp Ptg Branch, Melbourne)

1912 (Dec). *Thin paper, white gum* (*as Victoria*, 1912). *W* w **11** (*sideways on* 3d.). *P* 12½.
261 **23** 1d. carmine-vermilion .. .. 16·00 8·00
a. Perf 11 .. .. 16·00 8·00
b. Perf comp of 12½ and 11 .. ..
262 **26** 3d. brown .. .. 48·00 55·00

STAMP BOOKLETS

There are very few surviving examples of Nos. SB1/4. Listings are provided for those believed to have been issued with prices quoted for those known to still exist.

1904 (1 Jan)–**09**. *Black on red cover as No.* SB1 *of New South Wales. Stapled.*
SB1 £1 booklet containing two hundred and forty 1d. in twelve blocks of 20 (5×4) .. .. ..
a. Red on pink cover (1909) .. .. ..
b. Blue on pink cover .. ..

1904 (1 Jan). *Black on grey cover as No.* SB1. *Stapled.*
SB2 £1 booklet containing one hundred and twenty 2d. in four blocks of 30 .. ..

1910 (May). *Black on white cover as No.* SB3 *of New South Wales. Stapled.*
SB3 2s. booklet containing eleven ½d. (No. 249), either in block of 6 plus block of 5 or block of 11, and eighteen 1d. (No. 250), either in three blocks of 6 or block of 6 plus block of 12 .. .. £2250

Unsold stock No. SB3 was uprated with one additional ½d. in May 1911.

1911 (Aug). *Red on pink cover as No.* SB3. *Stapled.*
SB4 2s. booklet containing twelve ½d. (No. 249), either in two blocks of 6 or block of 12, and eighteen 1d. (No. 250), either in three blocks of 6 or block of 6 plus block of 12 .. .. £1700

POSTAL FISCAL STAMPS

VALIDITY. Nos. F1/29 were authorised for postal purposes on 1 November 1882.

CLEANED STAMPS. Beware of postal fiscal stamps with pen-cancellations removed.

F 1

F 2

F 3

F 4

(Recess Alfred Bock, Hobart)

1863–80. *Wmk double-lined* "1", *W* **4**. (*a*) *Imperf.*
F 1 **F 1** 3d. green (1.65) .. .. .. £100 65·00
F 2 **F 2** 2s. 6d. carmine (11.63) .. .. £100 65·00
F 3 2s. 6d. lake (5.80) .. .. ..
F 4 **F 3** 5s. brown (1.64) £225 £180
F 5 5s. sage-green (1880) .. .. £120 90·00
F 6 **F 4** 10s. orange (1.64) £350 £180
F 7 10s. salmon (5.80) £225 £180

(*b*) *P* 10
F 8 **F 1** 3d. green .. .. 60·00 32·00
F 9 **F 2** 2s. 6d. carmine .. .. 65·00
F10 **F 3** 5s. brown £100
F11 **F 4** 10s. orange .. .. 75·00

(*c*) *P* 12
F12 **F 1** 3d. green .. .. 60·00 40·00
F13 **F 2** 2s. 6d. carmine .. .. 60·00 50·00
F14 **F 3** 5s. brown £110
F15 5s. sage-green .. .. 55·00 40·00
F16 **F 4** 10s. orange .. .. 70·00 50·00
F17 10s. salmon .. .. 55·00 40·00

(*d*) *P* 12½
F18 **F 1** 3d. green £120
F19 **F 2** 2s. 6d. carmine £110
F20 **F 3** 5s. brown £150
F21 **F 4** 10s. orange-brown £110

(*e*) *P* 11½
F22 **F 1** 3d. green .. ..
F23 **F 2** 2s. 6d. lake .. .. 60·00 50·00
F24 **F 3** 5s. sage-green .. .. 55·00 38·00
F25 **F 4** 10s. salmon .. .. 90·00 60·00

See also No. F30.

In 1879, the 3d., 2s. 6d., 5s. (brown), and 10s. (orange) were reprinted on thin, tough, white paper, and are found with or without "REPRINT". In 1889 another reprint was made on white card, imperforate and perforated 12. These are also found with or without "REPRINT".

F 5 Duck-billed Platypus

REVENUE

(F 6)

(Typo D.L.R.)

1880 (19 Apr). *W* **16** (*sideways*). *P* 14.
F26 **F 5** 1d. slate .. .. 15·00 4·50
F27 3d. chestnut .. .. 16·00 3·25
F28 6d. mauve .. .. 70·00 2·25
F29 1s. rose-pink .. .. 90·00 10·00
a. Perf comp of 14 and 11 .. ..

All values are known imperf, but not used.

Reprints are known of the 1d. in *deep blue* and the 6d. in lilac. The former is on yellowish white, the latter on white card. Both values also exist on wove paper, perf 12, with the word "REPRINT".

1888 (Aug). *W* **16**. *P* 12.
F30 **F 2** 2s. 6d. lake .. .. 22·00 17·00
a. Imperf between (horiz pair) .. £475

1900 (15 Nov). *Optd with Type* F **6**. (*a*) *On Types* F **2** *and* F **4**.
F32 **F 2** 2s. 6d. lake (No. F30) £200
a. "REVFNUE" £300
b. Opt inverted £400
c. Imperf £225
F33 **F 4** 10s. salmon (No. F17) .. ..
a. "REVFNUE" .. ..

(*b*) *On Nos.* F27 *and* F29
F34 **F 5** 3d. chestnut .. .. 20·00 20·00
a. Double opt, one vertical .. .. 80·00 £110
F35 1s. rose-pink .. ..

(*c*) *On stamps as Nos.* F26/9, *but typo locally. W* **16**. *P* 12
F36 **F 5** 1d. blue .. .. 20·00
a. Imperf between (horiz pair) .. £300
b. "REVENUE" inverted £100
c. "REVENUE" double £160
d. Pale blue .. .. 19·00
F37 6d. mauve .. .. 55·00
a. Double print £225
F38 1s. pink .. .. 80·00

(*d*) *On No.* 225
F39 **20** £1 green and yellow £130 £110
a. Opt double, one vertical £250 £250

It was not intended that stamps overprinted with Type F **6** should be used for postal purposes, but an ambiguity in regulations permitted such usage until all postal fiscal st[amps] were invalidated for postal purposes on 30 November 1900.

Printings of some of the above with different waterm[arks], together with a 2d. as Nos. F36/8, did not appear until afte[r] stamps had become invalid for postal purposes.

Tasmania became part of the Commonwealth of Australi[a on] 1 January 1901.

VICTORIA

PRICES FOR STAMPS ON COVER

Nos. 1/17	*from* × 2
Nos. 18/22	*from* × 4
Nos. 23/4	*from* × 2
No. 25	*from* × 3
Nos. 26/32	*from* × 2
No. 33	*from* × 6
No. 34	*from* × 8
Nos. 35/9	*from* × 4
No. 40	*from* × 3
Nos. 41/53	*from* × 2
No. 54	*from* × 3
No. 55	—
No. 56	*from* × 4
Nos. 57/72	*from* × 2
No. 73	*from* × 3
Nos. 74/80	*from* × 2
No. 81	*from* × 3
Nos. 82/7	*from* × 4
Nos. 88/200	*from* × 3
Nos. 201/6	*from* × 5
Nos. 207/8	*from* × 10
Nos. 209/14	*from* × 5
Nos. 215/19	—
Nos. 220/6	*from* × 20
Nos. 227/33	—
Nos. 234/7	*from* × 20
Nos. 238/52	—
Nos. 253/6	*from* × 20
No. 257	*from* × 10
No. 258	*from* × 20
No. 259	*from* × 10
Nos. 260/4	—
Nos. 265/6	*from* × 20
Nos. 267/73	*from* × 10
Nos. 274/91	—
Nos. 292/304	*from* × 10
Nos. 305/9	*from* × 5
Nos. 310/23	*from* × 10
Nos. 324/8	—
No. 329	*from* × 12
Nos. 330/50	*from* × 8
Nos. 351/2	—
Nos. 353/4	*from* × 4
No. 355	*from* × 10
Nos. 356/73	*from* × 15
Nos. 374/5	*from* × 3
Nos. 376/98	*from* × 10
Nos. 399/400	—
Nos. 401/6	*from* × 10
Nos. 407/15	—
Nos. 416/30	*from* × 10
Nos. 431/2	—
Nos. 433/43	*from* × 4
Nos. 444/53	—
Nos. 454/5	*from* × 10
Nos. 456/63	*from* × 6
No. 464	—
Nos. D1/8	*from* × 30
Nos. D9/10	—
Nos. D11/37	*from* × 30

During the expansion of the Australian settlements in t[he] fourth decade of the nineteenth century the growing populati[on] of the Port Phillip District in the south of New South Wales l[ed] to a movement for its creation as a separate colony. Th[is] aspiration received the approval of the British Government [in] 1849, but the colony of Victoria, as it was to be called, was not be created until 1 July 1851.

In the meantime the New South Wales Legislative Counc[il] voted for the introduction of postal reforms, including the use [of] postage stamps, from 1 January 1850, and this act was also [to] apply to the Port Phillip District where stamps inscribe[d] "VICTORIA" would predate the creation of that colony b[y] eighteen months.

Until the end of 1859 the stamps of Victoria, with th[e] exception of Nos. 40 and 73, were produced by local contracto[rs] working under the supervision of the colonial administration.

SPECIMEN OVERPRINTS. Those listed are from U.P.U. distributions in 1892 and 1897. Further "Specimen" overprin[ts] exist, but these were used for other purposes.

HAM PRINTINGS. The first contractor was Thomas Ham [of] Melbourne. He was responsible for the initial printings of th[e] "Half-Length" 1d., 2d. and 3d., together with the replacemen[t] "Queen on Throne" 2d. The first printings were produced fro[m] small sheets of 30 (5×6) laid down directly from the engrave[d] die which showed a single example of each value. Subsequen[t] printings, of which No. 4*a* was the first, were in sheets of 12[0] (two panes of 60) laid down using intermediate stones of variou[s] sizes. Impressions from the first printings were fine and clea[r] but the quality deteriorated when intermediate stones wer[e] used.

1 Queen Victoria ("Half Length")

(Lithographed by Thomas Ham, Melbourne)

3 Jan)–**53**. *Imperf.*

1d. Thin line at top

2d. Fine border and background

3d. White area to left of orb

riginal state of dies: 1*d*. (*tops of letters of* "VICTORIA" *reach top of stamp*); 2*d*. (*fine border and background*); 3*d*. (*thicker ite outline around left of orb, central band of orb does not trude at left*). *No frame-lines on dies.*

1d. orange-vermilion £13000 £1700
 a. Orange-brown .. .. † £850
 b. Dull chocolate-brown (shades) £5000 £950
2d. lilac-mauve (*shades*) (Stone A) £2750 £450
2d. brown-lilac (*shades*) (Stone B) £2500 £275
 a. Grey-lilac .. .. — £275
3d. bright blue (*shades*) £2000 £325
 a. Blue (shades) £2000 £180
 ab. Retouched (between Queen's head and right border) (No. 11 in transfer-group) (8 varieties) .. .. — £300
 ac. Retouched (under "V") (No. 10 in transfer group) £5000 £300

ith the exception of No. 4*a* the above were printed from l stones of 30 (5×6) laid down directly from the engraved which showed a single example of each value. There were stones of the 2d. and one for each of the other values. No. 4*a* e second printing of the 3d. for which the sheet size was eased to 120, the printing stone being constructed from an rmediate stone of 15 (5×3).

1d. Thick line at top

2d. Coarse background

3d. White area small and band protruding to left of orb

Second state of dies: 1*d*. (*more colour over top of letters of* VICTORIA"); 2*d*. (*fine border as* (*a*) *but with coarse ackground*); 3*d*. (*thinner white outline around left of orb, entral band of orb protrudes at left*).

1d. red-brown (*shades*) (2.50) £3500 £300
 a. Pale dull red-brown £2500 £300
2d. grey-lilac (*shades*) (1.50) £1100 £100
 a. Dull grey £1100 £110
3d. blue (*shades*) (6.51) £1000 £110
 a. Retouched (22 varieties) .. *from* £1600 £225

rinted in sheets of 120 (10×12) with the printing stones structed from intermediate stones of 30 (5×6) for the 1d. and or 10 (5×2) for the 3d. It is believed that the use of the aller intermediate stone for the latter resulted in the many ouches.

Frame-lines added

(*c*) *Third state of dies: As in* (*b*) *but with frame-lines added, very close up, on all four sides.*

8 **1** 1d. dull orange-vermilion (11.50) £1500 £400
 a. Dull red (shades) £1200 £120
9 1d. deep red-brown (5.51) .. .. .. — £450
 a. Brownish red (shades) £700 £110
 b. Dull rose (shades) £700 £110
10 2d. grey (*shades*) (8.50) £850 £130
 a. Olive-grey (shades) £1000 £130
11 3d. blue (*shades*) (12.52) .. .. .. £400 50·00
 a. Deep blue (shades) .. .. .. £500 50·00
 b. Pale greenish blue (shades) £650 £100

Printed in sheets of 120 (12×10) produced from intermediate stones of 30 (6×5) for No. 8 and 12 (6×2) for the others.

White veil

(*d*) *As* (*c*) *but altered to give, for the* 1*d. and* 3*d., the so-called "white veils", and for the* 2*d., the effect of vertical drapes to the veil.*

12 **1** 1d. reddish brown (6.51) £750 £100
 a. Bright pinky red (shades) £500 £100
13 2d. drab (1.51) £1000 £110
 a. Grey-drab £1000 £110
 b. Lilac-drab .. .. — £110
 c. Red-lilac .. .. — £500
 d. Void lower left corner .. .. .. — £1800
14 3d. blue (*shades*) (1.53) .. .. .. £400 48·00
 a. Deep blue (shades) .. .. .. £400 48·00
 b. Greenish blue (shades) .. .. .. £500 50·00
 c. Retouched (9 varieties) £750 £120

Printed in sheets of 120 (12×10) produced from intermediate stones of 12 (6×2) on which the details of the veil were amended as described above.

The "void corner" error occurred on the printing stone. It is believed that only four examples still exist.

2d. Coarse border and background

(*e*) *Fourth state of* 2*d. die only: Coarse border and background. Veil details as in original die.*

15 **1** 2d. red-lilac (*shades*) (5.50) £600 £180
 a. Lilac £600 £180
 b. Grey .. .. — £275
 c. Dull brownish lilac £400 £100
 d. Retouched lower label—value omitted *from* — £1800
 e. Other retouches (17 varieties) *from* £1000 £225

Printed in sheets of 120 (12×10) produced from an intermediate stone of 30 (6×5).

(*f*) 2*d. as* (*e*), *but with veils altered to give effect of vertical drapes.*

16 **1** 2d. lilac-grey (1.51) £750 £110
 a. Deep grey £850 £110
 b. Brown-lilac (shades) .. .. .. £600 60·00
17 2d. cinnamon (*shades*) (2.51) .. .. £500 95·00
 a. Drab (shades) .. .. £550 60·00
 b. Pale dull brown (shades) .. .. £650 70·00
 c. Greenish grey .. .. £500 60·00
 d. Olive-drab (shades) £600 £120
 e. Buff .. .. † £130

Printed in sheets of 120 (12×10) produced from two successive intermediate stones of 30 (6×5) on which the details of the veils were amended as described above.

This was the final printing of the 2d. "Half Length" as the die for this value had been damaged. A replacement 2d. design was ordered from Thomas Ham.

For the later printings of the 1d. and 3d. in this design see Nos. 23/4, 26/31, 48/9 and 78/9.

2 Queen on Throne **3**

(Recess-printed by Thomas Ham)

1852 (27 Dec). *Imperf.*

18 **2** 2d. reddish brown .. .. .. £170 22·00
 a. Chestnut .. .. — £110
 b. Purple-brown .. .. £250 22·00

Printed in sheets of 50 (10×5) from a hand-engraved plate of the same size. Each stamp in the sheet had individual corner letters made-up of various combinations, none of which contained the letter "J".

Reprints were made in 1891 using the original plate, on paper wmk V over Crown, both imperf and perf 12½.

For later printings of this design see Nos. 19/22 and 36/9.

CAMPBELL & CO PRINTINGS. In May 1853 the Victoria postal authorities placed an order for 1d. and 6d. stamps in the "Queen on Throne" design with Perkins, Bacon in London. These would not arrive for some time, however, and supplies of Ham's printings were rapidly becoming exhausted. Local tenders were, therefore, solicited for further supplies of the 1d. and 3d. "Half Lengths" and the 2d. "Queen on Throne". That received from J. S. Campbell & Co was accepted. The stamps were produced by lithography, using transfers from either the "Half Length" engraved die or the 2d. "Queen on Throne" engraved plate of 50. Stamps from the Campbell & Co printings can be distinguished from later printings in lithography by the good quality paper used.

(Lithographed by J. S. Campbell & Co, Melbourne, using transfers taken from Ham's engraved plate)

1854 (Jan–July). *Good quality white or toned paper. Imperf.*

(*a*) *Clear impressions with details around back of throne generally complete*

19 **2** 2d. brownish purple .. .. .. £170 25·00
 a. Grey-brown .. .. £250 25·00
 b. Purple-black .. .. — 25·00
 c. Dull lilac-brown (*toned paper only*) .. £300 40·00

(*b*) *Poor impressions with details around back of throne not fully defined*

20 **2** 2d. violet-black (2.54) .. .. .. £250 25·00
 a. Grey-black .. .. £350 26·00
 b. Grey-lilac .. .. £250 26·00
 c. Dull brown (*on toned*) .. .. £250 26·00
 ca. Substituted transfer (in pair) .. .. — £2000

(*c*) *Weak impressions with background generally white without details. Toned paper only*

21 **2** 2d. grey-purple (7.54) .. .. .. £130 22·00
 a. Purple-black .. .. £130 22·00

(*d*) *Printings using an intermediate stone. Impression flat and blurred. Background details usually complete. Toned paper only*

22 **2** 2d. grey-drab (*shades*) (5.54) .. .. £225 22·00
 a. Black .. .. — £100

Nos. 19/21 were produced using transfers taken directly from the original Ham engraved plate. It is believed that the different strengths of the impressions were caused by the amount of pressure exerted when the tranfers were taken. The stamps were printed in sheets of 100 (2 panes 10×5). On one stone a block of four at bottom left, lettered "FL GM" over "QV RW", was damaged and the stone was repaired by using a block of four substituted transfers. These were lettered "VZ WA" over "FL GM". No. 20ca covers any one of these substituted transfers in pair with normal. As horizontal pairs these are lettered "WA HN" or "GM SX" and as vertical "VZ" over "VZ" or "WA" over "WA".

For No. 22 an intermediate stone was used to produce a printing stone of 300 (6 panes 10×5). The insertion of a further stage into the process caused the blurred appearance of stamps from this printing. No. 22*a* is believed to come from proof sheets issued to post offices for normal use. Examples are usually cancelled with Barred Oval 108 and Barred Numerals 1 and 2.

(Lithographed by J. S. Campbell & Co, Melbourne)

1854 (Feb–June). *Good quality wove paper. Imperf.*

23 **1** 1d. orange-red (*shades*) £450 £110
 a. Rose £2000 £275
24 3d. blue (*shades*) (6.54) .. .. .. £475 32·00
 a. Retouch under "C" of "VICTORIA" .. — £120

The 1d. was produced in sheets of 192 (two panes of 96 (12×8)) and the 3d. in sheets of 320 (two panes of 160 (18×9)). Both printing stones were constructed from transfers taken from intermediate stones of 24 (6×4). The spacing between stamps is far wider than on the Ham printings. The 3d. panes of 160 were constructed using six complete transfers of 24 and three of 6 with the final impression in the bottom two rows removed.

The 1d. Campbell printings have the frame lines almost completely absent due to lack of pressure when taking transfers.

The 3d. retouch, No. 24a, occurs on R.3/5 of the intermediate stone.

CAMPBELL AND FERGUSSON PRINTINGS. Increased postal rates in early 1854 led to a requirement for a 1s. value and in April a contract for this stamp was awarded to Campbell and Fergusson (the new corporate style of J. S. Campbell & Co). Further contracts to print the 1d. and 3d. "Half Lengths" and the 2d. "Queen on Throne" followed. All were produced by lithography with the two "Half Lengths" using transfers from the original engraved die and the 2d. "Queen on Throne" transfers from Ham's original engraved plate.

All Campbell and Fergusson printings were on paper of a poorer quality than that used for the earlier contract.

(Lithographed by Campbell & Fergusson)

1854 (6 July). *Poorer quality paper. Imperf.*

25 **3** 1s. blue (*shades*) .. .. £650 22·00
 a. Greenish blue .. .. £750 22·00
 b. Indigo-blue .. .. — £110

No. 25 was produced in sheets of 100 (8×12 with an additional stamp appearing at the end of Rows 6 to 9). The printing stones used each contained four such sheets. They were constructed from an intermediate stone of 40 (8×5) taken from a single engraved die. Each pane of 100 showed two complete transfers of 40, one of 20 and one of a vertical strip of 4.

For this stamp rouletted or perforated see Nos. 54 and 81.

(Lithographed by Campbell & Fergusson)

1854 (July)–**57**. *Poorer quality paper. Imperf.*

26 **1** 1d. brown (*shades*) .. .. .. £450 95·00
 a. Brick-red (shades) .. .. .. £600 75·00
 b. Dull red (shades) .. .. .. £650 75·00
27 1d. orange-brown (*shades*) (8.55) £400 £100
 a. Dull rose-red (shades) .. .. .. £400 60·00
 b. Bright rose-pink £500 £100
 c. Retouched (6 varieties) £1400 £400

28 1 1d. pink (*shades*) (2.55) .. .. .. £375 35·00
a. Rose (shades) .. .. £375 35·00
b. Lilac-rose (shades) .. .. .. £400 35·00
c. Dull brown-red (shades) .. .. .. — £110
d. Retouched (8 varieties) £750 £325
29 3d. bright blue (*shades*) (7.57) .. .. £425 50·00
a. Greenish blue (shades) .. .. £375 42·00
b. Retouch under "C" of "VICTORIA" .. — 95·00
30 3d. Prussian blue (*shades*) (11.56) .. £500 70·00
a. Milky blue £750 £110
b. Retouch under "C" of "VICTORIA" .. — £225
31 3d. steel-blue (*shades*) (*heavier impression*) (5.55) .. .. — 48·00
a. Greenish blue (shades) .. .. £350 35·00
b. Blue (shades) .. .. £350 35·00
c. Deep blue (shades) .. .. .. £350 35·00
d. Indigo (shades) .. .. — 40·00

The 1d. was produced in sheets of 400 (2 panes 20×10) constructed from transfers originating from the J. S. Campbell & Co intermediate stone. Each pane contained six complete tranfers of 24, three of 12, two of 8 and one of 4.

The 3d. was produced in sheets of 320 (2 panes of 160) (No. 29), 200 (No. 30) or 400 (2 panes of 200) (No. 31.) The stone for No. 29 was constructed from transfers taken from the J. S. Campbell intermediate stone with the retouch on R.3/5 still present. The panes of 160 contained six transfers of 24 and three of 6 with the last impression in both rows 8 and 9 removed. Quality of impression is generally poor. The stone for No. 30, once again taken from the Campbell intermediate stone, was laid down in the same combination of transfers as the 1d. value. Impressions from it were, however, so poor that transfers from a new intermediate stone were used for No. 31. Impressions from this stone, on which the panes of 200 were in a similar layout to the 1d., were much further apart than those on the stones used to produce Nos. 29/30.

The Campbell and Fergusson printings of the "Half Lengths" are listed in the order in which they were printed.

CALVERT PRINTINGS. Contracts for the provision of other values required by the postal rate changes in 1853 were placed with Samuel Calvert of Melbourne who used typography as the printing process. Calvert continued to print, and later roulette, stamps for the Victoria Post Office until March 1858 when it was discovered that he had placed some of the stock in pawn.

4

5

6

(Typographed from woodblocks by Samuel Calvert)

1854 (1 Sept)–**55**. *Imperf.*
32 4 6d. reddish brown (13.9.54) .. .. £250 32·00
a. Dull orange .. .. £180 18·00
b. Orange-yellow .. .. .. £180 19·00
33 5 6d. ("TOO LATE") lilac and green (1.1.55) £750 £150
34 6 1s. ("REGISTERED") rose-pink and blue (1.12.54) £900 £120
35 4 2s. dull bluish green/*pale yellow* £1200 £150

No. 33 was provided to pay the additional fee on letters posted after the normal closure of the mails. This service was only available in the larger towns; examples are usually postmarked Castlemaine, Geelong or Melbourne. The service was withdrawn on 30 June 1857 and remaining stocks of the "TOO LATE" stamps were used for normal postal purposes.

No. 34 was issued to pay the registration fee and was so used until 5 January 1858 after which remaining stocks were used for normal postage.

These four values were produced from individually-engraved boxwood woodblocks. The 6d. was in sheets of 100 printed by two impressions from two plates of 25. The 2s. was in sheets of 50 from a single plate of 25. The bicoloured "TOO LATE" and "REGISTERED" stamps are unusual in that Calvert used a common woodblock "key" plate of 25 for both values combined with "duty" plates made up from metal screws. Both values were originally in sheets of 50, but the "REGISTERED" later appeared in sheets of 100 for which a second "key" plate of 25 was utilised.

For these stamps rouletted or perforated see Nos. 53, 55/8, 60/1 and 82.

(Lithographed by Campbell & Fergusson)

1855 (Mar)–**56**. *Poorer quality paper. Imperf.*

(*a*) *Printings from stones which were not over-used; background around top of throne generally full and detail good*
36 2 2d. lilac (*shades*) (7.55) .. .. .. £140 22·00
a. Purple (shades) .. .. .. £140 22·00
b. "TVO" for "TWO" £4000 £600

(*b*) *Early printings from stones which were over-used. Similar characteristics to those above, though detail is not quite so full. Distinctive shades.*
37 2 2d. brown .. .. — 70·00
a. Brown-purple .. .. £170 23·00
b. Warm purple .. .. — 23·00
c. Rose-lilac .. .. — 23·00
d. Substituted transfer (pair) .. .. — £600

(*c*) *Later printings from the same stones used for No. 37 when in a worn condition. Impressions heavy, coarse and overcoloured; details blurred; generally white background around top of throne.*
38 2 2d. dull lilac-mauve (1856) .. .. £170 25·00
a. Dull mauve .. .. £170 25·00
b. Grey-violet .. .. — 25·00
c. Red-lilac .. .. — 26·00
d. Substituted transfer (pair) .. .. — £600

(*d*) *Printings from a stone giving blotchy and unpleasing results, with poor definition. Mainly shows in extra colour patches found on most stamps.*
39 2 2d. dull purple (7.55) .. .. .. — 42·00
a. Dull grey-lilac .. .. £180 42·00
b. On thick card paper .. .. .. — £500

The Campbell and Fergusson 2d. "Queen on Throne" printings were in sheets of 200 (4 panes 10 × 5) constructed from transfers taken from the original Ham engraved plate.

Four separate stones were used. On Stone A a creased transfer running through R.4/8, 4/9 and 5/8 caused the "TVO" variety on the stamp from the bottom row of one pane. On Stone C the impression in the first vertical row of one pane were found to be so faulty that they were replaced by substituted transfers taken from elsewhere on the sheet causing abnormal horizontal pairs lettered "UY BF", "TX MQ", "DI WA", "SW GM" and "CH RW". The vertical pairs from the substituted transfers are lettered "UY" over "TX" and "DI" over "SW".

PERKINS BACON "CANCELLED". For notes on these handstamps, showing "CANCELLED" between horizontal bars forming an oval, see Catalogue Introduction.

7 Queen on Throne

8 "Emblems"

(Recess Perkins, Bacon & Co, London)

1856 (23 Oct). *Wmk Large Star, W w* **1**. *Imperf.*
40 7 1d. yellow-green (H/S "CANCELLED" in oval £3500) .. .. £120 20·00

Supplies of this stamp, and the accompanying 6d. which was only issued rouletted (see No. 73), arrived in the colony at the end of 1854, but the 1d. was not placed on sale until almost two years later.

No. 40 was reprinted from the original plate in 1891. Examples, in either dull yellow-green or bright blue-green, are imperforate and on V over Crown watermarked paper.

(Typographed from electrotypes by Calvert)

1857 (26 Jan–6 Sept). *Imperf.* (*a*) *Wmk Large Star, W w* **1**
41 8 1d. yellow-green (18 Feb) .. .. .. 95·00 13·00
a. Deep green .. .. £110 26·00
b. Printed on both sides .. .. .. † £700
42 4d. vermilion .. .. £250 10·00
a. Brown-vermilion .. .. .. £225 9·00
b. Printed on both sides .. .. .. † £700
43 4d. dull red (20 July) .. .. .. £160 7·50
44 4d. dull rose (6 Sept) .. .. .. £225 7·50

(*b*) *No wmk. Good quality medium wove paper*
45 8 2d. pale lilac (25 May) .. .. .. £170 10·00
a. Grey-lilac .. .. £170 10·00

Nos. 41/5 were produced in sheets of 120, arranged as four panes of 30 (6×5) (1d. and 4d.) or twelve panes of 10 (2×5) (2d.), using electrotypes taken from a single engraved die of each value. The setting of the 4d. was re-arranged before the printing of Nos. 43/4.

Only two examples of No. 41b and No. 42b have been recorded.

For this printing rouletted or perforated see Nos. 46/7, 50/2, 59, 74 and 77.

ROULETTES AND PERFORATIONS. In August 1857 a rouletting machine was provided at the G.P.O., Melbourne, to enable the counter clerks to separate stamp stocks before sale to the public. This machine produced roulettes of 7½–9 in one direction across six rows at a time. There was also a single wheel device which gauged 7–7½. Both were in use between the earliest known date of 12 August and the end of 1857.

Calvert was granted a separate contract in October 1857 to roulette the stamps he printed, but only Nos. 57/61 had been produced when it was found, in April 1858, that he had pawned a quantity of the sheets. His contracts were terminated and his successor, F. W. Robinson, used a roulette machine of a different gauge before switching to a gauge 12 perforating machine in January 1859.

1857 (12 Aug–Sept). *Rouletted* 7–9 *by counter clerks at G.P.O., Melbourne.*
46 8 1d. yellow-green (No. 41) .. .. .. £300 65·00
47 2d. pale lilac (No. 45) .. .. .. — 27·00
a. Grey-lilac .. .. — 27·00
48 1 3d. blue (*shades*) (No. 24) .. .. .. — £180
a. Retouch under "C" of "VICTORIA" ..
49 3d. bright blue (*shades*) (No. 29) .. .. — £190
a. Greenish blue (shades) £1000 £170
b. Retouch under "C" of "VICTORIA" ..
50 8 4d. vermilion (No. 42) .. .. .. — £100
51 4d. dull red (No. 43) .. .. .. — 38·00
52 4d. dull rose (No. 44) (Sept) .. .. — 26·00
53 4 6d. reddish brown (No. 32) .. .. .. — 50·00
a. Dull orange .. .. — 35·00
b. Orange-yellow .. .. — 42·00
54 3 1s. blue (*shades*) (No. 25) .. .. .. — 80·00
a. Greenish blue .. .. — 80·00
55 6 1s. ("REGISTERED") rose-pink and blue (No. 34) £3500 £180
56 4 2s. dull bluish green/*pale yellow* (No. 35) £3500 £350

With the exception of the 1s., Nos. 54/*a*, these stamps are normally found rouletted on one or two sides only.

1857 (Oct). *Rouletted by Calvert.* (*a*) *Rouletted* 7–9 *on all four sides and with finer points than No.* 53*b*
57 4 6d. orange-yellow (No. 32*b*) .. .. — 55·00

(*b*) *Serpentine roulette* 10–10½
58 4 6d. orange-yellow (No. 32*b*) .. .. — 60·00

(*c*) *Serrated* 18–19
59 8 2d. grey-lilac (No. 45*a*) £500 £350
60 4 6d. orange-yellow (No. 32*b*) .. .. — 65·00

(*d*) *Compound of serrated* 18–19 *and serpentine* 10–10½
61 4 6d. orange-yellow (No. 32*b*) .. .. — 65·00

No. 59 was not covered by the contract given to Calvert, but it is believed to be a test run for the rouletting machine. No. 61 always shows serrated 18–19 on three sides and the serpentine roulette at the top or bottom of the stamp.

(Typo from electrotypes by Calvert)

1858 (14 Jan–Apr). *No wmk. Good quality white wove pa*

(*a*) *Rouletted* 7–9 *on all four sides*
62 8 1d. pale emerald £300
a. Emerald-green £300
63 4d. rose-pink (18 Jan) £200
a. Bright rose £200
b. Reddish pink .. .. —
c. Imperf horiz (vert pair) .. .. †

(*b*) *Imperf* (Apr)
64 8 1d. pale emerald £190
a. Emerald-green .. .. .. —
65 4d. rose-pink £250
a. Bright rose .. .. —
b. Reddish pink .. .. —

Nos. 62/5 were produced in sheets of 120, arranged as panes of 30 (6×5).

The Royal Collection contains a used horizontal pair of th showing the vertical roulettes omitted.

The majority of Nos. 64/5 were issued in April after Calv contracts had been terminated, although there is some evid that imperforate sheets of the 4d., at least, were issued ea

For the 1d. of this issue perforated see No. 75.

ROBINSON PRINTINGS. Calvert's contracts were canc in April 1858 and the work was then placed with F Robinson, who had unsuccessfully tendered in 1856. The s electrotypes were used, but a perforating machine introduced from January 1859. Robinson continued to print perforate stamps under contract until the end of 1859 whe Victoria Post Office purchased his equipment to set up a St Printing Branch and appointed him Printer of Postage Sta

(Typo from electrotypes by Robinson)

1858 (May–Dec). (*a*) *Imperf.* (i) *Coarse quality wove paper*
66 8 4d. dull rose (*oily ink*) .. .. .. —

(ii) *Smooth vertically-laid paper*
67 8 4d. dull rose (*oily ink*) .. .. .. — 3
a. Dull rose-red .. .. — 3
68 4d. dull rose-red (*normal ink*) (20 May) .. £400 1

(*b*) *Rouletted* 5½–6½. (i) *Smooth laid paper*
69 8 2d. brown-lilac (*shades*) (*horiz laid*) (June) £120
a. Vert laid paper (21 Sept) £200
70 2d. violet (*horiz laid*) (27 Nov) £150
a. Dull violet £180 1
71 4d. pale dull rose (*vert laid*) (1 June) .. £150
a. Horiz laid paper .. .. .. †
b. Dull rose-red £120
c. Rose-red £120
ca. Serrated 19 .. .. †

(ii) *Good quality wove paper*
72 8 1d. yellow-green (24 Dec) £275 2

Nos. 66/72 were produced in sheets of 120, arranged as panes of 30 (6 × 5).

For stamps of this issue perforated see Nos. 76 and 80.

(Recess Perkins, Bacon & Co, London)

1858 (1 Nov). *Wmk Large Star, W w* **1**. *Rouletted* 5½–6½.
73 7 6d. bright blue £130 1
a. Light blue £170 25

No. 73 was received from London at the same time as the No. 40, but was kept in store until November 1858 when stock was rouletted by Robinson. When issued the gum was poor state.

Imperforate examples exist from Perkins, Bacon remaind Examples are known handstamped "CANCELLED" in ova bars. *Price* £3500.

Imperforate reprints, in shades of indigo, were made from original plate in 1891 on V over Crown watermarked paper.

1859 (Jan–May). *P 12 by Robinson.*
74 8 1d. yellow-green (No. 41) .. .. .. — £
75 1d. emerald-green (No. 64*a*) .. .. — £
a. Imperf between (horiz pair) .. ..
76 1d. yellow-green (as No. 72) (11 Jan) .. £160 13
a. Imperf horiz (vert pair) .. .. — £
b. Thin, glazed ("Bordeaux") paper .. † £1
77 2d. pale lilac (No. 45) .. .. .. — £2
a. Grey-lilac .. .. — £2
78 1 3d. blue (*shades*) (No. 24) (2 Feb) .. £750 £1
a. Retouch under "C" of "VICTORIA" .. — £2
79 3d. greenish blue (*shades*) (No. 29*a*) .. † £3
a. Retouch under "C" of "VICTORIA" .. † £10
80 8 4d. dull rose-red (No. 68) .. .. .. — £3
81 3 1s. blue (*shades*) (No. 25) (4 Feb)) .. £130 15
a. Greenish blue £150 12
b. Indigo-blue .. .. — 30
82 4 2s. dull bluish green/*pale yellow* (No. 35) (May) £250 32

The 1s. was reprinted in 1891 using transfers taken from t original die. These reprints were on V over Crown watermark paper and perforated 12½.

For perforated 6d. black and 2s. blue both as Type **4** see N 102 and 129/30.

(Typo from electrotypes by Robinson)

1859 (17 Feb–23 Dec). *P* 12. (*a*) *Good quality wove paper*
83 8 4d. dull rose £150 3
a. Roul 5½–6½ .. .. † £8

(*b*) *Poorer quality wove paper*
84 8 1d. dull green (July) .. .. .. £120 9·
a. Green (11 Nov) .. .. .. £120 9·
85 4d. rose-carmine (16 July) .. .. .. £150 5·
a. Rose-pink (*thick paper*) (30 Nov) .. — 10·

(*c*) *Horizontally laid paper with the lines wide apart*
86 8 1d. dull green (18 July) .. .. ..
a. Laid lines close together .. .. — 18·
b. Green (*shades*) (Oct) .. .. .. £130 9·
87 4d. rose-pink (*shades*) (23 Dec) .. .. £120 7·
a. Laid lines close together .. .. — 10·

STAMP PRINTING BRANCH. On 1 January 1860 F. W Robinson was appointed Printer of Postage Stamps and h equipment purchased by the Post Office to establish the Stan Printing Branch. All later Victoria issues were printed by th Branch which became part of the Victoria Government Printin Office in December 1885. In 1909 the Commonwealth Stan Printing Office under J. B. Cooke was established in Melbourn and produced stamps for both the states and Commonweal until 1918.

9

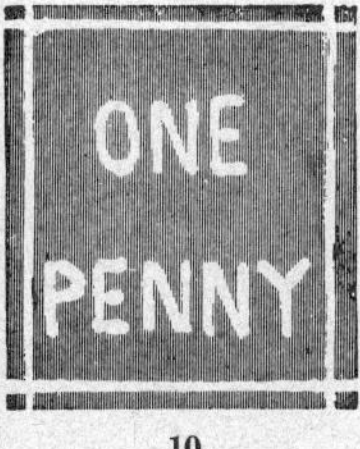

10

11

(Des and eng F. Grosse. Typo from electrotypes)

0 (31 Jan)–**66**. *P* 12. (*a*) *No wmk*

9 3d. deep blue (*horiz laid paper*) .. .. £300 30·00
a. Light blue .. ..
4d. rose-pink (*thin glazed Bordeaux paper*) (21.4.60) .. .. — 10·00
a. Rose .. .. £275 13·00
ab. Thick coarse paper (7.60) .. .. £275 10·00

) *On paper made by T. H. Saunders of London wmkd with the appropriate value in words as W* **10**

9 3d. pale blue (1.61) .. .. .. £120 7·00
a. Bright blue (10.61) .. .. .. £120 8·00
b. Blue (4.63) .. .. .. £130 6·00
c. Deep blue (4.64) .. .. .. £130 6·00
d. "TRREE" for "THREE" in wmk ..
3d. maroon (13.2.66) .. .. .. £100 25·00
a. Perf 13 .. .. £120 28·00
4d. rose-pink (1.8.60) .. .. .. — 6·00
a. Rose-red .. .. 80·00 3·25
b. Rose-carmine .. .. — 8·50
c. Dull rose .. .. 80·00 3·25
d. Printed on "FIVE SHILLINGS" diagonal wmk paper (11.9.62) .. .. £1500 20·00
6d. orange (25.10.60) £3000 £200
6d. black (20.8.61) .. .. .. £110 5·50
a. Grey-black .. .. £110 5·50

) *On paper made by De La Rue wmkd with the appropriate value as a single-lined numeral as W* **11**

9 4d. dull rose-pink (9.10.62) .. .. 90·00 5·00
a. Dull rose .. .. 95·00 5·50
b. Rose-red .. .. — 5·00
c. Roul 8 (28.7.63) .. .. .. — £250
d. Imperf (31.7.63) .. .. .. — 70·00
e. Perf 13×12 .. ..

All three values were produced in sheets of 120, initially as ır panes of 30 (6×5). Printings of the 3d. from 1864 were in a anged format of six panes of 20 (4×5).

The "TRREE" watermark error comes from early printings of . 90 on R. 10/7.

Two examples of the 4d. on Saunders paper are known sected in 1863, but such use was unauthorised.

Nos. 95c/e were issued during July and August 1863 when the rmal perforating machine had broken down.

Reprints, from new plates, were made of the 3d. and 4d. in 91 on "V over Crown" paper and perforated $12^1/_2$.

60 (Apr)–**63**. *P* 12. (*a*) *No wmk*

96 8 1d. bright green (*horiz laid paper*) .. ..
97 1d. bright green (*thin, glazed Bordeaux paper*) (25.5.60) .. .. — 28·00

(*b*) *On paper made by T. H. Saunders of London wmkd with the appropriate value in words as W* **10**

98 8 1d. pale yellowish green (8.7.60) .. .. 65·00 4·50
a. Yellow-green .. .. 75·00 4·75
b. Error. Wmkd "FOUR PENCE" .. † —
99 2d. brown-lilac (7.7.61) .. .. .. — 23·00
00 2d. bluish slate (8.61) .. .. .. £100 5·00
a. Greyish lilac (9.61) .. .. .. £110 5·00
b. Slate-grey (1.62) .. .. .. — 5·00
c. Printed on "THREE PENCE" wmkd paper. *Pale slate* (27.12.62) .. .. £110 10·00
ca. Bluish grey (2.63) .. .. .. £120 13·00

c) *On paper made by De La Rue wmkd single-lined "2", W* **11**

01 8 2d. dull reddish lilac (24.4.63) .. .. £160 7·00
a. Grey-lilac (10.63) .. .. .. £150 12·00
ab. Error. Wmkd "6" .. .. † £4000
b. Grey-violet (11.63) .. .. .. £100 9·00
c. Slate (12.63) .. .. £150 18·00

The only confirmed example of No. 98b is in the Royal Collection. There have been unconfirmed reports of the xistence of another.

861 (22 June). *On paper made by T. H. Saunders of London wmkd "SIX PENCE" as W* **10**. *P* 12.

02 4 6d. black .. .. £160 38·00

No. 102 was produced as an emergency measure after the ecision had been taken to change the colour of the current 6d. rom orange (No. 93) to black (No. 94). During the changeover he old Calvert "woodblock" plates were pressed into service to rovide two month's supply.

MINIMUM PRICE

The minimum price quote is 10p which represents a handling charge rather than a basis for valuing common stamps. For further notes about prices see introductory pages.

12

13

(Des, eng and electrotyped De Gruchy & Leigh, Melbourne. Typo)

1861 (1 Oct)–**64**. *P* 12. (*a*) *On paper made by T. H. Saunders of London wmkd "ONE PENNY" as W* **10**

103 **12** 1d. pale green .. .. 80·00 6·50
a. Olive-green .. .. — 7·50

(*b*) *On paper made by De La Rue wmkd single-lined "1" as W* **11**

104 **12** 1d. olive-green (1.2.63) .. .. .. 60·00 8·00
a. Pale green (9.63) .. .. .. 60·00 5·00
b. Apple-green (4.64) .. .. .. 60·00 5·00

(*c*) *On paper supplied to Tasmania by Perkins, Bacon and wmkd double-lined "1", W* **4** *of Tasmania*

105 **12** 1d. yellow-green (10.12.63) .. .. £110 7·50
a. Dull green .. .. — 7·50
b. Imperf between (pair) .. .. † —

All printings were in sheets of 120 containing four panes of 30 (6×5).

Reprints from new plates were made in 1891 on paper watermarked "V over Crown" and perforated $12^1/_2$.

(Frame die eng F. Grosse. Typo from electrotypes)

1862 (26 Apr)–**64**. *Centre vignette cut from T* **9** *with a new frame as T* **13**.

(*a*) *On paper made by T. H. Saunders of London wmkd "SIX PENCE" as W* **10**. *P* 12

106 **13** 6d. grey .. .. 80·00 5·00
a. Grey-black .. .. 80·00 6·50
b. Jet-black .. .. 85·00 7·50

(*b*) *On paper made by De La Rue wmkd with single-lined "6" as W* **11**

107 **13** 6d. grey (*p* 12) (18.6.63) .. .. 70·00 4·50
a. Jet-black .. .. — 5·50
b. Grey-black .. .. 70·00 4·75
c. Perf 13. *Jet-black* .. .. .. 80·00 5·50
ca. Grey-black .. .. 80·00 5·50

Printings before August 1863 were in sheets of 120 containing four panes of 30 (6×5). For subsequent printings of No. 107 the format was changed to six panes of 20 (4×5).

Reprints from new plates were made in 1891 on paper watermarked "V over Crown" and perforated $12^1/_2$.

SINGLE-LINED NUMERAL WATERMARK PAPERS. The first consignment of this paper, showing watermarks as W 11, arrived in Victoria during October 1862. Five further consignments followed, all but the last supplied by De La Rue.

The complexity of the scheme for different watermarks for each value, together with the time required to obtain further supplies from Great Britain, resulted in the emergency use of paper obtained from Tasmania and of the wrong numeral watermark on certain printings.

The final order for this paper was placed, in error with the firm of T. H. Saunders of London. Although the actual watermarks are the same (the dandy rolls were the property of the Victoria Government and supplied to each firm in turn) there are considerable differences between the two types of paper. That manufactured by Saunders is of a more even quality and is smoother, thicker, less brittle and less white than the De La Rue type.

De La Rue supplied white paper watermarked "1", "2", "4", "6" and "8", blue paper watermarked "1" and green paper watermarked "2".

The Saunders consignment of October 1865 contained white paper watermarked "1", "4" and "6", blue paper watermarked "1", green paper watermarked "2" and pink paper watermarked "10".

It is helpful for comparison purposes to note that all white paper watermarked "2" or "8" can only be De La Rue and all pink paper watermarked "10" can only be Saunders.

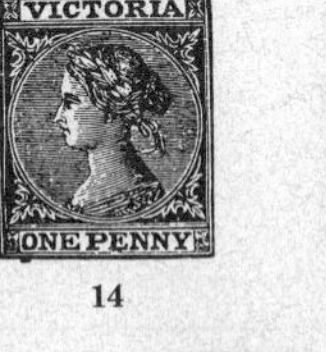

14

15

16

17

18

(Des and eng F. Grosse. Typo from electrotypes)

1863–74. *"Laureated" series.*

(*a*) *On paper made by De La Rue wmkd with the appropriate value in single-lined numerals as W* **11**

108 **14** 1d. pale green (*p* 12) (9.9.64) .. .. 75·00 7·00
a. Perf $12^1/_2$×12 (9.64) .. ..
b. Perf 13 (10.10.64) .. .. .. 70·00 3·75
c. Bluish green (*p* 13) (12.64) .. .. 65·00 3·25
ca. Printed double .. .. .. † £550
d. Green (*p* 12) (7.65) .. .. .. 70·00 3·25
da. Perf 13 .. .. 65·00 3·50
e. Deep green (*p* 12) (12.65) .. .. 85·00 3·50
ea. Perf 13 .. .. — 3·50
eb. Perf 12×13 .. .. — 6·50
f. Bright yellow-green (*p* 13) (1.67) .. — 15·00

109 **14** 2d. violet (*p* 12) (1.4.64) .. .. 65·00 6·00
a. Dull violet (*p* 12) (10.64) .. .. 70·00 6·00
ab. Perf $12^1/_2$×12 .. .. ..
ac. Perf $12^1/_2$ .. ..
ad. Perf 13 .. .. 70·00 4·50
b. Dull lilac (*p* 13) (4.65) .. .. 55·00 4·25
ba. Perf 12 (7.66) .. .. .. — 7·50
bb. Perf 12×13 (7.66) .. .. .. — 9·00
c. Reddish mauve (*p* 13) (11.65) .. 60·00 5·50
d. Rose-lilac (*p* 13) (1.66) .. .. 55·00 6·00
da. Perf 12×13 or 13×12 (2.66) .. 55·00 6·00
e. Grey (*p* 12) (7.66) .. .. .. 85·00 7·50
ea. Perf 13 .. .. 55·00 3·25
110 4d. deep rose (*p* 12) (11.9.63) .. .. £110 3·50
a. Printed double .. .. .. † £500
b. Rose-pink (*p* 12) (9.63) .. .. 85·00 2·50
c. Pink (*p* 12) (7.5.64) .. .. 85·00 2·50
ca. Error. Wmkd single-lined "8" .. † £2000
cb. Perf $12^1/_2$×12 (9.64) .. ..
d. Dull rose (*p* 13) (10.64) .. .. 75·00 2·50
e. Dull rose-red (*p* 13) (2.65) .. .. 75·00 2·50
ea. Perf 12 (8.65) .. .. .. £120 75·00
111 **16** 6d. blue (*p* 12) (13.2.66) .. .. 42·00 4·50
a. Perf 13 .. .. 42·00 2·75
b. Perf 12×13 .. .. .. 40·00 2·75
112 **14** 8d. orange (*p* 13) (22.2.65) .. .. £300 55·00
113 **17** 1s. blue/*blue* (*p* 13) (10.4.65) .. .. £100 3·50
a. Perf 12×13 (4.66) .. .. £100 3·50
ab. Imperf between (vert pair) .. † £1200
b. Bright blue/blue (*p* 13) (6.67) .. 85·00 3·00
c. Indigo-blue/blue (*p* 13) (3.68) .. — 3·00
d. Dull blue/blue (*p* 12) (6.74) .. .. — 3·50

(*b*) *Emergency printings on Perkins, Bacon paper borrowed from Tasmania wmkd double-lined "4" as W* **4** *of Tasmania*

114 **14** 4d. deep rose (*p* 12) (7.1.64) .. .. £110 4·00
a. Pale rose (*p* 12) .. .. .. — 3·50
b. Dull reddish rose (*p* 13) (11.8.65) .. £110 3·75
ba. Perf 12 .. .. — 3·75
bb. Perf 12×13 .. .. .. — 11·00
c. Red (*p* 13) (4.12.65) .. .. £120 3·75

(*c*) *Emergency printings on De La Rue paper as W* **11**, *but showing incorrect single-lined numeral. P* 13

115 **14** 1d. brt yellow-grn (*wmkd* "8") (27.12.66) £120 13·00
116 1d. brt yellow-green (*wmkd* "6") (6.67) — 22·00
117 2d. grey (*wmkd* "8") (18.1.67) .. .. £110 5·00
118 **15** 3d. lilac (*wmkd* "8") (29.9.66) .. .. £110 24·00
119 **16** 10d. grey (*wmkd* "8") (21.10.65) .. £475 £110
a. Grey-black £475 £120

(*d*) *On paper made by T. H. Saunders wmkd with the appropriate value in single-lined numerals as W* **11**

120 **14** 1d. deep yellow-green (*p* 12×13) (1.66) £120 8·00
a. Perf 13 (3.66) .. .. .. 65·00 3·25
b. Perf 12 (7.66) .. .. .. — 9·00
121 4d. rose-red (*p* 13) (12.12.65) .. .. 75·00 3·00
a. Perf 12×13 or 13×12 (2.66) .. £110 5·50
b. Perf 12 (4.66) .. .. .. — 4·75
122 **16** 6d. blue (*p* 13) (28.5.66) .. .. 38·00 1·50
a. Perf 12 .. .. 42·00 3·50
b. Perf 12×13 .. .. .. 38·00 1·75
ba. Imperf between (horiz pair) .. † £600
123 10d. dull purple/*pink* (*p* 13) (22.3.66) .. 85·00 5·00
a. Perf 12×13 .. .. .. £120 6·50
b. Blackish brown/pink (*p* 13) (12.69) 90·00 5·50
c. Purple-brown/pink (*p* 13) (11.70) ..
124 **17** 1s. bright blue/*blue* (*p* 13) (5.12.70) .. 55·00 2·50
a. Pale dull blue/blue (*p* 12) (1.73) .. £120 3·25
ab. Perf 13 .. .. — 8·00
b. Indigo-blue/blue (*p* 12) (9.73) .. — 5·00
ba. Perf 13 .. .. 55·00 3·50

(*e*) *Emergency printings on Saunders paper as W* **11**, *but showing incorrect single-lined numeral. P* 13

125 **14** 1d. brt yellow-green (*wmkd* "4") (6.3.67) 90·00 11·00
126 1d. brt yellow-green (*wmkd* "6") (6.67) £130 18·00
127 2d. grey (*wmkd* "4") (21.2.67) .. .. 90·00 5·00
128 2d. grey (*wmkd* "6") (13.5.67) .. .. £150 6·00

The 1d., 2d., 4d. and 8d. were originally produced in sheets of 120 containing eight panes of 15 (3×5). The 3d. and 6d. were in sheets of 120 (12×10) and the 1d. (from February 1866), 2d. (from July 1866) and 4d. (from April 1866) subsequently changed to this format. The 10d. was in sheets of 120 containing twenty panes of 6 (2×3). The 1s. was originally in sheets of 60 containing three panes of 20 (4×5), but this changed to 120 (12×10) in April 1866.

Only single examples are thought to exist of Nos. 110a, 110ca, 113ab, and 122ba and two of No. 108ca.

For later emergency printings on these papers see Nos.153/66.

(Typo from composite woodblock and electrotype plate)

1864 (22 Nov)–**80**. (*a*) *On De La Rue paper wmkd single-lined "2" as W* **11**

129 **4** 2s. light blue/*green* (*p* 13) (22.11.64) .. £160 6·00
a. Dark blue/green (*p* 12) (9.65) .. £180 10·00
ab. Perf 13 (6.66) .. .. .. £160 6·50
b. Blue/green (*p* 13) (6.68) .. .. £150 4·75
c. Greenish blue/green (*p* 13) (7.73) .. £150 6·00
ca. Perf 12 .. .. £170 7·00
d. Deep greenish blue/green (*p* $12^1/_2$) .. £150 5·50

(*b*) *On Saunders paper wmkd single-lined "2" as W* **11**

130 **4** 2s. dark blue/*green* (*p* 13) (23.11.67) .. £170 7·00
a. Blue/green (*p* 13) (10.71) .. .. £170 6·00
ab. Perf 12 (8.74) .. .. .. £190 7·00
c. Deep greenish blue/green (*p* $12^1/_2$) (7.80) £150 5·50

Nos. 129/30 were produced in sheets of 30 containing two panes of 15 (3×5). The plate contained eighteen of the original woodblock impressions and twelve electrotypes taken from them.

19

20

V OVER CROWN WATERMARKS. The changeover from the numeral watermarks to a general type to be used for all values was first suggested at the end of 1865, but the first supplies did not reach Melbourne until April 1867. Five different versions were used before the V over Crown watermark was superseded by the Commonwealth type in 1905. The five versions are listed as follows:

Type **19** De La Rue paper supplied 1867 to 1882. Shows four points at the top of the crown with the left and right ornaments diamond-shaped
Type **33** De La Rue paper supplied 1882 to 1895. No points at the top of the crown with the left and right ornaments oval-shaped
Type **82** Waterlow paper supplied 1896 to 1899. Wide base to crown
Type **85** Waterlow paper used for postal issues 1899 to 1905. Wide top to crown
Type **104** James Spicer and Sons paper used for postal issues August and September 1912. Narrow crown

(Typo from electrotypes)

1867–81. *Wmk V over Crown, W* **19**. (*a*) *P* 13
131 **14** 1d. bright yellow-green (10.8.67) .. 65·00 2·75
a. Bright olive-green (1.69) .. .. 95·00 17·00
b. Yellow-green (4.69) .. .. 65·00 2·50
c. Dull green (3.70) .. .. .. 65·00 2·50
d. Pale green (10.70) .. .. .. 60·00 2·50
e. Grass-green (1871) .. .. 60·00 2·75
f. Bluish green (*shades*) (7.72) .. 60·00 2·75
g. Green (*shades*) (9.72) .. .. 60·00 2·50
132 2d. slate-grey (*shades*) (26.8.67) .. 70·00 3·50
a. Grey-lilac (29.1.68) .. .. 70·00 4·75
b. Lilac (26.8.68) .. .. .. 50·00 3·25
c. Dull mauve (*shades*) (10.68) .. 50·00 3·25
d. Lilac-grey (1.69) .. .. .. — 3·50
e. Lilac-rose (2.69) .. .. .. 55·00 3·00
f. Mauve (4.69) .. .. .. 70·00 3·25
g. Red-lilac (5.69) .. .. .. 55·00 3·00
h. Dull lilac (6.69) .. .. .. 55·00 2·50
i. Silver-grey (9.69) .. .. .. £110 7·00
133 **15** 3d. lilac (28.8.67) .. .. .. £200 28·00
a. Grey-lilac (6.68) .. .. .. £225 30·00
134 3d. yellow-orange (12.6.69) .. .. 25·00 3·00
a. Dull orange (6.70) .. .. .. 23·00 2·50
b. Orange (3.73) .. .. .. — 2·50
c. Bright orange (3.73) .. .. .. 27·00 2·50
d. Orange-brown (*glazed paper*) (10.78) 27·00 6·50
135 **14** 4d. dull rose (28.11.67) .. .. 75·00 5·00
a. Wmk sideways .. .. .. † 60·00
b. Aniline red (*shades*) (21.4.69) .. — 6·50
c. Rose-pink (11.69) .. .. .. — 5·00
d. Rose (*shades*) (8.71) .. .. 70·00 3·00
e. Dull rose (*glazed paper*) (5.3.79) .. 70·00 3·00
f. Dull rose-red (*glazed paper*) (11.79) — 4·00
g. Bright lilac-rose (*aniline*) (*glazed paper*) (2.80) .. .. 80·00 3·75
h. Rosine (*aniline*) (*glazed paper*) (9.80) £200 5·00
136 **16** 6d. deep blue (15.1.68) .. .. — 3·00
a. Blue (21.12.68) .. .. .. 25·00 1·25
b. Indigo-blue (10.69) .. .. .. 25·00 1·25
c. Prussian blue (9.72) .. .. 23·00 1·25
d. Indigo (4.73) .. .. .. 25·00 1·40
e. Dull blue (*worn plate*) (3.74) .. — 1·25
f. Dull ultramarine (2.12.75) .. 32·00 1·25
g. Light Prussian blue (12.75) .. 48·00 1·25
h. Dull violet-blue (7.77) .. .. — 6·50
i. Blue (*glazed paper*) (6.78) .. .. 38·00 1·25
j. Dull milky-blue (*glazed paper*) (9.79) 32·00 1·25
k. Prussian blue (*glazed paper*) (4.80) — 1·25
l. Light blue (*glazed paper*) (4.81) .. 38·00 1·25
m. Deep blue (*glazed paper*) (10.81) .. 32·00 1·25
137 **14** 8d. lilac-brown/*pink* (24.1.77) .. .. 80·00 5·50
a. Purple-brown/pink (2.78) .. .. 80·00 5·50
b. Chocolate/pink (8.78) .. .. 85·00 5·00
ba. Compound perf 13×12 .. .. † £325
c. Red-brown/pink (12.78) .. .. 80·00 5·00
138 **17** 1s. light blue/*blue* (11.5.75) .. .. £100 7·00
139 **18** 5s. blue/*yellow* (26.12.67) £1700 £300
a. Wmk reversed .. .. .. — £500
140 5s. indigo-blue and carmine (I) (8.10.68) £200 20·00
a. Blue and carmine (4.69) .. .. £180 13·00
b. Pale bright blue and carmine (*glazed paper*) (24.7.77) .. .. .. — 17·00
c. Grey-blue and carmine (*glazed paper*) (4.78) .. .. .. £170 15·00
d. Wmk sideways. *Deep lavender-blue and carmine* (*glazed paper*) (4.6.80) £170 17·00
141 5s. bright blue and red (II) (*glazed paper*) (12.5.81) .. .. £150 14·00
a. Indigo-blue and red (*glazed paper*) — 18·00

(*b*) *P* 12
142 **14** 1d. pale green (10.71) .. .. .. 70·00 2·40
a. Grass-green (1871) .. .. .. 60·00 2·40
b. Bluish green (*shades*) (7.72) .. — 2·40
c. Green (*shades*) (9.72) .. .. 60·00 2·25
143 **15** 3d. dull orange (5.72) .. .. .. 23·00 2·00
a. Orange (3.73) .. .. .. — 2·10
b. Bright orange (3.73) .. .. — 2·50
c. Dull orange-yellow (*glazed paper*) (12.80) .. ..
144 **14** 4d. rose (*shades*) (8.71) .. .. 70·00 3·00
a. Compound perf 12×13 .. .. — £325
b. Dull rose (*glazed paper*) (3.79) .. — 3·00
c. Dull rose-red (*glazed paper*) (11.79) — 3·00
d. Bright lilac-rose (*aniline*) (*glazed paper*) (2.80) .. .. .. — 6·50
e. Rosine (*aniline*) (*glazed paper*) (9.80) 80·00 4·75
145 **16** 6d. deep blue (2.2.72) .. .. ..
a. Prussian blue (9.72) .. .. 25·00 1·75
b. Indigo (4.73) .. .. .. 32·00 2·00
c. Dull blue (*worn plate*) (3.74) ..
d. Blue (*glazed paper*) (6.78) .. .. — 1·75
e. Dull milky-blue (*glazed paper*) (9.79) — 1·75
f. Light blue (*glazed paper*) (4.81) .. — 2·75
146 **14** 8d. red-brn/*pink* (*glazed paper*) (11.80) .. 75·00 5·50
147 **17** 1s. light blue/*blue* (5.75) .. .. — 6·50
148 **18** 5s. bright blue and red (II) (*glazed paper*) (5.81) .. .. £150 13·00
a. Indigo-blue and red .. .. £225 17·00

(*c*) *P* 12½
149 **15** 3d. dull orange-yellow (*glazed paper*) (12.80) .. .. 32·00 3·75
150 **14** 4d. rosine (*aniline*) (*glazed paper*) (9.80)
151 **16** 6d. Prussian blue (*glazed paper*) (4.80) ..
a. Light blue (*glazed paper*) (4.81)
b. Deep blue (*glazed paper*) (10.81) .. 32·00 2·25
152 **14** 8d. lilac-brown/*pink* (8.77) .. .. 75·00 5·50
a. Red-brown/pink (*glazed paper*) (11.80) † —

The same electrotypes as the previous issues were used for this series with the exception of the 5s. which was a new value. The 1d., 2d., 3d., 4d., 6d. and 1s. plates were arranged to print sheets of 120 (12×10) and the 8d. conformed to this when reintroduced in 1877. New plates for the 1d. (1868), 2d. (1869) and 6d. (1875) were constructed by Robinson's successor, J. P. Atkinson, using the improved facilities then available.

Atkinson was also responsible for the printing of the 5s. value. The original printings in blue on yellow paper were produced in sheets of 25, or possibly 50, using a vertical strip of five electrotypes. Due to its size the 5s. did not exactly fit the watermarked paper and, to avoid a preprinted sheet number, a proportion of the printing was made on the back of the paper creating the reversed watermark variety, No. 139a. These varieties occur in the first printing only as Atkinson created a plate of 25 for the second printing in March 1868. Printings of the 5s. bicoloured to April 1880 were made from electrotypes taken from the monocoloured plate. These showed a blue line beneath the crown (Type I). In early 1881 this plate was found to be too worn for further use and a new die was made from which a plate of 100 was constructed. Stamps from this plate are without the blue line beneath the crown (Type II).

PERFORATIONS. Various perforating machines were in use during this period. The use of line machines gauging 12 ceased around 1883. Of the line machines gauging 13 two were converted to comb types in 1873 and were eventually replaced by the 12½ gauge line and comb machines first used in 1876.

(Typo from electrotypes)

1867–70. *Emergency printings on various papers due to shortages of V over Crown paper. P* 13.

(*a*) *Perkins, Bacon paper borrowed from Tasmania. Wmkd double-lined numerals as W* **4** *of Tasmania*
153 **14** 1d. pale yellowish green (*wmkd* "1") (24.9.67) .. .. 65·00 3·50
a. Deep yellow-green (10.67) .. .. 65·00 3·50
154 1d. pale yellow-green (*wmkd* "4") (27.5.68) £1300 85·00
155 2d. grey-lilac (*wmkd* "4") (3.2.68) .. £110 4·25
a. Slate (4.68) .. .. £110 3·50
b. Mauve (7.68) .. .. .. — 4·50
156 2d. mauve (*wmkd* "1") (30.6.68) .. £110 5·50
157 **15** 3d. grey-lilac (*wmkd* "1") (8.68) .. £150 42·00
158 **14** 4d. dull rose-red (*wmkd* "4") (5.68) .. £110 5·00
159 **16** 6d. blue (*wmkd* "4") (20.6.68) .. £150 13·00
a. Indigo-blue .. .. .. — 15·00
160 6d. blue (*wmkd* "1") (28.7.68) .. 55·00 4·25
161 6d. dull blue (*wmkd* "2") (1870) .. † £2250

(*b*) *Saunders paper. Wmkd in words as W* **10**
162 **14** 1d. pale yellow-green (wmkd "SIX PENCE") (23.3.68) .. .. £375 22·00
163 2d. slate-grey (*wmkd* "SIX PENCE") (6.68) .. .. † £2500
164 **16** 6d. blue (*wmkd* "SIX PENCE") (20.5.68) £250 16·00
a. Indigo-blue .. .. .. — 20·00
165 6d. dull blue (*wmkd* "THREE PENCE") (6.12.69) .. .. £130 6·00
a. Deep blue .. .. — 7·00
166 6d. dull blue (*wmkd* "FOUR PENCE") (21.5.70) .. .. £250 23·00
a. Deep blue .. .. — 24·00

(*c*) *V over Crown, W* **19**, *coloured paper*
167 **14** 2d. mauve/*lilac* (7.68) .. .. .. 65·00 6·50
a. Lilac/lilac .. .. .. 65·00 6·00

(*d*) *Saunders single-lined numeral "4" as W* **11**
168 **16** 6d. dull blue (21.5.70) .. † £1600

The supply of paper was so short during 1868 that many odds and ends were utilised. Nos. 161 (five known), 163 (one known) and 168 (ten known) are the rarest of these emergency printings.

(Printed in Melbourne from a double electrotyped plate of 240 supplied by D.L.R.)

1870 (28 Jan)–**73.** *Wmk V over Crown, W* **19**.
169 **20** 2d. brown-lilac (*p* 13) .. .. .. 60·00 1·50
a. Dull lilac-mauve (9.70) .. .. 50·00 1·00
b. Mauve (*worn plate*) (3.73) .. .. 50·00 1·25
170 2d. dull lilac-mauve (*p* 12) (28.7.71) .. 55·00 2·00
a. Mauve (*worn plate*) (3.73) .. .. 55·00 1·75

9 9
NINEPENCE
(**21**)

1871 (22 Apr). *No.* 123*c surch with T* **21** *in blue.*
171 **16** 9d. on 10d. purple-brown/*pink* .. £300 10·00
a. Blackish brown/pink .. .. £400 12·00
b. Surch double .. .. .. † £800

22

23

24

25

26
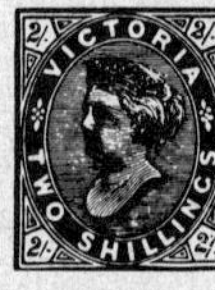
27

(Des and eng W. Bell. Typo from electrotyped plates)

1873 (25 Mar)–**74.** *Saunders paper wmkd single-lined "10" W* **11**.
172 **25** 9d. pale brown/*pink* (*p* 13) .. .. 65·00 10
a. Red-brown/pink (7.74) .. .. 60·00 10
173 9d. pale brown/*pink* (*p* 12) .. .. 70·00 12

½ ½
HALF
(**28**)

1873 (25 June). *No.* 131*g surch with T* **28** *in red.*
174 **14** ½d. on 1d. green (*p* 13) .. .. .. 48·00 12
a. Grass-green .. .. .. 50·00 12
b. Short "1" at right (R. 1/3) .. .. — 70
175 ½d. on 1d. green (*p* 12) .. .. .. 65·00 14
a. Grass-green .. .. .. 65·00 14
b. Short "1" at right (R. 1/3) .. .. — 75

Die I

Die II

Two Dies of 2d.:
Die I. Single-lined outer oval
Die II. Double-lined outer oval

(Des and eng W. Bell. Typo from electrotyped plates)

1873–87. *Wmk V over Crown, W* **19**, (*sideways on* ½*d.*).

(*a*) *P* 13
176 **22** ½d. rose-red (10.2.74) .. .. .. 8·50
a. Lilac-rose (1874) .. .. .. 9·00 1·2
b. Rosine (*shades*) (*glazed paper*) (12.80) .. .. 7·50
c. Pale red (*glazed paper*) (1882) .. 8·50
d. Mixed perf 13 and 12 .. .. † £2
177 **23** 1d. dull bluish green (14.12.75) .. 20·00 1·2
a. Green (*shades*) (1877) .. .. 20·00 1·2
b. Yellow-green (*glazed paper*) (1878) 20·00 1·0
178 **24** 2d. deep lilac-mauve (I) (1.10.73) .. 28·00
a. Dull violet-mauve .. .. .. 28·00
b. Dull mauve .. .. .. 28·00
c. Pale mauve (*worn plate*) (*glazed paper*) (1.79) .. .. .. 29·00
d. Mixed perf 13 and 12 .. .. £130 £10
179 2d. lilac-mauve (II) (*glazed paper*) (17.12.78) .. .. 26·00
a. Grey-mauve (1.80) .. .. .. —
b. Pale mauve (6.80) .. .. .. 35·00
c. Vert pair, lower stamp imperf horiz † £120
180 **26** 1s. indigo-blue/*blue* (16.8.76) .. .. 55·00 3·2
a. Deep blue/blue (7.77) .. .. 60·00 3·2
b. Pale blue/blue (3.80) .. .. 65·00 3·2
c. Bright blue/blue (9.80) .. .. 70·00 7·5
d. Bright blue/blue (*glazed paper*) (21.11.83) .. .. 70·00 5·0
e. Pale blue/blue (*glazed paper*) (7.84)
f. Mixed perf 13 and 12 .. .. † —

(*b*) *P* 12
181 **22** ½d. rose-red (1874) .. .. .. 9·00 1·7
a. Lilac-rose (1874) .. .. .. 8·50 1·7
b. Rosine (*shades*) (*glazed paper*) (12.80) 8·50 1·5
c. Pale red (*glazed paper*) (1882) .. 8·50 1·7
182 **23** 1d. dull bluish green (1875) .. .. 23·00 2·0
a. Green (*shades*) (1877) .. .. 22·00 5·0
b. Yellow-green (*glazed paper*) (1878) — 3·0
183 **24** 2d. deep lilac-mauve (I) (1873) .. .. — 3·5
a. Dull violet-mauve .. .. .. — 3·5
b. Dull mauve .. .. .. 32·00 1·5
c. Pale mauve (*worn plate*) (*glazed paper*) (1879) .. .. .. — 1·7
184 2d. lilac-mauve (II) (*glazed paper*) (1878) 35·00 1·2
a. Grey-mauve (*glazed paper*) (1880) .. — 1·2
b. Pale mauve (*glazed paper*) (1880) .. — 2·5
185 **25** 9d. lilac-brown/*pink* (1.12.75) .. .. £100 12·0
186 **26** 1s. deep blue/*blue* (1880) .. .. — 7·5
a. Bright blue/blue (1880) .. .. — 7·5

(*c*) *P* 12½
187 **22** ½d. rosine (*shades*) (*glazed paper*) (1880)
a. Pale red (*glazed paper*) (1882) ..
188 **23** 1d. yellow-green (*glazed paper*) (1880)
189 **24** 2d. grey-mauve (II) (*glazed paper*) (1880)
a. Pale mauve (1880) .. ..
190 **27** 2s. deep blue/*green* (*glazed paper*) (8.7.81) .. .. £120 18·00
a. Light blue/green (*glazed paper*) (4.83)
ab. Wmk sideways .. .. .. £130 22·00
b. Ultramarine/green (*glazed paper*) (6.84) .. .. — 28·00
ba. Wmk sideways .. .. .. — 50·00

8d 8d
EIGHTPENCE
(**29**)

1876 (1 July). *No.* 185 *surch with T* **29**.
191 **25** 8d. on 9d. lilac-brown/*pink* .. .. £180 15·00
a. "F.IGHTPENCE" .. .. .. — £180

No. 191a was caused by a broken "E" and it occurred once in each sheet of 120.

24 Jan). *Saunders paper wmkd* "10" *as W* **11**.
4 8d. lilac-brown/*pink* (*p* 13) .. .. — £500
a. Purple-brown/pink (2.78) .. .. £100 8·50
b. Chocolate/pink (8.78) .. .. † £600
c. Red-brown/pink (8.79) .. .. 85·00 5·00
8d. red-brown/*pink* (*p* 12) (8.79) .. — 12·00
8d. red-brown/*pink* (*p* 12½) (8.79) .. — 50·00

. 192/4 occur amongst the V over Crown printings, the two of pink paper having become mixed.

Emergency printings on coloured papers wmkd V over wn, W **19**, (*sideways on* ½*d.*). *P* 13.
22 ½d. rose-red/*pink* (1.3.78) .. .. 26·00 16·00
23 1d. yellow-green/*yellow* (5.3.78) .. 80·00 14·00
1d. yellow-green/*drab* (5.4.78) .. .. £110 45·00
24 2d. dull violet-mauve/*lilac* (21.2.78) .. — £400
2d. dull violet-mauve/*green* (23.2.78) .. £140 16·00
2d. dull violet-mauve/*brown* (21.3.78) .. £130 16·00

ere was a shortage of white V over Crown, W **19**, marked paper in the early months of 1878 and various red papers were used for printings of the ½d., 1d. and 2d. s until fresh stocks of white paper were received.

30

31

32

Des and eng C. Naish. Typo from electrotyped plates)

(3 Nov)–**84.** *Wmk V over Crown, W* **19**.
30 1d. green (*p* 12½) (2.84) .. .. 90·00 10·00
31 2d. sepia (*p* 12½) .. .. .. 23·00 55
a. Sepia-brown (2.81) .. .. .. 21·00 55
b. Brown (*aniline*) (5.81) .. .. 24·00 55
c. Dull black-brown (10.81) .. .. — 55
d. Dull grey-brown (3.82) .. .. 20·00 55
2d. sepia (*p* 13) .. ..
a. Mixed perf 13 and 12 .. .. † £250
2d. sepia (*p* 12) .. .. — 45·00
a. Sepia-brown (2.81) .. .. .. — 45·00
b. Brown (*aniline*) (5.81) .. .. — 45·00
2d. mauve (*worn plate*) (*p* 12½) (2.84) .. — 6·50
32 4d. rose-carmine (*p* 12½) (10.81) .. 50·00 5·00
a. Rosine (7.82) .. .. .. 50·00 4·50

os. 201 and 205 are subsequent printings of stamps first uced on watermark W **33**.

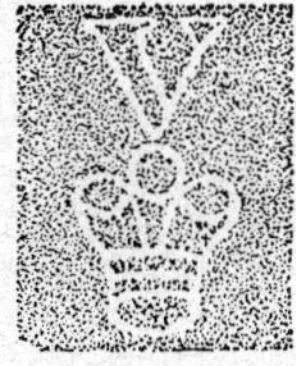
33

32–84. *Wmk V over Crown, W* **33**, (*sideways on* ½*d.*). *P* 12½.
22 ½d. rosine (3.83) .. .. .. 12·00 3·00
a. Perf 12 .. .. — 17·00
23 1d. yellow-green (9.82) .. .. 20·00 1·75
a. Perf 12 .. ..
30 1d. yellow-green (29.10.83) .. .. 20·00 1·25
a. Green (1.84) .. .. .. 18·00 1·25
b. Pale green (5.84) .. .. .. 18·00 1·25
31 2d. dull grey-brown (15.8.82) .. .. 21·00 85
a. Chocolate (3.83) .. .. .. 21·00 85
ab. Perf 12 .. .. — 19·00
1 2d. mauve (20.12.83) .. .. .. 13·00 80
a. Worn plate (2.84) .. .. .. 14·00 80
b. Perf 12 .. .. † £250
c. Mixed perf 12 and 12½ .. .. † £250
2 **15** 3d. yellow-orange (13.4.83) .. .. 35·00 8·00
a. Dull brownish orange .. .. 40·00 9·50
3 **32** 4d. rose-red (3.83) .. .. .. 48·00 7·00
4 **16** 6d. dull violet-blue (10.11.82) .. .. 24·00 1·25
a. Indigo-blue (11.83) .. .. .. 24·00 1·25
b. Light ultramarine (8.84) .. .. 24·00 1·40

Reprints were made in 1891 of the "Laureated" 1d., 2d., 3d. (in llow), 4d., 6d., 8d. (in orange-yellow), 10d. (in greenish slate) d 5s. (in blue and red), of the Bell ½d., 1d., 2d. (Die II), 9d. and and of the Naish 2d. (in brown), 4d. (in pale red) and 2s. With e exception of the Bell 9d., which was watermarked W **19**, all re watermarked W **33** and perforated 12½. Some were from w plates.

HE POST OFFICE ACT OF 1883. Following official concern to the number of different series of adhesive stamps, both scal and postal, used in Victoria it was decided that the system ould be unified to the extent that the postage stamps, Stamp atute fiscals and Stamp Duty fiscals should be replaced by a ngle series valid for all three purposes. As the Stamp Duty ries contained the largest number of values it was adopted as e basis of the new range.

The regulations for the changeover were detailed in the Post ffice Act of 1883 which came into force on 1 January 1884. rom that date all existing Stamp Statute (first produced in 371) and Stamp Duty (first produced in 1879) issues became alid for postal purposes, and the previous postage stamps could e used for fiscal fees.

Until matters could be organised printings of some of the xisting postage values continued and these will be found cluded in the listings above.

Printing of the Stamp Statute series was discontinued in early 884.

The existing Stamp Duty range was initially supplemented by ostage stamps overprinted "STAMP DUTY" for those values here the available fiscal design was considered to be too large to be easily used on mail. These overprints were replaced by smaller designs inscribed "STAMP DUTY".

Stamp Statute and Stamp Duty values which became valid for postal purposes on 1 January 1884 have previously been listed in this catalogue as Postal Fiscals. Under the circumstances this distinction appears somewhat arbitary and all such stamps are now shown in the main listing. Used prices quoted are for examples with postal cancellations. In some instances prices are also provided for fiscally used and these are marked "F.C.".

34

35

36

37

(Des and dies eng J. Turner (3d., 2s. 6d.), W. Bell (others). Typo from electrotypes)

1884 (1 Jan)*. *Stamp Statute series. Vert designs as T* **34/6**, *and others showing Queen Victoria, and T* **37**. *P* 13.

(*a*) *Wmk single-lined numerals according to face value, as W* **11**, (*sideways*). *Paper manufactured by T. H. Saunders unless otherwise stated*
215 1s. blue/*blue* .. .. 55·00 19·00
a. Perf 12 .. .. 70·00 25·00
216 2s. blue/*green* (*D.L.R. paper*) .. .. 85·00 60·00
a. Perf 12 .. .. 85·00 60·00
217 2s. deep blue/*green* .. .. .. 85·00
a. Perf 12 .. .. — 60·00
b. Wmk upright .. ..
218 10s. brown-olive/*pink* .. .. ..
219 10s. red-brown/*pink* £600 £150
a. Wmk upright. Perf 12 .. ..

(*b*) *Wmk V over Crown, W* **19**, (*sideways*). *P* 13
220 1d. pale green .. .. 32·00 25·00
a. Green (*wmk upright*) (*p* 12½) .. 65·00 48·00
221 3d. mauve £190 £130
222 4d. rose £180 £120
223 6d. blue .. .. 55·00 19·00
a. Ultramarine .. .. .. 48·00 16·00
ab. Perf 12 .. .. 55·00 17·00
224 1s. blue/*blue* .. .. 55·00 19·00
a. Perf 12 .. .. 60·00 23·00
b. Ultramarine/blue (*p* 12½) .. .. — 35·00
ba. Perf 12 .. .. — 27·00
c. Deep blue/blue (*p* 12½) .. .. 55·00 19·00
ca. Perf 12 .. .. — 19·00
225 2s. blue/*green* .. .. 80·00 55·00
a. Perf 12 .. .. 80·00
b. Deep blue/blue-green (*glazed paper*) .. 80·00 60·00
ba. Perf 12 .. .. 80·00 65·00
226 2s. 6d. orange .. .. — 95·00
a. Perf 12 .. ..
b. Yellow (*glazed paper*) £200
ba. Perf 12 .. .. £200 £100
c. Orange-yellow (*glazed paper*) (*p* 12½) — £110
ca. Perf 12 .. ..
227 5s. blue/*yellow* .. .. £190 60·00
a. Perf 12 .. .. £200
b. Wmk upright .. ..
ba. Perf 12 .. ..
c. Ultram/lemon (*glazed paper*) (*p* 12½) £190 60·00
ca. Wmk upright .. ..
228 10s. brown/*pink* £600 £150
a. Purple-brown/pink £600 £150
ab. Perf 12 .. ..
229 £1 slate-violet/*yellow* £425 £120
a. Wmk upright .. ..
b. Mauve/yellow .. ..
ba. Perf 12 .. .. £425 £120
bb. Perf 12½ £425 £120
230 £5 black and yellow-green £2250 £550
a. Perf 12 .. ..
b. Wmk upright. Perf 12½ £2250 £550

(*c*) *Wmk V over Crown, W* **33**, (*sideways*)
231 1d. yellowish green (*p* 12½) .. .. 48·00 48·00
232 2s. 6d. pale orange-yellow (*p* 12) .. .. £200 95·00
233 £5 black & yellow-grn (*wmk upright*) (*p* 12) — £550

OMNIBUS ISSUES

Details, together with prices for complete sets, of the various Omnibus issues from the 1935 Silver Jubilee to 1951 B.W.I. University College are included in a special section following Zanzibar at the end of this catalogue.

½d

HALF

(38)

1884 (1 Jan)*. *No.* 220 *surch with T* **38** *in red.*
234 ½d. on 1d. pale green .. .. .. 48·00 48·00

* The dates quoted are those on which the stamps became valid for postal purposes. The ½d., 1d., 4d., 6d., 1s., 5s. and £1 were issued for fiscal purposes on 26 April 1871. The 10s. was added to the series in June 1871, the £5 in September 1871, the 2s. 6d. in July 1876 and the 3d. in October 1879.

All values of the Stamp Statute series were reprinted in 1891 on paper watermarked W **19** (5s., 10s., £1) or W **33** (others). The £5 was pulled from the original plate, but the others were produced from new electrotypes taken from the original dies.

39

40

41

42

43

44

45

46

47

48

49

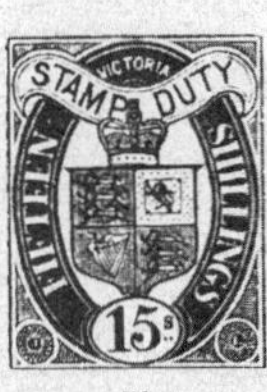

50

51

52

53

54

55

56

57

58

59

60

61

(Des H. Samson and F. Oxenbould (T **39**), C. Jackson and L. Lang (all others except T **40**). Dies eng C. Jackson, J. Turner, J. Whipple, A. Williams and other employees of Sands & MacDougall. T **40** die eng C. Naish)

1884 (1 Jan*)–**96.** *Existing Stamp Duty series.*

(*a*) *Litho. Wmk V over Crown, W* **19**, (*sideways*). *P* 13

235 **39** 1d. blue-green 55·00 16·00
a. Perf 12 55·00 16·00
b. Perf 12½
236 **43** 1s. 6d. rosine £150 18·00
a. Perf 12 — 25·00
b. Perf 12½
237 **45** 3s. purple/*blue* £325 32·00
a. Perf 12 — 40·00
b. Perf 12½
238 **46** 4s. orange-red 80·00 16·00
a. Perf 12 80·00 16·00
b. Perf 12½
239 **48** 6s. apple-green £225 27·00
a. Perf 12½
240 **49** 10s. brown/*rose* (*glazed paper*) £375 70·00
a. Perf 12
b. Perf 12½
c. Wmk upright
cb. Perf 12½
241 **50** 15s. mauve £900 £150
242 **51** £1 red-orange £375 65·00
a. Perf 12½ £375 65·00
243 **52** £1 5s. dull rose (*wmk upright*) £850 £160
244 **53** £1 10s. deep grey-olive £900 £110
a. Wmk upright — £140
245 – 35s. grey-violet (*wmk upright*) (F.C. £160) £3250
246 **54** £2 blue — 95·00
247 **55** 45s. dull brown-lilac £1600 £130
248 **56** £5 rose-red (*wmk upright*) (F.C. £50) £1400 £300
249 **57** £6 blue/*pink* (*wmk upright*) (*glazed paper*) (F.C. £100) — £500
250 **58** £7 violet/*blue* (*wmk upright*) (F.C. £100) — £500
251 **59** £8 brownish red/*yellow* (*wmk upright*) (*glazed paper*) (F.C. £100) — £650
252 **60** £9 yellow-green/*green* (*wmk upright*) (*glazed paper*) (F.C. £100) — £650

(*b*) *Typo from electrotypes*

(i) *Wmk V over Crown, W* **19**, (*sideways*). *P* 13

253 **39** 1d. yellowish green 38·00 16·00
a. Perf 12 38·00 16·00
b. Perf 12½
254 **40** 1d. pale bistre 13·00 2·50
a. Perf 12 13·00 3·25
b. Perf 12½
255 **41** 6d. dull blue 55·00 8·00
a. Perf 12 60·00 15·00
b. Perf 12½
256 **42** 1s. deep blue/*blue* 65·00 5·00
a. Perf 12 65·00 6·50
b. Perf 12½
c. *Brt blue/blue* (*glazed paper*) (*p* 12½) 65·00 6·00
ca. Perf 12 — 6·50
d. *Ultramarine/blue* (*glazed paper*) (*p* 12½) (11.84) £100 6·50
257 1s. chalky blue/*lemon* (*glazed paper*) (*p* 12½) (3.3.85) 80·00 22·00
258 **44** 2s. deep blue/*green* (*glazed paper*) £130 19·00
a. Perf 12 — 21·00
b. Perf 12½ — 23·00
c. *Indigo/green* £110 23·00
ca. Perf 12 £150 24·00
cb. Perf 12½
259 **45** 3s. mar/*bl* (*glazed paper*) (*p* 12½) (8.8.84) £250 27·00
260 **47** 5s. claret/*yellow* (*glazed paper*) 50·00 5·00
a. Perf 12 60·00 10·00
b. Perf 12½
c. *Pale claret/yellow* (*p* 12½) 50·00 11·00
ca. Perf 12 70·00 11·00
d. *Reddish purple/lemon* (*p* 12½) (6.87) 45·00 11·00
e. *Brown-red/yellow* (*p* 12½) (5.93) 75·00 25·00
261 **49** 10s. chocolate/*rose* (*glazed paper*) — 70·00
a. Perf 12
b. Perf 12½
c. Wmk upright
262 **51** £1 yellow-orange/*yellow* (*p* 12) £550 75·00
a. *Orange/yellow* (*p* 12½) (8.84) £500 55·00
b. *Reddish orange/yellow* (*p* 12½) (9.88) £325 55·00
263 **54** £2 deep blue (*p* 12) — 90·00
264 **61** £10 dull mauve (*p* 12)
a. *Deep red-lilac* (*p* 12) £1600 £110

(ii) *Wmk V over Crown, W* **33**, (*sideways*). *P* 12½

265 **40** 1d. ochre 22·00 3·50
a. Perf 12 22·00 3·50
266 **41** 6d. ultramarine 65·00 7·00
a. Perf 12 65·00 7·00
267 **43** 1s. 6d. pink (1.85) £130 25·00
a. *Bright rose-carmine* (4.86) £150 23·00
268 **45** 3s. drab (20.10.85) 75·00 16·00
a. *Olive-drab* (1.93) 70·00 16·00
269 **46** 4s. red-orange (5.86) 80·00 14·00
a. *Yellow-orange* (12.94)
ab. Wmk upright £100 12·00
270 **47** 5s. rosine (8.5.96) 75·00 19·00
271 **48** 6s. pea-green (12.11.91) £110 35·00
a. *Apple-green* (*wmk upright*) (3.96) £180 35·00
272 **49** 10s. dull bluish green (10.85) £160 32·00
a. *Grey-green* (5.86) £120 27·00
273 **50** 15s. purple-brown (12.85) £550 75·00
a. *Brown* (*wmk upright*) (5.95) £550 80·00
274 **52** £1 5s. pink (*wmk upright*) (6.8.90) £950 85·00
275 **53** £1 10s. pale olive (6.88) £700 75·00
276 **54** £2 bright blue — 75·00
a. *Blue* (7.88) £750 75·00
277 **55** 45s. lilac (15.8.90) £2000 95·00
278 **56** £5 rose-pink (*p* 12) — £275
a. *Pink* (*p* 12½) — £375
279 **61** £10 mauve (3.84) £1800 90·00
a. *Lilac* (6.85) — £100

*This is the date on which the stamps became valid for postal use. The 1d., 6d., 1s., 1s.6d., 2s., 3s., 4s., 5s., 10s., 15s., £1, £1 10s., £2, £5 and £10 were issued for fiscal purposes on 18 December 1879 with the £1 5s., 35s., 45s., £6 and £9 added to the range later the same month and the 6s., £7 and £8 in January 1880.

Used prices for the £1 5s., £1 10s., £2 (No. 276*a*), 45s. and £10 watermarked W **33** are for examples from the cancelled-to-order sets sold to collectors by the Victoria postal authorities between September 1900 and 30 June 1902.

Similar Stamp Duty designs were prepared for 7s., 8s., 9s., 11s., 12s., 13s., 14s., 16s., 17s., 18s., and 19s., but were never issued.

The two different 1d. designs were reprinted in 1891 on W **33** paper.

For these designs with later watermarks see Nos. 345/50 and 369/71.

62

(Des C. Jackson and L. Lang. Dies eng C. Jackson)

1884 (1 Jan*)–**1900.** *High value Stamp Duty series.*

(*a*) *Recess-printed direct from the die*

(i) *Wmk V over Crown, W* **19**, (*sideways*). *P* 12½

280 **62** £25 yellow-green (F.C. £55)
a. Wmk upright
b. Perf 13
c. *Deep green* (F.C. £55)
ca. Wmk upright
281 £50 bright mauve (F.C. £85)
a. Wmk upright
b. Perf 13
282 £100 crimson-lake (F.C. £110)
a. Wmk upright
b. Perf 13

(ii) *Wmk V over Crown, W* **33**, (*sideways*). *P* 12½

283 **62** £25 yellow-green
a. Perf 12
b. *Deep green* (1.85) (F.C. £55) — £425
c. *Bright blue-green* (10.90) (F.C. £55)
ca. Wmk upright
284 £50 dull lilac-mauve (*wmk upright*) (F.C.£85)
a. *Black-violet* (10.90) (F.C. £65) — £425
ab. Wmk upright
285 **62** £100 crimson (F.C. £120)
a. Wmk upright
b. Perf 12 (F.C. £120)
c. *Aniline crimson* (*wmk upright*) (2.85) (F.C. £120) —
d. *Scarlet-red* (5.95) —
da. Wmk upright —

(*b*) *Litho. Wmk V over Crown, W* **33**, (*sideways*). *P* 12½

286 **62** £25 dull yellowish green (1.86) (F.C. £45)
a. Wmk upright (11.87)
b. *Dull blue-green* (9.88) (F.C. £45)
ba. Wmk upright
287 £50 dull purple (1.86) (F.C. £60)
a. Wmk upright
b. *Bright violet* (11.89) (F.C. £60)
ba. Wmk upright
288 £100 rosine (1.86) (F.C. £95)
a. Wmk upright

(*c*) *Typo from electrotyped plates. Wmk V over Crown, W* *P* 12½

289 **62** £25 dull blue-green (12.97) —
290 £50 bright mauve (10.97) —
291 £100 pink-red (10.1900) —

*This is the date on which the stamps became valid for p use. All three values were issued for fiscal purpose 18 December 1879.

Used prices for Nos. 283*b*, 284*a*, 285*c/d* and 289/91 ar examples from the cancelled-to-order sets described beneat 279*a*. "F.C." indicates that the price quoted is for a stamp a fiscal cancellation.

For the £25 and £50 with watermark W **82** see Nos. 351/

63

(Des and die eng C. Naish. Typo from electrotyped plates

1884 (23 Apr)–**92.** *New design inscr* "STAMP DUTY". *Wm over Crown, W* **33** (*sideways*). *P* 12½.

292 **63** 2s. 6d. brown-orange 85·00 1
a. *Yellow* (8.85) 80·00 1
b. *Lemon-yellow* (2.92) 80·00 1

For this design on later watermarks see Nos. 344 and 370

64

65

66

67

68

(Des and dies eng C. Naish. Typo from electrotyped plates)

1885 (1 Jan)–**95.** *New designs inscr* "STAMP DUTY". *P* 12

(*a*) *W* **19**

293 **68** 8d. rose/*pink* 23·00 5·
a. *Rose-red/pink* (2.88) 25·00 5·
294 **66** 1s. deep dull blue/*lemon* (11.85) 65·00 8·
a. *Dull blue/yellow* (6.86) 65·00 8·
295 **68** 2s. olive/*bluish green* (12.85) 50·00 3·

(*b*) *W* **33**

296 **64** ½d. pale rosine 6·50
a. *Deep rosine* (7.85) 8·50 1·
b. *Salmon* (9.85) 9·00 1·
297 **65** 1d. yellowish green (1.85) 8·50
a. *Dull pea-green* (2.85) 14·00 1·
298 **66** 2d. lilac 8·00
a. *Mauve* (1886) 8·00
b. *Rosy-mauve* (1886) 9·50
299 **65** 3d. yellowish brown 12·00 1·0
a. *Pale ochre* (9.86) 9·50 1·0
b. *Bistre-yellow* (9.92) 10·00 1·0
300 **67** 4d. magenta 42·00 3·0
a. *Bright mauve-rose* (12.86) 45·00 3·5
b. Error. Lilac (12.86) £2500 £45
301 **65** 6d. chalky blue (1.85) 55·00 2·5
a. *Bright blue* (3.85) 38·00 2·1
b. *Cobalt* (7.85) 38·00 2·1
302 **68** 8d. bright scarlet/*pink* (3.95) 30·00 8·0
303 2s. olive-green/*pale green* (1.90) 27·00 4·2
304 2s. apple-green (12.8.95) 25·00 38·0
a. *Blue-green* (29.10.95) 18·00 7·5

The plates for the 1d., 6d., 1s. and 2s. were derived from th dies of the 2d. (1s.), 3d. (1d. and 6d.) and 8d. (2s.). In eac instance lead moulds of six impressions were taken from th original die and the face values altered by hand creating si slightly different versions.

Two states of the 2d. die exist with the second showing a break in the top frame line near the righthand corner. This damaged die was used for seven impressions on Plate 1 and all 120 or Plate 2.

No. 300b occured during the December 1886 printing of the 4d. when about fifty sheets were printed in the colour of the 2d istake. The sheets were issued to Melbourne post offices used examples are known postmarked between ecember 1886 and 4 March 1887. Nine unused are also ved to exist.

prints of the ½d., 1d., 2d., 4d., 6d. and 1s. values were made 91 from the existing plates. The 1s. was watermarked W **19** he remainder W **33**.

r some of these values used with later watermarks see Nos. 343, 361 and 369.

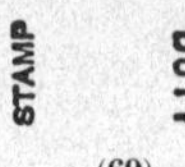

(**69**)

5 (Feb–Nov). *Optd with T* **69**. *P* 12½. (*a*) *W* **19**
15 3d. dull orge-yell (*glazed paper*) (B.) (Nov) — £130
26 1s. pale blue/*blue* (*glazed paper*) (*p* 13) 95·00 20·00
a. Deep blue/blue .. .. .. — 22·00
b. Blue opt (F.C. £14) £1200 £600
27 2s. ultramarine/*grn* (*glazed paper*) (Mar) 90·00 18·00
a. Wmk sideways .. .. .. £100 20·00

(*b*) *W* **33**
15 3d. yellow-orange (B.) (Nov) .. .. 60·00 22·00
a. Dull brownish orange (B.) .. .. 65·00 24·00
32 4d. rose-red (B.) (Nov) .. .. .. 55·00 27·00

nauthorised reprints of the 4d. and 1s., both with blue prints and watermarked W **33**, were made during 1895–96. 4d. reprint, which is in pale red, also exists without the print.

70 **71** **72**

73 **74** **75**

76 **77** **78**

79

80

(Des S. Reading (1d. (No. 313), M. Tannenberg (2½d., 5d.), C. Naish (1s. 6d.), P. Astley (others). Dies eng C. Naish (2d., 4d. (both existing dies with lines added behind Queen's head) and 1s. 6d.), S. Reading (originally as an employee of Fergusson & Mitchell) (others). Typo from electrotyped plates)

1886 (26 July)–**96**. *W* **33** (*sideways on* ½*d.*, 1*s.*, £5, £7 *to* £9). *P* 12½.
310 **70** ½d. lilac-grey (28.8.86) .. .. 20·00 4·25
a. Grey-black .. .. .. — 35·00
311 ½d. pink (15.2.87) .. .. .. 8·00 50
a. Rosine (*aniline*) (1889) .. .. 4·75 30
b. Rose-red (1891) .. .. .. 4·75 30
c. Vermilion (1896) .. .. .. 5·50 35
312 **71** 1d. green .. .. 6·50 65
a. Yellow-green (1887) .. .. 6·50 65
313 **72** 1d. dull chestnut (1.1.90) .. .. 6·50 30
a. Deep red-brown (1890) .. .. 6·50 40
b. Orange-brown (1890) .. .. 6·50 30
c. Brown-red (1890) .. .. .. 6·50 30
d. Yellow-brown (1891) .. .. 6·50 30
e. Bright yellow-orange (1893) .. 50·00 12·00
f. Brownish orange (1894) .. .. 4·50 30
314 **73** 2d. pale lilac (17.12.86) .. .. 7·00 20
a. Pale mauve (1887) .. .. 8·00 20
b. Deep lilac (1888, 1892) .. .. 6·00 20
c. Purple (1894) .. .. .. 3·50 25
d. Violet (1895) .. .. .. 3·50 20
e. Imperf .. .. — £700
315 **74** 2½d. red-brown/*lemon* (1.1.91) .. .. 15·00 2·50
a. Brown-red/yellow (1892) .. .. 11·00 80
b. Red/yellow (1893) .. .. .. 8·50 70
316 **75** 4d. rose-red (1.4.87) .. .. .. 14·00 1·00
a. Red (1893) .. .. .. 8·50 90
317 **76** 5d. purple-brown (1.1.91) .. .. 8·50 1·25
a. Pale reddish brown (1893) .. .. 7·00 1·25
318 **77** 6d. bright ultramarine (27.8.86) .. 14·00 80
a. Pale ultramarine (1887) .. .. 13·00 50
b. Dull blue (1891) .. .. .. 12·00 50
319 **25** 9d. apple-green (18.10.92) .. .. 22·00 9·00
320 9d. carmine-rose (15.10.95) .. .. 23·00 6·50
a. Rosine (*aniline*) (1896) .. .. 27·00 6·50
321 **78** 1s. dull purple-brown (14.3.87) .. 45·00 2·00
a. Lake (1890) .. .. .. 35·00 2·00
b. Carmine-lake (1892) .. .. 18·00 1·00
c. Brownish red (1896) .. .. 19·00 1·60
322 **79** 1s. 6d. pale blue (9.88) .. .. £130 65·00
323 1s. 6d. orange (19.9.89) .. .. 16·00 5·00
a. Red-orange (1893) .. .. 16·00 5·50
324 **80** £5 pale blue and maroon (7.2.88)† .. £1000 80·00
325 £6 yellow and pale blue (1.10.87)† .. £1200 £110
326 £7 rosine and black (17.10.89)† .. £1400 £120
327 £8 mauve & brown-orange (2.8.90)† £1500 £150
328 £9 apple-green and rosine (21.8.88)† £1800 £160

†The used prices provided for these stamps are for cancelled-to-order examples.

Unauthorised reprints of the ½d. lilac-grey and 1s. 6d. pale blue were made in 1894–95 on W **33** paper and perforated 12½. These differ in shade from the originals and have rougher perforations. It should be noted that the original printing of No. 322 does not occur with inverted watermark, but the reprint does.

A single example of No. 314e is known postmarked "737" (Foster). A second, postmarked "249" (Mortlake), was reported in 1892. It is known that an imperforate sheet was sold at Mortlake P.O. in 1890. Other examples are believed to be clandestine.

A later printing of the £5 value, as No. 324 but perforated 11, was not valid for postal use (*Price* £250 *unused*).

A £10 value as Type **80** was prepared, but not issued.

1891 (17 June). *W* **19**. *P* 12½.
329 **72** 1d. orange-brown/*pink* .. .. .. 4·75 2·00

No. 329 was an emergency printing during a shortage of white W **33** paper.

81

82

(Die eng A. Williams (1½d.). Typo from electrotyped plates)

1896 (11 June)–**99**. *W* **82** (*sideways on* ½*d.*, 1½*d.*, 1*s.*, 2*s.* 6*d. to* 15*s.*). *P* 12½.
330 **70** ½d. light scarlet (1.7.96) .. .. 3·25 35
a. Carmine-rose (1897) .. .. 3·50 35
b. Dp carmine-red (*coarse impression*) (1899) .. .. — 1·50
c. Wmk upright .. .. .. † —
331 ½d. emerald (1.8.99) .. .. .. 11·00 2·00
332 **72** 1d. brown-red (13.6.96) .. .. 4·50 10
a. Brownish orange (1897) .. .. 4·50 10
333 **81** 1½d. apple-green (7.10.97) .. .. 3·00 2·25
334 **73** 2d. violet .. .. 6·00 10
a. Wmk sideways .. .. .. † —
335 **74** 2½d. blue (1.8.99) .. .. .. 7·50 4·50
336 **65** 3d. ochre (11.96) .. .. .. 7·00 65
a. Buff (1898) .. .. .. 6·50 65
337 **75** 4d. red (6.97) .. .. 11·00 1·75
338 **76** 5d. red-brown (7.97) .. .. .. 14·00 1·00
339 **77** 6d. dull blue (9.96) .. .. .. 11·00 65
340 **25** 9d. rosine (8.96) .. .. .. 26·00 3·25
a. Rose-carmine (1898) .. .. — 3·25
b. Dull rose (1898) .. .. .. 23·00 3·25
341 **78** 1s. brownish red (3.97) .. .. 13·00 2·00
342 **79** 1s. 6d. brown-orange (8.98) .. .. 32·00 13·00
343 **68** 2s. blue-green (4.97) .. .. .. 27·00 6·50
344 **63** 2s. 6d. yellow (9.96) .. .. .. 90·00 12·00
a. Wmk upright (1898) .. .. £100 12·00
345 **45** 3s. olive-drab (12.96) .. .. .. 55·00 17·00
a. Wmk upright (1898) .. .. 55·00 16·00
346 **46** 4s. orange (9.97) .. .. .. 80·00 8·50
347 **47** 5s. rosine (2.97) .. .. .. 80·00 10·00
a. Rose-carmine (1897) .. .. 80·00 10·00
b. Wmk upright. *Rosine* (1899) .. 80·00 11·00
348 **48** 6s. pale yellow-green (4.99)† .. .. 85·00 23·00
349 **49** 10s. grey-green (4.97) .. .. .. £120 17·00
a. Blue-green (1898) .. .. .. £120 17·00
350 **50** 15s. brown (4.97)† .. .. .. £375 45·00
351 **62** £25 dull bluish green (1897)† .. .. — £110
352 £50 dull purple (1897)† .. .. .. — £140

†The used prices provided for these stamps are for cancelled-to-order examples.

83

84

(Des M. Tannenberg. Dies eng A. Mitchelhill. Typo from electrotyped plates)

1897 (22 Oct). *Hospital Charity Fund*. *W* **82** (*sideways*). *P* 12½.
353 **83** 1d. (1s.) blue .. .. 18·00 18·00
354 **84** 2½d. (2s. 6d.) red-brown .. .. 85·00 70·00
353s/4s Optd "Specimen" *Set of* 2 £140

These stamps were sold at 1s. and 2s. 6d., but only had postal validity for 1d. and 2½d. with the difference going to the Fund.

1899 (1 Aug). *W* **33** (*sideways*). *P* 12½.
355 **81** 1½d. brown-red/*yellow* .. .. .. 3·00 1·75

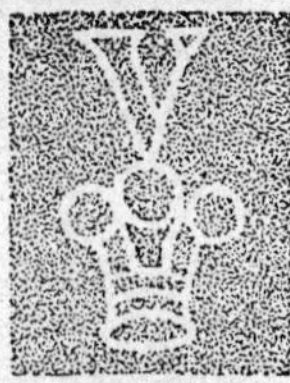

85

1899 (1 Aug)–**1901**. *W* **85** (*sideways on* ½*d.*, 1*s. and* 2*s.* 6*d. to* 10*s.*). *P* 12½.
356 **70** ½d. emerald (12.99) .. .. .. 4·75 40
a. Deep blue-green .. .. .. 5·00 40
b. Wmk upright .. .. ..
357 **72** 1d. rose-red .. .. 6·00 15
a. Rosine (1900) .. .. .. 4·25 10
358 1d. olive (6.6.01) .. .. .. 5·00 4·00
359 **73** 2d. violet .. .. 8·50 10
a. Wmk sideways .. .. .. † —
360 **74** 2½d. blue (10.99) .. .. .. 10·00 1·50
361 **65** 3d. bistre-yellow (9.99) .. .. 7·00 1·50
362 3d. slate-green (20.6.01) .. .. 21·00 8·50
363 **75** 4d. rose-red (12.99) .. .. .. 6·00 1·50
364 **76** 5d. red-brown (10.99) .. .. .. 12·00 1·50
365 **77** 6d. dull ultramarine (1.00) .. .. 8·50 1·25
366 **25** 9d. rose-red (9.99) .. .. .. 13·00 1·75
367 **78** 1s. brown-red (5.00) .. .. .. 14·00 2·00
368 **79** 1s. 6d. orange (2.00) .. .. .. 16·00 8·00
369 **68** 2s. blue-green (6.00) .. .. .. 17·00 6·50
370 **63** 2s. 6d. yellow (1.00) .. .. .. £300 16·00
371 **45** 3s. pale olive (4.00)† .. .. .. £130 20·00
372 **47** 5s. rose-red (4.00) .. .. .. £100 20·00
373 **49** 10s. green (3.00)† .. .. .. £130 20·00

†The used prices provided for these stamps are for cancelled-to-order examples.

From 1 July 1901 stamps inscribed "STAMP DUTY" could only be used for fiscal purposes.

86 Victoria Cross

87 Australian Troops in South Africa

(Des Sands and MacDougall (1d.), J. Sutherland (2d.). Dies eng S. Reading. Typo from electrotyped plates)

1900 (22 May). *Empire Patriotic Fund*. *W* **85** (*sideways*). *P* 12½.
374 **86** 1d. (1s.) olive-brown .. .. .. 65·00 40·00
375 **87** 2d. (2s.) emerald-green £130 £130

These stamps were sold at 1s. and 2s., but only had postal validity for 1d. and 2d. with the difference going to the Fund.

FEDERATION. The six Australian colonies were federated as the Commonwealth of Australia on 1 January 1901. Under the terms of the Post and Telegraph Act their postal services were amalgamated on 1 March 1901, but other clauses to safeguard the financial position of the individual States provided them with a large degree of independence until 13 October 1910 when issues of each state could be used throughout Australia. Postage stamps for the Commonwealth of Australia did not appear until January 1913.

It was agreed in 1901 that stamp printing should be centralised at Melbourne under J. B. Cooke of South Australia who was appointed Commonwealth Stamp Printer. By 1909 the Commonwealth Stamp Printing Branch in Melbourne was producing stamps for Papua, South Australia, Tasmania and Western Australia in addition to those of Victoria.

On federation it was decided to separate postal and fiscal stamp issues so Victoria needed urgent replacements for the current Stamp Duty series which reverted to fiscal use only on 30 June 1901.

1901 (29 Jan). *Re-use of previous designs without* "POSTAGE" *inscr*. *W* **82** (2*s.*) *or W* **85** (*others*) (*sideways on* ½*d.*). *P* 12×12½.
376 **22** ½d. bluish green .. .. .. 2·00 1·00
a. "VICTCRIA" (R. 7/19) .. .. 35·00 25·00
377 **31** 2d. reddish violet .. .. .. 6·50 85
378 **15** 3d. dull orange .. .. .. 15·00 1·25
379 **32** 4d. bistre-yellow .. .. .. 25·00 13·00
380 **16** 6d. emerald .. .. 9·00 6·00
381 **26** 1s. yellow .. .. 40·00 32·00
382 **27** 2s. blue/*pink* .. .. .. 42·00 18·00
383 **18** 5s. pale red and deep blue .. .. 45·00 35·00

88

89

90

91 92 93 94 95 96 97 98 99 100 101 102

I II III

Three die states of ½d.:

I. Outer vertical line of colour to left of "V" continuous except for a break opposite the top of "V". Triangles either end of "VICTORIA" are more or less solid colour.

II. Die re-engraved. Three breaks in outer line of colour left of "V". White lines added to left triangle.

III. Die re-engraved. As II, but equivalent triangle at right also contains white lines.

I

II

III

I and II

III

Three die states of 1d.:

I. Thick lines fill top of oval above Queen's head.

II. Die re-engraved. Lines thinner, showing white space between.

III. Die re-engraved. As II, but with bottom left value table recut to show full point separated from both "1" and the circular frame.

Two die states of 2d.:

I. Frame line complete at top right corner. Bottom right corner comes to a point.

II. Break in right frame line just below the top corner. Bottom right corner is blunted.

Two types of 1s.:

A. "POSTAGE" 6 mm long (produced by a hand punch applied twice to each impression on the previous 1s. electrotyped plate. Slight variations in position occur).

B. "POSTAGE" 7 mm long (produced from new electrotyped plates incorporating the "POSTAGE" inscriptions).

(Eng S. Reading after photo by W. Stuart (£1, £2))

1901 (29 Jan)–**10.** *Previous issues with* "POSTAGE" *added and new designs* (£1, £2). *W* **85** (*sideways on ½d., 1½d.*, £1, £2).

(*a*) *P* 12×12½

384	**88**	½d. blue-green (I) (26.6.01)	2·50	40
		a. Wmk upright (1903)	2·75	40
		b. Die state II (6.04)	4·00	40
		ba. Wmk upright	4·00	6·00
385	**89**	1d. rose (I)	4·50	15
		a. Dull red (12.02)	4·00	15
		ab. Wmk sideways	†	—
		b. Die state II (4.01)	1·75	15
		ba. Dull red (12.02)	1·25	15
		c. Die state III. *Pale rose-red* (4.05)	3·00	70
		ca. Wmk sideways	50·00	50·00
386	**90**	1½d. maroon/*yellow* (9.7.01)	7·50	4·00
		a. Wmk upright. *Brn-red/yell* (9.01)	2·10	55
		b. Dull red-brown/yellow (1906) ..	2·10	55
		ba. On yellow-buff back (1908) ..	3·50	1·00
387	**91**	2d. lilac (I) (26.6.01)	8·00	30
		a. Die state II	24·00	1·50
		b. Reddish violet (1902)	8·00	30
		ba. Die state II	24·00	1·50
		c. Bright purple (II) (1905) ..	7·00	30
		d. Rosy mauve (II) (1905)		
388	**92**	2½d. dull blue	8·50	35
		a. Deep blue (1902)	8·50	35
389	**93**	3d. dull orange-brown (5.7.01) ..	7·50	1·00
		a. Chestnut (1901)	7·00	55
		b. Yellowish brown (1903)	7·00	55
		ba. Wmk sideways	11·00	15·00
390	**94**	4d. bistre-yellow (26.6.01)	5·50	65
		a. Brownish bistre (1905)	9·00	70
391	**95**	5d. reddish brown	8·00	40
		a. Purple-brown (1903)	7·50	40
392	**96**	6d. emerald (5.7.01)	12·00	80
		a. Dull green (1904)	14·00	1·00
393	**97**	9d. dull rose-red (5.7.01)	13·00	2·00
		a. Wmk sideways (1901)	22·00	4·50
		b. Pale red (1901)	13·00	1·25
		c. Dull brownish red (1905) ..	17·00	2·25
394	**98**	1s. yellow-orange (A) (5.7.01) ..	14·00	1·75
		a. Yellow (1902)	16·00	1·75
		b. Type B (4.03)	17·00	3·00
		ba. Orange (1904)	16·00	2·50
		bb. Wmk sideways (1905)	29·00	7·50
395	**99**	2s. blue/*rose* (5.7.01)	22·00	2·00

(*b*) *P* 12½

396	**88**	½d. blue-green (III) (6.05)	8·00	60
397	**92**	2½d. dull blue (1901)	£250	£250
398	**100**	5s. rose-red and pale blue (5.7.01) ..	60·00	13·00
		a. Scarlet and deep blue (12.01) ..	70·00	11·00
		b. Rosine and blue (12.04)	70·00	11·00
399	**101**	£1 carmine-rose (18.11.01)	£225	£100
400	**102**	£2 deep blue (2.6.02)	£500	£250

(*c*) *P* 11

401	**88**	½d. blue-green (I) (9.02)	6·00	2·75
		a. Wmk upright (1903)	3·25	1·00
		b. Die state II (6.04)	5·50	1·00
		c. Die state III (6.05)	6·50	1·25
402	**89**	1d. dull red (I) (12.02)	55·00	40·00
		a. Die state II	45·00	18·00
		ab. Pale red (*aniline*) (3.03)	6·50	2·00
		ac. Pale rose (*aniline*) (1904) ..	26·00	3·75
		b. Die state III. *Pale rose-red* (7.05)	45·00	25·00
403	**90**	1½d. dull red-brown/*yellow* (1910) ..	50·00	50·00
404	**91**	2d. bright purple (II) (1905) ..	£500	£180
		a. Rosy mauve (II) (1905)	†	—
405	**93**	3d. yellowish brown (1903)	5·50	4·75
		a. Wmk sideways	15·00	21·00
406	**96**	6d. emerald (2.03)	12·00	16·00
		a. Dull green (1905)	£325	£160
407	**101**	£1 rose (5.05)	£275	£130
408	**102**	£2 deep blue (1905)	£850	£750

(*d*) *Compound or mixed perf* 12½ *and* 11

409	**88**	½d. blue-green (I) (1901)	26·00	9·50
		a. Wmk upright (1903)	—	9·50
		b. Die state II (1904)	23·00	20·00
		ba. Wmk upright	35·00	
410	**89**	1d. dull red (I) (1902)	—	£180
		a. Die state II	£350	£140
411	**90**	1½d. maroon/*yellow* (1903)	£500	£200
412	**91**	2d. reddish violet (I) (1903)	†	£300
413	**93**	3d. dull orange-brown (1902) ..	—	£475
414	**96**	6d. emerald (1903)	†	£425
415	**100**	5s. rosine and blue (12.04)	£850	

Examples of the 1d. Die state II perforated 12½ exist with two black lines printed across the face of the stamp. These were prepared in connection with stamp-vending machine trials.

1905–13. *Wmk Crown over A, W* w **11** (*sideways on ½d.*, £1, £2).

(*a*) *P* 12×12½

416	**88**	½d. blue-green (*shades*) (III) (21.10.05)	2·25	20
		a. Wmk upright. Thin, ready gummed paper (6.12)	3·75	4·75
417	**89**	1d. rose-red (III) (16.7.05)	1·50	
		a. Pale rose (1907)	1·25	
		b. Rose-carmine (1911)	3·50	
		ba. Wmk sideways	13·00	
		c. Thin, ready gummed paper (10.12)	4·50	
418	**91**	2d. dull mauve (II) (13.9.05) ..	6·00	
		a. Lilac (1906)	6·00	
		b. Reddish violet (1907)	6·00	
		c. Bright mauve (1910)	4·75	
		ca. Thin, ready gummed paper (8.12)	27·00	
419	**92**	2½d. blue (10.08)	3·00	
		a. Indigo (1909)	5·50	
420	**93**	3d. orange-brown (11.11.05) ..	8·00	
		a. Yellow-orange (1908)	8·00	
		b. Dull orange-buff (1909)	8·00	
		c. Ochre (1912)	8·00	
421	**94**	4d. yellow-bistre (15.1.06)	7·00	
		a. Olive-bistre (1908)	7·00	
		b. Yellow-olive (1912)	7·00	
422	**95**	5d. chocolate (14.8.06)	7·00	
		a. Dull reddish brown (1908) ..	7·00	
		ab. Thin, ready gummed paper (19.10.12)	13·00	1
423	**96**	6d. dull green (25.10.05)	12·00	
		a. Dull yellow-green (1907) ..	12·00	
		b. Emerald (1909)	12·00	1
		c. Yellowish green (1911)	12·00	2
		d. Emerald. Thin, ready gummed paper (11.12)	19·00	16
424	**97**	9d. brown-red (11.12.05)	13·00	2
		a. Orange-brown (1906)	13·00	1
		b. Red-brown (1908)	14·00	1
		c. Pale dull rose (1909)	14·00	3
		d. Rose-carmine (1910)	9·50	1
425	**98**	1s. orange (B) (13.2.06)	8·00	2
		a. Yellow-orange (1906)	11·00	2
		b. Yellow (1908)	13·00	2
		ba. Thin, ready gummed paper (11.12)	28·00	19
		c. Pale orange. Thin, ready gummed paper (1913)	28·00	20

(*b*) *P* 12½

426	**88**	½d. blue-green (*shades*) (III) (1905) ..	2·25	
		a. Wmk upright (1909)	15·00	3
		b. Thin, ready gummed paper (1912)	5·00	
		ba. Wmk upright	3·50	4
427	**89**	1d. rose-red (III) (1905)	3·50	
		a. Rose-carmine (1911)	6·00	2
428	**92**	2½d. indigo (1909)	12·00	2
429	**96**	6d. yellowish green (1911)	18·00	8
430	**100**	5s. rose-red and ultramarine (12.07)	70·00	13·
		a. Rose-red and blue (1911) ..	80·00	15·
		ab. Wmk sideways	85·00	18·
431	**101**	£1 salmon (12.2.07)	£225	£1
		a. Dull rose (1910)	£225	£1
		ab. Wmk upright (1911)	£275	£1
432	**102**	£2 dull blue (18.7.06)	£500	£3

(*c*) *P* 11

433	**88**	½d. blue-green (*shades*) (III) (1905) ..	1·60	
		a. Wmk upright. Thin, ready gummed paper (1912)	15·00	18·
434	**89**	1d. rose-red (III) (1905)	3·75	1·
		a. Pale rose (1907)	3·75	1·
		b. Rose-carmine (1911)	7·00	3·
		ba. Wmk sideways	11·00	6·
		c. Thin, ready gummed paper (10.12)	7·50	4·
435	**91**	2d. lilac (II) (1906)	†	£1
		a. Reddish violet (1907)	65·00	16·
		b. Bright mauve (1910)	25·00	9·
436	**92**	2½d. blue (1908)	60·00	10·
		a. Indigo (1909)	11·00	7·
437	**93**	3d. orange-brown (1905)	10·00	8·
		a. Yellow-orange (1908)	†	£1
		b. Dull orange-buff (1909)	15·00	17·
		c. Ochre (1912)	8·00	5·
438	**94**	4d. yellow-bistre (1906)	9·00	15·
		a. Olive-bistre (1909)		
		b. Yellow-olive (1912)	8·50	15·
439	**95**	5d. chocolate (1906)	†	£5
		a. Dull reddish brown (1908) ..	†	£5
440	**96**	6d. emerald (1909)	10·00	15·
		a. Yellowish green (1911)	15·00	20·
441	**97**	9d. rose-carmine (1910)	†	£40
442	**98**	1s. yellow-orange (B) (1906)	†	£18
		a. Orange (1910)	£400	
443	**100**	5s. rose-red and ultramarine (12.07)	70·00	9·5
444	**101**	£1 salmon (12.2.07)	£275	£11
445	**102**	£2 dull blue (1.07)	£700	£35

(*d*) *Compound or mixed perfs* 12½ *and* 11

446	**88**	½d. blue-green (*shades*) (III) (1905) ..	18·00	16·0
		a. Wmk upright. Thin, ready gummed paper (1912)	£110	80·0
447	**89**	1d. rose-red (III) (1905)	40·00	40·0
		a. Pale rose (1907)	—	45·0
		b. Rose-carmine (1911)	—	45·0
448	**91**	2d. reddish violet (II) (1907) ..	£350	£20
449	**93**	3d. orange-brown (1905)	†	£27
		a. Ochre (1912)	£250	
450	**94**	4d. bistre (1908)	†	£30
451	**96**	6d. emerald (1909)	—	£40
		a. Yellowish green (1911)	†	£27
452	**97**	9d. orange-brown (1906)	†	£47
		a. Red-brown (1908)	†	£47
453	**98**	1s. yellow-orange (1906)	£650	

(*e*) *Rotary comb perf* 11½×12¼

454	**89**	1d. pale rose (III) (2.10)	6·50	1·75
		a. Rose-carmine (1911)		
		ab. Thin, ready gummed paper (7.12)	3·25	3·50
		b. Rose-red. Thin, ready gummed paper (10.12)	3·25	3·50
455	**91**	2d. lilac (II) (1910)	10·00	1·50

The original Crown over A watermark paper used by Victoria was of medium thickness and had toned gum applied after printing. Stocks of this paper lasted until 1912 when further supplies were ordered from a new papermakers, Cowan and Sons. This paper was much thinner and was supplied with white gum already applied. The first delivery arrived in June 1912 and a second in September of the same year.

The rotary comb perforating gauging 11½×12¼ was transferred from South Australia in 1909 when J. B. Cooke moved to Melbourne.

mples of the 1d. perforated 12½ or 11 exist with two black across the face of the stamp. These were prepared in ction with stamp-vending machine trials.

(103) 104

(29 June). *No.* 455 *surch with T* **103** *in red.*

91 1d. on 2d. lilac (II) 70 45

(Aug–Sept). *W* **104**. *(a) P* 12×12½

89 1d. rose-carmine (III) .. .. 2·75 3·00

a. Wmk sideways .. .. .. 50·00

91 2d. reddish violet (II) (Sept) .. .. 3·00 3·50

a. Lilac .. .. 5·50 6·00

97 9d. rose-carmine .. .. 15·00 15·00

(b) P 12½

88 ½d. bluish green (III) .. .. 3·00 4·00

(c) P 11

88 ½d. bluish green (III) .. .. .. 20·00 20·00

89 1d. rose-carmine (III) .. .. .. 28·00 14·00

97 9d. rose-carmine .. .. 20·00 22·00

(d) Compound or mixed perfs 12½ *and* 11

97 9d. rose-carmine .. .. † £450

os. 457/64 were emergency printings caused by the non-val of stocks of the Cowan thin, ready gummed Crown over atermarked paper. Paper watermarked W **104** had been oduced in 1911 and was normally used for Victoria fiscal nps. This watermark can be easily distinguished from the ious W **85** by its narrow crown.

STAMP BOOKLETS

here are very few surviving examples of Nos. SB1/4. Listings provided for those believed to have been issued with prices ted for those known to still exist.

4 (Mar)–**09**. *Black on red cover as No.* SB1 *of New South Vales. Stapled.*

£1 booklet containing two hundred and forty 1d. in four blocks of 30 and two blocks of 60 ..

a. Red on pink cover (1909) £6000

b. Blue on pink cover £5000

4 (Mar). *Black on grey cover as No.* SB1. *Stapled.*

2 £1 booklet containing one hundred and twenty 2d. in four blocks of 30 .. ..

0 (May). *Black on white cover as No.* SB3 *of New South Vales. Stapled.*

3 2s. booklet containing eleven ½d. (No. 426), either in block of 6 plus block of 5 or block of 11, and eighteen 1d. (No. 427), either in three blocks of 6 or block of 6 plus block of 12 .. .. £2000

a. Black on pale green cover £2000

Jnsold stock of No. SB3 was uprated with one additional ½d. May 1911.

11 (Aug). *Red on pink cover as No.* SB3. *Stapled.*

4 2s. booklet containing twelve ½d. (No. 426), either in two blocks of 6 or block of 12, and eighteen 1d. (No. 427), either in three blocks of 6 or block of 6 plus block of 12 .. .. .. £1500

POSTAGE DUE STAMPS

D 1

ies eng A. Williams (values) and J. McWilliams (frame). Typo)

890 (12 Oct)–**94**. *Wmk V over Crown, W* **33**. *P* 12×12½.

1 D 1 ½d. dull blue and brown-lake (24.12.90) 3·75 2·75

a. Dull blue and deep claret .. 2·75 3·50

2 1d. dull blue and brown-lake .. 5·00 1·40

a. Dull blue and brownish red (1.93) 7·00 1·25

3 2d. dull blue and brown-lake .. 9·00 1·50

a. Dull blue and brownish red (3.93) 10·00 1·00

4 4d. dull blue and brown-lake .. 11·00 2·00

a. Dull blue and pale claret (5.94) .. 13·00 6·00

5 5d. dull blue and brown-lake .. 10·00 2·00

6 6d. dull blue and brown-lake .. 12·00 2·50

7 10d. dull blue and brown-lake .. 75·00 40·00

8 1s. dull blue and brown-lake .. 48·00 6·50

9 2s. dull blue and brown-lake .. £110 48·00

10 5s. dull blue and brown-lake .. £160 90·00

1/10 .. .. *Set of* 10 £400 £170

1as/10s Optd "Specimen" .. *Set of* 10 £300

A used example of the 6d. showing compound perforation of 2×12½ and 11 exists in the Royal Collection.

895 (17 Jan)–**96**. *Colours changed. Wmk V over Crown, W* **33**. *P* 12×12½.

11 D 1 ½d. rosine and bluish green .. .. 4·00 1·60

a. Pale scarlet and yellow-green (3.96) 3·50 1·50

12 1d. rosine and bluish green .. .. 3·50 80

a. Pale scarlet and yellow-green (3.96) 4·00 90

D13 D 1 2d. rosine and bluish green .. .. 6·00 1·00

a. Pale scarlet and yellow-green (3.96) 6·50 90

D14 4d. rosine and bluish green .. .. 9·00 1·50

a. Pale scarlet and yellow-green (3.96) 9·50 1·50

D15 5d. rosine and bluish green .. .. 9·00 8·50

a. Pale scarlet and yellow-green (3.96) 9·00 5·50

D16 6d. rosine and bluish green .. .. 8·50 4·00

D17 10d. rosine and bluish green .. .. 17·00 10·00

D18 1s. rosine and bluish green .. .. 13·00 3·25

D19 2s. pale red & yellowish green (28.3.95) 60·00 20·00

D20 5s. pale red & yellowish green (28.3.95) £100 40·00

D11/20 .. .. *Set of* 10 £200 75·00

1897 (July)–**99**. *Wmk V over Crown. W* **82**. *P* 12×12½.

D21 D 1 1d. pale scarlet and yellow-green .. 5·50 1·25

a. Dull red and bluish green (8.99) 7·50 1·25

D22 2d. pale scarlet and yellow-green .. 7·50 1·25

a. Dull red and bluish green (6.99) 8·50 1·00

D23 4d. pale scarlet and yellow-green .. 13·00 2·25

a. Dull red and bluish green (8.99) 16·00 1·75

D24 5d. pale scarlet and yellow-green .. 13·00 3·25

D25 6d. pale scarlet and yellow-green .. 8·00 3·50

D21/5 .. .. *Set of* 5 42·00 9·50

1900 (June)–**04**. *Wmk V over Crown, W* **85**. *P* 12×12½.

D26 D 1 ½d. rose-red and pale green .. .. 6·00 4·50

a. Pale red and deep green (8.01) .. 4·00 4·00

b. Scarlet and deep green (1.03) .. — 23·00

c. Aniline rosine and green (6.04) .. 6·50 7·00

D27 1d. rose-red and pale green .. .. 7·00 80

a. Pale red and deep green (9.01) .. 6·50 35

b. Scarlet and deep green (2.02) .. 7·50 60

c. Aniline rosine and green (9.03) .. 7·00 1·25

D28 2d. rose-red and pale green (7.00) .. 8·50 1·25

a. Pale red and deep green (9.01) .. 8·50 1·25

b. Scarlet and deep green (2.02) .. 8·50 75

c. Aniline rosine and green (9.03) .. 8·50 1·25

D29 4d. rose-red and pale green (5.01) .. 18·00 4·50

a. Pale red and deep green (9.01) .. 17·00 2·25

b. Scarlet and deep green (6.03) .. 17·00 3·00

c. Aniline rosine and green (6.04) .. 18·00 3·50

D30 5d. scarlet and deep green (1.03) .. 14·00 6·00

D31 1s. scarlet and deep green (3.02) .. 18·00 5·50

D32 2s. scarlet and deep green (1.03) .. £110 65·00

D33 5s. scarlet and deep green (1.03) .. £130 65·00

D26/33 .. .. *Set of* 8 £275 £130

1905 (Dec)–**09**. *Wmk Crown over A, W w* **11**. *P* 12×12½.

D34 D 1 ½d. aniline rosine and pale green (1.06) 9·00 9·00

a. Scarlet & pale yellow-green (7.07) 4·25 4·50

b. Dull scarlet and pea-green (3.09) 6·50 5·50

ba. Compound perf 12×12½ and 11 £180 £120

D35 1d. aniline rosine and pale green .. 38·00 5·00

a. Scarlet & pale yellow-green (5.06) 6·50 2·00

b. Dull scarlet and pea-green (1.07) 9·50 2·00

D36 2d. aniline scarlet & dp yell-grn (5.06) 10·00 2·25

a. Dull scarlet and pea-green (11.07) 10·00 2·00

D37 4d. dull scarlet and pea-green (1908) 18·00 8·50

D34/7 .. .. *Set of* 4 35·00 15·00

A printing of the 5d. in dull scarlet and pea-green on this paper was prepared in 1907–08, but not put into use. A few examples have survived, either mint or cancelled-to-order from presentation sets (*Price* £1000 *mint,* £750 *cancelled-to-order*).

WESTERN AUSTRALIA

PRICES FOR STAMPS ON COVER

Nos. 1/6	*from* × 6
Nos. 15/32	*from* × 4
Nos. 33/46	*from* × 5
Nos. 49/51	*from* × 6
Nos. 52/62	*from* × 10
Nos. 63/*a*	*from* × 8
No. 67	*from* × 6
Nos. 68/92*a*	*from* × 10
Nos. 94/102	*from* × 40
Nos. 103/5	*from* × 8
Nos. 107/10*a*	*from* × 12
Nos. 111*a*/*b*	—
Nos. 112/16	*from* × 25
Nos. 117/25	*from* × 10
Nos. 126/8	—
Nos. 129/34	*from* × 8
Nos. 135/6	—
Nos. 138/48	*from* × 12
Nos. 151/63	*from* × 5
Nos. 168/9	*from* × 20
Nos. 170/1	*from* × 4
Nos. 172/3	*from* × 40
Nos. F11/22	*from* × 10
Nos. T1/2	—

SPECIMEN OVERPRINTS. Those listed are from U.P.U. distributions between 1889 and 1892. Further "Specimen" overprints exist, but those were used for other purposes.

1

2

3

4

GUM. The 1854 issues are hardly ever seen with gum and so the unused prices quoted are for examples without gum.

(Eng W. Humphrys. Recess P.B.)

1854 (1 Aug). *W* **4** *(sideways). (a) Imperf.*

1 **1** 1d. black £800 £180

(b) Rouletted 7½ *to* 14 *and compound*

2 **1** 1d. black £1400 £400

In addition to the supplies received from London a further printing, using the original plate and watermarked paper from Perkins, Bacon, was made in the colony before the date of issue.

The 1d. is also known pin-perforated.

(Litho H. Samson (later A. Hillman), Government Lithographer)

1854 (1 Aug)–**55**. *W* **4** *(sideways). (a) Imperf.*

3 **2** 4d. pale blue £250 £160

a. Blue £250 £160

b. Deep dull blue £1200 £600

c. Slate-blue (1855) £1600 £750

d. "T" of "POSTAGE" shaved off to a point at foot (R. 7/5, 7/10, 7/15, 7/20) £800 £600

e. Top of letters of "AUSTRALIA" cut off so that they are barely 1 mm high .. † £7000

f. "PEICE" instead of "PENCE" .. † £7000

g. "CE" of "PENCE" close together .. † £9000

h. Frame inverted (R. 8/1, 8/6, 8/11, 8/16) † £60000

i. Tilted border (R. 7/4, 7/9, 7/14, 7/19) £950 £700

j. "WEST" in squeezed-down letters and "F" of "FOUR" with pointed foot (R. 2/17) £1000 £750

k. "ESTERN" in squeezed-down letters and "U" of "FOUR" squeezed-up (R. 3/17) £1700 £1300

l. Small "S" in "POSTAGE" (R. 4/17) .. £1000 £750

m. "EN" of "PENCE" shorter (R. 6/4) .. £900 £700

n. "N" of "PENCE" tilted to right with thin first downstroke (R. 6/16) .. £900 £700

o. Swan and water above "ENCE" damaged (R. 6/20) £900 £700

p. "F" of "FOUR" slanting to left (R. 7/17) £900 £700

q. "WESTERN" in squeezed-down letters only 1½ mm high (R. 8/17) £1100 £800

r. "P" of "PENCE" with small head (R. 9/15) £900 £700

s. "RALIA" in squeezed-down letters only 1½ mm high (R. 9/16) £1000 £750

t. "PE" of "PENCE" close together (R. 10/15) £900 £700

u. "N" of "PENCE" narrow (R. 10/16) .. £900 £700

v. Part of right cross-stroke and down-stroke of "T" of "POSTAGE" cut off (R. 11/15) £900 £700

w. "A" in "POSTAGE" with thin right limb (R. 11/16) £900 £700

x. Coloured line above "AGE" of "POSTAGE" (R. 8/6) £950 £750

y. No outer line above "GE" of "POSTAGE" and coloured line under "FOU" of "FOUR" (R. 8/11) £1000 £800

4 **3** 1s. salmon .. .. — £1800

a. Deep red-brown £1000 £450

b. Grey-brown (1.55) £475 £325

c. Pale brown (10.55) £350 £275

(b) Rouletted 7½ *to* 14 *and compound*

5 **2** 4d. pale blue £1200 £425

a. Blue .. .. — £425

b. Slate-blue (1855) .. .. — £1200

6 **3** 1s. grey-brown (1.55) £1800 £800

a. Pale brown (10.55) £1700 £750

The 1s. is also known pin-perforated.

The 4d. value was prepared from the Perkins, Bacon 1d. plate. A block of 60 (5 × 12) was taken as a transfer from this plate, the frames painted out and then individually replaced by transfers taken from a single impression master plate of the frame. Four transfers were then taken from this completed intermediate stone to construct the printing stone of 240 impressions. This first printing stone was used by H. Samson to print the initial supplies in July 1854.

The intermediate stone had carried several transfer errors, the most prominent of which was the "T" of "POSTAGE" sliced at foot, which appeared on four positions of the printing stone (No. 3d.)

The original printing stone also contained three scarce creased transfers, whose exact positions in the sheet have yet to be established (Nos. 3e/g.) These were corrected during the first printing.

Further supplies were required in January 1855 and A. Hillman, Samson's successor, found, after printing three further sheets from the first printing stone, that two of the impressions on the intermediate stone were defective giving one inverted and one tilted frame (Nos. 3h/i). A second printing stone was then prepared on which the four positions of the inverted frame were individually corrected.

None of the creased transfers from the first printing stone appear on the second, which exhibits its own range of similar varieties (Nos. 3j/w).

For the third printing in October 1855 the impressions showing the inverted frame were replaced on the printing stone with fresh individual transfers of the frame. On two of the positions traces of the original frame transfer remained visible (Nos. 3x/y).

The same stone was used for a further printing in December 1855 and it is believed that the slate-blue shade occurred from one of the 1855 printings.

The above varieties, with the exception of Nos. 3e/g, also occur on the rouletted stamps.

The 1s. value was produced in much the same way, based on a transfer from the Perkins, Bacon 1d. plate.

5

(Litho A. Hillman, Government Lithographer)

1857 (7 Aug)–**59.** W **4** (*sideways*). (*a*) *Imperf.*
15 **5** 2d. brown-black/*red* (26.2.58) .. £1900 £500
a. Printed both sides.. .. .. .. £2250 £800
16 2d. brown-black/*Indian red* (26.2.58) £2000 £800
a. Printed both sides.. .. .. .. £2250 £850
17 6d. golden bronze £6000 £1500
18 6d. black-bronze £3000 £600
19 6d. grey-black (1859) £3000 £500

(*b*) *Rouletted* 7½ *to* 14 *and compound*
20 **5** 2d. brown-black/*red* £4500 £1300
a. Printed both sides .. .. .. — £1500
21 2d. brown-black/*Indian red* .. .. .. — £1400
22 6d. black-bronze £4000 £850
23 6d. grey-black .. .. — £900

The 2d. and 6d. are known pin-perforated.

Prices quoted for Nos. 15/23 are for "cut-square" examples. Collectors are warned against "cut-round" copies with corners added.

(Recess in the colony from P.B. plates)

1860 (11 Aug)–**64.** W **4** (*sideways*). (*a*) *Imperf.*
24 **1** 2d. pale orange .. .. .. 70·00 65·00
25 2d. orange-vermilion .. .. .. 70·00 65·00
a. Wmk upright .. .. ..
25*b* 2d. deep vermilion £600 £400
26 4d. blue (21.6.64) £225 £1600
a. Wmk upright £225
27 4d. deep blue £225 £1700
28 6d. sage-green (27.7.61) £1100 £400
28*a* 6d. deep sage-green .. .. .. — £550

(*b*) *Rouletted* 7½ *to* 14
29 **1** 2d. pale orange £400 £170
30 2d. orange-vermilion £450 £180
31 4d. deep blue £2500
32 6d. sage-green £1900 £450

PERKINS BACON "CANCELLED". For notes on these handstamps, showing "CANCELLED" between horizontal bars forming an oval, see Catalogue Introduction.

(Recess P.B.)

1861. W **4** (*sideways*). (*a*) *Intermediate perf* 14–16.
33 **1** 1d. rose £350 £100
34 2d. blue .. .. £140 40·00
35 4d. vermilion £600 £1500
36 6d. purple-brown .. .. .. £375 70·00
37 1s. yellow-green £475 £130

(*b*) *P* 14 *at Somerset House*
38 **1** 1d. rose .. .. £180 48·00
39 2d. blue .. .. 80·00 29·00
40 4d. vermilion £180 £140

(*c*) *Perf clean-cut* 14–16
41 **1** 2d. blue .. .. 65·00 24·00
a. Imperf between (pair) .. ..
42 6d. purple-brown .. .. .. £200 42·00
43 1s. yellow-green .. .. .. £350 60·00
a. Wmk upright .. .. .. — 60·00

(*d*) *P* 14–16 *very rough* (*July*)
44 **1** 1d. rose-carmine (H/S "CANCELLED" in oval £5000) .. .. .. £200 38·00
45 6d. purple/*blued* (H/S "CANCELLED" in oval £4000) £1200 £275
46 1s. deep green (H/S "CANCELLED" in oval £4000) £1100 £250

Perkins, Bacon experienced considerable problems with their perforating machine during the production of these stamps.

The initial printing showed intermediate perforation 14–16. Further supplies were then sent, in late December 1860, to Somerset House to be perforated on their comb 14 machine. The Inland Revenue Board were only able to process the three lower values, although the 6d. purple-brown and 1s. yellow-green are known from this perforation overprinted "SPECIMEN".

The Perkins, Bacon machine was repaired the following month and the 6d., 1s. and a further supply of the 2d. were perforated on it to give a clean-cut 14–16 gauge.

A final printing was produced in July 1861, but by this time the machine had deteriorated so that it produced a very rough 14–16.

(Recess D.L.R. from P.B. plates)

1863 (16 Dec)–**64.** *No wmk. P* 13.
49 **1** 1d. carmine-rose .. .. .. 55·00 3·50
50 1d. lake .. .. 55·00 3·50
51 6d. deep lilac (15.4.64) .. .. £110 38·00
51*a* 6d. dull violet (15.4.64) .. .. £170 45·00

Both values exist on thin and on thick papers, the former being the scarcer.

Both grades of paper show a marginal sheet watermark, "T H SAUNDERS 1860" in double-lined large and small capitals, but parts of this watermark rarely occur on the stamps.

(Recess D.L.R. from P.B. plates)

1864 (27 Dec)–**79.** *Wmk Crown CC* (*sideways* on* 1d.). *P* 12½.
52 **1** 1d. bistre .. .. 55·00 4·00
w. Wmk Crown to right of CC .. .. 55·00 4·00
53 1d. yellow-ochre (16.10.74) .. .. 70·00 7·00
w. Wmk Crown to right of CC .. .. 70·00 7·00
54 2d. chrome-yellow (18.1.65) .. .. 55·00 1·75
55 2d. yellow .. .. 55·00 1·75
a. Wmk sideways (5.79) .. .. — 16·00
aw. Wmk Crown to right of CC .. .. — 16·00
b. Error. Mauve (1879) £5500 £4000
x. Wmk reversed .. .. .. 55·00 1·75
56 4d. carmine (18.1.65) .. .. .. 65·00 4·00
a. Doubly printed £5000
w. Wmk inverted .. .. .. — 20·00
57 **1** 6d. violet (18.1.65) .. .. .. 75·00 6·00
a. Doubly printed .. .. .. † £7000
b. Wmk sideways .. .. .. — £180
x. Wmk reversed .. .. .. — 6·00
58 6d. indigo-violet .. .. £300 30·00
x. Wmk reversed .. .. .. — 30·00
59 6d. lilac (1872) .. .. £150 6·00
60 6d. mauve (12.5.75) .. .. .. £140 6·00
x. Wmk reversed .. .. .. — 6·00
61 1s. bright green (18.1.65) .. .. £100 12·00
s. Handstamped "Specimen" .. .. 85·00
62 1s. sage-green (10.68) .. .. .. £275 24·00

*The normal sideways watermark shows Crown to left of CC, *as seen from the back of the stamp.*

Beware of fakes of No. 55b made by altering the value tablet of No. 60.

7

ONE PENNY

(8)

(Typo D.L.R.)

1871 (29 Oct)–**73.** *Wmk Crown CC* (*sideways*). *P* 14.
63 **7** 3d. pale brown .. .. 35·00 4·25
a. Cinnamon (1873) .. .. .. 35·00 3·75
s. Handstamped "Specimen" .. .. 75·00

1874 (10 Dec). *No.* 55 *surch with T* **8** *by Govt Printer.*
67 **1** 1d. on 2d. yellow (G.) .. .. .. £250 50·00
a. Pair, one without surch .. ..
b. Surch triple .. .. .. † £2250
c. "O" of "ONE" omitted .. ..

Forged surcharges of T **8** are known on stamps wmk Crown CC perf 14, and on Crown CA, perf 12 and 14.

(Recess D.L.R. from P.B. plates)

1876–81. *Wmk Crown CC* (*sideways**). *P* 14.
68 **1** 1d. ochre .. .. 50·00 2·25
w. Wmk Crown to right of CC .. .. 50·00 2·25
69 1d. bistre (1878) .. .. .. 80·00 3·25
70 1d. yellow-ochre (1879) .. .. .. 55·00 1·25
71 2d. chrome-yellow .. .. .. 50·00 80
a. Wmk upright (1877) .. .. .. 75·00 1·75
74 4d. carmine (1881) .. .. .. £350 80·00
75 6d. lilac (1877) .. .. £100 3·25
a. Wmk upright (1879) .. .. £475 15·00
bw. Wmk Crown to right of CC .. .. — 3·25
75*c* 6d. reddish lilac (1879) .. .. .. £100 5·50

*The normal sideways watermark shows Crown to left of CC, *as seen from the back of the stamp.*

(Recess D.L.R. from P.B. plates)

1882 (Mar)–**85.** *Wmk Crown CA* (*sideways**). (*a*) *P* 14.
76 **1** 1d. yellow-ochre .. .. .. 18·00 1·00
w. Wmk Crown to right of CA .. .. 18·00 1·00
x. Wmk sideways reversed .. ..
77 2d. chrome-yellow .. .. .. 23·00 90
a. Wmk upright .. .. .. †
78 4d. carmine (8.82) .. .. .. 90·00 6·50
a. Wmk upright (1885) .. .. — 27·00
w. Wmk Crown to right of CA .. .. — 6·50
79 6d. reddish lilac (1882) .. .. .. 75·00 3·00
80 6d. lilac (1884) .. .. 75·00 4·00
s. Handstamped "Specimen" .. .. 75·00
w. Wmk Crown to right of CA .. .. — 5·00
y. Wmk sideways inverted and reversed — 20·00

(*b*) *P* 12×14
81 **1** 1d. yellow-ochre (2.83) £1300 £150

(*c*) *P* 12
82 **1** 1d. yellow-ochre (2.83) .. .. .. 60·00 3·00
83 2d. chrome-yellow (6.83) .. .. .. 85·00 3·00
a. Imperf between (pair) .. ..
84 4d. carmine (5.83) .. .. .. £140 26·00
w. Wmk Crown to right of CA .. .. — 26·00
85 6d. lilac (6.83) .. .. £250 26·00
w. Wmk Crown to right of CA .. .. — 26·00

*The normal sideways watermark shows Crown to left of CA, *as seen from the back of the stamp.*

(Typo D.L.R.)

1882 (July)–**95.** *Wmk Crown CA* (*sideways*). *P* 14.
86 **7** 3d. pale brown .. .. 14·00 1·50
87 3d. red-brown (12.95) .. .. .. 8·50 1·50

The 3d. stamps in other colours, watermark Crown CA and perforated 12, are colour trials dating from 1883.

½ (9) 1d. (10) 1d. (11)

1884 (19 Feb). *Surch with T* **9**, *in red, by Govt Printer.*
89 **1** ½ on 1d. yellow-ochre (No. 76) .. .. 14·00 19·00
a. Thin bar .. .. 75·00 90·00
90 ½ on 1d. yellow-ochre (No. 82) .. .. 9·00 15·00

Inverted or double surcharges are forgeries made in London about 1886.

The "Thin bar" varieties occur on R12/3, R12/8, R12/13 and R12/18, and show the bar only 0.2 mm thick.

1885 (May). *Nos.* 63/*a surch, in green, by Govt Printer.*

(*a*) *Thick* "1" *with slanting top, T* **10** (*Horizontal Rows* 1/5)
91 1d. on 3d. pale brown .. .. .. 50·00 11·00
a. Cinnamon .. .. 42·00 10·00
b. Vert pair. Nos. 91/2 .. .. £180

(*b*) *Thin* "1" *with straight top, T* **11** (*Horizontal Row* 6)
92 1d. on 3d. pale brown .. .. .. £130 27·00
a. Cinnamon .. .. £100 28·00

12

13

14

15

(Typo D.L.R.)

1885 (May)–**93.** *Wmk Crown CA* (*sideways*). *P* 14.
94 **12** ½d. yellow-green .. .. .. 3·25
94*a* ½d. green .. .. 3·25
95 **13** 1d. carmine (2.90) .. .. .. 16·00
96 **14** 2d. bluish grey (6.90) .. .. .. 23·00
96*a* 2d. grey .. .. 22·00
97 **15** 2½d. deep blue (1.5.92) .. .. .. 9·50
97*a* 2½d. blue .. .. 8·50
98 4d. chestnut (7.90) .. .. .. 9·00
99 5d. bistre (1.5.92) .. .. .. 8·50
100 6d. bright violet (1.93) .. .. .. 15·00
101 1s. pale olive-green (4.90) .. .. 25·00
102 1s. olive-green .. .. 17·00
94s/101s (*ex* 1d., 6d.) Handstamped (Nos. 96, 98, 101) or Optd "Specimen" .. *Set of* 6 £225

(Recess D.L.R. from P.B. plates)

1888 (Mar–Apr). *Wmk Crown CA* (*sideways*). *P* 14.
103 **1** 1d. carmine-pink .. .. .. 15·00
104 2d. grey .. .. 42·00
105 4d. red-brown (April) .. .. .. 70·00 1
103s/5s H/S "Specimen" .. .. *Set of* 3 £150

ONE PENNY (16) Half-penny (17)

1893 (Feb). *Surch with T* **16**, *in green, by Govt Printer.*
107 **7** 1d. on 3d. pale brown (No. 63) .. .. 11·00
108 1d. on 3d. cinnamon (No. 63*a*) .. .. 11·00
a. Double surcharge £650
109 1d. on 3d. pale brown (No. 86) .. .. 38·00

1895 (21 Nov). *Surch with T* **17** *by Govt Printer.* (*a*) *In green.*
110 **7** ½d. on 3d. pale brown (No. 63) .. .. 7·50 2
110*a* ½d. on 3d. cinnamon (No. 63*a*) .. .. 5·50 2
b. Surcharge double £450

(*b*) *In red and in green*
111*a* **7** ½d. on 3d. cinnamon (No. 63*a*) .. .. 75·00 £
111*b* ½d. on 3d. red-brown (No. 87) .. .. 55·00 £

Green was the adopted surcharge colour but a trial had ear been made in red on stamps watermarked Crown CC. As t proved unsatisfactory they were given another surcharge in gre The trial stamps were inadvertently issued and, to prevent spe lation, a further printing of the duplicated surcharge was made, on both papers, Crown CC (No. 111*a*) and Crown CA (No. 111*b*).

18

19

20

21

(Typo D.L.R.)

1898 (Dec)–**1907.** *Wmk W Crown A*, W **18**. *P* 14.
112 **13** 1d. carmine .. .. 4·75
113 **14** 2d. bright yellow (1.99) .. .. 13·00 1
114 **19** 2½d. blue (1.01) .. .. .. 8·00
115 **20** 6d. bright violet (10.06) .. .. 22·00 1
116 **21** 1s. olive-green (4.07) .. .. .. 25·00 3

22

23

24

POSTAGE EIGHT PENCE

25

26

27

28 29 30

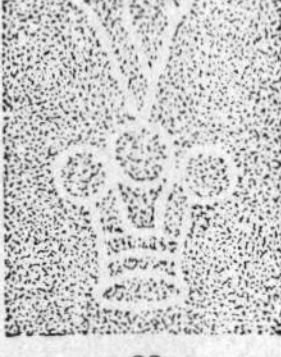

31 32 33

o Victoria Govt Printer, Melbourne, Commonwealth Stamp Ptg Branch from March, 1909)

2 (Oct)–**12.** *Wmk V and Crown, W* **33** (*sideways on horiz* *esigns*).

(*a*) *P* 12½ *or* 12½ × 12 (*horiz*), 12 × 12½ (*vert*)

Type	Description	Unused	Used
22	1d. carmine-rose (1.03)	10·00	30
	a. Wmk upright (10.02)	14·00	40
23	2d. yellow (4.1.03)	9·50	1·75
	a. Wmk upright (1903)	20·00	2·25
24	4d. chestnut (4.03)	11·00	1·50
	a. Wmk upright	£200	
15	5d. bistre (4.9.05)	70·00	48·00
25	8d. apple-green (3.03)	18·00	2·50
26	9d. yellow-orange (5.03)	27·00	6·00
	a. Wmk upright (11.03)	50·00	22·00
27	10d. red (3.03)	30·00	4·75
28	2s. bright red/*yellow*	80·00	18·00
	a. Wmk sideways	£170	16·00
	b. Orange/yellow (7.06)	40·00	8·50
	c. Brown-red/yellow (5.11)	40·00	8·50
29	2s. 6d. deep blue/*rose*	40·00	8·00
30	5s. emerald-green	60·00	20·00
31	10s. deep mauve	£140	65·00
	a. Bright purple (1910)	£325	£160
32	£1 orange-brown (1.11.02)	£275	£150
	a. Orange (10.7.09)	£550	£250

(*b*) *P* 11

Type	Description	Unused	Used
22	1d. carmine-rose	£120	14·00
	a. Wmk upright		
23	2d. yellow	£160	16·00
	a. Wmk upright	†	£250
24	4d. chestnut	£550	£180
15	5d. bistre	45·00	35·00
26	9d. yellow-orange	75·00	60·00
28	2s. bright red/*yellow*	£140	85·00
	a. Orange/yellow	£250	£120

(*c*) *Perf compound of* 12½ *or* 12 *and* 11

No.	Type	Description	Unused	Used
5	**22**	1d. carmine-rose	£500	£250
6	**23**	2d. yellow	£600	£300
7	**24**	4d. chestnut		

Type **22** is similar to Type **13** but larger.

34 35

05–12. *Wmk Crown and A, W* **34** (*sideways*).

(*a*) *P* 12½ *or* 12½ × 12 (*horiz*), 12 × 12½ (*vert*)

No.	Type	Description	Unused	Used
38	**12**	½d. green (6.10)	4·00	3·75
39	**22**	1d. rose-pink (10.05)	7·50	50
		a. Wmk upright (1.06)	7·50	50
		b. Carmine (1909)	9·50	50
		c. Carmine-red (1912)	11·00	6·00
40	**23**	2d. yellow (15.11.05)	6·50	1·75
		a. Wmk upright (4.10)		
41	**7**	3d. brown (2.06)	14·00	1·00
42	**24**	4d. bistre-brown (12.06)	15·00	4·25
		a. Pale chestnut (1908)	15·00	4·00
		b. Bright brown-red (14.10.10)	10·00	1·50
43	**15**	5d. pale olive-bistre (8.05)	14·00	5·00
		a. Olive-green (1.09)	14·00	5·00
		b. Pale greenish yellow (5.12)	55·00	65·00
44	**25**	8d. apple-green (22.4.12)	18·00	35·00
45	**26**	9d. orange (11.5.06)	24·00	3·75
		a. Red-orange (6.10)	35·00	3·75
		b. Wmk upright (7.12)	38·00	24·00
46	**27**	10d. rose-orange (16.2.10)	22·00	14·00
48	**30**	5s. emerald-grn (*wmk upright*) (9.07)	90·00	65·00

(*b*) *P* 11

No.	Type	Description	Unused	Used
50	**12**	½d. green		
51	**22**	1d. rose-pink	24·00	7·50
		a. Carmine-red	29·00	6·50
		b. Wmk upright	38·00	11·00
52	**23**	2d. yellow	26·00	11·00
53	**7**	3d. brown	14·00	2·75
54	**24**	4d. yellow-brown	£500	£160
		a. Pale chestnut	—	£225
55	**15**	5d. pale olive-bistre	28·00	10·00
		a. Olive-green	16·00	10·00
57	**26**	9d. orange	85·00	90·00
		a. Red-orange	—	70·00
		b. Wmk upright (1912)	†	£450

(*c*) *Perf compound of* 12½ *or* 12 *and* 11

No.	Type	Description	Unused	Used
161	**22**	1d. rose-pink (*wmk upright*)	£325	£150
162	**23**	2d. yellow	£275	£130
163	**7**	3d. brown	£425	£225
164	**26**	9d. red-orange		

1912 (Mar). *Wmk Crown and A* (*sideways*). *W* **35**. *P* 11½ × 12.

No.	Type	Description	Unused	Used
168	**20**	6d. bright violet	11·00	5·50
169	**21**	1s. sage-green	26·00	8·00
		a. Perf 12½ (single line)	—	£450

1912 (7 Aug). *W* **34** (*sideways*). *Thin paper and white gum* (*as Victoria*).

No.	Type	Description	Unused	Used
170	**7**	3d. brown (*p* 12½)	48·00	48·00
		a. Wmk upright	48·00	48·00
171		3d. brown (*p* 11)		
		a. Wmk upright		

ONE PENNY

(**36**)

1912 (6 Nov). *Nos.* 140 *and* 162 *surch with T* **36** *in Melbourne.*

(*a*) *P* 12½ *or* 12 × 12½

No.	Type	Description	Unused	Used
172	**23**	1d. on 2d. yellow	80	70
		a. Wmk upright	3·50	5·00

(*b*) *Perf compound of* 12½ *and* 11

No.	Type	Description	Unused	Used
173	**23**	1d. on 2d. yellow	£350	

STAMP BOOKLETS

There are very few surviving examples of Nos. SB1/4. Listings are provided for those believed to have been issued with prices quoted for those known to still exist.

1904 (1 Jan)–**09.** *Black on red cover as No.* SB1 *of New South Wales. Stapled.*

SB1 £1 booklet containing two hundred and forty 1d. in four blocks of 30 and two blocks of 60
a. Red on pink cover (1909) .. £7000
b. Blue on pink cover

1904 (1 Jan). *Black on grey cover as No.* SB1. *Stapled.*

SB2 £1 booklet containing one hundred and twenty 2d. in four blocks of 30

1910 (May). *Black on white cover as No.* SB3 *of New South Wales. Stapled.*

SB3 2s. booklet containing eleven ½d. (No. 138), either in block of 6 plus block of 5 or block of 11, and eighteen 1d. (No. 139) either in three blocks of 6 or block of 6 plus block of 12 .. £2500

Unsold stock of No. SB3 was uprated with one additional ½d. in May 1911.

1911 (Aug). *Red on pink cover as No.* SB3. *Stapled.*

SB4 2s. booklet containing twelve ½d. (No. 138), either in two blocks of 6 or block of 12, and eighteen 1d. (No. 139), either in three blocks of 6 or block of 6 plus block of 12 .. £1900

POSTAL FISCAL STAMPS

By the Post and Telegraph Act of 5 September 1893 the current issue of fiscal stamps up to and including the 1s. value, Nos. F11/15, was authorised for postal use.

These stamps had been initially supplied, for fiscal purposes, in February 1882 and had been preceded by a series of "I R" surcharges and overprints on postage stamps which were in use for a period of about six months. Examples of these 1881–82 provisionals can be found postally used under the terms of the 1893 Act but, as they had not been current for fiscal purposes for over eleven years, we no longer list them.

F 3

(Typo D.L.R.)

1893 (5 Sept). *Definitive fiscal stamps of Feb* 1882. *Wmk CA over Crown. P* 14.

No.	Type	Description	Unused	Used
F11	F **3**	1d. dull purple	10·00	1·75
F12		2d. dull purple	£110	40·00
F13		3d. dull purple	42·00	2·75
F14		6d. dull purple	48·00	4·00
F15	–	1s. dull purple	85·00	8·00

The 1s. value is as Type F **3** but with rectangular outer frame and circular frame surrounding swan.

Higher values in this series were not validated by the Act for postal use.

Two varieties of watermark exist on these stamps. Initial supplies showed an indistinct watermark with the base of the "A" 4 mm wide. From 1896 the paper used showed a clearer watermark on which the base of the "A" was 5 mm wide.

1897. *Wmk W Crown A, W* **18**. *P* 14.

No.	Type	Description	Unused	Used
F19	F **3**	1d. dull purple	8·50	1·75
F20		3d. dull purple	35·00	2·75
F21		6d. dull purple	35·00	3·00
F22	–	1s. dull purple	80·00	9·50

The above were invalidated for postal purposes from 1 January 1901.

TELEGRAPH STAMPS USED FOR POSTAGE

The 1d. Telegraph stamps were authorised for postal purposes from 25 October 1886.

T 1

1886 (25 Oct). *Wmk Crown CC.*

No.	Type	Description	Unused	Used
T1	T 1	1d. bistre (*p* 12½)	30·00	4·25
T2		1d. bistre (*p* 14)	30·00	4·75

Copies of a similar 6d. value are known postally used, but such use was unauthorised.

OFFICIAL STAMPS

Stamps of the various issues from 1854–85 are found with a circular hole punched out, the earlier size being about 3 mm. in diameter and the later 4 mm. These were used on official correspondence by the Commissariat and Convict Department, branches of the Imperial administration separate from the colonial government. This system of punching ceased by 1886. Subsequently many stamps between Nos. 94 and 148 may be found punctured, "PWD", "WA" or "OS".

Western Australia became part of the Commonwealth of Australia on 1 January 1901.

COMMONWEALTH OF AUSTRALIA

On 1 March 1901 control of the postal service passed to the federal administration although it was not until 13 October 1910 that the issues of the various states became valid for use throughout Australia. Postal rates were standardised on 1 May 1911.

The first national postage due stamps appeared in July 1902, but it was not until January 1913 that postage stamps inscribed "AUSTRALIA" were issued.

PRICES FOR STAMPS ON COVER TO 1945

Nos. 1/19	*from* × 4
Nos. 20/3	*from* × 2
Nos. 24/30	*from* × 4
Nos. 35/47*f*	*from* × 3
Nos. 51/5*a*	*from* × 4
Nos. 55*b*/75	*from* × 3
Nos. 76/84	*from* × 4
Nos. 85/104	*from* × 3
Nos. 105/6	*from* × 4
Nos. 107/15	*from* × 3
No. 116	*from* × 5
Nos. 117/20	*from* × 4
Nos. 121/39*a*	*from* × 2
Nos. 140/*a*	*from* × 5
Nos. 141/4	*from* × 3
No. 146	*from* × 6
Nos. 147/53	*from* × 3
Nos. 153*a*/*b*	*from* × 2
Nos. 154/63	*from* × 3
Nos. 164/211	*from* × 2
Nos. D1/118	*from* × 8
Nos. O123/36	*from* × 5

PRINTERS. Except where otherwise stated, all Commonwealth stamps to No. 581 were printed under Government authority at Melbourne. Until 1918 there were two establishments (both of the Treasury Dept)—the Note Printing Branch and the Stamp Printing Branch. The former printed T **3** and **4**.

In 1918 the Stamp Printing Branch was closed and all stamps were printed by the Note Printing Branch. In 1926 control was transferred from the Treasury to the Commonwealth Bank of Australia, and on 14 January 1960 the branch was attached to the newly established Reserve Bank of Australia.

Until 1942 stamps bore in the sheet margin the initials or names of successive managers and from 1942 to March 1952 the imprint "Printed by the Authority of the Government of the Commonwealth of Australia". After November 1952 (or Nos. D129/31 for Postage Dues) imprints were discontinued.

SPECIMEN OVERPRINTS. These come from Specimen sets, first made available to the public on 15 December 1913. In these sets the lower values were cancelled-to-order, but stamps with a face value of 7s. 6d. or 75 c. were overprinted "Specimen" in different types. These overprints are listed as they could be purchased from the Australian Post Office.

It is, however, believed that examples of No. 112 overprinted "Specimen" were distributed by the U.P.U. in 1929. Supplies of the 1902 and 1902–04 postage due stamps overprinted "Specimen" were supplied to the U.P.U. by some of the states.

MINIMUM PRICE

The minimum price quote is 10p which represents a handling charge rather than a basis for valuing common stamps. For further notes about prices see introductory pages.

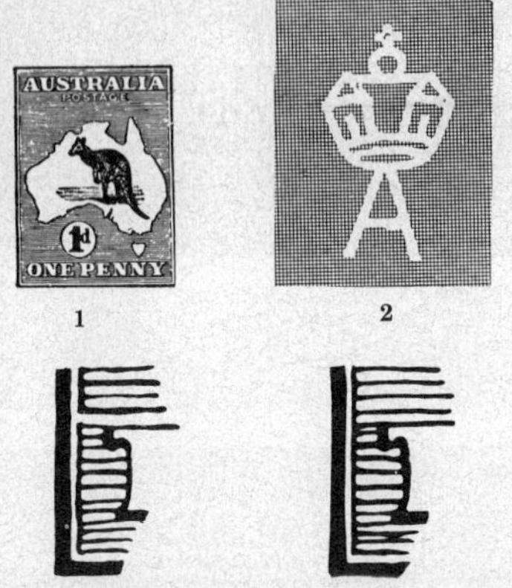

1 2

Die I Die II

of Type 1 (mono-coloured values only):—

I. Break in inner frame line at lower left level with top of words of value.

II. Die repaired showing no break.

e I was only used for the ½d., 1d., 2d. and 3d. Several plates produced for each except the 3d. When the second plate of the was being prepared the damage became aggravated after ing 105 out of the 120 units when the die was returned for ir. This gave rise to the *se-tenant* pairs showing the two states e die.

e II was used until 1945 and deteriorated progressively with age to the frame lines and rounding of the corners.

pecialists recognise seven states of this die, but we only list the most major of the later versions.

Die IIA. This state is as Die II, but, in addition, shows a break the inner left-hand frame line, 9 mm from the top of the ign (occurs on 1d., 2d. and 6d.).

Die IIB. As Die IIA, but now also showing break in outer me line above "ST", and (not illustrated) an incomplete corner the inner frame line at top right (occurs on 3d., 6d., 9d., 1s. d £1 (No. 75)).

(Des B. Young. Eng S. Reading. Typo J.B. Cooke)

13 (2 Jan)–**14.** *W* **2**. *P* 12.

No.	Type	Description	Unused	Used
1		½d. green (Die I) (14.1.13)	6·00	3·25
		a. Printed on the gummed side ..	£1300	
		bw. Wmk inverted	30·00	9·00
		c. Wmk sideways	†	£4250
		1d. red (Die I)	8·50	1·00
		a. Wmk sideways	£750	£140
		aw. Wmk sideways inverted		
		b. Carmine	8·50	1·00
		cw. Wmk inverted	25·00	3·00
		d. Die II. *Red* (16.1.13)	9·00	1·00
		da. Wmk sideways	£800	£150
		db. Carmine	8·50	1·00
		dw. Wmk inverted	25·00	3·00
		e. Die IIA. *Red* (4.14)	15·00	1·25
		eb. Carmine	15·00	1·25
		ew. Wmk inverted	40·00	5·00
3		2d. grey (Die I) (15.1.13)	28·00	4·50
		w. Wmk inverted	50·00	10·00
4		2½d. indigo (Die II) (27.1.13)	29·00	13·00
5		3d. olive (Die I) (28.1.13)	48·00	8·00
		a. Imperf three sides (horiz pair) ..	£16000	
		b. In pair with Die II	£450	£180
		c. Yellow-olive	48·00	9·50
		ca. In pair with Die II	£450	£200
		dw. Wmk inverted	90·00	27·00
		e. Die II. *Olive*	£160	50·00
		ea. Yellow-olive	£160	50·00
		ew. Wmk inverted	£300	£110
6		4d. orange (Die II) (19.2.13)	50·00	22·00
		a. Orange-yellow	£190	48·00
8		5d. chestnut (Die II) (18.1.13) ..	40·00	32·00
9		6d. ultramarine (Die II) (18.1.13) ..	48·00	20·00
		a. Retouched "E"	£1700	£550
		b. Die IIA (substituted cliché) (11.13)	£1300	£450
		w. Wmk inverted	£200	70·00
0		9d. violet (Die II) (1.2.13)	45·00	22·00
1		1s. emerald (Die II) (25.1.13)	48·00	17·00
		a. Blue-green	50·00	17·00
		w. Wmk inverted	£225	60·00
2		2s. brown (Die II) (28.1.13)	£160	75·00
3		5s. grey and yellow (Die II) (20.3.13)	£275	£150
4		10s. grey and pink (Die II) (20.3.13) ..	£600	£475
15	**1**	£1 brown & ultram (Die II) (20.3.13)	£1000	£1100
16		£2 black and rose (Die II) (8.4.13) ..	£2500	£1600
1/16		.. .. *Set of* 15	£4250	£3250
14s/16s		Optd "Specimen" .. *Set of* 3	£600	

Three examples, all used, are known of No. 1c.

The watermark on No. 2a shows the Crown pointing to the left and on No. 2aw pointing to the right, *both as seen from the back of the stamp.*

The 3d. was printed from two plates, one of which contained 105 stamps as Die I and 15 as Die II. The other plate contained Die I stamps only.

No. 5a. shows the stamp perforated at foot only. Examples are known from the top or bottom rows of different sheets.

No. 9a shows a badly distorted second "E" in "PENCE", which is unmistakable. It occurs on the Upper plate right pane R. 10/6 and was replaced by a substitute cliché in Die IIA (No. 9b) in the November 1913 printing.

See also Nos. 24/30 (*W* **5**), 35/45*b* (*W* **6**), 73/5 (*W* **6**, new colours), 107/14 (*W* **7**), 132/8 (*W* **15**), 212 (2s. re-engraved).

3 **4** Laughing Kookaburra

(Des R. A. Harrison. Eng and recess T. S. Harrison)

1913 (9 Dec)–**14.** *No wmk. P* 11.

No.	Type	Description	Unused	Used
17	**3**	1d. red	2·50	4·50
		a. Imperf between (horiz pair)	£2000	
		b. Imperf horiz (vert pair)	£1400	
		c. Pale rose-red	7·00	11·00
		ca. Imperf between (vert pair)	£1600	
		cb. Imperf between (horiz pair)	£2250	
19	**4**	6d. claret (26.8.14)	65·00	38·00

All printings from Plate 1 of the 1d. were in the shade of No. 17*c*. This plate shows many retouches.

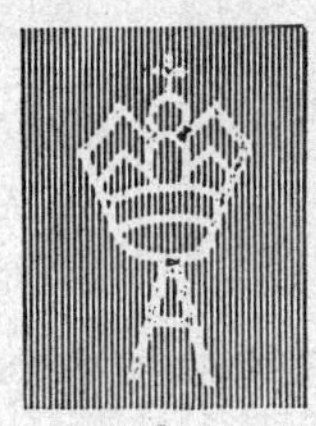

5 **5a**

1d. Die II

1d. Die II. The flaw distinguishing the so-called Die II, a white upward spur to the right of the base of the "1" in the left value tablet, is now known to be due to a defective roller-die. It occurred on all stamps in the second and third vertical rows of upper left plate right pane. Each of the twenty defective impressions differs slightly; a typical example is illustrated above.

(Dies eng P.B. Typo J. B. Cooke until May 1918, then T. S. Harrison)

1914 (17 July)–**20.** *W* **5**. *P* 14¼×14 (*comb*).

No.	Type	Description	Unused	Used
20	**5a**	½d. bright green (22.2.15)	3·75	1·00
		a. Perf 14¼ (line) (12.15)	£3000	£300
		b. Green (1916)	3·75	1·00
		c. Yellow-green (1916)	22·00	10·00
		d. Thin "1" in fraction at right (Pl 5 rt pane R. 8/1)	£5000	£1500
		w. Wmk inverted	12·00	4·00
21		1d. carmine-red (*shades*) (Die I) (*p* 14¼ (line))	25·00	4·00
		a. Die II	£4000	£400
		bw. Wmk inverted	†	£1000
		c. Perf 14¼×14 (comb) (7.8.14) ..	7·00	60
		ca. Rusted cliché (Pl 2 rt pane R. 6/4 and 5) (9.16)	£5000	£300
		cb. Substituted cliché (Pl 2 rt pane R. 6/5) (2.18)	£800	55·00
		cc. Pale carmine (*shades*) (1917) ..	10·00	60
		cd. Rose-red (1917)	11·00	2·50
		ce. Carmine-pink (1918)	90·00	8·00
		cf. Carmine (*aniline*) (1920)	16·00	3·25
		cw. Wmk inverted	12·00	2·00
		d. Die II. *Carmine-red* (*shades*) ..	£300	6·00
		db. Substituted cliché (Pl 2 right pane R. 6/4) (2.18)	£800	55·00
		dc. Pale carmine (*shades*)	£300	7·00
		dw. Wmk inverted	£425	15·00
22		4d. orange (6.1.15)	27·00	2·50
		a. Yellow-orange (1915)	27·00	3·25
		b. Lemon-yellow (3.16)	80·00	14·00
		c. Pale orange-yellow (1.17)	60·00	11·00
		d. Dull orange (1920)	42·00	3·25
		e. Line through "FOUR PENCE" (Pl 2 right pane R. 2/6) (*all shades*) *From*	£300	90·00
		w. Wmk inverted	40·00	12·00
23		5d. brown (*p* 14¼ (line)) (22.2.15) ..	25·00	4·00
		aw. Wmk inverted	£180	50·00
		b. Perf 14¼×14 (comb) (15.8.17) ..	18·00	2·00
		ba. Yellow-brown (1920)	25·00	2·75
		bw. Wmk inverted	80·00	20·00

The variety No. 20d was caused by the engraving of a new fraction in a defective electro in 1918.

No. 21ca was caused by rusting on two positions of the steel plate 2 and shows as white patches on the back of the King's neck and on, and besides, the top of the right frame (right pane R. 6/4) and on the left frame, wattles, head and ears of kangaroo (right pane R. 6/5). These were noticed in December 1916 when the damaged impressions were removed and replaced by a pair of copper electros (Die II for R. 6/4 and Die I for R. 6/5), showing rounded corners and some frame damage, the former also showing a white spot under tail of emu. In time the tops of the crown quickly wore away.

Most of Nos. 20/3 were perforated 14 by a comb machine (exact gauge 14.25×14), but printings of the ½d. in December 1915, of the 1d. in July and August 1914 and of the 5d. until June 1917 were perforated by a line machine measuring 14.2.

See also Nos. 47/fa (*W* **5**, rough paper), 48/52 (*W* **6***a*), 53/*ba* (1d. Die III), 56/66*b* and 76/81 (*W* **5**, new colours), 82 (*W* **6***a*), 83/4 (no wmk), 85/104 (*W* **7**), 124/31 (*W* **15**).

(Typo J. B. Cooke)

1915 (15 Jan–Aug). *W* **5**. *P* 12.

No.	Type	Description	Unused	Used
24	**1**	2d. grey (Die I)	50·00	12·00
		w. Wmk inverted	†	£800
25		2½d. indigo (Die II) (July)	50·00	28·00
26		6d. ultramarine (Die II) (April) ..	£130	22·00
		a. Bright blue	£170	48·00
		b. Die IIA. *Ultramarine* (substituted cliché) (Upper plate rt pane R. 10/6)	£1200	£350
		ba. Bright blue	£1500	£450
		w. Wmk inverted	†	£1500
27		9d. violet (Die II) (9 July)	£130	35·00
		w. Wmk inverted	£800	£325
28		1s. blue-green (Die II) (Apr)	£140	24·00
29		2s. brown (Die II) (March)	£425	90·00
30		5s. grey and yellow (Die II) (12 Feb) ..	£500	£250
		a. Yellow portion doubly printed ..	£5500	£1500
		w. Wmk inverted	£600	£300
24/30		.. .. *Set of* 7	£1300	£400

6 **6a**

Nos. 38ca and 73a (Upper plate lt pane R. 1/6)

(Typo J. B. Cooke (to May 1918), T. S. Harrison to February 1926), A. J. Mullett (to June 1927) and thereafter J. Ash)

1915 (8 Oct)–**28.** *W* **6** (*narrow Crown*). *P* 12.

No.	Type	Description	Unused	Used
35	**1**	2d. grey (Die I) (11.15)	25·00	6·50
		a. In pair with Die IIA (1917)* ..	£1300	£500
		bw. Wmk inverted	35·00	9·00
		c. Silver-grey (shiny paper) (3.18) ..	26·00	8·00
		d. Die IIA. *Silver-grey* (shiny paper) (3.18)	38·00	11·00
		da. Grey (1920)	40·00	11·00
36		2½d. deep blue (Die II) (9.17)	23·00	10·00
		aw. Wmk inverted	50·00	20·00
		b. Deep indigo (1919)	28·00	8·50
		ba "1" of fraction omitted (Lower plate left pane R. 6/3)	£12000	£4000
37		3d. yellow-olive (Die I)	28·00	4·50
		a. In pair with Die II	£200	95·00
		b. Olive-green (1917)	30·00	4·50
		ba. In pair with Die II	£200	95·00
		cw. Wmk inverted	45·00	10·00
		d. Die II. *Yellow-olive*	80·00	27·00
		da. Olive-green	80·00	27·00
		dw. Wmk inverted	£160	65·00
		e. Die IIB. *Light olive* (1.23) ..	35·00	11·00
38		6d. ultramarine (Die II) (15.12.15) ..	55·00	7·50
		a. Die IIA (substituted cliché) (Upper plate rt pane R. 10/6)	£1100	£300
		b. Dull blue (6.18)	65·00	11·00
		ba. Die IIA (substituted cliché) ..	£1200	£325
		cw. Wmk inverted	95·00	24·00
		d. Die IIB. *Brt ultramarine* (23.7.21)	55·00	7·50
		da. Leg of kangaroo broken	£2250	£450
		dw. Wmk inverted	—	40·00
39		9d. violet (Die II) (29.7.16)	38·00	8·00
		aw. Wmk inverted	80·00	24·00
		b. Die IIB. *Violet* (16.4.19)	38·00	8·00
		bw. Wmk inverted	65·00	18·00
40		1s. blue-green (Die II) (6.16)	35·00	3·75
		aw. Wmk inverted	75·00	20·00
		b. Die IIB (9.12.20)	38·00	3·25
		ba. Wmk sideways (13.12.27)	60·00	£120
		bw. Wmk inverted	70·00	18·00
41		2s. brown (Die II) (6.16)	£150	12·00
		a. Imperf three sides (horiz pair) ..	£30000	
		b. Red-brown (*aniline*)	£425	75·00
		w. Wmk inverted	£300	£110
42		5s. grey and yellow (Die II) (4.18) ..	£180	75·00
		a. Grey and orange (1920)	£190	80·00
		b. Grey and deep yellow	£180	75·00
		ba. Wmk sideways	†	£7000
		c. Grey and pale yellow (1928) ..	£180	75·00
		w. Wmk inverted	£375	£150

10s. grey and pink (Die II) (5.2.17) £400 £225
a. *Grey and bright aniline pink* (10.18) £350 £170
ab. Wmk sideways £7500 £3750
aw. Wmk inverted £800 £275
b. *Grey and pale aniline pink* (1922) £425 £190
£1 chocolate & dull blue (Die II) (7.16) £1400 £750
a. *Chestnut and bright blue* (6.17) £1500 £800
ab. Wmk sideways £14000 £6000
aw. Wmk inverted £1800 £1000
b. *Bistre-brown and bright blue* (7.19) £1400 £750
£2 black and rose (Die II) (12.19) £2250 £1400
a. *Grey and crimson* (1921) £2000 £1300
b. *Purple-black and pale rose* (6.24) £1800 £1100
Set of 11 £3500 £1900
Optd "Specimen" *Set of* 3 £500

e Die IIA of No. 35a is a substituted cliché introduced to e a cracked plate which occurred on R. 10/1 of the Upper eft pane. The Die IIA characteristics are more pronounced cliché than on the sheet stamps from this die. The break , for instance, extends to the outer, in addition to the frame line.

plate of the 3d. contained mixed Die I and Die II stamps cribed.

values were printed by both Cooke and Harrison, and the . and 5s. were also printed by Mullett and Ash.

(Nov)–**18.** *Rough, unsurfaced paper, locally gummed.* *P* 14.
1d. scarlet (Die I) 18·00 2·50
a. *Deep red* (1917) 18·00 2·50
b. *Rose-red* (1918) 28·00 2·75
ba. Substituted cliché (Pl 2 rt pane R. 6/5) £750 60·00
c. *Rosine* (1918) £100 13·00
ca. Substituted cliché (Pl 2 rt pane R. 6/5) £1200 £150
dw. Wmk inverted 30·00 3·75
e. Die II. *Rose-red* (1918) £275 21·00
ea. Substituted cliché (Pl 2 rt pane R. 6/4) £750 60·00
ew. Wmk inverted £400 32·00
f. Die II. *Rosine* (1918) £375 55·00
fa. Substituted cliché (Pl 2 rt pane R. 6/4) £1200 £150

examples of the 5d. on this paper were perforated "OS" and be found listed as No. O60.

ypo J. B. Cooke to May 1918 thereafter T. S. Harrison)

(4 Jan)–**20.** *W* **6a** (*Mult*). *P* 14.
½d. green (*shades*) 5·00 2·50
a. Thin 1 in fraction at right (Pl 5 rt pane R. 8/1) £100 50·00
b. Wmk sideways † £4000
w. Wmk inverted 16·00 9·50
1d. carmine-pink (Die I) (23.1.18) £120 70·00
aw. Wmk inverted † £1500
b. *Deep red* (1918) £1500 £325
1d. carmine (10.12.19) 35·00 8·00
aw. Wmk inverted £350 £180
b. *Deep red (aniline)* (1920) £225 65·00
1½d. black-brown (30.1.19) 5·00 3·00
a. Very thin paper (2.19) 25·00 13·00
w. Wmk inverted 18·00 8·00
1½d. red-brown (4.19) 12·00 2·25
a. *Chocolate* (1920) 11·00 2·25
w. Wmk inverted 32·00 9·50

. 48 was printed by Cooke and Harrison, Nos. 49/*a* by e only and Nos. 50/2*a* by Harrison only. Nos. 49/*a* have r yellowish gum, that of No. 50 being pure white.

1d. Die III

d. Die III. In 1917 a printing (in sheets of 120) was made on er originally prepared for printing War Savings Stamps, n watermark T **5**. A special plate was made for this printing, ering in detail from those previously used. The shading nd the background is even; the solid background of the words "ONE NNY" is bounded at each end by a white vertical line; and re is a horizontal white line cutting the vertical shading lines eft on the King's neck.

(Typo J. B. Cooke)

8 (15 July). *Printed from a new Die III plate on white unsurfaced paper, locally gummed. W* **5**. *P* 14.
5a 1d. rose-red 55·00 28·00
ba. *Rose-carmine* 55·00 30·00
bw. Wmk inverted 80·00 38·00

po T. S. Harrison or A. J. Mullett (1s. 4d. from March 1926))

8 (9 Nov)–**23.** *W* **5**. *P* 14.
5a ½d. orange (9.11.23) 2·50 2·75
w. Wmk inverted 6·00 7·00
1d. violet (*shades*) (12.2.22) 6·00 1·50
a. Imperf three sides (horiz pair) £11000
b. *Red-violet* 8·00 2·25
1½d. black-brown 8·50 1·50
w. Wmk inverted 14·00 3·25
1½d. deep red-brown (4.19) 6·50 70
a. *Chocolate* (1920) 6·50 60
w. Wmk inverted 17·00 4·50
1½d. bright red-brown (20.1.22) 13·00 3·75
1½d. green (7.3.23) 4·00 80
a. Coarse unsurfaced paper (1923) £110
w. Wmk inverted † £1400
2d. brown-orange (9.20) 15·00 1·00
a. *Dull orange* (1921) 18·00 1·00
w. Wmk inverted † £1500
2d. bright rose-scarlet (19.1.22) 9·00 1·50
a. *Dull rose-scarlet* 9·00 1·50
w. Wmk inverted £2000
4d. violet (21.6.21) 13·00 15·00
a. Line through "FOUR PENCE" (Pl 2 rt pane R. 2/6) £10000 £2500
b. "FOUR PENCE" in thinner letters (Pl 2 rt pane R. 2/6) £400 £225

65 **5a** 4d. ultramarine (*shades*) (23.3.22) 48·00 8·50
a. "FOUR PENCE" in thinner letters (Pl 2 rt pane R. 2/6) £400 £150
b. *Pale milky blue* 75·00 13·00
w. Wmk inverted 65·00 40·00
66 1s. 4d. pale blue (2.12.20) 55·00 23·00
a. *Dull greenish blue* 60·00 24·00
b. *Deep turquoise* (1922) £950 £425
56/66 *Set of* 11 £160 50·00

In addition to a number of mint pairs from two sheets purchased at Gumeracha, South Australia, with the bottom row imperforate on three sides, a single used example of No. 57 imperforate on three sides is known.

No. 61a was printed on a batch of coarse unsurfaced paper during 1923. Mint examples can be identified by the yellowish gum and a mesh effect in the paper, but there is no conclusive method of identifying used stamps from this printing.

The 4d. ultramarine was originally printed from the Cooke plates but the plates were worn in mid-1923 and Harrison prepared a new pair of plates. Stamps from these plates can only be distinguished by the minor flaws which are peculiar to them.

The variety of Nos. 64 and 65 with "FOUR PENCE" thinner, was caused by the correction of the line through "FOUR PENCE" flaw early in the printing of No. 64.

(Typo T. S. Harrison (to February 1926), A. J. Mullett (to June 1927), thereafter J. Ash)

1923 (6 Dec)–**24.** *W* **6**. *P* 12.
73 **1** 6d. chestnut (Die IIB) 24·00 1·75
a. Leg of kangaroo broken (Upper plate lt pane R. 1/6) 75·00 £100
w. Wmk inverted † £1600
74 2s. maroon (Die II) (1.5.24) 55·00 24·00
w. Wmk inverted £150 70·00
75 £1 grey (Die IIB) (1.5.24) £400 £225
s. Optd "Specimen" 75·00

The 6d. and 2s. were printed by all three printers, but the £1 only by Harrison.

No. 73a was corrected during the Ash printing.

(Typo T. S. Harrison (to February 1926), thereafter A. J. Mullett)

1924 (1 May–18 Aug). *P* 14. (*a*) *W* **5**.
76 **5a** 1d. sage-green 3·00 1·50
w. Wmk inverted 11·00 5·50
77 1½d. scarlet (*shades*) 2·25 40
a. Very thin paper 40·00 20·00
b. "HALEPENCE" (Pl 22 left pane R. 4/4) 30·00 20·00
c "RAL" of "AUSTRALIA" thin (Pl 22 left pane R. 5/4) 30·00 20·00
d. Curved "1" and thin fraction at left (Pl 24 rt pane R. 7/5) 30·00 20·00
w. Wmk inverted 30·00 9·00
78 2d. red-brown 20·00 7·00
a. *Bright red-brown* 26·00 8·00
w. Wmk inverted † £1600
79 3d. dull ultramarine 25·00 2·00
a. Imperf three sides (horiz pair) £6000
80 4d. olive-yellow 28·00 5·50
a. *Olive-green* 28·00 6·00
w. Wmk inverted † £1200
81 4½d. violet 23·00 3·50

(*b*) *W* **6a**
82 **5a** 1d. sage-green (20 May) 8·00 8·50
w. Wmk inverted † £1300

(*c*) *No wmk*
83 **5a** 1d. sage-green (18 August) 5·50 9·50
84 1½d. scarlet (14 August) 11·00 9·50
76/84 *Set of* 9 £110 42·00

Nos. 78/*a* and 82/4 were printed by Harrison only but the remainder were printed by both Harrison and Mullett.

In the semi-transparent paper of Nos. 54a and 77a the watermark is almost indistinguishable.

Nos. 77b, 77c and 77d are typical examples of retouching of which there are many others in these issues. In No. 77c the letters "RAL" differ markedly from the normal. There is a white stroke cutting the oval frame-line above the "L", and the right-hand outer line of the Crown does not cut the white frame-line above the "A".

It is believed that No. 79a occurs on the bottom row of at least four sheets purchased from post offices in Victoria during 1926.

7

I

II

New Dies

1d. For differences see note above No. 20.

1½d. From new steel plates made from a new die. Nos. 87*a* and 96*a* are the Ash printings, the ink of which is shiny.

2d. Die I. Height of frame 25.6 mm. Left-hand frame-line thick and uneven behind Kangaroo. Pearls in Crown vary in size.
Die II. Height of frame 25.6 mm. Left-hand frame-line thin and even. Pearls in Crown are all the same size.
Die III. Height 25.1 mm; lettering and figures of value bolder than Die I.

3d. Die II has bolder letters and figures than Die I, as illustrated above.

5d. Die II has a bolder figure "5" with flat top compared with Die I of the earlier issues.

(Typo A. J. Mullett or J. Ash (from June 1927))

1926–30. *W* **7**. (*a*) *P* 14.
85 **5a** ½d. orange (10.3.27) 6·00 7·50
w. Wmk inverted 50·00 35·00
86 1d. sage-green (23.10.26) 3·25 1·00
w. Wmk inverted 15·00 3·75
87 1½d. scarlet (5.11.26) 7·50 2·00
a. *Golden scarlet* (1927) 11·00 2·50
w. Wmk inverted 14·00 4·50
89 2d. red-brown (Die I) (17.8.27) 28·00 35·00
90 3d. dull ultramarine (12.26) 23·00 5·00
w. Wmk inverted † £1300
91 4d. yellow-olive (17.1.28) 48·00 35·00
92 4½d. violet (26.10.27) 18·00 3·75
93 1s. 4d. pale greenish blue (6.9.27) 90·00 80·00
w. Wmk inverted † £1500
85/93 *Set of* 8 £200 £150

(*b*) *P* 13½×12½
94 **5a** ½d. orange (21.11.28) 2·25 1·40
95 1d. sage-green (Die I) (23.12.26) 2·25 70
aw. Wmk inverted 10·00 4·50
b. Die II (6.28) 50·00 80·00
bw. Wmk inverted £275
96 1½d. scarlet (14.1.27) 2·25 1·00
a. *Golden scarlet* (1927) 2·25 1·00
w. Wmk inverted 10·00 2·50
97 1½d. red-brown (16.9.30) 5·50 5·50
98 2d. red-brown (Die II) (28.4.28) 8·00 9·00
99 2d. golden scarlet (Die II) (2.8.30) 12·00 2·25
a. Die III (9.9.30) 9·00 85
ab. No wmk £700 £900
ac. *Tête-bêche* (pair) £32000
aw. Wmk inverted (*from booklets*) 9·00 1·40
100 3d. dull ultramarine (Die I) (28.2.28) 38·00 6·50
aw. Wmk inverted £110 £170
b. Die II. *Deep ultramarine* (28.9.29) 23·00 1·40
bw. Wmk inverted † £1400
102 4d. yellow-olive (19.4.29) 23·00 3·25
w. Wmk inverted † £1300
103 4½d. violet (11.28) 48·00 22·00
103*a* 5d. orange-brown (Die II) (27.8.30) 23·00 7·00
104 1s. 4d. turquoise (30.9.28) 80·00 26·00
w. Wmk inverted † £1600
94/104 *Set of* 11 £190 65·00

Owing to defective manufacture, part of a sheet of the 2d. (Die III), discovered in July 1931, escaped unwatermarked; while the watermark in other parts of the same sheet was faint or normal.

Only one example of No. 99ac is known.

8 Parliament House, Canberra

9 "DH66" Biplane and Pastoral Scene

(Des R. A. Harrison. Die eng J. A. C. Harrison (Waterlow, London). Plates and printing by A. J. Mullett)

1927 (9 May). *Opening of Parliament House, Canberra. No wmk. P* 11.
105 **8** 1½d. brownish lake 50 50
a. Imperf between (vert pair) £2250
b. Imperf between (horiz pair) £3250 £3250

(Eng H. W. Bell. Recess J. Ash)

1928 (29 Oct–2 Nov). *4th National Stamp Exhibition, Melbourne. As T* **4**. *No wmk. P* 11.
106 3d. blue (2 Nov) 4·25 4·75
MS106*a* 65×70 mm. No. 106×4 £110 £200
ab. Imperf (pane of four) £18000

No. **MS**106*a* comes from special sheets of 60 stamps divided into 15 blocks of 4 (5×3) and separated by wide gutters perforated down the middle, printed and sold at the Exhibition.

(Typo J. Ash)

1929 (Feb)–**30.** *W* **7**. *P* 12.
107 **1** 6d. chestnut (Die IIB) (25.9.29) 23·00 4·50
108 9d. violet (Die IIB) 30·00 15·00
109 1s. blue-green (Die IIB) (12.6.29) 35·00 6·00
w. Wmk inverted † £1700
110 2s. maroon (Die II) (3.29) 45·00 15·00
111 5s. grey and yellow (Die II) (30.11.29) £190 80·00
112 10s. grey and pink (Die II) £300 £400
114 £2 black and rose (Die II) (11.30) £1900 £450
107/14 *Set of* 7 £2250 £850
112s/14s Optd "Specimen" *Set of* 2 £325

(Des R. A. Harrison and H. Herbert. Eng A. Taylor. Recess J. Ash)

1929 (20 May). *Air. No wmk. P* 11.
115 **9** 3d. green (*shades*) 10·00 4·00

Variations of up to ¾ mm in the design size of No. 115 are due to paper shrinkage on the printings produced by the "wet" process. The last printing, in 1935, was printed by the "dry" method.

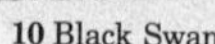

10 Black Swan **11** "Capt. Charles Sturt" (J. H. Crossland)

(Des G. Pitt Morrison. Eng F. D. Manley. Recess J. Ash)

1929 (28 Sept). *Centenary of Western Australia. No wmk. P* 11.
116 **10** 1½d. dull scarlet .. .. 1·25 1·60
a. Re-entry ("T" of "AUSTRALIA" clearly double) (Pl 2 R. 7/4) .. 55·00 60·00

(Des R. A. Harrison. Eng F. D. Manley. Recess J. Ash)

1930 (2 June). *Centenary of Exploration of River Murray by Capt. Sturt. No wmk. P* 11.
117 **11** 1½d. scarlet .. .. 1·00 1·00
118 3d. blue .. .. 3·25 6·50

No. 117 with manuscript surcharge of "2d. paid P M L H I" was issued by the Postmaster of Lord Howe Island during a shortage of 2d. stamps between 23 August and 17 October 1930. A few copies of the 1½d. value No. 96*a* were also endorsed. These provisionals are not recognized by the Australian postal authorities. (*Price* £500 *un. or us., either stamp*).

TWO

PENCE

(**12**)

13 Fokker F.VIIa/3m *Southern Cross* above Hemispheres

1930 (28 July–2 Aug). *T* 5*a surch as T* **12**. *W* **7**. *P* 13½×12½.
119 2d. on 1½d. golden scarlet .. .. 1·50 75
120 5d. on 4½d. violet (2 Aug) .. .. 6·00 8·50

No. 120 is from a redrawn die in which the words "FOURPENCE HALFPENNY" are noticeably thicker than in the original die and the figure "4" has square instead of tapering serifs. The redrawn die also shows thin white lines to the left and right of the tablet carrying "FOURPENCE HALFPENNY".

Stamps from the redrawn die without the surcharge were printed, but not issued thus. Some stamps, *cancelled to order*, were included in sets supplied by the post office. A few mint copies, which escaped, the cancellation were found and some may have been used postally (*Price* £2000 *unused*, £45 *used c.t.o.*).

(Des and eng F. D. Manley. Recess John Ash)

1931 (19 Mar). *Kingsford Smith's Flights. No wmk. P* 11.

(*a*) *Postage.*
121 **13** 2d. rose-red .. .. 1·00 1·00
122 3d. blue .. .. 4·50 5·00

(*b*) *Air. Inscr* "AIR MAIL SERVICE" *at sides*
123 **13** 6d. violet .. .. 6·50 12·00
a. Re-entry ("FO" and "LD" double) (Pl 1 R. 5/5) .. .. 50·00 80·00
121/3 .. .. *Set of* 3 11·00 16·00

15 **17** Superb Lyrebird

(Typo John Ash)

1931–36. *W* **15**. (*a*) *P* 13½×12½.
124 **5*a*** ½d. orange (2.33) .. .. .. 4·75 6·00
125 1d. green (Die I) (10.31) .. .. 1·75 20
w. Wmk inverted .. .. .. 14·00 3·00
x. Wmk reversed £200 £100
y. Wmk inverted and reversed .. £325 £150
126 1½d. red-brown (10.36) .. .. 6·00 10·00
127 2d. golden scarlet (Die III) (18.12.31) 1·75 10
w. Wmk inverted (*from booklets*) .. 2·25 50
128 3d. ultramarine (Die II) (30.9.32) .. 18·00 1·25
w. Wmk inverted £1600 £1300
129 4d. yellow-olive (2.33) .. .. 18·00 1·25
w. Wmk inverted .. .. .. † £1400
130 5d. orange-brown (Die II) (25.2.32) .. 15·00 20
w. Wmk inverted .. .. .. † £1400
131 1s. 4d. turquoise (18.8.32) .. .. 50·00 3·50
w. Wmk inverted .. .. .. † £1400
124/31 .. .. *Set of* 8 £100 20·00

(*b*) *P* 12
132 **1** 6d. chestnut (Die IIB) (20.4.32) .. 22·00 25·00
133 9d. violet (Die IIB) (20.4.32) .. .. 28·00 1·25
134 2s. maroon (Die II) (6.8.35) .. .. 5·00 60
135 5s. grey and yellow (Die II) (12.32) .. £120 12·00
136 10s. grey and pink (Die II) (31.7.32) .. £250 £100
137 £1 grey (Die IIB) (11.35) £425 £160
138 £2 black and rose (Die II) (6.34) .. £1600 £325
132/8 .. .. *Set of* 7 £2250 £550
136s/8s Optd "Specimen" .. .. *Set of* 3 75·00

Stamps as No. 127, but without watermark and perforated 11, are forgeries made in 1932 to defraud the P.O.

For re-engraved type of No. 134, see No. 212.

(Des and eng F. D. Manley. Recess John Ash)

1931 (4 Nov). *Air Stamp. As T* **13** *but inscr* "AIR MAIL SERVICE" *in bottom tablet. No wmk. P* 11.
139 6d. sepia .. .. 16·00 12·00

1931 (17 Nov). *Air. No.* 139 *optd with Type* O **4**.
139*a* 6d. sepia .. .. 35·00 50·00

This stamp was not restricted to official use but was on general sale to the public.

(Des and eng F. D. Manley. Recess John Ash)

1932 (15 Feb). *No wmk. P* 11.
140 **17** 1s. green .. .. 42·00 2·00
a. Yellow-green .. .. 48·00 2·75

18 Sydney Harbour Bridge **19** Laughing Kookaburra

(Des R. A. Harrison. Eng F. D. Manley. Printed John Ash)

1932 (14 Mar). *Opening of Sydney Harbour Bridge.* (*a*) *Recess. No wmk. P* 11.
141 **18** 2d. scarlet .. .. 2·25 2·75
142 3d. blue .. .. 4·25 7·00
143 5s. blue-green £375 £180

(*b*) *Typo. W* **15**. *P* 10½.
144 **18** 2d. scarlet .. .. 2·00 1·40
141/4 .. .. *Set of* 4 £375 £180

Stamps as No. 144 without wmk and perf 11 are forgeries made in 1932 to defraud the P.O.

(Des F. D. Manley. Die eng E. Broad. Typo John Ash)

1932 (1 June). *W* **15**. *P* 13½×12½.
146 **19** 6d. red-brown .. .. 25·00 55
w. Wmk inverted .. .. † £800

20 Melbourne and R. Yarra **21** Merino Ram

(Des and eng F. D. Manley. Recess John Ash)

1934 (2 July–Aug). *Centenary of Victoria. W* **15**. *P* 10½.
147 **20** 2d. orange-vermilion .. .. .. 2·50 1·75
a. Perf 11½ (Aug) .. .. .. 5·00 1·50
148 3d. blue .. .. 5·00 5·50
a. Perf 11½ (Aug) .. .. .. 5·00 8·00
149 1s. black .. .. 48·00 20·00
a. Perf 11½ (Aug) .. .. .. 48·00 22·00
147/9 .. .. *Set of* 3 50·00 25·00
147a/9a .. .. *Set of* 3 55·00 28·00

Stamps were originally issued perforated 10½, but the gauge was subsequently changed to 11½ in August 1934 due to difficulties in separating stamps in the first perforation.

(Des and eng F. D. Manley. Recess John Ash)

1934 (1–26 Nov). *Death Centenary of Capt. John Macarthur (founder of Australian sheep farming). W* **15**. *P* 11½.
150 **21** 2d. carmine-red (A) .. .. .. 4·25 1·50
150*a* 2d. carmine-red (B) (26 Nov) .. 25·00 3·25
151 3d. blue .. .. 10·00 9·50
152 9d. bright purple .. .. 38·00 42·00
150/2 .. .. *Set of* 3 48·00 48·00

Type A of the 2d. shows shading on the hill in the background varying from light to dark (as illustrated). Type B has the shading almost uniformly dark.

22 Hermes **23** Cenotaph, Whitehall

(Des F. D. Manley. Eng E. Broad and F. D. Manley. Recess John Ash until April 1940; W. C. G. McCracken thereafter)

1934 (1 Dec)–**48**. (*a*) *No wmk. P* 11.
153 **22** 1s. 6d. dull purple .. .. .. 32·00 1·00

(*b*) *W* **15**. *Chalk-surfaced paper. P* 13½×14
153*a* **22** 1s. 6d dull purple (22.10.37) .. 9·00 45
b. Thin rough ordinary paper (12.2.48) .. .. 2·50 1·40

(Des B. Cottier; adapted and eng F. D. Manley. Recess John Ash)

1935 (18 Mar). *20th Anniv of Gallipoli Landing. W* **15**. *P* 13½×12½ *or* 11 (1*s*.).
154 **23** 2d. scarlet 80 30
155 1s. black (*chalk-surfaced*) .. .. 42·00 38·00

The 1s. perforated 13½×12½ is a plate proof (*Price* £1500 *used*).

24 King George V on "Anzac" **25** Amphitrite and Telephon[e] Cable

(Des and eng F. D. Manley. Recess John Ash)

1935 (2 May). *Silver Jubilee. Chalk-surfaced paper. W* **15** *(… ways). P* 11½.
156 **24** 2d. scarlet .. .. 1·50
157 3d. blue .. .. 5·00
158 2s. bright violet .. .. 27·00
156/8 .. .. *Set of* 3 30·00

(Des and eng F. D. Manley. Recess John Ash)

1936 (1 Apr). *Opening of Submarine Telephone Lin[e] … Tasmania. W* **15**. *P* 11½.
159 **25** 2d. scarlet 75
160 3d. blue .. .. 2·75

26 Site of Adelaide, 1836; Old Gum Tree, Glenelg; King William St., Adelaide

(Des and eng F. D. Manley. Recess John Ash)

1936 (3 Aug). *Centenary of South Australia. W* **15**. *P* 11½.
161 **26** 2d. carmine .. .. 1·25
162 3d. blue .. .. 4·00
163 1s. green .. .. 10·00
161/3 .. .. *Set of* 3 14·00 1

27 Wallaroo **28** Queen Elizabeth **28*a***

29 **30** King George VI **30*a***

31 King George VI **32** Koala **33** Merino Ra[m]

34 Laughing Kookaburra **35** Platypus **36** Superb Lyreb[ird]

38 Queen Elizabeth **39** King George VI

40 King George VI and Queen Elizabeth

of 3d.:

Die I Die Ia Die II

Die I. The letters "TA" of "POSTAGE" at right are joined by a white flaw; the outline of the chin consists of separate strokes. No. 168a is a preliminary printing made with unsuitable ink and may be detected by the absence of finer details; the King's face appears whitish and the wattles are blank. The greater part of this printing was distributed to the Press with advance notices of the issue.

Die Ia. As Die I, but "T" and "A" have been clearly separated by individual retouches made on the plates.

Die II. A completely new die. "T" and "A" are separate and a continuous line has been added to the chin. The outline of the neck extends to about 1 mm above the lobe of the King's right ear.

Die III. Differs from Dies I and II in the King's left eyebrow which is shaded downwards from left to right instead of from right to left.

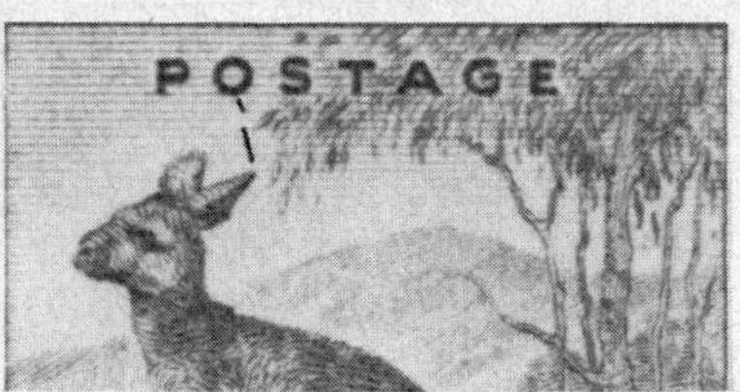

Line to Kangaroo's ear (Rt pane R. 6/8)

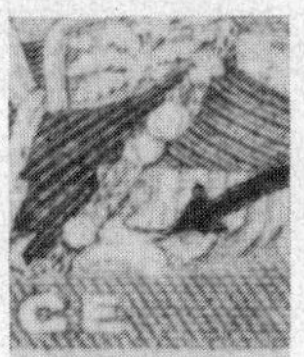

Medal flaw
(Right pane R. 2/5)

(Des R. A. Harrison (T **28/30**), F. D. Manley (T **27, 31/6**), H. Barr (T **38/9**), H. Barr and F. D. Manley (T **40**). Eng F. D. Manley and T. C Duffell (T **34**), T. C Duffell (revised lettering for T **28a, 30a**), F. D. Manley (others). All recess with John Ash, W. C. G. McCracken or "By Authority ..." imprints)

1937–49. *W* **15** (*sideways on* 5*d*., 9*d*., 5*s*. *and* 10*s*.). *Chalk-surfaced paper* (3*d*. (*No*. 168), 5*s*., 10*s*., £1).

(*a*) *P* 13½ × 14 (*vert designs*) *or* 14 × 13½ (*horiz*)

	27	½d. orange (3.10.38)	2·50	45
	28	1d. emerald-green (10.5.37)	60	20
	29	1½d. maroon (20.4.38)	9·00	3·50
	30	2d. scarlet (10.5.37)	60	10
	31	3d. blue (Die I) (2.8.37)	60·00	12·00
		a. "White wattles" (from 1st ptg)	£120	70·00
		b. Die Ia	£140	6·50
		c. Die II (3.38)	60·00	3·75
		ca. Bright blue (*ordinary thin paper*) (20.12.38)	60·00	2·75
	32	4d. green (1.2.38)	11·00	1·25
	33	5d. purple (1.12.38)	1·50	60
2	**34**	6d. purple-brown (2.8.37)	20·00	1·25
3	**35**	9d. chocolate (1.9.38)	4·00	1·25
4	**36**	1s. grey-green (2.8.37)	48·00	2·25
5	**31**	1s. 4d. pale magenta (3.10.38)	1·50	1·50
		a. Deep magenta (1943)	3·25	2·00

(*b*) *P* 13½

6	**38**	5s. claret (1.4.38)	14·00	1·50
		a. Thin rough ordinary paper (4.2.48)	3·50	2·25
7	**39**	10s. dull purple (1.4.38)	38·00	13·00
		a. Thin rough ordinary paper (11.48)	42·00	30·00
		s. Optd "Specimen"	30·00	
8	**40**	£1 blue-slate (1.11.38)	60·00	30·00
		a. Thin rough ordinary paper (4.4.49)	55·00	60·00
		s. Optd "Specimen"	£400	
4/78		*Set of* 14	£225	55·00

(*c*) *P* 15×14 (*vert designs*) *or* 14×15 (*horiz*) (1*d*. *and* 2*d*. *redrawn with background evenly shaded and lettering strengthened*)

9	**27**	½d. orange (28.1.42)	55	10
		a. Line to kangaroo's ear	14·00	
		b. Coil pair (1942)	16·00	19·00
		ba. Coil block of four (1943)	£325	
0	**28a**	1d. emerald-green (1.8.38)	3·00	20
1		1d. maroon (10.12.41)	1·50	20
		a. Coil pair (1942)	13·00	18·00
32	**29**	1½d. maroon (21.11.41)	4·00	7·50
33		1½d. emerald-green (10.12.41)	1·00	1·00
34	**30a**	2d. scarlet (11.7.38)	3·00	10
		a. Coil pair (10.41)	£325	£375
		b. Medal flaw	£120	
		w. Wmk inverted (*from booklets*)	5·50	50
35		2d. bright purple (10.12.41)	50	1·00
		a. Coil pair (1942)	42·00	55·00
		b. Medal flaw	42·00	
		w. Wmk inverted (*from coils*)	95·00	38·00
36	**31**	3d. bright blue (Die III) (11.40)	45·00	2·75
37		3d. purple-brown (Die III) (10.12.41)	40	10
38	**32**	4d. green (10.42)	1·00	10
		w. Wmk inverted	†	£800
39	**33**	5d. purple (17.12.45)	50	1·50
90	**34**	6d. red-brown (6.42)	2·00	10
		a. Purple-brown (1944)	1·75	10

191	**35**	9d. chocolate (12.9.43)	1·00	20
192	**36**	1s. grey-green (29.3.41)	1·25	10
		w. Wmk inverted	£850	£500
179/92		*Set of* 14	55·00	13·00

For unwmkd issue, see Nos. 228/30*d*.

Thin paper. Nos. 176a, 177a, 178a. In these varieties the watermark is more clearly visible on the back and the design is much less sharp. On early printings of No. 176a the paper appears tinted.

SPECIAL COIL PERFORATION. This special perforation of large and small holes on the narrow sides of the stamps was introduced after 1939 for stamps issued in coils and was intended to facilitate separation. Where they exist they are listed as "Coil pairs".

The following with "special coil" perforation were placed on sale in *sheets*: Nos. 179, 205, 222*a* (1952), 228, 230, 237, 262 (1953), 309, 311, and 314. These are listed as "Coil blocks of four".

Coils with "normal" perforations also exist for Nos. 180 and 184.

41 "Governor Phillip at Sydney Cove" (J. Alcott)

"Tail" flaw (Left pane R. 7/1. Later retouched)

(Des and eng E. Broad and F. D. Manley. Recess J. Ash)

1937 (1 Oct). 150*th Anniv of Foundation of New South Wales.* *W* **15**. *P* 13½ × 14.

193	**41**	2d. scarlet	2·25	20
		a. "Tail" flaw	£300	70·00
194		3d. bright blue	6·00	2·25
195		9d. purple	16·00	10·00
193/5		*Set of* 3	22·00	11·00

42 A.I.F. and Nurse

(Des and eng F. D. Manley from drawing by Virgil Reilly. Recess W. C. G. McCracken)

1940 (15 July). *Australian Imperial Forces.* *W* **15** (*sideways*). *P* 14 × 13½.

196	**42**	1d. green	1·75	1·75
197		2d. scarlet	1·75	60
198		3d. blue	12·00	8·00
199		6d. brown-purple	22·00	14·00
196/9		*Set of* 4	35·00	22·00

(43) (44) (45)

(Opts designed by F. D. Manley)

1941 (10 Dec). *Nos.* 184, 186 *and* 171 *surch with T* **43/5**.

200	**40b**	2½d. on 2d. scarlet (V.)	60	60
		a. Pair, one without surcharge	£4000	
		b. Medal flaw	£120	
201	**31**	3½d. on 3d. bright blue (Y. on Black)	75	1·75
202	**33**	5½d. on 5d. purple (V.)	3·50	4·25
200/2		*Set of* 3	4·25	6·00

Nos 200/2 were prepared in connection with the imposition of a ½d. "war tax" increase on most postage rates.

One sheet of the 2½d on 2d. was discovered showing the surcharge omitted on R.1/4 and R.1/5.

46 Queen Elizabeth **46a** **47** King George VI

48 King George VI **49** King George VI **50** Emu

(Des F. D. Manley. Eng F. D. Manley and T. C. Duffell (T **46/a**) or F. D. Manley (others))

1942–50. *Recess.* *W* **15**. *P* 15×14.

203	**46**	1d. brown-purple (2.1.43)	80	10
		a. Coil pair (1944)	18·00	25·00
204	**46a**	1½d. green (1.12.42)	80	10
205	**47**	2d. bright purple (4.12.44)	65	85
		b. Coil pair (1.49)	90·00	£100
		ba. Coil block of four (5.50)	£850	
206	**48**	2½d. scarlet (7.1.42)	30	10
		a. Imperf (pair)*	£3000	
		w. Wmk inverted (*from booklets*)	3·75	60
207	**49**	3½d. bright blue (3.42)	60	40
		a. Deep blue	80	40
208	**50**	5½d. slate-blue (12.2.42)	65	10
203/8		*Set of* 6	3·50	1·25

*No. 206a comes in horizontal pair with the right-hand stamp completely imperforate and the left-hand stamp imperforate at right only.

Coils with normal perforations exist for 1d.

For stamps as Nos. 204/5 but without watermark see Nos. 229/30.

The following items are understood to have been the subject of unauthorised leakages from the Commonwealth Note and Stamp Printing Branch and are therefore not listed by us.

It is certain that none of this material was distributed to post offices for issue to the public.

Imperforate all round. 1d. Princess Elizabeth; 1½d. Queen; 2½d. King; 4d. Koala; 6d. Kookaburra; 9d. Platypus; 1s. Lyrebird (small) (also imperf three sides); 1s. 6d. Air Mail (Type **22**); 2½d. Mitchell; 2½d. Newcastle (also imperf three sides or imperf vertically).

Also 2½d. Peace, unwatermarked; 2½d. King, *tête-bêche*; 3½d. Newcastle, in dull ultramarine; 2½d. King on "toned" paper.

52 Duke and Duchess of Gloucester

(Des F. D. Manley. Eng F. D. Manley and T. C. Duffell. Recess)

1945 (19 Feb). *Arrival of Duke and Duchess of Gloucester in Australia.* *W* **15**. *P* 14½.

209	**52**	2½d. lake	10	10
210		3½d. ultramarine	15	70
211		5½d. indigo	20	70
209/11		*Set of* 3	40	1·25

A B

1945 (24 Dec). *Kangaroo type, as No.* 134, *but re-engraved as* B. *W* **15**. *P* 12.

212	**1**	2s. maroon	2·00	4·50
		w. Wmk inverted	†	£2000

No. 134 has two background lines between the value circle and "TWO SHILLINGS"; No. 212 has only one line in this position. There are also differences in the shape of the letters.

53 Star and Wreath **56** Sir Thomas Mitchell and Queensland

(Des F. D. Manley (2½d.), F. D. Manley and G. Lissenden (3½d.), G. Lissenden (5½d.). Eng F. D. Manley. Recess)

1946 (18 Feb). *Victory Commemoration.* *T* **53** *and similar designs.* *W* **15** (*sideways on* 5½*d*.). *P* 14½.

213		2½d. scarlet	10	10
214		3½d. blue	25	75
215		5½d. green	30	50
213/15		*Set of* 3	60	1·25

Designs: *Horiz*—3½d. Flag and dove. *Vert*—5½d. Angel.

These designs were re-issued in 1995 with face values in decimal currency.

(Des F. D. Manley. Eng F. D. Manley and T. C. Duffell. Recess)

1946 (14 Oct). *Centenary of Mitchell's Exploration of Central Queensland.* *W* **15**. *P* 14½.

216	**56**	2½d. scarlet	10	10
217		3½d. blue	35	1·00
218		1s. grey-olive	35	45
216/18		*Set of* 3	70	1·40

57 Lt. John Shortland R.N.

58 Steel Foundry

59 Coal Carrier Cranes

(Des and eng G. Lissenden (5½d.), F. D. Manley (others). Recess)

1947 (8 Sept). *150th Anniv of City of Newcastle, New South Wales. W* **15** *(sideways on 3½d.). P 14½ or 15×14 (2½d.).*

219 **57** 2½d. lake 10 10
220 **58** 3½d. blue 40 80
221 **59** 5½d. green 40 45
219/21 .. .. *Set of* 3 80 1·25

60 Queen Elizabeth II when Princess

(Des R. A. Harrison. Eng. F. D. Manley. Recess)

1947 (20 Nov)–**52**. *Marriage of Princess Elizabeth. P 14×15.*

(a) W **15** *(sideways)*

222 **60** 1d. purple 15 20

(b) No wmk

222*a* **60** 1d. purple (8.48) 10 10
b. Coil pair (1.50) .. .. .. 2·25 4·50
c. Coil block of four (9.52) .. .. 4·75

61 Hereford Bull

61*a* Hermes and Globe

62 Aboriginal Art

62*a* Commonwealth Coat of Arms

(Des G. Sellheim (T **62**), F. D. Manley (others). Eng G. Lissenden (T **62**), F. D. Manley (1s. 3d., 1s. 6d., 5s.), F. D. Manley and R. J. Becker (10s., £1, £2). Recess)

1948 (16 Feb)–**56**. *(a) W* **15** *(sideways). P 14½*

223 **61** 1s. 3d. brown-purple .. .. 1·75 1·10
223*a* **61*a*** 1s. 6d. blackish brown (1.9.49) .. 70 10
224 **62** 2s. chocolate .. .. .. 2·00 10

(b) W **15**. *P 14½×13½*

224*a* **62*a*** 5s. claret (11.4.49) .. .. .. 2·75 20
ab. Thin paper (1951) .. .. 30·00 16·00
224*b* 10s. purple (3.10.49) .. .. .. 14·00 70
224*c* £1 blue (28.11.49) .. .. .. 30·00 3·50
224*d* £2 green (16.1.50) .. .. .. 80·00 14·00
224*bs/ds* Optd "Specimen" .. *Set of* 3 £140

(c) No wmk. P 14½

224*e* **61*a*** 1s. 6d. blackish brown (2.12.56) .. 11·00 1·50
224*f* **62** 2s. chocolate (27.6.56) .. .. 11·00 60
223/4*f* .. .. *Set of* 9 £130 19·00

No. 224ab is an emergency printing on white Harrison paper instead of the toned paper used for No. 224*a*.

No. 224*b* exists with watermark inverted and overprinted "SPECIMEN".

63 William J. Farrer

64 F. von Mueller

65 Boy Scout

(Des and eng F. D. Manley. Recess)

1948 (12 July). *William J. Farrer (wheat research) Commemoration. W* **15**. *P 15×14.*

225 **63** 2½d. scarlet 10 10

(Des and eng F. D. Manley. Recess)

1948 (13 Sept). *Sir Ferdinand von Mueller (botanist) Commemoration. W* **15**. *P 15×14.*

226 **64** 2½d. lake 10 10

(Des and eng F. D. Manley. Recess)

1948 (15 Nov). *Pan-Pacific Scout Jamboree, Wonga Park. W* **15** *(sideways). P 14 × 15.*

227 **65** 2½d. lake 10 10

See also No. 254.

Sky retouch (normally unshaded near hill) (Rt pane R. 6/8) (No. 228a retouched in 1951)

"Green mist" retouch. A large area to the left of the bird's feathers is recut (upper plate left pane R. 9/3)

1948–56. *No wmk. P 15×14 or 14×15 (9d.).*

228 **27** ½d. orange (15.9.49) 20 10
a. Line to kangaroo's ear .. 11·00
b. Sky retouch .. .. 25·00
c. Coil pair (1950) .. .. 75 2·25
ca. Line to kangaroo's ear .. 38·00
cb. Sky retouch (in pair) .. £110
d. Coil block of four (1953) .. 2·75
229 **46*a*** 1½d. green (17.8.49) .. .. 1·25 1·25
230 **47** 2d. bright purple (20.12.48) .. 80 1·25
aa. Coil pair .. .. 3·00 5·50
230*a* **32** 4d. green (18.8.56) .. .. 2·00 1·25
230*b* **34** 6d. purple-brown (18.8.56) .. 5·50 80
230*c* **35** 9d. chocolate (13.12.56) .. 22·00 2·75
230*d* **36** 1s. grey green (13.12.56) .. 4·00 1·00
da. "Green mist" retouch .. £700
228/30*d* .. .. *Set of* 7 32·00 7·50

66 "Henry Lawson" (Sir Lionel Lindsay)

67 Mounted Postman and Convair CV 240 Aircraft

(Des F. D. Manley. Eng. E. R. M. Jones. Recess)

1949 (17 June). *Henry Lawson (poet) Commemoration. P 15×14.*

231 **66** 2½d. maroon 15 10

(Des Sir Daryl Lindsay and F. D. Manley. Eng F. D. Manley. Recess)

1949 (10 Oct). *75th Anniv of Founding of U.P.U. P 15 × 14.*

232 **67** 3½d. ultramarine 30 50

68 John, Lord Forrest of Bunbury

69 Queen Elizabeth

70 King George VI

(Des and eng F. D. Manley. Recess)

1949 (28 Nov). *John, Lord Forrest of Bunbury (explorer and politician) Commemoration. W* **15**. *P 15×14.*

233 **68** 2½d. lake 15 10

(Des and eng F. D. Manley. Recess)

1950 (12 Apr)–**52**. *P 15×14. (a) W* **15**

234 **70** 2½d. scarlet (12.4.50) 10 10
235 3d. scarlet (28.2.51) 15 10
aa. Coil pair (4.51) .. .. 17·00 24·00

(b) No wmk

236 **69** 1½d. green (19.6.50) 40 20
237 2d. yellow-green (28.3.51) .. 15 10
a. Coil pair .. .. 5·00 8·00
b. Coil block of four (11.52) .. 10·00
237*c* **70** 2½d. purple-brown (23.5.51) .. 15 20
237*d* 3d. grey-green (14.11.51) .. 15 10
da. Coil pair (12.51) .. .. 24·00 30·00
234/7*d* .. .. *Set of* 6 1·00 50

On 14 October 1951 No. 235 was placed on sale in sheets of 144 originally intended for use in stamp booklets. These sheets contain 3 panes of 48 (16×3) with horizontal gutter margin between.

71 Aborigine

72

73

Reproductions of First Stamps of N[ew] South Wales and Victoria

(Des and eng F. D. Manley. Recess)

1950 (14 Aug). *W* **15**. *P 15×14.*

238 **71** 8½d. brown 15

For T **71** in a larger size, see Nos. 253/*b*.

(Des and eng G. Lissenden (T **72**), E. R. M. Jones (T **73**). Rec[ess])

1950 (27 Sept). *Centenary of First Adhesive Postage Stamp[s in] Australia. P 15×14.*

239 **72** 2½d. maroon 25
a. Horiz pair. Nos. 239/40 50
240 **73** 2½d. maroon 25

Nos. 239/40 were printed alternately in vertical colu[mns] throughout the sheet.

74 Sir Edmund Barton

75 Sir Henry Parkes

76 "Opening First Federal Parliament" (T. Roberts)

77 Federal Parliament Hou[se,] Canberra

(Des and eng F. D. Manley. Recess)

1951 (1 May). *50th Anniv of Commonwealth of Austral[ia]. P 15×14.*

241 **74** 3d. lake 30
a. Horiz pair. Nos. 241/2 .. .. 1·75 2·
242 **75** 3d. lake 30
243 **76** 5½d. blue .. .. 20 2·
244 **77** 1s. 6d. purple-brown 35
241/4 .. .. *Set of* 4 2·00 2·

Nos. 241/2 are printed alternately in vertical colum[ns] throughout the sheet.

78
E. H. Hargraves

79
C. J. Latrobe

(Des and eng F. D. Manley. Recess)

1951 (2 July). *Centenaries of Discovery of Gold in Austral[ia] and of Responsible Government in Victoria. P 15×14.*

245 **78** 3d. maroon 30
a. Horiz pair. Nos. 245/6 .. .. 80 1·
246 **79** 3d. maroon 30

Nos. 245/6 were printed alternately in vertical colum[ns] throughout the sheet.

80

81

82

King George VI

(Des E. R. M. Jones (7½d.), F. D. Manley (others). Eng. F. D. Manley. Recess)

1951–52. *W* **15** *(sideways on 1s. 0½d.). P 14½ (1s. 0½d.) or 15×14 (others).*

247 **80** 3½d. brown-purple (28.11.51) 10 1
a. Imperf between (horiz pair) .. £6500
248 4½d. scarlet (20.5.52) 15 8
249 6½d. brown (20.2.52) 15 6
250 6½d. emerald-green (9.4.52) 10 1
251 **81** 7½d. blue (31.10.51) 15 4
a. Imperf three sides (vert pr) .. £8500
252 **82** 1s. 0½d. indigo (19.3.52) 60 3
247/52 .. .. *Set of* 6 1·10 2·2

No. 251a occurs on the left-hand vertical row of one sheet.

(Des F. D. Manley. Eng E. R. M. Jones. Recess)

1952 (19 Mar)–**65**. *P 14½. (a) W* **15** *(sideways*)*

253 2s. 6d. deep brown .. .. .. 1·50 3
aw. Wmk Crown to left of C of A .. † £70

(*b*) *No wmk*

2s. 6d. deep brown (30.1.57) .. .. 4·00 75
ba. Sepia (10.65) .. .. 12·00 12·00

gn:—2s. 6d. As T **71** but larger (21×25½ *mm*).
normal sideways watermark on No. 253 shows Crown to f C of A, *as seen from the back of the stamp.*
253*ba* was an emergency printing and can easily be uished from No. 253*b* as it is on white Harrison paper, 3*b* being on toned paper.

(Des and eng F. D. Manley. Recess)

9 Nov). *Pan-Pacific Scout Jamboree, Greystanes. As T* **65**, *nscr* "1952–53". *W* **15** (*sideways*). *P* 14 × 15.
3½d. brown-lake 10 10

STAMP BOOKLETS

strations of booklet covers are reduced to ½ size, *unless vise stated.*
booklets from 1913 to 1949 were stapled.

17 Jan). *Red on pink cover* (SB1) *or blue on pink cover map of Australia on front and picture of State G.P.O. on* (SB2)
2s. booklet containing twelve ½d. and eighteen 1d. (Nos. 1/2) in blocks of 6 .. .. .. £1200
£1 booklet containing two hundred and forty 1d. (No. 2) in blocks of 30 .. .. .. £5000

6 Oct)–**18.** *Red on pink cover* (*Nos.* SB2*a*/3), *black on red er* (*No.* SB4) *or blue on pink cover with map of Australia on t and picture of State G.P.O. on back* (*No.* SB5).
2s. booklet containing twelve ½d. and eighteen 1d. (Nos. 1, 21c) in blocks of 6 .. .. £1500
2s. booklet containing twelve ½d. and eighteen 1d. (Nos. 20, 21c) in blocks of 6 (1915) .. £1500
2s. booklet containing twenty-four 1d. (No. 21c) in blocks of 6 (10.5.17) £1800
a. Black on green cover £1800
b. Red on green cover £1800
£1 booklet containing two hundred and forty 1d. (No. 21c) in blocks of 30 .. .. .. £5000
a. Back cover without G.P.O. picture (1918) ..

ords show that a £1 booklet containing one hundred and ty 2d. stamps was issued in very limited quantities during No examples are known to have survived.

(Jan–Apr). *Black on pink* (*Nos.* SB6/7) *or black on green* s. SB8/9*c*) *covers.*
2s. 3d. booklet containing eighteen 1½d. (No. 58) in blocks of 6 .. .. £1300
a. Black on green cover £1300
2s. 3d. booklet containing eighteen 1½d. (No. 51) in blocks of 6 .. .. £1300
a. Black on green cover £1300
2s. 3d. booklet containing eighteen 1½d. (No. 59) in blocks of 6 (Apr) £1300
a. Black on pink cover £1300
2s. 3d. booklet containing eighteen 1½d. (No. 52) in blocks of 6 (Apr) £1300
a. Black on pink cover .. ..
b. Black on blue cover £1300
c £1 booklet containing one hundred and sixty 1½d. (No. 52) in blocks of 20 (Apr) £5000

) (Dec)–**22.** *Black on blue* (*Nos.* SB10, SB12), *black on hite* (*No.* SB11) *or black on brown* (*No.* SB14) *covers.*
0 2s. booklet containing twelve 2d. (No. 62) in blocks of 6 .. .. £1500
a. Black on pink cover £1500
b. Black on orange cover (3.22) £2000
1 2s. booklet containing twelve 2d. (No. 63) in blocks of 6 (3.22) £1500
a. Black on orange cover (7.22) £2000
b. Black on pink cover £1500
c. Brown on buff cover £1500
d. Black on pink cover £1500
2 £1 booklet containing one hundred and twenty 2d. (No. 62) in blocks of 15 (1.21) £5000
a. Black on pink cover .. .. ..
3 £1 booklet containing ninety 2d. and fifteen 4d. (Nos. 63, 65) in blocks of 15 (3.22) .. ..
4 £1 booklet containing one hundred and twenty 2d. (No. 63) in blocks of 15 (8.22) £2000

3 (Oct)–**24.** *Black on rose* (*No.* SB15), *or green on pale green Nos.* SB16/18) *covers.*
15 2s. 3d. booklet containing eighteen 1½d. (No. 61) in blocks of 6 .. .. £1200
a. Black on pale green cover £1200
b. Green on pale green cover £1200
16 2s. 3d. booklet containing eighteen 1½d. (No. 77) in blocks of 6 (5.24) £1200
17 £1 booklet containing one hundred and sixty 1½d. (No. 61) in blocks of 20 (3.24) .. £4000
18 £1 booklet containing one hundred and sixty 1½d. (No. 77) in blocks of 20 (5.24) .. £4000

27 (Jan–June). *Green on pale green covers.*
19 2s. 3d. booklet containing eighteen 1½d. (No. 87) in blocks of 6 .. .. £750
20 2s. 3d. booklet containing eighteen 1½d. (No. 96) in blocks of 6 .. .. £750
21 £1 booklet containing one hundred and sixty 1½d. (No. 96) in blocks of 20 (June) .. £3750

27 (9 May). *Opening of Parliament House, Canberra. Green on pale green cover with picture of H. M. S.* Renown *on back* (2*s.*).
22 2s. booklet containing sixteen 1½d. (No. 105) in blocks of 8 .. .. 80·00
22*a* 10s. booklet containing eighty 1½d. (No. 105) in blocks of 8 .. ..
Surviving examples of No. SB22*a* are without front cover and ve a blank back cover.

1928 (Nov). *Green on pale green cover.*
SB23 2s. 3d. booklet containing eighteen 1½d. (No. 96a or 96w) in blocks of 6 .. .. .. £325

1930 (July)–**35.** *Air. Black on blue cover inscr* "AIR MAIL. SAVES TIME" *and biplane.*
SB24 3s. booklet containing twelve 3d. (No. 115) in blocks of 4 plus two panes of air mail labels £650
a. Cover inscr "USE THE AIR MAIL" and monoplane (5.35) £1200
b. Black on pale green cover inscr "USE THE AIR MAIL" (5.35) £900

1930 (9 Sept)–**33.** *Green on pale green covers inscr* "USE THE AIR MAIL" *on the back* (2*s*)
SB25 2s. booklet containing twelve 2d. (No. 99a or 99aw) in blocks of 6 .. .. .. £300
SB25*a* 2s. booklet containing twelve 2d. (No. 127 or 127w) in blocks of 6 (1.32) £275
ab. Cover with parcel rates on back (1933) .. £375
SB26 £1 booklet containing one hundred and twenty 2d. (No. 99) in blocks of 20 .. .. £3750
SB26*a* £1 booklet containing one hundred and twenty 2d. (No. 99a) in blocks of 20 .. .. £3750

1934 (June). *Black on cream cover inscr* "Address your mail fully..." *on front.*
SB26*b* 2s. booklet containing twelve 2d. (No. 127 or 127w) in blocks of 6 .. .. .. £450

1935–38. *Black on green cover with Commonwealth Savings Bank advertisement on front inscr* "WHEREVER THERE IS A MONEY ORDER POST OFFICE".
SB26*c* 2s. booklet containing twelve 2d. (No. 127 or 127w) in blocks of 6 .. .. .. £325
ca. Front cover inscr "IN MOST MONEY ORDER OFFICES" (1936) £300
cb. Ditto with waxed interleaves (1938) .. £350

1938 (Dec). *Black on green cover as No.* SB26*c*. *Postal rates on interleaves.*
SB27 2s. booklet containing twelve 2d. (No. 184 or 184w) in blocks of 6 .. .. .. £350
a. With waxed interleaves. Postal rates on back cover £450
b. Black on buff cover £450

1942 (Aug). *Black on buff cover, size* 73×47½ *mm. Postal rates on interleaves.*
SB28 2s. 6d. booklet containing twelve 2½d. (No. 206 or 206w) in blocks of 6, upright within the booklet £110
a. With waxed interleaves. Postal rates on back cover £200

1949 (Sept). *Black on buff cover, size* 79½×42½ *mm including figure of Hermes.*
SB29 2s. 6d. booklet containing twelve 2½d. (No. 206) in blocks of 6, sideways within the booklet 80·00

B 1

1952 (24 June). *Vermilion and deep blue on green cover as Type* B **1**. *Stitched.*
SB30 3s. 6d. booklet containing twelve 3½d. (No. 247) in blocks of 6 .. .. 17·00
a. With waxed interleaves .. .. .. 90·00

POSTAGE DUE STAMPS

POSTAGE DUE PRINTERS. Nos. D1/62 were typographed at the New South Wales Government Printing Office, Sydney. They were not used in Victoria.

D 1 D 2 D 3

Type D 1 adapted from plates of New South Wales Type D 1. No letters at foot.

1902 (1 July). *Chalk-surfaced paper. Wmk Type* D **2** (*inverted on 1d., 3d. and 4d.*). (*a*) *P* 11½, 12
D 1 D **1** ½d. emerald-green *or* dull green .. 3·25 4·25
D 2 1d. emerald-green .. .. .. 12·00 6·00
w. Wmk upright .. .. .. 30·00 20·00
D 3 2d. emerald-green .. .. .. 30·00 7·00
D 4 3d. emerald-green .. .. .. 30·00 20·00
w. Wmk upright .. .. .. 35·00 24·00
D 5 4d. emerald-green .. .. .. 42·00 12·00
w. Wmk upright .. .. .. 50·00 22·00
D 6 6d. emerald-green .. .. .. 55·00 9·50
w. Wmk inverted .. .. .. 55·00 9·50
D 7 8d. emerald-green *or* dull green .. 95·00 75·00
D 8 5s. emerald-green *or* dull green .. £180 70·00
D1/8 .. .. *Set of* 8 £400 £180
D1s/7s Optd "Specimen" .. .. *Set of* 7 £275

(*b*) *P* 11½, 12, *compound with* 11
D 9 D **1** 1d. emerald-green £225 £130
w. Wmk upright £250 £120
D10 2d. emerald-green £300 £120
w. Wmk inverted .. .. .. — £130

(*c*) *P* 11
D12 D **1** 1d. emerald-green (*wmk upright*) .. £900 £375
Stamps may be found showing portions of the marginal watermark "NEW SOUTH WALES POSTAGE".

1902 (July)–**04.** *Type* D **3** (*with space at foot filled in*). *Chalk-surfaced paper. Wmk Type* D **2** (*inverted on* 3*d.,* 4*d.,* 6*d.,* 8*d. and* 5*s.*). (*a*) *P* 11½, 12
D13 D **3** 1d. emerald-green (10.02) .. .. £150 80·00
D14 2d. emerald-green (3.03) .. .. — 85·00
D15 3d. emerald-green (3.03) .. .. £180 65·00
D17 5d. emerald-green .. .. .. 42·00 9·50
D18 10d. emerald-green *or* dull green .. 70·00 17·00
D19 1s. emerald-green .. .. .. 55·00 10·00
D20 2s. emerald-green .. .. .. £100 18·00

(*b*) *P* 11½, 12 *compound with* 11
D22 D **3** ½d. emerald-green *or* dull green (3.04) 7·50 7·00
w. Wmk inverted .. .. .. 8·50 7·00
D23 1d. emerald-green *or* dull grn (10.02) 6·50 2·75
w. Wmk inverted .. .. .. 6·50 2·75
D24 2d. emerald-green *or* dull green (3.03) 20·00 2·75
w. Wmk inverted .. .. .. 20·00 2·75
D25 3d. emerald-green *or* dull green (3.03) 60·00 12·00
w. Wmk upright .. .. .. 85·00 25·00
D26 4d. emerald-green *or* dull green (5.03) 50·00 9·00
w. Wmk upright .. .. .. 50·00 11·00
D27 5d. emerald-green .. .. .. 50·00 18·00
D28 6d. emerald-green (3.04) .. .. 50·00 10·00
D29 8d. emerald-green (3.04) .. .. £120 50·00
D30 10d. emerald-green *or* dull green .. 90·00 18·00
D31 1s. emerald-green .. .. .. 85·00 18·00
D32 2s. emerald-green .. .. .. £120 27·00
D33 5s. emerald-green *or* dull green (5.03) £180 21·00

(*c*) *P* 11
D34 D **3** ½d. emerald-green *or* dull green (*wmk inverted*) (3.04) £190 £130
D35 1d. emerald-green *or* dull grn (10.02) 65·00 22·00
w. Wmk inverted .. .. .. 80·00 30·00
D36 2d. emerald-green (3.03) .. .. £100 24·00
w. Wmk inverted .. .. .. £100 24·00
D37 3d. emerald-green *or* dull green (3.03) 65·00 30·00
w. Wmk upright .. .. .. 65·00 30·00
D38 4d. emerald-green *or* dull green (5.03) £120 45·00
w. Wmk upright .. .. .. £120 45·00
D39 5d. emerald-green .. .. .. £170 40·00
D40 6d. emerald-green (3.04) .. .. 85·00 16·00
D41 1s. emerald-green .. .. .. £190 38·00
D42 5s. emerald-green (5.03) £475 £100
D43 10s. dull green (10.03) £1600 £1300
D44 20s. dull green (10.03) £3500 £2250
D13/44 .. .. *Set of* 14 £5000 £3250
D13s/44s .. .. *Set of* 14 £850
The 10s. and 20s. values were only issued in New South Wales.

D 4 D 6

1906 (Jan)–**08.** *Chalk-surfaced paper. Wmk Type* D **4**.

(*a*) *P* 11½, 12, *compound with* 11
D45 D **3** ½d. green (1.07) .. .. .. 9·50 8·00
w. Wmk inverted .. .. .. 9·50 8·00
D46 1d. green .. .. 13·00 2·75
w. Wmk inverted .. .. .. 13·00 2·75
D47 2d. green .. .. 28·00 4·25
w. Wmk inverted .. .. .. 28·00 4·25
D48 3d. green (7.08) £475 £225
D49 4d. green (4.07) .. .. .. 60·00 21·00
w. Wmk inverted .. .. .. 60·00 21·00
D50 6d. green (3.08) .. .. .. £180 21·00
w. Wmk inverted .. .. .. £180 21·00
D45/50 .. .. *Set of* 6 £700 £250

(*b*) *P* 11
D51 D **3** 1d. green £1200 £475
aw. Wmk inverted .. .. .. — £475
D51*b* 2d. green .. .. † £1000
D52 4d. green (4.07) £1600 £700
No. D51*b* is only known pen-cancelled.
Shades exist.

1907 (July–Sept). *Chalk-surfaced paper. Wmk Type* w **11** (*Crown over double-lined A*) (*inverted on ½d.*). *P* 11½×11.
D53 D **3** ½d. dull green .. .. .. 20·00 55·00
w. Wmk upright .. .. .. 35·00 75·00
D54 1d. dull green (August) .. .. 60·00 35·00
w. Wmk inverted .. .. .. 60·00 35·00
D55 2d. dull green (Sept) .. .. £100 85·00
w. Wmk inverted .. .. .. £120 85·00
D56 4d. dull green (Sept) .. .. £170 85·00
w. Wmk inverted .. .. .. £170 85·00
y. Wmk inverted and reversed .. £300
D57 6d. dull green (Sept) £200 £110
w. Wmk inverted .. .. .. — £190
D53/7 .. .. *Set of* 5 £500 £325

1908 (Sept)–**09.** *Stroke after figure of value. Chalk-surfaced paper. Wmk Type* D **4** (*inverted on* 10*s*).

(*a*) *P* 11½×11
D58 D **6** 1s. dull green (1909) .. .. 75·00 8·50
D59 5s. dull green .. .. .. £200 48·00

(b) P 11

No.	Type	Description	Unused	Used
D60	D 6	2s. dull green (1909)	£850	£1400
D61		10s. dull green (1909)	£2000	£2500
D62		20s. dull green (1909)	£5500	£7000
D58/62		*Set of* 5	£7500	£10000

Nos. D61/2 were only issued in New South Wales.

D 7

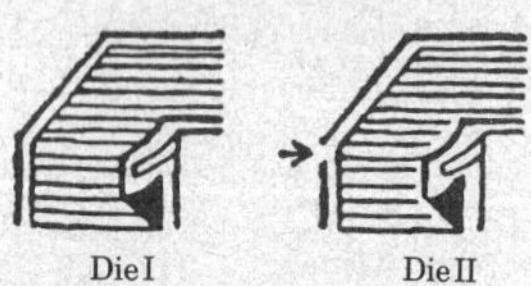

Die I　　Die II

1d.

Die I　　Die II

2d.

(Typo J. B. Cooke, Melbourne)

1909 (1 July)–**10.** *Wmk Crown over A, Type* w **11**.

(a) P 12×12½ (comb)

No.	Type	Description	Unused	Used
D63	D 7	½d. rosine and yellow-green (8.09)	14·00	26·00
D64		1d. rosine and yellow-green (I)	14·00	4·00
		b. Die II (7.10)	18·00	1·75
D65		2d. rosine and yellow-green (I)	24·00	3·50
		a. Die II (8.10)	22·00	1·75
D66		3d. rosine and yellow-green (9.09)	25·00	13·00
D67		4d. rosine and yellow-green (8.09)	22·00	5·00
D68		6d. rosine and yellow-green (8.09)	27·00	7·00
D69		1s. rosine and yellow-green (8.09)	30·00	4·00
D70		2s. rosine and yellow-green (8.09)	70·00	13·00
D71		5s. rosine and yellow-green (10.09)	90·00	15·00
D72		10s. rosine and yellow-green (11.09)	£250	£150
D73		£1 rosine and yellow-green (11.09)	£475	£275
D63/73		*Set of* 11	£900	£450

(b) P 11

No.	Type	Description	Unused	Used
D74	D 7	1d. rose and yellow-green (II)	£1400	£550
D74*a*		2d. rose and yellow-green (II)	£6000	£1500
D75		6d. rose and yellow-green	£6500	£3250

Only one unused example, without gum, and another pen-cancelled are known of No. D74*a*.

The 1d. of this printing is distinguishable from No. D78 by the colours, the green being very yellow and the rose having less of a carmine tone. The paper is thicker and slightly toned, that of No. D78 being pure white; the gum is thick and yellowish, No. D78 having thin white gum.

All later issues of the 1d. and 2d. are Die II.

(Typo J. B. Cooke (later ptgs by T. S. Harrison))

1912 (Dec)–**23.** *Thin paper. White gum.* W w **11**.

(a) P 12½ (line)

No.	Type	Description	Unused	Used
D76	D 7	½d. scarlet & pale yellow-green (7.13)	23·00	26·00
		w. Wmk inverted	38·00	32·00

(b) P 11

No.	Type	Description	Unused	Used
D77	D 7	½d. rosine & brt apple-green (10.14)	11·00	16·00
		a. Wmk sideways	6·50	7·00
D78		1d. rosine & bright apple-green (8.14)	6·00	2·00
		a. Wmk sideways	10·00	2·00
		w. Wmk inverted	40·00	16·00

(c) P 14

No.	Type	Description	Unused	Used
D79	D 7	½d. rosine & brt apple-green (11.14)	80·00	£100
		a. *Carmine & apple-green* (Harrison) (1919)	9·00	16·00
D80		1d. rosine & bright apple-green (9.14)	55·00	12·00
		a. *Scarlet & pale yellow-green* (2.18)	20·00	4·25
		aw. Wmk inverted	†	£300
		b. *Carmine & apple-green* (Harrison) (1919)	12·00	3·75
D81		2d. scarlet & pale yellow-green (1.18)	17·00	6·50
		a. *Carmine & apple-green* (Harrison) (10.18)	18·00	3·50
D82		3d. rosine and apple-green (5.16)	75·00	32·00
		a. Wmk sideways	£1700	£1000
D83		4d. carmine & apple-green (Harrison) (5.21)	90·00	55·00
		b. *Carmine and pale yellow-green*	65·00	50·00
		ba. Wmk sideways	£475	£325
D85		1s. scarlet & pale yellow-green (6.23)	25·00	13·00
D86		10s. scarlet & pale yellow-green (5.21)	£850	
D87		£1 scarlet & pale yellow-green (5.21)	£700	£950

(d) Perf 14 compound with 11

No.	Type	Description	Unused	Used
D88	D 7	1d. carmine and apple-green	£4000	
D76/88		*Set of* 8	£1500	

(Typo T. S. Harrison (to Feb. 1926), A. J. Mullet (to June 1927) and J. Ash (thereafter))

1922 (1 Mar)–**30.** W **6**. *(a) P 14*

No.	Type	Description	Unused	Used
D91	D 7	½d. carmine & yellow-green (17.5.23)	2·50	5·50
D92		1d. carmine and yellow-green	4·00	1·00
D93		1½d. carmine and yellow-green (3.25)	1·50	9·00
D94		2d. carmine and yellow-green (3.3.22)	3·50	2·25
D95		3d. carmine and yellow-green	9·50	3·50
D96		4d. carmine and yellow-green (7.2.22)	35·00	13·00
D97		6d. carmine and yellow-green (8.22)	26·00	12·00

(b) P 11

No.	Type	Description	Unused	Used
D98	D 7	4d. carmine & yellow-green (22.9.30)	6·50	4·50
D91/8		*Set of* 8	75·00	45·00

All values perforated 14 were printed by Harrison and all but the 1d. by Mullett and Ash. The 4d. perforated 11 was produced by J. Ash. There is a wide variation of shades in this issue.

(Typo J. Ash)

1931 (Oct)–**36.** W **15**. *(a) P 14*

No.	Type	Description	Unused	Used
D100	D 7	1d. carmine and yellow-green (10.31)	7·00	11·00
		a. Imperf between (horiz pair)	†	£6500
D102		2d. carmine & yellow-grn (19.10.31)	7·00	11·00

(b) P 11

No.	Type	Description	Unused	Used
D105	D 7	½d. carmine and yellow-green (4.34)	12·00	14·00
D106		1d. carmine & yellow-grn (21.11.32)	7·50	1·50
D107		2d. carmine and yellow-green (1933)	8·50	60
D108		3d. carmine and yellow-green (5.36)	70·00	70·00
D109		4d. carmine & yellow-green (23.5.34)	6·50	2·25
D110		6d. carmine and yellow-green (4.36)	£300	£275
D111		1s. carmine and yellow-green (8.34)	48·00	35·00
D105/11		*Set of* 7	£375	£350

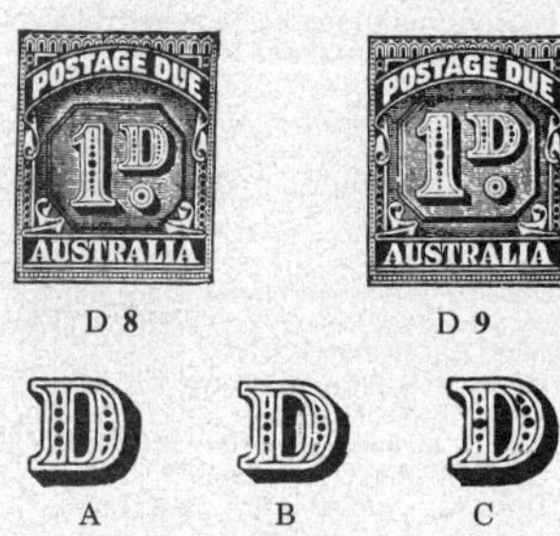

D 8　　D 9

A　　B　　C

Type A. Solid rectangle inside "D" (ptgs of ½d., 1d., 2d., 4d. and 6d. from 1909 to 1945)

Type B. Shaded area inside "D" (ptgs of 3d. from 1909 to 1945)

Type C. Solid segment of circle inside "D" (ptgs of all values below 1s. from 1946)

D　　E

Type D. Six lines of shading above numeral and four below (ptgs of 1s. from 1909 to 1945)

Type E. Larger "1" with only three background lines above; hyphen more upright (ptgs of 1s. from 1946 to 1953)

(Frame recess. Value typo J. Ash to 1940, then W.C.G. McCracken)

1938 (July–Sept). W **15**. *P* 14½×14.

No.	Type	Description	Unused	Used
D112	D 8	½d. carmine and green (A) (Sept)	3·75	2·75
D113		1d. carmine and green (A)	10·00	60
D114		2d. carmine and green (A)	11·00	1·25
D115		3d. carmine and green (B) (Aug)	30·00	13·00
D116		4d. carmine and green (A) (Aug)	13·00	60
D117		6d. carmine and green (A) (Aug)	70·00	42·00
D118		1s. carmine and green (D) (Aug)	50·00	12·00
D112/18		*Set of* 7	£170	65·00

Shades exist

1946–57. *Redrawn as Type* C *and* E *(1s).* W **15**. *P* 14½×14.

No.	Type	Description	Unused	Used
D119	D 9	½d. carmine and green (9.56)	1·25	3·25
D120		1d. carmine and green (17.6.46)	1·25	80
D121		2d. carmine and green (9.46)	4·50	1·25
D122		3d. carmine and green (6.8.46)	6·00	1·25
D123		4d. carmine and green (30.7.52)	9·00	2·00
D124		5d. carmine and green (16.12.48)	12·00	3·50
D125		6d. carmine and green (9.47)	11·00	2·00
D126		7d. carmine and green (26.8.53)	4·25	8·50
D127		8d. carmine and green (24.4.57)	10·00	26·00
D128		1s. carmine and green (9.47)	18·00	1·75
D119/28		*Set of* 10	65·00	45·00

There are many shades in this issue.

OFFICIAL STAMPS

From 1902 the departments of the Commonwealth government were issued with stamps of the various Australian States perforated "OS" to denote official use. These were replaced in 1913 by Commonwealth of Australia issues with similar perforated initials as listed below.

During the same period the administrations of the Australian States used their own stamps and those of the Commonwealth perforated with other initials for the same purpose. These States issues are outside the scope of this catalogue.

Most shades listed under the postage issues also exist perforated "OS". Only those which are worth more than the basic colours are included below.

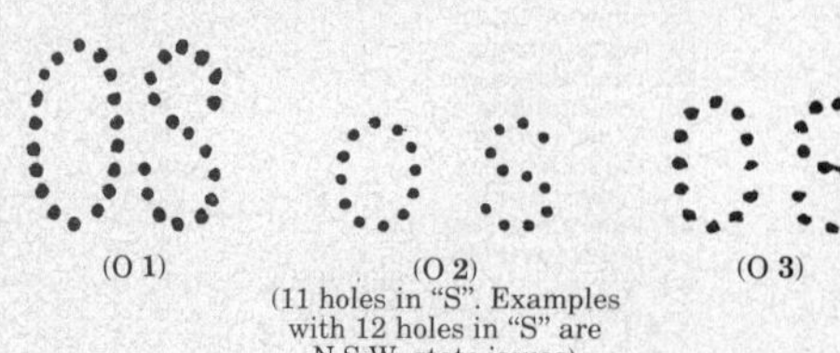

(O 1)　　(O 2) (11 holes in "S". Examples with 12 holes in "S" are N.S.W. state issues)　　(O 3)

1913 (Jan–Apr). *Nos.* 1/16 *punctured as Type* O **1**. *W* **2**.

No.	Type	Description	Unused	Used
O1	1	½d. green (Die I)	13·00	
		w. Wmk inverted	†	
O2		1d. red (Die I)	12·00	
		cw. Wmk inverted	60·00	
		d. Die II	16·00	
		da. Wmk sideways	†	
		dw. Wmk inverted	60·00	
O3		2d. grey (Die I)	25·00	
O4		2½d. indigo (Die II)	£200	
O5		3d. olive (Die I)	75·00	
		ca. In pair with Die II	£550	
		dw. Wmk inverted	85·00	
		e. Die II	£225	
		ew. Wmk inverted	£275	
O6		4d. orange (Die II)	£120	
		a. *Orange-yellow*	£180	
O7		5d. chestnut (Die II)	£100	
O8		6d. ultramarine (Die II)	75·00	
		w. Wmk inverted	£130	
O9		9d. violet (Die II)	90·00	
		w. Wmk inverted	†	
O10		1s. emerald (Die II)	£120	
		w. Wmk inverted	£225	
O11		2s. brown (Die II)	£200	
		a. Double print	†	
O12		5s. grey and yellow	£475	
O13		10s. grey and pink	£1400	
O14		£1 brown and ultramarine	£2250	
O15		£2 black and rose	£4000	
O1/15		*Set of* 15	£8000	

1914. *Nos.* 1/16 *punctured as Type* O **2**. *W* **2**. *P* 12.

No.	Type	Description	Unused	Used
O16	1	½d. green (Die I)	10·00	
		w. Wmk inverted	†	
O17		1d. red (Die I)	12·00	
		d. Die II	19·00	
		e. Die IIA	14·00	
O18		2d. grey (Die I)	45·00	
		w. Wmk inverted	60·00	
O19		2½d. indigo (Die II)	£140	
O20		3d. olive (Die I)	60·00	
		dw. Wmk inverted		
		e. Die II	£150	
		ew. Wmk inverted	£225	
O21		4d. orange (Die II)	£130	
		a. *Orange-yellow*	£180	
O22		5d. chestnut (Die II)	£100	
O23		6d. ultramarine (Die II)	65·00	
		w. Wmk inverted	£110	
O24		9d. violet (Die II)	65·00	
O25		1s. emerald (Die II)	70·00	
O26		2s. brown (Die II)	£170	7
O27		5s. grey and yellow	£750	
O28		10s. grey and pink	£1600	
O29		£1 brown and ultramarine	£2750	
O30		£2 black and rose	£4250	
O16/30		*Set of* 15	£9000	

1915. *Nos.* 24 *and* 26/30 *punctured as Type* O **2**. *W* **5**. *P* 12

No.	Type	Description	Unused	Used
O31	1	2d. grey (Die I)	60·00	1
O33		6d. ultramarine (Die II)	90·00	1
		b. Die IIA	£850	
O34		9d. violet (Die II)	£140	5
O35		1s. blue-green (Die II)	£140	3
O36		2s. brown (Die II)	£425	7
O37		5s. grey and yellow	£500	
		a. Yellow portion doubly printed	†	£1
		w. Wmk inverted	£600	

1914–21. *Nos.* 20/3 *punctured as Type* O **2**. *W* **5**. *P* 14¼ *(comb)*.

No.	Type	Description	Unused	Used
O38	5*a*	½d. bright green	9·00	
		a. Perf 14¼ (line)	†	
		w. Wmk inverted	14·00	
O39		1d. carmine-red (I) (No. 21c)	11·00	
		gw. Wmk inverted	15·00	
		h. Die II	£275	1
O41		4d. orange	38·00	
		a. *Yellow-orange*	55·00	
		b. *Pale orange-yellow*	90·00	1
		c. *Lemon-yellow*	£200	4
		w. Wmk inverted	50·00	1
O42		5d. brown (*p* 14¼ (line))	48·00	3
		aw. Wmk inverted	80·00	18
		b. Printed on the gummed side (wmk inverted)	£650	
		c. Perf 14¼×14 (comb)	48·00	
		cw. Wmk inverted	80·00	1

1915–28. *Nos.* 35/45 *punctured as Type* O **2**. *W* **6**. *P* 12.

No.	Type	Description	Unused	Used
O43	1	2d. grey (Die I)	17·00	4
		bw. Wmk inverted	21·00	6
		d. Die IIA	26·00	13
		da. Printed double	†	
O44		2½d. deep blue (Die II)	42·00	10
		w. Wmk inverted	†	22
O45		3d. yellow-olive (Die I)	22·00	3
		cw. Wmk inverted	26·00	6
		d. Die II	80·00	38
		dw. Wmk inverted	£110	50
		e. Die IIB	22·00	11
		ew. Wmk inverted	32·00	13
O46		6d. ultramarine (Die II)	30·00	4
		a. Die IIA	£550	£1
		d. Die IIB	42·00	11
		dw. Wmk inverted	55·00	16
O47		9d. violet (Die II)	24·00	9
		b. Die IIB	24·00	9
		bw. Wmk inverted	†	13
O48		1s. blue-green (Die II)	23·00	2
		aw. Wmk inverted	50·00	13
		b. Die IIB	23·00	3
O49		2s. brown (Die II)	£110	13
		b. *Red-brown (aniline)*	£250	40
		w. Wmk inverted	£225	65
O50		5s. grey and yellow	£150	42
		w. Wmk inverted	£250	85
O51		10s. grey and pink	£250	60
O52		£1 chocolate and dull blue	£1500	£10
		ab. Wmk sideways. *Chestnut & brt blue*	†	£45
		aw. Wmk inverted	£1900	£13
O53		£2 black and rose	£2000	£8
O43/53		*Set of* 11	£3750	£18

–20. *Nos. 47/f and 5d. as No. 23 punctured as Type* O **2**.
5. *Rough paper. P* 14.
5*a* 1d. scarlet (Die I) . . . . 20·00 4·75
a. Deep red . . . . 20·00 4·75
b. Rose-red . . . . 20·00 4·75
c. Rosine . . . . 55·00 10·00
dw. Wmk inverted . . . . . . 24·00 6·50
e. Die II. *Rose-red* . . . . . . £200 12·00
f. Die II. *Rose* . . . . . . £400 38·00
fw. Wmk inverted . . . . . .
5d. bright chestnut (9.20) £1300 £110
examples of the 5d. on this paper were perforated "OS".

–20. *Nos. 48/52 punctured as Type* O **2**. *W* **6***a*. *P* 14.
5*a* ½d. green . . . . 13·00 2·00
w. Wmk inverted . . . . . . 17·00 8·50
1d. carmine-pink (I) . . . . . . † —
1d. carmine (I) . . . . . . 55·00 28·00
1½d. black-brown . . . . . . 18·00 2·50
a. Very thin paper . . . . . . 35·00 12·00
w. Wmk inverted . . . . . . 42·00 8·50
1½d. red-brown . . . . . . 18·00 2·25
w. Wmk inverted . . . . . . 35·00 8·50
5 . . . . *Set of* 4 95·00 32·00

–23. *Nos. 56/9 and 61/6 punctured as Type* O **2**. *W* **5**. *P* 14.
5*a* ½d. orange . . . . 14·00 10·00
1d. violet . . . . 20·00 9·00
w. Wmk inverted . . . . . . † £2000
1½d. black-brown . . . . . . 22·00 2·75
w. Wmk inverted . . . . . . 32·00 6·50
1½d. deep red-brown . . . . . . 19·00 1·50
aw. Wmk inverted . . . . . . 30·00 6·50
5 1½d. bright red-brown . . . . . . † —
1½d. green . . . . 12·00 1·25
2d. brown-orange . . . . . . 12·00 1·25
w. Wmk inverted . . . . . . 35·00 8·50
2d. bright rose-scarlet . . . . 13·00 4·00
w. Wmk inverted . . . . . . 35·00 13·00
4d. violet . . . . 38·00 13·00
4d. ultramarine . . . . . . 60·00 11·00
1s. 4d. pale blue . . . . . . 50·00 17·00
b. Deep turquoise £600 £350
/75 . . . . *Set of* 10 £225 65·00

–24. *Nos. 73/5 punctured as Type* O **2**. *W* **6**. *P* 12.
1 6d. chestnut (Die IIB) . . . . . . 18·00 2·50
2s. maroon (Die II) . . . . . . 55·00 12·00
£1 grey (Die IIB) £550 £325
/8 . . . . *Set of* 3 £600 £325

4. *Nos. 76/84 punctured as Type* O **2**. *P* 14. (*a*) *W* **5**.
5*a* 1d. sage-green . . . . . . 6·50 2·00
1½d. scarlet . . . . 6·00 60
w. Wmk inverted . . . . . . 55·00 10·00
wa. Printed on the gummed side . . £180
2d. red-brown . . . . . . 20·00 13·00
a. Bright red-brown . . . . . . 35·00 20·00
2 3d. dull ultramarine . . . . . . 32·00 6·00
3 4d. olive-yellow . . . . . . 38·00 6·00
4 4½d. violet . . . . 70·00 12·00
w. Wmk inverted . . . . . . † £1600

(*b*) *W* **6***a*
5 **5***a* 1d. sage-green . . . . 14·00 14·00

(*c*) *No wmk*
6 **5***a* 1d. sage-green . . . . 60·00 55·00
7 1½d. scarlet . . . . 65·00 55·00
9/87 . . . . *Set of* 9 £275 £140

26–30. *Nos. 85/104 punctured as Type* O **2**. *W* **7**. (*a*) *P* 14
8 **5***a* ½d. orange . . . . £150 65·00
9 1d. sage-green . . . . . . 10·00 1·25
0 1½d. scarlet . . . . 18·00 2·00
a. Golden scarlet . . . . . . 20·00 4·50
w. Wmk inverted . . . . . . 19·00 3·00
2 2d. red-brown (Die I) . . . . . . £110 40·00
3 3d. dull ultramarine . . . . . . 50·00 13·00
w. Wmk inverted . . . . . . 50·00 13·00
4 4d. yellow-olive . . . . . . £110 38·00
5 4½d. violet . . . . £110 35·00
6 1s. 4d. pale greenish blue £250 £110
8/96 . . . . *Set of* 8 £700 £275

(*b*) *P* 13½×12½
97 **5***a* ½d. orange . . . . 3·00 1·25
98 1d. sage-green (Die I) . . . . . . 3·00 1·25
b. Die II . . . . 85·00 £110
00 1½d. scarlet . . . . 6·50 1·50
a. Golden scarlet . . . . . . 4·25 1·75
w. Wmk inverted . . . . . . 5·50 2·50
02 1½d. red-brown . . . . . . 14·00 3·75
03 2d. red-brown (Die II) . . . . . . 23·00 12·00
04 2d. golden scarlet (Die II) . . . . 16·00 3·25
a. Die III . . . . 13·00 2·25
aw. Wmk inverted . . . . . . 19·00 6·50
06 3d. dull ultramarine (Die I) . . . . 28·00 5·00
aw. Wmk inverted . . . . . . 28·00 12·00
b. Die II. *Deep ultramarine* . . . . 14·00 1·50
bw. Wmk inverted £2000 £1200
08 4d. yellow-olive . . . . . . 22·00 3·75
09 4½d. violet . . . . 65·00 65·00
10 5d. orange-brown (Die II) . . . . 45·00 7·00
11 1s. 4d. turquoise . . . . . . £170 22·00
7/111 . . . . *Set of* 11 £325 £110

27 (9 May). *Opening of Parliament House, Canberra. No.* 105 *punctured as Type* O **3**.
12 **8** 1½d. brownish lake . . . . . . 14·00 7·50

28 (29 Oct). *National Stamp Exhibition, Melbourne. No.* 106 *punctured as Type* O **2**.
13 3d. blue . . . . 13·00 9·00

29–30. *Nos. 107/14 punctured as Type* O **2**. *W* **7**. *P* 12.
14 **1** 6d. chestnut (Die IIB) . . . . . . 20·00 3·25
15 9d. violet (Die IIB) . . . . . . 38·00 5·50
16 1s. blue-green (Die IIB) . . . . 23·00 3·25
117 2s. maroon (Die II) . . . . . . 65·00 8·00
118 5s. grey and yellow . . . . . . £160 40·00
118*a* 10s. grey and pink . . . . . .
118*b* £2 black and rose £2250

1929 (20 May). *Air. No.* 115 *punctured as Type* O **3**.
O119 **9** 3d. green . . . . 20·00 12·00

1929 (28 Sept). *Centenary of Western Australia. No.* 116 *punctured as Type* O **3**.
O120 **10** 1½d. dull scarlet . . . . . . 13·00 9·00

1930 (2 June). *Centenary of Exploration of River Murray by Capt. Sturt. Nos.* 117/18 *punctured as Type* O **2**.
O121 **11** 1½d. scarlet . . . . 8·00 7·00
O122 3d. blue . . . . 13·00 8·00

OS

(O 4)

1931 (4 May). Nos. 121/2 *optd with Type* O **4**.
O123 **13** 2d. rose-red . . . . 55·00 16·00
O124 3d. blue . . . . £200 32·00
For No. 139 overprinted with Type O **4**, see No. 139*a*.

1932 (Feb)–**33**. *Optd as Type* O **4**. (*a*) *W* **7**. (i) *P* 13½×12½
O125 **5***a* 2d. golden scarlet (Die III) . . . . 8·50 1·50
a. Opt inverted . . . . . . † £3500
w. Wmk inverted . . . . . .
O126 4d. yellow-olive (3.32) . . . . . . 16·00 3·75

(ii) *P* 12
O127 **1** 6d. chestnut (3.32) . . . . . . 40·00 48·00

(*b*) *W* **15**. (i) *P* 13½×12½
O128 **5***a* ½d. orange (11.7.32) . . . . . . 4·75 1·50
a. Opt inverted £5000 £2500
O129 1d. green (3.32) . . . . . . 3·25 45
w. Wmk inverted £200 £100
x. Wmk reversed £325 £150
O130 2d. golden scarlet (Die III) . . . . 7·00 55
a. Opt inverted . . . . . . † £3750
O131 3d. ultramarine (Die II) (2.33) . . 7·50 4·00
O132 5d. orange-brown (7.32) . . . . 35·00 27·00

(ii) *P* 12
O133 **1** 6d. chestnut (9.32) . . . . . . 20·00 20·00
a. Opt inverted . . . . . . † £6000

(*c*) *Recess. No wmk. P* 11
O134 **18** 2d. scarlet (3.32) . . . . . . 5·00 2·00
O135 3d. blue (3.32) . . . . . . 14·00 5·00
O136 **17** 1s. green (3.32) . . . . . . 40·00 27·00
No. O128a and probably the other inverted overprints were caused by the insertion of a stamp upside down into sheets repaired before surcharging.

Issue of overprinted official stamps ceased in February 1933 and thereafter mail from the federal administration was carried free.

BRITISH COMMONWEALTH OCCUPATION FORCE (JAPAN)

Nos. J1/7 were used by the Australian forces occupying Japan after the Second World War. Initially their military post offices supplied unoverprinted Australian stamps, but it was decided to introduce the overprinted issue to prevent currency speculation.

B.C.O.F.
JAPAN
1946
(1)

B.C.O.F.
JAPAN
1946
(2)

1946 Wrong fount "6" (left pane R. 9/4)

O.F.O.F. AN AN — Normal / Narrow "N" (right pane R. 1/8)

1946 (11 Oct)–**48**. *Stamps of Australia optd as T* **1** (*1d., 3d.*) *or T* **2** (*others*) *at Hiroshima Printing Co, Japan.*
J1 **27** ½d. orange (No. 179) . . . . . . 3·25 4·75
a. Wrong fount "6" . . . . . . 75·00 85·00
b. Narrow "N" . . . . 75·00 85·00
c. Stop after "JAPAN" (right pane R.5/5) 75·00 85·00
J2 **46** 1d. brown-purple (No. 203) . . . . 2·50 2·25
a. Blue-black overprint . . . . 55·00 95·00
J3 **31** 3d. purple-brown (No. 187) . . . . 2·00 2·00
a. Opt double £600
J4 **34** 6d. purple-brown (No. 189*a*) (8.5.47) . . 15·00 9·00
a. Wrong fount "6" £200 £150
b. Stop after "JAPAN" (right pane R. 5/5) £200 £150
c. Narrow "N" £200 £150
J5 **36** 1s. grey-green (No. 191) (8.5.47) . . 15·00 11·00
a. Wrong fount "6" £225 £170
b. Stop after "JAPAN" (right pane R. 5/5) £225 £170
c. Narrow "N" £225 £170
J6 **1** 2s. maroon (No. 212) (8.5.47) . . 42·00 45·00
J7 **38** 5s. claret (No. 176) (8.5.47) . . 95·00 £120
a. Thin rough paper (No. 176*a*) (1948) 80·00 £120
J1/7 . . . . *Set of* 7 £140 £170
The ½d., 1d. and 3d. values were first issued on 11 October 1946, and withdrawn two days later, but were re-issued together with the other values on 8 May 1947.
The following values with T **2** in the colours given were from proof sheets which, however, were used for postage: ½d. (red), 1d. (red or black) and 3d. (gold, red or black). (*Prices for black opts £100, each, and for red or gold from £300 each, all un*)

The use of B.C.O.F. stamps ceased on 12 February 1949.

NAURU

Stamps of MARSHALL ISLANDS were used in Nauru from the opening of the German Colonial Post Office on 14 July 1908 until 8 September 1914.
Following the occupation by Australian forces on 6 November 1914 the "N.W. PACIFIC ISLANDS" overprints on Australia (see NEW GUINEA) were used from 2 January 1915.

PRICES FOR STAMPS ON COVER TO 1945	
Nos. 1/12	*from* ×10
Nos. 13/16	*from* ×4
Nos. 17/25	—
Nos. 26/39	*from* × 6
Nos. 40/3	*from* × 10
Nos. 44/7	*from* × 15

BRITISH MANDATE

NAURU (1) NAURU (2) NAURU (3)

1916 (2 Sept)–**23**. *Stamps of Great Britain (1912–22) overprinted at Somerset House.*

(*a*) *With T* **1** (*12½ mm long*) *at foot*
1 ½d. yellow-green . . . . 2·25 6·50
a. "NAUP.U" £350
b. Double opt, one albino . . . . 60·00
2 1d. bright scarlet . . . . . . 1·75 5·00
a. "NAUP.U" £600
2*b* 1d. carmine-red . . . . . . 11·00
bb. Double opt, one albino £225
3 1½d. red-brown (1923) . . . . . . 55·00 80·00
4 2d. orange (Die I) . . . . . . 2·00 13·00
a. "NAUP.U" £350 £450
b. Double opt, one albino £110
y. Wmk inverted and reversed . . £110
5 2d. orange (Die II) (1923) . . . . 70·00 £100
6 2½d. blue . . . . 2·75 7·00
a. "NAUP.U" £400 £500
b. Double opt, one albino £225
7 3d. bluish violet . . . . . . 2·00 3·50
a. "NAUP.U" £425 £550
b. Double opt, one albino £250
8 4d. slate-green . . . . . . 2·00 8·50
a. "NAUP.U" £550 £750
b. Double opt, one albino £225
9 5d. yellow-brown . . . . . . 2·25 8·50
a. "NAUP.U" £850
b. Double opt, one albino £150
10 6d. purple (*chalk-surfaced paper*) . . 3·50 10·00
a. "NAUP.U" £800
b. Double opt, one albino £275

11 9d. agate . . . . 8·50 22·00
a. Double opt, one albino . . £275
12 1s. bistre-brown . . . . 7·00 19·00
a. Double opt, one albino . . £300
s. Optd "Specimen" . . £130
1/12 . . . . *Set of* 11 80·00 £160

(*b*) *With T* 2 (13½ *mm long*) *at centre* (1923)
13 ½d. green . . . . 4·50 42·00
14 1d. scarlet . . . . 19·00 32·00
15 1½d. red-brown . . . . 24·00 42·00
a. Double opt, one albino . . £150
16 2d. orange (Die II) . . . . 30·00 60·00
13/16 . . *Set of* 4 70·00 £160

The "NAUP.U" errors occur on R.6/2 from Control I 16 only. The ink used on this batch of overprints was shiny jet-black.

There is a constant variety consisting of short left stroke to "N" which occurs on Nos. 1, 2, 2*b*, 4 (£30 *each*); 3 (£175); 5 (£200); 6, 7 (£40 *each*); 8, 9, 10 (£60 *each*); 11, 12 (£85 *each*). All unused prices.

(*c*) *With T* 3. (i) *Waterlow printing*
17 5s. rose-carmine £2250 £1600
18 10s. indigo-blue (R.) . . £6000 £4500
a. Double opt, one albino . . £7000 £7000
s. Optd "Specimen" . . £1000

(ii) *De La Rue printing*
19 2s. 6d. deep brown . . £600 £700
a. Double opt, one albino . . £1300
b. Treble opt, two albino . . £1400
s. Optd "Specimen" . . £275
20 2s. 6d. yellow-brown . . 65·00 95·00
21 2s. 6d. pale brown (worn plate) . . 70·00 90·00
a. Re-entry (R. 2/1) . .
s. Optd "Specimen" . . £250
22 5s. bright carmine (*shades*) . . £100 £140
a. Treble opt, two albino . . £650
s. Optd "Specimen" . . £250
23 10s. pale blue (R.) . . £250 £325
a. Treble opt (Blk. + R. + albino) . . £2250
b. Double opt, one albino . . £900
23*c* 10s. deep bright blue (R.) . . £500 £550

(iii) *Bradbury, Wilkinson printing* (1919)
24 2s. 6d. chocolate-brown . . 75·00 £110
a. Major re-entry (R. 1/2) . .
b. Double opt, one albino . . £375
25 2s. 6d. pale brown . . 65·00 95·00
a. Double opt, one albino . . £350

Examples of most values between Nos. 1 and 25 are known showing a forged P.O. Pleasant Island postmark dated "NO 2 21".

AUSTRALIAN MANDATE

4 *Century* (freighter)

(Des R. A. Harrison. Eng T. S. Harrison. Recess Note Printing Branch of the Treasury, Melbourne and from 1926 by the Commonwealth Bank of Australia)

1924–48. *No wmk. P* 11.

A. *Rough surfaced, greyish paper* (1924–34).
26A 4 ½d. chestnut . . . . 1·75 2·75
27A 1d. green . . . . 3·50 2·75
28A 1½d. scarlet . . . . 4·00 4·00
29A 2d. orange . . . . 4·00 11·00
30A 2½d. slate-blue . . . . 6·00 22·00
c. *Greenish blue* (1934) . . 8·00 15·00
31A 3d. pale blue . . . . 4·00 13·00
32A 4d. olive-green . . . . 7·50 17·00
33A 5d. brown . . . . 4·25 6·50
34A 6d. dull violet . . . . 4·75 12·00
35A 9d. olive-brown . . . . 9·50 19·00
36A 1s. brown-lake . . . . 6·50 13·00
37A 2s. 6d. grey-green . . . . 28·00 50·00
38A 5s. claret . . . . 50·00 £100
39A 10s. yellow £130 £180
26A/39A . . *Set of* 14 £225 £400

B. *Shiny surfaced, white paper* (1937–48)
26B 4 ½d. chestnut . . . . 8·00 13·00
c. Perf 14 (1947) . . 1·40 10·00
27B 1d. green . . . . 2·50 3·00
28B 1½d. scarlet . . . . 1·00 1·50
29B 2d. orange . . . . 2·25 8·00
30*d*B 2½d. dull blue (1948) . . 3·00 4·00
da. Imperf between (vert pair) . . £4750 £4750
db. Imperf between (horiz pair) . . £4750 £4750
31cB 3d. greenish grey (1947) . . 3·50 11·00
32B 4d. olive-green . . . . 4·25 13·00
33B 5d. brown . . . . 3·50 4·00
34B 6d. dull violet . . . . 3·25 5·00
35B 9d. olive-brown . . . . 7·50 21·00
36B 1s. brown-lake . . . . 6·50 2·75
37B 2s. 6d. grey-green . . . . 28·00 35·00
38B 5s. claret . . . . 38·00 50·00
39B 10s. yellow £100 £130
26B/39B . . *Set of* 14 £180 £275

HIS MAJESTY'S JUBILEE.

1910 - 1935

(5)

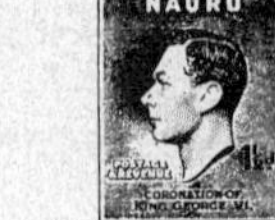

6

1935 (12 July). *Silver Jubilee. T* 4 (*shiny surfaced, white paper*) *optd with T* 5.
40 1½d. scarlet 75 80
41 2d. orange . . . . 1·25 4·00
42 2½d. dull blue . . . . 1·50 1·50
43 1s. brown-lake . . . . 5·00 3·50
40/3 . . *Set of* 4 7·75 9·00

(Recess John Ash, Melbourne)

1937 (10 May). *Coronation. P* 11.
44 6 1½d. scarlet . . . . 45 1·75
45 2d. orange . . . . 45 2·25
46 2½d. blue . . . . 45 1·25
47 1s. purple . . . . 65 1·25
44/7 . . *Set of* 4 1·75 6·00

Japanese forces invaded Nauru on 26 August 1942 and virtually all the inhabitants were removed to Truk in the Caroline Islands.

The Australian army liberated Nauru on 13 September 1945. After an initial period without stamps Australian issues were supplied during October 1945 and were used from Nauru until further supplies of Nos. 26/39 became available. The deportees did not return until early in 1946.

NEW GUINEA

Stamps of Germany and later of GERMAN NEW GUINEA were used in New Guinea from 1888 until 1914.

During the interim period between the "G.R.I." surcharges and the "N.W. PACIFIC ISLANDS" overprints, stamps of AUSTRALIA perforated "OS" were utilised.

PRICES FOR STAMPS ON COVER

Nos. 1/30	*from* × 3
Nos. 31/2	—
Nos. 33/49	*from* × 3
Nos. 50/9	*from* × 2
Nos. 60/2	—
Nos. 63/4	*from* × 2
Nos. 64*c*/*q*	—
Nos. 65/81	*from* × 5
Nos. 83/5	—
Nos. 86/97	*from* × 5
No. 99	—
Nos. 100/16	*from* × 4
Nos. 117/18	—
Nos. 119/24	*from* × 4
Nos. 125/203	*from* × 2
Nos. 204/5	—
Nos. 206/11	*from* × 8
Nos. 212/25	*from* × 2
Nos. O1/33	*from* × 8

AUSTRALIAN OCCUPATION

Stamps of German New Guinea surcharged

G.R.I. 2d. (1) G.R.I. 1s. (2) 1 (3)

SETTINGS. The "G.R.I" issues of New Guinea were surcharged on a small hand press which could only accommodate one horizontal row of stamps at a time. In addition to complete sheets the surcharges were also applied to multiples and individual stamps which were first lightly affixed to plain paper backing sheets. Such backing sheets could contain a mixture of denominations, some of which required different surcharges.

Specialists recognise twelve settings of the low value surcharges (1d. to 8d.):

Setting 1 (Nos. 1/4, 7/11) shows the bottom of the "R" 6 mm from the top of the "d"

Setting 2 (Nos. 16/19, 22/6) shows the bottom of the "R" 5 mm from the top of the "d"

Setting 3 was used for the Official stamps (Nos. O1/2)

Setting 4, which included the 2½d. value for the first time, and Setting 5 showed individual stamps with either 6 mm or 5 mm spacing.

These five settings were for rows of ten stamps, but the remaining seven, used on odd stamps handed in for surcharging, were applied as strips of five only. One has, so far, not been reconstructed, but of the remainder three show the 6 mm spacing, two the 5 mm and one both.

On the shilling values the surcharges were applied as horizontal rows of four and the various settings divide into two groups, one with 3½ to 4½ mm between the bottom of the "R" and the top of numeral, and the second with 5½ mm between the "R" and numeral. The first group includes the very rare initial setting on which the space is 4 to 4½ mm.

G.R.I, 2d. "I" for "1" (Setting 1) G.R.I. 1d. Short "1" (Setting 1) G.R.I. 1s. Large "S" (Setting 1)

1914 (17 Oct)–**15.** *Stamps of* 1901 *surch.*

(*a*) *As T* 1. "G.R.I." *and value* 6 *mm apart*
1 1d. on 3 pf. brown £300 £350
a. "1" for "I" . . £800
b. Short "1" . . £800
c. "1" with straight top serif (Setting 6) £800
d. "I" for "1" (Setting 12) . . £1100
2 1d. on 5 pf. green . . . . 45·00 60·00
a. "1" for "I" . . £200 £275
b. Short "1" . . £200 £275
c. "1" with straight top serif (Settings 6 and 9) . . £325 £375
3 2d. on 10 pf. carmine . . . . 50·00 75·00
a. "1" for "I" . . £250 £325
4 2d. on 20 pf. ultramarine . . 50·00
a. "1" for "I" . . £225
e. Surch double, one "G.R.I." albino . . £2500
f. Surch inverted . . £5000
5 2½d. on 10 pf. carmine (27.2.15) . . 65·00
a. Fraction bar omitted (Setting 9) . . £1200 £
6 2½d. on 20 pf. ultramarine (27.2.15) . . 75·00
a. Fraction bar omitted (Setting 9) . .
7 3d. on 25 pf. black and red/*yellow* . . £190
a. "1" for "I" . . £700
8 3d. on 30 pf. black and orange/*buff* . . £250
a. "1" for "I" . . £750
e. Surch double . . £4750 £
9 4d. on 40 pf. black and carmine . . £250
a. "1" for "I" . . £850
e. Surch double . . £1100 £
f. Surch inverted . . £5000
10 5d. on 50 pf. black and purple/*buff* . . £450
a. "1" for "I" . . £1300 £
e. Surch double . . £5000
11 8d. on 80 pf. black and carmine/*rose* . . £650
a. "1" for "I" . . £1800 £
d. No stop after "d" . . £2250
e. Error. Surch "G.R.I. 4d." . . £4250

(*b*) *As T* 2. "G.R.I." *and value* 3½ *to* 4 *mm apart*
12 1s. on 1 m. carmine . . £1500 £
a. Large "s" . . £4750 £4
13 2s. on 2 m. blue . . £1700 £
a. Large "s" . . £4500 £6
c. Error. Surch "G.R.I. 5s." . . £15000
d. Error. Surch "G.R.I. 2d." corrected by handstamped "S" . . £15000
14 3s. on 3 m. violet-black . . £3250 £4
a. Large "s" . . £6000
b. No stop after "I" (Setting 3) . . £6500 £6
15 5s. on 5 m. carmine and black . . £6500 £8
a. Large "s" . . £13000
b. No stop after "I" (Setting 3) . . £9500 £12
c. Error. Surch "G.R.I. 1s." . . £21000

G.R.I. 3d. Thick "3" (Setting 2) G.R.I. 5d. Thin "5" (Setting 2)

1914 (16 Dec)–**15.** *Stamps of* 1901 *surch.*

(*a*) *As T* 1. "G.R.I." *and value* 5 *mm apart*
16 1d. on 3 pf. brown . . 45·00 5
a. "I" for "1" (Setting 11) . . £425
b. Short "1" (Setting 2) . . £200
c. "1" with straight top serif (Settings 2 and 6) . . 75·00 9
e. Surch double . . £475 £
f. Surch double, one inverted . . £2000
g. Surch inverted . . £1200 £1
h. Error. Surch "G.R.I. 4d." . . £4750
17 1d. on 5 pf. green . . 18·00 3
b. Short "1" (Setting 2) . . £110 £
c. "1" with straight top serif (Setting 2) 35·00 6
e. "d" inverted . . † £1
f. "1d" inverted . . † £3
g. "G.R.I." without stops or spaces . . £3500
ga. "G.R.I." without stops, but with normal spaces . . — £3
h. "G.I.R." instead of "G.R.I." . . £4500 £4
i. Surch double . . £1300
18 2d. on 10 pf. carmine . . 24·00 40
e. No stop after "d" (Setting 2) . . £130 £
f. Stop before, instead of after, "G" (Settings 4 and 5) . . £3500
g. Surch double . . £5000 £5
h. Surch double, one inverted . . — £3
i. In vert pair with No. 20 . . £12000
j. In horiz pair with No. 20 . . £12000
k. Error. Surch ".GR.I. 1d." . . £3750 £3
l. Error. Surch "G.I.R. 3d." . . £4750
19 2d. on 20 pf. ultramarine . . 28·00 4
e. No stop after "d" (Setting 2) . . 95·00 £1
f. No stop after "I" (Setting 11) . . £800
g. "R" inverted (Settings 4 and 5) . . — £3
h. Surch double . . £1000 £1
i. Surch double, one inverted . . £1600 £1
j. Surch inverted . . £3250 £3
k. Albino surch (in horiz pair with normal) . . £9000
l. In vert pair with No. 21 . . £8000 £9
m. Error. Surch "G.R.I. 1d." . . £4750 £4
20 2½d. on 10 pf. carmine (27.2.15) . . £160 £
21 2½d. on 20 pf. ultramarine (27.2.15) . . £1500 £1
a. Error. Surch "G.R.I. 3d." (in vert pair with normal) . . £20000
22 3d. on 25 pf. black and red/*yellow* . . £110 £1
e. Thick "3" . . £500
f. Surch double . . £3750 £4
g. Surch inverted . . £3750 £4
h. Surch omitted (in horiz pair with normal) . . £9000
i. Error. Surch "G.R.I. 1d." . . £8500
23 3d. on 30 pf. black and orange/*buff* . . 90·00 £1
e. No stop after "d" (Setting 2) . . £550
f. Thick "3" . . £475
g. Surch double . . £1200 £1
h. Surch double, one inverted . . £1500 £1
i. Surch double, both inverted . . £3750 £4
j. Surch inverted . . £3250
k. Albino surch . . £6000
l. Surch omitted (in vert pair with normal) . . £4750
m. Error. Surch "G.R.I. 1d." . . £3750 £4
24 4d. on 40 pf. black and carmine . . £100 £1
e. Surch double . . £1000
f. Surch double, one inverted . . £1900
g. Surch double, both inverted . . £4250
h. Surch inverted . . £2500
i. Error. Surch "G.R.I. 1d." . . £2500
ia. Surch "G.R.I. 1d." inverted . . £4250
j. Error. Surch "G.R.I. 3d." double . . £7000
k. No stop after "I" (Setting 11) . . £1900

5d. on 50 pf. black and purple/*buff* .. £160 £190
e. Thin "5" £750 £1300
f. Surch double £1500
g. Surch double, one inverted .. £3250 £4500
h. Surch double, both inverted .. £3750 £4500
i. Surch inverted £2500
j. Error. Surch "G.I.R. 3d." £7500
8d. on 80 pf. black and carmine/*rose* .. £325 £400
e. Surch double £2500 £3000
f. Surch double, one inverted .. £2500 £3000
g. Surch triple £2750 £3250
h. Surch inverted £4000 £4500
i. Error. Surch "G.R.I. 3d." £8000

(*b*) *As T* **2**. "G.R.I." *and value* 5½ *mm apart*
1s. on 1 m. carmine £2500 £3500
a. No stop after "I" (Setting 7) .. £5000
2s. on 2 m. blue £2750 £4250
a. No stop after "I" (Setting 7) .. £5000
3s. on 3 m. violet-black £4500 £7500
a. G.R.I." double £14000
5s. on 5 m. carmine and black £17000 £19000

(Jan). *Nos.* 18 *and* 19 *further surch with T* **3**.
1d. on 2d. on 10 pf. £14000 £14000
1d. on 2d. on 20 pf. £13000 £8500

rman New Guinea Registration Labels surcharged

4

4*a*

G.R.I.

3d.

Sans serif "G" and different "3"

(Jan). *Registration Labels surch* "G.R.I. 3d." *in settings of e or ten and used for postage. Each black and red on buff. scr* "(Deutsch Neuguinea)" *spelt in various ways as licated. P* 14 (*No.* 43) *or* 11½ (*others*).

I. *With name of town in sans-serif letters as T* **4**
Rabaul "(Deutsch Neuguinea)" £180 £200
a. "G.R.I. 3d." double £2000 £2750
b. No bracket before "Deutsch" £700 £900
ba. No bracket and surch double £5000
d. "(Deutsch-Neuguinea)" £250 £375
da. "G.R.I. 3d." double £5000 £5000
db. No stop after "I" £650
dc. "G.R.I. 3d" inverted £5000
dd. No bracket before "Deutsch" £1000 £1400
de. No bracket after "Neuguinea" £1000 £1400
Deulon "(Deutsch Neuguinea)" .. £12000
Friedrich-Wilhelmshafen "(Deutsch Neuguinea)" £170 £450
a. No stop after "d" £325
b. "G" omitted £2750
c. Sans-serif "G" £5500
d. Sans-serif "G" and different "3" .. £4750
e. Surch inverted .. .. † £5000
f. "(Deutsch-Neuguinea)" £180 £450
fa. No stop after "d" £375
Herbertshöhe "(Deutsch Neuguinea)" .. £190 £500
a. No stop after "d" £400
b. No stop after "I" £700
c. "G" omitted £3000
d. Surch omitted (in horiz pair with normal) £7000
e. "(Deutsch Neu-Guinea)" £350 £600
Käwieng "(Deutsch-Neuguinea)" £600
a. No bracket after "Neuguinea" £2500
b. "Deutsch Neu-Guinea" £250 £475
ba. No stop after "d" £425
bb. "G.R.I." double £2500
bc. "3d." double £2500
bd. "G" omitted £3500
Kieta "(Deutsch-Neuguinea)" £350 £600
a. No bracket before "Deutsch" £1200 £1800
b. No stop after "d" £650
c. Surch omitted (righthand stamp of horiz pair) £5500
e. No stop after "I" £950
f. "G" omitted £3250
Manus "(Deutsch Neuguinea)" £200 £550
a. "G.R.I. 3d." double £3000
b. No bracket before "Deutsch" £900 £1400
Stephansort "(Deutsch Neu-Guinea)" .. † £1800
a. No stop after "d" .. .. .. † £3750

II. *With name of town in letters with serifs as T* **4a**
Friedrich Wilhelmshafen "(Deutsch-Neuguinea)" £160 £425
b. No stop after "d" £325 £700
c. No stop after "I" £650 £1000
d. No bracket before "Deutsch" £1000 £1500
e. No bracket after "Neuguinea" £1000 £1500
Käwieng "(Deutsch Neuguinea)" £150 £400
a. No stop after "d" £375
b. No stop after "I" .. .. ..
Manus "(Deutsch-Neuguinea)" £2000 £3000
a. No stop after "I" £3500 £3500

Examples of Nos. 33db, 36b, 38e, 41c and 43a also show the op after "R" either very faint or missing completely.

Stamps of Marshall Islands surcharged

TTINGS. The initial supply of Marshall Islands stamps, ained from Nauru, was surcharged with Setting 2 (5 mm tween "R" and "d") on the penny values and with the 3½ to 4 ting on the shilling stamps.

Small quantities subsequently handed in were surcharged, en on the same backing sheet as German New Guinea values, th Settings 6, 7 or 12 (all 6 mm between "R" and "d") for the nny values and with a 5½ mm setting for the shilling stamps.

1914 (16 Dec). *Stamps of* 1901 *surch*.

(*a*) *As T* **1**. "G.R.I." *and value* 5 *mm apart*
50 1d. on 3 pf. brown .. .. .. 50·00 85·00
c. "1" with straight top serif (Setting 2) £110 £180
d. ".GR.I." and "1" with straight top serif (Settings 4 and 5) .. .. .. † £4500
e. Surch inverted £2750
51 1d. on 5 pf. green .. .. .. 50·00 55·00
c. "1" with straight top serif (Settings 2 and 11) £100 £120
d. "I" for "1" (Setting 11) £700
e. "1" and "d" spaced £275 £300
f. Surch double £1200 £1800
g. Surch inverted £1400
52 2d. on 10 pf. carmine .. .. .. 17·00 26·00
e. No stop after "G" (Setting 2) £550
f. Surch double £1100 £1800
g. Surch double, one inverted £1400 £1800
h. Surch inverted £2250
i. Surch sideways £4000
53 2d. on 20 pf. ultramarine .. .. 18·00 30·00
e. No stop after "d" (Setting 2) .. 45·00 80·00
g. Surch double £1400 £1900
h. Surch double, one inverted £2750 £3000
i. Surch inverted £3500 £3500
54 3d. on 25 pf. black and red/*yellow* .. £275 £375
e. No stop after "d" (Settings 2 and 11) £500 £700
f. Thick "3" £750
g. Surch double £1400 £1900
h. Surch double, one inverted £1400
i. Surch inverted £3500
55 3d. on 30 pf. black and orange/*buff* .. £300 £400
e. No stop after "d" (Setting 2) .. £550 £700
f. Thick "3" £800
g. Surch inverted £2500 £3000
h. Surch double £2250
56 4d. on 40 pf. black and carmine .. £100 £130
e. No stop after "d" (Setting 2) .. £250 £400
f. "d" omitted (Setting 2) .. .. † £3750
g. Surch double £2500 £3000
h. Surch triple £4250
i. Surch inverted £3000
j. Error. Surch "G.R.I. 1d." £6000
k. Error. Surch "G.R.I. 3d." £6000
57 5d. on 50 pf. black and purple/*buff* .. £140 £180
e. Thin "5" £2500
f. "d" omitted (Setting 2) £1400
g. Surch double £3750
h. Surch inverted £4250
58 8d. on 80 pf. black and carmine/*rose* £400 £500
e. Surch double £3000
f. Surch double, both inverted £3750 £4250
g. Surch triple £4500
h. Surch inverted £3500

(*b*) *As T* **2**. "G.R.I." *and value* 3½–4 *mm apart*
59 1s. on 1 m. carmine £1800 £3000
b. No stop after "I" £3250 £4500
e. Surch double £11000
60 2s. on 2 m. blue £1200 £2000
b. No stop after "I" £2500 £3750
e. Surch double £11000
f. Surch double, one inverted £10000 £10000
61 3s. on 3 m. violet-black £3250 £4750
b. No stop after "I" £4500
e. Surch double £12000 £15000
62 5s. on 5 m. carmine and black £6500 £8500
e. Surch double, one inverted .. .. † £19000

1915 (Jan). *Nos.* 52 *and* 53 *further surch with T* **3**.
63 1d. on 2d. on 10 pf. carmine £140 £170
a. "1" double £8000
b. "1" inverted £8500 £8500
c. Small "1" £350
64 1d. on 2d. on 20 pf. ultramarine £3000 £2250
a. On No. 53e £5000 £3000
b. "1" inverted £9000 £9000

The surcharged "1" on No. 63c is just over 4 mm tall. Type **3** is 6 mm tall.

1915. *Stamps of* 1901 *surch*.

(*a*) *As T* **1**. "G.R.I." *and value* 6 *mm apart*
64*c* 1d. on 3 pf. brown £950
cc. "1" with straight top serif (Setting 6) £1400
cd. "I" for "1" (Setting 12) £4250
ce. Surch inverted £1400
64*d* 1d. on 5 pf. green £1000
dc. "1" with straight top serif (Setting 6) £1400
dd. "I" for "1" (Setting 12) £1400
de. Surch inverted £4250
df. Surch double £4250
64*e* 2d. on 10 pf. carmine £1500
ea. Surch sideways £4750
64*f* 2d. on 20 pf. ultramarine £1300
fe. Surch inverted £4250
64*g* 2½d. on 10 pf. carmine £7000
64*h* 2½d. on 20 pf. ultramarine £10000
64*i* 3d. on 25 pf. black and red/*yellow* .. £1700
64*j* 3d. on 30 pf. black and orange/*buff* .. £1700
je. Error. Surch "G.R.I. 1d." £5500
64*k* 4d. on 40 pf. black and carmine £1700
ke. Surch double £4500
kf. Surch inverted £4500
64*l* 5d. on 50 pf. black and purple/*buff* .. £1500
le. Surch double £4500
64*m* 8d. on 80 pf. black and carmine/*rose* .. £2250
me. Surch inverted £5000

(*b*) *As T* **2**. "G.R.I." *and value* 5½ *mm apart*
64*n* 1s. on 1 m. carmine £6500
na. Large "s" (Setting 5) £8000
nb. No stop after "I" (Setting 7) £8000
64*o* 2s. on 2 m. blue £5000
oa. Large "s" (Setting 5) £7500
oe. Surch double, one inverted £19000
64*p* 3s. on 3 m. violet-black £9500
pa. Large "s" (Setting 5) £13000
pb. No stop after "I" (Setting 7) £13000
pe. Surch inverted £19000
64*q* 5s. on 5 m. carmine and black £17000
qa. Large "s" (Setting 5) £20000

Stamps of Australia overprinted

T **1** *of Australia*

T **5a** *of Australia*

W **2** *of Australia*

W **5** *of Australia*

W **6** *of Australia*

N. W. PACIFIC ISLANDS. (*a*) **N. W. PACIFIC ISLANDS.** (*b*) **N. W. PACIFIC ISLANDS.** (*c*)

(6)

1915–16. *Stamps of Australia optd in black as T* **6** (*a*), (*b*) *or* (*c*).

(i) *T* **5a**. *W* **5** *of Australia. P* 14¼×14 (4 Jan–15 Mar 1915)
65 ½d. green .. .. 2·75 7·50
a. Bright green .. .. 3·00 8·50
aw. Wmk inverted .. .. 60·00
67 1d. pale rose (Die I) (4.1) .. .. 7·00 6·50
a. Dull red .. .. 7·00 6·50
b. Carmine-red .. .. 7·00 6·50
ba. Substituted cliché (Pl 2 rt pane R. 6/5) £1200 £750
c. Die II. *Carmine-red* £140 £140
ca. Substituted cliché (Pl 2 rt pane R. 6/4) £1200 £750
70 4d. yellow-orange .. .. 4·00 15·00
a. Pale orange-yellow .. .. .. 17·00 28·00
b. Chrome-yellow £250 £275
c. Line through "FOUR PENCE" (Pl 2 rt pane R. 2/6) (*all shades*) .. *from* £350 £550
72 5d. brown .. .. 2·25 16·00

(ii) *T* **1**. *W* **2** *of Australia. P* 12 (4 Jan 1915–March 1916)
73 2d. grey (Die I) .. .. 18·00 48·00
74 2½d. indigo (Die II) (4.1.15) .. .. 2·75 16·00
76 3d. yellow-olive (Die I) .. .. .. 20·00 48·00
a. Die II £300 £400
ab. In pair with Die I £500 £700
c. Greenish olive £190 £275
ca. Die II £1300
cb. In pair with Die I £2250
78 6d. ultramarine (Die II) .. .. .. 48·00 60·00
a. Retouched "E" £5000 £5500
w. Wmk inverted .. .. 90·00 £110
79 9d. violet (Die II) .. .. 45·00 55·00
81 1s. green (Die II) .. .. 48·00 55·00
83 5s. grey and yellow (Die II) (3.16) .. £750 £1100
84 10s. grey and pink (Die II) (12.15) .. £110 £160
85 £1 brown and ultramarine (Die II) (12.15) £425 £600

(iii) *T* **1**. *W* **5** *of Australia. P* 12 (Oct 1915–July 1916)
86 2d. grey (Die I) .. .. 15·00 18·00
87 2½d. indigo (Die II) (7.16) £10000 £10000
88 6d. ultramarine (Die II) .. .. .. 10·00 12·00
89 9d. violet (Die II) (12.15) .. .. 16·00 21·00
90 1s. emerald (Die II) (12.15) .. .. 11·00 24·00
91 2s. brown (Die II) (12.15) .. .. 85·00 £100
92 5s. grey and yellow (Die II) (12.15) .. 70·00 £100

(iv) *T* **1**. *W* **6** *of Australia. P* 12 (Dec 1915–1916)
94 2d. grey (Die I) .. .. 5·50 13·00
a. In pair with Die IIA £350
96 3d. yellow-olive (Die I) .. .. .. 5·50 11·00
a. Die II .. .. 75·00 £120
ab. In pair with Die I £160
97 2s. brown (Die II) (8.16) .. .. .. 30·00 45·00
w. Wmk inverted .. .. 30·00 70·00
99 £1 chocolate and dull blue (Die II) (8.16) £250 £400

Dates for Nos. 67 and 74 are issue dates at Rabaul. The stamps were in use from 2 January 1915 on Nauru. All other dates are those of despatch. Nos. 65/6, 68/73, 76/81 were despatched on 15 March 1915.

For Die IIA of 2d. see note below Australia No. 45.

SETTINGS. Type **6** exists in three slightly different versions, illustrated above as (*a*), (*b*), *and* (*c*). These differ in the letters "S" of "ISLANDS" as follows:

(*a*) Both "SS" normal.
(*b*) First "S" with small head and large tail and second "S" normal.
(*c*) Both "SS" with small head and large tail.

Type **11**, which also shows the examples of "S" as the normal version, can be identified from Type **6**(*a*) by the relative position of the second and third lines of the overprint. On Type **6***a* the "P" of "PACIFIC" is exactly over the first "S" of "ISLANDS". On Type **11** the "P" appears over the space between "I" and "S".

It has been established, by the study of minor variations, that there are actually six settings of the "N.W. PACIFIC ISLANDS" overprint, including that represented by T **11**, but the following are the different arrangements of Type **6**(*a*), (*b*), and (*c*) which occur.

A. Horizontal rows 1 and 2 all Type (*a*). Row 3 all Type (*b*). Rows 4 and 5 all Type (*c*).

B. (½d. green only). As A, except that the types in the bottom row run (*c*) (*c*) (*c*) (*c*) (*b*) (*c*).

C. As A, but bottom row now shows types (*a*) (*c*) (*c*) (*c*) (*b*) (*c*).

Horizontal strips and pairs showing varieties (*a*) and (*c*), or (*b*) and (*c*) *se-tenant* are scarce.

The earliest printing of the 1d. and 2½d. values was made on sheets with margin attached on two sides, the later printings being on sheets from which the margins had been removed. In this printing the vertical distances between the overprints are less than in later printings, so that in the lower horizontal rows of the sheet the overprint is near the top of the stamp.

The settings used on King George stamps and on the Kangaroo type are similar, but the latter stamps being smaller the overprints are closer together in the vertical rows.

PURPLE OVERPRINTS. We no longer differentiate between purple and black overprints in the above series. In our opinion the two colours are nowadays insufficiently distinct to warrant separation.

PRICES. The prices quoted for Nos. 65 to 101 apply to stamps with opts Types **6** (*a*) or **6** (*c*). Stamps with opt Type **6** (*b*) are worth a 25 per cent premium. Vertical strips of three, showing (*a*), (*b*) and (*c*), are worth from four times the prices quoted for singles as Types **6** (*a*) or **6** (*c*).

One Penny

(10)

N. W.
PACIFIC
ISLANDS.

(11)

1918 (23 May). *Nos. 72 and 81 surch locally with T* **10**.

100	1d. on 5d. brown	90·00	80·00
101	1d. on 1s. green	90·00	75·00

Types **6** (*a*), (*b*), (*c*) occur on these stamps also.

1918–23. *Stamps of Australia optd with T* **11** ("P" *of* "PACIFIC" *over space between* "I" *and* "S" *of* "ISLANDS").

(i) *T* **5a**. *W* **5** *of Australia. P* 14¼×14

102	½d. green	1·25	3·50
103	1d. carmine-red (Die I)	2·50	1·60
	a. Substituted cliché (Pl 2 rt pane R. 6/5)	£650	£375
	b. Die II	£110	48·00
	ba. Substituted cliché (Pl 2 rt pane R. 6/4)	£650	£375
104	4d. yellow-orange (1919)	3·25	16·00
	a. Line through "FOUR PENCE" (Pl 2 rt pane R. 2/6)	£800	£1200
105	5d. brown (1919)	2·00	12·00

(ii) *T* **1**. *W* **6** *of Australia. P* 12

106	2d. grey (Die I) (1919)	7·00	18·00
	a. Die II	11·00	40·00
107	2½d. indigo (Die II) (1919)	3·00	16·00
	a. "1" of "½" omitted	£5500	£7000
	b. Blue (1920)	7·00	25·00
109	3d. greenish olive (Die I) (1919)	23·00	26·00
	a. Die II	48·00	60·00
	ab. In pair with Die I	£325	£400
	b. Light olive (Die IIB) (1923)	23·00	32·00
110	6d. ultramarine (Die II) (1919)	4·50	14·00
	a. Greyish ultramarine (1922)	42·00	65·00
112	9d. violet (Die IIB) (1919)	8·00	35·00
113	1s. emerald (Die II)	6·50	30·00
	a. Pale blue-green	14·00	30·00
115	2s. brown (Die II) (1919)	21·00	38·00
116	5s. grey and yellow (Die II) (1919)	60·00	65·00
117	10s. grey and bright pink (Die II) (1919)	£150	£200
118	£1 bistre-brown & grey-bl (Die II) (1922)	£2750	£4000

(iii) *T* **5a**. *W* **6a** *of Australia* (*Mult Crown A*). *P* 14

119	½d. green (1919)	75	3·50
	w. Wmk inverted	38·00	

(iv) *T* **5a**. *W* **5** *of Australia. Colour changes and new value*

120	1d. violet (*shades*) (1922)	1·75	6·50
121	2d. orange (1921)	5·50	3·25
122	2d. rose-scarlet (1922)	9·00	4·50
123	4d. violet (1922)	20·00	40·00
	a. "FOUR PENCE" in thinner letters (Pl 2 rt pane R. 2/6)	£650	£1000
124	4d. ultramarine (1922)	11·00	55·00
	a. "FOUR PENCE" in thinner letters (Pl 2 rt pane R. 2/6)	£750	
120/4	*Set of* 5	42·00	£100

Type **11** differs from Type **6** (*a*) in the position of the "P" of "PACIFIC", which is further to the left in Type **11**.

For 1d. rosine Dies I and II on rough unsurfaced paper see Nos. O16/b.

MANDATED TERRITORY OF NEW GUINEA

A civil administration for the Mandated Territory of New Guinea was established on 9 May 1921.

PRINTERS. See note at the beginning of Australia.

12 Native Village

(13)

(Des R. Harrison. Eng T. Harrison. Recess Note Printing Branch, Treasury, Melbourne, from 1926 Note Ptg Branch, Commonwealth Bank of Australia, Melbourne)

1925 (23 Jan)–**28.** *P* 11.

125	**12**	½d. orange	2·50	7·00
126		1d. green	2·50	5·50
126*a*		1½d. orange-vermilion (1926)	3·25	2·75
127		2d. claret	2·50	4·50
128		3d. blue	4·50	4·00
129		4d. olive-green	13·00	19·00
130		6d. dull yellow-brown	20·00	48·00
		a. Olive-bistre (1927)	6·00	48·00
		b. Pale yellow-bistre (1928)	4·50	48·00
131		9d. dull purple (*to violet*)	13·00	45·00
132		1s. dull blue-green (6.4.25)	15·00	26·00
133		2s. brown-lake (6.4.25)	30·00	48·00
134		5s. olive-bistre (6.4.25)	48·00	65·00
135		10s. dull rose (6.4.25)	£100	£180
136		£1 dull olive-green (6.4.25)	£190	£300
125/36		*Set of* 13	£375	£600

1931 (8 June). *Air. Optd with T* **13.** *P* 11.

137	**12**	½d. orange	1·50	5·50
138		1d. green	1·60	5·00
139		1½d. orange-vermilion	1·25	5·00
140		2d. claret	1·25	7·00
141		3d. blue	1·75	13·00
142		4d. olive-green	1·25	9·00
143		6d. pale yellow-bistre	1·75	14·00
144		9d. violet	3·00	17·00
145		1s. dull blue-green	3·00	17·00
146		2s. brown-lake	7·00	40·00
147		5s. olive-bistre	20·00	65·00
148		10s. bright pink	75·00	£100
149		£1 olive-grey	£130	£225
137/49		*Set of* 13	£225	£475

14 Raggiana Bird of Paradise (Dates either side of value)

AIR MAIL

(15)

(Recess John Ash, Melbourne)

1931 (2 Aug). *Tenth Anniv of Australian Administration. T* **14** (*with dates*). *P* 11.

150	**14**	1d. green	4·00	1·00
151		1½d. vermilion	5·00	10·00
152		2d. claret	5·00	2·25
153		3d. blue	5·00	4·75
154		4d. olive-green	6·50	18·00
155		5d. deep blue-green	5·00	18·00
156		6d. bistre-brown	5·00	18·00
157		9d. violet	8·50	18·00
158		1s. pale blue-green	6·00	15·00
159		2s. brown-lake	10·00	28·00
160		5s. olive-brown	42·00	55·00
161		10s. bright pink	80·00	£130
162		£1 olive-grey	£180	£250
150/62		*Set of* 13	£325	£500

1931 (2 Aug). *Air. Optd with T* **15**.

163	**14**	½d. orange	3·25	3·25
164		1d. green	3·75	4·75
165		1½d. vermilion	3·75	10·00
166		2d. claret	3·25	3·00
167		3d. blue	6·00	6·50
168		4d. olive-green	6·00	6·00
169		5d. deep blue-green	6·00	11·00
170		6d. bistre-brown	7·00	26·00
171		9d. violet	8·00	15·00
172		1s. pale blue-green	7·50	15·00
173		2s. dull lake	16·00	48·00
174		5s. olive-brown	42·00	70·00
175		10s. bright pink	60·00	£120
176		£1 olive-grey	£110	£225
163/76		*Set of* 14	£250	£500

1932 (30 June)–**1934.** *T* **14** (*redrawn without dates*). *P* 11.

177	1d. green	1·50	20
178	1½d. claret	1·50	11·00
179	2d. vermilion	1·50	20
179*a*	2½d. green (14.9.34)	6·50	18·00
180	3d. blue	2·25	80
180*a*	3½d. aniline carmine (14.9.34)	13·00	9·50
181	4d. olive-green	1·75	6·00
182	5d. deep blue-green	1·75	70
183	6d. bistre-brown	3·25	3·25
184	9d. violet	9·50	22·00
185	1s. blue-green	4·50	10·00
186	2s. dull lake	4·00	17·00
187	5s. olive	27·00	45·00
188	10s. pink	48·00	70·00
189	£1 olive-grey	95·00	£100
177/89	*Set of* 15	£200	£275

1932 (30 June)–**34.** *Air. T* **14** (*redrawn without dates*), *optd with T* **15.** *P* 11.

190	½d. orange	60	1·50
191	1d. green	1·25	1·50
192	1½d. claret	1·75	7·00
193	2d. vermilion	1·75	30
193*a*	2½d. green (14.9.34)	6·00	2·50
194	3d. blue	3·25	3·00
194*a*	3½d. aniline carmine (14.9.34)	4·50	3·25
195	4d. olive-green	4·50	10·00
196	5d. deep blue-green	7·00	7·50
197	6d. bistre-brown	4·50	15·00
198	9d. violet	6·00	9·00
199	1s. pale blue-green	6·00	9·00
200	2s. dull lake	10·00	
201	5s. olive-brown	48·00	
202	10s. pink	75·00	
203	£1 olive-grey	75·00	
190/203	*Set of* 16	£225	

The ½d. orange redrawn without dates exists wi overprint, but it is believed that this was not issued (*Price un*).

16 Bulolo Goldfields

(Recess John Ash, Melbourne)

1935 (1 May). *Air. P* 11.

204 **16**	£2 bright violet	£200	
205	£5 emerald-green	£500	

(17)

18

1935 (27 June). *Silver Jubilee. As Nos.* 177 *and* 179, *but s... paper. Optd with T* **17**.

206	1d. green	60
207	2d. vermilion	1·75

(Recess John Ash, Melbourne)

1937 (18 May). *Coronation. P* 11.

208 **18**	2d. scarlet	50	
209	3d. blue	50	
210	5d. green	50	
	a. Re-entry (design completely duplicated) (Pl 2a R. 5/2)	55·00	8
211	1s. purple	50	
208/11	*Set of* 4	1·75	

(Recess John Ash, Melbourne)

1939 (1 Mar). *Air. Inscr* "AIR MAIL POSTAGE" *at foot. P* 11.

212 **16**	½d. orange	3·50	
213	1d. green	3·25	
214	1½d. claret	3·75	
215	2d. vermilion	7·50	
216	3d. blue	11·00	1
217	4d. yellow-olive	12·00	
218	5d. deep green	10·00	
219	6d. bistre-brown	22·00	1
220	9d. violet	22·00	2
221	1s. pale blue-green	22·00	1
222	2s. dull lake	60·00	4
223	5s. olive-brown	£130	95
224	10s. pink	£325	£
225	£1 olive-green	£100	£
212/25	*Set of* 14	£650	£

OFFICIAL STAMPS

O. S.

G.R.I.

1d.

(O 1)

O S

(O 2)

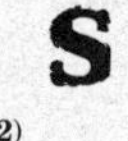

(O 3)

1915 (27 Feb). *Stamps of* 1901 *surch as Type* O **1**. "G.R.I." *a... value* 3½ *mm apart.*

O1	1d. on 3 pf. brown	25·00	75
	a. "1" and "d" spaced	75·00	£1
	b. Surch double	£2250	
O2	1d. on 5 pf. green	80·00	£1
	a. "1" and "d" spaced	£160	£3

1919–23. *Stamps of Australia optd with T* **11** *and punctur...* "O S" (8×15½ *mm with eleven holes in the perforated* "S").

(i) *T* **5a** *of Australia. W* **5**. *P* 14¼×14

O 3	1d. carmine-red (Die I)	90·00	20·
	b. Die II	—	£2
O 4	4d. yellow-orange	£100	40·
	a. Line through "FOUR PENCE" (Pl 2 rt pane R. 2/6)		
O 5	5d. brown (1921)	£150	40·

(ii) *T* **1** *of Australia. W* **6**. *P* 12

O 6	2d. grey (Die I)	£150	30·
O 7	2½d. indigo (Die II)	£250	£1
	b. Blue	£350	£1
O 8	3d. greenish olive (Die I) (1921)	£300	60·
O 9	6d. ultramarine (Die II) (1921)	£300	£1
	a. Greyish ultramarine	£250	£1
O10	9d. violet (Die IIB) (1921)	75·00	60·
O11	1s. emerald (Die II) (1921)	£150	75·
	a. Pale blue-green	£200	75·
O12	2s. brown (Die II) (1922)	£120	75·
O13	5s. grey and yellow (Die II) (1922)	—	£2
O14	10s. grey and bright pink (Die II) (1921)		

(iii) *T* **5a** *of Australia. W* **5**. *Rough unsurfaced paper, locally gummed. P* 14

O16	1d. rosine (Die I) (1920)	£400	£12
	b. Die II	£1100	£40

T 5a *of Australia.* W 5. *Colour changes and new value.*
P 14

1d. violet (*shades*) (1923) .. .. £150 20·00
2d. orange (1921) .. .. .. 60·00 20·00
2d. rose-scarlet (1923) .. .. £150 15·00
4d. violet (1921) .. .. .. £100 50·00
a. "FOUR PENCE" in thinner letters (Pl 2 rt pane R. 2/6) .. ..
4d. ultramarine (1922) .. .. .. £130 60·00

·tes quoted for Nos. O3/21 are those of despatch from ·ralia. The earliest postmark date recorded is 2 April 1919 ·o. O3. Their continued use on mail from government ·rtments after the establishment of the civil administration ·firmed by a notice in the official *New Guinea Gazette* of ·gust 1921.

·stralian postal archives indicate that nine sheets of the £1 1 perforated "O S" were sent to New Guinea in September . There is a pane of 30 of this stamp in the Royal Collection, ·s no other examples are known it may not have been issued ·stal purposes.

(6 Apr)–**31.** *Optd with Type* O 2. *P* 11.

12 1d. green .. .. 1·00 4·50
1½d. orange-vermilion (1931) .. 5·50 17·00
2d. claret .. .. 1·75 3·75
3d. blue .. .. 3·50 7·00
4d. olive-green .. .. .. 4·50 8·50
6d. olive-bistre .. .. .. 20·00 35·00
a. Pale yellow-bistre (1931) .. 7·00 35·00
9d. violet .. .. 4·00 35·00
1s. dull blue-green .. .. .. 5·50 35·00
2s. brown-lake .. .. .. 28·00 60·00
·30 .. .. *Set of* 9 55·00 £180

(2 Aug). *Optd with Type* O 3. *P* 11.

14 1d. green .. .. 5·00 13·00
1½d. vermilion .. .. .. 6·50 12·00
2d. claret .. .. 10·00 7·00
3d. blue .. .. 6·50 6·00
4d. olive-green .. .. .. 5·00 8·50
5d. deep blue-green .. .. .. 10·00 12·00
6d. bistre-brown .. .. .. 13·00 17·00
9d. violet .. .. 16·00 28·00
1s. pale blue-green .. .. .. 16·00 28·00
2s. brown-lake .. .. .. 40·00 70·00
5s. olive-brown .. .. .. 95·00 £170
·41 .. .. *Set of* 11 £200 £350

· (30 June)–**34.** T 14 (*redrawn without dates*), *optd with* ·*pe* O 3. *P* 11.

1d. green .. .. 5·50 5·50
1½d. claret .. .. 6·50 12·00
2d. vermilion .. .. .. 6·50 3·25
2½d. green (14.9.34) .. .. 3·25 6·00
3d. blue .. .. 7·00 23·00
3½d. aniline carmine (14.9.34) .. 3·25 9·00
4d. olive-green .. .. .. 6·50 17·00
5d. deep blue-green .. .. .. 6·00 17·00
6d. bistre-brown .. .. .. 10·00 38·00
9d. violet .. .. 10·00 40·00
1s. pale blue-green .. .. .. 15·00 28·00
2s. dull lake .. .. 35·00 75·00
5s. olive-brown £120 £170
·/54 .. .. *Set of* 13 £200 £400

·ivil Administration in New Guinea was suspended in 1942, ·owing the Japanese invasion.

·arious New Guinea stamps exist overprinted with an anchor · three Japanese characters in a style similar to the Japanese ·val Control Area overprints found on the stamps of ·therlands Indies. These overprints on New Guinea are bogus. ·o different versions are known, one produced in Japan during ·7 and the other in Australia during the late 1980s.

·n resumption, after the Japanese defeat in 1945, Australian ·mps were used until the appearance of the issue for the ·bined territories of Papua & New Guinea.

NORFOLK ISLAND

·Norfolk Island, first settled in 1788 from New South Wales, ·s transferred to Tasmania on 29 September 1844. It became a ·parate settlement on 1 November 1856 under the control of · Governor of New South Wales. The island was declared an ·stralian Territory on 1 July 1914. Unlike the other External ·rritories it retains an independent postal administration.

A Post Office was opened on Norfolk Island in 1832. The ·stamps of TASMANIA were used on Norfolk Island from July 1854 until May 1855, such use being identified by the "72" numeral cancellation. Stamps of NEW SOUTH WALES were first used on the island in 1877, but were not regularly available until 1898. The first "NORFOLK ISLAND" cancellation was supplied in 1892, but not used until 1898. Stamps of AUSTRALIA were in use from 1913 to 1947.

1 Ball Bay

·es and eng F. Manley. Recess Note Printing Branch, Reserve Bank of Australia)

·**47** (10 June)–**59.** *Toned paper. P* 14.

1 ½d. orange 85 60
a. White paper (11.56) .. .. 1·10 5·50
· 1d. bright violet 50 60
a. White paper (8.57) .. .. 5·00 15·00
· 1½d. emerald-green 50 70
a. White paper (11.56) .. .. 7·50 20·00
· 2d. reddish violet 55 40
a. White paper (11.56) .. .. 90·00 £130
· 2½d. scarlet 80 30

6 1 3d. chestnut 70 70
6*a* 3d. emerald-green (*white paper*) (6.7.59) 16·00 7·50
7 4d. claret .. .. 1·50 40
8 5½d. indigo 70 30
9 6d. purple-brown 70 30
10 9d. magenta .. .. 1·25 40
11 1s. grey-green 70 40
12 2s. yellow-bistre .. .. .. 1·00 1·00
12*a* 2s. deep blue (*white paper*) (6.7.59) .. 24·00 8·00
1/12*a* .. .. *Set of* 14 45·00 19·00

Stamps as Type 1, some in different colours, perforated 11 were prepared in 1940, but never issued. Examples exist from sheets stolen prior to the destruction of these stocks.

PAPUA (BRITISH NEW GUINEA)

Stamps of QUEENSLAND were used in British New Guinea (Papua) from at least 1885 onwards. Post Offices were opened at Daru (1894), Kulumadau (Woodlarks) (1899), Nivani (1899), Port Moresby (1885), Samarai (1888), Sudest (1899) and Tamata (1899). Stamps were usually cancelled "N.G." (at Port Moresby from 1885) or "BNG" (without stops at Samarai or with stops at the other offices) from 1888. Queensland stamps were replaced in Papua by the issue of 1901.

PRICES FOR STAMPS ON COVER

Nos. 1/7	*from* × 15
No. 8	—
Nos. 9/15	*from* × 20
No. 16	—
Nos. 17/27	*from* × 6
No. 28	—
Nos. 39/45*a*	*from* × 5
Nos. 47/71	*from* × 8
Nos. 72/4	—
Nos. 75/92*a*	*from* × 8
Nos. 93/103	*from* × 6
Nos. 104/5	—
Nos. 106/11	*from* × 10
Nos. 112/14	*from* × 6
No. 115	—
Nos. 116/28	*from* × 5
Nos. 130/53	*from* × 4
Nos. 154/7	*from* × 12
Nos. 158/67	*from* × 4
No. 168	*from* × 3
Nos. O1/54	*from* × 10
Nos. O55/66*a*	*from* × 7

1 Lakatoi (trading canoe) with Hanuabada Village in Background

2 (Horizontal)

Deformed "d" at left (R. 4/3)

(Recess D.L.R.)

1901 (1 July)–**05.** *Wmk Mult Rosettes,* W 2. *P* 14.

A. *Wmk horizontal. Thick paper. Line perf*

1 1 ½d. black and yellow-green .. .. 9·50 16·00
a. Thin paper £170 £140
2 1d. black and carmine .. .. .. 7·00 10·00
3 2d. black and violet .. .. .. 9·00 7·00
4 2½d. black and ultramarine .. .. 18·00 10·00
a. Thin paper £225 £160
ab. Black and dull blue £500 £350
5 4d. black and sepia .. .. .. 48·00 35·00
a. Deformed "d" at left £250 £200
6 6d. black and myrtle-green .. .. 45·00 35·00
7 1s. black and orange .. .. .. 60·00 65·00
8 2s. 6d. black and brown (1.1.05) .. £550 £500

B. *Wmk vertical. Medium to thick paper. Line or comb perf*

9 1 ½d. black and yellow-green .. .. 6·50 3·75
a. Thin paper (*comb perf*) (1905) .. 14·00 23·00
10 1d. black and carmine .. .. .. 3·50 2·00
11 2d. black and violet .. .. .. 9·50 4·00
a. Thin paper (*comb perf*) (1905) .. 48·00 16·00
12 2½d. black and ultramarine (*shades*) .. 9·50 12·00
13 4d. black and sepia .. .. .. 32·00 50·00
a. Deformed "d" at left £200 £275
b. Thin paper (*comb perf*) (1905) .. £190
ba. Deformed "d" at left £850
14 6d. black and myrtle-green .. .. 48·00 70·00
a. Thin paper (*comb perf*) (1905) .. £600
15 1s. black and orange .. .. .. 55·00 80·00
a. Thin paper (*comb perf*) (1905) .. £550
16 2s. 6d. black and brown (1905) .. £3000 £2250
a. Thin paper (*comb perf*) £500 £1000
1/16 .. .. *Set of* 8 £600 £600

The paper used for Nos. 1/8 is white, of consistent thickness and rather opaque. The thin paper used for the horizontal watermark printings is of variable thickness, readily distinguishable from the thick paper by its greater transparency and by the gum which is thin and smooth.

Nos. 9/16 were initially printed on the same thick paper as the stamps with horizontal watermark and were line perforated. Values from ½d. to 2½d. were subsequently printed on medium paper on which the watermark was more visible. These were comb perforated. The thin paper with vertical watermark, produced in 1905. is much more transparent and has smooth gum. Printings were made on this paper for all values except the 2½d., but only the ½d. and 2d. were issued in Papua although used examples of the 2s. 6d. are also known. The entire printing of the 1d. on thin paper with vertical watermark was used for subsequent overprints.

The sheets of the ½d., 2d. and 2½d. show a variety known as "white leaves" on R. 4/5 while the 2d. and 2½d. (both R. 6/2) and the ½d. and 1s. (both R. 6/3) show what is known as the "unshaded leaves" variety.

Papua. (3) **Papua.** (4)

1906–07. I. *Optd with* T 3 (*large opt*), *at Port Moresby* (8 Nov 1906).

A. *Wmk horizontal. Thick paper. Line perf*

17 1 4d. black and sepia £190 £150
a. Deformed "d" at left £600 £500
18 6d. black and myrtle-green .. .. 38·00 48·00
19 1s. black and orange .. .. .. 20·00 38·00
20 2s. 6d. black and brown £140 £150

B. *Wmk vertical. Thin paper* (½d., 1d., 2d.) *or medium to thick paper* (*others*). *Comb perf* (½d. *to* 2½d.) *or line perf* (*others*)

21 1 ½d. black and yellow-green .. .. 4·75 20·00
22 1d. black and carmine .. .. .. 10·00 18·00
23 2d. black and violet .. .. .. 5·00 3·00
24 2½d. black and ultramarine .. .. 3·75 15·00
25 4d. black and sepia £170 £130
a. Deformed "d" at left £550
26 6d. black and myrtle-green .. .. 28·00 55·00
27 1s. black and orange £1200 £900
28 2s. 6d. black and brown £7500 £6500
17/28 .. .. *Set of* 8 £325 £375

II. *Optd with* T 4 (*small opt*), *at Brisbane* (May–June 1907)

A. *Wmk horizontal. Thick paper. Line perf*

34 1 ½d. black and yellow-green .. .. ..
a. Thin paper .. .. 60·00 80·00
35 2½d. black and ultramarine .. .. ..
a. Thin paper .. .. 30·00 60·00
ac. Black and dull blue £140 £150
36 1s. black and orange £150 £200
37 2s. 6d. black and brown .. .. 32·00 48·00
a. Opt reading downwards £4000
c. Opt double (horiz) .. .. .. † £3000
d. Opt triple (horiz) .. .. .. † £2500

B. *Wmk vertical. Thin paper* (½d., 1d., 2d., 4d., 6d.) *or medium to thick paper* (2½d., 1s., 2s. 6d.). *Line or comb perf* (2½d.), *line perf* (1s., 2s. 6d.) *or comb perf* (*others*)

38 1 ½d. black and yellow-green .. .. 7·00 9·00
a. Opt double £1700
39 1d. black and carmine .. .. .. 3·50 5·00
a. Opt reading upwards £1900 £1200
40 2d. black and violet .. .. .. 4·50 2·25
41 2½d. black and ultramarine .. .. 8·50 18·00
42 4d. black and sepia .. .. .. 25·00 48·00
a. Deformed "d" at left £170 £275
43 6d. black and myrtle-green .. .. 27·00 42·00
a. Opt double £2250 £4000
44 1s. black and orange .. .. .. 60·00 75·00
b. Thin paper (*comb perf*) .. .. 27·00 40·00
ba. Opt double, one diagonal £6500 £4000
45 2s. 6d. black and brown £6000 £4500
a. Thin paper (*comb perf*) .. .. 38·00 48·00
34/45 (*cheapest*) .. .. .. *Set of* 8 £110 £180

In the setting of this overprint Nos. 10, 16, and 21 have the "p" of "Papua" with a defective foot or inverted "d" for "p", and in No. 17 the "pua" of "Papua" is a shade lower than the first "a".

No. 37a comes from a single sheet on which the overprints were sideways. Examples exist showing one, two or four complete or partial overprints.

PRINTERS. All the following issues were printed at Melbourne by the Stamp Ptg Branch (to 1928) or Note Ptg Branch.

WATERMARK VARIETIES. When printing the lithographed issues, Nos. 47/83, little attention was paid to the position of the watermark. Nos. 47, 49/58 and 75/83 all come either upright or inverted while Nos. 48 and 59/71 all occur with watermark sideways to left or right. Nos. 51/2 are known with watermark reversed and others may well exist.

5 Large "PAPUA"

B

C

Three types of the 2s. 6d.:—

A. Thin top to "2" and small ball. Thin "6" and small ball. Thick uneven stroke.
B. Thin top to "2" and large, well shaped ball. Thin "6" and large ball. Very thick uneven stroke.
C. Thick top to "2" and large, badly shaped ball. Thick "6" and uneven ball. Thin even line.

Type A is not illustrated as the stamp is distinguishable by perf and watermark.

The litho stones were prepared from the engraved plates of the 1901 issue, value for value except the 2s. 6d. for which the original plate was mislaid. No. 48 containing Type A was prepared from the original ½d. plate with the value inserted on the stone and later a fresh stone was prepared from the 1d. plate and this contained Type B. Finally, the original plate of the 2s. 6d. was found and a third stone was prepared from this, and issued in 1911. These stamps show Type C.

6 Small "PAPUA"

(Litho Stamp Ptg Branch, Melbourne, from transfers taken from original engraved plates)

1907–10. *Wmk Crown over A, W w* **11.**

A. *Large* "PAPUA". (*a*) *Wmk upright. P* 11

47 5 ½d. black and yellow-green (11.07) .. 1·50 3·50

(*b*) *Wmk sideways. P* 11

48 5 2s. 6d. black and chocolate (A) (12.09) .. 48·00 60·00
a. "POSTAGIE" at left (R. 1/5) .. £550 £650

B. *Small* "PAPUA"

I. *Wmk upright.* (*a*) *P* 11 (1907–8)

49 6 1d. black and rose (6.08) .. 4·75 5·00
50 2d. black and purple (10.08) .. 8·50 4·50
51 2½d. black and bright ultramarine (7.08) 19·00 27·00
a. Black and pale ultramarine .. 5·50 6·50
52 4d. black and sepia (20.11.07) .. 4·25 9·50
a. Deformed "d" at left .. 30·00 48·00
53 6d. black and myrtle-green (4.08) .. 11·00 16·00
54 1s. black and orange (10.08) .. 20·00 20·00

(*b*) *P* 12½ (1907–9)

55 6 2d. black and purple (10.08) .. 18·00 6·50
56 2½d. black and bright ultramarine (7.08) £120 £130
b. Black and pale ultramarine .. 48·00 75·00
57 4d. black and sepia (20.11.07) .. 8·00 8·00
a. Deformed "d" at left .. 50·00 50·00
58 1s. black and orange (1.09) .. 60·00 85·00

II. *Wmk sideways.* (*a*) *P* 11 (1909–10)

59 6 ½d. black and yellow-green (12.09) .. 2·25 2·75
a. Black and deep green (1910) .. 28·00 42·00
60 1d. black and carmine (1.10) .. 9·00 8·00
61 2d. black and purple (1.10) .. 9·00 9·00
62 2½d. black and dull blue (1.10) .. 4·25 18·00
63 4d. black and sepia (1.10) .. 4·75 9·00
a. Deformed "d" at left .. 27·00 45·00
64 6d. black and myrtle-green (11.09) .. 10·00 18·00
65 1s. black and orange (3.10) .. 42·00 60·00

(*b*) *P* 12½ (1909–10)

66 6 ½d. black and yellow-green (12.09) .. 1·60 3·75
a. Black and deep green (1910) .. 30·00 38·00
67 1d. black and carmine (12.09) .. 6·50 12·00
68 2d. black and purple (1.10) .. 3·50 5·50
69 2½d. black and dull blue (1.10) .. 9·00 35·00
70 6d. black and myrtle-green (11.09) .. £2750 £3750
71 1s. black and orange (3.10) .. 13·00 35·00

(*c*) *Perf compound of* 11 *and* 12½

72 6 ½d. black and yellow-green .. £2250 £2250
73 2d. black and purple .. £850

(*d*) *Mixed perfs* 11 *and* 12½

74 6 4d. black and sepia .. £5500

Compound perforations on the 4d. are fakes.

The only known examples of No. 74 come from the top row of a sheet perforated 11 and with an additional line perf 12½ in the top margin.

(Litho Stamp Ptg Branch, Melbourne, by J. B. Cooke, from new stones made by fresh transfers)

1910 (Sept)–**11.** *Large* "PAPUA". *W w* **11** (*upright*). *P* 12½.

75 5 ½d. black and green (12.10) .. 3·50 11·00
76 1d. black and carmine .. 9·00 8·50
77 2d. black & dull purple (*shades*) (12.10) 4·00 5·00
a. "C" for "O" in "POSTAGE" (R. 4/3) 65·00 65·00
78 2½d. black and blue-violet (10.10) .. 4·50 17·00
79 4d. black and sepia (10.10) .. 4·75 10·00
a. Deformed "d" at left .. 24·00 50·00
80 6d. black and myrtle-green .. 7·50 7·50
81 1s. black and deep orange (12.10) .. 5·50 19·00
82 2s. 6d. black and brown (B) .. 35·00 45·00
83 2s. 6d. black and brown (C) (1911) .. 42·00 55·00
75/82 .. *Set of* 8 65·00 £110

A variety showing a white line or "rift" in clouds occurs on R. 5/3 in Nos. 49/74 and the "white leaves" variety mentioned below No. 16 occurs on the 2d. and 2½d. values in both issues. They are worth about three times the normal price.

8

ONE PENNY

(9)

(Eng S. Reading. Typo J. B. Cooke)

1911–15. *Printed in one colour. W* **8** (*sideways**).

(*a*) *P* 12½ (1911–12)

84 6 ½d. yellow-green .. 1·25 3·75
a. Green .. 50 2·25
w. Wmk Crown to right of A .. 10·00
85 1d. rose-pink .. 70 75
w. Wmk Crown to right of A .. 20·00 20·00
86 2d. bright mauve .. 70 75
w. Wmk Crown to right of A .. — 40·00
87 2½d. bright ultramarine .. 4·75 8·50
a. Dull ultramarine .. 5·50 8·50
aw. Wmk Crown to right of A .. 50·00
88 4d. pale olive-green .. 2·25 11·00
w. Wmk Crown to right of A .. — 40·00
89 6 6d. orange-brown .. 3·75 5·00
w. Wmk Crown to right of A .. 75·00
90 1s. yellow .. 9·00 15·00
w. Wmk Crown to right of A .. 75·00
91 2s. 6d. rose-carmine .. 32·00 38·00
w. Wmk Crown to right of A .. £170
84/91 .. *Set of* 8 48·00 70·00

(*b*) *P* 14

92 6 1d. rose-pink (6.15) .. 22·00 6·00
a. Pale scarlet .. 6·50 2·00
w. Wmk Crown to right of A .. — 40·00

*The normal sideways watermark shows Crown to left of A, *as seen from the back of the stamp.*

(Typo J. B. Cooke (1916–18), T. S. Harrison (1918–26), A. J. Mullett (No. 95*b* only) (1926–27), or John Ash (1927–31))

1916 (Aug)–**31.** *Printed in two colours.* **W 8** (*sideways**). *P* 14.

93 6 ½d. myrtle and apple green (Harrison and Ash) (1919) .. 80 1·00
a. Myrtle and pale olive-green (1927) 1·75 2·25
w. Wmk Crown to right of A .. 5·00 5·00
94 1d. black and carmine-red .. 1·40 1·25
a. Grey-black and red (1918) .. 1·60 1·25
aw. Wmk Crown to right of A .. 3·00 40
b. Intense black and red (Harrison) (*wmk Crown to right of A*) (1926) 2·50 2·50
95 1½d. pale grey-blue (*shades*) & brn (1925) 2·00 80
aw. Wmk Crown to right of A .. 15·00 5·00
b. Cobalt and light brown (Mullett) (*wmk Crown to right of A*) (1927) 6·00 3·25
c. Bright blue and bright brown (1929) 2·75 2·00
d. "POSTACE" at right (R. 1/1) (all printings) .. *From* 32·00 32·00
96 2d. brown-purple & brown-lake (1919) 1·75 75
a. Deep brown-purple and lake (1931) 25·00 1·75
aw. Wmk Crown to right of A .. 30·00 1·75
b. Brown-purple and claret (1931) .. 2·00 75
97 2½d. myrtle and ultramarine (1919) .. 4·75 12·00
98 3d. black and bright blue-green (12.16) 1·50 1·75
a. Error. Black and deep greenish Prussian blue† .. £500 £500
b. Sepia-black & brt bl-grn (Harrison) 22·00 19·00
c. Black and blue-green (1927) .. 4·50 8·00
99 4d. brown and orange (1919) .. 2·50 5·00
a. Light brown and orange (1927) .. 8·50 16·00
aw. Wmk Crown to right of A .. 7·50 14·00
100 5d. bluish slate and pale brown (1931) 4·25 16·00
101 6d. dull and pale purple (*wmk Crown to right of A*) (1919) .. 3·25 9·50
aw. Wmk Crown to left of A .. 10·00
b. Dull purple and red-purple (*wmk Crown to left of A*) (1927) .. 11·00 16·00
c. "POSTACE" at left (R. 6/2) (all printings) .. *From* 70·00 £100
102 1s. sepia and olive (1919) .. 3·50 7·00
a. Brown and yellow-olive (1927) .. 6·50 14·00
103 2s. 6d. maroon and pale pink (1919) .. 18·00 40·00
a. Maroon & brt pink (*shades*) (1927) 19·00 50·00
104 5s. black and deep green (12.16) .. 40·00 48·00
105 10s. green and pale ultramarine (1925) £140 £160
93/105 .. *Set of* 13 £200 £275

*The normal sideways watermark shows Crown to left of A, *as seen from the back of the stamp.*

†Beware of similar shades produced by removal of yellow pigment. No. 98a is a colour trial, prepared by Cooke, of which, it is believed, five sheets were sold in error.

The printers of various shades can be determined by their dates of issue. The Ash printings are on whiter paper.

For 9d. and 1s. 3d. values, see Nos. 127/8.

1917 (Oct). *Nos.* 84, 86/9 *and* 91 *surch with T* **9** *by Govt Ptg Office, Melbourne.*

106 6 1d. on ½d. yellow-green .. 1·50 1·60
a. Green .. 1·00 1·25
w. Wmk Crown to right of A .. 4·00 4·00
107 1d. on 2d. bright mauve .. 12·00 15·00
108 1d. on 2½d. ultramarine .. 1·25 3·75
109 1d. on 4d. pale olive-green .. 1·75 4·50
w. Wmk Crown to right of A .. — 40·00
110 1d. on 6d. orange-brown .. 8·00 17·00
111 1d. on 2s. 6d. rose-carmine .. 1·50 6·00
106/11 .. *Set of* 6 23·00 42·00

AIR MAIL

(10)

(11)

1929 (Oct)–**30.** *Air. Optd with T* **10** *by Govt Printer, Port Moresby.*

(*a*) *Cooke printing. Yellowish paper*

112 6 3d. black and bright blue-green .. 1·25 11·00
a. Opt omitted in vert pair with normal £3250

(*b*) *Harrison printing. Yellowish paper*

113 6 3d. sepia-black and bright blue-green 50·00 65·00

(*c*) *Ash printing. White paper*

114 6 3d. black and blue-green .. 1·00 7·00
a. Opt omitted (in horiz pair with normal) .. £3750
b. Ditto, but vert pair .. £3250
c. Opt vertical, on back .. £3000
d. Opts *tête-bêche* (vert pair) .. £3250

1930 (15 Sept). *Air. Optd with T* **11**, *in carmine by Govt Printer, Port Moresby.* (*a*) *Harrison printings. Yellowish paper.*

115 6 3d. sepia-black and bright blue-green £1600 £2750
116 6d. dull and pale purple .. 3·00 16·00
a. "POSTACE" at left (R. 6/2) .. 65·00 £110
117 1s. sepia and olive .. 8·00 23·00
a. Opt inverted .. £4500

(*b*) *Ash printings. White paper*

118 6 3d. black and blue-green .. 1·00 6·00
119 6d. dull purple and red-purple .. 7·00 10·00
a. "POSTACE" at left (R. 6/2) .. 70·00 £100
120 1s. brown and yellow-olive .. 4·25 15·00
118/20 .. *Set of* 3 11·00 28·00

The rare Harrison printing with this overprint, No. should not be confused with examples of the Ash printing 118, which have been climatically toned.

5d.

TWO PENCE

(12)

FIVE PENCE

(13)

1931 (1 Jan). *Surch with T* **12** *by Govt Printer, Port Moresby*

(*a*) *Mullett printing*

121 6 2d. on 1½d. cobalt and light brown .. 12·00
a. "POSTACE" at right (R. 1/1) .. £140

(*b*) *Ash printing*

122 6 2d. on 1½d. bright blue and bright brown .. 1·00
a. "POSTACE" at right (R. 1/1) .. 25·00 4

1931. *Surch as T* **13** *by Govt Printer, Port Moresby.*

(*a*) *Cooke printing*

123 6 1s. 3d. on 5s. black and deep green 4·25

(*b*) *Harrison printing. Yellowish paper*

124 6 9d. on 2s. 6d. maroon and pale pink (Dec) 6·00 2

(*c*) *Ash printings. White paper*

125 6 5d. on 1s. brown and yellow-olive (26.7) 1·00
126 9d. on 2s. 6d. maroon and bright pink 5·50

(Typo J. Ash)

1932. *W* **15** *of Australia* (*Mult* "C of A"). *P* 11.

127 5 9d. lilac and violet .. 4·50 3
128 1s. 3d. lilac and pale greenish blue .. 7·50 3
127s/8s Optd "Specimen" .. *Set of* 2 £450

15 Motuan Girl

18 Raggiana Bird of Paradis

20 Native Mother and Child

22 Papuan Motherhood

(Des F. E. Williams (2s., £1 and frames of other values), E. Wh house (2d., 4d., 6d., 1s., and 10s.); remaining centres from pho by Messrs F. E. Williams and Gibson. Recess J. Ash (all valu and W. C. G. McCracken (½d., 1d., 2d., 4d.))

1932 (14 Nov). *T* **15, 18, 20, 22** *and similar designs. No w P* 11.

130 ½d. black and orange .. 1·50 3
a. Black and buff (McCracken) .. 13·00 22
131 1d. black and green .. 1·75
132 1½d. black and lake .. 1·50 8
133 2d. red .. 11·00
134 3d. black and blue .. 3·25 6
135 4d. olive-green .. 5·50 9
136 5d. black and slate-green .. 3·00 3
137 6d. bistre-brown .. 7·50 5
138 9d. black and violet .. 10·00 21
139 1s. dull blue-green .. 4·00 8
140 1s. 3d. black and dull purple .. 15·00 24
141 2s. black and slate-green .. 15·00 23
142 2s. 6d. black and rose-mauve .. 25·00 38
143 5s. black and olive-brown .. 55·00 50
144 10s. violet .. 80·00 80
145 £1 black and olive-grey .. £180 £1
130/145 .. *Set of* 16 £350 £3

Designs: *Vert* (*as T* **15**)—1d. A Chieftain's son; 1½d. Tr houses; 3d. Papuan dandy; 5d. Masked dancer; 9d. Papu shooting fish; 1s. 3d. Lakatoi; 2s. Papuan art; 2s. 6d. Potte making; 5s. Native policeman; £1 Delta house. (*As T* **18**)— *Dubu*—or ceremonial platform. *Horiz* (*as T* **20**)—10s. Lighting fire.

31 Hoisting the Union Jack

32 Scene on H.M.S. *Nelson*

(Recess J. Ash)

1934 (6 Nov). *50th Anniv of Declaration of British Protectorate P* 11.

146 31 1d. green .. 1·00 3·5
147 32 2d. scarlet .. 1·75 3·0
148 31 3d. blue .. 1·75 3·0
149 32 5d. purple .. 11·00 13·0
146/9 .. *Set of* 4 14·00 20·0

HIS MAJESTY'S JUBILEE.

1910 1935

(33)

HIS MAJESTY'S JUBILEE. 1910 — 1935

(34)

MAJESTY'S MAJESTY'S

Normal "Accent" flaw (R. 5/4)

(9 July). *Silver Jubilee. Nos.* 131, 133/4 *and* 136 *optd with* 33 *or* 34 (2*d*.).
1d. black and green .. 75 2·75
a. "Accent" flaw .. 27·00 50·00
2d. scarlet .. 2·00 2·75
3d. black and blue .. 1·75 2·75
a. "Accent" flaw .. 45·00 70·00
5d. black and slate-green .. 2·50 3·00
a. "Accent" flaw .. 60·00 80·00
.. *Set of* 4 6·25 10·00

35

36 Port Moresby

(Recess J. Ash)

7 (14 May). *Coronation. P* 11.
35 1d. green .. 45 15
2d. scarlet .. 45 50
3d. blue .. 45 70
5d. purple .. 45 1·25
7 .. *Set of* 4 1·60 2·40

ome covers franked with these stamps and posted on 2 June 7 were postmarked 2 April 1937 in error.

(Recess J. Ash)

3 (6 Sept). *Air. 50th Anniv of Declaration of British* ossession. *P* 11.
36 2d. rose-red .. 3·75 2·25
3d. bright blue .. 3·75 2·25
5d. green .. 3·75 3·25
8d. brown-lake .. 8·00 14·00
1s. mauve .. 22·00 15·00
'62 .. *Set of* 5 35·00 32·00

37 Natives poling Rafts

(Recess J. Ash)

9 (6 Sept). *Air. P* 11.
37 2d. rose-red .. 3·00 3·75
3d. bright blue .. 3·00 7·50
5d. green .. 3·00 1·50
8d. brown-lake .. 8·00 2·50
1s. mauve .. 10·00 7·00

(Recess W. C. G. McCracken)

41 (2 Jan). *Air. P* 11½.
3 37 1s. 6d. olive-green .. 30·00 32·00
3/168 .. *Set of* 6 50·00 48·00

OFFICIAL STAMPS

08 (Oct). *Punctured "OS".*
1 2s. 6d. black and brown (No. 37) .. £600 35·00
2s. 6d. black and brown (No. 45) .. £2500 £2250
a. Thin paper (No. 45a) .. £700 £550

08 (Dec)–**10**. *Nos.* 49/71 *punctured "OS".* I. *Wmk upright.*

(*a*) *P* 11
4 6 1d. black and rose .. 14·00 5·00
5 2d. black and purple .. 18·00 4·50
6 2½d. black and bright ultramarine .. 28·00 26·00
a. Black and pale ultramarine .. 14·00 4·25
7 4d. black and sepia .. 15·00 4·50
a. Deformed "d" at left .. 80·00 24·00
8 6d. black and myrtle-green .. 38·00 18·00
9 1s. black and orange .. 38·00 18·00
4/9 .. *Set of* 6 £120 48·00

(*b*) *P* 12½
10 6 2d. black and purple .. 30·00 8·00
11 2½d. black and bright ultramarine .. £120 85·00
b. Black and pale ultramarine .. 70·00 55·00
12 4d. black and sepia .. 30·00 9·00
a. Deformed "d" at left .. £130 50·00
13 1s. black and orange .. 95·00 50·00
10/13 .. *Set of* 4 £200 £110

II. *Wmk sideways.* (*a*) *P* 11
14 6 ½d. black and yellow-green .. 15·00 4·50
a. Black and deep green .. 50·00 30·00
15 1d. black and carmine .. 32·00 9·50
16 2d. black and purple .. 14·00 2·00
17 2½d. black and dull blue .. 22·00 5·00
18 4d. black and sepia .. 18·00 9·00
a. Deformed "d" at left .. 90·00 42·00

O19 6 6d. black and myrtle-green .. 32·00 5·00
O20 1s. black and orange .. 90·00 32·00
O14/20 .. *Set of* 7 £200 60·00

(*b*) *P* 12½
O21 6 ½d. black and yellow-green .. 11·00 1·50
a. Black and deep green .. 50·00 30·00
O22 1d. black and carmine .. 28·00 4·00
O23 2d. black and purple .. 18·00 3·00
O24 2½d. black and dull blue .. 40·00 14·00
O25 6d. black and myrtle-green .. — £1100
O26 1s. black and orange .. 40·00 14·00

1910. *Nos.* 47/8 *punctured "OS".*
O27 5 ½d. black & yellow-green (*wmk upright*) 14·00 13·00
O28 2s. 6d. black & chocolate (*wmk sideways*) £110 85·00

1910–11. *Nos.* 75/83 *punctured "OS".*
O29 5 ½d. black and green .. 15·00 6·00
O30 1d. black and carmine .. 32·00 6·00
O31 2d. black and dull purple .. 14·00 6·50
a. "C" for "O" in "POSTAGE" .. £140 70·00
O32 2½d. black and blue-violet .. 23·00 6·50
O33 4d. black and sepia .. 23·00 6·00
a. Deformed "d" at left .. £100 32·00
O34 6d. black and myrtle-green .. 23·00 6·00
O35 1s. black and deep orange .. 35·00 9·00
O36 2s. 6d. black and brown (B) .. 80·00 30·00
O37 2s. 6d. black and brown (C) .. 95·00 65·00
O29/36 .. *Set of* 8 £225 65·00

1911–12. *Nos.* 84/91 *punctured "OS".*
O38 6 ½d. yellow-green .. 7·50 2·00
O39 1d. rose-pink .. 9·50 1·25
O40 2d. bright mauve .. 9·50 1·25
w. Wmk Crown to right of A .. — 20·00
O41 2½d. bright ultramarine .. 16·00 7·50
O42 4d. pale olive-green .. 19·00 15·00
O43 6d. orange-brown .. 17·00 6·00
O44 1s. yellow .. 24·00 11·00
O45 2s. 6d. rose-carmine .. 60·00 65·00
O38/45 .. *Set of* 8 £140 95·00

1930. *Nos.* 93/6*a and* 98*c*/103 *punctured "OS".*
O46 6 ½d. myrtle and apple green .. 5·00 10·00
O47 1d. intense black and red .. 12·00 3·25
O48 1½d. bright blue and bright brown .. 7·50 10·00
a. "POSTACE" at right .. 75·00 90·00
O49 2d. deep brown-purple and lake .. 21·00 28·00
O50 3d. black and blue-green .. 40·00 55·00
O51 4d. light brown and orange .. 23·00 27·00
O52 6d. dull purple and pale purple .. 14·00 26·00
a. "POSTACE" at left .. £140 £170
O53 1s. brown and yellow-olive .. 26·00 42·00
O54 2s. 6d. maroon and pale pink .. 75·00 £100
O46/54 .. *Set of* 9 £200 £275

O S

(O 1)

(Typo T. S. Harrison (1d. and 2s. 6d.) and J. Ash)

1931 (29 July)–**32**. *Optd with Type* O 1. *W* **8** *or W* **15** *of Australia* (9*d*., 1*s*. 3*d*.). *P* 14 *or* 11 (9*d*., 1*s*. 3*d*.).
O55 6 ½d. myrtle and apple-green .. 1·75 4·75
O56 1d. grey-black and red ..
a. Intense black and red .. 3·75 7·50
O57 1½d. bright blue and bright brown .. 1·40 12·00
a. "POSTACE" at right .. 45·00 £120
O58 2d. brown-purple and claret .. 3·50 9·00
O59 3d. black and blue-green .. 2·50 22·00
O60 4d. light brown and orange (No. 99aw) 2·50 18·00
O61 5d. bluish slate and pale brown .. 6·00 38·00
O62 6d. dull purple and red-purple .. 4·00 8·50
a. "POSTACE" at left .. 85·00 £170
O63 9d. lilac and violet (1932) .. 40·00 55·00
O64 1s. brown and yellow-olive .. 9·00 30·00
O65 1s. 3d. lilac & pale greenish blue (1932) 40·00 55·00
O66 2s. 6d. maroon & pale pink (Harrison) 40·00 85·00
a. Maroon and bright pink (Ash) .. 40·00 85·00
O55/66 .. *Set of* 12 £130 £300

Civil Administration, in Papua, was suspended in 1942; on resumption, after the Japanese defeat in 1945, Australian stamps were used until the appearance of the issue of the combined territories of Papua & New Guinea.

Baghdad
see Iraq

Bahamas

The British Post Office at Nassau was established during the early days of the West Indies packet system, and was certainly operating by 1733. The first known local postmark dates from 1802.

The crowned-circle handstamp No. CC1 was issued in 1846 and was generally replaced, for the public mails, by various stamps of Great Britain in 1858.

Local mail deliveries were rudimentary until 1859 when Nos. 1/2 were issued by the colonial authorities for interisland mails. Examples used for this purpose are usually cancelled in manuscript or with a "27" postmark. The "local" 1d. stamp became valid for overseas mails in May, 1860, when the colonial authorities took over this service from the British G.P.O.

For illustrations of the handstamp and postmark types see BRITISH POST OFFICES ABROAD notes, following GREAT BRITAIN.

NASSAU

CROWNED-CIRCLE HANDSTAMPS

CC1 CC **2** BAHAMAS (Nassau) (18.5.1846) (R.)
Price on cover £2250

No. CC1 was later struck in black and used as an Offical Paid mark between July 1899 and September 1935. Handstamps as Types CC 1 and CC 3 (only three known) struck in black were used for the same purpose from 1933 until 1953; but it is believed that these were never employed during the pre-stamp period. *Price on cover from* £50.

Stamps of GREAT BRITAIN *cancelled* "A 05" *as Type* **2**.

1858 *to* **1860.**
Z1 1d. rose-red (1857), *perf* 14 .. £1800
Z2 2d. blue (1858) (Plate Nos. 7, 8) .. £1300
Z3 4d. rose (1857) .. £450
Z4 6d. lilac (1856) .. £350
Z5 1s. green (1856) .. £2250

PRICES FOR STAMPS ON COVER TO 1945

No. 1	*from* × 8
No. 2	—
Nos. 3/6	*from* × 8
No. 7	—
Nos. 8/11	*from* × 10
Nos. 12/15	*from* × 4
Nos. 16/19*a*	*from* × 6
Nos. 20/5	*from* × 15
Nos. 26/8	*from* × 4
No. 29	—
Nos. 30/2	*from* × 15
No. 33	*from* × 30
Nos. 35/7	*from* × 6
Nos. 38/9	*from* × 10
No. 39*b*	*from* × 30
No. 40	*from* × 50
No. 41	*from* × 6
No. 42	*from* × 15
No. 43	*from* × 5
Nos. 44/*a*	*from* × 10
No. 45	*from* × 40
Nos. 47/57	*from* × 4
Nos. 58/89	*from* × 2
Nos. 90/130	*from* × 3
Nos. 131/2	*from* × 10
Nos. 141/5	*from* × 4
Nos. 146/8	*from* × 6
Nos. 149/57	*from* × 3
Nos. 158/60	*from* × 4
No. 161	*from* × 8
Nos. 162/75	*from* × 5
Nos. S1/3	*from* × 20

CROWN COLONY

1

2

3

(Eng and recess P.B.)

1859 (10 June)–**60.** *No wmk. Imperf.* (*a*) *Thick, opaque paper*
1 1 1d. reddish lake (*shades*) .. £4500 £2250

(*b*) *Thin paper*
2 1 1d. dull lake (4.60) .. 50·00 £1500

No. 1, the printing on thick opaque paper, is very rare in unused condition. Unused remainders, on medium to thick, but slightly transparent, paper are worth about £250.

Collectors are warned against false postmarks upon the remainder stamps of 1d., imperf, on thin paper.

1860 (Oct). *No wmk. Clean-cut perf* 14 *to* 16.
3 **1** 1d. lake (H/S "CANCELLED" in oval £6000) £3750 £700

For notes on "CANCELLED" examples see Catalogue Introduction. Examples with this handstamp on No. 3 are imperforate horizontally.

1861 (June)–**62.** *No wmk.* (*a*) *Rough perf* 14 *to* 16
4 **1** 1d. lake £750 £300
5 **2** 4d. dull rose (Dec, 1861) £1400 £375
a. Imperf between (pair) £24000
6 6d. grey-lilac (Dec, 1861) £3500 £550
a. Pale dull lilac £3000 £500

(*b*) *P* 11 *to* 12½ (1862)
7 **1** 1d. lake £2000

No. 7 was a perforation trial on a new machine at Perkins, Bacon. It was not sent out to the Colony and is also known part perforated.

(Recess D.L.R.)

1862. *No wmk.** (*a*) *P* 11½, 12.
8 **1** 1d. carmine-lake £1000 £170
9 1d. lake £1200 £180
10 **2** 4d. dull rose £3250 £400
11 6d. lavender-grey £9500 £475

(*b*) *P* 11½, 12, *compound with* 11
12 **1** 1d. carmine-lake £2000 £850
13 1d. lake £2250 £950
14 **2** 4d. dull rose £16000 £1800
15 6d. lavender-grey £17000 £1800

(*c*) *P* 13
16 **1** 1d. lake £900 £160
17 1d. brown-lake £750 £130
18 **2** 4d. dull rose £2750 £375
19 6d. lavender-grey £3250 £475
a. Lilac £2750 £450

*Stamps exist with part of papermaker's sheet wmk ("T. H. SAUNDERS" and date).

1863–77. *Wmk Crown CC.* (*a*) *P* 12½
20 **1** 1d. brown-lake 90·00 55·00
w. Wmk inverted £140 90·00
x. Wmk reversed
21 1d. carmine-lake £100 60·00
w. Wmk inverted £140 80·00
x. Wmk reversed £110 60·00
22 1d. carmine-lake (aniline) £110 60·00
w. Wmk inverted £160
x. Wmk reversed
23 1d. rose-red 60·00 40·00
w. Wmk inverted £100
x. Wmk reversed 60·00 40·00
24 1d. red 60·00 40·00
w. Wmk inverted
x. Wmk reversed — 40·00
25 1d. vermilion 65·00 40·00
w. Wmk inverted £100 70·00
x. Wmk reversed 65·00 40·00
y. Wmk inverted and reversed £150
26 **2** 4d. bright rose £275 60·00
w. Wmk inverted — £160
x. Wmk reversed
27 4d. dull rose £400 60·00
w. Wmk inverted — £160
x. Wmk reversed £375 60·00
y. Wmk inverted and reversed £750
28 4d. brownish rose (*wmk reversed*) £450 80·00
w. Wmk inverted
29 6d. rose-lilac — £2250
w. Wmk inverted £6000
30 6d. lilac (*shades*) £375 70·00
w. Wmk inverted — £160
x. Wmk reversed
31 6d. deep violet £160 60·00
w. Wmk inverted — £160
x. Wmk reversed £180 65·00
y. Wmk inverted and reversed
32 6d. violet (aniline) £250 90·00
x. Wmk reversed — 95·00

(*b*) *P* 14
33 **1** 1d. scarlet-vermilion (1877) 50·00 15·00
x. Wmk reversed 60·00 22·00
34 1d. scarlet (or scarlet-vermilion) (aniline) £1000
x. Wmk reversed
35 **2** 4d. bright rose (1876) £350 40·00
w. Wmk inverted — £160
36 4d. dull rose £1500 40·00
w. Wmk inverted
37 4d. rose-lake £425 40·00

No. 29 is believed to be the shade of the first printing only and should not be confused with other lilac shades of the 6d.

No. 34 is not known postally used, although manuscript fiscal cancellations on this shade do exist.

(Typo D.L.R.)

1863–80. *Wmk Crown CC.* (*a*) *P* 12½.
38 **3** 1s. green (1865) £2500 £300

(*b*) *P* 14
39 **3** 1s. deep green £190 35·00
aw. Wmk inverted
b. Green £120 25·00
ba. Thick paper (1880) 8·00 7·00
bw. Wmk inverted (thick paper) — £150

1882 (Mar). *Wmk Crown CA.* (*a*) *P* 12.
40 **1** 1d. scarlet-vermilion 48·00 12·00
x. Wmk reversed — 50·00
41 **2** 4d. rose £550 45·00

(*b*) *P* 14
42 **1** 1d. scarlet-vermilion £425 60·00
x. Wmk reversed
43 **2** 4d. rose £800 60·00
x. Wmk reversed £850 60·00

1882 (Mar)–**98.** *Wmk Crown CA. P* 14.
44 **3** 1s. green 32·00 14·00
44*a* 1s. blue-green (1898) 35·00 23·00

FOURPENCE

(4)

5

1883. *No.* 31 *surch with T* **4**.
45 **2** 4d. on 6d. deep violet £550 £400
a. Surch inverted £12000 £8000
x. Wmk reversed £600 £450

Type **4** was applied by handstamp and occurs in various positions.

Caution is needed in buying Nos. 45 and 45a.

Sloping "2" (R. 10/6)

Malformed "E"

(Typo D.L.R.)

1884–90. *Wmk Crown CA. P* 14.
47 **5** 1d. pale rose 65·00 12·00
48 1d. carmine-rose 7·00 2·50
49 1d. bright carmine (aniline) 2·75 6·50
50 2½d. dull blue (1888) 65·00 17·00
51 2½d. blue 42·00 7·50
a. Sloping "2" £400 £120
52 2½d. ultramarine 9·50 2·25
a. Sloping "2" £140 70·00
s. Optd "Specimen" 65·00
w. Wmk inverted £140 75·00
53 4d. deep yellow 9·50 4·00
54 6d. mauve (1890) 6·00 26·00
a. Malformed "E" (R. 6/6) £180 £325
s. Optd "Specimen" 65·00
56 5s. sage-green 65·00 75·00
57 £1 Venetian red £275 £225
47/57 *Set of* 6 £325 £300

Examples of Nos. 54/7 are known showing a forged Bahamas postmark dated "AU 29 94".

6 Queen's Staircase, Nassau

7

8

(Recess D.L.R.)

1901 (23 Sept)–**03.** *Wmk Crown CC. P* 14.
58 **6** 1d. black and red 7·50 3·00
w. Wmk inverted 80·00 80·00
59 5d. black and orange (1.03) 8·50 48·00
y. Wmk inverted and reversed 95·00 £140
60 2s. black and blue (1.03) 27·00 50·00
61 3s. black and green (1.03) 35·00 60·00
w. Wmk inverted
y. Wmk inverted and reversed £100 £110
58/61 *Set of* 4 70·00 £140
58s/61s Optd "Specimen" *Set of* 4 £120

For stamps in this design, but with Mult Crown CA or Mult Script CA watermarks see Nos 75/80 and 111/14.

(Typo D.L.R.)

1902 (18 Dec)–**10.** *Wmk Crown CA. P* 14.
62 **7** 1d. carmine 1·50 2·50
63 2½d. ultramarine 6·50 1·25
a. Sloping "2" £250 £120
64 4d. orange 15·00 55·00
65 4d. deep yellow (3.10) 22·00 65·00
66 6d. brown 3·50 18·00
a. Malformed "E" (R. 6/6) £150 £200
67 1s. grey-black and carmine 20·00 48·00
68 1s. brownish grey and carmine (6.07) 22·00 48·00
69 5s. dull purple and blue 65·00 80·00
70 £1 green and black £250 £325
62/70 *Set of* 7 £300 £450
62s/70s Optd "Specimen" *Set of* 7 £250

Examples of most values are known showing a forged Nassau postmark dated "2 MAR 10".

1906 (Apr)–**11.** *Wmk Mult Crown CA. P* 14.
71 **7** ½d. pale green (5.06) 5·00 2·75
s. Optd "Specimen" 50·00
72 1d. carmine-rose 24·00 1·25
73 2½d. ultramarine (4.07) 25·00 26·00
a. Sloping "2" £350 £400
w. Wmk inverted £110 £110
74 6d. bistre-brown (8.11) 17·00 48·00
a. Malformed "E" (R. 6/6) £275 £475
71/4 *Set of* 4 60·00 70·00

1911 (Feb)–**19.** *Wmk Mult Crown CA. P* 14.
75 **6** 1d. black and red 16·00 2·75
a. Grey-black and scarlet (1916) 4·75 2·50
b. Grey-black & deep carmine-red (1919) 6·50 6·00
76 3d. purple/*yellow* (*thin paper*) (18.5.17) 4·75 25·00
a. Reddish pur/buff (*thick paper*) (1.19) 5·50 4·50
s. Optd "Specimen" 35·00
77 3d. black and brown (23.3.19) 2·00 2·25
s. Optd "Specimen" 35·00
w. Wmk inverted
78 5d. black and mauve (18.5.17) 2·75 5·50
s. Optd "Specimen" 35·00
79 2s. black and blue (11.16) 29·00 50·00
w. Wmk inverted
80 **6** 3s. black and green (8.17) 55·00
w. Wmk inverted £130
y. Wmk inverted and reversed £110
75/80 *Set of* 6 85·00

(Typo D.L.R.)

1912–19. *Wmk Mult Crown CA. Chalk-surfaced paper* (
£1). *P* 14.
81 **8** ½d. green 80
a. Yellow-green 2·50
82 1d. carmine (aniline) 3·50
a. Deep rose 8·00
b. Rose 11·00
w. Wmk inverted —
83 2d. grey (1919) 2·25
84 2½d. ultramarine 4·75
a. Deep dull blue 14·00
85 4d. orange-yellow 5·50
a. Yellow 2·50
86 6d. bistre-brown 1·75
a. Malformed "E" (R. 6/6) 90·00
87 1s. grey-black and carmine 1·75
a. Jet-black and carmine 14·00
88 5s. dull purple and blue 40·00
a. Pale dull purple and deep blue 50·00
89 £1 dull green and black £150
a. Green and black £190
81/9 *Set of* 9 £180
81s/9s Optd "Specimen" *Set of* 9 £325

1.1.17.

(9)

WAR TAX

(10)

1917 (18 May). *No.* 75*b optd with T* **9** *in red by D.L.R.*
90 **6** 1d. grey-black and deep carmine-red 40
a. Long stroke to "7" (R. 4/6) 40·00
s. Optd "Specimen" 60·00

It was originally intended to issue No. 90 on 1 January 19
but the stamps were not received in the Bahamas until M
Half the proceeds from their sale were donated to the Bri
Red Cross Society.

1918 (21 Feb–10 July). *Nos.* 75/6, 81/2 *and* 87 *optd at Nas with T* **10**.
91 **8** ½d. green 9·00
a. Opt double
b. Opt inverted
92 1d. carmine (aniline) 1·00
a. Opt double
b. Opt inverted
w. Wmk inverted £190
x. Wmk reversed £190
93 **6** 1d. black and red (10 July) 3·50
a. Opt double, one inverted £800
b. Opt double £1600
c. Opt inverted £1400
x. Wmk reversed £160
94 3d. purple/*yellow* (*thin paper*) 2·25
a. Opt double £1500
b. Opt inverted £1000
95 **8** 1s. grey-black and carmine 95·00
a. Opt double
91/5 *Set of* 5 £100

No. 93 was only on sale for ten days.

WAR TAX

(11)

WAR TAX

(12)

WAR CHARITY 3.6.18.

(13)

1918 (1 June–20 July). *Optd by D.L.R. in London with T* **11**
12 (*3d*).
96 **8** ½d. green 1·75
w. Wmk inverted
x. Wmk reversed
97 1d. carmine 1·00
a. Wmk sideways £350
w. Wmk inverted
y. Wmk inverted and reversed £250
98 **6** 3d. purple/*yellow* (20 July) 1·00
w. Wmk inverted 75·00
x. Wmk reversed
99 **8** 1s. grey-black and carmine (R.) 9·00
96/9 *Set of* 4 11·50
96s/9s Optd "Specimen" *Set of* 4 £130

1919 (21 Mar). *No.* 77 *optd with T* **12** *by D.L.R.*
100 **6** 3d. black and brown 45 4·0
a. "C" and "A" missing from wmk £1200
s. Optd "Specimen" 45·00
w. Wmk inverted 50·00

No. 100a shows the "C" omitted from one impression and th
"A" missing from the next one to the right (as seen from th
front of the stamp). The "C" is badly distorted in the secon
watermark.

1919 (1 Jan). *No.* 75*b optd with T* **13** *by D.L.R.*
101 **6** 1d. grey-black and deep carmine-red (R.) 30 2·5
a. Opt double £1500
s. Optd "Specimen" 50·00
w. Wmk inverted 50·00
x. Wmk reversed 50·00
y. Wmk inverted and reversed 75·00

The date is that originally fixed for the issue of the stamp. Th
year 1918 was also the bicentenary of the appointment of the firs
Royal governor.

WAR WAR

TAX TAX

(14) (15)

(14 July). (a) *Optd with T* **14** *by D.L.R.*
3 ½d. green (R.) .. .. 30 1·25
1d. carmine .. .. 1·50 1·50
1s. grey-black and carmine (R.) .. 15·00 29·00

(b) *No.* 77 *optd with T* **15**
6 3d. black and brown .. .. .. 75 8·00
w. Wmk inverted .. .. .. 50·00
x. Wmk reversed .. .. .. 60·00
y. Wmk inverted and reversed .. 55·00
.. .. *Set of* 4 16·00 35·00
5s .. .. *Set of* 4 £120

16

17 Great Seal of the Bahamas.

(Recess D.L.R.)

(1 Mar). *Peace Celebration. Wmk Mult Crown CA (sideways*). P* 14.
16 ½d. green .. .. 1·00 5·50
x. Wmk sideways reversed £275 £275
1d. carmine .. .. 2·75 1·00
x. Wmk sideways reversed £375
y. Wmk Crown to right of CA and reversed £375
2d. slate-grey .. .. 2·75 7·50
a. "C" of "CA" missing from wmk .. £800
3d. deep brown .. .. .. 2·75 9·00
w. Wmk Crown to right of CA .. £200
1s. deep myrtle-green .. .. 12·00 35·00
a. Substituted crown in wmk .. £1100
x. Wmk sideways reversed £500
/10 .. .. *Set of* 5 19·00 50·00
s/10s Optd "Specimen" .. *Set of* 5 £150
The normal sideways watermark shows Crown to left of CA, *een from the back of the stamp.*
or illustration of the substituted watermark crown see alogue Introduction.

(29 Mar)–**29**. *Wmk Script CA. P* 14.
6 1d. grey and rose-red .. .. .. 80 1·25
5d. black and purple (8.29) .. .. 3·75 42·00
2s. black and blue (11.22) .. .. 18·00 22·00
3s. black and green (9.24) .. .. 45·00 65·00
/14 .. .. *Set of* 4 60·00 £110
s/14s Optd or Perf (5d.) "Specimen" *Set of* 4 £160
xamples of all values are known showing a forged Nassau tmark dated "2 MAR 10".

F PENN

Elongated "E"
(left pane R. 9/6)

21 (8 Sept)–**37**. *Wmk Mult Script CA. Chalk-surfaced paper 3d., 1s., 5s., £1). P* 14.
5 **8** ½d. green (1924) 50 40
a. Elongated "E" .. .. .. 35·00
6 1d. carmine .. .. 1·00 15
7 1½d. brown-red (1934) .. .. .. 3·25 1·00
8 2d. grey (1927) .. .. .. 1·25 2·75
9 2½d. ultramarine (1922) .. .. 1·00 2·75
0 3d. purple/*pale yellow* (1931) .. .. 6·50 16·00
a. Purple/orange-yellow (1937) .. 7·50 17·00
1 4d. orange-yellow (1924) .. .. 1·50 5·00
2 6d. bistre-brown (1922) .. .. 70 1·25
a. Malformed "E" (R.6/6) .. .. 85·00 £120
3 1s. black and carmine (1926) .. .. 2·75 5·50
4 5s dull purple and blue (1924) .. 35·00 65·00
5 £1 green and black (1926) £160 £300
5/25 .. .. *Set of* 11 £190 £350
5s/25s Optd or Perf (1½d., 3d.) "Specimen" *Set of* 11 £375

(Recess B. W.)

30 (2 Jan). *Tercentenary of Colony. Wmk Mult Script CA. P* 12.
6 **17** 1d. black and scarlet .. .. .. 2·00 2·75
7 3d. black and deep brown .. .. 4·00 15·00
8 5d. black and deep purple .. .. 4·00 15·00
9 2s. black and deep blue .. .. 18·00 45·00
0 3s. black and green .. .. .. 42·00 85·00
26/30 .. .. *Set of* 5 60·00 £140
26s/30s Perf "Specimen" .. *Set of* 5 £150

18

(Recess B.W.)

1931 (14 July)–**46**. *Wmk Mult Script CA. P* 12.
131 **18** 2s. slate-purple and deep ultramarine .. 20·00 25·00
a. Slate-purple and indigo (9.42) .. 70·00 38·00
b. Brownish black and indigo (13.4.43) 7·00 3·00
c. Brownish black and steel-blue (6.44) 12·00 1·25
132 3s. slate-purple and myrtle-green .. 28·00 26·00
a. Brownish black and green (13.4.43) 7·00 2·00
b. Brownish blk & myrtle-grn (1.10.46) 8·00 3·25
131s/2s Perf "Specimen" .. *Set of* 2 70·00
Most of the stamps from the September 1942 printing (No. 131*a* and further stocks of the 3s. similar to No. 132) were used for the 1942 "LANDFALL" overprints

1935 (6 May). *Silver Jubilee. As Nos.* 91/4 *of Antigua. P* 13½ × 14.
141 1½d. deep blue and carmine .. .. 1·00 2·75
h. Dot by flagstaff .. .. .. 80·00
i. Dash by turret £120
142 2½d. brown and deep blue .. .. 5·00 9·00
f. Diagonal line by turret £120
g. Dot to left of chapel £160
143 6d. light blue and olive-green .. 7·00 13·00
g. Dot to left of chapel £200
h. Dot by flagstaff £200
144 1s. slate and purple .. .. .. 7·00 9·00
h. Dot by flagstaff £200
141/4 .. .. *Set of* 4 18·00 30·00
141s/4s Perf "Specimen" .. .. *Set of* 4 90·00
For illustrations of plate varieties see Omnibus section following Zanzibar.

19 Greater Flamingos in flight

20 King George VI

(Recess Waterlow)

1935 (22 May). *Wmk Mult Script CA. P* 12½.
145 **19** 8d. ultramarine and scarlet .. .. 6·00 3·25
s. Perf "Specimen" .. .. .. 42·00

1937 (12 May). *Coronation. As Nos.* 95/7 *of Antigua, but printed by D.L.R. P* 14.
146 ½d. green 15 15
147 1½d. yellow-brown 30 75
148 2½d. bright blue 50 75
146/8 .. .. *Set of* 3 85 1·50
146s/8s Perf "Specimen" .. .. *Set of* 3 60·00

Accent flaw (right pane R. 1/5) (1938 ptg only)

Short "T" in "TWO" (right pane R. 3/6) (Retouched on No. 152*c*, although bottom of letter is still pointed)

(Typo D.L.R.)

1938 (11 Mar)–**52**. *Wmk Mult Script CA. Chalk-surfaced paper (1s. to £1). P* 14.
149 **20** ½d. green .. .. 50 1·25
a. Elongated "E" .. .. .. 60·00
b. Accent flaw .. .. .. 95·00
c. Bluish green (11.9.42) .. .. 1·75 1·75
ca. Elongated "E" £110
d. Myrtle-green (11.12.46) .. .. 6·50 6·00
da. Elongated "E" £225
149*e* ½d. brown-purple (18.2.52) .. .. 1·00 2·50
ea. Error. Crown missing £6500
eb. Error. St. Edward's Crown .. £2750
ec. Elongated "E" .. .. .. 95·00
150 1d. carmine .. .. 8·50 4·75
150*a* 1d. olive-grey (17.9.41) .. .. 3·25 3·25
ab. Pale slate (11.9.42) 60 70
151 1½d. red-brown (19.4.38) .. .. 1·50 1·25
a. Pale red-brown (19.4.48) .. .. 4·75 2·50
152 2d. pale slate (19.4.38) .. .. 18·00 6·00
a. Short "T" £550
152*b* 2d. scarlet (17.9.41) .. .. 1·00 65
ba. Short "T" .. .. .. 90·00
bb. "TWO PENCE" printed double .. † £6000
bc. Dull rose-red (19.4.48) .. .. 3·25 3·25
152*c* 2d. green (1.5.51) .. .. .. 1·00 80
153 2½d. ultramarine .. .. .. 3·25 2·00
153*a* 2½d. violet (1.7.43) .. .. .. 1·25 1·25
ab. "2½ PENNY" printed double .. £3000
154 3d. violet (19.4.38) .. .. .. 16·00 4·25
154*a* 3d. blue (4.43) .. .. .. 60 1·25
ab. Bright ultramarine (19.4.48) .. 4·25 4·75
154*b* 3d. scarlet (1.2.52) .. .. .. 60 3·25
154*c* 10d. yellow-orange (18.11.46) .. 2·50 20
155 1s. grey-black and carmine (*thick paper*) (15.9.38) .. .. .. 18·00 6·00
a. Brownish grey and scarlet (4.42) £325 60·00
b. Ordinary paper. *Black and carmine* (9.42) .. .. .. 18·00 7·00
c. Ordinary paper. *Grey-black and bright crimson* (6.3.44) .. .. 9·50 75
d. Pale brownish grey and crimson (19.4.48) .. .. .. 10·00 1·50
156 5s. lilac & blue (*thick paper*) (19.4.38) £170 £100
a. Reddish lilac and blue (4.42) .. £1400 £450
b. Ordinary paper. *Purple & bl* (9.42) 28·00 17·00
c. Ordinary paper. *Dull mauve and deep blue* (11.46) .. .. 85·00 45·00
d. Brown-purple & dp brt bl (19.4.48) 35·00 10·00
e. Red-purple & dp bright blue (8.51) 24·00 14·00
157 **20** £1 deep grey-green and black (*thick paper*) (15.9.38) £250 £140
a. Ordinary paper. *Blue-green and black* (13.4.43) .. .. .. 60·00 45·00
b. Ordinary paper. *Grey-green and black* (3.44) .. .. .. £110 70·00
149/57a .. .. *Set of* 17 £130 70·00
149s/57s Perf "Specimen" .. *Set of* 14 £425
Nos. 149/50*a* exist in coils, constructed from normal sheets.
No. 149eb occurs on a row in the watermark in which the crowns and letters "CA" alternate.
The thick chalk-surfaced paper, used for the initial printing of the 1s., 5s. and £1, was usually toned and had streaky gum. The April 1942 printing for the 1s. and 5s., which was mostly used for the "LANDFALL" overprints, was on thin, white chalk-surfaced paper with clear gum. Printings of the three values between September 1942 and November 1946 were on a thick, smooth, opaque ordinary paper.

21 Sea Garden, Nassau

22 Fort Charlotte

23 Greater Flamingos in Flight

3d.

(24)

(Recess Waterlow)

1938 (1 July). *Wmk Mult Script CA. P* 12½.
158 **21** 4d. light blue and red-orange .. .. 1·00 1·00
159 **22** 6d. olive-green and light blue .. .. 60 1·00
160 **23** 8d. ultramarine and scarlet .. .. 6·75 2·25
158/60 .. .. *Set of* 3 7·50 3·75
158s/60s Perf "Specimen" .. *Set of* 3 £100

1940 (28 Nov). *No.* 153 *surcharged with T* **24** *by* The Nassau Guardian.
161 **20** 3d. on 2½d. blue .. .. 1·00 1·00

1492
LANDFALL
OF
COLUMBUS
1942

(25)

"RENCE" flaw (Right pane R. 9/3. Later corrected so that it does not occur on No. 154*a*)

1942 (12 Oct). *450th Anniv of Landing of Columbus in New World. Optd as T* **25** *by* The Nassau Guardian.
162 **20** ½d. bluish green 30 60
a. Elongated "E" .. .. .. 45·00
b. Opt double £1000
163 1d. pale slate 30 60
164 1½d. red-brown 40 60
165 2d. scarlet 30 65
a. Short "T" .. .. .. 80·00
166 2½d. ultramarine 50 65
167 3d. ultramarine 30 65
a. "RENCE" flaw £110
168 **21** 4d. light blue and red-orange 40 90
a. "COIUMBUS" (R. 5/2) £650 £750
169 **22** 6d. olive-green and light blue .. 40 1·75
a. "COIUMBUS" (R. 5/2) £650 £800
170 **23** 8d. ultramarine and scarlet .. 1·00 70
a. "COIUMBUS" (R. 5/2) £4750 £2250
171 **20** 1s. brownish grey and scarlet .. 5·50 3·50
a. Ordinary paper. *Black and carmine* 5·50 4·50
b. Ordinary paper. *Grey-black and bright crimson* .. .. .. 10·00 6·50
172 **18** 2s. slate-purple and indigo .. 15·00 18·00
a. Brownish black and indigo .. 8·00 10·00
b. Brownish black and steel-blue .. 24·00 24·00
c. Stop after "COLUMBUS" (R. 2/12) £3000
173 3s. slate-purple and myrtle-green .. 5·50 6·50
a. Brownish black and green .. 40·00 32·00
b. Stop after "COLUMBUS" (R. 2/12) £2000
174 **20** 5s. reddish lilac and blue .. .. 35·00 15·00
a. Ordinary paper. *Purple and blue* .. 18·00 14·00
175 £1 deep grey-green & blk (*thick paper*) 70·00 60·00
a. Ordinary paper. *Grey-green & black* 30·00 25·00
162/75a .. .. *Set of* 14 60·00 60·00
162s/75s Perf "Specimen" .. *Set of* 14 £400
These stamps replaced the definitive series for a period of six months. Initially stocks of existing printings were used, but when further supplies were required for overprinting a number of new printings were produced, some of which, including the new colour of the 3d., did not appear without overprint until much later.

1946 (11 Nov). *Victory. As Nos.* 110/11 *of Antigua.*
176 1½d. brown 10 40
177 3d. blue 10 40
176s/7s Perf "Specimen" .. .. *Set of* 2 55·00

NEW INFORMATION

The editor is always interested to correspond with people who have new information that will improve or correct the Catalogue.

26 Infant Welfare Clinic

(Recess C.B.N.)

1948 (11 Oct). *Tercentenary of Settlement of Island of Eleuthera. T* **26** *and similar horiz designs. P* 12.

No.	Description	Unused	Used
178	½d. orange	30	1·00
179	1d. sage-green	30	35
180	1½d. yellow	30	80
181	2d. scarlet	30	40
182	2½d. brown-lake	45	75
183	3d. ultramarine	1·50	85
184	4d. black	60	70
185	6d. emerald-green	1·75	80
186	8d. violet	70	70
187	10d. carmine	60	35
188	1s. sepia	1·00	50
189	2s. magenta	4·00	8·50
190	3s. blue	8·00	8·50
191	5s. mauve	11·00	4·50
192	10s. grey	9·50	9·00
193	£1 vermilion	9·00	14·00
178/93	*Set of* 16	40·00	45·00

Designs:—1d. Agriculture (combine harvester); 1½d. Sisal; 2d. Straw work; 2½d. Dairy farm; 3d. Fishing fleet; 4d. Hatchet Bay, Eleuthera; 6d. Tuna fishing; 8d. Paradise Beach; 10d. Modern hotels; 1s. Yacht racing; 2s. Water sports (skiing); 3s. Shipbuilding; 5s. Transportation; 10s. Salt production, Inagua, £1, Parliament Buildings.

1948 (1 Dec). *Royal Silver Wedding. As Nos.* 112/13 *of Antigua.*

No.	Description	Unused	Used
194	1½d. red-brown	20	25
195	£1 slate-green	32·00	32·00

1949 (10 Oct). *75th Anniv of Universal Postal Union. As Nos.* 114/17 *of Antigua.*

No.	Description	Unused	Used
196	2½d. violet	35	40
197	3d. deep blue	2·25	2·25
198	6d. greenish blue	55	2·25
199	1s. carmine	55	75
196/9	*Set of* 4	3·25	5·00

STAMP BOOKLETS

1938. *Black on pink cover with map and* "BAHAMAS ISLES OF JUNE" *on reverse. Stapled.*

SB1 2s. booklet containing twelve 1d. (No. 150) in blocks of 6 and eight 1½d. (No. 151) in folded block of 8 .. .. £9000

SPECIAL DELIVERY STAMPS

SPECIAL
DELIVERY

(S 1)

1916 (1 May). *No.* 59 *optd with Type* S 1 *by* The Nassau Guardian.

No.		Description	Unused	Used
S1	**6**	5d. black and orange	5·50	32·00
		a. Opt double	£800	£1200
		b. Opt double, one inverted	£950	£1300
		c. Opt inverted	£1300	£1400
		d. Pair, one without opt	£20000	£30000
		x. Wmk reversed		

There were three printings from similar settings of 30, and each sheet had to pass through the press twice. The first printing of 600 was on sale from 1 May 1916 in Canada at Ottawa, Toronto, Westmount (Montreal) and Winnipeg; and under an agreement with the Canadian P.O. were used in combination with Canadian stamps and were cancelled in Canada. The second printing (number unknown) was made about the beginning of December 1916, and the third of 6000, issued probably on 1 March 1917, were on sale only in the Bahamas. These printings caused the revocation, in mid-December 1916, of the agreement by Canada, which no longer accepted the stamps as payment of the special delivery fee and left them to be cancelled in the Bahamas.

It is not possible to identify the printings of the normal stamps without plating both the basic stamp and the overprint, though, in general, the word "SPECIAL" is further to the right in relation to "DELIVERY" in the third printing than in the first or second. Our prices for No. S1 are for the third printing and any stamps which can be positively identified as being from the first or second printings would be worth about eight times as much unused, and any on cover are very rare. All the errors appear to be from the third printing.

SPECIAL
DELIVERY

(S 2)

SPECIAL
DELIVERY

(S 3)

1917 (2 July). *As No.* 59, *but Wmk Mult Crown CA. Optd with Type* S **2** *by D.L.R.*

No.		Description	Unused	Used
S2	**6**	5d. black and orange	45	6·50
		s. Optd "Specimen"	65·00	

1918. *No.* 78 *optd with Type* S **3** *by D.L.R.*

No.		Description	Unused	Used
S3	**6**	5d. black and mauve (R.)	30	2·50
		s. Optd "Specimen"	65·00	

Nos. S2/3 were only on sale in the Bahamas.

Bahrain

An independent shaikhdom, with an Indian postal administration from 1884. A British postal administration operated from 1 April 1948 to 31 December 1965.

The first, and for 62 years the only, post office in Bahrain opened at the capital, Manama, on 1 August 1884 as a sub-office of the Indian Post Office at Bushire (Iran), both being part of the Bombay Postal Circle.

Unoverprinted postage stamps of India were supplied to the new office, continuing on sale there until 1933.

Z 1

Z 2

Stamps of INDIA *cancelled with Type* Z 1 (*this was normally struck elsewhere on the envelope with the stamps obliterated with* "B" *enclosed in a circular background of horizontal bars*) (1885–86)

1882–90. *Queen Victoria* (*Nos.* 84/101).

No.	Description	Price
Z1	½ a. deep blue-green	
Z2	2 a. pale blue	

Stamps of INDIA *cancelled with Type* Z **2** (*squared-circle*) (1886–1902)

1882–90. *Queen Victoria* (*Nos.* 84/101).

No.	Description	Price
Z 5	½ a. deep blue-green	6·00
Z 5*a*	½ a. blue-green	7·00
Z 6	1 a. brown-purple	8·00
Z 6*a*	1 a. plum	8·00
Z 7	1 a. 6 p. sepia	
Z 8	2 a. pale blue	12·00
Z 9	3 a. orange	
Z 9*a*	3 a. brown-orange	10·00
Z10	4 a. olive-green	
Z11	8 a. dull mauve	

1891. *Surch on Queen Victoria* (*No.* 102).

No.	Description	Price
Z12	2½ a. on 4 a. 6 p. yellow-green	

1892–97. *Queen Victoria* (*Nos.* 103/6).

No.	Description	Price
Z13	2 a. 6 p. yellow-green	8·00
Z14	1 r. green and aniline carmine	

1900–02. *Queen Victoria* (*Nos.* 112/18).

No.	Description	Price
Z15	½ a. pale yellow-green	10·00
Z15*a*	½ a. yellow-green	10·00
Z16	1 a. carmine	10·00
Z17	2½ a. ultramarine	20·00

OFFICIAL STAMPS

1883–99. *Queen Victoria* (*Nos.* O37*a*/48).

No.	Description	Price
Z18	½ a. blue-green	25·00
Z19	1 a. brown-purple	

Z 3

Z 4

Stamps of INDIA *cancelled with Type* Z 3 (*single circle, principally intended for use as a backstamp*) (1897–1920)

1882–90. *Queen Victoria* (*Nos.* 84/101).

No.	Description	Price
Z21	½ a. blue-green	
Z22	3 a. brown-orange	

1892–97. *Queen Victoria* (*Nos.* 103/6).

No.	Description	Price
Z23	1 r. green and aniline carmine	

1899. *Queen Victoria* (*No.* 111).

No.	Description	Price
Z24	3 p. carmine	

1900–02. *Queen Victoria* (*Nos.* 112/18).

No.	Description	Price
Z25	½ a. pale yellow-green	
Z25*a*	½ a. yellow-green	
Z26	1 a. carmine	
Z27	2 a. 6 p. ultramarine	

1902–11. *King Edward VII* (*Nos.* 119/47).

No.	Description	Price
Z28	½ a. green	
Z29	2 a. mauve	
Z30	2 a. 6 p. ultramarine	10·00

1906–07. *King Edward VII* (*Nos.* 149/50).

No.	Description	Price
Z31	½ a. green	
Z32	1 a. carmine	

1911–22. *King George V. Wmk Star* (*Nos.* 151/91).

No.	Description	Price
Z33	3 p. grey	
Z34	½ a. light green	
Z35	2 a. purple	1
Z36	2 a. 6 p. ultramarine (No. 171)	

Stamps of INDIA *cancelled with Type* Z **4** (*double circle date band and black lines in centre*) (1902–23)

1876. *Queen Victoria* (*Nos.* 80/2).

No.	Description	Price
Z40	6 a. pale brown	

1882–90. *Queen Victoria* (*Nos.* 84/101).

No.	Description	Price
Z41	3 a. brown-orange	
Z42	4 a. olive-green	
Z43	8 a. dull mauve	2
Z44	12 a. purple/*red*	

1895. *Queen Victoria* (*Nos.* 107/9).

No.	Description	Price
Z45	2 r. carmine and yellow-brown	
Z46	5 r. ultramarine and violet	

1899. *Queen Victoria* (*No.* 111).

No.	Description	Price
Z47	3 p. aniline carmine	

1900–02. *Queen Victoria* (*Nos.* 112/18).

No.	Description	Price
Z48	½ a. pale yellow-green	8
Z48*a*	½ a. yellow-green	8
Z49	1 a. carmine	
Z50	2 a. pale violet	
Z51	2 a. 6 p. ultramarine	

1902–11. *King Edward VII* (*Nos.* 119/47).

No.	Description	Price
Z52	3 p. grey	6
Z52*a*	3 p. slate-grey	7
Z53	½ a. yellow-green	4
Z53*a*	½ a. green	4
Z54	1 a. carmine	
Z55	2 a. violet	10
Z55*a*	2 a. mauve	10
Z56	2 a. 6 p. ultramarine	6
Z57	3 a. orange-brown	
Z58	4 a. olive	
Z59	6 a. olive-bistre	25
Z60	8 a. purple	
Z61	2 r. rose-red and yellow-brown	

1905. *Surcharged on King Edward VII* (*No.* 148).

No.	Description	Price
Z62	¼ a. on ½ a. green	

1906–07. *King Edward VII* (*Nos.* 149/50).

No.	Description	Price
Z63	½ a. green	5·
Z64	1 a. carmine	6

1911–22. *King George V. Wmk Star* (*Nos.* 151/91).

No.	Description	Price
Z65	3 p. grey	
Z66	½ a. light green	4·
Z67	1 a. carmine	6·
Z68	1½ a. chocolate (Type A)	
Z69	2 a. purple	
Z70	2 a. 6 p. ultramarine (No. 171)	
Z71	3 a. orange	
Z72	6 a. yellow-bistre	

1922–26. *King George V. Wmk Star* (*Nos.* 197/200).

No.	Description	Price
Z73	1 a. chocolate	10·

OFFICIAL STAMPS

1902–09. *King Edward VII* (*Nos.* O54/65)

No.	Description	Price
Z74	2 a. mauve	25·

1906. *King Edward VII* (*Nos.* O66/7).

No.	Description	Price
Z75	1 a. carmine	

Z 5

Stamps of INDIA *cancelled with Type* Z **5** (*large double circ primarily intended for use as a backstamp*) (1915–33)

1911–22. *King George V. Wmk Star* (*Nos.* 151/91).

No.	Description	Price
Z79	3 p. grey	
Z80	½ a. light green	7·0
Z80*a*	½ a. emerald	8·0
Z81	1 a. aniline carmine	
Z81*a*	1 a. pale rose-carmine	
Z82	1½ a. chocolate (Type A)	
Z83	2 a. purple	
Z83*a*	2 a. reddish purple	
Z83*b*	2 a. bright reddish violet	
Z84	2 a. 6 p. ultramarine (No. 171)	
Z85	3 a. orange	
Z86	6 a. yellow-bistre	
Z87	1 r. brown and green	

-26. *King George V. Wmk Star* (*Nos.* 197/200).
1 a. chocolate .. ..
3 a. ultramarine .. ..

-33. *King George V. Wmk Multiple Star* (*Nos.* 201/19).
3 p. slate .. .. 6·00
½ a. green .. ..
1 a. chocolate .. .. 5·00
2 a. bright purple (No. 205) .. ..
2 a. purple (No. 206) .. .. ..
3 a. ultramarine .. ..
a 3 a. blue .. ..
4 a. sage-green (No. 211) .. .. ..
8 a. reddish purple .. ..
1 r. chocolate and green .. .. ..
2 r. carmine and orange .. .. ..
5 r. ultramarine and purple .. .. ..
e 1 a. is known with inverted watermark.

Air (*Nos.* 220/5).
2 a. deep blue-green .. ..
3 a. blue .. ..
4 a. olive-green .. ..
6 a. bistre .. ..

Inauguration of New Delhi (*Nos.* 226/31).
¼ a. olive-green and orange-brown .. ..
1 a. mauve and chocolate .. .. ..
s. Z101/6 and Z136/41 come with watermark sideways to r right.

OFFICIAL STAMPS

-09. *King Edward VII* (*Nos.* O54/65).
2 a. mauve .. ..

-13. *King George V. Wmk Star* (*Nos.* O73/96).
½ a. light green .. ..
1 a. rose-carmine .. ..
2 a. reddish purple .. ..

BAHRAIN
9 JAN 28

Z 6

mps of INDIA *cancelled with Type* Z **6** (*double circle with black arc in lower segment*) (1924–33)

1–22. *King George V. Wmk Star* (*Nos.* 151/91).
5 3 p. grey .. ..
6 ½ a. light green .. ..
7 1 a. aniline carmine .. ..
8 2 a. purple .. ..
9 6 a. yellow-bistre .. .. 15·00

2–26. *King George V. Wmk Star* (*Nos.* 197/200).
0 1 a. chocolate .. .. 7·00
1 3 a. ultramarine .. ..

6–33. *King George V. Wmk Multiple Star* (*Nos.* 201/19).
2 3 p. slate .. .. 4·00
3 ½ a. green .. .. 4·00
4 1 a. chocolate .. .. 4·00
5 1½ a. rose-carmine .. .. 15·00
6 2 a. bright purple (No. 205) .. .. .. 15·00
7 2 a. purple (No. 206) .. .. 6·00
8 3 a. blue .. .. 7·00
0 4 a. sage-green (No. 211) .. .. ..
1 8 a. reddish purple .. ..
he ½ a. and 1 a. are known with watermark inverted.

29. *Air* (*Nos.* 220/5).
32 2 a. deep blue-green .. .. 8·00
33 3 a. blue .. ..
34 4 a. olive-green .. ..
35 6 a. bistre .. ..

31. *Inauguration of New Delhi* (*Nos.* 226/31).
36 ½ a. violet and green .. .. 12·00
37 2 a. green and blue .. ..

32–36. *King George V. Wmk Multiple Star* (*Nos.* 232/9).
38 1 a. chocolate .. ..
39 1 a. 3 p. mauve .. ..
40 2 a. vermilion .. ..
41 3 a. carmine .. ..

PRICES FOR STAMPS ON COVER TO 1945

Nos. 1/14	*from* × 5
Nos. 15/19	*from* × 6
Nos. 20/37	*from* × 2
Nos. 38/50	*from* × 6

(Currency. 12 pies = 1 anna; 16 annas = 1 rupee)

BAHRAIN BAHRAIN
(1) (2)

Stamps of India overprinted with T 1 or T 2 (rupee values)

1933 (10 Aug)–**37.** *King George V. Wmk Mult Star, T* **69**.
1 **55** 3 p. slate (11.33) .. .. .. 3·50 45
2 **56** ½ a. green .. .. 7·50 3·25
w. Wmk inverted .. .. .. 32·00 20·00
3 **80** 9 p. deep green (*litho*) .. .. .. 3·75 1·50
a. Typo ptg (1937) .. .. .. 10·00 10·00
4 **57** 1 a. chocolate .. .. 7·00 2·50
w. Wmk inverted .. .. .. 21·00 8·00
5 **82** 1 a. 3 p. mauve .. .. .. 5·00 1·00
w. Wmk inverted .. .. .. 6·50 1·50
6 **70** 2 a. vermilion .. .. 10·00 12·00
w. Wmk inverted .. .. .. 11·00 13·00
7 **62** 3 a. blue .. .. 19·00 45·00
8 **83** 3 a. 6 p. ultramarine .. .. .. 3·75 30
w. Wmk inverted .. .. .. 7·00 60
9 **71** 4 a. sage-green .. .. .. 18·00 45·00
10 **65** 8 a. reddish purple .. .. .. 6·00 30
w. Wmk inverted .. .. .. † 48·00
11 **66** 12 a. claret .. .. 7·50 1·25
w. Wmk inverted .. .. .. † 45·00
12 **67** 1 r. chocolate and green .. .. 16·00 7·50
13 2 r. carmine and orange .. .. 32·00 38·00
14 5 r. ultramarine and purple £110 £140
w. Wmk inverted .. .. .. 90·00 £130
1/14 .. .. *Set of* 14 £200 £250

1934–37. *King George V. Wmk Mult Star. T* **69**.
15 **79** ½ a. green (1935) .. .. .. 4·50 75
w. Wmk inverted .. .. .. 8·50 1·00
16 **81** 1 a. chocolate .. .. 10·00 40
w. Wmk inverted (from booklets) .. 25·00 32·00
17 **59** 2 a. vermilion (1935) .. .. .. 40·00 7·50
17*a* 2 a. vermilion (*small die*) (1937) .. 55·00 25
18 **62** 3 a. carmine .. .. 4·75 50
19 **63** 4 a. sage-green (1935) .. .. .. 4·50 40
15/19 .. .. *Set of* 6 £110 8·50

1938–41. *King George VI.*
20 **91** 3 p. slate (5.38) .. .. .. 9·00 3·25
21 ½ a. red-brown (5.38) .. .. .. 5·00 10
22 9 p. green (5.38) .. .. .. 5·00 5·50
23 1 a. carmine (5.38) .. .. .. 4·50 10
24 **92** 2 a. vermilion (1939) .. .. .. 6·50 1·50
26 – 3 a. yellow-green (1941) .. .. 12·00 5·00
27 – 3 a. 6 p. bright blue (7.38) .. .. 4·75 3·25
28 – 4 a. brown (1941) .. .. .. £120 65·00
30 – 8 a. slate-violet (1940) .. .. .. £140 35·00
31 – 12 a. lake (1940) .. .. .. £100 45·00
32 **93** 1 r. grey and red-brown (1940) .. 2·75 1·75
33 2 r. purple and brown (1940) .. .. 13·00 4·75
34 5 r. green and blue (1940) .. .. 15·00 13·00
35 10 r. purple and claret (1941) .. .. 65·00 35·00
36 15 r. brown and green (1941) .. .. 60·00 65·00
w. Wmk inverted .. .. .. 50·00 55·00
37 25 r. slate-violet and purple (1941) .. £100 85·00
20/37 .. .. *Set of* 16 £600 £300

1942–45. *King George VI on white background.*
38 **100*a*** 3 p. slate .. .. 2·25 1·00
39 ½ a. purple .. .. 4·00 1·50
40 9 p. green .. .. 13·00 14·00
41 1 a. carmine .. .. 4·00 50
42 **101** 1 a. 3 p. bistre .. .. .. 8·00 16·00
43 1½ a. dull violet .. .. 4·75 4·25
44 2 a. vermilion .. .. 5·50 1·50
45 3 a. bright violet .. .. 17·00 4·25
46 3½ a. bright blue .. .. 4·00 15·00
47 **102** 4 a. brown .. .. 2·25 1·50
48 6 a. turquoise-green .. .. .. 12·00 9·00
49 8 a. slate-violet .. .. 3·75 2·50
50 12 a. lake .. .. 6·00 4·00
38/50 .. .. *Set of* 13 75·00 65·00

Unoverprinted India Victory stamps, Nos. 278/81, were placed on sale in Bahrain during January 1946.

Although the stamps of Pakistan were never placed on sale in Bahrain examples of the 1947 "PAKISTAN" overprints on India can be found cancelled in Bahrain from air mail originating at Dubai or Sharjah.

Stamps of Great Britain surcharged

For similar surcharges without the name of the country, see BRITISH POSTAL AGENCIES IN EASTERN ARABIA.

BAHRAIN 1 ANNA (3)

BAHRAIN 5 RUPEES (4)

1948 (1 Apr)–**49.** *Surch as T* **3**, **4** (2 *r. and* 5 *r.*) *or similar surch with bars at foot* (10 *r.*).
51 **128** ½ a. on ½d. pale green .. .. .. 50 1·25
52 1 a. on 1d. pale scarlet .. .. .. 50 1·50
53 1½ a. on 1½d. pale red-brown .. .. 50 1·75
54 2 a. on 2d. pale orange 50 20
55 2½ a. on 2½d. light ultramarine .. .. 50 2·75
56 3 a. on 3d. pale violet 50 10
57 **129** 6 a. on 6d. purple 50 10
58 **130** 1 r. on 1s. bistre-brown .. .. 1·25 10
59 **131** 2 r. on 2s. 6d. yellow-green .. .. 5·50 4·75
60 5 r. on 5s. red .. .. .. 5·50 4·75
60*a* **132** 10 r. on 10s. ultramarine (4.7.49) .. 65·00 48·00
51/60*a* .. .. *Set of* 11 70·00 60·00

BAHRAIN 2½ ANNAS (5)

BAHRAIN 15 RUPEES (6)

1948 (26 Apr). *Silver Wedding, surch as T* **5** *or* **6**.
61 **137** 2½ a. on 2½d. ultramarine .. .. 1·00 30
62 **138** 15 r. on £1 blue .. .. .. 35·00 48·00

1948 (29 July). *Olympic Games, surch as T* **5**, *but in one line* (6 *a.*) *or two lines* (*others*); *the* 1 *r. also has a square of dots as T* **7**.
63 **139** 2½ a. on 2½d. ultramarine .. .. 55 2·00
a. Surch double £900 £1500
64 **140** 3 a. on 3d. violet .. .. .. 55 2·50
65 **141** 6 a. on 6d. bright purple .. .. 1·50 2·75
66 **142** 1 r. on 1s. brown .. .. .. 1·50 2·75
63/6 .. .. *Set of* 4 3·75 9·00

Fifteen used examples of No. 63a are known, of which thirteen, including a block of 4, were postmarked at Experimental P.O. K-121 (Muharraq), one on cover from F.P.O. 756 (Shaibah) on 25 October 1948 and one apparently cancelled-to-order at Bahrain on 10 October 1949.

BAHRAIN
3 ANNAS

(7)

1949 (10 Oct). *75th Anniv of U.P.U., surch as T* **7**, *in one line* (2½ *a.*) *or in two lines* (*others*).
67 **143** 2½ a. on 2½d. ultramarine .. .. 40 2·25
68 **144** 3 a. on 3d. violet .. .. .. 60 2·75
69 **145** 6 a. on 6d. bright purple .. .. 50 3·00
70 **146** 1 r. on 1s. brown .. .. .. 1·25 2·00
67/70 .. .. *Set of* 4 2·50 9·00

BAHRAIN 2 RUPEES (7*a*)

BAHRAIN 2 RUPEES Type II

BAHRAIN
Extra bar (R. 6/1)

Three Types of 2 r.:

Type I. As Type 7*a* showing "2" level with "RUPEES" and "BAHRAIN" sharp.

Type II. "2" raised. "BAHRAIN" worn. 15 mm between "BAHRAIN" and "2 RUPEES".

Type III. As Type II, but 16 mm between "BAHRAIN" and "2 RUPEES". Value is set more to the left of "BAHRAIN".

1950 (2 Oct)–**55.** *Surch as T* **3** *or* **7*a*** (*rupee values*).
71 **128** ½ a. on ½d. pale orange (3.5.51) .. 2·00 2·00
72 1 a. on 1d. light ultramarine (3.5.51) 2·50 20
73 1½ a. on 1½d. pale green (3.5.51) .. 2·50 12·00
74 2 a. on 2d. pale red-brown (3.5.51) .. 1·00 30
75 2½ a. on 2½d. pale scarlet (3.5.51) .. 2·50 12·00
76 **129** 4 a. on 4d. light ultramarine .. .. 2·50 1·50
77 **147** 2 r. on 2s. 6d. yellow-green (3.5.51) 22·00 7·50
a. Surch Type II (1953) .. .. 65·00 32·00
b. Surch Type III (1955) .. .. £750 80·00
ba. "I" inverted and raised (R.2/1) £2750 £600
78 **148** 5 r. on 5s. red (3.5.51) .. .. 13·00 3·75
a. Extra bar £275
79 **149** 10 r. on 10s. ultramarine (3.5.51) .. 26·00 7·50
71/79 .. .. *Set of* 9 65·00 42·00

STAMP BOOKLETS

1934. *Red and black on tan cover. Mysore Sandal Soap advertisement on front.*
SB1 16 a. booklet containing sixteen 1 a. (No. 16w) in blocks of 4 .. .. £950

The Bahrain Post Department took over the postal services on 1 January 1966. Later stamp issues will be found in Part 19 (*Middle East*) of the Stanley Gibbons catalogue.

Bangkok
see **British Post Office in Siam**

Barbados

Regular mails between Barbados and Great Britain were established at an early date in the island's development and it is believed that the British Mail Packet Agency at Bridgetown was opened in 1688 as part of the considerable expansion of the Packet Service in that year.

From 1 August 1851 the colonial authorities were responsible for the internal post system, but the British G.P.O. did not relinquish control of the overseas post until 1858.

For illustrations of the handstamp types see BRITISH POST OFFICES ABROAD notes, following GREAT BRITAIN.

CROWNED-CIRCLE HANDSTAMPS

CC1 CC 1 BARBADOES (3.10.1849) (R.) *Price on cover* £450

Combination covers exist with the local postage paid by a Barbados 1d. stamp and the overseas fee by an example of No. CC1.

During shortages of ½d. stamps in 1893 (17 February to 15 March) and of the ¼d. in 1896 (23 January to 4 May) No. CC1 was utilised, struck in black, on local mail. *Price on cover from* £90.

PRICES FOR STAMPS ON COVER TO 1945

Nos. 1/35	*from* × 5
Nos. 43/63	*from* × 4
Nos. 64/6	*from* × 10
Nos. 67/83	*from* × 5
Nos. 86/8	*from* × 3
Nos. 89/103	*from* × 4
No. 104	*from* × 20
Nos. 105/15	*from* × 4
Nos. 116/24	*from* × 8
Nos. 125/33	*from* × 5
Nos. 135/44	*from* × 4
Nos. 145/52	*from* × 6
No. 153	*from* × 8
Nos. 158/62	*from* × 5
Nos. 163/9	*from* × 3
Nos. 170/96	*from* × 4
Nos. 197/8	*from* × 10
Nos. 199/212	*from* × 6
Nos. 213/39	*from* × 3
No. 240	*from* × 10
Nos. 241/4	*from* × 5
Nos. 245/7	*from* × 6
Nos. 248/56*a*	*from* × 4
Nos. 257/61	*from* × 5
Nos. D1/3	*from* × 25

PERKINS BACON "CANCELLED". For notes on these handstamps, showing "CANCELLED" between horizontal bars forming an oval, see Catalogue Introduction.

CROWN COLONY

1 Britannia 2

(Recess Perkins, Bacon & Co)

1852 (15 April)–**55.** *Paper blued. No wmk. Imperf.*

1 1 (½d.) yellow-green .. .. — £650
2 (½d.) deep green .. .. 90·00 £300
3 (1d.) blue .. .. 32·00 £190
4 (1d.) deep blue .. .. 22·00 65·00
4*a* (2d.) greyish slate £200 £1100
b. Bisected (1d.) (on cover) (1854) .. † £6000
5 (4d.) brownish red (1855) .. .. .. 80·00 £275

The bisect, No. 4b, was authorised for use between 4 August and 21 September 1854 during a shortage of 1d. stamps.

Nos. 5*a*/*b* were never sent to Barbados and come from the Perkins Bacon remainders sold in the 1880's.

Apart from the shade, which is distinctly paler, No. 4*a* can be distinguished from No. 5*b* by the smooth even gum, the gum of No. 5*b* being yellow and patchy, giving a mottled appearance to the back of the stamp. No. 5*a* also has the latter gum.

Prepared for use but not issued

5*a* 1 (No value), slate-blue (*shades*) .. .. 19·00
5*b* (No value), deep slate £200

1855–58. *White paper. No wmk. Imperf.*

7 1 (½d.) yellow-green (1857) £425 £110
8 (½d.) green (1858) £110 £200
9 (1d.) pale blue .. .. 80·00 65·00
10 (1d.) deep blue (H/S "CANCELLED" in oval £5000) .. .. .. 27·00 55·00

1858 (10 Nov). *No wmk. Imperf.*

11 2 6d. pale rose-red £700 £120
11*a* 6d. deep rose-red £700 £180
12 1s. brown-black £250 £110
12*a* 1s. black .. .. £180 75·00

1860. *No wmk.* (*a*) *Pin-perf* 14.

13 1 (½d.) yellow-green £1700 £400
14 (1d.) pale blue £1600 £150
15 (1d.) deep blue £1600 £170

(*b*) *Pin-perf* 12½

16 1 (½d.) yellow-green £6000 £600
16*a* (1d.) blue .. .. — £1200

(*c*) *Pin-perf* 14 × 12½

16*b* 1 (½d.) yellow-green .. .. .. — £6000

Two examples of No. 15 are known bisected and used on separate pieces.

1861. *No wmk. Clean-cut perf* 14 *to* 16.

17 1 (½d.) deep green (H/S "CANCELLED" in oval £5000) .. .. 85·00 8·50
18 (1d.) pale blue .. .. £600 55·00
19 (1d.) blue .. .. £700 55·00
a. Bisected (½d.) (on cover) .. .. † £3000

1861–70. *No wmk.* (*a*) *Rough perf* 14 *to* 16

20 1 (½d.) deep green .. .. .. 19·00 18·00
21 (½d.) green .. .. 14·00 10·00
21*a* (½d.) blue-green .. .. .. 55·00 75·00
b. Imperf (pair) £500
22 (½d.) grass-green .. .. .. 24·00 18·00
a. Imperf (pair) £600
23 (1d.) blue (1861) .. .. .. 38·00 2·25
a. Imperf (pair) £500
24 (1d.) deep blue .. .. 28·00 3·50
a. Bisected diag (½d.) (on cover) (1863) .. .. .. † £1900
25 (4d.) dull rose-red (1861) .. .. 80·00 35·00
a. Imperf (pair) £700
26 (4d.) dull brown-red (1865) .. .. £110 45·00
a. Imperf (pair) £950
27 (4d.) lake-rose (1868) .. .. .. 90·00 65·00
a. Imperf (pair) £1000
28 (4d.) dull vermilion (1869) .. .. £200 70·00
a. Imperf (pair) £950
29 2 6d. rose-red (1861) (Handstamped "CANCELLED" in oval £5000) .. £225 13·00
30 6d. orange-red (1864) .. .. .. 85·00 19·00
31 6d. bright orange-vermilion (1868) .. 75·00 19·00
32 6d. dull orange-vermilion (1870) .. 85·00 13·00
a. Imperf (pair) £450
33 6d. orange (1870) .. .. .. 95·00 26·00
34 1s. brown-black (1863) .. .. .. 55·00 4·50
a. Error. Blue £13000
35 1s. black (1866) .. .. .. 48·00 7·00
a. Imperf between (horiz pair) .. £5000

(*b*) *Prepared for use, but not issued. P* 11 *to* 12

36 1 (½d.) grass-green £7000
37 (1d.) blue £2000

The bisect, No. 24a, was authorised for use in April 1863 and November 1866 during shortages of ½d. stamps.

No. 34a was an error on the part of the printer who supplied the first requisition of the 1s. value in the colour of the 1d. The 1s. blue stamps were never placed on sale, but the Barbados Colonial Secretary circulated some samples which were defaced by a manuscript corner-to-corner cross. A number of these samples subsequently had the cross removed.

Nos. 36/7 were never sent to Barbados and come from the Perkins Bacon remainders. It is believed that the imperforate pairs came from the same source.

1870. *Wmk Large Star, Type* w **1**. *Rough perf* 14 *to* 16.

43 1 (½d.) green .. .. 95·00 6·50
a. Imperf (pair) £850
43*b* (½d.) yellow-green .. .. .. £130 42·00
44 (1d.) blue .. .. £1300 48·00
a. Blue paper .. .. .. £3000 90·00
45 (4d.) dull vermilion .. .. .. £800 90·00
46 2 6d. orange-vermilion .. .. .. £750 55·00
47 1s. black .. .. £300 18·00

1871. *Wmk Small Star, Type* w **2**. *Rough perf* 14 *to* 16.

48 1 (1d.) blue .. .. £110 1·50
49 (4d.) dull rose-red .. .. .. £850 29·00
50 2 6d. orange-vermilion .. .. .. £475 12·00
51 1s. black .. .. £140 7·50

1872. *Wmk Small Star, Type* w **2**. (*a*) *Clean-cut perf* 14½ *to* 15½.

52 1 (1d.) blue .. .. £225 2·00
a. Bisected diag (½d.) (on cover) .. † £1700
53 2 6d. orange-vermilion .. .. .. £700 60·00
54 1s. black .. .. £130 7·50

(*b*) *P* 11 *to* 13 × 14½ *to* 15½

56 1 (½d.) green .. .. £250 32·00
57 (4d.) dull vermilion .. .. .. £550 90·00

1873. *Wmk Large Star, Type* w **1**. (*a*) *Clean-cut perf* 14½ *to* 15½.

58 1 (½d.) green .. .. £225 13·00
59 (4d.) dull rose-red £900 £150
60 2 6d. orange-vermilion .. .. .. £650 60·00
a. Imperf between (horiz pair) .. £4750
b. Imperf (pair) .. .. .. 75·00
61 1s. black .. .. £120 9·00
a. Imperf between (horiz pair) .. £4500

(*b*) *Prepared for use, but not issued. P* 11 *to* 12

62 2 6d. orange-vermilion £4750

Only eight mint examples, in two strips of four, are known of No. 62.

Two used singles of No. 60b have been seen.

1873 (June). *Wmk Small Star, Type* w **2** (*sideways = two points upwards*). *P* 14.

63 2 3d. brown-purple £325 £110

3

1873 (June). *Wmk Small Star, Type* w **2** (*sideways*). *P* 15½×15.

64 3 5s. dull rose £950 £300
s. Handstamped "Specimen" £300

1874 (May). *Wmk Large Star, Type* w **1**. (*a*) *Perf* 14.

65 2 ½d. deep green .. .. .. 26·00 6·50
66 1d. deep blue .. .. 75·00 2·00

(*b*) *Clean-cut perf* 14½ *to* 15½

66*a* 2 1d. deep blue .. .. † £8000
b. Imperf (pair) .. ..

(Recess D.L.R.)

1875–80. *Wmk Crown CC* (*sideways* on* 6*d.*, 1*s.*). (*a*) *P* 1

67 2 ½d. bright green .. .. 40·00
x. Wmk reversed .. .. .. —
68 4d. deep red £190
w. Wmk inverted £275 2
x. Wmk reversed £190
69 6d. bright yellow (aniline) £850
70 6d. chrome-yellow £550
a. Wmk upright .. .. .. † £
w. Wmk Crown to right of CC .. .. —
x. Wmk sideways reversed .. ..
71 1s. violet (aniline) £450
x. Wmk sideways reversed £450
y. Wmk sideways inverted and reversed —

(*b*) *P* 14

72 2 ½d. bright green (1876) .. .. .. 9·50
s. Handstamped "Specimen" in red .. 80·00
sa. Handstamped "Specimen" in black .. £110
w. Wmk inverted .. .. .. — 1
x. Wmk reversed .. .. .. 9·50
73 1d. dull blue .. .. 50·00
a. Bisected (½d.) (on cover) (1877) .. † £1
s. Handstamped "Specimen" in red .. 80·00
sa. Handstamped "Specimen" in black .. £110
w. Wmk inverted .. .. ..
x. Wmk reversed .. .. ..
74 1d. grey-blue .. .. 50·00
a. Wmk sideways .. .. .. †
w. Wmk inverted .. .. .. 90·00 2
x. Wmk reversed .. .. .. 65·00
y. Wmk inverted and reversed .. .. — 3
75 3d. mauve-lilac (1878) .. .. .. 95·00
s. Handstamped "Specimen" in black .. £110
76 4d. red (1878) .. .. 95·00
s. Handstamped "Specimen" in black .. £110
x. Wmk reversed .. .. ..
77 4d. carmine £150
w. Wmk inverted .. .. ..
x. Wmk reversed .. .. ..
78 4d. crimson-lake £500
79 6d. chrome-yellow (1876) £100
s. Handstamped "Specimen" in black .. £110
w. Wmk Crown to right of CC £110 2
x. Wmk sideways reversed .. .. — 2
80 6d. yellow £300 5
w. Wmk Crown to right of CC .. .. — 1
81 1s. purple (1876) £120
s. Handstamped "Specimen" in red .. £110
w. Wmk Crown to right of CC £110
x. Wmk sideways reversed .. ..
82 1s. violet (aniline) £3000 32
w. Wmk Crown to right of CC .. .. — 32
x. Wmk sideways reversed .. ..
83 1s. dull mauve £400 3
a. Bisected (6d.) (on cover) (1.80) .. † £4
x. Wmk sideways reversed .. ..

(*c*) *P* 14×12½

84 2 4d. red £5000

*The normal sideways watermark shows Crown to left of C *as seen from the back of the stamp.*

Only two examples, both used, of No. 70a have been report

Nos. 72sa/3sa were from postal stationery and are witho gum.

Very few examples of No. 84 have been found unused and o one used specimen is known.

1D. (3*a*) 1D. (3*b*) 1D. (3*c*)

1878 (28 Mar). *No. 64 surch by West Indian Press with T* **3** *sideways twice on each stamp and then divided vertically* 11½ *to* 13 *perforations. The lower label, showing the origin face value, was removed before use.*

(*a*) *With T* **3***a*. *Large numeral* "1", 7 *mm high with curved serif, and large letter* "D", 2¾ *mm high.*

86 3 1d. on half 5s. dull rose £4000 £6
a. No stop after "D" £11000 £16
b. Unsevered pair (both No. 86) .. £16000 £18
c. Ditto, Nos. 86 and 87 .. .. — £35
ca. Pair without dividing perf .. .. † £220
d. Ditto, Nos. 86 and 88 .. .. £24000 £55

(*b*) *With T* **3***b*. *As last, but numeral with straight serif*

87 3 1d. on half 5s. dull rose £4750 £7
a. Unsevered pair .. .. .. † £25

(*c*) *With T* **3***c*. *Smaller numeral* "1", 6 *mm high and smaller* "D", 2½ *mm high.*

88 3 1d. on half 5s dull rose £6000 £8
a. Unsevered pair £19000 £35

All types of the surcharge are found reading upwards as well downwards, and there are minor varieties of the type.

4

HALF-PENNY (5)

(Typo D.L.R.)

1882 (28 Aug)–**86.** *Wmk Crown CA. P* 14.

89 4 ½d. dull green (1882) .. .. .. 14·00 1·5
w. Wmk inverted .. .. ..
90 ½d. green .. .. 14·00 1·5
91 1d. rose (1882) .. .. 60·00 2·2
a. Bisected (½d.) (on cover) .. .. † £100
w. Wmk inverted .. .. ..
92 1d. carmine .. .. 15·00 1·0
93 2½d. ultramarine (1882) .. .. .. 80·00 1·5
w. Wmk inverted .. .. .. — 90·0
94 2½d. deep blue .. .. 90·00 1·5
95 3d. deep purple (1885) .. .. .. £100 29·0
96 3d. reddish purple .. .. .. 4·25 15·0
97 4d. grey (1882) .. .. £250 2·7

4 4d. pale brown (1885) 7·50 3·00
w. Wmk inverted — 60·00
x. Wmk reversed
y. Wmk inverted and reversed † £170
4d. deep brown 4·75 1·50
6d. olive-black (1886) 75·00 40·00
1s. chestnut (1886) 25·00 21·00
5s. bistre (1886) £150 £190
3 *Set of* 9 £550 £250
)3s (*ex* 4d. grey) Optd "Specimen" *Set of* 5 £400

(July). *No. 99 surch with T* **5** *by West Indian Press.*
4 ½d. on 4d. deep brown 2·25 3·75
a. No hyphen 10·00 19·00
b. Surch double (R.+Bk.) £550 £750
ba. Surch double (R.+Bk.) both without hyphen £1500 £1500
c. Surch double, one albino
d. Surch "PENNY HALF" — £200

s. 104b/ba come from a sheet with a trial surcharge in red
1 was subsequently surcharged again in black and put back
stock.
. 104c is known in a horizontal pair with the left hand
p showing the first two letters of the second impression
l. The right hand stamp shows a complete albino surcharge.

6 Seal of Colony **7**

(Typo D.L.R.)

(July)–**1903.** *Wmk Crown CA. P* 14.
6 ¼d. slate-grey and carmine (5.5.96) 2·25 10
w. Wmk inverted
½d. dull green 2·50 10
w. Wmk inverted — 65·00
1d. carmine 4·75 10
2d. slate-black and orange (5.99) 8·00 75
2½d. ultramarine 17·00 20
5d. grey-olive 7·00 4·50
6d. mauve and carmine 15·00 2·00
8d. orange and ultramarine 4·00 21·00
10d. dull blue-green and carmine 8·00 6·50
2s. 6d. blue-black and orange 48·00 48·00
w. Wmk inverted 95·00 £100
2s. 6d. violet and green (29.5.03) 80·00 £130
15 *Set of* 11 £180 £190
s/15s Optd "Specimen" *Set of* 11 £190
ee also Nos. 135/44 and 163/9.

(Typo D.L.R.)

7 (16 Nov)–**98.** *Diamond Jubilee. T* **7**. *Wmk Crown CC.* 14.

(a) White paper
¼d. grey and carmine 3·50 60
½d. dull green 3·50 60
1d. rose 3·50 60
2½d. ultramarine 7·00 85
w. Wmk inverted
5d. olive-brown 16·00 15·00
6d. mauve and carmine 21·00 21·00
8d. orange and ultramarine 8·50 23·00
10d. blue-green and carmine 48·00 55·00
2s. 6d. blue-black and orange 60·00 55·00
w. Wmk inverted
/24 *Set of* 9 £150 £150
s/24s Optd "Specimen" *Set of* 9 £150

(b) Paper blued
¼d. grey and carmine 28·00 30·00
½d. dull green 29·00 30·00
1d. carmine 38·00 40·00
2½d. ultramarine 40·00 45·00
5d. olive-brown £225 £250
6d. mauve and carmine £130 £140
8d. orange and ultramarine £140 £150
10d. dull green and carmine £190 £225
2s. 6d. blue-black and orange £120 £130

05. *Wmk Mult Crown CA. P* 14.
5 **6** ¼d. slate-grey and carmine 8·00 2·75
6 ½d. dull green 14·00 10
7 1d. carmine 14·00 10
9 2½d. blue 13·00 15
1 6d. mauve and carmine 11·00 14·00
2 8d. orange and ultramarine 40·00 80·00
4 2s. 6d. violet and green 40·00 90·00
5/144 *Set of* 7 £130 £170
See also Nos. 163/9.

8 Nelson Monument

(Des Mrs. G. Goodman. Recess D.L.R.)

906 (1 Mar). *Nelson Centenary. Wmk Crown CC. P* 14.
45 **8** ¼d. black and grey 8·00 1·75
w. Wmk inverted 32·00 35·00
46 ½d. black and pale green 9·50 15
w. Wmk inverted
x. Wmk reversed † 55·00
47 1d. black and red 12·00 15
w. Wmk inverted 45·00
x. Wmk reversed † 55·00

148 **8** 2d. black and yellow 1·75 4·50
149 2½d. black and bright blue 3·75 1·25
w. Wmk inverted
150 6d. black and mauve 18·00 25·00
151 1s. black and rose 21·00 50·00
145/51 *Set of* 7 65·00 75·00
145s/51s Optd "Specimen" *Set of* 7 £150

Two sets may be made of the above: one on thick, opaque, creamy white paper; the other on thin, rather transparent, bluish white paper.

See also Nos. 158/62*a*.

9 *Olive Blossom*, 1605

Kingston Relief Fund. 1d.

(10)

(Des Lady Carter. Recess D.L.R.)

1906 (15 Aug). *Tercentenary of Annexation. Wmk Multiple Crown CA (sideways). P* 14.
152 **9** 1d. black, blue and green 10·00 25
s. Optd "Specimen" 65·00

1907 (25 Jan–25 Feb). *Kingston Relief Fund. No.* 108 *surch with T* **10** *by T. E. King & Co., Barbados.*
153 **6** 1d. on 2d. slate-black and orange (R.) 2·50 4·75
a. Surch inverted (25.2.07) 1·75 6·50
b. Surch double £700 £750
c. Surch double, both inverted £700
d. Surch *tête-bêche* (pair) £850
e. No stop after "1d." 38·00 65·00
ea. Do., surch inverted (25.2.07) 38·00 80·00
eb. Do., surch double — £1100
f. Vert pair, one normal, one surch double — £850

The above stamp was sold for 2d. of which 1d. was retained for the postal revenue, and the other 1d. given to a fund for the relief of the sufferers by the earthquake in Jamaica.

An entire printing as No. 153a was created after a sheet of inverted surcharges was found in the initial supply.

1907 (6 July). *Nelson Centenary. Wmk Mult Crown CA. P* 14.
158 **8** ¼d. black and grey 5·00 3·50
161 2d. black and yellow 20·00 26·00
162 2½d. black and bright blue 10·00 21·00
a. Black and indigo £700 £800
158/62 *Set of* 3 32·00 45·00

1909 (July)–**10.** *Wmk Mult Crown CA. P* 14.
163 **6** ¼d. brown 5·50 30
164 ½d. blue-green 18·00 1·00
165 1d. red 14·00 10
166 2d. greyish slate (8.10) 7·50 9·50
167 2½d. bright blue (1910) 45·00 7·50
168 6d. dull and bright purple (1910) 9·50 15·00
169 1s. black/*green* (8.10) 9·50 14·00
163/9 *Set of* 7 £100 42·00
163s/9s (*ex* ½d., 2½d.) Optd "Specimen" *Set of* 5 £120

11

12

13

(Typo D.L.R.)

1912 (23 July)–**16.** *Wmk Mult Crown CA. P* 14.
170 **11** ¼d. brown 1·50 1·50
a. Pale brown (1916) 1·25 2·50
aw. Wmk inverted
171 ½d. green 3·50 10
a. Wmk sideways † —
172 1d. red (13.8.12) 7·50 10
a. Scarlet (1915) 23·00 3·25
173 2d. greyish slate (13.8.12) 2·75 14·00
174 2½d. bright blue (13.8.12) 1·50 40
175 **12** 3d. purple/*yellow* (13.8.12) 1·50 14·00
176 4d. red and black/*yellow* (13.8.12) 1·50 16·00
177 6d. purple and dull purple (13.8.12) 12·00 12·00
178 **13** 1s. black/*green* (13.8.12) 8·50 12·00
179 2s. blue and purple/*blue* (13.8.12) 42·00 45·00
180 3s. violet and green (13.8.12) 80·00 95·00
170/80 *Set of* 11 £140 £190
170s/80s Optd "Specimen" *Set of* 11 £140

14

WAR TAX

(15)

(Recess D.L.R.)

1916 (16 June)–**19.** *Wmk Mult Crown CA. P* 14.
181 **14** ¼d. deep brown 75 40
a. Chestnut-brown (9.17) 1·50 35
b. Sepia-brown (4.18) 3·75 2·75
w. Wmk inverted 17·00 18·00
y. Wmk inverted and reversed 32·00

182 **14** ½d. green 1·10 15
a. Deep green (9.17) 1·60 15
b. Pale green (4.18) 2·25 80
w. Wmk inverted 27·00
y. Wmk inverted and reversed
183 1d. deep red 17·00 6·00
a. Bright carmine-red (4.17) 2·50 15
b. Pale carmine-red (9.17) 6·00 65
w. Wmk inverted 27·00
x. Wmk reversed
y. Wmk inverted and reversed 26·00
184 2d. grey 3·50 19·00
a. Grey-black (9.19) 30·00 70·00
y. Wmk inverted and reversed
185 2½d. deep ultramarine 3·50 2·00
a. Royal blue (11.17) 3·50 2·00
w. Wmk inverted
y. Wmk inverted and reversed 32·00 32·00
186 3d. purple/*yellow* (thin paper) 2·25 5·50
a. Dp purple/yell (thick paper) (9.19) 28·00 38·00
187 4d. red/*yellow* 80 14·00
188 6d. purple 3·00 3·75
189 1s. black/*green* 7·00 9·00
190 2s. purple/*blue* 16·00 7·50
y. Wmk inverted and reversed 48·00
191 3s. deep violet 48·00 £110
w. Wmk inverted
y. Wmk inverted and reversed
181/91 *Set of* 11 80·00 £150
181s/91s "Specimen" *Set of* 11 £180

Dates quoted for shades are those of despatch from Great Britain.

Examples of the ½d. and 1d. values can be found perforated either by line or by comb machines.

See also Nos. 199/200*a*.

1917 (10 Oct)–**18.** *War Tax. Optd in London with T* **15**.
197 **11** 1d. bright red 50 15
s. Optd "Specimen" 55·00
w. Wmk inverted
198 1d. pale red (*thicker bluish paper*) (4.18) 3·00 50

1918 (18 Feb)–**20.** *Colours changed. Wmk Mult Crown CA. P* 14.
199 **14** 4d. black and red 80 3·75
x. Wmk reversed £120
200 3s. green and deep violet 17·00 60·00
a. Green and bright violet (1920) £225 £325
199s/200s Optd "Specimen" *Set of* 2 £120

The centres of these are from a new die having no circular border line.

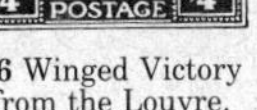

16 Winged Victory from the Louvre

17 Victory from Victoria Memorial, London

(Recess D.L.R.)

1920 (9 Sept)–**21.** *Victory. P* 14.

(a) Wmk Mult Crown CA (sideways on T* **17**)
201 **16** ¼d. black and bistre-brown 30 70
a. "C" of "CA" missing from wmk £250
c. Substituted crown in wmk £300
w. Wmk inverted
x. Wmk reversed 35·00
y. Wmk inverted and reversed 42·00
202 ½d. black and bright yellow-green 1·00 15
a. "C" of "CA" missing from wmk £275 £225
b. "A" of "CA" missing from wmk £275
c. Substituted crown in wmk
w. Wmk inverted — 80·00
x. Wmk reversed 80·00
y. Wmk inverted and reversed 80·00 80·00
203 1d. black and vermilion 4·00 10
a. "A" of "CA" missing from wmk † £300
c. Substituted crown in wmk † £275
w. Wmk inverted 38·00
y. Wmk inverted and reversed
204 2d. black and grey 2·00 7·00
a. "C" of "CA" missing from wmk £325
205 2½d. indigo and ultramarine 2·75 16·00
a. "C" of "CA" missing from wmk £325
w. Wmk inverted — 80·00
y. Wmk inverted and reversed 80·00 90·00
206 3d. black and purple 3·00 6·00
w. Wmk inverted 30·00 35·00
207 4d. black and blue-green 3·25 7·00
208 6d. black and brown-orange 3·75 14·00
w. Wmk inverted 60·00 80·00
wa. "C" of "CA" missing from wmk £800
209 **17** 1s. black and bright green 10·00 26·00
a. "C" of "CA" missing from wmk £750
w. Wmk Crown to left of CA
x. Wmk sideways reversed £110
y. Wmk sideways inverted and reversed £120
210 2s. black and brown 24·00 35·00
w. Wmk Crown to left of CA 65·00 80·00
x. Wmk sideways reversed £110
y. Wmk sideways inverted and reversed
211 3s. black and dull orange 30·00 45·00
a. "C" of "CA" missing from wmk £650
w. Wmk Crown to left of CA 70·00
x. Wmk sideways reversed

(b) Wmk Mult Script CA
212 **16** 1d. black and vermilion (22.8.21) .. 17·00 30
201/12 .. .. *Set of* 12 90·00 £140
201s/12s Optd "Specimen" .. *Set of* 12 £200

*The normal sideways watermark on Nos. 209/11 shows Crown to right of CA, *as seen from the back of the stamp.*

For illustration of the substituted watermark crown see Catalogue Introduction.

18

19

(Recess D.L.R.)

1921 (14 Nov)–**24**. *P* 14. *(a) Wmk Mult Crown CA.*
213 **18** 3d. purple/*pale yellow* .. .. .. 2·00 6·00
x. Wmk reversed .. .. .. † £120
214 4d. red/*pale yellow* .. .. .. 1·75 13·00
215 1s. black/*emerald* .. .. .. 5·50 11·00
w. Wmk inverted .. .. ..

(b) Wmk Mult Script CA
217 **18** ¼d. brown 25 10
x. Wmk reversed .. .. .. 24·00
y. Wmk inverted and reversed .. 35·00
219 ½d. green .. .. 1·50 10
220 1d. red 80 10
aw. Wmk inverted .. .. .. 24·00 30·00
ax. Wmk reversed .. .. ..
ay. Wmk inverted and reversed ..
b. Bright rose-carmine .. .. 6·50 1·00
bw. Wmk inverted .. .. .. 24·00
221 2d. grey .. .. 1·75 20
y. Wmk inverted and reversed ..
222 2½d. ultramarine .. .. .. 1·50 6·50
225 6d. reddish purple .. .. .. 3·50 5·50
226 1s. black/*emerald* (18.9.24) .. .. 48·00 90·00
227 2s. purple/*blue* .. .. .. 10·00 19·00
228 3s. deep violet .. .. .. 14·00 50·00
y. Wmk inverted and reversed
213/28 .. .. *Set of* 12 75·00 £180
213s/28s Optd "Specimen" .. *Set of* 12 £170

1925 (1 Apr)–**35**. *Wmk Mult Script CA. P* 14.
229 **19** ¼d. brown 25 10
230 ½d. green 50 10
a. Perf 13½×12½ (2.32) .. .. 6·50 10
231 1d. scarlet 50 10
a. Perf 13½×12½ (2.32) .. .. 5·50 50
231*b* 1½d. orange (1933) .. .. .. 14·00 3·25
ba. Perf 13½×12½ (15.8.32) .. 2·00 1·00
232 2d. grey .. .. 50 3·25
233 2½d. blue 50 80
a. Bright ultramarine (1933) .. .. 14·00 1·75
ab. Perf 13½×12½ (2.32) .. .. 6·00 3·00
234 3d. purple/*pale yellow* .. .. 1·00 45
a. Reddish purple/yellow (1935) .. 6·00 6·00
235 4d. red/*pale yellow* .. .. .. 75 1·00
236 6d. purple .. .. 1·00 90
237 1s. black/*emerald* .. .. .. 2·00 6·50
a. Perf 13½×12½ (8.32) .. .. 48·00 27·00
b. Brownish black/bright yellow-green (1934) .. .. .. 4·50 10·00
238 2s. purple/*blue* .. .. .. 7·00 6·50
238*a* 2s. 6d. carmine/*blue* (1.9.32) .. 22·00 25·00
239 3s. deep violet .. .. .. 11·00 13·00
229/39 .. .. *Set of* 13 42·00 50·00
229s/39s Optd or Perf (1½d., 2s. 6d.) "Specimen" *Set of* 13 £180

Nos. 230/1 exist in coils constructed from normal sheets.

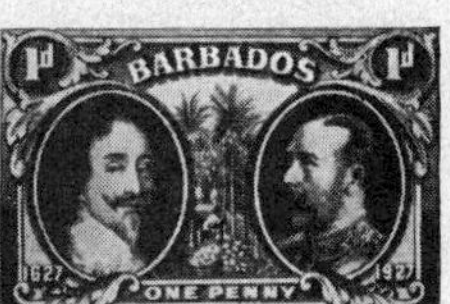

20 King Charles I and King George V

21 Badge of the Colony

(Recess B.W.)

1927 (17 Feb). *Tercentenary of Settlement of Barbados. Wmk Mult Script CA. P* 12½.
240 **20** 1d. carmine .. .. 1·00 75
s. Optd "Specimen" .. .. .. 42·00

1935 (6 May). *Silver Jubilee. As Nos.* 91/4 *of Antigua, but ptd by Waterlow. P* 11 × 12.
241 1d. deep blue and scarlet 50 20
j. Damaged turret .. .. .. 95·00
242 1½d. ultramarine and grey .. .. 3·75 6·00
j. Damaged turret £130
243 2½d. brown and deep blue .. .. 2·25 4·00
m. "Bird" by turret £170
244 1s. slate and purple .. .. 17·00 18·00
l. Kite and horizontal log £275
241/4 .. .. *Set of* 4 21·00 25·00
241s/4s Perf "Specimen" .. .. *Set of* 4 75·00

For illustrations of plate varieties see Omnibus section following Zanzibar.

1937 (14 May). *Coronation. As Nos.* 95/7 *of Antigua, but printed by D.L.R. P* 14.
245 1d. scarlet 30 15
246 1½d. yellow-brown 40 60
247 2½d. bright blue 70 45
245/7 .. .. *Set of* 3 1·25 1·10
245s/7s Perf "Specimen" .. .. *Set of* 3 50·00

Recut line (R. 10/6)

Extra frame line (R. 11/9)

Mark on central ornament (R. 1/3, 2/3, 3/3)

Vertical line over horse's head (R. 4/10) (corrected on Dec 1947 ptg)

"Flying mane" (R. 4/1) (corrected on Dec 1947 ptg)

Curved line at top right (R. 7/8) (corrected on Dec 1947 ptg)

Cracked plate (extends to top right ornament) (R. 6/10))

(Recess D.L.R.)

1938 (3 Jan)–**47**. *Wmk Mult Script CA. P* 13½×13.
248 **21** ½d. green .. .. 6·00 15
a. Recut line .. .. £120 40·00
b. Perf 14 (8.42) .. .. .. 70·00 1·25
ba. Recut line .. .. £325 75·00
248*c* ½d. yellow-bistre (16.10.42) 15 30
ca. "A" of "CA" missing from wmk .. £1100
cb. Recut line .. .. 19·00 24·00
249 1d. scarlet (1941) .. .. .. £275 4·00
a. Perf 14 (3.1.38) .. .. .. 16·00 10
249*b* 1d. blue-green (1943) .. .. .. 3·50 80
c. Perf 14 (16.10.42) 15 10
ca. "A" of "CA" missing from wmk .. £1100
250 1½d. orange 15 40
a. "A" of "CA" missing from wmk .. £1100
b. Perf 14 (11.41) .. .. .. 4·75 65
250*c* 2d. claret (3.6.41) .. .. .. 50 2·50
ca. Extra frame line .. .. .. 35·00 60·00
250*d* 2d. carmine (20.9.43) 20 70
da. Extra frame line .. .. .. 24·00 35·00
db. "A" of "CA" missing from wmk .. † —
e. Perf 14 (11.9.44) .. .. .. 15 1·75
ea. Extra frame line .. .. .. 24·00 50·00
251 2½d. ultramarine 50 60
a. Mark on central ornament .. 38·00 38·00
b. Blue (17.2.44) .. .. .. 1·75 4·50
ba. "A" of "CA" missing from wmk .. £1000
bb. Mark on central ornament .. 50·00 65·00
252 3d. brown .. .. 20 1·90
a. Vertical line over horse's head .. 75·00 £120
b. Perf 14 (4.41) 20 60
ba. Vertical line over horse's head .. 75·00 90·00
252*c* 3d. blue (1.4.47) .. .. .. 20 1·75
ca. Vertical line over horse's head .. 75·00 £100
253 4d. black 20 10
a. Flying mane .. .. .. 85·00 60·00
b. Curved line at top right .. .. 70·00 50·00
c. Cracked plate .. .. .. 70·00 50·00
d. Perf 14 (11.9.44) .. .. .. 20 4·00
da. Flying mane .. .. .. 85·00 £120
db. Curved line at top right .. .. 70·00 £100
dc. Cracked plate .. .. .. 70·00 £100
254 6d. violet 80 40
254*a* 8d. magenta (9.12.46) .. .. .. 55 2·00
255 1s. olive-green .. .. .. 16·00 2·50
a. Deep brown-olive (19.11.45) .. 1·00 10
256 2s. 6d. purple .. .. 7·00 1·50
256*a* 5s. indigo (3.6.41) .. .. .. 3·25 6·00
ab. "A" of "CA" missing from wmk .. £1400
248/56*a* .. .. *Set of* 16 32·00 14·00
248s/56as Perf "Specimen" .. *Set of* 16 £190

No. 249a was perforated by two machines, one gauging 13.8×14.1 line (1938), the other 14.1 comb (October 1940).

Nos. 248/c and 249/c exist in coils constructed from normal sheets.

22 Kings Charles I, George VI, Assembly Chamber and Mace

(Recess D.L.R.)

1939 (27 June). *Tercentenary of General Assembly. Wmk Script CA. P* 13½ × 14.
257 **22** ½d. green .. .. 2·25
258 1d. scarlet .. .. 2·25
259 1½d. orange .. .. 2·25
260 2½d. bright ultramarine .. .. .. 2·25
261 3d. brown .. .. 2·25
257/61 .. .. *Set of* 5 10·00
257s/61s Perf "Specimen" .. *Set of* 5 £140

Two flags on tug (R. 5/2)

1946 (18 Sept). *Victory. As Nos.* 110/11 *of Antigua.*
262 1½d. red-orange 15
a. Two flags on tug .. .. .. 20·00
263 3d. brown 15
262s/3s Perf "Specimen" .. .. *Set of* 2 48·00

ONE
PENNY
(23)

NY PEN

Short "Y" (R. 6/2)

Broken "E" (R. 7/4 and 11/4)

(Surch by Barbados Advocate Co)

1947 (21 Apr). *Surch with T* **23**. *(a) P* 14.
264 **21** 1d. on 2d. carmine (No. 250e) .. .. 1·25 2
a. Extra frame line .. .. .. 60·00 75
b. Short "Y" .. .. .. 60·00 75
c. Broken "E" .. .. .. 30·00 38

(b) P 13½×13
264*d* **21** 1d. on 2d. carmine (No. 250*d*) .. .. 3·00 5
da. Extra frame line £160 £1
db. Short "Y" £160 £1
dc. Broken "E" .. .. .. 95·00 £1

The relationship of the two words in the surcharge differs each position of the sheet.

1948 (24 Nov). *Royal Silver Wedding. As Nos.* 112/13 *Antigua.*
265 1½d. orange 30
266 5s. indigo .. .. 10·00 6·

1949 (10 Oct). *75th Anniv of Universal Postal Union. As N 114/17 of Antigua.*
267 1½d. red-orange 30
268 3d. deep blue .. .. 1·50 1·
269 4d. grey .. .. 35 2·
270 1s. olive 35 4
267/70 .. .. *Set of* 4 2·25 4·

(New Currency. 100 cents = 1 West Indian, later Barbados, dollar)

24 Dover Fort

27 Statue of Nelson

(Recess B.W.)

1950 (1 May). *T* **24, 27** *and similar designs. Wmk Mult Script CA P* 11 × 11½ *(horiz)*, 13½ *(vert)*.
271 1 c. indigo .. .. 30 2·2
272 2 c. emerald-green .. .. 15 2·0
273 3 c. reddish brown and blue-green .. .. 1·25 2·7
274 4 c. carmine 15 4
275 6 c. light blue .. .. 15 2·0
276 8 c. bright blue and purple-brown .. .. 1·25 2·5
277 12 c. greenish blue and brown-olive .. .. 1·00 1·0
278 24 c. scarlet and black .. .. .. 1·00 5
279 48 c. violet .. .. 8·00 6·5
280 60 c. green and claret .. .. .. 7·50 8·5
281 $1.20, carmine and olive-green .. .. 8·50 3·7
282 $2.40, black .. .. 15·00 15·0
271/282 .. .. *Set of* 12 38·00 42·0

Designs: *Horiz*—2 c. Sugar cane breeding; 3 c. Public buildings; 6 c. Casting net; 8 c. *Frances W. Smith* (schooner); 12 c. Four-winged Flyingfish; 24 c. Old Main Guard Garrison; 60 c. Careenage; $2.40, Seal of Barbados. *Vert*—48 c. St. Michael's Cathedral; $1.20, Map of Barbados and wireless mast.

1951 (16 Feb). *Inauguration of B.W.I. University College. As Nos. 118/19 of Antigua.*
283 3 c. brown and blue-green 30 30
284 12 c. blue-green and brown-olive .. .. 55 1·75

36 King George VI and Stamp of 1852

(Recess Waterlow)

(15 Apr). *Barbados Stamp Centenary. Wmk Mult Script CA.* 13½.

36	3 c. green and slate-green		15	40
	4 c. blue and carmine		15	1·00
	12 c. slate-green and bright green		15	1·00
	24 c. red-brown and brownish black		15	55
8		*Set of* 4	55	2·75

STAMP BOOKLETS

6 (Feb).
2s. ½d. booklet containing twenty-four 1d. (No. 137) in blocks of 6

9. *Black on red cover. Stapled.*
a 1s. 6d. booklet containing eighteen 1d. (No. 165) in blocks of 6

3 (June). *Black on red cover. Stapled.*
2s. booklet containing twelve ½d. and eighteen 1d. (Nos. 171/2) in blocks of 6 .. .. £1200

6 (16 June). *Black on red cover. Stapled.*
2s. booklet containing twelve ½d. and eighteen 1d. (Nos. 182/3) in pairs £900

0 (Sept). *Black on red cover. Stapled.*
4 2s. booklet containing twelve ½d. and eighteen 1d. (Nos. 202/3) in pairs

2 (12 Nov). *Black on pale green cover. Austin Cars and Post ffice Guide advertisements on front. Stapled.*
5 2s. booklet containing ½d. and 1d. (Nos. 230a, 231a) each in block of 10 and 1½d. (No. 231ba) in block of 6

33 (4 Dec). *Black on pale green cover. Advocate Co. Ltd. dvertisement on front. Stapled.*
6 2s. booklet containing ½d. and 1d. (Nos. 230/1) each in block of 10 and 1½d. (No. 231*b*) in block of 6

38 (3 Jan). *Black on light blue cover. Advocate Co. Ltd. dvertisement on front. Stapled.*
7 2s. booklet containing ½d. and 1d. (Nos. 248, 249a) each in block of 10 and 1½d. (No. 250) in block of 6 .. .. £1500

POSTAGE DUE STAMPS

D 1

(Typo D.L.R.)

934 (2 Jan)–**47**. *Wmk Mult Script CA. P* 14.

1	D 1	½d. green (10.2.35)		1·25	7·50
2		1d. black		1·25	1·25
		a. Bisected (½d.) (on cover)		†	£1000
3		3d. carmine (13.3.47)		20·00	18·00
1/3			*Set of* 3	20·00	24·00
1s/3s Perf "Specimen"			*Set of* 3	70·00	

The bisected 1d. was officially authorised for use between arch 1934 and February 1935. Some specimens had the value ½d." written across the half stamp in red or black ink (*Price on over* £1200).

(Typo D.L.R.)

950 (8 Dec)–**53**. *Values in cents. Wmk Mult Script CA. Ordinary paper. P* 14.

4 D 1	1 c. green		3·75	23·00
	a. Chalk-surfaced paper. *Deep green* (29.11.51)		30	3·00
	ab. Error. Crown missing, W **9***a*		£350	
	ac. Error. St. Edward's Crown, W **9***b*		£190	
5	2 c. black		7·00	12·00
	a. Chalk-surfaced paper (20.1.53)		1·00	5·50
	ac. Error. St. Edward's Crown, W **9***b*		£350	
6	6 c. carmine		16·00	17·00
	a. Chalk-surfaced paper (20.1.53)		1·00	8·50
	ab. Error. Crown missing, W **9***a*		£190	
	ac. Error. St. Edward's Crown, W **9***b*		£150	
D4/6		*Set of* 3	24·00	48·00
D4a/6a		*Set of* 3	2·10	15·00

The 1 c. has no dot below "c".

Barbuda
(*see after* Antigua)

(see after Antigua)

Basutoland

Stamps of CAPE OF GOOD HOPE were used in Basutoland from about 1876, initially cancelled by upright oval with framed number type postmarks of that colony. Cancellation numbers known to have been used in Basutoland are 133 (Quthing), 156 (Mafeteng), 210 (Mohaleshoek), 277 (Morija), 281 (Maseru), 317 (Thlotse Heights) and 688 (Teyateyaneng).

From 1910 until 1933 the stamps of SOUTH AFRICA were in use. Stamps of the Union provinces are also known used in Basutoland during the early years of this period and can also be found cancelled-to-order during 1932–33.

The following post offices and postal agencies existed in Basutoland before December 1933. Stamps of Cape of Good Hope or South Africa with recognisable postmarks from them are worth a premium. For a few of the smaller offices or agencies there are, as yet, no actual examples recorded. Dates given are those generally accepted as the year in which the office was first opened.

Bokong (1931)	Motsekuoa (1915)
Butha Buthe (1907)	Mount Morosi (1918)
Jonathan's (1927)	Mphotos (1914)
Khabos (1927)	Peka (1908)
Khetisas (1930)	Phamong (1932)
Khukhune (1933)	Pitseng (1921)
Kolonyama (1914)	Qachasnek (1895)
Kueneng (1914)	Qalo (1923?)
Leribe (1890)	Quthing (1882)
Mafeteng (1874)	Rankakalas (1933)
Majara (1912)	Roma Mission (1913)
Makhoa (1932)	Sebapala (1930)
Makoalis (1927)	Seforong (1924)
Mamathes (1919)	Sehlabathebe (1921)
Mapoteng (1925)	Sekake (1931)
Marakabeis (1932)	Teyateyaneng (1886)
Maseru (1872)	Thaba Bosigo (1913)
Maseru Rail (1915?)	Thabana Morena (1922)
Mashai (1929)	Thabaneng (1914)
Matsaile (1930)	Thaba Tseka (1929)
Mekading (1914)	Thlotse Heights (1872)
Mofokas (1915)	Tsepo (1923)
Mohaleshoek (1873)	Tsoelike (1927)
Mokhotlong (1921)	Tsoloane (1918)
Morija (1884)	

For further details of the postal history of Basutoland see *The Cancellations and Postal Markings of Basutoland/Lesotho* by A. H. Scott, published by Collectors Mail Auctions (Pty) Ltd, Cape Town, from which the above has been, with permission, extracted.

PRICES FOR STAMPS ON COVER TO 1945

Nos. 1/19	*from* × 5
Nos. 11/14	*from* × 6
Nos. 15/17	*from* × 10
Nos. 18/28	*from* × 6
Nos. 29/31	*from* × 10
Nos. O1/4	*from* × 4
Nos. D1/2	*from* × 25

CROWN COLONY

1 King George V, Nile Crocodile and Mountains

(Recess Waterlow)

1933 (1 Dec). *Wmk Mult Script CA. P* 12½.

1	**1**	½d. emerald		1·00	1·75
2		1d. scarlet		75	1·25
3		2d. bright purple		1·00	80
4		3d. bright blue		75	1·25
5		4d. grey		2·00	7·00
6		6d. orange-yellow		2·25	1·75
7		1s. red-orange		2·25	4·50
8		2s. 6d. sepia		21·00	45·00
9		5s. violet		48·00	65·00
10		10s. olive-green		£110	£120
1/10			*Set of* 10	£170	£225
1s/10s Perf "Specimen"			*Set of* 10	£250	

1935 (4 May). *Silver Jubilee. As Nos.* 91/4 *of Antigua. P* 13½×14.

11	1d. deep blue and carmine	55	50
	f. Diagonal line by turret	70·00	
12	2d. ultramarine and grey	65	1·25
	f. Diagonal line by turret	60·00	
	g. Dot to left of chapel	90·00	
13	3d. brown and deep blue	3·75	3·75
	g. Dot to left of chapel	£150	
	h. Dot by flagstaff	£150	
14	6d. slate and purple	3·75	3·75
	g. Dot to left of chapel	£170	
	h. Dot by flagstaff	£170	
	i. Dash by turret	£170	
11/14	*Set of* 4	8·00	8·00
11s/14s Perf "Specimen"	*Set of* 4	80·00	

For illustrations of plate varieties see Omnibus section following Zanzibar.

1937 (12 May). *Coronation. As Nos.* 95/7 *of Antigua, but printed by D.L.R. P* 14.

15	1d. scarlet	35	50
16	2d. bright purple	50	85
17	3d. bright blue	60	85
15/17	*Set of* 3	1·25	2·00
15s/17s Perf "Specimen"	*Set of* 3	55·00	

2 King George VI, Nile Crocodile and Mountains

Tower flaw (R. 2/4)

(Recess Waterlow)

1938 (1 Apr). *Wmk Mult Script CA. P* 12½.

18	**2**	½d. green		30	1·25
19		1d. scarlet		50	70
		a. Tower flaw		90·00	
20		1½d. light blue		40	50
21		2d. bright purple		30	60
22		3d. bright blue		30	1·25
23		4d. grey		1·50	3·50
24		6d. orange-yellow		50	1·50
25		1s. red-orange		50	1·00
26		2s. 6d. sepia		8·50	8·50
27		5s. violet		22·00	9·50
28		10s. olive-green		22·00	17·00
18/28			*Set of* 11	50·00	40·00
18s/28s Perf "Specimen"			*Set of* 11	£190	

Basutoland

(3)

1945 (3 Dec). *Victory. Stamps of South Africa, optd with T* **3**, *inscr alternately in English and Afrikaans.*

				Un. pair	*Used pair*	*Used single*
29	**55**	1d. brown and carmine		40	40	10
30	**56**	2d. slate-blue and violet		40	40	10
31	**57**	3d. deep blue and blue		40	70	15
29/31			*Set of* 3	1·10	1·40	30

4 King George VI

5 King George VI and Queen Elizabeth

6 Queen Elizabeth II as Princess, and Princess Margaret

7 The Royal Family

(Recess Waterlow)

1947 (17 Feb). *Royal Visit. Wmk Mult Script CA. P* 12½.

32	**4**	1d. scarlet		10	10
33	**5**	2d. green		10	10
34	**6**	3d. ultramarine		10	10
35	**7**	1s. mauve		15	10
32/5			*Set of* 4	40	30
32s/5s Perf "Specimen"			*Set of* 4	80·00	

1948 (1 Dec). *Royal Silver Wedding. As Nos.* 112/13 *of Antigua.*

36	1½d. ultramarine	20	10
37	10s. grey-olive	30·00	27·00

1949 (10 Oct). *75th Anniv of Universal Postal Union. As Nos. 114/17 of Antigua.*

38	1½d. blue	20	1·00
39	3d. deep blue	1·75	2·00
40	6d. orange	1·00	2·00
41	1s. red-brown	50	1·00
38/41	*Set of* 4	3·00	5·50

OFFICIAL STAMPS

OFFICIAL

(O 1)

1934 (4 May). *Nos. 1/3 and 6 optd with Type* O 1.

O1 1	½d. emerald	£3500	£3500
O2	1d. scarlet	£1500	£1000
O3	2d. bright purple	£900	£550
O4	6d. orange-yellow	£10000	£4750
O1/4	*Set of* 4	£14000	£9000

Collectors are advised to buy these stamps only from reliable sources. They were not sold to the public.

POSTAGE DUE STAMPS

D 1

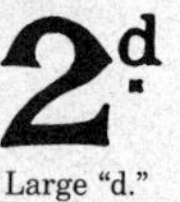

Normal

2d

Large "d." (R. 9/6, 10/6)

(Typo D.L.R.)

1933 (1 Dec)–**52**. *Wmk Mult Script CA. Ordinary paper. P* 14.

D1 D 1	1d. carmine	1·75	8·00
	a. Scarlet (1938)	32·00	40·00
	b. Chalk-surfaced paper. *Deep carmine* (24.10.51)	1·00	2·25
	ba. Error. Crown missing, W9*a*	£130	
	bb. Error. St. Edward's Crown, W9*b*	65·00	
D2	2d. violet	7·50	16·00
	a. Chalk-surfaced paper (6.11.52)	30	9·50
	ab. Error. Crown missing, W9*a*	£140	
	ac. Error. St. Edward's Crown, W9*a*	65·00	
	ad. Large "d"	6·00	
D1s/2s Perf "Specimen"	*Set of* 2	42·00	

Batum

Batum, the outlet port on the Black Sea for the Russian Transcaucasian oilfields, was occupied by the Turks on 15 April 1918.

Under the terms of the armistice signed at Mudros on 30 October 1918 the Turks were to withdraw and be replaced by an Allied occupation of Batum, the Baku oilfields and the connecting Transcaucasia Railway. British forces arrived off Batum in early December and the oblast, or district, was declared a British military governorship on 25 December 1918. The Turkish withdrawal was completed five days later.

The provision of a civilian postal service was initially the responsibility of the Batum Town Council. Some form of mail service was in operation by February 1919 with the postage prepaid in cash. Letters are known showing a framed oblong handstamp, in Russian, to this effect. The Town Council was responsible for the production of the first issue, Nos. 1/6, but shortly after these stamps were placed on sale a strike by Council employees against the British military governor led to the postal service being placed under British Army control.

SURCHARGES. Types **2** and **4/8** were all applied by handstamp. Most values from No. 19 onwards are known showing the surcharge inverted, surcharge double or in pairs with surcharge *tête-bêche*.

BRITISH OCCUPATION

(Currency. 100 kopeks = 1 rouble)

PRICES FOR STAMPS ON COVER

Nos. 1/6	*from* × 60
Nos. 7/10	*from* × 15
Nos. 11/18	*from* × 60
Nos. 19/20	*from* × 15
Nos. 21/44	—
Nos. 45/53	*from* × 200

1 Aloe Tree

БАТУМ. ОБ.

Руб 10 Руб

(2)

1919 (4 Apr). *Litho. Imperf.*

1 1	5 k. green	6·50	11·00
2	10 k. ultramarine	6·50	11·00
3	50 k. yellow	2·50	3·25
4	1 r. chocolate	3·25	3·75
5	3 r. violet	9·50	14·00
6	5 r. brown	10·00	16·00
1/6	*Set of* 6	35·00	55·00

Nos. 1/6 were printed in sheets of 198 (18×11).

1919 (13 Apr). *Russian stamps (Arms types) handstamped with T* **2**.

7	10 r. on 1 k. orange (*imperf*)	42·00	50·00
8	10 r. on 3 k. carmine-red (*imperf*)	18·00	23·00
9	10 r. on 5 k. brown-lilac (*perf*)	£325	£325
10	10 r. on 10 on 7 k. deep blue (*perf*)	£275	£275

A similar handstamped surcharge, showing the capital letters without serifs, is bogus.

BRITISH
OCCUPATION

(3)

1919 (10 Nov.) *Colours changed and new values. Optd with T* **3**.

11 1	5 k. yellow-green	11·00	12·00
12	10 k. bright blue	11·00	12·00
13	25 k. orange-yellow	11·00	12·00
14	1 r. pale blue	3·50	9·00
15	2 r. pink	1·00	3·00
16	3 r. bright violet	1·00	3·00
17	5 r. brown	1·25	3·25
	a. "CCUPATION" (R.5/1)	£350	
18	7 r. brownish red	4·00	6·50
11/18	*Set of* 8	40·00	55·00

Nos. 11/18 were printed in sheets of 432 (18×24).

БАТУМ ОБЛАС.
P 10 P.
BRITISH
OCCUPATION

(4)

БАТУМЪ
BRITISH
P. 15 P.
OCCUPATION
ОБЛ.

(5)

1919 (27 Nov)–**20**. *Russian stamps (Arms types) handstamped with T* **4** *or* **5**. *Imperf.*

19	10 r. on 3 k. carmine-red	14·00	18·00
20	15 r. on 1 k. orange	45·00	50·00
	a. Red surch	38·00	42·00
	b. Violet surch (10.3.20)	48·00	55·00

Nos. 20a/b have the handstamp in soluble ink.

1920 (12 Jan). *Russian stamps (Arms types) handstamped as T* **4**.

(a) Imperf

21	50 r. on 1 k. orange	£325	£350
22	50 r. on 2 k. yellow-green (R.)	£425	£475

(b) Perf

23	50 r. on 2 k. yellow-green	£425	£450
24	50 r. on 3 k. carmine-red	£900	£950
25	50 r. on 4 k. red	£700	£750
26	50 r. on 5 k. brown-lilac	£400	£425
27	50 r. on 10 k. deep blue (R.)	£1100	£1200
28	50 r. on 15 k. blue and red-brown	£425	£475

(6)

1920 (30 Jan–21 Feb). *Russian stamps (Arms types) handstamped as T* **6**. *(a) Perf*

29	25 r. on 5 k. brown-lilac (21 Feb)	35·00	38·00
	a. Blue surch	35·00	38·00
30	25 r. on 10 on 7 k. blue (21 Feb)	95·00	£100
	a. Blue surch	55·00	60·00
31	25 r. on 20 on 14 k. dp carmine & bl (21 Feb)	60·00	65·00
	a. Blue surch	55·00	60·00
32	25 r. on 25 k. deep violet & lt green (21 Feb)	95·00	£100
	a. Blue surch	80·00	85·00
33	25 r. on 50 k. green and copper-red (21 Feb)	55·00	60·00
	a. Blue surch	60·00	65·00
34	50 r. on 2 k. yellow-green	85·00	90·00
35	50 r. on 3 k. carmine-red	85·00	90·00
36	50 r. on 4 k. red	75·00	80·00
37	50 r. on 5 k. brown-lilac	55·00	60·00

(b) Imperf

38	50 r. on 2 k. yellow-green	£300	£325
39	50 r. on 3 k. carmine-red	£375	£400
40	50 r. on 5 k. brown-lilac	£1000	£1100

1920 (10 Mar). *Romanov issue, as T* **25** *of Russia, handstamped with T* **6**.

41	50 r. on 4 k. rose-carmine (B.)	45·00	55·00

РУБ 25 ЛЕЙ
25 РУБ. 25

(7)

R. 50 R.
BRITISH
OCCUPATION
РУБ.

(8)

1920 (1 Apr). *Nos. 3, 11 and 13 handstamped with T* **7** (

42/3) *or* **8** (*No.* 44).

42	25 r. on 5 k. yellow-green	26·00	2
	a. Blue surch	35·00	3
43	25 r. on 25 k. orange-yellow	21·00	2.
	a. Blue surch	85·00	8
44	50 r. on 50 k. yellow	16·00	1
	a. "50" cut	12·00	1
	b. Blue surch	80·00	8
	ba. "50" cut	£140	£

Nos. 44a and 44ba show the figures broken by intentional cuts applied as a protection against forgery. The "5" is cut at base and on the right side of the loop. The "0" is chipped at and foot, and has both vertical lines severed.

1920 (19 June). *Colours changed and new values. Optd u T* **3**. *Imperf.*

45 1	1 r. chestnut	70	6
	a. "BPITISH"	45·00	
46	2 r. pale blue	80	6
	a. "BPITISH"	55·00	
47	3 r. pink	1·00	6
	a. "BPITISH"	55·00	
48	5 r. black-brown	80	6
	a. "BPITISH"	55·00	
49	7 r. yellow	80	6
	a. "BPITISH"	55·00	
50	10 r. myrtle-green	70	6
	a. "BPITISH"	55·00	
51	15 r. violet	1·00	7
	a. "BPITISH"	£110	
52	25 r. scarlet	90	7
	a. "BPITISH"	£100	
53	50 r. deep blue	1·00	10
	a. "BPITISH"	£170	
45/53	*Set of* 9	7·00	55

Nos. 45/53 were printed in sheets of 308 (22×14). T "BPITISH" error occurs on R. 1/19 of the overprint.

POSTCARD STAMPS

When Nos. 7/10 were issued on 13 April 1919 a similar 35 surcharge was applied to stocks of various Russian postcar held by the post office. The majority of these had star impressions printed directly on to the card, but there were als few cards, originally intended for overseas mail, on which Russ 4 k. stamps had been affixed.

PRICES. Those in the left-hand column are for unus examples on complete postcard; those on the right for us examples off card. Examples used on postcard are worth mor

1919 (13 Apr). *Russian stamps handstamped as T* **2**.

P1	35 k. on 4 k. red (Arms type)	£2750	£32
P2	35 k. on 4 k. carmine-red (Romanov issue)	£7500	£85

Batum was handed over to the National Republic of Georg on 7 July 1920.

Bechuanaland

Before the 1880s the only Europeans in the area whic became Bechuanaland were scattered hunters and trader together with the missionaries who were established a Kuruman as early as 1816.

Tribal conflicts in the early years of the decade led to th intervention of Boers from the Transvaal who established th independent republics of Goshen and Stellaland.

STELLALAND

The Boer republic of Stellaland was proclaimed towards th end of 1882. A postal service was organised from the capital Vryburg, and stamps were ordered from a firm in Cape Town These were only valid within the republic. Until June 1885 mai to other parts of South Africa was sent through Christiana, ir the Transvaal, and was franked with both Stellaland and Transvaal stamps.

No date stamps or obliterators were used by the Stellaland Post Office. Stamps were pen-cancelled with the initials of a postal official and the date.

PRICES FOR STAMPS ON COVER

The issues of Stellaland are very rare on cover.

1 Arms of the Republic

(Litho by Van der Sandt, de Villiers & Co., Cape Town)

1884 (29 Feb). *P* 12.

1 1	1d. red	£180	£325
	a. Imperf between (horiz pair)	£3750	
	b. Imperf between (vert pair)	£3750	
2	3d. orange	21·00	£325
	a. Imperf between (horiz pair)	£650	
	b. Imperf between (vert pair)	£1200	
	c. Imperf vert (horiz pair)	£900	
3	4d. olive-grey	21·00	£350
	a. Imperf between (horiz pair)	£650	
	b. Imperf between (vert pair)	£1400	

6d. lilac-mauve .. .. 21·00 £350
a. Imperf between (horiz pair) £950
b. Imperf between (vert pair) £1200
1s. green .. .. 42·00 £600

1884 the British Government, following appeals from local ; for protection, decided to annex both Goshen and ıland. A force under Sir Charles Warren from the Cape ed Vryburg on 7 February 1885 and continued to king, the principal town of Goshen.

30 September 1885 Stellaland and other territory to the of the Molopo River was constituted the Crown Colony of sh Bechuanaland. A protectorate was also proclaimed over t tract of land to the north of the Molopo.

llaland stamps continued to be used until 2 December 1885 external mail, franked with Stellaland and Cape of Good stamps, postmarked at Barkly West and Kimberley in ıaland West.

(Oct). *Handstamped "Twee" sideways in violet-lake.*
2d. on 4d. olive-grey £3500

2 December 1885 Cape of Good Hope stamps overprinted ish Bechuanaland" were placed on sale at the Vryburg post .

BRITISH BECHUANALAND

CROWN COLONY

PRICES FOR STAMPS ON COVER

Nos. 1/8	*from* × 12
No. 9	*from* × 80
Nos. 10/21	*from* × 8
Nos. 22/8	*from* × 10
No. 29	*from* × 10
No. 30	*from* × 10
Nos. 31/2	*from* × 12
Nos. 33/7	*from* × 20
Nos. 38/9	*from* × 25

BRITISH

British
Bechuanaland
(1)

BECHUANALAND
(2)

5 (2 Dec)–**87**. *Stamps of Cape of Good Hope ("Hope" seated) otd with T* **1**, *by W. A. Richards & Sons, Cape Town.*

(*a*) *Wmk Crown CC (No. 3) or Crown CA (others)*
½d. grey-black (No. 40*a*) (R.) .. .. 13·00 19·00
a. Opt in lake £3250
b. Opt double (Lake+Black) £650
3d. pale claret (No. 43) .. .. .. 35·00 40·00
4d. dull blue (No. 30) (12.86?) .. .. 55·00 65·00

(*b*) *Wmk Anchor (Cape of Good Hope. Type* **13**)
½d. grey-black (No. 48*a*) (3.87) .. .. 7·00 11·00
a. Error. "ritish" £2000
b. Opt double £3000
1d. rose-red (No. 49) .. .. .. 9·50 9·00
a. Error. "ritish" £2750 £2250
b. Opt double .. .. † £1900
2d. pale bistre (No. 50) .. .. .. 35·00 8·00
a. Error. "ritish" £5000 £3500
b. Opt double .. .. † £1800
6d. reddish purple (No. 52) .. .. 90·00 38·00
1s. green (No. 53) (11.86?) £250 £150
a. Error. "ritish" £15000 £11000

Nos. 1/8 were overprinted from settings of 120. The missing " errors are believed to have occurred on one position for one these settings only.

Overprints with stop after "Bechuanaland" are forged.

87 (1 Nov). *No. 197 of Great Britain optd with T* **2**, *by D.L.R.*
½d. vermilion .. .. 1·25 1·25
a. Opt double £2250
s. Handstamped "Specimen" .. .. 80·00

3

4

5

(Typo D.L.R.)

887 (1 Nov). (*a*) *Wmk Orb (Great Britain Type* **48**). *P* 14.
0 **3** 1d. lilac and black .. .. .. 15·00 1·75
1 2d. lilac and black .. .. .. 65·00 1·75
a. Pale dull lilac and black .. .. 42·00 23·00
2 3d. lilac and black .. .. .. 3·50 5·50
a. Pale reddish lilac and black .. 55·00 18·00
3 4d. lilac and black .. .. .. 42·00 2·25
4 6d. lilac and black .. .. .. 50·00 2·50

(*b*) *Wmk Script "V R" (sideways, reading up). P* 13½
5 **4** 1s. green and black .. .. .. 29·00 5·50
6 2s. green and black .. .. .. 50·00 35·00
7 2s. 6d. green and black.. .. .. 60·00 55·00
8 5s. green and black .. .. .. 80·00 £150
9 10s. green and black £170 £350

(*c*) *Two Orbs (sideways). P* 14×13½
20 **5** £1 lilac and black £800 £700
21 £5 lilac and black £2750 £1500
10s/21s H/S "Specimen" .. .. *Set of* 12 £900

Nos. 10/21 were produced by overprinting a series of "Unappropriated Die" designs originally produced by the Board of Inland Revenue for use as Great Britain fiscal stamps.

Several values are known on blued paper. No. 11*a* is the first printing of the 2d. (on safety paper?) and has a faded appearance.

When purchasing Nos. 20/21 in used condition beware of copies with fiscal cancellations cleaned off and bearing forged postmarks.

For No. 15 surcharged "£5" see No. F2.

1d.
(6)

1s.
(7)

One
Half-
Penny
(8)

1888 (7 Aug). *Nos.* 10/11 *and* 13/15 *surch as T* **6** *or* **7**, *by P. Townshend & Co, Vryburg.*
22 **3** 1d. on 1d. lilac and black .. .. .. 7·50 6·50
23 2d. on 2d. lilac and black (R.) .. .. 20·00 3·00
a. Pale dull lilac and black (No. 11*a*) .. 80·00 48·00
b. Curved foot to "2" £200 £150
c. Surch in green .. .. .. † £3250
25 4d. on 4d. lilac and black (R.) £225 £300
26 6d. on 6d. lilac and black .. .. 90·00 10·00
a. Surch in blue .. .. .. † £10000
28 **4** 1s. on 1s. green and black .. .. £130 75·00

Nos. 23c and 26a are from two sheets of surcharge trials subsequently put into stock and used at Vryburg (2d.) or Mafeking (6d.) during 1888–89.

1888 (Dec.) *No.* 12*a surch with T* **8**, *by P. Townshend & Co, Vryburg.*
29 **3** ½d. on 3d. pale reddish lilac and black £130 £140
a. Broken "f" in "Half" £4500

No. 29 was produced from a setting of 60 (12×5).

No. 29a shows the letter "f" almost completely missing and occurs on R. 5/11 of the setting. Five examples are known, one being in the Royal Collection.

Errors of spelling on this surcharge are bogus.

British
Bechuanaland.
(9)

British
Bechuanaland.
(10)

BRITISH
BECHUANALAND
(11)

1889 (Jan). *No. 48a of Cape of Good Hope (wmk Anchor) optd with T* **9**, *by P. Townshend & Co, Vryburg.*
30 ½d. grey-black (G.) .. .. 3·25 22·00
b. Opt double, one inverted.. .. .. £1100
c. Opt double, one vertical £550
ca. *Se-tenant* with stamp without opt .. £3250
e. "British" omitted.. .. .. .. £2000

No. 30 was produced using a setting of 30 (6×5). No. 30e occurred on R. 5/1 of the setting on some sheets only.

1891 (Nov). *Nos.* 49/50 *of Cape of Good Hope (wmk Anchor), optd with T* **10**, *reading upwards.*
31 1d. rose-red .. .. 10·00 8·00
a. Horiz pair, one without opt £2750
b. "British" omitted .. .. .. — £1200
c. "Bechuanaland" omitted £1200
32 2d. pale bistre .. .. 3·25 2·25
a. No stop after "Bechuanaland" £250 £300
31s/2s H/S "Specimen" .. .. *Set of* 2 £130

Nos. 31/2 were produced from separate sett.ngs of 120 (12×10). No. 32a occurs on R. 3/3.

See also Nos. 38 and 39.

1891 (1 Dec)–**1904**. *Nos.* 172, 200, 205, 208 *and* 211 *of Great Britain optd with T* **11**, *by D.L.R.*
33 1d. lilac .. .. 6·00 1·50
34 2d. grey-green and carmine .. .. 8·00 4·00
35 4d. green and purple-brown .. .. 2·50 50
a. Bisected (2d.) (on cover) (11.99) .. † £2000
36 6d. purple/*rose-red* .. .. .. 3·00 2·00
37 1s. dull green (7.94) .. .. .. 13·00 16·00
a. Bisected (6d.) (on cover) (12.04) .. † —
33/7 .. .. *Set of* 5 29·00 22·00
33s/6s H/S "Specimen" .. .. *Set of* 4 £170

No. 35a was used at Palapye Station and No. 37a at Kanye, both in the Protectorate.

1893 (Dec)–**95**. *As Nos.* 31/2, *but T* **10** *reads downwards.*
38 1d. rose-red .. .. 2·25 2·25
a. Pair, one without opt .. .. ..
b. "British" omitted £1400
c. Optd "Bechuanaland. British" £850 £950
d. No dots to "i" of "British" (R. 1/10) .. 95·00 95·00
e. Opt reading up, no dots to "i" of "British" £1500
39 2d. pale bistre (15.3.95) .. .. .. 4·50 2·25
a. Opt double £1100 £650
b. "British" omitted £500 £500
c. Optd "Bechuanaland. British" £375 £225
d. No dots to "i" of "British" (R. 1/10) .. £120 £120
e. Opt reading up, no dots to "i" of "British"

A common setting of 120 (12×10) was used for Nos. 38/9. Some sheets of both values were overprinted the wrong way up, resulting in Nos. 38e and 39e.

On 16 November 1895 British Bechuanaland was annexed to the Cape of Good Hope and ceased to have its own stamps, but they remained in use in the Protectorate until superseded in 1897. The Postmaster-General of Cape Colony had assumed control of the Bechuanaland postal service on 1 April 1893 and the Cape, and subsequently the South African, postal authorities continued to be responsible for the postal affairs of the Bechuanaland Protectorate until 1963.

BECHUANALAND PROTECTORATE

PRICES FOR STAMPS ON COVER TO 1945

Nos. 40/51	*from* × 10
Nos. 52/71	*from* × 6
Nos. 72/82	*from* × 5
Nos. 83/98	*from* × 4
Nos. 99/110	*from* × 6
Nos. 111/17	*from* × 10
Nos. 118/28	*from* × 4
Nos. 129/31	*from* × 10
Nos. D1/3	*from* × 50
Nos. D4/6	*from* × 60
No. F1	*from* × 5
No. F2	—
No. F3	*from* × 5

This large area north of the Molopo River was proclaimed a British Protectorate on 30 September 1885 at the request of the native chiefs.

A postal service using runners was inaugurated on 9 August 1888 and Nos. 40 to 55 were issued as a temporary measure with the object of assessing the cost of this service.

Protectorate
(12) 15½ mm

Protectorate
1d
(13)

1888 (7 Aug). *No.* 9 *optd with T* **12** *and Nos.* 10/19 *surch or optd only as T* **13** *by P. Townshend & Co. Vryburg.*
40 – ½d. vermilion .. .. 3·50 25·00
a. "Protectorate" double £325
s. Handstamped "Specimen" .. .. 80·00
41 **3** 1d. on 1d. lilac and black .. .. 8·00 14·00
a. Small figure "1" (R. 5/4, 7/2, 10/2) .. £375 £400
42 2d. on 2d. lilac and black .. .. 23·00 17·00
b. Curved foot to "2" £550 £425
43 3d. on 3d. pale reddish lilac and black £120 £170
44 4d. on 4d. lilac and black £275 £275
a. Small figure "4" £3250 £3250
45 6d. on 6d. lilac and black .. .. 70·00 40·00
46 **4** 1s. green and black .. .. .. 75·00 50·00
a. First "o" omitted £4250 £3000
s. Handstamped "Specimen" £110
47 2s. green and black £600 £850
a. First "o" omitted £9500
48 2s. 6d. green and black £500 £750
a. First "o" omitted £9000
49 5s. green and black £1100 £1900
a. First "o" omitted £13000
50 10s. green and black £3250 £5000
a. First "o" omitted £18000

Nos. 40/5 were produced from a basic setting of 120 (12×10) on which a faulty first "o" in "Protectorate" occurred on R.5/12. For Nos. 46/50 the setting was reduced to 84 (12×7) and on many sheets the first "o" on R.5/12 failed to print.

See also Nos. 54/5

1888 (Dec). *No.* 25 *optd with T* **12** *by P. Townshend & Co, Vryburg.*
51 **3** 4d. on 4d. lilac and black .. .. .. 70·00 32·00

Bechuanaland
Protectorate.
(14)

Protectorate
Fourpence
(15)

1889 (Jan). *No. 48a of Cape of Good Hope (wmk Anchor), optd with T* **14** *by P. Townshend & Co., Vryburg.*
52 ½d. grey-black (G.) .. .. 2·75 35·00
a. Opt double £450 £600
ab. Ditto, one reading "Protectorate Bechuanaland" £900
b. "Bechuanaland" omitted £1000
c. Optd "Protectorate Bechuanaland" .. £425 £500

1889 (Aug). *No.* 9 *surch with T* **15** *by P. Townshend & Co., Vryburg.*
53 4d. on ½d. vermilion .. .. .. 18·00 3·50
a. "rpence" omitted (R. 9/2) .. .. † £6000
b. "ourpence" omitted (R. 9/2) £10000
c. Surch (T **15**) inverted .. .. .. † £4000
cb. Ditto. "ourpence" omitted .. .. † £11000
s. Handstamped "Specimen" £130

Examples of No. 53c are postmarked "679" (Tati).

Protectorate
(16) 15 mm

Protectorate
(17)

1890. *No.* 9 *optd.*
54 **16** ½d. vermilion £140 £150
a. Type **16** inverted .. .. .. 75·00 95·00
b. Type **16** double .. .. .. 90·00 £130
c. Type **16** double and inverted £600 £600
d. Optd "Portectorate" inverted £6000
w. Wmk inverted .. .. ..
55 **17** ½d. vermilion £170 £275
a. Type **17** double £900
b. Optd "Protectorrte" .. .. ..
c. Optd "Protectorrte" double £12000

These were trial printings made in 1888 which were subsequently issued.

In June 1890 the Bechuanaland Protectorate and the Colony of British Bechuanaland came under one postal administration and the stamps of British Bechuanaland were used in the Protectorate until 1897.

BRITISH

BECHUANALAND
(18)

BECHUANALAND
PROTECTORATE
(19)

1897. *No.* 61 *of Cape of Good Hope (wmk Anchor), optd as T* **18**.

(a) Lines 13 mm apart, bottom line 16 mm long, by Taylor & Marshall, Cape Town

56 ½d. yellow-green (July?) .. .. 2·50 9·00

(b) Lines 13½ mm apart, bottom line 15 mm long, by P. Townshend & Co, Vryburg

57 ½d. yellow-green (April) .. .. 19·00 75·00
a. Opt double, one albino inverted .. £200

(c) Lines 10½ mm apart, bottom line 15 mm long, by W. A. Richards & Sons, Cape Govt Printers

58 ½d. yellow-green (July?) .. .. 8·00 42·00

Although issued only in the Protectorate, the above were presumably overprinted "BRITISH BECHUANALAND" because stamps bearing this inscription were in use there at the time.

1897 (Oct)–**1902.** *Nos.* 172, 197, 200, 202, 205 *and* 208 *of Great Britain (Queen Victoria) optd with T* **19** *by* D.L.R.

59 ½d. vermilion .. .. 1·00 2·25
60 ½d. blue-green (25.2.02) .. .. 1·40 3·50
61 1d. lilac .. .. 4·00 75
62 2d. grey-green and carmine .. .. .. 3·25 4·50
63 3d. purple/*yellow* (12.97) .. .. .. 5·50 8·50
64 4d. green and purple-brown .. .. .. 15·00 11·00
65 6d. purple/*rose-red* .. .. 23·00 11·00
59/65 .. .. *Set of* 7 48·00 38·00
59s/65s Optd or H/S (No. 60s) "Specimen" *Set of* 7 £225

BECHUANALAND
PROTECTORATE
(20)

BECHUANALAND
PROTECTORATE
(21)

1904 (29 Nov)–**13.** *Nos.* 216, 218/19, 230 *and* 313/14 *(Somerset House ptgs) of Great Britain (King Edward VII) optd with T* **20**, *by* D.L.R.

66 ½d. blue-green (3.06) .. .. 2·00 2·00
67 ½d. yellowish green (11.08) .. .. .. 3·75 3·50
68 1d. scarlet (4.05) .. .. 7·50 30
s. Optd "Specimen" .. .. 60·00
69 2½d. ultramarine .. .. 7·00 5·00
a. Stop after "P" in "PROTECTORATE" £900 £1200
70 1s. deep green and scarlet (10.12) .. 35·00 £120
71 1s. green and carmine (1913) .. .. 40·00 £110
s. Optd "Specimen" .. .. 90·00

No. 69a occurs on R. 5/9 of the lower pane.

1912 (Sept)–**14.** *No.* 342 *of Great Britain (King George V, wmk Crown) optd with T* **20**.

72 1d. scarlet .. .. 1·50 60
a. No cross on crown .. .. — 75·00
b. Aniline scarlet (No. 343) (1914) .. £120 80·00

1913 (July)–**24.** *Stamps of Great Britain (King George V) optd.*

(a) Nos. 351, 357, 362, 367, 370/1, 376, 379, 385 *and* 395 *(wmk Simple Cypher, T* **100**) *optd with T* **20**

73 ½d. green (*shades*) .. .. 1·25 1·75
74 1d. scarlet (*shades*) (4.15) .. .. .. 2·75 75
a. Carmine-red (1922) .. .. 20·00 2·50
75 1½d. red-brown (12.20) .. .. 2·50 3·00
76 2d. reddish orange (Die I) .. .. .. 2·75 4·25
a. Orange (Die I) (1921) .. .. .. 15·00 4·50
aw. Wmk inverted .. ..
77 2d. orange (Die II) (1924) .. .. .. 35·00 5·00
78 2½d. cobalt-blue .. .. 3·50 20·00
a. Blue (1915) .. .. 7·50 23·00
79 3d. bluish violet .. .. 6·00 12·00
80 4d. grey-green .. .. 6·50 16·00
81 6d. reddish purple (*shades*) .. .. .. 7·00 16·00
a. Opt double, one albino .. .. ..
82 1s. bistre .. .. 9·50 20·00
a. Bistre-brown (1923) .. .. 23·00 32·00
s. Optd "Specimen" .. .. 75·00
73/82 .. .. *Set of* 9 38·00 80·00

(b) With T **21**

(i) Waterlow printings (Nos. 399 *and* 401) *(1914–15)*

83 2s. 6d. deep sepia-brown (1.15) £120 £250
a. Re-entry (R.2/1) £1000 £1500
b. Opt double, one albino £275
84 5s. rose-carmine (1914) £160 £375
a. Opt double, one albino £375
83s/4s Optd "Specimen" .. .. *Set of* 2 £275

(ii) D.L.R. printings (Nos. 407/8 *and* 409) *(1916–19)*

85 2s. 6d. pale brown (7.16) £110 £250
a. Re-entry (R. 2/1) £1100 £1500
86 2s. 6d. sepia (1917) £130 £225
a. Opt treble, two albino .. .. ..
b. Re-entry (R. 2/1) .. ..
87 5s. bright carmine (8.19) £300 £425
a. Opt double, one albino £450

(iii) B.W. printings (Nos. 414 *and* 416) *(1920–23)*

88 2s. 6d. chocolate-brown (7.23) .. .. 80·00 £160
a. Major re-entry (R. 1/2) £1900
b. Opt double, one albino £550
c. Opt treble, two albino £500
89 5s. rose-red (7.20) £110 £275
a. Opt treble, two albino £375
b. Opt double, one albino .. .. ..

Examples of Nos. 83/9 are known showing a forged Lobatsi postmark dated "6 MAY 35" or "6 MAY 39".

1925 (July)–**27.** *Nos.* 418/19, 421, 423/4, 426/*a and* 429 *of Great Britain (wmk Block Cypher, T* **111**) *optd with T* **20**.

91 ½d. green (1927) .. .. 1·50 1·75
92 1d. scarlet (8.25) .. .. 2·00 70
w. Wmk inverted .. ..
93 2d. orange (Die II) .. .. 1·75 1·00
94 3d. violet (10.26) .. .. 4·75 16·00
a. Opt double, one albino £250
w. Wmk inverted £170
95 4d. grey-green (10.26) .. .. 4·75 30·00
a. Printed on the gummed side .. ..
96 6d. reddish purple (*chalk-surfaced paper*) (12.25) .. .. 35·00 60·00
97 6d. purple (*ordinary paper*) (1926) .. 48·00 48·00
98 1s. bistre-brown (10.26) .. .. .. 9·00 24·00
w. Wmk inverted £325 £300
91/8 .. .. *Set of* 8 95·00 £160

22 King George V, Baobab Tree and Cattle drinking

23 King George VI, Baobab Tree and Cattle drinking

(Des from photo by Resident Commissioner, Ngamiland, Recess Waterlow)

1932 (12 Dec). *Wmk Mult Script CA. P* 12½.

99 **22** ½d. green .. .. 1·00 30
a. Imperf between (horiz pair) .. £14000
100 1d. scarlet .. .. 1·00 25
101 2d. brown .. .. 1·00 30
102 3d. ultramarine .. .. 1·00 1·75
103 4d. orange .. .. 1·25 5·50
104 6d. purple .. .. 2·50 3·00
105 1s. black and olive-green .. .. .. 3·00 7·00
106 2s. black and orange .. .. 24·00 40·00
107 2s. 6d. black and scarlet .. .. .. 19·00 30·00
108 3s. black and purple .. .. 35·00 42·00
109 5s. black and ultramarine .. .. .. 55·00 65·00
110 10s. black and brown £110 £120
99/110 .. .. *Set of* 12 £225 £275
99s/110s Perf "Specimen" .. *Set of* 12 £250

Examples of most values are known showing a forged Lobatsi postmark dated "6 MAY 35" or "6 MAY 39".

1935 (4 May). *Silver Jubilee. As Nos.* 91/4 *of Antigua but ptd by* B.W. *P* 11 × 12.

111 1d. deep blue and scarlet .. .. .. 30 2·75
a. Extra flagstaff £225
b. Short extra flagstaff £275
c. Lightning conductor £250
d. Flagstaff on right-hand turret £250
e. Double flagstaff £250
112 2d. ultramarine and grey-black .. .. 1·00 2·75
a. Extra flagstaff .. .. 95·00
b. Short extra flagstaff .. .. .. 95·00
c. Lightning conductor .. .. .. 80·00
113 3d. brown and deep blue .. .. .. 2·50 2·75
a. Extra flagstaff £130
b. Short extra flagstaff £130
c. Lightning conductor £110
114 6d. slate and purple .. .. 4·00 2·75
a. Extra flagstaff £120
b. Short extra flagstaff £110
c. Lightning conductor £110
111/14 .. .. *Set of* 4 7·00 10·00
111s/14s Perf "Specimen" .. .. *Set of* 4 80·00

For illustrations of plate varieties see Omnibus section following Zanzibar.

1937 (12 May). *Coronation. As Nos.* 95/7 *of Antigua, but printed by* D.L.R. *P* 14.

115 1d. scarlet 45 40
116 2d. yellow-brown .. .. 60 1·00
117 3d. bright blue .. .. 60 1·25
115/17 .. .. *Set of* 3 1·50 2·40
115s/17s Perf "Specimen" .. .. *Set of* 3 55·00

(Recess Waterlow)

1938 (1 Apr)–**52.** *Wmk Mult Script CA. P* 12½.

118 **23** ½d. green .. .. 2·00 2·25
a. Light yellowish green (1941) .. 7·00 6·00
b. Yellowish green (4.43) .. .. 4·50 3·75
c. Deep green (4.49) .. .. .. 3·00 8·00
119 1d. scarlet 75 50
120 1½d. dull blue .. .. 8·50 2·00
a. Light blue (4.43) .. .. .. 1·00 1·00
121 2d. chocolate-brown 75 50
122 3d. deep ultramarine .. .. 1·00 2·50
123 4d. orange .. .. 2·00 3·50
124 6d. reddish purple .. .. 4·75 3·00
a. Purple (1944) .. .. 4·00 2·50
ab. "A" of "CA" missing from wmk .. † —
125 1s. black and brown-olive .. .. .. 4·00 4·25
a. Grey-black & olive-green (21.5.52) 15·00 18·00
126 2s. 6d. black and scarlet .. .. .. 14·00 14·00
127 5s. black and deep ultramarine .. .. 30·00 16·00
a. Grey-black & dp ultram (10.46) .. 70·00 50·00
128 10s. black and red-brown .. .. .. 14·00 19·00
118/28 .. .. *Set of* 11 65·00 60·00
118s/28s Perf "Specimen" .. .. *Set of* 11 £170

NEW INFORMATION

The editor is always interested to correspond with people who have new information that will improve or correct the Catalogue.

Bechuanaland
(24)

1945 (3 Dec). *Victory. Stamps of South Africa optd with T Inscr alternately in English and Afrikaans.*

			Un. pair	*Used pair*
129	**55**	1d. brown and carmine	50	55
130	**56**	2d. slate-blue and violet	50	1·00
131	**57**	3d. deep blue and blue	50	1·00
		a. Opt omitted (in vert pair with normal)	£7000	
129/31		.. .. .. *Set of* 3	1·40	2·25

No. 131a comes from a sheet on which the overprint displaced downwards so that it is omitted from stamps in the row and shown on the sheet margin at foot.

(Recess Waterlow)

1947 (17 Feb). *Royal Visit. As Nos.* 32/5 *of Basutoland. W Mult Script CA. P* 12½.

132 1d. scarlet 10
133 2d. green 10
134 3d. ultramarine 10
135 1s. mauve 10
132/5 .. .. *Set of* 4 35
132s/5s Perf "Specimen" .. .. *Set of* 4 80·00

1948 (1 Dec). *Royal Silver Wedding. As Nos.* 112/13 *Antigua.*

136 1½d. ultramarine 30
137 10s. black .. .. 27·00 35

1949 (10 Oct). *75th Anniv of Universal Postal Union. As N* 114/17 *of Antigua.*

138 1½d. blue 30
139 3d. deep blue .. .. 1·00 2
140 6d. magenta 45 1
141 1s. olive 45 1
138/41 .. .. *Set of* 4 2·00 4

POSTAGE DUE STAMPS

BECHUANALAND
PROTECTORATE
(D 1)

BECHUANALAND
PROTECTORATE
(D 2)

1926 (Jan). *Nos.* D9/10 *and* D13 *of Great Britain, optd wi Types* D **1** *or* D **2** *(2d.).*

D1 ½d. emerald (wmk sideways - inverted) .. 4·00 65
D2 1d. carmine .. .. 4·00 48·
D3 2d. agate .. .. 6·00 85·
D1/3 .. .. *Set of* 3 12·50 £1

D 3

2d
Normal

2d
Large "d"
(R. 9/6, 10/6)

Serif on "d" (R.1/6)

(Typo D.L.R.)

1932 (12 Dec)–**58.** *Wmk Mult Script CA. Ordinary paper. P* 14

D4 D **3** ½d. sage-green .. .. 6·00 38·0
D5 1d. carmine .. .. 7·00 9·0
a. Chalk-surfaced paper (27.11.58) .. 1·00 15·0
D6 2d. violet .. .. 9·00 42·0
a. Large "d" .. .. 95·00
b. Chalk-surfaced paper (27.11.58) .. 1·50 19·0
ba. Large "d" .. .. 26·00
bb. Serif on "d" .. .. 35·00
D4/6b .. .. *Set of* 3 7·75 60·0
D4s/6s Perf "Specimen" .. .. *Set of* 3 65·00

No. D6a first occurred on the 1947 printing.

POSTAL FISCAL STAMPS

The following stamps issued for fiscal purposes were each allowed to be used for postal purposes for a short time. No. F2 was used by the public because the word "POSTAGE" had not been obliterated and No. F3 because the overprint did not include the words "Revenue only" as did the contemporary fiscal overprints for Basutoland and Swaziland.

Bechuanaland
Protectorate
(F 1)

£5
(F 2)

Bechuanaland
Protectorate.
(F 3)

(July). *No.* 266a *of Transvaal, optd with Type* **F 1** *by* ·*nsvaal Govt Ptg Wks, Pretoria.*

6d. black and brown-orange (Bl-Blk) ..	£150	£300

F1 was supplied to Assistant Commissioners in January for revenue purposes. The "POSTAGE" inscription was not ·rated, however, and the stamp is known postally used for a d of a year from July 1910.

No. 15 *surch with Type* F **2** *at top.*

4	£5 on 1s. green and black ..	£10000	

. *No.* 4*b of South Africa optd with Type* F **3**, *in varying* ·*itions.*

1d. scarlet	42·00	£130
a. Opt double, one albino	£150	

Bermuda

The first internal postal system for Bermuda was organised by Joseph Stockdale, the proprietor of the *Bermuda Gazette*, in January 1784. This service competed with that of the colonial post office, set up in May 1812, until 1818.

Control of the overseas postal services passed to the British G.P.O. in 1818. The internal delivery system was discontinued between 1821 and 1830. The overseas posts became a colonial responsibility in September 1859.

For illustrations of the handstamp types see BRITISH POST OFFICES ABROAD notes, following GREAT BRITAIN.

CROWNED-CIRCLE HANDSTAMPS

CC1 CC1	ST. GEORGES BERMUDA (R.) (1.8.1845) .. .. *Price on cover*	£7000
CC2	IRELAND ISLE BERMUDA (R.) (1.8.1845) .. .. *Price on cover*	£7000
CC3	HAMILTON BERMUDA (R.) (13.11.1846) .. .. *Price on cover*	£3750

For Nos. CC1 and CC3 used as adhesive Postmasters' Stamps see Nos. O7 and O6.

PRICES FOR STAMPS ON COVER TO 1945

Nos. 1/11	*from* × 5
Nos. 12/17	*from* × 10
Nos. 19/29*a*	*from* × 8
Nos. 30/a	*from* × 10
Nos. 31/4	*from* × 4
Nos. 34*a*/55	*from* × 3
Nos. 56/8	*from* × 10
Nos. 59/76	*from* × 4
Nos. 76*a*/93	*from* × 3
Nos. 94/7	*from* × 4
Nos. 98/106	*from* × 3
Nos. 107/15	*from* × 4
Nos. 116/21	*from* × 5
No. 122	*from* × 20

COLONY

O 1

O 2

1848–61. *Postmasters' Stamps. Adhesives prepared and issued by the postmasters at Hamilton and St. Georges. Dated as given in brackets.*

(a) By W. B. Perot at Hamilton

O1	O 1	1d. black/*bluish grey* (1848)	—	£110000
O2		1d. black/*bluish grey* (1849)	—	£120000
O3		1d. red/*thick white* (1853)	—	£90000
O4		1d. red/*bluish wove* (1854)	—	£275000
O5		1d. red/*bluish wove* (1856)	—	£170000
O6	O 2	(1d.) carmine-red/*bluish laid* (1861) ..	—	£75000

(b) By J. H. Thies at St. Georges
As Type O **2** *but inscr* "ST. GEORGES"

O7	–	(1d.) carmine-red/*buff* (1860)	†	£65000

Stamps of Type O **1** bear manuscript value and signature, the dates being those shown on the eleven known examples. The stamps are distributed between the dates as follows: 1848 three examples, 1849 two examples, 1853 three examples, 1854 two examples, 1856 one example.

It is believed that the franking value of Nos. O6/7 was 1d., although this is not shown on the actual stamps. Four examples are known of this type used from Hamilton, from March 1861 (and one unused), and five used from St. Georges between July 1860 and January 1863, both issues being cancelled by pen.

Prices shown reflect our estimation of value based on known copies. For instance of the two copies known of No. O4, one is in the Royal collection and the other is on entire.

It is possible that a fourth postmaster's provisional was used by Robert Ward at Hamilton in late 1862 when two examples of Type O **2** on laid paper are known cancelled by blue crayon.

1

2

3

4

5

(Typo D.L.R.)

1865–1903. *Wmk Crown CC. (a) P* 14

1	**1**	1d. rose-red (25.9.65)	90·00	1·25
		a. Imperf	£25000	£15000
		w. Wmk inverted	£250	95·00
2	**1**	1d. pale rose	£120	7·00
		w. Wmk inverted	£275	£110
3	**2**	2d. dull blue (14.3.66)	£325	22·00
		w. Wmk inverted	—	£275
4		2d. bright blue (1877)	£350	16·00
		w. Wmk inverted	—	£275
5	**3**	3d. yellow-buff (10.3.73)	£475	65·00
		aw. Wmk inverted	£950	£160
		ax. Wmk reversed		
5*b*		3d. orange (1875)	£1700	£130
6	**4**	6d. dull purple (25.9.65)	£950	75·00
		w. Wmk inverted	—	£650
7		6d. dull mauve (2.7.74)	23·00	12·00
		w. Wmk inverted	85·00	85·00
8	**5**	1s. green (25.9.65)	£275	50·00
		w. Wmk inverted	£500	£225

(b) P 14×12½

10	**3**	3d. yellow-buff (12.81)	£170	60·00
10*a*	**4**	6d. bright mauve (1903)	13·00	22·00
		aw. Wmk inverted	£450	
11	**5**	1s. green (11.93)	11·00	£120
		a. Imperf between (vert strip of 3) ..	£12000	
		w. Wmk inverted		

No. 11a occurs from Rows 8, 9, and 10 of four panes, possibly from a single sheet. Some of the stamps have become partially separated. One *used* vertical pair is known (*Price* £12000).

Although they arrived in Bermuda in March 1880, stamps perforated 14×12½ were not issued until the dates given above.

THREE PENCE (6)

THREE PENCE (6*a*)

THREE PENCE (7)

One Penny. (8)

1874 (12 Mar–19 May). *Nos.* 1 *and* 8 *surch diagonally.*

(a) With T **6** *("P" and "R" different type)*

12	**1**	3d. on 1d. rose-red	£15000	
13	**5**	3d. on 1s. green	£2500	£850

(b) With T **6a** *("P" same type as "R")*

13*b*	**5**	3d. on 1s. green	£2000	£800

(c) With T **7** (19 May)

14	**5**	3d. on 1s. green	£1400	£650

The 3d. on 1d. was a trial surcharge which was not regularly issued, though a few specimens were postally used before 1879. Nos. 13, 13*b* and 14, being handstamped, are found with double or partial double surcharges.

(Surch by Queen's Printer, Donald McPhee Lee)

1875 (March–May). *Surch with T* **8**.

15	**2**	1d. on 2d. (No. 4) (23 Apr)	£700	£375
		a. No stop after "Penny"	£12000	£8000
16	**3**	1d. on 3d. (No. 5) (8 May)	£450	£350
17	**5**	1d. on 1s. (No. 8) (11 Mar)	£500	£250
		a. Surch inverted	†	£21000
		b. No stop after "Penny"	£15000	£10000

It is emphasised that the prices quoted for Nos. 12/17 are for fine examples. The many stamps from these provisional issues which are in inferior condition are worth much less.

9

10

11

(Typo D.L.R.)

1880 (25 Mar). *Wmk Crown CC. P* 14.

19	**9**	½d. stone	2·75	4·25
		w. Wmk inverted	70·00	£120
		y. Wmk inverted and reversed ..		
20	**10**	4d. orange-red	17·00	1·75
		w. Wmk inverted		
		x. Wmk reversed		

(Typo D.L.R.)

1883–1904. *Wmk Crown CA. P* 14.

21	**9**	½d. dull green (10.92)	2·75	2·75
21*a*		½d. deep grey-green (1893)	2·50	80
22	**1**	1d. dull rose (12.83)	£150	4·25
		w. Wmk inverted	—	£140
23		1d. rose-red	80·00	3·25
		w. Wmk inverted	—	£140
24		1d. carmine-rose (3.86)	48·00	70
24*a*		1d. aniline carmine (1889)	9·00	20
		aw. Wmk inverted	£140	75·00
25	**2**	2d. blue (12.86)	55·00	3·50
26		2d. aniline purple (7.93)	14·00	3·75
26*a*		2d. brown-purple (1898)	3·50	1·50
27	**11**	2½d. deep ultramarine (10.11.84) ..	13·00	2·50
		aw. Wmk inverted	£275	90·00
27*b*		2½d. pale ultramarine	5·00	40
		bw. Wmk inverted	—	90·00
28	**3**	3d. grey (20.1.86)	22·00	6·50
28*a*	**10**	4d. orange-brown (18.1.04)	27·00	48·00
		ax. Wmk reversed	£325	
29	**5**	1s. yellow-brown (1893)	15·00	17·00
		ax. Wmk reversed	—	£425
29*b*		1s. olive-brown	13·00	16·00
		bx. Wmk reversed		
21/9*b*		.. .. *Set of* 8	£120	70·00
21s, 26s & 29s Optd "Specimen"		.. *Set of* 3	£375	

1893 PROVISIONAL POSTCARD. Following the reduction of the overseas postcard rate to 1d. in 1893 existing stocks of postal stationery postcards, including some from the September 1880 issue franked with Nos. 19 and 22, were surcharged "One

ASDA

PTS

BERMUDA
2/6 2/6
TWO SHILLINGS & SIXPENCE

SG89d

BERMUDA
2/6 2/6
TWO SHILLINGS & SIXPENCE

SG89f

y". This surcharge was applied by the *Royal Gazette* press. generally believed that an individual in the Post Office red all the examples showing Nos. 19 and 22, but sional postcards are known used to Europe or locally. *Price* £550 *unused*, £1400 *used*.

ONE
RTHING

(12)

13 Dry Dock

14

. *As Nos. 29/a but colour changed, surch with T* **12** *by* L.R.
5 ¼d. on 1s. dull grey (11.1.01) .. .. 1·50 50
as. Optd "Specimen" .. .. .. 75·00
¼d. on 1s. bluish grey (18.3.01) .. 1·75 85
ba. "F" in "FARTHING" inserted by handstamp £6000 £7000

ven examples of No. 30ba are known, five unused (one g in the Royal Collection) and two used (one on postcard). It d appear that the "F" in position one of an unspecified zontal row was damaged and an additional impression of the r was then inserted by a separate handstamp.

(Typo D.L.R.)

2 (Nov)–**03**. *Wmk Crown CA. P* 14.
13 ½d. black and green (12.03) .. .. 12·00 1·50
1d. brown and carmine .. .. 8·00 10
3d. magenta and sage-green (9.03) .. 3·00 2·00
.. .. *Set of* 3 21·00 3·25
3s Optd "Specimen" .. .. *Set of* 3 £130

–**10**. *Wmk Mult Crown CA. P* 14.
13 ¼d. brown and violet (9.08) .. .. 1·75 1·50
½d. black and green (12.06) .. .. 19·00 65
½d. green (3.09) .. .. .. 13·00 2·75
1d. brown and carmine (4.06) .. .. 25·00 20
w. Wmk inverted £350 £200
1d. red (5.08) .. .. 18·00 10
2d. grey and orange (10.07) .. .. 7·50 11·00
2½d. brown and ultramarine (12.06) .. 15·00 7·00
2½d. blue (14.2.10) .. .. .. 12·00 6·50
4d. blue and chocolate (11.09) .. .. 3·00 16·00
42 .. .. *Set of* 9 £100 40·00
, 36s, 38s/42s Optd "Specimen" *Set of* 7 £350

(Recess D.L.R.)

0–**25**. *Wmk Mult Crown CA. P* 14.
14 ¼d. brown (26.3.12) .. .. .. 1·75 2·50
a. Pale brown .. .. .. 60 1·50
½d. green (4.6.10) .. .. .. 1·25 25
a. Deep green (1918) .. .. .. 7·00 1·25
w. Wmk inverted .. .. ..
x. Wmk reversed .. .. .. — £225
y. Wmk inverted and reversed ..
1d. red (I) (15.10.10) .. .. .. 14·00 30
a. Rose-red (1916) .. .. .. 18·00 30
b. Carmine (12.19) .. .. .. 50·00 8·00
w. Wmk inverted £400 £400
x. Wmk reversed .. .. ..
y. Wmk inverted and reversed .. £300
2d. grey (1.13) .. .. .. 3·00 8·00
x. Wmk reversed .. .. ..
2½d. blue (27.3.12) .. .. .. 3·50 60
w. Wmk inverted .. .. ..
x. Wmk reversed .. .. .. — £225
y. Wmk inverted and reversed .. £150 £100
3d. purple/*yellow* (1.13) .. .. 1·75 6·00
a 4d. red/*yellow* (1.9.19) .. .. 5·50 11·00
6d. purple (26.3.12) .. .. .. 16·00 20·00
a. Pale claret (2.6.24) .. .. 11·00 8·00
1s. black/*green* (26.3.12) .. .. 4·00 4·00
a. Jet black/olive (1925) .. .. 4·75 13·00
/51 .. .. *Set of* 9 40·00 35·00
s/51s .. .. *Set of* 9 £400

Nos. 44 to 51*a* are comb-perforated 13.8×14 or 14. No. 45 its also line-perforated 14, probably from the printing spatched to Bermuda on 13 March 1911.
See also Nos. 76*b*/87*a*.

15

IGH VALUE KEY TYPES. The reign of King Edward VII aw the appearance of the first in a new series of "key type" esigns, initially on the issues of Malaya — Straits Settlements nd Nyasaland, to be used for high value denominations where a maller design was felt to be inappropriate. The system was xtended during the reign of King George V, using the portrait s Bermuda Type **15**, to cover Bermuda, Ceylon, Leeward slands, Malaya — Straits Settlements, Malta and Nyasaland. A umber of these territories continued to use the key type concept or high value King George VI stamps and one, Leeward Islands, or stamps of Queen Elizabeth II.

In each instance the King George V issues were printed in heets of 60 (12×5) on various coloured papers. The system tilised a common "head" plate used with individual "duty" lates which printed the territory name and face value.

Two major plate flaws occur on the King George V head plate: he break in scroll on R.1/12 and the broken crown and scroll on R.2/12. Both of these occur in different states, having been epaired and then damaged once again, perhaps on several ccasions. Later printings of R. 1/12 show additional damage to he crown and upper scrolls. The prices quoted in the listings are or examples approximately as illustrated.

Break in scroll (R. 1/12)

Broken crown and scroll (R. 2/12)

Break through scroll (R. 1/9. Ptgs from June 1929. Some show attempts at repair)

(Typo D.L.R.)

1918 (1 Apr)–**22**. *Wmk Mult Crown CA. Chalk-surfaced paper. P* 14.
51*b* **15** 2s. purple and blue/*blue* (19.6.20) .. 18·00 50·00
ba. Break in scroll £225
bb. Broken crown and scroll £190
bx. Wmk reversed £1700
52 2s. 6d. black and red/*blue* .. .. 28·00 80·00
a. Break in scroll £275
52*b* 4s. black and carmine (19.6.20) .. 60·00 £160
ba. Break in scroll £275
bb. Broken crown and scroll £275
53 5s. deep green and deep red/*yellow* .. 55·00 £110
a. Break in scroll £375
c. Green & carmine-red/pale yell (1920) 45·00 90·00
ca. Break in scroll £325
cb. Broken crown and scroll £325
cw. Wmk inverted £325
cx. Wmk reversed £2250
cy. Wmk inverted and reversed .. £2250
54 10s. green and carmine/*pale bluish green* £170 £350
a. Break in scroll £600
c. Green & red/pale bluish green (10.22) £225 £375
ca. Break in scroll £700
cb. Broken crown and scroll £700
cw. Wmk inverted .. .. ..
55 £1 purple and black/*red* £325 £550
a. Break in scroll £800
b. Broken crown and scroll £950
c. Break through scroll £1500
w. Wmk inverted £1600
51*b*/5 .. .. *Set of* 6 £600 £1100
51bs/5s Optd "Specimen" .. *Set of* 6 £800

Beware of cleaned copies of the 10s. with faked postmarks.
Examples of Nos. 51*b*/5 are known showing a forged Hamilton double ring postmark dated "22 JAN 13".
See also Nos. 88/93.

WAR TAX
(16)

WAR TAX
(17)

1918 (4 May). *Nos. 46 and 46a optd with T* **16** *by the Bermuda Press.*
56 **14** 1d. red .. .. 50 1·00
a. Rose-red .. .. 50 1·25
ay. Wmk inverted and reversed ..

1920 (5 Feb). *No. 46b optd with T* **17** *by the Bermuda Press.*
58 **14** 1d. carmine .. .. 1·50 2·25

The War Tax stamps represented a compulsory levy in addition to normal postal fees until 31 Dec 1920. Subsequently they were valid for ordinary postage.

18

19

(Des by the Governor (Gen. Sir James Willcocks). Typo D.L.R.)

1920 (11 Nov)–**21**. *Tercentenary of Representative Institutions (1st issue). Chalk-surfaced paper (3d. to 1s.). P* 14.

(*a*) *Wmk Mult Crown CA* (*sideways**) (19.1.21)
59 **18** ¼d. brown .. .. 3·25 17·00
a. "C" of "CA" missing from wmk .. £425
b. "A" of "CA" missing from wmk .. £425
w. Wmk Crown to right of CA .. £150
x. Wmk sideways reversed £180
60 ½d. green .. .. 3·25 9·00
w. Wmk Crown to right of CA .. £225
x. Wmk sideways reversed £180
y. Wmk sideways inverted and reversed .. ..
61 2d. grey .. .. 13·00 38·00
a. "C" of "CA" missing from wmk .. £650
w. Wmk Crown to right of CA .. £325
y. Wmk sideways inverted and reversed £400
62 3d. dull and deep purple/*pale yellow* .. 12·00 35·00
w. Wmk Crown to right of CA ..
x. Wmk sideways reversed .. ..
63 4d. black and red/*pale yellow* .. .. 12·00 35·00
a. "C" of "CA" missing from wmk .. £950
64 1s. black/*blue-green* .. .. .. 16·00 48·00

(*b*) *Wmk Mult Script CA* (*sideways*)
65 **18** 1d. carmine .. .. 3·75 30
66 2½d. bright blue .. .. 13·00 11·00
67 6d. dull and bright purple (19.1.21) .. 26·00 65·00
59/67 .. .. *Set of* 9 90·00 £225
59s/67s Optd "Specimen" .. *Set of* 9 £350

*The normal sideways watermark shows Crown to left of CA, *as seen from the back of the stamp.*

(Des H. J. Dale. Recess D.L.R.)

1921 (12 May). *Tercentenary of Representative Institutions (2nd issue). P* 14. (*a*) *Wmk Mult Crown CA* (*sideways**).
68 **19** 2d. slate-grey .. .. 5·50 28·00
a. "C" of "CA" missing from wmk ..
w. Wmk Crown to left of CA £400
69 2½d. bright ultramarine .. .. .. 9·00 3·00
a. "C" of "CA" missing from wmk .. £700
b. "A" of "CA" missing from wmk .. £700
x. Wmk sideways reversed .. .. — £350
70 3d. purple/*pale yellow* .. .. .. 5·50 16·00
71 4d. red/*pale yellow* .. .. .. 16·00 21·00
x. Wmk sideways reversed £200
72 6d. purple .. .. 12·00 48·00
a. "C" of "CA" missing from wmk .. £850
b. "A" of "CA" missing from wmk .. £900
c. Substituted crown in wmk .. † £1300
73 1s. black/*green* .. .. .. 23·00 48·00

(*b*) *Wmk Mult Script CA* (*sideways**)
74 **19** ¼d. brown .. .. 1·25 3·75
w. Wmk Crown to left of CA ..
x. Wmk sideways reversed .. ..
75 ½d. green .. .. 2·75 6·00
w. Wmk Crown left of CA £130 £150
y. Wmk sideways inverted and reversed £250
76 1d. deep carmine .. .. .. 2·50 35
a. "C" of "CA" missing from wmk ..
68/76 .. .. *Set of* 9 65·00 £150
68s/76s Optd "Specimen" *Set of* 9 £325

*The normal sideways watermark shows Crown to right of CA, *as seen from the back of the stamp.*

For illustration of the substituted watermark crown see Catalogue Introduction.

Examples of most values of Nos. 59/76 are known showing part strikes of the forged Hamilton postmark mentioned below Nos. 51*b*/5.

I II III

Three Types of the 1d.
I. Scroll at top left very weak and figure "1" has pointed serifs.
II. Scroll weak. "1" has square serifs and "1d" is heavy.
III. Redrawn. Scroll is completed by a strong line and "1" is thinner with long square serifs.

I II

Two Types of the 2½d.
I. Short, thick figures, especially of the "1", small "d".
II. Figures taller and thinner, "d" larger.

1922–34. *Wmk Mult Script CA. P* 14.

No.	Type	Description	Unused	Used
76*b*	**14**	¼d. brown (7.28)	1·50	3·00
77		½d. green (11.22)	1·50	15
		w. Wmk inverted		
		x. Wmk reversed		
78		1d. scarlet (I) (11.22)	17·00	60
		a. Carmine (7.24)	18·00	60
		bx. Wmk reversed		
78*c*		1d. carmine (II) (12.25)	38·00	6·00
		cx. Wmk reversed		
		d. Scarlet (8.27)	10·00	80
79		1d. scarlet (III) (10.28)	12·00	30
		a. Carmine-lake (1934)	24·00	2·25
79*b*		1½d. red-brown (27.3.34)	9·00	35
80		2d. grey (12.23)	1·50	1·50
		x. Wmk reversed	60·00	
81		2½d. pale sage-green (12.22)	2·25	1·50
		a. Deep sage-green (1924)	1·75	1·50
		aw. Wmk inverted		
		ax. Wmk reversed		
		ay. Wmk inverted and reversed		
82		2½d. ultramarine (I) (1.12.26)	2·50	50
		aw. Wmk inverted	£110	
82*b*		2½d. ultramarine (II) (3.32)	1·75	70
83		3d. ultramarine (12.24)	16·00	26·00
		w. Wmk inverted	£110	
84		3d. purple/*yellow* (10.26)	4·00	1·00
85		4d. red/*yellow* (8.24)	2·00	1·00
		x. Wmk reversed		
86		6d. purple (8.24)	1·00	80
87		1s. black/*emerald* (10.27)	4·75	9·00
		a. Brownish black/yellow-green (1934)	35·00	50·00
76*b*/87		*Set of* 12	50·00	40·00
76*b*s/87s Optd or Perf (1½d.) "Specimen"		*Set of* 12	£500	

Both comb and line perforations occur on Nos. 76*b*/87*a*. Detailed gauges are as follows:

13.7×13.9 comb — Nos. 77, 78/*a*, 80, 81/*a*, 83, 84, 85, 86, 87
13.75 line — Nos. 76*b*, 77, 78*c*/*d*, 79/*a*, 79*b*, 80, 82, 82*b*, 84, 85, 86, 87/*a*
13.75×14 line — Nos. 77, 78*c*/*d*, 79*b*, 80, 82*b*, 86, 87*a*
14×13.75 line — Nos. 79/*a*
14 line — Nos. 81/*a*

Breaks in scrolls at right (R. 1/3. Ptgs of 12s. 6d. from July 1932)

1924–32. *Wmk Mult Script* CA. *Chalk-surfaced paper. P* 14.

No.	Type	Description	Unused	Used
88	**15**	2s. purple and brt blue/*pale blue* (1.9.27)	42·00	70·00
		a. Break in scroll	£200	
		b. Broken crown and scroll	£200	
		c. Purple and blue/grey-blue (1931)	50·00	75·00
		ca. Break in scroll	£250	
		cb. Broken crown and scroll	£250	
		cc. Break through scroll	£300	
89		2s. 6d. black and carmine/*pale blue* (4.27)	55·00	£110
		a. Break in scroll	£250	
		b. Broken crown and scroll	£250	
		c. Black and red/blue to deep blue (6.29)	65·00	£110
		ca. Break in scroll	£325	
		cb. Broken crown and scroll	£325	
		cc. Break through scroll	£375	
		d. Grey-black and pale orange-vermilion/grey-blue (3.30)	£2750	£2750
		da. Break in scroll	£4500	
		db. Broken crown and scroll	£4500	
		dc. Break through scroll	£4500	
		e. Black and carmine-red/deep grey-blue (8.30)	75·00	£120
		ea. Break in scroll	£375	
		eb. Broken crown and scroll	£375	
		ec. Break through scroll	£425	
		f. Black & scarlet-vermilion/dp bl (9.31)	80·00	£120
		fa. Break in scroll	£375	
		fb. Broken crown and scroll	£375	
		fc. Break through scroll	£425	
		g. Black & brt orge-verm/dp blue (8.32)	£3000	£2750
		ga. Broken crown and scroll	£4750	
		gb. Break through scroll	£4750	
92		10s. green and red/*pale emerald* (12.24)	£120	£250
		a. Break in scroll	£550	
		b. Broken crown and scroll	£475	
		c. Break through scroll	£550	
		d. Green and red/deep emerald (1932)	£130	£275
		da. Break in scroll	£550	
		db. Broken crown and scroll	£500	
		dc. Break through scroll	£600	
93		12s. 6d. grey and orange (8.32)	£250	£350
		a. Break in scroll	£700	
		b. Broken crown and scroll	£750	
		c. Break through scroll	£850	
		d. Breaks in scrolls at right	£850	
		e. Error. Ordinary paper		
88/93		*Set of* 4	£425	£700
88s/93s Optd or Perf (12s. 6d) "Specimen"		*Set of* 4	£500	

The true No. 89*d* is the only stamp on grey-blue paper, other deeper orange-vermilion shades exist on different papers. No. 89*g* was despatched to Bermuda in July/August 1932, but is not known used before 1937.

Beware of fiscally used 2s. 6d. 10s. and 12s. 6d. stamps cleaned and bearing faked postmarks. Large quantities were used for a "head tax" levied on travellers leaving the country.

For 12s. 6d. design inscribed "Revenue" at both sides see No. F1 under POSTAL FISCAL.

1935 (6 May). *Silver Jubilee. As Nos.* 91/4 *of Antigua, but ptd by Waterlow. P* 11×12.

No.	Type	Description	Unused	Used
94		1d. deep blue and scarlet	45	60
		j. Damaged turret	£110	
		m. "Bird" by turret	95·00	£110
95		1½d. ultramarine and grey	70	2·25
		m. "Bird" by turret	£110	
96		2½d. brown and deep blue	1·40	1·00
		m. "Bird" by turret	£150	£150
97		1s. slate and purple	15·00	24·00
		k. Kite and vertical log	£150	
		l. Kite and horizontal log	£275	
94/7		*Set of* 4	16·00	25·00
94s/7s Perf "Specimen"		*Set of* 4	£160	

For illustrations of plate varieties see Omnibus section following Zanzibar.

20 Red Hole, Paget

21 South Shore

22 *Lucie* (yacht)

23 Grape Bay, Paget Parish

24 Point House, Warwick Parish

25 Gardener's Cottage, Par-la-Ville, Hamilton

(Recess B.W.)

1936 (14 Apr)–**47**. *Wmk Mult Script CA* (*sideways on horiz designs*). *P* 12.

No.	Type	Description	Unused	Used
98	**20**	½d. bright green	10	10
99	**21**	1d. black and scarlet	30	30
100		1½d. black and chocolate	1·00	50
101	**22**	2d. black and pale blue	5·00	2·00
102	**23**	2½d. light and deep blue	1·00	25
103	**24**	3d. black and scarlet	2·75	1·40
104	**25**	6d. carmine-lake and violet	80	10
		a. Claret and dull violet (6.47)	3·50	1·25
105	**23**	1s. green	5·00	8·50
106	**20**	1s. 6d. brown	50	10
98/106		*Set of* 9	15·00	11·50
98s/106s Perf "Specimen"		*Set of* 9	£250	

All are line-perf 11.9, except printings of the 6d. from July 1951 onwards, which are comb-perf 11.9 × 11.75.

1937 (14 May). *Coronation. As Nos.* 95/7 *of Antigua, but printed by D.L.R. P* 14.

No.	Description	Unused	Used
107	1d. scarlet	50	50
108	1½d. yellow-brown	60	1·50
109	2½d. bright blue	70	1·50
107/9	*Set of* 3	1·60	3·25
107s/9s Perf "Specimen"	*Set of* 3	£110	

26 Ships in Hamilton Harbour

27 St. David's Lighthouse

28 White-tailed Tropic Bird, Arms of Bermuda and Native Flower

29 King George VI

(Des Miss Higginbotham (T **28**). Recess B.W.)

1938 (20 Jan)–**1952**. *T* **22**, *T* **23** (*but with portrait of King George VI*) *and T* **26** *to* **28**. *Wmk Mult Script CA. P* 12.

No.	Type	Description	Unused	Used
110	**26**	1d. black and red (*a*) (*b*)	85	20
111		1½d. deep blue and purple-brown (*a*) (*b*)	7·00	1·50
		a. Blue and brown (*a*) (3.43)	7·00	3·25
		b. Lt blue & purple-brn (*a*) (*b*) (9.45)	2·25	35
		ba. "A" of "CA" missing from wmk	£1500	
112	**22**	2d. light blue and sepia (*a*)	45·00	
112*a*		2d. ultramarine and scarlet (*a*) (*b*) (8.11.40)	1·50	
113	**23**	2½d. light and deep blue (*a*)	11·00	
113*a*		2½d. lt blue & sepia-black (*a*) (18.12.41)	3·00	
		b. Pale blue & sepia-black (*a*) (3.43)	2·75	
		c. Bright blue and deep sepia-black (*b*) (23.9.52)	5·00	
114	**27**	3d. black and rose-red (*a*)	18·00	
114*a*		3d. black & deep blue (*a*) (*b*) (16.7.41)	1·75	
114*b*	**28**	7½d. black, blue & brt grn (*a*) (18.12.41)	6·50	
		c. Black, blue & yellow-grn (*a*) (3.43)	4·50	
115	**23**	1s. green (*a*) (*b*)	2·00	
		a. Bluish green (*b*) (20.6.52)	6·50	

Perforations. Two different perforating machines were use[d for] the various printings of these stamps: (*a*) the original 11.9 [line] perforation; (*b*) 11.9 × 11.75 comb perforation, introduced in [...] 1950. These perforations occur as indicated above.

Shading omitted from top right scroll (R. 1/1. March 1943 ptgs of 2s. and £1)

Lower right scroll with broken tail (R. 2/10. Line perforated printings only)

Broken top right scroll (R. 5/11. Line perforated ptgs only. A retouched state of the flaw is visible in later ptgs up to March 1943)

Broken lower right scroll (R. 5/12. Occurs on printings made between May 1941 and March 1943)

Gash in chin (R.2/5. Ptgs between May 1941 and March 1943

Missing pearl (R.5/1, Nov 1945 ptg of 5s. only)

"ER" joined (R. 1/2. Occurs in its complete state on 1938 ptg only. Subsequent ptgs show it incomplete)

Damaged left value tablet (R. 1/11. Part of 1951 ptg only)

(Typo D.L.R.)

(20 Jan)–**53.** *T* **29.** *Wmk Mult Crown CA* (£1) *or Mult ipt CA* (*others*). *Chalk-surfaced paper. P* 14 (*comb*).

2s. deep purple and ultramarine/*grey-blue* £110 10·00
a. Deep reddish purple and ultram/grey-blue (21.11.40)* .. .. .. £300 24·00
b. Perf 14¼ line. *Deep purple and ultram/grey-blue* (14.11.41)* .. .. .. £300 85·00
bc. Lower right scroll with broken tail .. £1600 £650
bd. Broken top right scroll £1200 £475
be. Broken lower right scroll £1200 £475
bf. Gash in chin £1300 £550
c. Ordinary paper. *Pur & bl /dp bl* (7.6.42) 7·00 1·50
ce. Broken lower right scroll .. .. £200 80·00
cf. Gash in chin .. .. £225 85·00
d. Ordinary paper. *Purple and deep blue/pale blue* (5.3.43) .. .. 11·00 1·50
db. Shading omitted from top right scroll £1000 £550
de. Broken lower right scroll £550 £300
df. Gash in chin £600 £325
e. Perf 13. Ordinary paper. *Dull purple and blue/pale blue* (15.2.50) .. .. 17·00 15·00
f. Perf 13. Ordinary paper. *Reddish purple and blue/pale blue* (10.10.50) .. .. 8·50 16·00
2s. 6d. black and red/*grey-blue* .. .. 70·00 8·50
a. Perf 14¼ line. *Black and red/grey-blue* (21.2.42)* £500 £110
ac. Lower right scroll with broken tail .. £1800 £700
ad. Broken top right scroll £1400 £550
ae. Broken lower right scroll £1400 £550
af. Gash in chin £1500 £600
b. Ordinary paper. *Black and red/pale blue* (5.3.43) .. .. 19·00 6·50
be. Broken lower right scroll £500 £225
bf. Gash in chin £550 £250
c. Perf 13. Ordinary paper. *Black and orange-red/pale blue* (10.10.50) .. 19·00 11·00
d. Perf 13. Ordinary paper. *Black and red/pale blue* (18.6.52) .. .. .. 16·00 12·00
5s. green and red/*yellow* .. .. .. £140 26·00
a. Pale green and red/yellow (14.3.39)* £300 65·00
b. Perf 14¼ line. *Dull yellow-green and red/yellow* (5.1.43)* .. .. .. £250 30·00
bc. Lower right scroll with broken tail .. £1200 £450
bd. Broken top right scroll £850 £300
be. Broken lower right scroll £850 £300
bf. Gash in chin £900 £350
c. Ordinary paper. *Dull yellow-green and carmine-red/pale yellow* (5.42)* .. £550 95·00
ce. Broken lower right scroll £3500 £1000
cf. Gash in chin £3500 £1000
d. Ordinary paper. *Pale bluish green and carmine-red/pale yellow* (5.3.43) .. £100 50·00
de. Broken lower right scroll £750 £425
df. Gash in chin £750 £425
e. Ordinary paper. *Green and red/pale yellow* (11.45)* .. .. .. 50·00 20·00
ea. Missing pearl £750
f. Perf 13. Ordinary paper. *Yellow-green and red/pale yellow* (15.2.50) .. 23·00 20·00
g. Perf 13. *Green and scarlet/yellow* (*chalk-surfaced*) (10.10.50) .. .. 35·00 45·00
10s. green and deep lake/*pale emerald* .. £450 £300
a. Bluish green and deep red/green (8.39)* £225 £130
b. Perf 14¼ line. Ordinary paper. *Yellow-green and carmine/green* (1942)* .. £425 £120
bc. Lower right scroll with broken tail .. £1700 £850
bd. Broken top right scroll £1300 £650
be. Broken lower right scroll £1300 £650
bf. Gash in chin £1400 £700
c. Ordinary paper. *Yellowish green and deep carmine-red/green* (5.3.43) .. 70·00 60·00
ce. Broken lower right scroll £2250
cf. Gash in chin £2250
d. Ordinary paper. *Deep green and dull red/green* (*emerald back*) (11.12.46) .. 80·00 60·00
e. Perf 13. Ordinary paper. *Green and vermilion/green* (19.9.51) .. 35·00 42·00
f. Perf 13. Ordinary paper. *Green and dull red/green* (16.4.53) .. .. 35·00 48·00
0 12s. 6d. deep grey and brownish orange .. £475 £425
a. Grey and brownish orange (*shades*) .. £180 65·00
b. Grey and pale orange (9.11.40)* .. 95·00 50·00
c. Ordinary paper (2.3.44)* .. .. £100 65·00
ce. Broken lower right scroll £1800 £1900
cf. Gash in chin £1800
d. Ordinary paper. *Grey & yell*† (17.9.47)* £600 £475
e. Perf 13. *Grey and pale orange* (*chalk-surfaced*) (10.10.50) .. .. .. 95·00 75·00
1 £1 purple and black/*red* £275 £100
a. "ER" joined £700
b. Pale purple & black/pale red (13.5.43)* 80·00 60·00
bb. Shading omitted from top right scroll £1800
be. Broken lower right scroll £1300 £850
bf. Gash in chin £1300 £850
c. Dp reddish pur & blk/pale red (5.3.43)* 60·00 60·00
ce. Broken lower right scroll £1200
cf. Gash in chin £1200
d. Perf 13. *Violet & black/scarlet* (7.12.51) 48·00 75·00
da. Damaged left value tablet £1800
e. Perf 13. *Brt violet & blk/scar* (10.12.52) £160 £170
0/21d .. .. *Set of* 16 £275 £180
0s/21s Perf "Specimen" .. *Set of* 16 £1500

Following extensive damage to their printing works on 29 ecember 1940 much of De La Rue's work was transferred to ther firms operating under their supervision. It is understood at Williams Lea & Co produced those new printings ordered r the Bermuda high value stamps during 1941. The first batch f these printings showed the emergency use, by Williams Lea, f a 14¼ line perforating machine (exact gauge 14.15) instead of e comb perforation (exact gauge 13.9 × 13.8).

Dates marked * are those of earliest known use.

In No. 116c the coloured surfacing of the paper is mottled with hite specks sometimes accompanied by very close horizontal nes. In Nos. 116d, 117b and 118c/d the surfacing is the same olour as the back, sometimes applied in widely spaced orizontal lines giving the appearance of laid paper.

†No. 120d is the so-called "lemon" shade.

HALF
PENNY

X **X**

(30)

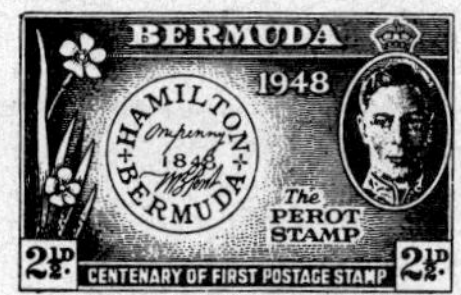

31 Postmaster Perot's Stamp

1940 (20 Dec). *No.* 110 *surch with T* **30** *by* Royal Gazette, *Hamilton.*
122 **26** ½d. on 1d. black and red (*shades*) .. 40 45

The spacing between "PENNY" and "X" varies from 12½ mm to 14 mm.

1946 (6 Nov). *Victory. As Nos.* 110/11 *of Antigua.*
123 1½d. brown 15 15
124 3d. blue 15 15
123s/4s Perf "Specimen" .. .. *Set of* 2 80·00

1948 (1 Dec). *Royal Silver Wedding. As Nos.* 112/13 *of Antigua.*
125 1½d. red-brown 30 50
126 £1 carmine .. .. 40·00 48·00

(Recess B.W.)

1949 (11 Apr). *Centenary of Postmaster Perot's Stamp. Wmk Mult Script CA. P* 13½.
127 **31** 2½d. blue and brown 15 15
128 3d. black and blue 15 15
129 6d. violet and green 15 15
127/9 .. .. *Set of* 3 40 40

1949 (10 Oct). *75th Anniv of Universal Postal Union. As Nos.* 114/17 *of Antigua.*
130 2½d. blue-black 30 75
131 3d. deep blue .. .. 1·40 1·25
132 6d. purple 40 75
133 1s. blue-green 40 75
130/3 .. .. *Set of* 4 2·25 3·25

STAMP BOOKLETS

1948 (5 Apr–10 May). *Pink* (*No.* SB1), *or light blue* (*No.* SB2) *covers. Stapled.*
SB1 5s. booklet containing six 1d., 1½d., 2d., 2½d. and 3d. (Nos. 110, 111*b*, 112*a*, 113*b*, 114*a*) in blocks of 6 (10 May) £130
SB2 10s. 6d. booklet containing six 3d. and eighteen 6d. (Nos. 114*a*, 104) in blocks of 6 with twelve air mail labels £150

POSTAL FISCAL

1937 (1 Feb). *As T* **15**, *but inscr* "REVENUE" *at each side. Wmk Mult Script CA. Chalk-surfaced paper. P* 14.
F1 12s. 6d. grey and orange £1000 £1100
a. Break in scroll (R. 1/12) £3000
b. Broken crown and scroll (R. 2/12) .. £3000
c. Breaks in scrolls at right (R. 1/3) .. £3000

No. F1 was issued for fiscal purposes towards the end of 1936. Its use as a postage stamp was authorised from 1 February to April 1937. The used price quoted above is for examples postmarked during this period. Later in the same year postmarks with other dates were obtained by favour.

For illustration of No. F1a/c see above Nos. 51*b* and 88.

British Central Africa *see* Nyasaland Protectorate

British Columbia and Vancouver Island *see* Canada

British Commonwealth Occupation Force *see after* Australia

British East Africa *see* Kenya, Uganda and Tanganyika

British Forces in Egypt *see* Egypt

British Guiana

The postal service from what was to become British Guiana dates from 1796, being placed on a more regular basis after the final British occupation.

An inland postal system was organised in 1850, using the adhesive stamps of British Guiana, but, until 1 May 1860, overseas mails continued to be the province of the British G.P.O. The stamps of Great Britain were supplied for use on such letters from 11 May 1858 and examples of their use in combination with British Guiana issues have been recorded.

For illustration of the handstamp and postmark type see BRITISH POST OFFICES ABROAD notes, following GREAT BRITAIN.

CROWNED-CIRCLED HANDSTAMPS

The provision of a handstamp, probably as Type CC 1, inscribed "DEMERARA", is recorded in the G.P.O. proof book under 1 March 1856. No examples have been reported. A further handstamp, as Type CC **6**, recorded in the proof book on 17 February 1866, is known used as a cancellation in at least two instances, *circa* 1868.

GEORGETOWN (DEMERARA)

Stamps of GREAT BRITAIN *cancelled* "A 03" *as Type* **2**.

1858 to 1860.
Z1 1d. rose-red (1857), *perf* 14 .. .. £275
Z2 4d. rose (1857) £140
Z3 6d. lilac (1856) £100
a. Azure paper .. ..
Z4 1s. green (1856) £1200

NEW AMSTERDAM (BERBICE)

Stamps of GREAT BRITAIN *cancelled* "A 04" *as Type* **2**.

1858 to 1860.
Z5 1d. rose-red (1857), *perf* 14 .. .. £700
Z6 2d. blue (1858) (Plate Nos. 7, 8) £750
Z7 4d. rose (1857) £325
Z8 6d. lilac (1856) £200
Z9 1s. green (1856) £1400

PRICES FOR STAMPS ON COVER TO 1945

Nos. 1/21	*from* × 3
No. 23	†
Nos. 24/7	*from* × 3
Nos. 29/115	*from* × 4
Nos. 116/24	*from* × 6
Nos. 126/36	*from* × 5
Nos. 137/59	*from* × 6
Nos. 162/5	*from* × 8
Nos. 170/4	*from* × 5
Nos. 175/89	*from* × 6
No. 192	*from* × 20
Nos. 193/210	*from* × 4
Nos. 213/15	*from* × 5
Nos. 216/21	*from* × 3
Nos. 222/4	*from* × 8
Nos. 233/50	*from* × 3
No. 251	—
Nos. 252/7	*from* × 3
Nos. 259/82	*from* × 4
Nos. 283/7	*from* × 5
Nos. 288/300	*from* × 4
Nos. 301/4	*from* × 5
Nos. 305/7	*from* × 6
Nos. 308/19	*from* × 5
Nos. D1/4	*from* × 12
Nos. O1/12	*from* × 12

CROWN COLONY

(Currency. 100 cents = 1 dollar)

1

2

(Set up and printed at the office of the *Royal Gazette*, Georgetown, British Guiana)

1850 (1 July)–**51**. *Type-set. Black impression. (a) Medium wove paper. Prices are for*—I. *Cut square.* II. *Cut round.*

I *Used* II *Used*

1 1 2 c. *rose* (1.3.51) .. .. — £70000
2 4 c. *orange* £26000 £4250
3 4 c. *lemon-yellow* (1851) £40000 £5000
4 8 c. *green* £15000 £3250
5 12 c. *blue* £5500 £2000
6 12 c. *indigo* £9500 £2750
7 12 c. *pale blue* (1851) £8500 £3000
a. "2" of "12" with straight foot .. — £5000
b. "1" of "12" omitted .. .. † £35000

(*b*) *Pelure paper* (1851)

8 1 4 c. *pale yellow* £50000 £5500

These stamps were usually initialled by the postmaster, or the Post Office clerks, before they were issued. The initials are—E. T. E. D(alton), E. D. W(ight), J. B. S(mith), H. A. K(illikelley), and W. H. L(ortimer). There are several types of each value and it has been suggested that the setting contained one horizontal row of four slightly different impressions.

Ten examples of No. 1 have been recorded, including three pairs on separate covers.

(Litho Waterlow)

1852 (1 Jan). *Surface-coloured paper. Imperf.*

Un *Used*

9 2 1 c. black/*magenta* £8500 £4250
10 4 c. black/*deep blue* £11000 £6000

There are two types of each value.

Reprints on thicker paper and perf 12½, were made in 1865 (*Price £17 either value*).

Such reprints with the perforations removed are sometimes offered as genuine originals.

CONDITION. Prices for Nos. 9 to 21 are for fine copies. Poor to medium specimens can be supplied when in stock at much lower rates.

3

4

5

(Dies eng and stamps litho Waterlow)

1853–59. *Imperf. (a) Original printing.*

11 3 1 c. vermilion £3000 £1000

This 1 c. in *reddish brown* is probably a proof (*Price* £650).

A B

C

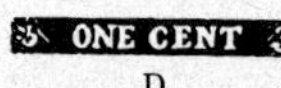
D

A. "O" large and 1 mm from left corner.
B. "O" small and ¾ mm from left corner.
C. "O" small and ¾ mm from left corner. "NT" widely spaced.
D. "ONE" close together, "O" 1¼ mm from left corner.

(*b*) *Fresh lithographic transfers from the 4 c. with varying labels of value. White line above value* (1857–59).

12 3 1 c. dull red (A) £2750 £1000
13 1 c. brownish red (A) £6000 £1400
14 1 c. dull red (B) £3250 £1100
15 1 c. brownish red (B) £6500 £1500
16 1 c. dull red (C) £4000 £1400
16*a* 1 c. brownish red (C) .. .. .. — £1700
17 1 c. dull red (D) £11000 £4500

1853–55. *Imperf.*

18 4 4 c. deep blue £1900 £650
a. Retouched £3000 £900
19 4 c. blue (1854) £1200 £425
a. Retouched £2000 £600
20 4 c. pale blue (1855) £900 £350
a. Retouched £1500 £550

The 4 c. value was produced from transfers from the original 1 c., with the bottom inscription removed, teamed with a new face value. The join often shows as a white line or traces of it above the label of value and lower corner figures. In some stamps on the sheet this line is missing, owing to having been retouched, and in these cases a line of colour usually appears in its place.

The 1 c. and 4 c. stamps were printed in 1865 from fresh transfers of five varieties. These are on thin paper and perf 12½ (*Price £14 each unused*).

1860 (May). *Figures in corners framed. Imperf.*

21 5 4 c. blue £3500 £475

6

(Type-set and printed at the *Official Gazette* by Baum and Dallas, Georgetown.)

1856 (*a*) *Surface-coloured paper*

23 6 1 c. black/*magenta* .. .. .. † —
24 4 c. black/*magenta* (Jan) .. .. † £6000
25 4 c. black/*rose-carmine* (Aug) £20000 £8500
26 4 c. black/*blue* (Sept) .. .. .. † £40000

(*b*) *Paper coloured through*

27 6 4 c. black/*deep blue* (Aug) .. .. † £55000

Since only one example of No. 23 is known, no market price can be given. This celebrated stamp frequently termed "the world's rarest", was last on the market in 1980. It is initialled by E. D. Wight and postmarked at Demerara on 4 April 1856.

These stamps, like those of the first issue, were initialled before being issued; the initials are—E.T.E.D (alton), E.D.W. (ight), C.A. W(atson), and W.H.L (ortimer). C.A.W. only appears on stamps postmarked between 14 March and 4 April and also 16–20 May. E.T.E.D. is only known on stamps between 1–5 July and on 1 August. All examples on the rose-carmine or blue papers show E.D.W.

Stamps as Type **6** were printed in sheets of 4 (2×2) each stamp differing slightly in the position of the inscriptions. There is evidence that the setting was re-arranged at some point before August, *possibly* to accommodate the production of the 1 c.

PAPERMAKERS' WATERMARKS. Seven different papermakers' watermarks were used in the period 1860 to 1875 and stamps bearing portions of these are worth a premium.

7

A B

C D

E F

(Dies eng and litho Waterlow)

1860 (July)–**63**. *Tablets of value as illustrated. Thick paper. P* 12.

29 7 1 c. pale rose £1300 £200
30 2 c. deep orange (8.60) .. .. .. £180 40·00
31 2 c. pale orange .. .. £180 42·00
32 4 c. deep blue (8.60) .. .. .. £425 75·00
33 4 c. blue .. .. £275 50·00
34 8 c. brownish rose .. .. .. £450 85·00
35 8 c. pink .. .. £375 65·00
36 12 c. lilac .. .. £450 38·00
37 12 c. grey-lilac .. .. £375 35·00
38 24 c. deep green (6.63) £1100 £100
39 24 c. green .. .. £900 65·00

The 1 c. was reprinted in 1865 on *thin* paper, P 12½–13, and in a different shade. *Price* £14.

The 12 c. in both shades is frequently found surcharged with a large "5d" in *red*; this is to denote the proportion of postage repayable by the colony to Great Britain for overseas letters.

1861 (3 Aug*). *Colour changed. Thick paper. P* 12.

40 7 1 c. reddish brown £325 9

*Earliest known postmark date.

1862–65. (*a*) *Thin paper. P* 12.

41 7 1 c. brown £450
42 1 c. black (1863) .. .. 90·00 5
43 2 c. orange .. .. 85·00 4
44 4 c. blue £100 3
45 4 c. pale blue .. .. 90·00 2
46 8 c. pink (1863) £120 5
47 12 c. dull purple (1863) £140 2
48 12 c. purple £160 2
49 12 c. lilac £170 3
50 24 c. green £800 9

(*b*) *Thin paper. P* 12½–13 (1863)

51 7 1 c. black .. .. 55·00 1
52 2 c. orange .. .. 70·00 1
53 4 c. blue .. .. 75·00 1
54 8 c. pink £200 7
55 12 c. brownish lilac .. .. .. £475 £
56 24 c. green £550 6

Copies are found on *pelure* paper.

(*c*) *Medium paper. P* 12½–13

57 7 1 c. black (1864) .. .. 45·00 3
58 2 c. deep orange (1864) .. .. .. 60·00 2
59 2 c. orange .. .. 65·00 1
60 4 c. greyish blue (1864) .. .. .. 75·00 1
61 4 c. blue .. .. 90·00 2
62 8 c. pink (1864) £140 5
63 12 c. brownish lilac (1865) £425 9
64 24 c. green (1864) £170 5
65 24 c. deep green £300 7

(*d*) *Medium paper. P* 10 (Nov 1865)

65*a* 7 12 c. grey-lilac £450 75

8

9

G

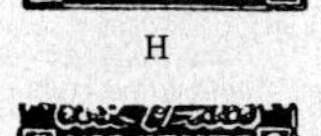
H

I

K

New transfers for the 1 c., 2 c., 8 c., and 12 c. with the spa between values and the word "CENTS" about 1 mm.

1863–76. *Medium paper* (*a*) *P* 12½–13 (1863–68).

66 8 1 c. black (1866) .. .. 40·00 23·
67 2 c. orange-red (1865) .. .. .. 48·00 5·
68 2 c. orange .. .. 42·00 5·
69 9 6 c. blue (1865) .. .. £100 50·
70 6 c. greenish blue .. .. £110 55·
71 6 c. deep blue .. .. £160 60·
72 6 c. milky blue .. .. £100 50·
73 8 8 c. pink (1868) .. .. £180 17·
74 8 c. carmine .. .. £200 19·
75 12 c. grey-lilac (1867) .. .. .. £425 27·
76 12 c. brownish purple .. .. .. £500 38·
77 9 24 c. green (*perf* 12) .. .. .. £225 19·
78 24 c. yellow-green (*perf* 12) .. .. .. £140 9·
79 24 c. yellow-green (*perf* 12½–13) .. .. £140 8·
80 24 c. green (*perf* 12½–13) (1864) .. .. £140 9·
81 24 c. blue-green (*perf* 12½–13) .. .. £180 19·
82 48 c. pale red .. .. £225 48·
83 48 c. deep red .. .. £250 50·
84 48 c. carmine-rose .. .. £275 50·

The 4 c. corresponding to this issue can only be distinguish from that of the previous issue by minor plating flaws.

There is a variety of the 6 c. with stop before "VICISSIM".

Varieties of most of the values of issues of 1863–64 and 1866 a to be found on both very thin and thick papers.

(*b*) *P* 10 (1866–71)

85 8 1 c. black (1869) .. .. 9·50 4·0
86 1 c. grey-black .. .. 11·00 8·5
87 2 c. orange (1868) .. .. 24·00 3·0
88 2 c. reddish orange .. .. 35·00 4·2
89 4 c. slate-blue .. .. 80·00 13·0
90 4 c. blue .. .. 80·00 7·5
a. Bisected (on cover) .. .. .. † £500
b. Ditto. Imperf (on cover) .. .. .. † –
91 4 c. pale blue .. .. 75·00 9·5
92 9 6 c. milky blue (1867) .. .. .. £110 29·0
93 6 c. ultramarine .. .. £120 50·0
94 6 c. dull blue .. .. £110 32·0
95 8 8 c. pink (5.71) .. .. £110 23·0
96 8 c. brownish pink .. .. £130 25·0
96*a* 8 c. carmine .. .. £200 29·0
97 12 c. pale lilac (1867) .. .. .. £200 14·0
98 12 c. grey-lilac .. .. £160 13·0
99 12 c. brownish grey .. .. £150 16·0
100 12 c. lilac .. .. £150 16·0
101 9 24 c. deep green .. .. £225 9·5
102 24 c. bluish green .. .. £200 8·0
103 24 c. yellow-green .. .. £160 7·5
104 48 c. crimson (1867) .. .. .. £300 28·0
s. Handstamped "Specimen" £225
sa. Perf "Specimen" £170
105 48 c. red .. .. £300 24·0

(*c*) *P* 15 (1875–76)

106 8 1 c. black .. .. 45·00 7·5
107 2 c. orange-red .. .. £130 8·5
108 2 c. orange .. .. £130 8·5
109 4 c. bright blue .. .. £225 95·0
111 9 6 c. ultramarine .. .. £550 75·0
112 8 8 c. deep rose (1876) .. .. .. £225 80·0
113 12 c. lilac .. .. £550 55·0

9 24 c. yellow-green £600 35·00
24 c. deep green £900 60·00
ere is a variety of the 48 c. with stop after "P" in IMUSQUE".
perforate stamps of this and of the previous issue are dered to be proofs, although examples of the 24 c. rforate from the 1869–73 period are known commercially

CES for stamps of the 1862 issue are for good average copies. es with roulettes on all sides very seldom occur and do not exist arginal positions.

10 11 12

13 14 15

e-set and printed at the Office of the *Royal Gazette*, Georgetown)

2 (Sept). *Black on coloured paper. Roul* 6.
10 1 c. *rose* £2500 £475
a. Unsigned £300
b. Wrong ornament (as T **13**) at left (R. 1/1) — £800
c. "1" for "I" in "BRITISH" (R. 1/5) — £800
11 1 c. *rose* £3250 £650
a. Unsigned £350
b. Narrow "T" in "CENTS" (R. 3/1) — £800
c. Wrong ornament (as T **15**) at top (R. 3/3) — £800
d. "1" for "I" in "BRITISH" and italic "S" in "POSTAGE" (R. 3/5) — £800
12 1 c. *rose* £4750 £850
a. Unsigned £600
b. "1" for "I" in "GUIANA" (R. 4/4) — £850
c. Wrong ornament (as T **15**) at left (R. 4/5) — £850
d. "C" for "O" in "POSTAGE" (R. 4/6) — £850
10 2 c. *yellow* £2500 £325
a. Unsigned £950
b. Wrong ornament (as T **13**) at left (R. 1/1) — £550
c. "1" for "I" in "BRITISH" (R. 1/5) — £550
11 2 c. *yellow* £3250 £400
a. Unsigned £1000
b. "C" for "O" in "TWO" and narrow "T" in "CENTS" (R. 3/1) — £550
c. Wrong ornament (as T **15**) at top (R. 3/3) — £550
d. Italic "S" in "CENTS" (R. 3/4) — £550
e. "1" for "I" in "BRITISH" and italic "S" in "POSTAGE" (R. 3/5) — £550
f. Italic "T" in "TWO" (R. 3/6) — £550
12 2 c. *yellow* £4750 £650
a. Unsigned £1200
b. "1" for "I" in "GUIANA" (R. 4/4) — £650
c. Wrong ornament (as T **15**) at left (R. 4/5) — £650
d. "C" for "O" in "POSTAGE" (R. 4/6) — £650
2 13 4 c. *blue* £2750 £550
a. Unsigned £550
b. Wrong ornament (as T **15**) at left (R. 1/6) — £900
c. Wrong ornament (as T **15**) at top and italic "S" in "CENTS" (R. 2/2) — £900
d. Ornament omitted at right (R. 2/4) — £900
3 14 4 c. *blue* £3500 £750
a. Unsigned £600
b. With inner frame lines (as in T **10/13**) (R. 2/5–6) £5000 £1300
ba. "1" for "I" in "BRITISH" (R. 2/5) £5000 £1300
c. "1" for "I" in "BRITISH" and "GUIANA" (R. 4/1) — £900
4 15 4 c. blue £3500 £750
a. Unsigned £650
b. Wrong ornament (as T **12**) at foot (R. 3/1) — £900
c. Italic "S" in "CENTS" (R. 3/2) — £900
d. Italic "S" in "BRITISH" (R. 3/3) — £900

Stamps were initialled across the centre before use by the cting Receiver-General, Robert Mather. Black was used on the c., red for the 2 c. and an ink which appears white for the 4 c. The three values of this provisional were each printed in eets of 24 (6 × 4). The 1 c. and 2 c. were produced from the same tting of the border ornaments which contained 12 examples as ype **10** (Rows 1 and 2), 8 as Type **11** (R. 3/1 to R. 4/2) and 4 as ype **12** (R. 4/3–6).
The setting of the 4 c. contained 10 examples as Type **13** (R. 1/1 R. 2/4), 8 as Type **14** (R. 2/5–6 and Row 4) and 6 as Type **15** Row 3).

16

(17)

(Typo D.L.R.)

1876 (1 July)–**79**. *Wmk Crown CC.* (*a*) *P* 14.
126 **16** 1 c. slate 2·75 1·40
127 2 c. orange 48·00 1·75
w. Wmk inverted
128 4 c. blue £120 9·00
129 6 c. brown 75·00 7·00
130 8 c. rose £100 75
w. Wmk inverted
131 12 c. pale violet 50·00 1·25
w. Wmk inverted
132 24 c. emerald-green 60·00 3·00
w. Wmk inverted
133 48 c. red-brown £110 27·00
134 96 c. olive-bistre £475 £250
126/34 *Set of* 9 £900 £250
126s/32s, 134s Handstamped "Specimen" *Set of* 8 £600
131sa/2sa Perf "Specimen" *Set of* 2 £150

(*b*) *P* 12½ (1877)
135 **16** 4 c. blue £1200 £200

(*c*) *Perf compound of* 14×12½ (1879)
136 **16** 1 c. slate — £200

1878. *Provisionals. Various stamps with old values ruled through with thick bars, in black ink, the bars varying in depth of colour.*
(*a*) *With two horiz bars* (17 Apr)
137 **16** (1 c.) on 6 c. brown 38·00 £110
(*b*) *Official stamps with horiz bars across* "OFFICIAL" (end Aug)
138 **8** 1 c. black £200 70·00
139 **16** 1 c. slate £150 55·00
140 2 c. orange £300 65·00
(*c*) *With horiz and vert bars as T* **17** (6 Nov)
141 **9** (1 c.) on 6 c. ultramarine (93) £150 75·00
142 **16** (1 c.) on 6 c. brown £300 £100
a. Optd with vert bar only † £4000
(*d*) *Official stamps with bars across* "OFFICIAL" (23 Nov)
(i) *With two horiz bars and one vert*
144 **16** (1 c.) on 4 c. blue £250 95·00
145 (1 c.) on 6 c. brown £375 90·00
146 **8** (2 c.) on 8 c. rose £1500 £250
(ii) *With one horiz bar and one vert*
147 **16** (1 c.) on 4 c. blue † £2000
148 (2 c.) on 8 c. rose £325 95·00

1 2 2
(18) (19) (20)

1881 (21 Dec). *No. 134 with old value ruled through with bar in black ink and surch.*
149 **18** 1 on 96 c. olive-bistre 3·50 6·00
a. Bar in red
b. Bar omitted
150 **19** 2 on 96 c. olive-bistre 4·25 11·00
a. Bar in red
b. Bar omitted
151 **20** 2 on 96 c. olive-bistre 48·00 85·00
a. Bar in red

In the setting of 60 Type **19** occurs on the first five vertical rows and Type **20** on the sixth.

1 2 2
(21) (23) (24)

1881 (28 Dec). *Various stamps with old value ruled with bar and surch.* (*a*) *On No.* 105.
152 **21** 1 on 48 c. red 42·00 5·00
a. Bar omitted — £550
(*b*) *On Official stamps* (*including unissued* 48 c. *optd with Type* O **2**)
153 **21** 1 on 12 c. brownish purple (O4) £120 70·00
154 1 on 48 c. red-brown £130 90·00
155 **23** 2 on 12 c. pale violet (O11) 65·00 26·00
a. Pair. Nos. 155/6 £950 £1000
b. Surch double £700 £400
c. Surch double (T **23** + **24**) £2500
d. Extra bar through "OFFICIAL"
156 **24** 2 on 12 c. pale violet (O11) £450 £300
157 **23** 2 on 24 c. emerald-green (O12) 75·00 42·00
a. Pair. Nos. 157/8 £1100 £1200
b. Surch double £1000
158 **24** 2 on 24 c. emerald-green (O12) £600 £600
159 **19** 2 on 24 c. green (O5) £250 £130

On Nos. 149/59 the bar is found in various thicknesses ranging from 1 to 4 mm.
It is believed that the same composite surcharge setting of 60 (6×10) was used for Nos. 155/6 and 157/8. Type **24** occurs on R. 7/2, 4–6 and R. 8/1.

26

27

(Type-set, Baldwin & Co. Georgetown)

1882 (9 Jan). *Black impression. P* 12. *Perforated with the word* "SPECIMEN" *diagonally.*
162 **26** 1 c. *magenta* 42·00 28·00
a. Imperf between (horiz pair) † —
b. Without "SPECIMEN" £500 £350
c. "1" with foot 90·00 65·00
163 2 c. *yellow* 75·00 50·00
a. Without "SPECIMEN" £450 £400
b. Small "2" 75·00 50·00
164 **27** 1 c. *magenta* 42·00 28·00
a. Without "SPECIMEN" £500 £350
b. "1" with foot 90·00 65·00
c. Imperf between (horiz pair) † £4250
165 2 c. *yellow* 70·00 42·00
a. Bisected diagonally (1 c.) (on cover)
b. Without "SPECIMEN" £450 £400
c. Small "2" £110 85·00

These stamps were perforated "SPECIMEN" as a precaution against fraud. Stamps are known with "SPECIMEN" double.
The 1 c. and 2 c. stamps were printed in separate sheets; but utilising the same clichés, these being altered according to the face value required. Two settings were used, common to both values:—
1st setting. Four rows of three, T **26** being Nos. 5, 6, 7, 8, 11 and 12, and T **27** the remainder.
From this setting there were two printings of the 2 c., but only one of the 1 c.
2nd setting. Six rows of two, T **26** being Nos. 3, 7, 8, 9, 11 and 12, and T **27** the remainder.
There were two printings of each value from this setting.
Se-tenant pairs are worth about 20% more.
The "1" with foot occurs on T **27** on No. 9 in the first setting and on T **26** on No. 7 in the first printing only of the second setting.
The small "2" appears on T **26** in the first setting on Nos. 6, 7, 8 and 12 in the first printing and on Nos. 7, 8 and 12 only in the second printing: in the second setting it comes on Nos. 3, 9 and 12 in the first printing and on Nos. 9, 11 and 12 in the second printing. On T **27** the variety occurs in the first setting on No. 9 of the second printing only and in the second setting on No. 10 in both printings.

(Typo D.L.R.)

1882. *Wmk Crown C.A. P* 14.
170 **16** 1 c. slate (27 Jan) 8·50 30
171 2 c. orange (27 Jan) 22·00 15
a. Value doubly printed † £3250
x. Wmk reversed
172 4 c. blue 90·00 5·00
173 6 c. brown 5·00 6·50
w. Wmk inverted
174 8 c. rose 90·00 40
x. Wmk reversed
170/4 *Set of* 5 £190 11·00
170s/4s Perf "Specimen" *Set of* 5 £250

INLAND 4 CENTS 4 CENTS
(*a*) (*b*)
Two types of "4"

2 CENTS
REVENUE
(28)

6 6
(*c*) (*d*)
Two types of "6"

1888–89. *T* **16** (*without value in lower label*) *optd.* "INLAND REVENUE", *and surch with value as T* **28**, *by D.L.R. Wmk Crown CA. P* 14.
175 1 c. dull purple (8.89) 1·25 20
176 2 c. dull purple (25.5.89) 1·25 30
177 3 c. dull purple 1·00 20
178 4 c. dull purple (*a*) 7·00 30
a. Larger figure "4" (*b*) 20·00 6·00
179 6 c. dull purple (*c*) 8·00 3·75
a. Figure 6 with straight top (*d*) 19·00 4·00
180 8 c. dull purple (8.89) 1·50 30
181 10 c. dull purple 6·00 2·50
182 20 c. dull purple 20·00 11·00
183 40 c. dull purple 21·00 19·00
184 72 c. dull purple (1.10.88) 38·00 48·00
185 $1 green (1.10.88) £425 £450
186 $2 green (1.10.88) £200 £225
187 $3 green (1.10.88) £140 £150
188 $4 green (*a*) (1.10.88) £450 £500
a. Larger figure "4" (*b*) £1200 £1300
189 $5 green (1.10.88) £250 £250
175/89 *Set of* 15 £1400 £1500

Nos. 175/89 were surcharged in settings of 60 (6×10). No. 178a occurs on all stamps in the third vertical row, No. 179a in the fourth and sixth vertical rows and No. 188a in the second vertical row.

2
(29)

30

(31)

1889 (6 June). *No.* 176 *surch with T* **29** *in red by* Official Gazette.
192 "2" on 2 c. dull purple 1·50 15

The varieties with figure "2" *inverted* or *double* were made privately by a postal employee in Demerara.

1889 (Sept). *Wmk Crown CA. P* 14.
193 **30** 1 c. dull purple and slate-grey 3·25 1·75
194 2 c. dull purple and orange 1·75 10
w. Wmk inverted
195 4 c. dull purple and ultramarine 4·50 1·75
196 4 c. dull purple and cobalt 21·00 2·25
197 6 c. dull purple and brown 35·00 14·00
198 6 c. dull purple and maroon 7·00 11·00
199 8 c. dull purple and rose 12·00 1·00
w. Wmk inverted — 60·00
200 12 c. dull purple and bright purple 18·00 1·75
200*a* 12 c. dull purple and mauve 8·50 2·25
201 24 c. dull purple and green 6·00 2·50
202 48 c. dull purple and orange-red 16·00 9·00
x. Wmk reversed
203 72 c. dull purple and red-brown 28·00 38·00
204 72 c. dull purple and yellow-brown 65·00 75·00

205 **30** 96 c. dull purple and carmine .. .. 65·00 70·00
x. Wmk reversed .. ..
206 96 c. dull purple and rosine .. .. 75·00 80·00
193/205 .. .. *Set of* 10 £140 £120
193s/205s Optd "Specimen" .. *Set of* 10 £140

1890 (15 July). *Stamps of* 1888–89 *surch locally* "One Cent", *in red, as in T* **31**.
207 1 c. on $1 (No. 185) .. .. 1·25 35
a. Surch double .. .. — 90·00
208 1 c. on $2 (No. 186) .. .. 2·00 60
a. Surch double .. .. 75·00
209 1 c. on $3 (No. 187) .. .. 2·00 1·25
a. Surch double .. .. 90·00
210 1 c. on $4 (No. 188) .. .. 2·00 6·50
a. Surch double .. .. 80·00
b. Larger figure "4" (*b*) .. .. .. 12·00 25·00
207/10 .. .. *Set of* 4 6·50 8·00

1890–91. *Colours changed. Wmk Crown CA. P* 14
213 **30** 1 c. sea-green (12.90) 75 10
214 5 c. ultramarine (1.91) .. .. .. 2·75 10
215 8 c. dull purple and greenish black (10.90) .. .. 2·75 1·10
213/15 .. .. *Set of* 3 5·50 1·10
213s/15s Optd "Specimen" .. *Set of* 3 60·00

32 Mount Roraima **33** Kaieteur Falls

(Recess D.L.R.)

1898 (18 July). *Queen Victoria's Jubilee. Wmk Crown CC (sideways* on T* **32**). *P* 14.
216 **32** 1 c. blue-black and carmine-red .. 4·00 75
w. Wmk Crown to left of CC ..
x. Wmk sideways reversed .. ..
y. Wmk sideways inverted and reversed .. ..
217 **33** 2 c. brown and indigo .. .. 20·00 2·25
a. Imperf between (horiz pair) .. £5000
x. Wmk reversed .. .. .. — £100
218 2 c. brown and blue .. .. .. 24·00 2·50
219 **32** 5 c. deep green and sepia .. .. 42·00 3·50
a. Imperf between (horiz pair) ..
w. Wmk Crown to left of CC ..
220 **33** 10 c. blue-black and brown-red .. 22·00 20·00
221 **32** 15 c. red-brown and blue .. .. 30·00 16·00
216/21 .. .. *Set of* 5 £110 38·00
216s/21s Optd "Specimen" .. *Set of* 5 £110

*The normal sideways watermark on Type **32** shows Crown to right of CC, *as seen from the back of the stamp.*

A second plate was later used for the 1 c. on which the lines of shading on the mountains in the background are strengthened, and those along the ridge show distinct from each other, whereas, in the original, they are more or less blurred. In the second plate the shading of the sky is less pronounced.

TWO CENTS.
(**34**)

Shaved "E"

35

(Surch at Printing Office of the *Daily Chronicle*, Georgetown)

1899 (24 Feb–15 June). *Surch with T* **34**.
222 **32** 2 c. on 5 c. (No. 219) (15 June) .. 3·25 2·00
a. No stop after "CENTS" .. .. 95·00 65·00
b. Comma after "CENTS" (R. 7/2) ..
c. "CINTS" (R. 4/1) £100
d. Shaved "E" (R. 6/2) .. .. 32·00
w. Wmk Crown to left of CC .. ..
223 **33** 2 c. on 10 c. (No. 220) .. .. 2·25 2·00
a. No stop after "CENTS" (R. 5/5 or 2/9) 20·00 50·00
b. "GENTS" for "CENTS" (R. 5/7) .. 50·00 70·00
c. Surch inverted £400 £475
ca. Surch inverted and stop omitted .. £2750
d. Shaved "E" (R. 4/2 or 3/8) .. 22·00
224 **32** 2 c. on 15 c. (No. 221) .. .. 1·50 1·25
a. No stop after "CENTS" (R. 9/2) .. 65·00 65·00
b. Surch double £600 £750
ba. Surch double, one without stop ..
d. Surch inverted £425 £550
da. Surch inverted and stop omitted ..
f. Shaved "E" (R. 6/2) .. .. 26·00
222/4 .. .. *Set of* 3 6·25 4·75

No. 222c was caused by damage to the first "E" of "CENTS" which developed during surcharging. The listing is for an example with only the upright stroke of the letter visible.

There were two settings of No. 223 with the no stop and shaved "E" varieties occurring on R.5/5 and R.4/2 of the first and on R.2/9 and R.3/8 of the second.

No. 224b occurred on the first five vertical columns of one sheet, the surcharges on the right hand vertical column being normal.

Only two examples of No. 224ba are known.

There is only one known example of No. 224da.

1900–7. *Wmk Crown CA. P* 14.
233 **30** 1 c. grey-green (1907) .. .. .. 1·75 3·25
234 2 c. dull purple and carmine .. .. 3·25 30
235 2 c. dull purple and black/*red* (1901) .. 1·25 10
w. Wmk inverted .. .. .. — 60·00
236 **30** 6 c. grey-black and ultramarine (1902) 6·50 11·00
237 48 c. grey and purple-brown (1901) .. 50·00 35·00
a. Brownish grey and brown (1907) .. 29·00 28·00
238 60 c. green and rosine (1903) .. .. 60·00 £170
233/8 .. .. *Set of* 6 90·00 £190
233s/8s Optd "Specimen" .. *Set of* 6 95·00

No. 233 is a reissue of No. 213 in non-fugitive ink.

1905–7. *Wmk Multiple Crown CA. Ordinary paper* (1 c. *to* 60 c.) *or chalk-surfaced paper* (72, 96 c.).
240 **30** 1 c. grey-green .. .. .. 4·00 30
aw. Wmk inverted .. ..
b. Chalk-surfaced paper .. .. 4·25 30
241 2 c. purple and black/*red* .. .. 9·00 10
a. Chalk-surfaced paper .. .. 3·50 10
242 4 c. dull purple and ultramarine .. 8·00 14·00
a. Chalk-surfaced paper .. .. 6·00 12·00
243 5 c. dull purple and blue/*blue* (1.5.05) .. 11·00 9·00
a. Chalk-surfaced paper .. .. 3·50 6·50
s. Optd "Specimen" .. .. .. 20·00
244 6 c. grey-black and ultramarine .. 16·00 45·00
a. Chalk-surfaced paper .. .. 15·00 42·00
aw. Wmk inverted .. .. ..
245 12 c. dull and bright purple .. .. 22·00 32·00
a. Chalk-surfaced paper .. .. 22·00 42·00
246 24 c. dull purple and green (1906) .. 11·00 10·00
a. Chalk-surfaced paper .. .. 3·75 4·50
247 48 c. grey and purple-brown .. .. 25·00 29·00
a. Chalk-surfaced paper .. .. 14·00 20·00
248 60 c. green and rosine .. .. .. 25·00 85·00
a. Chalk-surfaced paper .. .. 14·00 85·00
249 72 c. purple and orange-brown (1907) .. 32·00 65·00
250 96 c. black & vermilion/*yellow* (20.11.05) 35·00 45·00
s. Optd "Specimen" .. .. .. 30·00
240/50 .. .. *Set of* 11 £140 £275

1905. *Optd* "POSTAGE AND REVENUE". *Wmk Multiple Crown CA. Chalk-surfaced paper. P* 14.
251 **35** $2.40, green and violet £160 £275
s. Optd "Specimen" .. .. .. 75·00

1907–10. *Colours changed. Wmk Mult Crown CA. P* 14
252 **30** 1 c. blue-green .. .. 15·00 2·75
253 2 c. rose-red .. .. 16·00 10
a. Redrawn (1910) .. .. .. 8·50 10
254 4 c. brown and purple .. .. .. 2·25 60
255 5 c. ultramarine .. .. 13·00 1·50
256 6 c. grey and black .. .. .. 13·00 7·00
257 12 c. orange and mauve .. .. .. 4·00 4·00
252/7 .. .. *Set of* 6 50·00 14·00
253s/7s Optd "Specimen" .. *Set of* 5 75·00

In No. 253a the flag at the main truck is close to the mast, whereas in the original type it appears to be flying loose from halyards. There are two background lines above the value "2 CENTS" instead of three and the "S" is further away from the end of the tablet.

37

War
Tax
(**38**)

(Typo D.L.R.)

1913–21. *Wmk Mult Crown CA. Chalk-surfaced paper* (4 c. *and* 48 c. *to* 96 c.). *P* 14.
259 **37** 1 c. yellow-green .. .. .. 2·00 80
a. Blue-green (1917) .. .. .. 1·50 25
260 2 c. carmine .. .. 1·25 10
a. Scarlet (1916) .. .. .. 3·00 10
b. Wmk sideways .. .. .. † £1600
261 4 c. brown and bright purple (1914) .. 5·00 25
aw. Wmk inverted .. .. ..
b. Deep brown and purple .. .. 3·75 25
262 5 c. bright blue .. .. 1·75 1·00
263 6 c. grey and black .. .. .. 2·75 1·00
264 12 c. orange and violet .. .. .. 1·25 1·00
265 24 c. dull purple and green (1915) .. 3·25 4·00
266 48 c. grey and purple-brown (1914) .. 22·00 17·00
267 60 c. green and rosine (1915) .. .. 15·00 50·00
268 72 c. purple and orange-brown (1915) .. 40·00 70·00
269 96 c. black and vermilion/*yellow* (1915) .. 30·00 60·00
a. White back (1913) .. .. .. 18·00 45·00
b. On lemon (1916) .. .. .. 18·00 48·00
bs. Optd "Specimen" .. .. .. 30·00
c. On pale yellow (1921) .. .. 19·00 60·00
cs. Optd "Specimen" .. .. .. 30·00
259/69*a* .. .. *Set of* 11 £100 £170
259s/69as Optd "Specimen" .. *Set of* 11 £130

Examples of Nos. 267/9c are known with part strikes of forged postmarks of Grove dated "29 OCT 1909" and of Georgetown dated "30 OCT 1909".

1918 (4 Jan). *No.* 260*a optd with T* **38**, *by D.L.R.*
271 **37** 2 c. scarlet .. .. 1·00 15

The relative position of the words "WAR" and "TAX" vary considerably in the sheet.

1921–27. *Wmk Mult Script CA. Chalk-surfaced paper* (24 c. *to* 96 c.). *P* 14.
272 **37** 1 c. green (1922) .. .. .. 4·75 30
273 2 c. rose-carmine .. .. .. 4·25 20
w. Wmk inverted .. .. .. † £110
274 2 c. bright violet (1923) .. .. .. 2·50 10
275 4 c. brown and bright purple (1922) .. 4·75 10
276 6 c. bright blue (1922) .. .. .. 3·00 30
277 12 c. orange and violet (1922) .. .. 2·75 1·50
278 24 c. dull purple and green .. .. 2·00 4·50
279 48 c. black and purple (1926) .. .. 9·50 3·50
280 60 c. green and rosine (1926) .. .. 10·00 48·00
281 72 c. dull purple & orange-brown (1923) 22·00 55·00
282 96 c. black and red/*yellow* (1927) .. 19·00 45·00
272/82 .. .. *Set of* 11 75·00 £140
272s/82s Optd "Specimen" .. *Set of* 11 £160

39 Ploughing a Rice Field **40** Indian shooting Fish

(Recess Waterlow)

1931 (21 July). *Centenary of County Union T* **39/40** *and si designs. Wmk Mult Script CA. P* 12½.
283 1 c. emerald-green .. .. 2·50
284 2 c. brown .. .. 2·00
285 4 c. carmine .. .. 1·75
286 6 c. blue .. .. 2·25
287 $1 violet .. .. 21·00 4
283/7 .. .. *Set of* 5 27·00 4
283s/7s Perf "Specimen" .. .. *Set of* 5 75·00

Designs: *Vert*—4 c., $1 Kaieteur Falls. *Horiz*—6 c. Pu buildings, Georgetown.

43 Ploughing a Rice Field **44** Gold Mining

(Recess Waterlow)

1934 (1 Oct)–**51**. *T* **40** (*without dates at top of frame*), **43/4** *similar designs. Wmk Mult Script CA* (*sideways on h designs*). *P* 12½.
288 **43** 1 c. green 60
289 **40** 2 c. red-brown .. .. 1·50
290 **44** 3 c. scarlet.. 30
aa. Wmk error. Crown missing .. . — £1
a. Perf 12½ × 13½ (30.12.43) 60
b. Perf 13 × 14 (28.4.49) 60
291 – 4 c. slate-violet .. .. 2·00
a. Imperf between (vert pair) .. .. † £14
b. Imperf horiz (vert pair) .. . £6500 £7
292 – 6 c. deep ultramarine .. .. .. 2·75 3
293 – 12 c. red-orange 20
a. Perf 14 × 13 (16.4.51) 50 1
294 – 24 c. purple.. .. .. 3·50 5
295 – 48 c. black .. .. 7·00 8
296 – 50 c. green .. ..10·00 17
297 – 60 c. red-brown .. ..26·00 27
298 – 72 c. purple.. .. .. 1·25 2
299 – 96 c. black .. ..20·00 30
300 – $1 bright violet .. ..32·00 30
288/300 .. .. *Set of* 13 95·00 £1
288s/300s Perf "Specimen" .. *Set of* 13 £140

Designs: *Vert*—4 c., 50 c. Kaieteur Falls (as No. 285, but w dates omitted); 96 c. Sir Walter Raleigh and his son. *Horiz*— Shooting logs over falls; 12 c. Stabroek Market; 24 c. Sugar ca in punts; 48 c. Forest road; 60 c. Victoria Regia Lilies; 7 Mount Roraima; $1 Botanical Gardens.

Examples of Nos. 295/300 are known with forged Georgeto postmarks dated "24 JY 31" or "6 MY 35".

1935 (6 May). *Silver Jubilee. As Nos.* 91/4 *of Antigua.*
301 2 c. ultramarine and grey 20
f. Diagonal line by turret .. .. 27·00
h. Dot by flagstaff .. .. .. 60·00
302 6 c. brown and deep blue .. .. 1·00 1
f. Diagonal line by turret .. .. 55·00
g. Dot to left of chapel .. .. .. 85·00
h. Dot by flagstaff .. .. .. 85·00
303 12 c. green and indigo .. .. .. 4·00 8·
f. Diagonal line by turret .. .. 85·00
h. Dot by flagstaff £140
i. Dash by turret £140
304 24 c. slate and purple .. .. .. 5·50 8·
h. Dot by flagstaff £170
i. Dash by turret £170
301/4 .. .. *Set of* 4 9·50 16·
301s/4s .. .. *Set of* 4 75·00

For illustrations of plate varieties see Omnibus secti following Zanzibar.

1937 (12 May). *Coronation. As Nos.* 95/7 *of Antigua, but ptd D.L.R. P* 14.
305 2 c. yellow-brown 15
306 4 c. grey-black 50
307 6 c. bright blue .. .. 60 1·
305/7 .. .. *Set of* 3 1·10 1·
305s/7s Perf "Specimen" .. .. *Set of* 3 55·00

53 South America **54** Victoria Regia Lilies

(Recess Waterlow)

1938 (1 Feb)–**1952**. *As earlier types but with portrait of Ki George VI as in T* **53/4**. *Wmk Mult Script CA. P* 12½
308 **43** 1 c. yellow-green .. ..16·00
aa. Green (1944) 30
a. Perf 14 × 13 (1949) 30
309 – 2 c. slate-violet 60
a. Perf 13 × 14 (28.4.49) 30

53 4 c. scarlet and black 70 30
a. Imperf horiz (vert pair) .. £14000 £10000
b. Perf 13×14 (1952) 50 15
40 6 c. deep ultramarine 40 10
a. Perf 13×14 (24.10.49) 50 30
– 24 c. blue-green .. ..26·00 10·00
a. Wmk sideways .. .. .. 1·25 10
– 36 c. bright violet (7.3.38) .. .. .. 2·00 20
a. Perf 13×14 (13.12.51) .. .. 3·00 30
– 48 c. orange 60 40
a. Perf 14×13 (8.5.51*) .. .. 1·50 1·25
– 60 c. red-brown .. ..11·00 3·75
– 96 c. purple.. .. .. 2·50 2·75
a. Perf 12½×13½ (1944) .. .. 6·00 8·50
b. Perf 13×14 (8.2.51) .. .. .. 2·75 6·50
– $1 bright violet .. ..11·00 35
a. Perf 14×13(1951) £300 £400
– $2 purple (11.6.45) .. .. .. 4·50 14·00
a. Perf 14×13 (9.8.50) .. .. ..10·00 15·00
54 $3 red-brown (2.7.45) .. .. ..27·00 25·00
a. Bright red-brown (12.46) .. ..28·00 28·00
b. Perf 14×13. *Red-brown* (29.10.52) ..25·00 45·00
a/19 .. .. *Set of* 12 55·00 40·00
s/19s Perf "Specimen" .. *Set of* 12 £200

esigns: *Vert*—2 c., 36 c. Kaieteur Falls; 96 c. Sir Walter igh and his son. *Horiz*—24 c. Sugar cane in punts; 48 c. st road; 60 c. Shooting logs over falls; $1 Botanical Gardens; Iount Roraima.
Earliest known postmark date.

6 (1 Oct). *Victory. As Nos.* 110/11 *of Antigua.*
3 c. carmine 10 20
6 c. blue 30 50
s/1s Perf "Specimen" .. .. *Set of* 2 48·00

8 (20 Dec). *Royal Silver Wedding. As Nos.* 112/13 *of ntigua, but $3 in recess.*
3 c. scarlet 10 40
$3 red-brown .. .. 12·00 23·00

9 (10 Oct). *75th Anniv of Universal Postal Union. As Nos.* 14/17 *of Antigua.*
4 c. carmine 10 20
6 c. deep blue .. .. 1·00 65
12 c. orange 15 45
24 c. blue-green 15 60
/7 .. .. *Set of* 4 1·25 1·75

1 (16 Feb). *University College of B.W.I. As Nos.* 118/19 *of ntigua.*
3 c. black and carmine 30 30
6 c. black and blue 30 60

STAMP BOOKLETS

9 (14 June). *Black on pink cover without face value. tapled.*
1 49 c. booklet containing twelve 1 c. and eighteen 2 c. (Nos. 252/3) in blocks of 6 .. ..

23. *Black on pink cover without face value. Stapled.*
2 30 c. booklet containing six 1 c. and twelve 2 c. (Nos. 272, 274) in blocks of 6 .. ..

23. *Black on pink without face value. Stapled.*
3 48 c. booklet containing twelve 1 c. and eighteen 2 c. (Nos. 272, 274) in blocks of 6 .. .. £1100
a. With face value on front cover .. ..

23. *Black on red cover without face value. Stapled.*
4 72 c. booklet containing twelve 1 c., six 2 c. and twelve 4 c. (Nos. 272, 274/5) in blocks of 6 £1500

34. *Black on orange cover. Stitched.*
5 24 c. booklet containing eight 1 c. and eight 2 c. (Nos. 288/9) in blocks of 4 .. .. ..

34. *Black on orange cover. Stitched.*
6 36 c. booklet containing four 1 c., eight 2 c. and four 4 c. (Nos. 288/9, 291) in blocks of 4 ..

38. *Black on orange cover. Stitched.*
7 36 c. booklet containing four 1 c., eight 2 c. and four 4 c. (Nos. 308/10) in blocks of 4 .. £250

44. *Black on orange cover. Stitched.*
8 24 c. booklet containing eight 1 c. and eight 2 c. (Nos. 308/9) in blocks of 4 .. .. .. £170

45–49. *Black on red cover. Stitched.*
9 24 c. booklet containing 1 c., 2 c. and 3 c. (Nos. 290, 308, 309), each in block of 4 .. .. £150
a. Containing Nos. 290, 308aa, 309 .. .. 65·00
b. Containing Nos. 290, 308aa, 309a .. .. 65·00
c. Containing Nos. 290a, 308aa, 309 .. .. 65·00
d. Containing Nos. 290b, 308aa, 309 .. .. 65·00
e. Containing Nos. 290b, 308aa, 309a .. 65·00
f. Containing Nos. 290b, 308a, 309a .. .. 65·00

POSTAGE DUE STAMPS

D 1

(Typo D.L.R.)

940 (Mar)–55. *Wmk Mult Script CA. Chalk-surfaced paper* (4 c.). *P* 14.
1 D 1 1 c. green .. .. 4·75 6·50
a. Chalk-surfaced paper. *Deep green*, (30.4.52) .. .. 1·50 9·50
ab. W9*a* (Crown missing) £225
ac. W9*b* (St. Edward's Crown) .. 95·00
D2 D 1 2 c. black .. .. 18·00 2·00
a. Chalk-surfaced paper (30.4.52) .. 1·50 3·50
ab. W9*a* (Crown missing) £180
ac. W9*b* (St. Edward's Crown) .. 85·00
D3 4 c. bright blue (1.5.52) .. .. 30 8·50
a. W9*a* (Crown missing) £160
b. W9*b* (St. Edward's Crown) .. 85·00
D4 12 c. scarlet .. .. 27·00 4·00
a. Chalk-surfaced paper (19.7.55) .. 14·00 24·00
D1a/4a .. .. *Set of* 4 15·00 40·00
D1s, D2s and D4s Perf "Specimen" *Set of* 3 50·00

OFFICIAL STAMPS

OFFICIAL (O 1) **OFFICIAL** (O 1*a*) **OFFICIAL** (O 2)

1875. *Optd with Type* O **1** (1 c.) *or* O **1***a* (*others*) *by litho. P* 10.
O1 8 1 c. black (R.) .. .. 48·00 17·00
a. Imperf between (horiz pair) .. — £5500
O2 2 c. orange .. .. £170 14·00
O3 8 c. rose £325 £120
O4 7 12 c. brownish purple £1800 £500
O5 9 24 c. green £1000 £225

Two types of the word "OFFICIAL" are found on each value. On the 1 c., the word is either 16 or 17 mm long. On the other values the chief difference is in the shape and position of the letter "o" in "OFFICIAL". In one case the "o" is upright, in the other it slants to the left.

1877. *Optd with Type* O **2** *by typo. Wmk Crown CC. P* 14.
O 6 16 1 c. slate .. .. £225 65·00
a. Imperf between (vert pair) .. .. — £8000
O 7 2 c. orange .. .. £100 15·00
O 8 4 c. blue .. .. 80·00 20·00
O 9 6 c. brown £4750 £600
O10 8 c. rose £1900 £450

Prepared for use, but not issued

O11 16 12 c. pale violet £1200
O12 24 c. green £1300

The "OFFICIAL" overprints have been extensively forged.

The use of Official stamps was discontinued in June 1878, but was resumed in June 1981.

British Honduras

It is recorded that the first local post office was established by the inhabitants in 1809, but Belize did not become a regular packet port of call until December 1829. The post office came under the control of the British G.P.O. in April 1844 and the stamps of Great Britain were supplied for use on overseas mail from May 1858.

The colonial authorities took over the postal service on 1 April, 1860, the Great Britain stamps being withdrawn at the end of the month. There was no inland postal service until 1862.

For illustrations of the handstamp and postmark types see BRITISH POST OFFICES ABROAD notes, following GREAT BRITAIN.

BELIZE

CROWNED-CIRCLE HANDSTAMPS

CC1 CC 1*b* BELIZE (R.)(13.11.1841) .. *Price on cover* £4000

Stamps of GREAT BRITAIN *cancelled* "A 06" *as Type* **2**.

1858 *to* **1860**.
Z1 1d. rose-red (1857), *perf* 14 .. .. £900
Z2 4d. rose (1857) £375
Z3 6d. lilac (1856) £375
Z4 1s. green (1856) £1500

PRICES FOR STAMPS ON COVER TO 1945

Nos. 1/4	*from* × 20
Nos. 5/16	*from* × 25
Nos. 17/22	*from* × 20
Nos. 23/6	*from* × 10
Nos. 27/30	*from* × 15
Nos. 35/42	*from* × 20
Nos. 43/4	*from* × 30
Nos. 49/50	*from* × 25
Nos. 51/69	*from* × 15
Nos. 80/100	*from* × 6
Nos. 101/10	*from* × 5
Nos. 111/20	*from* × 15
Nos. 121/2	*from* × 8
No. 123	*from* × 10
Nos. 124/37	*from* × 6
Nos. 138/42	*from* × 10
Nos. 143/9	*from* × 8
Nos. 150/61	*from* × 5
Nos. D1/3	*from* × 30

CROWN COLONY

1

(Typo D.L.R.)

1865 (1 Dec). *No wmk. P* 14.
1 1 1d. pale blue .. .. 60·00 50·00
a. Imperf between (pair) .. ..
2 1d. blue .. .. 70·00 55·00
3 6d. rose £300 £130
4 1s. green £325 £120
a. In horiz pair with 6d. £18000
b. In vert pair with 1d. £25000

In the first printing all three values were printed in the same sheet separated by horizontal and vertical gutter margins. The sheet comprised two panes of 60 of the 1d. at the top with a pane of 60 of the 1s. at bottom left and another of 6d. at bottom right. Copies of 1d. *se-tenant* with the 6d. are not known. There were two later printings of the 1d. but they were in sheets without the 6d. and 1s.

1872–79. *Wmk Crown CC.* (*a*) *P* 12½
5 1 1d. pale blue .. .. 65·00 16·00
w. Wmk inverted £170
y. Wmk inverted and reversed ..
6 1d. deep blue (1874) .. .. .. 75·00 16·00
7 3d. red-brown .. .. £110 70·00
8 3d. chocolate (1874) .. .. .. £130 85·00
9 6d. rose .. .. £225 35·00
9*a* 6d. bright rose-carmine (1874) .. £375 45·00
10 1s. green .. .. £375 28·00
10*a* 1s. deep green (1874) .. .. .. £325 21·00
b. Imperf between (horiz pair) .. † £13000
w. Wmk inverted .. .. ..

(*b*) *P* 14 (1877–79)
11 1 1d. pale blue (1878) .. .. .. 60·00 16·00
12 1d. blue .. .. 55·00 10·00
a. Imperf between (horiz pair) .. £4500
13 3d. chestnut .. .. £120 17·00
14 4d. mauve (1879) .. .. .. £170 8·50
x. Wmk reversed .. .. ..
15 6d. rose (1878) £350 £170
w. Wmk inverted .. .. .. — £300
16 1s. green .. .. £190 11·00
a. Imperf between (pair) .. .. ..

1882–87. *Wmk Crown CA. P* 14.
17 1 1d. blue (4.84) .. .. 40·00 13·00
18 1d. rose (1884) .. .. 23·00 13·00
a. Bisected (½d.) (on cover) .. ..
s. Optd "Specimen" £150
19 1d. carmine (1887) .. .. .. 50·00 18·00
20 4d. mauve (7.82) .. .. .. 70·00 4·75
w. Wmk inverted .. .. ..
21 6d. yellow (1885) £275 £190
22 1s. grey (1.87) £250 £160
s. Optd "Specimen" .. .. .. 75·00

(New Currency. 100 cents = 1 British Honduras dollar)

2 CENTS (2) TWO (3) 2 CENTS (4)

1888 (1 Jan). *Stamps of* 1872–79 (*wmk Crown CC*), *surch locally as T* **2.** (*a*) *P* 12½.
23 1 2 c. on 6d. rose £180 £120
24 3 c. on 3d. chocolate £11000 £4750
(*b*) *P* 14
25 1 2 c. on 6d. rose .. .. £100 90·00
a. Surch double £1700
b. Bisected (1 c.) (on cover) .. .. † £200
c. Slanting "2" with curved foot .. £1100
w. Wmk inverted .. .. .. — £300
26 3 c. on 3d. chestnut .. .. .. 75·00 75·00
There are very dangerous forgeries of these surcharges.

1888. *Stamps of* 1882–87 (*wmk Crown CA*), *surch locally as T* **2**, *P* 14.
27 1 2 c. on 1d. rose .. .. .. 8·50 21·00
a. Surch inverted £1900 £1800
b. Surch double £900 £900
c. Bisected (1 c.) (on cover) .. .. † £180
28 10 c. on 4d. mauve .. .. .. 50·00 16·00
29 20 c. on 6d. yellow .. .. .. 27·00 35·00
30 50 c. on 1s. grey £325 £450
a. Error. "5" for "50" £7500

Various settings were used for the surcharges on Nos. 23/30, the most common of which was of 36 (6 × 6) impressions. For No. 29 this setting was so applied that an albino surcharge occurs in the margin above each stamp in the first horizontal row.

The same setting was subsequently amended, by altering the "2" to "1", to surcharge the 4d. value. As this was in sheets of 30 it was only necessary to alter the values on the bottom five rows of the setting. Albino surcharges once again occur in the top margin of the sheet, but, as the type in the first horizontal row remained unaltered, these read "20 CENTS" rather than the "10 CENTS" on the actual stamps.

1888 (Mar). *No.* 30 *further surch locally with T* **3.**
35 1 "TWO" on 50c. on 1s. grey (R.) .. 45·00 90·00
a. Bisected (1 c.) (on cover) .. .. † £200
b. Surch in black £9500 £8000
c. Surch double (R. + Blk.) £9500 £8000

1888 (July)–**91.** *Surch in London as T* **4.** *Wmk Crown CA. P* 14.
36 1 1 c. on 1d. dull green (?12.91) .. .. 80 1·50
37 2 c. on 1d. carmine .. .. .. 60 2·25
a. Bisected (1 c.) (on cover) .. .. † 90·00
w. Wmk inverted .. ..
38 3 c. on 3d. red-brown .. .. .. 3·00 1·40
39 6 c. on 3d. ultramarine (?4.91) .. .. 2·75 13·00
40 10 c. on 4d. mauve .. .. .. 8·50 50
a. Surch double £1800
41 20 c. on 6d. yellow (2.89) .. .. 12·00 14·00
42 50 c. on 1s. grey (11.88) .. .. 29·00 75·00
36/42 .. .. .. *Set of* 7 50·00 95·00
36s/42s Optd "Specimen" .. *Set of* 7 £350

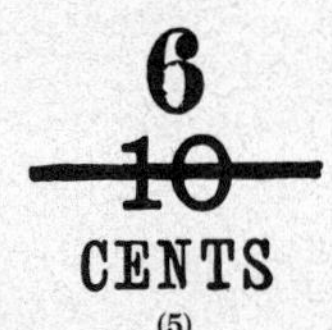
(5)

FIVE (6) 15 (7)

1891. *Stamps of* 1888–9 *surch locally.* (*a*) *With T* **5** (May).
43 1 6 c. on 10 c. on 4d. mauve (R.) .. .. 1·50 2·00
a. "6" and bar inverted £400 £400
b. "6" only inverted .. .. — £2750
44 6 c. on 10 c. on 4d. mauve (Blk.) .. .. 1·25 1·50
a. "6" and bar inverted £2750 £750
b. "6" only inverted .. .. † £2750

Of variety (b) only six copies of each can exist, as one of each of these errors came in the first six sheets, and the mistake was then corrected. Of variety (a) more copies exist.

Essays are known with "SIX" in place of "6" both with and without bars (*price* £85 *and* £400 *respectively*). Although not issued we mention them, as three contemporary covers franked with them are known.

(*b*) *With T* **6/7** (23 Oct)
49 1 5 c. on 3 c. on 3d. red-brown .. .. 1·25 1·40
a. Wide space between "I" and "V" .. 50·00 65·00
b. "FIVE" and bar double £300 £325
50 15 c. on 6 c. on 3d. ultramarine (R.) .. 13·00 24·00
a. Surch double .. .. ..

8

9

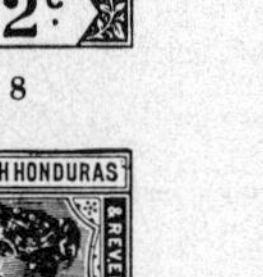
10

11

(Typo D.L.R.)

1891 (July)–**1901.** *Wmk Crown CA. P* 14.
51 8 1 c. dull green (4.95) .. .. .. 2·50 1·25
a. Malformed "S" .. .. .. £140 75·00
w. Wmk inverted .. .. ..
52 2 c. carmine-rose .. .. .. 2·00 20
a. Malformed "S" .. .. .. £120 45·00
b. Repaired "S" .. .. .. £100 45·00
53 3 c. brown .. .. 6·00 4·00
w. Wmk inverted .. .. ..
54 5 c. ultramarine (4.95) .. .. .. 12·00 75
a. Malformed "S" £300 £100
55 11 5 c. grey-black & ultram/*blue* (10.00) .. 16·00 2·50
56 8 6 c. ultramarine .. .. .. 6·00 2·00
57 9 10 c. mauve and green (4.95) .. .. 10·00 8·50
58 10 10 c. dull purple and green (1901) .. 11·00 7·50
59 9 12 c. pale mauve and green .. .. 23·00 7·00
a. Violet and green .. .. .. 2·50 2·00
60 24 c. yellow and blue .. .. .. 5·50 14·00
a. Orange and blue .. .. .. 30·00 55·00
61 25 c. red-brown and green (4.95) .. .. 65·00 £110
62 10 50 c. green and carmine (3.98) .. .. 24·00 55·00
63 11 $1 green and carmine (12.99) .. .. 70·00 £110
64 $2 green and ultramarine (12.99) .. 90·00 £140
65 $5 green and black (12.99) £275 £325
51/65 .. .. .. *Set of* 15 £550 £700
51s/65s Optd "Specimen" .. *Set of* 15 £350

For illustrations of Nos. 51a, 52a/b and 54a see above Gambia No. 37.

Most values are known with a forged Belize postmark dated "OC 23 09".

1899 (1 July). *Optd* "REVENUE" 12 *mm long.*
66 8 5 c. ultramarine .. .. .. 11·00 2·50
a. "BEVENUE" .. .. .. 90·00 95·00
b. Malformed "S" at right .. .. — £250
c. Repaired "S" at right £225
d. Opt 11 mm long .. .. .. 22·00 8·00
67 9 10 c. mauve and green .. .. .. 3·50 16·00
a. "BEVENUE" £180 £250
b. "REVENU" £425
c. Opt 11 mm long .. .. .. 19·00 45·00
cb. "REVENU" £450 £500
68 25 c. red-brown and green .. .. 2·75 35·00
a. "BEVENUE" £120 £300
b. "REVE UE" .. .. ..
c. Opt 11 mm long .. .. .. 4·00 50·00
69 1 50 c. on 1s. grey £140 £300
a. "BEVENUE" £2750
c. Opt 11 mm long £250 £400

Two minor varieties, a small "U" and a tall, narrow "U" are found in the word "REVENUE".

The overprint setting of 60 (6 × 10) contained 43 examples of the 12 mm size and 17 of the 11 mm. The smaller size overprints occur on R.8/1, R8/3 to 6 and on all positions in Rows 9 and 10.

The "BEVENUE" error appears on R. 6/4 and, it is believed, "REVE UE" comes from R. 6/6. Both occur on parts of the printing only. The missing "E" developed during the overprinting and damage to this letter can be observed on at least eight positions in the setting.

14

15

(Typo D.L.R.)

1902 (10 Oct)–**04.** *Wmk Crown CA. P* 14.
80 14 1 c. grey-green and green (28.4.04) .. 1·25 22·00
81 2 c. purple and black/*red* (18.3.03) .. 75 25
w. Wmk inverted .. .. .. — 60·00
82 5 c. grey-black and blue/*blue* .. .. 6·00 30
w. Wmk inverted .. .. ..
83 15 20 c. dull and bright purple (28.4.04) .. 6·00 17·00
80/3 .. .. .. *Set of* 4 12·50 35·00
80s/3s Optd "Specimen" .. *Set of* 4 55·00

1904 (Dec)–**07.** *Wmk Mult Crown CA. Ordinary paper* (1, 2 c.) *or chalk-surfaced paper* (*others*). *P* 14.
84 14 1 c. grey-green and green (8.05) .. 9·00 10·00
a. Chalk-surfaced paper (1906) .. 75 1·75
85 2 c. purple and black/*red* .. .. 2·75 30
a. Chalk-surfaced paper (1906) .. 75 20
86 5 c. grey-black and blue/*blue* (5.2.06) .. 1·75 20
87 15 10 c. dull purple & emerald-green (20.9.07) 5·00 11·00
89 25 c. dull purple and orange (20.9.07) .. 7·00 48·00
90 50 c. grey-green and carmine (20.9.07) .. 15·00 70·00
91 14 $1 grey-green and carmine (20.9.07) .. 50·00 75·00
92 $2 grey-green and blue (20.9.07) .. 90·00 £150
93 $5 grey-green and black (20.9.07) .. £200 £250
84/93 .. .. .. *Set of* 9 £325 £550
87s/93s .. .. .. *Set of* 6 £225

Examples of most values are known showing a forged Belize postmark dated "OC 23 09".

1908 (7 Dec)–**11.** *Colours changed. Wmk Mult Crown* *Chalk-surfaced paper* (25 c.). *P* 14.
95 14 1 c. blue-green (1.7.10) .. .. 11·00
96 2 c. carmine .. .. 12·00
w. Wmk inverted .. ..
97 5 c. ultramarine (1.6.09) .. .. 1·75
100 15 25 c. black/*green* (14.10.11) .. .. 3·00 4
95/100 .. .. .. *Set of* 4 25·00 4
96s/100s Optd "Specimen" .. *Set of* 3 70·00

16

17

(18)

1913–21. *Wmk Mult Crown CA. Chalk-surfaced paper* (10 $5). *P* 14.
101 16 1 c. blue-green .. .. .. 3·75
a. Yellow-green (13.3.17) .. .. 6·00
w. Wmk inverted .. ..
102 2 c. red .. .. 3·50
a. Bright scarlet (1915) .. .. 6·00
b. Dull scarlet (8.17) .. .. 3·00
c. Red/bluish .. .. .. 12·00
w. Wmk inverted .. ..
103 3 c. orange (16.4.17) 80
104 5 c. bright blue .. .. .. 2·00
105 17 10 c. dull purple and yellow-green .. 3·00
a. Dull purple and bright green (1917) 13·00 2
106 25 c. black/*green* .. .. .. 1·25 1
a. On blue-green, olive back (8.17) .. 5·00 1
b. On emerald back (1921) .. .. 1·75 2
107 50 c. purple and blue/*blue* .. .. 10·00 1
108 16 $1 black and carmine .. .. 19·00 4
109 $2 purple and green .. .. 65·00 8
110 $5 purple and black/*red* .. .. £200 £
101/10 .. .. .. *Set of* 10 £275 £
101s/10s Optd "Specimen" .. *Set of* 10 £225

1915–16. *Optd with T* **18**, *in violet.*
111 16 1 c. green (30.12.15) .. .. 3·00 1
a. Yellow-green (6.6.16) 50 1
112 2 c. scarlet (3.11.15) .. .. 3·50
113 5 c. bright blue (29.7.15) 30 6
111s/13s Optd "Specimen" .. *Set of* 3 90·00

These stamps were shipped early in the 1914–18 war, and w thus overprinted, so that if seized by the enemy, they could distinguished and rendered invalid.

WAR (19) WAR (20)

21

1916 (23 Aug). *No.* 111 *optd locally with T* **19.**
114 16 1 c. green 10 1
a. Opt inverted .. .. .. £190 £

1917. *Nos.* 101 *and* 103 *optd with T* **19.**
116 16 1 c. blue-green .. .. 1·50 3
aw. Wmk inverted £200
ax. Wmk reversed £200
b. Yellow-green 20 1
118 3 c. orange .. .. 3·75 4
a. Opt double £325

1918. *Nos.* 101 *and* 103 *optd with T* **20.**
119 16 1 c. blue-green 10
a. Yellow-green .. .. .. 3·50 4
120 3 c. orange 70 1
y. Wmk inverted and reversed .. £200
119s/20s Optd "Specimen" .. *Set of* 2 £100

(Recess D.L.R.)

1921 (28 Apr). *Peace Commemoration. Wmk Mult Crown C* (*sideways*). *P* 14.
121 21 2 c. rose-red .. .. 3·25
a. "C" of "CA" missing from wmk .. £275
s. Optd "Specimen" .. .. .. 45·00

1921 (26 Nov). *Wmk Mult Script CA. P* 14.
122 16 1 c. green .. .. 3·50 12
s. Optd "Specimen" .. .. .. 45·00

1922 (4 Jan). *As T* **21** *but with words* "PEACE" *omitted. Wm* *Mult Script CA* (*sideways*). *P* 14.
123 4 c. slate .. .. 6·50
s. Optd "Specimen" .. .. .. 45·00

22

BELIZE RELIEF FUND PLUS 3 CENTS (23)

(Typo D.L.R.)

(1 Aug)–**33**. *Ordinary paper* (1 c. *to* 5 c.) *or chalk-surfaced* *er* (*others*). *P* 14 (*a*) *Wmk Mult Crown CA.*

22 25 c. black/*emerald* .. .. .. 6·50 35·00
$5 purple and black/*red* (1.10.24) .. £190 £200

(*b*) *Wmk Mult Script CA*

22 1 c. green (2.1.29) .. .. .. 4·00 6·50
2 c. brown (1.3.23) .. .. .. 1·50 1·50
2 c. rose-carmine (10.12.26) .. .. 2·25 1·50
3 c. orange (1933) .. .. .. 15·00 4·00
4 c. grey (1.10.29) .. .. .. 6·00 85
5 c. ultramarine .. .. .. 1·50 55
a. *Milky blue* (1923) .. .. .. 4·75 3·75
10 c. dull purple and sage-green (1.12.22) 1·25 30
25 c. black/*emerald* (1.10.24) .. .. 1·25 8·50
50 c. purple and blue/*blue* (1.11.23) .. 4·75 16·00
$1 black and scarlet (2.1.25) .. .. 8·00 23·00
$2 yellow-green and bright purple .. 32·00 80·00
37 .. .. *Set of* 13 £250 £325
37s Optd or Perf (1 c., 3 c., 4 c.) "Specimen" *Set of* 13 £250

(2 May). *Belize Relief Fund. Surch as T* **23**. *Wmk Mult Script* . *P* 14.

22 1 c. + 1 c. green .. .. 70 7·00
2 c. + 2 c. rose-carmine .. .. .. 75 6·50
3 c. + 3 c. orange .. .. .. 85 16·00
4 c. + 4 c. grey (R.) .. .. .. 10·00 21·00
5 c. + 5 c. ultramarine .. .. .. 6·50 14·00
42 .. .. *Set of* 5 17·00 55·00
/42s Perf "Specimen" .. *Set of* 5 £110

5 (6 May). *Silver Jubilee. As Nos.* 91/4 *of Antigua, but ptd by* W. & *Co. P* 11 × 12.

3 c. ultramarine and grey-black .. .. 1·75 50
a. Extra flagstaff .. .. 55·00
b. Short extra flagstaff .. .. .. 70·00
c. Lightning conductor .. .. .. 55·00
d. Flagstaff on right-hand turret.. .. £100
4 c. green and indigo .. .. .. 1·75 3·50
a. Extra flagstaff £180
c. Lightning conductor £180
d. Flagstaff on right-hand turret.. .. £190
e. Double flagstaff.. .. .. .. £190
5 c. brown and deep blue .. .. 1·75 1·00
25 c. slate and purple .. .. .. 3·75 4·00
a. Extra flagstaff £250
b. Short extra flagstaff £275
c. Lightning conductor £225
d. Flagstaff on right-hand turret.. .. £300
e. Double flagstaff.. .. .. .. £300
6 .. .. *Set of* 4 8·00 8·00
s/6s Perf "Specimen" .. .. *Set of* 4 75·00

or illustrations of plate varieties see Omnibus section wing Zanzibar.

7 (12 May). *Coronation. As Nos.* 95/7 *of Antigua, but* *rinted by D.L.R. P* 14.

3 c. orange 30 30
4 c. grey-black 70 30
5 c. bright blue .. .. 80 1·60
/9 .. .. *Set of* 3 1·60 2·00
s/9s "Specimen" .. .. *Set of* 3 50·00

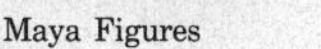

24 Maya Figures

25 Chicle Tapping

(Recess B.W.)

38 (10 Jan)–**47**. *T* **24/5** *and similar designs. Wmk Mult Script* *CA* (*sideways on horizontal stamps*). *P* 11½ × 11 (*horiz designs*) *or* 11 × 11½ (*vert designs*).

1 c. bright magenta and green (14.2.38) .. 10 1·50
2 c. black and scarlet (14.2.38) .. .. 20 1·00
a. Perf 12 (1947) .. .. 1·90 1·00
2 3 c. purple and brown 30 80
3 4 c. black and green 30 70
4 5 c. mauve and dull blue .. .. .. 1·00 70
5 10 c. green and reddish brown (14.2.38) .. 1·00 60
6 15 c. brown and light blue (14.2.38) .. 2·25 70
7 25 c. blue and green (14.2.38).. .. 2·25 1·25
8 50 c. black and purple (14.2.38) .. .. 11·00 3·50
9 $1 scarlet and olive (28.2.38) .. .. 20·00 10·00
0 $2 deep blue and maroon (28.2.38).. .. 27·00 16·00
1 $5 scarlet and brown (28.2.38) .. .. 27·00 23·00
0/61 .. .. *Set of* 12 80·00 55·00
0s/61s Perf "Specimen" .. .. *Set of* 12 £160

Designs: *Vert*—3 c. Cohune palm; $1 Court House, Belize. $2 ahogany felling; $5 Arms of Colony. *Horiz*—4 c. Local products; . Grapefruit; 10 c. Mahogany logs in river; 15 c. Sergeant's Cay; c. Dorey; 50 c. Chicle industry.

46 (9 Sept). *Victory. As Nos.* 110/11 *of Antigua.*

62 3 c. brown 10 10
63 5 c. blue 10 10
62s/3s Perf "Specimen" .. .. *Set of* 2 50·00

48 (1 Oct). *Royal Silver Wedding. As Nos.* 112/13 *of Antigua.*

64 4 c. green 15 50
65 $5 brown .. .. 16·00 40·00

36 Island of St George's Cay

37 H.M.S. *Merlin*

(Recess Waterlow)

1949 (10 Jan). *150th Anniv of Battle of St. George's Cay. Wmk Mult Script CA. P* 12½.

166 **36** 1 c. ultramarine and green 10 75
167 3 c. blue and yellow-brown .. .. 10 1·25
168 4 c. olive and violet 10 50
169 **37** 5 c. brown and deep blue 80 20
170 10 c. green and red-brown 70 30
171 15 c. emerald and ultramarine 70 30
166/71 .. .. *Set of* 6 2·00 3·00

1949 (10 Oct). *75th Anniv of U.P.U. As Nos.* 114/17 *of Antigua.*

172 4 c. blue-green 30 30
173 5 c. deep blue .. .. 1·25 50
174 10 c. red-brown .. .. 30 2·50
175 25 c. blue 35 50
172/5 .. .. *Set of* 4 2·00 3·50

1951 (16 Feb). *Inauguration of B.W.I. University College. As Nos.* 118/19 *of Antigua.*

176 3 c. reddish violet and brown .. .. 45 1·50
177 10 c. green and brown 45 30

STAMP BOOKLETS

1920. *Black on pink cover inscr* "British Honduras–100–Two Cent Stamps". *Stapled.*

SB1 $2 booklet containing one hundred 2 c. (No. 102*b*) in blocks of 10 (5×2) .. ..

1920. *Grey-blue cover inscr* "British Honduras–100–Three Cent Stamps". *Stapled.*

SB2 $3 booklet containing one hundred 3 c. (No. 103) in blocks of 10 (5×2) .. ..

1923. *Black on pink cover inscr* "British Honduras–100–Two Cent Stamps". *Stapled.*

SB3 $2 booklet containing one hundred 2 c. brown (No. 127) in blocks of 10 (5×2) .. .. ..

1927. *Black on pink cover inscr* "British Honduras–100–Two Cent Stamps". *Stapled.*

SB4 $2 booklet containing one hundred 2 c. rose-carmine (No. 128) in blocks of 10 (5×2) ..

POSTAGE DUE STAMPS

D 1

(Typo D.L.R.)

1923–64. *Wmk Mult Script CA. Ordinary paper. P* 14.

D1 D **1** 1 c. black .. .. 2·25 13·00
a. Chalk-surfaced paper (25.9.56) .. 50 19·00
b. White uncoated paper (9.4.64) .. 14·00 27·00
D2 2 c. black .. .. 2·25 7·50
a. Chalk-surfaced paper (25.9.56) .. 50 18·00
D3 4 c. black .. .. 1·25 6·00
a. Missing top serif on "C" (R. 6/6) .. 17·00
b. Chalk-surfaced paper (25.9.56) .. 90 13·00
ba. Missing top serif on "C" (R. 6/6) .. 16·00
w. Wmk inverted £170
D1/3 .. .. *Set of* 3 5·25 24·00
D1a/3b .. .. *Set of* 3 1·75 45·00
D1s/3s Optd "Specimen" .. .. *Set of* 3 55·00

The early ordinary paper printings were yellowish and quite distinct from No. D1b.

Stamps in this design, but with different watermark, were issued between 1965 and 1972.

British Levant

The term "British Levant" is used by stamp collectors to describe the issues made by various British Post Offices within the former Turkish Empire.

Arrangements for the first such service were included amongst the terms of a commercial treaty between the two countries in 1832, but the system did not start operations until September 1857 when a post office for civilian use was opened in Constantinople, replacing the Army Post Office which had existed there since June 1854.

Eventually the number of British Post Offices grew to five:

Beyrout (Beirut, Lebanon). Opened 1873, closed 30 September 1914.

Constantinople (Istanbul). Opened 1 September 1857, closed 30 September 1914, re-opened 4 February 1919, finally closed 27 September 1923.

Salonica (Thessalonika, Greece). Opened 1 May 1900, closed October 1914. The city was captured by Greek troops on 7 November 1912 and incorporated into Greece by the Treaty of London (July 1913).

Smyrna (Izmir). Opened 1872, closed 30 September 1914, re-opened 1 March 1919, finally closed September 1922. Between 15 May 1919 and 8 September 1922 the city was under Greek occupation.

Stamboul (a sub-office of Constantinople). Opened 1 April 1884, closed 25 August 1896, re-opened 10 February 1908, finally closed 30 September 1914.

Stamps from the two British Post Offices in Egypt, still technically part of the Turkish Empire, are listed under EGYPT.

A. BRITISH POST OFFICES IN TURKISH EMPIRE, 1857–1914

For illustrations of the postmark types see BRITISH POST OFFICES ABROAD notes, following GREAT BRITAIN.

From 1 August 1885 letter and registered charges were prepaid with surcharged stamps (No. 1 onwards). Until 14 August 1905 postcards and parcels continued to be franked with unoverprinted Great Britain stamps. Only a limited range of values were stocked for this purpose and these are listed. Other values exist with Levant postmarks, but these stamps did not originate from the local post offices.

After 15 August 1905 the post offices were supplied with Great Britain stamps overprinted "LEVANT". Subsequent examples of unoverprinted stamps with Levant postmarks are omitted from the listing. The use of such stamps during 1919–22 at Constantinople and Smyrna is, however, covered by a later note.

BEYROUT (BEIRUT)

Between 1873 and 1876 much of the mail from the British Post Office in Beyrout sent to European addresses was forwarded through the French or Italian Post Offices at Alexandria. Such covers show Great Britain stamps used in combination with those of French or Italian P.O's in the Turkish Empire.

Stamps of GREAT BRITAIN *cancelled* "G 06" *or circular postmark as in Types* **8**, **18** *or* **20**.

1873.

Z 1 ½d. rose-red (1870–79) .. .. .. *From* 38·00
Plate Nos. 12, 13, 14, 19, 20.
Z 2 1d. rose-red (1864–79).. .. .. *From* 16·00
Plate Nos. 107, 118, 130, 140, 145, 148, 155, 157, 162, 167, 177, 179, 180, 184, 185, 186, 187, 195, 198, 200, 203, 204, 211, 213, 215, 218, 220, 222.
Z 3 1½d. lake-red (1870–74) (Plate 3) £250
Z 4 2d. blue (1858–69) .. .. .. *From* 21·00
Plate Nos. 13, 14, 15.
Z 5 2½d. rosy mauve (1875) (*blued paper*) .. .. 75·00
Plate No. 1.
Z 6 2½d. rosy mauve (1875–76) .. .. *From* 32·00
Plate Nos. 1, 2, 3.
Z 7 2½d. rosy mauve (1876–79) .. .. *From* 25·00
Plate Nos. 3, 4, 5, 6, 7, 8, 9, 10, 11, 12, 13, 14, 15, 16, 17.
Z 8 2½d. blue (1880).. .. .. .. *From* 15·00
Plate Nos. 17, 18, 19, 20.
Z 9 2½d. blue (1881).. .. .. .. *From* 11·00
Plate Nos. 21, 22, 23.
Z10 3d. rose (1867–73) (Plate No. 10) .. ..
Z11 3d. rose (1873–76) .. .. 40·00
Plate Nos. 12, 15, 16, 18, 19, 20.
Z12 3d. rose (1881) (Plate Nos. 20, 21) .. ..
Z13 4d. vermilion (1865–73) .. .. *From* 38·00
Plate Nos. 11, 12, 13, 14.
Z14 4d. vermilion (1876) (Plate No. 15) £180
Z15 4d. sage-green (1877) £120
Plate Nos. 15, 16.
Z16 4d. grey-brown (1880) *wmk* Large Garter (Plate No. 17) .. ..
Z17 4d. grey-brown (1880) *wmk* Crown .. .. 48·00
Plate Nos. 17, 18.
Z18 6d. mauve (1870) (Plate Nos. 8, 9) .. ..
Z19 6d. buff (1872–73) .. .. .. *From* 85·00
Plate Nos. 11, 12.
Z20 6d. chestnut (1872) (Plate No. 11) .. .. 42·00
Z21 6d. grey (1873) (Plate No. 12).. .. ..
Z22 6d. grey (1874–80) .. .. .. *From* 30·00
Plate Nos. 13, 14, 15, 16, 17.
Z23 8d. orange (1876) £350
Z24 10d. red-brown (1867) £160
Z25 1s. green (1867–73) .. .. .. 30·00
Plate Nos. 6, 7.
Z26 1s. green (1873–77) .. .. .. *From* 42·00
Plate Nos. 8, 9, 10, 12, 13.
Z27 1s. orange-brown (1880) (Plate No. 13) ..
Z28 1s. orange-brown (1881) .. .. .. 55·00
Plate Nos. 13, 14.
Z29 2s. blue (1867).. .. .. £150
Z30 5s. rose (1867) (Plate Nos. 1, 2) .. *From* £600

1880.

Z31	½d. deep green	9·50
Z32	½d. pale green	11·00
Z33	1d. Venetian red	13·00
Z34	1½d. Venetian red	16·00
Z35	2d. pale rose	45·00
Z36	2d. deep rose	45·00
Z37	5d. indigo	75·00

1881.

Z38	1d. lilac (14 *dots*)	
Z39	1d. lilac (16 *dots*)	6·00

1884.

Z40	½d. slate-blue	12·00
Z41	1½d. lilac	75·00
Z42	2d. lilac	65·00
Z43	2½d. lilac	11·00
Z44	4d. dull green	£170
Z45	5d. dull green	£110
Z46	1s. dull green	£250

1887–92.

Z47	½d. vermilion	6·00
Z54	6d. purple/*rose-red*	21·00
Z55	1s. dull green	£130

1900.

Z56	½d. blue-green	9·00
Z57	1s. green and carmine	£170

1902–04. *De La Rue ptgs.*

Z58	½d. blue-green	4·75
Z59	½d. yellowish green	5·00
Z60	1d. scarlet	4·25
Z64	1s. dull green and carmine	29·00

CONSTANTINOPLE

Stamps of GREAT BRITAIN *cancelled* "C" *or circular postmark as in Types* **1**, **10**, **18** *or* **19**.

1857.

Z 68	½d. rose-red (1870–79) .. *From* Plate Nos. 5, 6, 10, 11, 12, 13, 14, 15, 20.	24·00
Z 69	1d. red-brown (1854), Die I, *wmk* Small Crown, *perf* 16	
Z 70	1d. red-brown (1855), Die II, *wmk* Small Crown, *perf* 14	
Z 71	1d. red-brown, (1855), Die II, *wmk* Large Crown, *perf* 14	19·00
Z 72	1d. rose-red (1857)	7·00
Z 73	1d. rose-red (1861) Alphabet IV	
Z 74	1d. rose-red (1864–79) .. *From* Plate Nos. 71, 72, 73, 74, 76, 78, 79, 80, 81, 83, 85, 87, 89, 90, 92, 93, 94, 95, 96, 97, 99, 101, 102, 105, 106, 108, 109, 110, 113, 116, 118, 119, 120, 121, 122, 123, 124, 125, 127, 129, 130, 131, 134, 135, 136, 137, 138, 140, 141, 143, 144, 145, 146, 147, 148, 149, 150, 151, 152, 155, 156, 157, 158, 159, 160, 161, 162, 163, 164, 165, 166, 167, 170, 171, 172, 173, 174, 175, 176, 177, 178, 179, 180, 181, 183, 184, 186, 187, 188, 189, 190, 191, 192, 193, 194, 195, 196, 197, 198, 200, 201, 203, 204, 205, 206, 207, 208, 210, 212, 214, 215, 216, 220, 222, 224.	8·00
Z 75	1½d. rose-red (1870) (Plate 1)	£200
Z 76	2d. blue (1855), *wmk* Large Crown, *perf* 14. (Plate Nos. 5, 6)	
Z 77	2d. blue (1858–69) .. *From* Plate Nos. 7, 8, 9, 12, 13, 14, 15.	12·00
Z 78	2½d. rosy mauve (1875–76) (*blued paper*) (Plate Nos. 1, 2) .. *From*	55·00
Z 79	2½d. rosy mauve (1875–76) .. *From* Plate Nos. 1, 2, 3.	30·00
Z 80	2½d. rosy mauve (*Error of Lettering*)	
Z 81	2½d. rosy mauve (1876–79) .. *From* Plate Nos. 3 to 17.	23·00
Z 82	2½d. blue (1880–81) .. *From* Plate Nos. 17, 18, 19, 20.	11·00
Z 83	2½d. blue (1881) (Plate Nos. 21, 22, 23)	7·50
Z 84	3d. carmine-rose (1862) (Plate No. 2)	£130
Z 85	3d. rose (1865) (Plate No. 4)	75·00
Z 86	3d. rose (1867–73) (Plate Nos. 4 to 10)	70·00
Z 87	3d. rose (1873–76) Plates, 11, 12, 15, 16, 17, 18, 19.	21·00
Z 88	3d. rose (1881) (Plate No. 21)	
Z 89	3d. on 3d. lilac (1883) (Plate No. 21)	
Z 90	4d. rose (1857)	45·00
	a. *Rose-carmine*	
Z 91	4d. red (1862) (Plate Nos. 3, 4) .. *From*	38·00
Z 92	4d. vermilion (1865–73) .. *From* Plate Nos. 7 to 14.	26·00
Z 93	4d. vermilion (1876) (Plate No. 15)	£150
Z 94	4d. sage-green (1877) Plate Nos. 15, 16.	90·00
Z 95	4d. grey-brown (1880) *wmk* Large Garter (Plate No. 17)	
Z 96	4d. grey-brown (1880) *wmk* Crown (Plate Nos. 17, 18) .. *From*	35·00
Z 97	6d. lilac (1856)	60·00
Z 98	6d. lilac (1862) (Plate Nos. 3, 4) .. *From*	38·00
Z 99	6d. lilac (1865–67) Plate Nos. 5, 6.	35·00
Z100	6d. lilac (1867) (Plate No. 6)	40·00
Z101	6d. violet (1867–70) .. *From* Plate Nos. 6, 8, 9.	32·00
Z102	6d. buff (1872–73) Plate Nos. 11, 12.	50·00
Z103	6d. chestnut (1872) (Plate No. 11)	30·00
Z104	6d. grey (1873) (Plate No. 12)	75·00
Z105	6d. grey (1874–76) .. *From* Plate Nos. 13, 14, 15, 16.	24·00
Z106	6d. grey (1881–82) (Plate Nos. 17, 18)	26·00
Z107	6d. on 6d. lilac (1883)	70·00
	a. Dots slanting (Letters MI or SJ)	£110
Z108	8d. orange (1876)	£325
Z109	10d. red-brown (1867), *wmk* Emblems	£14000
Z110	10d. red-brown (1867)	£160
Z111	1s. green (1856)	£110
Z112	1s. green (1862)	60·00
Z113	1s. green (1862) ("K" *variety*)	
Z114	1s. green (1862) (*thick paper*)	
Z115	1s. green (1865) (Plate No. 4)	65·00
Z116	1s. green (1867–73) .. *From* Plate Nos. 4, 5, 6, 7.	16·00
Z117	1s. green (1873–77) .. *From* Plate Nos. 8, 9, 10, 11, 12, 13.	27·00
Z118	1s. orange-brown (1880) (Plate No. 13)	£180
Z119	1s. orange-brown (1881) .. *From* Plate Nos. 13, 14.	45·00
Z120	2s. blue (1867)	90·00
Z121	5s. rose (1867–74) .. *From* Plate Nos. 1, 2.	£250
Z122	5s. rose (1882) (*white paper*)	£850
Z123	5s. rose (1882) (*blued paper*)	£1000

1880.

Z124	½d. deep green	6·50
Z125	½d. pale green	7·50
Z126	1d. Venetian red	7·50
Z127	2d. pale rose	38·00
Z128	2d. deep rose	38·00
Z129	5d. indigo	

1881.

Z130	1d. lilac (14 *dots*)	
Z131	1d. lilac (16 *dots*)	2·50

1883–84.

Z132	½d. slate-blue	6·50
Z133	1½d. lilac	
Z134	2d. lilac	55·00
Z135	2½d. lilac	7·00
Z136	3d. lilac	
Z137	4d. dull green	
Z138	5d. dull green	90·00
Z139	6d. dull green	
Z140	9d. dull green	
Z141	1s. dull green	£190
Z142	2s. 6d. lilac (*blued paper*)	£500
Z143	2s. 6d. lilac (*white paper*)	80·00
Z144	5s. rose (*blued paper*)	
Z145	5s. rose (*white paper*)	

1887–92.

Z146	½d. vermilion	2·50
Z154	6d. purple/*rose-red*	10·00
Z157	1s. dull green	75·00

1900.

Z158	½d. blue-green	4·00
Z159	1s. green and carmine	£140

1902–04. *De La Rue ptgs.*

Z160	½d. blue-green	3·00
Z161	½d. yellowish green	3·50
Z162	1d. scarlet	2·50
Z169	6d. purple	11·00
Z172	1s. green and carmine	18·00
Z173	2s. 6d. lilac	
Z174	5s. carmine	

POSTAL FISCALS

Z175	1d. purple (*wmk Anchor*) (1868)	
Z176	1d. purple (*wmk Orb*) (1881)	£600

SALONICA

Stamps of GREAT BRITAIN *cancelled with circular postmark as in Type* **18** *or double-circle datestamp.*

1900.

Z202	½d. vermilion (1887)	17·00
Z203	½d. blue-green (1900)	19·00
Z204	1d. lilac (1881)	19·00
Z205	6d. purple/*red* (1887)	25·00
Z206	1s. green and carmine (1900)	£160
Z207	5s. rose (*white paper*) (1883)	£800

1902.

Z208	½d. blue-green	23·00
Z209	½d. yellow-green	17·00
Z209*a*	1d. scarlet	17·00
Z209*c*	1s. green and carmine	42·00

SMYRNA (IZMIR)

Stamps of GREAT BRITAIN *cancelled* "F 87" *or circular postmark as in Type* **8**, **16** *or* **18**.

1872.

Z210	½d. rose-red (1870–79) .. *From* Plates 11, 12, 13, 14, 15.	28·00
Z211	1d. rose-red (1864–79) .. *From* Plate Nos. 120, 124, 134, 137, 138, 139, 140, 142, 143, 145, 146, 148, 149, 150, 151, 152, 153, 155, 156, 157, 158, 159, 160, 161, 162, 163, 164, 166, 167, 168, 169, 170, 171, 172, 173, 174, 175, 176, 177, 178, 183, 184, 185, 186, 187, 188, 191, 193, 195, 196, 198, 200, 201, 204, 210, 212, 215, 217, 218.	13·00
Z212	1½d. lake-red (1870–74) (Plate Nos. 1, 3) *From*	£225
Z213	2d. blue (1858) *wmk* Large Crown, *perf* 16	
Z214	2d. blue (1858–69) .. *From* Plate Nos. 13, 14, 15.	16·00
Z215	2½d. rosy mauve (1875) (*blued paper*) Plate No. 1.	60·00
Z216	2½d. rosy mauve (1875–76) .. *From* Plate Nos. 1, 2, 3.	27·00
Z217	2½d. rosy mauve (*Error of lettering*)	
Z218	2½d. rosy mauve (1876–79) .. *From* Plate Nos. 3, 4, 5, 6, 7, 8, 9, 10, 11, 12, 13, 14, 15, 16, 17.	22·00
Z219	2½d. blue (1880) .. *From* Plate Nos. 17, 18, 19, 20.	11·00
Z220	2½d. blue (1881) Plate Nos. 21, 22, 23.	
Z221	3d. rose (1867–73) Plate Nos. 5, 7, 9, 10.	
Z222	3d. rose (1873–76) (Plate No. 14)	
Z223	4d. vermilion (1865–73) Plate Nos. 12, 13, 14.	
Z224	4d. vermilion (1876) (Plate No. 15)	
Z225	4d. sage-green (1877) Plate Nos. 15, 16.	
Z226	4d. grey-brown (1880) *wmk* Large Garter (Plate No. 17)	
Z227	4d. grey-brown (1880) *wmk* Crown (Plate Nos. 17, 18) .. *From*	3
Z228	6d. buff (1872–73) .. *From* Plate Nos. 11, 12.	7
Z229	6d. chestnut (1872) (Plate No. 11)	
Z230	6d. grey (1873) (Plate No. 12)	7
Z231	6d. grey (1874–80) .. *From* Plate Nos. 13, 14, 15, 16, 17.	2
Z232	6d. grey (1881–82) (Plate Nos. 17, 18)	5
Z233	6d. on 6d. lilac (1883)	8
Z234	8d. orange (1876)	
Z235	9d. straw (1867)	
Z236	10d. red-brown (1867)	£
Z237	1s. green (1867–73) (Plate Nos. 6, 7)	
Z238	1s. green (1873–77) .. *From* Plate Nos. 8, 9, 10, 11, 12, 13.	3
Z239	1s. orange-brown (1880) (Plate No. 13)	
Z240	1s. orange-brown (1881) (Plate Nos. 13, 14)	4
Z241	5s. rose (1867–74) (Plate No. 2)	

1880.

Z242	½d. deep green	
Z243	½d. pale green	
Z244	1d. Venetian red	1
Z245	1½d. Venetian red	8
Z246	2d. pale rose	3
Z247	2d. deep rose	3
Z248	5d. indigo	5

1881.

Z249	1d. lilac (16 *dots*)	4

1884.

Z250	½d. slate-blue	9
Z251	2d. lilac	60
Z252	2½d. lilac	10
Z253	4d. dull green	
Z254	5d. dull green	£
Z255	1s. dull green	£

1887.

Z256	½d. vermilion	4
Z263	6d. purple/*rose-red*	16
Z264	1s. dull green	£

1900.

Z265	½d. blue-green	7
Z266	1s. green and carmine	

1902–04. *De La Rue ptgs.*

Z267	½d. blue-green	4
Z268	½d. yellowish green	5
Z269	1d. scarlet	4
Z276	6d. purple	13
Z279	1s. green and carmine	24
Z280	2s. 6d. purple	
Z281	5s. carmine	

STAMBOUL (CONSTANTINOPLE)

Stamps of GREAT BRITAIN *cancelled* "S" *as Type* **10**, *or circu* *postmarks inscribed either* "BRITISH POST OFFI CONSTANTINOPLE S" *or* "BRITISH POST OFFICE STA BOUL" *as Type* **18**.

1884.

Z296	½d. slate-blue	18·
Z297	1d. lilac	9·
Z298	2d. lilac	
Z299	2½d. lilac	11·
Z300	5d. dull green	£1

1887–92.

Z306	½d. vermilion	9·
Z314	6d. purple/*rose-red*	26·
Z317	1s. dull green	

The "S" cancellation was in use from 1885 to 1891 and the "Sta boul" mark from 1892 to 1896, when the office was closed, and fro its reopening in 1908 to 1914. The "CONSTANTINOPLE S" har stamp was normally used as a back stamp, but can be found canc ling stamps in the period 1885 to 1892.

PRICES FOR STAMPS ON COVER	
Nos. 1/3a	*from* × 8
Nos. 4/6a	*from* × 5
Nos. 7/40	*from* × 3
Nos. L1/10	*from* × 6
Nos. L11/17	*from* × 3

I. TURKISH CURRENCY

(40 paras = 1 piastre)

Following the depreciation of the Turkish piastre against ste ling in 1884 it was decided to issue stamps surcharged in Turkis currency to avoid speculation. During the early period unsu charged stamps of Great Britain remained on sale from the Britis Post Offices at the current rate of exchange until replaced b "LEVANT" overprints.

80 PARAS	4 PIASTRES	12 PIASTRES
(1)	(2)	(3)

PRINTERS. Nos. 1/24 were surcharged or overprinted by De L Rue, *unless otherwise stated.*

ıps of Great Britain (Queen Victoria) surch as T 1 to 3

1 Aug)–88.
40 pa. on 2½d. lilac .. .. .. 90·00 1·25
80 pa. on 5d. green .. .. .. £180 9·50
12 pi. on 2s. 6d. lilac/*bluish* £275 £200
a. On white paper (4.88) .. .. 45·00 22·00

June)–96.
40 pa. on 2½d. purple/*blue* .. .. 2·75 10
a. Surch double £1900 £2500
80 pa. on 5d. purple and blue (7.90) .. 15·00 30
a. Small "0" in "80" .. .. .. £170 85·00
w. Wmk inverted .. .. .. † £500
4 pi. on 10d. dull purple & carm (10.10.96) 42·00 8·00
a. Dull purple and deep bright carmine 42·00 11·00
b. Large, wide "4" (R. 1/2, 1/4) .. £130 55·00

5a first appeared on the June 1895 printing when the size surcharge plate was increased from 60 to 120. On the rian stamp the variety comes on R. 4/1 and 4/7. The same g was used for the first printing of the Edward VII arge, but here the sheet size was further increased to 240 ıt No. 9a occurs on R. 4/1, 4/7, 14/1 and 14/7.

25 Feb). *Roughly handstamped at Constantinople, as T 1.*
/1 40 pa. on ½d. vermilion £425 £100

ıs provisional was in use for five days only at the tantinople and Stamboul offices. As fraudulent copies were with the original handstamp, and can be found "used" on cancelled by fraudulent use of the usual canceller, this p should only be purchased from undoubted sources.

e handstamp became damaged during use so that by 1 h the top of the "S" was broken. Used examples dated 25 or ebruary showing the broken "S" *must* be fraudulent. It is known with genuine handstamp inverted (*Price* £800 *ed*, £300 *used*).

–5. *Stamps of King Edward VII surch as T 1 to 3.*
6 40 pa. on 2½d. ultramarine (3.02) .. 12·00 10
a. Pale ultramarine .. .. .. 13·00 10
ab. Surch double .. .. .. † £2000
9 80 pa. on 5d. dull purple & ultram (5.6.02) 4·75 2·50
a. Small "0" in "80" £200 £190
2 4 pi. on 10d. dull purple & carm (6.9.02) 9·50 4·00
a. No cross on crown .. .. .. 90·00 90·00
b. Chalk-surfaced paper .. .. 6·00 10·00
ba. Chalk-surfaced paper. No cross on crown .. .. 85·00 £100
4 12 pi. on 2s. 6d. lilac (29.8.03) .. 35·00 35·00
a. Chalk-surfaced paper. *Pale dull pur* 70·00 75·00
b. Chalk-surfaced paper. *Dull purple* 35·00 35·00
5 24 pi. on 5s. bright carmine (15.8.05) .. 32·00 40·00
.. .. *Set of* 5 80·00 70·00
1s Optd "Specimen" .. .. *Set of* 3 £150
o. 9a only occurs on the first printing of 80 pa. on 5d.

1 PIASTRE
(4)

–08. *Surch in "PIASTRES" instead of "PARAS" as T 4 and 2.*
6 1 pi. on 2½d. ultramarine (17.4.06) .. 11·00 10
a. Surch double .. .. .. † £1300
9 2 pi. on 5d. dull purple & ultram (11.11.05) 24·00 2·50
a. Chalk-surfaced paper (1.08) .. 22·00 1·75
ab. Slate-purple and ultramarine .. 25·00 7·00

1 Piastre (5) — 1 PIASTRE 10 PARAS (6)

3 (2 July). *Issued at Beyrout. No. L4 surch with T 5 by merican Press, Beyrout.*
85 1 pi. on 2d. grey-green and carmine .. £1300 £600

9 (16 Nov–Dec.) *Stamps of King Edward VII surch as T 1 0 pa.), 6, and 2 (5 pi). Ordinary paper (No. 19) or halk-surfaced paper (others).*
84 30 pa. on 1½d. pale dull purple and green 10·00 1·25
a. Surch double, one albino ..
87 1 pi. 10 pa. on 3d. dull purple/*orange-yell* 12·00 30·00
88 1 pi. 30 pa. on 4d. green & chocolate-brn 5·00 17·00
1 pi. 30 pa. on 4d. pale orange (16.12.09) 17·00 50·00
83 2 pi. 20 pa. on 6d. dull purple .. .. 18·00 50·00
93 5 pi. on 1s. dull green and carmine .. 4·25 8·50
s. Optd "Specimen" .. .. .. 60·00
21 .. .. *Set of* 6 60·00 £140

1¾ PIASTRE (7) — 4 Normal "4" — 4 Pointed "4"

0 (24 Jan). *Stamps of King Edward VII surch as T 7. halk-surfaced paper (Nos. 22 and 24).*
87 1¼ pi. on 3d. dull purple/*orange-yellow* .. 40 1·00
88 1¾ pi. on 4d. pale orange 40 60
a. Orange-red .. .. .. 4·75 5·50
b. Thin, pointed "4" in fraction .. 5·50 26·00
83 2½ pi. on 6d. dull purple .. .. 1·40 65
4 .. .. *Set of* 3 2·00 2·00
No. 23b occurs in the first and seventh vertical rows of the sheet. e variety also occurs on No. 38, but not on No. 38b.

1 PIASTRE (8) — **1 PIASTRE** (9)

PE DIFFERENCES. In T 4 the letters are tall and narrow and space enclosed by the upper part of the "A" is small.
In T 8 the opening of the "A" is similar but the letters are shorter d broader, the "P" and the "E" being particularly noticeable.
In T 9 the letters are short and broad, but the "A" is thin and en.

1911–13. *Stamps of King Edward VII, Harrison or Somerset House ptgs, surch at Somerset House.*

(*a*) *Surch with T 4* (20 July)
25 **86** 1 pi. on 2½d. bright blue (*perf* 14) .. 15·00 9·00
a. Surch double, one albino .. £200
26 1 pi. on 2½d. bright blue (*perf* 15×14) (14.10.11) 12·00 2·50
a. Dull blue .. .. .. 12·00 2·00

(*b*) *Surch with T 8*
27 **86** 1 pi. on 2½d. bright blue (*perf* 15×14) (3.12) .. .. .. 12·00 2·00
a. Dull blue .. .. .. 21·00 3·25

(*c*) *Surch with T 9* (7.12)
28 **86** 1 pi. on 2½d. bright blue (*perf* 15×14) 60·00 60
a. Dull blue .. .. .. 60·00 60

(*d*) *Surch with T 1 to 3* (1911–13)
29 **84** 30 pa. on 1½d. reddish purple and bright green (22.8.11) .. .. 6·50 55
a. Slate-purple and green .. 10·00 2·25
b. Surch double, one albino .. 50·00
30 **89** 2 pi. on 5d. dull reddish purple and bright blue (13.5.12) .. .. 9·50 1·50
a. Deep dull reddish purple and bright blue .. .. .. 11·00 2·25
31 **92** 4 pi. on 10d. dull purple & scar (26.6.12) 26·00 11·00
a. Dull reddish purple & aniline pink £150 70·00
b. Dull reddish purple and carmine 11·00 11·00
c. No cross on crown
32 **93** 5 pi. on 1s. green and carmine (1913) .. 23·00 5·50
a. Surch double, one albino .. £200
33 **94** 12 pi. on 2s. 6d. dull reddish pur (3.2.12) 50·00 38·00
a. Dull greyish purple .. .. 50·00 38·00
34 **95** 24 pi. on 5s. carmine (1913) .. .. 55·00 75·00
a. Surch double, one albino £225
29/34 .. .. *Set of* 6 £140 £110

1913 (Apr)–**14.** *Stamps of King George V, wmk Royal Cypher, surch as T 1 (30 pa.), 9 (1 pi.), 7 or 2 (4 and 5 pi.).*
35 **105** 30 pa. on 1½d. red-brown (4.13) .. 3·50 14·00
a. Surch double, one albino .. £100
36 **104** 1 pi. on 2½d. cobalt-blue (6.13) .. 4·75 10
a. Bright blue .. .. .. 3·75 15
37 **106** 1¼ pi. on 3d. dull reddish violet (9.13) .. 4·50 4·25
a. Violet .. .. 5·00 5·50
b. Surch double, one albino .. £300
38 1¾ pi. on 4d. deep grey-green (7.13) .. 3·00 6·00
a. Thin, pointed "4" in fraction .. 45·00 80·00
b. Grey-green .. .. .. 3·75 5·00
39 **108** 4 pi. on 10d. turquoise-blue (12.13) .. 7·50 17·00
40 5 pi. on 1s. bistre-brown (1.14) .. 40·00 60·00
35/40 .. .. *Set of* 6 55·00 90·00

II. BRITISH CURRENCY

Stamps overprinted "LEVANT" were for use on parcels, with the ½d. and 1d. principally used for printed paper and post cards. They replaced unoverprinted Great Britain stamps, Nos. Z58/64, Z160/74, Z208/9c and Z267/81, which had previously been used for these purposes.

From October 1907 the three lowest values were also used for certain other amended postal rates until Nos. 16/21 were introduced.

LEVANT
(L 1)

1905 (15 Aug)–**12.** *Stamps of King Edward VII optd with Type L 1.*

(*a*) *De La Rue ptgs*
L 1 **83** ½d. pale yellowish green .. .. 8·50 15
a. Yellowish green .. .. 8·50 15
L 2 1d. scarlet .. .. .. 6·00 15
a. Bright scarlet .. .. .. 6·00 90
L 3 **84** 1½d. dull purple and green .. .. 4·50 1·75
a. Chalk-surfaced paper. *Pale dull purple and green* .. .. 13·00 2·75
L 4 **85** 2d. grey-green and carmine-red .. 5·00 23·00
a. Chalk-surfaced paper. *Pale grey-green and carmine-red* .. 3·00 7·00
ab. Dull blue-green and carmine .. 3·00 8·00
L 5 **86** 2½d. ultramarine .. .. .. 8·50 20·00
L 6 **87** 3d. dull purple/*orange-yellow* .. 6·00 12·00
L 7 **88** 4d. green and grey-brown .. .. 8·00 35·00
a. Green and chocolate-brown .. 16·00 40·00
L 8 **89** 5d. dull purple and ultramarine .. 16·00 27·00
L 9 **83** 6d. pale dull purple .. .. 12·00 25·00
L10 **93** 1s. dull green and carmine .. 35·00 48·00
a. Chalk-surfaced paper .. .. 35·00 48·00
L1/10 .. .. .. *Set of* 10 90·00 £160

(*b*) *Harrison ptgs optd at Somerset House*
L11 **83** ½d. dull yellow-green (*p.* 14) (2.12) .. 25·00 22·00
a. Dull green .. .. .. 25·00 22·00
b. Deep dull green .. .. .. 30·00 25·00

On 28 December 1909 all values, except for the ½d. and 1d. were withdrawn from sale. A further consignment of the 2d, No. L 4*ab*, probably ordered in error was, however, received, and, as there was no requirement for this value, sold mainly to collectors. Subsequently dated cancellations on the withdrawn values are philatelic, being worth much less than the used prices quoted.

Distorted "N" (R. 2/10, 12/10)

1911–13. *Stamps of King George V optd with Type L 1 at Somerset House. (a) Die A. Wmk Crown.*
L12 **98** ½d. green (No. 322) (12.9.11) .. 1·00 1·00
a. Distorted "N" .. .. .. 20·00
L13 **99** 1d. carmine-red (No. 327) (1.1.12) .. 50 4·50
a. No cross on crown £150
b. Opt double, one albino £100
c. Distorted "N" .. .. .. 17·00

(*b*) *Redrawn types. Wmk Crown*
L14 **101** ½d. green (No. 339) (19.3.12) .. 50 20
a. Yellow-green .. .. .. 1·25 40
b. Distorted "N" .. .. .. 16·00
L15 **102** 1d. bright scarlet (No. 341) (24.2.12) 50 1·60
a. Scarlet (No. 342) .. .. 2·00 1·60
b. Opt triple, two albino .. .. 42·00
c. Distorted "N" .. .. .. 16·00

(*c*) *New types. Wmk Royal Cypher* (7.13)
L16 **105** ½d. green (No. 351) .. .. .. 30 1·00
a. Yellow-green .. .. .. 70 1·50
b. Distorted "N" .. .. .. 13·00
L17 **104** 1d. scarlet (No. 357) .. .. .. 30 4·25
a. Vermilion .. .. .. 7·00 9·00
b. Distorted "N" .. .. .. 13·00

Similar overprints were issued when the British Post Offices reopened in 1919, and are listed below.

B. BRITISH POST OFFICES IN CONSTANTINOPLE AND SMYRNA, 1919–1923

CONSTANTINOPLE

Following the occupation of Constantinople by Allied forces a British Military Post Office was opened for civilian use on 4 February 1919. During the period of its existence stamps of Great Britain with face values to 10s. were available and such use can be identified by the following cancellations:

"FIELD POST OFFICE H12" (4 February 1919 to 18 March 1919)
"ARMY POST OFFICE Y" (20 March 1919 to June 1920)
"ARMY POST OFFICE S.X.3" (March 1919 to April 1920)
"British A.P.O. CONSTANTINOPLE" (July 1919 to July 1920).

Of these four marks the first two types were also used for military mail.

The office reverted to civilian control on 29 July 1920, Nos. 41/50 and L18/24 being intended for its use.

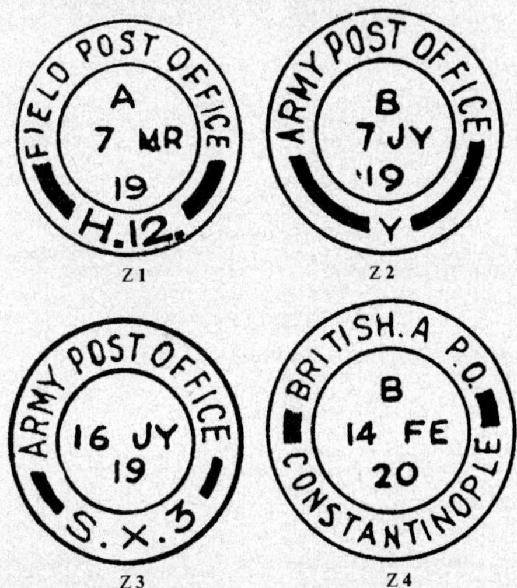

Z 1 Z 2 Z 3 Z 4

1919–20. *Used at the Army Post Office. Stamps of* GREAT BRITAIN *cancelled with Types* Z 1, Z 2, Z 3, Z 4.
Z176 ½d. green .. .. 2·00
Z177 1d. scarlet .. .. 2·00
Z178 1½d. brown .. .. 3·25
Z179 2d. orange (Die I) .. .. .. 2·50
Z180 2½d. blue .. .. 4·00
Z181 4d. grey-green .. .. 8·50
Z182 6d. purple .. .. 4·50
Z183 9d. agate .. .. 22·00
Z184 1s. bistre .. .. 5·50
Z185 2s. 6d. brown .. .. 32·00
Z186 5s. rose-red .. .. 50·00
Z187 10s. dull grey-blue .. .. .. 90·00

1920–21. *Used at the Civilian Post Office. Stamps of* GREAT BRITAIN *cancelled with Type* 18 *or double-circle datestamp.*
Z188 ½d. green .. .. 2·00
Z189 1d. scarlet .. .. 2·00
Z190 1½d. brown .. .. 3·25
Z191 2d. orange (Die I) .. .. .. 2·50
Z192 2½d. blue .. .. 4·00
Z193 3d. violet .. .. 6·50
Z194 4d. grey-green .. .. 8·50
Z195 5d. brown .. .. 13·00
Z196 6d. purple .. .. 4·50
Z197 10d. turquoise-blue .. .. .. 22·00
Z198 1s. bistre .. .. 5·50
Z199 2s. 6d. brown .. .. 32·00
Z200 5s. rose-red .. .. 50·00
Z201 10s. dull grey-blue .. .. .. 90·00

PRICES FOR STAMPS ON COVER

Nos. 41/50	*from* × 2
Nos. L18/24	*from* × 5

Stamps of Great Britain surch at Somerset House

I. TURKISH CURRENCY

1½ PIASTRES (10) 15 PIASTRES (11)

18¾

Short hyphen bar (R. 4/12, 14/12.)

1921 (Aug). *Stamps of King George V, wmk Royal Cypher, surch as T* **1** *(30 pa.),* **10** *and* **11** *(15 and 18¾ pi.).*

41 **105** 30 pa. on ½d. green .. 75 11·00
a. *Yellow-green* .. 2·75 13·00
42 **104** 1½ pi. on 1d. bright scarlet .. 1·50 1·00
a. *Vermilion* .. 6·50 3·00
b. *Scarlet-vermilion* .. 6·00 3·75
43 3¾ pi. on 2½d. blue .. 1·25 25
a. *Dull Prussian blue* .. 24·00 2·75
44 **106** 4½ pi. on 3d. violet .. 2·00 3·75
a. *Bluish violet* .. 2·50 3·00
45 **107** 7½ pi. on 5d. brown .. 30 10
a. *Yellow-brown* .. 2·00 20
46 **108** 15 pi. on 10d. turquoise-blue .. 70 15
47 18¾ pi. on 1s. bistre-brown .. 4·25 3·75
a. Short hyphen bar .. 55·00
b. *Olive-bistre* .. 6·00 4·50
ba. Short hyphen bar .. 70·00

45 PIASTRES (12) 45

Joined figures (second stamp in each horiz row)

1921. *Stamps of King George V (Bradbury, Wilkinson printing) surch as T* **12**.

48 **109** 45 pi. on 2s. 6d. chocolate-brown .. 20·00 45·00
a. Joined figures .. 35·00 65·00
b. *Olive-brown* .. 50·00 60·00
ba. Joined figures .. 70·00 85·00
49 90 pi. on 5s. rose-red .. 25·00 30·00
a. Surch double, one albino .. £225
50 180 pi. on 10s. dull grey-blue .. 45·00 40·00
a. Surch double, one albino .. £225
41/50 .. *Set of* 10 90·00 £120
47s/50s Optd "Specimen" .. *Set of* 4 £250

II. BRITISH CURRENCY

1921. *Stamps of King George V optd as Type* L **1**.

L18 **106** 2d. reddish orange (Die I) .. 1·25 27·00
a. *Bright orange* .. 2·25 27·00
L19 3d. bluish violet .. 7·50 10·00
L20 4d. grey-green .. 5·00 13·00
L21 **107** 5d. yellow-brown .. 12·00 28·00
L22 6d. dull purple (*chalk-surfaced paper*) 24·00 42·00
a. *Reddish purple* .. 26·00 8·50
L23 **108** 1s. bistre-brown .. 13·00 8·50
a. *Olive-bistre* .. 13·00 8·50
s. Optd "Specimen" .. 65·00
L24 **109** 2s. 6d. chocolate-brown .. 38·00 85·00
a. *Olive-brown* .. 65·00 £120
s. Optd "Specimen" .. £130
L18/24 .. *Set of* 7 85·00 £160

On No. L24 the letters of the overprint are shorter, being only 3 mm high.

Nos. 41/50 and L18/24 were used at the Constantinople office only.

SMYRNA

When the office re-opened on 1 March 1919 existing stocks of surcharged or overprinted issues were utilised until they were exhausted in mid-1920. During this period examples of Nos. 24, 29*a*, 30*a*, 33*b*/7, 39/40, L4*b*, L14/17 are known with commercial postmarks. These stamps were supplemented and finally replaced in mid-1920 by ordinary stamps of Great Britain.

Stamps of GREAT BRITAIN *cancelled with circular postmark as Type* **18** *or with* "REGISTERED" *oval.*

Z282 ½d. green .. 2·50
Z283 1d. scarlet .. 2·50
Z284 1½d. brown .. 3·50
Z285 2d. orange (Die I) .. 3·00
Z286 2d. orange (Die II) .. 26·00
Z287 2½d. blue (*shades*) .. 5·00
Z288 2½d. dull Prussian blue .. £400
Z289 4d. grey-green .. 11·00
Z290 6d. purple .. 8·00
Z291 10d. turquoise-blue .. 29·00
Z292 1s. bistre .. 8·50
Z293 2s. 6d. brown .. 60·00
Z294 5s. rose-red .. 85·00
Z295 10s. dull grey-blue .. £140

NEW INFORMATION

The editor is always interested to correspond with people who have new information that will improve or correct the Catalogue.

C. BRITISH FIELD OFFICE IN SALONICA

These overprints were originally prepared for use by a civilian post office to be set up on Mt Athos, Northern Greece. When the project was abandoned they were placed on sale at the Army Field Office in Salonica.

PRICES FOR STAMPS ON COVER
Nos. S1/8 *from* × 8

Levant (S 1)

1916 (end Feb–9 Mar). *Stamps of Gt. Britain, optd with Type* S **1** *by Army Printing Office, Salonica.*

S 1 **105** ½d. green .. 38·00 £180
a. Opt double .. £1800 £2250
b. Vert pair, one without opt .. £900 £1200
S 2 **104** 1d. scarlet .. 38·00 £180
a. Opt double .. £1200 £1500
S 3 **106** 2d. reddish orange (Die I) .. £120 £300
S 4 3d. bluish violet .. 90·00 £300
a. Opt double ..
S 5 4d. grey-green .. £120 £300
S 6 **107** 6d. reddish pur (*chalk-surfaced paper*) 70·00 £250
a. Vert pair, one without opt .. £1000 £1400
S 7 **108** 9d. agate .. £275 £500
a. Opt double .. £8000 £6500
S 8 1s. bistre-brown .. £225 £450
S1/8 .. *Set of* 8 £850 £2000

There are numerous forgeries of this overprint.

All values can be found with an additional albino overprint, inverted on the gummed side.

British New Guinea
see New Guinea
after Australia

British Occupation of Iraq
see Iraq

British Occupation of Italian Colonies

PRICES FOR STAMPS ON COVER TO 1945
Nos. M1/21 *from* × 4
Nos. MD1/5 *from* × 10
Nos. S1/9 *from* × 4
The above prices refer to covers from the territor concerned, not examples used in Great Britain.

MIDDLE EAST FORCES

For use in territory occupied by British Forces in Er (1942), Italian Somaliland (from 13 April 1942), Cyren (1943), Tripolitania (1943), and some of the Dodecanese Isl (1945).

PRICES. Our prices for used stamps with "M.E.F." overpr are for specimens with identifiable postmarks of the territo in which they were issued. These stamps were also used in United Kingdom with official sanction, from the summer of 1 onwards, and with U.K. postmarks are worth considerably

PRINTERS. Considerable research has been undertake discover the origins of Nos. M1/10. It is now suggested that M1/5, previously assigned to Harrison and Sons, were prod by the Army Printing Services, Cairo, and that the sma printing, Nos. M6/10, previously identified as the work of Army Printing Services, Cairo, was from an unidentified pri within the Middle East Forces area.

M.E.F. (M 1) M.E.F (M 2)

Opt. 14 mm long. Regular lettering and upright oblong stops.

Opt. 13½ mm long. Reg lettering and square st

M.E.F. (M 2*a*)

Opt. 13½ mm long. Rough lettering and round stops.

(*Illustrations twice actual size*)

M.E.F.

Sliced "M" (R.6/10)

1942 (2 Mar). *Stamps of Great Britain optd.* W **127**. *P* 15 × 14.

(*a*) *With Type* M **1**

M 1 **128** 1d. scarlet (No. 463) .. 80 1
a. Sliced "M" .. 55·00
M 2 2d. orange (No. 465) .. 30 2
a. Sliced "M" .. 35·00
M 3 2½d. ultramarine (No. 466) .. 30
a. Sliced "M" .. 35·00
M 4 3d. violet (No. 467) .. 30
M 5 **129** 5d. brown .. 30
a. Sliced "M" .. 35·00

(*b*) *With Type* M **2**

M 6 **128** 1d. scarlet (No. 463) .. 55·00 12
a. Optd with Type M 2*a* .. 45·00 8
b. Nos. M6/a *se-tenant* vert .. £200 80
M 7 2d. orange (No. 465) .. 75·00 85
a. Optd with Type M 2*a* .. 65·00 75
b. Nos. M7/a *se-tenant* vert .. £325 £2
M 8 2½d. ultramarine (No. 466) .. 40·00 7
a. Optd with Type M 2*a* .. 38·00 5
b. Nos. M8/a *se-tenant* vert .. £180 60
M 9 3d. violet (No. 467) .. £110 30
a. Optd with Type M 2*a* .. £100 28
ab. Opt double .. † £22
b. Nos. M9/a *se-tenant* vert .. £425 £1
M10 **129** 5d. brown .. £400 90
a. Optd with Type M 2*a* .. £375 80
b. Nos. M10/a *se-tenant* vert .. £1200 £6

See note after No. M21.

Nos. M6/10 were issued in panes of 60 (6 × 10), rows 2, 3, an being overprinted with Type M **2** and the other seven rows wi Type M 2*a*.

M.E.F. (M 3)

Optd 13½ mm long. Regular lettering and upright oblong stops.

(*Illustration twice actual size*)

; (1 Jan)–**1947.** *Stamps of Great Britain optd with Type* M 3 *Harrison & Sons. W* **127**, *P* 15 × 14 (*1d. to* 1*s.*); *W* **133**, *P* 14 *hers*).

128 1d. pale scarlet (No. 486) .. .. 1·50 10
2d. pale orange (No. 488) .. .. 1·50 1·25
2½d. light ultramarine (No. 489) .. 45 10
3d. pale violet (No. 490) .. .. 1·50 10
129 5d. brown .. .. .. 2·50 10
6d. purple 40 10
130 9d. deep olive-green 85 10
1s. bistre-brown 50 10
131 2s. 6d. yellow-green .. .. .. 7·00 1·00
5s. red (1947) .. .. .. 11·00 17·00
132 10s. ultramarine (1947) .. .. 14·00 10·00
/21 .. .. .. *Set of* 11 35·00 27·00
s/21s Optd "Specimen" .. *Set of* 4 £500

ne overprint on No. M15 should not be confused with the other prints on the 5d. value. It can be distinguished from No. M5 by ½ mm difference in length; and from No. M10 by the more nse colour, thicker lettering and larger stops.

POSTAGE DUE STAMPS

M.E.F.

(MD 1)

2. *Postage Due stamps of Great Britain Nos.* D27/30 *and* 33 *optd with Type* MD 1, *in blue-black.*

1 **D 1** ½d. emerald .. .. .. 30 10·00
2 1d. carmine .. .. .. 30 1·75
3 2d. agate .. .. .. 1·25 1·25
4 3d. violet .. .. .. 50 4·25
5 1s. deep blue .. .. .. 3·25 11·00
s. Optd "Specimen" £150
1/5 .. .. .. *Set of* 5 5·00 25·00

CYRENAICA

n June 1949 the British authorities recognised the leader of the ussi, Amir Mohammed Idris Al-Senussi, as Amir of Cyrenaica n autonomy in internal affairs.

(Currency. 10 millièmes = 1 piastre, 100 piastres = 1 Egyptian pound)

24 Mounted Warrior **25**

(Recess Waterlow)

50 (16 Jan). *P* 12½.

6 **24** 1 m brown .. .. .. 1·25 2·75
7 2 m. carmine .. .. .. 1·50 2·75
8 3 m. orange-yellow .. .. .. 1·50 2·75
9 4 m. blue-green .. .. .. 1·50 3·25
0 5 m. grey-black .. .. .. 1·25 1·25
1 8 m. orange .. .. .. 1·50 1·50
2 10 m. violet .. .. .. 1·50 1·25
3 12 m. scarlet .. .. .. 1·50 1·00
4 20 m. blue .. .. .. 1·50 1·00
5 **25** 50 m. ultramarine and purple-brown .. 2·50 3·00
6 100 m. carmine and black .. .. 6·50 9·00
7 200 m. violet and deep blue .. .. 11·00 25·00
8 500 m. orange-yellow and green .. 42·00 65·00
6/148 .. .. .. *Set of* 13 65·00 £110

POSTAGE DUE STAMPS

D 26

(Recess Waterlow)

950 (16 Jan). *P* 12½

149 **D 26** 2 m. brown .. .. .. 45·00 95·00
150 4 m. blue-green .. .. .. 45·00 95·00
151 8 m. scarlet .. .. .. 45·00 £100
152 10 m. orange .. .. .. 45·00 £100
153 20 m. orange-yellow .. .. .. 45·00 £110
154 40 m. blue .. .. .. 45·00 £130
155 100 m. grey-brown .. .. .. 45·00 £140
149/155 .. .. .. *Set of* 7 £275 £700

On 24 December 1951 Cyrenaica united with Tripolitania, ezzan and Ghadames to form the independent Kingdom of Libya, hose issues are listed in Part 13 (*Africa since Independence —M*) of this catalogue.

PRICES OF SETS

Set prices are given for many issues, generally those containing three stamps or more. Definitive sets include one of each value or major colour change, but do not cover different perforations, die types or minor shades. Where a choice is possible the set prices are based on the cheapest versions of the stamps included in the listings.

ERITREA

From early 1950 examples of Nos. E1/32 exist precancelled in manuscript by a black or blue horizontal line for use by British troops on concession rate mail.

BRITISH MILITARY ADMINISTRATION

(Currency. 100 cents = 1 shilling)

B. M. A. ERITREA 10 CENTS (E 1)

B. M. A. ERITREA 5 SHILLINGS (E 2)

SH. 50 Normal **SH .50** Misplaced Stop

1948–9. *Stamps of Great Britain surch as Types* E 1 *or* E 2.

E 1 **128** 5 c. on ½d. pale green 60 65
E 2 10 c. on 1d. pale scarlet .. .. 75 2·50
E 3 20 c. on 2d. pale orange .. .. 50 2·25
E 4 25 c. on 2½d. light ultramarine .. 50 60
E 5 30 c. on 3d. pale violet .. .. 1·25 4·50
E 6 **129** 40 c. on 5d. brown .. .. 30 4·25
E 7 50 c. on 6d. purple .. .. 30 1·00
E 7*a* **130** 65 c. on 8d. bright carmine (1.2.49) .. 7·00 2·00
E 8 75 c. on 9d. deep olive-green 50 75
E 9 1 s. on 1s. bistre-brown 50 50
E10 **131** 2 s. 50 c. on 2s. 6d. yellow-green .. 7·00 10·00
a. Misplaced stop (R. 4/7) .. .. 90·00 £120
E11 5 s. on 5s. red .. .. 7·00 16·00
E12 **132** 10 s. on 10s. ultramarine .. .. 20·00 22·00
E1/12 .. .. .. *Set of* 13 42·00 60·00

BRITISH ADMINISTRATION

1950 (6 Feb). *As Nos.* E1/12, *but surch* "B.A. ERITREA" *and new values instead of* "B.M.A." *etc.*

E13 **128** 5 c. on ½d. pale green .. .. 65 7·00
E14 10 c. on 1d. pale scarlet .. .. 30 2·75
E15 20 c. on 2d. pale orange 30 70
E16 25 c. on 2½d. light ultramarine .. 30 60
E17 30 c. on 3d. pale violet .. .. 30 1·75
E18 **129** 40 c. on 5d. brown .. .. 40 1·50
E19 50 c. on 6d. purple 30 20
E20 **130** 65 c. on 8d. bright carmine .. .. 1·25 1·50
E21 75 c. on 9d. deep olive-green 30 25
E22 1 s. on 1s. bistre-brown 30 15
E23 **131** 2 s. 50 c. on 2s. 6d. yellow-green .. 4·50 4·75
E24 5 s. on 5s. red .. .. 6·00 10·00
E25 **132** 10 s. on 10s. ultramarine .. .. 55·00 55·00
E13/25 .. .. .. *Set of* 13 60·00 70·00

1951 (28 May*). *Nos.* 503/4, 506/7 *and* 509/11 *of Great Britain surch* "B.A. ERITREA" *and new values.*

E26 **128** 5 c. on ½d. pale orange 30 60
E27 10 c. on 1d. light ultramarine 30 60
E28 20 c. on 2d. pale red-brown 30 30
E29 25 c. on 2½d. pale scarlet 30 30
E30 **147** 2 s. 50 c. on 2s. 6d. yellow-green .. 7·50 21·00
E31 **148** 5 s. on 5s. red .. .. 21·00 21·00
E32 10 s. on 10s. ultramarine .. .. 21·00 21·00
E26/32 .. .. .. *Set of* 7 45·00 60·00

*This is the local release date. The stamps were placed on sale in London on 3 May.

POSTAGE DUE STAMPS

B. M. A. ERITREA 10 CENTS

(ED 1)

1948. *Postage Due stamps of Great Britain Nos.* D27/30 *and* D33 *surch as Type* ED 1.

ED1 **D 1** 5 c. on ½d. emerald .. .. 9·50 20·00
ED2 10 c. on 1d. carmine .. .. 9·50 22·00
a. No stop after "B" £110
ED3 20 c. on 2d. agate .. .. 7·00 15·00
a. No stop after "A" .. .. 60·00
b. No stop after "B" (R. 1/9) .. £120
ED4 30 c. on 3d. violet .. .. 9·50 14·00
ED5 1 s. on 1s. deep blue .. .. 17·00 28·00
ED1/5 .. .. .. *Set of* 5 48·00 90·00

1950 (6 Feb). *As Nos.* ED1/5, *but surch* "B.A. ERITREA" *and new values instead of* "B.M.A." *etc.*

ED6 **D 1** 5 c. on ½d. emerald .. .. 11·00 45·00
ED7 10 c. on 1d. carmine .. .. 9·00 15·00
a. "C" of "CENTS" omitted .. £1800
ab. "C" omitted and vertical oblong for "E" of "CENTS" .. £3250
ED8 20 c. on 2d. agate .. .. 9·50 13·00
ED9 30 c. on 3d. violet .. .. 11·00 17·00
w. Wmk sideways-inverted* .. — 55·00
ED10 1 s. on 1s. deep blue .. .. 15·00 22·00
a. Stop after "A" omitted (R. 2/13) £275
ED6/10 .. .. .. *Set of* 5 50·00 £100

No. ED7a, and probably No. ED7ab, occurred on R.7/17, but the error was quickly corrected.

*No. ED9w shows the Crowns pointing to the left, *as seen from the back of the stamp.*

Stamps of Ethiopia were used in Eritrea after 15 September 1952 following federation with Ethiopia.

SOMALIA

BRITISH OCCUPATION

E.A.F.

(S 1. "East Africa Forces")

1943 (15 Jan)–**46.** *Stamps of Great Britain optd with Type* S 1, *in blue.*

S1 **128** 1d. pale scarlet 60 40
S2 2d. pale orange .. .. .. 1·50 1·25
S3 2½d. light ultramarine .. .. 30 3·50
S4 3d. pale violet 50 15
S5 **129** 5d. brown 50 40
S6 6d. purple 30 90
S7 **130** 9d. deep olive-green .. .. 80 2·25
S8 1s. bistre-brown .. .. .. 1·50 15
S9 **131** 2s. 6d. yellow-green (1946) .. 7·50 6·50
S1/9 .. .. .. *Set of* 9 12·00 14·00
S8s/9s Optd "Specimen" .. *Set of* 2 £250

The note *re* used prices above Type M 1 of Middle East Forces also applies to the above issue.

BRITISH MILITARY ADMINISTRATION

(Currency. 100 cents = 1 shilling)

1948 (27 May). *Stamps of Great Britain surch* "B.M.A./ SOMALIA" *and new values, as Types* E 1 *and* E 2 *of Eritrea.*

S10 **128** 5 c. on ½d. pale green .. .. 1·00 1·75
S11 15 c. on 1½d. pale red-brown .. .. 1·50 14·00
S12 20 c. on 2d. pale orange .. .. 2·50 4·00
S13 25 c. on 2½d. light ultramarine .. 2·25 4·50
S14 30 c. on 3d. pale violet .. .. 2·25 9·00
S15 **129** 40 c. on 5d. brown 85 20
S16 50 c. on 6d. purple .. .. 50 2·00
S17 **130** 75 c. on 9d. deep olive-green .. .. 2·00 17·00
S18 1 s. on 1s. bistre-brown .. .. 1·25 20
S19 **131** 2 s. 50 c. on 2s. 6d. yellow-green .. 3·75 25·00
a. Misplaced stop (R. 4/7) .. .. 85·00 £250
S20 5 s. on 5s. red .. .. 8·50 35·00
S10/20 .. .. .. *Set of* 11 23·00 £100

For illustration of No. S19a, see previous column above No. E1 of Eritrea.

BRITISH ADMINISTRATION

1950 (2 Jan). *As Nos.* S10/20, *but surch* "B.A./SOMALIA" *and new values, instead of* "B.M.A." *etc.*

S21 **128** 5 c. on ½d. pale green .. .. 20 3·00
S22 15 c. on 1½d. pale red-brown .. .. 60 16·00
S23 20 c. on 2d. pale orange .. .. 60 6·50
S24 25 c. on 2½d. light ultramarine .. 50 7·00
S25 30 c. on 3d. pale violet .. .. 1·00 4·25
S26 **129** 40 c. on 5d. brown 55 85
S27 50 c. on 6d. purple .. .. 50 1·00
S28 **130** 75 c. on 9d. deep olive-green .. .. 1·25 6·50
S29 1 s. on 1s. bistre-brown .. .. 60 1·50
S30 **131** 2 s. 50 c. on 2s. 6d. yellow-green .. 4·00 24·00
S31 5 s. on 5s. red .. .. 9·50 29·00
S21/31 .. .. .. *Set of* 11 17·00 90·00

Somalia reverted to Italian Administration on 1 April 1950 later becoming independent. Later issues will be found listed in Part 8 (*Italy and Switzerland*) of this catalogue.

TRIPOLITANIA

BRITISH MILITARY ADMINISTRATION

(Currency. 100 centesimi = 1 Military Administration lira)

4 M.A.L. Normal **4 M.A.L.** Misaligned surcharge (R.8/8, 18/8)

1948 (1 July). *Stamps of Great Britain surch* "B.M.A./TRIPOLITANIA" *and new values, as Types* E 1 *and* E 2 *of Eritrea, but expressed in M(ilitary) A(dministration) L(ire).*

T 1 **128** 1 l. on ½d. pale green .. .. 50 1·00
T 2 2 l. on 1d. pale scarlet 30 15
T 3 3 l. on 1½d. pale red-brown 30 50
a. Misaligned surch .. .. 23·00
T 4 4 l. on 2d. pale orange 30 50
a. Misaligned surch .. .. 25·00
T 5 5 l. on 2½d. light ultramarine .. 30 20
T 6 6 l. on 3d. pale violet 30 40
T 7 **129** 10 l. on 5d. brown 30 15
T 8 12 l. on 6d. purple 30 20
T 9 **130** 18 l. on 9d. deep olive-green 50 65
T10 24 l. on 1s. bistre-brown .. .. 50 1·00
T11 **131** 60 l. on 2s. 6d. yellow-green .. .. 2·50 7·50
T12 120 l. on 5s. red .. .. 13·00 16·00
T13 **132** 240 l. on 10s. ultramarine .. .. 20·00 90·00
T1/13 .. .. .. *Set of* 13 35·00 £110

BRITISH ADMINISTRATION

1950 (6 Feb). *As Nos.* T1/13, *but surch.* "B.A. TRIPOLITANIA" *and new values, instead of* "B.M.A." *etc.*

T14 **128** 1 l. on ½d. pale green .. .. 1·50 11·00
T15 2 l. on 1d. pale scarlet .. .. 1·75 40
T16 3 l. on 1½d. pale red-brown .. .. 50 11·00
a. Misaligned surch .. .. 35·00
T17 4 l. on 2d. pale orange .. .. 40 4·50
a. Misaligned surch .. .. 27·00
T18 5 l. on 2½d. light ultramarine .. 30 70
T19 6 l. on 3d. pale violet .. .. 1·25 3·25
T20 **129** 10 l. on 5d. brown .. .. 30 4·00
T21 12 l. on 6d. purple .. .. 1·25 50

T22 **130** 18 l. on 9d. deep olive-green .. .. 1·50 2·50
T23 24 l. on 1s. bistre-brown .. .. .. 1·50 3·50
T24 **131** 60 l. on 2s. 6d. yellow-green .. .. 4·50 12·00
T25 120 l. on 5s. red .. .. 17·00 22·00
T26 **132** 240 l. on 10s. ultramarine .. .. 28·00 60·00
T14/26 .. .. *Set of* 13 50·00 £120

1951 (3 May). *Nos.* 503/7 *and* 509/11 *of Great Britain surch* "B.A. TRIPOLITANIA" *and new values.*

T27 **128** 1 l. on ½d. pale orange .. .. .. 20 5·00
T28 2 l. on 1d. light ultramarine 20 90
T29 3 l. on 1½d. pale green .. .. .. 30 7·50
T30 4 l. on 2d. pale red-brown .. .. 20 1·25
T31 5 l. on 2½d. pale scarlet .. .. 30 7·50
T32 **147** 60 l. on 2s. 6d. yellow-green .. .. 4·50 20·00
T33 **148** 120 l. on 5s. red .. .. .. 8·00 26·00
T34 **149** 240 l. on 10s. ultramarine .. .. 35·00 42·00
T27/34 .. .. *Set of* 8 42·00 £100

POSTAGE DUE STAMPS

1948. *Postage Due stamps of Great Britain Nos.* D27/30 *and* D33 *surch.* "B.M.A./TRIPOLITANIA" *and new values, as Type* ED **1** *of Eritrea, but expressed in M(ilitary) A(dministration) L(ire).*

TD1 **D 1** 1 l. on ½d. emerald .. .. .. 5·50 48·00
a. No stop after "A" .. .. 65·00
TD2 2 l. on 1d. carmine .. .. .. 2·50 30·00
a. No stop after "A" .. .. 42·00
b. No stop after "M" (R.1/17) .. 80·00
TD3 4 l. on 2d. agate .. .. .. 7·50 28·00
a. No stop after "A" £120
b. No stop after "M" £150
TD4 6 l. on 3d. violet .. .. .. 7·50 20·00
TD5 24 l. on 1s. deep blue .. .. .. 28·00 £100
TD1/5 .. .. *Set of* 5 45·00 £200

1950 (6 Feb). *As Nos.* TD1/5, *but surch* "B.A. TRIPOLITANIA" *and new values, instead of* "B.M.A." *etc.*

TD 6 **D 1** 1 l. on ½d. emerald .. .. 12·00 80·00
a. No stop after "B" £120
TD 7 2 l. on 1d. carmine .. .. 2·50 27·00
a. No stop after "B" .. .. 65·00
TD 8 4 l. on 2d. agate .. .. 2·75 30·00
a. No stop after "B" .. .. 75·00
TD 9 6 l. on 3d. violet .. .. 18·00 60·00
a. No stop after "B" £190
w. Wmk sideways-inverted* .. 55·00
TD10 24 l. on 1s. deep blue .. .. 48·00 £140
a. No stop after "A" £375
b. No stop after "B" £375
TD6/10 .. .. *Set of* 5 75·00 £300

*No. TD9w shows the Crowns pointing to the left, *as seen from the back of the stamp.*

Tripolitania became part of the independent kingdom of Libya on 24 December 1951.

British P.Os in Crete

BRITISH ADMINISTRATION OF CANDIA PROVINCE (HERAKLEION)

Crete, formerly part of the Turkish Empire, was made autonomous, under Turkish suzerainty, in November 1898 with British, French, Italian and Russian troops stationed in separate zones to keep the peace.

Overseas mail franked with Nos. B1/5 was forwarded through the Austrian post office at Canea, being additionally franked with stamps of the Austro-Hungarian Post Offices in the Turkish Empire.

(Currency. 40 paras = 1 piastre)

PRICES FOR STAMPS ON COVER	
No. B1	*from* × 10
Nos. B2/5	—

B 1

B 2

1898 (25 Nov). *Handstruck locally. Imperf.*

B1 **B 1** 20 pa. bright violet £425 £225

1898 (3 Dec). *Litho by M. Grundmann, Athens. P* 11½.

B2 **B 2** 10 pa. blue .. .. 8·00 17·00
a. Imperf (pair) £250
B3 20 pa. green .. .. 12·00 15·00
a. Imperf (pair) £250

1899. *P* 11½.

B4 **B 2** 10 pa. brown .. .. 8·00 24·00
a. Imperf (pair) £250
B5 20 pa. rose .. .. 17·00 15·00
a. Imperf (pair) £250

The British postal service closed at the end of 1899.

British P.O. in Siam

(Bangkok)

An overseas postal service for foreign residents was operated by the British Consulate at Bangkok from 1858. Mail was despatched by steamer to Singapore and from 1876 onwards was increasingly franked with Straits Settlements stamps. These were initially cancelled on arrival at Singapore, but later an oval postmark inscribed "BRITISH CONSULATE BANGKOK" was used. In 1883 a circular "BANGKOK" datestamp was introduced for use with Nos. 1/23. Both cancellations can also be found used on Hong Kong stamps between 1881 and 1885.

(Currency. 100 cents = 1 Straits dollar)

Stamps of Straits Settlements (see Malaysia) cancelled with oval postmark inscribed "BRITISH CONSULATE BANGKOK" *around Royal Arms.*

1877 *to* **1882.** *Wmk Crown CC* (*Nos.* 11/15, 33 *and* 35).

Z1 2 c. brown £350
Z2 4 c. rose £350
Z3 6 c. dull lilac £400
Z4 8 c. orange-yellow £350
Z5 10 c. on 30 c. claret (thin "0") (No. 33) £1000
Z6 10 c. on 30 c. claret (thick "10") (No. 34) £1000
Z7 10 c. on 30 c. claret (thin "1", thick "0".) (No. 35) £1100
Z8 12 c. blue £450

Subsequent Straits Settlements values to 8 c. watermarked Crown CA are known used at Bangkok in 1883 and 1884. During this period the stamps overprinted "B" were on sale at the British Post Office.

PRICES FOR STAMPS ON COVER
The issues of the British Post Offices in Siam are worth from × 100 the prices quoted for used stamps when on cover.

(1)

1882 (May)–**85.** *Stamps of Straits Settlements optd with T* **1.**

(*a*) *On No.* 9 *of* 1867

1 32 c. on 2 a. yellow (1885) £35000

(*b*) *On Nos.* 11/13, 14*a*, 15/17 *and* 19 *of* 1867–72 *and Nos.* 48/9 *of* 1882. *Wmk Crown CC*

2 2 c. brown £2750 £1400
3 4 c. rose £2250 £1100
a. Opt double .. .. – £7500
4 5 c. purple-brown £275 £300
5 6 c. lilac £200 £110
6 8 c. orange £1900 £200
7 10 c. slate £350 £150
8 12 c. blue £900 £475
9 24 c. green £700 £150
10 30 c. claret £30000 £20000
11 96 c. grey £5000 £2750

(*c*) *On Nos.* 59/60 *of April* 1883

12 2 c. on 32 c. pale red (*Wide* "S") .. £2000 £
13 2 c. on 32 c. pale red (*Wide* "E") .. £2500 £

(*d*) *On Nos.* 50/3 *of* 1882 *and Nos.* 63/7 *of* 1883–84. *W Crown CA*

14 2 c. brown £475
15 2 c. pale rose (1883) .. .. .. 55·00 4
a. Opt inverted .. .. .. — £
b. Opt double £2750 £2
c. Opt treble £10000
16 4 c. rose (1883) .. .. £500 £
17 4 c. pale brown (1883) .. .. .. 75·00 7
a. Opt double £3500
b. Broken oval £1100 £1
18 5 c. blue (1884) .. .. £225 £
19 6 c. lilac (1884) .. .. £160 £
20 8 c. orange (1883) £140 6
a. Opt inverted £17000 £10
21 10 c. slate (1883) £150 8
22 12 c. brown-purple (1883) .. .. £275 £
23 24 c. yellow-green (1884?) £4000 £2

The prices quoted for the overprint double errors, Nos. 3a, and 17a, are for stamps showing two clear impressions of overprint. Examples showing partial doubling, on these other values, are worth a small premium over the price quo for normal stamps.

No. 17b shows the edge of the central oval broken above "O" of "POSTAGE". It occurs on R. 10/5 of the lower right pa

The use of these stamps ceased on 30 June 1885. Siam joi the Universal Postal Union on 1 July 1885.

British Postal Agencies in Eastern Arabia

Certain Arab States in Eastern Arabia, whilst remaining in pendent, had British postal administrations.

Bahrain and Kuwait (from 1948) and Qatar (from 1957) u British stamps overprinted and surcharged in local currency. Dhabi (from 1964) and Trucial States (from 1961 and used only Dubai) had definitive issues made under the auspices of the Brit Agencies.

In addition, British stamps were surcharged with value only use in Muscat and certain other states. They were formerly lis under Muscat as they were first put on sale there, but in view their more extended use, the list has been transferred he retaining the same numbering.

The stamps were used in Muscat from 1 April 1948 to 29 A 1966; in Dubai from 1 April 1948 to 6 January 1961; in Qatar: D from August 1950, Umm Said from February 1956, to 31 Ma 1957; and in Abu Dhabi from 30 March 1963 (Das Island fr December 1960) to 29 March 1964.

Nos. 21/2 were placed on sale in Kuwait Post Offices in Ap and May 1951 and from February to November 1953 due shortages of stamps with "KUWAIT" overprint. Isola examples of other values can be found commercially used fr Bahrain or Kuwait.

(Currency. 12 pies = 1 anna; 16 annas = 1 rupee)

Stamps of Great Britain surcharged

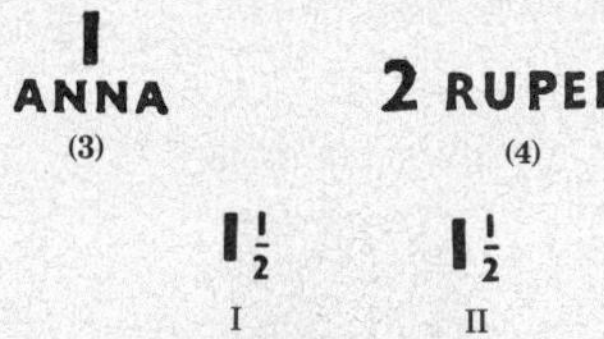

(3) (4)

1½ 1½
I II

Two types of 1½ a. surcharge:
I. "1" 3¼ mm high and aligns with top of "2" in "½" (Rows 1 to 10).
II. "1" 3½ mm high with foot of figure below top of "2" (Rows 11 to 20).

1948 (1 Apr). *Surch with T* **3** (½ *a. to* 1 *r.*) *or* **4** (2 *r.*).

16 **128** ½ a. on ½d. pale green .. .. 2·75 6·
17 1 a. on 1d. pale scarlet .. .. 2·75
18 1½ a. on 1½d. pale red-brown (I) .. 7·00 2·0
a. Type II .. .. 7·00 2·0
b. Vert pair. Nos. 18/a .. .. 38·00
19 2 a. on 2d. pale orange .. .. 1·75 2·2
20 2½ a. on 2½d. light ultramarine .. 3·00 5·
21 3 a. on 3d. pale violet .. .. .. 3·00
22 **129** 6 a. on 6d. purple .. .. .. 3·00
23 **130** 1 r. on 1s. bistre-brown .. .. 3·50
24 **131** 2 r. on 2s. 6d. yellow-green .. .. 8·50 32·0
16/24 .. .. *Set of* 9 32·00 45·0

One example of No. 22 is known with the surcharge almo completely omitted from position R. 20/2 in the sheet.

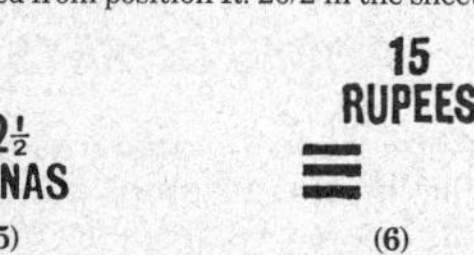

(5) (6)

1948 (26 Apr). *Royal Silver Wedding. Nos.* 493/4 *surch with T or* **6**.

25 **137** 2½ a. on 2½d. ultramarine .. .. 2·00 2·0
26 **138** 15 r. on £1 blue .. .. 23·00 35·0

29 July). *Olympic Games. Nos. 495/8 surch with new values ANNAS" or "1 RUPEE", as T 5/6, but in one line on 2½ a. t) or 6 a. and 1 r. (horiz) and grills obliterating former values ll except 2½ a.*

.39 2½ a. on 2½d. ultramarine .. .. 35 2·00
.40 3 a. on 3d. violet .. .. 45 2·00
.41 6 a. on 6d. bright purple .. .. 45 2·00
.42 1 r. on 1s. brown .. .. 1·25 2·25
a. Surch double £800
.. .. *Set of* 4 2·25 7·50

(10 Oct). *75th Anniv of Universal Postal Union. Nos. 499/ surch with new values in "ANNAS" or "1 RUPEE" as T 3/4, all in one line, with grills obliterating former values.*

.43 2½ a. on 2½d. ultramarine .. .. 50 2·50
.44 3 a. on 3d. violet .. .. 60 2·50
.45 6 a. on 6d. bright purple .. .. 60 1·75
.46 1 r. on 1s. brown .. .. 2·00 2·75
.. .. *Set of* 4 3·25 8·50

2 RUPEES (6*a*) **2 RUPEES** (6*b*)

6*a*. "2" and "RUPEES" level and in line with lower of the two bars.

6*b*. "2" raised in relation to "RUPEES" and whole surcharge below the lower bar.

(2 Oct)–**55**. *Nos. 503/8 surch as T* **3** *and No.* 509 *with 6a.*

28 ½ a. on ½d. pale orange (3.5.51) .. 30 9·00
1 a. on 1d. light ultramarine (3.5.51) .. 30 7·50
1½ a. on 1½d. pale green (I) (3.5.51) .. 7·00 22·00
a. Type II .. .. 7·00 22·00
b. Vert pair. Nos. 37/a .. .. 38·00
2 a. on 2d. pale red-brown (3.5.51) .. 30 8·50
2½ a. on 2½d. pale scarlet (3.5.51) .. 30 16·00
29 4 a. on 4d. light ultramarine .. .. 30 3·50
.47 2 r. on 2s. 6d. yellow-green (3.5.51) .. 24·00 7·00
a. Surch with Type 6*b* (1955) .. £150 65·00
.. .. *Set of* 7 29·00 65·00

British Solomon Islands

he first British Resident Commissioner, Charles Woodford, appointed in 1896 and a administrative centre established ulagi.

ail was initially sent unstamped by sealed bag to Sydney re New South Wales stamps were applied and cancelled. er the Resident Commissioner kept a stock of New South es stamps which were still not cancelled until arrival at ney. From April 1906 Mr. Woodford used a vertical oblong ITISH SOLOMON ISLANDS PAID" handstamp in place of v South Wales stamps which were then added to many of the ers by the postal authorities in Sydney.

PRICES FOR STAMPS ON COVER TO 1945

Nos. 1/7	*from* × 12
Nos. 8/17	*from* × 25
Nos. 18/36	*from* × 6
Nos. 37/8	—
Nos. 39/51	*from* × 6
No. 52	—
Nos. 53/6	*from* × 2
Nos. 57/9	*from* × 6
Nos. 60/72	*from* × 2
Nos. D1/8	*from* × 5

BRITISH PROTECTORATE

1

2

(Des C. M. Woodford. Litho W. E. Smith & Co, Sydney)

)7 (14 Feb). *No wmk. P* 11.

1 ½d. ultramarine .. .. .. 9·00 14·00
1d. rose-carmine .. .. .. 23·00 25·00
2d. indigo .. .. .. 28·00 30·00
a. Imperf between (horiz pair) .. £11000
2½d. orange-yellow .. .. .. 32·00 42·00
a. Imperf between (vert pair) £4000
b. Imperf between (horiz pair) .. £5500 £4250
5d. emerald-green .. .. .. 55·00 65·00
6d. chocolate .. .. .. 50·00 60·00
a. Imperf between (vert pair) £3750
1s. bright purple .. .. .. 70·00 75·00
.. .. *Set of* 7 £250 £275

Nos. 1/7 did not become valid for international postage until rly September 1907. Overseas covers before that date show ditional New South Wales values.

Three types exist of the ½d. and 2½d., and six each of the ner values, differing in minor details.

Forgeries of Nos. 1/7 show different perforations and have the at paddle touching the shore. Genuine stamps show a gap tween the paddle and the shore.

(Recess D.L.R.)

1908 (1 Nov)–**11**. *Wmk Mult Crown CA (sideways). P* 14.

8 **2** ½d. green .. .. 1·50 1·00
9 1d. red .. .. 1·25 1·00
10 2d. greyish slate .. .. .. 1·25 1·00
11 2½d. ultramarine .. .. .. 3·75 2·00
11*a* 4d. red/*yellow* (6.3.11) .. .. 3·25 11·00
12 5d. olive .. .. 8·50 7·00
13 6d. claret .. .. 10·00 6·50
14 1s. black/*green* .. .. .. 8·50 7·00
15 2s. purple/*blue* (7.3.10) .. .. 40·00 55·00
16 2s. 6d. red/*blue* (7.3.10) .. .. 48·00 70·00
17 5s. green/*yellow* (7.3.10) .. .. 75·00 £100
8/17 .. .. .. *Set of* 11 £170 £225
8s/17s Optd "Specimen" .. .. *Set of* 11 £250

The ½d. and 1d. were issued in 1913 on rather thinner paper and with brownish gum.

3

½d ½d POSTAGE REVENUE BRITISH SOLOMON ISLANDS
4

(T **3** and **4**. Typo D.L.R.)

1913. *Inscribed* "POSTAGE POSTAGE". *Wmk Mult Crown CA. P* 14.

18 **3** ½d. green (1.4) .. .. .. 80 3·50
19 1d. red (1.4) .. .. .. 80 14·00
20 3d. purple/*yellow* (27.2) .. .. 80 4·00
a. On orange-buff .. .. .. 7·00 24·00
21 11d. dull purple and scarlet (27.2) .. 3·00 12·00
18/21 .. .. .. *Set of* 4 4·75 30·00
18s/21s Optd "Specimen" .. *Set of* 4 70·00

1914 (Mar)–**23**. *Inscribed* "POSTAGE REVENUE". *Wmk Mult Crown CA. Chalk-surfaced paper* (3d. *to* £1). *P* 14.

22 **4** ½d. green .. .. 80 12·00
23 ½d. yellow-green (1917) .. .. 4·50 18·00
24 1d. carmine-red .. .. .. 1·50 1·25
25 1d. scarlet (1917) .. .. .. 4·75 6·50
26 2d. grey (7.14) .. .. .. 3·00 9·00
27 2½d. ultramarine (7.14) .. .. 2·00 5·00
28 3d. purple/*pale yellow* (3.23) .. 20·00 80·00
29 4d. black and red/*yellow* (7.14) .. 2·00 2·50
30 5d. dull purple and olive-green (7.14) .. 20·00 30·00
31 5d. brown-purple and olive-green (7.14) 20·00 30·00
32 6d. dull and bright purple (7.14) .. 6·00 14·00
33 1s. black/*green* (7.14) .. .. 4·75 7·00
a. On blue-green, olive back (1923) .. 7·50 24·00
34 2s. purple and blue/*blue* (7.14) .. 7·00 10·00
35 2s. 6d. black and red/*blue* (7.14) .. 9·50 20·00
36 5s. green and red/*yellow* (7.14) .. 27·00 48·00
a. On orange-buff (1920) .. .. 45·00 70·00
37 10s. green and red/*green* (7.14) .. 75·00 80·00
38 £1 purple and black/*red* (7.14) .. £225 £120
22/38 .. .. .. *Set of* 14 £350 £400
22s/38s Optd "Specimen" .. *Set of* 14 £400

Variations in the coloured papers are mostly due to climate and do not indicate separate printings.

1922–31. *Wmk Mult Script CA. Chalk-surfaced paper* (4*d. and* 5*d. to* 10*s.*). *P* 14.

39 **4** ½d. green (10.22) .. .. .. 30 3·50
40 1d. scarlet (4.23) .. .. .. 11·00 11·00
41 1d. dull violet (2.27) .. .. .. 1·00 7·50
42 **3** 1½d. bright scarlet (7.24) .. .. 2·25 60
43 **4** 2d. slate-grey (4.23) .. .. .. 3·75 15·00
44 3d. pale ultramarine (11.23) .. .. 70 4·50
45 4d. black and red/*yellow* (7.27) .. 3·50 23·00
45*a* 4½d. red-brown (1931) .. .. 3·00 20·00
46 5d. dull purple and olive-green (12.27) 3·00 27·00
47 6d. dull and bright purple (12.27) .. 3·75 27·00
48 1s. black/*emerald* (12.27) .. .. 2·75 12·00
49 2s. purple and blue/*blue* (2.27) .. 8·00 35·00
50 2s. 6d. black and red/*blue* (12.27) .. 7·50 38·00
51 5s. green and red/*pale yellow* (12.27) .. 26·00 55·00
52 10s. green and red/*emerald* (1.25) .. 90·00 95·00
39/52 .. .. .. *Set of* 15 £150 £325
39s/52s Optd or Perf (4½d.) "Specimen" *Set of* 15 £300

1935 (6 May). *Silver Jubilee. As Nos.* 91/4 *of Antigua. P* 13½×14.

53 1½d. deep blue and carmine .. .. 1·00 1·00
f. Diagonal line by turret .. .. 50·00
h. Dot by flagstaff .. .. .. 90·00
54 3d. brown and deep blue .. .. 3·00 6·00
f. Diagonal line by turret .. .. 90·00
h. Dot by flagstaff £170
55 6d. light blue and olive-green .. .. 9·00 12·00
a. Frame printed double, one albino
b. Frame printed triple, two albino .. £1200
h. Dot by flagstaff £250
i. Dash by turret £250
56 1s. slate and purple .. .. .. 7·50 10·00
a. Frame printed double, one albino .. £1500
f. Diagonal line by turret £180
h. Dot by flagstaff £250
i. Dash by turret £250
53/6 .. .. .. *Set of* 4 18·00 26·00
53s/6s Perf "Specimen" .. .. *Set of* 4 90·00

The second albino impression on No. 55b is sometimes almost co-incidental with the inked impression of the frame.

For illustrations of plate varieties see Omnibus section following Zanzibar.

1937 (13 May). *Coronation. As Nos.* 95/7 *of Antigua. P* 11×11½.

57 1d. violet 30 70
58 1½d. carmine 30 60
59 3d. blue 50 50
57/9 .. .. .. *Set of* 3 1·00 1·60
57s/9s Perf "Specimen" .. .. *Set of* 3 60·00

5 Spears and Shield

6 Native Constable and Chief

7 Canoe House

8 Roviana Canoe

(Recess D.L.R. (2d., 3d., 2s. and 2s. 6d.), Waterlow (others))

1939 (1 Feb)–**1951**. *T* 5/8 *and similar designs. Wmk Mult Script CA. P* 13½ (2*d.*, 3*d.*, 2*s. and* 2*s.* 6*d.*) *or* 12½ (*others*).

60 ½d. blue and blue-green .. .. .. 15 1·00
61 1d. brown and deep violet .. .. 30 1·25
62 1½d. blue-green and carmine .. .. 70 1·25
63 2d. orange-brown and black .. .. 80 1·50
a. Perf 12 (7.11.51) .. .. .. 30 1·50
64 2½d. magenta and sage-green .. .. 1·75 1·75
a. Imperf horiz (vert pair) £9000
65 3d. black and ultramarine .. .. 1·00 1·50
a. Perf 12 (29.11.51) .. .. .. 1·50 2·50
66 4½d. green and chocolate .. .. 4·00 13·00
67 6d. deep violet and reddish purple .. 75 1·00
68 1s. green and black .. .. .. 1·25 1·00
69 2s. black and orange .. .. .. 6·50 5·50
70 2s. 6d. black and violet .. .. 26·00 4·50
71 5s. emerald-green and scarlet .. .. 32·00 9·50
72 10s. sage-green and magenta (27.4.42) .. 4·00 8·50
60/72 .. .. .. *Set of* 13 70·00 45·00
60s/72s Perf "Specimen" .. *Set of* 13 £275

Designs: *Horiz* (*as T* 8)—1½d. Artificial Island, Malaita; 1s. Breadfruit; 5s. Malaita canoe. (*As T* 7)—3d. Roviana canoes; 2s. Tinakula volcano; 2s.6d. Common Scrub Hen. *Vert* (*as T* 6)—4½d., 10s. Native house, Reef Islands; 6d. Coconut plantation.

Examples of No. 64a from the first two rows of the only known sheet are perforated between stamp and top margin.

1946 (15 Oct). *Victory. As Nos.* 110/11 *of Antigua.*

73 1½d. carmine 15 80
74 3d. blue 15 10
73s/4s Perf "Specimen" .. .. *Set of* 2 55·00

Pocket handkerchief flaw (R. 1/6)

1949 (14 Mar). *Royal Silver Wedding. As Nos.* 112/13 *of Antigua.*

75 2d. black 50 50
a. Pocket handkerchief flaw .. .. 24·00
76 10s. magenta .. .. .. 10·00 8·00

1949 (10 Oct). *75th Anniv of U.P.U. As Nos.* 114/17 *of Antigua.*

77 2d. red-brown .. .. 50 1·00
78 3d. deep blue .. .. 2·25 1·00
79 5d. deep blue-green .. .. .. 50 1·40
80 1s. blue-black .. .. 50 1·00
77/80 .. .. .. *Set of* 4 3·25 4·00

POSTAGE DUE STAMPS

D 1

(Typo B.W.)

1940 (1 Sept). *Wmk Mult Script CA. P* 12.

D1 **D 1** 1d. emerald-green .. .. .. 6·50 7·00
D2 2d. scarlet .. .. 7·00 7·00
D3 3d. brown .. .. 7·00 11·00
D4 4d. blue .. .. 11·00 11·00
D5 5d. grey-green .. .. .. 12·00 21·00
D6 6d. purple .. .. 12·00 15·00
D7 1s. violet .. .. 15·00 26·00
D8 1s. 6d. turquoise-green .. .. 27·00 48·00
D1/8 .. .. .. *Set of* 8 85·00 £130
D1s/8s Perf "Specimen" .. .. *Set of* 8 £150

Brunei

Sultan Hashim Jalil-ul-alam Akamudin, 1885–1906

(Currency. 100 cents = 1 Straits, later Malayan and Brunei, dollar)

For many years the status of the 1895 issue remained uncertain to such an extent that the 1906 provisionals on Labuan were taken to be the first issue of Brunei.

The 1895 "Star and Crescent" design stamps were, from their first appearance, considered bogus or, at best, as an issue made purely for philatelic purposes. Research into the background of the events surrounding the set led to the publication, in 1933, of the original agreement between Sultan Hashim and J. C. Robertson dated 20 August 1894 which made clear that the stamps fulfilled a genuine postal purpose. Although Robertson and his partners intended to exploit the philatelic sales for their own benefit the agreement testifies, as does other evidence, to the use of the stamps by the Sultan for his postal service. As Brunei did not, at that time, belong to any local or international postal union the stamps were only valid within the state or on mail to Labuan or Sarawak. Items for further afield required franking with Labuan stamps in addition. Although most covers surviving are addressed to Robertson's associates enough commercial covers and cards exist to show that there was, indeed, a postal service.

PRICES FOR STAMPS ON COVER TO 1945

Nos. 1/10 are rare used on cover.
Nos. 11/22 *from* × 30
Nos. 23/33 *from* × 25
Nos. 34/50 *from* × 10
Nos. 51/9 *from* × 12
Nos. 60/78 *from* × 8

The Sarawak Government maintained a post office at the coal mining centre of Brooketon, and the stamps of SARAWAK were used there from 1893 until the office was handed over to Brunei in February 1907.

1 Star and Local Scene

(Litho in Glasgow)

1895 (22 July). *P* 13–13½.
1 **1** ½ c. brown .. .. 2·75 20·00
2 1 c. brown-lake .. .. 3·00 15·00
3 2 c. black .. .. 4·00 15·00
4 3 c. deep blue .. .. 3·50 14·00
5 5 c. deep blue-green .. .. 6·50 16·00
6 8 c. plum .. .. 6·50 26·00
7 10 c. orange-red .. .. 8·00 26·00
a. Imperf (pair) £1300
8 25 c. turquoise-green .. .. 60·00 75·00
9 50 c. yellow-green .. .. 18·00 90·00
10 $1 yellow-olive .. .. 20·00 £110
1/10 .. .. *Set of* 10 £120 £375

BRUNEI. BRUNEI.

BRUNEI. TWO CENTS. 25 CENTS.

(2) (3) (4)

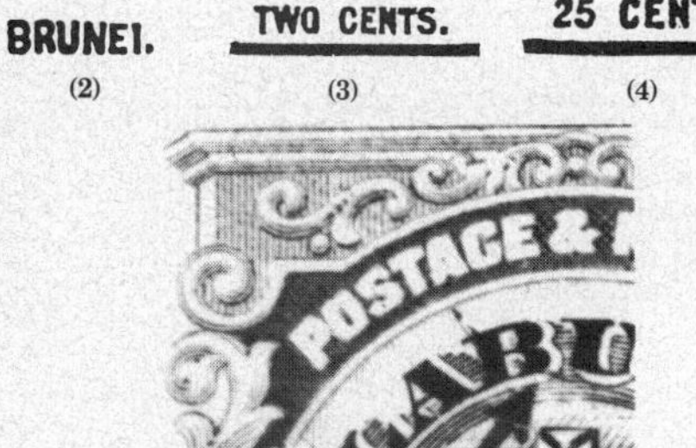

Line through "B" (R.5/10)

(Optd by Govt Printer, Singapore)

1906 (1 Oct). *Nos. 117/26 of Labuan (see North Borneo), optd with T* **2**, *or surch as T* **3** *or* **4** *(25 c.), in red. P* 13½ *or* 14 *(1 c.).*
11 1 c. black and purple .. .. .. 28·00 55·00
a. Error. Opt in black £1800 £2500
b. Line through "B" £350
c. Perf 13½–14, comp 12–13 .. ..
12 2 c. on 3 c. black and sepia .. .. .. 2·75 9·00
a. "BRUNEI" double £3750 £2500
b. "TWO CENTS" double £9000
c. Line through "B" £110
13 2 c. on 8 c. black and vermilion .. .. .. 27·00 80·00
a. "TWO CENTS" double £8500
b. "TWO CENTS" omitted (in vert pair with normal) £9500
c. Line through "B" £325
14 3 c. black and sepia .. .. .. 28·00 85·00
a. Line through "B" £325
15 4 c. on 12 c. black and yellow .. .. 3·75 5·00
a. Line through "B" £120
16 5 c. on 16 c. green and brown .. .. 45·00 75·00
a. Line through "B" £375
17 8 c. black and vermilion .. .. 9·00 32·00
a. Line through "B" £190
18 10 c. on 16 c. green and brown .. .. 6·50 22·00
a. Line through "B" £170
19 25 c. on 16 c. green and brown £100 £120
a. Line through "B" £700
20 30 c. on 16 c. green and brown .. .. 95·00 £120
a. Line through "B" £700
21 50 c. on 16 c. green and brown .. .. 95·00 £120
a. Line through "B" £700
22 $1 on 8 c. black and vermilion .. .. 95·00 £120
a. Line through "B" £700
11/22 .. .. *Set of* 12 £475 £750

Only one sheet of the 1 c. received the black overprint.

The surcharges were applied in settings of 50. Nos. 13a/b occur from one sheet on which the surcharge from the second impression of the setting was misplaced to give two surcharges on row five and none on row ten.

Examples of all values are known showing a forged Brunei postmark dated "13 JUL".

Sultan Mohamed Jemal-ul-Alam, 1906–1924

PRINTERS. All Brunei stamps from Nos. 23 to 113 were recess-printed by De La Rue.

5 View on Brunei River

1907 (26 Feb)–**09**. *Wmk Mult Crown CA. P* 14.
23 **5** 1 c. grey-black and pale green .. .. 2·25 11·00
x. Wmk reversed .. .. 15·00
24 2 c. grey-black and scarlet .. .. 2·50 4·50
x. Wmk reversed .. .. 32·00
25 3 c. grey-black and chocolate .. .. 10·00 22·00
x. Wmk reversed .. .. 35·00
26 4 c. grey-black and mauve .. .. 7·50 10·00
a. Grey-black and reddish purple (1909) 70·00 60·00
w. Wmk inverted .. ..
x. Wmk reversed .. .. 55·00
27 5 c. grey-black and blue .. .. 50·00 90·00
x. Wmk reversed .. .. 90·00
28 8 c. grey-black and orange .. .. 7·50 23·00
29 10 c. grey-black and deep green .. .. 4·50 7·00
30 25 c. pale blue and ochre-brown .. .. 32·00 48·00
31 30 c. violet and black .. .. 23·00 22·00
32 50 c. green and deep brown .. .. 15·00 22·00
33 $1 red and grey .. .. 60·00 90·00
23/33 .. .. .. *Set of* 11 £190 £300
23s/33s Optd "Specimen" .. *Set of* 11 £275

I

II

I Double plate. Lowest line of shading on water is dotted.
II Single plate. Dotted line of shading removed.

Stamps printed in two colours are as I.

1908 (12 June)–**22**. *Colours changed. Double or single plates. Wmk Mult Crown CA. P* 14.
34 **5** 1 c. green (I) .. .. .. 80 2·25
35 1 c. green (II) (1911) .. .. .. 60 2·00
a. "A" missing from wmk £200
b. "C" missing from wmk £200
36 2 c. black and brown (5.4.11) .. .. 3·00 1·25
w. Wmk inverted .. .. 55·00
37 3 c. scarlet (I) .. .. .. 3·00 1·25
a. Substituted crown in wmk £450
38 3 c. scarlet (II) (1916) .. .. 80·00 38·00
39 4 c. claret (II) (17.4.12) .. .. 3·00 75
40 5 c. black and orange (1916) .. .. 7·00 7·00
41 8 c. blue and indigo-blue (10.08) .. .. 7·00 11·00
42 10 c. purple/*yellow* (II) (11.12) .. .. 2·00 1·75
a. On pale yellow (1922) .. .. 1·25 4·00
as. Optd "Specimen" .. .. 45·00
w. Wmk inverted .. .. 95·00
x. Wmk reversed .. .. 70·00
y. Wmk inverted and reversed .. ..
43 25 c. deep lilac (II) (30.5.12) .. .. 4·00 16·00
a. Deep dull purple (1920) .. .. 12·00 16·00
44 30 c. purple and orange-yellow (18.3.12) 9·00 12·00
45 50 c. black/*green* (II) (1912) .. .. 27·00 65·00
a. On blue-green (1920) .. .. 8·50 35·00
46 $1 black and red/*blue* (18.3.12) .. 20·00 48·00
47 $5 carmine/*green* (I) (1910) £110 £180
48 $25 black/*red* (I) (1910) £475 £850
34/47 .. .. .. *Set of* 12 £160 £275
34s/48s Optd "Specimen" .. *Set of* 13 £500

The used price for No. 48 is for a cancelled-by-favour example, dated before December 1941; there being no actual postal rate for which this value could be used. Examples dated after 1945 are worth much less.

For illustration of the substituted watermark crown see Catalogue Introduction.

Retouch Normal

(6)

RETOUCHES. We list the very distinctive 5 c. Retouch (to
value tablet, R. 1/8) but there are others of interest, notab
the clouds.

1916. *Colours changed. Single plates. Wmk Mult Crown CA.*
49 **5** 5 c. orange .. .. 16·00
a. "5 c." retouch £400
50 8 c. ultramarine .. .. 6·00
49s/50s Optd "Specimen" .. *Set of* 2 £100

MALAYA-BORNEO EXHIBITION OVERPRINTS. T
were produced from a setting of 30 examples, applied twice to
print the complete sheet of 60 stamps. Three prominent over
flaws exist, each occurring on all the stamps in two vertical ro
the sheet.

HI EX NE

Short "I" (all stamps in 2nd and 8th vertical rows)
Broken "E" (all stamps in 4th and 10th vertical rows)
Broken "N (all stamps in 6 12th vertical

(Optd by Govt Printer, Singapore)

1922 (31 Mar). *Optd with T* **6**, *in black.*
51 **5** 1 c. green (II) .. .. 3·50
a. Short "I" .. .. 6·50
b. Broken "E" .. .. 6·50
c. Broken "N" .. .. 6·50
52 2 c. black and brown .. .. .. 4·50
a. Short "I" .. .. 10·00
b. Broken "E" .. .. 10·00
c. Broken "N" .. .. 10·00
53 3 c. scarlet (II) .. .. 6·00
a. Short "I" .. .. 12·00
b. Broken "E" .. .. 12·00
c. Broken "N" .. .. 12·00
54 4 c. claret (II) .. .. 8·00
a. Short "I" .. .. 13·00
b. Broken "E" .. .. 13·00
c. Broken "N" .. .. 13·00
55 5 c. orange (II) .. .. 11·00
a. "5 c." retouch (and short "I") £325
b. Short "I" .. .. 17·00
c. Broken "E" .. .. 17·00
d. Broken "N" .. .. 17·00
56 10 c. purple/*yellow* (II) .. .. .. 6·50
a. Short "I" .. .. 14·00
b. Broken "E" .. .. 14·00
c. Broken "N" .. .. 14·00
57 25 c. deep dull purple (II) .. .. .. 14·00
a. Short "I" .. .. 30·00
b. Broken "E" .. .. 30·00
c. Broken "N" .. .. 30·00
x. Wmk reversed .. .. ..
58 50 c. black/*blue-green* (II) .. .. 45·00
a. Short "I" .. .. 80·00
b. Broken "E" .. .. 80·00
c. Broken "N" .. .. 80·00
59 $1 black and red/*blue* .. .. .. 70·00
a. Short "I" £120
b. Broken "E" £120
c. Broken "N" £120
51/9 .. .. *Set of* 9 £140

Examples of all values are known showing forged Bru
postmarks dated "28 MAR 1922" or "13 JUL".

Sultan Ahmed Tajudin Akhazul Khairi Wadin, 1924–1

7 Native houses, Water Village

1924 (Feb)–**37**. *Printed from single plates as Type* II, *exc*
30 c. and $1 *as Type* I. *Wmk Mult Script CA. P* 14.
60 **5** 1 c. black (9.26) .. .. 1·00
61 2 c. brown (3.24) 90
62 2 c. green (3.33) .. .. .. 1·50
63 3 c. green (3.24) 80
64 4 c. maroon (3.24) .. .. .. 1·50
65 4 c. orange (1929) .. .. .. 2·00
66 5 c. orange-yellow* (3.24) .. .. 4·50
a. "5 c." retouch £180
67 5 c. grey (1931) .. .. .. 11·00
a. "5 c." retouch £400
68 5 c. chocolate (1933) .. .. .. 11·00
a. "5 c." retouch £190
69 **7** 6 c. intense black** (3.24) .. .. 14·00
x. Wmk reversed .. .. ..
70 6 c. scarlet (1931) .. .. .. 3·75
71 **5** 8 c. ultramarine (9.27) .. .. .. 6·00
72 8 c. grey-black (1933) .. .. .. 11·00
73 10 c. purple/*yellow* (3.37) .. .. 14·00
74 **7** 12 c. blue .. .. 4·50
a. Pale greenish blue (1927) £130
75 **5** 25 c. slate-purple (1931) .. .. .. 7·00
76 30 c. purple and orange-yellow (1931) .. 9·50
77 50 c. black/*emerald* (1931) .. .. 7·50
78 $1 black and red/*blue* (1931) .. .. 24·00
60/78 .. .. *Set of* 19 £120
60s/78s (*ex* 10 c.) Optd (Nos. 60/1, 63/4, 66, 69, 71, 74) or Perf "Specimen" .. *Set of* 18 £350

*For 5 c. orange, see No. 82. No. 66 is a "Wet" printing and No.
a "Dry".

**For 6 c. black, see No. 83. Apart from the difference in sha
there is a variation in size, No. 69 being 37¾ mm long and No.
39 mm.

2 c. orange and 3 c. blue-green in Type **5**, and the 6 c. ish grey, 8 c. red and 15 c. ultramarine in Type **7** were not without the Japanese Occupation overprint although rprinted examples exist. It is believed that these 1941 ngs were produced and possibly perforated, by other firms eat Britain following bomb damage to the De La Rue works end of 1940 (*Price for set of* 5, £500 *un*).

ring the life of this issue De La Rue changed the method of ction from a "Wet" to a "Dry" process. Initially the stamps printed on ungummed paper which was dampened before put on the press. Once the paper had dried, and contracted in ocess, the gum was then applied. "Dry" printings, introduced d 1934, were on pre-gummed paper. The contraction of the printings was considerable and usually involves a difference ween 0.5 mm and 1 mm when compared with the larger "Dry" ngs. The following stamps occur from both "Wet" and "Dry" ns: 1 c., 2 c. green, 4 c. orange, 5 c. chocolate, 6 c. scarlet, 8 c. black, 10 c. and 25 c.

mps of this issue can be found either line or comb perforated.

nei was occupied by the Japanese Army in January 1942 emained under Japanese administration until liberated by h Australian Division in June 1945.

After the cessation of hostilities with the Japanese postal ervices were re-introduced by the British Military Administration. Post offices under B.M.A. control were opened at runei Town and Kuala Belait on 17 December 1945 where .M.A. overprints on the stamps of NORTH BORNEO and ARAWAK were used until the reappearance of Brunei ssues on 2 January 1947.

Redrawn clouds (R. 1/1 of No. 80*ab* only)

(2 Jan)–**51.** *Colours changed and new values. Wmk Mult ript CA. P* 14.

5		1 c. chocolate	50	1·75
		a. "A" of "CA" missing from wmk	£1100	
		2 c. grey	60	3·50
		a. Perf $14^1/_2\times13^1/_2$ (25.9.50)	1·50	4·50
		ab. Black (27.6.51)	2·00	6·50
		ac. Redrawn clouds	65·00	
7		3 c. green	1·00	5·00
5		5 c. orange*	80	1·25
		a. "5 c." retouch	55·00	75·00
		b. Perf $14^1/_2\times13^1/_2$ (25.9.50)	4·00	13·00
		c. Ditto "5 c." retouch	£120	£190
7		6 c. black*	1·00	4·00
5		8 c. scarlet	40	1·00
		a. Perf 13 (25.1.51)	55	8·50
		10 c. violet	70	30
		a. Perf $14^1/_2\times13^1/_2$ (25.9.50)	2·00	5·50
		15 c. ultramarine	1·50	60
		25 c. deep claret	2·25	1·00
		a. Perf $14^1/_2\times13^1/_2$ (25.1.51)	1·50	8·00
		30 c. black and orange	1·50	1·00
		a. Perf $14^1/_2\times13^1/_2$ (25.1.51)	1·50	11·00
		50 c. black	3·00	70
		a. Perf 13 (25.9.50)	1·75	15·00
		$1 black and scarlet	6·50	75
		$5 green and red-orange (2.2.48)	16·00	17·00
		$10 black and purple (2.2.48)	55·00	30·00
92		*Set of* 14	75·00	60·00
/92s Perf "Specimen"		*Set of* 14	£200	

See also Nos. 66 and 69.

he 1, 2, 3, 5, 6, 10 and 25 c. values utilised the plates of the -war issue and were line perforated until the introduction of $14^1/_2\times13^1/_2$ comb machine for some values in 1950–51. The 5, 50 c., $1, $5 and $10 were from new plates with the sheets nb perforated. The 30 c. was initially a pre-war plate, but it is ieved that a new plate was introduced in 1951.

8 Sultan Ahmed Tajudin and Water Village

49 (22 Sept). *Sultan's Silver Jubilee. Wmk Mult Script CA.* P 13.

8		8 c. black and carmine	70	1·00
		25 c. purple and red-orange	70	1·40
		50 c. black and blue	70	1·40
5		*Set of* 3	1·90	3·50

49 (10 Oct). *75th Anniv of Universal Postal Union. As Nos.* 114/17 *of Antigua.*

	8 c. carmine	1·00	1·25
	15 c. deep blue	3·50	1·50
	25 c. magenta	1·00	1·50
	50 c. blue-black	1·00	1·25
/9	*Set of* 4	6·00	5·00

JAPANESE OCCUPATION OF BRUNEI

Japanese forces landed in Northern Borneo on 15 December 1941 and the whole of Brunei had been occupied by 6 January 1942.

Brunei, North Borneo, Sarawak and, after a short period, Labuan, were administered as a single territory by the Japanese. Until September–October 1942, previous stamp issues, without overprint, continued to be used in conjunction with existing postmarks. From the Autumn of 1942 onwards unoverprinted stamps of Japan were made available and examples can be found used from the area for much of the remainder of the War. Japanese Occupation issues for Brunei, North Borneo and Sarawak were equally valid throughout the combined territory but not, in practice, equally available.

PRICES FOR STAMPS ON COVER

Nos. J1/16	*from* × 8
Nos. J17/20	—

本日大

府政國帝本日大 (1) ("Imperial Japanese Government")

便郵國帝 (2) ("Imperial Japanese Postal Service $3")

1942 (Oct)–**44.** *Stamps of Brunei handstamped with T* **1** *in violet to blue. Wmk Mult Script CA (except Nos.* J18/19, *Mult Crown CA). P* 14.

J 1	**5**	1 c. black	6·00	23·00
		a. Red opt	60·00	80·00
J 2		2 c. green	50·00	£110
J 3		2 c. orange (1943)	3·50	9·00
J 4		3 c. blue-green	28·00	75·00
		a. Opt omitted (in pair with normal)	£1700	
J 5		4 c. orange	3·00	13·00
J 6		5 c. chocolate	3·00	13·00
		a. "5 c." retouch	£150	£375
J 7	**7**	6 c. greenish grey (*p* $14\times11^1/_2$) (1944)	40·00	£200
J 8		6 c. scarlet	£550	£550
J 9	**5**	8 c. grey-black	£650	£850
J10	**7**	8 c. red	4·00	12·00
		a. Opt omitted (in pair with normal)	£1300	
J11	**5**	10 c. purple/*yellow*	8·50	26·00
J12	**7**	12 c. blue	24·00	26·00
		a. Red opt	£160	£250
J13		15 c. ultramarine (1944)	13·00	26·00
J14	**5**	25 c. slate-purple	23·00	50·00
		a. Red opt	£275	£350
J15		30 c. purple and orange-yellow	95·00	£180
J16		50 c. black/*emerald*	38·00	60·00
		a. Red opt	£300	
J17		$1 black and red/*blue* (1944)	55·00	70·00
		a. Red opt	—	£650
J18		$5 carmine/*green* (1944)	£850	£1800
J19		$25 black/*red* (1944)	£900	£1800

The overprint varies in shade from violet to blue, and being handstamped, exists double, double one inverted and treble.

Nos. J3, J7, J10 and J13 were not issued without the overprint.

1944 (11 May). *No.* J1 *surch with T* **2** *in orange-red.*

J20	**5**	$3 on 1 c. black	£6000	£5500
		a. Surch on No. 60 of Brunei	£7500	

Three separate handstamps were used to apply Type **2**, one for the top line, one for the bottom and the third for the two central characters.

Burma

(Currency. 12 pies = 1 anna; 16 annas = 1 rupee)

Stamps of India were used in Burma from 1854 and, after 1856, individual examples can be identified by the use of the concentric octagonal postmarks of the Bengal Postal Circle of which the following were supplied to Burmese post offices:

Type A
No. B 156
(Rangoon)

Type B
No. B 5
(Akyab)

B5	Akyab	B146	Pegu
B12*	Bassein	B150	Prome
B22	Nga Thine Khyoung	B156*	Rangoon
B56	Amherst	B159	Sandoway
B108	Kyouk Phyoo	B165	Sarawah (*to* 1860)
B111	Meeaday	B165	Henzada (*from* 1861)
B112	Mengyee	B171	Shoay Gyeen
B127	Moulmein	B173	Sittang
B128	Mergui	B179	Thayetmyo
B129	Tavoy	B181	Toungoo
B133	Myanoung	B227	Port Blair
B136	Namayan		

*Exists in black or blue. Remainder in black only.

Akyab, Moulmein and Rangoon used postmarks as both Type A and Type B, Port Blair as Type B only and the remainder as Type A only.

From 1860 various types of duplex cancellations were introduced and Burmese examples can be identified when sufficient of the left-hand portion is visible on the stamp. Such marks were issued for the following offices:

Akyab	Rangoon
Bassein	Rangoon C.R.H.
Mandalay	(Cantonment Receiving House)
Moulmein	Thayetmyo
Port Blair	Toungoo
Prome	

1862 Duplex from Toungoo

1865 Duplex from Akyab

During 1875, a further series of duplex marks was introduced in which the right-hand portion of the cancellation included the office code number, prefixed by the letter "R" for Rangoon:

R–1	Rangoon	R–9	Myanoung
R–1/1	Rangoon Cantonment	R–10	Port Blair
R–2	Akyab	1/R–10	Nancowry
R–3	Bassein	R–11	Prome
R–4	Henzada	R–12	Sandoway
R–5	Kyouk Phyoo	R–13	Shwegyeen
R–6	Mandalay	R–14	Tavoy
R–7	Mergui	R–15	Thayetmyo
R–8	Moulmein	R–16	Tounghoo
1/R–8	Amherst		

1875 type from Rangoon

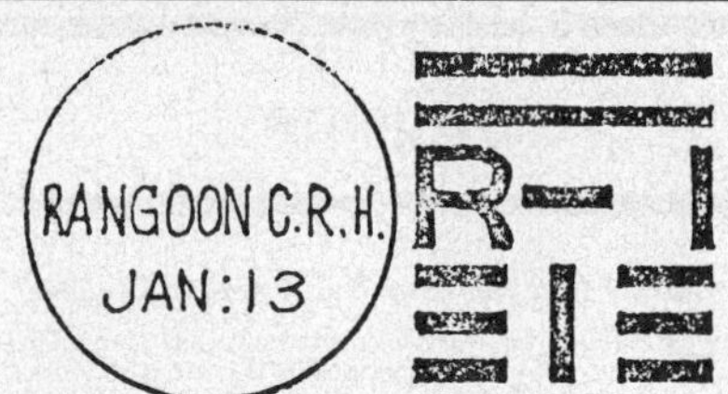

1875 type from Rangoon Cantonment Receiving House

From 1886 the whole of Burma was united under the Crown and the post offices were supplied with circular date stamps giving the name of the town.

Most Indian stamps, both postage and official, issued during the period were supplied to post offices in Burma. None of the imperforates printed by De La Rue have been seen however, and from the later issues the following have not been recorded with Burma postmarks:

Nos. 39a, 66a, 68, 85a, 92a, 110a/b, 148a, 155a, 165, 192a/c, 195a/b, O15, O38, O40b, O50a/b, O76a, O101a, O102, O103/a, O104/5 and O142.

The value of most India stamps used in Burma coincides proportionately with the used prices quoted for India, but some, especially the provisional surcharges, are extremely rare with Burmese postmarks. Stamps of the face value of 2 r. and above from the reigns of Victoria and Edward VII are more common with telegraph cancellations than with those of the postal service.

PRICES FOR STAMPS ON COVER TO 1945	
Nos. 1/18	*from* × 6
Nos. 18*a*/33	*from* × 4
No. 34	*from* × 5
Nos. 35/50	*from* × 8
Nos. O1/27	*from* × 15

BRITISH ADMINISTRATION

From 1 January 1886 Burma was a province of the Indian Empire but was separated from India and came under direct British administration on 1 April 1937.

BURMA (1) **BURMA** (1*a*)

1937 (1 Apr). *Stamps of India (King George V inscr* "INDIA POSTAGE") *optd with T* **1** *or* **1a** *(rupee values). W* **69**. *P* 14.

No.	Description	Unused	Used
1	3 p. slate	60	10
	w. Wmk inverted	1·50	60
2	½ a. green	1·00	10
	w. Wmk inverted	1·75	60
3	9 p. deep green (*typo*)	1·00	10
	w. Wmk inverted	1·50	60
4	1 a. chocolate	75	10
	w. Wmk inverted	1·50	60
5	2 a. vermilion (*small die*)	75	10
6	2½ a. orange	60	10
	w. Wmk inverted	1·50	60
7	3 a. carmine	1·00	30
	w. Wmk inverted	3·00	1·25
8	3½ a. deep blue	1·75	10
	aw. Wmk inverted	2·25	30
	b. *Dull blue*	7·50	6·00
	bw. Wmk inverted	4·75	4·00
9	4 a. sage-green	1·00	10
	w. Wmk inverted	—	28·00
10	6 a. bistre	75	35
	w. Wmk inverted	—	28·00
11	8 a. reddish purple	1·50	10
12	12 a. claret	3·50	1·00
	w. Wmk inverted	10·00	2·00
13	1 r. chocolate and green	17·00	2·75
14	2 r. carmine and orange	28·00	9·50
	w. Wmk inverted	40·00	14·00
15	5 r. ultramarine and purple	38·00	17·00
16	10 r. green and scarlet	80·00	60·00
	w. Wmk inverted	†	—
17	15 r. blue and olive (*wmk inverted*)	£275	£110
18	25 r. orange and blue	£550	£275
	w. Wmk inverted	£600	£300
1/18	*Set of* 18	£900	£425

The opt is at top on all values except the 3 a.

The 1 a. has been used from Yenangyaung on 22 Mar 1937.

2 King George VI and "Chinthes"

3 King George VI and "Nagas"

4 *Karaweik* (royal barge)

8 King George VI and Peacock

10 Elephants' Heads

Extra trees flaw (R. 11/8)

(Des Maung Kyi (2 a. 6 p.), Maung Hline (3 a.), Maung Ohn Pe (3 a. 6 p.) and N. K. D. Naigamwalla (8 a.). Litho Security Ptg Press, Nasik)

1938 (15 Nov)–**40**. *T* **2/4**, **8** *and similar designs. W* **10**. *P* 14 *(vert) or* 13½×13 *(horiz).*

No.	Type	Description	Unused	Used
18*a*	**2**	1 p. red-orange (1.8.40)	3·00	1·00
19		3 p. bright violet	20	50
20		6 p. bright blue	20	10
21		9 p. yellow-green	1·00	80
22	**3**	1 a. purple-brown	20	10
23		1½ a. turquoise-green	20	80
24		2 a. carmine	45	10
25	**4**	2 a. 6 p. claret	14·00	1·25
26	–	3 a. dull violet	14·00	1·75
27	–	3 a. 6 p. light blue and blue	1·25	4·00
		a. Extra trees flaw	45·00	
28	**3**	4 a. greenish blue	60	10
29	–	8 a. myrtle-green	5·00	30
30	**8**	1 r. purple and blue	6·00	20
31		2 r. brown and purple	16·00	1·75
32	–	5 r. violet and scarlet	48·00	23·00
33	–	10 r. brown and myrtle	55·00	50·00
18*a*/33		*Set of* 16	£150	75·00

Designs: *Horiz (as T* **4**)—3 a. Burma teak; 3 a. 6 p. Burma rice; 8 a. River Irrawaddy. *Vert (as T* **8**)—5 r., 10 r. King George VI and "Nats".

The 1 a. exists lithographed or typographed, the latter having a "Jubilee" line in the sheet margin.

(11)

1940 (6 May) *Centenary of First Adhesive Postage Stamps. No.* 25 *surch with T* **11**.

No.	Type	Description	Unused	Used
34	**4**	1 a. on 2 a. 6 p. claret	3·75	1·50

For stamps issued in 1942–45 see under Japanese Occupation.

CHIN HILLS DISTRICT. This area, in the far north-west of the country, remained in British hands when the Japanese overran Burma in May 1942.

During the period July to December 1942 the local officials were authorised to produce provisional stamps and the letters "OHMS" are known overprinted by typewriter on Nos. 3, 20, 22/4, 28/9 and 31 of Burma or handstamped, in violet, on Nos. 25, 27 and 29. The two types can also occur together or in combination with a handstamped "SERVICE".

From early in 1943 ordinary postage stamps of India were used from the Chin Hills post offices of Falam, Haka, Fort White and Tiddim, this expedient continuing until the fall of Falam to the Japanese on 7 November 1943.

The provisional stamps should only be collected on Official cover where dates and the sender's handwriting can be authenticated.

BRITISH MILITARY ADMINISTRATION

Preparations for the liberation of Burma commenced in February 1943 when the Civil Affairs Service (Burma) (CAS(B)) was set up at Delhi as part of the proposed military administration structure. One of the specific tasks assigned to CAS(B) was the operation of a postal service for the civilian population.

Operations against the Japanese intensified during the second half of 1944. The port of Akyab in the Arakan was reoccupied in January 1945. The 14th Army took Mandalay on 29 March and Rangoon was liberated from the sea on 3 May.

Postal services for the civilian population started in Akyab on 13 April 1945 while post offices in the Magwe Division around Meiktila were operating from 4 March. Mandalay post offices opened on 8 June and those in Rangoon on 16 June, but the full network was only completed in December 1945, just before the military administration was wound-up.

MILY ADMN (12) **MILY ADMN** (13)

1945 (from 11 Apr). *Nos.* 18*a to* 33 *optd with T* **12** *(small sta[…] or* **13** *(others) by Security Printing Press, Nasik.*

No.	Type	Description	Unused
35	**2**	1 p. red-orange	10
		a. Opt omitted (in pair with normal)	£1600
36		3 p. bright violet	10
37		6 p. bright blue	10
38		9 p. yellow-green	30
39	**3**	1 a. purple-brown (16.6)	10
40		1½ a. turquoise-green (16.6)	10
41		2 a. carmine	10
42	**4**	2 a. 6 p. claret	2·00
43	–	3 a. dull violet	1·50
44	–	3 a. 6 p. light blue and blue	10
		a. Extra trees flaw	20·00
45	**3**	4 a. greenish blue	10
46	–	8 a. myrtle-green	10
47	**8**	1 r. purple and blue	40
48		2 r. brown and purple	40
49	–	5 r. violet and scarlet	40
50	–	10 r. brown and myrtle	40
35/50		*Set of* 16	4·75

Only the typographed version of the 1 a., No. 22, received[…] overprint.

The missing overprints on the 1 p. occur on the stamps […] the bottom row of one sheet. A further block with two exam[…] of the variety caused by a paper fold also exists.

The exact dates of issue for Nos. 35/50 are difficu[…] establish.

The initial stock of overprints is known to have rea[…] CAS(B) headquarters, Imphal, at the beginning of April 1[…] Postal directives issued on 11 April refer to the use of […] overprints in Akyab and in the Magwe Division w[…] surcharged pre-war postal stationery envelopes had previo[…] been in use. The 6 p., 1 a., 1½ a. and 2 a. values were place[…] sale at Mandalay on 8 June and the 1 a. and 2 a. at Rangoo[…] 16 June. It has been suggested that only a limited service […] initially available in Rangoon. All values were on sal[…] 9 August 1945.

BRITISH CIVIL ADMINISTRATION

1946 (1 Jan). *As Nos.* 19/33, *but colours changed.*

No.	Type	Description	Unused	Used
51	**2**	3 p. brown	10	
52		6 p. deep violet	10	
53		9 p. green	15	
54	**3**	1 a. blue	15	
55		1½ a. orange	15	
56		2 a. claret	15	
57	**4**	2 a. 6 p. greenish blue	2·75	
57*a*	–	3 a. blue-violet	6·50	
57*b*	–	3 a. 6 p. black and ultramarine	30	
		ba. Extra trees flaw	45·00	
58	**3**	4 a. purple	50	
59	–	8 a. maroon	1·75	
60	**8**	1 r. violet and maroon	1·25	
61		2 r. brown and orange	6·00	
62	–	5 r. green and brown	6·00	14[…]
63	–	10 r. claret and violet	8·50	18[…]
51/63		*Set of* 15	30·00	45[…]

No. 54 was printed in typography only.

14 Burman

(Des A. G. I. McGeogh. Litho Nasik)

1946 (2 May). *Victory. T* **14** *and similar vert designs. W* **10** *(si[…] ways). P* 13.

No.	Description	Unused
64	9 p. turquoise-green	20
65	1½ a. violet	20
66	2 a. carmine	20
67	3 a. 6 p. ultramarine	50
64/7	*Set of* 4	1·00

Designs:—1½ a. Burmese woman; 2 a. Chinthe; 3 a. 6[…] Elephant.

INTERIM BURMESE GOVERNMENT

ကြားဖြတ် အစိုးရ။ (18 *Trans.* "Interim Government")

ားဖြတ်ကြ အစိုးရ။ (**18***a*)

တ်ကြား[…] အစိုးရ[…] (**18***b*)

Type **18***a* shows the first character transposed to the end […] the top line (R. 6/15).

Type **18***b* shows the last two characters transposed to t[…] front of the top line (R. 14/14).

Some sheets of the 3 p. show both errors corrected by […] handstamp as Type **18**.

1947 (1 Oct). *Stamps of* 1946 *optd with T* **18** *(small stamps) […] larger opt (others).*

No.	Type	Description	Unused	Used
68	**2**	3 p. brown	70	
		a. Opt Type **18***a*	28·00	
		ab. Corrected by handstamp as Type **18**		
		b. Opt Type **18***b*	28·00	
		ba. Corrected by handstamp as Type **18**		
69		6 p. deep violet	10	
		a. Opt Type **18***a*	15·00	
70		9 p. green	10	
		a. Opt inverted	19·00	23·[…]

		1 a. blue	10	30
		a. Vert pair, one with opt omitted ..		
		1½ a. orange	1·00	10
		2 a. claret	30	15
		a. Horiz pair, one with opt omitted ..		
		b. Opt Type **18***a*	25·00	
		2 a. 6 p. greenish blue	1·75	1·00
		3 a. blue-violet	2·50	1·75
		3 a. 6 p. black and ultramarine	50	2·00
		a. Extra trees flaw	40·00	
		4 a. purple	1·75	30
		8 a. maroon	1·75	1·50
		1 r. violet and maroon	4·00	50
		2 r. brown and orange	4·50	3·25
		5 r. green and brown	4·50	3·50
		10 r. claret and violet	3·25	3·50
		.. .. *Set of* 15	24·00	17·00

3 p., 6 p., 2 a., 2 a. 6 p., 3 a. 6 p. and 1 r. are also known with rint inverted.

OFFICIAL STAMPS

BURMA BURMA

SERVICE SERVICE

(O 1) (O 1*a*)

(Apr–June). *Stamps of India* (*King George V inscr* IDIA POSTAGE") *optd with Type* O **1** *or* O **1***a* (*rupee ues*). *W* **69**. *P* 14.

		3 p. slate	1·75	10
		w. Wmk inverted	—	14·00
		½ a. green	7·50	10
		w. Wmk inverted	†	—
		9 p. deep green	4·00	30
		1 a. chocolate	5·00	10
		2 a. vermilion (*small die*)	8·00	35
		w. Wmk inverted	—	14·00
		2½ a. orange	4·25	2·00
		4 a. sage-green	5·00	10
		6 a. bistre	4·25	7·00
		8 a. reddish purple (1.4.37)	4·00	80
		12 a. claret (1.4.37)	4·00	4·25
		1 r. chocolate and green (1.4.37) ..	20·00	3·75
		2 r. carmine and orange	48·00	38·00
		w. Wmk inverted	60·00	45·00
		5 r. ultramarine and purple	95·00	48·00
		10 r. green and scarlet	£250	£130
.4		.. .. *Set of* 14	£425	£200

r the above issue the stamps were either overprinted RMA" and "SERVICE" at one operation or had the two ls applied separately. Research has yet to establish if all es exist with both forms of overprinting.

SERVICE SERVICE

(O 2) (O 3)

). *Nos.* 19/24 *and* 28 *optd with Type* O **2** (*typo*) *and Nos.* 25 *and* /33 *optd with Type* O **3** (*litho*).

	2	3 p. bright violet	15	20
		6 p. bright blue	15	20
		9 p. yellow-green	5·00	3·00
	3	1 a. purple-brown	15	15
		1½ a. turquoise-green	4·50	1·75
		2 a. carmine	1·25	20
	4	2 a. 6 p. claret	26·00	12·00
	3	4 a. greenish blue	5·50	45
	–	8 a. myrtle-green	25·00	4·00
	8	1 r. purple and blue	38·00	5·50
)		2 r. brown and purple	45·00	14·00
;	–	5 r. violet and scarlet	42·00	29·00
7	–	10 r. brown and myrtle	£120	38·00
5/27		.. .. *Set of* 13	£275	95·00

Both versions of the 1 a. value exist with this overprint.

46. *British Civil Administration. Nos.* 51/6 *and* 58 *optd with Type* O **2** (*typo*) *and Nos.* 57 *and* 59/63 *optd with Type* O **3** (*litho*).

3	**2**	3 p. brown	1·50	3·00
9		6 p. deep violet	1·50	2·25
)		9 p. green	20	3·00
1	**3**	1 a. blue	20	2·00
2		1½ a. orange	20	20
3		2 a. claret	20	2·00
4	**4**	2 a. 6 p. greenish blue	1·40	5·50
5	**3**	4 a. purple	20	70
6	–	8 a. maroon	2·25	3·50
7	**8**	1 r. violet and maroon	60	3·75
8		2 r. brown and orange	7·00	40·00
9	–	5 r. green and brown	9·00	45·00
)	–	10 r. claret and violet	17·00	50·00
8/40		.. .. *Set of* 13	35·00	£140

47. *Interim Burmese Government. Nos.* O28/40 *optd with T* **18** *small stamps*) *or larger opt* (*others*).

1	**2**	3 p. brown	20	40
2		6 p. deep violet	1·25	10
3		9 p. green	2·00	90
4	**3**	1 a. blue	2·25	80
5		1½ a. orange	4·50	30
6		2 a. claret	2·25	15
7	**4**	2 a. 6 p. greenish blue	25·00	11·00
8	**3**	4 a. purple	10·00	40
9	–	8 a. maroon	8·00	4·00
0	**8**	1 r. violet and maroon	14·00	2·25
1		2 r. brown and orange	14·00	20·00
2	–	5 r. green and brown	14·00	20·00
3	–	10 r. claret and violet	14·00	30·00
1/53		.. .. *Set of* 13	£100	80·00

Later stamp issues will be found listed in Part 21 (*South-East sia*) of this catalogue.

JAPANESE OCCUPATION OF BURMA

PRICES FOR STAMPS ON COVER

Nos. J1/44	—
Nos. J45/6	*from* × 6
Nos. J47/56	*from* × 8
No. J56*g*	—
Nos. J57/72	*from* × 6
Nos. J73/5	*from* × 25
No. J76	*from* × 8
No. J77	*from* × 20
Nos. J78/81	*from* × 25
Nos. J82/4	*from* × 10
Nos. J85/7	*from* × 40
No. J88	*from* × 12
Nos. J89/97	*from* × 30
Nos. J98/104	*from* × 50
Nos. J105/111	*from* × 30

BURMA INDEPENDENCE ARMY ADMINISTRATION

The Burma Independence Army, formed by Aung San in 1941, took control of the Delta area of the Irrawaddy in May 1942. They reopened a postal service in the area and were authorised by the Japanese to overprint local stocks of stamps with the Burmese emblem of a peacock.

Postage and Official stamps with the peacock overprints or handstamps were used for ordinary postal purposes with the probable exception of No. J44.

DISTINGUISHING FEATURES. Type **1**. Body and head of Peacock always clearly outlined by broad uncoloured band. There are four slightly different sub-types of overprint Type **1**.

Type **2**. Peacock with slender neck and more delicately detailed tail. Clear spur on leg at right. Heavy fist-shaped blob of ink below and parallel to beak and neck.

Type **4**. No basic curve. Each feather separately outlined. Straight, short legs.

Type **5**. Much fine detail in wings and tail in clearly printed overprints. Thin, long legs ending in claws which, with the basic arc, enclose clear white spaces in well-printed copies. Blob of colour below beak shows shaded detail and never has the heavy fist-like appearance of this portion in Type **2**.

Two sub-types may be distinguished in Type **5**, the basic arc of one having a chord of 14–15 mm and the other 12½–13 mm.

Type **6**. Similar to Type **5**, but with arc deeply curved and reaching nearly to the top of the wings. Single diagonal line parallel to neck below beak.

Collectors are warned against forgeries of these overprints, often in the wrong colours or on the wrong values.

(1)

(2)

(3)

1942 (May). *Stamps of Burma overprinted with the national device of a Peacock.*

I. *Overprinted at Myaungmya*

A. *With Type* **1** *in black*

On Postage Stamps of King George V

J 1		9 p. deep green (No. 3)	£110
J 2		3½ a. deep blue (No. 8)	50·00

On Official Stamp of King George V

J 3		6 a. bistre (No. O8)	70·00

On Postage Stamps of King George VI

J 4	**2**	9 p. yellow-green	£150
J 5	**3**	1 a. purple-brown	£550
J 6		4 a. greenish blue (opt black on red) ..	£160
		a. Triple opt, black on double red ..	£425

On Official Stamps of King George VI

J 7	**2**	3 p. bright violet	24·00	80·00
J 8		6 p. bright blue	16·00	55·00
J 9	**3**	1 a. purple-brown	16·00	48·00
J 9*a*		1½ a. turquoise-green	£650	
J10		2 a. carmine	23·00	90·00
J11		4 a. greenish blue	22·00	70·00

The overprint on No. J6 was apparently first done in red in error, and then corrected in black. Some stamps have the black overprint so accurately superimposed that the red hardly shows. These are rare.

Nos. J5 and J9 exist with the Peacock overprint on both the typographed and the litho printings of the original stamps.

B. *With Types* **2** *or* **3** (*rupee values*), *in black*

On Postage Stamps of King George VI

J12	**2**	3 p. bright violet	17·00	65·00
J13		6 p. bright blue	48·00	95·00
J14		9 p. yellow-green	19·00	60·00
J15	**3**	1 a. purple-brown	14·00	55·00
J16		2 a. carmine	19·00	75·00
J17	**3**	4 a. greenish blue	35·00	95·00
		a. Opt double		
		b. Opt inverted	£650	
		c. Opt double, one inverted	£425	
		d. Opt double, both inverted	£650	
J18		1 r. purple and blue	£250	
J19		2 r. brown and purple	£150	

The Myaungmya overprints (including No. J44) are usually clearly printed.

(4)

(5)

(6)

Type **5** generally shows the details of the peacock much less clearly and, due to heavy inking, or careless impression, sometimes appears as almost solid colour.

Type **6** was officially applied only to postal stationery. However, the handstamp remained in the possession of a postal official who used it on postage stamps after the war. These stamps are no longer listed.

II. *Handstamped* (*at Pyapon?*) *with T* **4**, *in black* (*so-called experimental type*)

On Postage Stamps of King George VI

J19*a*	**2**	6 p. bright blue	85·00	
J19*b*	**3**	1 a. purple-brown	£100	£250
J20		2 a. carmine	£120	£275
J21		4 a. greenish blue	£650	£650

Unused specimens of Nos. J20/1 are usually in poor condition.

III. *Overprinted at Henzada with T* **5** *in blue, or blue-black*

On Postage Stamps of King George V

J22		3 p. slate (No. 1)	3·00	18·00
		a. Opt double	10·00	48·00
J23		9 p. deep green (No. 3)	22·00	60·00
		a. Opt double	80·00	
J24		2 a. vermilion (No. 5)	£100	£180

On Postage Stamps of King George VI

J25	**2**	1 p. red-orange	£180	£275
J26		3 p. bright violet	30·00	75·00
J27		6 p. bright blue	25·00	50·00
		a. Opt double	£100	£150
		b. Clear opt, on back and front ..	£275	
J28		9 p. yellow-green	£800	
J29	**3**	1 a. purple-brown	9·00	40·00
		a. Opt inverted	£600	
J30		1½ a. turquoise-green	21·00	65·00
		a. Opt omitted (in pair with normal)	£1700	
J31		2 a. carmine	21·00	65·00
		a. Opt double	£600	
J32		4 a. greenish blue	42·00	95·00
		a. Opt double	£250	
		b. Opt inverted	£1100	

On Official Stamps of King George VI

J33	**2**	3 p. bright violet	£110	£225
J34		6 p. bright blue	£140	£225
J35	**3**	1½ a. turquoise-green	£160	£275
J35*a*		2 a. carmine	£350	£425
J36		4 a. greenish blue	£1000	

(6*a*)

("Yon Thon" = "Office use")

V. *Official Stamp of King George VI optd at Myaungmya with Type* **6***a in black*

J44	**7**	8 a. myrtle-green	85·00

No. J44 was probably for official use.

There are two types of T **6***a*, one with base of peacock 8 mm long and the other with base about 5 mm long. The neck and other details also vary. The two types are found *se-tenant* in the sheet.

Stocks of the peacock types were withdrawn when the Japanese Directorate-General took control of the postal services in the Delta in August 1942.

JAPANESE ARMY ADMINISTRATION

7

8 Farmer

1942 (1 June). *Impressed by hand. Thick yellowish paper. P* 12 × 11. *No gum.*

J45	**7**	(1 a.) red	38·00	65·00

This device was the personal seal of Yano Sitza, the Japanese official in charge of the Posts and Telegraphs department of the Japanese Army Administration. It was impressed on paper already perforated by a line machine. Some stamps show part of the papermaker's watermark, either "ABSORBO DUPLICATOR" or "ELEPHANT BRAND", each with an elephant.

Other impressions of this seal on different papers, and showing signs of wear, were not valid for postal purposes.

(Des T. Kato. Typo *Rangoon Gazette* Press)

1942 (15 June). *Value in annas. P* 11 *or* 11 × 11½. *Laid bâtonné paper. No gum.*

J46 **8** 1 a. scarlet .. .. 15·00 15·00

Some stamps show part of the papermaker's watermark, either "ELEPHANT BRAND" or "TITAGHUR SUPERFINE", each with an elephant.

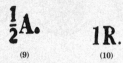

(9) (10)

1942 (22 Sept). (*a*) *Nos.* 314/17, 320/2, 325, 327 *and* 396 *of Japan surch as T* **9**/**10**.

J47 **9** ¼ a. on 1 s. chestnut (Rice harvesting) 25·00 30·00
a. Surch inverted £100 £100
b. Surch double, one inverted .. £150
J48 ½ a. on 2 s. bright scarlet (General Nogi) 28·00 32·00
a. Surch inverted .. .. .. 90·00 95·00
b. Surch double, one inverted .. £150
J49 ¾ a. on 3 s. green (Power station) .. 60·00 65·00
a. Surch inverted £120 £120
b. Surch double, one inverted .. — £160
J50 1 a. on 5 s. claret (Admiral Togo) .. 45·00 42·00
a. Surch inverted £170 £170
b. Surch double, one inverted .. £190 £190
c. Surch omitted (in pair with normal) — £250
J51 3 a. on 7 s. green (Diamond Mts) .. 85·00 95·00
a. Surch inverted £170
J52 4 a. on 4 s. emerald (Togo) .. .. 42·00 45·00
a. Surch inverted £170
J53 8 a. on 8 s. violet (Meiji Shrine) .. £150 £150
a. Surch inverted £225 £225
b. Surch double, one inverted .. £350
c. Surch in red £225 £250
d. Red surch inverted £350
e. Surch double (black and red) .. £600
J54 **10** 1 r. on 10 s. deep carmine (Yomei Gate) 17·00 24·00
a. Surch inverted .. .. .. 80·00 90·00
b. Surch double .. .. .. 80·00 £100
c. Surch double (black and red) .. £400 £400
d. Surch omitted (in pair with normal) £225 £225
e. Surch omitted (in pair with inverted surch) £325
J55 2 r. on 20 s. ultramarine (Mt Fuji) .. 50·00 50·00
a. Surch inverted £110 £110
b. Surch double, one inverted .. £130
c. Surch omitted (in pair with normal black surch) £160 £160
d. Surch in red .. .. .. 48·00 48·00
e. Red surch inverted £110 £110
f. Red surch double £110 £110
g. Surch omitted (in pair with normal red surch) £200 £200
ga. Surch omitted (in pair with double red surch)
h. Surch double (black and red) .. £350
J56 **9** 5 r. on 30 s. turquoise (Torii Shrine) 12·00 27·00
a. Surch inverted .. .. .. 85·00
b. Surch double £110
c. Surch double, one inverted .. £150
d. Surch omitted (in pair with normal surch) £190 £190
e. Surch omitted (in pair with inverted black surch) £275
f. Surch in red .. .. .. 24·00 32·00
fa. Red surch inverted .. .. 90·00 90·00
fb. J56a and J56fa *se-tenant* .. £425 £425
fc. Surch omitted (in pair with normal red surch) £190 £190

(*b*) *No.* 386 *of Japan commemorating the fall of Singapore similarly surch*

J56*g* **9** 4 a. on 4 + 2 s. green and red .. £150 £160
h. Surch omitted (in pair with normal) £500
ha. Surch omitted (in pair with inverted surch) £550
i. Surch inverted £350

(New Currency. 100 cents = 1 rupee)

(11) (12) (13)

1942 (15 Oct). *Previous issues, with "anna" surcharges obliterated, handstamped with new value in cents, as T* **11** *and* **12** (*No. J57 handstamped with new value only*).

(*a*) *On No.* J46

J57 5 c. on 1 a. scarlet .. .. .. 12·00 16·00
a. Surch omitted (in pair with normal) £1100

(*b*) *On Nos.* J47/53

J58 1 c. on ¼ a. on 1 s. chestnut .. .. 45·00 45·00
a. "1 c." omitted (in pair with normal) .. £500
b. "¼ a." inverted £250
J59 2 c. on ½ a. on 2 s. bright scarlet .. 42·00 45·00
J60 3 c. on ¾ a. on 3 s. green .. .. 48·00 48·00
a. Surch in blue £170
J61 5 c. on 1 a. on 5 s. claret .. .. 65·00 65·00
J62 10 c. on 3 a. on 7 s. green £110 £100
J63 15 c. on 4 a. on 4 s. emerald .. .. 32·00 35·00
J64 20 c. on 8 a. on 8 s. violet £425 £375
a. Surch on No. J53c (surch in red) .. £250 £150

The "anna" surcharges were obliterated by any means available, in some cases by a bar or bars, and in others by the butt of a pencil dipped in ink. In the case of the fractional surcharges, the letter "A" and one figure of the fraction, were sometimes barred out, leaving the remainder of the fraction to represent the new value, e.g. the "1" of "½" deleted to create the 2 c. surcharge or the "4" of "¾" to create the 3 c. surcharge.

1942. *Nos.* 314/17, 320/1 *and* 396 *of Japan surcharged in cents only as T* **13**.

J65 1 c. on 1 s. chestnut (Rice harvesting) .. 21·00 20·00
a. Surch inverted £110 £110
J66 2 c. on 2 s. brt scarlet (General Nogi) .. 42·00 32·00
J67 3 c. on 3 s. green (Power station) .. 50·00 45·00
a. Pair, with and without surch .. — £250
b. Surch inverted £120
c. Surch in blue .. .. .. 85·00 95·00
d. Surch in blue inverted £200 £225
J68 5 c. on 5 s. claret (Admiral Togo) .. 55·00 42·00
a. Pair, with and without surch .. £300
b. Surch in violet £130 £150
ba. Surch inverted .. .. .. — £225
J69 10 c. on 7 s. green (Diamond Mts) .. 70·00 60·00
J70 15 c. on 4 s. emerald (Togo) .. .. 16·00 20·00
a. Surch inverted £120 £130
b. Pair, with and without surch .. — £225
J71 20 c. on 8 s. violet (Meiji Shrine) .. £150 85·00
a. Surch double £300

Nos. J67c and J68b were issued for use in the Shan States.

BURMESE GOVERNMENT

On 1 November 1942 the Japanese Army Administration handed over the control of the postal department to the Burmese Government. On 1 August 1943 Burma was declared by the Japanese to be independent.

14 Burma State Crest

15 Farmer

(Des U Tun Tin and Maung Tin from drawing by U Ba Than. Typo Rangoon)

1943 (15 Feb). *P* 11. *No gum.*

J72 **14** 5 c. scarlet .. .. 17·00 20·00
a. Imperf .. .. 18·00 21·00
ab. Printed on both sides .. .. 85·00

No. J72 was usually sold affixed to envelopes, particularly those with the embossed 1 a. King George VI stamp, which it covered. Unused specimens off cover are not often seen and blocks are rare.

1943. *Typo. No gum. P* 11½.

J73 **15** 1 c. orange (22 March) .. .. 2·00 4·00
a. Brown-orange .. .. .. 1·50 4·25
J74 2 c. yellow-green (24 March) .. 60 1·00
a. "3" for "2" in face value (R.2/10) .. £160
b. Blue-green .. .. .. 8·50
J75 3 c. light blue (25 March) .. .. 2·00 1·00
a. On laid paper .. .. .. 18·00 27·00
b. Imperf between (horiz pair) .. — £275
J76 5 c. carmine (small "c") (17 March) .. 16·00 10·00
J77 5 c. carmine (large "C") .. .. 2·50 3·50
a. Imperf (pair) £110
b. "G" for "C" (R.2/6) £170
J78 10 c. grey-brown (25 March) .. .. 4·50 4·00
a. Imperf (pair) £110
b. Imperf between (horiz pair) .. — £275
J79 15 c. magenta (26 March) .. .. 30 1·50
a. Imperf between (vert strip of 3) ..
b. On laid paper .. .. .. 6·00 17·00
ba. Inverted "C" in value (R. 2/3) .. £140
J80 20 c. grey-lilac (29 March) 30 80
J81 30 c. deep blue-green (29 March) .. 30 1·00

The 1 c., 2 c. and 3 c. have large "C" in value as illustrated. The 10 c. and higher values have small "c". Nos. J73/81 had the face values inserted individually into the plate used for No. J46 with the original face value removed. There were a number of printings for each value, often showing differences such as missing stops, various founts of figures or "c", etc., in the value tablets.

The face value error, No. J74a, was later corrected.

Some sheets of No. J75a show a sheet watermark of Britannia seated within a crowned oval spread across fifteen stamps in each sheet. This paper was manufactured by T. Edmonds and the other half of the sheet carried the watermark inscription "FOOLSCAP LEDGER". No stamps have been reported showing letters from this inscription, but a block of 25 is known on laid paper showing a different sheet watermark "HERTFORDSHIRE LEDGER MADE IN ENGLAND". Examples showing parts of these sheet watermarks are rare.

No. J79a shows the horizontal perforations omitted between rows 3/4 and 4/5.

There are marked varieties of shade in this issue.

16 Soldier carving word "Independence"

17 Rejoicing Peasant

18 Boy with National Flag

Normal

Skyline flaw (R. 5/6)

(Des Maung Ba Thit (**16**), Naung Ohn Maung (**17**), and Maur Yi (**18**). Typo State Press, Rangoon)

1943 (1 Aug). *Independence Day.* (*a*) *P* 11.

J82 **16** 1 c. orange .. .. 9·00
J83 **17** 3 c. light blue .. .. 9·50
J84 **18** 5 c. carmine .. .. 17·00
a. Skyline flaw .. .. .. 75·00
J82/4 .. .. *Set of* 3 32·00

(*b*) *Rouletted*

J85 **16** 1 c. orange .. .. 1·00
b. Perf×roul .. .. 95·00
c. Imperf (pair) .. .. .. 45·00
J86 **17** 3 c. light blue .. .. 1·75
b. Perf×roul .. .. 85·00
c. Imperf (pair) .. .. .. 45·00
J87 **18** 5 c. carmine .. .. 1·50
a. Horiz roulette omitted (vert pair) ..
b. Perf×roul .. .. 55·00
c. Imperf (pair) .. .. .. 45·00
d. Skyline flaw .. .. .. 10·00
J85/7 .. .. *Set of* 3 3·75

The stamps perf × rouletted may have one, two or three s perforated.

The rouletted stamps often appear to be roughly perfor owing to failure to make clean cuts. These apparent perforat are very small and quite unlike the large, clean holes of the sta perforated 11.

A few imperforate sets, mounted on a special card folder cancelled with the commemorative postmark were presente officials. These are rare.

19 Burmese Woman

20 Elephant carrying Log

21 Watch Tov Mandalay

(Litho G. Kolff & Co, Batavia)

1943 (1 Oct). *P* 12½.

J88 **19** 1 c. red-orange .. .. .. 27·00 15
J89 2 c. yellow-green 50 2
J90 3 c. deep violet 50 2
a. Bright violet .. .. .. 1·25 3
J91 **20** 5 c. carmine 55
J92 10 c. blue .. .. 1·25 1
J93 15 c. red-orange 65 2
J94 20 c. yellow-green 65 1
J95 30 c. olive-brown 65 1
J96 **21** 1 r. red-orange 30 2
J97 2 r. bright violet 30 2
J88/97 .. .. *Set of* 10 29·00 28

22 Bullock Cart

23 Shan Woman

(**24** "Burma Sta and value)

(Litho G. Kolff & Co, Batavia)

1943 (1 Oct). *Issue for Shan States. P* 12½.

J 98 **22** 1 c. olive-brown .. .. .. 25·00 32·
J 99 2 c. yellow-green .. .. .. 25·00 32·
J100 3 c. bright violet .. .. .. 3·50 10·
J101 5 c. ultramarine .. .. .. 2·00 5·
J102 **23** 10 c. blue .. .. 12·00 17·
J103 20 c. carmine .. .. 26·00 17·
J104 30 c. olive-brown .. .. .. 17·00 40·
J98/104 .. .. *Set of* 7 £100 £1

The Shan States, except for the frontier area around Ke Tung which was ceded to Thailand on 20 August 1943, we placed under the administration of the Burmese Government 24 December 1943, and these stamps were later overprinted T **24** for use throughout Burma.

1 Nov). *Optd as T* **24** *(the lower characters differ for each* e).

No.	Type	Description	Unused	Used
22		1 c. olive-brown	3·00	6·00
		2 c. yellow-green	40	2·25
		a. Opt inverted	£375	£600
		3 c. bright violet	2·00	7·00
		5 c. ultramarine	1·00	1·25
23		10 c. blue	2·75	2·00
		20 c. carmine	40	1·50
		30 c. olive-brown	40	1·75
1		.. .. *Set of* 7	9·00	20·00

Bushire

BRITISH OCCUPATION

(Currency. 20 chahis = 1 kran; 10 kran = 1 toman)

Bushire, a seaport town of Persia, was occupied by the British on 8 August 1915. The Persian postal authorities resumed control on 18 October 1915. British forces returned to Bushire during 1916, but mail from this period was carried by Indian Army F.P.O. No. 319.

PRICES FOR STAMPS ON COVER
Nos. 1/29 *from* × 5

Types of Iran (Persia) overprinted

57

66

67

68

BUSHIRE
Under British
Occupation.
(1)

1915 (15 Aug). *Nos.* 361/3, 365, 367/70, 372, 374/6 *and* 378/9 *of Iran optd with T* **1** *at the British Residency.*

No.	Type	Description	Unused	Used
1	**57**	1 ch. orange and green	38·00	40·00
		a. No stop	£100	£110
2		2 ch. sepia and carmine	38·00	35·00
		a. No stop	£100	£100
3		3 ch. green and grey	45·00	50·00
		a. No stop	£130	£150
4		5 ch. carmine and brown	£275	£275
5		6 ch. brown-lake and green	35·00	24·00
		a. No stop	£100	90·00
6		9 ch. indigo-lilac and brown	35·00	40·00
		a. No stop	£110	£120
		b. Opt double		
7		10 ch. brown and carmine	38·00	40·00
		a. No stop	£120	£120
8		12 ch. blue and green	45·00	48·00
		a. No stop	£140	£150
9		24 ch. green and purple	70·00	50·00
		a. No stop	£190	£160
10		1 kr. carmine and blue	70·00	28·00
		a. Double overprint	£6000	
		b. No stop	£190	95·00
11		2 kr. claret and green	£190	£150
		a. No stop	£600	£400
12		3 kr. black and lilac	£160	£170
		a. No stop	£500	£500
13		5 kr. blue and red	£110	95·00
		a. No stop	£375	£350
14		10 kr. rose and bistre-brown	95·00	90·00
		a. No stop	£350	£325

Nos. 1/3 and 5/14 were overprinted in horizontal strips of 10 and No. 4 in horizontal strips of 5. Eight different settings are recognized, with the "No stop" variety occurring on stamp 9 from the four settings with 3 mm between "Under" and "British" and on stamp 10 from one setting where the gap is 2 mm.

1915 (Sept). *Nos.* 426/40 *and* 441 *of Iran optd with T* **1**.

No.	Type	Description	Unused	Used
15	**66**	1 ch. deep blue and carmine	£325	£325
16		2 ch. carmine and deep blue	£6000	£6500
17		3 ch. deep green	£400	£400
18		5 ch. vermilion	£5000	£5000
19		6 ch. carmine and green	£4000	£4250
20		9 ch. deep violet and brown	£550	£600
21		10 ch. brown and deep green	£850	£900
22		12 ch. ultramarine	£1000	£1100
23		24 ch. sepia and brown	£400	£400
24	**67**	1 kr. black, brown and silver	£400	£425
25		2 kr. carmine, slate and silver	£350	£375
26		3 kr. sepia, dull lilac and silver ..	£475	£500
27		5 kr. slate, sepia and silver	£450	£475
		a. Opt inverted	†	£11000
28	**68**	1 t. black, violet and gold	£400	£450
29		3 t. red, crimson and gold	£2750	£3000

Nos. 15/29 were overprinted in strips of 5.

Examples of overprint Type 1 on Iran No. 414, 1 ch. on 5 ch. (previously No. 30), are now believed to be forged.

Cameroon

Allied operations against the German protectorate of Kamerun commenced in September 1914 and were completed on 18 February 1916. The territory was divided, under an Anglo-French agreement, on 31 March 1916 with the British administering the area in the west along the Nigerian border. League of Nations mandates were issued for the two sections of Cameroon, which were converted into United Nations trusteeships in 1946.

Supplies of Kamerun stamps were found on the German steamer *Professor Woermann* captured at Freetown and these were surcharged, probably in Sierra Leone, and issued by the Cameroons Expeditionary Force at Duala in July 1915.

A French Post Office opened in Duala on 10 November 1915 using stamps of Gabon overprinted "Corps Expeditionnaire Franco-Anglais Cameroun". Although under the overall control of the British combined force commander this office remained part of the French postal system.

PRICES FOR STAMPS ON COVER
The stamps of British Occupation of Cameroons are rare used on cover.

CAMEROONS EXPEDITIONARY FORCE

A

B

C. E. F.
1d.
(1)

C. E. F.
1s.
(2)

SETTINGS. Nos. B1/3 were surcharged from a setting of 100 (10×10) with the face value changed for the 1d.

Nos. B4 and B6/9 were surcharged from a common setting of 50 (5×10) with the face value amended.

No. B5 was surcharged from a setting of 10 in a vertical strip repeated across the sheet. The figures of the surcharge on this value are in a different style from the remainder of the pence stamps.

Nos. B10/13 were surcharged from a common setting of 20 (4×5) with the face value amended.

Different fount "d" (R. 1/10, 6/9, 10/10)

"1" with thin serifs (R. 5/1)

Large "3" (R. 3/5, 3/10)

Short "4" (R. 10/2, 10/7)

"s" inverted (R. 3/4)

"s" broken at top (R. 3/1)

1915 (12 July). *Stamps of German Kamerun. Types* A *and* B, *surch as T* **1** (*Nos.* B1/9) *or* **2** (*Nos.* B10/13) *in black or blue.*

No.	Type	Description	Unused	Used
B1	A	½d. on 3 pf. (No. K7) (B.)	13·00	29·00
		a. Different fount "d"	£110	£225
B2		½d. on 5 pf. (No. K21 *wmk lozenges*) (B.)	2·75	9·00
		a. Different fount "d"	30·00	85·00
		b. Surch double	†	£800
		ba. Surch double, one albino	£180	
B3		1d. on 10 pf. (No. K22 *wmk lozenges*) (B.)	1·25	9·50
		a. "1" with thin serifs	13·00	65·00
		b. Surch double	£275	
		ba. Surch double, one albino	85·00	
		c. "1d." only double	£1800	
		d. Surch triple, two albino	£190	
		e. Surch in black	14·00	55·00
		ea. "1" with thin serifs	£150	
		eb. "C.E.F." omitted	£2750	
B4		2d. on 20 pf. (No. K23 *wmk lozenges*)	3·50	19·00
		a. Surch double, one albino	£180	
B5		2½d. on 25 pf. (No. K11)	12·00	42·00
		a. Surch double	£6500	
		ab. Surch double, one albino		
B6		3d. on 30 pf. (No. K12)	12·00	42·00
		a. Large "3"	£700	
		b. Surch triple, two albino	£200	
B7		4d. on 40 pf. (No. K13)	12·00	42·00
		a. Short "4"	£550	£850
		b. Surch triple, two albino	£190	
		c. Surch quadruple, three albino ..	£1500	
B8		6d. on 50 pf. (No. K14)	12·00	42·00
		a. Surch double, one albino	£170	
B9		8d. on 80 pf. (No. K15)	12·00	42·00
		a. Surch triple, two albino	£900	
B10	B	1s. on 1 m. (No. K16)	£150	£600
		a. "s" inverted	£700	£2000
B11		2s. on 2 m. (No. K17)	£150	£600
		a. "s" inverted	£700	£2000
		b. Surch double, one albino	£1200	

B12 B 3s. on 3 m. (No. K18) £150 £600
a. "s" inverted £700 £2000
b. "s" broken at top £475
c. Surch double £7000
ca. Surch triple, two albino £1200
B13 5s. on 5 m. (No. K25a *wmk lozenges*) £180 £650
a. "s" inverted £800 £2250
b. "s" broken at top £550
B1/13 .. .. *Set of* 13 £650 £2500

Examples of all values exist showing a forged Duala Kamerun postmark dated "11 10 15". Another forged cancel dated "16 11 15" is also known. This can be identified by the lack of a serif on the index letter "b".

The stamps of Nigeria were subsequently used in British Cameroons and the area was administered as part of Nigeria from February 1924.

For issues of Cameroun under French administration see *Part 6 (France)*.

Canada

Separate stamp issues appeared for British Columbia and Vancouver Island, Canada, New Brunswick, Newfoundland, Nova Scotia and Prince Edward Island before these colonies joined the Dominion of Canada.

BRITISH COLUMBIA & VANCOUVER ISLAND

Vancouver Island was organised as a Crown Colony in 1849 and the mainland territory was proclaimed a separate colony as British Columbia, in 1858. The two colonies combined, as British Columbia, on 19 November 1866.

PRICES FOR STAMPS ON COVER	
Nos. 2/3	*from* × 6
Nos. 11/12	*from* × 2
Nos. 13/14	*from* × 6
Nos. 21/2	*from* × 10
Nos. 23/7	*from* × 6
Nos. 28/9	*from* × 10
No. 30	—
No. 31	*from* × 10
Nos. 32/3	—

1

(Typo D.L.R.)

1860. *No wmk. P* 14.
2 1 $2^1/_2$d. deep reddish rose £325 £180
3 $2^1/_2$d. pale reddish rose £325 £180

When Vancouver Island adopted the dollar currency in 1862 the $2^1/_2$d. was sold at 5 c. From 18 May until 1 November 1865 examples of Nos. 2/3 were used to prepay mail from Vancouver Island to British Columbia at the price of 15 cents a pair.

From 20 June 1864 to 1 November 1865, the $2^1/_2$d. was sold in British Columbia for 3d. and was subsequently used for the same purpose during a shortage of 3d. stamps in 1867.

Imperforate plate proofs exist in pale dull red (*Price* £2750 *un*)

VANCOUVER ISLAND

(New Currency. 100 cents = 1 dollar)

2

3

(Typo D.L.R.)

1865 (19 Sept). *Wmk Crown CC.* (a) *Imperf* (1866)
11 2 5 c. rose £20000 £8000
12 3 10 c. blue £1500 £850

(b) *P* 14
13 2 5 c. rose £250 £150
w. Wmk inverted £1100
x. Wmk reversed .. .. .. † £550
14 3 10 c. blue £225 £140
w. Wmk inverted £750 £500

Medium or poor copies of Nos. 11 and 12 can be supplied at much lower prices, when in stock.

After the two colonies combined Nos. 13/14 were also used in British Columbia.

BRITISH COLUMBIA

4

(Typo D.L.R.)

1865 (1 Nov)–**67.** *Wmk Crown CC. P* 14.
21 4 3d. deep blue .. .. 80·00 65·00
22 3d. pale blue (19.7.67) .. .. .. 80·00 65·00
w. Wmk inverted £250 £170

British Columbia changed to the dollar currency on 1 January 1866. Remaining stocks of No. 21 and the supply of No. 22, when it finally arrived, were sold at $12^1/_2$ c. a pair.

(New Currency. 100 cents = 1 dollar)

TWO CENTS (5) 5.CENTS.5 (6)

1868–71. *T* 4 *in various colours. Wmk Crown CC. Surch as T* 5 *or* **6.** (a) *P* $12^1/_2$ (3.69)
23 5 c. red (Bk.) £700 £650
24 10 c. lake (B.) £550 £475
25 25 c. yellow (V.) £400
26 50 c. mauve (R.) £475
27 $1 green (G.) £750

(b) *P* 14
28 2 c. brown (Bk.) (1.68) £110
29 5 c. pale red (Bk.) (5.69) £140
30 10 c. lake (B.) £750
31 25 c. yellow (V.) (21.7.69) £140
32 50 c. mauve (R.) (23.2.71) £450
w. Wmk inverted £600
33 $1 green (G.) £650

Nos. 30 and 33 were not issued.

British Columbia joined the Dominion of Canada on 20 1871.

COLONY OF CANADA

The first British post offices in what was to become the colo Canada were opened at Quebec, Montreal and Trois Riv during 1763. These, and subsequent, offices remained part o British G.P.O. system until 6 April 1851.

The two provinces of Upper Canada (Ontario) and Lo Canada (Quebec) were united in 1840.

For illustration of the handstamp types see BRITISH P OFFICES ABROAD notes, following GREAT BRITAIN.

NEW CARLISLE, GASPÉ

POSTMASTER'S PROVISIONAL ENVELOPE

1

1851 (7 April).
1 1 3d. black .. ..

Only one example is known, addressed to Toronto, with impression cancelled by the signature of the postmaster, R Kelly.

QUEBEC

CROWNED-CIRCLE HANDSTAMPS

CC1 CC 1*b* QUEBEC L.C. (R.) (13.1.1842) *Price on cover* £

PRICES FOR STAMPS ON COVER	
Nos. 1/23	*from* × 2
Nos. 25/8	*from* × 3
Nos. 29/43*a*	*from* × 3
Nos. 44/5	*from* × 8

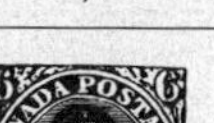

1 American Beaver (Designed by Sir Sandford Fleming) **2** Prince Albert **3**

Major re-entry: Line though "EE PEN" (Upper pane R. 5/7)

(T **1/6.** Eng and recess Rawdon, Wright, Hatch and Edson, N York)

1851. *Imperf. Laid paper.*
1 1 3d. red (23 April) £11000 £6
1*a* 3d. orange-vermilion £11000 £6
b. Major re-entry .. .. .. — £16
2 2 6d. slate-violet (15 May) £14000 £9
3 6d. brown-purple £15000 £12
a. Bisected (3d.) on cover .. .. † £200
4 3 12d. black (14 June) £60000 £400

There are several re-entries on the plate of the 3d. in addition the major re-entry listed. All re-entries occur in this stamp on papers.

Forgeries of the 3d. are known without the full stop af "PENCE". They also omit the foliage in the corners, as similar forgeries of the 6d.

4

5

6 Jacques Cart

1852–57. *Imperf.*

A. *Handmade wove paper, varying in thickness* (1852–56)
5 1 3d. red £1100 £1
a. Bisected ($1^1/_2$d.) on cover (1856) .. † £220
6 3d. deep red £1200 £1
7 3d. scarlet-vermilion £1500 £1

3d. brown-red £1200 £160
a. Bisected (1½d.) on cover (1856) .. † £22000
b. Major re-entry (*all shades*) *from* £2750 £650
6d. slate-violet £12000 £950
a. Bisected (3d.) on cover .. .. † £12000
6d. greenish grey £12000 £950
6d. brownish grey £13000 £1100
7½d. yellow-green (*shades*) (2.6.57) .. £7000 £1500
10d. bright blue (1.55) £7000 £1200
10d. dull blue £6500 £1100
10d. blue *to* deep blue £7000 £1200
a. Major re-entry (*all shades*) *from* — £2000
12d. black .. .. — £48000

achine-made medium to thick wove paper of a more even texture with more visible mesh. Clearer impressions (1857)
½d. deep rose (1.8.57) £700 £400
3d. red £1600 £450
a. Bisected (1½d.) on cover .. † £20000
b. Major re-entry .. .. .. — £1200
6d. grey-lilac £14000 £2000
10d. blue *to* deep blue £7000 £2000
a. Major re-entry £11000 £2500

C. *Thin soft horizontally ribbed paper* (1857)
½d. deep rose £5500 £1600
a. Vertically ribbed paper £6000 £2250
3d. red £3000 £400
a. Major re-entry .. .. .. — £1100

D. *Very thick soft wove paper* (1857)
6d. reddish purple £14000 £2500
a. Bisected (3d.) on cover .. .. † £18000

sected examples of the 3d. value were used to make up the . Canadian Packet rate to England from May 1856 until the oduction of the 7½d. value on 2 June 1857.

e 7½d. and 10d. values can be found in wide and narrow ions. These differences are due to shrinkage of the paper, h was wetted before printing and then contracted unevenly ng drying. The width of these stamps varies between 17 and m.

e listed major re-entry on the 10d. occurs on R.3/5 and s strong doubling of the top frame line and the left-hand stg." with a line through the lower parts of "ANAD" and "CE". Smaller re-entries occur on all values.

xamples of the 12d. on wove paper come from a proof sheet for postal purposes by the postal authorities.

e 3d. is known perforated 14 and also *percé en scie* 13. Both contemporary, but were unofficial.

-59. *P* 11¾. A. *Machine-made medium to thick wove per with a more even hard texture.*
4 ½d. deep rose (12.58) £1800 £600
a. Lilac-rose £2000 £650
1 3d. red (1.59) £2500 £300
a. Major re-entry .. .. .. — £1000
2 6d. brownish grey (1.59) £6500 £2500
a. Slate-violet £6500 £2250

B. *Thin soft horizontally ribbed paper*
4 ½d. deep rose-red .. .. .. — £3250
1 3d. red .. .. — £1200
a. Major re-entry .. .. ..

(New Currency. 100 cents = 1 dollar)

7

8 American Beaver

Prince Albert

10

11 Jacques Cartier

(Recess A.B.N. Co)

(On 1 May 1858, Messrs. Rawdon, Wright, Hatch and Edson ned with eight other firms to form "The American Bank Note " and the "imprint" on sheets of the following stamps has the w title of the firm with "New York" added.)

359 (1 July). *P* 12.
) 7 1 c. pale rose (to rose-red) .. .. £225 27·00
) 1 c. deep rose (to carmine-rose) .. £300 45·00
a. Imperf (pair) £2500
b. Imperf × perf .. .. ..
8 5 c. pale red .. .. £250 11·00
2 5 c. deep red .. .. £250 11·00
a. Re-entry* (R.3/8) £2500 £450
b. Imperf (pair) £7000
c. Bisected (2½ c.) with 10 c. on cover † £4000
3 9 10 c. black-brown £6000 £1300
a. Bisected (5 c.), on cover .. .. † £5500
3b 10 c. deep red-purple £2500 £500
ba. Bisected (5 c.), on cover .. † £3750
4 10 c. purple (*shades*) .. .. .. £800 42·00
a. Bisected (5 c.), on cover .. .. † £3750
5 10 c. brownish purple .. .. .. £750 42·00
6 10 c. brown (to pale) .. .. .. £750 42·00
a. Bisected (5 c.), on cover .. .. † £4500
7 10 c. dull violet .. .. £800 50·00
8 10 c. bright red-purple .. .. .. £800 42·00
a. Imperf (pair) £6000
9 10 12½ c. deep yellow-green .. .. £600 40·00
0 12½ c. pale yellow-green .. .. .. £550 40·00
1 12½ c. blue-green .. .. £700 48·00
a. Imperf (pair) £2500
b. Imperf between (vert pair) .. ..

42 11 17 c. deep blue .. .. £750 60·00
a. Imperf (pair) £3000
43 17 c. slate-blue .. .. £900 90·00
43*a* 17 c. indigo .. .. £800 65·00

*The price of No. 32a is for the very marked re-entry showing oval frame line doubled above "CANADA". Slighter re-entries are worth from £30 upwards in used condition.

As there were numerous P.O. Dept. orders for the 10 c., 12½ c. and 17 c. and some of these were executed by more than one separate printing, with no special care to ensure uniformity of colour, there is a wide range of shade, especially in the 10 c., and some shades recur at intervals after periods during which other shades predominated. The colour-names given in the above list therefore represent groups only.

It has been proved by leading Canadian specialists that the perforations may be an aid to the approximate dating of a particular stamp, the gauge used measuring 11¾ × 11¾ from mid-July, 1859 to mid 1863, 12 × 11¾ from March 1863 to mid 1865 and 12 × 12 from April 1865 to 1868. Exceptionally in the 5 c. value many sheets were perforated 12 × 12 between May and October, 1862, whilst the last printings of the 12½ c. and 17 c. perf 11¾ × 11¾ were in July 1863, the perf 12 × 11¾ starting towards the end of 1863.

12

(Recess A.B.N. Co)

1864 (1 Aug). *P* 12.
44 12 2 c. rose-red £400 £140
45 2 c. bright rose £400 £140
a. Imperf (pair) £1600

The Colony of Canada became part of the Dominion of Canada on 1 July 1867.

NEW BRUNSWICK

New Brunswick, previously part of Nova Scotia, became a separate colony in June 1784. The colony became responsible for its postal service on 6 July 1851.

PRICES FOR STAMPS ON COVER

Nos. 1/4	*from* × 2
Nos. 5/6	*from* × 3
Nos. 7/9	*from* × 10
Nos. 10/12	*from* × 30
No. 13	—
Nos. 14/17	*from* × 2
No. 18	*from* × 5
No. 19	*from* × 100

1 Royal Crown and Heraldic Flowers of the United Kingdom

(Recess P.B.)

1851 (5 Sept). *Blue paper. Imperf.*
1 1 3d. bright red £2000 £350
2 3d. dull red £2000 £325
a. Bisected (1½d.) (on cover) .. .. † £2750
2*b* 6d. mustard-yellow £6000 £1500
3 6d. yellow £4500 £800
4 6d. olive-yellow £4500 £700
a. Bisected (3d.) (on cover) .. .. † £3000
b. Quartered (1½d.) (on cover) .. † £35000
5 1s. reddish mauve £13000 £4000
6 1s. dull mauve £14000 £4500
a. Bisected (6d.) (on cover) .. .. † £20000
b. Quartered (3d.) (on cover) .. .. † £28000

Reprints of all three values were made in 1890 on thin, hard, white paper. The 3d. is bright orange, the 6d. and 1s. violet-black.

Nos. 2a and 4b were to make up the 7½d. rate to Great Britain, introduced on 1 August 1854.

(New Currency. 100 cents = 1 dollar)

2 Locomotive

3

3*a* Charles Connell

4

5

6 Paddle-steamer *Washington*

7 King Edward VII when Prince of Wales

(Recess A.B.N. Co)

1860 (15 May)–**63**. *No wmk. P* 12.
7 2 1 c. brown-purple .. .. .. 55·00 38·00
8 1 c. purple .. .. 32·00 32·00
9 1 c. dull claret .. .. 32·00 32·00
a. Imperf vert (horiz pair) £550
10 3 2 c. orange (1863) .. .. .. 17·00 17·00
11 2 c. orange-yellow .. .. .. 19·00 17·00
12 2 c. deep orange .. .. .. 22·00 17·00
a. Imperf horiz (vert pair) £450
13 3*a* 5 c. brown £4250
14 4 5 c. yellow-green .. .. .. 15·00 13·00
15 5 c. deep green .. .. .. 15·00 13·00
16 5 c. sap-green (deep yellowish green) .. £300 40·00
17 5 10 c. red .. .. 38·00 38·00
a. Bisected (5 c.) (on cover) (1860) .. † £600
18 6 12½ c. indigo .. .. 50·00 40·00
19 7 17 c. black .. .. 35·00 42·00

Beware of forged cancellations.

No. 13 was not issued due to objections to the design showing Charles Connell, the Postmaster-General. Most of the printing was destroyed.

New Brunswick joined the Dominion of Canada on 1 July 1867 and its stamps were withdrawn in March of the following year.

NEWFOUNDLAND

Newfoundland became a self-governing colony in 1855 and a Dominion in 1917. In 1934 the adverse financial situation led to the suspension of the constitution.

The first local postmaster, at St. John's, was appointed in 1805, the overseas mails being routed via Halifax, Nova Scotia. A regular packet service was established between these two ports in 1840, the British G.P.O. assuming control of the overseas mails at the same time.

The responsibility for the overseas postal service reverted to the colonial administration on 1 July 1851.

For illustrations of the handstamp types see BRITISH POST OFFICES ABROAD notes, following GREAT BRITAIN.

ST. JOHN'S

CROWNED-CIRCLE HANDSTAMPS

CC1 CC 1a ST. JOHNS NEWFOUNDLAND (R.) (27.6.1846) .. .. *Price on cover* £900

PRICES FOR STAMPS ON COVER TO 1945

No. 1	*from* × 30
Nos. 2/4	*from* × 3
No. 5	*from* × 20
No. 6	*from* × 10
No. 7	*from* × 3
No. 8	*from* × 30
No. 9	*from* × 8
No. 10	—
No. 11	*from* × 8
No. 12	*from* × 3
Nos. 13/14	*from* × 20
Nos. 15/17	—
Nos. 18/20	*from* × 20
No. 21	*from* × 15
Nos. 22/3	—
No. 25	*from* × 30
No. 26	*from* × 5
No. 27	*from* × 8
No. 28	*from* × 3
Nos. 29/30	*from* × 10
No. 31	*from* × 30
No. 32	*from* × 8
No. 33	*from* × 5
No. 33*a*	—
Nos. 34/9	*from* × 8
Nos. 40/1	*from* × 5
Nos. 42/3	*from* × 30
Nos. 44/8	*from* × 8
No. 49	*from* × 50
Nos. 50/3	*from* × 10
No. 54	*from* × 4
No. 55/8*b*	*from* × 10
No. 59	*from* × 100
No. 59*a*	*from* × 10
Nos. 60/1	*from* × 4
Nos. 62/5	*from* × 8
Nos. 65*a*/79	*from* × 3
Nos. 83/90	*from* × 10
Nos. 91/3	*from* × 2
No. 94	*from* × 50
Nos. 95/141	*from* × 3
Nos. 142/*a*	*from* × 1½
No. 143	*from* × 8
Nos. 144/8*f*	*from* × 2
Nos. 149/62	*from* × 3

No. 163	—
Nos. 164/78	*from* × 2
Nos. 179/90	*from* × 3
No. 191	—
Nos. 192/220	*from* × 2
No. 221	—
Nos. 222/9	*from* × 3
Nos. 230/4	*from* × 2
No. 235	—
Nos. 236/91	*from* × 2
Nos. D1/6	*from* × 10

1

2

4

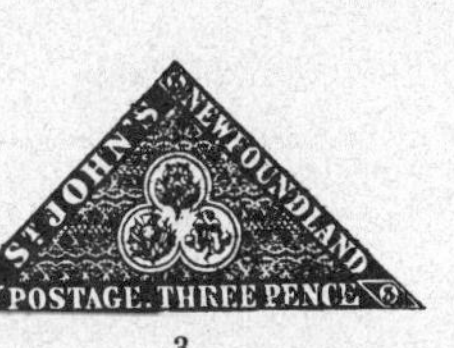
3

5

Royal Crown and Heraldic flowers of the United Kingdom

(Recess P.B.)

7 (1 Jan)–**64.** *No wmk. Thick, machine-made paper with a istinct mesh. Imperf.*
1 1d. brown-purple .. .. .. 90·00 £160
a. Bisected (½d.) (1864) (on cover) .. †£12000
2 2d. scarlet-vermilion (15 Feb) .. £9000 £4500
3 3d. yellowish green £700 £400
4 4d. scarlet-vermilion £6000 £2500
1 5d. brown-purple £180 £350
4 6d. scarlet-vermilion £12000 £3000
5 6½d. scarlet-vermilion £2250 £2500
4 8d. scarlet-vermilion £225 £400
a. Bisected (4d.) (1859) (on cover) .. † £3750
2 1s. scarlet-vermilion £13000 £4750
a. Bisected (6d.) (1860) (on cover) .. †£12000

he 6d. and 8d. differ from the 4d. in many details, as does the 1s. from the 2d.

RKINS BACON "CANCELLED". For notes on these dstamps, showing "CANCELLED" between horizontal bars ning an oval, see Catalogue Introduction.

0 (15 Aug–Dec). *Medium, hand-made paper without mesh. nperf.*
2 2d. orange-vermilion £325 £400
3 3d. grn *to* dp grn* (H/S "CANCELLED" in oval £5000) .. .. .. 70·00 £150
4 4d. orange-verm (H/S "CANCELLED" in oval £8000) £2250 £800
a. Bisected (2d.) (12.60) (on cover) .. †£13000
1 5d. Venetian red (H/S "CANCELLED" in oval £6500) .. .. .. 90·00 £275
4 6d. orange-vermilion £2750 £600
2 1s. orange-verm (H/S "CANCELLED" in oval £11000) £19000 £8000
a. Bisected (6d.) (12.60) (on cover) .. †£40000

No. 11 includes stamps from the July and November 1861 ntings which are very difficult to distinguish.

The 1s. on horizontally or vertically *laid* paper is now nsidered to be a proof (*Price* £10000).

Stamps of this and the following issue may be found with part the paper-maker's watermark "STACEY WISE 1858".

ISECTS. Collectors are warned against buying bisected stamps these issues without a reliable guarantee.

62–64. *New colours. Hand-made paper without mesh. Imperf.*
1 1d. chocolate-brown £160 £275
a. Red-brown £4000
2 2d. rose-lake £160 £375
4 4d. rose-lake (H/S "CANCELLED" in oval £6000) .. .. .. 29·00 90·00
a. Bisected (2d.) (1864) (on cover) .. † —
1 5d. chocolate-brown .. .. .. 60·00 £300
a. Red-brown .. .. .. 48·00 £190
4 6d. rose-lake (H/S "CANCELLED" in oval £6000) .. .. .. 21·00 £100
a. Bisected (3d.) (1863) (on cover) .. † £9000
5 6½d. rose-lake (H/S "CANCELLED" in oval £5000) .. .. .. 65·00 £425
2 **4** 8d. rose-lake .. .. .. 75·00 £550
3 **2** 1s. rose-lake ("H/S "CANCELLED" in oval £5000) .. .. .. 35·00 £300
a. Bisected (6d.) (1863) (on cover) .. †£14000

Nos. 16/23 come from printings made in July (2d., 4d., 6d., ½d., and 1s. only) or November 1861 (all values). The paper sed was from the same manufacturer as that for Nos. 11/15, it was of more variable thickness and texture, ranging from a elatively soft medium paper, which can be quite opaque, to a hin hard transparent paper. The rose-lake stamps also show a onsiderable variation in shade ranging from pale to deep. The xtensive remainders of this issue were predominately in pale hades on thin hard paper, but it is not possible to distinguish etween stamps from the two printings with any certainty. Deep hades of the 2d., 4d., 6d., 6½d. and 1s. on soft opaque paper do, owever, command a considerable premium.

Beware of buying used specimens of the stamps which are worth much less in unused condition, as many unused stamps have been rovided with faked postmarks. A guarantee should be obtained.

(New Currency. 100 cents = 1 dollar)

6 Atlantic Cod

7 Common Seal on Ice-floe

8 Prince Consort

9 Queen Victoria

10 Schooner

11 Queen Victoria

(Recess A.B.N. Co, New York)

1865 (15 Nov)–**71.** *P* 12. (*a*) *Thin yellowish paper.*
25 **6** 2 c. yellowish green .. .. .. £100 42·00
a Bisected (1 c.) (on cover) (1870) † £3750
26 **7** 5 c. brown £475 £170
a. Bisected (2½ c.) (on cover) ..
27 **8** 10 c. black .. .. £275 75·00
a. Bisected (5 c.) (on cover) (1869) † £2750
28 **9** 12 c. red-brown £400 £150
a. Bisected (6 c.) (on cover) .. .. † £2750
29 **10** 13 c. orange-yellow .. .. .. 90·00 70·00
30 **11** 24 c. blue .. .. 32·00 32·00

(*b*) *Medium white paper*
31 **6** 2 c. bluish green (*to* deep) (1870) .. 70·00 30·00
32 **8** 10 c. black (1871) .. .. .. £170 38·00
33 **9** 12 c. chestnut (1870) .. .. .. 45·00 45·00
33*a* **11** 24 c. blue (1870?) £900 £325

The inland postage rate was reduced to 3 c. on 8 May, 1870. Until the 3 c. value became available examples of No. 25 were bisected to provide 1 c. stamps.

12 King Edward VII when Prince of Wales

14 Queen Victoria

I

II

In Type II the white oval frame line is unbroken by the scroll containing the words "ONE CENT", the letters "N.F." are smaller and closer to the scroll, and there are other minor differences.

(Recess National Bank Note Co, New York)

1868 (Nov). *P* 12.
34 **12** 1 c. dull purple (I) .. .. .. 50·00 48·00

(Recess A.B.N. Co)

1868 (Nov)–**73.** *P* 12.
35 **12** 1 c. brown-purple (II) (5.71) .. .. 85·00 55·00
36 **14** 3 c. vermilion (7.70) £250 £100
37 3 c. blue (1.4.73) .. .. .. £275 18·00
38 **7** 5 c. black £250 £100
39 **14** 6 c. rose (7.70) .. .. .. 7·50 17·00

1876–79. *Rouletted.*
40 **12** 1 c. lake-purple (II) (1877) .. .. 90·00 45·00
41 **6** 2 c. bluish green (1879) .. .. .. £120 45·00
42 **14** 3 c. blue (1877) .. .. .. £275 4·25
43 **7** 5 c. blue .. .. £180 3·50
a. Imperf (pair) .. .. ..

15 King Edward VII when Prince of Wales

16 Atlantic Cod

17

18 Common Seal on Ice-floe

(Recess British American Bank Note Co, Montreal)

1880–82. *P* 12.
44 **15** 1 c. dull grey-brown .. .. .. 27·00 8·50
a. Dull brown .. .. .. 25·00 8·50
b. Red-brown .. .. .. 28·00 13·00
46 **16** 2 c. yellow-green (1882) .. .. .. 45·00 22·00
47 **17** 3 c. pale dull blue .. .. .. 75·00 5·00
a. Bright blue .. .. .. 80·00 3·00
48 **18** 5 c. pale dull blue .. .. .. £200 8·00

19 Newfoundland Dog

20 Atlantic Brigantine

21 Queen Victoria

(Recess British American Bank Note Co, Montreal)

1887 (15 Feb)–**88.** *New colours and values. P* 12.
49 **19** ½ c. rose-red .. .. 9·50 7·00
50 **15** 1 c. blue-green (1.88) .. .. .. 11·00 6·50
a. Green .. .. .. 6·00 3·00
b. Yellow-green .. .. .. 11·00 8·50
51 **16** 2 c. orange-vermilion (1.88) .. .. 15·00 4·50
52 **17** 3 c. deep brown (1.88) .. .. .. 60·00 1·50
53 **18** 5 c. deep blue (1.88) .. .. .. 95·00 4·50
54 **20** 10 c. black (1.88) .. .. .. 48·00 50·00
49/54 .. .. *Set of* 6 £220 65·00

For reissues of 1880/8 stamps in similar colours, see Nos. 62/5*a*.

(Recess B.A.B.N.)

1890 (Nov). *P* 12.
55 **21** 3 c. deep slate .. .. .. 27·00 1·50
a. Imperf (pair) .. ..
56 3 c. slate-grey (*to* grey) .. .. 28·00 1·50
a. Imperf horiz (vert pair) .. £400
57 3 c. slate-violet .. .. .. 35·00 3·50
58 3 c. grey-lilac .. .. .. 35·00 1·50
58*a* 3 c. brown-grey .. .. .. 35·00 6·00
58*b* 3 c. purple-grey .. .. .. 38·00 5·50

There is a very wide range of shades in this stamp, and those given only cover the main groups.

Stamps on pink paper are from a consignment recovered from the sea and which were affected by the salt water.

(Recess British American Bank Note Co, Montreal)

1894 (Aug–Dec). *Changes of colour. P* 12.
59 **19** ½ c. black (11.94) .. .. .. 9·50 5·00
59*a* **18** 5 c. bright blue (12.94) .. .. .. 60·00 3·50
60 **14** 6 c. crimson-lake (12.94) .. .. 16·00 16·00
61 **9** 12 c. deep brown .. .. .. 48·00 50·00

The 6 c. is printed from the old American Bank Note Company's plates.

1896 (Jan)–**98.** *Reissues. P* 12.
62 **19** ½ c. orange-vermilion .. .. .. 45·00 50·00
63 **15** 1 c. deep brown .. .. .. 60·00 55·00
63*a* 1 c. deep green (1898) .. .. 16·00 11·00
64 **16** 2 c. green .. .. 85·00 50·00
65 **17** 3 c. deep blue .. .. .. 70·00 15·00
65*a* 3 c. chocolate-brown .. .. .. 80·00 80·00
62/5*a* .. .. *Set of* 6 £325 £225

The above were *reissued* for postal purposes. The colours were generally brighter than those of the original stamps.

22 Queen Victoria

23 John Cabot

24 Cape Bonavista

25 Caribou hunting

26 Mining

27 Logging

28 Fishing

29 *Matthew* (Cabot)

30 Willow Grouse

31 Group of Grey Seals

32 Salmon-fishing

33 Seal of the Colony

34 Iceberg off St. John's

35 Henry VII

(Des R. O. Smith. Recess A.B.N. Co)

1897 (24 June). *400th Anniv of Discovery of Newfoundland and 60th year of Queen Victoria's reign. P* 12.

No.	Type	Description	Unused	Used
66	**22**	1 c. green	2·50	5·50
67	**23**	2 c. bright rose	2·25	2·75
		a. Bisected (1 c.) on cover	†	£250
68	**24**	3 c. bright blue	3·50	1·00
		a. Bisected (1½ c.) on cover	†	£250
69	**25**	4 c. olive-green	9·50	3·00
70	**26**	5 c. violet	13·00	3·00
71	**27**	6 c. red-brown	9·50	3·25
		a. Bisected (3 c.) on cover	†	£250
72	**28**	8 c. orange	21·00	9·00
73	**29**	10 c. sepia	42·00	6·50
74	**30**	12 c. deep blue	35·00	6·00
75	**31**	15 c. bright scarlet	20·00	18·00
76	**32**	24 c. dull violet-blue	25·00	19·00
77	**33**	30 c. slate-blue	45·00	60·00
78	**34**	35 c. red	60·00	60·00
79	**35**	60 c. black	17·00	12·00
66/79		*Set of* 14	£275	£190

The 60 c. surcharged "TWO-2-CENTS" in three lines is an essay made in December 1918 (*Price* £300).

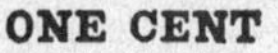

ONE CENT (36)

ONE CENT (37)

ONE CENT (38)

1897 (19 Oct). *T* **21** *surch with T* **36/8** *by Royal Gazette, St. Johns, on stamps of various shades.*

No.	Type	Description	Unused	Used
80	**36**	1 c. on 3 c. grey-purple	48·00	20·00
		a. Surch double, one diagonal	£1100	
		d. Vert pair, one without lower bar and "ONE CENT"	£3500	
81	**37**	1 c. on 3 c. grey-purple	£100	85·00
82	**38**	1 c. on 3 c. grey-purple	£450	£375

Nos. 80/2 occur in the same setting of 50 (10×5) applied twice to each sheet. Type **36** appeared in the first four horizontal rows, Type **37** on R. 5/1–8 and Type **38** on R. 5/9 and 10.

Trial surcharges in red or red and black were not issued.

(*Price*: Type **36** *in red* £750, *in red and black* £750: Type **37** *in red* £2250, *in red and black* £2500: Type **38** *in red* £5000, *in red and black* £6000).

These surcharges exist on stamps of various shades, but those on brown-grey are clandestine forgeries, having been produced by one of the printers at the *Royal Gazette*.

39 Prince Edward later Duke of Windsor

40 Queen Victoria

41 King Edward VII when Prince of Wales

42 Queen Alexandra when Princess of Wales

43 Queen Mary when Duchess of York

44 King George V when Duke of York

(Recess A.B.N. Co)

1897 (4 Dec)–**1918.** *P* 12.

No.	Type	Description	Unused	Used
83	**39**	½ c. olive (8.98)	2·25	1·50
		a. Imperf (pair)	£325	
84	**40**	1 c. carmine	3·25	3·50
85		1 c. blue-green (6.98)	9·50	20
		a. Yellow-green	7·50	20
		b. Imperf horiz (vert pair)	£170	
86	**41**	2 c. orange	3·25	3·50
		a. Imperf (pair)	—	£300
87		2 c. scarlet (6.98)	14·00	40
		a. Imperf (pair)	£225	£225
		b. Imperf between (pair)	£300	
88	**42**	3 c. orange (6.98)	17·00	30
		a. Imperf horiz (vert pair)	£275	
		b. Imperf (pair)	£225	£225
		c. Red-orange/bluish (6.18)	30·00	2·75
89	**43**	4 c. violet (21.10.01)	23·00	4·50
		a. Imperf (pair)	£350	
90	**44**	5 c. blue (6.99)	38·00	3·00
83/90		*Set of* 8	95·00	15·00

No. 88*c* was an emergency war-time printing made by the American Bank Note Co from the old plate, pending receipt of the then current 3 c. from England.

The imperforate errors of this issue are found used, but only as philatelic "by favour" items. It is possible that No. 86*a* only exists in this condition.

45 Map of Newfoundland

(Recess A.B.N. Co)

1908 (31 Aug). *P* 12.

No.	Type	Description	Unused	Used
94	**45**	2 c. lake	27·00	1·00

46 King James I

47 Arms of Colonisation Co

48 John Guy

49 *Endeavour* (immigrant ship), 1610

50 Cupids

51 Sir Francis Bacon

52 View of Mosquito

53 Logging Camp, Red Indian Lake

54 Paper Mills, Grand Falls

55 King Edward VII

56 King George V

6 c. (A) "Z" in "COLONIZATION" reversed. (B) "Z" correc

(Litho Whitehead, Morris & Co Ltd)

1910 (15 Aug). (*a*) *P* 12

No.	Type	Description	Unused	Used
95	**46**	1 c. green	7·50	2
		a. "NFWFOUNDLAND" (Right pane R. 5/1)	55·00	85
		b. "JAMRS" (Right pane R. 5/2)	55·00	85
		c. Imperf between (horiz pair)	£275	£
96	**47**	2 c. rose-carmine	12·00	2
97	**48**	3 c. olive	6·00	15
98	**49**	4 c. violet	15·00	13
99	**50**	5 c. bright blue	25·00	7
100	**51**	6 c. claret (A)	45·00	£1
100*a*		6 c. claret (B)	22·00	75
101	**52**	8 c. bistre-brown	48·00	95
102	**53**	9 c. olive-green	40·00	80
103	**54**	10 c. purple-slate	55·00	£1
104	**55**	12 c. pale red-brown	55·00	80
		a. Imperf (pair)	£300	
105	**56**	15 c. black	65·00	£1
95/105		*Set of* 11	£300	£5
		(*b*) *P* 12×14		
106	**46**	1 c. green	4·25	8
		a. "NFWFOUNDLAND"	50·00	£1
		b. "JAMRS"	50·00	£1
		c. Imperf between (horiz pair)	£475	£5
107	**47**	2 c. rose-carmine	4·00	
		a. Imperf between (horiz pair)	£475	
108	**50**	5 c. bright blue (*p* 14×12)	8·00	2
		(*c*) *P* 12×11		
109	**46**	1 c. green	1·25	
		a. Imperf between (horiz pair)	£250	
		b. Imperf between (vert pair)	£300	
		c. "NFWFOUNDLAND"	23·00	48
		e. "JAMRS"	23·00	48
		(*d*) *P* 12×11½		
110	**47**	2 c. rose-carmine	£225	£2

(Dies eng Macdonald & Sons. Recess A. Alexander & Sons, Ltd

1911 (7 Feb). *As T* **51** *to* **56**, *but recess printed. P* 14.

No.	Description	Unused	Used
111	6 c. claret (B)	18·00	42
112	8 c. yellow-brown	48·00	65
	a. Imperf between (horiz pair)	£450	
	b. Imperf (pair)	£300	
113	9 c. sage-green	45·00	95
	a. Imperf between (horiz pair)	£425	
114	10 c. purple-black	90·00	£1
	a. Imperf between (horiz pair)	£400	
	b. Imperf (pair)	£250	
115	12 c. red-brown	60·00	60
116	15 c. slate-green	65·00	£1
111/16	*Set of* 6	£275	£45

The 9 c. and 15 c. exist with papermaker's watermark "I TOWGOOD FINE".

57 Queen Mary

58 King George V

59 Duke of Windsor whe Prince of Wale

60 King George VI when Prince Albert

61 Princess Mary, the Princess Royal

62 Prince Henry Duke of Glouceste

63 Prince George, Duke of Kent

64 Prince John

65 Queen Alexandra

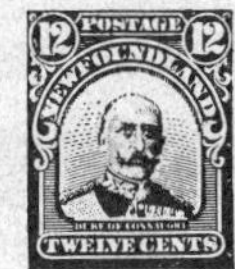
66 Duke of Connaught

67 Seal of Newfoundland

to 5 c., 10 c. eng and recess D.L.R.; others eng Macdonald & Co, recess A. Alexander & Sons)

(19 June)–**16**. *Coronation. P* 13½ × 14 (*comb*) (1 *c. to* 5 *c.,* c.) *or* 14 (*line*) (*others*).

No.		Description	Unused	Used
57		1 c. yellow-green	7·00	30
		a. *Blue-green* (1915)	8·00	30
58		2 c. carmine	3·75	20
		a. *Rose-red* (*blurred impression*). Perf 14 (1916)	7·50	55
59		3 c. red-brown	20·00	29·00
60		4 c. purple	19·00	26·00
61		5 c. ultramarine	7·00	1·50
62		6 c. slate-grey	13·00	25·00
63		8 c. aniline blue	55·00	75·00
		a. *Greenish blue*	65·00	90·00
64		9 c. violet-blue	16·00	42·00
65		10 c. deep green	28·00	40·00
66		12 c. plum	23·00	42·00
67		15 c. lake	18·00	45·00
/27		*Set of* 11	£180	£275

he 2 c. rose-red, No. 118*a* is a poor war-time printing by Alexer & Sons.

lthough No. 123 has a typical aniline appearance it is believed t the shade results from the thinning of non-aniline ink.

68 Reindeer

FIRST
TRANS-
ATLANTIC
AIR POST
April, 1919.

(69)

(Des J. H. Noonan. Recess D.L.R.)

19 (2 Jan). *Newfoundland Contingent,* 1914–1918. *P* 14.

No.	Type	Description	Unused	Used
)	**68**	1 c. green (*a*) (*b*)	3·75	20
1		2 c. scarlet (*a*) (*b*)	3·75	85
		a. *Carmine-red* (*b*)	11·00	45
2		3 c. brown (*a*) (*b*)	6·00	20
		a. *Red-brown* (*b*)	7·00	30
3		4 c. mauve (*a*)	6·00	70
		a. *Purple* (*b*)	11·00	30
4		5 c. ultramarine (*a*) (*b*)	7·00	1·25
5		6 c. slate-grey (*a*)	5·00	35·00
6		8 c. bright magenta (*a*)	11·00	42·00
7		10 c. deep grey-green (*a*)	6·00	4·00
8		12 c. orange (*a*)	18·00	50·00
9		15 c. indigo (*a*)	15·00	55·00
		a. *Prussian blue* (*a*)	80·00	£140
40		24 c. bistre-brown (*a*)	22·00	28·00
41		36 c. sage-green (*a*)	15·00	27·00
30/41		*Set of* 12	£100	£225

Each value bears with "Trail of the Caribou" the name of a fferent action: 1 c. Suvla Bay; 3 c. Gueudecourt; 4 c. Beaumont amel; 6 c. Monchy; 10 c. Steenbeck; 15 c. Langemarck; 24 c. ambrai; 36 c. Combles; 2 c., 5 c., 8 c., and 12 c. inscribed "Royal aval Reserve-Ubique".

Perforations. Two perforating heads were used: (*a*) comb 4 × 13.9; (*b*) line 14.1 × 14.1.

919 (12 Apr). *Air. No.* 132 *optd with T* **69**, *by Robinson & Co Ltd, at the offices of the "Daily News".*

No.	Type	Description	Unused	Used
42	**68**	3 c. brown	£15000	£8000

These stamps franked correspondence carried by Lieut. H. Hawker on his Atlantic flight. 18 were damaged and destroyed, 5 used on letters, 11 given as presentation copies, and the emaining 76 were sold in aid of the Marine Disasters Fund.

919 (19 April). *Nos.* 132 *optd in MS.* "Aerial Atlantic Mail. J.A.R."

No.	Type	Description	Unused	Used
42*a*	**68**	3 c. brown	—	£20000

This provisional was made by W. C. Campbell, the Secretary of he Postal Department, and the initials are those of the Postmaster, J. A. Robinson, for use on correspondence intended o be carried on the abortive Morgan-Raynham Trans-Atlantic light. The mail was eventually delivered by sea.

In addition to the 25 to 30 used examples, one unused, no gum, copy of No. 142*a* is known.

Single examples of a similar overprint on the 2 c. (No. 131) and 5 c. (No. 134) are known used on covers, the former with an unoverprinted example of the same value.

Trans-Atlantic
AIR POST,
1919.
ONE DOLLAR.

(70)

THREE
CENTS

(71)

1919 (9 June). *Air. No.* 75 *surch with T* **70** *by Royal Gazette, St. Johns.*

No.	Type	Description	Unused	Used
143	**31**	$1 on 15 c. bright scarlet	£110	£110
		a. No comma after "AIR POST"	£140	£150
		b. As Var a and no stop after "1919"	£350	£375
		c. As Var a and "A" of "AIR" under "a" of "Trans"	£350	£375

These stamps were issued for use on the mail carried on the first successful flight across the Atlantic by Capt. J. Alcock and Lieut. A. Brown, and on other projected Trans-Atlantic flights (Alcock flown cover, *Price* £3000).

The surcharge was applied in a setting of which 16 were normal, 7 as No. 143a, 1 as No. 143b and 1 as No. 143c.

1920 (Sept). *Nos.* 75 *and* 77/8 *surch as T* **71**, *by Royal Gazette* (2 *c. with only one bar, at top of stamp*).

A. *Bars of surch* 10½ *mm apart.* B. *Bars* 13½ *mm apart*

No.	Type	Description	Unused	Used
144	**33**	2 c. on 30 c. slate-blue (24 Sept)	4·25	17·00
		a. Surch inverted	£500	£550
145	**31**	3 c. on 15 c. bright scarlet (A) (13 Sept)	£160	£170
		a. Surch inverted	£1100	
146		3 c. on 15 c. bright scarlet (B) (13 Sept)	15·00	15·00
147	**34**	3 c. on 35 c. red (15 Sept)	6·50	11·00
		a. Surch inverted	£900	
		b. Lower bar omitted	£120	£150
		c. "THREE" omitted	£1100	

Our prices for Nos. 147b and 147c are for stamps with lower bar or "THREE" entirely missing. The bar may be found in all stages of incompleteness and stamps showing broken bar are not of much value.

On the other hand, stamps showing either only the top or bottom of the letters "THREE" are scarce, though not as rare as No. 147c.

The 6 c. T **27** surcharged "THREE CENTS", in red or black, is an essay (*Price* £425). The 2 c. on 30 c. with red surcharge is a colour trial (*Price* £500).

AIR MAIL
to Halifax, N.S.
1921.

(72)

1921 (16 Nov). *Air. No.* 78 *optd with T* **72** *by Royal Gazette.*

I. 2¾ *mm between* "AIR" *and* "MAIL"

No.	Type	Description	Unused	Used
148	**34**	35 c. red	90·00	90·00
		a. No stop after "1921"	80·00	80·00
		b. No stop and first "1" of "1921" below "f" of "Halifax"	£180	£180
		c. As No. 148, inverted	£4000	
		d. As No. 148a, inverted	£3750	
		e. As No. 148b, inverted	£8000	

II. 1½ *mm between* "AIR" *and* "MAIL"

No.	Type	Description	Unused	Used
148*f*	**34**	35 c. red	£100	£100
		g. No stop after "1921"	£120	£120
		h. No stop and first "1" of "1921" below "f" of "Halifax"	£180	£180
		i. As No. 148f, inverted	£4500	
		k. As No. 148g, inverted	£5500	
		l. As No. 148h, inverted	£8000	

Type **72** was applied as a setting of 25 which contained ten stamps as No. 148a, seven as No. 148, four as No. 148*f*, two as No. 148g, one as No. 148b and one as No. 148h.

73 Twin Hills, Tor's Cove

74 South-West Arm, Trinity

75 Statue of the Fighting Newfoundlander, St. John's

(Recess D.L.R.)

1923 (9 July)–**26**. *T* **73/5** *and similar designs. P* 14 (*comb or line*).

No.		Description	Unused	Used
149		1 c. green	1·25	20
150		2 c. carmine	75	10
		a. Imperf (pair)	£160	
151		3 c. brown	80	10
152		4 c. deep purple	1·00	30
153		5 c. ultramarine	2·25	1·75
154		6 c. slate	3·50	8·00
155		8 c. purple	4·50	3·50
156		9 c. slate-green	18·00	29·00
157		10 c. violet	5·00	3·00
		a. *Purple*	6·50	2·75
158		11 c. sage-green	3·75	16·00
159		12 c. lake	3·25	9·50
160		15 c. Prussian blue	3·25	16·00
161		20 c. chestnut (28.4.24)	8·00	11·00
162		24 c. sepia (22.4.24)	45·00	75·00
149/62		*Set of* 14	85·00	£150

Designs: *Horiz* (*as T* **73**)—6 c. Upper Steadies, Humber River; 11 c. Shell Bird Island; 20 c. Placentia. (*As T* **74**)—8 c. Quidi Vidi, near St. John's; 9 c. Caribou crossing lake; 12 c. Mount Moriah, Bay of Islands. *Vert* (*as T* **75**)—4 c. Humber River, 5 c. Coast at Trinity; 10 c. Humber River Canon; 15 c. Humber River near Little Rapids; 24 c. Topsail Falls.

Perforations. Three perforating heads were used: comb 13.8×14 (all values); line 13.7 and 14, and combinations of these two (for all except 6, 8, 9 and 11 c.).

Air Mail
DE PINEDO
1927

(87)

1927 (18 May). *Air. No.* 79 *optd with T* **87**, *by Robinson & Co, Ltd.*

No.	Type	Description	Unused	Used
163	**35**	60 c. black (R.)	£25000	£7500

For the mail carried by De Pinedo to Europe 300 stamps were overprinted, 230 used on correspondence, 66 presented to De Pinedo, Government Officials, etc., and 4 damaged and destroyed. Stamps without overprint were also used.

NEW INFORMATION

The editor is always interested to correspond with people who have new information that will improve or correct the Catalogue.

88 Newfoundland and Labrador

89 S.S. *Caribou*

90 King George V and Queen Mary

91 Duke of Windsor when Prince of Wales

92 Express Train

93 Newfoundland Hotel, St. John's

94 Heart's Content

95 Cabot Tower, St. John's

96 War Memorial, St. John's

97 G.P.O., St. John's

98 Vickers "Vimy" Aircraft

99 Parliament House, St. John's

100 Grand Falls, Labrador

(Recess D.L.R.)

1928 (3 Jan)–**29**. *Publicity issue. P* 14 (1 *c.*), 13½×13 (2, 3, 5, 6, 10, 14, 20 *c.*), 13×13½ (4 *c.*) (*all comb*), *or* 14–13½* (*line*) (*others*).

No.	Type	Description	Unused	Used
164	**88**	1 c. deep green	2·25	1·25
165	**89**	2 c. carmine	3·25	50
166	**90**	3 c. brown	4·00	1·25
		a. Perf 14–13½ (line)	2·25	1·25
167	**91**	4 c. mauve	7·50	2·50
		a. *Rose-purple* (1929)	7·50	6·50
168	**92**	5 c. slate-grey	13·00	4·50
		a. Perf 14–13½ (line)	25·00	6·50
169	**93**	6 c. ultramarine	3·00	21·00
		a. Perf 14–13½ (line)	8·00	21·00
170	**94**	8 c. red-brown	3·25	26·00
171	**95**	9 c. deep green	2·00	13·00
172	**96**	10 c. deep violet	13·00	14·00
		a. Perf 14–13½ (line)	6·00	16·00
173	**97**	12 c. carmine-lake	2·00	19·00
174	**95**	14 c. brown-purple (8.28)	12·00	12·00
		a. Perf 14–13½ (line)	5·00	8·50
175	**98**	15 c. deep blue	3·25	27·00
176	**99**	20 c. grey-black	13·00	14·00
		a. Perf 14–13½ (line)	2·50	7·00
177	**97**	28 c. deep green (12.28)	28·00	48·00
178	**100**	30 c. sepia	6·00	17·00
164/78 (*cheapest*)		*Set of* 15	75·00	£190

*Exact gauges for the various perforations are: 14 comb = 14×13.9; 13½×13 comb = 13.5×12.75; 14–13½ line = 14–13.75.

See also Nos. 179/87 and 198/208.

D 1 c. P D 2 c. P

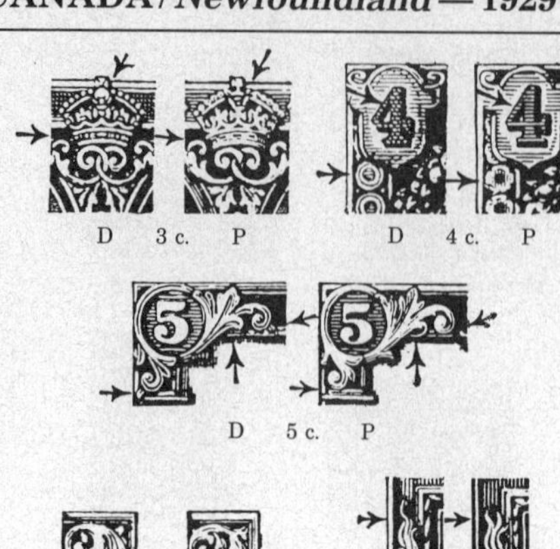

D 3 c. P D 4 c. P

D 5 c. P

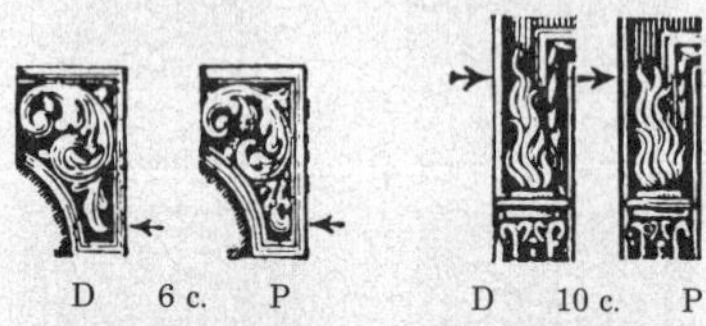

D 6 c. P D 10 c. P

D 15 c. P

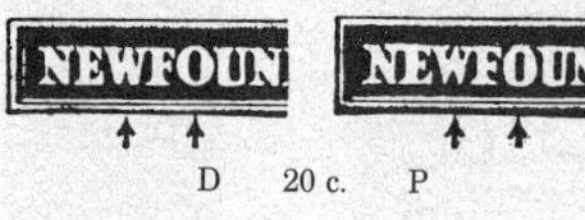

D 20 c. P

D. De La Rue printing

P. Perkins, Bacon printing

1929 (10 Aug)–**31.** *Perkins, Bacon printing. Former types re-engraved. No wmk. P* 14 (*comb*) (1 *c.*), $13^{1}/_{2}$ (*comb*) (2, 6 *c.*), 14–$13^{1}/_{2}$ (*line*) (20 *c.*) *or* $13^{1}/_{2}\times14$ (*comb*) (*others*)*.

179	**88**	1 c. green (26.9.29)	3·50	30
		a. Perf 14–$13^{1}/_{2}$ (line)	3·50	30
		b. Imperf between (vert pair)	£130	
		c. Imperf (pair)	£120	
180	**89**	2 c. scarlet	1·75	40
		a. Imperf (pair)	£110	
		b. Perf 14–$13^{1}/_{2}$ (line)	3·00	90
181	**90**	3 c. red-brown	1·00	20
		a. Imperf (pair)	£110	
182	**91**	4 c. reddish purple (26.8.29)	2·75	80
		a. Imperf (pair)	£120	
183	**92**	5 c. deep grey-green (14.9.29)	7·00	2·75
184	**93**	6 c. ultramarine (8.11.29)	7·00	14·00
		a. Perf 14–$13^{1}/_{2}$ (line)	2·25	15·00
185	**96**	10 c. violet (5.10.29)	4·25	3·50
186	**98**	15 c. blue (1.30)	17·00	80·00
187	**99**	20 c. black (1.1.31)	50·00	48·00
179/87		*Set of* 9	80·00	£130

*Exact gauges for the various perforations are: 14 comb = 14×13.9; $13^{1}/_{2}$ comb = 13.6×13.5; 14–$13^{1}/_{2}$ line = 14–13.75; $13^{1}/_{2}\times14$ comb = 13.6×13.8.

THREE
CENTS

(101)

Trans-Atlantic
AIR MAIL
By B. M.
"Columbia"
September
1930
Fifty Cents

(102)

(Surch by Messrs D. R. Thistle, St. John's)

1929 (23 Aug). *No.* 154 *surch with T* **101**.

188		3 c. on 6 c. slate (R.)	1·00	4·75
		a. Surch inverted	£600	£900
		b. Surch in black	£700	

1930 (25 Sept). *Air. No.* 141 *surch with T* **102** *by Messrs D. R. Thistle.*

191	**68**	50 c. on 36 c. sage-green	£4750	£4250

103 Aeroplane and Dog-team

104 Vickers-Vimy Biplane and early Sailing Packet

105 Routes of historic Transatlantic Flights

106

(Des A. B. Perlin. Recess P.B.)

1931. *Air. P* 14. (*a*) *Without wmk* (2.1.31)

192	**103**	15 c. chocolate	6·00	12·00
		a. Imperf between (horiz or vert pair)	£650	
		b. Imperf (pair)	£375	
193	**104**	50 c. green	32·00	55·00
		a. Imperf between (horiz or vert pair)	£700	£550
		b. Imperf (pair)	£500	
194	**105**	$1 deep blue	50·00	95·00
		a. Imperf between (horiz or vert pair)	£650	
		b. Imperf (pair)	£500	
192/4		*Set of* 3	80·00	£150

(*b*) *Wmk W* **106**, (*sideways*) (13.3.31)

195	**103**	15 c. chocolate	6·00	18·00
		a. Pair, with and without wmk	30·00	
		b. Imperf between (horiz or vert pair)	£600	
		ba. Ditto, one without wmk (vert pair)	£850	
		c. Imperf (pair)	£400	
		d. Wmk Cross (pair)	85·00	
196	**104**	50 c. green	28·00	65·00
		a. Imperf between (horiz or vert pair)	£650	
		b. Imperf (pair)		
		c. Pair, with and without wmk	£190	
197	**105**	$1 deep blue	80·00	£140
		a. Imperf between (horiz or vert pair)	£650	
		b. Imperf horiz (vert pair)	£500	
		c. Pair, with and without wmk	£350	
		d. Imperf (pair)	£425	
195/7		*Set of* 3	£100	£200

"WITH AND WITHOUT WMK" PAIRS listed in the issues from No. 195a onwards must have one stamp *completely* without any trace of watermark.

1931 (25 March–July). *Perkins, Bacon printing* (*re-engraved types*). *W* **106** (*sideways on* 1 *c.*, 4 *c.*, 30 *c.*). *P* $13^{1}/_{2}$ (1 *c.*) *or* $13^{1}/_{2}\times14$ (*others*), *both comb**.

198	**88**	1 c. green (7.31)	7·00	3·00
		a. Imperf between (horiz pair)	£500	
199	**89**	2 c. scarlet (7.31)	6·00	3·75
		w. Wmk inverted	40·00	
200	**90**	3 c. red-brown (7.31)	2·00	2·00
		w. Wmk inverted	40·00	
201	**91**	4 c. reddish purple (7.31)	2·00	1·25
202	**92**	5 c. deep grey-green (7.31)	7·00	10·00
203	**93**	6 c. ultramarine	10·00	23·00
204	**94**	8 c. chestnut (1.4.31)	24·00	29·00
		w. Wmk inverted	55·00	
205	**96**	10 c. violet (1.4.31)	12·00	9·00
206	**98**	15 c. blue (1.7.31)	21·00	55·00
207	**99**	20 c. black (1.7.31)	60·00	16·00
208	**100**	30 c. sepia (1.7.31)	28·00	42·00
198/208		*Set of* 11	£160	£170

*Exact gauges for the two perforations are: $13^{1}/_{2}$ = 13.6×13.5; $13^{1}/_{2}\times14$ = 13.6×13.8.

107 Atlantic Cod

108 King George V

109 Queen Mary

110 Duke of Windsor when Prince of Wales

111 Caribou

112 Queen Elizabeth II when Princess

113 Atlantic Salmon

114 Newfoundland Dog

115 Harp Seal

116 Cape Race

117 Sealing Fleet

118 Fishing Fleet

(Recess P.B.)

1932 (2 Jan). *W* **106** (*sideways* on vert designs*). *P* $13^{1}/_{2}$ (*com*

209	**107**	1 c. green	2·25	
		a. Imperf (pair)	£100	
		b. Perf 13 (line)	15·00	25·
		ba. Imperf between (vert pair)	£110	
		w. Wmk top of shield to right	40·00	
210	**108**	2 c. carmine	1·50	
		a. Imperf (pair)	£100	
		c. Perf 13 (line)	10·00	20·
		w. Wmk top of shield to right	40·00	
211	**109**	3 c. orange-brown	1·50	
		a. Imperf (pair)	75·00	
		c. Perf 13 (line)	15·00	26·
		d. Perf 14 (line). Small holes	18·00	22·
		da. Imperf between (vert pair)	£150	
		w. Wmk top of shield to right	40·00	
212	**110**	4 c. bright violet	5·50	2·
		w. Wmk top of shield to right		
213	**111**	5 c. maroon	4·00	1·
		a. Imperf (pair)	£150	
		w. Wmk top of shield to right		
214	**112**	6 c. light blue	4·00	14·
215	**113**	10 c. black-brown	70	
		a. Imperf (pair)	60·00	
		w. Wmk inverted	10·00	
216	**114**	14 c. black	4·25	5·
		a. Imperf (pair)	£120	
217	**115**	15 c. claret	1·25	2·
		a. Imperf (pair)	£140	
		b. Perf 14 (line)	8·00	10·
218	**116**	20 c. green	1·00	1·
		a. Imperf (pair)	£120	
		b. Perf 14 (line)	70·00	65·
		w. Wmk inverted	20·00	
219	**117**	25 c. slate	2·00	2·2
		a. Imperf (pair)	£130	
		b. Perf 14 (line)	35·00	48·0
		ba. Imperf between (vert pair)	£300	
220	**118**	30 c. ultramarine	32·00	32·0
		a. Imperf (pair)	£325	
		b. Imperf between (vert pair)	£650	
		c. Perf 14 (line)	£225	
209/20		*Set of* 12	55·00	55·0

*The normal sideways watermark shows the top of the shiel to left, *as seen from the back of the stamp.*

Nos. 209b, 210c and 211c were only issued in stamp booklets.

For similar stamps in different perforations see Nos. 222/8 and 276/89.

TRANS-ATLANTIC
WEST TO EAST
Per Dornier DO-X
May, 1932.
One Dollar and Fifty Cents

(119)

1932 (19 May). *Air. No.* 197 *surch as T* **119**, *by Messrs. D. R. Thistle. P* 14.

221	**105**	$1.50 on $1 deep blue (R.)	£190	£225
		a. Surch inverted	£10000	

120 Queen Mother, when Duchess of York

121 Corner Brook Paper Mills

122 Loading Iron Ore, Bell Island

(Recess P.B.)

1932 (15 Aug)–**38**. *W* **106** (*sideways* on vert designs*). *P* $13^{1}/_{2}$ (*comb*).

222	**107**	1 c. grey	1·25	10
		a. Imperf (pair)	40·00	
		c. Perf 14 (line)	6·50	9·50
		d. Perf 14 (line). Small holes	15·00	25·00
		e. Pair, with and without wmk	40·00	
		w. Wmk top of shield to right	50·00	

108 2 c. green 50 10
a. Imperf (pair) .. .. .. 35·00
c. Perf 14 (line) .. .. .. 7·50 9·50
ca. Imperf between (horiz pair) .. £250
d. Perf 14 (line). Small holes .. 18·00 25·00
e. Pair, with and without wmk .. 42·00
w. Wmk top of shield to right .. 35·00
110 4 c. carmine (21.7.34) .. .. 2·00 40
a. Imperf (pair) .. .. .. 50·00
b. Perf 14 (line) .. .. .. 3·75 5·00
ba. Imperf between (horiz or vert pair) £120
w. Wmk top of shield to right .. 50·00
111 5 c. violet (Die I) .. .. .. 2·00 1·75
a. Imperf (pair) .. .. .. 55·00
b. Perf 14 (line). Small holes .. 24·00 22·00
c. Die II 70 30
ca. Imperf (pair) .. .. .. 60·00
cb. Perf 14 (line) .. .. .. 22·00 19·00
cbw. Wmk top of shield to right .. 40·00
cc. Imperf between (horiz pair) .. £190
cd. Pair, with and without wmk .. £120
120 7 c. red-brown .. .. .. 2·75 3·75
b. Perf 14 (line) £130
ba. Imperf between (horiz pair) .. £450
c. Imperf (pair) £140
w. Wmk top of shield to right ..
121 8 c. brownish red .. .. .. 3·25 2·00
a. Imperf (pair) .. .. .. 85·00
w. Wmk inverted .. .. ..
122 24 c. bright blue .. .. .. 85 3·25
a. Imperf (pair) £200
b. Doubly printed £800
w. Wmk inverted .. .. .. 25·00
118 48 c. red-brown (1.1.38) .. .. 6·00 10·00
ca. Imperf (pair) .. .. .. 85·00
...c .. .. *Set of* 8 15·00 17·00

...he normal sideways watermark shows the top of the shield ...t, *as seen from the back of the stamp.*

... 223. Two dies exist of the 2 c. Die I was used for No. 210 and ... dies for No. 223. The differences, though numerous, are very ...t.

... 225. There are also two dies of the 5 c., Die I only being used ...o. 213 and both dies for the violet stamp. In Die II the antler ...ing to the "T" of "POSTAGE" is taller than the one pointing to ...S" and the individual hairs on the underside of the caribou's ...re distinct.

...r similar stamps in a slightly larger size and perforated ... or 13½ (5 c.) see Nos. 276/89.

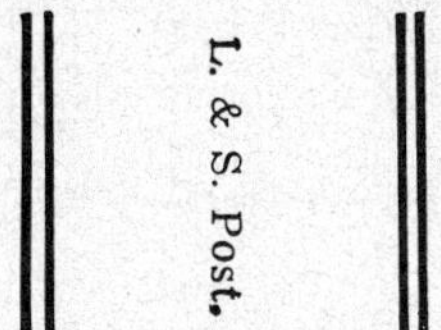

(123) "L.&S."—Land and Sea

...3 (9 Feb). *No. 195 optd with T* **123** *for ordinary postal use, ...y Messrs D. R. Thistle. W* **106** *(sideways). P* 14.
103 15 c. chocolate .. .. .. 3·50 11·00
a. Pair, one without wmk .. .. 23·00
b. Opt reading up £1600
c. Vertical pair, one without opt .. £3000

124 Put to Flight

125 Land of Heart's Delight

(Des J. Scott. Recess P.B.)

...33 (31 May). *Air. T* **124/5** *and similar horiz designs. W* **106** *(sideways). P* 14 (5, 30, 75 c.) *or* 11½ (10, 60 c.).
...0 5 c. red-brown .. .. .. 16·00 17·00
a. Imperf(pair) £160
b. Imperf between (horiz or vert pair) .. £950
...1 10 c. orange-yellow .. .. .. 12·00 30·00
a. Imperf(pair) £130
...2 30 c. light blue .. .. .. 30·00 42·00
a. Imperf(pair) £375
...3 60 c. green .. .. 48·00 90·00
a. Imperf(pair) £425
...4 75 c. yellow-brown .. .. .. 48·00 85·00
a. Imperf(pair) £375
b. Imperf between (horiz or vert pair) .. £1800
...0/4 .. .. *Set of* 5 £130 £225

Designs:—30 c. Spotting the herd; 60 c. News from home; 75 c. ...abrador.

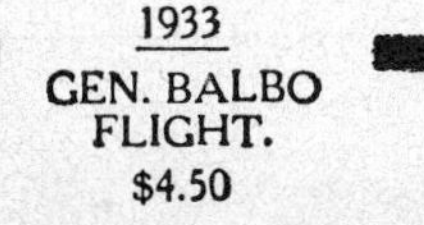

(129)

(Surch by Robinson & Co, St. John's)

...933 (24 July). *Air. Balbo Transatlantic Mass Formation Flight. No.* 234 *surch with T* **129**. *W* **106**. *P* 14.
...35 $4.50 on 75 c. yellow-brown £250 £300
a. Surch inverted £35000
b. Surch on 10 c. (No. 231) £35000

No. 235a. When this error was discovered the stamps were ...rdered to be officially destroyed but four copies which had been ...orn were recovered and skilfully repaired. In addition four undamaged examples exist and the price quoted is for one of these.

130 Sir Humphrey Gilbert

131 Compton Castle, Devon

132 Gilbert Coat of Arms

(Recess P.B.)

1933 (3 Aug). *350th Anniv of the Annexation by Sir Humphrey Gilbert. T* **130/2** *and similar designs. W* **106** *(sideways* on vert designs). P* 13½ *(comb†).*
236 1 c. slate .. .. 80 1·50
a. Imperf (pair) .. .. .. 45·00
237 2 c. green .. .. 1·00 70
a. Imperf (pair) .. .. .. 48·00
b. Doubly printed £300
238 3 c. chestnut .. .. 2·00 1·25
239 4 c. carmine 80 50
a. Imperf (pair) .. .. .. 45·00
240 5 c. violet .. .. 2·00 80
241 7 c. greenish blue .. .. .. 13·00 17·00
a. Perf 14 (line) .. .. .. 10·00 35·00
242 8 c. vermilion .. .. .. 7·50 13·00
a. Brownish red £275
b. Bisected (4 c.) (on cover) .. † £375
243 9 c. ultramarine .. .. .. 7·00 12·00
a. Imperf (pair) £200
b. Perf 14 (line) .. .. .. 48·00 60·00
244 10 c. brown-lake .. .. .. 4·00 9·00
a. Imperf (pair) £275
b. Perf 14 (line) .. .. .. 65·00 70·00
245 14 c. grey-black .. .. .. 14·00 30·00
a. Perf 14 (line) .. .. .. 17·00 48·00
246 15 c. claret .. .. 11·00 23·00
w. Wmk top of shield to right .. 7·50 17·00
247 20 c. grey-green .. .. .. 13·00 18·00
a. Perf 14 (line) .. .. .. 23·00 35·00
w. Wmk inverted .. .. .. 45·00
248 24 c. maroon .. .. .. 14·00 23·00
a. Imperf (pair) £100
b. Perf 14 (line) .. .. .. 23·00 38·00
w. Wmk top of shield to right .. 35·00
249 32 c. olive-black .. .. .. 7·00 50·00
a. Perf 14 (line) .. .. .. 22·00 70·00
w. Wmk top of shield to right .. 20·00
236/49 .. .. .. *Set of* 14 65·00 £170

Designs: *Horiz*—4 c. Eton College; 7 c. Gilbert commissioned by Elizabeth I; 8 c. Fleet leaving Plymouth, 1583; 9 c. Arrival at St. John's; 10 c. Annexation, 5 August 1583; 20 c. Map of Newfoundland, 1626. *Vert*—5 c. Anchor token; 14 c. Royal Arms; 15 c. Gilbert in the *Squirrel*; 24 c. Queen Elizabeth I. 32 c. Gilbert's statue at Truro.

*The normal sideways watermark shows the top of the shield to left, *as seen from the back of the stamp.*

†Exact gauges for the two perforations are: 13½ comb = 13.4; 14 line = 13.8.

1935 (6 May). *Silver Jubilee. As Nos.* 91/4 *of Antigua, but ptd by B.W. P* 11 × 12.
250 4 c. rosine .. .. 1·00 1·75
251 5 c. bright violet .. .. .. 1·25 1·75
252 7 c. blue .. .. 1·75 7·00
253 24 c. olive-green .. .. .. 5·00 9·50
250/3 .. .. .. *Set of* 4 8·00 18·00
250s/3s Perf "Specimen" .. *Set of* 4 £120

1937 (12 May). *Coronation Issue. As Nos.* 95/7 *of Antigua, but name and value uncoloured on coloured background. P* 11×11½.
254 2 c. green .. .. 1·00 2·25
255 4 c. carmine .. .. 1·60 2·75
256 5 c. purple .. .. 3·00 2·75
254/6 .. .. .. *Set of* 3 5·00 7·00
254s/6s Perf "Specimen" .. *Set of* 3 75·00

144 Atlantic Cod

Die I

Die II

No. 258. In Die II the shading of the King's face is heavier and dots have been added down the ridge of the nose. The top frame line is thicker and more uniform.

NEW INFORMATION

The editor is always interested to correspond with people who have new information that will improve or correct the Catalogue.

Fish-hook flaw (R. 1/7 or 3/3)

Re-entry to right of design (inscr oval, tree and value) (R.4/8)

Extra chimney (R. 6/5)

(Recess P.B.)

1937 (12 May). *Additional Coronation Issue. T* **144** *and similar horiz designs. W* **106**. *P* 14 *(line)**.
257 1 c. grey .. .. 2·75 30
a. Pair, with and without wmk .. 23·00
b. Fish-hook flaw .. .. .. 22·00
c. Perf 13½ (line) .. .. .. 3·25 40
ca. Pair, with and without wmk .. 26·00
cb. Fish-hook flaw .. .. .. 26·00
d. Perf 13 (comb) .. .. .. 25·00 45·00
da. Pair, with and without wmk ..
db. Fish-hook flaw £170
258 3 c. orange-brown (I) .. .. 7·50 3·50
a. Pair, with and without wmk .. 60·00
b. Imperf between (horiz pair) ..
c. Perf 13½ (line) .. .. .. 7·50 4·50
ca. Pair, with and without wmk ..
cb. Imperf between (vert pair) .. £375
d. Perf 13 (comb) .. .. .. 4·75 3·25
e. Die II (p 14, line) .. .. 4·25 3·50
ea. Pair, with and without wmk .. 90·00
ec. Perf 13½ (line) .. .. .. 4·50 3·75
eca. Pair, with and without wmk .. £100
ecb. Imperf between (vert pair) .. £450
ed. Perf 13 (comb) .. .. .. 6·00 3·00
eda. Pair, with and without wmk .. 95·00
259 7 c. bright ultramarine .. .. 2·50 1·25
a. Pair, with and without wmk ..
b. Re-entry at right .. .. 48·00
c. Perf 13½ (line) .. .. .. 2·50 1·75
ca. Pair, with and without wmk ..
cb. Re-entry at right .. .. 48·00
d. Perf 13 (comb) £300 £400
db. Re-entry at right £1200
260 8 c. scarlet .. .. 1·75 3·00
a. Pair, with and without wmk .. 60·00
b. Imperf between (horiz or vert pair) .. £600
c. Imperf (pair) £300
d. Perf 13½ (line) .. .. .. 2·25 3·75
da. Pair, with and without wmk .. 65·00
db. Imperf between (vert pair) ..
e. Perf 13 (comb) .. .. .. 7·00 10·00
261 10 c. blackish brown .. .. .. 3·75 8·00
a. Pair, with and without wmk .. 75·00
b. Perf 13½ (line) .. .. .. 4·00 8·50
ba. Pair, with and without wmk .. 65·00
c. Perf 13 (comb) .. .. .. 3·25 10·00
cw. Wmk inverted .. .. .. 75·00
262 14 c. black .. .. 1·40 2·75
a. Pair, with and without wmk .. 55·00
b. Perf 13½ (line) .. .. .. 2·25 3·50
ba. Pair, with and without wmk .. 55·00
c. Perf 13 (comb) £5500 £3250
263 15 c. claret .. .. 9·50 4·25
a. Pair, with and without wmk .. 65·00
bw. Wmk inverted .. .. .. 75·00
c. Perf 13½ (line) .. .. .. 11·00 4·50
ca. Pair, with and without wmk .. 65·00
cb. Imperf between (vert pair) .. £425
d. Perf 13 (comb) .. .. .. 19·00 22·00
da. Pair, with and without wmk .. £100
264 20 c. green .. .. 2·25 8·00
a. Pair, with and without wmk ..
c. Extra chimney .. .. .. 38·00
dw. Wmk inverted .. .. .. 85·00
e. Perf 13½ (line) .. .. .. 3·50 8·50
ea. Pair, with and without wmk .. £130
eb. Imperf between (vert pair) .. £650
ec. Extra chimney .. .. .. 50·00
f. Perf 13 (comb) .. .. .. 2·50 8·00
fc. Extra chimney .. .. .. 45·00
265 24 c. light blue .. .. .. 2·50 2·50
a. Pair, with and without wmk .. £130
c. Perf 13½ (line) .. .. .. 2·50 3·00
ca. Pair, with and without wmk .. £130
cb. Imperf between (vert pair) .. £700
d. Perf 13 (comb) .. .. .. 24·00 25·00

266 **25** c. slate .. .. 2·75 1·75
a. Pair, with and without wmk .. £120
b. Perf 13½ (line) .. .. .. 2·75 3·25
ba. Pair, with and without wmk .. £120
c. Perf 13 (comb) .. .. .. 25·00 50·00
267 48 c. slate-purple .. .. 8·50 5·00
a. Pair, with and without wmk .. £160
c. Perf 13½ (line) .. .. .. 9·00 6·00
ca. Pair, with and without wmk .. £160
cb. Imperf between (vert pair) £650
d. Perf 13 (comb) .. .. .. 30·00 65·00
257/67 .. .. *Set of* 11 35·00 35·00

Designs:—3 c. Map of Newfoundland; 7 c. Reindeer; 8 c. Corner Brook paper mills; 10 c. Atlantic Salmon; 14 c. Newfoundland dog; 15 c. Harp Seal; 20 c. Cape Race; 24 c. Bell Island; 25 c. Sealing fleet; 48 c. The Banks fishing fleet.

The line perforations measure 14.1 (14) or 13.7 (13½). The comb perforation measures 13.3×13.2. One example of the 7 c. has been reported perforated 13½×14.

Four used examples of No. 259d have now been identified on separate covers.

The paper used had the watermarks spaced for smaller format stamps. In consequence the individual watermarks are out of alignment so that stamps from the second vertical row were sometimes without watermark.

155 King George VI

156 Queen Mother

(Recess P.B.)

1938 (12 May). *T* **155/6** *and similar vert designs. W* **106** *(sideways). P* 13½ *(comb).*
268 2 c. green .. .. 1·50 70
a. Pair, with and without wmk .. £130
b. Imperf (pair) .. .. 75·00
269 3 c. carmine .. .. 1·00 80
a. Perf 14 (line) £375 £250
b. Pair, with and without wmk .. £180
c. Imperf (pair) .. .. 75·00
270 4 c. light blue .. .. 1·75 30
a. Pair, with and without wmk .. 85·00
b. Imperf (pair) .. .. 70·00
w. Wmk inverted .. .. .. 65·00
271 7 c. deep ultramarine .. .. .. 75 4·00
a. Imperf (pair) £110
268/71 .. .. *Set of* 4 4·50 5·25

Designs:—4 c. Queen Elizabeth II as princess; 7 c. Queen Mary.

For similar designs, perf 12½, see Nos. 277/81.

159 King George VI and Queen Elizabeth

(Recess B.W.)

1939 (17 June). *Royal Visit. No wmk. P* 13½.
272 **159** 5 c. deep ultramarine .. .. .. 2·00 55

2

 **CENTS** 

(160)

1939 (20 Nov). *No.* 272 *surch as T* **160**, *at St. John's.*
273 **159** 2 c. on 5 c. deep ultramarine (Br.) .. 2·00 30
274 4 c. on 5 c. deep ultramarine (C.) .. 1·25 60

161 Grenfell on the *Strathcona* (after painting by Gribble)

162 Memorial University College

(Recess C.B.N.)

1941 (1 Dec). 50*th Anniv of Sir Wilfred Grenfell's Labrador Mission. P* 12.
275 **161** 5 c. blue 30 55

Damaged "A" (R. 5/9)

(Recess Waterlow)

1941–44. *W* **106** *(sideways* on vert designs). P* 12½ *(line).*
276 **107** 1 c. grey 20 65
277 **155** 2 c. green 30 30
w. Wmk top of shield to right .. 35·00
278 **156** 3 c. carmine 30 10
a. Pair, with and without wmk .. 75·00
b. Damaged "A" .. .. 45·00 30·00
w. Wmk top of shield to right .. 35·00
279 – 4 c. blue (As No. 270) .. .. 2·25 20
a. Pair, with and without wmk .. £140
w. Wmk top of shield to right .. 35·00
280 **111** 5 c. violet (Die I) (*p* 13½ *comb*) .. 95·00
a. Perf 12½ (line) (6.42) .. .. 2·75 50
ab. Pair, with and without wmk .. £120
ac. Printed double £350
ad. Imperf vert (horiz pair) £350
b. Imperf (pair) £120
281 – 7 c. deep ultramarine (As No. 271) .. 6·00 12·00
a. Pair, with and without wmk .. £150
282 **121** 8 c. rose-red .. .. 1·75 2·00
a. Pair, with and without wmk .. £140
283 **113** 10 c. black-brown .. .. .. 1·75 1·25
284 **114** 14 c. black .. .. 4·00 6·00
285 **115** 15 c. claret .. .. 5·50 8·00
286 **116** 20 c. green .. .. 5·50 5·50
287 **122** 24 c. blue .. .. 3·25 14·00
w. Wmk top of shield to right .. 55·00
288 **117** 25 c. slate .. .. 7·00 8·50
289 **118** 48 c. red-brown (1944) .. .. 3·75 6·00
276/89 .. .. *Set of* 14 35·00 60·00

*The normal sideways watermark shows the top of the shield to left, *as seen from the back of the stamp.*

Nos. 276/89 are redrawn versions of previous designs with slightly larger dimensions; the 5 c. for example, measures 21 mm in width as opposed to the 20.4 mm of the Perkins Bacon printings.

No. 280. For Die I see note relating to No. 225.

(Recess C.B.N.)

1943 (1 Jan). *P* 12.
290 **162** 30 c. carmine .. .. .. 1·00 2·25

163 St. John's

TWO

CENTS

(164)

(Recess C.B.N.)

1943 (1 June). *Air. P* 12.
291 **163** 7 c. ultramarine 40 65

1946 (21 Mar). *No.* 290 *surch locally with T* **164**.
292 **162** 2 c. on 30 c. carmine 30 75

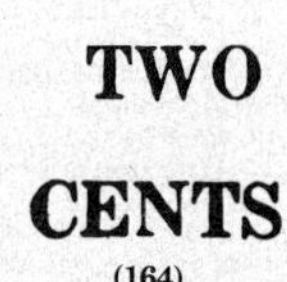

165 Queen Elizabeth II when Princess

166 Cabot off Cape Bonavista

(Recess Waterlow)

1947 (21 Apr). *Princess Elizabeth's* 21*st Birthday. W* **106** *(sideways). P* 12½.
293 **165** 4 c. light blue 30 75
a. Imperf vert (horiz pair) £300

(Recess Waterlow)

1947 (24 June). 450*th Anniv of Cabot's Discovery of Newfoundland. W* **106** *(sideways). P* 12½.
294 **166** 5 c. mauve 20 80
a. Imperf between (horiz pair) .. £1300

STAMP BOOKLETS

1926. *Black on pink cover with Ayre and Sons advertisement on front. Stapled.*
SB1 40 c. booklet containing eight 1 c. and sixteen 2 c. (Nos. 149/50) in blocks of 8 .. .. £1200

B 1

1932 (2 Jan). *Black on buff cover as Type* B 1. *Stapled.*
SB2 40 c. booklet containing four 1 c., twelve 2 c. and four 3 c. (Nos. 209b, 210c, 211c) in blocks of 4 £350
a. Contents as No. SB2, but containing Nos. 209b, 210 and 211c £425
b. Contents as No. SB2, but containing Nos. 222d, 223d and 211d £400

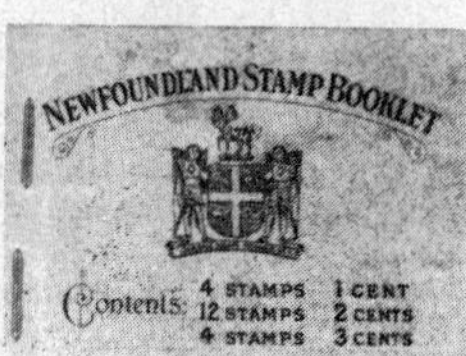

B 2

1932. *Black on cream cover as Type* B 2. *Stapled.*
SB3 40 c. booklet containing four 1 c., twelve 2 c. and four 3 c. (Nos. 222, 223, 211) in blocks of 4

POSTAGE DUE STAMPS

D 1

D **6**ac

(Litho John Dickinson & Co, Ltd)

1939 (1 May)–**49.** *P* 10.
D1 D 1 1 c. green .. .. 2·25
a. Perf 11 (1949) .. .. .. 3·25 1
D2 2 c. vermilion .. .. 13·00
a. Perf 11 × 9 (1946) .. .. .. 13·00 1
D3 3 c. ultramarine .. .. 5·00 2
a. Perf 11 × 9 (1949) .. .. .. 13·00 3
b. Perf 9 .. .. £600
D4 4 c. orange .. .. 9·00 1
a. Perf 11 × 9 (May 1948) .. .. 12·00 4
D5 5 c. brown .. .. 5·50 2
D6 10 c. violet .. .. 6·00 1
a. Perf 11 (W **106**) (1949) .. .. 22·00 8
ab. Ditto. Imperf between (vert pair) .. £700
ac. "POSTAGE LUE" (R 3/3 or 3/8) .. £110 £
D1/6 .. .. *Set of* 6 38·00 9

Newfoundland joined the Dominion of Canada on 31 Ma 1949.

NOVA SCOTIA

Organised postal services in Nova Scotia date from April 17 when the first of a series of Deputy Postmasters was appoint under the authority of the British G.P.O. This arrangem continued until 6 July 1851 when the colony assumed respon bility for its postal affairs.

For illustrations of the handstamp types see BRITISH PO OFFICES ABROAD notes, following GREAT BRITAIN.

AMHERST

CROWNED-CIRCLE HANDSTAMPS

CC1 CC 1 AMHERST. N.S.(R) (25.2.1845)
Price on cover £1

ST. MARGARETS BAY

CROWNED-CIRCLE HANDSTAMPS

CC2 CC 1 ST. MARGARETS BAY. N.S.(R) (30.6.1845)
Price on cover £90

Nos. CC1/2 were later used during temporary shortages stamps, struck in red or black.

PRICES FOR STAMPS ON COVER

No. 1	*from* × 5
Nos. 2/4	*from* × 2
Nos. 5/8	*from* × 4
Nos. 9/10	*from* × 10
Nos. 11/13	*from* × 2
Nos. 14/15	—
No. 16	*from* × 4
Nos. 17/19	*from* × 10
Nos. 20/5	*from* × 2
No. 26	*from* × 50
Nos. 27/8	*from* × 4
No. 29	*from* × 10

1

2

Crown and Heraldic Flowers of United Kingdom and Mayflower o Nova Scotia.

(Recess P.B.)

(1 Sept)–**57.** *Bluish paper. Imperf.*

No.	Type	Description	Unused	Used
1		1d. red-brown (12.5.53)	£2000	£400
		a. Bisected (½d.) (on cover)	†	£55000
2		3d. deep blue	£1000	£160
		a. Bisected (1½d.) (on cover)	†	£2500
		3d. bright blue	£900	£120
		a. Bisected (1½d.) (on cover)	†	£2500
		3d. pale blue (1857)	£750	£140
		a. Bisected (1½d.) (on cover)	†	£2500
		6d. yellow-green	£4000	£425
		a. Bisected (3d.) (on cover)	†	£3250
		6d. deep green (1857)	£10000	£750
		a. Bisected (3d.) (on cover)	†	£5500
		b. Quartered (1½d.) (on cover)	†	£40000
		1s. cold violet	£19000	£5000
		a. Bisected (6d.) (on cover)	†	£45000
		b. Quartered (3d.) (on cover)	†	£60000
		1s. deep purple (1851)	£15000	£3750
		d. Watermarked	£20000	£5000
		1s. purple (1857)	£14000	£2500
		a. Bisected (6d.) (on cover)	†	£35000

…e watermark on No. 7d consists of the whole or part of a …r from the name "T. H. SAUNDERS" (the papermakers).

…e stamps formerly catalogued on almost white paper are …ably some from which the bluish paper has been discharged.

…eprints of all four values were made in 1890 on thin, hard, …e paper. The 1d. is brown, the 3d. blue, the 6d. deep green, …the 1s. violet-black.

…e 3d. bisects, which were authorized on 19 October 1854, …usually found used to make up the 7½d. rate.

(New Currency. 100 cents = 1 dollar)

3

4

5

(Recess American Bank Note Co, New York)

…0–**63.** *P* 12. (*a*) *Yellowish paper.*

No.	Type	Description	Unused	Used
	3	1 c. jet black	3·50	12·00
		a. Bisected (½ c.) (on cover)	†	£10000
		1 c. grey-black	3·50	12·00
		2 c. grey-purple	11·00	15·00
		2 c. purple	17·00	14·00
		5 c. blue	£325	17·00
		5 c. deep blue	£325	17·00
	4	8½ c. deep green	2·75	40·00
		8½ c. yellow-green	2·75	40·00
		10 c. scarlet	14·00	24·00
	5	12½ c. black	26·00	26·00
		12½ c. greyish black	—	26·00

(*b*) *White paper*

No.	Type	Description	Unused	Used
	3	1 c. black	3·25	12·00
		a. Imperf vert (horiz pair)	£150	
		1 c. grey	3·25	12·00
		2 c. dull purple	3·50	14·00
		2 c. purple	3·50	14·00
		2 c. grey-purple	3·50	14·00
		a. Bisected (1 c.) (on cover)	†	£4500
		2 c. slate-purple	3·50	12·00
		5 c. blue	£350	17·00
		5 c. deep blue	£350	17·00
	4	8½ c. deep green	17·00	40·00
		10 c. scarlet	5·00	23·00
		10 c. vermilion	4·00	23·00
		a. Bisected (5 c.) (on cover)	†	£750
	5	12½ c. black	45·00	30·00

Nova Scotia joined the Dominion of Canada on 1 July 1867.

PRINCE EDWARD ISLAND

Prince Edward Island, previously administered as part of Nova Scotia, became a separate colony in 1769.

PRICES FOR STAMPS ON COVER

Nos. 1/4	*from* × 3
Nos. 5/6	—
Nos. 7/8	*from* × 5
Nos. 9/20	*from* × 6
Nos. 21/6	*from* × 3
Nos. 27/31	*from* × 6
Nos. 32/3	*from* × 50
Nos. 34/7	*from* × 6
Nos. 38/41	*from* × 20
No. 42	*from* × 50
Nos. 43/7	*from* × 5

1 4

2

3

5

6

Two Dies of 2d:

Die I. Left-hand frame and circle merge at centre left (all stamps in the sheet of 60 (10×6) except R. 2/5)

Die II. Left-hand frame and circle separate at centre left (R. 2/5). There is also a break in the top frame line.

(Typo Charles Whiting, London)

1861 (1 Jan). *Yellowish toned paper.* (*a*) *P* 9.

No.	Type	Description	Unused	Used
1	1	2d. rose (I)	£250	£120
		a. Imperf between (horiz pair)	£4500	
		b. Imperf horiz (vert pair)		
		c. Bisected (1d.) (on cover)	†	£3000
		d. Die II		
2		2d. rose-carmine (I)	£275	£130
		a. Die II		
3	2	3d. blue	£500	£225
		a. Bisected (1½d.) (on cover)	†	£3000
		b. Double print	£1500	
4	3	6d. yellow-green	£750	£350

(*b*) *Rouletted*

No.	Type	Description	Unused	Used
5	1	2d. rose (I)	£3000	£2250

The 2d. and 3d., perf 9, were authorised to be bisected and used for half their normal value.

1862. *Yellowish toned paper. P* 11.

No.	Type	Description	Unused	Used
6	4	1d. brown-orange	38·00	65·00
6*a*		2d. rose (I)	†	—
7	6	9d. bluish lilac (29.3.62)	75·00	60·00
8		9d. dull mauve	75·00	60·00

1863–69. *Yellowish toned paper.* (*a*) *P* 11½–12

No.	Type	Description	Unused	Used
9	4	1d. yellow-orange	26·00	35·00
		a. Bisected (½d.) (on cover)	†	£2000
		b. Imperf between (horiz pair)	£325	
10		1d. orange-buff	27·00	35·00
11		1d. yellow	29·00	35·00
12	1	2d. rose (I)	9·50	9·50
		a. Imperf vert (horiz pair)		
		b. Bisected (1d.) (on cover)	†	£1700
		c. Die II	75·00	80·00
13		2d. deep rose (I)	10·00	12·00
		a. Die II	80·00	90·00
14	2	3d. blue	17·00	18·00
		a. Imperf horiz (vert pair)		
		b. Bisected (1½d.) (on cover)		
15		3d. deep blue	17·00	17·00
16	5	4d. black (1869)	18·00	23·00
		a. Imperf vert (horiz pair)	£225	
		b. Bisected (2d.) (on cover)	†	£1600
		c. Imperf between (horiz strip of 3)	£300	
17	3	6d. yellow-green (15.12.66)	90·00	80·00
		a. Bisected (3d.) (on cover)	†	£3000
18		6d. blue-green (1868)	80·00	85·00
19	6	9d. lilac	65·00	65·00
20		9d. reddish mauve	65·00	65·00
		a. Imperf vert (horiz pair)	£425	
		b. Bisected (4½d.) (on cover)	†	£2500

(*b*) *Perf compound of* 11 *and* 11½–12

No.	Type	Description	Unused	Used
21	4	1d. yellow-orange	£150	65·00
22	1	2d. rose (I)	£150	65·00
		a. Die II		
23	2	3d. blue	£190	65·00
24	5	4d. black	£250	£200
25	3	6d. yellow-green	£225	£225
26	6	9d. reddish mauve	£250	£225

1870. *Coarse, wove bluish white paper. P* 11½–12.

No.	Type	Description	Unused	Used
27	1	2d. rose (I)	11·00	12·00
		a. Die II	85·00	95·00
28		2d. rose-pink (I)	6·50	9·50
		a. Die II	65·00	75·00
		b. "TWC" (R. 6/4)	70·00	80·00
		c. Imperf between (horiz pair)	£130	
29	2	3d. pale blue	10·00	13·00
30		3d. blue	10·00	13·00
		a. Imperf between (horiz pair)	£275	
31	5	4d. black	4·75	27·00
		a. Imperf between (horiz pair)	£130	
		b. Bisected (2d.) (on cover)	†	£1700
		c. Perf compound 11 and 11½–12		

(New Currency. 100 cents = 1 dollar)

7

(Recess British-American Bank Note Co., Montreal and Ottawa)

1870 (1 June). *P* 12.

No.	Type	Description	Unused	Used
32	7	4½d. (3d. stg), yellow-brown	40·00	48·00
33		4½d. (3d. stg), deep brown	42·00	50·00

8 9 10

11

12 13

(Typo Charles Whiting, London)

1872 (1 Jan). (*a*) *P* 11½–12.

No.	Type	Description	Unused	Used
34	8	1 c. orange	4·25	13·00
35		1 c. yellow-orange	4·25	11·00
36		1 c. brown-orange	4·75	14·00
37	10	3 c. rose	15·00	21·00
		a. Stop between "PRINCE. EDWARD"	42·00	55·00
		b. Bisected (1½ c.) (on cover)		
		c. Imperf horiz (vert pair)	£375	

(*b*) *Perf* 12 *to* 12¼, *large holes*

No.	Type	Description	Unused	Used
38	9	2 c. blue	14·00	32·00
		a. Bisected (1 c.) (on cover)	†	£2500
39	11	4 c. yellow-green	4·75	16·00
40		4 c. deep green	5·50	14·00
		a. Bisected (2 c.) (on cover)	†	£2500
41	12	6 c. black	4·25	15·00
		a. Bisected (3 c.) (on cover)	†	£1300
		b. Imperf between (horiz pair)	£225	
		c. Imperf vert (horiz pair)		
42	13	12 c. reddish mauve	4·00	26·00

(*c*) *P* 12½–13, *smaller holes*

No.	Type	Description	Unused	Used
43	8	1 c. orange	14·00	
44		1 c. brown-orange	4·75	13·00
45	10	3 c. rose	15·00	24·00
		a. Stop between "PRINCE. EDWARD"	55·00	70·00
45*b*	12	6 c. black	—	£250

(*d*) *Perf compound of* (*a*) *and* (*c*) 11½–12 × 12½–13

No.	Type	Description	Unused	Used
46	8	1 c. orange	35·00	38·00
47	10	3 c. rose	38·00	38·00
		a. Stop between "PRINCE. EDWARD"	£180	£190

Prince Edward Island joined the Dominion of Canada on 1 July 1873.

DOMINION OF CANADA

On July 1867, Canada, Nova Scotia and New Brunswick were united to form the Dominion of Canada.

The provinces of Manitoba (1870), British Columbia (1871), Prince Edward Island (1873), Alberta (1905), Saskatchewan (1905), and Newfoundland (1949) were subsequently added, as were the Northwest Territories (1870) and Yukon Territory (1898).

PRICES FOR STAMPS ON COVER TO 1945

Nos. 46/67	*from* × 2
Nos. 68/71	*from* × 10
Nos. 72/89	*from* × 3
Nos. 90/100	*from* × 2
Nos. 101/2	*from* × 5
Nos. 103/11	*from* × 3
Nos. 115/20	*from* × 6
Nos. 121/49	*from* × 3
Nos. 150/65	*from* × 2
Nos. 166/72	*from* × 3
Nos. 173/87	*from* × 5
Nos. 188/95	*from* × 2
Nos. 196/215	*from* × 3
Nos. 219/224*b*	*from* × 4
Nos. 225/45	*from* × 2
Nos. 246/55	*from* × 8
Nos. 256/310	*from* × 2
No. 312	*from* × 20
No. 313	*from* × 10
Nos. 315/18	*from* × 2
Nos. 319/28	*from* × 3
Nos. 329/40	*from* × 2
Nos. 341/400	*from* × 1
Nos. R1/11	*from* × 5
Nos. S1/3	*from* × 8
No. S4	*from* × 6
No. S5	*from* × 5
Nos. S6/11	*from* × 3
Nos. S12/14	*from* × 5
Nos. D1/8	*from* × 4
Nos. D9/13	*from* × 5
Nos. D14/24	*from* × 4

13

14

15

Large types

PRINTERS. Nos. 46/120 were recess-printed by the British American Bank Note Co at Ottawa or Montreal.

1868 (1 Apr)–**90.** *As T* **13/15** (*various frames*).

I. *Ottawa printings. P* 12.

(*a*) *Thin rather transparent crisp paper*

No.	Type	Description	Unused	Used
46	13	½ c. black (1.4.68)	70·00	60·00
47	14	1 c. red-brown (1.4.68)	£325	50·00
48		2 c. grass-green (1.4.68)	£350	40·00
49		3 c. red-brown (1.4.68)	£600	21·00
50		6 c. blackish brown (1.4.68)	£900	£150
51		12½ c. bright blue (1.4.68)	£550	£110
52		15 c. deep reddish purple	£800	£160

In these first printings the impression is generally blurred and the lines of the background are less clearly defined than in later printings.

(b) *Medium to stout wove paper* (1868–71)
½ c. black . . . . 50·00 50·00
½ c. grey-black . . . . 50·00 50·00
a. Imperf between (pair) . .
b. Watermarked £11000 £6000
1 c. red-brown . . . . £300 40·00
a. Laid paper £6500 £1600
b. Watermarked (1868) £1800 £190
1 c. deep orange (Jan, 1869) . . £750 80·00
1 c. orange-yellow (May (?), 1869) . . £650 60·00
1 c. pale orange-yellow . . £750 75·00
ba. Imperf . . . .
2 c. deep green . . . . £325 28·00
2 c. pale emerald-green (1871) . . £400 42·00
ab. Bisected (1 c. with 2 c. to make 3 c. rate) on cover . . † £4000
ac. Laid paper . . † £60000
2 c. bluish green . . £325 28·00
da. Watermarked (1868) . . £1500 £200
3 c. brown-red . . £650 15·00
a. Laid paper . . £6000 £300
b. Watermarked (1868) . . £2250 £160
6 c. blackish brown (*to* chocolate) . . £700 40·00
a. Watermarked (1868) . . £3000 £600
6 c. yellow-brown (1870) . . £650 38·00
ba. Bisected (3 c.), on cover . . † £2000
12½ c. bright blue . . £450 40·00
a. Imperf horiz (vert pair) . . † £10000
b. Watermarked (1868) . . £1700 £225
12½ c. pale dull blue (milky) . . £475 40·00
15 c. deep reddish purple . . £450 60·00
15 c. pale reddish purple . . £400 60·00
ab. Watermarked (1868) . . — £1200
15 c. dull violet-grey . . £225 30·00
ba. Watermarked (1868) . . £3000 £500
15 c. dull grey-purple . . £300 30·00

[Th]e official date of issue was 1 April 1868. Scattered examples [of m]ost values can be found used in the second half of March.

[Th]e watermark on the stout paper stamps consists of the [wor]ds "E & G BOTHWELL CLUTHA MILLS", in large double-[line]d capitals which can be found upright, inverted or reversed. [Por]tions of one or two letters only may be found on these [sta]mps, which occur in the early printings of 1868.

[Th]e paper may, in most cases, be easily divided if the stamps [are l]aid face downwards and carefully compared. The thin hard [pap]er is more or less transparent and shows the design through [the] stamp; the thicker paper is softer to the feel and more [opa]que.

[O]f the 2 c. laid paper No. 57ac two examples only are known.

II. *Montreal printings. Medium to stout wove paper.*

(a) *P* 11½×12 *or* 13¾×12

13 ½ c. black (1873) . . 65·00 65·00
15 5 c. olive-green (1.10.75) . . £700 65·00
a. Perf 12 . . £3500 £800
14 15 c. dull grey-purple (1874) . . £700 £160
15 c. lilac-grey (3.77) . . £900 £160
a. Script watermark . . £7000 £1800
b. "BOTHWELL" watermark . . † £750
15 c. slate . . £900 £300

(b) *P* 12

14 15 c. clear deep violet (1879) . . £2250 £500
15 c. deep slate (1881) . . £140 28·00
15 c. slaty blue (1887) . . £140 28·00
15 c. slate-purple (*shades*) (7.88–92) . . 65·00 17·00

[N]o. 63a gauges 12 or above on all four sides.

[T]he watermark on No. 65a is part of "Alex.Pirie & Sons" [whi]ch appeared as script letters once per sheet in a small batch [of t]he paper used for the 1877 printing. For a description of the [she]et watermark on No. 65b see note after No. 61c.

[S]everal used examples of the 12½ c. have been reported [per]forated 11½×12 or 13¾×12.

[T]he last printing of the 15 c. slate-purple, No. 70, took place at [Ott]awa.

[I]II. *Ottawa printings. Thinnish paper of poor quality, often toned grey or yellowish. P* 12

14 15 c. slate-violet (*shades*) (5.90) . . 65·00 20·00
a. Imperf (pair). *Brown-purple* . . £1000

[E]xamples of No. 71 are generally found with yellowish [str]eaky gum.

21

Small type

[18]70–88. *As T* 21 (*various frames*). *Ottawa* (1870–73) *and Montreal printings. P* 12 (*or slightly under*).
Papers (a) 1870–80. *Medium to stout wove.*
(b) 1870–72. *Thin, soft, very white.*
(c) 1878–97. *Thinner and poorer quality.*

[7]2 21 1 c. bright orange (*a, b*) (1870–73) . . £130 22·00
a. Thick soft paper (1871) . . £375 £120
[7]3 1 c. orange-yellow (*a*) (1876–79) . . 50·00 2·00
[7]4 1 c. pale dull yellow (*a*) (1877–79) . . 32·00 1·50
[7]5 1 c. bright yellow (*a, c*) (1878–97) . . 24·00 1·00
a. Imperf (pair) (c) . . £300
b. Bisected (½ c.) (on *Railway News*) . . † £3000
c. Printed both sides . . £1500
[7]6 1 c. lemon-yellow (*c*) (1880) . . 85·00 16·00
[7]7 2 c. dp green (*a, b*) (1872–73 & 1876–78) 75·00 1·75
[7]8 2 c. grass-green (*c*) (1878–88) . . 42·00 1·00
a. Imperf (pair) . . £350
b. Bisected (1 c. with 2 c. to make 3 c. rate) on cover . . † £1400
[7]9 3 c. Indian red (*a*) (1.70) . . £900 50·00
a. Perf 12½ (2.70) . . £4500 £500
[8]0 3 c. pale rose-red (*a*) (9.70) . . £275 8·00
[8]1 3 c. deep rose-red (*a, b*) (1870–73) . . £300 8·50
a. Thick soft paper (1.71) . . — £150
[8]2 3 c. dull red (*a, c*) (1876–88) . . 60·00 1·75
[8]3 3 c. orange-red (*shades*) (*a, c*) (1876–88) 45·00 1·25
[8]4 3 c. rose-carm (*c*) (10.88–4.89) . . £350 11·00
85 21 5 c. olive-green (*a, c*) (2.76–88) . . £200 8·00
86 6 c. yellowish brown (*a, b, c*) (1872–73 and 1876–90) . . £180 11·00
a. Bisected (3 c.) on cover . . † £1600
b. Perf 12×11½ (1873) . . † —
87 10 c. pale lilac-magenta (*a*) (1876–?) . . £475 50·00
88 10 c. deep lilac-magenta (*a, c*) (3.76–88) £450 55·00
89 10 c. lilac-pink (3.88) . . £250 30·00

Nos. 75 and 78 were printed in the same shades during the second Ottawa period. Nos. 75a and 78a date from *circa* 1894–95.

Examples of paper (*a*) can often be found showing traces of ribbing, especially on the 2 c. value.

No. 79a was issued in New Brunswick and Nova Scotia.

One used copy of the 10 c. perf 12½ has been reported.

1873–79. *Montreal printings. Medium to stout wove paper. P* 11½×12 *or* 13¾×12.

90 21 1 c. bright orange . . £190 28·00
91 1 c. orange-yellow (1873–79) . . £160 12·00
92 1 c. pale dull yellow (1877–79) . . £150 17·00
93 1 c. lemon-yellow (1879) . . £180 17·00
94 2 c. deep green (1873–78) . . £225 19·00
95 3 c. dull red (1875–79) . . £225 15·00
96 3 c. orange-red (1873–79) . . £225 15·00
97 5 c. olive-green (1.2.76–79) . . £400 26·00
98 6 c. yellowish brown (1873–79) . . £400 32·00
99 10 c. very pale lilac magenta (1874) . . £900 £250
100 10 c. deep lilac-magenta (1876–79) . . £600 £190

27

1882–97. *Montreal* (*to March* 1889) *and Ottawa printings. Thinnish paper of poor quality. P* 12.

101 27 ½ c. black (7.82–97) . . 10·00 6·50
102 ½ c. grey-black . . 10·00 6·50
ab. Imperf (pair) (1891–93?) . . £400
ac. Imperf between (pair) . . £700

1889–97. *Ottawa printings. Thinnish paper of poor quality, often toned grey or yellowish. P* 12.

103 21 2 c. dull sea-green . . 40·00 1·25
104 2 c. blue-green (7.89–91) . . 32·00 1·50
105 3 c. bright vermilion (4.89–97) . . 28·00 80
a. Imperf (pair) (1891–93?) . . £300
106 5 c. brownish grey (5.89) . . 60·00 1·75
a. Imperf (pair) (1891–93) . . £400
107 6 c. deep chestnut (10.90) . . 30·00 8·50
a. "5 c." re-entry* . . £2000 £1300
b. Imperf (pair) (1891–93?) . . £400
108 6 c. pale chestnut . . 38·00 8·50
109 10 c. salmon-pink . . £250 £110
110 10 c. carmine-pink (4.90) . . £160 23·00
ab. Imperf (pair) (1891–93?) . . £450
111 10 c. brownish red (1894?) . . £160 23·00
ba. Imperf (pair) . . £400

*No. 107a shows traces of the 5 c. value 2½ mm below the 6 c. design.

The 1 c. showed no change in the Ottawa printings, so is not included. The 2 c. reverted to its previous grass-green shade in 1891.

The 3 c. is known bisected and used as a ⅔ stamp for the 2 c. "drop letter" rate at Halifax in 1892.

28

29

(Recess B.A.B.N.)

1893 (17 Feb). *P* 12.

115 28 20 c. vermilion . . £160 42·00
a. Imperf (pair) . . £1200
116 50 c. blue . . £225 24·00
a. Imperf (Prussian blue) (pair) . . £1200

1893 (1 Aug). *P* 12.

117 29 8 c. pale bluish grey . . 90·00 4·25
a. Imperf (pair) . . £475
118 8 c. bluish slate . . £100 4·25
119 8 c. slate-purple . . 90·00 4·25
120 8 c. blackish purple . . 75·00 4·25
a. Imperf (pair) . . £500

PRINTERS. The following stamps to No. 287 were recess-printed by the American Bank Note Co, Ottawa, which in 1923 became the Canadian Bank Note Co.

30

(Des L. Pereira and F. Brownell)

1897 (19 June). *Jubilee issue. P* 12.

121 30 ½ c. black . . 48·00 48·00
122 1 c. orange . . 10·00 4·50
123 1 c. orange-yellow . . 10·00 4·50
a. Bisected (½ c.) on cover . . † £2500
124 2 c. green . . 15·00 9·00
125 2 c. deep green . . 15·00 9·00
126 3 c. carmine . . 12·00 2·25
127 5 c. slate-blue . . 40·00 14·00
128 5 c. deep blue . . 40·00 14·00
129 6 c. brown . . 85·00 85·00
130 8 c. slate-violet . . 32·00 29·00
131 10 c. purple . . 50·00 42·00
132 15 c. slate . . 85·00 85·00
133 20 c. vermilion . . 85·00 85·00
134 50 c. pale ultramarine . . £120 95·00
135 50 c. bright ultramarine . . £120 £100
136 $1 lake . . £400 £400
137 $2 deep violet . . £700 £350
138 $3 bistre . . £800 £650
139 $4 violet . . £800 £600
140 $5 olive-green . . £800 £600
121/40 . . *Set of* 16 £3500 £2500
133s/40s Handstamped "Specimen" . . *Set of* 7 £1800

No 123a was used on issues of the *Railway News* of 5, 6 and 8 November 1897 and must be on a large part of the original newspaper with New Glasgow postmark.

31

32

(From photograph by W. & D. Downey, London)

1897–98. *P* 12.

141 31 ½ c. grey-black (9.11.97) . . 6·00 4·75
142 ½ c. black . . 7·50 5·00
a. Imperf (pair) . . £375
143 1 c. blue-green (12.97) . . 18·00 90
a. Imperf (pair) . . £375
144 2 c. violet (12.97) . . 18·00 1·50
a. Imperf (pair) . . £375
145 3 c. carmine (1.98) . . 24·00 40
a. Imperf (pair) . . £700
146 5 c. deep blue/*bluish* (12.97) . . 60·00 2·75
a. Imperf (pair) . . £375
147 6 c. brown (12.97) . . 55·00 21·00
a. Imperf (pair) . . £700
148 8 c. orange (12.97) . . 75·00 7·00
a. Imperf (pair) . . £400
149 10 c. brownish purple (1.98) . . £130 55·00
a. Imperf (pair) . . £425
141/9 . . *Set of* 8 £350 80·00

BOOKLET PANES. Most definitive booklets issued from 1900 onwards had either the two horizontal sides or all three outer edges imperforate. Stamps from the panes show one side or two adjacent sides imperforate.

Two types of the 2 c.

Die Ia. Frame consists of four fine lines.

Die Ib. Frame has one thick line between two fine lines.

The die was retouched in 1900 for Plates 11 and 12 producing weak vertical frame lines and then retouched again in 1902 for Plates 15 to 20 resulting in much thicker frame lines. No. 155*b* covers both states of the retouching.

1898–1902. *P* 12.

150 32 ½ c. black (9.98) . . 3·25 1·10
a. Imperf (pair) . . £375
151 1 c. blue-green (6.98) . . 22·00 40
152 1 c. deep green/*toned paper* . . 22·00 50
a. Imperf (pair) . . £700
153 2 c. dull purple (Die Ia) (9.98) . . 23·00 30
a. Thick paper (6.99) . . 90·00 10·00
154 2 c. violet (Die Ia) . . 22·00 30
154*a* 2 c. reddish purple (Die Ia) . . 40·00 1·00
155 2 c. rose-carmine (Die Ia) (20.8.99) . . 30·00 30
a. Imperf (pair) . . £300
155*b* 2 c. rose-carmine (Die Ib) (1900) . . 40·00 65
ba. Booklet pane of 6 (11.6.00) . . £750
156 3 c. rose-carmine (6.98) . . 42·00 1·00
157 5 c. slate-blue/*bluish* . . 95·00 1·60
a. Imperf (pair) . . £750
158 5 c. Prussian blue/*bluish* . . £100 1·60
159 6 c. brown (9.98) . . 85·00 48·00
a. Imperf (pair) . . £650
160 7 c. greenish yellow (23.12.02) . . 55·00 13·00
161 8 c. orange-yellow (10.98) . . £110 25·00
162 8 c. brownish orange . . £100 25·00
a. Imperf (pair) . . £650
163 10 c. pale brownish purple (11.98) . . £160 14·00
164 10 c. deep brownish purple . . £160 14·00
a. Imperf (pair) . . £650
165 20 c. olive-green (29.12.00) . . £300 48·00
150/65 . . *Set of* 11 £750 £120

The 7 c. and 20 c. also exist imperforate, but unlike the values listed in this condition, they have no gum. (*Price*, 7 c. £350, 20 c. £1400 *pair, un*).

33

(Des R. Weir Crouch, G. Hahn, A. H. Howard and R. Holmes. Eng C. Skinner. Design recess, colours added by typo)

1898 (7 Dec). *Imperial Penny Postage. Design in black. British possessions in red. Oceans in colours given. P* 12.

166	**33**	2 c. lavender	29·00	5·50
167		2 c. greenish blue	25·00	5·00
168		2 c. blue	25·00	4·75
		a. Imperf (pair)	£350	

Forgeries of Type **33** are without horizontal lines across the continents and have a forged Montreal postmark of 24.12.98.

1899 (4 Jan). *Provisionals used at Port Hood, Nova Scotia. No.* 156 *divided vertically and handstamped.*

169	**32**	"1" in blue, on 1/3 of 3 c.	—	£3500
170		"2" in violet, on 2/3 of 3 c.	—	£3000

Nos. 169/70 were prepared by the local postmaster during a shortage of 2 c. stamps caused by a change in postage rates.

2 CENTS

(**34**)

35 King Edward VII

1899. *Surch with T* **34**, *by Public Printing Office.*

171	**31**	2 c. on 3 c. carmine (8 Aug)	12·00	8·00
		a. Surch inverted	£275	
172	**32**	2 c. on 3 c. rose-carmine (28 July)	17·00	4·25
		a. Surch inverted	£275	

(Des King George V when Prince of Wales and J. A. Tilleard)

1903 (1 July)–**12.** *P* 12.

173	**35**	1 c. pale green	22·00	50
174		1 c. deep green	20·00	50
175		1 c. green	20·00	50
176		2 c. rose-carmine	20·00	50
		a. Booklet pane of 6	£750	
177		2 c. pale rose-carmine	20·00	50
		a. Imperf (pair) (18.7.09)	28·00	32·00
178		5 c. blue/*bluish*	70·00	2·50
179		5 c. indigo/*bluish*	70·00	2·75
180		7 c. yellow-olive	55·00	2·75
181		7 c. greenish bistre	65·00	2·75
181*a*		7 c. straw (1.12)	£110	35·00
182		10 c. brown-lilac	£110	9·50
183		10 c. pale dull purple	£110	9·50
184		10 c. dull purple	£110	9·50
185		20 c. pale olive-green (27.9.04)	£200	23·00
186		20 c. deep olive-green	£225	23·00
		s. Handstamped "Specimen"	75·00	
187		50 c. deep violet (19.11.08)	£350	85·00
173/87		*Set of* 7	£700	£110

The 1 c., 5 c., 7 c. and 10 c. exist imperforate but are believed to be proofs. (*Prices per pair,* 1 c. £400, 5 c. £600, 7 c. £400, 10 c. £600).

IMPERFORATE AND PART-PERFORATED SHEETS. Prior to 1946 many Canadian issues exist imperforate, or with other perforation varieties, in the colours of the issued stamps and, usually, with gum. In the years before 1927 such examples are believed to come from imprimatur sheets, removed from the Canadian Post Office archives. From 1927 until 1946 it is known that the printers involved in the production of the various issues submitted several imperforate plate proof sheets of each stamp to the Post Office authorities for approval. Some of these sheets or part sheets were retained for record purposes, but the remainder found their way onto the philatelic market.

Part-perforated sheets also occur from 1927–29 issues.

From 1908 until 1946 we now only list and price such varieties of this type which are known to be genuine errors, sold from post offices. Where other imperforate or similar varieties are known they are recorded in footnotes.

It is possible, and in some cases probable, that some imperforate varieties listed before 1908 may have also been removed from the archives as mentioned above, but it is far harder to be explicit over the status of this earlier material.

36 King George V and Queen Mary when Prince and Princess of Wales

37 Jacques Cartier and Samuel Champlain

(Des Machado)

1908 (16 July). *Quebec Tercentenary T* **36/7** *and similar horiz designs. P* 12.

188	½ c. sepia	3·50	3·25
189	1 c. blue-green	13·00	2·75
190	2 c. carmine	18·00	1·00
191	5 c. indigo	45·00	20·00
192	7 c. olive-green	50·00	40·00
193	10 c. violet	55·00	45·00
194	15 c. brown-orange	75·00	65·00
195	20 c. dull brown	£100	80·00
188/95	*Set of* 8	£300	£225

Designs:—2 c. King Edward VII and Queen Alexandra; 5 c. Champlain's House in Quebec; 7 c. Generals Montcalm and Wolfe; 10 c. Quebec in 1700; 15 c. Champlain's departure for the West; 20 c. Cartier's arrival before Quebec.

Some values exist on both toned and white papers.

Nos. 188/95 exist imperforate. (*Price* £350, *un, for each pair*).

WET AND DRY PRINTINGS. Until the end of December 1922 all Canadian stamps were produced by the "wet" method of recess-printing in which the paper was dampened before printing, dried and then gummed.

In late December 1922 the Canadian Bank Note Co. began to use the "dry" process in which the paper was gummed before printing. Late printings of the 3 c. brown were the first stamps to be produced by this method, but the changeover was not completed until January 1926.

"Dry" printings have a sharper appearance and can often be found with a degree of embossing showing on the reverse. Stamps from "wet" printings shrink during drying and are narrower than "dry" examples. In many cases the difference can be as great as 0.5 mm. On some early booklet panes the difference is in the vertical, rather than the horizontal, measurement.

On Nos. 196/215 all values only exist from "wet" printings except the 3 c., 20 c. and 50 c. which come from both types of printing.

44

1911–22. *P* 12.

196	**44**	1 c. yellow-green (22.12.11)	5·50	50
		a. With fine horiz lines across stamp	35·00	8·50
197		1 c. bluish green	5·50	50
		a. Booklet pane of 6 (1.5.13)	50·00	
198		1 c. deep bluish green	6·00	50
199		1 c. deep yellow-green	6·00	65
		a. Booklet pane of 6	18·00	
200		2 c. rose-red (15.12.11)	4·50	50
201		2 c. deep rose-red	4·75	50
		a. Booklet pane of 6 (1.12)	32·00	
202		2 c. pale rose-red	4·50	50
		a. With fine horiz lines across stamp	25·00	10·00
203		2 c. carmine	5·50	50
204		3 c. brown (6.8.18)	6·00	50
205		3 c. deep brown	5·00	50
		a. Booklet pane of 4 + 2 labels (2.22)	50·00	
205*b*		5 c. deep blue (17.1.12)	60·00	75
206		5 c. indigo	90·00	2·75
206*a*		5 c. grey-blue	80·00	1·75
206*b*		7 c. straw (12.1.12)	75·00	13·00
207		7 c. pale sage-green (1914)	£180	30·00
208		7 c. olive-yellow (1915)	20·00	3·00
209		7 c. yellow-ochre (1916)	20·00	3·00
210		10 c. brownish purple (12.1.12)	90·00	2·75
211		10 c. reddish purple	£100	3·25
212		20 c. olive-green (23.1.12)	29·00	1·50
213		20 c. olive	29·00	1·75
214		50 c. grey-black (26.1.12)	£100	8·00
215		50 c. sepia	48·00	3·75
196/215		*Set of* 8	£225	11·00

The 20 c. and 50 c. values exist imperforate (*Price* £1200 *un, for each pair*).

1912 (Nov)–**21.** *For use in coil-machines.* (*a*) *P* 12×*imperf.*

216	**44**	1 c. yellow-green (1914)	3·50	10·00
217		1 c. blue-green	12·00	23·00
		a. Two large holes at top and bottom (vert pair) (7.18)	65·00	80·00
218		2 c. deep rose-red (1914)	25·00	18·00
218*a*		3 c. brown (1921)	3·50	6·00

No. 217a has two large holes about 3½ mm in diameter in the top and bottom margins. They were for experimental use in a vending machine at Toronto in July 1918 and were only in use for two days.

The 1 c. and 2 c. also exist with two small "V" shaped holes about 9.5 mm apart at top which are gripper marks due to modifications made in vending machines in 1917.

(*b*) *Imperf* × *perf* 8

219	**44**	1 c. yellow-green (9.12)	12·00	4·50
220		1 c. blue-green	15·00	4·75
		a. With fine horiz lines across stamp	55·00	
221		2 c. carmine (9.12)	11·00	1·50
222		2 c. rose-red	12·00	2·25
223		2 c. scarlet	32·00	5·00
224		3 c. brown (8.18)	5·00	2·00

(*c*) *P* 8 × *imperf*

224*a*	**44**	1 c. blue-green (15.2.13)	60·00	48·00
224*b*		2 c. carmine (15.2.13)	60·00	48·00

The stamps imperf × perf 8 were sold in coils over the counter; those perf 8 × imperf were on sale in automatic machines. Varieties showing perf 12 on 2 or 3 adjacent sides and 1 or 2 sides imperf are from booklets, or the margins of sheets.

WAR TAX

(**45**)

46

47

1915 (12 Feb). *Optd with T* **45**.

225	**44**	5 c. blue	£110	£190
226		20 c. olive-green	55·00	95·00
227		50 c. sepia (R.)	£110	£150
225/7		*Set of* 3	£250	£400

These stamps were intended for tax purposes, but owing to ambiguity in an official circular dated 16 April 1915, it was for a time believed that their use for postal purposes was authorised. The position was clarified by a further circular on 20 May 1916 which made clear that Nos. 225/7 were for fiscal use only.

1915. *P* 12.

228	**46**	1 c. green (15.4.15)	8·00	50
229		2 c. carmine-red (16.4.15)	12·00	70
230		2 c. rose-carmine	13·00	3·00

Die I

Die II

In Die I there is a long horizontal coloured line under the fo the "T", and a solid bar of colour runs upwards from the "1" to "T".

In Die II this solid bar of colour is absent, and there is a s horizontal line under the left side of the "T", with two short vert dashes and a number of dots under the right-hand side.

1916 (1 Jan). *P* 12.

231	**47**	2 c. + 1 c. rose-red (Die I)	24·00	
232		2 c. + 1 c. bright carmine (Die I)	24·00	
233		2 c. + 1 c. scarlet (Die I)	21·00	

1916 (Feb). *Imperf* × *perf* 8 (*coils*).

234	**47**	2 c. + 1 c. rose-red (Die I)	55·00	1[illegible]

1916 (July). *P* 12 × 8.

235	**47**	2 c. + 1 c. carmine-red (Die I)	16·00	4[illegible]
236		2 c. + 1 c. bright rose-red (Die I)	16·00	4[illegible]

1916 (Aug). *P* 12.

237	**47**	2 c. + 1 c. carmine-red (Die II)	95·00	18[illegible]

1916 (Aug). *Colour changed.* (*a*) *P* 12.

238	**47**	2 c. + 1 c. brown (Die I)	£180	2[illegible]
239		2 c. + 1 c. yellow-brown (Die II)	4·00	
		a. Imperf (pair)	£850	
240		2 c. + 1 c. deep brown (Die II)	10·00	

(*b*) *Imperf* × *perf* 8

241	**47**	2 c. + 1 c. brown (Die I)	£100	7
		a. Pair, 241 and 243	£350	
243		2 c. + 1 c. deep brown (Die II)	35·00	3

No. 239a, which is a genuine error, should not be confus with ungummed proofs of the Die I stamp, No. 238 (*Price pair,* £140).

This value also exists p 12×imperf or imperf×p 12, but w not issued with these perforations (*Price, in either instan* £300, *un, per pair*).

48 Quebec Conference, 1864, from painting "The Fathers of Confederation", by Robert Harris

1917 (15 Sept). 50*th Anniv of Confederation. P* 12.

244	**48**	3 c. bistre-brown	18·00	1·
245		3 c. deep brown	20·00	2·

No. 244 exists imperforate (*Price per pair,* £275 *un*).

I

II

Die I. Space between top of "N" and oval frame line and spa between "CENT" and lower frame line.

Die II. "ONE CENT" appears larger so that "N" touches oval ar "CENT" almost touches frame line. There are other differences b this is the most obvious one.

I

II

Die I. The lowest of the three horizontal lines of shading belov the medals does not touch the three heavy diagonal lines; thre complete white spaces over both "E's" of "THREE"; long centre ba to figures "3". Vertical spandrel lines fine.

Die II. The lowest horizontal line of shading touches the first c the three diagonal lines; two and a half spaces over first "E" an spaces over second "E" partly filled by stem of maple leaf; shor centre bar to figures "3". Vertical spandrel lines thick. There ar numerous other minor differences.

WET AND DRY PRINTINGS. See notes above No. 196.

On Nos. 246/63 all listed items occur from both "wet" and "dry printings except Nos. 246aa/ab, 248aa, 256, 259, 260 and 262 whic come "wet" only, and Nos. 246a, 248/a, 252/4*a*, 256b and 263 whic are "dry" only.

–31. *As T* **44**. (a) *P* 12.
44 1 c. chrome-yellow (Die I) (7.6.22) .. 2·50 60
aa. Booklet pane of 4 + 2 labels (7.22) 50·00
ab. Booklet pane of 6 (12.22) .. .. 27·00
a. Die II (1925) .. .. .. 5·50 30
2 c. deep green (6.6.22) .. .. .. 2·25 10
aa. Booklet pane of 4 + 2 labels (7.22) 30·00
ab. Booklet pane of 6 (12.22) £250
b. Thin paper (9.24) .. .. .. 3·00 4·50
3 c. carmine (Die I) (18.12.23) .. .. 3·75 10
aa. Booklet pane of 4 + 2 labels (12.23) 29·00
a. Die II (11.24) .. .. .. 21·00 80
4 c. olive-yellow (7.7.22) .. .. 8·00 3·50
a. Yellow-ochre .. .. .. 8·00 3·50
5 c. violet (2.2.22) .. .. .. 5·00 1·75
a. Thin paper (9.24) .. .. .. 5·00 8·00
b. Reddish violet (1925) .. .. 7·00 2·00
7 c. red-brown (12.12.24) .. .. 12·00 7·00
a. Thin paper .. .. £130 30·00
8 c. blue (1.9.25) .. .. .. 19·00 10·00
10 c. blue (20.2.22) .. .. .. 20·00 3·25
10 c. bistre-brown (1.8.25) .. .. 18·00 3·00
a. Yellow-brown .. .. .. 18·00 3·00
$1 brown-orange (22.7.23) .. .. 50·00 8·00
55 .. .. *Set of* 10 £130 32·00
e $1 differs from T **44** in that the value tablets are oval.
os. 249/55 exist imperforate (*Prices per un pair* 4 c. *to* 8 c. *each*, 10 c. £1000, $1 £1200).

(b) *Imperf* × *perf* 8
44 1 c. chrome-yellow (Die I) (1922) .. 4·00 5·50
a. Imperf horiz (vert pair) (1924) .. £160
b. Die II (1925) .. .. .. 4·50 7·00
c. Do. Imperf horiz (vert pair) (1927) 11·00 27·00
2 c. deep green (26.7.22) .. .. 9·00 2·25
b. Imperf horiz (vert pair) (1927) .. 12·00 27·00
3 c. carmine (Die I) (9.4.24) .. .. 60·00 10·00
a. Imperf horiz (vert pair) (1924) .. £250
b. Die II (1925) .. .. .. 80·00 23·00
/8 .. .. *Set of* 3 65·00 16·00
os. 256a, 256c, 257b and 258a come from coil printings sold heet form. Those issued in 1924 were from "wet" printings those in 1927 from "dry". A "wet" printing of No. 257b, ed in 1924, also exists (*Price £160 mint*), but cannot be tified from that issued in 1927 except by the differences veen "wet" and "dry" stamps.

(c) *Imperf* (*pairs*)
44 1 c. chrome-yellow (Die I) (6.10.24) .. 50·00 70·00
2 c. deep green (6.10.24) .. .. 50·00 70·00
3 c. carmine (Die I) (31.12.23)† .. .. 28·00 42·00

(d) *P* 12 × *imperf*
44 2 c. deep green (9.24) .. .. .. 65·00 65·00

(e) *P* 12 × 8
44 3 c. carmine (Die II) (24.6.31) .. .. 2·50 3·25
Earliest known postmark.
Nos. 259 to 261 were on sale only at the Philatelic Branch,). Dept, Ottawa.
No. 263 was produced by adding horizontal perforations to used sheet stock of No. 258b. The stamps were then issued in 31 pending the delivery of No. 293.

2 CENTS (49)

2 CENTS (50)

26. *No.* 248 *surch.*

(a) *With T* **49**, *by the Govt Printing Bureau*
4 **44** 2 c. on 3 c. carmine (12.10.26) .. .. 42·00 50·00
a. Pair, one without surch £300
b. On Die II £375

(b) *With T* **50**, *by the Canadian Bank Note Co*
5 **44** 2 c. on 3 c. carmine (4.11.26) .. .. 16·00 20·00
a. Surch double (partly treble) .. £200

51 Sir J. A. Macdonald

52 "The Fathers of Confederation"

53 Parliament Buildings, Ottawa

54 Sir W. Laurier

55 Canada, Map 1867–1927

927 (29 June). *60th Anniv of Confederation. P* 12. I. *Commemorative Issue. Inscr* "1867–1927 CANADA CONFEDERATION".
66 **51** 1 c. orange .. .. 2·50 1·50
67 **52** 2 c. green .. .. 2·25 30
68 **53** 3 c. carmine .. .. 7·00 5·00
69 **54** 5 c. violet .. .. 3·25 3·50
70 **55** 12 c. blue .. .. 23·00 5·00
66/70 .. .. *Set of* 5 35·00 14·00
Nos. 266/70 exist imperforate, imperf×perf or perf×imperf *Prices from £65, un, per pair*).

56 Darcy McGee

57 Sir W. Laurier and Sir J. A. Macdonald

58 R. Baldwin and L. H. Lafontaine

II. *Historical Issue*
271 **56** 5 c. violet .. .. 3·00 2·50
272 **57** 12 c. green .. .. 15·00 4·50
273 **58** 20 c. carmine .. .. 17·00 12·00
271/3 .. .. *Set of* 3 32·00 17·00
Nos. 271/3 exist imperforate, imperf×perf or perf×imperf (*Prices from £65, un, per pair*).

59

(Des H. Schwartz)

1928 (21 Sept). *Air. P* 12.
274 **59** 5 c. olive-brown .. .. 6·00 3·50
No. 274 exists imperforate, imperf×perf or perf×imperf (*Price per pair, £140, un*).

60 King George V

61 Mt Hurd and Indian Totem Poles

62 Quebec Bridge

63 Harvesting with Horses

64 *Bluenose* (fishing schooner)

65 Parliament Buildings, Ottawa

1928–29. (a) *P* 12.
275 **60** 1 c. orange (25.10.28) .. .. .. 2·75 60
a. Booklet pane of 6 .. .. .. 18·00
276 2 c. green (16.10.28) .. .. .. 1·25 20
a. Booklet pane of 6 .. .. .. 18·00
277 3 c. lake (12.12.28) .. .. .. 17·00 15·00
278 4 c. olive-bistre (16.8.29) .. .. 13·00 6·50
279 5 c. violet (12.12.28) .. .. .. 6·50 3·25
a. Booklet pane of 6 (6.1.29) .. .. 90·00
280 8 c. blue (21.12.28) .. .. .. 7·50 4·75
281 **61** 10 c. green (5.12.28) .. .. .. 8·50 1·25
282 **62** 12 c. grey-black (8.1.29) .. .. 22·00 10·00
283 **63** 20 c. lake (8.1.29) .. .. .. 27·00 12·00
284 **64** 50 c. blue (8.1.29) .. .. .. £100 38·00
285 **65** $1 olive-green (8.1.29) .. .. £110 60·00
a. Brown-olive .. .. .. £225 95·00
275/85 .. .. *Set of* 11 £275 £130

(b) *Imperf* × *perf* 8 (5.11.28)
286 **60** 1 c. orange .. .. 13·00 22·00
287 2 c. green .. .. 13·00 4·25
Slight differences in the size of many Canadian stamps, due to paper shrinkage, are to be found.
Nos. 275/85 exist imperforate, imperf×perf or perf×imperf (*Prices per unused pair*, 1 c. to 8 c., *from* £60, 10 c. to 20 c., *from* £100, 50 c. and $1, *from* £375). *Tête-bêche* horizontal pairs of the 1 c., 2 c. and 5 c. are also known from uncut booklet sheets (*Prices per pair, £225, un*).

PRINTERS. The following stamps to No. 334 were recess-printed by the British American Bank Note Co, Ottawa.

66

67 Parliamentary Library, Ottawa

68 The Old Citadel, Quebec

69 Harvesting with Tractor

70 Acadian Memorial Church and Statue of "Evangeline", Grand Pre, Nova Scotia

71 Mt Edith Cavell, Canadian Rockies

Die I 1 c. Die II Die I 2 c. Die II

1 c. Die I. Three thick coloured lines and one thin between "P" and ornament, at right. Curved line in ball-ornament short.
Die II. Four thick lines. Curved line longer.

2 c. Die I. Three thick coloured lines between "P" and ornament, at left. Short line in ball.
Die II. Four thick lines. Curved line longer.

1930–31. (a) *P* 11.
288 **66** 1 c. orange (I) (17.7.30) .. .. 1·75 1·00
289 1 c. green (I) (6.12.30) .. .. 1·50 10
b. Booklet pane of 6 (21.7.31) .. 25·00
d. Die II (8.31) .. .. .. 1·25 10
da. Imperf (pair) £900
db. Booklet pane of 4 + 2 labels (13.11.31) .. .. .. 75·00
290 2 c. green (I) (6.6.30) .. .. 1·75 10
a. Booklet pane of 6 (17.6.30) .. 35·00
291 2 c. scarlet (I) (17.11.30) 70 75
a. Booklet pane of 6 (17.11.30) .. 23·00
b. Die II 90 10
292 2 c. deep brown (I) (4.7.31) .. .. 1·50 3·00
a. Booklet pane of 6 (23.7.31) .. 35·00
b. Die II (4.7.31) .. .. .. 1·25 10
ba. Booklet pane of 4 + 2 labels (13.11.31) £100
293 3 c. scarlet (13.7.31) 90 10
a. Booklet pane of 4 + 2 labels .. 35·00
294 4 c. yellow-bistre (5.11.30) .. .. 6·50 4·50
295 5 c. violet (18.6.30) .. .. .. 2·75 4·50
296 5 c. deep slate-blue (13.11.30) .. 5·00 20
a. Dull blue .. .. 14·00 50
297 8 c. blue (13.8.30) .. .. .. 11·00 16·00
298 8 c. red-orange (5.11.30) .. .. 7·00 5·50
299 **67** 10 c. olive-green (15.9.30) .. .. 14·00 1·00
a. Imperf (pair) £900
300 **68** 12 c. grey-black (4.12.30) .. .. 14·00 5·50
301 **69** 20 c. red (4.12.30) .. .. .. 22·00 1·00
302 **70** 50 c. blue (4.12.30) .. .. .. 80·00 17·00
303 **71** $1 olive-green (4.12.30) .. .. 95·00 23·00
288/303 .. .. *Set of* 16 £225 70·00

(b) *Imperf* × *perf* $8^1/_2$
304 **66** 1 c. orange (I) (14.7.30) .. .. 11·00 15·00
305 1 c. green (I) (4.2.31) .. .. .. 6·00 7·00
306 2 c. green (I) (27.6.30) .. .. 4·00 5·00
307 2 c. scarlet (I) (19.11.30) .. .. 4·50 5·00
308 2 c. deep brown (I) (4.7.31) .. .. 9·00 1·50
309 3 c. scarlet (13.7.31) .. .. .. 14·00 1·50
304/9 .. .. *Set of* 6 42·00 32·00
Nos. 300/3 exist imperforate (*Prices per unused pair*, 12 c. £500, 20 c. £500, 50 c. £600, $1 £700).
Some low values in the above and subsequent issues have been printed by both Rotary and "Flat plate" processes. The former can be distinguished by the gum, which has a striped appearance.
For 13 c. bright violet, T **68**, see No. 325.

PRICES OF SETS

Set prices are given for many issues, generally those containing three stamps or more. Definitive sets include one of each value or major colour change, but do not cover different perforations, die types or minor shades. Where a choice is possible the set prices are based on the cheapest versions of the stamps included in the listings.

72 Mercury and Western Hemisphere 73 Sir Georges Etienne Cartier

(Des H. Schwartz)

1930 (4 Dec). *Air. P* 11.
310 **72** 5 c. deep brown .. .. 18·00 18·00

1931 (30 Sept). *P* 11.
312 **73** 10 c. olive-green .. .. 5·00 20
No. 312 exists imperforate (*Price per pair, £350, un*).

(74) (75)

1932 (22 Feb). *Air. No.* 274 *surch with T* **74**.
313 **59** 6 c. on 5 c. olive-brown .. .. .. 3·00 2·50
Examples of this stamp with surcharge inverted, surcharge double, surcharge triple or surcharge omitted in pair with normal are not now believed to have been regularly issued. Such "errors" have also been forged and collectors are warned against forged examples, some of which bear unauthorized markings which purport to be the guarantee of Stanley Gibbons Ltd.

1932 (21 June). *Nos.* 291/*b surch with T* **75**.
314 **66** 3 c. on 2 c. scarlet (I) .. .. .. 2·00 2·50
a. Die II .. .. 1·00 60

76 King George V 77 Duke of Windsor when Prince of Wales

78 Allegory of British Empire

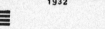

6 6
OTTAWA CONFERENCE
1932

(79)

1932 (12 July). *Ottawa Conference. P* 11. (*a*) *Postage stamps.*
315 **76** 3 c. scarlet 70 80
316 **77** 5 c. blue .. .. 8·50 4·75
317 **78** 13 c. green .. .. 9·00 6·00
(*b*) *Air. No.* 310 *surch with T* **79**
318 **72** 6 c. on 5 c. deep brown (B.) .. .. 10·00 12·00
315/18 .. .. .. *Set of* 4 25·00 21·00

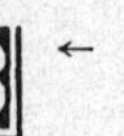

80 King George V "3" level Die I "3" raised Die II

1932 (1 Dec)–**33.** (*a*) *P* 11.
319 **80** 1 c. green 60 10
a. Booklet pane of 6 (28.12.33) .. 15·00
b. Booklet pane of 4 + 2 labels (19.9.33) 75·00
320 2 c. sepia 70 10
a. Booklet pane of 6 (7.9.33) .. 15·00
b. Booklet pane of 4 + 2 labels (19.9.33) 75·00
321 3 c. scarlet (Die I) .. .. .. 1·00 10
a. Booklet pane of 4 + 2 labels (22.8.33) 40·00
b. Die II (29.11.32) 85 10
ba. Booklet pane of 4 + 2 labels (19.9.33) 30·00
322 4 c. yellow-brown .. .. .. 35·00 9·00
323 5 c. blue .. .. 10·00 10
a. Imperf vert (horiz pair) £950
324 8 c. red-orange .. .. .. 23·00 4·25
325 **68** 13 c. bright violet .. .. .. 32·00 2·25
319/25 .. .. .. *Set of* 7 90·00 14·00
A plate block of four from Plate 1 exists printed in varnish ink.
Nos. 319/25 exist imperforate (*Prices per unused pair*, 1 c. *to* 8 c. £150, 13 c. £450).

(*b*) *Imperf × perf* 8½ (1933)
326 **80** 1 c. green .. .. 13·00 3·50
327 2 c. sepia .. .. 19·00 2·50
328 3 c. scarlet (Die II) .. .. .. 12·00 1·50
326/8 .. .. .. *Set of* 3 40·00 6·75

81 Parliament Buildings, Ottawa

1933 (18 May). *U.P.U. Congress Preliminary Meeting. P* 11.
329 **81** 5 c. blue .. .. 6·00 2·75
No. 329 exists imperforate (*Price per pair £450, un*)

WORLD'S
GRAIN EXHIBITION &
CONFERENCE

REGINA 1933

(82)

1933 (24 July). *World's Grain Exhibition and Conference, Regina. No.* 301 *optd with T* **82** *in blue.*
330 **69** 20 c. red .. .. 16·00 7·00
No. 330 exists imperforate (*Price per pair £450, un*).

83 S.S. *Royal William* (after S. Skillett) 84 Jacques Cartier approaching Land

1933 (17 Aug). *Centenary of First Trans-Atlantic Steamboat Crossing. P* 11.
331 **83** 5 c. blue .. .. 9·50 3·00
No. 331 exists imperforate (*Price per pair £450, un*).

1934 (1 July). *Fourth Centenary of Discovery of Canada. P* 11.
332 **84** 3 c. blue .. .. 2·50 1·50
No. 332 exists imperforate (*Price per pair £450, un*).

85 U.E.L. Statue, Hamilton 86 Seal of New Brunswick

1934 (1 July). 150*th Anniv of Arrival of United Empire Loyalists. P* 11.
333 **85** 10 c. olive-green .. .. .. 8·50 4·75
No. 333 exists imperforate (*Price per pair £750, un*).

1934 (16 Aug). 150*th Anniv of Province of New Brunswick. P* 11.
334 **86** 2 c. red-brown .. .. .. 1·50 2·25
No. 334 exists imperforate (*Price per pair £400, un*).

PRINTERS. The following stamps were recess-printed (except where otherwise stated) by the Canadian Bank Note Co, Ottawa, until No. 616.

87 Queen Elizabeth II when Princess 89 King George V and Queen Mary

1935 (4 May). *Silver Jubilee. T* **87**, **89** *and similar designs. P* 12.
335 1 c. green 55 55
336 2 c. brown 60 50
337 3 c. carmine-red .. .. .. 1·75 50
338 5 c. blue .. .. 5·50 5·50
339 10 c. green .. .. 3·25 3·75
340 13 c. blue .. .. 6·50 6·00
335/40 .. .. .. *Set of* 6 16·00 15·00
Designs: *Vert* (*as T* **87**)—2 c. King George VI when Duke of York; 5 c. King Edward VIII when Prince of Wales. *Horiz* (*as T* **89**)—10 c. Windsor Castle; 13 c. Royal Yacht *Britannia*.
Nos. 335/40 exist imperforate (*Price £180, un, for each pair*).

93 King George V 94 Royal Canadian Mounted Policeman

99 Daedalus

1935 (1 June–5 Nov). *T* **93/4**, **99** *and similar designs.* (*a*) *Postc*
(i) *P* 12.
341 **93** 1 c. green 70
a. Booklet pane of 6 (19.8.35) .. 22·00
b. Booklet pane of 4+2 labels (22.7.35) .. .. .. 55·00
342 2 c. brown 75
a. Booklet pane of 6 (16.11.35) .. 26·00
b. Booklet pane of 4+2 labels (22.7.35) .. .. .. 55·00
343 3 c. scarlet 80
a. Booklet pane of 4+2 labels .. 28·00
b. Printed on the gummed side .. £225
344 4 c. yellow .. .. 3·00 1
345 5 c. blue .. .. 2·00
a. Imperf vert (horiz pair) £200
346 8 c. orange .. .. 3·25 3
347 **94** 10 c. carmine .. .. 6·00
348 – 13 c. purple .. .. 6·00
349 – 20 c. olive-green .. .. .. 17·00
350 – 50 c. deep violet .. .. .. 25·00 4
351 – $1 bright blue .. .. .. 40·00 11
341/51 .. .. .. *Set of* 11 90·00 20
(ii) *Coil stamps. Imperf × perf* 8
352 **93** 1 c. green (5.11.35) .. .. .. 13·00 4
353 2 c. brown (14.10.35) .. .. .. 9·50 4
354 3 c. scarlet (20.7.35) .. .. .. 9·00 1
352/4 .. .. .. *Set of* 3 28·00 9
(*b*) *Air. P* 12
355 **99** 6 c. red-brown .. .. 2·75 1
a. Imperf vert (horiz pair) £4750
Designs: *Horiz* (*as T* **94**)—13 c. Confederation Conferenc Charlottetown, 1864; 20 c. Niagara Falls; 50 c. Parliame Buildings, Victoria, British Columbia; $1 Champla Monument, Quebec.
Nos. 341/51 (*Prices per pair*, 1 c. *to* 8 c. *each* £110, 10 c. *to each* £200, *un.*) and 355 (*Price per pair £425, un*) ex imperforate.

100 King George VI and Queen Elizabeth

1937 (10 May). *Coronation. P* 12.
356 **100** 3 c. carmine 85
No. 356 exists imperforate (*Price per pair £450, un*).

101 King George VI 102 Memorial Chamber Parliament Buildings, Ottawa

107 Fairchild 45-80 Sekani Seaplane over *Distributor* on River Mackenzie

(T **101**. Photograph by Bertram Park)

1937–38. *T* **101/2**, **107** *and similar designs.* (*a*) *Postage.*
(i) *P* 12.
357 **101** 1 c. green (1.4.37) .. .. .. 1·50 10
a. Booklet pane of 4 + 2 labels (14.4.37) .. .. .. 28·00
b. Booklet pane of 6 (18.5.37) .. 3·50
358 2 c. brown (1.4.37) .. .. .. 1·75 10
a. Booklet pane of 4 + 2 labels (14.4.37) .. .. .. 55·00
b. Booklet pane of 6 (3.5.38) .. 11·00

101 3 c. scarlet (1.4.37) .. .. .. 1·75 10
a. Booklet pane of 4 + 2 labels (14.4.37) .. .. .. 4·25
4 c. yellow (10.5.37) .. .. .. 4·00 1·75
5 c. blue (10.5.37) .. .. .. 4·00 10
8 c. orange (10.5.37) .. .. 3·75 1·75
102 10 c. rose-carmine (15.6.38) .. .. 5·00 10
a. Red .. .. 5·00 10
– 13 c. blue (15.11.38) .. .. .. 14·00 1·25
– 20 c. red-brown (15.6.38) .. .. 22·00 70
– 50 c. green (15.6.38) .. .. .. 45·00 8·00
– $1 violet (15.6.38) .. .. .. 60·00 9·00
a. Imperf horiz (vert pair) .. £2500
67 .. .. *Set of* 11 £150 20·00
›s. 357/67 exist imperforate (*Prices per pair* 1 c. *to* 8 c. *each* , 10 c. *to* 50 c. *each* £250, $1 £350 *un*).

(ii) *Coil stamps. Imperf × perf* 8
101 1 c. green (15.6.37) .. .. .. 3·50 2·50
2 c. brown (18.6.37) .. .. .. 3·50 2·75
3 c. scarlet (15.4.37) .. .. .. 17·00 75
70 .. .. *Set of* 3 22·00 5·50

(*b*) *Air. P* 12
107 6 c. blue (15.6.38) .. .. .. 11·00 60
esigns: *Horiz* (*as T* **107**)—13 c. Entrance to Halifax Harbour; :. Fort Garry Gate, Winnipeg; 50 c. Entrance, Vancouver bour; $1 Chateau de Ramezay, Montreal.
o. 371 exists imperforate (*Price per pair* £375, *un*).

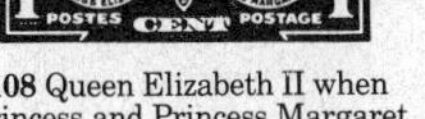

108 Queen Elizabeth II when Princess and Princess Margaret

109 National War Memorial, Ottawa

110 King George VI and Queen Elizabeth

39 (15 May). *Royal Visit. P* 12.
2 **108** 1 c. black and green .. .. .. 1·75 10
3 **109** 2 c. black and brown 60 50
4 **110** 3 c. black and carmine 60 10
2/4 .. .. *Set of* 3 2·75 60
Nos. 372/4 exist imperforate (*Price* £325, *un, for each pair*).

111 King George VI in Naval uniform

112 King George VI in Military uniform

113 King George VI in Air Force uniform

114 Grain Elevator

116 Parliament Buildings

117 Ram Tank

121 Air Training Camp

942 (1 July)–**48.** *War Effort. T* **111/14**, **116/17**, **121** *and similar designs.* (*a*) *Postage.* (i) *P* 12.
75 **111** 1 c. green .. .. 1·50 10
a. Booklet pane of 4 + 2 labels (12.9.42) .. .. .. 23·00
b. Booklet pane of 6 (24.11.42) .. 2·50
76 **112** 2 c. brown .. .. 1·75 10
a. Booklet pane of 4 + 2 labels (12.9.42) .. .. .. 27·00
b. Booklet pane of 6 (6.10.42) .. 18·00
77 **113** 3 c. carmine-lake .. .. .. 1·25 60
a. Booklet pane of 4 + 2 labels (20.8.42) .. .. .. 4·25

378 **113** 3 c. purple (30.6.43) 90 10
a. Booklet pane of 4 + 2 labels (28.8.43) .. .. 5·50
b. Booklet pane of 6 (24.11.47) .. 11·00
379 **114** 4 c. slate .. .. 5·50 1·00
380 **112** 4 c. carmine-lake (9.4.43) 70 10
a. Booklet pane of 6 (3.5.43) .. 3·50
381 **111** 5 c. blue .. .. 3·00 10
382 – 8 c. red-brown .. .. .. 5·50 75
383 **116** 10 c. brown .. .. 5·50 10
384 **117** 13 c. dull green .. .. .. 6·50 6·50
385 14 c. dull green (16.4.43) .. .. 15·00 1·00
386 – 20 c. chocolate .. .. .. 14·00 20
387 – 50 c. violet .. .. 26·00 3·00
388 – $1 blue .. .. 42·00 5·50
375/88 .. .. *Set of* 14 £110 16·00
Nos. 375/88 exist imperforate (*Prices per pair* 1 c. *to* 8 c. *each* £180, 10 c. to 20 c. *each* £250, 50 c. and $1 *each* £350, *un*).

(ii) *Coil stamps. Imperf×perf* 8
389 **111** 1 c. green (9.2.43) .. .. .. 1·00 1·50
390 **112** 2 c. brown (24.11.42) .. .. .. 2·25 1·75
391 **113** 3 c. carmine-lake (23.9.42) .. .. 2·00 5·00
392 3 c. purple (19.8.43) .. .. 5·50 3·25
393 **112** 4 c. carmine-lake (13.5.43) .. .. 6·00 1·50
389/93 .. .. *Set of* 5 15·00 11·50

(iii) *Booklet stamps. Imperf×perf* 12 (1.9.43)
394 **111** 1 c. green .. .. .. 3·00 1·25
a. Booklet pane of 3 .. .. .. 9·00
395 **113** 3 c. purple .. .. .. 3·00 1·50
a. Booklet pane of 3 .. .. .. 9·00
396 **112** 4 c. carmine-lake .. .. .. 3·00 1·75
a. Booklet pane of 3 .. .. .. 9·00
394/6 .. .. *Set of* 3 8·00 4·00
Nos. 394/6 are from booklets in which the stamps are in strips of three, imperforate at top and bottom and right-hand end.

(iv) *Coil stamps. Imperf × perf* 9½
397 **111** 1 c. green (13.7.48) .. .. .. 3·00 4·00
397*a* **112** 2 c. brown (1.10.48) .. .. .. 7·50 19·00
398 **113** 3 c. purple (2.7.48) .. .. .. 4·75 6·00
398*a* **112** 4 c. carmine-lake (22.7.48) .. .. 7·00 3·50
397/8*a* .. .. *Set of* 4 20·00 29·00

(*b*) *Air. P* 12
399 **121** 6 c. blue (1.7.42) .. .. .. 17·00 4·75
400 7 c. blue (16.4.43) .. .. .. 3·00 10
Designs: *Horiz* (*as T* **114**)—8 c. Farm scene. (*As T* **117**)—20 c. Launching of corvette H.M.C.S. *La Malbaie*, Sorel; 50 c. Munitions factory; $1 H.M.S. *Cossack* (destroyer).
Nos. 399/400 exist imperforate (*Price* £425, *un, for each pair*).

122 Ontario Farm Scene

129 Alexander Graham Bell and "Fame"

1946 (16 Sept)–**47.** *Peace Re-conversion. T* **122** *and similar horiz designs. P* 12. (*a*) *Postage.*
401 8 c. brown .. .. 1·25 2·00
402 10 c. olive-green .. .. .. 1·75 10
403 14 c. sepia .. .. 4·00 1·00
404 20 c. slate .. .. 3·00 10
405 50 c. green .. .. 17·00 2·75
406 $1 purple .. .. 27·00 3·00

(*b*) *Air*
407 7 c. blue .. .. 4·00 10
a. Booklet pane of 4 (24.11.47) .. .. 9·00
401/7 .. .. *Set of* 7 50·00 8·00
Designs:—7 c. Canada Geese in flight; 10 c. Great Bear Lake; 14 c. St. Maurice River Power Station; 20 c. Combine Harvester; 50 c. Lumbering in British Columbia; $1 *Abegweit* (train ferry), Prince Edward Is.

1947 (3 Mar). *Birth Centenary of Bell (inventor of telephone). P* 12.
408 **129** 4 c. blue 15 10

130 "Canadian Citizenship".

131 Queen Elizabeth II when Princess

1947 (1 July). *Advent of Canadian Citizenship and Eightieth Anniv of Confederation. P* 12.
409 **130** 4 c. blue 10 10

(From photograph by Dorothy Wilding)

1948 (16 Feb). *Princess Elizabeth's Marriage. P* 12.
410 **131** 4 c. blue 10 10

132 Queen Victoria, Parliament Building, Ottawa, and King George VI

133 Cabot's Ship *Matthew*

1948 (1 Oct). *One Hundred Years of Responsible Government. P* 12.
411 **132** 4 c. grey 10 10

1949 (1 Apr). *Entry of Newfoundland into Canadian Confederation. P* 12.
412 **133** 4 c. green 30 10

134 "Founding of Halifax, 1749" (C. W. Jefferys)

1949 (21 June). *Bicentenary of Halifax, Nova Scotia. P* 12.
413 **134** 4 c. violet 30 10

135

136

137

138 King George VI **139**

(From photographs by Dorothy Wilding)

1949 (15 Nov)–**51.** (i) *P* 12.
414 **135** 1 c. green 10 10
415 **136** 2 c. sepia 60 30
415*a* 2 c. olive-green (25.7.51) 30 10
416 **137** 3 c. purple 30 10
a. Booklet pane of 4+2 labels (12.4.50) 2·25
417 **138** 4 c. carmine-lake 20 10
a. Booklet pane of 6 (5.5.50) .. .. 27·00
417*b* 4 c. vermilion (2.6.51) 40 10
ba. Booklet pane of 6 .. .. 6·00
418 **139** 5 c. blue .. .. .. 2·00 10
414/18 .. .. *Set of* 7 3·50 40

(ii) *Imperf × perf* 9½ (*coil stamps*)
419 **135** 1 c. green (18.5.50) .. .. .. 1·25 1·00
420 **136** 2 c. sepia (18.5.50) .. .. .. 5·50 6·00
420*a* 2 c. olive-green (9.10.51) .. .. 1·75 2·25
421 **137** 3 c. purple (18.5.50) .. .. 2·25 2·50
422 **138** 4 c. carmine-lake (20.4.50) .. .. 14·00 9·00
422*a* 4 c. vermilion (27.11.51) .. .. 2·00 2·75
419/22*a* .. .. *Set of* 6 24·00 21·00

(iii) *Imperf × perf* 12 (*booklets*)
422*b* **135** 1 c. green (18.5.50) .. .. .. 50 1·75
ba. Booklet pane of 3 .. .. 1·50
423 **137** 3 c. purple (18.5.50) .. .. 1·25 1·00
a. Booklet pane of 3 .. .. 3·75
423*b* **138** 4 c. carmine-lake (18.5.50) .. .. 15·00 8·00
ba. Booklet pane of 3 .. .. 45·00
423*c* 4 c. vermilion (25.10.51) .. .. 7·00 7·00
ca. Booklet pane of 3 .. .. 21·00
422*b*/3*c* .. .. *Set of* 4 21·00 16·00
These booklet panes are imperforate at top, bottom and right-hand end.

140 King George VI

141 Oil Wells in Alberta

(From photograph by Dorothy Wilding)

1950 (19 Jan). *As T* **135/9** *but without* "POSTES POSTAGE", *as T* **140**. (i) *P* 12.
424 1 c. green 10 50
425 2 c. sepia .. .. 10 1·25
426 3 c. purple 10 65
427 4 c. carmine-lake 10 20
428 5 c. blue .. .. 30 1·25
424/8 .. .. *Set of* 5 60 3·50

(ii) *Imperf × perf* 9½ (*coil stamps*)
429 1 c. green .. .. 30 1·00
430 3 c. purple .. .. 80 1·50

1950 (1 Mar). *P* 12.
431 **141** 50 c. green .. .. 6·00 1·00

142 Drying Furs

143 Fisherman

1950 (2 Oct). *P* 12.
432 **142** 10 c. brown-purple .. .. 1·60 10

1951 (1 Feb). *P* 12.
433 **143** $1 ultramarine .. .. .. 38·00 5·00

144 Sir R. L. Borden

145 W. L. Mackenzie King

1951 (25 June). *Prime Ministers* (1*st issue*). *P* 12.
434 **144** 3 c. blue-green 10 50
435 **145** 4 c. rose-carmine 10 10
See also Nos. 444/5, 475/6 and 483/4.

146 Mail Trains, 1851 and 1951

147 SS. *City of Toronto* and SS. *Prince George*

148 Mail Coach and DC-4M North Star

149 Reproduction of 3d., 1851

1951 (24 Sept). *Canadian Stamp Centenary*. *P* 12.
436 **146** 4 c. black 35 10
437 **147** 5 c. violet .. .. 65 1·75
438 **148** 7 c. blue .. .. 35 1·00
439 **149** 15 c. scarlet .. .. 1·40 10
436/9 .. .. *Set of* 4 2·50 2·75

150 Queen Elizabeth II when Princess and Duke of Edinburgh

1951 (26 Oct). *Royal Visit*. *P* 12.
440 **150** 4 c. violet 10 10

STAMP BOOKLETS

Booklet Nos. SB1/48 are stapled.

All booklets up to and including No. SB41 contain panes consisting of two rows of three (3×2).

B 1

1900 (11 June). *Red on pink cover. Two panes of six* 2 c. (*No.* 155ba).
SB1 25 c. booklet. Cover as Type B **1** with English text £1700

1903 (1 July). *Red on pink cover. Two panes of six* 2 c. (*No.* 176a).
SB2 25 c. booklet. Cover as Type B **1** with English text £1800

1912 (Jan)–**16.** *Red on pink cover. Two panes of six* 2 c. (*No.* 201a).
SB3 25 c. booklet. Cover as Type B **1** with English text 60·00
a. Cover handstamped "NOTICE Change in Postal Rates For New Rates See Postmaster" 60·00
b. French text (4.16) £100
ba. Cover handstamped "AVIS Changement des tarifs Postaux Pour les nouveaux tarifs consulter le maitre de poste" £100

1913 (1 May)–**16.** *Green on pale green cover. Four panes of six* 1 c. (*No.* 197a).
SB4 25 c. booklet. Cover as Type B **1** with English text £350
a. Containing pane No. 199a .. .. .. 65·00
ab. Cover handstamped "NOTICE Change in Postal Rates For New Rates See Postmaster" 65·00
b. French text (28.4.16) £500
ba. Containing pane No. 199a £130
bb. Cover handstamped "AVIS Changement des tarifs Postaux Pour les nouveaux tarifs consulter le maitre de poste" £275

1922 (Mar). *Black on brown cover. Two panes of four* 3 c. *and* 2 *labels* (*No.* 205a).
SB5 25 c. booklet. Cover as Type B **1** with English text £300
a. French text £600

1922 (July–Dec). *Black on blue cover. Panes of four* 1 c., 2 c. *and* 3 c. (*Nos.* 246aa, 247aa, 205a) *and* 2 *labels.*
SB6 25 c. booklet. Cover as Type B **1** with English text £300
a. French text (Dec) £475

1922 (Dec). *Black on orange cover. Four panes of six* 1 c. (*No.* 246ab).
SB7 25 c. booklet. Cover as Type B **1** with English text £100
a. French text £130

1922 (Dec). *Black on green cover. Two panes of six* 2 c. (*No.* 247ab).
SB8 25 c. booklet. Cover as Type B **1** with English text £600
a. French text £700

1923 (Dec). *Black on blue cover. Panes of four* 1 c., 2 c. *and* 3 c. (*Nos.* 246aa, 247aa, 248aa) *and* 2 *labels.*
SB9 25 c. booklet. Cover as Type B **1** with English text £200
a. French text £325

1923 (Dec)–**24.** *Black on brown cover. Two panes of four* 3 c. (*No.* 248aa) *and* 2 *labels.*
SB10 25 c. booklet. Cover as Type B **1** with English text £180
a. French text (5.24) £275

B 2

1928 (16 Oct). *Black on green cover. Two panes of six* 2 c. (*No.* 276a).
SB11 25 c. booklet. Cover as Type B **2** with English text 55·00
a. French text .. .. 75·00

1928 (25 Oct). *Black on orange cover. Four panes of six* 1 c. (*No.* 275a).
SB12 25 c. booklet. Cover as Type B **2** with English text £100
a. French text £190

1929 (6 Jan). *Plain manilla cover. Three panes of six* 1 c., *two panes of six* 2 c. *and one pane of six* 5 c. (*Nos.* 275a, 276a, 279a).
SB13 72 c. booklet. Plain cover £300
a. With "Philatelic Div., Fin. Br. P.O. Dept., Ottawa" circular cachet on front cover £800
b. With "1928" in the centre of the circular cachet £900

1930 (17 June). *Black on green cover. Two panes of six* 2 c. (*No.* 290a).
SB14 25 c. booklet. Cover as Type B **2** with English text 80·00
a. French text £110

1930 (17 Nov). *Black on red cover. Two panes of six* 2 c. (*No.* 291a).
SB15 25 c. booklet. Cover as Type B **2** with English text 55·00
a. French text .. .. 75·00

1931 (13 July). *Black on red cover. Two panes of four* 3 c. (*No.* 293a) *and* 2 *labels.*
SB16 25 c. booklet. Cover as Type B **2** with English text 80·00
a. French text £110

1931 (21 July). *Black on green cover. Four panes of six* 1 c. (*No.* 289b).
SB17 25 c. booklet. Cover as Type B **2** with English text £120
a. French text £160

1931 (23 July). *Black on brown cover. Two panes of six* 2 c. (*No.* 292a).
SB18 25 c. booklet. Cover as Type B **2** with English text 80·00
a. French text £110

1931 (13 Nov). *Black on blue cover. Panes of four* 1 c., 2 c
3 c. (*Nos.* 289db, 292ba, 293a) *and* 2 *labels.*
SB19 25 c. booklet. Cover as Type B **2** with English text
a. French text .. ..

1933 (22 Aug–13 Nov). *Black on red cover. Two panes of*
3 c. (No. 321a) *and* 2 *labels.*
SB20 25 c. booklet. Cover as Type B **2** with English text
(13 Nov) 8
a. French text (22 Aug) .. .. ..

1933 (7 Sept). *Black on brown cover. Two panes of six* 2 c.
320a).
SB21 25 c. booklet. Cover as Type B **2** with English text 6
a. French text .. ..

1933 (19 Sept–5 Dec). *Black on blue cover. Panes of four*
2 c. *and* 3 c. (*Nos.* 319b, 320b, 321ba) *and* 2 *labels.*
SB22 25 c. booklet. Cover as Type B **2** with English text
a. French text (5 Dec) .. .. ..

1933 (28 Dec)–**34.** *Black on green cover. Four panes of six*
(*No.* 319a).
SB23 25 c. booklet. Cover as Type B **2** with English text 8
a. French text (26.3.34) .. .. .. £

B 3

1935 (1 June–8 Aug). *Red on white cover. Two panes of*
3 c. (*No.* 343a) *and* 2 *labels.*
SB24 25 c. booklet. Cover as Type B **3** with English text
(8 Aug) 55
a. French text (1 June) 70

1935 (22 July–1 Sept). *Blue on white cover. Panes of four*
2 c. *and* 3 c. (*Nos.* 341b, 342b, 343a) *and* 2 *labels.*
SB25 25 c. booklet. Cover as Type B **3** with English text £
a. French text (1 Sept) .. .. .. £

1935 (19 Aug–18 Oct). *Green on white cover. Four panes of*
1 c. (*No.* 341a).
SB26 25 c. booklet. Cover as Type B **3** with English text 90
a. French text (18 Oct) £1

1935 (16–18 Mar). *Brown on white cover. Two panes of six*
(*No.* 342a).
SB27 25 c. booklet. Cover as Type B **3** with English text 70
a. French text (18 Mar) £1

B 4

1937 (14 Apr)–**38.** *Blue and white cover. Panes of four* 1 c., 2
and 3 c. (*Nos.* 357a, 358a, 359a) *and* 2 *labels.*
SB28 25 c. booklet. Cover as Type B **3** with English text 85·
a. French text (4.1.38) £1
SB29 25 c. booklet. Cover as Type B **4** with English text
57 mm wide .. .. 70·
a. English text 63 mm wide .. .. .. 95·
b. French text 57 mm wide (4.1.38) .. .. 90·
ba. French text 63 mm wide £1

1937 (23–27 Apr). *Red and white cover. Two panes of four* 3
(*No.* 359a) *and* 2 *labels.*
SB30 25 c. booklet. Cover as Type B **3** with English text
(27 Apr) .. .. 22·0
a. French text (23 Apr) .. .. .. 40·0
SB31 25 c. booklet. Cover as Type B **4** with English text
57 mm wide (27 Apr) .. .. .. 10·0
a. English text 63 mm wide .. .. .. 40·0
b. French text 57 mm wide (23 Apr) .. 13·0
ba. French text 63 mm wide £15

1937 (18 May)–**38.** *Green and white cover. Four panes of si*
1 c. (*No.* 357b).
SB32 25 c. booklet. Cover as Type B **3** with English text 35·0
a. French text (14.10.38) .. .. .. 50·0
SB33 25 c. booklet. Cover as Type B **4** with English text
57 mm wide .. .. 20·0
a. English text 63 mm wide .. .. .. 60·0
b. French text 57 mm wide (14.10.38) .. 18·0
ba. French text 63 mm wide £13

(3 May)–**39.** *Brown and white cover. Two panes of six* 2 c.
). 358b).
25 c. booklet. Cover as Type B **3** with English text 50·00
a. French text (3.3.39) .. .. .. 65·00
25 c. booklet. Cover as Type B **4** with English text
57 mm wide .. .. 23·00
a. English text 63 mm wide .. .. 65·00
b. French text 57 mm wide .. .. .. 42·00
ba. French text 63 mm wide .. .. .. 90·00

(20–29 Aug) *Red and white cover. Two panes of four* 3 c.
). 377a) *and* 2 *labels.*
25 c. booklet. Cover as Type B **4** with English text 8·50
a. French text (29 Aug) .. .. .. 12·00

(12–14 Sept). *Violet and white cover. Panes of four* 1 c.,
. *and* 3 *c.* (*Nos.* 375a, 376a, 377a), *each with* 2 *labels.*
7 25 c. booklet. Cover as Type B **4** with English text
(14 Sept) .. .. 48·00
a. French text (12 Sept) .. .. .. 90·00

(6 Oct)–**43.** *Brown and white cover. Two panes of six* 2 c.
o. 376b).
3 25 c. booklet. Cover as Type B **4** with English text 45·00
a. French text (6.4.43) .. .. .. 70·00

(24 Nov)–**46.** *Green and white cover. Four panes of six* 1 c.
o. 375b).
9 25 c. booklet. Cover as Type B **4** with English text 11·00
a. French text (16.2.43) .. .. .. 17·00
b. Bilingual text (8.1.46) .. .. .. 23·00

3 (3 May)–**46.** *Orange and white cover. One pane of six* 4 c.
o. 380a).
0 25 c. booklet. Cover as Type B **4** with English text 4·00
a. French text (12.5.43) .. .. .. 13·00
b. Bilingual text (8.1.46) .. .. .. 16·00

3 (28 Aug)–**46.** *Purple and white cover. Two panes of four*
c. (*No.* 378a) *and* 2 *labels.*
1 25 c. booklet. Cover as Type B **4** with English text 10·00
a. French text (7.9.43) .. .. .. 26·00
b. Bilingual text (8.1.46) .. .. .. 20·00

B 5

3 (1 Sept)–**46.** *Black and white cover. Panes of three* 1 c.,
c. *and* 4 *c.* (*Nos.* 394a, 395a, 396a) (3×1).
42 25 c. booklet. Cover as Type B **5** with English text 27·00
a. French text (18.9.43) .. .. .. 35·00
c. Bilingual text (23.1.46) .. .. .. 32·00

B 6

47 (24 Nov). *Brown on orange cover. Panes of six* 3 c. *and* 4 c.
(3×2) *and two panes of four* 7 c. (2×2) (*Nos.* 378b, 380a, 407a).
43 $1 booklet. Cover as Type B **6** with English text 25·00
a. French text .. .. 40·00

50 (12 Apr–18 May). *Purple and white cover. Two panes of four* 3 c. (*No.* 416a) *and* 2 *labels* (3×2).
44 25 c. booklet. Cover as Type B **4** with English text 5·00
a. Bilingual text (18 May) .. .. .. 5·00

50 (5–10 May). *Orange and white cover. One pane of six* 4 c.
(*No.* 417a) (3×2).
345 25 c. booklet. Cover as Type B **4** with English text 30·00
a. Stitched .. .. 60·00
b. Bilingual text (10 May) .. .. .. 35·00

950 (18 May). *Black and white cover. Panes of three* 1 c., 3 c.
and 4 *c.* (*Nos.* 422ba, 423a, 423ba) (3×1).
B46 25 c. booklet. Cover as Type B **5** with English text 50·00
a. Bilingual text .. .. 55·00

951 (2 June). *Orange and white cover. One pane of six* 4 c.
(*No.* 417ba) (3×2).
B47 25 c. booklet. Cover as Type B **4** with English text 6·00
a. Stitched .. .. 12·00
b. Bilingual text .. .. 10·00

951 (25 Oct)–**52.** *Black and white cover. Panes of three* 1 c.,
3 *c. and* 4 *c.* (*Nos.* 422ba, 423a, 423ca) (3×1).
B48 25 c. booklet. Cover as Type B **5** with English text 28·00
a. Bilingual text (9.7.52) .. .. .. 32·00

REGISTRATION STAMPS

R 1

(Eng and recess – printed British-American Bank Note Co, Montreal and Ottawa)

1875 (15 Nov)–**92.** *White wove paper.* (*a*) *P* 12 (*or slightly under*).

R 1	R 1	2 c. orange	60·00	1·00
R 2		2 c. orange-red (1889)	70·00	6·00
R 3		2 c. vermilion	75·00	7·50
		a. Imperf (pair)	†	£2500
R 4		2 c. rose-carmine (1888)	£150	55·00
R 5		5 c. yellow-green (1878)	£100	1·50
R 6		5 c. deep green	80·00	1·25
		a. Imperf (pair)	£650	
R 7		5 c. blue-green (1888)	90·00	1·50
R 7*a*		5 c. dull sea-green (1892)	£130	3·25
R 8		8 c. bright blue	£325	£225
R 9		8 c. dull blue	£300	£200
		(*b*) *P* 12 × 11½ *or* 12 × 11¾		
R10	R 1	2 c. orange	£300	60·00
R11		5 c. green (*shades*)	£750	£150

SPECIAL DELIVERY STAMPS

PRINTERS. The following Special Delivery and Postage Due Stamps were recess-printed by the American Bank Note Co (to 1928), the British American Bank Note Co (to 1934), and the Canadian Bank Note Co (1935 onwards).

S 1

1898–1920. *P* 12.

S1	S 1	10 c. blue-green (28.6.98)	80·00	7·00
S2		10 c. deep green (12.13)	45·00	6·00
S3		10 c. yellowish green (8.20)	55·00	6·00

The differences between Types I and II (figures "10" with and without shading) formerly illustrated were due to wear of the plate. There was only one die.

S 2

S **3** Mail-carrying, 1867 and 1927

1922 (21 Aug). *P* 12.
S4 S **2** 20 c. carmine-red .. .. .. 35·00 6·50
No. S4 exists in two slightly different sizes due to the use of "wet" or "dry" printing processes. See note below No. 195.

1927 (29 June). *60th Anniversary of Confederation. P* 12.
S5 S **3** 20 c. orange .. .. .. 11·00 10·00
No. S5 exists imperforate, imperf×perf or perf×imperf (*Price, in each instance,* £130 *per pair, un*).

S 4

1930 (2 Sept). *P* 11.
S6 S **4** 20 c. brown-red .. .. .. 42·00 7·00

1932 (24 Dec). *Type as* S **4**, *but inscr* "CENTS" *in place of* "TWENTY CENTS". *P* 11.
S7 20 c. brown-red .. .. .. 45·00 15·00
No. S7 exists imperforate (*Price per pair* £375, *un*).

S **5** Allegory of Progress

(Des A. Foringer)

1935 (1 June). *P* 12.
S8 S **5** 20 c. scarlet .. .. 3·50 2·75
No. S8 exists imperforate (*Price per pair* £400, *un*).

S **6** Canadian Coat of Arms

1938–39. *P* 12.
S 9 S **6** 10 c. green (1.4.39) .. .. .. 18·00 3·00
S10 20 c. scarlet (15.6.38) .. .. .. 40·00 24·00
Nos. S9/10 exist imperforate (*Price* £425, *un, for each pair*).

≡10 10≡

(S **7**)

1939 (1 Mar). *Surch with Type* **S 7.**
S11 S **6** 10 c. on 20 c. scarlet .. .. .. 10·00 8·00

S **8** Coat of Arms and Flags

S **9** Lockheed L.18 Lodestar

1942 (1 July)–**43.** *War Effort. P* 12. (*a*) *Postage.*
S12 S **8** 10 c. green .. .. 5·00 30
(*b*) *Air*
S13 S **9** 16 c. ultramarine .. .. .. 5·50 45
S14 17 c. ultramarine (1.4.43) .. .. 4·25 55
Nos. S12/14 exist imperforate (*Prices per un pair* 10 c. £400, 16 c. £450, 17 c. £450).

S **10** Arms of Canada and Peace Symbols

S **11** Canadair DC-4M North Star

1946 (16 Sept–5 Dec). *P* 12. (*a*) *Postage*
S15 S **10** 10 c. green .. .. 2·75 30
(*b*) *Air.* (i) *Circumflex accent in* "EXPRÊS"
S16 S **11** 17 c. ultramarine .. .. .. 4·50 4·00
(ii) *Grave accent in* "EXPRÈS"
S17 S **11** 17 c. ultramarine (5.12.46) .. .. 5·00 4·00

POSTAGE DUE STAMPS

PRINTERS. See note under "Special Delivery Stamps".

D 1

D 2

1906 (1 July)–**28.** *P* 12.

D1 **D 1** 1 c. dull violet 8·50 2·75
D2 1 c. red violet (1916) 10·00 3·75
a. Thin paper (10.24) 15·00 19·00
D3 2 c. dull violet 18·00 1·00
D4 2 c. red-violet (1917) 19·00 1·25
a. Thin paper (10.24) 27·00 20·00
D5 4 c. violet (3.7.28) 45·00 50·00
D6 5 c. dull violet 24·00 3·00
D7 5 c. red-violet (1917) 24·00 3·00
a. Thin paper (10.24) 17·00 27·00
D8 10 c. violet (3.7.28) 32·00 17·00
D1/8 *Set of* 5 £110 65·00

The 1 c., 2 c. and 5 c. values exist imperforate (*Price £275 for each un pair*).

Printings up to October 1924 used the "wet" method, those from mid 1925 onwards the "dry". For details of the differences between these two methods, see above No. 196.

1930–2. *P* 11.

D 9 **D 2** 1 c. bright violet (14.7.30) 8·50 10·00
D10 2 c. bright violet (21.8.30) 7·50 1·90
D11 4 c. bright violet (14.10.30) 15·00 6·50
D12 5 c. bright violet (12.12.31) 16·00 27·00
D13 10 c. bright violet (24.8.32) 65·00 27·00
D9/13 *Set of* 5 £100 65·00

Nos. D9/11 and D13 exist imperforate, No. D13 also exists imperf × perf (*Price for vertical pair £550, un*).

D 3

D 4

1933–4. *P* 11.

D14 **D 3** 1 c. violet (5.5.34) 9·50 14·00
D15 2 c. violet (20.12.33) 7·50 4·50
D16 4 c. violet (12.12.33) 12·00 14·00
D17 10 c. violet (20.12.33) 24·00 29·00
D14/17 *Set of* 4 48·00 55·00

No. D14 exists imperforate (*Price per pair £300, un*).

1935–65. *P* 12.

D18 **D 4** 1 c. violet (14.10.35) 80 10
D19 2 c. violet (9.9.35) 1·00 10
D20 3 c. violet (4.65) 4·25 5·00
D21 4 c. violet (2.7.35) 1·50 10
D22 5 c. violet (12.48) 3·50 1·75
D23 6 c. violet (1957) 2·00 3·00
D24 10 c. violet (16.9.35) 70 10
D18/24 *Set of* 7 12·00 8·75

The 1 c., 2 c., 4 c. and 10 c. exist imperforate (*Price £150 for each un pair*).

OFFICIAL STAMPS

Stamps perforated "O H M S" were introduced in May 1923 for use by the Receiver General's department in Ottawa and by the Assistant Receiver Generals' offices in provincial cities. From 1 July 1939 this use was extended to all departments of the federal government and such stamps continued to be produced until replaced by the "O.H.M.S." overprinted issue of 1949.

The perforated initials can appear either upright, inverted or sideways on individual stamps. The prices quoted are for the cheapest version. Stamps perforated with Type O 1 are only priced used. Only isolated examples are known mint and these are very rare.

A number of forged examples of the perforated "O.H.M.S." are known, in particular of Type O 1. Many of these forged perforated initials were applied to stamps which had already been used and this can aid their detection. Genuine examples, postmarked after the perforated initials were applied, often show the cancellation ink bleeding into the holes.

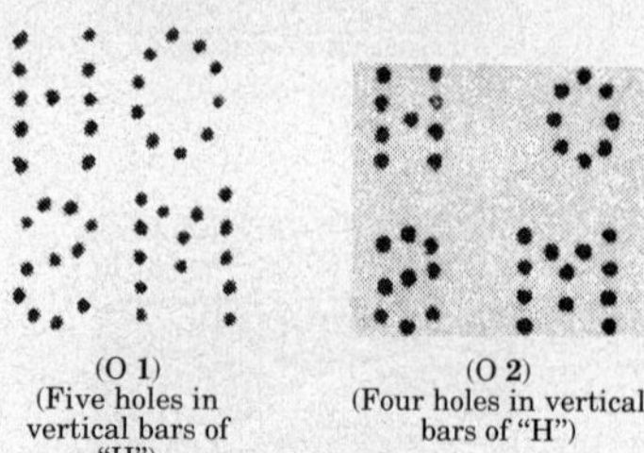
(O 1) (Five holes in vertical bars of "H")

(O 2) (Four holes in vertical bars of "H")

1923 (May). *Nos.* 196/215 *punctured as Type* O 1.

O1 **44** 1 c. yellow-green — 20·00
O2 2 c. carmine — 18·00
O3 3 c. deep brown — 16·00
O4 5 c. deep blue — 20·00
O5 7 c. yellow-ochre — 35·00
O6 10 c. reddish purple — 35·00
O7 20 c. olive — 22·00
O8 50 c. sepia — 35·00
O1/8 *Set of* 8 — £180

1923 (May). *50th Anniv of Confederation. No.* 244 *punctured as Type* O 1.

O9 **48** 3 c. bistre-brown — £110

1923 (May)–**31.** *Nos.* 246/55 *and* 263 *punctured as Type* O 1.

(*a*) *P* 12

O10 **44** 1 c. chrome-yellow (Die I) — 18·00
a. Die II (1925) — 18·00
O11 2 c. deep green — 13·00
O12 3 c. carmine (Die I) (12.23) — 13·00
a. Die II (1924) — 16·00
O13 4 c. olive-yellow — 18·00
O14 5 c. violet — 18·00
a. Thin paper (1924) — 22·00
O15 7 c. red-brown (1924) — 27·00
O16 8 c. blue (1925) — 32·00
O17 10 c. blue — 22·00
O18 10 c. bistre-brown (1925) — 13·00
O19 $1 brown-orange (7.23) — 55·00
O10/19 *Set of* 10 — £200

(*b*) *P* 12×8

O20 **44** 3 c. carmine (Die II) (1931) — 42·00

1927 (29 June). *60th Anniv of Confederation. Nos.* 266/73 *punctured as Type* O 1. (*a*) *Commemorative issue.*

O21 **51** 1 c. orange — 18·00
O22 **52** 2 c. green — 25·00
O23 **53** 3 c. carmine — 35·00
O24 **54** 5 c. violet — 23·00
O25 **55** 12 c. blue — £140
O21/5 *Set of* 5 — £225

(*b*) *Historical issue*

O26 **56** 5 c. violet — 18·00
O27 **57** 12 c. green — £110
O28 **58** 20 c. carmine — 70·00
O26/8 *Set of* 3 — £180

1928 (21 Sept). *Air. No.* 274 *punctured as Type* O 1.

O29 **59** 5 c. olive-brown — 90·00

1928–29. *Nos.* 275/85 *punctured as Type* O 1.

O30 **60** 1 c. orange — 23·00
O31 2 c. green — 15·00
O32 3 c. lake — 40·00
O33 4 c. olive-bistre — 48·00
O34 5 c. violet — 16·00
O35 8 c. blue — 45·00
O36 **61** 10 c. green — 13·00
O37 **62** 12 c. grey-black — £120
O38 **63** 20 c. lake — 38·00
O39 **64** 50 c. blue — £140
O40 **65** $1 olive-green — £120
O30/40 *Set of* 11 — £550

1930–31. *Nos.* 288/97, *and* 300/5 *punctured as Type* O 1.

O41 **66** 1 c. orange (Die I) — 23·00
O42 1 c. green (Die I) — 13·00
a. Die II — 11·00
O43 2 c. green (Die I) — 35·00
O44 2 c. scarlet (Die I) — 18·00
a. Die II — 16·00
O45 2 c. deep brown (Die I) — 22·00
a. Die II — 18·00
O46 3 c. scarlet — 13·00
O47 4 c. yellow-bistre — 42·00
O48 5 c. violet — 29·00
O49 5 c. deep slate-blue — 23·00
O50 8 c. blue — 55·00
O51 8 c. red-orange — 40·00
O52 **67** 10 c. olive-green — 18·00
O53 **68** 12 c. grey-black — 75·00
O54 **69** 20 c. red — 38·00
O55 **70** 50 c. blue — 55·00
O56 **71** $1 olive-green — £130
O41/56 *Set of* 15 — £500

1930 (4 Dec). *Air. No.* 310 *punctured as Type* O 1.

O57 **72** 5 c. deep brown — £140

1931 (30 Sept). *No.* 312 *punctured as Type* O 1.

O58 **73** 10 c. olive-green — 18·00

1932 (22 Feb). *Air. No.* 313 *punctured as Type* O 1.

O59 **59** 6 c. on 5 c. olive-brown — 95·00

1932 (21 June). *Nos.* 314/a *punctured as Type* O 1.

O60 **66** 3 c. on 2 c. scarlet (Die I) — 30·00
a. Die II — 23·00

1932 (12 July). *Ottawa Conference. Nos.* 315/18 *punctured as Type* O 1. (*a*) *Postage.*

O61 **76** 3 c. scarlet — 15·00
O62 **77** 5 c. blue — 27·00
O63 **78** 13 c. green — £160

(*b*) *Air*

O64 **72** 6 c. on 5 c. deep brown — £120
O61/4 *Set of* 4 — £300

1932–33. *Nos.* 319/25 *punctured as Type* O 1.

O65 **80** 1 c. green — 13·00
O66 2 c. sepia — 13·00
O67 3 c. scarlet — 13·00
O68 4 c. yellow-brown — 45·00
O69 5 c. blue — 20·00
O70 8 c. red-orange — 45·00
O71 **68** 13 c. bright violet — 45·00
O65/71 *Set of* 7 — £180

1933 (18 May). *U.P.U. Congress Preliminary Meeting. No.* 329 *punctured as Type* O 1.

O72 **81** 5 c. blue — 38·00

1933 (24 July). *World's Grain Exhibition and Conference, Regina. No.* 330 *punctured as Type* O 1.

O73 **69** 20 c. red — 45·00

1933 (17 Aug). *Centenary of First Trans-Atlantic Stear Crossing. No.* 331 *punctured as Type* O 1.

O74 **83** 5 c. blue —

1934 (1 July). *Fourth Centenary of Discovery of Canada* 332 *punctured as Type* O 1.

O75 **84** 3 c. blue —

1934 (1 July). *150th Anniv of Arrival of United E Loyalists. No.* 333 *punctured as Type* O 1.

O76 **85** 10 c. olive-green —

1934 (16 Aug). *150th Anniv of Province of New Brunswick* 334 *punctured as Type* O 1.

O77 **86** 2 c. red-brown —

1935 (4 May). *Silver Jubilee. Nos.* 335/40 *punctured as* O 1.

O78 **87** 1 c. green — 2
O79 – 2 c. brown — 3
O80 **89** 3 c. carmine-red — 4
O81 – 5 c. blue — 3
O82 – 10 c. green —
O83 – 13 c. blue —
O78/83 *Set of* 6 —

1935. *Nos.* 341/51 *and* 355 *punctured as Type* O 1. (*a*) *Pos*

O84 **93** 1 c. green — 1
O85 2 c. brown — 2
O86 3 c. scarlet — 2
O87 4 c. yellow — 4
O88 5 c. blue — 2
O89 8 c. orange — 4
O90 **94** 10 c. carmine — 3
O91 – 13 c. purple — 4
O92 – 20 c. olive-green — 4
O93 – 50 c. deep violet — 3
O94 – $1 bright blue — 9

(*b*) *Air*

O95 **99** 6 c. red-brown — 7
O84/95 *Set of* 12 — £

1937 (10 May). *Coronation. No.* 356 *punctured as Type* O

O96 **100** 3 c. carmine — 4

1937–38. *Nos.* 357/67, 370 *and* 371 *punctured as Type* O 1.

(*a*) *Postage*

O 97 **101** 1 c. green —
O 98 2 c. brown —
O 99 3 c. scarlet —
O100 4 c. yellow — 8
O101 5 c. blue — 6
O102 8 c. orange — 13
O103 **102** 10 c. rose-carmine — 20
a. Red — 23
O104 – 13 c. blue — 28
O105 – 20 c. red-brown — 28
O106 – 50 c. green — 65
O107 – $1 violet — 95
O97/107 *Set of* 11 — £

(*b*) *Coil stamp*

O108 **101** 3 c. scarlet — 65

(*c*) *Air*

O109 **107** 6 c. blue — 28

1939 (15 May). *Royal Visit. Nos.* 372/4 *punctured as Type* O

O110 **108** 1 c. black and green — 32
O111 **109** 2 c. black and brown — 42
O112 **110** 3 c. black and carmine — 32
O110/12 *Set of* 3 — 95

1939 (1 July). *Air. No.* 274 *punctured as Type* O 2.

O113 **59** 5 c. olive-brown 20·00 14

1939 (1 July). *Nos.* 347/50 *and* 355 *punctured as Type* O 2.

(*a*) *Postage*

O114 **94** 10 c. carmine 55·00 38
O115 – 13 c. purple 60·00 38
O116 – 20 c. olive-green 75·00 48
O117 – 50 c. deep violet 60·00 38

(*b*) *Air*

O118 **99** 6 c. red-brown 50·00 42
O114/18 *Set of* 5 £275 £1

1939 (1 July). *Coronation. No.* 356 *punctured as Type* O 2.

O119 **100** 3 c. carmine 70·00 45

1939 (1 July). *Nos.* 357/67, 369/70 *and* 371 *punctured as Ty* O 2. (*a*) *Postage*

O120 **101** 1 c. green 1·50
O121 2 c. brown 2·25
O122 3 c. scarlet 2·50
O123 4 c. yellow 5·00 2
O124 5 c. blue 3·50
O125 8 c. orange 13·00 4
O126 **102** 10 c. rose-carmine 55·00 3
a. Red 8·00
O127 – 13 c. blue 13·00 1
O128 – 20 c. red-brown 35·00 2
O129 – 50 c. green 48·00 8
O130 – $1 violet £110 30
O120/30 *Set of* 11 £225 42

(*b*) *Coil stamps*

O131 **101** 2 c. brown 70·00 45
O132 3 c. scarlet 70·00 45

(*c*) *Air*

O133 **107** 6 c. blue 3·00

(1 July). *Royal Visit. Nos.* 372/4 *punctured as Type* O **2**.
108 1 c. black and green .. .. .. 80·00 38·00
109 2 c. black and brown .. .. 80·00 38·00
110 3 c. black and carmine .. .. 80·00 38·00
/6 .. .. *Set of* 3 £225 £100

–**43.** *War Effort. Nos.* 375/88 *and* 399/400 *punctured as* *pe* O **2**. (*a*) *Postage*
111 1 c. green 40 10
112 2 c. brown 50 10
113 3 c. carmine-lake .. .. .. 1·10 40
3 c. purple 60 10
114 4 c. slate .. .. 2·75 75
112 4 c. carmine-lake 55 10
111 5 c. blue .. .. 1·25 15
– 8 c. red-brown .. .. .. 7·50 2·00
116 10 c. brown .. .. 4·50 20
117 13 c. dull green .. .. .. 5·50 5·50
14 c. dull green .. .. .. 9·00 85
3 – 20 c. chocolate .. .. .. 12·00 70
– 50 c. violet .. .. 35·00 5·50
) – $1 blue .. .. 90·00 25·00
(*b*) *Air*
121 6 c. blue .. .. 4·00 2·00
2 7 c. blue .. .. 3·25 25
7/52 .. .. *Set of* 16 £160 40·00

. *Peace Re-conversion. Nos.* 401/7 *punctured as Type* O **2**.
(*a*) *Postage*
3 **122** 8 c. brown .. .. 11·00 3·50
4 – 10 c. olive-green .. .. .. 3·25 15
5 – 14 c. sepia .. .. 4·25 65
6 – 20 c. slate .. .. 4·50 50
7 – 50 c. green .. .. 23·00 5·00
8 – $1 purple .. .. 60·00 15·00
(*b*) *Air*
9 – 7 c. blue .. .. 3·00 40
3/9 .. .. *Set of* 7 95·00 23·00

9. *Nos.* 415 *and* 416 *punctured as Type* O **2**.
0 **136** 2 c. sepia 75 75
1 **137** 3 c. purple 75 75

O.H.M.S.
(O **3**)

9. *Nos.* 375/6, 378, 380 *and* 402/7 *optd as Type* O **3** *by* *pography.*
(*a*) *Postage*
62 **111** 1 c. green .. .. 1·75 2·25
a. Missing stop after "S" .. .. £160 50·00
63 **112** 2 c. brown .. .. 12·00 12·00
a. Missing stop after "S" .. .. £150 85·00
64 **113** 3 c. purple .. .. 1·25 1·40
65 **112** 4 c. carmine-lake .. .. .. 2·00 1·40
66 – 10 c. olive-green .. .. .. 3·75 15
a. Missing stop after "S" .. .. 85·00 35·00
67 – 14 c. sepia .. .. 4·50 2·00
a. Missing stop after "S" .. .. £110 48·00
68 – 20 c. slate .. .. 12·00 60
a. Missing stop after "S" .. .. £150 50·00
69 – 50 c. green £160 £120
a. Missing stop after "S" £900 £550
70 – $1 purple .. .. 45·00 48·00
a. Missing stop after "S" £1600
(*b*) *Air*
71 – 7 c. blue .. .. 24·00 7·00
a. Missing stop after "S" .. .. £140 65·00
62/71 .. .. *Set of* 10 £225 £140
Forgeries exist of this overprint. Genuine examples are ×15 mm and show the tops of all letters aligned, as are the ps.
Only a few sheets of the $1 showed the variety, No. O170a.

ISSING STOP VARIETIES. These occur on R. 6/2 of the wer left pane (Nos. O162a, O163a and O176a) or R. 10/2 of the wer left pane (O166a, O167a, O168a, O169a, O170a and 71a). No. O176a also occurs on R. 8/8 of the upper left pane in dition to R. 6/2 of the lower left pane.

49–50. *Nos.* 414/15, 416/17, 418 *and* 431 *optd as Type* O **3** *by* *ypography.*
172 **135** 1 c. green .. .. 1·25 1·00
173 **136** 2 c. sepia .. .. 2·25 1·50
174 **137** 3 c. purple .. .. 1·50 1·00
175 **138** 4 c. carmine-lake .. .. .. 1·75 15
176 **139** 5 c. blue (1949) .. .. .. 3·00 2·00
a. Missing stop after "S" .. .. 85·00 38·00
177 **141** 50 c. green (1950) .. .. .. 32·00 28·00
172/7 .. .. *Set of* 6 38·00 30·00

G **G** **G**
(O **4**) (O **5**) (O **6**)

Type O **6** differs from Type O **5** in having a thinner ppearance and an upward sloping left serif to the lower arm. It sults from a new plate introduced in 1961/62. Variations in ickness are known in Type O 4 but these are due to wear and ibsequent cleaning of the plate. All are produced by pography. Examples showing the "G" applied by lithography re forgeries.

50 (2 Oct)–**52.** *Nos.* 402/4, 406/7, 414/18 *and* 431 *optd with* *Type* O **4** (1 *to* 5 *c.*) *or* O **5** (7 *c. to* $1). (*a*) *Postage.*
178 **135** 1 c. green 80 10
179 **136** 2 c. sepia .. .. 1·75 1·75
180 2 c. olive-green (11.51) .. .. 1·75 10
181 **137** 3 c. purple .. .. 1·50 10
182 **138** 4 c. carmine-lake .. .. .. 1·75 30
183 4 c. vermilion (1.5.52) .. .. 1·90 10

O184 **139** 5 c. blue .. .. 2·50 60
O185 – 10 c. olive-green .. .. .. 3·00 10
O186 – 14 c. sepia .. .. 12·00 3·50
O187 – 20 c. slate .. .. 20·00 20
O188 **141** 50 c. green .. .. 11·00 10·00
O189 – $1 purple .. .. 65·00 65·00
(*b*) *Air*
O190 – 7 c. blue .. .. 24·00 13·00
O178/90 .. .. *Set of* 13 £130 85·00

1950–51. *Nos.* 432/3 *optd with Type* O **5**.
O191 **142** 10 c. brown-purple .. .. .. 2·75 10
a. Opt omitted in pair with normal £425 £350
O192 **143** $1 ultramarine (1.2.51) .. .. 60·00 65·00

OFFICIAL SPECIAL DELIVERY STAMPS

1923 (May). *Nos.* S3/4 *punctured as Type* O **1**.
OS1 S **1** 10 c. yellowish green .. .. .. — 85·00
OS2 S **2** 20 c. carmine-red .. .. .. — 70·00

1927 (29 June). *60th Anniv of Confederation. No.* S5 *punctured as Type* O **1**.
OS3 S **3** 20 c. orange .. .. — 80·00

1930 (2 Sept). *Inscr* "TWENTY CENTS" *at foot. No.* S6 *punctured as Type* O **1**.
OS4 S **4** 20 c. brown-red .. .. .. — 65·00

1932 (24 Dec). *Inscr* "CENTS" *at foot. No.* S7 *punctured as Type* O **1**.
OS5 S **4** 20 c. brown-red .. .. .. — 65·00

1935 (1 June). *No.* S8 *punctured as Type* O **1**.
OS6 S **5** 20 c. scarlet .. .. — 65·00

1938–39. *Nos.* S9/10 *punctured as Type* O **1**.
OS7 S **6** 10 c. green .. .. — 40·00
OS8 20 c. scarlet .. .. — 60·00

1939 (1 Mar). *No.* S11 *punctured as Type* O **1**.
OS9 S **6** 10 c. on 20 c. scarlet .. .. .. — 60·00

1939 (1 July). *Inscr* "CENTS" *at foot. No.* S7 *punctured as Type* O **2**.
OS10 S **4** 20 c. brown-red .. .. .. £150 80·00

1939 (1 July). *No.* S8 *punctured as Type* O **2**.
OS11 S **5** 20 c. scarlet .. .. 85·00 40·00

1939 (1 July). *No.* S9 *punctured as Type* O **2**.
OS12 S **6** 10 c. green .. .. 7·00 4·75

1939 (1 July). *No.* S11 *punctured as Type* O **2**.
OS13 S **6** 10 c. on 20 c. scarlet .. .. .. £100 50·00

1942–43. *Nos.* S12/14 *punctured as Type* O **2**. (*a*) *Postage*
OS14 S **8** 10 c. green .. .. 9·00 6·50
(*b*) *Air*
OS15 S **9** 16 c. ultramarine .. .. .. 17·00 13·00
OS16 17 c. ultramarine .. .. .. 10·00 8·00

1946–47. *Nos.* S15/17 *punctured as Type* O **2**. (*a*) *Postage*
OS17 S **10** 10 c. green .. .. 6·50 4·50
(*b*) *Air*
OS18 S **11** 17 c. ultramarine (circumflex accent) 26·00 22·00
OS19 17 c. ultramarine (grave accent) .. 55·00 55·00

1950. *No.* S15 *optd as Type* O **3**, *but larger.*
OS20 S **10** 10 c. green .. .. 17·00 22·00

1950 (2 Oct). *No.* S15 *optd as Type* O **4**, *but larger.*
OS21 S **10** 10 c. green .. .. 26·00 27·00

The use of official stamps was discontinued on 31 December 1963.

Cape of Good Hope *see* South Africa

Cayman Islands

The first post office was opened at Georgetown in April 1889. The stamps of Jamaica with the following cancellations were used until 19 February 1901. At some stage, probably around 1891, a supply of the Jamaica 1889 1d., No. 27, was overprinted "CAYMAN ISLANDS", but these stamps were never issued. Two surviving examples are known, one unused and the other cancelled at Richmond in Jamaica.

Types of Jamaica

2

3

4

8 11

13

PRICES OF NOS. Z1/27. These are for a single stamp showing a clear impression of the postmark. Nos. Z1, 2, 6/8, 11/13, 18, 22 and Z25 are known used on cover and these are worth considerably more.

GEORGETOWN, GRAND CAYMAN

Z 1

Z 2

Z 3

Stamps of JAMAICA *cancelled with Type* Z **1** *in purple.*

1889 *to* **1894.**
Z1 **8** ½d. yellow-green (No. 16) £475
Z2 **11** 1d. purple and mauve (No. 27) £475
Z2*a* **2** 2d. slate (No. 20*a*) £4000
Z3 **11** 2d. green (No. 28) £850
Z4 2½d. dull purple and blue (No. 29) .. £1000
Z5 **4** 4d. red-orange (No. 22) £2500

Stamps of JAMAICA *cancelled with Type* Z **2** *in purple or black.*

1895 *to* **1898.**
Z6 **8** ½d. yellow-green (No. 16) £550
Z7 **11** 1d. purple and mauve (No. 27) £450
Z8 2½d. dull purple and blue (No. 29) £750
Z9 **3** 3d. sage-green (No. 21) £3000

Stamps of JAMAICA *cancelled with Type* Z 3.

1898 *to* **1901.**
Z10 **8** ½d. yellow-green (No. 16) £450
a. Green (No. 16*a*) £450
Z11 **11** 1d. purple and mauve (No. 27) £450
Z12 **13** 1d. red (No. 31) (1900) £475
Z13 **11** 2½d. dull purple and blue (No. 29) £650

OFFICIAL STAMPS

Stamps of JAMAICA *cancelled with Type* Z 1 *in purple.*

1890 *to* **1894.**
Z14 **8** ½d. green (No. O1) (*opt 17–17½ mm long*) .. £1000
Z15 ½d. green (No. O3) (*opt 16 mm long*) (1893) £2500
Z16 **11** 1d. rose (No. O4) £1100
Z17 2d. grey (No. O5) £3000

Stamps of JAMAICA *cancelled with Type* Z 2 *in purple or black.*

1895 *to* **1898.**
Z18 **8** ½d. green (No. O3) £2000
Z19 **11** 1d. rose (No. O4) £3250
Z20 2d. grey (No. O5) £3250

STAKE BAY, CAYMAN BRAC

CAYMAN BRAC
CAYMAN ISLANDS

Z 4

Z 5

Stamps of JAMAICA *cancelled with Type* Z 4.

1898 *to* **1900.**
Z21 **8** ½d. yellow-green (No. 16) £3000
Z22 **11** 1d. purple and mauve (No. 27) £3250
Z23 2d. green (No. 28) £4000
Z24 2½d. dull purple and blue (No. 29) £3250

Stamps of JAMAICA *cancelled with Type* Z 5.

1900 *to* **1901.**
Z25 **8** ½d. yellow-green (No. 16) £3250
Z26 **11** 1d. purple and mauve (No. 27) £3000
Z27 **13** 1d. red (No. 31) £3000
Z28 **11** 2½d. dull purple and blue (No. 29) £2500

PRICES FOR STAMPS ON COVER TO 1945

Nos. 1/2	*from* × 25
Nos. 3/12	*from* × 5
Nos. 13/16	*from* × 4
Nos. 17/19	*from* × 10
Nos. 25/34	*from* × 5
Nos. 35/52*b*	*from* × 4
Nos. 53/67	*from* × 5
Nos. 69/83	*from* × 4
Nos. 84/95	*from* × 6
Nos. 96/9	*from* × 5
Nos. 100/11	*from* × 4
Nos. 112/14	*from* × 6
Nos. 115/26	*from* × 2

DEPENDENCY OF JAMAICA

1

2

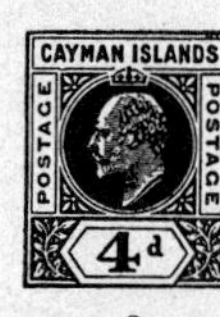

3

(T **1/3**, **8/9** and **12/13** typo D.L.R.)

1900 (Nov). *Wmk Crown CA. P* 14.
1 **1** ½d. deep green .. .. 8·00 19·00
a. Pale green .. .. 4·25 15·00
2 1d. rose-carmine .. .. 3·50 2·25
a. Pale carmine .. .. 11·00 10·00
1s/2s Optd "Specimen" .. .. *Set of* 2 95·00

(Dented frame under "A" (R. 1/6 of left pane) (The variety is believed to have occurred at some point between 9 January and 9 April 1902 and is then present on all subsequent printings of the "POSTAGE POSTAGE" design)

1902 (Jan)–**03.** *Wmk Crown CA. P* 14.
3 **2** ½d. green (15.9.02) .. .. .. 4·50 25·00
a. Dented frame £100
4 1d. carmine (6.3.03) .. .. .. 10·00 9·00
a. Dented frame £150 £180
5 **2** 2½d. bright blue .. .. 10·00 12·00
a. Dented frame £160
6 6d. brown .. .. 29·00 60·00
a. Dented frame £300
7 **3** 1s. orange .. .. 60·00 £110
a. Dented frame £400 £600
3/7 .. .. .. *Set of* 5 £100 £190
3s/7s Optd "Specimen" .. .. *Set of* 5 £170

1905 (Feb–18 Oct). *Wmk Mult Crown CA. P* 14.
8 **2** ½d. green .. .. 6·50 7·50
a. Dented frame £100 £150
9 1d. carmine (18 Oct) .. .. .. 14·00 17·00
a. Dented frame £200 £275
10 2½d. bright blue .. .. 6·50 3·25
a. Dented frame £120 £140
11 6d. brown .. .. 16·00 38·00
a. Dented frame £250 £375
12 **3** 1s. orange .. .. 32·00 48·00
a. Dented frame £325
8/12 .. .. .. *Set of* 5 65·00 £100

1907 (13 Mar). *Wmk Mult Crown CA. P* 14.
13 **3** 4d. brown and blue .. .. .. 32·00 55·00
a. Dented frame £300 £475
14 **2** 6d. olive and rose .. .. .. 32·00 65·00
a. Dented frame £300
15 **3** 1s. violet and green .. .. .. 55·00 75·00
a. Dented frame £375
16 5s. salmon and green £170 £275
a. Dented frame £1100 £1500
13/16 .. .. .. *Set of* 4 £250 £400
13s/16s Optd "Specimen" .. .. *Set of* 4 £200

One Halfpenny. (4) ½D (5) 1D (6)

1907 (30 Aug). *No. 9 surch at Govt Printing Office, Kingston, with T* 4.
17 **2** ½d. on 1d. carmine .. .. .. 42·00 65·00
a. Dented frame £375 £550

1907 (Nov). *No. 16 handstamped at Georgetown P.O. with T* **5** *or* **6**.
18 **3** ½d. on 5s. salmon and green (26 Nov) .. £225 £325
a. Surch inverted £24000
b. Surch double £9000 £9000
c. Surch double, one inverted ..
d. Surch omitted (in pair with normal) £38000
e. Dented frame £1100
19 1d. on 5s. salmon and green (23 Nov) .. £225 £300
a. Surch double £14000
b. Surch inverted £40000
c. Dented frame £1100 £1500

The ½d. on 5s. may be found with the figures "1" or "2" omitted, owing to defective handstamping.

8

9

2½D (10)

1907 (27 Dec)–**09.** *Chalk-surfaced paper* (3d. *to* 10s.). *P* 14.

(*a*) *Wmk Mult Crown CA*
25 **8** ½d. green .. .. 2·00 4·00
26 1d. carmine .. .. 1·50 75
27 2½d. ultramarine (30.3.08) .. .. 3·50 3·50
28 **9** 3d. purple/*yellow* (30.3.08) .. .. 3·25 6·50
29 4d. black and red/*yellow* (30.3.08) .. 50·00 70·00
30 **8** 6d. dull and bright purple (2.10.08) .. 9·50 35·00
a. Dull purple and violet-purple .. 32·00 55·00
31 **9** 1s. black/*green* (5.4.09) .. .. 7·50 22·00
32 5s. green and red/*yellow* (30.3.08) .. 38·00 60·00

(*b*) *Wmk Crown CA* (30.3.08)
33 **9** 1s. black/*green* .. .. 55·00 80·00
34 **8** 10s. green and red/*green* £160 £225
25/34 .. .. .. *Set of* 10 £300 £450
25s/30s, 32s/4s Optd "Specimen" .. *Set of* 9 £300

1908 (12 Feb). *No. 13 handstamped locally with T* 10.
35 **3** 2½d. on 4d. brown and blue £1500 £2250
a. Surch double £30000 £18000
b. Dented frame £8500

No. 35 should only be purchased when accompanied by an expert committee's certificate or similar form of guarantee.

MANUSCRIPT PROVISIONALS. During May and June 1908 supplies of ½d. and 1d. stamps became exhausted, and the payment of postage was indicated by the Postmistress, Miss Gwendolyn Parsons, using a manuscript endorsement. Such endorsements were in use from 12 May to 1 June.

Price on cover
MP1 "(Postage Paid G.A.P.)" (12 May to 1 June) .. £3000
MP1*a* "(Postage Paid G.A.P.) ½ or 1d." (23 May) .. £4500

In October of the same year there was a further shortage of ¼d. stamps and the manuscript endorsements were again applied by either the new Postmaster, William Graham McCausland, or by Miss Parsons who remained as his assistant.

MP2 "Pd ¼d/W.G. McC" (4 to 27 October) £250
MP2*a* "¼d Pd./W.G. McC" (14 October) £1200
MP3 "Paid" (7 October) £6500
MP4 "Pd ¼d" (8 October) £5500
MP5 "(Paid ¼GAP. asst.)" (15 October) £5000

No. MP2 exists in different inks and formats.

Manuscript endorsement for the 2½d. rate is also known, but this is thought to have been done by oversight.

A 1d. surcharge on 4d. (No. 29), issued in mid-May intended as a revenue stamp and was never authorise postal use (*price* £225 *un.*). Used examples were either can by favour or passed through the post in error. Exists surcharge inverted (*price* £1600 *un.*), surcharge double £2500 *un.*) or surcharge double, both inverted (*price* £250

11

12

13

1908 (30 June)–**09.** *Wmk Mult Crown CA. Litho. P* 14.
38 **11** ¼d. brown .. .. 1·75
a. Grey-brown (2.09) .. .. .. 2·50
s. Optd "Specimen" .. .. .. 70·00

1912 (24 Apr)–**20.** *Die I. Wmk Mult Crown CA. Chalk-surf paper* (3d. *to* 10s.). *P* 14.
40 **13** ¼d. brown (10.2.13) .. .. .. 1·00
41 **12** ½d. green .. .. 2·75
42 1d. red (25.2.13) .. .. .. 3·25
43 **13** 2d. pale grey .. .. 1·00
44 **12** 2½d. bright blue (26.8.14) .. .. 7·00 1
a. Deep bright blue (9.11.17) .. 18·00 2
45 **13** 3d. purple/*yellow* (26.11.14) .. 14·00 3
a. White back (19.11.13) .. .. 3·50
b. On lemon (12.3.18) .. .. 2·25 1
bs. Optd "Specimen" .. .. 55·00
c. On orange-buff (1920) .. .. 10·00 3
d. On buff (1920) .. ..
e. On pale yellow (1920) .. .. 3·50 3
46 4d. black and red/*yellow* (25.2.13) .. 1·00 1
47 **12** 6d. dull and bright purple (25.2.13) .. 3·75
48 **13** 1s. black/*green* (15.5.16) .. .. 3·50 2
as. Optd "Specimen" .. .. 55·00
b. White back (19.11.13) .. .. 3·50
49 2s. purple and bright blue/*blue* .. 12·00 4
50 3s. green and violet .. .. .. 19·00 6
51 5s. green and red/*yellow* (26.8.14) .. 75·00 £
52 **12** 10s. deep green and red/*green* (26.11.14) £100 £
as. Optd "Specimen" .. .. 85·00
b. White back (19.11.13) .. .. 80·00 £
c. On blue-green, olive back (5.10.18) 90·00 £
40/52*b* .. .. .. *Set of* 13 £190 £
40s/4s, 45as, 46s/7s, 48bs, 49s/51s, 52bs Optd "Specimen" .. .. .. *Set of* 13 £325

WAR STAMP. 1½d (14) WAR STAMP. 1½d (15) 1½d Straight serif (Left-hand pane R. 10/2)

1917 (26 Feb). *T* **12** *surch with T* **14** *or* **15** *at Kingst Jamaica.*
53 **14** 1½d. on 2½d. deep blue .. .. .. 7·00 1
a. No fraction bar .. .. .. 95·00 £
b. Missing stop after "STAMP" (R.1/4) £350
54 **15** 1½d. on 2½d. deep blue .. .. .. 1·75 6
a. No fraction bar .. .. .. 60·00 £
b. Straight serif .. .. .. 70·00 £

On No. 53 "WAR STAMP" and "1½d." were appl separately.

WAR STAMP 1½d (16) WAR STAMP 1½d (17) WAR STAMP 1½d. (18)

1917 (4 Sept). *T* **12** *surch with T* **16** *or* **17** *by D.L.R.*
55 **16** 1½d. on 2½d. deep blue £700 £19
56 **17** 1½d. on 2½d. deep blue 30
a. Short opt (right pane R. 10/1) .. 20·00
s. Optd "Specimen" £100
x. Wmk reversed .. .. .. 85·00

De La Rue replaced surcharge Type **16** by Type **17** (whi shows different figures) after only a few sheets as it did n adequately obliterate the original face value. A small quanti said to be 3½ sheets, of Type **16** was included in t consignment in error.

1919–20. *T* **12** *and* **13** (2½d. *special printing*), *optd only, surch in addition at Kingston* (No. 58) *or by D.L.R.* (*others*).
57 **16** ½d. green (4.2.19) .. .. .. 60 2·
a. Short opt (right pane R. 10/1) .. 24·00
58 **18** 1½d. on 2d. grey (10.3.20) .. .. 1·50 7·
59 **17** 1½d. on 2½d. orange (4.12.19) .. .. 80 1·
a. Short opt (right pane R. 10/1) .. 27·00
57s, 59s Optd "Specimen" .. .. *Set of* 2 80·00

The ½d. stamps on *buff* paper, and later consignments of t 2d. T **13** on *pinkish*, derived their colour from the paper in whic they were packed for despatch from England.

Nos. 56a, 57a and 59a show the overprint 2 mm high inste of 2½ mm.

A further surcharge as No. 58, but in red, was prepared Jamaica during April 1920, but these were not issued.

19

20 King William IV and King George V

4 Apr)–**26.** *P* 14. (*a*) *Wmk Mult Crown CA.*
3d. purple/*orange-buff* .. .. .. 1·50 8·00
aw. Wmk inverted £100 £150
ay. Wmk inverted and reversed .. 75·00 £110
b. Purple/pale yellow .. .. .. 45·00 60·00
bw. Wmk inverted .. .. ..
4d. red/*yellow* (1.4.22) .. .. .. 1·00 4·00
1s. black/*green* .. .. .. 1·25 9·50
x. Wmk reversed .. .. ..
5s. yellow-green/*pale yellow* .. .. 16·00 70·00
a. Deep green/pale yellow .. .. 70·00 £110
b. Blue-green/pale yellow .. .. 75·00 £130
c. Deep green/orange-buff (19.11.21) .. £100 £170
10s. carmine/*green* (19.11.21) .. .. 55·00 £100
.. .. *Set of* 5 70·00 £170
Optd "Specimen" .. .. *Set of* 5 £180

(*b*) *Wmk Mult Script CA*
9 ¼d. yellow-brown (1.4.22) .. .. 50 1·50
y. Wmk inverted and reversed .. £200
½d. pale grey-green (1.4.22) 50 30
w. Wmk inverted .. .. ..
y. Wmk inverted and reversed ..
1d. deep carmine-red (1.4.22) .. .. 1·40 85
1½d. orange-brown .. .. .. 1·75 30
2d. slate-grey (1.4.22) .. .. .. 1·75 4·00
2½d. bright blue (1.4.22) 50 50
x. Wmk reversed £200
3d. purple/*yellow* (29.6.23) .. .. 75 4·00
y. Wmk inverted and reversed .. £200
4½d. sage-green (29.6.23) .. .. 2·25 3·00
6d. claret (1.4.22) .. .. .. 5·50 32·00
a. Deep claret .. .. 19·00 40·00
1s. black/*green* (15.5.25) .. .. 9·50 32·00
2s. violet/*blue* (1.4.22) .. .. .. 14·00 24·00
3s. violet (1.4.22) .. .. .. 23·00 16·00
5s. green/*yellow* (15.2.25) .. .. 24·00 45·00
10s. carmine/*green* (5.9.26) .. .. 60·00 85·00
.. .. *Set of* 14 £130 £225
3s Optd "Specimen" .. *Set of* 14 £325

example of the 4d, No. 62, is known with the 'C' missing the watermark in the top sheet margin.

.R." **PROVISIONAL.** On the night of 9/10 November the Cayman Brac Post Office at Stake Bay, and its nts, was destroyed by a hurricane. Pending the arrival of cement stamp stocks and cancellation the Postmaster, Mr. Rutty, initialled covers to indicate that postage had been Those destined for overseas addresses additionally ved a "Postage Paid" machine postmark in red when they ed through Kingston, Jamaica.

Price on cover
Endorsed "A.S.R." in manuscript £5000
Endorsed "A.S.R." in manuscript and "Postage Paid" machine postmark in red £7500

ese emergency arrangements lasted until 19 December.

(Recess Waterlow)

(5 Dec). *Centenary of the "Assembly of Justices and stry". Wmk Mult Script CA. P* 12½.
20 ¼d. brown .. .. 1·50 1·00
a. "A" of "CA" missing from wmk .. £1100 £1100
½d. green .. .. 2·75 7·50
a. "A" of "CA" reversed in wmk .. £1300
1d. scarlet .. .. 2·75 6·50
1½d. red-orange .. .. 2·75 2·75
a. "A" of "CA" missing from wmk ..
2d. grey .. .. 2·75 3·25
2½d. ultramarine .. .. .. 2·75 1·50
3d. olive-green .. .. 3·00 5·00
6d. purple .. .. 9·50 23·00
1s. black and brown .. .. .. 17·00 32·00
2s. black and ultramarine .. .. 45·00 75·00
5s. black and green .. .. .. 80·00 £120
10s. black and scarlet £250 £350
5 .. .. *Set of* 12 £350 £500
95s Perf "Specimen" .. .. *Set of* 12 £450

o. 85a shows one "A" of the watermark reversed so that its d points to right when seen from the back. It is believed that stamp may also exist with "A" missing.
xamples of all values are known showing a forged George vn postmark dated "DE 31 1932".

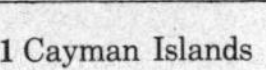

21 Cayman Islands

24 Queen or Pink Conch Shells

(Recess Waterlow)

35 (1 May)–**36.** *T* **21, 24** *and similar designs. Wmk Mult Script CA. P* 12½.
6 **21** ¼d. black and brown .. .. .. 50 1·00
7 – ½d. ultramarine & yellow-green (1.1.36) 1·00 1·00
8 – 1d. ultramarine and scarlet .. .. 4·00 2·25
9 **24** 1½d. black and orange .. .. .. 1·50 1·75
0 – 2d. ultramarine and purple .. .. 3·75 1·10
1 – 2½d. blue and black (1.1.36) .. .. 3·25 1·25
2 **21** 3d. black and olive-green .. .. 2·50 3·00
3 – 6d. bright purple and black (1.1.36) .. 8·50 4·00
4 – 1s. ultramarine and orange (1.1.36) .. 6·00 6·50
5 – 2s. ultramarine and black .. .. 45·00 35·00
6 – 5s. green and black .. .. .. 50·00 50·00
7 **24** 10s. black and scarlet .. .. .. 70·00 85·00
/107 .. .. *Set of* 12 £170 £170
s/107s Perf "Specimen" .. *Set of* 12 £250

Designs: *Horiz*—½d., 2d., 1s. Cat boat; 1d., 2s. Red-footed Booby; ½d., 6d. 5s. Hawksbill Turtles.
Examples of all values are known showing a forged George wn postmark dated "AU 23 1936"

1935 (6 May). *Silver Jubilee. As Nos.* 91/4 *of Antigua.*
108 ½d. black and green .. .. .. 15 1·00
f. Diagonal line by turret .. .. 30·00
h. Dot by flagstaff .. .. .. 48·00
i. Dash by turret .. .. .. 60·00
109 2½d. brown and deep blue .. .. 1·00 1·00
110 6d. light blue and olive-green .. .. 1·00 3·25
h. Dot by flagstaff £150
i. Dash by turret £150
111 1s. slate and purple .. .. .. 7·00 7·00
h. Dot by flagstaff £250
i. Dash by turret £275
108/11 .. .. .. *Set of* 4 8·25 11·00
108s/11s Perf "Specimen" .. *Set of* 4 £100

For illustrations of plate varieties see Omnibus section following Zanzibar.

1937 (13 May). *Coronation Issue. As Nos.* 95/7 *of Antigua. P* 11×11½.
112 ½d. green .. .. 30 1·10
113 1d. carmine 50 20
114 2½d. blue 95 40
112/14 .. .. .. *Set of* 3 1·60 1·50
112s/14s .. .. .. *Set of* 3 80·00

26 Beach View

27 Dolphin (fish) (*Coryphaena hippurus*)

(Recess D.L.R. (½d., 2d., 6d., 1s., 10s.), Waterlow (others))

1938 (5 May)–**48.** *T* **26/7** *and similar designs. Wmk Mult Script CA (sideways on* ¼d., 1d., 1½d., 2½d., 3d., 2s., 5s.). *Various perfs.*
115 **26** ¼d. red-orange (*p* 12½) 70 55
a. Perf 13½×12½ (16.7.43) .. 10 65
116 **27** ½d. green (*p* 13×11½) 75 55
a. Perf 14 (16.7.43) .. .. 1·25 1·40
ab. "A" of "CA" missing from wmk .. £1100
117 – 1d. scarlet (*p* 12½) 30 75
118 **26** 1½d. black (*p* 12½) 30 10
119 – 2d. violet (*p* 11½×13) .. .. 3·00 40
a. Perf 14 (16.7.43) 60 30
120 – 2½d. bright blue (*p* 12½) 40 20
120*a* – 2½d. orange (*p* 12½) (25.8.47) .. 2·25 50
121 – 3d. orange (*p* 12½) 40 15
121*a* – 3d. bright blue (*p* 12½) (25.8.47) .. 2·25 30
122 – 6d. olive-green (*p* 11½×13) .. 11·00 4·00
a. Perf 14 (16.7.43) .. .. 2·00 1·25
b. Brownish ol (*p* 11½×13) (8.7.47) 3·00 1·50
123 **27** 1s. red-brown (*p* 13×11½) .. .. 6·50 1·50
a. Perf 14 (16.7.43) .. .. 4·50 2·00
ab. "A" of "CA" missing from wmk .. £1200
124 **26** 2s. yellow-green (*shades*) (*p* 12½) .. 48·00 14·00
a. Deep green (16.7.43) .. .. 25·00 9·00
125 – 5s. carmine-lake (*p* 12½) .. .. 32·00 15·00
a. Crimson (1948) .. .. 70·00 22·00
126 – 10s. chocolate (*p* 11½×13) .. .. 23·00 9·00
a. Perf 14 (16.7.43) .. .. 21·00 9·00
aw. Wmk inverted .. ..
115/26a .. .. .. *Set of* 14 80·00 35·00
115s/26s Perf "Specimen" .. *Set of* 14 £300

Designs: *Horiz* (*as T* **26**)—1d., 3d. Cayman Islands map; 2½d., 5s. *Rembro* (schooner). *Vert* (*as T* **27**)—2d., 6d., 10s. Hawksbill Turtles.

Stop after "1946" (Plate B1 R.2/1)

1946 (26 Aug). *Victory. As Nos.* 110/11 *of Antigua.*
127 1½d. black 20 10
128 3d. orange-yellow 20 10
a. Stop after "1946" .. .. .. 17·00
127s/8s Perf "Specimen" .. .. *Set of* 2 70·00

1948 (29 Nov). *Royal Silver Wedding. As Nos.* 112/13 *of Antigua.*
129 ½d. green 10 10
130 10s. violet-blue .. .. 13·00 13·00

1949 (10 Oct). *75th Anniv of Universal Postal Union. As Nos.* 114/17 *of Antigua.*
131 2½d. orange 30 50
132 3d. deep blue .. .. .. 1·50 1·75
133 6d. olive .. .. 60 1·75
134 1s. red-brown 60 30
131/4 .. .. *Set of* 4 2·75 3·75

31 Cat Boat

32 Coconut Grove, Cayman Brac

(Recess B.W.)

1950 (2 Oct). *T* **31/2** *and similar horiz designs. Wmk Mult Script CA. P* 11½ × 11.
135 ¼d. bright blue and pale scarlet 15 60
136 ½d. reddish violet and emerald-green .. 15 1·25
137 1d. olive-green and deep blue 60 75
138 1½d. green and brown 30 75
139 2d. reddish violet and rose-carmine .. 1·25 1·50
140 2½d. turquoise and black .. .. 1·25 60
141 3d. bright green and light blue .. .. 1·40 1·50
142 6d. red-brown and blue .. .. 2·00 1·25
143 9d. scarlet and grey-green .. .. 5·50 2·00
144 1s. brown and orange .. .. 3·25 2·75
145 2s. violet and reddish purple .. .. 8·50 9·00
146 5s. olive-green and violet .. .. 13·00 7·00
147 10s. black and scarlet .. .. .. 15·00 14·00
135/47 .. .. *Set of* 13 45·00 38·00

Designs:—1d. Green Turtle; 1½d. Thatch rope industry; 2d. Cayman seamen; 2½d. Map of Cayman Islands; 3d. Parrotfish; 6d. Bluff, Cayman Brac; 9d. Georgetown harbour; 1s. Turtle in "crawl"; 2s. *Ziroma* (schooner); 5s. Boat-building; 10s. Government Offices, Grand Cayman.

Ceylon

PRICES FOR STAMPS ON COVER TO 1945

No. 1	*from* × 5
Nos. 2/12	*from* × 4
Nos. 16/17	*from* × 5
Nos. 18/59	*from* × 8
Nos. 60/2	*from* × 15
Nos. 63/72	*from* × 8
Nos. 121/38	*from* × 6
Nos. 139/41	†
Nos. 142/3	*from* × 10
Nos. 146/51	*from* × 6
Nos. 151*a*/2	†
Nos. 153/93	*from* × 8
Nos. 195/201	*from* × 12
Nos. 202/43	*from* × 6
Nos. 245/9	*from* × 4
Nos. 250/5	*from* × 5
Nos. 256/64	*from* × 4
Nos. 265/76	*from* × 3
Nos. 277/88	*from* × 4
Nos. 289/300	*from* × 8
Nos. 301/18	*from* × 2
Nos. 319/23	—
Nos. 330/7*b*	*from* × 4
Nos. 338/56	*from* × 2
Nos. 357/60	—
Nos. 361/2	*from* × 5
Nos. 363/7	*from* × 3
Nos. 368/78	*from* × 2
Nos. 379/82	*from* × 4
Nos. 383/5	*from* × 3
Nos. 386/97	*from* × 2
Nos. 398/9	*from* × 8
Nos. O1/17	*from* × 30

CROWN COLONY

PRICES. The prices of the imperf stamps of Ceylon vary greatly according to condition. The following prices are for fine copies with four margins.
Poor to medium specimens can be supplied at much lower prices.

1

2

3

NOTE. Beware of stamps of Type **2** which are often offered with corners added.

(Recess P.B.)

1857 (1 Apr). *Blued paper. Wmk Star W w* **1.** *Imperf.*
1 **1** 6d. purple-brown £7500 £450

Collectors should beware of proofs with faked watermark, often offered as originals.

PERKINS BACON "CANCELLED". For notes on these handstamps, showing "CANCELLED" between horizontal bars forming an oval, see Catalogue Introduction.

1857 (2 July)–**59.** *Wmk Star,* W w **1.** *White paper.* (*a*) *Imperf*
2 **1** 1d. deep turquoise-blue (24.8.57) .. £650 26·00
a. Blue .. .. .. £750 42·00
b. Blued paper .. .. .. — £180
3 2d. green (*shades*) (24.8.57) .. .. £150 55·00
a. Yellowish green .. .. £500 90·00
4 **2** 4d. dull rose (23.4.59) £50000 £4500
5 **1** 5d. chestnut £1500 £150
6 6d. purple-brown (1859) £1800 £140
a. Brown £6000 £475
b. Deep brown £7000 £1000
c. Light brown .. .. .. — £900

7 2 8d. brown (23.4.59) £22000 £1500
8 9d. purple-brown (23.4.59) £32000 £900
9 3 10d. dull vermilion £800 £300
10 1s. slate-violet £4500 £200
11 2 1s. 9d. green (H/S "CANCELLED" in oval £5500) £700 £800
a. *Yellow-green* £4000 £3000
12 2s. dull blue (23.4.59) £5500 £1200

(b) Unofficial perf 7½ (1s. 9d.) or roul (others)
13 1 1d. blue £5500
14 2d. green £2500 £1200
15 2 1s. 9d. green £6500

Nos. 13/15 were privately produced, probably by commercial firms for their own convenience.

The 10d. also exists with "CANCELLED" in oval, but no examples are believed to be in private hands.

4

(Typo D.L.R.)

1857 (Oct)–**64.** *No wmk. Glazed paper. (a) Imperf*
16 4 ½d. reddish lilac (*blued paper*) £3250 £475
17 ½d. dull mauve (1858) £170 £180
a. Private roul £5500

(b) P 12½
18 4 ½d. dull mauve (1864) £200 £160

(Recess P.B.)

1861–64. *Wmk Star, W w 1.*

(a) Clean-cut and intermediate perf 14 to 15½
19 1 1d. light blue £850 £160
a. Dull blue (H/S "CANCELLED" in oval £5500) £140 12·00
20 2d. green (*shades*) £140 28·00
a. Imperf between (vert pair) † —
b. Yellowish green (H/S "CANCELLED" in oval £5500) £150 24·00
21 2 4d. dull rose (H/S "CANCELLED" in oval £6000) £1800 £250
22 1 5d. chestnut (H/S "CANCELLED" in oval £4000) 80·00 8·00
23 6d. brown (H/S "CANCELLED" in oval £6000) £1800 95·00
a. Bistre-brown — £160
24 2 8d. brown (H/S "CANCELLED" in oval £5000) £1700 £475
25 9d. purple-brown £5500 £225
26 3 1s. slate-violet (H/S "CANCELLED" in oval £5500) 85·00 13·00
27 2 2s. dull blue £2500 £600

(b) Rough perf 14 to 15½
28 1 1d. dull blue £100 6·00
a. Blued paper £475 20·00
29 2d. green £400 75·00
30 2 4d. rose-red £375 70·00
a. Deep rose-red £400 80·00
31 1 6d. deep brown £850 90·00
a. Light brown £1400 £120
b. Olive-sepia £750 80·00
32 2 8d. brown £1300 £550
a. Yellow-brown £1300 £350
33 9d. deep brown (H/S "CANCELLED" in oval £4500) 70·00 60·00
a. Light brown £800 85·00
b. Olive-sepia £500 50·00
34 3 10d. dull vermilion £225 22·00
a. Imperf vert (horiz pair) † —
35 1s. slate-violet £225 15·00
36 2 1s. 9d. light green (*prepared for use, but not issued*) £650
37 2s. dull blue (H/S "CANCELLED" in oval £5000) £600 £130
a. Deep dull blue £800 £160

(c) P 12½ by D.L.R.
38 3 10d. dull vermilion (9.64) £225 16·00

The line machine used for Nos. 19/37 produced perforations of variable quality due to wear, poor cleaning and faulty servicing, but it is generally accepted that the clean-cut and intermediate versions occurred on stamps perforated up to March 1861 and the rough variety when the machine was used after that date.

(Recess D.L.R.)

1862. *No wmk. Smooth paper. (a) P 13*
39 1 1d. dull blue £110 6·00
40 5d. lake-brown £1300 £150
41 6d. brown £140 25·00
a. Deep brown £130 23·00
42 2 9d. brown £1200 90·00
43 3 1s. slate-purple £1600 75·00

(b) P 11½, 12
44 1 1d. dull blue £1200 £120
a. Imperf between (horiz pair) † £9000

Nos. 39/44 were printed on paper showing a papermaker's watermark of "T H SAUNDERS 1862", parts of which can be found on individual stamps. Examples are rare and command a premium.

The 1s. is known imperforate, but was not issued in this condition.

MINIMUM PRICE

The minimum price quote is 10p which represents a handling charge rather than a basis for valuing common stamps. For further notes about prices see introductory pages.

5
(23 mm high. "CC" oval)

6
(21½ mm high. "CC" round and smaller)

(Typo (½d.) or recess (others) D.L.R.)

1863–66. W **5**. *Paper medium thin and slightly soft.*

(a) P 11½, 12
45 1 1d. deep blue £2500 £300
x. Wmk reversed £3250 £400

(b) P 13
46 1 6d. sepia £1400 £150
x. Wmk reversed — £130
y. Wmk inverted and reversed £1900 £300
47 2 9d. sepia £3250 £650

(c) P 12½
48 4 ½d. dull mauve (1864) 35·00 26·00
aw. Wmk inverted £150 48·00
b. Reddish lilac 48·00 35·00
c. Mauve 25·00 26·00
49 1 1d. deep blue 95·00 4·00
a. Imperf
w. Wmk inverted † 26·00
x. Wmk reversed £100 4·50
y. Wmk inverted and reversed † 32·00
50 2d. grey-green (1864) 60·00 9·00
a. Imperf
bw. Wmk inverted £170 38·00
by. Wmk inverted and reversed † 75·00
c. Bottle-green † £3500
d. Yellowish green £7500 £400
dx. Wmk reversed † £650
e. Emerald (*wmk reversed*) £110 90·00
ew. Wmk inverted £325 £180
51 2d. ochre (*wmk reversed*) (1866) £225 £225
w. Wmk inverted £425 £425
y. Wmk inverted and reversed £350 £325
52 2 4d. rose-carmine (1865) £500 £130
ax. Wmk reversed £650
b. Rose £325 70·00
bx. Wmk reversed £375 90·00
53 1 5d. red-brown (*shades*) (1865) £150 60·00
w. Wmk inverted † £130
x. Wmk reversed £180 50·00
54 5d. grey-olive (1866) £1700 £325
ax. Wmk reversed £1400 £275
b. Yellow-olive £750 £225
bx. Wmk reversed £750 £200
55 6d. sepia £120 4·00
aw Wmk inverted † 48·00
b. Reddish brown £150 11·00
c. Blackish brown £120 9·00
ca. Double print † £2500
cw. Wmk inverted † 42·00
cx. Wmk reversed £160 32·00
cy. Wmk inverted and reversed † 85·00
56 2 8d. reddish brown (*shades*) (1864) 80·00 40·00
x. Wmk reversed £110 55·00
y. Wmk inverted and reversed £190 70·00
57 9d. sepia £300 40·00
x. Wmk reversed £425 65·00
58 3 10d. vermilion (1866) £1600 55·00
ax. Wmk reversed † £110
b. Orange-red £3750 £350
bx. Wmk reversed † £450
59 2 2s. steel-blue (*shades*) (1864) £200 30·00
x. Wmk reversed † 75·00
y. Wmk inverted and reversed † £130

Watermarks as Type **5** were arranged in four panes, each of 60, with the words "CROWN COLONIES" between the panes. Parts of this marginal watermark often appear on the stamps.

The ½d. dull mauve, 2d. ochre and 5d. grey-olive with this watermark also exist imperforate, but are not known used. The 6d. sepia and 2s. steel-blue also exist imperforate on wove paper without watermark.

One used example of the 2d. grey-green is known showing private roulettes added to an imperforate stamp (*Price* £2750).

7

8

(Typo D.L.R.)

1866–68. *Wmk Crown CC. (a) P 12½*
60 7 3d. rose £160 70·00

(b) P 14
61 8 1d. blue (*shades*) (1868) 18·00 7·50
w. Wmk inverted † 80·00
62 7 3d. carmine-rose (1867) 60·00 35·00
a. Bright rose 65·00 40·00

Nos. 60/1 exist imperforate.

(Recess D.L.R.)

1867–70. W **6**. *Specially produced hand-made paper. P 12½.*
63 1 1d. dull blue £130 9·00
aw. Wmk inverted £300 65·00
ax. Wmk reversed £130 9·00
b. Deep blue £120 7·00
bx. Wmk reversed £180 27·00
64 1 2d. ochre 95·00
ax. Wmk reversed —
b. Bistre 45·00
bw. Wmk inverted 95·00
c. Olive-bistre £140
cw. Wmk inverted £140
d. Yellow 75·00
dx. Wmk reversed 48·00
65 2 4d. rose £190
ax. Wmk reversed £170
b. Rose-carmine 48·00
bw. Wmk inverted †
bx. Wmk reversed 48·00
by. Wmk inverted and reversed £300
66 1 5d. yellow-olive 75·00
ax. Wmk reversed 65·00
ay. Wmk inverted and reversed
b. Olive-green 95·00
c. Bronze-green 28·00
67 6d. deep brown (1869) 65·00
a. Blackish brown 85·00
aw. Wmk inverted †
ax. Wmk reversed £110
b. Red-brown 28·00
68 2 8d. chocolate 50·00
ax. Wmk reversed —
b. Lake-brown £110
bx. Wmk reversed —
69 9d. bistre-brown (1869) £375
ax. Wmk reversed £300
b. Blackish brown 40·00
70 3 10d. dull vermilion (*wmk reversed*) £2500
ay. Wmk inverted and reversed †
b. Red-orange 42·00
bx. Wmk reversed —
by. Wmk inverted and reversed £350
c. Orange 75·00
71 1s. reddish lilac (1870) £275
ax. Wmk reversed £375
b. Reddish violet 80·00
bw. Wmk inverted †
bx. Wmk reversed £180
72 2 2s. steel-blue £160
ax. Wmk reversed †
b. Deep blue £100
bx. Wmk reversed £130

Watermarks as Type **6** were arranged in one pane o (12×20) with the words "CROWN COLONIES" twice in side margin.

Unused examples of the 1d. dull blue, 1d. deep blu yellow-olive, 6d. deep brown, 9d. blackish brown and 10d orange with this watermark exist imperforate.

PRINTERS. All stamps from No. 121 to 367 were typogra by De La Rue & Co. Ltd, London.

(New Currency. 100 cents = 1 rupee)

9 10 11

12

13

14

15 16 17

18

19

1872–80. *Wmk Crown CC. (a) P 14.*
121 9 2 c. pale brown (*shades*) 13·00 2
w. Wmk inverted 80·00 40
122 10 4 c. grey 30·00 1
w. Wmk inverted — 42
123 4 c. rosy-mauve (1880) 48·00 1
124 11 8 c. orange-yellow 40·00 5
a. Yellow 28·00 6
w. Wmk inverted †
126 12 16 c. pale violet 75·00 2
w. Wmk inverted † 90
127 13 24 c. green 48·00 2
w. Wmk inverted † £1
128 14 32 c. slate (1877) £140 15
w. Wmk inverted £325
129 15 36 c. blue £130 17
x. Wmk reversed £275

16 48 c. rose 65·00 5·00
w. Wmk inverted — 38·00
17 64 c. red-brown (1877) £250 60·00
18 96 c. drab £180 26·00
w. Wmk inverted † £120
y. Wmk inverted and reversed † —
2 Set of 11 £850 £110

(b) P 14×12½
9 2 c. brown £350 60·00
10 4 c. grey £1200 26·00
11 8 c. orange-yellow £375 45·00
w. Wmk inverted † £150

(c) P 12½
9 2 c. brown £2250 £160
10 4 c. grey £1200 £225

(d) P 12½ × 14
19 2 r. 50 c. dull-rose (1879) £450 £300

repared for use and sent out to Ceylon, but not issued unsurcharged
14 32 c. slate (p 14 × 12½) £800
17 64 c. red-brown (p 14 × 12½) £950
19 2 r. 50, dull rose (p 12½) £1300

:GERIES.—Beware of forged overprint and surcharge ties on Victorian issues.

SIXTEEN
16
CENTS
(20)

2 (Oct). *Nos.* 127 *and* 131 *surch as T* **20** *by Govt Printer.*
13 16 c. on 24 c. green 22·00 6·50
a. Surch inverted
17 20 c. on 64 c. red-brown 9·00 5·00
a. Surch double † £1100

–98. *Wmk Crown CA. (a) P* 14.
9 2 c. pale brown 50·00 1·75
2 c. dull green (1884) 2·50 15
s. Optd "Specimen" £250
w. Wmk inverted £110 45·00
10 4 c. rosy mauve 3·00 30
4 c. rose (1884) 3·75 11·00
s. Optd "Specimen" £250
11 8 c. orange 4·25 8·00
a. Yellow (1898) 3·50 7·00
12 16 c. pale violet £1400 £150

(b) Trial perforation. P 12
a 9 2 c. dull green £2250
b 10 4 c. rose £2250
c 13 24 c. brown-purple £2500

c) Prepared for use and sent out to Ceylon, but not issued unsurcharged. P 14
13 24 c. brown-purple £1000
s. Optd "Specimen" £475

Although delivered in 1884 it is believed that the 4 c. rose, No. , was not used until the early 1890s.

Postage &
FIVE
CENTS
Revenue
(21)

TEN
CENTS
(22)

Twenty
Cents
(23)

One Rupee
Twelve
Cents
(24)

85. *T* **10/19** *surch locally as T* **21/24**.

I. *Wmk Crown CC. (a) P* 14
3 21 5 c. on 16 c. pale violet † £2500
4 5 c. on 24 c. green £2250 £100
5 5 c. on 32 c. slate 55·00 15·00
a. Surch inverted † £1100
b. Dark grey £110 32·00
6 5 c. on 36 c. blue £225 8·00
a. Surch inverted † £1700
x. Wmk reversed † 55·00
7 5 c. on 48 c. rose £950 50·00
8 5 c. on 64 c. red-brown 85·00 4·50
a. Surch double † £900
9 5 c. on 96 c. drab £400 60·00
1 22 10 c. on 16 c. pale violet £4500 £1600
2 10 c. on 24 c. green £400 £100
3 10 c. on 36 c. blue £375 £160
4 10 c. on 64 c. red-brown £400 £130
5 20 c. on 24 c. green 50·00 18·00
6 23 20 c. on 32 c. slate 55·00 50·00
a. Dark grey 55·00 42·00
7 25 c. on 32 c. slate 13·00 4·50
a. Dark grey 24·00 8·00
8 28 c. on 48 c. rose 35·00 6·00
a. Surch double † £1000
9 22 30 c. on 36 c. blue 14·00 9·00
x. Wmk reversed 10·00 8·50
xa. Surch inverted £200 £100
70 56 c. on 96 c. drab 22·00 18·00

(b) P 14 × 12½
172 21 5 c. on 32 c. slate £550 45·00
173 5 c. on 64 c. red-brown £550 38·00
174 22 10 c. on 64 c. red-brown 55·00 90·00
a. Imperf between (vert pair) £2750
175 24 1 r. 12 c. on 2 r. 50 c. dull rose *(p* 12½) £425 85·00
176 1 r. 12 c. on 2 r. 50 c. dull rose *(p* 12½ × 14) 85·00 42·00

II. *Wmk Crown CA. P* 14
178 21 5 c. on 4 c. rose 18·00 3·50
a. Surch inverted † £275
179 5 c. on 8 c. orange-yellow 55·00 6·50
a. Surch double † £1200
b. Surch inverted † £1500
180 5 c. on 16 c. pale violet 85·00 10·00
a. Surch inverted † £170
182 5 c. on 24 c. brown-purple — £500
184 22 10 c. on 16 c. pale violet £4500 £950
185 10 c. on 24 c. brown-purple 12·00 5·50
186 15 c. on 16 c. pale violet 9·50 6·50

Only seven examples, all used, are recorded of No. 153.

The 5 c. on 4 c. rosy mauve and 5 c. on 24 c. green, both watermarked Crown CA, previously catalogued are now considered to be forgeries.

REVENUE AND POSTAGE

5 CENTS
(25)

10 CENTS
(26)

1 R. 12 C.
(27)

1885. *T* **11/15, 18** *and* **19** *surch with T* **25/7** *by D.L.R. P* 14.

(a) Wmk Crown CA
187 25 5 c. on 8 c. lilac 14·00 1·40
w. Wmk inverted † 60·00
188 26 10 c. on 24 c. brown-purple 8·50 6·50
189 15 c. on 16 c. orange-yellow 50·00 8·50
190 28 c. on 32 c. slate 20·00 2·50
191 30 c. on 36 c. olive-green 28·00 14·00
192 56 c. on 96 c. drab 45·00 13·00

(b) Wmk Crown CC (sideways)
193 27 1 r. 12 on 2 r. 50, dull rose 38·00 80·00
187/93 Set of 7 £180 £110
187s/93s Optd "Specimen" Set of 7 £750

28

29

1886. *Wmk Crown CA. P* 14.
195 28 5 c. dull purple 2·25 10
w. Wmk inverted † 70·00
196 29 15 c. sage-green 4·50 1·25
w. Wmk inverted † £110
197 15 c. olive-green 4·75 1·25
198 25 c. yellow-brown 3·50 1·00
a. Value in yellow £100 70·00
199 28 c. slate 16·00 1·40
195s, 197s/9s Optd "Specimen" Set of 4 £200

Six plates were used for the 5 c., No. 195, between 1885 and 1901, each being replaced by its successor as it became worn. Examples from the worn plates show thicker lines in the background and masses of solid colour under the chin, in front of the throat, at the back of the neck and at the base.

30

1887. *Wmk Crown CC (sideways). White or blued paper. P* 14.
201 30 1 r. 12, dull rose 22·00 20·00
a. Wmk upright 40·00 55·00
aw. Wmk inverted † £140
s. Optd "Specimen" £100

TWO CENTS
(31)

Two
(32)

2 Cents
(33)

Two Cents
(34)

2 Cents
(35)

1888–90. *Nos.* 148/9 *surch with T* **31/5**.
202 31 2 c. on 4 c. rosy mauve 1·40 80
a. Surch inverted 20·00 19·00
b. Surch double, one inverted — £180
203 2 c. on 4 c. rose 2·25 30
a. Surch inverted 13·00 14·00
b. Surch double — £190
204 32 2 (c). on 4 c. rosy mauve 75 30
a. Surch inverted 28·00 30·00
b. Surch double 55·00 55·00
c. Surch double, one inverted 50·00 45·00
205 2 (c) on 4 c. rose 4·50 20
a. Surch inverted £190
b. Surch double 60·00 65·00
c. Surch double, one inverted 65·00 70·00
206 33 2 c. on 4 c. rosy mauve 55·00 28·00
a. Surch inverted 90·00 38·00
b. Surch double, one inverted £110
207 2 c. on 4 c. rose 2·25 75
a. Surch inverted 10·00 8·50
b. Surch double £110 £110
c. Surch double, one inverted 8·00 10·00
208 34 2 c. on 4 c. rosy mauve 42·00 16·00
a. Surch inverted £110 30·00
209 2 c. on 4 c. rose 2·50 1·10
a. Surch inverted 11·00 5·50
b. Surch double 85·00 85·00
c. Surch double, one inverted 11·00 5·50
210 35 2 c. on 4 c. rosy mauve 42·00 24·00
a. Surch inverted 60·00 40·00
b. Surch double, one inverted 75·00 75·00
c. Surch double — £190
d. "s" of "Cents" inverted — £375
e. As d. Whole surch inverted
211 2 c. on 4 c. rose 9·50 1·00
a. Surch inverted 15·00 5·50
b. Surch double 75·00 75·00
c. Surch double, one inverted 17·00 8·50
d. "s" of "Cents" inverted — £160
x. Wmk reversed † 75·00
209s, 211s Optd "Specimen" Set of 2 60·00

The 4 c. rose and the 4 c. rosy mauve are found surcharged "Postal Commission 3 (or "Three") Cents". They denote the extra commission charged by the Post Office on postal orders which had not been cashed within three months of the date of issue. For a short time the Post Office did not object to the use of these stamps on letters.

POSTAGE
Five Cents
REVENUE
(36)

FIFTEEN
CENTS
(37)

1890. *No.* 197 *surch with T* **36**.
233 5 c. on 15 c. olive-green 2·00 1·90
a. Surch inverted 38·00 40·00
b. Surch double 95·00 £100
c. "Flve" for "Five" (R. 1/1) 95·00 80·00
d. Variety as c, inverted — £850
e. "REVENUE" omitted £140 £120
f. Inverted "s" in "Cents" 50·00 60·00
g. Variety as f, and whole surch inverted £900
h. "REVENUE" omitted and inverted "s" in "Cents" £750
i. "POSTAGE" spaced between "T" and "A" (R. 1/5) 55·00 60·00
j. Variety as i, and whole surch inverted — £700
s. Optd "Specimen" 30·00

1891. *Nos.* 198/9 *surch with T* **37**.
239 29 15 c. on 25 c. yellow-brown 9·00 10·00
240 15 c. on 28 c. slate 14·00 8·50

3 Cents
(38)

39

1892. *Nos.* 148/9 *and* 199 *surch with T* **38**.
241 10 3 c. on 4 c. rosy mauve 1·00 3·25
242 3 c. on 4 c. rose 3·00 6·00
s. Optd "Specimen" 30·00
w. Wmk inverted 85·00
243 29 3 c. on 28 c. slate 3·50 3·00
a. Surch double £100
241/3 Set of 3 6·75 11·00

1893–99. *Wmk Crown CA. P* 14.
245 39 3 c. terracotta and blue-green 3·25 45
246 10 4 c. carmine-rose (1898) 7·50 8·00
247 29 30 c. bright mauve and chestnut 4·25 2·00
a. Bright violet and chestnut 5·00 2·50
249 19 2 r. 50, purple/*red* (1899) 28·00 48·00
245/9 Set of 4 38·00 55·00
245s, 247s/9s Optd "Specimen" Set of 3 60·00

Six Cents
(40)

2 R. 25 C.
(41)

1898 (Dec)–**99.** *(a) No.* 196 *surch with T* **40**.
250 29 6 c. on 15 c. sage-green 70 75

(b) As No. 138, *but colour changed and perf* 14, *surch as T* **41** (1899)
254 19 1 r. 50 on 2 r. 50, slate 20·00 42·00
w. Wmk inverted £100
255 2 r. 25 on 2 r. 50, yellow 35·00 75·00
250s/5s Optd "Specimen" Set of 3 70·00

43

1899–1900. *Wmk Crown CA* (1 *r.* 50, 2 *r.* 25 *wmk Crown CC*). *P* 14.

No.	Type	Description	Unused	Used
256	**9**	2 c. pale orange-brown	2·25	30
257	**39**	3 c. deep green	2·25	55
258	**10**	4 c. yellow	3·00	2·75
259	**29**	6 c. rose and black	1·25	45
260	**39**	12 c. sage-green and rose (1900)	4·00	7·00
261	**29**	15 c. blue	5·50	1·25
262	**39**	75 c. black and red-brown	4·75	6·00
263	**43**	1 r. 50, rose	19·00	35·00
264		2 r. 25, dull blue	30·00	35·00
256/64		*Set of* 9	65·00	80·00
256s/64s Optd "Specimen"		*Set of* 9	£160	

44

45

46

47

48

1903 (29 May)–**05.** *Wmk Crown CA. P* 14.

No.	Type	Description	Unused	Used
265	**44**	2 c. red-brown (21.7.03)	2·00	20
266	**45**	3 c. green (11.6.03)	2·00	1·00
267		4 c. orange-yellow and blue	2·00	3·50
268	**46**	5 c. dull purple (2.7.03)	1·50	60
269	**47**	6 c. carmine (5.11.03)	9·50	1·50
		w. Wmk inverted	55·00	
270	**45**	12 c. sage-green and rosine (13.8.03)	5·00	8·50
271	**48**	15 c. blue (2.7.03)	6·50	3·00
272		25 c. bistre (11.8.03)	4·00	8·00
273		30 c. dull violet and green	3·25	4·00
274	**45**	75 c. dull blue and orange (31.3.05)	3·00	17·00
275	**48**	1 r. 50, greyish slate (7.4.04)	65·00	55·00
276		2 r. 25, brown and green (12.4.04)	60·00	48·00
265/76		*Set of* 12	£140	£130
265s/76s Optd "Specimen"		*Set of* 12	£150	

1904 (13 Sept)–**05.** *Wmk Mult Crown CA. Ordinary paper. P* 14.

No.	Type	Description	Unused	Used
277	**44**	2 c. red-brown (17.11.04)	1·25	10
278	**45**	3 c. green (17.11.04)	1·25	15
279		4 c. orange and ultramarine	1·50	1·50
280	**46**	5 c. dull purple (29.11.04)	1·75	1·25
		a. Chalk-surfaced paper (5.10.05)	3·50	70
281	**47**	6 c. carmine (11.10.04)	1·10	15
282	**45**	12 c. sage-green and rosine (29.9.04)	1·50	1·75
283	**48**	15 c. blue (1.12.04)	1·50	60
284		25 c. bistre (5.1.05)	6·00	3·75
285		30 c. violet and green (7.9.05)	2·50	2·75
286	**45**	75 c. dull blue and orange (25.5.05)	5·25	8·00
287	**48**	1 r. 50, grey (5.1.05)	24·00	10·00
288		2 r. 25, brown and green (22.12.04)	20·00	29·00
277/88		*Set of* 12	60·00	50·00

50

51

1908. *Wmk Mult Crown CA. P* 14.

No.	Type	Description	Unused	Used
289	**50**	5 c. deep purple (26 May)	2·00	10
290		5 c. dull purple	3·00	30
291	**51**	6 c. carmine (6 June)	1·00	10
289s, 291s Optd "Specimen"		*Set of* 2	60·00	

1910 (1 Aug)–**11.** *Wmk Mult Crown CA. P* 14.

No.	Type	Description	Unused	Used
292	**44**	2 c. brown-orange (20.5.11)	1·50	50
293	**48**	3 c. green (5.7.11)	1·00	75
294		10 c. sage-green and maroon	2·50	2·00
295		25 c. grey	2·50	1·50
296		50 c. chocolate	4·00	7·50
297		1 r. purple/*yellow*	7·50	10·00
298		2 r. red/*yellow*	15·00	27·00
299		5 r. black/*green*	38·00	65·00
300		10 r. black/*red*	75·00	£170
292/300		*Set of* 9	£130	£250
292s/300s Optd "Specimen"		*Set of* 9	£190	

NEW INFORMATION

The editor is always interested to correspond with people who have new information that will improve or correct the Catalogue.

52

53

(A)

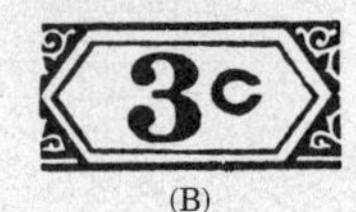
(B)

Most values in Type **52** were produced by two printing operations, using "Key" and "Duty" plates. Differences in the two Dies of the Key plate are described in the introduction to this catalogue.

In the Ceylon series, however, the 1 c. and 5 c. values, together with later printings of the 3 c. and 6 c., were printed from special plates at one operation. These plates can be identified by the large "C" in the value tablet (see illustration A). Examples of these values from Key and Duty plates printing have value tablet as illustration B. The 3 c. and 5 c. stamps from the single plates *resemble* Die I, and the 1 c. and 6 c. Die II, although in the latter case the inner top corners of the side panels are square and not curved.

1912–25. *Wmk Mult Crown CA. Chalk-surfaced paper* (30 *c. to* 100 *r.*). *P* 14.

(*a*) *Printed from single plates. Value tablet as* A

No.	Type	Description	Unused	Used
301	**52**	1 c. brown (1919)	1·00	10
		w. Wmk inverted	18·00	
302		3 c. blue-green (1919)	2·50	45
		w. Wmk inverted	18·00	27·00
		y. Wmk inverted and reversed	22·00	35·00
303		5 c. purple	6·00	2·75
		a. Wmk sideways (Crown to right of CA)	£325	
		y. Wmk inverted and reversed	70·00	
304		5 c. bright magenta	1·00	60
		w. Wmk inverted	—	65·00
305		6 c. pale scarlet (1919)	8·50	85
		a. Wmk sideways (Crown to left of CA)	32·00	65·00
		w. Wmk inverted	24·00	35·00
306		6 c. carmine	13·00	1·25
		a. Wmk sideways (Crown to right of CA)	42·00	
		y. Wmk inverted and reversed	24·00	

(*b*) *Printed from Key and Duty plates. Die I.* 3 *c. and* 6 *c. have value tablet as* B

No.	Type	Description	Unused	Used
307	**52**	2 c. brown-orange	40	30
		a. Deep orange-brown	30	20
308		3 c. yellow-green	6·50	2·25
		a. Deep green (1917)	4·50	1·10
309		6 c. scarlet (*shades*)	1·10	50
		a. Wmk sideways	†	—
310		10 c. sage-green	3·00	1·75
		a. Deep sage-green (1917)	5·00	2·50
		w. Wmk inverted	80·00	
311		15 c. deep bright blue	2·50	1·25
		a. Ultramarine (1918)	1·75	1·25
		aw. Wmk inverted	23·00	
312		25 c. orange and blue	6·50	4·50
		a. Yellow and blue (1917)	1·75	1·75
		aw. Wmk inverted	80·00	80·00
313		30 c. blue-green and violet	4·00	3·25
		a. Yellow-green and violet (1915)	7·00	4·00
		ab. Wmk sideways (Crown to right of CA)	22·00	
		abw. Wmk Crown to left of CA	24·00	
		aw. Wmk inverted	38·00	
314		50 c. black and scarlet	1·25	1·75
		w. Wmk inverted	17·00	
315		1 r. purple/*yellow*	2·50	3·50
		a. White back (1913)	2·25	4·75
		as. Optd "Specimen"	48·00	
		b. On lemon (1915)	4·25	8·00
		bs. Optd "Specimen"	45·00	
		c. On orange-buff (1918)	26·00	35·00
		cw. Wmk inverted	55·00	
		d. On pale yellow (1922)	4·50	10·00
		ds. Optd "Specimen"	42·00	
316		2 r. black and red/*yellow*	3·25	11·00
		a. White back (1913)	2·75	12·00
		as. Optd "Specimen"	48·00	
		b. On lemon (1915)	21·00	27·00
		bs. Optd "Specimen"	40·00	
		c. On orange-buff (1919)	38·00	42·00
		cw. Wmk inverted	50·00	
		d. On pale yellow (1921)	38·00	40·00
317		5 r. black/*green*	17·00	28·00
		a. White back (1914)	19·00	32·00
		as. Optd "Specimen"	48·00	
		b. On blue-grn (*olive back*) (1917)	16·00	30·00
		bs. Optd "Specimen"	55·00	
		bw. Wmk inverted	55·00	70·00
		c. Die II. *On emerald back* (1923)	45·00	90·00
		cs. Optd "Specimen"	55·00	
318		10 r. purple and black/*red*	60·00	80·00
		aw. Wmk inverted	£130	
		b. Die II (1923)	75·00	£120
		bw. Wmk inverted	£250	
319		20 r. black and red/*blue*	£100	£110
320	**53**	50 r. dull purple	£350	
		a. Break in scroll	£700	
		b. Broken crown and scroll	£700	
		s. Optd "Specimen"	£130	
321		100 r. grey-black	£1300	
		a. Break in scroll	£2250	
		b. Broken crown and scroll	£2250	
		s. Optd "Specimen"	£250	
		w. Wmk inverted	£2750	
322		500 r. dull green	£4250	
		a. Break in scroll	£7000	
		b. Broken crown and scroll	£7000	
		s. Optd "Specimen"	£450	
323	**53**	1000 r. purple/*red* (1925)	£15000	
		b. Broken crown and scroll	£20000	
		s. Optd "Specimen"	£850	
301/18		*Set of* 14	85·00	
301s/19s Optd "Specimen"		*Set of* 15	£325	

For illustrations of the varieties on Nos. 320/3 see above
58 of Leeward Islands.

The 2 c. and 5 c. exist in coils, constructed from normal sh
used in stamp-affixing machines introduced in 1915.

Sideways watermark varieties are described as seen *fron*
back of the stamp.

The "substituted crown" watermark variety is known o
sheet margin of the 1 c., No. 301.

WAR
STAMP

(54)

WAR
STAMP
ONE CENT

(55)

1918 (18 Nov)–**19.** (*a*) *Optd with T* **54** *by Govt Pri*
Colombo.

No.	Type	Description	Unused	Used
330	**52**	2 c. brown-orange	20	
		a. Opt inverted	32·00	3
		b. Opt double	26·00	3
		c. Opt omitted in pair with opt inverted	£350	
331		3 c. blue-green (No. 302) (1919)	1·75	
332		3 c. deep green (No. 308*a*)	20	
		a. Opt double	60·00	6
333		5 c. purple	50	
		a. Opt double	32·00	3
		w. Wmk inverted	70·00	
334		5 c. bright magenta	2·00	
		a. Opt inverted	32·00	3
		b. Opt double	26·00	3

(*b*) *Surch with T* **55**

No.	Type	Description	Unused	Used
335	**52**	1 c. on 5 c. purple	50	
		y. Wmk inverted and reversed	70·00	
336		1 c. on 5 c. bright magenta	1·25	
330s, 332s/3s, 335s Optd "Specimen"		*Set of* 4	90·00	

Collectors are warned against forgeries of the errors in
"WAR STAMP" overprints.

1918. *Surch as T* **55**, *but without* "WAR STAMP".

No.	Type	Description	Unused	Used
337	**52**	1 c. on 5 c. purple	15	
		a. Surch double	£130	
		bs. Optd "Specimen"	30·00	
337*c*		1 c. on 5 c. bright magenta	1·75	2

1921–32. *Wmk Mult Script CA. Chalk-surfaced paper* (30 *c.*
100 *r.*). *P* 14.

(*a*) *Printed from single plates. Value tablet as* A

No.	Type	Description	Unused	Used
338	**52**	1 c. brown (1927)	60	
339		3 c. green (5.5.22)	2·75	
		w. Wmk inverted	18·00	27
340		3 c. slate-grey (1923)	75	
		a. Wmk sideways	£850	
		w. Wmk inverted	20·00	
341		5 c. purple (1927)	50	
342		6 c. carmine-red (3.8.21)	2·00	
		w. Wmk inverted	19·00	27
		y. Wmk inverted and reversed	30·00	
343		6 c. bright violet (1922)	90	
		w. Wmk inverted	20·00	
		y. Wmk inverted and reversed	30·00	

(*b*) *Printed from Key and Duty plates*

No.	Type	Description	Unused	Used
344	**52**	2 c. brown-orange (Die II) (1927)	60	
345		9 c. red/*pale yellow* (Die II) (1926)	80	
346		10 c. sage-green (Die I) (16.9.21)	1·40	
		aw. Wmk inverted	25·00	
		ay. Wmk inverted and reversed	20·00	29·
		b. Die II (1924)	1·75	
		c. Vert gutter pair. Die I and Die II. Nos. 346 and 346b	£190	
347		12 c. rose-scarlet (Die I) (1925)	4·25	5·
		a. Die II	1·00	2·
		as. Optd "Specimen"	70·00	
		b. Vert gutter pair. Die I and Die II. Nos. 347/a	£100	
348		15 c. ultramarine (Die I) (30.5.22)	3·25	8·
349		15 c. green/*pale yellow* (Die I) (1923)	1·25	1·
		a. Die II (1924)	1·50	1·(
		aw. Wmk inverted	20·00	
		b. Vert gutter pair. Die I and Die II. Nos. 349/a	£190	
350		20 c. bright blue (Die I) (1922)	3·00	6·(
		aw. Wmk inverted	40·00	
		b. Die II (1924)	3·50	4
		c. Vert gutter pair. Die I and Die II. Nos. 350 and 350b	£190	
351		25 c. yellow and blue (Die I) (17.10.21)	1·40	1·9
		aw. Wmk inverted	50·00	
		b. Die II (1924)	2·75	1·2
		c. Vert gutter pair. Die I and Die II. Nos. 351/b	£130	
352		30 c. yellow-green & vio (Die I) (15.3.22)	1·40	2·5
		a. Die II (1924)	2·50	1·2
		b. Vert gutter pair. Die I and Die II. Nos. 352/a	£325	
353		50 c. black and scarlet (Die II) (1922)	1·40	8
		a. Die I (1932)	50·00	75·0
354		1 r. purple/*pale yellow* (Die I) (1923)	15·00	25·0
		a. Die II (1925)	13·00	23·0
		b. Vert gutter pair. Die I and Die II. Nos. 354/a	£250	
355		2 r. black & red/*pale yell* (Die II) (1923)	7·00	7·5
356		5 r. black/*emerald* (Die II) (1924)	27·00	48·0
357		20 r. black and red/*blue* (Die II) (1924)	£120	£16
358	**53**	50 r. dull purple (1924)	£350	
		a. Break in scroll	£600	
		b. Broken crown and scroll	£600	
		s. Optd "Specimen"	£130	
359		100 r. grey-black (1924)	£1400	
		a. Break in scroll	£2250	
		b. Broken crown and scroll	£2250	
		s. Optd "Specimen"	£300	

3 100 r. dull purple and blue (24.10.27) .. £1300
a. Break in scroll £2000
b. Broken crown and scroll £2000
s. Optd "Specimen" £300
. .. . *Set of* 19 60·00 85·00
7s Optd "Specimen" .. *Set of* 20 £425

2 c. to 30 c. and 1 r. values produced from Key and Duty were printed in sheets of 240 using two plates one above her. Nos. 346c, 347b, 349b, 350c, 351b, 353b and 354b from printings in 1924 and 1925 which combined Key 7 (Die I) with Key Plate 12 (Die II).

353a, from Key Plate 23, was a mistake; the "retired" Die g issued in error when it became necessary to replace Key 21.

illustrations of the varieties on Nos. 358/60 see above No. Leeward Islands.

2 Cents.

(56)

57

(Surch at Ceylon Govt Printing Works)

(27 Nov). *Surch as T* **56**.
52 2 c. on 3 c. slate-grey .. .. .. 80 1·00
a. Surch double .. .. .. 70·00
b. Bar omitted .. .. .. 70·00 80·00
5 c. on 6 c. bright violet 50 40
2s Optd "Specimen" .. *Set of* 2 50·00

. 361b comes from the bottom horizontal row of the sheet h was often partially obscured by the selvedge during narging.

(27 Nov)–**29**. *Wmk Mult Script CA. Chalk-surfaced per. P* 14.
57 1 r. dull and bright purple (1928) .. 2·50 1·25
2 r. green and carmine (1929) .. .. 3·75 2·75
5 r. green and dull purple (1928) .. 13·00 19·00
10 r. green and brown-orange .. .. 30·00 80·00
20 r. dull purple and blue .. .. 90·00 £180
7 .. .. *Set of* 5 £120 £250
7s Optd "Specimen" .. *Set of* 5 £140

. 364. Collectors are warned against faked 2 r. stamps, ing what purports to be a double centre.

58 Tapping Rubber

60 Adam's Peak

(Recess D.L.R. (2, 3, 20, 50 c.), B.W. (others))

5 (1 May)–**36**. *T* **58, 60** *and similar designs. Wmk Mult Script A (sideways on* 10, 15, 25, 30 *c. and* 1 *r.). Various perfs.*
2 c. black and carmine (*p* 12 × 13) 30 40
a. Perf 14 .. .. 9·00 40
3 c. blk & ol-green (*p* 13 × 12) (1.10.35) .. 35 40
a. Perf 14 .. .. 26·00 35
6 c. black & blue (*p* 11 × 11½) (1.1.36) .. 30 30
9 c. green & orange (*p* 11 × 11½) (1.1.36) .. 1·00 65
10 c. black & purple (*p* 11½ × 11) (1.6.35) .. 1·25 2·25
15 c. red-brown and green (*p* 11½ × 11) .. 1·00 50
20 c. black & grey-blue (*p* 12 × 13) (1.1.36) .. 1·75 2·50
25 c. deep blue & chocolate (*p* 11½ × 11) .. 1·40 1·25
30 c. carm & green (*p* 11½ × 11) (1.8.35) .. 3·00 2·75
50 c. black and mauve (*p* 14) (1.1.36) .. 8·50 1·75
1 r. vio-bl & chocolate (*p* 11½ × 11) (1.7.35) .. 17·00 16·00
/78 .. .. *Set of* 11 32·00 26·00
s/78s Perf "Specimen" .. *Set of* 11 £150

Designs: *Vert*—6 c. Colombo Harbour; 9 c. Plucking tea; 20 c. onut Palms. *Horiz*—10 c. Hill paddy (rice); 15 c. River scene; c. Temple of the Tooth, Kandy; 30 c. Ancient irrigation tank; . Wild elephants; 1 r. Trincomalee.

5 (6 May). *Silver Jubilee. As Nos.* 91/4 *of Antigua.* 13½×14.
6 c. ultramarine and grey 65 30
f. Diagonal line by turret .. .. 50·00 28·00
g. Dot to left of chapel .. .. 75·00 42·00
h. Dot by flagstaff .. .. 75·00 42·00
i. Dash by turret .. .. 80·00 45·00
9 c. green and indigo .. .. 70 1·25
f. Diagonal line by turret .. .. 70·00
g. Dot to left of chapel .. .. 85·00
h. Dot by flagstaff .. .. 95·00
1 20 c. brown and deep blue .. .. 4·25 2·75
f. Diagonal line by turret £160
g. Dot to left of chapel £225
2 50 c. slate and purple .. .. 5·25 9·00
f. Diagonal line by turret £225 £275
h. Dot by flagstaff £275 £300
9/82 .. .. *Set of* 4 9·75 12·00
9s/82s Perf "Specimen" .. *Set of* 4 90·00

For illustrations of plate varieties, see Omnibus section lowing Zanzibar.

37 (12 May). *Coronation. As Nos.* 95/7 *of Antigua. P* 11×11½.
3 6 c. carmine 65 15
4 9 c. green .. .. 2·50 3·25
5 20 c. blue .. .. 3·50 3·00
3/5 .. .. *Set of* 3 6·00 5·75
3s/5s Perf "Specimen" .. *Set of* 3 70·00

69 Tapping Rubber

70 Sigiriya (Lion Rock)

71 Ancient Guard-stone, Anuradhapura

72 King George VI

Apostrophe flaw (Frame Pl 1A R.6/6) (ptg of 1 Jan 1943 only)

(Recess B.W. (6, 10, 15, 20, 25, 30 c., 1 r., 2 r. (both)), D.L.R. (others)) T **72** typo D.L.R.)

1938–49. *T* **69/72** *and designs as* 1935–36, *but with portrait of King George VI instead of King George V,* "POSTAGE & REVENUE" *omitted and some redrawn. Wmk Mult Script CA (sideways on* 10, 15, 25, 30 *c. and* 1 *r.). Chalk-surfaced paper (*5 *r.). P* 11×11½ (6, 20 *c.*, 2 *r.* (*both*)), 11½×11 (10, 15, 25, 30 *c.*, 1 *r.*), 11½×13 (2 *c.*), 13×11½ (3, 50 *c.*), 13½ (5 *c.*) *or* 14 (5 *r.*).

386 **69** 2 c. black and carmine (25.4.38) .. 11·00 1·75
a. Perf 13½×13 (1938) .. .. £120 1·75
b. Perf 13½ (25.4.38) .. .. 2·00 10
c. Perf 11×11½ (17.2.44) 65 85
cw. Wmk inverted .. .. .. — £500
d. Perf 12 (22.4.49) .. .. 2·00 3·50
387 **60** 3 c. black and deep blue-green (21.3.38) 10·00 50
a. Perf 13×13½ (1938) .. .. £250 8·00
b. Perf 13½ (21.3.38) .. .. 4·00 10
c. Perf 14 (line) (7.41) £120 95
d. Perf 11½×11 (14.5.42) 80 10
da. "A" of "CA" missing from wmk .. £800 £800
dw. Wmk inverted .. .. .. † —
e. Perf 12 (14.1.46) 65 85
387*f* – 5 c. sage-green & orange (1.1.43) .. 30 10
fa. Apostrophe flaw .. .. .. 55·00
g. Perf 12 (1947) .. .. .. 1·25 30
388 – 6 c. black and blue (1.1.38) 30 10
389 **70** 10 c. black and light blue (1.2.38) .. 2·25 10
a. Wmk upright (1.6.44) .. .. 2·50 50
390 – 15 c. green and red-brown (1.1.38) .. 2·00 10
a. Wmk upright (23.7.45) .. .. 2·75 60
391 – 20 c. black and grey-blue (15.1.38) .. 3·25 10
392 – 25 c. deep blue and chocolate (15.1.38) 5·00 30
a. Wmk upright (1944) .. .. 4·25 10
393 – 30 c. carmine and green (1.2.38) .. 11·00 1·75
a. Wmk upright (16.4.45) .. .. 12·00 2·75
394 – 50 c. black and mauve (25.4.38) .. £160 42·00
a. Perf 13×13½ (25.4.38) .. .. £350 2·75
b. Perf 13½ (25.4.38) .. .. 17·00 30
c. Perf 14 (line) (4.42) .. .. £100 27·00
d. Perf 11½×11 (14.5.42) .. .. 4·25 3·25
e. Perf 12 (14.1.46) .. .. 3·75 20
395 – 1 r. blue-violet and chocolate (1.2.38) 16·00 1·25
a. Wmk upright (1944) .. .. 18·00 2·25
396 **71** 2 r. black and carmine (1.2.38) .. 13·00 2·50
a. "A" of "CA" missing from wmk ..
396*b* 2 r. black and violet (15.3.47) .. 2·00 1·60
397 **72** 5 r. green and purple (1.7.38) .. 38·00 4·50
a. Ordinary paper. *Green and pale purple* (19.2.43) .. .. 14·00 2·75
386/97a (*cheapest*) .. *Set of* 14 65·00 9·00
386s/97s Perf "Specimen" .. *Set of* 14 £300

Designs: *Vert*—5 c. Coconut palms; 6 c. Colombo Harbour; 20 c. Plucking tea. *Horiz*—15 c. River scene; 25 c. Temple of the Tooth, Kandy; 30 c. Ancient irrigation tank; 50 c. Wild elephants; 1 r. Trincomalee.

Printings of the 2 c., 3 c. and 50 c. perforated 11×11½ or 11½×11 were produced by Bradbury, Wilkinson after the De La Rue works had been bombed in December 1940.

3 CENTS

(73)

3 CENTS

(74)

1940–41. *Nos.* 388 *and* 391 *surch by Govt Ptg Office, Colombo.*
398 **73** 3 c. on 6 c. black and blue (10.5.41) .. 10 10
399 **74** 3 c. on 20 c. black and grey-blue (5.11.40) 2·00 1·50

1946 (10 Dec). *Victory. As Nos.* 110/11 *of Antigua.*
400 6 c. blue 10 10
401 15 c. brown 10 40
400s/1s Perf "Specimen" .. *Set of* 2 55·00

75 Parliament Building

76 Adam's Peak

(Des R. Tenison and M. S. V. Rodrigo. Recess B.W.)

1947 (25 Nov). *Inauguration of New Constitution. T* **75/6** *and similar designs. Wmk Mult Script CA. P* 11 × 12 (*horiz*) *or* 12 × 11 (*vert*).
402 6 c. black and blue 10 15
403 10 c. black, orange and carmine 15 20
404 15 c. green and purple 15 80
405 25 c. ochre and emerald-green 15 20
402/5 .. .. *Set of* 4 50 1·25
402s/5s Perf "Specimen" .. *Set of* 4 85·00

Designs: *Horiz*—15 c. Temple of the Tooth. *Vert*—25 c. Anuradhapura.

DOMINION

79 Lion Flag of Dominion

80 D. S. Senanayake

81 Lotus Flowers and Sinhalese Letters "Sri"

(Recess (flag typo) B.W.)

1949 (4 Feb–5 Apr). *First Anniv of Independence. (a) Wmk Mult Script CA (sideways on* 4 *c.). P* 12½×12 (4 *c.*) *or* 12×12½ (5 *c.*).
406 **79** 4 c. yellow, carmine and brown .. 15 20
407 **80** 5 c. brown and green 10 10

(*b*) *W* **81** (*sideways on* 15 *c.*). *P* 13 × 12½ (15 *c.*) *or* 12 × 12½ (25 *c.*) (5 April)
408 **79** 15 c. yellow, carmine and vermilion .. 30 15
409 **80** 25 c. brown and blue 15 65
406/9 .. .. *Set of* 4 50 1·00

The 15 c. is larger, measuring 28 × 12 mm.

82 Globe and Forms of Transport

83

84

(Recess D.L.R.)

1949 (10 Oct). *75th Anniv of Universal Postal Union. W* **81**. *P* 13 (25 *c.*) *or* 12 (*others*).
410 **82** 5 c. brown and bluish green 75 10
411 **83** 15 c. black and carmine .. .. 1·10 1·75
412 **84** 25 c. black and ultramarine .. .. 1·10 1·10
410/12 .. .. *Set of* 3 2·75 2·50

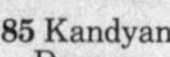
85 Kandyan Dancer

88 Sigiriya (Lion Rock)

89 Octagon Library, Temple of the Tooth

90 Ruins at Madirigiriya

(Recess B.W.)

1950 (4 Feb). *T* **85, 88/90** *and similar designs.* *W* **81.** *P* 11 × 11½ (75 *c.*), 11½ × 11 (1 *r.*), 12 × 12½ (*others*).

413	4 c. purple and scarlet	10	10
414	5 c. green	10	10
415	15 c. blue-green and violet	1·50	30
416	30 c. carmine and yellow	30	40
417	75 c. ultramarine and orange	3·50	10
418	1 r. deep blue and brown	1·75	30
413/18	.. .. *Set of* 6	6·50	1·00

Designs: *Vert* (*as T* **88**)—5 c. Kiri Vehera, Polonnaruwa; 15 c. Vesak Orchid.

For these values with redrawn inscriptions see Nos. 450/1, 454, 456, 460 and 462.

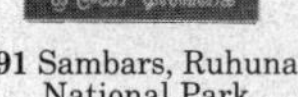
91 Sambars, Ruhuna National Park

92 Ancient Guard-stone, Anuradhapura

96 Star Orchid

97 Rubber Plantation

99 Tea Plantation

I. No. 424

II. No. 424a (Dot added)

(Photo Courvoisier)

1951 (1 Aug)–**54.** *T* **91/2, 96/7, 99** *and similar designs. No wmk.* *P* 11½.

419	2 c. brown and blue-green (15.5.54)	10	75
420	3 c. black and slate-violet (15.5.54)	10	75
421	6 c. brown-black & yellow-green (15.5.54) ..	10	30
422	10 c. green and blue-grey	75	65
423	25 c. orange-brown & bright blue (15.3.54) ..	10	20
424	35 c. red and deep green (I) (1.2.52)	1·50	1·50
	a. Type II (1954)	5·50	60
425	40 c. deep brown (15.5.54)	4·50	90
426	50 c. indigo and slate-grey (15.3.54)	30	10
427	85 c. black and deep blue-green (15.5.54) ..	50	10
428	2 r. blue and deep brown (15.5.54)	6·50	1·00
429	5 r. brown and orange (15.3.54)	4·75	1·25
430	10 r. red-brown and buff (15.3.54)	35·00	9·00
419/30	.. .. *Set of* 12	48·00	14·00

Designs: *Vert* (*as T* **91**)—6 c. Harvesting rice; 10 c. Coconut trees; 25 c. Sigiriya fresco. (*As T* **99**)—5 r. Bas-relief, Anuradhapura; 10 r. Harvesting rice. *Horiz* (*as T* **97**)—50 c. Outrigger canoe; (*as T* **99**)—2 r. River Gal Dam.

These values with redrawn inscriptions were issued in 1958–62, see Nos. 488, etc.

PRICES OF SETS

Set prices are given for many issues, generally those containing three stamps or more. Definitive sets include one of each value or major colour change, but do not cover different perforations, die types or minor shades. Where a choice is possible the set prices are based on the cheapest versions of the stamps included in the listings.

STAMP BOOKLETS

1905 (Oct). *Black on grey* (*No.* SB1) *or black on buff* (*No.* SB1*a*) *covers. Stapled.*

SB1	1 r. 21, booklet containing twenty-four 5 c. (No. 280) in blocks of 12	
SB1*a*	1 r. 45, booklet containing twenty-four 6 c. (No. 281) in blocks of 6	£2000

1908. *Black on grey cover. Advertisement on back cover. Stapled.*

SB2	1 r. 20, booklet containing twenty-four 5 c. (No. 289) in blocks of 12	

1912. *Black on grey cover. Advertisement on back cover. Stapled.*

SB2*a*	1 r. 20, booklet containing twenty-four 5 c. (No. 304) in blocks of 12	

1919. *Black on orange covers. Telegraph details on back cover. Stapled.*

SB3	1 r. 44, booklet containing twenty-four 6 c. (No. 311) in blocks of 6	
	a. Black on grey cover. Advertisement on back cover	
SB4	1 r. 44, booklet containing twenty-four 3 c. and twelve 6 c. (Nos. 310/11) in blocks of 6 ..	
	a. Advertisement on back cover	

1922. *Black on green covers. "Fiat" advertisement on back cover. Stapled.*

SB5	1 r. 44, booklet containing twenty-four 6 c. (No. 356) in blocks of 6	
SB6	1 r. 46, booklet containing twenty-four 3 c. and twelve 6 c. (Nos. 355/6) in blocks of 6 ..	
	a. Black on orange cover. "Colombo Jewelry Store" advertisement on back cover	

1926. *Black on green covers. Kennedy & Co.* (*No.* SB7) *or Fiat* (*No.* SB8) *advertisements on back cover. Stapled.*

SB7	2 r. 06, booklet containing twelve 3 c., 5 c. on 6 c. and 9 c. (Nos. 355, 362 and 357) in blocks of 6	£2500
SB8	2 r. 16, booklet containing twenty-four 9 c. (No. 357) in blocks of 6	

1932. *Black on green covers. Stapled.*

SB9	1 r. 80, booklet containing thirty 6 c. (No. 356) in blocks of 6 and pane of three airmail labels	£950
SB10	2 r. 70, booklet containing thirty 9 c. (No. 357) in blocks of 6 and pane of three airmail labels	

1935 (May). *Silver Jubilee of King George V. Black on light blue* (*No.* SB11) *or light green* (*No.* SB12) *covers. Stapled.*

SB11	1 r. 80, booklet containing thirty 6 c. (No. 379) in blocks of 6	£1000
SB12	2 r. 70, booklet containing thirty 9 c. (No. 380) in blocks of 6	£1300

1935 (Dec)–**36.** *Black on blue* (*No.* SB13) *or green* (*No.* SB14) *covers. Stapled.*

SB13	1 r. 80, booklet containing thirty 6 c. (No. 370) in blocks of 6 and pane of four airmail labels	
	a. Stamps in blocks of 10	£650
SB14	2 r. 70, booklet containing thirty 9 c. (No. 371) in blocks of 6 and pane of four airmail labels	£750
	a. Stamps in blocks of 10 (1936)	£750

1937 (Apr–June). *Coronation of King George VI. Black on blue* (*No.* SB15) *or olive-green* (*No.* SB16) *covers. Stapled.*

SB15	1 r. 80, booklet containing thirty 6 c. (No. 383) in blocks of 10 and pane of four airmail labels (June)	£800
SB16	2 r. 70, booklet containing thirty 9 c. (No. 384) in blocks of 10 and pane of four airmail labels	£850

1938. *Black on blue* (*No.* SB17) *or grey* (*No.* SB18) *covers. Stapled.*

SB17	1 r. 80, booklet containing thirty 6 c. (No. 388) in blocks of 10 and pane of four airmail labels	
SB18	3 r. booklet containing fifteen 20 c. (No. 391) in blocks of 5 or 10 and pane of four airmail labels	£950

1941. *Black on pink cover, with contents amended in manuscript. Stapled.*

SB19	1 r. 80, booklet containing sixty 3 c. on 6 c. (No. 398) in blocks of 10	
	a. Black on blue cover	

1951 (5 Dec). *Black on buff cover. Stitched.*

SB20	1 r. booklet containing twenty 5 c. (No. 414) in blocks of four and pane of airmail labels ..	12·00
	a. Containing two blocks of ten 5 c. stamps and no airmail labels	45·00

1952 (21 Jan). *Black on green cover. Stitched.*

SB21	6 r. booklet containing eight 75 c. (No. 417) in blocks of 4 and two panes of four airmail labels	18·00

OFFICIAL STAMPS

1869. *Issues of* 1867–68 *overprinted* "SERVICE" *in block letters.*
Although these stamps were prepared for use and sent out to the colony, they were never issued.

Prices:

Narrow "SERVICE"		Wide "SERVICE"	
No. 64*d*, 2d. ..	65·00	No. 61, 1d. ..	65·00
67, 6d. ..	65·00	62, 3d. ..	£110
68, 8d. ..	70·00		
71, 1s. ..	£130		
72*b*, 2s. ..	£120		
72*b*, 2s. *imp* ..	£800		

Until 1 October 1895 all Official mail was carried free. After that date postage was paid on Official letters to the general public, on certain interdepartmental mail and on all packets over 1lb in weight. Nos. O1/17 were provided for ths purpose.

On

Service

(O 3)

1895. *Optd with Type* O **3** *by the Govt Printer, Colombo.*

O1	**9**	2 c. green (No. 147)	8·00	
O2	**39**	3 c. terracotta and blue-green (No. 245)	10·00	
O3	**28**	5 c. dull purple (No. 195)	3·25	
O4	**29**	15 c. sage-green (No. 196)	12·00	
O5		25 c. yellow-brown (No. 198)	10·00	
O6		30 c. bright mauve and chestnut (No. 247)	13·00	
O7	**30**	1 r. 12, dull rose (*wmk sideways*) (No. 201)	70·00	5
		a. Opt double, one albino	£225	
		b. Wmk upright	85·00	7
O1/7		.. .. *Set of* 7	£110	5

1899 (June)–**1900.** *Nos.* 256/7 *and* 261/2 *optd with Type* C

O 8	**9**	2 c. pale orange-brown (3.00)	7·00	
O 9	**39**	3 c. deep green (9.00)	8·00	
O10	**29**	15 c. blue (9.00)	16·00	
O11	**39**	75 c. black and red-brown (R.)	5·50	
O8/11		.. .. *Set of* 4	32·00	

1903 (26 Nov)–**04.** *Nos.* 265/6, 268 *and* 271/3 *optd with* T O **3.**

O12	**44**	2 c. red-brown (4.1.04)	12·00	
O13	**45**	3 c. green	7·00	
O14	**46**	5 c. dull purple	18·00	
O15	**48**	15 c. blue	27·00	
O16		25 c. bistre (15.7.04)	21·00	1
O17		30 c. dull violet and green (14.3.04) ..	11·00	
O12/17		.. .. *Set of* 6	85·00	2

Stamps overprinted "On Service" were withdrawn o October 1904.

POSTAL FISCALS

1952 (1 Dec). *As T* **72** *but inscr* "REVENUE" *at si Chalk-surfaced paper.*

F1	10 r. dull green and yellow-orange	60·00 2

This revenue stamp was on sale for postal use from 1 Decem 1952, until 14 March 1954.

Cook Islands
see after New Zealand

Cyprus

prus was part of the Turkish Ottoman Empire from 1571. e first records of an organised postal service date from 1871 a post office was opened at Nicosia (Lefkosa) under the juris- n of the Damascus Head Post Office. Various stamps of ey from the 1868 issue onwards are known used from this , cancelled "KIBRIS", in Arabic, within a double-lined oblong. ascript cancellations have also been reported. The records t the opening of a further office at Larnaca (Tuzla) in 1873, but ncellation for this office has been identified.

provide an overseas postal service the Austrian Empire ed a post office in Larnaca during 1845. Stamps of the rian Post Offices in the Turkish Empire were placed on sale from 1 June 1864 and were cancelled with an unframed ght-line mark or circular date stamp. This Austrian post closed on 6 August 1878.

BRITISH ADMINISTRATION

llowing the convention with Turkey, Great Britain med the administration of Cyprus on 11 July 1878 and the post office, as part of the British G.P.O. system, was opened arnaca on 27 July 1878. Further offices as Famagusta, enia, Limassol, Nicosia and Paphos followed in September 8.

he stamps of Great Britain were supplied to the various es as they opened and continued to be used until the Cyprus ninistration assumed responsibility for the postal service on pril 1880. With the exception of "969" (Nicosia) similar neral cancellations had previously been used at offices in at Britain.

umeral postmarks for Headquarters Camp, Nicosia ("D48") Polymedia (Polemidhia) Camp, Limassol ("D47") were plied by the G.P.O. in London during January 1881. These cellations had three bars above and three bars below the neral. Similar marks, but with four bars above and below, previously been used in London on newspapers and bulk l.

lthough both three bar cancellations subsequently occur on rus issues only isolated examples have been found on loose at Britain stamps and there are no known covers or pieces ch confirm such usage in Cyprus.

or illustrations of the postmark types see BRITISH POST FICES ABROAD notes, following GREAT BRITAIN.

FAMAGUSTA

mps of GREAT BRITAIN *cancelled* "982" *as Type* **9**

'8 *to* 1880.

½d. rose-red (1870–79) (Plate Nos. 11, 13) .. £700
1d. rose-red (1864–79) £475
Plate Nos. 145, 174, 181, 193, 202, 204, 206, 215, 217.
2d. blue (1858–69) (Plate Nos. 13, 14, 15) .. £950
2½d. rosy mauve (1876) (Plate Nos. 13, 16) .. £1100
6d. grey (1874–80) (Plate No. 15)
1s. green (1873–77) (Plate No. 12) £1900

KYRENIA

mps of GREAT BRITAIN *cancelled* "974" *as Type* **9**

78 *to* 1880.

8 ½d. rose-red (1870–79) (Plate No. 13)
9 1d. rose-red (1864–79) .. .. *From* £550
Plate Nos. 168, 171, 193, 196, 206, 207, 209, 220.
0 2d. blue (1858–69) (Plate Nos. 13, 15) *From* £850
1 2½d. rosy mauve (1876–79) .. *From* £1000
Plate Nos. 12, 13, 14, 15.
2 4d. sage-green (1877) (Plate No. 16)
3 6d. grey (1874–80) (Plate No. 16)

LARNACA

amps of GREAT BRITAIN *cancelled* "942" *as Type* **9**

78 *to* 1880.

4 ½d. rose-red (1870–79) .. .. *From* £250
Plate Nos. 11, 12, 13, 14, 15, 19, 20.
5 1d. rose-red (1864–79) .. .. *From* £170
Plate Nos. 129, 131, 146, 154, 170, 171, 174, 175, 176, 177, 178, 179, 181, 182, 183, 184, 187, 188, 190, 191, 192, 193, 194, 195, 196, 197, 198, 199, 200, 201, 202, 203, 204, 205, 206, 207, 208, 209, 210, 212, 213, 214, 215, 216, 217, 218, 220, 221, 222, 225.
6 1½d. lake-red (1870) (Plate No. 3) .. £1700
7 2d. blue (1858–69) (Plate Nos. 9, 13, 14, 15) .. £225
8 2½d. rosy mauve (1876–79) .. *From* 50·00
Plate Nos. 4, 5, 6, 8, 9, 10, 11, 12, 13, 14, 15, 16, 17.
9 2½d. blue (1880) (Plate Nos. 17, 18) .. £500
21 4d. sage-green (1877) (Plate Nos. 15, 16) .. £550
22 6d. grey (1874–76) (Plate Nos. 15, 16, 17) .. £500
23 6d. pale buff (1872–73) (Plate No. 11) .. £1900
24 8d. orange (1876) £4250
25 1s. green (1873–77) (Plate Nos. 12, 13) .. £900
27 5s. rose (1874) (Plate No. 2) £4500

LIMASSOL

Stamps of GREAT BRITAIN *cancelled* "975" *as Type* **9**

1878 *to* 1880.

Z28 ½d. rose-red (1870–79) (Plate Nos. 11, 13, 15, 19) £450
Z29 1d. rose-red (1864–79) .. .. .. *From* £275
Plate Nos. 159, 160, 171, 173, 174, 177, 179, 184, 187, 190, 193, 195, 196, 197, 198, 200, 202, 206, 207, 208, 209, 210, 213, 215, 216, 218, 220, 221, 222, 225
Z30 1½d. lake-red (1870–74) (Plate No. 3) .. £1800
Z31 2d. blue (1858–69) (Plate Nos. 14, 15) .. *From* £400
Z32 2½d. rosy-mauve (1876–80) .. .. *From* £160
Plate Nos. 11, 12, 13, 14, 15, 16.
Z33 2½d. blue (1880) (Plate No. 17) £1200
Z34 4d. sage-green (Plate No. 16) £700

NICOSIA

Stamps of GREAT BRITAIN *cancelled* "969" *as Type* **9**

1878 *to* 1880.

Z35 ½d. rose-red (1870–79) £450
Plate Nos. 12, 13, 14, 15, 20.
Z36 1d. rose-red (1864–79) .. .. *From* £275
Plate Nos. 170, 171, 174, 189, 190, 192, 193, 195, 196, 198, 200, 202, 203, 205, 206, 207, 210, 212, 214, 215, 218, 221, 222, 225.
Z37 2d. blue (1858–69) (Plate Nos. 14, 15) .. £450
Z38 2½d. rosy mauve (1876–79) .. *From* £170
Plate Nos. 10, 11, 12, 13, 14, 15, 16.
Z42 4d. sage-green (1877) (Plate No. 16) .. £800
Z43 6d. grey (1873) (Plate No. 16) £800

PAPHOS

Stamps of GREAT BRITAIN *cancelled* "981" *as Type* **9**

1878 *to* 1880.

Z44 ½d. rose-red (1870–79) (Plate Nos. 13, 15) ..
Z45 1d. rose-red (1864–79) .. .. *From* £500
Plate Nos. 196, 201, 202, 204, 206, 213, 217.
Z46 2d. blue (1858–69) (Plate No. 15) .. £850
Z47 2½d. rosy mauve (1876–79) .. *From* £500
Plate Nos. 13, 14, 15, 16.

PRICES FOR STAMPS ON COVER TO 1945

No. 1	*from* × 10
No. 2	*from* × 50
No. 3	*from* × 100
No. 4	*from* × 8
Nos. 5/6	—
Nos. 7/10	*from* × 15
Nos. 11/15	*from* × 5
No. 16	—
Nos. 16*a*/24	*from* × 10
No. 25	*from* × 40
No. 26	—
No. 27	*from* × 10
No. 28	—
No. 29	*from* × 30
Nos. 31/5*a*	*from* × 10
Nos. 36/7	—
Nos. 40/9	*from* × 8
Nos. 50/71	*from* × 5
Nos. 74/99	*from* × 4
Nos. 100/2	—
Nos. 103/17	*from* × 4
No. 117*a*	—
Nos. 118/31	*from* × 5
No. 132	—
Nos. 133/43	*from* × 5
Nos. 144/7	*from* × 6
Nos. 148/63	*from* × 5

PERFORATION. Nos. 1/122 are perf 14.

Stamps of Great Britain overprinted

CYPRUS (1) CYPRUS (2)

(Optd by D.L.R.)

1880 (1 Apr).

1 1 ½d. rose £100 £100
a. Opt double (Plate 15) .. .. †£12000

Plate No.	*Un.*	*Used.*	*Plate No.*	*Un.*	*Used*
12. ..	£170	£250	19. ..	£5000	£700
15. ..	£100	£100			

2 2 1d. red .. .. 9·50 29·00
a. Opt double (Plate 208) .. £14000
aa. Opt double (Plate 218) .. £4250
b. Vert pair, top stamp without opt (Plate 208) £16000

174. ..	£1200	£1200	208. ..	90·00	55·00
181. ..	£325	£170	215. ..	11·00	45·00
184. ..	£12000	£2250	216. ..	15·00	30·00
193. ..	£650	†	217. ..	10·00	48·00
196. ..	£550	†	218. ..	16·00	48·00
201. ..	10·00	48·00	220. ..	£350	£375
205. ..	48·00	48·00			

3 2 2½d. rosy mauve .. .. .. 2·25 7·50
a. Large thin "C" (Plate 14) (BK, JK) 40·00 £160
b. Large thin "C" (Plate 15) (BK, JK) 65·00 £375
w. Wmk inverted (Plate 15) £275

14. ..	2·25	7·50	15. ..	3·25	22·00

4 2 4d. sage-green (Plate 16) .. £120 £200
5 6d. grey (Plate 16) £500 £650
6 1s. green (Plate 13) £650 £450

No. 3 has been reported from Plate 9.

HALF-PENNY (3) 18 mm HALF-PENNY (4) 16 or 16½ mm

HALF-PENNY (5) 13 mm 30 PARAS (6)

(Optd by Govt Ptg Office, Nicosia)

1881 (Feb–June). *No. 2 surch.*

7 3 ½d. on 1d. red (Feb) .. .. .. 70·00 85·00
a. "HALFPENN" (BG, LG) (*all plates*) .. .. .. *From* £1700 £1700

Plate No.	*Un.*	*Used.*	*Plate No.*	*Un.*	*Used.*
174. ..	£150	£300	215. ..	£600	£650
181. ..	£140	£160	216. ..	70·00	85·00
201. ..	85·00	£110	217. ..	£750	£650
205. ..	70·00	85·00	218. ..	£425	£550
208. ..	£160	£275	220. ..	£250	£300

8 4 ½d. on 1d. red (Apr) £120 £160
a. Surch double (Plates 201 and 216) £2500 £2500

201. ..	£120	£160	218. ..	—	—
216. ..	£350	£400			

9 5 ½d. on 1d. red (1 June) .. .. 45·00 65·00
aa. Surch double (Plate 205) £650
ab. Surch double (Plate 215) £450 £550
b. Surch treble (Plate 205) £3000
ba. Surch treble (Plate 215) £650
bc. Surch treble (Plate 218) £3000
c. Surch quadruple (Plate 205) .. £3750
ca. Surch quadruple (Plate 215) .. £3750

205. ..	£225	—	217. ..	£120	75·00
215. ..	45·00	65·00	218. ..	65·00	90·00

The surcharge on No. 8 was handstamped; the others were applied by lithography.

(New Currency: 40 paras = 1 piastre, 180 piastres = £1)

1881 (June). *No. 2 surch with T* **6** *by lithography.*

10 6 30 paras on 1d. red .. .. .. £100 80·00
a. Surch double, one invtd (Plate 216) £3250
aa. Surch double, one invtd (Plate 220) £1300 £1000

201. ..	£120	85·00	217. ..	£170	£160
216. ..	£100	80·00	220. ..	£150	£160

7

"US" damaged at foot (Left pane R. 5/5)

(Typo D.L.R.)

1881 (1 July). *Die I. Wmk Crown CC.*

11 7 ½ pi. emerald-green .. .. .. £180 42·00
w. Wmk inverted £475 £275
12 1 pi. rose .. .. £375 30·00
13 2 pi. blue .. .. £450 30·00
w. Wmk inverted .. .. .. — £475
14 4 pi. pale olive-green £900 £275
15 6 pi. olive-grey £1400 £425

Stamps of Queen Victoria initialled "J.A.B." or overprinted "POSTAL SURCHARGE" with or without the same initials were employed for accounting purposes between the Chief Post Office and sub-offices, the initials are those of the then Postmaster, Mr. J. A. Bulmer.

1882 (May)–**86.** *Die I*. Wmk Crown CA.*

16 7 ½ pi. emerald-green (5.82) £5000 £400
a. Dull green (4.83) .. .. 14·00 1·00
ab. Top left triangle detached .. — £130
17 30 pa. pale mauve (7.6.82) .. .. 60·00 18·00
a. Top left triangle detached .. £700 £300
b. Damaged "US" £600 £300
18 1 pi. rose (3.83) .. .. .. 80·00 1·75
a. Top left triangle detached .. — £150
19 2 pi. blue (4.83) .. .. .. £110 1·75
a. Top left triangle detached .. — £150
20 4 pi. deep olive-green (10.83) .. £500 30·00
a. Pale olive-green .. .. £350 23·00
ab. Top left triangle detached .. — £425
21 6 pi. olive-grey (7.82) .. .. 42·00 17·00
a. Top left triangle detached .. — £350
22 12 pi. orange-brown (1886) .. .. £170 35·00
a. Top left triangle detached .. — £550
s. Optd "Specimen" £650
16*a*/22 .. .. .. *Set of* 7 £750 85·00

*For description and illustrations of Dies I and II see Introduction.

For illustration of "top left triangle detached" variety see above No. 21 of Antigua.

See also Nos. 31/7.

½ ½ (8) 30 PARAS (9)

Spur on "1" (position 3 in setting)

(Surch litho by Govt Ptg Office, Nicosia)

1882. *Surch with T* **8/9**. (*a*) *Wmk Crown CC.*
23 **7** ½ on ½ pi. emerald-green (6.82) .. £500 75·00
c. Spur on "1" .. £700 £110
w. Wmk inverted
24 30 pa. on 1 pi. rose (22.5.82) .. £1400 £100

(*b*) *Wmk Crown CA*
25 **7** ½ on ½ pi. emerald-green (27.5.82) .. £120 6·50
a. Surch double .. † £2750
b. "½" inserted by hand .. † —
c. Spur on "1" .. £180 12·00

Nos. 23 and 25 were surcharged by a setting of 6 arranged as a horizontal row.

No. 25b shows an additional handstamped "½" applied to examples on which the surcharge was so misplaced as to almost omit one of the original "½s".

1/2 1/2
(10)

11

Varieties of numerals:

1 Normal — 1 Large — 1 Small

2 Normal — 2 Large

1886 (Apr). *Surch with T* **10** (*fractions approx 6 mm apart*) *in typography.*

(*a*) *Wmk Crown CC*
26 **7** ½ on ½ pi. emerald-green .. £15000

(*b*) *Wmk Crown CA*
27 **7** ½ on ½ pi. emerald-green .. £225 70·00
a. Large "2" at right .. £2000 £750

1886 (May–June). *Surch with T* **10** (*fractions approx 8 mm apart*) *in typography.*

(*a*) *Wmk Crown CC*
28 **7** ½ on ½ pi. emerald-green .. £7000 £425
a. Large "1" at left .. — £1700
b. Small "1" at right .. £13000 £2250
c. Large "2" at left .. — £2250
d. Large "2" at right .. † £2250

(*b*) *Wmk Crown CA*
29 **7** ½ on ½ pi. emerald-green (June) .. £325 9·00
a. Large "1" at left .. £2250 £200
b. Small "1" at right .. £2750 £275
c. Large "2" at left .. £2500 £275
d. Large "2" at right .. £2500 £275

Nos. 28/9 were surcharged in a setting of 60. The large "1" at left and large "2" at right both occur in the fourth vertical row, the large "2" at left in the fifth vertical row and the small "1" at right in the top horizontal row.

A third type of this surcharge is known with the fractions spaced approximately 10 mm apart on CA paper with postmarks from August 1886. This may be due to the shifting of type.

1892–94. *Die II. Wmk Crown CA.*
31 **7** ½ pi. dull green .. 4·00 70
32 30 pa. mauve .. 4·25 4·25
a. Damaged "US" .. £140
33 1 pi. carmine .. 10·00 1·50
34 2 pi. ultramarine .. 14·00 1·75
35 4 pi. olive-green .. 50·00 28·00
a. Pale olive-green .. 18·00 23·00
36 6 pi. olive-grey (1894) .. £140 £500
37 12 pi. orange-brown (1893) .. £120 £325
31/7 .. *Set of* 7 £275 £750

1894 (14 Aug)–**96.** *Colours changed and new values. Die II. Wmk Crown CA.*
40 **7** ½ pi. green and carmine (1896) .. 4·00 1·25
w. Wmk inverted
41 30 pa. bright mauve and green (1896) .. 2·00 1·25
a. Damaged "US" .. £100
42 1 pi. carmine and blue (1896) .. 5·00 1·25
43 2 pi. blue and purple (1896) .. 6·00 1·25
44 4 pi. sage-green and purple (1896) .. 14·00 4·25
45 6 pi. sepia and green (1896) .. 11·00 13·00
46 9 pi. brown and carmine .. 15·00 16·00
47 12 pi. orange-brown and black (1896) .. 16·00 50·00
48 18 pi. greyish slate and brown .. 45·00 45·00
49 45 pi. grey-purple and blue .. 90·00 £130
40/9 .. *Set of* 10 £180 £225
40s/9s Optd "Specimen" .. *Set of* 10 £300

LIMASSOL FLOOD HANDSTAMP. Following a flood on 14 November 1894, which destroyed the local stamp stocks, the postmaster of Limassol produced a temporary handstamp showing "½C.P." which was applied to local letters with the usual c.d.s.

(Typo D.L.R.)

1902–04. *Wmk Crown CA.*
50 **11** ½ pi. green and carmine (12.02) .. 3·75 1·25
w. Wmk inverted .. 65·00 42·00
51 30 pa. violet and green (2.03) .. 6·00 2·75
a. Mauve and green .. 15·00 6·50
b. Damaged "US" .. — £110
52 1 pi. carmine and blue (9.03) .. 15·00 3·00
53 2 pi. blue and purple (2.03) .. 50·00 9·00
54 4 pi. olive-green and purple (9.03) .. 28·00 19·00
55 6 pi. sepia and green (9.03) .. 40·00 £110
56 9 pi. brown and carmine (5.04) .. 95·00 £190
57 **11** 12 pi. chestnut and black (4.03) .. 13·00 50·00
58 18 pi. black and brown (5.04) .. 70·00 £140
59 45 pi. dull purple and ultramarine (10.03) £200 £500
50/9 .. *Set of* 10 £450 £900
50sw/9s Optd "Specimen" .. *Set of* 10 £450

The ½ pi "SPECIMEN" is only known with watermark inverted.

Broken top left triangle (Left pane R.7/5)

1904–10. *Wmk Mult Crown CA.*
60 **11** 5 pa. bistre and black (14.1.08) .. 1·00 70
a. Broken top left triangle .. 45·00 45·00
w. Wmk inverted .. £800
61 10 pa. orange and green (12.06) .. 3·00 50
aw. Wmk inverted .. — 70·00
b. Yellow and green .. 35·00 5·50
bw. Wmk inverted .. — 80·00
c. Broken top left triangle .. 60·00 38·00
62 ½ pi. green and carmine (1.7.04) .. 4·25 20
a. Broken top left triangle .. 80·00 27·00
w. Wmk inverted .. 85·00 55·00
63 30 pa. purple and green (1.7.04) .. 13·00 1·50
a. Violet and green (1910) .. 15·00 2·50
b. Broken top left triangle .. £150 55·00
c. Damaged "US" .. £150 55·00
w. Wmk inverted .. † £650
64 1 pi. carmine and blue (11.04) .. 4·00 1·00
a. Broken top left triangle .. 90·00 48·00
65 2 pi. blue and purple (11.04) .. 5·50 1·75
a. Broken top left triangle .. £120 65·00
66 4 pi. olive-green and purple (2.05) .. 10·00 7·00
a. Broken top left triangle .. £170 £150
67 6 pi. sepia and green (17.7.04) .. 12·00 14·00
a. Broken top left triangle .. £170
68 9 pi. brown and carmine (30.5.04) .. 28·00 8·50
a. Yellow-brown and carmine .. 25·00 21·00
aw. Wmk inverted .. £110 70·00
b. Broken top left triangle .. £275 £190
69 12 pi. chestnut and black (4.06) .. 23·00 35·00
a. Broken top left triangle .. £275
70 18 pi. black and brown (16.6.04) .. 30·00 11·00
a. Broken top left triangle .. £350 £250
71 45 pi. dull purple and ultram (15.6.04) .. 75·00 £140
a. Broken top left triangle .. £600
60/71 .. *Set of* 12 £180 £200
60s/1s Optd "Specimen" .. *Set of* 2 £120

12

13

Broken bottom left triangle (Right pane R.10/6)

(Typo D.L.R.)

1912 (July)–**15.** *Wmk Mult Crown CA.*
74 **12** 10 pa. orange and green (11.12) .. 3·00 2·50
a. Wmk sideways .. † £2000
b. Orange-yellow & brt green (8.15) .. 2·25 1·25
ba. Broken bottom left triangle .. 60·00 40·00
75 ½ pi. green and carmine .. 1·75 20
a. Yellow-green and carmine .. 7·50 1·90
ab. Broken bottom left triangle .. 80·00 50·00
w. Wmk inverted .. † £750
76 30 pa. violet and green (3.13) .. 2·50 60
a. Broken bottom left triangle .. 60·00 40·00
w. Wmk inverted
77 1 pi. rose-red and blue (9.12) .. 3·75 1·75
a. Carmine and blue (1.15?) .. 13·00 4·25
ab. Broken bottom left triangle .. £120 60·00
78 2 pi. blue and purple (7.13) .. 6·50 2·00
a. Broken bottom left triangle .. 95·00 50·00
79 4 pi. olive-green and purple .. 4·25 4·50
a. Broken bottom left triangle .. 75·00 85·00
80 6 pi. sepia and green .. 3·50 8·50
a. Broken bottom left triangle .. 75·00
81 9 pi. brown and carmine (3.15) .. 23·00 26·00
a. Yellow-brown and carmine .. 25·00 27·00
b. Broken bottom left triangle .. £250
82 12 pi. chestnut and black (7.13) .. 13·00 30·00
b. Broken bottom left triangle .. £170
83 18 pi. black and brown (3.15) .. 24·00 28·00
a. Broken bottom left triangle .. £225
84 45 pi. dull purple and ultramarine (3.15) 70·00 £120
a. Broken bottom left triangle .. £475
74/84 .. *Set of* 11 £140 £200
74s/84s Optd "Specimen" .. *Set of* 11 £350

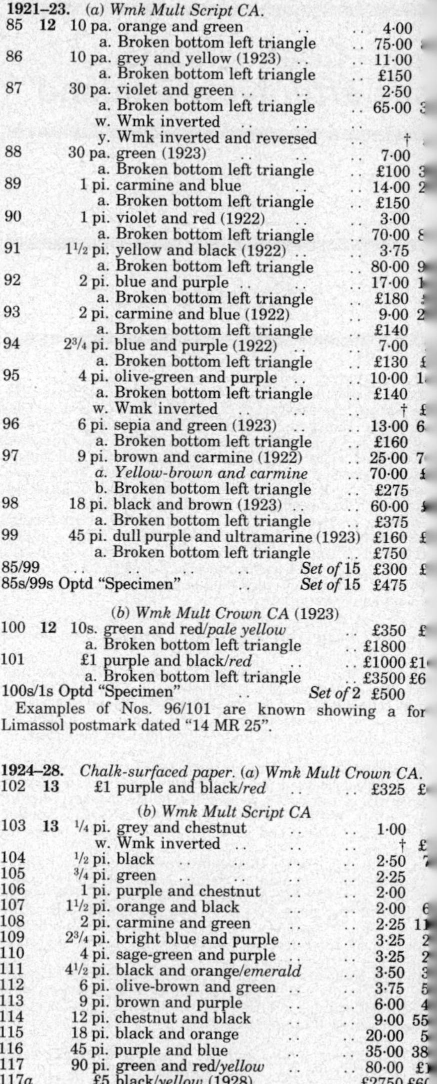

1921–23. (*a*) *Wmk Mult Script CA.*
85 **12** 10 pa. orange and green .. 4·00
a. Broken bottom left triangle .. 75·00
86 10 pa. grey and yellow (1923) .. 11·00
a. Broken bottom left triangle .. £150
87 30 pa. violet and green .. 2·50
a. Broken bottom left triangle .. 65·00
w. Wmk inverted
y. Wmk inverted and reversed .. †
88 30 pa. green (1923) .. 7·00
a. Broken bottom left triangle .. £100
89 1 pi. carmine and blue .. 14·00
a. Broken bottom left triangle .. £150
90 1 pi. violet and red (1922) .. 3·00
a. Broken bottom left triangle .. 70·00
91 1½ pi. yellow and black (1922) .. 3·75
a. Broken bottom left triangle .. 80·00
92 2 pi. blue and purple .. 17·00
a. Broken bottom left triangle .. £180
93 2 pi. carmine and blue (1922) .. 9·00
a. Broken bottom left triangle .. £140
94 2¾ pi. blue and purple (1922) .. 7·00
a. Broken bottom left triangle .. £130
95 4 pi. olive-green and purple .. 10·00
a. Broken bottom left triangle .. £140
w. Wmk inverted .. †
96 6 pi. sepia and green (1923) .. 13·00
a. Broken bottom left triangle .. £160
97 9 pi. brown and carmine (1922) .. 25·00
a. Yellow-brown and carmine .. 70·00
b. Broken bottom left triangle .. £275
98 18 pi. black and brown (1923) .. 60·00
a. Broken bottom left triangle .. £375
99 45 pi. dull purple and ultramarine (1923) £160
a. Broken bottom left triangle .. £750
85/99 .. *Set of* 15 £300
85s/99s Optd "Specimen" .. *Set of* 15 £475

(*b*) *Wmk Mult Crown CA* (1923)
100 **12** 10s. green and red/*pale yellow* .. £350
a. Broken bottom left triangle .. £1800
101 £1 purple and black/*red* .. £1000
a. Broken bottom left triangle .. £3500
100s/1s Optd "Specimen" .. *Set of* 2 £500

Examples of Nos. 96/101 are known showing a for[ged] Limassol postmark dated "14 MR 25".

1924–28. *Chalk-surfaced paper.* (*a*) *Wmk Mult Crown CA.*
102 **13** £1 purple and black/*red* .. £325

(*b*) *Wmk Mult Script CA*
103 **13** ¼ pi. grey and chestnut .. 1·00
w. Wmk inverted .. †
104 ½ pi. black .. 2·50
105 ¾ pi. green .. 2·25
106 1 pi. purple and chestnut .. 2·00
107 1½ pi. orange and black .. 2·00
108 2 pi. carmine and green .. 2·25
109 2¾ pi. bright blue and purple .. 3·25
110 4 pi. sage-green and purple .. 3·25
111 4½ pi. black and orange/*emerald* .. 3·50
112 6 pi. olive-brown and green .. 3·75
113 9 pi. brown and purple .. 6·00
114 12 pi. chestnut and black .. 9·00
115 18 pi. black and orange .. 20·00
116 45 pi. purple and blue .. 35·00
117 90 pi. green and red/*yellow* .. 80·00
117*a* £5 black/*yellow* (1928) .. £2750
as. Optd "Specimen" .. £900

Examples of No. 102 are known showing a forged Limas[sol] postmark dated "14 MR 25" and of No. 117*a* showing a forg[ed] Registered Nicosia postmark dated "6 MAY 35".

CROWN COLONY

1925. *Wmk Mult Script CA. Chalk-surfaced paper* (½, ¾ *a*[*nd*] 2 *pi.*)
118 **13** ½ pi. green .. 2·25
119 ¾ pi. brownish black .. 1·75
120 1½ pi. scarlet .. 2·50
121 2 pi. yellow and black .. 5·50
122 2½ pi. bright blue .. 2·75
102/22 (*ex* £5) .. *Set of* 21 £400
102s/22s (*ex* £5) Optd "Specimen" .. *Set of* 21 £600

In the above set the fraction bar in the value is horizontal. In N[os.] 91, 94, 107 and 109 it is diagonal.

14 Silver Coin of Amathus, 6th-cent B.C.

16 Map of Cyprus

(Recess B.W.)

1928 (1 Feb). 50*th Anniv of British Rule. T* **14**, **16** *and simil*[*ar*] *designs. Wmk Mult Script CA. P* 12.
123 ¾ pi. deep dull purple .. 2·75
124 1 pi. black and greenish blue .. 3·00
125 1½ pi. scarlet .. 4·50
126 2½ pi. light blue .. 3·50
127 4 pi. deep brown .. 5·00
128 6 pi. blue .. 6·50
129 9 pi. maroon .. 7·50
130 18 pi. black and brown .. 17·00
131 45 pi. violet and blue .. 35·00
132 £1 blue and bistre-brown .. £200
123/32 .. *Set of* 10 £250
123s/32s Optd "Specimen" .. *Set of* 10 £500

Designs: *Vert*—1 pi. Zeno (philosopher); 2½ pi. Discovery of bod[y] of St Barnabas; 4 pi. Cloister, Abbey of Bella Paise; 9 pi. Tekke o[f] Umm Haram; 18 pi. Statue of Richard I, Westminster; 45 pi. St. Nicholas Cathedral, Famagusta (now Lala Mustafa Pasha Mosque); £1 King George V. *Horiz*—6 pi. Badge of Cyprus.

24 Ruins of Vouni Palace

25 Small Marble Forum, Salamis

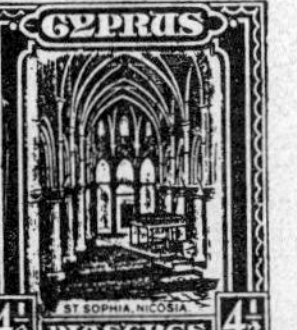

30 St. Sophia Cathedral, Nicosia (now Selimiye Mosque)

31 Bayraktar Mosque, Nicosia

(Recess Waterlow)

(1 Dec). *T* **24/5, 30/1** *and similar designs. Wmk Mult* ·ipt *CA (sideways on* ½ *pi.,* 1½ *pi.,* 2½ *pi.,* 4½ *pi.,* 6 *pi.,* ·i. *and* 18 *pi.). P* 12½.

¼ pi. ultramarine and orange-brown .. 1·00 50
a. Imperf between (vert pair) .. £21000 £16000
½ pi. green .. .. 1·25 1·00
a. Imperf between (vert pair) .. £11000 £12000
¾ pi. black and violet .. .. .. 1·00 10
a. Imperf between (vert pair) .. £23000
1 pi. black and red-brown .. .. 1·00 80
a. Imperf between (vert pair) .. £13000 £13000
b. Imperf between (horiz pair) .. £10000
1½ pi. carmine .. .. 1·50 55
2½ pi. ultramarine .. .. .. 1·50 1·75
4½ pi. black and crimson .. .. 3·00 3·50
6 pi. black and blue .. .. .. 8·50 12·00
9 pi. sepia and violet .. .. .. 6·50 4·25
18 pi. black and olive-green .. .. 40·00 27·00
45 pi. green and black .. .. .. 65·00 48·00
43 .. .. *Set of* 11 £110 90·00
·/43s Perf "Specimen" .. *Set of* 11 £275

·esigns: *Horiz.*—¾ pi. Church of St. Barnabas and St. ·rion, Peristerona; 1 pi. Roman theatre, Soli; 1½ pi. Kyrenia ·bour; 2½ pi. Kolossi Castle; 45 pi. Forest scene, Troodos. ·—9 pi. Queen's Window, St. Hilarion Castle; 18 pi. Buyuk ·n, Nicosia.

·5 (6 May). *Silver Jubilee. As Nos.* 91/4 *of Antigua, but ptd by* ·*aterlow & Sons. P* 11 × 12.

¾ pi. ultramarine and grey .. .. 1·75 40
1½ pi. deep blue and scarlet .. .. 3·50 2·50
l. Kite and horizontal log £190
2½ pi. brown and deep blue .. .. 3·75 1·50
9 pi. slate and purple .. .. .. 13·00 12·00
·/7 .. .. *Set of* 4 20·00 15·00
·s/7s Perf "Specimen" .. .. *Set of* 4 £130

·or illustration of plate variety see Omnibus section following ·zibar.

·7 (12 May). *Coronation. As Nos.* 95/7 *of Antigua.* · 11×11½.

¾ pi. grey 60 20
1½ pi. carmine 90 80
2½ pi. blue .. .. 2·00 1·25
·/50 .. .. *Set of* 3 3·25 2·00
·s/50s Perf "Specimen" .. *Set of* 3 £100

35 Vouni Palace

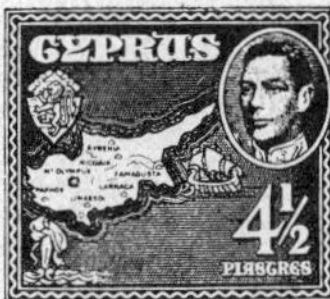

36 Map of Cyprus

37 Othello's Tower, Famagusta

38 King George VI

(Recess Waterlow)

·**38** (12 May)–**1951**. *T* **35** *to* **38** *and other designs as* 1934, *but with portrait of King George VI. Wmk Mult Script CA. P* 12½.

·1 **35** ¼ pi. ultramarine and orange-brown .. 20 20
·2 **25** ½ pi. green 40 10
·2*a* – ½ pi. violet (2.7.51) .. .. .. 2·25 20
·3 – ¾ pi. black and violet .. .. .. 14·00 40
·4 – 1 pi. orange 80 10
a. Perf 13½×12½ (5.44) .. .. £400 27·00
·5 – 1½ pi. carmine .. .. 5·50 1·50
·5*a* – 1½ pi. violet (15.3.43) 50 30
·5*ab* – 1½ pi. green (2.7.51) .. .. .. 2·75 40
·5*b* – 2 pi. black and carmine (2.2.42) .. 70 10
c. Perf 12½×13½ (10.44) . .. 2·25 7·00
·6 – 2½ pi. ultramarine .. .. .. 22·00 2·50
·6*a* – 3 pi. ultramarine (2.2.42) .. .. 1·25 15
·6*b* – 4 pi. ultramarine (2.7.51) .. .. 3·00 30

157 **36** 4½ pi. grey 70 10
158 **31** 6 pi. black and blue .. .. .. 1·25 1·00
159 **37** 9 pi. black and purple .. .. .. 2·25 20
160 – 18 pi. black and olive-green .. .. 6·00 85
a. Black and sage-green (19.8.47) .. 8·00 1·50
161 – 45 pi. green and black .. .. .. 17·00 2·50
162 **38** 90 pi. mauve and black .. .. .. 22·00 4·75
163 £1 scarlet and indigo .. .. .. 48·00 23·00
151/63 .. .. *Set of* 19 £130 32·00
151s/63s Perf "Specimen" .. *Set of* 19 £375

Designs: *Horiz*—¾ pi., 2 pi. Peristerona Church; 1 pi. Soli Theatre; 1½ pi. Kyrenia Harbour; 2½ pi., 3 pi., 4 pi. Kolossi Castle; 45 pi. Forest scene. *Vert*—18 pi. Buyuk Khan, Nicosia.

Dot between "1" and "½" in right-hand value tablet (Pl B1 R. 9/1)

1946 (21 Oct). *Victory. As Nos.* 110/11 *of Antigua.*

164 1½ pi. deep violet 15 10
a. Dot between "1" and "½" .. .. 20·00
165 3 pi. blue 15 15
164s/5s Perf "Specimen" .. .. *Set of* 2 90·00

Extra decoration (R. 3/5)

1948 (20 Dec). *Royal Silver Wedding. As Nos.* 112/13 *of Antigua.*

166 1½ pi. violet 50 20
a. Extra decoration .. .. .. 32·00
167 £1 indigo .. .. 42·00 48·00

1949 (10 Oct). *75th Anniv of Universal Postal Union. As Nos.* 114/17 *of Antigua but inscr* "CYPRUS" *(recess).*

168 1½ pi. violet 40 70
169 2 pi. carmine-red .. .. 1·50 1·50
170 3 pi. deep blue .. .. 70 1·00
171 9 pi. purple .. .. 70 1·25
168/71 .. .. *Set of* 4 3·00 4·00

Cyrenaica
see British Occupation of Italian Colonies

Dominica

CROWN COLONY

A British packet agency was operating on Dominica from about 1778, the date of the earliest known use of a postal marking. This was replaced by a branch office of the British G.P.O. which opened at Roseau on 8 May 1858. The stamps of Great Britain were used from that date until 1 May 1860, after which the colonial authorities assumed responsibility for the postal service. Until the introduction of Nos. 1/3 in 1874 No. CC1 and later handstamps were utilised.

For illustrations of handstamp and postmark types see BRITISH POST OFFICES ABROAD notes, following GREAT BRITAIN.

ROSEAU

CROWNED/CIRCLE HANDSTAMPS

CC1 CC 1 DOMINICA (Black or R.) (17.5.1845)
Price on cover £500

No. CC1 is also known struck in black on various adhesive stamps as late as 1883.

Stamps of GREAT BRITAIN *cancelled* "A 07" *as Type* **2**.

1858 *to* **1860**

Z1 1d. rose-red (1857), *perf* 14 .. .. £225
Z2 2d. blue (1858) (Plate No. 7) £650
Z3 4d. rose (1857) £275
Z4 6d. lilac (1856) £275
Z5 1s. green £1200

PRICES FOR STAMPS ON COVER TO 1945

Nos. 1/3	*from* × 25
No. 4	*from* × 40
No. 5	*from* × 100
No. 6	*from* × 40
Nos. 7/8	*from* × 100
No. 9	*from* × 40
Nos. 10/12	*from* × 15
Nos. 13/15	*from* × 100
No. 17	*from* × 50
Nos. 18/a	—
No. 19	*from* × 40
Nos. 20/5	*from* × 30
No. 26	—
Nos. 27/90	*from* × 5
No. 91	—
Nos. 92/8	*from* × 10
Nos. 99/109	*from* × 3
Nos. R1/3	*from* × 15
No. R4	*from* × 50
No. R6	*from* × 3

ONE PENNY — 1

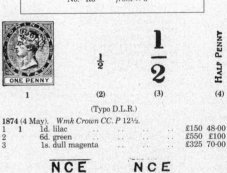

½ — (2)

1/2 — (3)

HALF PENNY — (4)

(Typo D.L.R.)

1874 (4 May). *Wmk Crown CC. P* 12½.

1 1 1d. lilac .. .. £150 48·00
2 6d. green £550 £100
3 1s. dull magenta .. .. £325 70·00

NCE — Normal

NCE — Malformed "CE" (R.10/6)

1877–79. *Wmk Crown CC. P* 14.

4 1 ½d. olive-yellow (1879) .. .. .. 11·00 48·00
5 1d. lilac .. .. 5·00 2·00
a. Bisected vert or diag (½d.) (on cover or card) .. .. † £1700
w. Wmk inverted .. .. 60·00
6 2½d. red-brown (1879) .. .. .. £225 29·00
w. Wmk inverted .. .. † £150
7 4d. blue (1879) .. .. £110 2·50
a. Malformed "CE" in "PENCE" .. £1500 £225
8 6d. green .. .. £150 20·00
9 1s. magenta .. .. £120 48·00

1882 (25 Nov)–**83.** *No. 5 bisected vertically and surch.*

10 **2** ½ (d.), in *black*, on half 1d. .. .. £160 38·00
a. Surch inverted £950 £800
b. Surcharges *tête-bêche* (pair) .. £1600
11 **3** ½ (d.), in *red*, on half 1d. (12.82) .. 28·00 15·00
a. Surch inverted £1000 £475
c. Surch double £1600 £650
12 **4** ½d. in *black*, on half 1d. (3.83) .. 60·00 20·00
b. Surch double £800

Type 4 is found reading up or down.

1883–86. *Wmk Crown CA. P* 14.
13 **1** ½d. olive-yellow .. .. 2·50 10·00
14 1d. lilac (1886) .. .. 26·00 11·00
a. Bisected (½d.) (on cover) .. .. † £1900
15 2½d. red-brown (1884) .. .. .. £140 2·00
w. Wmk inverted £275

Half Penny (5) **One Penny** (6)

1886 (Mar). *Nos. 8 and 9 surch locally.*
17 **5** ½d. on 6d. green .. .. .. 4·25 3·50
18 **6** 1d. on 6d. green £20000 £10000
a. Thick bar (approx 1 mm) .. .. † £16000
19 1d. on 1s. magenta .. .. .. 14·00 16·00
a. Surch double £5000 £2750

It is believed that only two sheets of the 1d. on 6d. were surcharged. On one of these sheets the six stamps in the top row showed the thick bar variety, No. 18a.

1886–90. *Wmk Crown CA. P* 14.
20 **1** ½d. dull green .. .. 1·50 5·50
22 1d. rose (1887) .. .. 14·00 15·00
a. Deep carmine (1889) .. .. .. 2·75 6·00
b. Bisected (½d.) (on cover) .. .. † £1800
w. Wmk inverted £110
23 2½d. ultramarine (1888) .. .. .. 3·75 5·00
24 4d. grey .. .. 2·75 4·00
a. Malformed "CE" in "PENCE" £160 £200
25 6d. orange (1888) .. .. .. 7·00 40·00
26 1s. dull magenta (1890) £150 £250
20/6 .. .. *Set of* 6 £150 £275
20s/5s Optd "Specimen" .. .. *Set of* 5 £225

The stamps of Dominica were superseded by the general issue for Leeward Islands on 31 October 1890, but the sets following were in concurrent use with the stamps inscribed "LEEWARD ISLANDS" until 31 December 1939, when the island came under the administration of the Windward Islands.

9 "Roseau from the Sea" (Lt. Caddy)

10

(T 9 to 11 typo D.L.R.)

1903 (1 Sept)–**07.** *Wmk Crown CC* (*sideways* on T* **9**). *Ordinary paper. P* 14.
27 **9** ½d. green and grey-green .. .. 4·00 2·50
a. Chalk-surfaced paper (1906) .. .. 13·00 18·00
28 1d. grey and red .. .. .. 8·00 75
a. Chalk-surfaced paper (1906) .. .. 29·00 6·00
29 2d. green and brown .. .. .. 2·50 4·50
a. Chalk-surfaced paper (1906) .. .. 25·00 38·00
30 2½d. grey and bright blue .. .. 5·00 4·00
a. Chalk-surfaced paper (3.9.07) .. .. 20·00 45·00
31 3d. dull purple and grey-black .. .. 8·00 3·25
a. Chalk-surfaced paper (1906) .. .. 35·00 30·00
32 6d. grey and chestnut .. .. .. 4·50 18·00
33 1s. magenta and grey-green .. .. 27·00 42·00
a. Chalk-surfaced paper (1906) .. .. 75·00 £150
34 2s. grey-black and purple .. .. 26·00 29·00
35 2s. 6d. grey-green and maize .. .. 18·00 75·00
36 **10** 5s. black and brown .. .. .. 90·00 £140
27/36 .. .. *Set of* 10 £170 £275
27s/36s Optd "Specimen" .. *Set of* 10 £130

*The normal sideways watermark shows Crown to right of CC, *as seen from the back of the stamp.*

1907–08. *Wmk Mult Crown CA* (*sideways* on T* **9**). *Chalk-surfaced paper. P* 14.
37 **9** ½d. green .. .. 3·50 3·25
38 1d. grey and red .. .. .. 2·00 40
39 2d. green and brown .. .. .. 5·50 15·00
40 2½d. grey and bright blue .. .. 4·50 21·00
41 3d. dull purple and grey-black .. 4·00 13·00
42 6d. black and chestnut .. .. 50·00 85·00
43 1s. magenta and grey-green (1908) .. 3·75 55·00
44 2s. grey-black and purple (1908) .. 22·00 32·00
45 2s. 6d. grey-green and maize (1908) .. 22·00 60·00
46 **10** 5s. black and brown (1908) .. .. 60·00 60·00
37/46 .. .. *Set of* 10 £160 £300

*The normal sideways watermark shows Crown to right of CA, *as seen from the back of the stamp.*

Examples of Nos. 27/36 and 37/46 are known showing a forged Gen. Post Office Dominica postmark dated "JU 1 11".

11

WAR TAX
ONE HALFPENNY
(12)

1908–21. *Wmk Mult Crown CA* (*sideways* on T* **9**). *Chalk-surfaced paper* (*3d., 6d., 1s.*). *P* 14.
47 **9** ½d blue-green .. .. .. 3·00 3·75
aw. Wmk Crown to left of CA .. 2·50 2·75
ay. Wmk sideways inverted and reversed .. .. ..
b. Dp green (wmk Crown to left of CA) 3·50 2·25
48 1d. carmine-red .. .. .. 3·00 30
aw. Wmk Crown to left of CA .. 3·50 40
b. Scarlet (1916) .. .. .. 1·50 40
bw. Wmk Crown to left of CA .. 1·00 50
49 2d. grey (1909) .. .. .. 4·00 12·00
aw. Wmk Crown to left of CA .. 3·50 16·00
b. Slate (wmk Crown to left of CA) (1918) .. .. .. 3·50 12·00
50 2½d. blue .. .. .. 8·50 6·00
aw. Wmk Crown to left of CA .. — 9·00
b. Bright blue (1918) .. .. 5·00 9·00
bw. Wmk Crown to left of CA .. 6·00 13·00
51 3d. purple/*yellow* (1909) .. .. 3·00 4·25
a. Ordinary paper (wmk Crown to left of CA) (1912) .. .. .. 3·00 4·50
ab. *On pale yellow* (1920) .. .. 8·50 15·00
52 6d. dull and bright purple (1909) .. 10·00 15·00
a. Ordinary paper. *Dull purple* (wmk Crown to left of CA) (1915) .. 3·50 18·00
53 1s. black/*green* (1910) .. .. 3·00 2·75
a. Ordinary paper (wmk Crown to left of CA) (1912) .. .. .. 3·00 4·00
as. Optd "Specimen" in red .. 65·00
53*b* 2s. purple and deep blue/*blue* (wmk Crown to left of CA) (1919) .. 25·00 85·00
53*c* 2s. 6d. black and red/*blue* (wmk Crown to left of CA) (1921) .. .. 25·00 90·00
54 **11** 5s. red and green/*yellow* (1914) .. 55·00 80·00
47/54 .. .. *Set of* 10 £110 £275
48s/54s Optd "Specimen" (1s. optd in blk) *Set of* 9 £180

*The normal sideways watermark shows Crown to right of CA, *as seen from the back of the stamp.*

1916 (Sept). *No. 47b surch with T* **12** *by De La Rue.*
55 **9** ½d. on ½d. deep green (R.) 60 75
a. Small "O" in "ONE" .. .. 6·50 16·00

No. 55a occurs on ten stamps within each sheet of 60.

1918 (18 Mar). *No. 47b optd with T* **12** *locally, from D.L.R. plate, but with* "ONE HALF-PENNY" *blanked out.*
56 **9** ½d. deep green (Blk.) .. .. .. 2·75 6·00
w. Wmk Crown to right of CA .. ..

The blanking out of the surcharge was not completely successful so that it almost always appears as an albino to a greater or lesser extent.

WAR TAX
(14)

1918 (June)–**19.** *Nos. 47b and* 51a *optd with T* **14** *by De La Rue.*
57 **9** ½d. deep green 15 50
w. Wmk Crown to right of CA .. 50·00
x. Wmk reversed .. .. ..
58 3d. purple/*yellow* (R.) (1919) .. .. 1·25 4·00

WAR TAX
=1½D.=
(15)

1½D.
Short Fraction Bar (R.6/4)

1919. *As No.* 50aw, *but colour changed, surch with T* **15** *by De La Rue.*
59 **9** 1½d. on 2½d. orange (R.) 15 55
a. Short fraction bar .. .. 7·50 35·00
b. "C" and "A" missing from wmk ..

No. 59b shows the "C" omitted from one impression with the "A" missing from the next one to the left (as seen from the back of the stamp). The "C" is badly distorted in the second watermark.

1920 (1 June). *As No.* 59, *but without* "WAR TAX".
60 **9** 1½d. on 2½d. orange (Blk.) .. .. 2·50 4·50
a. Short fraction bar .. .. 55·00 70·00
b. "A" of "CA" missing from wmk ..
55s/60s Optd "Specimen" .. *Set of* 6 £170

1921–22. *Wmk Mult Script CA* (*sideways**). *Chalk-surfaced paper* (*6d.*). *P* 14.
62 **9** ½d. blue-green .. .. .. 2·50 14·00
63 1d. carmine-red .. .. .. 1·75 3·75
w. Wmk Crown to right of CA .. — 13·00
64 1½d. orange .. .. .. 3·00 11·00
65 2d. grey .. .. .. 2·75 3·25
66 2½d. bright blue .. .. .. 2·00 8·50
67 6d. purple .. .. .. 2·50 35·00
69 2s. purple and blue/*blue* (1922) .. 32·00 85·00
70 2s. 6d. black and red/*blue* .. .. 32·00 85·00
62/70 .. .. *Set of* 8 70·00 £225
62s/70s Optd "Specimen" .. *Set of* 8 £140

*The normal sideways watermark shows Crown to left of CA, *as seen from the back of the stamp.*

The 1½d. has figures of value, in the lower corner and no ornamentation below words of value.

16

(Typo D.L.R.)

1923 (1 Mar)–**33.** *Chalk-surfaced paper. P* 14.

(*a*) *Wmk Mult Script CA* (*sideways**)
71 **16** ½d. black and green .. .. .. 1·75
72 1d. black and bright violet .. .. 2·00
73 1d. black and scarlet (1933) .. .. 9·00
74 1½d. black and scarlet .. .. .. 2·75
75 1½d. black and red-brown (1933) .. 9·00
76 2d. black and grey .. .. .. 1·75
77 2½d. black and orange-yellow .. .. 1·50
78 2½d. black and ultramarine (1927) .. 4·25
79 3d. black and ultramarine .. .. 1·50
80 3d. black and red/*yellow* (1927) .. 1·50
81 4d. black and brown .. .. .. 2·50
82 6d. black and bright magenta .. .. 3·50
83 1s. black/*emerald* .. .. .. 2·25
84 2s. black and blue/*blue* .. .. 10·00
85 2s. 6d. black and red/*blue* .. .. 18·00
86 3s. black and purple/*yellow* (1927) .. 3·25
87 4s. black and red/*emerald* .. .. 11·00
88 5s. black and green/*yellow* (1927) .. 22·00

(*b*) *Wmk Mult Crown CA* (*sideways**)
89 **16** 3s. black and purple/*yellow* .. .. 4·00
90 5s. black and green/*yellow* .. .. 9·00
91 £1 black and purple/*red* £225
71/91 .. .. *Set of* 21 £300
71s/91s Optd or Perf (Nos. 73s, 75s) "Specimen" *Set of* 21 £350

*The normal sideways watermark shows Crown to left of *as seen from the back of the stamp.*

Examples of most values are known showing a forged G. Dominica postmark dated "MY 19 27".

1935 (6 May). *Silver Jubilee. As Nos. 91/4 of Antigua.*
92 1d. deep blue and carmine 75
f. Diagonal line by turret .. .. 35·00
h. Dot by flagstaff .. .. 55·00
93 1½d. ultramarine and grey .. .. 1·50
f. Diagonal line by turret .. .. 50·00
h. Dot by flagstaff .. .. 80·00
94 2½d. brown and deep blue .. .. 1·50
95 1s. slate and purple .. .. 1·50
h. Dot by flagstaff £130
i. Dash by turret £130
92/5 .. .. .. *Set of* 4 4·75
92s/5s Perf "Specimen" .. .. *Set of* 4 75·00

For illustrations of plate varieties see Omnibus sect following Zanzibar.

1937 (12 May). *Coronation. As Nos. 95/7 of Antig* *P* 11×11½.
96 1d. carmine 40
97 1½d. yellow-brown 40
98 2½d. blue 60
96/8 .. .. *Set of* 3 1·25
96s/8s Perf "Specimen" .. .. *Set of* 3 55·00

17 Fresh Water Lake

18 Layou River

(Recess Waterlow)

1938 (15 Aug)–**47.** *T* **17/18** *and similar horiz designs. Wmk M Script CA. P* 12½.
99 **17** ½d. brown and green 10
100 **18** 1d. grey and scarlet 20
101 – 1½d. green and purple 30
102 – 2d. carmine and grey-black 50
103 – 2½d. purple and bright blue .. .. 4·00
a. Purple & bright ultramarine (8.42) 20
104 **18** 3d. olive-green and brown 30
104*a* – 3½d. ultramarine and purple (15.10.47) 2·00
105 **17** 6d. emerald-green and violet .. 1·75
105*a* 7d. green and yellow-brown (15.10.47) 1·75
106 – 1s. violet and olive-green .. .. 2·75
106*a* **18** 2s. slate and purple (15.10.47) .. 5·50
107 **17** 2s. 6d. black and vermilion .. .. 12·00
108 **18** 5s. light blue and sepia .. .. 7·50
108*a* – 10s. black and brown-orange (15.10.47) 12·00
99/108*a* .. .. *Set of* 14 42·00

Designs:–1½d., 2½d., 3½d. Picking limes; 2d., 1s., 10s. Boili Lake.

21 King George VI

(Photo Harrison)

1940 (15 Apr)–**42.** *Wmk Mult Script CA. Chalk-surface paper. P* 15×14.
109 **21** ¼d. chocolate .. .. 1·00
a. Ordinary paper (1942) 10
99s/109s Perf "Specimen" .. *Set of* 15 £225

1946 (14 Oct). *Victory. As Nos.* 110/11 *of Antigua.*
110 1d. carmine 20
111 3½d. blue 20
110s/11s Perf "Specimen" .. *Set of* 2 48·00

1948 (1 Dec). *Royal Silver Wedding. As Nos.* 112/13 *o Antigua.*
112 1d. scarlet 15
113 10s. red-brown .. .. 9·50

New Currency. 100 cents = 1 B.W.I., later East Caribbean dollar)

(10 Oct). *75th Anniv of Universal Postal Union. As Nos.* 17 *of Antigua.*
5 c. blue 15 15
6 c. brown 1·00 2·00
12 c. purple 45 1·00
24 c. olive 30 30
7 *Set of* 4 1·75 3·00

16 Feb). *Inauguration of B.W.I. University College. As Nos.* /19 *of Antigua.*
3 c. yellow-green and reddish violet 50 70
12 c. deep green and carmine 75 30

22 King George VI

23 Drying Cocoa

(Photo Harrison (½ c.). Recess B.W. (others))

(1 July). *T* **22** *and designs as T* **23**. *Wmk Mult Script CA.* *alk-surfaced paper* (½ *c.*). *P* 15×14 (½ *c.*), 13½×13 ($2.40), ×13½ (*others*).
½ c. chocolate 10 30
1 c. black and vermilion 10 30
  b. "A" of "CA" missing from wmk £500
  c. "JA" for "CA" in wmk £500
2 c. red-brown and deep green 10 30
  a. "C" of "CA" missing from wmk £600
  b. "A" of "CA" missing from wmk £600
3 c. green and reddish violet 15 1·25
  a. "C" of "CA" missing from wmk
  c. "JA" for "CA" in wmk £500
4 c. brown-orange and sepia 60 1·40
  a. "C" of "CA" missing from wmk £600
  b. "A" of "CA" missing from wmk £600
5 c. black and carmine 85 30
  a. "C" of "CA" missing from wmk £800
  b. "A" of "CA" missing from wmk £800
  c. "JA" for "CA" in wmk
6 c. olive and chestnut 90 30
  a. "C" of "CA" missing from wmk
  b. "A" of "CA" missing from wmk £1000
8 c. blue-green and blue 80 70
  b. "A" of "CA" missing from wmk
12 c. black and bright green 60 1·25
  a. "C" of "CA" missing from wmk £1200
14 c. blue and violet 95 1·25
  a. "C" of "CA" missing from wmk £1200
  b. "A" of "CA" missing from wmk † —
  c. "JA" for "CA" in wmk
24 c. reddish violet and rose-carmine 75 30
  a. "C" of "CA" missing from wmk £1200
48 c. bright green and red-orange 3·50 7·50
  a. "C" of "CA" missing from wmk £1200
  b. "A" of "CA" missing from wmk £1200
  c. "JA" for "CA" in wmk
60 c. carmine and black 3·50 5·50
  c. "JA" for "CA" in wmk £800
$1.20, emerald and black 4·25 6·00
  a. "C" of "CA" missing from wmk £1400
  b. "A" of "CA" missing from wmk £1400
$2.40, orange and black 23·00 35·00
'34 *Set of* 15 30·00 55·00

esigns: *Horiz*—2 c., 60 c. Making Carib baskets; 3 c., 48 c. Lime tation; 4 c. Picking oranges; 5 c. Bananas; 6 c. Botanical dens; 8 c. Drying vanilla beans; 12 c., $1.20, Fresh Water Lake; :. Layou River; 24 c. Boiling Lake. *Vert*—$2.40, Picking ages.

xamples of Nos. 121b, 122b, 124b, 125b, 126b, 129b, 131b 133b show traces of the *left leg* of the "A", *as seen from the k of the stamp.*

'os. 121c, 123c, 125c, 129c and 131c may represent an mpt to repair the missing "C" variety.

NEW CONSTITUTION 1951

(34)

1 (15 Oct). *New Constitution. Nos.* 123, 125, 127 *and* 129 *optd ith T* **34** *by B.W.*
3 c. green and reddish violet 15 70
  a. "C" of "CA" missing from wmk £600
5 c. black and carmine 15 80
  a. "JA" for "CA" in wmk £700
8 c. blue-green and blue (R.) 15 15
  a. "JA" for "CA" in wmk
14 c. blue and violet (R.) 35 20
  b. "A" of "CA" missing from wmk £900
5/8 *Set of* 4 70 1·60

POSTAL FISCALS

REVENUE (R 1) **Revenue** (R 2)

79–88. *Optd with Type* R **1** *by De La Rue. P* 14. (*a*) *Wmk Crown CC.*
1 1d. lilac 80·00 8·00
  a. Bisected vert (½d.) on cover † —
6d. green 3·00 23·00
  w. Wmk inverted £100
1s. magenta 9·00 16·00
/3 *Set of* 3 80·00 42·00

(*b*) *Wmk Crown CA*
1 1d. lilac (1888) 4·25 3·50

88. *Optd with Type* R **2** *locally. Wmk Crown CA.*
1 1d. rose £250 70·00

East Africa (G.E.A.) *see* Tanganyika

East Africa and Uganda Protectorates *see* Kenya, Uganda and Tanganyika

Egypt

TURKISH SUZERAINTY

In 1517 Sultan Selim I added Egypt to the Ottoman Empire, and it stayed more or less under Turkish rule until 1805, when Mohammed Ali became governor. He established a dynasty of governors owing nominal allegiance to the Sultan of Turkey until 1914.

Khedive Ismail

18 January 1863–26 June 1879

He obtained the honorific title of Khedive (viceroy) from the Sultan in 1867.

The operations of British Consular Post Offices in Egypt date from August 1839 when the first packet agency, at Alexandria, was opened. Further agencies at Suez (1 January 1847) and Cairo (1856) followed. Alexandria became a post office on 17 March 1858 with Cairo following on 23 February 1859 and Suez on 1 January 1861.

Great Britain stamps were issued to Alexandria in March 1858 and to the other two offices in August/September 1859. "B 01" cancellations as Type **2** were issued to both Alexandria and Cairo. Cancellations with this number as Types **8, 12** and **15** were only used at Alexandria.

Before 1 July 1873 combination covers showing Great Britain stamps and the first issue of Egypt exist with the latter paying the internal postage to the British Post Office at Alexandria.

The Cairo office closed on 30 June 1873 and the other two on 30 March 1878. Suez continued to function as a transit office for a number of years.

Stamps issued after 1877 can be found with the Egyptian cancellation "Port Said", but these are on letters posted from British ships.

For cancellations used during the 1882 and 1885 campaigns, see BRITISH FORCES IN EGYPT at the end of the listing.

For illustrations of the handstamp and postmark types see BRITISH POST OFFICES ABROAD notes, following GREAT BRITAIN.

ALEXANDRIA

CROWNED-CIRCLE HANDSTAMPS

CC1 CC1b ALEXANDRIA (R.) (13.5.1843) *Price on cover* £2750

Stamps of GREAT BRITAIN *cancelled* "B 01" *as in Types* **2** (*also used at Cairo*), **8**, **12**, *or* **15**.

1858 (Mar) *to* **1878.**
Z 1 ½d. rose-red (1870–79) *From* 19·00
  Plate Nos. 5, 6, 8, 10, 13, 14, 15, 19, 20.
Z 2 1d. rose-red (1857) 7·00
Z 3 1d. rose-red (1861) (Alph IV)
Z 4 1d. rose-red (1864–79) *From* 9·50
  Plate Nos. 71, 72, 73, 74, 76, 78, 79, 80, 81, 82, 83, 84, 85, 86, 87, 88, 89, 90, 91, 92, 93, 94, 95, 96, 97, 98, 99, 101, 102, 103, 104, 106, 107, 108, 109, 110, 111, 112, 113, 114, 115, 117, 118, 119, 120, 121, 122, 123, 124, 125, 127, 129, 130, 131, 133, 134, 136, 137, 138, 139, 140, 142, 143, 144, 145, 146, 147, 148, 149, 150, 152, 154, 156, 157, 158, 159, 160, 162, 163, 165, 168, 169, 170, 171, 172, 174, 175, 177, 179, 180, 181, 182, 183, 185, 188, 190, 198, 200, 203, 206, 210, 220.
Z 5 2d. blue (1858–69) *From* 9·50
  Plate Nos. 7, 8, 9, 13, 14, 15.
Z 6 2½d. rosy mauve (1875) (blued *paper*) *From* 60·00
  Plate Nos. 1, 2.
Z 7 2½d. rosy mauve (1875–6) (Plate Nos. 1, 2, 3) 29·00
Z 8 2½d. rosy mauve (*Error of Lettering*) £1300
Z 9 2½d. rosy mauve (1876–79) *From* 25·00
  Plate Nos. 3, 4, 5, 6, 7, 8, 9.
Z10 3d. carmine-rose (1862) £120
Z11 3d. rose (1865) (Plate No. 4) 60·00
Z12 3d. rose (1867–73) (Plate Nos. 4, 5, 6, 7, 8, 9) *From* 23·00
Z13 3d. rose (1873–76) *From* 21·00
  Plate Nos. 11, 12, 14, 15, 16, 18, 19.
Z15 4d. rose (1857) 42·00
Z16 4d. red (1862) (Plate Nos. 3, 4) *From* 42·00
Z17 4d. vermilion (1865–73) 23·00
  Plate Nos. 7, 8, 9, 10, 11, 12, 13, 14.
Z18 4d. vermilion (1876) (Plate No. 15) £160
Z19 4d. sage-green (1877) (Plate No. 15) £110
Z20 6d. lilac (1856) 48·00
Z21 6d. lilac (1862) (Plate Nos. 3, 4) *From* 42·00
Z22 6d. lilac (1865–67) (Plate Nos. 5, 6) *From* 32·00
Z23 6d. lilac (1867) (Plate No. 6) 42·00
Z24 6d. violet (1867–70) (Plate Nos. 6, 8, 9) *From* 30·00
  a. Imperf (Plate No. 8) £1200
Z25 6d. buff (1872–73) (Plate Nos. 11, 12) *From* 55·00
Z26 6d. chestnut (1872) (Plate No. 11) 27·00
Z27 6d. grey (1873) (Plate No. 12) 80·00
Z28 6d. grey (1874–76) (Plate Nos. 13, 14, 15) *From* 23·00
Z29 9d. straw (1862) £150
Z30 9d. bistre (1862)
Z31 9d. straw (1865)
Z32 9d. straw (1867)
Z33 10d. red-brown (1867) £130
Z34 1s. green (1856) £120
Z35 1s. green (1862) 75·00
Z36 1s. green (1862) ("K" *variety*)
Z37 1s. green (1865) (Plate No. 4) 35·00
Z38 1s. green (1867–73) (Plate Nos. 4, 5, 6, 7) *From* 15·00
Z39 1s. green (1873–77) *From* 27·00
  Plate Nos. 8, 9, 10, 11, 12, 13.
Z40 2s. blue (1867) £100
Z41 5s. rose (1867–74) (Plate Nos. 1, 2) *From* £250

CAIRO

CROWNED-CIRCLE HANDSTAMPS

CC2 CC **6** CAIRO (R. or Blk.) (23.3.1859) *Price on cover* £3750

Cancellation "B 01" as Type **2** (also issued at Alexandria) was used to cancel mail franked with Great Britain stamps between April 1859 and June 1873.

SUEZ

CROWNED-CIRCLE HANDSTAMPS

CC3 CC **1** SUEZ (B. *or* Black) (16.7.1847) *Price on cover* £4250

Stamps of GREAT BRITAIN *cancelled* "B 02" *as in Types* **2** *and* **8**, *or with circular date stamp as Type* **5**.

1859 (Aug) *to* **1878.**
Z42 ½d. rose-red (1870–79) 28·00
  Plate Nos. 6, 10, 11, 12, 13, 14.
Z43 1d. rose-red (1857) 9·00
Z44 1d. rose-red (1864–79) *From* 11·00
  Plate Nos. 73, 74, 78, 79, 80, 81, 83, 84, 86, 87, 90, 91, 93, 94, 96, 97, 100, 101, 106, 107, 108, 110, 113, 118, 119, 120, 121, 122, 123, 124, 125, 129, 130, 131, 134, 136, 137, 138, 140, 142, 143, 144, 145, 147, 148, 149, 150, 151, 152, 153, 154, 156, 158, 159, 160, 161, 162, 163, 164, 165, 166, 167, 168, 170, 174, 176, 177, 178, 179, 180, 181, 182, 184, 185, 186, 187, 189, 190, 205.
Z45 2d. blue (1858–69) *From* 14·00
  Plate Nos. 8, 9, 13, 14, 15.
Z46 2½d. rosy mauve (1875) (blued *paper*) *From* 60·00
  Plate Nos. 1, 2, 3.
Z47 2½d. rosy mauve (1875–76) (Plate Nos. 1, 2, 3) *From* 32·00
Z48 2½d. rosy mauve (*Error of Lettering*) £1300
Z49 2½d. rosy mauve (1876–79) *From* 24·00
  Plate Nos. 3, 4, 5, 6, 7, 8, 9, 10.
Z50 3d. carmine-rose (1862) £130
Z51 3d. rose (1865) (Plate No. 4) 70·00
Z52 3d. rose (1867–73) (Plate Nos. 5, 6, 7, 8, 10)
Z53 3d. rose (1873–76) (Plate Nos. 12, 16) *From* 24·00
Z54 4d. rose (1857) 50·00
Z55 4d. red (1862) (Plate Nos. 3, 4) *From* 45·00
Z56 4d. vermilion (1865–73) *From* 27·00
  Plate Nos. 7, 8, 9, 10, 11, 12, 13, 14.
Z57 4d. vermilion (1876) (Plate No. 15)
Z58 4d. sage-green (1877) (Plate No. 15) £120
Z59 6d. lilac (1856) 48·00
Z60 6d. lilac (1862) (Plate Nos. 3, 4) *From* 42·00
Z61 6d. lilac (1865–67) (Plate Nos. 5, 6) *From* 35·00
Z62 6d. lilac (1867) (Plate No. 6) 45·00
Z63 6d. violet (1867–70) (Plate Nos. 6, 8, 9) *From* 35·00
Z64 6d. buff (1872–73) (Plate Nos. 11, 12) *From* 60·00
Z65 6d. pale chestnut (Plate No. 12) (1872) £2250
Z66 6d. chestnut (1872) (Plate No. 11) 30·00
Z67 6d. grey (1873) (Plate No. 12) 90·00
Z68 6d. grey (1874–76) (Plate Nos. 13, 14, 15, 16) *From* 25·00
Z69 8d. orange (1876)
Z70 9d. straw (1862) £160
  a. Thick paper
Z71 9d. bistre (1862)
Z72 9d. straw (1867)
Z73 10d. red-brown (1867) £175
Z74 1s. green (1856) £140
Z75 1s. green (1862) 80·00
Z76 1s. green (1862) ("K" *variety*)
Z77 1s. green (1865) (Plate No. 4) 45·00
Z78 1s. green (1867–73) (Plate Nos. 4, 5, 6, 7) *From* 18·00
Z79 1s. green (1873–77) *From* 27·00
  Plate Nos. 8, 9, 10, 11, 12.
Z80 2s. blue (1867) £150
Z81 5s. rose (1867–74) (Plate Nos. 1, 2) *From* £275

PRICES FOR STAMPS ON COVER

Nos. 1/41	*from* × 8
Nos. 42/3	*from* × 30
Nos. 44/83	*from* × 5
Nos. 84/97	*from* × 2
Nos. D57/70	*from* × 12
Nos. D71/86	*from* × 5
Nos. D84/103	*from* × 2
Nos. O64/87	*from* × 5
Nos. O88/101	*from* × 2

(Currency: 40 paras = 1 piastre)

1

2

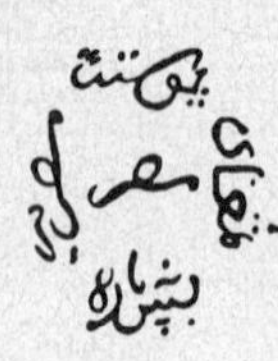
(3)

(Typo (1 pi) or litho (others) Pellas Brothers, Genoa. Inscr (T 3) applied typo (1, 2 pi.) or litho (others))

1866 (1 Jan). *Various designs as T* **1** *with black inscriptions as T* **3**. *The lowest group of characters indicates the value. 1 pi. no wmk, others W* **2** *(inverted). P* 12½.

1 5 pa. grey .. .. 40·00 26·00
a. *Greenish grey* .. .. .. 40·00 26·00
b. Imperf (pair) £180
c. Imperf between (pair) £300
d. Perf 12½×13 and compound .. .. 50·00 48·00
e. Perf 13 .. .. £250 £300
w. Wmk upright £250 £200
2 10 pa. brown .. .. 55·00 28·00
a. Imperf (pair) £160
b. Imperf between (pair) £350
c. Perf 12½×13 and compound .. .. 80·00 48·00
d. Perf 12½×15 .. .. .. £250 £275
e. Perf 13 .. .. £170 £190
w. Wmk upright .. .. .. 65·00 28·00
3 20 pa. pale blue .. .. .. 70·00 29·00
a. *Greenish blue* .. .. .. 70·00 29·00
b. Imperf (pair) £240
c. Imperf between (pair) £400
d. Perf 12½×13 and compound .. .. £100 80·00
e. Perf 13 .. .. £425 £250
w. Wmk upright .. .. .. 70·00 29·00
4 1 pi. claret .. .. 60·00 4·50
a. Imperf (pair) £100
b. Imperf between (pair) £400
c. Perf 12½×13 and compound .. .. 90·00 20·00
d. Perf 13 .. .. £300 £190
5 2 pi. yellow .. .. 90·00 40·00
a. *Orange-yellow* .. .. .. 90·00 40·00
b. Imperf (pair) .. .. ..
c. Imperf between (pair) £350 £350
d. Bisected diag (1 pi.) (on cover) .. † £2250
e. Perf 12½×13 and compound .. .. £120 45·00
f. Perf 12½×15 .. .. .. £130
w. Wmk upright .. .. .. 90·00 40·00
6 5 pi. rose £250 £170
a. Imperf (pair) .. .. ..
b. Imperf between (pair) £1000
c. Perf 12½×13 and compound £275
d. Error. Inscr 10 pi., perf 12½×15 .. £900 £750
da. Imperf £500
w. Wmk upright £250 £170
7 10 pi. slate £275 £250
a. Imperf (pair) .. .. ..
b. Imperf between (pair) £2000
c. Perf 12½×13 and compound £425 £425
d. Perf 13 .. .. £1600
w. Wmk upright £275 £250

The 2 pi. bisected was authorised for use between 16 and 31 July 1867 at Alexandria or Cairo.

Stamps perforated 12½, 12½×13 and compound, and 13 occur in the same sheets with the 13 gauge usually used on the top, left-hand, right-hand or bottom rows. Each sheet of 200 contained one stamp perforated 13 all round, two 13 on three sides, one 13 on two adjacent sides, eighteen 13×12½, eight 12½×13, eight 13 on one side and eighteen 13 at top or bottom. So many sheets were received imperforate or part-perforated that some stock was passed to V. Penasson of Alexandria who applied the 12½×15 gauge.

The two halves of each background differ in minor details of the ornamentation. All values can be found with either half at the top.

Proofs of all values exist on smooth paper, without watermark. Beware of forgeries.

All values also exist with the watermark reversed (*same price as upright*) or inverted and reversed (*same price as inverted*).

4

5

6

(Des F. Hoff. Litho V. Penasson, Alexandria)

1867 (1 Aug)–**71**. *W* **6** *(impressed on reverse). P* 15×12½.

11 4 5 pa. orange-yellow .. .. .. 25·00 8·00
a. Imperf (pair) .. .. ..
b. Imperf between (horiz pair) .. £170
w. Wmk inverted £250 £200
12 10 pa. dull lilac .. .. .. 70·00 8·50
b. *Bright mauve* (7.69) .. .. 50·00 9·00
ba. Bisected diag (5 pa.) (on piece) (17.11.71) .. .. .. † £750
w. Wmk inverted £300 £200
13 20 pa. deep blue-green .. .. .. £100 13·00
a. *Pale blue-green* .. .. .. £100 13·00
b. *Yellowish green* (7.69) .. .. £110 12·00
w. Wmk inverted £350 £200
14 5 1 pi. dull rose-red *to* rose .. .. 12·00 1·00
a. *Lake* .. .. £120 32·00
b. Imperf (pair) £100
c. Imperf between (horiz pair) .. £170
d. Bisected diag (20 pa.) (on piece) .. † £750
e. Rouletted .. .. 55·00
w. Wmk inverted .. .. .. 50·00 30·00
15 2 pi. bright blue .. .. .. £110 15·00
a. *Pale blue* .. .. .. £110 15·00
b. Imperf (pair) .. .. ..
c. Imperf between (pair) £425
d. Bisected diag (1 pi.) (on cover) .. † —
e. Perf 12½ £225
w. Wmk inverted £400 £300
16 5 pi. brown £300 £180
w. Wmk inverted £500 £300

Each value was engraved four times, the resulting blocks being used to form sheets of 200. There are therefore four types showing minor variations for each value.

No. 12ba was used on newspapers from Alexandria between 17 November 1871 and 20 January 1872.

Stamps printed both sides, both imperf and perf, come from printer's waste. The 1 pi. rose without watermark is a proof.

7

8 (Side panels transposed and inverted)

8*a* (I)

8*a* (II)

WATERMARK 8*a*. There are two types of this watermark which, as they are not always easy to distinguish, we do not list separately. Type II is slightly wider and less deep and the crescent is flatter than in Type I. The width measurement for Type I is generally about 14 mm and for Type II about 15 mm, but there is some variation within the sheets for both types.

Nos. 26/43, 45/7*a*, 49/*a*, 50/1 and 57 come with Type I only. Nos. 44*a*, 48/*a*, 52, 54*b*, 73/7 and 78 exist with both types of watermark (but No. 83 and official overprints on these stamps still require research); our prices are generally for Type II. Other watermarked issues between 1888 and 1907 have Type II watermarks only.

1872 (1 Jan)–**75**. *T* **7** *(the so-called "Penasson" printing*). Thick opaque paper. W* **8***a*. *P* 12½×13½.

A. LITHOGRAPHED

26 7 20 pa. blue (*shades*) .. .. .. £120 50·00
a. Imperf (pair) .. .. ..
b. Imperf between (pair) .. .. — £2000
c. Perf 13½ .. .. £200 55·00
w. Wmk inverted .. .. .. £200 75·00
27 1 pi. red (*shades*) .. .. .. £225 9·00
a. Perf 13½ .. .. £500 20·00
w. Wmk inverted .. .. .. £600 27·00

B. TYPOGRAPHED

28 7 5 pa. brown (*shades*) .. .. .. 7·00 4·50
a. Perf 13½ .. .. 24·00 9·00
w. Wmk inverted .. .. .. £100 60·00
29 10 pa. mauve .. .. 6·00 3·00
a. Perf 13½ .. .. 6·00 3·25
w. Wmk inverted .. .. .. 40·00 25·00
30 20 pa. blue (*shades*) .. .. .. 50·00 3·75
a. Perf 13½ .. .. 80·00 20·00
w. Wmk inverted .. .. .. 45·00 30·00
31 1 pi. rose-red .. .. 50·00 1·00
a. Bisected (20 pa.) (on piece with No. 31) (7.75) .. .. .. † £600
b. Perf 13½ .. .. 80·00 3·50
w. Wmk inverted .. .. .. 35·00 25·00
32 2 pi. chrome-yellow .. .. .. 85·00 4·00
a. Bisected (1 pi.) (on piece) (7.74) .. — £650
b. Perf 13½ .. .. 18·00 4·00
w. Wmk inverted .. .. ..
33 2½ pi. violet .. .. 80·00 14·00
a. Perf 13½ £700 £190
w. Wmk inverted .. .. .. 90·00 30·00
34 5 pi. yellow-green .. .. .. £180 32·00
a. *Tête-bêche* (pair) .. .. ..
b. Perf 13½ .. .. £275 55·00
w. Wmk inverted .. .. .. £200 90·00

*It is now accepted that stamps in both processes were printed by the Government Printing Works at Bûlâq, Cairo, although Penasson may have been involved in the production of the dies.

The lithographed and typographed stamps each show the characteristic differences between these two processes:—

The typographed stamps show the coloured lines of the design impressed into the paper and an accumulation of ink along the margins of the lines.

The lithographed stamps are essentially flat in appearance, without the heaping of the ink. Many of the 20 pa. show evidence of retouching, particularly of the outer frame lines.

The 1 p. bisected was used at Gedda, on 5 July 1875, or Scio and the 2 pi. vertically bisected at Gallipoli or Scio.

See also footnote below No. 41.

1874 (Nov)–**75**. *Typo from new stereos at Bûlâq, on thinner paper. W* **8***a*. *P* 12½.

35 8 5 pa. brown (3.75) .. .. .. 7·50 3·75
a. Tête-bêche (vert pair) .. .. 35·00 35·00
b. Tête-bêche (horiz pair) £275 £300
c. Imperf (pair) .. .. ..
d. Imperf between (pair) £100 £120
ew. Wmk inverted .. .. .. 7·50 3·75
f. Perf 13½×12½ .. .. .. 12·00 3·75
fa. Tête-bêche (vert pair) .. .. 60·00 60·00
fb. Tête-bêche (horiz pair) £325 £350
fw. Wmk inverted .. .. .. 12·00 3·75
36 7 10 pa. grey-lilac (*shades*) (8.75) .. .. 8·00
a. Tête-bêche (vert pair) £140
b. Tête-bêche (horiz pair) .. ..
c. Imperf (pair) .. .. ..
dw. Wmk inverted .. .. ..
e. Perf 13½×12½ .. .. .. 17·00
ea. Tête-bêche (vert pair) £140
eb. Tête-bêche (horiz pair) .. ..
ew. Wmk inverted .. .. .. 17·00
37 20 pa. grey-blue (*shades*) (2.75) .. .. 90·00
b. Bisected diag (10 pa.) (on cover) .. †
cw. Wmk inverted .. .. ..
d. Perf 13½×12½ .. .. .. 8·50
da. Imperf between (pair) £300
38 1 pi. red (*shades*) (4.75) .. .. 6·00
a. Tête-bêche (vert pair) .. .. 90·00
b. Tête-bêche (horiz pair) £300
c. Imperf (pair) .. .. ..
d. Imperf between (pair) .. .. —
ew. Wmk inverted .. .. .. 8·00
f. Perf 13½×12½ .. .. .. 70·00
fa. Tête-bêche (vert pair) £350
fb. Tête-bêche (horiz pair) .. ..
fw. Wmk inverted .. .. .. 80·00
39 2 pi. yellow (12.74) .. .. .. 75·00
a. Tête-bêche (pair) £400
bw. Wmk inverted .. .. .. 90·00
c. Perf 13½×12½ .. .. .. 5·50
ca. Tête-bêche (pair) £400
cb. Bisected diag (1 pi.) (on cover) (4.75) †
cw. Wmk inverted .. .. .. 7·50
d. Perf 12½×13½ .. .. .. 65·00
da. Tête-bêche (pair) £850
dw. Wmk inverted .. .. .. 80·00
40 2½ pi. violet .. .. 8·50
a. Tête-bêche (pair) £350
bw. Wmk inverted .. .. .. 12·00
c. Perf 12½×13½ .. .. .. 55·00
ca. Tête-bêche (pair) £1000
cw. Wmk inverted .. .. .. 50·00
41 5 pi. green .. .. 55·00
a. Imperf (pair) .. .. .. †
bw. Wmk inverted £100
c. Perf 12½×13½ £300

The 2 pi. bisected was used at Gedda and are all postmar[illegible] 13 April.

The 1872 printings have a thick line of colour in the [illegible] margin of the sheet and the other margins are all plain, [illegible] exception being the 5 pa., which on the majority of the sh[illegible] has the line at the righthand side of the sheet. The 1874[illegible] printings have a wide fancy border all round every sheet.

The 1872 printings are on thick opaque paper, with [illegible] impressions sharp and clear. The 1874–75 printings are on thi[illegible] paper, often semi-transparent and oily in appearance, and ha[illegible] the impressions very blurred and badly printed. These are [illegible] general distinctions and there are a number of exceptions.

The majority of the 1874–75 stamps have blind or defec[illegible] perforations, while the 1872 stamps have clean-cut perfs.

The two printings of the 5 pa. to 1 pi. values can be identi[illegible] by their perforation gauges, which are always different; [illegible] 5 pa. also differs in the side panels (Types **7** and **8**). Only the [illegible] 12½×13½ varieties of the three higher values may need t[illegible] distinguished. As well as the general points noted above [illegible] following features are also helpful:

2 pi. In the 1872 issue the left-hand Arabic character in [illegible] top inscription is one complete shape, resembling an inve[illegible] "V" with a horizontal line on top. In the 1874 issue the chara[illegible] has three separate components, a line with two dots below.

2½ pi. There is a distinct thinning of the frame line in the [illegible] right-hand corner of the 1872 issue. This sometimes takes [illegible] form of a short white line within the frame.

5 pi. In the 1872 issue the top frame line is split for its en[illegible] length; in the 1874 issue the line is solid for all or most of [illegible] length. The 1872 printing always has a white dot above the [illegible] of "PIASTRE"; this dot appears on only a few positions of [illegible] 1874 printing.

There seem to be many different compositions of the she[illegible] containing the *tête-bêche* varieties, settings being known wit[illegible] 3, 9 and 10 inverted stamps in various sheets. Sheets of the 5 [illegible] are known with 9 of the 20 horizontal rows inverted, giv[illegible] vertical *tête-bêche* pairs; four stamps were inverted within th[illegible] row giving four horizontal *tête-bêche* pairs.

(9)

1878 (Dec). *No.* 40 *surch as T* **9** *at Bûlâq. P* 12½.

42 7 5 pa. on 2½ pi. violet .. .. .. 6·00
a. Surch inverted .. .. .. 70·00
b. Tête-bêche (pair) £3500
dw. Wmk inverted .. .. .. 7·50
e. Perf 12½×13½ .. .. .. 6·50
ea. Surch inverted £140
eb. Tête-bêche (pair) .. .. ..
ew. Wmk inverted .. .. .. 8·00
43 10 pa. on 2½ pi. violet .. .. .. 11·00
a. Surch inverted .. .. .. 75·00
b. Tête-bêche (pair) £1500
dw. Wmk inverted .. .. .. 15·00
e. Perf 12½×13½ .. .. .. 15·00
ea. Surch inverted £110
eb. Tete-bêche (pair) £1500
ew. Wmk inverted .. .. .. 25·00

ALTERED CATALOGUE NUMBERS

Any Catalogue numbers altered from the las[illegible] edition are shown as a list in the introductor[illegible] pages.

10

11

12

13 14

15

(Typo De La Rue)

(1 Apr). *Ordinary paper. W* 8*a* (*inverted on* 10 *pa.*). *P* 14.

10 5 pa. deep brown 1·50 30
 a. Pale brown 1·50 30
 w. Wmk inverted £120 £100
11 10 pa. reddish lilac 50·00 3·00
12 20 pa. pale blue 60·00 1·75
 w. Wmk inverted 90·00 15·00
13 1 pi. rose 25·00 20
 a. Pale rose 25·00 20
 w. Wmk inverted 60·00 10·00
14 2 pi. orange 29·00 50
 a. Orange-yellow 26·00 80
 w. Wmk inverted 32·00 2·00
15 5 pi. green 55·00 10·00
 a. Blue-green 55·00 9·00
 w. Wmk inverted 50·00 11·00

ee also Nos. 50/6

Khedive Tewfik

26 June 1879–7 January 1892

ritish troops were landed in Egypt in 1882 to secure the Suez ial against a nationalist movement led by Arabi Pasha. Arabi defeated at Tel-el-Kebir and British troops remained in Egypt il 1954. A British resident and consul-general advised the edive. Holders of this post were Sir Evelyn Baring (Lord mer), 1883–1907; Sir Eldon Gorst, 1907–11; and Lord Kitchr, 1911–14.

31–1902. *Colours changed. Ordinary paper. W* 8*a* (*inverted n No.* 50). *P* 14.

11 10 pa. claret (1.81) 50·00 7·00
 10 pa. bluish grey (25.1.82) 7·50 1·75
 w. Wmk inverted 40·00 3·00
 10 pa. green (15.12.84) 1·50 70
 w. Wmk inverted 20·00 3·00
12 20 pa. rose-carmine (15.12.84) 13·00 55
 a. Bright rose 13·00 50
 w. Wmk inverted 35·00 7·00
13 1 pi. blue (15.12.84) 5·00 20
 a. Deep ultramarine 6·00 20
 b. Pale ultramarine 4·00 20
 cw. Wmk inverted 26·00 10·00
 d. Chalk-surfaced paper. *Ultramarine* (1902) 2·50 10
 da. Blue 2·50 10
 dw. Wmk inverted 75·00 40·00
14 2 pi. orange-brown (1.8.93) 12·00 30
 aw. Wmk inverted 80·00 40·00
 b. Chalk-surfaced paper (1902) 12·00 10
 ba. Orange 22·00 1·00
 bw. Wmk inverted
15 5 pi. pale grey (15.12.84) 13·00 50
 a. Slate 11·00 40
 bw. Wmk inverted
 c. Chalk-surfaced paper. *Slate-grey* (1902) 16·00 15

PARAS 20

(17)

884 (1 Feb). *Surch with T* 17 *at Bûlâq.*

7 15 20 pa. on 5 pi. green 7·00 1·25
 a. Surch inverted 65·00 60·00
 w. Wmk inverted 50·00 30·00

New Currency: 1000 milliemes = 100 piastres = £1 Egyptian)

18

19

20

21

22

1888 (1 Jan)–**1909.** *Ordinary paper. W* 8*a*. *P* 14.

58 **18** 1 m. pale brown 1·50 10
 a. Deep brown 2·25 10
 bw. Wmk inverted 25·00 4·00
 c. Chalk-surfaced paper. *Pale brown* (1902) 1·50 10
 ca. Deep brown 1·60 10
 cw. Wmk inverted 40·00 5·00
59 **19** 2 m. blue-green 75 10
 a. Green 75 10
 bw. Wmk inverted 40·00 5·00
 c. Chalk-surfaced paper. *Green* (1902) 60 10
 cw. Wmk inverted 40·00 5·00
60 **20** 3 m. maroon (1.1.92) 2·50 1·00
61 3 m. yellow (1.8.93) 3·50 50
 a. Orange-yellow 2·75 15
 bw. Wmk inverted 45·00 15·00
 c. Chalk-surfaced paper. *Orange-yellow* (1902) 2·00 10
 cw. Wmk inverted 75·00 30·00
62 **21** 4 m. verm (*chalk-surfaced paper*) (1906) 2·00 10
 a. Bisected (2 m.) (on cover) (11.09) † —
63 5 m. rose-carmine 2·25 10
 a. Bright rose 2·25 10
 b. Aniline rose 3·50 10
 cw. Wmk inverted
 d. Chalk-surfaced paper. *Rose* (1902) 1·75 10
 da. Deep aniline rose 3·75 20
64 **22** 10 p. mauve (1.1.89) 15·00 80
 a. Aniline mauve 18·00 80
 bw. Wmk inverted
 c. Chalk-surfaced paper. *Mauve* (1902) 22·00 50

No. 62a was used at Gizira in conjunction with the 1 m. value and the Official, No. O64.

No. 63d exists in coils constructed from normal sheets.

Khedive Abbas Hilmi

7 January 1892–19 December 1914

A set of three values, in a common design showing Cleopatra and a Nile boat, was prepared in 1895 for the Nile Winter Fête, but not issued. Examples survive from the De La Rue archives.

29 Nile Feluccas

30 Cleopatra from Temple of Dendera

31 Ras-el-Tin Palace, Alexandria

35 Archway of Ptolemy III, Karnak

37 Rock Temple of Abu Simbel

(Typo D.L.R.)

1914 (8 Jan). *W* 8*a*. *P* 13½×14 (1 *m. to* 10 *m.*) *or* 14 (20 *m. to* 200 *m.*).

73 **29** 1 m. sepia 80 40
74 **30** 2 m. green 1·25 20
 w. Wmk inverted
75 **31** 3 m. yellow-orange 80 35
 a. Double impression
 w. Wmk inverted — 3·00
76 – 4 m. vermilion 1·75 65
 w. Wmk inverted — 1·75
77 – 5 m. lake 2·00 10
 a. Wmk sideways star to right* (booklets) 10·00 22·00
 aw. Wmk sideways star to left 10·00 22·00
 w. Wmk inverted 15·00 10·00
78 – 10 m. dull blue 3·25 10
 w. Wmk inverted — 15·00
79 **35** 20 m. olive 6·50 30
 w. Wmk inverted — 6·00
80 – 50 m. purple 11·00 40
 w. Wmk inverted — 50·00
81 **37** 100 m. slate 12·00 60
82 – 200 m. maroon 26·00 3·50
73/82 *Set of* 10 55·00 6·00

Designs: *As T* **29**—4 m. Pyramids at Giza; 5 m. Sphinx; 10 m. Colossi of Amenophis III at Thebes. *As T* **35**—50 c. Cairo Citadel; 200 m. Aswân Dan.

*The normal sideways watermark shows the star to the right of the crescent, *as seen from the back of the stamp.*

All the above exist imperforate, but imperforate stamps without watermark are proofs.

See also Nos. 84/95.

BRITISH PROTECTORATE

On 18 December 1914, after war with Turkey had begun, Egypt was declared to be a British protectorate. Abbas Hilmi was deposed, and his uncle, Hussein Kamil, was proclaimed Sultan of Egypt.

Sultan Hussein Kamil

19 December 1914–9 October 1917

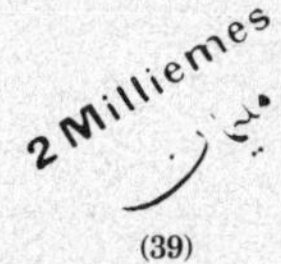

(39)

1915 (15 Oct). *No.* 75 *surch with T* **39**, *at Bûlâq.*

83 **31** 2 m. on 3 m. yellow-orange 55 1·50
 a. Surch inverted £200 £200
 b. Surch double, one albino £120
 w. Wmk inverted

Sultan Ahmed Fuad

9 October 1917–15 March 1922

40

(A)

(B)

41 Statue of Rameses II, **42** Luxor

(Typo Harrison)

1921–22. *As Nos.* 73/82 *and new designs* (15 *m.*). *W* **40**. *P* 14 (20, 50, 100 *m.*) *or* 13½×14 (*others*).

84 **29** 1 m. sepia (A) 1·00 2·00
 a. Two dots omitted (B) (R. 10/10) 35·00 45·00
 w. Wmk inverted 10·00 7·50
85 **30** 2 m. green 3·50 3·75
 a. Imperf between (pair)
 w. Wmk inverted 15·00 10·00
86 2 m. vermilion (1922) 2·75 55
 w. Wmk inverted 15·00 10·00
87 **31** 3 m. yellow-orange 3·50 1·50
 w. Wmk inverted 16·00 10·00
88 – 4 m. green (1922) 4·25 6·00
 w. Wmk inverted — 10·00
89 – 5 m. lake (1.21) 3·50 10
 a. Imperf between (pair)
 w. Wmk inverted 15·00 10·00
90 – 5 m. pink (11.21) 3·50 10
 w. Wmk inverted 15·00 10·00
91 – 10 m. dull blue 3·50 20
 w. Wmk inverted — 10·00
92 – 10 m. lake (9.22) 1·75 30
 w. Wmk inverted — 10·00
93 **41** 15 m. indigo (3.22) 3·75 15
 w. Wmk inverted — 8·00
94 **42** 15 m. indigo 20·00 3·00
 w. Wmk inverted 22·00 10·00
95 **35** 20 m. olive 7·50 30
 w. Wmk inverted 20·00 10·00
96 – 50 m. purple 10·00 1·00
 w. Wmk inverted 18·00 12·00
97 **37** 100 m. slate (1922) 70·00 7·50
84/97 *Set of* 13 £100 20·00

Type **42** was printed first; but because the Arabic inscription at right was felt to be unsuitable the stamps were withheld and the corrected Type **41** printed and issued. Type **42** was released later.

STAMP BOOKLETS

1903 (1 Jan). *Black on pink cover inscr* "Egyptian Post Office" *in English and French. Stapled.*

SB1 121 m. booklet containing twenty-four 5 m. (No. 63c) in blocks of 6
 Price reduced to 120 m. from 1 July 1911.

1903 (1 July). *Black on blue cover inscr* "Egyptian Post Office" *in English and French. Stapled.*

SB2 73 m. booklet containing twenty-four 3 m. (No. 61ab) in blocks of 6

1911 (1 July). *Black on pink cover inscr* "Egyptian Post Office" *in English and Arabic. Stapled.*

SB3 120 m. Contents as No. SB1

1914 (8 Jan). *Black on pink cover inscr* "Egyptian Post Office" *in English and Arabic. Stapled.*

SB4 125 m. booklet containing twenty-four 5 m. (No. 77a) in blocks of 6

1919 (1 Jan). *Black on pink cover inscr* "Egyptian Post Office" *in English and Arabic. Stapled.*

SB5 120 m. Contents as No. SB4

1921 (12 June). *Deep blue on pink cover inscr* "POST OFFICE" *in English and Arabic. Stapled.*

SB6 120 m. booklet containing twenty-four 5 m. (No. 89) in blocks of 6
 a. Stitched

1921 (Nov). *Deep blue or pink cover inscr* "POST OFFICE" *in English and Arabic. Stapled.*

SB7 120 m. booklet containing twenty-four 5 m. (No. 90) in blocks of 6

POSTAGE DUE STAMPS

D 16

D 23

D 24

(Des L. Barkhausen. Litho V. Penasson, Alexandria)

1884 (1 Jan). *W* **6** *(impressed on reverse). P* 10½.

D57 **D 16** 10 pa. red .. .. 45·00 9·00
a. Imperf (pair) .. ..
b. Imperf between (pair) .. £110
w. Wmk inverted .. .. 75·00 15·00
D58 20 pa. red .. .. £110 26·00
w. Wmk inverted .. .. £190 40·00
D59 1 pi. red .. .. £130 40·00
w. Wmk inverted £200 £100
D60 2 pi. red .. .. £225 10·00
w. Wmk inverted .. .. £325 20·00
D61 5 pi. red .. .. 14·00 42·00
w. Wmk inverted .. .. 32·00 48·00

1886 (1 Aug)–**87**. *No wmk. P* 10½.

D62 **D 16** 10 pa. rose-red (1887) .. .. 55·00 9·50
a. Imperf between (pair) .. 90·00
D63 20 pa. rose-red .. .. .. £225 35·00
a. Imperf between (pair) ..
D64 1 pi. rose-red .. .. .. 28·00 7·00
a. Imperf between (pair) .. £120 £120
D65 2 pi. rose-red .. .. .. 28·00 3·75
a. Imperf between (pair) .. £120

Specialists distinguish four types of each value in both these issues.

(Litho V. Penasson, Alexandria)

1888 (1 Jan). *No wmk. P* 11½.

D66 **D 23** 2 m. green .. .. .. 11·00 17·00
a. Imperf between (pair) £170 £170
D67 5 m. rose-carmine .. .. .. 29·00 17·00
D68 1 p. blue .. .. £130 35·00
a. Imperf between (pair) £170
D69 2 p. orange .. .. £150 12·00
D70 5 p. grey £200 £180
a. With stop after left-hand "PIASTRES" £275 £225

Specialists distinguish four types of each value. No. D70a occurs on all examples of one of these types in the sheet except that on R. 2/1.

Beware of forgeries of the 5 p.

(Typo De La Rue)

1889 (Apr)–**1907**. *Ordinary paper. W* **8a**. *P* 14.

D71 **D 24** 2 m. green .. .. .. 7·00 50
a. Bisected (1 m.) (on cover with unbisected 2 m.) (2.98) .. † £250
bw. Wmk inverted .. .. 8·00 50
c. Chalk-surfaced paper (1906) .. 14·00 50
D72 4 m. maroon .. .. .. 2·25 50
aw. Wmk inverted .. .. 4·00 1·00
b. Chalk-surfaced paper (1906) .. 2·75 50
D73 1 p. ultramarine .. .. .. 5·50 50
aw. Wmk inverted .. .. 7·50 50
b. Chalk-surfaced paper (1906) .. 6·50 50
D74 2 p. orange .. .. .. 5·50 70
a. Bisected diagonally (1 p.) (on cover) .. .. .. † —
bw. Wmk inverted .. .. 5·00 70
c. Chalk-surfaced paper (1907) .. 5·00 70

No. D71a was authorised for use on Egyptian Army letters from the Sudan campaign which were only charged 3 m. postage due.

See also Nos. 84/6 for stamps with watermark sideways.

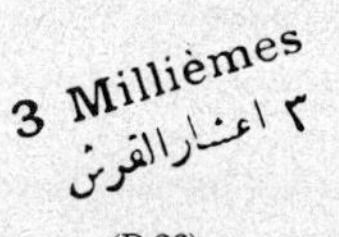

(D 26)

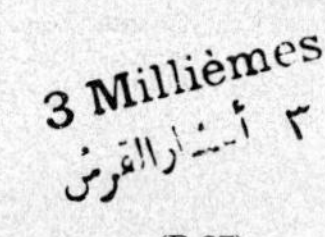

(D 27)

Type D 26

The Arabic figure at right is less than 2 mm from the next character, which consists of a straight stroke only.

Type D 27

The distance is 3 mm and the straight character has a comma-like character above it. There are other minor differences.

1898 (7 May)–**1907**. *No.* D74 *surch at Bûlâq. Ordinary paper.*

(a) With Type D **26**

D75 **D 24** 3 m. on 2 p. orange .. .. 1·25 3·50
a. Surch inverted .. .. 60·00 75·00
b. Pair, one without surch ..
c. Arabic "2" for "3" .. ..
d. Arabic "3" over "2" £100

No. D75c occurred in the first printing on positions 10, 20, 30, 40, 50 and 60 of the pane of 60 (the Arabic figure is the right-hand character of the second line—see illustration on page xvii). In the second printing the correct figure was printed on top to form No. D75d. The error was corrected in subsequent printings.

(b) With Type D **27** (11.04)

D76 **D 24** 3 m. on 2 p. orange .. .. 3·75 11·00
a. Surch inverted .. .. 50·00 60·00
b. Surch double £200
c. Chalk-surfaced paper (1907) ..

1914–15. *As Nos.* D71/3 *but wmk sideways*.*

D84 **D 24** 2 m. bright green (1915) .. .. 10·00 3·25
w. Wmk star to left of crescent .. 17·00 11·00
D85 4 m. maroon .. .. .. 10·00 12·00
w. Wmk star to left of crescent .. 20·00
D86 1 p. dull ultramarine .. .. 18·00 8·50
w. Wmk star to left of crescent .. 14·00 9·00

*The normal sideways watermark shows star to right of crescent, *as seen from the back of the stamp.*

D 43

D 44

(Typo Harrison)

1921 (Apr)–**22**. *Chalk-surfaced paper. W* **40** *(sideways*). P* 14×13½.

D 98 **D 43** 2 m. green .. .. .. 2·75 3·50
w. Wmk stars below crescents .. 9·00 3·50
D 99 2 m. scarlet (1922) .. .. 1·00 1·50
w. Wmk stars below crescents .. 7·50 4·00
D100 4 m. scarlet .. .. .. 5·00 13·00
D101 4 m. green (1922) .. .. .. 3·00 1·00
w. Wmk stars below crescents .. 12·00 5·00
D102 **D 44** 10 m. deep slate-blue (11.21) .. 5·50 17·00
D103 10 m. lake (1922) .. .. .. 5·50 70
w. Wmk stars below crescents .. 10·00 4·00
D98/103 .. .. *Set of* 6 20·00 32·00

*The normal sideways watermark shows the stars above the crescents.

OFFICIAL STAMPS

O 25

O.H.H.S.
(O 28)

"O.H.H.S."
(O 29)

(Typo De La Rue)

1893 (1 Jan)–**1914**. *Ordinary paper. W* **8a**. *P* 14.

O64 **O 25** (–) chestnut .. .. .. 1·90 10
a. Chalk-surfaced paper (1903) ..
bw. Wmk inverted .. ..
c. Wmk sideways star to right. Chalk-surfaced paper (1914) .. 10·00 8·50
cw. Wmk sideways star to left ..

From January 1907 No. O64 was used on most official mail to addresses within Egypt. In 1907 it was replaced by Nos. O73/8, but the use of No. O64 for unregistered official mail to Egyptian addresses was resumed on 1 January 1909.

After No. O64c was withdrawn in 1915 the remaining stock was surcharged 1 p., 2 p., 3 p. or 5 p. for fiscal use.

1907 (1 Feb–Aug). *Nos.* 54*da*, 56*c*, 58*c*, 59*c*, 61*c and* 63*d optd with Type* O **28** *by De La Rue.*

O73 **18** 1 m. pale brown .. .. .. 1·75 30
O74 **19** 2 m. green .. .. .. 3·75 10
a. Opt double .. ..
O75 **20** 3 m. orange-yellow .. .. 2·75 1·25
O76 **21** 5 m. rose .. .. .. 5·00 10
O77 **13** 1 p. blue .. .. .. 2·00 20
O78 **15** 5 p. slate-grey (Aug) .. .. 16·00 2·00
O73/8 .. .. *Set of* 6 28·00 3·50

Nos. O73/8 were used on all official mail from February 1907 until 1 January 1909 after which their use was restricted to registered items and those sent to addresses overseas.

1913 (Nov). *No.* 63d *optd at Bûlâq.*

(a) With Type O **29**

O79 **21** 5 m. rose .. .. — £300
a. Opt inverted .. .. ..

(b) As Type O **29** *but without inverted commas*

O80 **21** 5 m. rose .. .. .. 5·00 40
a. No stop after "S" (R. 11/10) .. 50·00 16·00
b. Opt inverted .. .. £200 75·00

O.H.H.S.
(O 38)

O.H.H.S.
(O 39)

O.H.H.S.
(O 43)

1914 (Dec)–**15**. *Stamps of* 1902–6 *and* 1914 *optd with Type* O **38** *at Bûlâq.*

O83 **29** 1 m. sepia (1.15) .. .. 1·25 3·50
a. No stop after "S" (R. 10/10) .. 12·00 25·00
O84 **19** 2 m. green (3.15) .. .. 3·50 4·75
a. No stop after "S" .. .. 14·00 23·00
b. Opt inverted .. .. 35·00 35·00
c. Opt double £325
O85 **31** 3 m. yellow-orange (3.15) .. 2·00 3·50
a. No stop after "S" (R. 10/10) .. 14·00 25·00
O86 **21** 4 m. vermilion (12.14) .. .. 4·00 1·75
a. Opt inverted £190 £140
b. Pair, one without opt ..
O87 – 5 m. lake (1.15) .. .. 3·75 80
a. No stop after "S" (R. 10/10) .. 15·00 22·00
O83/7 .. .. *Set of* 5 13·00 13·00

No. O84a occurs on three positions from the first printing and on two different positions from the second.

1915 (Oct). *Nos.* 59ab, 62 *and* 77 *optd lithographically Type* O **39** *at Bûlâq.*

O88 **19** 2 m. green .. .. 1·75
a. Opt inverted .. .. .. 20·00 2
b. Opt double .. .. .. 25·00
O89 **21** 4 m. vermilion .. .. 4·50
O90 – 5 m. lake .. .. 5·50
a. Pair, one without opt £275

1922. *Nos.* 84, *etc optd lithographically with Type* O 4 *Bûlâq.*

O 98 **29** 1 m. sepia (A) (28.6) .. .. .. 3·50
a. Two dots omitted (B) £200
w. Wmk inverted .. .. ..
O 99 **30** 2 m. vermilion (16.6) .. .. 7·00 1
O100 **31** 3 m. yellow-orange (28.6) .. .. 65·00
O101 – 5 m. pink (13.3) .. .. .. 17·00

Egypt was declared to be an independent kingdom on 15 M 1922, and Sultan Ahmed Fuad became king.

Later stamp issues will be found listed in Part 19 (*Middle E* of this catalogue.

EGYPTIAN POST OFFICES ABROAD

From 1865 Egypt operated various post offices in fore countries. No special stamps were issued for these offices use in them of unoverprinted Egyptian stamps can only identified by the cancellation. Stamps with such cancellati are worth more than the used prices quoted in the Eg listings.

Such offices operated in the following countries. An * indica that details will be found under that heading elsewhere in catalogue.

ETHIOPIA

A

B

C

D

MASSAWA. *Open Nov* 1867 *to* 5 Dec 1885. *Postmark types (also without* REGIE), B, C, D. *An Arabic seal type is al known on stampless covers.*

SENHIT (near Keren). *Open* 1878 *to* April 1885. *Only o cover, cancelled* "Mouderie Senhit" *in* 1879, *is know together with one showing a possible hand-draw cancellation.*

A post office is also recorded at Harar in 1878, but no posta marking has so far been reported.

SOMALILAND*

Unoverprinted stamps of Egypt used from 1876 until 1884.

SUDAN*

Unoverprinted stamps of Egypt used from 1867 until 1897.

TURKISH EMPIRE

E

F

G H I J K L M N O

he offices are listed according to the spelling on the cellation. The present-day name (if different) and country given in brackets.

ALESSANDRETTA (Iskenderun, Turkey). *Open* 14 July 1870 *to* Feb 1872. *Postmark types* E, I.
BAIROUT (Beirut, Lebanon). *Open* 14 July 1870 *to* Feb 1872. *Postmark types* E, J.
CAVALA (Kavala, Greece). *Open* 14 July 1870 *to* Feb 1872. *Postmark type* E.
COSTANTINOPOLI (Istanbul, Turkey). *Open* 13 June 1865 *to* 30 June 1881. *Postmark types* E, F, O.
DARDANELLI (Canakkle, Turkey). *Open* 10 June 1868 *to* 30 June 1881. *Postmark types* H, K.
DJEDDAH, *see* GEDDA.
GALIPOLI (Gelibolu, Turkey). *Open* 10 June 1868 *to* 30 June 1881. *Postmark types* E, L.
GEDDA, DJEDDAH (Jeddah, Saudi Arabia). *Open* 8 June 1865 *to* 30 June 1881. *Postmark types* F, G (*also with year replacing solid half-circle*), O (*all spelt* GEDDA), D (*spelt* DJEDDAH).
IAFFA (Jaffa, Israel). *Open* 14 July 1870 *to* Feb 1872. *Postmark type* E.
LAGOS (Port Lago, Greece). *Open* 14 July 1870 *to* Feb 1872. *Postmark type* E.
LATAKIA (Syria). *Open* 14 July 1870 *to* Feb 1872. *Postmark type* E.
LEROS (Aegean Is). *Open* July 1873 *to* January 1874 *and* May *to* October 1874. *Postmark type* E.
MERSINA (Mersin, Turkey). *Open* 14 July 1870 *to* Feb 1872. *Postmark type* E.
METELINO (Lesbos, Greece). *Open* 14 July 1870 *to* 30 June 1881. *Postmark types* E, M.
RODI (Rhodes, Greece). *Open* 13 Aug 1872 *to* 30 June 1881. *Postmark type* E.
SALONNICCHI (Thessaloniki, Greece). *Open* 14 July 1870 *to* Feb 1872. *Postmark type* E.
SCIO (Chios, Aegean Is.). *Open* 14 July 1870 *to* 30 June 1881. *Postmark types* E, N.
SMIRNE (Izmir, Turkey). *Open* 14 Nov 1865 *to* 30 June 1881. *Postmark types* E (*also without* "V. R."), F.
TENEDOS (Bozcaada, Turkey). *Open* 14 July 1870 *to* March 1871. *Postmark type* E.
TRIPOLI (Lebanon). *Open* 14 July 1870 *to* Feb 1872. *Postmark type* E.
VOLO (Volos, Greece). *Open* 14 July 1870 *to* Feb 1872. *Postmark type* E.

BRITISH FORCES IN EGYPT

Following the rise of a nationalist movement led by Arabi Pasha, and serious disturbances in Alexandria, British troops landed at Ismalia in August 1882 and defeated the nationalists at Tel-el-Kebir on 13 September. A British Army Post Office detachment landed at Alexandria on 21 August and provided a postal service for the troops, using Great Britain stamps, from various locations until it was withdrawn on 7 October.

During the Gordon Relief Expedition of 1884–85 a postal detachment was sent to Suakin on the Red Sea. This operated between 25 March and 30 May 1885 using Great Britain stamps.

ZA 1

Stamps of GREAT BRITAIN *cancelled with Type* ZA **1**.

1882 (Aug–Oct).

ZA1	½d. rose-red (Plate No. 20)	
ZA2	½d. green (1880)	£300
ZA3	1d. Venetian red (1880)	
ZA4	1d. lilac (1881)	£175
ZA5	2½d. blue (1881) (Plate Nos. 21, 22, 23)	£100

1885. *Used at Suakin.*

ZA6	½d. slate-blue (1884)	
ZA7	1d. lilac (1881)	£300
ZA8	2½d. lilac (1884)	£225
ZA9	5d. dull green (1884)	£500

From 1 November 1932, to 29 February 1936 members of the British Forces in Egypt and their families were allowed to send letters to the British Isles at reduced rates. Special seals, which were on sale in booklets at N.A.A.F.I. Institutes and Canteens, were used instead of Egyptian stamps. These seals were stuck on the back of the envelopes, letters bearing the seals being franked on the front with a hand-stamp inscribed "EGYPT POSTAGE PREPAID" in a double circle surmounted by a crown.

PRICES FOR STAMPS ON COVER

Nos. A1/9	*from* × 5
No. A10	*from* × 2
No. A11	*from* × 5
No. A12	*from* × 100
No. A13	*from* × 20
No. A14	*from* × 100
No. A15	*from* × 20

A 1

A 2

(Des Lt-Col. C. Fraser. Typo Hanbury, Tomsett & Co. Ltd, London)

1932 (1 Nov)–**33.** *P* 11. (*a*) *Inscr* "POSTAL SEAL".

A1	A **1**	1 p. deep blue and red	80·00	3·50

(*b*) *Inscr* "LETTER SEAL"

A2	A **1**	1 p. deep blue and red (8.33)	25·00	85

(Des Sgt. W. F. Lait. Litho Walker & Co, Amalgamated Press, Cairo)

1932 (26 Nov)–**35.** *Christmas Seals. P* 11½.

A3	A **2**	3 m. black/*azure*	48·00	70·00
A4		3 m. brown-lake (13.11.33)	7·50	48·00
A5		3 m. deep blue (17.11.34)	7·00	25·00
A6		3 m. vermilion (23.11.35)	1·25	32·00
		a. Pale vermilion (19.12.35)	7·50	18·00

A 3

(Des Miss Waugh. Photo Harrison)

1934 (1 June)–**35.** (*a*) *P* 14½ × 14.

A7	A **3**	1 p. carmine	35·00	85
A8		1 p. green (5.12.34)	4·00	4·00

(*b*) *P* 13½ × 14

A9	A **3**	1 p. carmine (24.4.35)	2·25	3·00

JUBILEE
COMMEMORATION
1935

(A **4**)

1935 (6 May). *Silver Jubilee. As No.* A9, *but colour changed and optd with Type* A **4**, *in red.*

A10	A **3**	1 p. ultramarine	£200	£180

Xmas 1935
3 Milliemes

(A **5**)

1935 (16 Dec). *Provisional Christmas Seal. No.* A9 *surch with Type* A **5**.

A11	A **3**	3 m. on 1 p. carmine	16·00	70·00

The seals and letter stamps were replaced by the following Army Post stamps issued by the Egyptian Postal Administration. No. A9 was accepted for postage until 15 March 1936.

A **6** King Fuad I

A **7** King Farouk

W **48** of Egypt

(Types A **6**/A **7**. Photo Survey Dept, Cairo)

1936. *W* **48** *of Egypt. P* 13½×14.

A12	A **6**	3 m. green (9.11.36)	1·00	1·00
A13		10 m. carmine (1.3.36)	3·00	10
		w. Wmk inverted		

1939 (16 Dec). *W* **48** *of Egypt. P* 13×13½.

A14	A **7**	3 m. green	3·00	4·50
A15		10 m. carmine	3·75	10
		w. Wmk inverted		

These stamps were withdrawn in April 1941 but the concession, without the use of special stamps, continued until October 1951 when the postal agreement was abrogated.

SUEZ CANAL COMPANY

PRICES FOR STAMPS ON COVER

Nos. 1/4	*from* × 20

100 Centimes = 1 Franc

On 30 November 1855 a concession to construct the Suez Canal was granted to Ferdinand de Lesseps and the Compagnie Universelle du Canal Maritime de Suez was formed. Work began in April 1859 and the canal was opened on 17 November 1869. In November 1875 the Khedive sold his shares in the company to the British Government, which then became the largest shareholder.

The company transported mail free of charge between Port Said and Suez from 1859 to 1867, when it was decided that payment should be made for the service and postage stamps were introduced in July 1868. Letters for destinations beyond Port Said or Suez required additional franking with Egyptian or French stamps.

The imposition of charges for the service was not welcomed by the public and in August the Egyptian Government agreed to take it over.

1

(Litho Chézaud, Ainé & Tavernier, Paris)

1868 (8 July). *Imperf.*

1	**1**	1 c. black	£250	£1000
2		5 c. green	85·00	£500
3		20 c. blue	75·00	£500
4		40 c. pink	£130	£750

Shades of all values exist.

Stamps can be found showing parts of the papermaker's watermark "LA+-F" (La Croix Frères).

These stamps were withdrawn from sale on 16 August 1868 and demonetised on 31 August.

Many forgeries exist, unused and cancelled. The vast majority of these forgeries show vertical lines, instead of cross-hatching, between "POSTES" and the central oval. It is believed that other forgeries, which do show cross-hatching, originate from the plate of the 40 c. value which is missing from the company's archives. These are, however, on thin, brittle paper with smooth shiny gum.

Falkland Islands

PRICES FOR STAMPS ON COVER TO 1945

No. 1	*from* × 100
No. 2	*from* × 50
Nos. 3/4	*from* × 10
No. 5	—
Nos. 6/10	*from* × 30
Nos. 11/12	*from* × 15
Nos. 13/17	*from* × 10
Nos. 17*b/c*	*from* × 100
Nos. 18/21	*from* × 10
Nos. 22/*b*	*from* × 30
Nos. 23/4	*from* × 100
Nos. 25/6	*from* × 30
No. 27	*from* × 20
No. 28	*from* × 40
No. 29	*from* × 5
Nos. 30/*b*	*from* × 50
No. 30*c*	*from* × 15
No. 31	*from* × 5
Nos. 32/8	*from* × 15
Nos. 41/2	—
Nos. 43/8	*from* × 12
Nos. 49/50	—
Nos. 60/5	*from* × 10
Nos. 66/9	—
Nos. 70/1	*from* × 10
Nos. 72/*b*	—
Nos. 73/9	*from* × 4
No. 80	—
No. 115	*from* × 2
Nos. 116/19	*from* × 20
Nos. 120/2	*from* × 6
Nos. 123/6	—
Nos. 127/34	*from* × 5
Nos. 135/8	—
Nos. 139/45	*from* × 50
Nos. 146/63	*from* × 5

CROWN COLONY

FALKLAND PAID. ISLANDS.

1 2

1869–76. *The Franks.*
FR1 **1** In black, *on cover* £6500
FR2 **2** In red, *on cover* (1876) £12000

On *piece*, No. FR1 on white or coloured paper £90; No. FR2 on white £140.

The first recorded use of No. FR1 is on a cover to London datestamped 4 January 1869. The use of these franks ceased when the first stamps were issued.

½d.

3 (4)

In the ½d., 2d., 2½d. and 9d. the figures of value in the lower corners are replaced by small rosettes and the words of value are in colour.

NOTE. Nos. 1, 2, 3, 4, 8, 10, 11 and 12 exist with one or two sides imperf from the margin of the sheets.

(Recess B.W.)

1878–79. *No wmk. P* 14, 14½.
1 **3** 1d. claret (19.6.78) £600 £350
2 4d. grey-black (Sept 1879) £1100 £150
a. On wmkd paper £2750 £500
3 6d. blue-green (19.6.78) .. .. 65·00 60·00
4 1s. bistre-brown (1878) .. .. 60·00 60·00

No. 2a shows portions of the papermaker's watermark—"R. TURNER, CHAFFORD MILLS"—in ornate double-lined capitals.

NOTES. The dates shown for Nos. 5/12 and 15/38 are those on which the printer delivered the various printings to the Crown Agents. Several months could elapse before the stamps went on sale in the Colony, depending on the availability of shipping.

The plates used for these stamps did not fit the paper so that the watermark appears in all sorts of positions on the stamp. Well centred examples are scarce. Examples can also be found showing parts of the marginal watermarks, either CROWN AGENTS horizontally in letters 12 mm high or "CROWN AGENTS FOR THE COLONIES" vertically in 7 mm letters. Both are in double-lined capitals.

1882 (22 Nov). *Wmk Crown CA (upright). P* 14, 14½.
5 **3** 1d. dull claret £325 £130
a. Imperf vert (horiz pair) £45000
x. Wmk reversed £750
y. Wmk inverted and reversed £450 £275
6 4d. grey-black .. .. £300 75·00
w. Wmk inverted £450 £180

1885 (23 Mar)–**87.** *Wmk Crown CA (sideways*). P* 14, 14½.
7 **3** 1d. pale claret .. .. 55·00 42·00
w. Wmk Crown to right of CA .. .. 80·00 55·00
x. Wmk sideways reversed £170 £100
y. Wmk Crown to right of CA and reversed £160 £100
8 1d. brownish claret (3.10.87) .. .. 80·00 38·00
a. Bisected (on cover) (1891) † .. .. † £2000
w. Wmk Crown to right of CA .. .. 95·00 42·00
x. Wmk sideways reversed £140 £100
y. Wmk Crown to right of CA and reversed £160 £130
9 4d. pale grey-black .. .. .. £475 48·00
w. Wmk Crown to right of CA .. .. £500 60·00
x. Wmk sideways reversed £600 £160
y. Wmk Crown to right of CA and reversed £600 £110
10 4d. grey-black (3.10.87) .. .. .. £325 35·00
w. Wmk Crown to right of CA .. .. £325 38·00
x. Wmk sideways reversed .. .. £650 90·00
y. Wmk Crown to right of CA and reversed .. .. £500 60·00

*The normal sideways watermark shows Crown to left of CA, *as seen from the back of the stamp.*

†See note below No. 14.

1889 (26 Sept)–**91.** *Wmk Crown CA (upright). P* 14, 14½.
11 **3** 1d. red-brown (21.5.91) .. .. .. £160 65·00
a. Bisected (on cover)* .. .. .. † £2250
x. Wmk reversed £350 £170
12 4d. olive grey-black .. .. .. £110 45·00
w. Wmk inverted £400 £250
x. Wmk reversed £325 £130

See note below No. 14.

1891 (Jan). *Nos.* 8 *and* 11 *bisected diagonally and each half handstamped with T* 4.
13 **3** ½d. on half of 1d. brownish claret (No. 8) £500 £300
a. Unsevered pair £2250 £1000
b. Unsevered pair *se-tenant* with unsurcharged whole stamp £15000
c. Bisect *se-tenant* with unsurcharged whole stamp .. .. † £1300
14 ½d. on half 1d. red-brown (No. 11) .. £550 £250
a. Unsevered pair £2750 £1300
b. Bisect *se-tenant* with unsurcharged whole stamp .. .. † £1200

1891 PROVISIONALS. In 1891 the postage to the United Kingdom and Colonies was reduced from 4d. to 2½d. per half ounce. As no ½d. or 2½d. stamps were available the bisection of the 1d. was authorised from 1 January 1891. This authorisation was withdrawn on 11 January 1892, although bisects were accepted for postage until July of that year. The ½d. and 2½d. stamps were placed on sale from 10 September 1891.

Cork Cancel used in 1891

The Type 4 surcharge was not used regularly; unsurcharged bisects being employed far more frequently. Genuine bisects should be cancelled with the cork cancel illustrated above. The use of any other postmark, including a different cork cancel, requires date evidence linked to known mail ship sailings to prove authenticity.

Posthumous strikes of the surcharge on "souvenir" bisects usually show a broken "2" and/or a large full stop. These are known on bisected examples of No. 18 and on varieties such as surcharge inverted, double or sideways. Forgeries exist of all these provisionals.

1891 (10 Sept*)–**1902.** *Wmk Crown CA (upright). P* 14, 14½.
15 **3** ½d. blue-green (Aug–Nov 1891) .. .. 20·00 26·00
x. Wmk reversed £250 £250
y. Wmk inverted and reversed £275 £275
16 ½d. green (20.5.92) .. .. .. 16·00 15·00
ax. Wmk reversed £120 £120
ay. Wmk inverted and reversed £250 £250
b. Deep dull green (15.4.96) .. .. 40·00 30·00
17 ½d. deep yellow-green (1894–95) .. .. 17·00 21·00
ay. Wmk inverted and reversed £120 £120
b. Yellow-green (19.6.99) .. .. 2·00 2·50
c. Dull yellowish green (13.1.1902) .. 5·00 4·25
cx. Wmk reversed £250 £250
18 1d. orange red-brown (14.10.91) .. .. 70·00 50·00
a. Brown .. .. 90·00 55·00
w. Wmk inverted £650 £300
x. Wmk reversed £160 £160
19 1d. reddish chestnut (20.4.92) .. .. 40·00 42·00
20 1d. orange-brn (wmk reversed) (18.1.94) 45·00 42·00
21 1d. claret (23.7.94) .. .. .. 90·00 80·00
x. Wmk reversed .. .. .. 65·00 50·00
22 1d. Venetian red (pale to deep) (1895–96) 17·00 15·00
ax. Wmk reversed .. .. .. 10·00 10·00
b. Venetian claret (1898?) .. .. 30·00 12·00
23 1d. pale red (19.6.99) .. .. .. 5·00 2·00
x. Wmk reversed £200 £200
24 1d. orange-red (13.1.1902) .. .. 9·00 4·00
25 2d. purple (pale to deep) (1895–98) .. 6·50 12·00
x. Wmk reversed £300 £325
26 2d. reddish purple (15.4.96) .. .. 5·00 11·00
27 2½d. pale chalky ultramarine (8.91) .. £120 40·00
28 **3** 2½d. dull blue (19.11.91) .. .. .. £130 20·00
x. Wmk reversed £275 £250
29 2½d. Prussian blue (18.1.94) £225 £130
30 2½d. ultramarine (1894–96) .. .. 22·00 9·50
ax. Wmk reversed .. .. .. 42·00 11·00
ay. Wmk inverted and reversed £475
b. Pale ultramarine (10.6.98) .. .. 27·00 13·00
bx. Wmk reversed .. .. .. £100 75·00
c. Deep ultramarine (18.9.1901) .. 32·00 32·00
cx. Wmk reversed £200 £200
31 4d. brownish black (wmk reversed) (18.1.94) £600 £275
32 4d. olive-black (11.5.95) .. .. 10·00 21·00
33 6d. orange-yellow (19.11.91) £150 £130
x. Wmk reversed .. .. .. 48·00 40·00
34 6d. yellow (15.4.96) .. .. .. 27·00 38·00
35 9d. pale reddish orange (15.11.95) .. 32·00 55·00
x. Wmk reversed £250 £275
y. Wmk inverted and reversed £350 £350
36 9d. salmon (15.4.96) .. .. .. 38·00 50·00
x. Wmk reversed £250 £275
37 1s. grey-brown (15.11.95) .. .. 45·00 50·00
x. Wmk reversed £140 £150
38 1s. yellow-brown (15.4.96) .. .. 42·00 45·00
x. Wmk reversed £130 £140
15/38 .. .. *Set of* 8 £130 £160
15s, 26s, 28s, 33s, 35s Optd "Specimen" *Set of* 5 £600

*The ½d. and 2½d. were first placed on sale in the Falkland Islands on 10 September 1891. Such stamps came from the August 1891 printing. It is now believed that the stock of the May printings sent to the Falkland Islands was lost at sea.

The 2½d. ultramarine printing can sometimes be found in a violet shade, but the reason for this is unknown.

5 6

(Recess B.W.)

1898 (5 Oct). *Wmk Crown CC. P* 14, 14½.
41 **5** 2s. 6d. deep blue £200 £250
42 **6** 5s. red £170 £200
41s/2s Optd "Specimen" .. .. *Set of* 2 £450

7 8

(Recess D.L.R.)

1904 (16 July)–**12.** *Wmk Mult Crown CA. P* 14.
43 **7** ½d. yellow-green .. .. .. 4·25 1·50
aw. Wmk inverted £200 £140
ax. Wmk reversed £550
b. Pale yellow-grn (on thick paper) (6.08) 13·00 9·00
bw. Wmk inverted
c. Deep yellow-green (7.11) .. .. 9·00 3·00
44 1d. vermilion .. .. 9·50 1·50
aw. Wmk inverted £200 £150
ax. Wmk reversed £300 £250
b. Wmk sideways (7.06) .. .. 1·00 2·50
c. Thick paper (1908) .. .. .. 15·00 1·75
cw. Wmk inverted £300 £250
cx. Wmk reversed £375 £250
d. Dull coppery red (on thick paper) (3.08) .. .. £180 35·00
dx. Wmk reversed £550 £300
e. Orange-vermilion (7.11) .. .. 15·00 2·75
ex. Wmk reversed £300 £300
45 2d. purple (27.12.04) .. .. .. 14·00 26·00
ax. Wmk reversed £110 £110
b. Reddish purple (13.1.12) £225 £275
46 2½d. ultramarine (*shades*) .. .. 29·00 7·50
aw. Wmk inverted £180 £140
ay. Wmk inverted and reversed .. .. — £425
b. Deep blue (13.1.12) £250 £150
47 6d. orange (27.12.04) .. .. .. 38·00 48·00
48 1s. brown (27.12.04) .. .. .. 40·00 32·00
49 **8** 3s. green £150 £130
aw. Wmk inverted £1200 £950
b. Deep green (4.07) £120 £120
bx. Wmk reversed £1200 £850
50 5s. red (27.12.04) £170 £150
43/50 .. .. *Set of* 8 £375 £350
43s/50s Optd "Specimen" .. .. *Set of* 8 £500

Examples of Nos. 41/50 and earlier issues are known with a forged Falkland Islands postmark dated "OCT 15 10".

For details of South Georgia underprint, South Georgia provisional handstamps and Port Foster handstamp see under FALKLAND ISLANDS DEPENDENCIES.

9 10

s B. MacKennal. Eng J. A. C. Harrison. Recess D.L.R.)

(3 July)–20. *Wmk Mult Crown CA. P 13¾×14 (comb)* . to 1s.) *or 14 (line)* (3s. *to* £1).

) ½d. yellow-green .. .. 2·75 3·50
a. Perf 14 (line). *Dp yell-green* (1914) 18·00 35·00
b. Perf 14 (line). *Deep olive* (1918) .. 24·00 95·00
c. *Deep olive* (4.19) .. .. 3·50 29·00
ca. Printed both sides .. .. .. † £5500
d. *Dull yellowish green* (on thick greyish paper) (1920) .. .. 4·50 29·00
1d. orange-red .. .. 6·00 2·50
a. Perf 14 (line). *Orange-vermilion* (1914, 1916) .. .. .. 25·00 2·50
b. Perf 14 (line). *Vermilion* (1918) .. † £700
c. *Orange-vermilion* (4.19) .. .. 3·75 3·00
d. *Orange-vermilion* (on thick greyish paper) (1920) .. .. .. 7·00 2·00
dx. Wmk reversed £150
2d. maroon .. .. 25·00 23·00
a. Perf 14 (line). *Dp reddish pur* (1914) £110 90·00
b. Perf 14 (line). *Maroon* (4.18) .. £110 90·00
c. *Deep reddish purple* (4.19) .. .. 7·00 16·00
2½d. deep bright blue .. .. .. 19·00 24·00
a. Perf 14 (line). *Dp bright blue* (1914) 27·00 32·00
b. Perf 14 (line). *Deep blue* (1916, 4.18) 28·00 35·00
c. *Deep blue* (4.19) .. .. .. 7·00 17·00
6d. yellow-orange (6.7.12) .. .. 14·00 20·00
aw. Wmk inverted £350 £325
b. *Brown-orange* (4.19) .. .. 12·00 40·00
1s. light bistre-brown (6.7.12) .. .. 30·00 30·00
a. *Pale bistre-brown* (4.19) .. .. 50·00 95·00
b. *Brn* (on thick greyish paper) (1920) 32·00 £140
10 3s. slate-green .. .. 75·00 80·00
5s. deep rose-red .. .. 85·00 95·00
a. *Reddish maroon* (1914) £190 £200
b. *Maroon* (1916) .. .. .. 75·00 £100
bx. Wmk reversed £2250 £1400
10s. red/*green* (11.2.14) £160 £250
£1 black/*red* (11.2.14) £375 £450
(*inc* 67*b*) .. .. .. *Set of* 11 £750 £950
9s (*inc both* 67*s and* 67*as*) Optd "Specimen" *Set of* 11 £1400

ne exact measurement of the comb perforation used for Type **9** .7 × 13.9. The line perforation, used for the 1914, 1916 and printings and for all the high values in Type **10**, measured ×14.1.

was previously believed that all examples of the 1d. in nilion with the line perforation were overprinted to form No. but it has now been established that some unoverprinted ets of No. 61b were used during 1919.

Many of the sheets showed stamps from the left-hand side in a ter shade than those from the right. It is believed that this due to the weight of the impression. Such differences are ticularly noticeable on the 2½d. 1916 and 1918 printings ere the lighter shades, approaching milky blue in earance, are scarce.

ll 1919 printings show weak impressions of the background er side of the head caused by the poor paper quality.

Examples of all values are known with forged postmarks, luding one of Falkland Islands dated "5 SP 19" and another of th Shetlands dated "20 MR 27".

WAR STAMP

(11)

2½D

(12)

18 (22 Oct*)–20. *Optd by Govt Printing Press, Stanley, with* T **11**.

9 ½d. deep olive (line perf) (No. 60b) .. 1·00 9·00
a. *Yellow-green* (No. 60) (4.19) .. 16·00
ab. Albino opt £1200
b. *Deep olive* (comb perf) (No. 60c) (4.19) 50 6·50
c. *Dull yellowish green* (on thick greyish paper) (No. 60*d*) (5.20) .. .. 12·00 65·00
cx. Wmk reversed £180
1d. vermilion (line perf) (No. 61b) .. 2·00 18·00
a. Opt double, one albino £400
b. *Orge-verm* (line perf) (No. 61a) (4.19) 16·00 †
c. *Orge-verm* (comb perf) (No. 61c) (4.19) 50 3·50
ca. Opt double £1800
cx. Wmk reversed £350
d. *Orange-vermilion* (on thick greyish paper) (No. 61*d*) (5.20) .. .. 80·00 £160
1s. light bistre-brown (No. 65) .. .. 30·00 75·00
a. *Pale bistre-brown* (No. 65a) (4.19) .. 4·00 42·00
ab. Opt double, one albino £1300
ac. Opt omitted (in pair with normal) .. £6500
b. *Brown* (on thick greyish paper) (No. 65*b*) (5.20) .. .. 5·50 42·00
ba. Opt double, one albino £1300
bw. Wmk inverted £170 £250
bx. Wmk reversed £650

*Earliest known postal use. Cancellations dated 8 October ere applied much later.

There were five printings of the "WAR STAMP" overprint, but ll, except that in May 1920, used the same setting. Composition the five printings was as follows:

October 1918. Nos. 70, 71 and 72
January 1919. Nos. 70, 71 and 72
April 1919, Nos. 70/*b*, 71*b*/*c* and 72*a*
October 1919. Nos. 70*b*, 71*c* and 72*a*
May 1920. Nos. 70*c*, 71*d* and 72*b*.

It is believed that the entire stock of No. 70*a* was sold to stamp ealers. Only a handful of used examples are known which may ave subsequently been returned to the colony for cancellation.

No. 71ca exists in a block of 12 (6×2) from the bottom of a heet on which the first stamp in the bottom row shows a single verprint, but the remainder have overprint double.

Examples of Nos. 70/2 are known with a forged Falkland slands postmark dated "5 SP 19".

921–28. *Wmk Mult Script CA. P* 14.

3 9 ½d. yellowish green .. .. .. 3·00 4·00
a. *Green* (1925) .. .. .. 3·00 4·00
4 1d. dull vermilion (1924) .. .. 5·00 1·25
aw. Wmk inverted .. .. .. † £1300
ay. Wmk inverted and reversed .. £250
b. *Orange-vermilion* (*shades*) (1925) .. 5·50 1·25

75 9 2d. deep brown-purple (8.23) .. .. 14·00 7·00
aw. Wmk inverted .. .. .. — £1100
ax. Wmk reversed £1200
b. *Purple-brown* (1927) .. .. 16·00 24·00
c. *Reddish maroon* (1.28) .. .. 8·00 24·00
cy. Wmk inverted and reversed .. ..
76 2½d. deep blue .. .. 22·00 16·00
a. *Indigo* (28.4.27) .. .. .. 16·00 20·00
b. *Deep steel-blue* (1.28) .. .. 6·00 16·00
c. *Prussian blue* (10.28) £300 £450
77 2½d. deep purple/*pale yellow* (8.23) .. 4·50 32·00
a. *Pale purple*/*pale yellow* (1925) .. 4·25 32·00
ay. Wmk inverted and reversed .. £300
78 6d. yellow-orange (1925) .. .. 8·00 38·00
w. Wmk inverted £190
x. Wmk reversed £1000
79 1s. deep ochre .. .. 16·00 48·00
80 10 3s. slate-green (8.23) .. .. .. 80·00 £150
73/80 .. .. *Set of* 8 £120 £275
73s/80s (*inc both* 76s *and* 76as) Optd "Specimen" *Set of* 9 £650

Dates quoted above are those of despatch from Great Britain.

No. 76c only occurred in part of the October 1928 printing. The remainder were in the deep steel-blue shade of the January 1928 despatch, No. 76*b*.

1928 (7 Feb). *No. 75b surch with* T **12**.

115 9 2½d. on 2d. purple-brown £750 £750
a. Surch double £30000

No. 115 was produced on South Georgia during a shortage of 2½d. stamps. The provisional was withdrawn on 22 February 1928.

13 Fin Whale and Gentoo Penguins **14**

(Recess P.B.)

1929 (2 Sept)–**36**. *P* 14 (*comb*). (*a*) *Wmk Mult Script CA*.

116 13 ½d. green .. .. 1·25 3·00
a. Line perf (1936) .. .. .. 4·00 8·00
117 1d. scarlet .. .. 3·75 80
a. Line perf. *Deep red* (1936) .. 7·00 14·00
118 2d. grey .. .. 2·75 2·50
119 2½d. blue .. .. 2·75 2·25
120 14 4d. orange (*line perf*) (18.2.32) .. 16·00 13·00
a. *Deep orange* (1936) .. .. 38·00 48·00
121 13 6d. purple .. .. 15·00 13·00
a. Line perf. *Reddish purple* (1936) 40·00 25·00
122 1s. black/*emerald* .. .. .. 19·00 32·00
a. Line perf. *On bright emerald* (1936) 23·00 27·00
123 2s. 6d carmine/*blue* .. .. .. 42·00 48·00
124 5s. green/*yellow* .. .. .. 65·00 85·00
125 10s. carmine/*emerald* £120 £160

(*b*) *Wmk Mult Crown CA*

126 13 £1 black/*red* £300 £375
116/26 .. .. .. *Set of* 11 £500 £650
116s/26s Perf "Specimen" .. *Set of* 11 £1000

Two kinds of perforation exist:

A. Comb perf 13.9:—original values of 1929.

B. Line perf 13.9×14.2 or 14.2 (small holes)—4d. and 1936 printings of ½d., 1d., 6d. and 1s. On some sheets the last vertical row of perforations shows larger holes.

Examples of most values are known with forged postmarks, including one of Port Stanley dated "14 JY 31" and another of South Georgia dated "AU 30 31".

15 Romney Marsh Ram

26 King George V

(Des (except 6d.) by G. Roberts. Eng and recess B.W.)

1933 (2 Jan–Apr). *Centenary of British Administration*. T **15**, **26** *and similar designs. Wmk Mult Script CA. P* 12.

127 ½d. black and green .. .. .. 1·75 5·50
128 1d. black and scarlet .. .. .. 3·50 2·25
129 1½d. black and blue .. .. .. 12·00 15·00
130 2d. black and brown .. .. .. 10·00 22·00
131 3d. black and violet .. .. .. 13·00 15·00
132 4d. black and orange .. .. .. 14·00 16·00
133 6d. black and slate .. .. .. 50·00 60·00
134 1s. black and olive-green .. .. 40·00 60·00
135 2s. 6d. black and violet £150 £170
136 5s. black and yellow £500 £650
a. *Black and yellow-orange* (Apr) .. £1300 £1400
137 10s. black and chestnut £550 £750
138 £1 black and carmine £1500 £2000
127/38 .. .. .. *Set of* 12 £2500 £3250
127s/38s Perf "Specimen" .. *Set of* 12 £2250

Designs: *Horiz*—1d. Iceberg; 1½d. Whale-catcher *Bransfield*; 2d. Port Louis; 3d. Map of Falkland Islands; 4d. South Georgia; 6d. Fin Whale; 1s. Government House, Stanley. *Vert*—2s. 6d. Battle Memorial; 5s. King Penguin; 10s. Coat of Arms.

Examples of all values are known with forged Port Stanley postmarks dated "6 JA 33". Some values have also been seen with part strikes of the forged Falkland Islands postmark mentioned below Nos. 60/9 and 70/2.

1935 (7 May). *Silver Jubilee. As Nos. 91/4 of Antigua, but printed by B.W. P* 11 × 12.

139 1d. deep blue and scarlet .. .. .. 3·25 40
b. Short extra flagstaff £375 £250
d. Flagstaff on right-hand turret .. £250 £170
e. Double flagstaff £300 £200
140 2½d. brown and deep blue .. .. .. 9·00 1·75
b. Short extra flagstaff £900 £475
d. Flagstaff on right-hand turret .. £275 £180
e. Double flagstaff £400 £250
l. Re-entry on value tablet (R. 8/1) .. £200 £100
141 4d. green and indigo .. .. .. 11·00 4·50
b. Short extra flagstaff £600 £375
d. Flagstaff on right-hand turret .. £375 £250
e. Double flagstaff £425 £300
142 1s. slate and purple .. .. .. 8·00 3·50
a. Extra flagstaff £2750 £2250
b. Short extra flagstaff £600 £325
c. Lightning conductor £1600 £800
d. Flagstaff on right-hand turret .. £600 £350
e. Double flagstaff £650 £375
139/42 .. .. .. *Set of* 4 28·00 9·00
139s/42s Perf "Specimen" .. *Set of* 4 £300

For illustrations of plate varieties see Omnibus section following Zanzibar.

1937 (12 May). *Coronation. As Nos. 95/7 of Antigua. P* 11×11½.

143 ½d. green 30 10
144 1d. carmine 40 45
145 2½d. blue 80 80
143/5 .. .. .. *Set of* 3 1·40 1·25
143s/5s Perf "Specimen" .. .. *Set of* 3 £180

27 Whales' Jaw Bones

(Des G. Roberts (Nos. 146, 148/9, 158 and 160/3), K. Lellman (No. 159). Recess B.W.)

1938 (3 Jan)–**50**. *Horiz designs as* T **27**. *Wmk Mult Script CA. P* 12.

146 ½d. black and green (*shades*) 30 75
147 1d. black and carmine .. .. .. 29·00 80
a. *Black and scarlet* .. .. .. 3·75 85
148 1d. black and violet (14.7.41) .. .. 2·50 1·75
a. *Black and purple-violet* (1.43) .. 7·50 1·75
149 2d. black and deep violet .. .. .. 1·00 50
150 2d. black and carmine-red (14.7.41) .. 1·00 2·25
a. *Black and red* (1.43) .. .. .. 2·75 1·00
151 2½d. black and bright blue .. .. .. 1·25 30
152 2½d. black and blue (15.6.49) .. .. 6·50 7·00
153 3d. black and blue (14.7.41) .. .. 6·50 2·50
a. *Black and deep blue* (1.43) .. .. 10·00 2·50
154 4d. black and purple .. .. .. 3·00 65
155 6d. black and brown .. .. .. 2·50 1·50
156 6d. black (15.6.49) .. .. .. 5·00 4·25
157 9d. black and grey-blue .. .. .. 16·00 1·00
158 1s. pale blue .. .. 65·00 18·00
a. *Deep blue* (1941) .. .. .. 18·00 2·50
159 1s. 3d. black and carmine-red (11.12.46) .. 2·50 1·40
160 2s. 6d. slate .. .. 55·00 11·00
161 5s. bright blue and pale brown .. .. £110 65·00
b. *Indigo and yellow-brown* (1942) .. £600 90·00
c. *Blue and buff-brown* (9.2.50) .. £150 £200
162 10s. black and orange .. .. .. 60·00 27·00
163 £1 black and violet .. .. .. £120 48·00
146/63 .. .. .. *Set of* 18 £375 £150
146s/51s, 153s/5s, 157s/63s Perf "Specimen" *Set of* 16 £1000

Designs:—Nos. 147 and 150, Black-necked Swan; Nos. 148/9, Battle Memorial; Nos. 151 and 153, Flock of sheep; Nos. 152 and 154, Magellan Goose; Nos. 155/6, *Discovery II* (polar supply vessel); No. 157, *William Scoresby* (research ship); No. 158, Mount Sugar Top; No. 159; Turkey Vultures; No. 160 Gentoo Penguins; No. 161, Southern Sealion; No. 162, Deception Island; No. 163, Arms of Falkland Islands.

Examples of values issued before 1946 are known with forged Port Stanley postmarks dated "14 JY 41" and "28 JY 43".

1946 (7 Oct). *Victory. As Nos. 110/11 of Antigua.*

164 1d. dull violet 30 15
165 3d. blue 45 15
164s/5s Perf "Specimen" .. .. *Set of* 2 £160

1948 (1 Nov). *Royal Silver Wedding. As Nos. 112/13 of Antigua.*

166 2½d. ultramarine .. .. 2·00 1·00
167 £1 mauve .. .. 90·00 55·00

1949 (10 Oct). *75th Anniv of Universal Postal Union. As Nos. 114/17 of Antigua.*

168 1d. violet .. .. 1·50 75
169 3d. deep blue .. .. 5·00 2·00
170 1s. 3d. deep blue-green .. .. .. 3·00 2·25
171 2s. blue .. .. 3·00 7·50
168/71 .. .. *Set of* 4 11·00 11·00

39 Sheep

43 Arms of the Colony

(Des from sketches by V. Spencer. Recess Waterlow)

1952 (2 Jan). *T* **39, 43** *and similar designs. Wmk Mult Script CA. P* 13×13½ (*vert*) *or* 13½×13 (*horiz*).

172 ½d. green 70 70
173 1d. scarlet .. .. 1·50 40
174 2d. violet .. .. 3·50 2·50
175 2½d. black and light ultramarine 95 50
176 3d. deep ultramarine .. .. 1·00 1·00
177 4d. reddish purple .. .. 7·50 1·50
178 6d. bistre-brown .. .. 12·00 1·00
179 9d. orange-yellow .. .. 9·00 2·00
180 1s. black .. .. 23·00 80
181 1s. 3d. orange .. .. 13·00 5·00
182 2s. 6d. olive-green .. .. 16·00 11·00
183 5s. purple .. .. 10·00 9·00
184 10s. grey .. .. 23·00 11·00
185 £1 black .. .. 25·00 17·00
172/185 .. .. *Set of* 14 £130 55·00

Designs: *Horiz*—1d. *Fitzroy* (supply ship); 2d. Magellan Goose; 2½d. Map of Falkland Islands; 4d. Auster Autocrat aircraft; 6d. *John Biscoe I* (research ship); 9d. View of the Two Sisters; 1s. 3d. Kelp goose and gander; 10s. Southern Sealion and South American Fur Seal; £1 Hulk of *Great Britain*. *Vert*—1s. Gentoo Penguins; 2s. 6d. Sheep-shearing; 5s. Battle Memorial.

FALKLAND ISLANDS DEPENDENCIES

PRICES FOR STAMPS ON COVER TO 1945
Nos. A1/D8 *from* × 20

A. GRAHAM LAND

For use at Port Lockroy (established 1 February 1944) and Hope Bay (established 12 February 1945) bases.

Falkland Islands definitive stamps with face values of 1s. 3d. and above were valid for use from Graham Land in conjunction with Nos. A1/8 and subsequently Nos. G1/16.

Stamps of FALKLAND ISLANDS *cancelled at Port Lockroy or Hope Bay with Graham Land circular datestamps between* 12 February 1944 *and* 31 January 1954.

1938–50. *King George VI* (*Nos.* 159/63).

Z1 1s. 3d. black and carmine-red .. .. .. 90·00
Z2 2s. 6d. slate .. .. 42·00
Z3 5s. indigo and yellow-brown £130
Z4 10s. black and orange .. .. 48·00
Z5 £1 black and violet .. .. 70·00

1952. *King George VI* (*Nos.* 181/5)

Z 6 1s. 3d. orange .. .. 75·00
Z 7 2s. 6d. olive-green .. .. 85·00
Z 8 5s. purple .. .. 95·00
Z 9 10s. grey £100
Z10 £1 black £110

GRAHAM LAND

DEPENDENCY OF

(A 1)

1944 (12 Feb)–**45.** *Falkland Islands Nos.* 146, 148, 150, 153/5, 157 *and* 158*a optd with Type* A **1**, *in red, by B.W.*

A1 ½d. black and green .. .. 30 1·75
 a. Blue-black and green £700 £400
A2 1d. black and violet .. .. 30 1·00
A3 2d. black and carmine-red .. .. .. 50 1·00
A4 3d. black and blue .. .. 30 1·00
A5 4d. black and purple .. .. 3·00 1·75
A6 6d. black and brown .. .. 15·00 2·25
 a. Blue-black and brown (24.9.45) .. .. 20·00
A7 9d. black and grey-blue .. .. 1·00 1·25
A8 1s. deep blue .. .. 1·00 1·25
A1/8 .. .. *Set of* 8 19·00 10·00
A1s/8s Perf "Specimen" .. .. *Set of* 8 £375

B. SOUTH GEORGIA

The stamps of Falkland Islands were used at the Grytviken whaling station on South Georgia from 3 December 1909.

Mr. J. Innes Wilson, the Stipendary Magistrate whose duties included those of postmaster, was issued with a stock of stamps, values ½d. to [illegible], together with an example of the current "FALKLAND ISLANDS" circular datestamp. This was used to cancel the stamps, but, as it gave no indication that mail had originated at South Georgia, a straight-line handstamp inscribed "SOUTH GEORGIA", or subsequently "South Georgia", was also supplied. It was intended that this should be struck directly on to each letter or card below the stamp, but it can sometimes be found struck across the stamp instead.

The use of the "South Georgia" handstamp continued after the introduction of the "SOUTH GEORGIA" circular datestamp in June 1910 apparently for philatelic purposes, but no example has been reported used after June 1912.

SOUTH GEORGIA.

Z 1

South Georgia.

Z 2

		On piece	On cover /card
ZU1	Example of Type Z 1 used in conjunction with "FALKLAND ISLANDS" postmark (22 Dec 1909 to 30 March 1910) *Price from*	£1200	£4250
ZU2	Example of Type Z 2 used in conjunction with "FALKLAND ISLANDS" postmark (May 1910) .. .. *Price from*	£850	£3500
ZU3	Example of Type Z 2 used in conjunction with "SOUTH GEORGIA" postmark (June 1910 to June 1912) .. *Price from*	£250	£900

Stamps of FALKLAND ISLANDS *cancelled at Grytviken with South Georgia circular datestamps between* June 1910 *and* 31 January 1954.

1891–1902. *Queen Victoria* (*Nos.* 32, 36 *and* 38)

Z11 4d. olive-black £160
Z12 9d. salmon £160
Z13 1s. yellow-brown £170

1904–12. *King Edward VII* (*Nos.* 43/50).

Z14 ½d. green .. .. 13·00
Z15 1d. vermilion .. .. 13·00
 d. Dull coppery red (on thick paper) .. .. 40·00
Z16 2d. purple .. .. 60·00
 b. Reddish purple £275
Z17 2½d. ultramarine .. .. 22·00
 b. Deep blue £180
Z18 6d. orange £120
Z19 1s. brown £120
Z20 3s. green £250
Z21 5s. red £300

SOUTH GEORGIA PROVISIONAL HANDSTAMPS. During October 1911 the arrival of the German South Polar Expedition at Grytviken, South Georgia, resulted in the local supply of stamps becoming exhausted. The Acting Magistrate, Mr. E. B. Binnie, who was also responsible for the postal facilities, produced a handstamp reading "Paid at (or At) SOUTH GEORGIA" which, together with a manuscript indication of the postage paid and his signature, was used on mail from 18 October 1911 to January 1912. Further examples, signed by John Innes Wilson, are known from February 1912, but these may be philatelic.

PH1 "Paid 1 at SOUTH GEORGIA EBB" *Price on cover* £4250
PH1*a* "Paid 1 At SOUTH GEORGIA EBB" (16 Dec) *Price on cover* £4500
PH2 "Paid 2½ at SOUTH GEORGIA EBB" *Price on cover* £4750
PH2*a* "Paid 2½ At SOUTH GEORGIA EBB" (16 Dec) *Price on cover* £5250

1912–23. *King George V. Wmk Mult Crown CA* (*Nos.* 60/9).

Z22 ½d. green .. .. 16·00
 a. Perf 14 (line). *Deep yellow-green* .. .. 35·00
 d. Dull yellowish green (on thick greyish paper) 35·00
Z23 1d. orange-red .. .. 10·00
 a. Perf 14 (line). *Orange-vermilion* .. .. 10·00
 d. Orange-vermilion .. .. 10·00
Z24 2d. maroon .. .. 42·00
Z25 2½d. deep bright blue .. .. 28·00
 c. Deep blue .. .. 27·00
Z26 6d. yellow-orange .. .. 50·00
 b. Brown-orange .. .. 50·00
 ba. Bisected (diag) (3d.) (on cover) (3.23) .. £11000
Z27 1s. bistre-brown £100
 a. Pale bistre-brown £120
 b. Brown (on thick greyish paper) £160
Z28 3s. slate-green £160
Z29 5s. deep rose-red £190
 a. Reddish maroon £300
 b. Maroon £250
Z30 10s. red/*green* £350
Z31 £1 black/*red* £500

1918–20. "WAR STAMP" *ovpts* (*Nos.* 70/2)

Z32 ½d. deep olive .. .. 16·00
Z33 1d. vermilion .. .. 16·00
Z34 1s. light bistre-brown .. .. 85·00

1921–28. *King George V. Wmk Mult Script CA* (*Nos.* 73/80).

Z35 ½d. yellowish green .. .. 5·00
Z36 1d. dull vermilion .. .. 4·00
Z37 2d. deep brown-purple .. .. 25·00
Z38 2½d. deep blue .. .. 22·00
 a. Bisected (diag) (1d.) (on cover) (3.23) .. £7000
 b. Prussian blue £450
Z39 2½d. deep purple/*pale yellow* .. .. .. 48·00
Z40 6d. yellow-orange .. .. 50·00
Z41 1s. deep ochre .. .. 60·00
Z42 3s. slate-green £180

1928 PROVISIONAL. For listing of the 2½d. on 2d. surcharge issued at Grytviken on 7 February 1928 see No. 115 of Falkland Islands.

1929–36. *King George V. Whale and Penguins design* (*Nos.* 116/26).

Z43 ½d. green .. .. 5·00
Z44 1d. scarlet .. .. 4·00
Z45 2d. grey .. .. 10·00
Z46 2½d. blue .. .. 4·00
Z47 4d. orange .. .. 20·00
Z48 6d. purple .. .. 30·00
Z49 1s. black/*emerald* .. .. 40·00
Z50 2s. 6d. carmine/*blue* .. .. 85·00
Z51 5s. green/*yellow* £130
Z52 10s. carmine/*emerald* £250
Z53 £1 black/*red* £550

Examples of most values are known with forged postmarks dated "Au 30" in 1928, 1930 and 1931.

1933. *Centenary of British Administration* (*Nos.* 127/38).

Z54 ½d. black and green .. ..
Z55 1d. black and scarlet .. ..
Z56 1½d. black and blue .. ..
Z57 2d. black and brown .. ..
Z58 3d. black and violet .. ..
Z59 4d. black and orange .. ..
Z60 6d. black and slate .. ..
Z61 1s. black and olive-green .. .. ..
Z62 2s. 6d. black and violet .. ..
Z63 5s. black and yellow .. ..
 a. Black and yellow-orange .. .. .. £
Z64 10s. black and chestnut .. ..
Z65 £1 black and carmine .. .. .. £

1935. *Silver Jubilee* (*Nos.* 139/42).

Z66 1d. deep blue and scarlet .. .. ..
Z67 2½d. brown and deep blue .. .. ..
Z68 4d. green and indigo .. ..
Z69 1s. slate and purple .. ..

1937. *Coronation* (*Nos.* 143/5).

Z70 ½d. green .. ..
Z71 1d. carmine .. ..
Z72 2½d. blue .. ..

1938–50. *King George VI* (*Nos.* 146/63).

Z73 ½d. black and green .. ..
Z74 1d. black and carmine .. ..
 a. Black and scarlet .. ..
Z75 1d. black and violet .. ..
Z76 2d. black and deep violet .. .. ..
Z77 2d. black and carmine-red .. .. ..
Z78 2½d. black and bright blue (No. 151) .. ..
Z79 3d. black and blue .. ..
Z80 4d. black and purple .. ..
Z81 6d. black and brown .. ..
Z82 9d. black and grey-blue 11
Z83 1s. pale blue 32
 a. Deep blue 32
Z84 1s. 3d. black and carmine-red 38
Z85 2s. 6d. slate 26
Z86 5s. bright blue and pale brown .. .. £
 a. Indigo and yellow-brown .. .. £
 b. Blue and buff-brown .. .. .. £
Z87 10s. black and orange 48
Z88 £1 black and violet 70

Falkland Islands definitive stamps with values of 1s. 3d. a above continued to be valid from South Georgia after introduction of Nos. B1/8 and subsequently Nos. G1/16. For South Georgia postmarks exist dated "30 MR 49".

1952. *King George VI* (*Nos.* 181/5).

Z89 1s. 3d. orange 40
Z90 2s. 6d. olive-green 75
Z91 5s. purple 85
Z92 10s. grey 95
Z93 £1 black £1

1944 (24 Feb)–**45.** *Falkland Islands Nos.* 146, 148, 150, 153 157 *and* 158*a optd* "SOUTH GEORGIA/DEPENDENCY O *in red, as Type* A **1** *of Graham Land.*

B1 ½d. black and green .. .. .. 30 1·
 a. Wmk sideways £2750
B2 1d. black and violet .. .. .. 30 1·
B3 2d. black and carmine-red .. .. 50 1·
B4 3d. black and blue .. .. .. 30 1·
B5 4d. black and purple .. .. .. 3·00 1·
B6 6d. black and brown .. .. .. 15·00 2·
 a. Blue-black and brown (24.9.45) .. 20·00
B7 9d. black and grey-blue .. .. .. 1·00 1·
B8 1s. deep blue .. .. 1·00 1·
B1/8 .. .. *Set of* 8 19·00 10·
B1s/8s Perf "Specimen" .. .. *Set of* 8 £375

C. SOUTH ORKNEYS

Used from the *Fitzroy* in February 1944 and at Laurie Islan (established January 1946).

Falkland Islands definitive stamps with face values of 1s. 3 and above were valid for use from the South Orkneys i conjunction with Nos. C1/8 and subsequently Nos. G1/16.

Stamps of FALKLAND ISLANDS *cancelled on the* Fitzroy, *a Laurie Island or at Signy Island with South Orkneys circula datestamps between* 21 February 1944 *and* 31 January 1954

1938–50. *King George VI* (*Nos.* 160/3).

Z95 2s. 6d. slate .. .. 42·0
Z96 5s. indigo and yellow-brown £13
Z97 10s. black and orange .. .. .. 48·0
Z98 £1 black and violet .. .. .. 70·0

1952. *King George VI* (*Nos.* 181/5).

Z 99 1s. 3d. orange .. .. 75·0
Z100 2s. 6d. olive-green .. .. 85·0
Z101 5s. purple .. .. 95·0
Z102 10s. grey £10
Z103 £1 black £11

1944 (21 Feb)–**45.** *Falkland Islands Nos.* 146, 148, 150, 153/5, 15 *and* 158*a optd* "SOUTH ORKNEYS/DEPENDENCY OF", *in rec as Type* A **1** *of Graham Land.*

C1 ½d. black and green .. .. .. 30 1·75
C2 1d. black and violet .. .. .. 30 1·00
 w. Wmk inverted £3750
C3 2d. black and carmine-red .. .. 50 1·00
C4 3d. black and blue .. .. .. 30 1·00
C5 4d. black and purple .. .. .. 3·00 1·75
C6 6d. black and brown .. .. .. 15·00 2·25
 a. Blue-black and brown (24.9.45) .. 20·00
C7 9d. black and grey-blue .. .. .. 1·00 1·25
C8 1s. deep blue .. .. 1·00 1·25
C1/8 .. .. *Set of* 8 19·00 10·00
C1s/8s Perf "Specimen" .. .. *Set of* 8 £375

D. SOUTH SHETLANDS

…tal facilities were first provided at the Port Foster whaling …n on Deception Island for the 1912–13 whaling season and available each year between November and the following until March 1931.

… postmark was provided for the 1912–13 season and the postmaster was instructed to cancel stamps on cover with a …ght-line "PORT FOSTER" handstamp. Most letters so …elled subsequently received a "FALKLAND ISLANDS" …lar postmark dated between 19 and 28 March 1913. It is …n that only low value stamps were available at Port Foster. …er values, often with other "FALKLAND ISLANDS" …nark dates, were, it is believed, subsequently "made to …".

…ps of FALKLAND ISLANDS *cancelled at Port Foster, …ception Island with part of* "PORT FOSTER" *straight-line …ndstamp.*

…–12. *King Edward VII* (*Nos.* 43*c*, 44*e*).
… ½d. deep yellow-green £1200
… 1d. orange-vermilion £1200

… *King George V. Wmk Mult Crown CA* (*Nos.* 60/1).
… ½d. yellow-green £1200
… 1d. orange-red £1200

…ps of FALKLAND ISLANDS *cancelled at Port Foster with …rt of oval* "DECEPTION ISLAND SOUTH SHETLANDS" *…stmark in black or violet between* 1914 *and* 1927.

…–12. *King Edward VII* (*No.* 43*c*)
…3 ½d. deep yellow-green £250

…2–20. *King George V. Wmk Mult Crown CA* (*Nos.* 60/9).
…0 ½d. yellow-green .. .. 85·00
…1 1d. orange-red .. .. 85·00
…2 2d. maroon £110
…3 2½d. deep bright blue £110
…4 6d. yellow-orange £140
…5 1s. light bistre-brown £160
…6 3s. slate-green £350
…7 5s. deep rose-red £400
…8 10s. red/*green* £500
…9 £1 black/*red* £700

…18–20. "WAR STAMP" *ovpts* (*Nos.* 70/2).
…20 ½d. deep olive £110
…21 1d. vermilion £110
…22 1s. light bistre-brown £225

…21–28. *King George V. Wmk Mult Script CA* (*Nos.* 73/80).
…23 ½d. yellowish green £110
…26 2½d. deep blue £140
…29 1s. deep ochre £160

…amps of FALKLAND ISLANDS *cancelled at Port Foster with* "SOUTH SHETLANDS" *circular datestamp between* 1923 *and* March 1931

…12–20. *King George V. Wmk Mult Crown CA* (*Nos.* 60/9).
…30 1d. orange-vermilion .. .. 55·00
…31 2d. deep reddish purple .. .. 65·00
…32 2½d. deep bright blue .. ..
…33 6d. brown-orange .. .. 85·00
…34 1s. bistre-brown .. ..
…35 3s. slate-green £190
…36 5s. maroon £225
…37 10s. red/*green* £375
…38 £1 black/*red* £650

Examples of all values are known with forged postmarks …ted "20 MR 27".

…918–20. "WAR STAMP" *ovpts* (*Nos.* 70/2).
…139 1d. vermilion .. ..
…140 1s. light bistre brown .. ..

…921–28. *King George V. Wmk Mult Script CA* (*Nos.* 73/80).
…141 ½d. yellowish green .. .. 38·00
…142 1d. dull vermilion .. .. 38·00
…143 2d. deep brown-purple .. .. 55·00
…144 2½d. deep blue .. .. 45·00
a. Prussian blue .. ..
…145 2½d. deep purple/*pale yellow* .. .. .. 80·00
…146 6d. yellow-orange .. .. 65·00
…147 1s. deep ochre .. .. 65·00
…148 3s. slate-green £200

…929. *King George V. Whale and Penguins design* (*Nos.* 116/26).
…149 ½d. green .. .. 55·00
…150 1d. scarlet .. .. 55·00
…151 2d. grey .. .. 75·00
…152 2½d. blue .. .. 65·00
…153 6d. purple .. .. 85·00
…154 1s. black/*emerald* .. .. 85·00
…155 2s. 6d. carmine/*blue* £140
Z156 5s. green/*yellow* £150
Z157 10s. carmine/*emerald* £325
Z158 £1 black/*red* £700

The whaling station at Port Foster was abandoned at the end of the 1930–31 season.

It was reoccupied as a Falkland Islands Dependencies Survey base on 3 February 1944.

Falkland Islands definitive stamps with face values of 1s. 3d. and above were valid for use from the South Shetlands in conjunction with Nos. D1/8 and subsequently Nos. G1/16.

Stamps of FALKLAND ISLANDS *cancelled at Port Foster or Admiralty Bay with South Shetlands circular datestamps between* 5 February 1944 *and* 31 January 1954

1938–50. *King George VI* (*Nos.* 160/3).
Z159 2s. 6d. slate .. .. 42·00
Z160 5s. indigo and yellow-brown £130
Z161 10s. black and orange .. .. 48·00
Z162 £1 black and violet .. .. 70·00

1952. *King George VI* (*Nos.* 181/5).
Z163 1s. 3d. orange .. .. 75·00
Z164 2s. 6d. olive-green .. .. 85·00
Z165 5s. purple .. .. 95·00
Z166 10s. grey £100
Z167 £1 black £110

1944 (5 Feb)–**45**. *Falkland Islands Nos.* 146, 148, 150, 153/5, 157 *and* 158*a optd* "SOUTH SHETLANDS/DEPENDENCY OF", *in red, as Type* A 1 *of Graham Land.*
D1 ½d. black and green .. .. .. 30 1·75
D2 1d. black and violet .. .. .. 30 1·00
D3 2d. black and carmine-red .. .. .. 50 1·00
D4 3d. black and blue .. .. .. 30 1·00
D5 4d. black and purple .. .. .. 3·00 1·75
D6 6d. black and brown .. .. .. 15·00 2·25
a. Blue-black and brown (24.9.45) .. 20·00
D7 9d. black and grey-blue .. .. .. 1·00 1·25
D8 1s. deep blue .. .. 1·00 1·25
D1/8 .. .. *Set of* 8 19·00 10·00
D1s/8s Perf "Specimen" .. .. *Set of* 8 £375

From 12 July 1946 to 16 July 1963, Graham Land, South Georgia, South Orkneys and South Shetlands used FALKLAND ISLANDS DEPENDENCIES stamps.

E. FALKLAND ISLANDS DEPENDENCIES

For use at the following bases:
Admiralty Bay (South Shetlands) (*opened* January 1948, *closed* January 1961)
Argentine Islands (Graham Land) (*opened* 1947)
Deception Island (South Shetlands)
Grytviken (South Georgia)
Hope Bay (Graham Land) (*closed* 4 February 1949, *opened* February 1952)
Laurie Island (South Orkneys) (*closed* 1947)
Port Lockroy (Graham Land) (*closed* 16 January 1962)
Signy Island (South Orkneys) (*opened* 1946)
Stonington Island (Graham Land) (*opened* 1946, *closed* 1950, *opened* 1958, *closed* 1959, *opened* 1960)

G 1

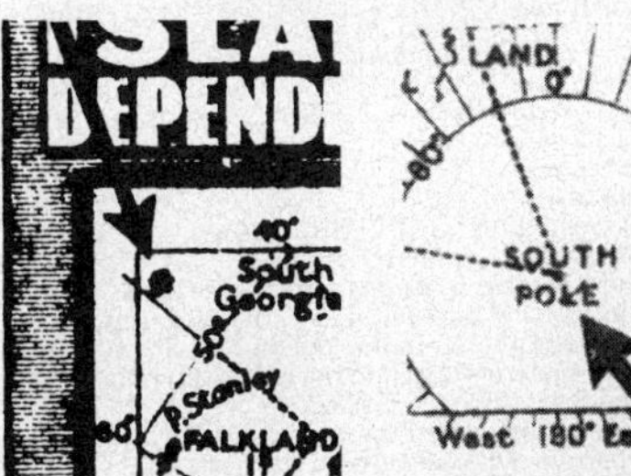

Extra island (Plate 1 R. 3/9)

"SOUTH POKE" flaw (Plate 2 R. 6/8)

Missing "I" in "S. Shetland Is." (Plate 1 R. 1/2)

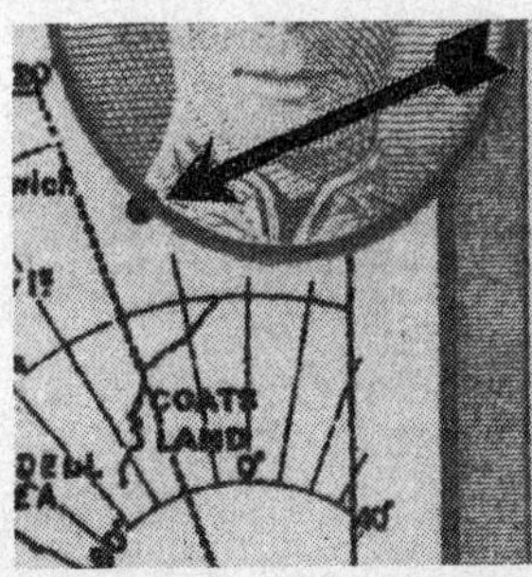

Extra dot by oval (Plate 1 R. 4/6)

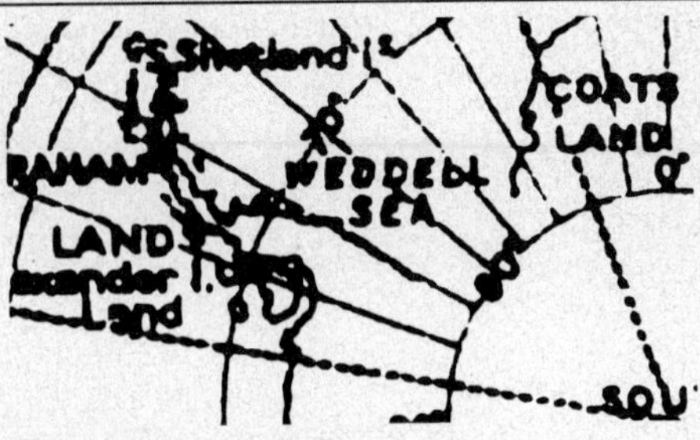

Nos. G1/8

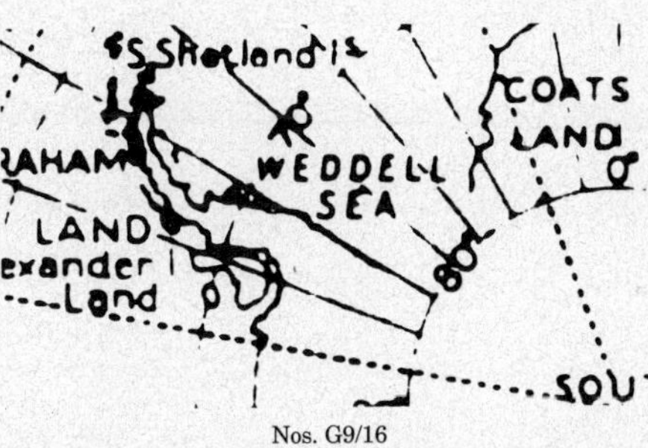

Nos. G9/16

On Nos. G9 to G16 the map is redrawn; the "0°" meridian does not pass through the "S" of "COATS", the "n" of "Alexander" is not joined to the "L" of "Land" below, and the loops of letters "s" and "t" are generally more open.

(Map litho, frame recess D.L.R.)

1946 (12 July*)–**49.** *Wmk Mult Script CA* (*sideways*). *P* 12.

(*a*) *Map thick and coarse*
G 1 **G 1** ½d. black and green .. .. 1·00 2·25
a. Extra island .. .. .. 75·00
b. Missing "I" .. .. .. 75·00
c. "SOUTH POKE" .. .. 75·00
d. Extra dot by oval .. .. 75·00
G 2 1d. black and violet .. .. 1·25 1·75
a. Extra island .. .. .. 75·00
b. Missing "I" .. .. .. 75·00
d. Extra dot by oval .. .. 75·00
G 3 2d. black and carmine .. .. 1·25 2·50
a. Extra island .. .. .. 80·00
b. Missing "I" .. .. .. 80·00
d. Extra dot by oval .. .. 80·00
G 4 3d. black and blue .. .. 1·25 4·00
a. Extra island .. .. .. 90·00
b. Missing "I" .. .. .. 90·00
d. Extra dot by oval .. .. 90·00
G 5 4d. black and claret .. .. 2·25 4·75
c. "SOUTH POKE" £110
G 6 6d. black and orange .. .. 3·25 4·75
a. Extra island £120
b. Missing "I" £120
c. "SOUTH POKE" £120
d. Extra dot by oval £120
e. Black and ochre .. .. 50·00 95·00
ea. Extra island £300
eb. Missing "I" £300
ec. "SOUTH POKE" £300
ed. Extra dot by oval £300
G 7 9d. black and brown .. .. 2·00 3·75
c. "SOUTH POKE" £110
G 8 1s. black and purple .. .. 2·00 4·25
c. "SOUTH POKE" £110
G1/8 .. .. *Set of* 8 13·00 25·00
G1s/8s Perf "Specimen" .. .. *Set of* 8 £500

(*b*) *Map thin and clear* (16.2.48)
G 9 **G 1** ½d. black and green .. .. 2·25 11·00
a. Recess frame printed double, one albino and inverted £1000
G10 1d. black and violet .. .. 1·50 14·00
G11 2d. black and carmine .. .. 2·75 20·00
G11*a* 2½d. black and deep blue (6.3.49) .. 7·50 6·00
G12 3d. black and blue .. .. .. 2·75 4·50
G13 4d. black and claret .. .. 19·00 22·00
G14 6d. black and orange .. .. 23·00 9·00
G15 9d. black and brown .. .. 23·00 9·00
G16 1s. black and purple .. .. 24·00 9·00
G9/16 .. .. *Set of* 9 95·00 95·00

*This is the date of issue for South Georgia. Nos. G1/8 were released in London on 11 February.

In Nos. G1/8 a variety with a gap in the 80th parallel occurs six times in each sheet of all values in positions R. 1/4, 1/9, 3/4, 3/9, 5/4 and 5/9 (*Price for set of* 8 £40 *mint, in pairs with normal*).

A constant variety, dot on "T" of "SOUTH", occurs on R. 5/2, 5/4, 5/6, 5/8 and 5/10 of all values of the "thin map" set with the exception of the 2½d.

1946 (4 Oct*). *Victory. As Nos.* 110/11 *of Antigua.*
G17 1d. deep violet 50 15
G18 3d. blue 75 15
G17s/18s Perf "Specimen" .. *Set of* 2 £130

*This is the date of issue for South Georgia. The stamps were placed on sale from the South Orkneys on 17 January 1947, from the South Shetlands on 30 January 1947 and from Graham Land on 10 February 1947.

1948 (6 Dec). *Royal Silver Wedding. As Nos.* 112/13 *of Antigua, but* 1s. *in recess.*
G19 2½d. ultramarine .. .. 1·50 1·25
G20 1s. violet-blue .. .. 1·75 1·75

1949 (10 Oct). *75th Anniv of U.P.U. As Nos.* 114/17 *of Antigua.*
G21 1d. violet . . . . 1·00 1·50
G22 2d. carmine-red . . . . 4·00 2·50
G23 3d. deep blue . . . . 3·00 1·25
G24 6d. red-orange . . . . 4·00 3·00
G21/4 . . . . *Set of* 4 11·00 7·50

Fiji

PRICES FOR STAMPS ON COVER TO 1945

Nos. 1/9	*from* × 6
Nos. 10/34	*from* × 5
Nos. 35/59	*from* × 8
Nos. 60/3	—
Nos. 64/9	*from* × 20
Nos. 70/5	*from* × 5
Nos. 76/103	*from* × 8
Nos. 104/14	*from* × 5
Nos. 115/24	*from* × 4
Nos. 125/37	*from* × 3
Nos. 138/241	*from* × 4
Nos. 242/5	*from* × 3
Nos. 246/8	*from* × 8
Nos. 249/66*b*	*from* × 2
No. 267	*from* × 8
Nos. D1/5*c*	*from* × 4
Nos. D6/10	*from* × 20
Nos. D11/18	*from* × 15

King Cakobau 1852–Oct 1874

Christian missionaries reached Fiji in 1835 and early letters are known to and from their mission stations, sent via Sydney, Hobart or Auckland.

In 1852 Cakobau, the chief of the island of Bau, declared himself King of Fiji and converted to Christianity two years later. Internal problems and difficulties with the American government led the king to offer to cede Fiji to Great Britain. The offer was refused, but resulted in the appointment of a British Consul in 1858. A Consular Post Office operated from September 1858 until 1872 and franked mail with New South Wales stamps from 1863.

The destruction of plantations in the Confederacy during the American Civil War led to an increased demand for Fijian cotton and this upsurge in commercial activity encouraged the *Fiji Times* newspaper on Levuka to establish a postal service on 1 November 1870.

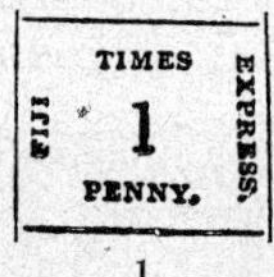

1

(Type-set and printed at the office of *The Fiji Times*, Levuka, Ovalau, Fiji)

1870 (1 Nov)–**71.** *Rouletted in the printing.* (*a*) *Quadrillé paper.*
1 **1** 1d. black/*rose* £3250 £3500
2 3d. black/*rose* £3500 £3500
3 6d. black/*rose* £2000 £2000
4 1s. black/*rose* £1500 £1800

(*b*) *Laid bâtonné paper* (1871)
5 **1** 1d. black/*rose* £900 £1800
a. Vert strip of 4. Nos. 5, 7/9 . . . . £35000
6 3d. black/*rose* £1500 £2750
7 6d. black/*rose* £1100 £1800
8 9d. black/*rose* £1900 £3000
a. Comma after "EXPRESS" (R.4/4) . . £2750
9 1s. black/*rose* £1200 £1400

Nos. 1/4 were printed *se-tenant* as a sheet of 24 (6 × 4) with the 6d. stamps in the first horizontal row, the 1s. in the second, the 1d. in the third and the 3d. in the fourth. Nos. 5/9 were produced from the same plate on which three of the 3d. impressions had been replaced with three 9d. values.

The issued stamps showed the vertical frame lines continuous from top to bottom of the sheet with the horizontal rules broken and not touching the verticals. Used examples are cancelled in manuscript or by the star cancellation used at Bua.

There are no reprints of these stamps, but the 1d., 3d., 6d. and 1s. are known in the correct type on *yellow wove* paper and are believed to be proofs.

There are also three different sets of imitations made by the proprietors of *The Fiji Times* to meet the demands of collectors:—

The first was produced in 1876 on *white wove* or *vertically laid* paper, rouletted on dotted lines and arranged in sheets of 40 (5 rows of 8) comprising 1d., 3d., 6d., 9d. and 1s.; the horizontal frame lines are continuous and the vertical ones broken.

The second was produced before 1888 on *thick rosy mauve wove* paper, rouletted on dotted lines and arranged in sheets of 30 (5 rows of 6) comprising 1s., 9d., 6d., 3d. and 1d.; the vertical frame lines are continuous and the horizontal ones broken.

The third only came to light in the 1960s and is rare, only one complete sheet being recorded, which has since been destroyed. The sheet arrangement is the same as Nos. 1/4, which suggests that this was the first imitation to be produced. It is on *off-white wove* paper, rouletted on closely dotted or solid lines, with vertical frame lines continuous and the horizontal ones broken, as in the originals. These differ from the proofs mentioned above in that the lettering is slightly larger and the figures also differ.

King Cakobau established a formal government in June 1871 and stamps for the royal post office were ordered from Sydney. These arrived in October 1871 and the postal service was placed on a firm basis by the First Postal Act in December of that year. Under its terms the *Fiji Times* service closed on 17 January 1872 and the British Consular Post Office followed six months later.

NEW INFORMATION

The editor is always interested to correspond with people who have new information that will improve or correct the Catalogue.

2

3

(Eng and electrotyped by A. L. Jackson. Typo Govt Printing O Sydney)

1871 (Oct). *Wove paper. Wmk* "FIJI POSTAGE" *in small s serif capitals across the middle row of stamps in the sheet. P*
10 **2** 1d. blue . . . . 50·00
11 3d. pale yellow-green £110
12 **3** 6d. rose £130

The 3d. differs from T **2** in having a white circle contai square dots surrounding the centre.

All three values are known *imperf*, but were not issued in condition.

See notes after No. 33b.

1872 (13 Jan). *Surch as T* **4**, *in local currency, by Govt Office, Sydney.*
13 **2** 2 c. on 1d. pale blue . . . . . . 50·00 6
a. Deep blue . . . . 30·00 4
14 6 c. on 3d. yellow-green. . . . . . . 65·00 6
15 **3** 12 c. on 6d. carmine-rose. . . . . . 90·00 7

CROWN COLONY

King Cakobau renewed his offer to cede Fiji to Great Bri and this took place on 12 October 1874.

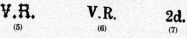

V.R. (5) **V.R.** (6) **2d.** (7)

Varieties:—

V.R. **V.R.**

(*Enlarged*)

Cross pattée stop Inverted "A"

Cross pattée stop after "R" (R. 3/6).
Round raised stop after "V" (R. 3/8).
Round raised stops after "V" and "R" (R. 3/9).
Inverted "A" for "V" (R. 3/10).
No stop after "R" (R. 2/3 on T **5**, R. 5/3 on T **6**).
Large stop after "R" (R. 5/10).

(Optd at *Polynesian Gazette* Office, Levuka)

1874 (21 Oct). *Nos.* 13/15 *optd.* (*a*) *With T* **5**.
16 **2** 2 c. on 1d. blue £900 £2
a. No stop after "R" £2250 £10
b. Cross pattée stop after "R" £2250 £10
c. Round raised stop after "V" £2250 £10
d. Round raised stops after "V" and "R" £2250 £10
e. Inverted "A" for "V" £2250 £10
f. Vert pair. Nos. 16 and 19 . . . . £2500
17 6 c. on 3d. green £1400 £6
a. No stop after "R" £3500 £16
b. Cross pattée stop after "R" £3500 £16
c. Round raised stop after "V" £3500 £16
d. Round raised stops after "V" and "R" £3500 £16
e. Inverted "A" for "V" £3500 £16
f. Vert pair. Nos. 17 and 20 . . . . £4000
18 **3** 12 c. on 6d. rose £600 £2
a. No stop after "R" £2000 £10
b. Cross pattée stop after "R" £2000 £10
c. Round raised stop after "V" £2000 £10
d. Round raised stops after "V" and "R" £2000 £10
e. Inverted "A" for "V" £2000 £10
f. Opt inverted . . . . — £40
g. Vert pair. Nos. 18 and 21 . . . . £1800

(*b*) *With T* **6**
19 **2** 2 c. on 1d. blue £1000 £27
a. No stop after "R" £2250 £100
f. Large stop after "R" . . . . . . — £100
20 6 c. on 3d. green £1800 £90
a. No stop after "R" £3500 £160
21 **3** 12 c. on 6d. rose £750 £22
a. No stop after "R" £2000 £100
b. Opt inverted £4500

Nos. 16/21 were produced in sheets of 50 (10 × 5) of which th top three rows were overprinted with Type **5** and the lower tw with Type **6**.

1875. *Stamps of* 1874 *surch at* Polynesian Gazette *Office Levuka, with T* **7**.

(*a*) *In red* (May)
22 **2** 2d. on 6 c. on 3d. green (No. 17) . . £500 £18
a. No stop after "R" £1500 £65
b. Cross pattée stop after "R" £1500 £65
c. Round raised stop after "V" £1500 £65
d. Round raised stops after "V" and "R" £1500 £65
e. Inverted "A" for "V" £1500 £65
f. No stop after "2d" (R. 1/2) £1500 £650
g. Vert pair. Nos. 22/3 . . . . . . £1600
23 2d. on 6 c. on 3d. green (No. 20) . . £650 £275
a. No stop after "R" £1500 £650
b. Stop between "2" and "d" (R. 5/7) . . £1500 £650

(*b*) *In black* (30 Sept)
24 **2** 2d. on 6 c. on 3d. green (No. 17) . . £1300 £450
a. No stop after "R" £3000 £1200
b. Cross pattée stop after "R" £3000 £1200
c. Round raised stop after "V" £3000 £1200
d. Round raised stops after "V" and "R" £3000 £1200
e. Inverted "A" for "V" £3000 £1200
f. No stop after "2d" (R. 1/2) £3000 £1200
g. "V.R." double . . . . . .
h. Vert pair. Nos. 24/5 . . . . . . £4000
25 2d. on 6 c. on 3d. green (No. 20) . . £1700 £650
a. No stop after "R" £3000 £1200
b. Stop between "2" and "d" (R. 5/7) . . £3000 £1200
c. "V.R." double . . . . — £3250

(20 Nov). *No. 15 surch at* Polynesian Gazette *Office,* ...*uka, with T* **7** *and* "V.R." *at one operation.* (*a*) "V.R." *T* **5**.
2d. on 12 c. on 6d. rose £1500 £650
aa. Round raised stop after "R" .. .. — £1000
a. Inverted "A" for "V" (R. 1/3, 2/8, 4/4) £1900 £800
b. Do. and round raised stop after "V" (R. 3/3, 3/6, 3/8, 3/10) £1700 £750
c. As "a" and round raised stops after "R" and "V" (R. 3/2, 3/9) £2000 £850
d. Surch double .. .. .. — £3250
e. Vert pair. Nos. 26/7 .. .. .. £4000

(*b*) "V.R." *T* **6**
2d. on 12 c. on 6d. rose £1600 £700
a. Surch double .. .. .. — £3500

...e setting used for Nos. 26/7 was similar to that of Nos. 16/21, ...he fourth stamp in the fourth row had a Type **5** "V.R." ...ad of a Type **6**.
...position of No. 26aa is not known.

(8)

Two Pence

(9)

(Typo Govt Printing Office, Sydney, from plates of 1871)

...-77. *On paper previously lithographed* "VR" *as T* **8**, *the 3d. ...ch with T* **9**. *P* 12½. (*a*) *Wove paper* (31.1.76).
1d. grey-blue .. .. 50·00 50·00
a. Dull blue .. .. 50·00 50·00
b. Doubly printed £550
c. Void corner (R. 2/1) £500 £300
d. Imperf vert (horiz pair) £850
2d. on 3d. pale green .. .. .. 45·00 55·00
a. Deep green .. .. 42·00 55·00
6d. pale rose .. .. 65·00 65·00
a. Dull rose .. .. 50·00 55·00
b. Carmine-rose .. .. 55·00 55·00
c. Doubly printed £2500

(*b*) *Laid paper* (5.1.77)
1d. blue .. .. 16·00 27·00
a. Deep blue .. .. 17·00 27·00
b. Void corner (R. 2/1) £275 £225
c. Imperf vert (horiz pair) £700
2d. on 3d. yellow-green .. .. .. 60·00 70·00
a. Deep yellow-green .. .. .. 60·00 70·00
b. Imperf between (pair) £850
c. Perf 10 .. .. £300
ca. Imperf vert (horiz pair) .. ..
d. Perf 11 .. .. £300
6d. rose .. .. 50·00 28·00
a. Carmine-rose .. .. 50·00 35·00
b. Imperf vert (horiz pair) £700

...he 3d. *green* is known without the surcharge T **9** on wove paper ...also without the surcharge and the monogram. In this latter ...dition it can only be distinguished from No. 11 by its colour, ...ch is a fuller, deeper yellow-green.
...tamps on both wove and laid paper *imperf* are from printer's ...l or waste sheets and were not issued.
...ll values are known on laid paper without the monogram ..." and the 3d. stamp also without the surcharge but these are ...believed to be from printer's trial sheets which were never ...ed for postal purposes. Being on laid paper they are easily ...inguishable from Nos. 10/12.

...7 (12 Oct). *Optd with T* **8** *and surch as T* **9**. *Laid paper. P* 12½.
2 4d. on 3d. mauve .. .. .. 85·00 25·00
a. Imperf vert (horiz pair) £850

10

11

A Four Pence

B Four Pence

Type A: Length 12½ mm
Type B: Length 14 mm

Note also the different shape of the two "e"s.

(...ypo from new plates made from original dies of 1871 with "CR" altered to "VR" at Govt Printing Office, Sydney. 2d. and 4d. made from old 3d. die.)

...78–99. *Surcharges as T* **9** *or as Types* A *or* B *for 4d. value. Wove paper with paper-maker's name* "T. H. SAUNDERS" *or* "SANDERSON" *in double-lined capitals extending over seven stamps in each full sheet.* (*a*) *P* 12½ (1878–80).
10 1d. pale ultramarine (19.2.79) .. 8·00 8·00
a. Ultramarine .. .. .. 11·00 8·50
2d. on 3d. green (17.10.78) .. .. 5·00 17·00
2d. yellow-green (1.9.79) .. .. 16·00 9·00
a. Blue-green .. .. 27·00 13·00
b. Error. Ultramarine £25000
11 6d. rose (30.7.80) .. .. .. £100 20·00

(*b*) *P* 10 (1881–90)
10 1d. dull blue (11.5.82) .. .. .. 55·00 3·00
a. Ultramarine .. .. .. 17·00 2·75
b. Cambridge blue (12.7.83) .. .. 48·00 3·75
...0 2d. yellow-green (20.10.81) .. .. 13·00 1·00
a. Blue-green .. .. 23·00 4·50
...1 4d. on 1d. mauve (29.1.90) .. .. 38·00 26·00
...2 4d. on 2d. pale mauve (A) (23.5.83) .. 70·00 10·00
a. Dull purple .. .. 70·00 10·00
...3 4d. on 2d. dull purple (B) (7.11.88) .. — £140
...4 4d. mauve (13.9.90) .. .. .. 60·00
a. Deep purple .. .. 60·00 60·00
...5 **11** 6d. pale rose (11.3.85) .. .. .. 70·00 17·00
a. Bright rose .. .. 16·00 16·00

(*c*) *P* 10×12½ (1881–82)
46 **10** 1d. ultramarine (11.5.82) .. .. .. 95·00 29·00
47 2d. green (20.10.81) .. .. .. £160 55·00
48 **11** 6d. rose (20.10.81) .. .. .. £325 48·00
a. Pale rose .. .. £325 48·00

(*d*) *P* 12½×10 (1888–90)
49 **10** 1d. ultramarine (1890) .. .. — £300
49*a* 2d. green (1888) .. .. ..
49*b* 4d. on 2d. dull purple (A) .. .. † —

(*e*) *P* 10×11¾ (3.9.86)
50 **10** 1d. dull blue .. .. 70·00 11·00
a. Ultramarine .. ..
51 2d. yellow-green .. .. .. 65·00 7·50

(*f*) *P* 11¾×10 (1886–88)
51*a* **10** 1d. dull blue (7.11.88) .. .. £225 38·00
ab. Ultramarine .. .. ..
51*b* 2d. yellow-green (3.9.86) .. .. — £500
52 **11** 6d. rose (1887) .. .. ..

(*g*) *P* 11×10 (1892–93)
53 **10** 1d. ultramarine (18.8.92) .. .. 13·00 9·00
54 4d. pale mauve (18.8.92) .. .. 9·50 10·00
55 **11** 6d. pale rose (14.2.93) .. .. 7·50 17·00
a. Rose .. .. 13·00 21·00

(*h*) *P* 11 (1897–99)
56 **10** 4d. mauve (14.7.96) .. .. .. 11·00 7·50
57 **11** 6d. dull rose (14.7.96) .. .. 25·00 40·00
a. Printed both sides (12.99) .. £950 £800
b. Bright rose .. .. 42·00 48·00

(*i*) *P* 11×11¾ (1896)*
58 **10** 4d. deep purple (14.7.96) .. .. 32·00
a. Bright purple .. .. .. 7·50 6·50
59 **11** 6d. rose (23.7.96) .. .. .. 32·00
a. Bright rose .. .. .. 7·00 3·75

(*j*) *Imperf* (*pairs*) (1882–90)
60 **10** 1d. ultramarine .. .. ..
61 2d. yellow-green .. .. ..
62 4d. on 2d. pale mauve .. .. ..
63 **11** 6d. rose .. .. — £1200

*Under this heading are included stamps from several perforating machines with a gauge varying between 11·6 and 12.

No. 37b was printed in the colour of the 1d. in error. Only four examples have been reported, one of which was subsequently destroyed.

In the absence of detailed information on dates of issue printing dates are quoted for Nos. 35/63 and 76/103.

12

13

(Typo Govt Printing Office, Sydney)

1881–99. *Paper-maker's name wmkd as previous issue.*

(*a*) *P* 10 (19.10.81)
64 **12** 1s. pale brown .. .. .. 85·00 19·00
a. Deep brown .. .. .. 85·00 21·00

(*b*) *P* 11×10 (1894)
65 **12** 1s. pale brown .. .. .. 40·00 40·00

(*c*) *P* 11 (1897)
66 **12** 1s. pale brown .. .. .. 38·00 14·00

(*d*) *P* 11×11¾ (5.99)
67 **12** 1s. pale brown .. .. .. 32·00 9·00
a. Brown .. .. 32·00 9·00
b. Deep brown .. .. .. 45·00 45·00

(*e*) *P* 11¾×11 (3.97)
68 **12** 1s. brown .. .. 50·00 42·00

Dates given of earliest known use.
Forgeries exist.

(Centre typo, frame litho Govt Printing Office, Sydney)

1882 (23 May). *Toned paper wmkd with paper-maker's name* "Cowan" *in old English outline type once in each sheet. P* 10.
69 **13** 5s. dull red and black .. .. 55·00 28·00

In July 1900, an electrotyped plate of a 5s. stamp was made and stamps were printed from it with pale orange-red centre and grey-black frame; these are known *perf* 10, *perf* 11¾, and *imperf*. These stamps were not used for postal purposes, but, like surplus stocks of No. 69, were sold as remainders with a special obliteration dated "15 Dec., 00". The design differs in many particulars from the issued stamp.

2½d. (**14**)   2½d. (**15**)

Types **14** (fraction bar 1 mm from "2") and **15** (fraction bar 2 mm from "2") are from the same setting of 50 (10×5) with Type **15** occurring on R. 1/2, 2/2, 3/2 and 4/2.

(Stamps typo in Sydney and surch at Govt Printing Office, Suva)

1891 (1 Jan). *T* **10** *surch. P* 10.
70 **14** 2½d. on 2d. green .. .. .. 42·00 48·00
71 **15** 2½d. on 2d. green £130 £140

½d. (**16**)   5d (**17**)

FIVE PENCE (**18**) 2 mm spacing   FIVE PENCE (**19**) 3 mm spacing

1892 (1 Mar)–**93**. *P* 10. (*a*) *Surch on T* **10**.
72 **16** ½d. on 1d. dull blue .. .. .. 50·00 75·00
a. Ultramarine .. .. .. 42·00 70·00
73 **17** 5d. on 4d. deep purple (25.7.92) .. 50·00 70·00
a. Dull purple .. .. .. 50·00 70·00

(*b*) *Surch on T* **11**
74 **18** 5d. on 6d. brownish rose (30.11.92) .. 55·00 65·00
a. Bright rose .. .. .. 55·00 60·00
b. Perf 10×12½ .. .. ..
75 **19** 5d. on 6d. rose (4.1.93) .. .. 70·00 80·00
a. Deep rose .. .. .. 60·00 70·00
b. Brownish rose .. .. .. 60·00

20

21 Native Canoe

22

(Typo in Sydney)

1891–1902. *Wmk in sheet, either* "SANDERSON" *or* "NEW SOUTH WALES GOVERNMENT" *in outline capitals.*

(*a*) *P* 10 (1891–94)
76 **20** ½d. slate-grey (26.4.92) .. .. 4·50 3·75
77 **21** 1d. black (19.9.94) .. .. .. 10·00 4·25
78 2d. pale green (19.9.94) .. .. 90·00 10·00
79 **22** 2½d. chocolate (8.6.91) .. .. 38·00 14·00
80 **21** 5d. ultramarine (14.2.93) .. .. 75·00 50·00

(*b*) *P* 11×10 (1892–93)
81 **20** ½d. slate-grey (20.10.93) .. .. 5·50 15·00
82 **21** 1d. black (14.2.93) .. .. .. 6·00 3·25
83 2d. green (14.2.93) .. .. .. 14·00 4·50
84 **22** 2½d. chocolate (17.8.92) .. .. 19·00 22·00
a. Brown .. .. 7·50 8·00
b. Yellowish brown .. .. ..
85 **21** 5d. ultramarine (14.2.93) .. .. 12·00 7·50

(*c*) *P* 11 (1893–96)
86 **20** ½d. slate-grey (2.6.96) .. .. 3·00 5·50
a. Greenish slate .. .. .. 2·50 6·00
87 **21** 1d. black (31.10.95) .. .. .. 4·00 3·75
88 1d. pale mauve (2.6.96) .. .. 4·75 1·00
a. Rosy mauve .. .. .. 6·00 1·00
89 2d. dull green (17.3.94) .. .. 5·50 80
a. Emerald-green .. .. .. 6·50 2·00
90 **22** 2½d. brown (31.10.95) .. .. 21·00 8·50
a. Yellowish brown .. .. .. 13·00 17·00
91 **21** 5d. ultramarine (14.2.93) £200

(*d*) *P* 10×11¾ (1893–94)
92 **20** ½d. greenish slate £600
93 **21** 1d. black (20.7.93) .. .. .. 15·00 5·50
94 2d. dull green (19.9.94) £600 £375

(*e*) *P* 11¾×10 (19.9.94)
94*a* **20** ½d. greenish slate .. .. .. — £1000

(*f*) *P* 11¾ (1894–98)
95 **20** ½d. greenish slate (19.9.94) .. .. 2·75 8·00
a. Grey .. .. 28·00
96 **21** 1d. black (19.9.94) .. .. .. £190 26·00
97 1d. rosy mauve (4.5.98) .. .. 4·75 7·50
98 2d. dull green (19.9.94) .. .. 85·00 35·00

(*g*) *P* 11×11¾ (1895–97)
99 **20** ½d. greenish slate (8.10.97) .. .. 1·00 2·75
100 **21** 1d. black (31.10.95) £1500 £1500
101 1d. rosy mauve (14.7.96) .. .. 4·50 80
a. Pale rosy mauve .. .. .. 4·00 2·00
102 2d. dull green (26.7.97) .. .. 32·00 4·00
103 **22** 2½d. brown (26.7.97) .. .. 11·00 17·00
a. Yellow-brown .. .. .. 5·00 5·00

(*h*) *P* 11¾×11 (1897–98)
103*b* **20** ½d. greenish slate (8.10.97) .. .. 4·00 6·50
103*c* **21** 1d. rosy mauve (10.2.97) .. .. 10·00 5·00
103*d* 2d. dull green (4.5.98) £200

The 2½d. brown is known doubly printed, but only occurs in the remainders and with the special obliteration (*Price* £110 *cancelled-to-order*). It was never issued for postal use.

23

24

(Typo D.L.R.)

1903 (1 Feb). *Wmk Crown CA. P* 14.
104 **23** ½d. green and pale green .. .. 2·25 2·00
105 1d. dull purple and black/*red* .. .. 13·00 55
106 **24** 2d. dull purple and orange .. .. 3·75 1·25
107 **23** 2½d. dull purple and blue/*blue* .. 14·00 5·50
108 3d. dull purple and purple .. .. 1·50 4·50
109 **24** 4d. dull purple and black .. .. 1·50 2·50
110 **23** 5d. dull purple and green .. .. 1·50 4·00
111 **24** 6d. dull purple and carmine .. .. 1·50 1·75
112 **23** 1s. green and carmine .. .. 11·00 60·00
113 **24** 5s. green and black .. .. .. 48·00 £120
114 **23** £1 grey-black and ultramarine .. £300 £375
104/14 .. .. *Set of* 11 £350 £500
104s/14s Optd "Specimen" .. *Set of* 11 £300

1904–9. *Wmk Mult Crown CA. Chalk-surfaced paper* (1s.). *P* 14.
115 **23** ½d. green and pale green .. .. 14·00 3·00
116 1d. purple and black/*red* .. .. 26·00 10
117 1s. green and carmine (1909) .. 26·00 40·00
115/17 .. .. *Set of* 3 60·00 40·00

1906–12. *Colours changed. Wmk Mult Crown CA. Chalk-surfaced paper* (6d. *to* £1). *P* 14.
118 **23** ½d. green (1908) .. .. 11·00 3·25
119 1d. red (1906) .. .. 8·00 10
w. Wmk inverted .. .. .. † —
120 2½d. bright blue (1910) .. .. .. 6·50 7·50
121 **24** 6d. dull purple (1910) .. .. .. 11·00 27·00
122 **23** 1s. black/*green* (1911) .. .. .. 4·00 10·00
123 **24** 5s. green and red/*yellow* (1911) .. 55·00 60·00
124 **23** £1 purple and black/*red* (1912) .. £300 £275
118/24 .. .. *Set of* 7 £350 £350
119s/24s Optd "Specimen" .. *Set of* 6 £300

Nos. 112/14, 117 and 120/4 are known with a forged registered postmark of Suva dated "10 DEC 1909".

25 26 WAR STAMP (27)

(Typo D.L.R.)

1912 (Oct)–**23.** *Die I. Wmk Mult Crown CA. Chalk-surfaced paper* (5d. *to* £1). *P* 14.
125 **26** ¼d. brown (1.4.16) .. .. .. 2·50 30
a. Deep brown (1917) .. .. .. 1·50 40
y. Wmk inverted and reversed ..
126 **25** ½d. green .. .. 1·50 1·00
a. Yellow-green (1916) .. .. 8·50 8·50
b. Blue-green (1917) .. .. 1·25 50
w. Wmk inverted .. .. 90·00
y. Wmk inverted and reversed .. 90·00
127 **25** 1d. carmine .. .. 2·00 10
a. Bright scarlet (1916) .. .. 2·00 75
ax. Wmk reversed .. .. .. † —
b. Deep rose (1916) .. .. .. 9·50 2·00
bw. Wmk inverted .. .. .. † —
128 **26** 2d. greyish slate (5.14) .. .. 1·75 10
a. Wmk sideways .. .. ..
b. "C" of "CA" missing from wmk .. † —
129 **25** 2½d. bright blue (5.14) .. .. 3·00 3·50
130 3d. purple/*yellow* (5.14) .. .. 4·25 5·50
a. Wmk sideways £350 £425
b. On lemon (1915) .. .. 2·00 8·50
c. On pale yellow (1921) .. .. 1·75 14·00
ca. "A" of "CA" missing from wmk ..
cw. Wmk inverted .. ..
d. Die II. *On pale yellow* (1922) .. 2·50 24·00
131 **26** 4d. black and red/*yellow* (5.14) .. 23·00 20·00
a. On lemon .. .. .. 4·00 16·00
b. On orange-buff (1920) .. .. 50·00 65·00
c. On pale yellow (1921) .. .. 8·00 14·00
cw. Wmk inverted .. ..
d. Die II. *On pale yellow* (1922) .. 3·75 24·00
ds. Optd "Specimen" .. .. 40·00
132 **25** 5d. dull purple and olive-green (5.14) 5·50 11·00
133 **26** 6d. dull and bright purple (5.14) .. 2·00 5·50
134 **25** 1s. black/*green* (10.13) .. .. 1·25 14·00
a. White back (4.14) .. .. 1·00 11·00
b. On blue-green, olive back (1916) 4·75 10·00
c. On emerald back (1921) .. .. 6·50 35·00
cs. Optd "Specimen" .. .. 42·00
d. Die II. *On emerald back* (1922) .. 2·75 22·00
135 **26** 2s. 6d. black and red/*blue* (19.1.16) .. 32·00 30·00
136 5s. green and red/*yellow* .. .. 32·00 40·00
137 **25** £1 purple and black/*red* (5.14) .. £250 £275
a. Die II (1923) £250 £275
125/37 .. .. .. *Set of* 13 £275 £325
125s/37s Optd "Specimen" .. *Set of* 13 £425

1915 (1 Dec)–**19.** *Optd with T* **27** *by Govt Printer, Suva.*
138 **25** ½d. green .. ..
a. Yellow-green (1916) .. .. 75 4·25
b. Blue-green (1917) .. .. .. 75 2·75
c. Opt inverted £600
d. Opt double .. .. ..
139 1d. carmine .. .. 25·00 23·00
a. Bright scarlet .. .. .. 1·75 75
ab. Horiz pair, one without opt .. £5500
c. Opt inverted £700
d. Deep rose (1919) .. .. 2·25 2·25
138s/9s H/S "Specimen" .. .. *Set of* 2 £120

No. 139ab occurred on one pane of 120 only, the overprint being so misplaced that all the stamps of the last vertical row escaped it entirely.

Nos. 140/227 are no longer used.

1922–29. *Die II. Wmk Mult Script CA. Chalk-surfaced paper* (1s. *to* 5s.). *P* 14.
228 **26** ¼d. deep brown (1923) .. .. 2·50 24·00
229 **25** ½d. green (1923) .. .. .. 75 2·50
w. Wmk inverted .. ..
230 1d. carmine-red .. .. .. 2·50 2·00
231 1d. violet (6.1.27) .. .. .. 1·25 10
232 **26** 1½d. scarlet (6.1.27) .. .. .. 4·00 3·25
233 2d. grey .. .. 1·25 10
a. Face value omitted £7000
234 **25** 3d. bright blue (1924) .. .. 2·75 1·50
235 **26** 4d. black and red/*lemon* (1924) .. 5·00 7·00
a. On pale yellow (1929) .. .. 40·00 24·00
236 **25** 5d. dull purple and sage-green (1927) 1·50 2·00
237 **26** 6d. dull and bright purple .. .. 2·00 1·25
238 **25** 1s. black/*emerald* (1924) .. .. 4·00 6·00
w. Wmk inverted .. ..
239 **26** 2s. purple and blue/*blue* (6.1.27) .. 25·00 60·00
240 2s. 6d. black and red/*blue* (1925) .. 11·00 32·00
241 5s. green and red/*pale yellow* (1926) 30·00 65·00
228/41 .. .. .. *Set of* 14 85·00 £180
228s/41s Optd "Specimen" *Set of* 14 £300

The 2d. imperforate with watermark Type **10** of Ireland came from a trial printing and was not issued.

Only one example of No. 233a is known. It was caused by an obstruction during the printing of the duty plate.

1935 (6 May). *Silver Jubilee. As Nos.* 91/4 *of Antigua.*
242 1½d. deep blue and carmine .. .. 80 7·00
a. Deep blue and aniline red .. 8·00 20·00
b. Frame printed double, one albino .. £1000
f. Diagonal line by turret .. .. 45·00
h. Dot by flagstaff .. .. .. 95·00
i. Dash by turret .. .. .. 95·00
243 2d. ultramarine and grey .. .. 1·50 35
f. Diagonal line by turret .. .. 60·00
g. Dot to left of chapel £130
244 3d. brown and deep blue .. .. 2·50 3·00
f. Diagonal line by turret .. .. 90·00
h. Dot by flagstaff £170
i. Dash by turret £170
245 1s. slate and purple .. .. .. 4·50 6·00
a. Frame printed double, one albino .. £1500
f. Diagonal line by turret £140
h. Dot by flagstaff £225
242/5 .. .. *Set of* 4 8·50 15·00
242s/5s Perf "Specimen" .. .. *Set of* 4 85·00

For illustrations of plate varieties see Omnibus section following Zanzibar.

1937 (12 May). *Coronation. As Nos.* 95/7 *of Antigua. P* 11×11½.
246 1d. purple 60 45
247 2d. grey-black .. .. 60 1·25
248 3d. Prussian blue .. .. 60 1·25
246/8 .. .. *Set of* 3 1·60 2·75
246s/8s Perf "Specimen" .. .. *Set of* 3 55·00

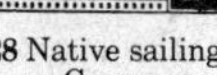
28 Native sailing Canoe

29 Native Village

30 Camakua (canoe)

31 Map of Fiji Islands

Two Dies of Type **30**:

Die I Empty Canoe
Die II Native in Canoe

Two Dies of Type **31**:

Die I Without "180°"

Die II With "180°"

Extra palm frond (R. 5/8)

Extra line (R. 2/1)

Extra island (R. 10/5)

Spur on arms medallion (Pl 2 R. 4/2) (ptg of 26 Nov 1945)

(Des V. E. Ousey (½d., 1s., 2s. 6d.), Miss C. D. Lovejoy (1d., 1 5d.), Miss I. Stinson (3d., 5s.) and A. V. Guy (2d. (Nos. 25 2½d., 6d., 2s.). Recess De La Rue (½d., 1½d., 2d., (253/5a), 2½d., 6d., 8d., 1s. 5d., 1s. 6d.), Waterlow (others

1938 (5 Apr)–**1955.** *T* **28/31** *and similar designs. Wmk Mult S CA. Various perfs.*
249 **28** ½d. green (*p* 13½) 20
a. Perf 14 (5.41) .. .. .. 20·00
b. Perf 12 (8.48) 80
ba. Extra palm frond .. .. 45·00
250 **29** 1d. brown and blue (*p* 12½) .. 50
251 **30** 1½d. carmine (Die I) (*p* 13½) .. 15·00
252 1½d. carmine (Die II) (*p* 13½) (1.10.40) 1·40
a. Deep carmine (10.42) .. .. 4·00
b. Perf 14 (6.42) .. .. .. 18·00 1
c. Perf 12 (21.7.49) .. .. 1·00
253 **31** 2d. brown and green (Die I) (*p* 13½) 38·00
a. Extra line £300 65
254 2d. brown and green (Die II) (*p* 13½) (1.10.40) .. .. .. 16·00 16
255 – 2d. green & mag (*p* 13½) (19.5.42) .. 40
a. Perf 12 (27.5.46) 55
256 **31** 2½d. brown & grn (Die II) (*p* 14) (6.1.42) 60 1
a. Extra island .. .. .. 25·00
b. Perf 13½ (1.44) 70
ba. Extra island .. .. .. 25·00
c. Perf 12 (19.1.48) .. .. 1·00
ca. Extra island .. .. .. 25·00
257 – 3d. blue (*p* 12½) .. .. .. 1·00
a. Spur on arms medallion .. £180 £
258 – 5d. blue and scarlet (*p* 12½) .. 42·00 10
259 – 5d. yell-green & scar (*p* 12½) (1.10.40) 20
260 **31** 6d. black (Die I) (*p* 13×12) .. .. 60·00 12
261 6d. black (Die II) (*p* 13½) (1.10.40) 3·00 2
a. Violet-black (1.44) .. .. 25·00 28
b. Perf 12. *Black* (5.6.47) .. .. 1·50 1
261*c* – 8d. carmine (*p* 14) (15.11.48) .. 1·00 2
d. Perf 13 (7.6.50) 70 2
262 – 1s. black and yellow (*p* 12½) .. 75
263 – 1s. 5d. black & carm (*p* 14) (13.6.40) 20
263*a* – 1s. 6d. ultramarine (*p* 14) (1.8.50) .. 3·50 2
b. Perf 13 (16.2.55) .. .. 1·25 15
264 – 2s. violet and orange (*p* 12½) .. 2·50
265 – 2s. 6d. green and brown (*p* 12½) .. 2·75 1
266 – 5s. green and purple (*p* 12½) .. 2·75 1
266*a* – 10s. orange & emer (*p* 12½) (13.3.50) 35·00 40
266*b* – £1 ultram & carm (*p* 12½) (13.3.50) 48·00 50
249/66*b* .. .. *Set of* 22 £250 £1
249s/66s (*excl* 8*d. and* 1*s.* 6*d.*) Perf "Specimen" *Set of* 18 £450

Designs: *Horiz* (*as T* **30**)—2d. (Nos. 255/a) Government Offic (*As T* **29**)—3d. Canoe and arms of Fiji; 8d., 1s. 5d., 1s. 6d. Arms Fiji; 2s. Suva Harbour; 2s. 6d. River scene; 5s. Chief's hut. *Vert* (*T* **29**)—5d. Sugar cane; 1s. Spearing fish by torchlight; 10s. Pa paw Tree; £1 Police bugler.

2½d.

(42)

1941 (10 Feb). *No.* 254 *surch with T* **42** *by Govt Printer, Suv*
267 **31** 2½d. on 2d. brown and green .. .. 1·00 2

1946 (17 Aug). *Victory. As Nos.* 110/11 *of Antigua.*
268 2½d. green 10 7
a. Printed double, one albino £275
269 3d. blue 10 1
268s/9s Perf "Specimen" .. .. *Set of* 2 60·00

1948 (17 Dec). *Royal Silver Wedding. As Nos.* 112/13 *o Antigua.*
270 2½d. green .. .. 40 1·0
271 5s. violet-blue .. .. 14·00 7·0

1949 (10 Oct). *75th Anniv of U.P.U. As Nos.* 114/17 *of Antigua.*
272 2d. bright reddish purple 30 3
273 3d. deep blue .. .. 1·75 2·2
274 8d. carmine-red .. .. 30 1·5
275 1s. 6d. blue .. .. 30 1·0
272/5 .. .. *Set of* 4 2·40 4·5

43 Children Bathing

44 Rugby Football

(Recess B.W.)

(17 Sept). *Health Stamps. Wmk Mult Script CA. P* 13½.

43	1d. + 1d. brown	10	60
44	2d. + 1d. green	30	60

STAMP BOOKLETS

•. *Black and red cover. Stapled.*
2s. booklet containing eleven ½d. (No. 118) in blocks of 5 and 6, and eighteen 1d. (No. 119) in blocks of 6 .. .. £2750

•. *Black on red cover. Stapled.*
2s. booklet containing eleven ½d. (No. 126) in blocks of 5 and 6, and eighteen 1d. (No. 127) in blocks of 6 .. .. £2250

9 (10 Mar)–**40.** *Black on green covers. No advertising ages. Stapled.*
3s. booklet containing eight ½d. and eight 1d. (Nos. 249/50) in blocks of 8 and twelve 2d. (No. 253) in blocks of 6 .. .. £750
a. Including four advertising pages (black on buff cover) (1940) .. ..
5s. 9d. booklet containing ten ½d. and ten 1d. (Nos. 249/50) in blocks of 10 and twenty-seven 2d. (No. 253) in blocks of 9 .. .. .. £2250
a. Including four advertising pages (black on pink cover) (1940) .. ..
los. SB3/4 were produced locally and Nos. SB3a/4a by De La e.

POSTAGE DUE STAMPS

D 1

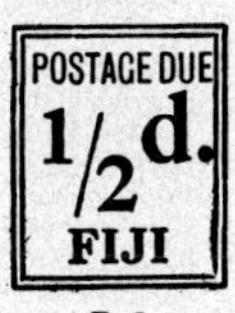

D 2

(Typo Govt Printer, Suva)

7 (1 Jan). *Thick yellowish white laid paper. No gum. P* 11.

D 1	½d. black	£700	£375
	a. *Se-tenant* strip of 8: 1d. (×3) + ½d. + 4d. + 3d. (×3)	£13000	
	1d. black	£300	75·00
	2d. black	£250	65·00
	3d. black	£300	80·00
	4d. black	£700	£375

Nos. D1/2 and D4/5 were printed, *se-tenant*, in sheets of 96 ×12) with each horizontal row containing three 1d., one ½d., e 4d. and three 3d. in that order. Only thirty-one such sheets re issued. The 2d. was printed separately in sheets of 84 ×12). On all these sheets marginal copies were imperforate on e outer edge.

17 (21 April)–**18.** *Narrower setting, value in ½d. as Type* D **2**.

5*a*	½d. black	£475	£250
5*b*	1d. black	£250	£120
5*c*	2d. black (5.4.18)	£850	£500

1d. and 2d. stamps must have wide margins (3½ to 4 mm) on the ertical sides to be Nos. D2 or D3. Stamps with narrow margins of pproximately the same width on all four sides are Nos. D5*b* or D5*c*. Nos. D5*a/c* were printed in separate sheets of 84 (7 × 12). The arginal copies are perforated on all sides.

D 3

D 4

(Typo D.L.R.)

918 (1 June). *Wmk Mult Crown CA. P* 14.

D 6	D 3	½d. black	3·00	18·00
D 7		1d. black	3·50	5·00
D 8		2d. black	3·25	7·50
D 9		3d. black	3·25	48·00
D10		4d. black	6·00	27·00
D6/10		.. .. *Set of* 5	17·00	95·00
D6s/10s		Optd "Specimen" .. *Set of* 5	£150	

No postage due stamps were in use between 31 August 1931 and 3 July 1940.

(Typo Waterlow)

1940 (3 July). *Wmk Mult Script CA. P* 12½.

D11	D 4	1d. emerald-green	7·00	60·00
D12		2d. emerald-green	9·00	60·00
D13		3d. emerald-green	12·00	65·00
D14		4d. emerald-green	15·00	70·00
D15		5d. emerald-green	16·00	70·00
D16		6d. emerald-green	18·00	75·00
D17		1s. carmine-lake	22·00	£100
D18		1s. 6d. carmine-lake	23·00	£150
D11/18		.. .. *Set of* 8	£110	£600
D11s/18s		Perf "Specimen" .. *Set of* 8	£180	

All values are known with forged postmarks, including one of Levuka dated "8 APR 41" and others of Suva dated "12 AUG 42", "14 AU 42" or "20 MR 45".

The use of postage due stamps was discontinued on 30 April 1946.

Gambia

PRICES FOR STAMPS ON COVER TO 1945

Nos. 1/4	*from* × 20
Nos. 5/8	*from* × 15
Nos. 10/20	*from* × 20
Nos. 21/31	*from* × 40
Nos. 32/6	*from* × 20
Nos. 37/44	*from* × 10
Nos. 45/68	*from* × 8
Nos. 69/70	*from* × 20
Nos. 72/85	*from* × 8
Nos. 86/142	*from* × 5
Nos. 143/6	*from* × 6
Nos. 147/9	*from* × 8
Nos. 150/61	*from* × 3

WEST AFRICAN SETTLEMENT

British traders were active in the River Gambia area from the beginning of the 17th century, but it was not until 1808 that it was officially recognised as a Settlement. Administration passed from the merchants to the Governor of Freetown (Sierra Leone) in 1821 and in 1843 Gambia became a separate colony with a Protectorate declared over the banks of the river for 300 miles inland in 1857. A period of colonial retrenchment in 1865 saw a return to Settlement status under Sierra Leone, but Gambia once again became a Crown Colony in 1888.

There was no government postal service before 1858.

PRICES. The prices of Nos. 1 to 8 are for fine copies, with good margins and embossing. Brilliant or poor copies can be supplied at prices consistent with their condition.

DOUBLE EMBOSSING. The majority of the stamps of T **1** with so-called "double embossing" are merely specimens in which the printing and embossing do not register accurately and have no special value. We no longer list "twice embossed" or "twice embossed, once inverted" varieties as they are considered to be outside the scope of this catalogue.

1

(Typo and embossed by D.L.R.)

1869 (18 Mar)–**72.** *No wmk. Imperf.*

1	**1**	4d. brown	£475	£160
2		4d. pale brown (1871)	£400	£200
3		6d. deep blue	£425	£180
3*a*		6d. blue	£500	£150
4		6d. pale blue (17.2.72)	£2250	£1000

Our prices for the 6d. pale blue, No. 4, are for stamps which are pale by comparison with specimens of the "deep blue" and "blue" colour groups listed under Nos. 3 and 3*a*. The date given is the earliest known postmark. An exceptionally pale shade is recognized by specialists and this is rare.

1874 (Aug). *Wmk Crown CC. Imperf.*

5	**1**	4d. brown	£350	£180
		w. Wmk inverted	£475	£275
		x. Wmk reversed	£475	£275
		y. Wmk inverted and reversed	£550	£325
6		4d. pale brown	£350	£180
7		6d. deep blue	£300	£200
		w. Wmk inverted	£400	£275
		x. Wmk reversed	£450	£300
		y. Wmk inverted and reversed	£450	£300
8		6d. blue	£300	£180
		a. Sloping label	£550	£325
		b. Wmk sideways	†	—
		w. Wmk inverted	£400	£275

SLOPING LABEL VARIETY. Traces of this flaw first occur in the 6d. imperforate on R.1/1 and R.1/5. In the perforated printings the variety on R.1/5 is much more pronounced and appears as illustrated above. Our listings are these examples from R.1/5, less noticeable varieties of this type from R.1/1, which slope from right to left, being worth less. These varieties continued to appear until the introduction of a new 6d. plate in 1893, used for No. 34.

1880–81. *Wmk Crown CC. P* 14*. A. *Wmk sideways*†
10A 1 ½d. orange £190 £150
w. Wmk Crown to left of CC .. ..
12A 1d. maroon £325 £250
w. Wmk Crown to left of CC .. ..
y. Wmk sideways inverted and reversed .. ..
13A 2d. rose .. .. .. £100 55·00
w. Wmk Crown to left of CC .. ..
14A 3d. bright ultramarine £375 £300
w. Wmk Crown to left of CC .. ..
15A 4d. brown .. .. .. £375 60·00
w Wmk Crown to left of CC .. £350 55·00
16A 4d. pale brown .. .. .. £350 55·00
w. Wmk Crown to left of CC .. £325 50·00
17A 6d. deep blue .. .. .. £140 85·00
c. Sloping label £375 £225
18A 6d. blue .. .. .. £140 85·00
c. Sloping label £375 £225
w. Wmk Crown to left of CC ..
19A 1s. green £375 £250
20A 1s. deep green £375 £250
w. Wmk Crown to left of CC £500
10A/20A .. .. *Set of* 7 £1600 £1000

B. *Wmk upright*
10B 1 ½d. orange .. .. .. 7·00 12·00
11B ½d. dull orange .. .. .. 7·00 12·00
w. Wmk inverted .. .. .. 45·00
x. Wmk reversed .. .. .. 38·00
12B 1d. maroon .. .. .. 4·50 6·00
w. Wmk inverted .. .. .. 90·00 90·00
13B 2d. rose .. .. .. 23·00 11·00
w. Wmk inverted .. .. .. † £200
14B 3d. bright ultramarine .. .. 65·00 32·00
14cB 3d. pale dull ultramarine .. .. 50·00 26·00
w. Wmk inverted .. .. .. 65·00 40·00
15B 4d. brown .. .. .. £170 14·00
w. Wmk inverted .. .. .. † £150
16B 4d. pale brown .. .. .. £170 15·00
17B 6d. deep blue .. .. .. 80·00 45·00
c. Sloping label £225 £150
18B 6d. blue .. .. .. 80·00 45·00
c. Sloping label £225 £150
19B 1s. green £225 £130
w. Wmk inverted .. .. .. † £325
20B 1s. deep green £225 £130
10B/20B .. .. *Set of* 7 £500 £225

*There were three different printings of these stamps. The original supply, sent in June 1880 and covering all seven values, had watermark sideways and was perforated by a line machine. In October of the same year a further printing of the lowest five values had the watermark changed to upright, but was still with line perforation. The final printing, sent May 1881 and containing all values, also had watermark upright, but was perforated on a comb machine.

†The normal sideways watermark shows Crown to right of CC, *as seen from the back of the stamp.*

1886–93. *Wmk Crown CA (sideways*). P* 14.
21 1 ½d. myrtle-green (1887) .. .. 2·50 2·25
w. Wmk Crown to right of CA .. 26·00
x. Wmk sideways reversed .. .. 38·00
22 ½d. grey-green .. .. .. 3·00 3·25
22*b* 1d. maroon .. .. .. † £15000
23 1d. crimson (1887) .. .. 5·00 7·00
23*a* 1d. aniline crimson .. .. 6·50 9·00
23*b* 1d. pale carmine .. .. .. 6·00 9·00
24 2d. orange (1887) .. .. .. 10·00 5·00
25 2d. deep orange .. .. .. 1·60 8·00
26 2½d. ultramarine (1887) .. .. 2·75 2·00
27 2½d. deep bright blue .. .. .. 2·25 1·25
w. Wmk Crown to right of CA .. 90·00
28 3d. slate-grey (1886) .. .. 5·00 14·00
29 3d. grey .. .. .. 3·50 15·00
30 4d. brown (1887) .. .. .. 4·50 2·00
31 4d. deep brown .. .. .. 4·50 2·00
a. Wmk upright .. .. .. † £1100
w. Wmk Crown to right of CA .. 65·00 65·00
32 6d. yellowish olive-green (1886) .. 75·00 30·00
a. Sloping label .. .. .. £180 75·00
bw. Wmk Crown to right of CA .. £140
32*d* 6d. olive-green (1887) .. .. 60·00 55·00
da. Sloping label £160 £140
33 6d. bronze-green (1889) .. .. 26·00 55·00
a. Sloping label .. .. .. 60·00 £100
bw. Wmk Crown to right of CA .. £150
33*c* 6d. deep bronze-green (1889) .. 27·00 55·00
ca. Sloping label .. .. .. 60·00 £100
34 6d. slate-green (1893) .. .. 11·00 45·00
35 1s. violet (1887) .. .. .. 3·25 16·00
36 1s. deep violet .. .. .. 4·50 17·00
36*b* 1s. aniline violet £1100
21/36 .. .. *Set of* 8 30·00 70·00
21s/4s, 32s Optd "Specimen" .. *Set of* 4 £400

*The normal sideways watermark shows Crown to left of CA, *as seen from the back of the stamp.*

The above were printed in panes of 15 on paper intended for larger panes. Hence the watermark is sometimes misplaced or omitted and letters from "CROWN AGENTS FOR THE COLONIES" from the margin may appear on the stamps.

The ½d., 2d., 3d., 4d., 6d. (No. 32) and 1s. with watermark Crown CA are known imperforate (*price from* £1100, *unused*).

Only three examples, all used, are recorded of the 1d. maroon, No. 22*b*.

The previously listed 3d. "pearl-grey" shade has been deleted as it is impossible to distinguish from other 3d. shades when it occurs on a single stamp. Sheets from this late printing can be identified by three coloured dots in the left sheet margin and one in the right, this being the reverse of the normal arrangement.

Only three used examples are known of the 4d. with upright watermark, No. 31a.

NEW INFORMATION

The editor is always interested to correspond with people who have new information that will improve or correct the Catalogue.

CROWN COLONY

2

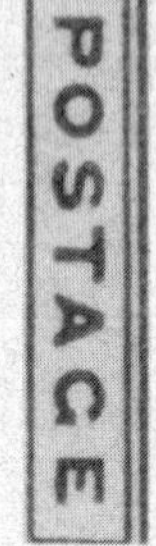

Normal

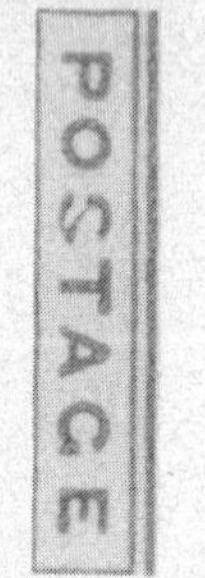

Malformed "S"

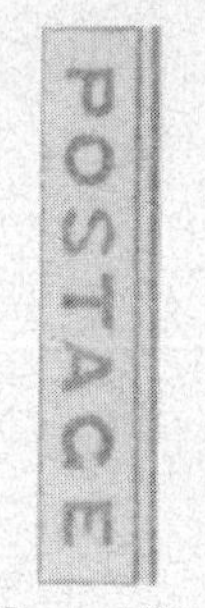

Repaired "S"

The Malformed "S" occurs on R. 7/3 of the left pane from Key Plate 2. This was used to print the initial supply all values. Printings of the ½d., 1d. and 2½d. despatched on 24 September 1898 had the "S" repaired as shown above. Subsequent printings of the ½d., 1d. and 3d. were from Key Plate 3.

(Typo D.L.R.)

1898 (2 May)–**1902.** *Wmk Crown CA. P* 14.
37 2 ½d. dull green (*shades*) .. .. .. 2·75 1·75
a. Malformed "S" £190
b. Repaired "S" £225 £180
38 1d. carmine (*shades*) .. .. .. 1·50 75
a. Malformed "S" £190
b. Repaired "S" £225 £225
39 2d. orange and mauve .. .. .. 6·00 3·50
a. Malformed "S" £225 £225
40 2½d. ultramarine .. .. 1·75 2·50
a. Malformed "S" £190
b. Repaired "S" £250
41 3d. reddish purple and blue .. .. 18·00 12·00
a. Malformed "S" £300
b. Deep purple and ultramarine (1902) 85·00 £100
42 4d. brown and blue .. .. .. 9·00 30·00
a. Malformed "S" £275
43 6d. olive-green and carmine .. .. 10·00 25·00
a. Malformed "S" £300
44 1s. violet and green .. .. .. 28·00 65·00
a. Malformed "S" £400
37/44 .. .. *Set of* 8 70·00 £130
37s/44s Optd "Specimen" .. *Set of* 8 £150

3

4

Dented frame (R. 1/6 of left pane)

1902 (13 Mar)–**05.** *Wmk Crown CA. P* 14.
45 3 ½d. green (19.4.02) .. .. .. 2·50 2·50
a. Dented frame .. .. .. 65·00
46 1d. carmine .. .. 3·00 1·00
a. Dented frame .. .. .. 70·00
47 2d. orange and mauve (14.6.02) .. 3·25 2·00
a. Dented frame £100
48 2½d. ultramarine (14.6.02) .. .. 28·00 18·00
a. Dented frame £250
49 3d. purple and ultramarine (19.4.02) .. 12·00 3·50
a. Dented frame £180
50 4d. brown and ultramarine (14.6.02) .. 3·00 24·00
a. Dented frame £140
51 6d. pale sage-green & carmine (14.6.02) 3·50 12·00
a. Dented frame £140
52 1s. violet and green (14.6.02) .. .. 48·00 85·00
a. Dented frame £350
53 4 1s. 6d. green and carmine/*yellow* (6.4.05) 7·00 18·00
a. Dented frame £190
54 2s. deep slate and orange (14.6.02) .. 48·00 60·00
a. Dented frame £325
55 2s. 6d. purple and brown/*yellow* (6.4.05) 15·00 60·00
a. Dented frame £250
56 3s. carmine and green/*yellow* (6.4.05) .. 20·00 60·00
a. Dented frame £250
45/56 .. .. *Set of* 12 £170 £300
45s/56s Optd "Specimen" .. *Set of* 12 £180

1904 (Aug)–**06.** *Wmk Mult Crown CA. P* 14.
57 3 ½d. green (9.05) .. .. 4·50
a. Dented frame .. .. 90·00
58 1d. carmine .. .. 4·50
a. Dented frame .. .. 95·00
59 2d. orange and mauve (23.2.06) .. 12·00
a. Dented frame £180
60 2½d. bright blue (8.05) .. .. .. 5·50
a. Bright blue and ultramarine .. 12·00
b. Dented frame £110
61 3d. purple and ultramarine (9.05) .. 7·00
a. Dented frame £130
62 4d. brown and ultramarine (23.2.06) .. 18·00
a. Dented frame £225
63 4 5d. grey and black (6.4.05) .. .. 14·00
a. Dented frame £190
64 3 6d. olive-green and carmine (23.2.06) .. 18·00
a. Dented frame £225
65 4 7½d. green and carmine (6.4.05) .. .. 10·00
a. Dented frame £150
66 10d. olive and carmine (6.4.05) .. .. 20·00
a. Dented frame £225
67 3 1s. violet and green (9.05) .. .. 20·00
a. Dented frame £225
68 4 2s. deep slate and orange (7.05) .. 70·00
a. Dented frame £350
57/68 .. .. *Set of* 12 £180
63s, 65s/6s Optd "Specimen" .. *Set of* 3 70·00
See also Nos. 72/85.

HALF PENNY
(5)

ONE PENNY
(6)

1906 (10 Apr). *Nos.* 55 *and* 56 *surch with T* **5** *or* **6** *by* (
Printer.
69 ½d. on 2s. 6d. purple and brown/*yellow* .. 50·00 65
a. Dented frame £400
70 1d. on 3s. carmine and green/*yellow* .. 55·00 30
a. Surch double £1800 £5
b. Dented frame £450

No. 69 was surcharged in a setting of 30 (6 × 5), the spa between the words and the bars being 5 mm on rows 1, 2 and 5; 4 mm on rows 3 and 4. Constant varieties occur on R.2/1 (bro "E") and R.5/1 (dropped "Y") of the setting.

No. 70 was surcharged in a setting of 60 (6 × 10) and a sim dropped "Y" variety occurs on R.6/3 and R.8/5.

Both values were withdrawn on 24 April when fresh supp of ½d. and 1d. definitives were received from London.

1909 (1 Oct). *Colours changed. Wmk Mult Crown CA. P* 14
72 3 ½d. blue-green .. .. 2·75 3
a. Dented frame .. .. .. 75·00
73 1d. red .. .. 5·50
a. Dented frame £100
74 2d. greyish slate .. .. .. 1·60 11
a. Dented frame £100
75 3d. purple/*yellow* .. .. .. 3·50 1
a. Purple/lemon-yellow .. .. 5·50 1
b. Dented frame £110
76 4d. black and red/*yellow* .. .. 1·00
a. Dented frame £110
77 4 5d. orange and purple .. .. .. 1·50 1
a. Dented frame £120
78 3 6d. dull and bright purple .. .. 2·25 2
a. Dented frame £130
79 4 7½d. brown and blue .. .. .. 2·50 2
a. Dented frame £130
80 10d. pale sage-green and carmine .. 2·50 7
a. Dented frame £140
81 3 1s. black/*green* .. .. .. 3·25 17
a. Dented frame £140
82 4 1s. 6d. violet and green .. .. 12·00 60
a. Dented frame £200
83 2s. purple and bright blue/*blue* .. 14·00 20
a. Dented frame £200
84 2s. 6d. black and red/*blue* .. .. 21·00 20
a. Dented frame £250
85 3s. yellow and green .. .. .. 22·00 48
a. Dented frame £250
72/85 .. .. *Set of* 14 85·00 £1
73s/85s Optd "Specimen" .. *Set of* 13 £225

Most values between Nos. 45 and 85 are known with forg postmarks. These include circular types of Bathurst, dated "JA 97", and Macarthy Island, dated "FE 17 10", and an ov registered Gambia postmark dated "22 JU 10".

7

8

Split "A" (R. 8/3 of left pane) (ptgs to 1918)

(Typo D.L.R.)

1912 (1 Sept)–**22.** *Wmk Mult Crown CA. Chalk-surfaced pape* (5s.). *P* 14.
86 7 ½d. deep green .. .. 1·75 1·5
a. Green .. .. 2·50 1·5
b. Pale green (1916) .. .. .. 3·25 3·2
c. Split "A" .. .. 65·00
87 1d. red .. .. 2·50 8
a. Rose-red .. .. 1·75 3
b. Scarlet (1916) .. .. .. 3·25 9
c. Split "A" .. .. 75·00

8 1½d. olive-green and blue-green .. 50 30
a. Split "A" .. .. 75·00
7 2d. greyish slate .. .. 50 2·75
a. Split "A" .. .. 75·00
2½d. deep bright blue .. .. .. 4·00 3·00
a. Bright blue .. .. 4·50 2·50
b. Split "A" £120
3d. purple/*yellow* 50 30
a. On lemon (1917) .. .. .. 14·00 18·00
b. On orange-buff (1920) .. .. 10·00 8·50
c. On pale yellow .. .. .. 1·25 1·00
d. Split "A" .. .. 90·00
4d. black and red/*yellow* .. .. 1·00 10·00
a. On lemon (1917) .. .. .. 2·50 7·50
b. On orange-buff (1920) .. .. 8·00 11·00
c. On pale yellow .. .. .. 1·50 6·00
d. Split "A" £100
w. Wmk inverted .. .. 90·00
8 5d. orange and purple .. .. .. 1·00 2·00
a. Split "A" £110
7 6d. dull and bright purple .. .. 1·00 2·50
a. Split "A" £110
8 7½d. brown and blue .. .. .. 1·25 6·50
a. Split "A" £160
10d. pale sage-green and carmine .. 2·00 17·00
a. Deep sage-green and carmine .. 2·00 15·00
b. Split "A" £180
7 1s. black/*green* .. .. 2·00 1·00
a. On emerald back (1921) .. .. 1·00 18·00
b. Split "A" £130
8 1s. 6d. violet and green .. .. .. 11·00 10·00
a. Split "A" £325
2s. purple and blue/*blue* .. .. 3·50 6·00
a. Split "A" £300
2s. 6d. black and red/*blue* .. .. 3·25 14·00
a. Split "A" £300
3s. yellow and green .. .. .. 8·50 25·00
a. Split "A" £425
5s. green and red/*pale yellow* (1922) 70·00 £110
)2 .. .. *Set of* 17 95·00 £180
102s Optd "Specimen" .. *Set of* 17 £325

–22. *Wmk Mult Script CA. Chalk-surfaced paper* (4s.). 14.
7 ½d. dull green .. .. 30 15·00
x. Wmk reversed .. .. 85·00
1d. carmine-red .. .. 1·00 4·25
x. Wmk reversed .. .. 80·00 80·00
8 1½d. olive-green and blue-green .. 1·25 13·00
7 2d. grey .. .. 1·00 2·25
x. Wmk reversed .. .. 70·00
2½d. bright blue .. .. 50 5·50
8 5d. orange and purple .. .. .. 1·75 16·00
x. Wmk reversed .. .. 40·00
7 6d. dull and bright purple .. .. 1·75 16·00
x. Wmk reversed .. .. 21·00
8 7½d. brown and blue .. .. .. 2·00 28·00
x. Wmk reversed .. .. 21·00
10d. pale sage-green and carmine .. 7·00 15·00
x. Wmk reversed .. .. 45·00
4s. black and red (1922) .. .. 65·00 £110
w. Wmk inverted .. .. 60·00 £130
'17 .. .. *Set of* 10 70·00 £200
s/17s Optd "Specimen" .. *Set of* 10 £200

'orged postmarks of the types mentioned below No. 85 have) been seen on various values between No. 86 and 117. lectors should beware of partial strikes which do not show year date.

9

10

(Recess D.L.R.)

22 (1 Sept)–**29.** *Portrait and shield in black. P* 14*.

(*a*) *Wmk Mult Crown CA*

8 9 4d. red/*yellow* (*a*) .. .. .. 2·50 2·50
9 7½d. purple/*yellow* (*a*) .. .. .. 3·25 6·50
0 10 1s. purple/*yellow* (*a*) .. .. .. 8·00 21·00
w. Wmk inverted .. .. 80·00
1 5s. green/*yellow* (*c*) .. .. .. 38·00 £100
w. Wmk inverted .. .. 60·00
8/21 .. .. *Set of* 4 45·00 £120
8s/21s Optd or H/S (5s.) "Specimen" .. *Set of* 4 £140

(*b*) *Wmk Mult Script CA*

2 9 ½d. green (*abd*) 55 55
3 ½d. deep green (*bd*) (1925) .. .. 3·75 1·25
4 1d. brown (*abd*) 80 20
5 1½d. bright rose-scarlet (*abd*) 80 20
6 2d. grey (*ab*) .. .. 1·00 2·75
7 2½d. orange-yellow (*b*) .. .. .. 1·00 11·00
w. Wmk inverted .. .. 80·00
8 3d. bright blue (*abd*) .. .. .. 1·00 20
9 4d. red/*yellow* (*bd*) (1.3.27) .. .. 5·50 19·00
0 5d. sage-green (*a*) .. .. .. 2·00 10·00
1 6d. claret (*ad*) .. .. 1·25 30
2 7½d. purple/*yellow* (*ab*) (1927) .. 7·00 48·00
3 10d. blue (*a*) .. .. 4·50 18·00
4 10 1s. purple/*yellow* (*aef*) (9.24) .. .. 2·50 1·00
a. Blackish purple/yell-buff (*c*) (1929) 38·00 45·00
5 1s. 6d. blue (*af*) .. .. 11·00 12·00
6 2s. purple/*blue* (*ac*) .. .. .. 4·00 4·25
7 2s. 6d. deep green (*a*) .. .. .. 4·50 9·50
8 3s. bright aniline violet (*a*) .. .. 12·00 42·00
9 3s. slate-purple (*c*) (1928) £180 £350
0 4s. brown (*ace*) .. .. 5·50 16·00
1 5s. green/*yellow* (*acf*) (9.26) .. .. 12·00 38·00
2 10s. sage-green (*ce*) .. .. .. 70·00 £100
22/42 .. .. *Set of* 19 £130 £300
22s/42s Optd "Specimen" .. *Set of* 19 £400

Perforations. A number of different perforating machines were used for the various printings of these stamps and the following varieties are known: (*a*) the original 14 line perforation; (*b*) 14 × 13.8 comb perforation used for Type **9**; (*c*) 13.8 × 13.7 comb perforation used for Type **10**; (*d*) 13.7 line perforation used for Type **9**; (*e*) 14 × 13.8 compound line perforation used for Type **10**; (*f*) 13.8 × 14 compound line perforation used for Type **10**. The occurrence of these perforations on the individual values is indicated by the letters shown after the colour descriptions above.

No. 139 has been faked, but note that this stamp is comb perf 13.8 × 13.7 whereas No. 138 is line perf 14 exactly. There are also shades of the slate-purple.

Most values of the above issue are known with a forged oval registered Gambia postmark dated "22 JU 10", often with the year date not shown. Collectors should exercise particular caution in buying used examples of No. 139.

1935 (6 May). *Silver Jubilee. As Nos.* 91/4 *of Antigua, but printed by B.W. P* 11×12.
143 1½d. deep blue and scarlet 50 50
a. Extra flagstaff £250
b. Short extra flagstaff £150
c. Lightning conductor £275
d. Flagstaff on right-hand turret .. £200
e. Double flagstaff £200
144 3d. brown and deep blue 55 70
a. Extra flagstaff £160
b. Short extra flagstaff £160
c. Lightning conductor £150
145 6d. light blue and olive-green .. .. 1·00 2·50
a. Extra flagstaff £150
b. Short extra flagstaff £160
c. Lightning conductor £160
d. Flagstaff on right-hand turret .. £325
146 1s. slate and purple .. .. .. 3·00 7·00
a. Extra flagstaff £200
b. Short extra flagstaff £250
c. Lightning conductor £200
d. Flagstaff on right-hand turret .. £400
143/6 .. .. *Set of* 4 4·50 9·50
143s/6s Perf "Specimen" .. .. *Set of* 4 90·00

For illustrations of plate varieties see Omnibus section following Zanzibar.

Examples of Nos. 145a and 146a are known with the extra flagstaff erased from the stamp with a sharp point.

1937 (12 May). *Coronation. As Nos.* 95/7 *of Antigua. P* 11×11½
147 1d. yellow-brown 30 15
148 1½d. carmine 30 35
149 3d. blue 55 60
147/9 .. .. *Set of* 3 1·00 1·00
147s/9s Perf "Specimen" .. .. *Set of* 3 60·00

11 Elephant (from Colony Badge)

(Recess B.W.)

1938 (1 Apr)–**46.** *Wmk Mult Script CA. P* 12.
150 11 ½d. black and emerald-green 15 70
151 1d. purple and brown 20 50
152 1½d. brown-lake and bright carmine .. £150 12·00
a. Brown-lake and scarlet .. .. 3·00 2·25
b. Brown-lake and vermilion .. .. 30 2·00
152*c* 1½d. blue and black (2.1.45) .. .. 30 1·50
153 2d. blue and black .. .. .. 4·00 3·25
153*a* 2d. lake and scarlet (1.10.43) .. .. 60 2·25
154 3d. light blue and grey-blue 30 10
154*a* 5d. sage-green & purple-brn (13.3.41) 50 50
155 6d. olive-green and claret .. .. 1·50 35
156 1s. slate-blue and violet .. .. 2·00 10
156*a* 1s. 3d. chocolate & lt blue (28.11.46) 2·75 2·50
157 2s. carmine and blue .. .. .. 4·50 3·25
158 2s. 6d. sepia and dull green .. .. 12·00 2·25
159 4s. vermilion and purple .. .. 21·00 2·50
160 5s. blue and vermilion .. .. .. 21·00 4·00
161 10s. orange and black .. .. .. 21·00 7·00
150/61 .. .. *Set of* 16 80·00 28·00
150s/61s Perf "Specimen" .. *Set of* 16 £275

1946 (6 Aug). *Victory. As Nos.* 110/11 *of Antigua.*
162 1½d. black 10 10
163 3d. blue 10 10
162s/3s Perf "Specimen" .. .. *Set of* 2 55·00

1948 (24 Dec). *Royal Silver Wedding. As Nos.* 112/13 *of Antigua.*
164 1½d. black 25 10
165 £1 mauve .. .. 12·00 14·00

1949 (10 Oct). *75th Anniv of Universal Postal Union. As Nos.* 114/17 *of Antigua.*
166 1½d. blue-black 30 75
167 3d. deep blue .. .. 1·25 1·25
168 6d. magenta 35 40
169 1s. violet 35 35
166/9 .. .. *Set of* 4 2·00 2·50

MINIMUM PRICE

The minimum price quote is 10p which represents a handling charge rather than a basis for valuing common stamps. For further notes about prices see introductory pages.

Gibraltar

CROWN COLONY

Early details of postal arrangements in Gibraltar are hard to establish, although it is known that postal facilities were provided by the Civil Secretary's Office from 1749. Gibraltar became a packet port in July 1806, although the Civil Secretary's office continued to be responsible for other mail. The two services were amalgamated on 1 January 1857 as a Branch Office of the British G.P.O., the control of the postal services not reverting to Gibraltar until 1 January 1886.

Spanish stamps could be used at Gibraltar from their introduction in 1850 and, indeed, such franking was required on letters weighing over ½ oz. sent to Spain after 1 July 1854. From 1 July 1856 until 1 January 1876 all mail to Spain required postage to be prepaid by Spanish stamps and these issues were supplied by the Gibraltar postal authorities, acting as a Spanish Postal Agent. The mail forwarded under this system was cancelled at San Roque with a horizontal barred oval, later replaced by a cartwheel type mark showing numeral 63. From 1857 combination covers showing the 2d. ship mail fee paid in British stamps and the inland postage by Spanish issues exist.

Stamps of Great Britain were issued for use in Gibraltar from 3 September 1857 (earliest recorded cover is dated 7 September 1857) to the end of 1885.

The initial supply contained 1d., 4d. and 6d. values. No supplies of the 2d. or 1s. were sent until the consignment of October 1857. No other values were supplied until early 1862.

For illustrations of the postmark types see BRITISH POST OFFICES ABROAD notes, following GREAT BRITAIN.

Stamps of GREAT BRITAIN *cancelled* "G" *as Type* **1** (3 Sept 1857 *to* 19 Feb 1859)
Z 1 1d. red-brown (1854) Die I, *wmk* Small Crown, *Perf* 16 .. .. £350
Z 2 1d. red-brown (1855), Die II, *wmk* Small Crown, *perf* 16 .. .. £600
Z 3 1d. red-brown (1855), Die II, *wmk* Small Crown, *perf* 14 .. .. £300
Z 4 1d. red-brown (1855), Die II, *wmk* Large Crown, *perf* 14 .. .. 75·00
Z 5 1d. rose-red (1857), Die II, *wmk* Large Crown, *perf* 14 .. .. 21·00
Z 6 2d. blue (1855), *wmk* Small Crown, *perf* 14 .. £375
Z 7 2d. blue (1855–58), *wmk* Large Crown, *perf* 16 .. £325
Z 8 2d. blue (1855), *wmk* Large Crown, *perf* 14 *From* 55·00
Plate Nos. 5, 6.
Z 9 2d. blue (1858) (Plate No. 7) £225
Z10 4d. rose (1857) .. .. 55·00
a. Thick glazed paper .. ..
Z11 6d. lilac (1856) .. .. 40·00
Z12 6d. lilac (1856) (blued *paper*) £750
Z13 1s. green (1856) £110
a. Thick paper .. ..
Z14 1s. green (1856) (blued *paper*) £1300

Stamps of GREAT BRITAIN *cancelled* "A 26" *as in Types* **2, 5, 11** *or* **14** (20 Feb 1859 *to* 31 Dec 1885).
Z15 ½d. rose-red (1870–79) .. .. .. *From* 26·00
Plate Nos. 4, 5, 6, 8, 10, 11, 12, 13, 14, 15, 19, 20.
Z16 1d. red-brown (1841), *imperf* £1300
Z17 1d. red-brown (1855), *wmk* Large Crown, *perf* 14 .. £170
Z18 1d. rose-red (1857), *wmk* Large Crown, *perf* 14 .. 12·00
Z19 1d. rose-red (1864–79) .. .. .. *From* 20·00
Plate Nos. 71, 72, 73, 74, 76, 78, 79, 80, 81, 82, 83, 84, 85, 86, 87, 88, 89, 90, 91, 92, 93, 94, 95, 96, 97, 98, 99, 100, 101, 102, 103, 104, 105, 106, 107, 108, 109, 110, 111, 112, 113, 114, 115, 116, 117, 118, 119, 120, 121, 122, 123, 124, 125, 127, 129, 130, 131, 132, 133, 134, 135, 136, 137, 138, 139, 140, 141, 142, 143, 144, 145, 146, 147, 148, 149, 150, 151, 152, 153, 154, 155, 156, 157, 158, 159, 160, 161, 162, 163, 164, 165, 166, 167, 168, 169, 170, 171, 172, 173, 174, 175, 176, 177, 178, 179, 180, 181, 182, 183, 184, 185, 186, 187, 188, 189, 190, 191, 192, 193, 194, 195, 196, 197, 198, 199, 200, 201, 202, 203, 204, 205, 206, 207, 208, 209, 210, 211, 212, 213, 214, 215, 216, 217, 218, 219, 220, 221, 222, 223, 224, 225.
Z20 1½d. lake-red (1870) (Plate No. 3) £400
Z21 2d. blue (1855), *wmk* Large Crown, *perf* 14 .. £120
Plate No. 6.
Z22 2d. blue (1858–69) .. .. .. *From* 19·00
Plate Nos. 7, 8, 9, 12, 13, 14, 15.
Z23 2½d. rosy mauve (1875) (blued *paper*) .. *From* £100
Plate Nos. 1, 2, 3.
Z24 2½d. rosy mauve (1875–76) (Plate Nos. 1, 2, 3) *From* 27·00
Z25 2½d. rosy mauve (*Error of Lettering*) £1800
Z26 2½d. rosy mauve (1876–79) .. .. *From* 20·00
Plate Nos. 3, 4, 5, 6, 7, 8, 9, 10, 11, 12, 13, 14, 15, 16, 17.
Z27 2½d. blue (1880–81) (Plate Nos. 17, 18, 19, 20) *From* 12·00
Z28 2½d. blue (1881) (Plate Nos. 21, 22, 23) .. *From* 10·00
Z29 3d. carmine-rose (1862) £170
Z30 3d. rose (1865) (Plate No. 4) .. .. .. 55·00
Z31 3d. rose (1867–73) .. .. .. *From* 35·00
Plate Nos. 4, 5, 6, 7, 8, 9, 10.
Z32 3d. rose (1873–76) .. .. .. *From* 42·00
Plate Nos. 11, 12, 14, 15, 16, 17, 18, 19, 20.
Z33 3d. rose (1881) (Plate Nos. 20, 21) .. ..
Z34 3d. lilac (1883) (3d. *on* 3d) £120
Z35 4d. rose (1857) .. .. 50·00
Z36 4d. red (1862) (Plate Nos. 3, 4) .. .. *From* 48·00
Z37 4d. vermilion (1865–73) .. .. *From* 30·00
Plate Nos. 7, 8, 9, 10, 11, 12, 13, 14.
Z38 4d. vermilion (1876) (Plate No. 15) £250
Z39 4d. sage-green (1877) (Plate Nos. 15, 16) .. £110
Z40 4d. grey-brown (1880) *wmk* Large Garter .. £225
Plate No. 17.
Z41 4d. grey-brown (1880) *wmk* Crown .. *From* 45·00
Plate Nos. 17, 18.
Z42 6d. lilac (1856) .. .. 42·00
Z43 6d. lilac (1862) (Plate Nos. 3, 4) .. *From* 38·00
Z44 6d. lilac (1865–67) (Plate Nos. 5, 6) .. *From* 32·00
Z45 6d. lilac (1867) (Plate No. 6) .. .. .. 42·00
Z46 6d. violet (1867–70) (Plate Nos. 6, 8, 9) *From* 32·00
Z47 6d. buff (1872–73) (Plate Nos. 11, 12) *From* £150

Z48 6d. chestnut (1872) (Plate No. 11) .. .. .. 32·00
Z49 6d. grey (1873) (Plate No. 12) .. .. .. 95·00
Z50 6d. grey (1874–80) .. .. .. *From* 30·00
Plate Nos. 13, 14, 15, 16, 17.
Z51 6d. grey (1881) (Plate Nos. 17, 18) £190
Z52 6d. lilac (1883) (6d. *on* 6d.) .. .. .. 95·00
Z53 8d. orange (1876) £375
Z54 9d. bistre (1862) £200
Z55 9d. straw (1862) £600
Z56 9d. straw (1865) £550
Z57 9d. straw (1867) £170
Z58 10d. red-brown (1867) £150
Z59 1s. green (1856) £100
Z60 1s. green (1862) .. .. .. 70·00
Z61 1s. green (1862) ("K" *variety*) £2000
Z62 1s. green (1865) (Plate No. 4) .. .. 60·00
Z63 1s. green (1867–73) (Plate Nos. 4, 5, 6, 7) .. *From* 24·00
Z64 1s. green (1873–77) .. .. .. *From* 55·00
Plate Nos. 8, 9, 10, 11, 12, 13.
Z65 1s. orange-brown (1880) (Plate No. 13) £300
Z66 1s. orange-brown (1881) (Plate Nos. 13, 14) *From* 80·00
Z67 2s. blue (1867) £180
Z68 5s. rose (1867) (Plate No. 1) £650

1880.
Z69 ½d. deep green .. .. .. 24·00
Z70 ½d. pale green .. .. .. 24·00
Z71 1d. Venetian red .. .. .. 23·00
Z72 1½d. Venetian red £225
Z73 2d. pale rose .. .. .. 70·00
Z74 2d. deep rose .. .. .. 70·00
Z75 5d. indigo £120

1881.
Z76 1d. lilac (14 *dots*) .. .. .. 27·00
Z77 1d. lilac (16 *dots*) .. .. .. 9·00

1884.
Z78 ½d. slate-blue .. .. .. 22·00
Z79 2d. lilac .. .. .. 80·00
Z80 2½d. lilac .. .. .. 15·00
Z81 3d. lilac .. .. ..
Z82 4d. dull green £160
Z83 6d. dull green .. .. ..

POSTAL FISCAL
Z83*a* 1d. purple (Die 4) (1878) *wmk* Small Anchor £650
Z84 1d. purple (1881), *wmk* Orb £1100

PRICES FOR STAMPS ON COVER TO 1945

Nos. 1/2	*from* × 25
No. 3	*from* × 10
No. 4	*from* × 25
Nos. 5/6	*from* × 8
Nos. 7/33	*from* × 6
Nos. 39/45	*from* × 5
Nos. 46/109	*from* × 3
Nos. 110/13	*from* × 4
Nos. 114/17	*from* × 3
Nos. 118/20	*from* × 5
Nos. 121/31	*from* × 3

GIBRALTAR

(1)

1886 (1 Jan). *Contemporary types of Bermuda optd with T* **1** *by D.L.R. Wmk Crown CA. P* 14.
1 **9** ½d. dull green .. .. .. 11·00 7·00
2 **1** 1d. rose-red .. .. .. 50·00 4·25
3 **2** 2d. purple-brown .. .. .. £100 75·00
w. Wmk inverted .. ..
4 **11** 2½d. ultramarine .. .. .. £130 3·25
a. Optd in blue-black £500 £150
w. Wmk inverted .. .. .. — £325
5 **10** 4d. orange-brown .. .. .. £120 85·00
6 **4** 6d. deep lilac £200 £180
7 **5** 1s. yellow-brown £425 £350
1/7 .. .. *Set of* 7 £900 £650
1s/3s, 4as/7s Optd "Specimen" .. *Set of* 7 £2750

PRINTER. All Gibraltar stamps to No. 109 were typographed by De La Rue & Co, Ltd.

2

3

4

5

1886 (Nov)–**87**. *Wmk Crown CA. P* 14.
8 **2** ½d. dull green (1.87) .. .. .. 9·00 3·75
9 **3** 1d. rose (2.87) .. .. .. 42·00 4·25
10 **4** 2d. brown-purple (12.86) .. .. .. 30·00 17·00
w. Wmk inverted £350
11 **5** 2½d. blue .. .. .. 75·00 2·75
w. Wmk inverted .. .. .. £190 65·00
12 **4** 4d. orange-brown (16.4.87) .. .. 75·00 75·00
13 6d. lilac (16.4.87) £100 £100
14 1s. bistre (2.87) £180 £180
w. Wmk inverted .. .. ..
8/14 .. .. *Set of* 7 £450 £350
8s/14s Optd "Specimen" .. *Set of* 7 £500

Examples of Nos. 3, 6/7 and 14 are known showing a forged Gibraltar postmark dated "JU-13 87".

See also Nos. 39/45.

5 CENTIMOS

(6)

5

"5" with short foot (all stamps in 1st, 5th and 6th vertical columns (5 c. on ½d.) or all stamps in 2nd vertical column (25 c. on 2d., 25 c. on 2½d., 50 c. on 6d. and 75 c. on 1s.)

1889 (1 Aug). *Surch as T* **6**.
15 **2** 5 c. on ½d. green .. .. .. 6·00 17·00
a. "5" with short foot .. .. .. 6·00 17·00
16 **3** 10 c. on 1d. rose .. .. .. 12·00 8·00
17 **4** 25 c. on 2d. brown-purple .. .. 4·75 6·00
a. "5" with short foot .. .. 10·00 12·00
ab. Small "I" (R. 6/2) £100 £150
b. Broken "N" (R. 10/5) £100 £150
18 **5** 25 c. on 2½d. bright blue .. .. 20·00 2·25
a. "5" with short foot .. .. 35·00 5·00
ab. Small "I" (R. 6/2) £325 £100
b. Broken "N" (R. 10/5) £325 £100
19 **4** 40 c. on 4d. orange-brown .. .. 50·00 70·00
20 50 c. on 6d. bright lilac .. .. 55·00 70·00
a. "5" with short foot .. .. 90·00 £110
21 75 c. on 1s. bistre .. .. 55·00 65·00
a. "5" with short foot .. .. 90·00 £100
15/21 .. .. *Set of* 7 £180 £200
15s/21s Optd "Specimen" *Set of* 7 £350

10 c., 40 c. and 50 c. values from this issue and that of 1889–96 are known bisected and used for half their value from various post offices in Morocco (*price on cover from* £500). These bisects were never authorised by the Gibraltar Post Office.

Broken "M" (Pl 2 R. 4/5)

7

Flat top to "C" (Pl 2 R. 4/4)

1889 (8 Oct)*–**96**. *Issue in Spanish currency. Wmk Crown CA. P* 14.
22 **7** 5 c. green .. .. .. 4·50 80
a. Broken "M" .. .. .. £120 60·00
w. Wmk inverted £200 £160
23 10 c. carmine .. .. .. 4·50 50
b. Value omitted £5000
24 20 c. olive-green and brown (2.1.96) .. 38·00 18·00
w. Wmk inverted .. .. — £225
25 20 c. olive-green (8.7.96) .. .. 11·00 60·00
a. Flat top to "C" £170
26 25 c. ultramarine .. .. 15·00 70
a. Deep ultramarine .. .. 26·00 80
27 40 c. orange-brown .. .. 3·75 2·50
28 50 c. bright lilac (1890) .. .. 3·25 2·00
29 75 c. olive-green (1890) .. .. 32·00 32·00
30 1 p. bistre (11.89) .. .. 75·00 20·00
31 1 p. bistre and ultramarine (6.95) .. 4·75 4·50
32 2 p. black and carmine (2.1.96) .. 10·00 29·00
33 5 p. slate-grey (12.89) .. .. 42·00 £100
22/33 .. .. *Set of* 12 £225 £225
22s/4s, 26s/33s Optd "Specimen" *Set of* 11 £375

*Earliest recorded postmark date.

1898 (1 Oct). *Reissue in Sterling currency. Wmk Crown CA. P* 14.
39 **2** ½d. grey-green .. .. .. 5·00 1·75
w. Wmk inverted
40 **3** 1d. carmine .. .. .. 6·00 50
w. Wmk inverted .. .. .. † £1000
41 **4** 2d. brown-purple and ultramarine .. 22·00 1·75
42 **5** 2½d. bright ultramarine .. .. 27·00 50
w. Wmk inverted .. .. £200 75·00
43 **4** 4d. orange-brown and green .. .. 18·00 6·50
a. "FOUR PENCE" trimmed at top (Pl 2 R. 8/4) £400
44 6d. violet and red .. .. .. 40·00 20·00
45 1s. bistre and carmine .. .. 35·00 16·00
w. Wmk inverted
39/45 .. .. *Set of* 7 £140 42·00
39s/45s Optd "Specimen" *Set of* 7 £250

No. 39 is greyer than No. 8, No. 40 brighter and deeper than No. 9 and No. 42 much brighter than No. 11.

8

9

½ Normal **½** Large "2"

2½d.

This occurs on R.10/1 in each pane of 60. The diagonal stroke is also longer.

1903 (1 May). *Wmk Crown CA. P* 14.
46 **8** ½d. grey-green and green .. .. 10·00
47 1d. dull purple/*red* .. .. .. 30·00
48 2d. grey-green and carmine .. .. 17·00
49 2½d. dull purple and black/*blue* .. .. 4·50
a. Large "2" in "½" £190
50 6d. dull purple and violet .. .. 15·00
51 1s. black and carmine .. .. .. 28·00
52 **9** 2s. green and blue £110
53 4s. dull purple and green .. .. 80·00
54 8s. dull purple and black/*blue* £110
55 £1 dull purple and black/*red* £475
46/55 .. .. *Set of* 10 £800
46s/55s Optd "Specimen" .. *Set of* 10 £500

1904–8. *Wmk Mult Crown CA. Ordinary paper* (*½d. to 2d* *6d. to 2s.*) *or chalk-surfaced paper* (*others*). *P* 14.
56 **8** ½d. dull and bright green (4.4.04*) .. 9·00
a. Chalk-surfaced paper (10.05) .. 12·00
57 1d. dull purple/*red* (6.9.04*) .. .. 8·00
a. Bisected (½d.) (on card) .. .. †
bw. Wmk inverted .. .. ..
c. Chalk-surfaced paper (16.9.05) .. 4·25
58 2d. grey-green and carmine (9.1.05) .. 12·00
a. Chalk-surfaced paper (2.07) .. 8·50
59 2½d. purple and black/*blue* (4.5.07) .. 35·00
a. Large "2" in "½" £475
60 6d. dull purple and violet (19.4.06) .. 30·00
a. Chalk-surfaced paper (4.08) .. 26·00
61 1s. black and carmine (13.10.05) .. 42·00
a. Chalk-surfaced paper (4.06) .. 50·00
62 **9** 2s. green and blue (2.2.05) .. .. 70·00
a. Chalk-surfaced paper (10.07) .. 75·00
63 4s. deep purple and green (6.08) .. £200
64 £1 deep purple and black/*red* (15.3.08) £475
56/64 .. .. *Set of* 9 £750

*Earliest known date of use.

1906 (Oct)–**12.** *Colours changed. Wmk Mult Crown* *Chalk-surfaced paper* (*6d. to 8s.*). *P* 14.
66 **8** ½d. blue-green (1907) .. .. .. 3·50
67 1d. carmine .. .. .. 5·50
a. Wmk sideways .. .. .. —
w. Wmk inverted .. .. .. †
68 2d. greyish slate (5.10) .. .. 8·00
69 2½d. ultramarine (6.07) .. .. 5·00
a. Large "2" in "½" £200
70 6d. dull and bright purple (18.3.12) .. £120
71 1s. black/*green* (1910) .. .. 23·00
72 **9** 2s. purple and bright blue/*blue* (4.10) .. 48·00
73 4s. black and carmine (4.10) £100
x. Wmk reversed £1400
74 8s. purple and green (1911) £180
66/74 .. .. *Set of* 9 £450
67s/74s Optd "Specimen" .. *Set of* 8 £550

Examples of Nos. 55, 64 and 73/4 are known showing a for[ged] oval registered postmark dated "6 OC 10".

10

11

"HALEPENNY" (Pl 1 R. 7/3. Occurs on ptgs from 1917)

1912 (17 July)–**24.** *Wmk Mult Crown CA. Ordinary paper* (*½d. to 2½d*) *or chalk-surfaced paper* (*others*). *P* 14.
76 **10** ½d. blue-green .. .. .. 3·25
a. Yellow-green (4.17) .. .. 4·75
b. "HALEPENNY" £120
w. Wmk inverted .. .. ..
x. Wmk reversed .. .. .. †
77 1d. carmine-red .. .. .. 3·50
a. Scarlet (6.16) .. .. .. 3·50
ay. Wmk inverted and reversed ..
78 2d. greyish slate .. .. .. 9·00
79 2½d. deep bright blue .. .. .. 5·00
a. Large "2" in "½" £150
b. Pale ultramarine (1917) .. .. 7·00
ba. Large "2" in "½" £275
80 6d. dull purple and mauve .. .. 9·00
81 1s. black/*green* .. .. .. 9·00
a. Ordinary paper (8.18) £550
b. On blue-green, olive back (1919) .. 12·00
c. On emerald surface (12.23) .. 24·00
d. On emerald back (3.24) .. .. 18·00
ds. Optd "Specimen" .. .. .. 70·00
82 **11** 2s. dull purple and blue/*blue* .. .. 26·00
83 4s. black and carmine .. .. .. 30·00
84 8s. dull purple and green .. .. 80·00
85 £1 dull purple and black/*red* £130
76/85 .. .. *Set of* 10 £275
76s/85s Optd "Specimen" .. *Set of* 10 £475

WAR TAX

(12)

15 Apr). *Optd with T* **12** *by Beanland, Malin & Co, altar.*
½d. green .. .. 1·00 1·75
a. Opt double £800
w. Wmk inverted £375
y. Wmk inverted and reversed .. £375
printings of this overprint exist, the second being in slightly r type on a deeper shade of green.

3 PENCE (I) THREE PENCE (II)

27. *Wmk Mult Script CA. Chalk-surfaced paper* (6d. *to P* 14.
10 ½d. green (25.4.27) .. .. .. 1·50 1·50
1d. carmine-red (2.21) .. .. 1·75 1·00
1½d. chestnut (1.12.22) .. .. 1·75 55
a. Pale chestnut (7.24) .. .. 1·75 30
w. Wmk inverted .. .. .. † £550
2d. grey (17.2.21) .. .. .. 1·25 1·25
2½d. bright blue (2.21) .. .. .. 20·00 30·00
a. Large "2" in "½" £375 £400
3d. bright blue (I) (1.1.22) .. .. 3·00 4·25
a. Ultramarine .. .. .. 2·50 1·50
6d. dull purple and mauve (1.23) .. 6·00 3·75
a. Bright purple & magenta (22.7.26) 1·60 3·50
1s. black/*emerald* (20.6.24) .. .. 10·00 15·00
11 2s. grey-purple and blue/*blue* (20.6.24) 19·00 70·00
a. Reddish purple and blue/blue (1925) 7·00 42·00
4s. black and carmine (20.6.24) .. 60·00 £110
8s. dull purple and green (20.6.24) .. £190 £375
1 .. .. *Set of* 11 £250 £500
01s Optd "Specimen" .. *Set of* 11 £550
e ½d. exists in coils, constructed from normal sheets, first d in 1937.

(15 Oct)–**32**. *New values and colours changed. Wmk Mult ript CA. Chalk-surfaced paper. P* 14.
10 1s. sage-green and black (8.1.29) .. 14·00 22·00
a. Olive and black (1932) .. .. 14·00 12·00
11 2s. red-brown and black (8.1.29) .. 9·50 29·00
2s. 6d. green and black .. .. 9·50 17·00
5s. carmine and black .. .. .. 15·00 50·00
10s. deep ultramarine and black .. 32·00 70·00
£1 red-orange and black (16.11.27) .. £140 £180
£5 violet and black £1300 £4000
s. Optd "Specimen" £700
7 .. .. *Set of* 6 £200 £325
/7s Optd or Perf (1s., 2s.) "Specimen" *Set of* 6 £400
xamples of Nos. 83/5, 99/101 and 102/8 are known showing ed oval registered postmarks dated "24 JA 25" or "6 MY 35".

(11 Apr). *T* **10** *inscribed* "THREE PENCE". *Wmk Mult ript CA. P* 14.
3d. ultramarine (II) .. .. .. 7·50 2·00
s. Perf "Specimen" .. .. .. 70·00

13 The Rock of Gibraltar

(Des Capt. H. St. C. Garrood. Recess D.L.R.)

1–**33**. *Wmk Mult Script CA. P* 14.
13 1d. scarlet (1.7.31) .. .. .. 2·50 2·50
a. Perf 13½×14 .. .. .. 14·00 5·50
1½d. red-brown (1.7.31) .. .. 1·75 2·25
a. Perf 13½×14 .. .. .. 11·00 4·00
2d. pale grey (1.11.32) .. .. 5·50 1·50
a. Perf 13½×14 .. .. .. 13·00 2·25
3d. blue (1.6.33) .. .. .. 5·50 3·00
a. Perf 13½×14 .. .. .. 23·00 28·00
/13 .. .. *Set of* 4 14·00 8·00
a/13a .. .. *Set of* 4 55·00 35·00
s/13s Perf "Specimen" .. *Set of* 4 £170
Figures of value take the place of both corner ornaments at base of the 2d. and 3d.

35 (6 May). *Silver Jubilee. As Nos.* 91/4 *of Antigua but ptd by* *B.W. P* 11 × 12.
2d. ultramarine and grey-black .. .. 1·60 2·50
a. Extra flagstaff .. .. .. 60·00 75·00
b. Short extra flagstaff .. .. .. 95·00 £110
c. Lightning conductor .. .. .. 60·00 75·00
d. Flagstaff on right-hand turret .. £150 £160
e. Double flagstaff £150 £160
5 3d. brown and deep blue .. .. .. 3·25 3·50
a. Extra flagstaff £300 £325
b. Short extra flagstaff £250 £275
c. Lightning conductor £275 £300
6 6d. green and indigo .. .. .. 9·50 12·00
a. Extra flagstaff £225 £275
b. Short extra flagstaff £325 £350
c. Lightning conductor £225 £275
7 1s. slate and purple .. .. .. 9·50 9·50
a. Extra flagstaff £200 £200
b. Short extra flagstaff £300 £300
c. Lightning conductor £200 £200
4/17 .. .. *Set of* 4 21·00 25·00
4s/17s Perf "Specimen" *Set of* 4 £170
For illustrations of plate varieties see Omnibus section lowing Zanzibar.

37 (12 May). *Coronation. As Nos.* 95/7 *of Antigua. P* 11×11½.
8 ½d. green 25 15
9 2d. grey-black .. .. 1·00 2·25
0 3d. blue .. .. 2·25 2·25
8/20 .. .. *Set of* 3 3·25 4·00
8s/20s Perf "Specimen" *Set of* 3 85·00

14 King George VI

15 Rock of Gibraltar

16 The Rock (North Side)

Broken second "R" in "GIBRALTAR" (Frame Pl.2 R.9/4)

(Des Captain H. St. C. Garrood. Recess D.L.R.)

1938 (25 Feb)–**51**. *Designs as T* **14/16**. *Mult Script CA.*
121 ½d. deep green (*p* 13½×14) .. 10 40
122 1d. yellow-brown (*p* 14) .. .. 26·00 2·25
a. Perf 13½ (1940) .. .. .. 26·00 2·25
ab. Perf 13½. Wmk sideways (1940) .. 6·50 7·00
b. Perf 13. Wmk sideways. *Red-brown* (1942) 50 60
c. Perf 13. Wmk sideways. *Deep brown* (1944) .. .. 50 3·50
d. Perf 13. *Red-brown* (1949) .. .. 1·75 1·50
123 1½d. carmine (*p* 14) .. .. .. 35·00 75
a. Perf 13½ .. .. £250 35·00
123*b* 1½d. slate-violet (*p* 13) (1.1.43) .. 50 1·50
124 2d. grey (*p* 14) .. .. .. 26·00 40
a. Perf 13½ (1940) .. .. .. 1·25 35
ab. Perf 13½. Wmk sideways (1940) .. £600 42·00
b. Perf 13. Wmk sideways (1943) .. 50 1·25
ba. "A" of "CA" missing from wmk .. £1200
124*c* 2d. carm (*p* 13) (*wmk sideways*) (15.7.44) 50 60
125 3d. light blue (*p* 13½) .. .. 19·00 1·00
a. Perf 14 .. .. £130 5·00
b. Perf 13 (1942) 50 30
ba. Greenish blue (2.51) .. .. 3·50 2·50
125*c* 5d. red-orange (*p* 13) (1.10.47) .. 1·00 1·25
126 6d. carm & grey-violet (*p* 13½) (16.3.38) 48·00 3·00
a. Perf 14 .. .. £120 1·25
b. Perf 13 (1942) .. .. .. 3·50 1·75
c. Perf 13. *Scarlet and grey-violet* (1945) 4·50 3·75
127 1s. black and green (*p* 14) (16.3.38) .. 40·00 23·00
a. Perf 13½ .. .. 65·00 7·00
b. Perf 13 (1942) .. .. .. 3·25 4·25
ba. Broken "R" £190
128 2s. black and brown (*p* 14) (16.3.38) .. 65·00 25·00
a. Perf 13½ .. .. £120 32·00
b. Perf 13 (1942) .. .. .. 4·50 6·50
ba. Broken "R" £225
129 5s. black and carmine (*p* 14) (16.3.38) 95·00 £150
a. Perf 13½ .. .. 38·00 17·00
b. Perf 13 (1944) .. .. .. 14·00 17·00
ba. Broken "R" £300
130 10s. black and blue (*p* 14) (16.3.38) .. 65·00 £120
a. Perf 13 (1943) .. .. .. 35·00 25·00
ab. Broken "R" £400
131 £1 orange (*p* 13½×14) (16.3.38) .. 38·00 45·00
121/31 .. .. *Set of* 14 £120 85·00
121s/31s Perf "Specimen" *Set of* 14 £550
Designs:—½d., £1, Type **14**. *Horiz as T* **15/16**—1d., 1½d. (*both*), Type **15**; 2d. (*both*), Type **16**; 3d., 5d. Europa Point; 6d. Moorish Castle; 1s. Southport Gate; 2s. Eliott Memorial; 5s. Government House; 10s. Catalan Bay.
The ½d., 1d. and both colours of the 2s. exist in coils constructed from normal sheets. These were originally joined vertically, but, because of technical problems, the 1d. and 2d. grey were subsequently issued in horizontal coils. The 2d. carmine only exists in the horizontal version.
Examples of Nos. 129/31 are known showing forged oval registered postmarks dated "6 OC 43", "18 OC 43", "3 MR 44" and "4 AU 44."

1946 (12 Oct). *Victory. As Nos.* 110/11 *of Antigua.*
132 ½d. green 10 20
133 3d. ultramarine 30 50
132s/3s Perf "Specimen" .. *Set of* 2 70·00

1948 (1 Dec). *Royal Silver Wedding. As Nos.* 112/13 *of Antigua.*
134 ½d. green .. .. 70 1·25
135 £1 brown-orange .. .. 50·00 70·00

1949 (10 Oct). *75th Anniv of Universal Postal Union. As Nos.* 114/17 *of Antigua.*
136 2d. carmine .. .. 1·00 1·25
137 3d. deep blue .. .. 2·00 1·25
138 6d. purple .. .. 1·25 1·50
139 1s. blue-green .. .. 1·00 2·75
136/9 .. .. *Set of* 4 4·75 6·00

NEW CONSTITUTION 1950
(23)

1950 (1 Aug). *Inauguration of Legislative Council. Nos.* 124*c*, 125*ba*, 126*b and* 127*b optd as T* **23**.
140 **16** 2d. carmine .. .. 30 1·00
141 – 3d. greenish blue .. .. .. 55 1·00
142 – 6d. carmine and grey-violet .. .. 65 1·60
a. Opt double £750 £900
143 – 1s. black and green (R.) .. .. 65 1·60
a. Broken "R" .. .. 55·00
140/3 .. .. *Set of* 4 1·90 4·75
On stamps from the lower part of the sheet of No. 142a the two impressions are almost coincident.

STAMP BOOKLETS

1906 (Oct). *Black on red cover. Stapled.*
SB1 2s. ½d. booklet containing twenty-four ½d. and twelve 1d. (Nos. 56a, 67) in blocks of 6 ..

1912 (17 July). *Black on red cover with Edwardian cypher. Stapled.*
SB2 2s. ½d. booklet containing twenty-four ½d. and twelve 1d. (Nos. 76/7) in blocks of 6 .. ..

Gilbert and Ellice Islands

No organised postal service existed in the Gilbert and Ellice Islands before the introduction of stamp issues in January 1911. A New Zealand Postal Agency was, however, provided on Fanning Island, one of the Line Islands, primarily for the use of the staff of the Pacific Cable Board cable station which was established in 1902. The agency opened on 29 November 1902 and continued to operate until replaced by a Protectorate post office on 14 February 1939. The cable station closed on 16 January 1964. Fanning Island is now known as Tabuaeran.

Z 1

The following NEW ZEALAND *stamps are know postmarked on Fanning Island with Type* Z 1 *(in use from November* 1902 *until November* 1936. *The earliest known cover is postmarked* 20 *December* 1902.

1882–1900 Q.V. (*p* 11) ½d., 1d., 2d. (*Nos.* 236/8)
1898 Pictorials (*no wmk*) 1d., 2d. (*Nos.* 247/8)
1900 Pictorials (*W* **38**) ½d., 1½d., 2d. (*Nos.* 273, 275*b*, 276)
1901 1d. "Universal" (*W* **38**) (*No.* 278)
1902 1d. "Universal" (*no wmk*) (*No.* 295)
1902 ½d. Pictorial (*W* **43**) (*No.* 302*b*)
1902–09 Pictorials (*W* **43**) 2d., 2½d., 3d., 6d., 8d., 9d., 1s., 2s., 5s. (*Nos.* 309, 312/13, 315, 319/20, 326, 328/9)
1907–08 Pictorials (*W* **43**) 4d. (*No.* 379)
1908 1d. "Universal" (*De La Rue paper*) 1d. (*No.* 386)
1909–12 King Edward VII (*typo*) ½d. (*No.* 387)
1909–16 King Edward VII (*recess*) 2d., 3d., 4d., 5d., 6d., 8d., 1s. (*Nos.* 388/91, 393/6, 398)
1909–26 1d. "Universal" (*W* **43**) 1d. (*Nos.* 405, 410)
1915–30 King George V (*recess*) 1½d., 2d. bright violet, 2½d., 3d., 4d. bright violet, 6d., 7½d., 9d., 1s. (*Nos.* 416/17, 419/20, 422, 425/6, 429/30)
1915–34 King George V (*typo*) ½d., 1½d. (all 3), 2d., 3d. (*Nos.* 435/40, 446, 448, 449)
1915 "WAR STAMP" opt ½d. (*No.* 452)
1920 Victory 1d., 1½d. (*Nos.* 454/5)
1922 2d. on ½d. (*No.* 459)
1923–25 Penny Postage 1d. (*No.* 460)
1926–34 Admiral design 1d. (*No.* 468)
1935–36 Pictorials ½d., 2d., 4d., 8d., 1s. (*Nos.* 556, 559, 562 565, 567)
1935 Silver Jubilee ½d., 1d., 6d. (*Nos.* 573/5)
1936 Anzac 1d.+1d. (*No.* 592)

Z 2

The following NEW ZEALAND *stamps are known postmarked on Fanning Island with Type* Z 2 *(in use from* 7 *December* 1936 *to* 13 *February* 1939):

1935–36 Pictorials (*W* **43**) 1d (*No.* 557)
1936–39 Pictorials (*W* **98**) ½d., 1d., 1½d. (*Nos.* 577/9)
1936 Chambers of Commerce Congress ½d. (*No.* 593)
1936 Health 1d. + 1d. (*No.* 598)
1937 Coronation 1d., 2½d., 6d. (*Nos.* 599/601)
1938–39 King George VI ½d., 1d., 1½d. (*Nos.* 603, 605, 607)

The schooner which carried the mail from Fanning Island also called at Washington Island, another of the Line group. Problems arose, however, as the authorities insisted that mail from Washington must first pass through the Fanning Island Postal Agency before being forwarded which resulted in considerable delays. Matters were resolved by the opening of a New Zealand Postal Agency on Washington Island which operated from 1 February 1921 until the copra plantations were closed in early 1923. The postal agency was re-established on 15 May 1924, but finally closed on 30 March 1934. Covers from this second period occur with incorrectly dated postmarks. Manuscript markings on New Zealand Nos. 578, 599/600 and 692 are unofficial and were applied during the resettlement of the island between 1937 and 1948. Washington Island is now known as Teraina.

NEW INFORMATION

The editor is always interested to correspond with people who have new information that will improve or correct the Catalogue.

Z 3

The following NEW ZEALAND *stamps are known postmarked on Washington Island with Type* Z 3:

1909–16 King Edward VII 5d., 8d. (*Nos.* 402, 404*b*)
1915–30 King George V (*recess*) 6d., 7½d., 8d., 9d., 1s. (*Nos.* 425/7, 429/30)
1915–34 King George V (*typo*) ½d., 1½d., 2d., 3d. (*Nos.* 435, 438/9, 449)
1915 "WAR STAMP" opt ½d (*No.* 452)
1920 Victory 1d., 1½d., 6d. (*Nos.* 454/5, 457)
1922 2d. on ½d. (*No.* 459)
1926–34 Admiral design 1d. (*No.* 468)

The above information is based on a special survey undertaken by members of the Kiribati & Tuvalu Philatelic Society and the Pacific Islands Study Circle, co-ordinated by Mr. Michael Shaw.

PRICES FOR STAMPS ON COVER TO 1945

Nos. 1/7	*from* × 5
Nos. 8/11	*from* × 10
Nos. 12/23	*from* × 6
No. 24	—
No. 26	*from* × 15
Nos. 27/30	*from* × 6
No. 35	—
Nos. 36/9	*from* × 4
Nos. 40/2	*from* × 12
Nos. 43/54	*from* × 4
Nos. D1/8	*from* × 5

BRITISH PROTECTORATE

GILBERT&ELLICE

PROTECTORATE

(1)

2 Pandanus Pine

1911 (1 Jan). *Stamps of Fiji optd with T* 1. *Wmk Mult Crown CA. Chalk-surfaced paper* (5d. *to* 1s.).
1 **23** ½d. green .. .. 4·75 42·00
2 1d. red .. .. 45·00 28·00
3 **24** 2d. grey .. .. 8·50 15·00
4 **23** 2½d. ultramarine .. .. .. 12·00 27·00
5 5d. purple and olive-green .. .. 40·00 70·00
6 **24** 6d. dull and bright purple .. .. 20·00 45·00
7 **23** 1s. black/*green* (R.) .. .. .. 20·00 55·00
1/7 .. .. *Set of* 7 £130 £250
1s/7s Optd "Specimen" .. .. *Set of* 7 £275

The 2d. to 6d. are on special printings which were not issued without overprint.

Examples of Nos. 1/7 are known showing a forged Ocean Island postmark dated "JY 15 11".

(Recess D.L.R.)

1911 (Mar). *Wmk Mult Crown CA. P* 14.
8 **2** ½d. green .. .. 4·25 14·00
9 1d. carmine .. .. 2·00 7·00
w. Wmk inverted £275
10 2d. grey .. .. 1·50 7·00
11 2½d. blue .. .. 5·00 11·00
8/11 .. .. *Set of* 4 11·50 35·00
8s/11s Optd "Specimen" .. .. *Set of* 4 £140

3

WAR TAX

(5)

(Typo D.L.R.)

1912 (May)–**24**. *Die I* (½d. *to* 5s.) *or Die II* (£1). *Wmk Mult Crown CA. Chalk-surfaced paper* (3d. *to* £1). *P* 14.
12 **3** ½d. green (7.12) .. .. .. 50 4·50
a. Yellow-green (1914) .. .. 4·50 11·00
13 1d. carmine (12.12) .. .. .. 2·25 5·00
a. Scarlet (1915) .. .. .. 3·75 11·00
14 2d. greyish slate (1.16) .. .. 15·00 26·00
15 2½d. bright blue (1.16) .. .. 1·75 11·00
16 3d. purple/*yellow* (1918) .. .. 2·50 8·50
17 4d. black and red/*yellow* (10.12) .. 75 7·00
18 5d. dull purple and sage-green .. .. 1·75 7·00
19 6d. dull and bright purple .. .. 1·25 7·50
20 1s. black/*green* .. .. .. 1·25 5·50
21 2s. purple and blue/*blue* (10.12) .. 14·00 30·00
22 2s. 6d. black and red/*blue* (10.12) .. 15·00 25·00
23 5s. green and red/*yellow* (10.12) .. 32·00 60·00
24 £1 purple and black/*red* (Die II) (3.24) £550 £1400
12/24 .. .. .. *Set of* 13 £600 £1400
12s/24s Optd "Specimen" .. *Set of* 13 £550

CROWN COLONY

1918 (June). *Optd with T* 5.
26 **3** 1d. red 50
s. Optd "Specimen" .. .. .. 60·00

1922–27. *Die II. Wmk Mult Script CA. Chalk-surfaced* (10s.). *P* 14.
27 **3** ½d. green (1923) .. .. .. 3·25
28 1d. violet (1927) .. .. .. 4·50
29 1½d. scarlet (1924) .. .. .. 4·50
30 2d. slate-grey .. .. .. 7·00
35 10s. green and red/*emerald* (3.24) .. £160
27s/35s Optd "Specimen" .. *Set of* 5 £250

Examples of most values between Nos. 12 and 35 are k showing part strikes of the forged postmark mentioned Nos. 1/7. Collectors should exercise particular caution buying used examples of Nos. 24 and 35.

1935 (6 May). *Silver Jubilee. As Nos.* 91/4 *of Antigua, but B.W. P* 11 × 12.
36 1d. ultramarine and grey-black .. .. 2·25
d. Flagstaff on right-hand turret £160
e. Double flagstaff £225
37 1½d. deep blue and scarlet .. .. 1·75
d. Flagstaff on right-hand turret £160
e. Double flagstaff £225
38 3d. brown and deep blue .. .. 5·50
d. Flagstaff on right-hand turret £250
e. Double flagstaff £300
39 1s. slate and purple .. .. .. 25·00
d. Flagstaff on right-hand turret £375
e. Double flagstaff £425
36/9 .. .. *Set of* 4 30·00
36s/9s Perf "Specimen" .. *Set of* 4 £110

For illustrations of plate varieties see Omnibus se following Zanzibar.

1937 (12 May). *Coronation. As Nos.* 95/7 *of Antigua, but pt D.L.R. P* 14.
40 1d. violet 35
41 1½d. scarlet 35
42 3d. bright blue 40
40/2 .. .. *Set of* 3 1·00
40s/2s Perf "Specimen" .. *Set of* 3 70·00

6 Great Frigate Bird

7 Pandanus Pine

8 Canoe crossing Reef

(Recess B.W. (½d., 2d., 2s. 6d.), Waterlow (1d., 5d., 6d., 2s., D.L.R. (1½d., 2½d., 3d., 1s.))

1939 (14 Jan)–**55**. *T* **6/8** *and similar horiz designs. Wmk M Script CA (sideways on* ½d., 2d. *and* 2s. 6d.). *P* 11½×11 (½d., 2d., 2s. 6d.), 12½ (1d., 5d., 6d., 2s., 5s.) *or* 13½ (1½d., 2½d., 3d., 1s.).
43 ½d. indigo and deep bluish green 60
a. "A" of "CA" missing from wmk ..
44 1d. emerald and plum 30 1
45 1½d. brownish black and bright carmine .. 30 1
46 2d. red-brown and grey-black 75 1
47 2½d. brownish black and deep olive .. 40
a. Brownish black & olive-green (12.5.43) 3·50 3
48 3d. brownish black and ultramarine .. 45 1
a. Perf 12. *Black and bright blue* (24.8.55) 50 2
49 5d. deep ultramarine and sepia .. .. 4·25 1
a. Ultramarine and sepia (12.5.43) .. 4·75 6
b. Ultramarine & blackish brn (20.10.44) 4·25 5
50 6d. olive-green and deep violet 50
51 1s. brownish black and turquoise-green .. 11·00 2
a. Brownish black & turquoise-bl (12.5.43) 5·00 3
ab. Perf 12 (8.5.51) .. .. .. 2·75 14
52 2s. deep ultramarine and orange-red .. 12·00 12
53 2s. 6d. deep blue and emerald .. .. 14·00 14
54 5s. deep rose-red and royal blue .. .. 16·00 16
43/54 .. .. *Set of* 12 45·00 45
43s/54s Perf "Specimen" .. .. *Set of* 12 £250

Designs: *As T* **6**—2d. Canoe and boat-house; 2s. 6d. Gilb Islands canoe. *As T* **7**—5d. Ellice Islands canoe; 6d. Coconut palr 2s. H.M.C.S. *Nimanoa*; 5s. Coat of arms. *As T* **8**—2½d. Nat house; 3d. Seascape; 1s. Cantilever jetty, Ocean Island.

1946 (16 Dec). *Victory. As Nos.* 110/11 *of Antigua.*
55 1d. purple 15
56 3d. blue 15
55s/6s Perf "Specimen" .. .. *Set of* 2 55·00

1949 (29 Aug). *Royal Silver Wedding. As Nos.* 112/13 *Antigua.*
57 1d. violet 40
58 £1 scarlet .. .. 12·00 18

1949 (10 Oct). *75th Anniv of U.P.U. As Nos.* 114/17 *of Antigua.*
59 1d. purple 40
60 2d. grey-black .. .. 2·00 2
61 3d. deep blue 50 2
62 1s. blue 50 2
59/62 .. .. *Set of* 4 3·00 6

POSTAGE DUE STAMPS

D 1

(Typo B.W.)

(Aug). *Wmk Mult Script CA. P* 12.

D 1 1d. emerald-green .. .. 8·50 22·00
2d. scarlet .. .. 9·50 22·00
3d. brown .. .. 14·00 23·00
4d. blue .. .. 16·00 29·00
5d. grey-green .. .. 21·00 29·00
6d. purple .. .. 21·00 29·00
1s. violet .. .. 23·00 40·00
1s. 6d. turquoise-green .. .. .. 45·00 85·00
.. .. *Set of* 8 £140 £250
8s Perf "Specimen" .. .. *Set of* 8 £170

:amples of all values are known showing a forged Post Office
.n Island postmark dated "16 DE 46".

Gold Coast

Gold Coast originally consisted of coastal forts, owned by the Royal African Company, trading with the interior. In 1821, due to raids by the Ashanti king, the British Government took over the forts, together with some of the hinterland, and the Gold Coast was placed under the Governor of Sierra Leone.

The administration was handed back to a merchantile company in 1828, but the forts returned to British Government rule in 1843. The colony was reconstituted by Royal Charter on 24 July, 1874, and at that time also included the settlement at Lagos which became a separate colony in January, 1886.

Following the end of the final Ashanti War the whole of the territory was annexed in September 1901.

A postal service was established at Cape Coast Castle in 1853. There is no record of British stamps being officially issued in the Colony before 1875, apart from those used on board the ships of the West African Squadron, but examples do, however, exist cancelled by Gold Coast postmarks.

CROWN COLONY

PRICES FOR STAMPS ON COVER TO 1945

Nos. 1/3	*from* × 15
Nos. 4/8	*from* × 20
Nos. 9/10	*from* × 10
Nos. 11/20	*from* × 25
Nos. 22/5	—
Nos. 26/34	*from* × 10
Nos. 35/6	*from* × 20
Nos. 38/69	*from* × 6
Nos. 70/98	*from* × 3
Nos. 100/2	—
Nos. 103/12	*from* × 5
Nos. 113/16	*from* × 3
Nos. 117/19	*from* × 4
Nos. 120/32	*from* × 3
No. D1	*from* × 6
No. D2	*from* × 20
Nos. D3/4	*from* × 12

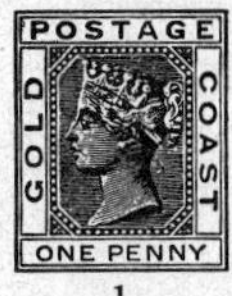

1

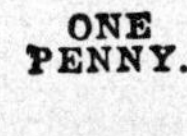

(2)

(Typo D.L.R.)

1875 (1 July). *Wmk Crown CC. P* 12½.

1 1 1d. blue .. .. £450 80·00
2 4d. magenta £425 £120
3 6d. orange .. .. £650 65·00

1876–84. *Wmk Crown CC. P* 14.

4 1 ½d. olive-yellow (1879) .. .. .. 55·00 22·00
5 1d. blue .. .. 17·00 6·50
a. Bisected (½d.) (on cover) (1884) .. † £3250
w. Wmk inverted £225 £110
6 2d. green (1879) .. .. 75·00 9·00
a. Bisected (1d.) (on cover) (1884) .. † £2750
b. Quartered (½d.) (on cover) (1884) .. † £4500
7 4d. magenta .. .. £170 6·00
a. Bisected (2d.) (on cover) (1884) .. † £5000
b. Quartered (1d.) (on cover) (1884) .. † £6500
w. Wmk inverted £425
8 6d. orange .. .. £110 18·00
a. Bisected (3d.) (on cover) (1884) .. † £6000
b. Sixth (1d.) (on cover) (1884) .. † £7500

During 1884 some values were in short supply and the use of bisects and other divided stamps is known as follows:

No. 5a. Used as part of 2½d. rate from Accra and Quittah
No. 6a. Used as 1d. rate from Addah, Cape Coast Castle, Quittah, Salt Pond, Secondee and Winnebah
No. 6b. Used as part of 2½d. rate from Cape Coast Castle
No. 7a. Used as 2d. or as part of 2½d. rate from Quittah
No. 7b. Used as 1d. rate from Appam, Axim, Cape Coast Castle and Winnebah
No. 8a. Used as 3d. rate from Secondee
No. 8b. Used as 1d. rate from Cape Coast Castle and Winnebah.

Examples of bisects used on piece are worth about 10% of the price quoted for those on cover.

The 4d., No. 7, is known surcharged "1 d". This was previously listed as No. 8c, but there are now serious doubts as to its authenticity. The three examples reported of this stamp all show *different* surcharges!

1883. *Wmk Crown CA. P* 14.

9 1 ½d. olive-yellow (January) .. .. £170 65·00
10 1d. blue (May) .. .. £850 70·00

PENNY

Short "P" and distorted "E" (Pl 1 R. 5/6) ("P" repaired for Pl 2)

1884 (Aug)–**91.** *Wmk Crown CA. P* 14.

11 1 ½d. green .. .. 2·50 75
a. Dull green .. .. 2·25 70
w. Wmk inverted £110 £110
12 1d. rose-carmine .. .. 3·00 50
a. Carmine .. .. 3·00 50
b. Bisected (½d.) (on cover) .. .. † £3750
c. Short "P" and distorted "E" .. .. 95·00

13 1 2d. grey .. .. 10·00 3·75
aw. Wmk inverted £170 £170
b. Slate .. .. 2·75 50
c. Bisected (1d.) (on cover) .. .. † £4250
d. Quartered (½d.) (on cover) .. ..
14 2½d. ultramarine and orange (13.3.91) .. 3·50 70
15 3d. olive-yellow (9.89) .. .. .. 8·00 4·50
a. Olive .. .. 8·00 4·50
16 4d. deep mauve (3.85) .. .. .. 8·00 1·50
a. Rosy mauve .. .. 10·00 3·00
17 6d. orange (1.89) .. .. 7·00 5·00
a. Orange-brown .. .. 7·00 5·00
b. Bisected (3d.) (on cover) .. ..
18 1s. violet (1888) .. .. 32·00 12·00
a. Bright mauve .. .. 4·50 1·25
19 2s. yellow-brown (1888) .. .. .. 80·00 35·00
a. Deep brown .. .. 40·00 15·00
11/19*a* .. .. *Set of* 9 70·00 26·00
14s/15s, 18s/19s Optd "Specimen" *Set of* 4 £150

During 1884 to 1886 and in 1889 some values were in short supply and the use of bisects and other divided stamps is known as follows:

No. 12b. Used as part of 2½d. rate from Cape Coast Castle
No. 13c. Used as 1d. or as part of 2d. rate from Cape Coast Castle, Chamah, Dixcove and Elmina
No. 13d. Used as part of 2½d. rate from Cape Coast Castle
No. 17b. Used as 3d. from Appam

1889 (Mar). *No.* 17 *surch with T* **2**.

20 1 1d. on 6d. orange .. .. £110 48·00
a. Surch double .. .. † £3000

In some sheets examples may be found with the bar and "PENNY" spaced 8 mm, the normal spacing being 7 mm.

USED HIGH VALUES. Until the introduction of airmail in 1929 there was no postal use for values over 10s. Post Offices did, however, apply postal cancellations to high value stamps required for telegram fees.

3 4

1889 (Sept)–**94.** *Wmk Crown CA. P* 14.

22 3 5s. dull mauve and blue .. .. 65·00 14·00
23 10s. dull mauve and red .. .. .. 75·00 15·00
a. Dull mauve and carmine £500 £180
24 20s. green and red £3250
25 20s. dull mauve and black/*red* (4.94) .. £150 35·00
w. Wmk inverted .. .. £200 75·00
22s/5s Optd "Specimen" .. *Set of* 4 £400

No. 24 was withdrawn from sale in April 1893 when a large part of the stock was stolen. No 20s. stamps were available until the arrival of the replacement printing a year later.

1898 (May)–**1902.** *Wmk Crown CA. P* 14.

26 3 ½d. dull mauve and green .. .. 2·00 1·00
27 1d. dull mauve and rose .. .. 2·00 50
aw. Wmk inverted .. .. .. — 90·00
27*b* 4 2d. dull mauve and orange-red (1902) 45·00 £120
28 3 2½d. dull mauve and ultramarine .. 4·50 5·00
29 4 3d. dull mauve and orange .. .. 4·75 1·50
30 6d. dull mauve and violet .. .. 5·50 1·50
31 3 1s. green and black (1899) .. .. 10·00 14·00
32 2s. green and carmine .. .. 10·00 17·00
33 5s. green and mauve (1900) .. .. 50·00 28·00
34 10s. green and brown (1900) .. .. £140 50·00
26/34 .. .. .. *Set of* 10 £250 £200
26s/34s Optd "Specimen" .. *Set of* 10 £180

1901 (6 Oct). *Nos.* 28 *and* 30 *surch with T* **2**.

35 1d. on 2½d. dull mauve and ultramarine .. 2·50 3·50
a. "ONE" omitted £1000
36 1d. on 6d. dull mauve and violet .. .. 2·50 3·50
a. "ONE" omitted £275 £550

6 7 8

1902. *Wmk Crown CA. P* 14.

38 6 ½d. dull purple and green (Aug) .. 1·50 40
39 1d. dull purple and carmine (May) .. 1·50 15
w. Wmk inverted .. .. .. — 65·00
40 7 2d. dull purple and orange-red (Apr) .. 21·00 7·00
w. Wmk inverted .. ..
41 6 2½d. dull purple and ultramarine (Aug) 4·50 9·00
42 7 3d. dull purple and orange (Aug) .. 3·00 1·50
43 6d. dull purple and violet (Aug) .. 3·75 1·50
w. Wmk inverted .. .. .. — 85·00
44 6 1s. green and black (Aug) .. .. 14·00 3·25
45 2s. green and carmine (Aug) .. .. 15·00 17·00
46 5s. green and mauve (Aug) .. .. 38·00 85·00
47 10s. green and brown (Aug) .. .. 55·00 £130
48 20s. purple and black/*red* (Aug) .. £130 £180
38/48 .. .. .. *Set of* 11 £250 £375
38s/48s Optd "Specimen" .. *Set of* 11 £200

Examples of Nos. 45/8 are known showing a forged Accra postmark dated "25 MAR 1902".

1904–06. *Wmk Mult Crown CA. Ordinary paper (½d. to 6d.) or chalk-surfaced paper (2s. 6d.).*

49 6 ½d. dull purple and green (3.06) .. 2·50 7·00
50 1d. dull purple and carmine (10.04) .. 7·50 30
a. Chalk-surfaced paper (5.06) .. 9·00 2·00
w. Wmk inverted .. .. ..

51 7 2d. dull purple and orange-red (11.04) 4·75 50
a. Chalk-surfaced paper (8.06) 23·00 2·00
52 6 2½d. dull purple and ultramarine (6.06) 48·00 45·00
53 7 3d. dull purple and orange (8.05) 60·00 5·50
a. Chalk-surfaced paper (4.06) 14·00 60
54 6d. dull purple and violet (3.06) 55·00 2·00
a. Chalk-surfaced paper (9.06) 40·00 1·25
57 2s. 6d. green and yellow (3.06) 28·00 £100
s. Optd "Specimen" 45·00
49/57 *Set of* 7 £130 £140

1907–13. *Wmk Mult Crown CA. Ordinary paper (½d. to 2½d. and 2s.) or chalk-surfaced paper (3d. to 1s., 2s. 6d., 5s.). P* 14.
59 6 ½d. dull green (5.07) 3·00 30
a. Blue-green (1909) 7·00 1·50
60 1d. red (2.07) 6·00 40
61 7 2d. greyish slate (4.09) 2·25 40
62 6 2½d. blue (4.07) 6·00 2·00
w. Wmk inverted
63 7 3d. purple/*yellow* (16.4.09) 8·00 55
64 6d. dull and deep purple (12.08) 15·00 55
a. Dull and bright purple (1911) 3·75 3·50
65 6 1s. black/*green* (10.09) 9·50 50
66 2s. purple and blue/*blue* (1910) 8·00 16·00
a. Chalk-surfaced paper (1912) 18·00 16·00
67 7 2s. 6d. blue and red/*blue* (1911) 27·00 80·00
68 6 5s. green and red/*yellow* (1913) 55·00 £160
59/68 *Set of* 10 £110 £225
59s/68s Optd "Specimen" *Set of* 10 £225

A 10s. green and red on green, and a 20s. purple and black on red, both Type **6**, were prepared for use but not issued. Both exist overprinted "SPECIMEN" (*Price for 10s. in this condition* £300). An example of the 10s. exists without "SPECIMEN" overprint.

(Typo D.L.R.)

1908 (Nov). *Wmk Mult Crown CA. P* 14.
69 8 1d. red 3·00 10
a. Wmk sideways † £1500
s. Optd "Specimen" 45·00

9 10 11

(Typo D.L.R.)

1913–21. *Die I. Wmk Mult Crown CA. Chalk-surfaced paper (3d. to 20s.). P* 14.
70 9 ½d. green 2·00 1·00
a. Yellow-green (1916) 2·75 1·25
72 10 1d. red 1·25 10
a. Scarlet (1917) 1·50 50
74 11 2d. grey 2·50 2·50
a. Slate-grey (1920) 8·00 8·00
w. Wmk inverted † £160
76 9 2½d. bright blue 4·50 1·00
a. "A" of "CA" missing from wmk £400
x. Wmk reversed † £160
77 11 3d. purple/*yellow* (8.15) 1·75 80
as. Optd "Specimen" 32·00
aw. Wmk inverted — 85·00
b. White back (9.13) 55 40
c. On orange-buff (1919) 4·50 7·00
cw. Wmk inverted
d. On buff (1920)
e. Die II. *On pale yellow* (1921) 30·00 5·00
78 6d. dull and bright purple 2·00 2·25
79 9 1s. black/*green* 2·00 1·25
a. Wmk sideways
bw. Wmk inverted
c. On blue-green, olive back (1916) 4·50 75
cs. Optd "Specimen" 40·00
cw. Wmk inverted
d. On emerald back (1920) 2·00 2·00
ds. Optd "Specimen" 35·00
e. Die II. *On emerald back* (1921) 1·50 50
es. Optd "Specimen" 40·00
ew. Wmk inverted
80 2s. purple and blue/*blue* 8·50 2·75
aw. Wmk inverted — £170
b. Die II (1921) £150 65·00
81 11 2s. 6d. black and red/*blue* 5·00 13·00
a. Die II (1921) 22·00 42·00
82 9 5s. green and red/*yellow* (1916) 8·50 50·00
as. Optd "Specimen" 42·00
b. White back (10.13) 9·50 50·00
c. On orange-buff (1919) 75·00 80·00
d. On buff (1920)
e. On pale yellow (1921) £100 £130
f. Die II. *On pale yellow* (1921) 30·00 £130
fw. Wmk inverted £180
83 10s. green and red/*green* 48·00 85·00
a. On blue-green, olive back (1916) 18·00 65·00
b. On emerald back (1921) 30·00 £120
84 20s. purple and black/*red* £120 80·00
70/84 *Set of* 12 £150 £190
70s/6s, 77bs, 78s/81s, 82bs/4s Optd "Specimen" *Set of* 12 £250

The 10s. and 20s. were withdrawn locally from September 1920 and, in common with other Gold Coast stamps, were not available to stamp dealers from the Crown Agents in London.

WAR TAX

ONE PENNY

(12)

13 King George V and Christiansborg Castle

1918 (17 June). *Surch with T* **12**.
85 10 1d. on 1d. red 1·50 50
s. Optd "Specimen" 50·00

1921–24. *Die I (15s., £2) or Die II (others). Wmk Mult Script CA. Chalk-surfaced paper (6d. to £2). P* 14.
86 9 ½d. green 80 50
87 10 1d. chocolate-brown (1922) 70 10
88 11 1½d. red (1922) 1·75 10
89 2d. grey 1·75 30
90 9 2½d. yellow-orange (1922) 75 9·00
91 11 3d. bright blue (1922) 1·75 60
94 6d. dull and bright purple 2·00 3·00
95 9 1s. black/*emerald* (1924) 2·75 3·25
96 2s. purple and blue/*blue* (1923) 3·00 3·25
97 11 2s. 6d. black and red/*blue* (1924) 7·00 20·00
98 9 5s. green and red/*pale yellow* (1924) 11·00 45·00
100 11 15s. dull purple and green (Die I) £120 £300
a. Die II (1924) £110 £300
as. Optd "Specimen" £100
102 £2 green and orange (Die I) £350 £850
86/100a *Set of* 12 £120 £350
86s/102s Optd "Specimen" *Set of* 13 £350

The Duty plate for the 1½d., 15s. and £2 has the words "GOLD COAST" in distinctly larger letters.

Examples of Nos. 100/a and 102 are known showing parts of forged Accra postmarks. These are dated "3 MAY 44" and "8 MAY 44", but are invariably positioned so that the year date is not shown.

(Des W. Palmer. Photo Harrison)

1928 (1 Aug). *Wmk Mult Script CA. P* 13½×15.
103 13 ½d. blue-green 70 40
104 1d. red-brown 70 10
105 1½d. scarlet 80 1·50
106 2d. slate 70 20
107 2½d. orange-yellow 1·25 3·50
108 3d. bright blue 70 40
109 6d. black and purple 1·25 40
110 1s. black and red-orange 2·75 75
111 2s. black and bright violet 16·00 4·75
112 5s. carmine and sage-green 50·00 45·00
103/12 *Set of* 10 65·00 50·00
103s/12s Optd "Specimen" *Set of* 10 £180

1935 (6 May). *Silver Jubilee. As Nos.* 91/4 *of Antigua, but printed by B.W. P* 11 × 12.
113 1d. ultramarine and grey-black 60 50
a. Extra flagstaff £120 £100
b. Short extra flagstaff £140
c. Lightning conductor 95·00
d. Flagstaff on right-hand turret £160
114 3d. brown and deep blue 3·00 6·00
a. Extra flagstaff £130
c. Lightning conductor £130
115 6d. green and indigo 6·00 14·00
a. Extra flagstaff £150 £160
b. Short extra flagstaff £250
c. Lightning conductor £150
d. Flagstaff on right-hand turret £300
116 1s. slate and purple 4·75 14·00
a. Extra flagstaff £160
b. Short extra flagstaff £180
c. Lightning conductor £160
113/16 *Set of* 4 13·00 30·00
113s/16s Perf "Specimen" *Set of* 4 85·00

For illustrations of plate varieties see Omnibus section following Zanzibar.

1937 (12 May). *Coronation. As Nos.* 95/7 *of Antigua. P* 11×11½.
117 1d. buff 1·00 2·00
118 2d. slate 1·10 3·50
119 3d. blue 1·25 1·25
117/19 *Set of* 3 3·00 6·00
117s/19s Perf "Specimen" *Set of* 3 50·00

14

15 King George VI and Christiansborg Castle, Accra

(Recess B.W.)

1938 (1 Apr)–**44**. *Wmk Mult Script CA. P* 11½×12 *(1s. 3d., 10s.) or* 12 *(others)*.
120 14 ½d. green 2·75 1·75
a. Perf 12×11½ (1940) 40 50
121 1d. red-brown 2·75 30
a. Perf 12×11½ (1939) 40 10
122 1½d. scarlet 4·00 2·25
a. Perf 12×11½ (1940) 40 50
123 2d. slate 4·00 1·50
a. Perf 12×11½ (1940) 40 10
124 3d. blue 2·75 1·00
a. Perf 12×11½ (1940) 40 35
125 4d. magenta 4·00 3·00
a. Perf 12×11½ (1942) 80 1·25
126 6d. purple 4·00 50
a. Perf 12×11½ (1939) 80 20
127 9d. orange 4·00 1·75
a. Perf 12×11½ (1944) 1·25 55
128 15 1s. black and olive-green 8·00 2·25
a. Perf 11½×12 (1940) 1·50 65
129 1s. 3d. brown & turquoise-bl (12.4.41) 2·00 50
130 2s. blue and violet 22·00 14·00
a. Perf 11½×12 (1940) 5·00 11·00
131 15 5s. olive-green & carmine 38·00
a. Perf 11½×12 (1940) 10·00
132 10s. black and violet (7.40) 7·00
120/32 *Set of* 13 27·00
120s/32s Perf "Specimen" *Set of* 13 £170

All values except 1s. 3d. and 10s. exist in two perforatior Line-perforated 12, from early printings; (*b*) Comb-perfo 12×11.8 (vertical design) or 11.8×12 (horiz design) from printings. The 1s. 3d. and 10s. only exist comb-perfo 11.8×12.

The ½d. and 1d. values exist in coils constructed from nc sheets.

1946 (14 Oct). *Victory. As Nos.* 110/11 *of Antigua. P* 13½
133 2d. slate-violet 12·00
a. Perf 13½ 10
134 4d. claret 1·50
a. Perf 13½ 1·00
133s/4s Perf "Specimen" *Set of* 2 50·00

16 Northern Territories Mounted Constabulary

17 Christiansborg Castle

(Des B. A. Johnston (1½d.), M. Ziorkley and B. A. Abban (2d.), draughtsman (2½d.), C. Gomez (1s.), M. Ziorkley (10s.); ot from photographs. Recess B.W.)

1948 (1 July). *T* **16/17** *and similar designs. Wmk Mult Script P* 12 × 11½ *(vert) or* 11½ × 12 *(horiz)*.
135 ½d. emerald-green 20
136 1d. blue 15
137 1½d. scarlet 1·25
138 2d. purple-brown 55
139 2½d. yellow-brown and scarlet 2·00
140 3d. light blue 4·00
141 4d. magenta 3·50
142 6d. black and orange 30
143 1s. black and vermilion 60
144 2s. sage-green and magenta 3·25
145 5s. purple and black 24·00
146 10s. black and sage-green 8·00
135/46 *Set of* 12 42·00
135s/46s Perf "Specimen" *Set of* 12 £225

Designs: *Horiz*—1½d. Emblem of Joint Provincial Cour 2½d. Map showing position of Gold Coast; 3d. Nsuta mangai mine; 4d. Lake Bosumtwi; 1s. Breaking cocoa pods; 2s. C Coast Regt Trooping the Colour; 5s. Surfboats. *Vert*— Talking drums; 6d. Cocoa farmer; 10s. Forest.

Nos. 135/6 exist in coils constructed from normal sheets.

1948 (20 Dec). *Royal Silver Wedding. As Nos.* 112/13 *Antigua.*
147 1½d. scarlet 30
148 10s. grey-olive 14·00

1949 (10 Oct). *75th Anniv of U.P.U. As Nos.* 114/17 *of Antig*
149 2d. red-brown 20
150 2½d. orange 1·50
151 3d. deep blue 25
152 1s. blue-green 25
149/52 *Set of* 4 2·00

POSTAGE DUE STAMPS

D 1

(Typo D.L.R.)

1923 (6 Mar). *Yellowish toned paper. Wmk Mult Script C P* 14.
D1 D 1 ½d. black 15·00 £1
D2 1d. black 75
D3 2d. black 13·00
D4 3d. black 22·00
D1/4 *Set of* 4 45·00 £1
D1s/4s Optd "Specimen" *Set of* 4 70·00

A bottom marginal strip of six of No. D2 is known showing t "A" of "CA" omitted from the watermark in the margin belo the third vertical column.

3d Normal

3d Lower serif at left of "3" missing (R. 9/1)

1/- Row 4 (No. D8)

1/- Row 5 (No. D8c)

The degree of inclination of the stroke on the 1s. value varie for each vertical row of the sheet: Rows 1, 2 and 6 104°, Row 108°, Row 4 107° and Row 5 (No. D8c) 100°.

52. *Chalk-surfaced paper. Wmk Mult Script CA. P* 14.
1 2d. black (13.12.51) .. .. .. 3·00 20·00
a. Error. Crown missing, W **9***a* .. £600
b. Error. St. Edward's Crown, W **9***b* £325
c. Large "d" (R. 9/6, 10/6) .. .. 20·00
3d. black (13.12.51) .. .. .. 1·50 18·00
a. Error. Crown missing, W **9***a* .. £600
b. Error. St. Edward's Crown. W **9***b* £325
c. Missing serif .. .. .. 26·00
6d. black (1.10.52) .. .. .. 1·75 8·00
a. Error. Crown missing, W **9***a* .. £750
b. Error. St. Edward's Crown, W **9***b* £550
1s. black (1.10.52) .. .. .. 1·75 60·00
b. Error. St. Edward's Crown, W **9***b* £700
c. Upright stroke .. .. .. 12·00
.. .. *Set of* 4 7·25 95·00
illustration of No. D5c see Nos. D4/6 of Bechuanaland.

Grenada

The earliest recorded postmark of the British administration of Grenada dates from 1784, and, although details of the early period are somewhat sparse, it would appear that the island's postal service was operated at a branch of the British G.P.O. In addition to a Packet Agency at St. George's, the capital, there was a further agency at Carriacou, in the Grenadines, which operated for a few years from 15 September 1847.

Stamps of Great Britain were supplied to the St. George's office from April 1858 until the colony assumed responsibility for the postal service on 1 May 1860. Following the take-over the crowned-circle handstamp, No. CC2, was again used until the Grenada adhesives were issued in 1861.

There was no internal postal service before 1861.

For illustrations of the handstamp and postmark types see BRITISH POST OFFICE ABROAD notes, following GREAT BRITAIN.

CARRIACOU

CROWNED-CIRCLE HANDSTAMPS

CC1 CC 1 CARRIACOU (13.11.1846) .. .. †
Although recorded in the G.P.O. proof book no example of No. CC1 has been reported used from Grenada.

ST. GEORGE'S

CROWNED-CIRCLE HANDSTAMPS

CC2 CC 1 GRENADA (R.) (24.10.1850) *Price on cover* **£1100**

Stamps of GREAT BRITAIN *cancelled* "A 15" *as Type* **2**

1858 *to* **1860**.
Z1 1d. rose-red (1857), *perf* 14 .. .. £375
Z2 2d. blue (1858) (Plate No. 7) £700
Z3 4d. rose (1857) £250
Z4 6d. lilac (1856) £120
Z5 1s. green (1856) £800

PRICES FOR STAMPS ON COVER TO 1945

Nos.	
Nos. 1/19	*from* × 15
Nos. 20/3	*from* × 20
Nos. 24/6	*from* × 10
No. 27	*from* × 15
No. 28	—
No. 29	*from* × 10
Nos. 30/6	*from* × 20
Nos. 37/9	*from* × 10
No. 40	*from* × 30
Nos. 41/7	*from* × 10
Nos. 48/101	*from* × 4
Nos. 109/11	*from* × 8
Nos. 112/48	*from* × 4
Nos. 149/51	*from* × 10
Nos. 152/63	*from* × 4
Nos. D1/3	*from* × 25
Nos. D4/7	*from* × 12
Nos. D8/14	*from* × 20

CROWN COLONY

PRINTERS. Types **1** and **5** recess-printed by Perkins, Bacon and Co.

PERKINS BACON "CANCELLED". For notes on these handstamps, showing "CANCELLED" between horizontal bars forming an oval, see Catalogue Introduction.

1

2 Small Star

(Eng C. Jeens)

1861 (3 June)–**62**. *No wmk. Wove paper.*

(*a*) *Rough perf* 14 *to* 16
1 **1** 1d. bluish green £4500 £300
2 1d. green (5.62) .. .. 50·00 40·00
a. Imperf between (horiz pair) ..
3 6d. rose (*shades*) (H/S "CANCELLED" in oval £6000) .. .. £800 90·00

(*b*) *Perf* 11 *to* $12\frac{1}{2}$
3*a* **1** 6d. lake-red (6.62) £750

The 1d. bluish green also exists handstamped "CANCELLED" in oval, but the only known example is in the Royal Collection.

No. 3*a* is only known unused, and may be the result of perforating machine trials undertaken by Perkins, Bacon. It has also been seen on horizontally laid paper (*Price* £1100).

SIDEWAYS WATERMARK. W **2/3** when sideways show two points of star downwards.

1863–71. *W* **2** (*Small Star*). *Rough perf* 14 *to* 16.
4 **1** 1d. green (3.64) .. .. 70·00 12·00
a. Wmk sideways .. .. — 22·00
5 1d. yellowish green .. .. £100 26·00
6 6d. rose (*shades*) (5.63) .. .. .. £600 12·00
a. Wmk sideways .. .. — 60·00
7 **1** 6d. orange-red (*shades*) (5.66) .. .. £650 12·00
8 6d. dull rose-red (*wmk sideways*) .. £3000 £225
9 6d. vermilion (5.71) .. .. .. £750 12·00
a. Double impression .. .. .. — £1800

1873 (Jan). *W* **2** (*Small Star, sideways*). *Clean-cut perf* 15.
10 **1** 1d. deep green .. .. 85·00 32·00
a. Bisected diag (on cover) .. .. † £6000
b. Imperf between (pair) .. .. — £4500

No. 10a, and later bisected 1d. values, were authorised until 1881 to pay the island newspaper rate ($\frac{1}{2}$d.) or the newspaper rate to Great Britain ($1\frac{1}{2}$d.). Examples also exist on covers to France.

3 Large Star

4 Broad-pointed Star

1873 (Sept)–**74**. *W* **3** (*Large Star*). *Intermediate perf* 15.
11 **1** 1d. blue-green (*wmk sideways*) (2.74) .. 75·00 19·00
a. Double impression .. .. ..
b. Bisected diag (on cover) .. .. † —
12 6d. orange-vermilion .. .. .. £600 26·00

5

POSTAGE

ONE SHILLING

(6)

NOTE. The early $\frac{1}{2}$d., $2\frac{1}{2}$d., 4d. and 1s. postage stamps were made by surcharging the undenominated Type **5** design.

The surcharges were from two founts of type—one about $1\frac{1}{2}$ mm high, the other 2 mm high—so there are short and tall letters on the same stamp; also the spacing varies considerably, so that the length of the words varies.

Examples of Type **5** with surcharges, but without the "POSTAGE" inscription, are revenue stamps.

1875 (July). *Surch with T* **6**. *W* **3**. *P* 14.
13 **5** 1s. deep mauve (B.) .. .. .. £650 9·50
a. "SHLLIING" .. .. † £700
b. "NE SHILLING" .. .. .. † £2500
c. Inverted "S" in "POSTAGE" .. £3500 £500
d. "OSTAGE" £5000 £2000

1875 (Dec). *W* **3** (*Large Star, upright*).
14 **1** 1d. green *to* yellow-green (*p* 14) .. 70·00 6·50
a. Bisected diag (on cover) .. .. † £6500
15 1d. green (*p* 15) £7000 £2000

No. 14 was perforated at Somerset House. 40 sheets of No. 15 were perforated by Perkins, Bacon to replace spoilages and to complete the order.

1878 (Aug). *W* **2** (*Small Star, sideways*). *Intermediate perf* 15.
16 **1** 1d. green .. .. £225 32·00
b. Bisected diag (on cover) .. .. † —
17 6d. deep vermilion .. .. .. £750 30·00
a. Double impression .. .. .. — £1500

1879 (Dec). *W* **2** (*Small Star, upright*). *Rough perf* 15.
18 **1** 1d. pale green (*thin paper*) .. .. £300 24·00
a. Double impression .. .. ..
b. Bisected diag (on cover) .. .. † —

1881 (Apr). *W* **2** (*Small Star, sideways*). *Rough perf* $14\frac{1}{2}$.
19 **1** 1d. green .. .. £120 7·50
a. Bisected diag (on cover) .. .. † £6500

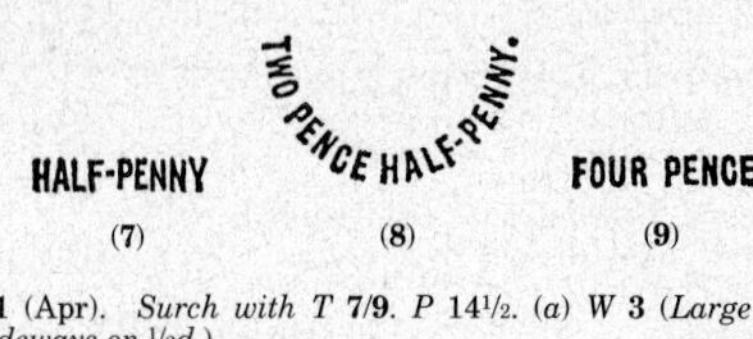

(7) (8) (9)

1881 (Apr). *Surch with T* **7/9**. *P* $14\frac{1}{2}$. (*a*) *W* **3** (*Large Star, sideways on* $\frac{1}{2}$*d.*)
20 **5** $\frac{1}{2}$d. pale mauve .. .. .. 30·00 10·00
21 $\frac{1}{2}$d. deep mauve .. .. .. 11·00 5·50
a. Imperf (pair) £300
ab. Ditto. "OSTAGE" (R.9/4) £4250
b. Surch double £275
c. "OSTAGE" (R.9/4) £190 £130
d. No hyphen £190 £130
e. "ALF-PENNY" £3000
f. Wmk upright £300 £140
g. Ditto. "OSTAGE" (R.9/4) £1700 £750
22 $2\frac{1}{2}$d. rose-lake .. .. 55·00 6·00
a. Imperf (pair) £450
b. Imperf between (horiz pair) .. £3500
c. No stop .. .. £250 75·00
d. "PENCF" (R.8/12) £450 £180
23 4d. blue .. .. £100 8·00
a. Wmk sideways .. ..
b. Inverted "S" in "POSTAGE" ..

(b) *W* **4** (*Broad-pointed Star*)

24 **5** 2½d. rose-lake .. .. £130 48·00
a. No stop £550 £200
b. "PENCF" (R.8/12) £750 £275
25 2½d. claret £400 £120
a. No stop £1000 £475
b. "PENCF" (R.8/12) £1500 £600
25*c* 2½d. deep claret £600 £225
d. No stop £2250 £900
e. "PENCF" (R.8/12) £2750 £1100
26 4d. blue £250 £180

Examples of the "F" for "E" error on the 2½d. value should not be confused with a somewhat similar broken "E" variety. The latter is always without the stop and shows other damage to the "E". The authentic error always occurs with the full stop shown.

The "no stop" variety occurs on R.3/4, R.6/2, R.8/3 and R.9/7.

ONE PENNY POSTAGE. POSTAGE POSTAGE

(10) (11) (12)

1883 (Jan). *Revenue stamps (T* **5** *with green surcharge as in T* **10**) *optd for postage. W* **2** (*Small Star*). *P* 14½.

(*a*) *Optd horizontally with T* **11**.

27 **5** 1d. orange .. .. £275 50·00
a. "POSTAGE" inverted £1700 £1200
b. "POSTAGE" double £1200 £1100
c. Inverted "S" in "POSTAGE" £800 £600
d. Bisected diag (on cover) .. .. .. † £3000

(*b*) *Optd diagonally with T* **11** *twice on each stamp, the stamp being cut and each half used as* ½*d*.

28 **5** Half of 1d. orange £650 £225
a. Unsevered pair £4250 £1200
b. "POSTAGE" inverted .. .. .. — £1100

(*c*) *Optd with T* **12**, *the stamps divided diagonally and each half used as* ½*d*.

29 **5** Half of 1d. orange £250 £110
a. Unsevered pair £1300 £450

Nos. 27/9 exist with wmk either upright or sideways.

1d. Revenue stamps with "POSTAGE" added in black manuscript were used at Gouyave during February and March 1883 (*Price* £2250, *used*). Similar manuscript overprints, in black or red, were also used at Sauteurs in September 1886 (*Price* £3250, *used*).

GRENADA POSTAGE ONE PENNY — 13
d. 1 POSTAGE. — (14)
GRENADA POSTAGE & REVENUE ONE PENNY — 15

(Typo D.L.R.)

1883. *Wmk Crown CA. P* 14.

30 **13** ½d. dull green (February) .. .. 1·25 1·00
a. *Tête-bêche* (vert pair) .. .. 4·00 14·00
31 1d. carmine (February) .. .. 65·00 3·25
a. *Tête-bêche* (vert pair) £225 £225
32 2½d. ultramarine (May) .. .. 7·00 1·00
a. *Tête-bêche* (vert pair) .. .. 24·00 50·00
33 4d. greyish slate (May) .. .. 4·75 1·75
a. *Tête-bêche* (vert pair) .. .. 17·00 55·00
34 6d. mauve (May) .. .. 3·25 4·00
a. *Tête-bêche* (vert pair) .. .. 18·00 55·00
35 8d. grey-brown (February) .. .. 8·50 12·00
a. *Tête-bêche* (vert pair) .. .. 32·00 75·00
36 1s. pale violet (April) .. .. £110 55·00
a. *Tête-bêche* (vert pair) £1100
30/36 .. .. *Set of* 7 £180 65·00

Types **13** and **15** were printed in rows *tête-bêche* in the sheets, so that 50% of the stamps have inverted watermarks.

1886 (1 Oct–Dec). *Revenue stamps (T* **5** *with green surch as T* **10**), *surch with T* **14**. *P* 14. (*a*) *Wmk Large Star, T* **3**.

37 **5** 1d. on 1½d. orange .. .. .. 38·00 30·00
a. Surch inverted £300 £300
b. Surch double £475 £300
c. "THRFE" £250 £225
d. "PFNCE" £250 £225
e. "HALH" £250 £225
f. Bisected diag (on cover) .. .. † £1900
38 1d. on 1s. orange (December) .. .. 32·00 30·00
a. "POSTAGE" (no stop) £375
b. "SHILLNG" £425 £375
c. Wide space (3½ mm) between "ONE" and "SHILLING" £300 £250
d. Bisected diag (on cover) .. .. † £2000

(*b*) *Wmk Small Star, T* **2**

39 **5** 1d. on 4d. orange (November) .. .. £140 90·00

1887 (Jan). *Wmk Crown CA. P* 14.

40 **15** 1d. carmine .. .. 1·00 75
a. *Tête-bêche* (vert pair) .. .. 2·50 17·00
s. Optd "Specimen" .. .. .. 50·00

Due to the sheet formation 50% of the stamps have inverted watermarks.

4*d*. POSTAGE — (16)
HALF PENNY POSTAGE — (17)

1888 (31 Mar)–**91**. *Revenue stamps (T* **5** *with green surch as T* **10**) *further surcharged. W* **2**. *P* 14½, *and No.* 35.

I. *Surch with T* **16**.

(*a*) 4 *mm between value and* "POSTAGE"

41 **5** 4d. on 2s. orange .. .. .. 38·00 17·00
a. Upright "d" (R. 5/6) £750 £400
b. Wide space (2¼ mm) between "TWO" and "SHILLINGS" .. £250 £150
c. First "S" in "SHILLINGS" inverted £450 £325
d. Imperf between (horiz pair) ..

(*b*) 5 *mm between value and* "POSTAGE"

42 **5** 4d. on 2s. orange .. .. .. 65·00 29·00
a. Wide space £300 £225
b. "S" inverted £650 £550

II. *Surch as T* **17** (December 1889)

43 **5** ½d. on 2s. orange .. .. .. 12·00 18·00
a. Surch double £300 £325
b. Wide space £110 £130
c. "S" inverted £275 £300

POSTAGE d. 1 AND REVENUE — (18)
POSTAGE AND REVENUE 1d. — (19)
2½d. — (20)

III. *Surch with T* **18** (December 1890)

44 **5** 1d. on 2s. orange .. .. .. 75·00 75·00
a. Surch inverted £650
b. Wide space £325 £325
c. "S" inverted £650 £650

IV. *Surch with T* **19** (January 1891)

45 **5** 1d. on 2s. orange .. .. .. 50·00 50·00
a. No stop after "1d" (R.3/8) £325
b. Wide space £250 £250
c. "S" inverted £500 £500
46 **13** 1d. on 8d. grey-brown .. .. 9·00 12·00
a. *Tête-bêche* (vert pair) .. .. 40·00 60·00
b. Surch inverted £300 £275
c. No stop after "1d" (R.6/5) £250 £250

V. *Surch with T* **20** (December 1891)

47 **13** 2½d. on 8d. grey-brown .. .. 8·00 11·00
a. *Tête-bêche* (vert pair) .. .. 40·00 60·00
b. Surch inverted .. .. ..
c. Surch double £750 £800
d. Surch double, one inverted £550 £500
e. Surch treble .. .. .. — £900
f. Surch treble, two inverted .. .. — £850
s. Optd "Specimen" .. .. .. 65·00

The wide space between "TWO" and "SHILLINGS" occurs on R. 1/4 and 10/3 of the original 2s. Revenue stamp which was printed in sheets of 120 (12×10).

The surcharges, Types **16/19**, were applied to half sheets as a setting of 60 (12×5).

There are two varieties of fraction in Type **20**, which each occur 30 times in the setting; in one the "1" has horizontal serif and the "2" commences in a ball; in the other the "1" has sloping serif and the "2" is without ball.

See also D4/7.

21

22

23 Flagship of Columbus. (Columbus named Grenada "La Concepcion")

(Typo D.L.R.)

1895 (6 Sept)–**99**. *Wmk Crown CA. P* 14.

48 **22** ½d. mauve and green (9.99) .. .. 2·50 1·75
49 **21** 1d. mauve and carmine (5.96) .. .. 4·50 75
50 2d. mauve and brown (9.99) .. .. 40·00 32·00
x. Wmk reversed .. .. .. — £160
51 2½d. mauve and ultramarine .. .. 5·00 1·50
52 **22** 3d. mauve and orange .. .. 6·50 16·00
53 **21** 6d. mauve and green .. .. 11·00 25·00
54 **22** 8d. mauve and black .. .. 12·00 42·00
55 1s. green and orange .. .. 18·00 35·00
48/55 .. .. *Set of* 8 90·00 £140
48s/55s Optd "Specimen" .. .. *Set of* 8 £150

(Recess D.L.R.)

1898 (15 Aug). 400*th Anniv of Discovery of Grenada by Columbus. Wmk Crown CC. P* 14

56 **23** 2½d. ultramarine .. .. .. 13·00 6·00
a. Bluish paper .. .. .. 32·00 40·00
s. Optd "Specimen" .. .. .. 85·00

24

25

(Typo D.L.R.)

1902. *Wmk Crown CA. P* 14.

57 **24** ½d. dull purple and green .. .. 3·25 1·25
58 **25** 1d. dull purple and carmine .. .. 4·50 30
59 2d. dull purple and brown .. .. 3·00 10·00
60 2½d. dull purple and ultramarine .. .. 3·50 2·75
61 **24** 3d. dull purple and orange .. .. 3·50
62 **25** 6d. dull purple and green .. .. 2·50
63 **24** 1s. green and orange .. .. 3·75
64 2s. green and ultramarine .. .. 21·00
65 **25** 5s. green and carmine .. .. 42·00
66 **24** 10s. green and purple £120
57/66 .. .. *Set of* 10 £180
57s/66s Optd "Specimen" .. .. *Set of* 10 £190

1904–6. *Wmk Mult Crown CA. Ordinary paper. P* 14.

67 **24** ½d. purple and green (1905) .. .. 17·00
68 **25** 1d. purple and carmine .. .. 9·00
69 2d. purple and brown (1905) .. .. 55·00
70 2½d. purple and ultramarine (1905) .. 55·00
71 **24** 3d. purple and orange (1905) .. .. 2·75
a. Chalk-surfaced paper .. .. 2·75
72 **25** 6d. purple and green (1906) .. .. 5·50
a. Chalk-surfaced paper .. .. 8·50
73 **24** 1s. green and orange (1905) .. .. 6·00
74 2s. green and ultramarine (1906) .. 45·00
a. Chalk-surfaced paper .. .. 26·00
75 **25** 5s. green and carmine (1906) .. .. 65·00
76 **24** 10s. green and purple (1906) £140
67/76 .. .. *Set of* 10 £300

Examples of most values between Nos. 57 and 76 are k showing a forged G.P.O. Grenada B.W.I. postmark "OC 6 09".

26 Badge of the Colony 27

(Recess D.L.R.)

1906. *Wmk Mult Crown CA. P* 14.

77 **26** ½d. green .. .. 4·00
78 1d. carmine .. .. 5·50
y. Wmk inverted and reversed ..
79 2d. orange .. .. 2·75
80 2½d. blue .. .. 6·00
a. Ultramarine .. .. .. 8·00

(Typo D.L.R.)

1908. *Wmk Crown CA. Chalk-surfaced paper. P* 14.

82 **27** 1s. black/*green* .. .. .. 27·00 5
83 10s. green and red/*green* .. .. 85·00

1908–11. *Wmk Mult Crown CA. Chalk-surfaced paper. P*

84 **27** 3d. dull purple/*yellow* .. .. 4·50
85 6d. dull purple and purple .. .. 20·00 2
86 1s. black/*green* (1911) .. .. 7·00
87 2s. blue and purple/*blue* .. .. 19·00 1
88 5s. green and red/*yellow* .. .. 55·00 7
77/88 .. .. .. *Set of* 11 £200
77s/80s, 82s/5s, 87s/8s Optd "Specimen" *Set of* 10 £200

Examples of Nos. 82/8 are known showing a forged G. Grenada B.W.I. postmark dated "OC 6 09".

28

WAR TAX — (29)
WAR T — (30

(Typo D.L.R.)

1913 (3 Jan)–**22**. *Wmk Mult Crown CA. Chalk-surfaced pa* (3*d. to* 10*s*.). *P* 14.

89 **28** ½d. yellow-green .. .. .. 1·00 1
90 ½d. green .. .. .. 1·00 1
91 1d. red .. .. .. 2·25
92 1d. scarlet (1916) .. .. .. 3·00
w. Wmk inverted ..
93 2d. orange .. .. .. 1·75
94 2½d. bright blue .. .. .. 1·75 3
95 2½d. dull blue (1920) .. .. 4·75 5
96 3d. purple/*yellow* 65
a. White back (3.14) 65 1
as. Optd "Specimen" .. .. 32·00
b. On lemon (1917) .. .. 4·00 9
c. On pale yellow (1921) .. .. 6·00 28
97 6d. dull and bright purple .. .. 1·50 9
98 1s. black/*green* .. .. .. 1·00 10
a. White back (3.14) .. .. 1·25 7
as. Optd "Specimen" .. .. 32·00
b. On blue-green, olive back (1917) .. 48·00 80
c. On emerald surface .. .. 1·50 12
d. On emerald back (6.22) .. .. 1·00 11
ds. Optd "Specimen" .. .. 32·00
dw. Wmk inverted .. .. 80·00
99 2s. purple and blue/*blue* .. .. 6·50 12
100 5s. green and red/*yellow* .. .. 17·00 60
a. On pale yellow (1921) .. .. 24·00 75
as. Optd "Specimen" .. .. 45·00
101 10s. green and red/*green* .. .. 55·00 90
a. On emerald back (6.22) .. .. 55·00 £1
as. Optd "Specimen" .. .. 55·00
89/101 .. .. .. *Set of* 10 75·00 £1
89s/101s Optd "Specimen" (1s. optd in red) *Set of* 10 £160
98sa 1s. optd in black .. .. .. 32·00

1916 (1 June). *Optd with T* **29** *by Govt Press, St. George's*.

109 **28** 1d. red (*shades*) .. .. .. 2·25 1
a. Opt inverted £275
b. Triangle for "A" in "TAX" .. .. 55·00 70
s. Handstamped "Specimen" .. .. 50·00

A small "A" in "WAR", 2 mm high is found on Nos. 29, 38 and of the setting of 60 and a very small "A" in "TAX", 1½ mm high, No. 11. Value about twice normal. The normal "A" is 2¼ mm hig No. 109b is on No. 56 of the setting.

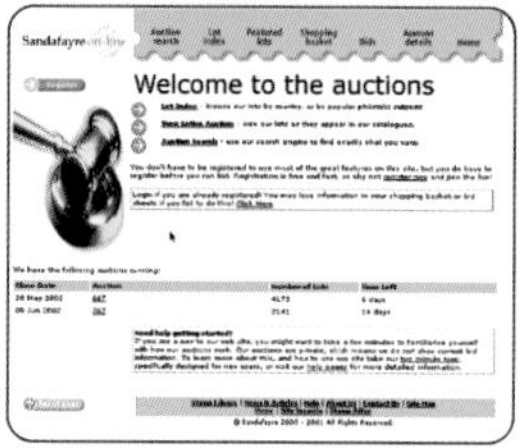

Welcome to the auctions

About us

News and Articles

Stamp library

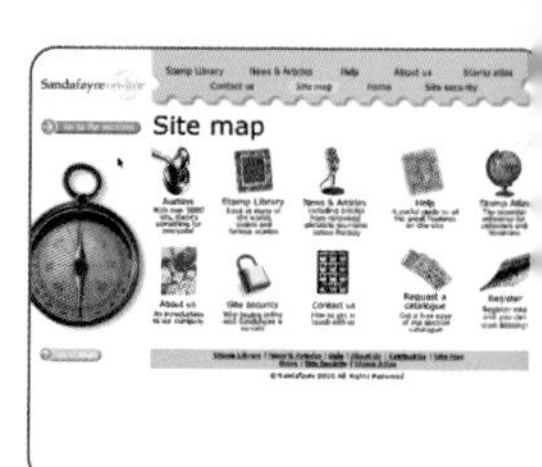

Site map

Falkland Islands
POSTAGE
ONE PENNY
GRAF ZEPPELIN
UNITED STATES POSTAGE

(1 Sept)–**18**. *Optd with T* **30** *in London.*
28 1d. scarlet 30 20
a. Carmine-red/bluish (5.18) .. .. 3·25 1·50
s. Optd "Specimen" .. .. .. 40·00
w. Wmk inverted £110

–**32**. *Wmk Mult Script CA. Chalk-surfaced paper* (3d.
o. 122) *to* 10s.) *P* 14.
28 ½d. green .. .. 1·25 30
1d. carmine-red 80 75
1d. brown (1923) .. .. .. 1·50 30
1½d. rose-red (6.22) .. .. .. 1·50 1·50
2d. orange .. .. 1·25 30
2d. grey (1926) .. .. .. 2·50 2·75
2½d. dull blue .. .. 4·50 3·50
2½d. grey (6.22) .. .. .. 1·00 9·00
2½d. bright blue (1926) .. .. 4·50 3·75
2½d. ultramarine (1931) .. .. 4·50 8·50
2½d. chalky blue and blue (1932) .. 50·00 50·00
3d. bright blue (6.22) .. .. 1·25 10·00
3d. purple/*yellow* (1926) .. .. 3·00 5·00
4d. black and red/*yellow* (1926) .. 1·00 3·75
5d. dull purple & sage-green (27.12.22) 1·50 4·25
6d. dull and bright purple .. .. 1·25 18·00
6d. black and carmine (1926) .. 2·25 2·50
9d. dull purple and black (27.12.22) 2·25 9·50
1s. black/*emerald* (1923) .. .. 2·50 40·00
1s. chestnut (1926) .. .. .. 3·00 10·00
2s. purple and blue/*black* (1922) .. 6·00 17·00
2s. 6d. black and carmine/*blue* (1929) 7·00 18·00
3s. green and violet (27.12.22) .. 6·00 27·00
5s. green and red/*pale yellow* (1923) 12·00 35·00
10s. green and red/*emerald* (1923) .. 50·00 £130
19, 121/34 .. .. .. *Set of* 22 £100 £300
/34s Optd or Perf (2s. 6d.) "Specimen" *Set of* 23 £325
me values of Nos. 89/101 and 112/34 have been seen with strikes of the forged postmark mentioned after Nos. 67/76 77/88.

31 Grand Anse Beach

32 Badge of the Colony

33 Grand Etang

34 St. George's

(Recess Waterlow)

34 (23 Oct)–**36**. *Wmk Mult Script CA* (*sideways on T* **32**).
P 12½.
5 **31** ½d. green .. .. 15 1·25
a. Perf 12½ × 13½ (1936) .. .. 4·50 40·00
6 **32** 1d. black and sepia .. .. .. 1·00 3·00
a. Perf 13½ × 12½ (1936) 60 35
7 **33** 1½d. black and scarlet .. .. .. 4·75 3·00
a. Perf 12½ × 13½ (1936) .. .. 1·25 55
8 **32** 2d. black and orange .. .. .. 1·00 50
9 **34** 2½d. blue 50 50
0 **32** 3d. black and olive-green .. .. 1·00 2·75
1 6d. black and purple .. .. .. 2·00 1·75
2 1s. black and brown .. .. .. 2·00 4·00
3 2s. 6d. black and ultramarine .. 8·00 28·00
4 5s. black and violet .. .. .. 38·00 50·00
5/44 .. .. *Set of* 10 48·00 80·00
5s/44s Perf "Specimen" .. .. *Set of* 10 £160

35 (6 May). *Silver Jubilee. As Nos.* 91/4 *of Antigua but ptd by Waterlow. P* 11×12.
5 ½d. black and green .. .. .. 80 1·25
k. Kite and vertical log .. .. 42·00
l. Kite and horizontal log .. .. 50·00
6 1d. ultramarine and grey .. .. 80 1·75
l. Kite and horizontal log .. .. 55·00
7 1½d. deep blue and scarlet .. .. 80 1·75
l. Kite and horizontal log .. .. 75·00
8 1s. slate and purple .. .. .. 6·50 17·00
l. Kite and horizontal log £180
5/8 .. .. *Set of* 4 8·00 20·00
5s/8s Perf "Specimen" .. .. *Set of* 4 70·00
For illustrations of plate varieties see Omnibus section llowing Zanzibar.

37 (12 May). *Coronation. As Nos.* 95/7 *of Antigua. P* 11x11½.
9 1d. violet 40 40
0 1½d. carmine 40 30
1 2½d. blue 80 40
9/51 .. .. *Set of* 3 1·40 1·00
9s/51s Perf "Specimen" .. .. *Set of* 3 50·00

35 King George VI

(Photo Harrison)

1937 (12 July)–**50**. *Wmk Mult Script CA. Chalk-surfaced paper. P* 15×14.
152 **35** ¼d. brown .. .. 1·40 20
a. Ordinary paper (11.42) 30 80
b. Ordinary paper. *Chocolate* (1.45) 20 80
c. Chalk-surfaced paper. *Chocolate* (8.50) .. .. 50 3·25
The ordinary paper is thick, smooth and opaque.

36 Grand Anse Beach

40 Badge of the Colony

Line on sail
(Centre Pl 3 R. 1/1.
Later partially retouched)

Colon flaw
(R. 5/6. Corrected on
ptg of Nov 1950)

(Recess D.L.R. (10s.), Waterlow (others))

1938 (16 Mar)–**50**. *As T* **31/4** (*but portrait of King George VI as in T* **36**) *and T* **40**. *Wmk Mult Script CA* (*sideways on T* **32**). *P* 12½ *or* 12 × 13 (10*s*.).
153 **36** ½d. yellow-green .. .. .. 4·50 1·00
a. Blue-green (10.9.43) .. .. 60 1·25
b. Perf 12½×13½ (1938) .. .. 6·00 80
ba. Blue-green .. .. .. 6·00 5·00
154 **32** 1d. black and sepia .. .. .. 1·00 20
a. Perf 13½×12½ (1938) 50 50
ab. Line on sail .. .. .. 60·00
155 **33** 1½d. black and scarlet 50 85
a. Perf 12½×13½ (1938) .. .. 2·25 30
156 **32** 2d. black and orange 30 50
a. Perf 13½×12½ (1938) .. .. 2·50 85
ab. Line on sail .. .. .. 75·00
157 **34** 2½d. bright blue 30 30
a. Perf 12½×13½ (?March 1950) .. £4500 £225
158 **32** 3d. black and olive-green .. .. 12·00 1·40
a. Perf 13½×12½ (16.3.38) .. 6·00 1·00
ab. Black and brown-olive (1942) .. 30 80
ac. Line on sail .. .. .. 60·00
b. Perf 12½. *Black & brn-ol* (16.8.50) 30 1·90
ba. Colon flaw .. .. .. 60·00
159 6d. black and purple .. .. .. 1·25 40
a. Perf 13½×12½ (1942) .. .. 2·25 50
160 1s. black and brown .. .. .. 2·25 40
a. Perf 13½×12½ (1941) .. .. 4·00 1·75
161 2s. black and ultramarine .. .. 17·00 1·75
a. Perf 13½×12½ (1941) .. .. 20·00 1·50
162 5s. black and violet .. .. .. 3·75 1·75
a. Perf 13½×12½ (1947) .. .. 2·75 5·50
163 **40** 10s. steel blue and carmine (*narrow*) (*p* 12×13) .. .. .. 55·00 9·00
a. Perf 14. *Steel blue and bright carmine* (*narrow*) .. .. £180 45·00
b. Perf 14. *Slate-blue and bright carmine* (*narrow*) (1943) £190 £110
c. Perf 12. *Slate-blue and bright carmine* (*narrow*) (1943) £450 £1000
d. Perf 14. *Slate-blue and carmine-lake* (*wide*) (1944) .. .. £100 8·00
e. Perf 14. *Blue-black and carmine* (*narrow*) (1943) .. .. .. 27·00 8·50
f. Perf 14. *Blue-black and bright carmine* (*wide*) (1947) .. .. 25·00 25·00
152/63*e* .. .. *Set of* 12 45·00 13·00
152s/63s Perf "Specimen" .. *Set of* 12 £225

In the earlier printings of the 10s. the paper was dampened before printing and the subsequent shrinkage produced narrow frames 23½ to 23¾ mm wide. Later printings were made on dry paper producing wide frames 24¼ mm wide.

No. 163a is one of the earlier printings line perf 13.8×14.1. Later printings of the 10s. are line perf 14.1.

Nos. 163b/c show a blurred centre caused by the use of a worn plate.

Nos. 163a and 163b may be found with gum more or less yellow due to local climatic conditions.

Examples of No. 163c are known showing forged St. George's postmarks dated "21 AU 42", "21 AU 43" or "2 OC 43".

1946 (25 Sept). *Victory. As Nos.* 110/11 *of Antigua.*
164 1½d. carmine 10 10
165 3½d. blue 10 30
164s/5s Perf "Specimen" .. .. *Set of* 2 50·00

1948 (27 Oct). *Royal Silver Wedding. As Nos.* 112/13 *of Antigua.*
166 1½d. scarlet 15 10
167 10s. slate-green .. .. 10·00 17·00

(New Currency. 100 cents = 1 West Indian, later Eastern Caribbean, dollar)

1949 (10 Oct). *75th Anniv of Universal Postal Union. As Nos.* 114/17 *of Antigua.*
168 5 c. ultramarine 10 10
169 6 c. olive .. .. 1·00 1·25
170 12 c. magenta 15 30
171 24 c. red-brown 15 30
168/71 .. .. *Set of* 4 1·25 1·60

41 King George VI

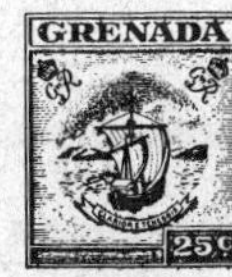

42 Badge of the Colony

43 Badge of the Colony

(Recess B.W. (T **41**), D.L.R. (others))

1951 (8 Jan). *Wmk Mult Script CA. P* 11½ (*T* **41**), 11½ × 12½ (*T* **42**), *and* 11½ × 13 (*T* **43**).
172 **41** ½ c. black and red-brown .. .. 15 1·25
173 1 c. black and emerald-green 15 25
174 2 c. black and brown 15 30
175 3 c. black and rose-carmine 15 10
176 4 c. black and orange 35 40
177 5 c. black and violet 20 10
178 6 c. black and olive 30 60
179 7 c. black and light blue .. .. 1·75 10
180 12 c. black and purple .. .. .. 2·25 30
181 **42** 25 c. black and sepia .. .. .. 2·25 60
182 50 c. black and blue .. .. .. 6·50 40
183 $1.50, black and yellow-orange .. 7·50 6·50
184 **43** $2.50, slate-blue and carmine .. .. 5·50 5·50
172/184 .. .. *Set of* 13 24·00 14·00

1951 (16 Feb). *Inauguration of B.W.I. University College. As Nos.* 118/19 *of Antigua.*
185 3 c. black and carmine 45 60
186 6 c. black and olive 45 30

NEW CONSTITUTION

1951

(**44**)

1951 (21 Sept). *New Constitution. Nos.* 175/7 *and* 180 *optd with T* **44** *by B.W.*
187 **41** 3 c. black and rose-carmine 15 30
188 4 c. black and orange 15 30
189 5 c. black and violet (R.) 15 30
190 12 c. black and purple 15 30
187/90 .. .. *Set of* 4 55 1·10

POSTAGE DUE STAMPS

D 1

1d.

SURCHARGE POSTAGE

(D **2**)

(Typo D.L.R.)

1892 (18 Apr–Oct). (*a*) *Type* D **1**. *Wmk Crown CA. P* 14.
D1 D **1** 1d. blue-black .. .. 25·00 1·50
D2 2d. blue-black .. .. £150 1·50
D3 3d. blue-black .. .. £160 2·50
D1/3 .. .. *Set of* 3 £300 5·00

(*b*) *Nos.* 34 *and* 35 *surch locoally as Type* D **2**
D4 **13** 1d. on 6d. mauve (10.92) .. .. 80·00 1·25
a. *Tête-bêche* (vert pair) £1100 £800
b. Surch double .. .. .. — £160
D5 1d. on 8d. grey-brown (8.92) .. £650 3·25
a. *Tête-bêche* (vert pair) £3250 £1400
D6 2d. on 6d. mauve (10.92) .. .. £150 2·50
a. *Tête-bêche* (vert pair) £1600 £1100
D7 2d. on 8d. grey-brown (8.92) .. £1200 10·00
a. *Tête-bêche* (vert pair) £4750 £3000

Nos. D4/7 were in use from August to November 1892. As supplies of Nos. D1/3 were available from April or May of that year it would not appear that they were intended for postage due purposes. There was a shortage of 1d. postage stamps in July and August, but this was alleviated by Nos. 44/5 which were still available. The provisionals *may* have been intended for postal purposes, but the vast majority appear to have been used philatelically.

1906 (July)–**11**. *Wmk Mult Crown CA. P* 14.
D 8 D **1** 1d. blue-black (1911) .. .. .. 3·50 7·50
D 9 2d. blue-black .. .. 11·00 1·75
D10 3d. blue-black (9.06) .. .. .. 13·00 6·00
D8/10 .. .. *Set of* 3 25·00 13·50

1921 (Dec)–**22**. *As Type* D **1**, *but inscr* "POSTAGE DUE". *Wmk Mult Script CA. P* 14.
D11 1d. black .. .. 90 1·00
D12 1½d. black (15.12.22) .. .. .. 8·50 20·00
D13 2d. black .. .. 2·00 1·75
D14 3d. black .. .. 2·00 4·50
D11/14 .. .. *Set of* 4 12·00 25·00
D11s/14s Optd "Specimen" .. *Set of* 4 80·00

1952 (1 Mar). *As Type* D 1, *but inscr* "POSTAGE DUE". *Value in cents. Chalk-surfaced paper. Wmk Mult Script CA. P* 14.

D15 2 c. black .. .. 30 6·50
a. Error. Crown missing. W **9***a* £100
b. Error. St. Edward Crown. W **9***b* .. .. 50·00

D16 4 c. black .. .. 30 11·00
a. Error. Crown missing. W **9***a* £100
b. Error. St. Edward Crown. W **9***b* .. .. 50·00

D17 6 c. black .. .. 45 11·00
a. Error. Crown missing. W **9***a* £150
b. Error. St. Edward Crown. W **9***b* .. .. 95·00

D18 8 c. black .. .. 75 11·00
a. Error. Crown missing. W **9***a* £275
b. Error. St. Edward Crown. W **9***b* £160

D15/18 .. .. *Set of* 4 1·60 35·00

Griqualand West *see* South Africa

Heligoland

Stamps of HAMBURG (see Part 7 (*Germany*) of this catalogue) were used in Heligoland until 16 April 1867. The Free City of Hamburg ran the Heligoland postal service between 1796 and 1 June 1866. Its stamps continued in use on the island until replaced by Heligoland issues.

PRICES FOR STAMPS ON COVER

Nos. 1/19 *from* × 3

PRINTERS. All the stamps of Heligoland were typographed at the Imperial Printing Works, Berlin.

REPRINTS. Many of the stamps of Heligoland were subsequently reprinted at Berlin (between 1875 and 1885), Leipzig (1888) and Hamburg (1892 and 1895). Of these only the Berlin productions are difficult to distinguish from the originals so separate notes are provided for the individual values. Leipzig reprints can be identified by their highly surfaced paper and those from Hamburg by their 14 perforation. All of these reprints are worth much less than the original stamps priced below.

There was, in addition, a small reprinting of Nos. 13/19, made by the German government in 1890 for exchange purposes, but examples of this printing are far scarcer than the original stamps.

Forgeries, printed by lithography instead of typography, also exist for Nos. 1/4, 6 and 8 perforated 12½ or 13. Forged cancellations can also be found on originals and, on occasion, genuine postmarks on reprints.

1

(Currency. 16 schillings = 1 mark)

Three Dies of Embossed Head for Types **1** and **2**:

Die I Die II

Die III

Die I. Blob instead of curl beneath the chignon. Outline of two jewels at top of diadem.
Die II. Curl under chignon. One jewel at top of diadem.
Die III. Shorter curl under chignon. Two jewels at top of diadem.

(Des Wedding. Die eng E. Schilling)

1867 (Mar)–**68**. *Head Die I embossed in colourless relief. Roul.*

1 **1** ½ sch. blue-green and rose £300 £800
a. Head Die II (7.68) £700 £1100
2 1 sch. rose and blue-green (21.3.67) .. £160 £180
3 2 sch. rose and grass-green (21.3.67) .. 10·00 55·00
4 6 sch. green and rose .. .. .. 12·00 £250

For Nos. 1/4 the second colour given is that of the spandrels on the ½ and 1 sch., and of the spandrels and central background for the 2 and 6 sch.

All four values exist from the Berlin, Leipzig and Hamburg reprintings. The following points are helpful in identifying originals from Berlin reprints; for Leipzig and Hamburg reprints see general note above:

½ sch. – Reprints are all in yellowish green and show Head Die II
1 sch. – All reprints are Head Die III
2 sch. – Berlin reprints are in dull rose with a deeper blue-green
6 sch. – Originals show white specks in green. Berlin reprints have a more solid bluish green

1869 (Apr)–**73**. *Head embossed in colourless* ... *P* 13½×14½.

5 **1** ¼ sch. rose and green (background) (I) (*quadrillé paper*) (8.73) .. .. 26·00
a. Error. Green and rose (background) (9.73) £110
b. Deep rose and pale green (background) (11.73) .. .. .. 85·00
6 ½ sch. blue-green and rose (II) £190
a. Yellow-green and rose (7.71) .. £140
b. Quadrillé paper (6.73) .. .. 95·00
7 ¾ sch. green and rose (I) (*quadrillé paper*) (12.73) .. .. 29·00
8 1 sch. rose and yellow-green (III) (7.71) .. £140
a. Quadrillé paper. *Rose and pale blue-green* (6.73) £120
9 1½ sch. grn & rose (I) (*quadrillé paper*) (9.73) 65·00

For Nos. 5/9 the second colour given is that of the spandr... the ½ and 1 sch., of the central background on the ¼ an... sch., and of the central background, side labels and marginal lines of the ¾ sch.

No. 5a was a printing of the ¼ sch. made in the c... combination of the 1½ sch. by mistake.

A further printing of the ¼ sch. (head die I) in deep ros... and yellowish green (background), on non-*quadrillé* paper, made in December 1874, but not issued (*Price* £15, *unused*...

All five values exist from the Berlin, Leipzig and Ham... reprintings. The following points are helpful in identi... originals from Berlin reprints; for Leipzig and Hamburg rep... see general note above:

¼ sch. – All Berlin and some Hamburg reprints are ... Die II
½ sch. – Berlin reprints on thinner paper with solid c... in the spandrels.
¾ sch. – Berlin reprints on thinner, non-quadrillé pap...
1 sch. – Berlin reprints are on thinner paper or show ... breaks in the rose line beneath "SCHILLIN... the top of the design or in the line above it a... foot.
1½ sch. – All Berlin and some Hamburg reprints are ... Die II

Berlin, Leipzig and Hamburg reprints also exist of the 2 a... sch., but these values do not come as perforated originals.

(New Currency. 100 pfennig = 1 mark)

2

3

4

5

(Des H. Gätke. Die eng E. Schilling (T **2**), A. Schiffner (oth...

1875 (Feb)–**90**. *Head Die II on T* **2** *embossed in colou... relief. P* 13½×14½.

10 **2** 1 pf. (¼d.) deep green and rose .. .. 10·00
11 2 pf. (½d.) deep rose and deep green .. 10·00
12 **3** 3 pf. (⅝d.) pale green, red and yellow (6.76) £225 £1...
a. Green, red and orange (6.77) .. £160
13 **2** 5 pf. (¾d.) deep yellow-green and rose .. 10·00 1...
a. Deep green and rose (6.90) .. .. 12·00 4...
14 10 pf. (1½d.) deep rose and deep green .. 30·00 20...
a. Scarlet and pale blue-green (5.87) 10·00 20...
15 **3** 20 pf. (2½d.) rose, green and yellow (6.76) £200
a. Rose-carmine, dp green & orge (4.80) £150 50...
b. Dull red, pale green and lemon (7.88) 12·00 28...
c. Aniline verm, brt grn & lemon (6.90) 12·00 50...
16 **2** 25 pf. (3d.) deep green and rose .. .. 12·00 26...
17 50 pf. (6d.) rose and green .. .. 18·00 32...
18 **4** 1 m. (1s.) deep green, scarlet & black (8.79) £140
a. Perf 11½ £1000
b. Deep green, aniline rose & black (5.89) £140
19 **5** 5 m. (5s.) deep green, aniline rose, black and yellow (8.79) £150
a. Perf 11½ £1000
ab. Imperf between (horiz pair) .. £3500

For stamps as Type **2** the first colour is that of the cent... background and the second that of the frame. On the 3 pf. ... first colour is of the frame and the top band of the shield, ... second is the centre band and the third the shield border. The ... pf. is similar, but has the centre band in the same colour as ... frame and the upper band on the shield in the second colou...

The 1, 2 and 3 pf. exist from the Berlin, Leipzig and Hamb... reprintings. There were no such reprints for the other valu... The following points are helpful in identifying originals fr... Berlin reprints; for Leipzig and Hamburg reprints see gene... note above:

1 pf. – Berlin printings show a peculiar shade of pink
2 pf. – All reprints are much lighter in shade than the de... rose and deep green of the originals
3 pf. – Berlin reprints either show the band around the shi... in brownish orange, or have this feature in de... yellow with the other two colours lighter.

Heligoland was ceded to Germany on 9 August 1890.

MINIMUM PRICE

The minimum price quote is 10p which represen... a handling charge rather than a basis for valui... common stamps. For further notes about pric... see introductory pages.

Hong Kong

CROWN COLONY

ng Kong island was formally ceded to Great Britain on anuary 1841. The Hong Kong Post Office was established in ber 1841, when much of the business previously transacted igh the Macao postal agency was transferred to the island. irst cancellation is known from April 1842, but local control e posts was shortlived as the Hong Kong Office became a ch of the British G.P.O. on 15 April 1843.
e colonial authorities resumed control of the postal service May 1860 although the previously established postal cies in the Chinese Treaty Ports remained part of the sh G.P.O. system until 1 May 1868.

r illustrations of the handstamp types see BRITISH POST ICES ABROAD notes, following GREAT BRITAIN.

CROWNED-CIRCLE HANDSTAMPS

CC1b HONG KONG (R.) (17.10.1843) *Price on cover* £550
CC1 HONG KONG (R.) (21.8.1844) *Price on cover* £800
CC3 HONG KONG (R.) (16.6.1852) *Price on cover* £350

'e no longer list the Great Britain stamps with obliteration 62" within oval. The Government notification dated 29 ember 1862 stated that only the Hong Kong stamps to be issued 3 December would be available for postage and the stamps erly listed were all issued in Great Britain later than the date e notice.

(Currency. 100 cents = 1 Hong Kong dollar)

PRICES FOR STAMPS ON COVER TO 1945	
Nos. 1/27	*from* × 6
Nos. 28/36	*from* × 4
Nos. 37/9	*from* × 5
Nos. 40/4	*from* × 4
Nos. 45/8	*from* × 10
Nos. 49/50	*from* × 4
No. 51	*from* × 15
Nos. 52/61	*from* × 5
Nos. 62/99	*from* × 4
Nos. 100/32	*from* × 3
Nos. 133/6	*from* × 2
Nos. 137/9	*from* × 4
Nos. 140/68	*from* × 2
Nos. D1/12	*from* × 8
Nos. F1/11	*from* × 4
No. F12	*from* × 3
Nos. P1/3	*from* × 2

RINTERS. All definitive issues up to 1962 were typographed De La Rue and Co., *except for some printings between 1941 1945.*

1

2

3

62 (8 Dec)–63. *No wmk. P* 14.
1 2 c. brown £375 90·00
a. Deep brown (1863) £500 £110
8 c. yellow-buff £650 65·00
12 c. pale greenish blue £500 48·00
3 18 c. lilac £550 48·00
24 c. green £1000 95·00
48 c. rose £2750 £325
96 c. brownish grey £3750 £425

63 (Aug)–71. *Wmk Crown CC. P* 14.
1 2 c. deep brown (11.64) £250 27·00
a. Brown £110 7·00
b. Pale yellowish brown £130 11·00
w. Wmk inverted £425 60·00
x. Wmk reversed — 80·00
2 4 c. grey £120 13·00
a. Slate £100 5·50
aw. Wmk inverted £350 60·00
b. Deep slate £140 10·00
c. Greenish grey £275 45·00
cw. Wmk inverted † £275
d. Bluish slate £450 21·00
dw. Wmk inverted £900 £110
e. Perf $12^1/_2$. *Slate* (12.70) £9000 £275
ew. Wmk inverted — £600
6 c. lilac £375 10·00
a. Mauve £475 11·00
w. Wmk inverted £850 60·00
x. Wmk reversed — 75·00
1 8 c. pale dull orange (10.64) £475 9·50
a. Brownish orange £425 11·00
b. Bright orange £375 11·00
w. Wmk inverted £850 75·00
x. Wmk reversed £900 85·00
12 c. pale greenish blue (4.65) £950 30·00
a. Pale blue 27·00 5·50
b. Deep blue £200 12·00
w. Wmk inverted — 65·00
x. Wmk reversed — 65·00
13 3 18 c. lilac (1866) £6000 £300
w. Wmk inverted † £750
x. Wmk reversed † £900
y. Wmk inverted and reversed † £1600
14 24 c. green (10.64) £500 8·50
a. Pale green £600 15·00
b. Deep green £800 28·00
w. Wmk inverted — 80·00
x. Wmk reversed £1400 90·00
15 2 30 c. vermilion £800 14·00
a. Orange-vermilion £700 15·00
w. Wmk inverted £2000 80·00
x. Wmk reversed — 90·00
16 30 c. mauve (14.8.71) £200 5·50
w. Wmk inverted £800 70·00
x. Wmk reversed — 90·00
17 48 c. pale rose (1.65) £950 45·00
a. Rose-carmine £800 25·00
w. Wmk inverted £1800 90·00
x. Wmk reversed — £120
18 96 c. olive-bistre (1.65) £30000 £550
w. Wmk inverted † £1400
19 96 c. brownish grey (1865) £1200 48·00
a. Brownish black £1300 40·00
w. Wmk inverted £1600 40·00
y. Wmk inverted and reversed † £1200

There is a wide range of shades in this issue, of which we can only indicate the main groups.

No. 12 is the same shade as No. 3 without wmk, the impression having a waxy appearance.

A single used example of the 48 c. in a bright claret shade is known. No other stamps in this shade, either mint or used, have been discovered.

See also Nos. 22 and 28/31.

16 cents. (4) 28 cents. (5) 5 cents. (6) 10 cents. (7)

No. 20b

1876 (Aug)–77. *Nos.* 13 *and* 16 *surch with T* 4 *or* 5 *by Noronha and Sons, Hong Kong.*
20 3 16 c. on 18 c. lilac (1.4.77) £2250 £150
a. Space between "n" and "t" £6500 £800
b. Space between "s" and stop £6500 £800
w. Wmk inverted £4500 £600
21 2 28 c. on 30 c. mauve £1300 48·00

1877 (Aug). *New value. Wmk Crown CC. P* 14.
22 3 16 c. yellow £1500 65·00
w. Wmk inverted £2750 £225

1880 (1 Mar–Sept). *Surch with T* 6 *or* 7 *by Noronha and Sons.*
23 1 5 c. on 8 c. brt orange (No. 11*b*) (Sept) £900 95·00
a. Surch inverted † £10000
b. Surch double † £15000
24 3 5 c. on 18 c. lilac (No. 13) £800 60·00
x. Wmk reversed £1600
25 1 10 c. on 12 c. pale blue (No. 12*a*) £950 55·00
a. Blue £1200 80·00
26 3 10 c. on 16 c. yellow (No. 22) (May) £4000 £150
a. Surch inverted † £40000
b. Surch double † £50000
w. Wmk inverted † £950
27 10 c. on 24 c. green (No. 14) (June) £1300 85·00
w. Wmk inverted † £400

Two examples of No. 26b are known, both used in Shanghai.

1880 (Mar–Dec). *Colours changed and new values. Wmk Crown CC. P* 14.
28 1 2 c. dull rose £130 20·00
a. Rose £140 21·00
29 2 5 c. blue (Dec) £350 35·00
w. Wmk inverted — 95·00
30 10 c. mauve (Nov) £500 14·00
w. Wmk inverted — 75·00
31 3 48 c. brown £1200 90·00

1882 (May)–96. *Wmk Crown CA. P* 14.
32 1 2 c. rose-lake (7.82) £150 26·00
a. Rose-pink £200 32·00
ab. Perf 12 £70000 £70000
w. Wmk inverted — 90·00
33 2 c. carmine (1884) 30·00 1·00
a. Aniline carmine 32·00 1·00
w. Wmk inverted — 65·00
34 2 4 c. slate-grey (1.4.96) 10·00 85
w. Wmk inverted — 65·00
35 5 c. pale blue 24·00 85
a. Blue 25·00 85
aw. Wmk inverted £225 65·00
x. Wmk reversed — £140
36 10 c. dull mauve (8.82) £600 11·00
w. Wmk inverted — £100
37 10 c. deep blue-green (1884) £1800 38·00
a. Green (2.84) £120 1·25
38 10 c. purple/*red* (1.1.91) 21·00 1·00
w. Wmk inverted £325 65·00
x. Wmk reversed £550 85·00
y. Wmk inverted and reversed
39 30 c. yellowish green (1.1.91) £130 38·00
a. Grey-green 70·00 18·00
38s, 39as Optd "Specimen" *Set of* 22 £400

Examples of No. 39 should not be confused with washed or faded stamps from the grey-green shade which tend to turn to a very yellow-green when dampened.

For other stamps with this watermark, but in colours changed to the U.P.U. scheme see Nos. 56/61.

20 CENTS (8) 50 CENTS (9) 1 DOLLAR (10)

1885 (Sept). *As Nos.* 15, 19 *and* 31, *but wmkd Crown CA, surch with T* 8 *to* 10 *by De La Rue.*
40 2 20 c. on 30 c. orange-red 95·00 5·50
a. Surch double
w. Wmk inverted £650 £130
41 3 50 c. on 48 c. yellowish brown £375 29·00
w. Wmk inverted — £110
42 $1 on 96 c. grey-olive £650 60·00
40s/2s Optd "Specimen" *Set of* 3 £950

7 cents. (11) 14 cents. (12)

弍 (13) (20 c.) 五十 (14) (50 c.) 壹員 (15) ($1)

1891 (1 Jan–Mar). *(a) Nos.* 16 *and* 37 *surch with T* 11 *or* 12 *by Noronha and Sons, Hong Kong*
43 2 7 c. on 10 c. green 65·00 8·00
a. Antique "t" in "cents" (R.1/1) £550 £150
b. Surch double £6000 £1300
44 14 c. on 30 c. mauve (Feb) £140 55·00
a. Antique "t" in "cents" (R.1/1) £2500 £900

(b) As Nos. 40/2 *(surch with T* 8 *to* 10 *by De La Rue), but colours changed*
45 2 20 c. on 30 c. yellowish green (No. 39) £170 £160
a. Grey-green (No. 39*a*) £110 £140
46 3 50 c. on 48 c. dull purple £250 £275
47 $1 on 96 c. purple/*red* £750 £350
45as/7s Optd "Specimen" *Set of* 3 £650

(c) Nos. 45/7 *with further surch, T* 13/15, *in Chinese characters, handstamped locally* (Mar)
48 2 20 c. on 30 c. yellowish green 55·00 7·00
a. Grey-green 29·00 6·00
b. Surch double £25000
49 3 50 c. on 48 c. dull purple 75·00 5·50
50 $1 on 96 c. purple/*red* £425 22·00
w. Wmk inverted

The true antique "t" variety (Nos. 43a and 44a) should not be confused with a small "t" showing a short foot. In the antique "t" the crossbar is accurately bisected by the vertical stroke, which is thicker at the top. The lower curve bends towards the right and does not turn upwards to the same extent as on the normal.

The handstamped surcharges on Nos. 48/50 were applied over the original Chinese face values. The single character for "2" was intended to convert "30 c." to "20 c.". There were six slightly different versions of the "2" handstamp and three for the "50 c.".

The errors of the Chinese surcharges previously listed on the above issue and also on Nos. 52 and 55 are now omitted as being outside the scope of the catalogue. While some without doubt possess philatelic merit, it is impossible to distinguish between the genuine errors and the clandestine copies made to order with the original chops. No. 55c is retained as this represents a distinctly different chop which was used for the last part of the printing.

1841 Hong Kong JUBILEE 1891 (16) 10 CENTS (17) 拾 (18) 拾 (19)

1891 (22 Jan). *50th Anniversary of Colony. Optd with T* 16 *by Noronha and Sons, Hong Kong.*
51 1 2 c. carmine (No. 33) £425 £100
a. Short "J" in "JUBILEE" (R. 1/6) £650 £150
b. Short "U" in "JUBILEE" (R. 1/1) £650 £150
c. Broken "1" in "1891" (R. 2/1) £800 £225
d. Tall narrow "K" in "Kong" (R. 1/3) £1200 £450
e. Opt double £16000 £12000
f. Space between "O" and "N" of "Hong" (R. 1/5) £1600 £700

Most of the supply of No. 51, which was only on sale for three days, was overprinted from a setting of 12 (6×2) applied five times to complete each sheet. There were six printings from this setting, but a second setting, possibly of 30 or 60, was used for the seventh. Positions quoted are from the setting of twelve. Most varieties only occur in some printings and many less marked overprint flaws also exist.

The prices quoted for No. 51e are for examples on which the two impressions are distinctly separated. Examples on which the two impressions are almost coincidental are worth considerably less.

1898 (1 Apr). *Wmk Crown CA. P* 14. *(a) Surch with T* 10 *by D.L.R. and handstamped Chinese characters as T* 15
52 3 $1 on 96 c. black £150 27·00
a. Grey-black £140 27·00

(b) Surch with T 10 *only*
53 3 $1 on 96 c. black £3000 £3750
a. Grey-black £2750 £3500
as. Optd "Specimen" £600

1898 (1 Apr). *(a) Surch with T* 17 *by Noronha and Sons, Hong Kong*
54 2 10 c. on 30 c. grey-green (No. 39*a*) £475 £750
a. Figures "10" widely spaced ($1^1/_2$ mm) £3500
b. Surch double

Type 17 was applied in a horizontal setting of 12, No. 54a appearing on position 12 for the early printings only.

As No. 54, but with handstamped Chinese characters, T 18, in addition
10 c. on 30 c. grey-green (No. 39*a*) .. 42·00 70·00
a. Yellowish green .. 80·00 £110
b. Figures "10" widely spaced (1½ mm) £700 £800
c. Chinese character large (Type **19**) .. £900 £1000
ca. Ditto. Figures "10" widely spaced .. £6500
d. Surch Type **17** double
s. Handstamped "Specimen" .. £130

(Aug)–**01.** *Wmk Crown CA. P* 14.
2 c. dull green .. 25·00 85
w. Wmk inverted .. £130 65·00
4 c. carmine (1901) .. 16·00 85
5 c. yellow .. 18·00 6·50
w. Wmk inverted .. — £275
10 c. ultramarine .. 48·00 1·75
w. Wmk inverted .. — 85·00
12 c. blue (1901) .. 35·00 48·00
30 c. brown (1901) .. 35·00 22·00
Set of 6 £160 70·00
s, 61s Optd "Specimen" *Set of* 5 £475

20

21

22

23

3 (Jan–July). *Wmk Crown CA. P* 14.
20 1 c. dull purple and brown .. 2·00 50
2 c. dull green (July) .. 7·50 1·50
w. Wmk inverted
21 4 c. purple/*red* (July) .. 9·00 40
5 c. dull green and brown-orange (July) 9·50 9·00
8 c. slate and violet (12 Feb) .. 8·50 1·25
20 10 c. purple and blue/*blue* (July) .. 32·00 1·50
23 12 c. green and purple/*yellow* (18 Feb) .. 8·00 4·25
20 c. slate and chestnut (June) .. 40·00 3·25
22 30 c. dull green and black (21 May) .. 40·00 20·00
23 50 c. dull green and magenta (June) .. 32·00 32·00
20 $1 purple and sage-green (June) .. 70·00 22·00
23 $2 slate and scarlet (July) .. £200 £225
22 $3 slate and dull blue (July) .. £250 £325
23 $5 purple and blue-green (June) .. £400 £450
22 $10 slate and orange/*blue* (July) .. £950 £425
76 *Set of* 15 £1800 £1300
76s Optd "Specimen" *Set of* 15 £1300
o. 63w is known used at Shanghai.

4 (4 Oct)–**06.** *Wmk Mult Crown CA. Chalk-surfaced paper , 12 c., $3, $5) or ordinary paper (others). P* 14.
20 2 c. dull green .. 5·50 1·25
a. Chalk-surfaced paper (1906) .. 9·00 2·75
aw. Wmk inverted .. † —
21 4 c. purple/*red* .. 12·00 40
a. Chalk-surfaced paper (1906) .. 7·00 75
5 c. dull green and brown-orange .. 22·00 7·00
a. Chalk-surfaced paper (1906) .. 13·00 5·00
aw. Wmk inverted
8 c. slate and violet (1906) .. 9·00 2·00
20 10 c. purple and blue/*blue* (3.05) .. 16·00 1·25
23 12 c. green and purple/*yellow* (1906) .. 11·00 5·50
20 c. slate and chestnut .. 30·00 2·25
a. Chalk-surfaced paper (1906) .. 27·00 2·25
w. Wmk inverted .. † £300
22 30 c. dull green and black .. 32·00 18·00
a. Chalk-surfaced paper (1906) .. 38·00 18·00
23 50 c. green and magenta .. 55·00 8·50
a. Chalk-surfaced paper (1906) .. 55·00 11·00
20 $1 purple and sage-green .. 95·00 21·00
a. Chalk-surfaced paper (1906) .. 90·00 21·00
23 $2 slate and scarlet .. £180 95·00
a. Chalk-surfaced paper (1905) .. £180 85·00
22 $3 slate and dull blue (1905) .. £190 £180
23 $5 purple and blue-green (1905) .. £375 £325
22 $10 slate and orange/*blue* (5.05) .. £1500 £1000
aw. Wmk inverted .. † —
b. Chalk-surfaced paper (1906) .. £1500 £800
/90 *Set of* 14 £2250 £1300
No. 77aw is known used at Shanghai in October 1908.

07–11. *Colours changed and new value. Wmk Mult Crown CA. Chalk-surfaced paper* (6 c. *and* 20 c. *to* $2). *P* 14.
20 1 c. brown (9.10) .. 3·50 1·00
x. Wmk reversed .. † —
2 c. deep green .. 19·00 1·75
a. Green .. 19·00 1·50
w. Wmk inverted
21 4 c. carmine-red .. 6·00 40
22 6 c. orange-vermilion and purple (10.07) 19·00 3·75
20 10 c. bright ultramarine .. 20·00 40
23 20 c. purple and sage-green (3.11) .. 40·00 40·00
22 30 c. purple and orange-yellow (3.11) .. 50·00 22·00
23 50 c. black/*green* (3.11) .. 38·00 15·00
$2 carmine-red and black (1910) .. £275 £250
/9 *Set of* 9 £425 £300
s, 93s/9s Optd "Specimen" *Set of* 8 £800
No. 91x was used at Canton during December 1912 and No. w at Shanghai during 1908.

24

25

26

27

28

(A)

(B)

In Type A of the 25 c. the upper Chinese character in the left-hand label has a short vertical stroke crossing it at the foot. In Type B this stroke is absent.

1912 (9 Nov)–**21.** *Wmk Mult Crown CA. Chalk-surfaced paper* (12 *c. to* $10). *P* 14.
100 24 1 c. brown .. 2·25 55
a. Black-brown .. 3·75 2·00
b. Crown broken at right (R. 9/2) .. £200 £150
101 2 c. deep green .. 5·50 30
a. Green .. 5·50 30
w. Wmk inverted .. † —
102 25 4 c. carmine-red .. 4·25 30
a. Scarlet (1914) .. 16·00 1·75
103 26 6 c. yellow-orange .. 4·00 85
a. Brown-orange .. 4·75 1·50
w. Wmk inverted .. £550
104 25 8 c. grey .. 23·00 4·50
a. Slate (1914) .. 32·00 4·50
105 24 10 c. ultramarine .. 30·00 30
a. Deep bright ultramarine .. 24·00 30
106 27 12 c. purple/*yellow* .. 4·50 6·00
a. White back (1914) .. 7·00 11·00
as. Optd "Specimen" .. 85·00
107 20 c. purple and sage-green .. 5·00 90
108 25 c. purple & magenta (Type A) (1.14) 17·00 19·00
109 25 c. purple & magenta (Type B) (8.19) £130 50·00
110 26 30 c. purple and orange-yellow .. 27·00 5·50
a. Purple and orange .. 15·00 5·00
w. Wmk inverted
111 27 50 c. black/*blue-green* .. 13·00 1·50
a. White back (5.14) .. 13·00 4·25
as. Optd "Specimen" .. £140
b. On blue-green, olive back (1917) £1200 30·00
c. On emerald surface (9.19) .. 22·00 8·00
d. On emerald back (7.12.21) .. 22·00 6·50
ds. Optd "Specimen" .. £140
112 24 $1 purple and blue/*blue* .. 38·00 2·50
w. Wmk inverted .. £120 85·00
113 27 $2 carmine-red and grey-black .. £120 42·00
114 26 $3 green and purple .. £180 70·00
115 27 $5 green and red/*green* .. £500 £325
a. White back (5.14) .. £500 £275
as. Optd "Specimen" .. £275
b. On blue-green, olive back (1917) £950 £250
bs. Optd "Specimen" .. £300
bw. Wmk inverted .. £2750
116 26 $10 purple and black/*red* .. £550 85·00
100/16 *Set of* 17 £1400 £450
100s/16s Optd "Specimen" *Set of* 17 £1600
No. 100b occurred on R. 9/2 of the lower right pane of the first MCA printing before being retouched.

Broken flower at top right
(Upper left pane R. 1/3)

1921 (Jan)–**37.** *Wmk Mult Script CA. Chalk-surfaced paper* (12 *c. to* $5). *P* 14.
117 24 1 c. brown .. 1·00 40
118 2 c. blue-green .. 2·25 40
a. Yellow-green (1932) .. 6·50 70
bw. Wmk inverted .. 60·00
118*c* 2 c. grey (14.4.37) .. 15·00 6·50
119 25 3 c. grey (8.10.31) .. 4·50 1·00
120 4 c. carmine-rose .. 3·50 70
a. Carmine-red (1932) .. 2·25 30
b. Top of lower Chinese characters at right broken off (R. 9/4) .. 80·00 60·00
121 5 c. violet (16.10.31) .. 6·50 30
122 8 c. grey .. 10·00 35·00
123 8 c. orange (7.12.21) .. 4·00 1·25
w. Wmk inverted .. £750
124 24 10 c. bright ultramarine .. 3·50 30
aw. Wmk inverted .. £110
124*b* 27 12 c. purple/*yellow* (3.4.33) .. 13·00 1·00
125 20 c. purple and sage-green (7.12.21) .. 4·00 30
126 28 25 c. purple and magenta (B) (7.12.21) 4·00 60
a. Broken flower .. 32·00 38·00
w. Wmk inverted .. † £150
127 26 30 c. purple & chrome-yellow (7.12.21) 10·00 1·50
a. Purple and orange-yellow .. 24·00 7·00
w. Wmk inverted .. £130
128 27 50 c. black/*emerald* (1924) .. 11·00 30
129 24 $1 purple and blue/*blue* (7.12.21) .. 27·00 50
130 27 $2 carmine-red & grey-black (7.12.21) 95·00 6·00
131 26 $3 green and dull purple (1926) .. £160 55·00
132 27 $5 green and red/*emerald* (1925) .. £450 70·00
117/32 *Set of* 18 £750 £160
117s/32s Optd or Perf (2 c. grey, 3, 5, 12 c.) "Specimen" *Set of* 18 £1500
No. 120b occurs on R. 9/4 of the lower left pane.

1935 (6 May). *Silver Jubilee. As Nos. 91/4 of Antigua, but ptd by B.W. P* 11×12.
133 3 c. ultramarine and grey-black .. 4·00 3·50
c. Lightning conductor .. £325 £225
134 5 c. green and indigo .. 8·50 3·50
a. Extra flagstaff .. £300 £275
b. Short extra flagstaff .. £375
c. Lightning conductor .. £300
d. Flagstaff on right-hand turret .. £350
135 10 c. brown and deep blue .. 20·00 1·75
136 20 c. slate and purple .. 38·00 8·00
b. Short extra flagstaff .. £700 £275
d. Flagstaff on right-hand turret .. £650 £275
e. Double flagstaff .. £650 £275
133/6 *Set of* 4 60·00 15·00
133s/6s Perf "Specimen" *Set of* 4 £325
For illustrations of plate varieties see Omnibus section following Zanzibar.

1937 (12 May). *Coronation. As Nos. 95/7 of Antigua. P* 11×11½.
137 4 c. green .. 4·50 3·00
138 15 c. carmine .. 10·00 3·25
139 25 c. blue .. 13·00 2·50
137/9 *Set of* 3 25·00 8·00
137s/9s Perf "Specimen" *Set of* 3 £180

29 King George VI

Short right leg to "R" (Right pane R. 7/3, left pane R. 3/1)

1938–52. *Wmk Mult Script CA. Chalk-surfaced paper* (80 *c.*, $1 (*No.* 155), $2 (*No.* 157), $5 (*No.* 159), $10 (*No.* 161)). *P* 14.
140 29 1 c. brown (24.5.38) .. 1·75 1·50
a. Pale brown (4.2.52) .. 2·25 5·50
141 2 c. grey (5.4.38) .. 2·00 30
a. Perf 14½×14 (28.9.45) .. 1·75 5·00
142 4 c. orange (5.4.38) .. 4·50 1·25
a. Perf 14½×14 (28.9.45) .. 4·50 3·25
143 5 c. green (24.5.38) .. 1·25 20
a. Perf 14½×14 (28.9.45) .. 2·50 5·00
144 8 c. red-brown (1.11.41) .. 1·75 2·50
a. Imperf (pair) .. £24000
145 10 c. bright violet (13.4.38) .. 50·00 75
a. Perf 14½×14. *Dull violet* (28.9.45) 9·50 20
b. Dull reddish violet (9.4.46) .. 6·00 70
c. Reddish lilac (9.4.47) .. 16·00 20
146 15 c. scarlet (13.4.38) .. 2·00 30
147 20 c. black (1.2.46) .. 1·25 30
148 20 c. scarlet-vermilion (1.4.48) .. 7·00 40
a. Rose-red (25.4.51) .. 15·00 5·50
149 25 c. bright blue (5.4.38) .. 29·00 1·50
150 25 c. pale yellow-olive (9.4.46) .. 4·75 1·50
151 30 c. yellow-olive (13.4.38) .. £150 1·40
a. Perf 14½×14. *Yellowish olive* (28.9.45) .. 24·00 8·50
152 30 c. blue (9.4.46) .. 7·00 20
153 50 c. purple (13.4.38) .. 55·00 70
a. Perf 14½×14. *Dp mag* (28.9.45) 30·00 1·10
ab. Printed both sides, inverted on reverse .. £7500
b. Reddish purple (9.4.46) .. 14·00 1·50
c. Chalk-surfaced paper. *Brt purple* (9.4.47) .. 9·00 20
154 80 c. carmine (2.2.48) .. 5·00 95
155 $1 dull lilac and blue (*chalk-surfaced paper*) (27.4.38) .. 8·00 2·50
a. Short right leg to "R" .. £110
b. Ordinary paper. *Pale reddish lilac and blue* (28.9.45) .. 12·00 7·50
156 $1 red-orange and green (9.4.46) .. 18·00 30
a. Short right leg to "R" .. £160
b. Chalk-surfaced paper (21.6.48) .. 48·00 3·50
ba. Short right leg to "R" .. £275
c. Chalk-surfaced paper. *Yellow-orange and green* (6.11.52) .. 75·00 15·00
157 $2 red-orange and green (24.5.38) .. 70·00 15·00
158 $2 reddish violet and scarlet (9.4.46) 28·00 2·25
a. Chalk-surfaced paper (9.4.47) .. 35·00 1·00
159 $5 dull lilac and scarlet (2.6.38) .. 55·00 50·00
160 $5 green and violet (9.4.46) .. 80·00 5·50
a. Yellowish green and violet (9.4.46) £170 16·00
ab. Chalk-surfaced paper (9.4.47) .. 95·00 3·00
161 $10 green and violet (2.6.38) .. £450 85·00
162 $10 bright lilac and blue (9.4.46) .. £140 27·00
a. Chalk-surfaced paper. *Reddish violet and blue* (9.4.47) .. £180 18·00
140/62 *Set of* 23 £800 £160
140s/62s Perf "Specimen" *Set of* 23 £2250

Following bomb damage to the De La Rue works on the night of 29 December 1940 various emergency arrangements were made to complete current requisitions for Hong Kong stamps:

Nos. 141a, 143a, 145a, 151a and 153a (all printings perforated 14½×14 except the 4 c.) were printed and perforated by Bradbury, Wilkinson & Co. Ltd. using De La Rue plates. These stamps are on rough-surfaced paper.

Nos. 142a and 144 were printed by Harrison & Sons in sheets of 120 (12×10) instead of the normal 120 two panes (6×10).

Printings of the $1 and $2 values were made by Williams, Lea & Co. using De La Rue plates.

With the exception of the 8 c. it is believed that none of these printings were issued in Hong Kong before its occupation by the Japanese on 25 December 1941, although examples could be obtained in London from late 1941. The issue dates quoted are those on which the stamps were eventually released in Hong Kong following liberation in 1945.

Nos. 160/*a* were separate printings released in Hong Kong on the same day.

No. 144a. One imperforate sheet was found and most of the stamps were sold singly to the public at a branch P.O. and used for postage.

30 Street Scene

31 *Empress of Japan* (liner) and Junk

(Des W. E. Jones. Recess B.W.)

1941 (26 Feb). *Centenary of British Occupation. T* **30/1** *and similar designs. Wmk Mult Script CA (sideways on horiz designs). P* 13½ × 13 (2 c. *and* 25 c.) *or* 13 × 13½ (*others*).
163 2 c. orange and chocolate .. .. .. 4·50 2·00
164 4 c. bright purple and carmine .. .. 5·00 2·25
165 5 c. black and green .. .. 2·50 50
166 15 c. black and scarlet.. .. .. .. 6·00 1·50
167 25 c. chocolate and blue .. .. .. 12·00 4·50
168 $1 blue and orange .. .. 45·00 7·00
163/8 .. .. *Set of* 6 65·00 16·00
163s/8s Perf "Specimen" .. .. *Set of* 6 £350

Designs: *Horiz*—5 c. The University; 15 c. The Harbour; $1 *Falcon* (clipper) and Short S.23 Empire "C" Class flying boat. *Vert*—25 c. The Hong Kong Bank.

Hong Kong was under Japanese occupation from 25 December 1941 until 30 August 1945. The Japanese post offices in the colony were closed from 31 August and mail was carried free, marked with cachets reading "HONG KONG/1945/ POSTAGE PAID". Military administration lasted until 1 May 1946. Hong Kong stamps were re-introduced on 28 September 1945.

36 King George VI and Phoenix

Extra stroke (R. 1/2)

(Des W. E. Jones. Recess D.L.R.)

1946 (29 Aug). *Victory. Wmk Mult Script CA. P* 13.
169 **36** 30 c. blue and red (*shades*) .. .. 2·50 1·25
a. Extra stroke .. .. 55·00
170 $1 brown and red .. .. .. 3·50 75
a. Extra stroke .. .. 80·00
169s/70s Perf "Specimen" .. *Set of* 2 £160

HONG KONG

Spur on "N" of "KONG" (R. 2/9)

1948 (22 Dec). *Royal Silver Wedding. As Nos.* 112/13 *of Antigua.*
171 10 c. violet .. .. 2·75 80
a. Spur on "N" .. .. 60·00 45·00
172 $10 carmine .. .. £275 80·00

1949 (10 Oct). *75th Anniv of Universal Postal Union. As Nos.* 114/17 *of Antigua.*
173 10 c. violet .. .. 4·00 50
174 20 c. carmine-red .. .. 16·00 3·00
175 30 c. deep blue .. .. 13·00 2·00
176 80 c. bright reddish purple .. .. 35·00 9·50
173/6 .. .. *Set of* 4 60·00 13·50

STAMP BOOKLETS

BOOKLET CONTENTS. In Nos. SB1/4 and SB6/7 the 1 c. and 2 c. were normally each in blocks of 12 or two blocks of 6 and the 4 c. in blocks of 12 and 4 or two blocks of 8, all having been taken from normal sheets. No. SB5 had both the 2 c. and 4 c. in blocks of 12 and 4 or as two blocks of 8. Other content formats exist.

1904 (1 Jan). *Black on white cover showing contents and postage rates with "K & W LD" imprint on front. Stapled.*
SB1 $1 booklet containing twelve 1 c (No. 62), twelve 2 c. (No. 56) and sixteen 4 c. (No. 57)
a. 4 c. No. 64 (King Edward VII) instead of No. 57 (Q.V.) £4500

1905–06. *Black on white cover showing contents and postage rates with "Hongkong Printing Press" imprint on front. Metal fastener.*
SB2 $1 booklet containing twelve 1 c., twelve 2 c. and sixteen 4 c. (Nos. 62/4) £3500
a. 2 c. and 4 c. (Nos. 77/8) (MCA ordinary paper) instead of Nos. 63/4 (CA) (1906) .. ..
b. 2 c. and 4 c. (Nos. 77a/8a) (MCA chalk-surfaced paper) instead of Nos. 77/8 (MCA ordinary paper) (1906) .. ..

Some examples of No. SB2 show the reference to Australia on the front cover deleted in manuscript. No. SB2a has the rate information reset to omit "EXCEPT AUSTRALIA".

1907 (Dec). *Black on white cover showing contents and postage rates for both Hong Kong and Agencies in China with "Hongkong Printing Press" imprint. Metal fastener.*
SB3 $1 booklet containing twelve 1 c. (No. 62), twelve 2 c. (No. 92) and sixteen 4 c. (No. 93) ..
a. Stapled £2750

1910 (May)–**11.** *Black on white cover showing contents, but no postage rates, with "Hongkong Printing Press" imprint on front. Stapled.*
SB4 $1 booklet containing twelve 1 c. (No. 62), twelve 2 c. (No. 92) and sixteen 4 c. (No. 93) ..
a. 1 c. No. 91 (MCA) instead of No. 62 (CA) (9.11) £2750

1912 (Apr). *Black on cream cover showing contents, but no postage rates, with "Hongkong Printing Press" imprint on front. Stapled.*
SB5 $1 booklet containing four 1 c., sixteen 2 c. and sixteen 4 c. (Nos. 91/3) £3500

1913 (Feb). *Black on cream cover showing contents, but no postage rates, with "Hongkong Printing Press" imprint on front. Stapled.*
SB6 $1 booklet containing twelve 1 c., twelve 2 c. and sixteen 4 c. (Nos. 100/2) (MCA wmk) .. £2500

1922–24. *Black on cream cover showing contents, but no postage rates, with "Hongkong Printing Press" imprint on front. Stapled.*
SB7 $1 booklet containing twelve 1 c., twelve 2 c. and sixteen 4 c. (Nos. 117/18, 120) (Script wmk) .. £2750
a. With Ye Olde Printerie Ltd imprint (1924) ..

POSTAGE DUE STAMPS

PRINTERS. Nos. D1/23 were typographed by De La Rue & Co.

D 1 Post-office Scales

1923 (Dec)–**56.** *Wmk Mult Script CA. Ordinary paper. P* 14.
D1 D 1 1 c. brown .. .. 2·50 65
a. Wmk sideways (1931) .. .. 1·50 3·25
ab. Chalk-surfaced paper (21.3.56) .. 30 1·00
D2 2 c. green .. .. 21·00 6·00
a. Wmk sideways (1928) .. .. 11·00 5·00
D3 4 c. scarlet .. .. 35·00 7·00
a. Wmk sideways (1928) .. .. 27·00 7·00
D4 6 c. yellow .. .. 26·00 13·00
a. Wmk sideways (1931) .. .. 60·00 35·00
D5 10 c. bright ultramarine .. .. .. 23·00 8·50
a. Wmk sideways (1934) .. .. 85·00 16·00
D1/5 .. .. *Set of* 5 95·00 30·00
D1a/5a .. .. *Set of* 5 £160 55·00
D1s/5s Optd "Specimen" .. .. *Set of* 5 £250

1938 (Feb)–**63.** *Wmk Mult Script CA (sideways). Ordinary paper. P* 14.
D 6 D 1 2 c. grey .. .. 13·00 9·00
a. Chalk-surfaced paper (21.3.56) .. 1·10 10·00
D 7 4 c. orange .. .. 18·00 6·50
a. Chalk-surfaced paper. *Orange-yellow* (23.5.61) .. .. .. 2·50 10·00
D 8 6 c. scarlet .. .. 9·50 5·50
D 9 8 c. chestnut (26.2.46) .. .. 5·50 32·00
D10 10 c. violet .. .. 35·00 50
a. Chalk-surfaced paper (17.9.63) .. 16·00 10·00
D11 20 c. black (26.2.46) .. .. .. 13·00 3·00
D12 50 c. blue (7.47) .. .. 48·00 15·00
D6a/12 .. .. *Set of* 7 85·00 65·00
D6s/12s Perf "Specimen" .. .. *Set of* 7 £325

POSTCARD STAMPS

Stamps specially surcharged for use on Postcards.

PRICES. Those in the left-hand column are for unused examples on complete postcards; those on the right for used examples off card. Examples used on postcards are worth more.

3
CENTS
(P 1)

THREE
(P 2)

1879 (1 Apr). *Nos.* 22 *and* 13 *surch as Type* **P 1** *by Noronha & Sons.*
P1 **3** 3 c. on 16 c. yellow (No. 22) £350 £350
P2 5 c. on 18 c. lilac (No. 13) £325 £350

1879 (Nov). *No.* P2 *handstamped with Type* **P 2**.
P3 **3** 3 c. on 5 c. on 18 c. lilac £6500 £7500

POSTAL FISCAL STAMPS

I. Stamps inscribed "STAMP DUTY"

NOTE. The dated circular "HONG KONG" cancellation "PAID ALL" in lower segment was used for fiscal purpos black, from 1877. Previously it appears in red on mail t U.S.A., but is usually not used as a cancellation.

F 1

F 2

10. 10.
HONG KONG
TEN DOLLARS

F 3

1874–1902. *Wmk Crown CC. (a) P* 15½×15
F1 **F 1** $2 olive-green £300 4
F2 **F 2** $3 dull violet £275 3
b. Bluish paper .. .. ..
F3 **F 3** $10 rose-carmine .. .. £7500 £

(*b*) *P* 14
F4 **F 1** $2 dull bluish green (10.97) .. £350 £
F5 **F 2** $3 dull mauve (3.02) .. .. £475 £
a. Bluish paper £1500
F6 **F 3** $10 grey-green £11000 £1
F4s/5s Optd "Specimen" *Set of* 2 £450

Nos. F1/3 and F7 exist on various papers, ranging from thi thick.

All three of the values perforated 15½×15 were authori for postal use in 1874. The $10 rose-carmine was withdr from such use in 1880, the $2 in September 1897 and the $ 1902.

The $2 and $3 perforated 14 were available for po purposes until July 1903. The $10 in grey-green was issue fiscal purposes in 1884 and is known with postal cancellatio

12
CENTS.
(F 4)

F 5

1880. *No.* F3 *surch with Type* **F 4** *by Noronha and Sons, H Kong.*
F7 **F 3** 12 c. on $10 rose-carmine .. .. £800 £

1890 (24 Dec). *Wmk Crown CA. P* 14.
F8 **F 5** 2 c. dull purple .. .. .. 75·00 17
w. Wmk inverted

No. F8 was authorised for postal use between 24 a 31 December 1890.

5
DOLLARS
(F 6)

ONE
DOLLAR
(F 7)

F 8

1891 (1 Jan). *Surch with Type* **F 6** *by D.L.R. Wmk Crown C P* 14.
F9 **F 3** $5 on $10 purple/*red* £300 £1
s. Optd "Specimen" £190

No. F9 was in use for postal purposes until June 1903.

1897 (Sept). *Surch with Type* **F 7** *by Noronha and Sons, Ho Kong, and with the value in Chinese characters subsequen applied twice by handstamp as T* **15**.
F10 **F 1** $1 on $2 olive-green (No. F1) £190 £1
a. Both Chinese handstamps omitted £3000 £20
F11 $1 on $2 dull bluish green (No. F4) .. £200 £1
a. Both Chinese handstamps omitted £1600 £13
b. Diagonal Chinese handstamp omitted £10000
c. Vertical Chinese handstamp omitted
s. Handstamped "Specimen" £140

1938 (11 Jan). *Wmk Mult Script CA. P* 14.
F12 **F 8** 5 c. green .. .. 50·00 11·(

No. F12 was authorised for postal use between 11 and 2 January 1938 due to a shortage of the 5 c., No. 121.

Forged cancellations are known on this stamp inscribe "VICTORIA 9.AM 11 JA 38 HONG KONG" without side ba between the rings.

…amps overprinted "S.O." (Stamp Office), or "S.D." (Stamp Duty)

S. O. S. D.

印 厘 印 厘

(S 1) (S 2)

(1 Jan). *Optd with Types* S **1** *or* S **2**.

…1	2 c. carmine (No. 33)	£900	£325
…2	2 c. carmine (No. 33)	£400	£180
	a. Opt inverted		† £4500
…1	10 c. purple/*red* (No. 38)	£1600	£400

…amples of No. S1 exist with the "O" amended to "D" in …uscript.

…her fiscal stamps are found apparently postally used, but there … evidence that this use was authorised.

…APANESE OCCUPATION OF HONG KONG

…ong Kong surrendered to the Japanese on 25 December …. The postal service was not resumed until 22 January 1942 …n the G.P.O. and Kowloon Central Office re-opened.

…apanese postmarks used in Hong Kong can be identified by …unique combination of horizontal lines in the central circle … three stars in the lower segment of the outer circle. Dates …wn on such postmarks are in the sequence Year/Month/Day … the first shown as a Japanese regnal year number so that …wa 17 = 1942 and so on.

…itially six current Japanese definitives, 1, 2, 3, 4, 10 and … (Nos. 297, 315/17, 322 and 327). were on sale, but the …ge gradually expanded to cover all values between ½ s. and … with Nos. 313/14, 318, 325, 328/31, 391, 395/6, 398/9 and … of Japan also available from Hong Kong post offices during …occupation. Philatelic covers exist showing other Japanese …mps, but these were not available from the local post offices. …ply of these Japanese stamps was often interrupted and, …ng the period between 28 July 1942 and 21 April 1943, …ular "Postage Paid" handstamps were sometimes used. A …stantial increase in postage rates on 16 April 1945 led to the …e of the local surcharges, Nos. J1/3.

PRICES FOR STAMPS ON COVER	
Nos. J1/3	*from* × 7

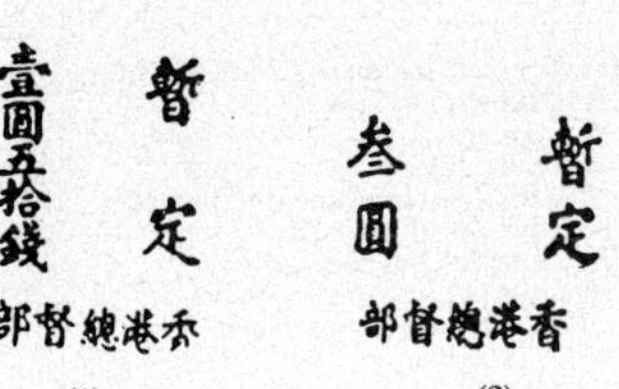

(1) (2)

…45 (16 Apr). *Stamps of Japan surch with* T **1** (*No.* J1) *or as* T **2**.

	1.50 yen on 1 s. brown	28·00	23·00
	3 yen on 2 s. scarlet	12·00	19·00
	5 yen on 5 s. claret	£900	£140

…Designs (18½ × 22 *mm*):—1 s. Girl Worker; 2 s. Gen. Nogi; 5 s. …miral Togo.

…No. J3 has four characters of value similarly arranged but …fering from T **2**.

BRITISH POST OFFICES IN CHINA

Under the terms of the 1842 Treaty of Nanking China granted …eat Britain and its citizens commercial privileges in five …eaty Ports, Amoy, Canton, Foochow, Ningpo and Shanghai. …itish Consuls were appointed to each Port and their offices, as …as usual during this period, collected and distributed mail for …e British community. This system was formally recognised by …Hong Kong Government notice published on 16 April 1844. …ail from the consular offices was postmarked when it passed …rough Hong Kong.

The number of Chinese Treaty Ports was increased to sixteen … the ratification of the Treaty of Peking in 1860 with British …stal facilities being eventually extended to the Ports of Chefoo, …ankow, Kiungchow (Hoihow), Swatow, Tainan (Anping) and …entsin.

As postal business expanded the consular agencies were …nverted into packet agencies or post offices which passed …nder the direct control of the Hong Kong postal authorities on May 1868.

In May 1898 the British Government leased the territory of …ei Hai Wei from China for use as a naval station to counter the …ussian presence at Port Arthur.

The opening of the Trans-Siberia Railway and the extension of …mperial Penny Postage to the Treaty Port agencies resulted in …em becoming a financial burden on the colonial post office. …ontrol of the agencies reverted to the G.P.O., London, on January 1911.

The pre-adhesive postal markings of the various agencies are fascinating, but complex, subject. Full details can be found in *…ong Kong & the Treaty Ports of China & Japan* by F.W. Webb …eprinted edition J. Bendon, Limassol, 1992) and in various …ublications of the Hong Kong Study Circle.

From 15 October 1864 the use of Hong Kong stamps on mail …om the Treaty Ports became compulsory, although such …amps were, initially, not cancelled (with the exception of …moy) until they reached Hong Kong where the "B62" killer was applied. Cancellation of mail at the actual Ports commenced during 1866 at Shanghai and Ningpo, spreading to all the agencies during the next ten years. Shanghai had previously used a c.d.s. on adhesives during 1863 and again in 1865–66.

The main types of cancellation used between 1866 and 1930 are illustrated below. The illustrations show the style of each postmark and no attempt has been made to cover differences in type letters or figures, arrangement, diameter or colour.

Until 1885 the vertical and horizontal killers were used to obliterate the actual stamps with an impression of one of the circular date stamps shown elsewhere on the cover. Many of the early postmarks were also used as backstamps or transit marks and, in the notes which follow, references to use are for the first appearance of the mark, not necessarily its first use as an obliterator.

Illustrations in this section are taken from *Hong Kong & the Treaty Ports of China & Japan* by F. W. Webb and are reproduced with the permission of the Royal Philatelic Society, London.

Details of the stamps known used from each post office are taken, with permission, from *British Post Offices in the Far East* by Edward B. Proud, published by Proud-Bailey Co. Ltd.

Postmark Types

Type **A**
Vertical killer

Type **B**
Horizontal killer

Type **C**
Name horizontal

Type **D**
Name curved

Type **E**
Double circle Name at top

Type **F**
Double circle Name at foot

SHANGHAI C AP 24 08 BR. P.O.

Type **G**
Single circle Name at top

PRICES. The prices quoted in this section are for fine used stamps which show a clear impression of a substantial part of the cancellation.

AMOY

One of the five original Treaty Ports, opened to British trade by the Treaty of Nanking in 1842. A consular postal agency was established in 1844 which expanded in 1876 into two separate offices, one on the off-shore island of Ku Lang Seu and the other in Amoy itself.

Amoy "PAID" (*supplied* 1858) *used* 1859–67
Type **A** ("A1") (*supplied* 1866) *used at Ku Lang Seu* 1869–82
Type **D** (*supplied* 1866) *used* 1867–1922
Type **B** ("D27") (*supplied* 1876) *used at Amoy* 1876–84
Type **C** *used* 1876–94
Type **F** (*supplied* 1913) *used* 1916–22

Stamps of HONG KONG *cancelled at Amoy between* 1864 *and* 1916 *with postmarks detailed above.*

1862. *No wmk* (*Nos.* 1/7).

Z1	2 c. brown	£150
Z2	8 c. yellow-buff	£140
Z3	12 c. pale greenish blue	£120
Z4	18 c. lilac	80·00
Z5	24 c. green	£150
Z6	48 c. rose	
Z7	96 c. brownish grey	£600

1863–71. *Wmk Crown CC* (*Nos.* 8/19).

Z 8	2 c. brown	35·00
Z 9	4 c. grey	32·00
	a. Perf 12½	
Z10	6 c. lilac	48·00
Z11	8 c. orange	40·00
Z12	12 c. blue	18·00
Z13	18 c. lilac	£550
Z14	24 c. green	45·00
Z15	30 c. vermilion	70·00
Z16	30 c. mauve	14·00
Z17	48 c. rose	42·00
Z18	96 c. olive-bistre	£1200
Z19	96 c. brownish grey	£170

1876–77. (*Nos.* 20/1).

Z20	16 c. on 18 c. lilac	£300
Z21	28 c. on 30 c. mauve	£130

1877. *Wmk Crown CC* (*No.* 22).

Z22	16 c. yellow	£110

1880. (*Nos.* 23/7).

Z23	5 c. on 8 c. orange	£120
Z24	5 c. on 18 c. lilac	95·00
Z25	10 c. on 12 c. blue	95·00
Z26	10 c. on 16 c. yellow	£190
Z27	10 c. on 24 c. green	£110

1880. *Wmk Crown CC* (*Nos.* 28/31).

Z28	2 c. rose	42·00
Z29	5 c. blue	60·00
Z30	10 c. mauve	48·00
Z31	48 c. brown	£150

1882–96. *Wmk Crown CA* (*Nos.* 32/9).

Z31*a*	2 c. rose-lake	
Z32	2 c. carmine	3·75
Z33	4 c. slate-grey	7·00
Z34	5 c. blue	3·75
Z35	10 c. dull mauve	26·00
Z36	10 c. green	4·25
Z37	10 c. purple/*red*	4·25
Z38	30 c. green	27·00

1885. (*Nos.* 40/2).

Z39	20 c. on 30 c. orange-red	11·00
Z40	50 c. on 48 c. yellowish brown	48·00
Z41	$1 on 96 c. grey-olive	80·00

1891. (*Nos.* 43/4, 48/50).

Z42	7 c. on 10 c. green	20·00
Z43	14 c. on 30 c. mauve	85·00
Z44	20 c. on 30 c. green	12·00
Z45	50 c. on 48 c. dull purple	15·00
Z46	$1 on 96 c. purple/*red*	38·00

1891. 50*th Anniv of Colony* (*No.* 51).

Z47	2 c. carmine	£850

1898. (*No.* 52).

Z48	$1 on 96 c. black	45·00

1898. (*No.* 55).

Z49	10 c. on 30 c. green	£190

1900–01. *Wmk Crown CA* (*Nos.* 56/61).

Z50	2 c. dull green	3·50
Z51	4 c. carmine	2·50
Z52	5 c. yellow	15·00
Z53	10 c. ultramarine	4·00
Z54	12 c. blue	£100
Z55	30 c. brown	55·00

1903. *Wmk Crown CA* (*Nos.* 62/76).

Z56	1 c. dull purple and brown	4·00
Z57	2 c. dull green	3·25
Z58	4 c. purple/*red*	2·25
Z59	5 c. dull green and brown-orange	16·00
Z60	8 c. slate and violet	6·00
Z61	10 c. purple and blue/*blue*	3·25
Z62	12 c. green and purple/*yellow*	11·00
Z63	20 c. slate and chestnut	8·50
Z64	30 c. dull green and black	38·00
Z65	50 c. dull green and magenta	55·00
Z67	$2 slate and scarlet	£325
Z68	$3 slate and dull blue	

1904–06. *Wmk Mult Crown CA* (*Nos.* 77/90).

Z71	2 c. dull green	3·25
Z72	4 c. purple/*red*	2·25
Z73	5 c. dull green and brown-orange	12·00
Z74	8 c. slate and violet	8·50
Z75	10 c. purple and blue/*blue*	3·00
Z76	12 c. green and purple/*yellow*	14·00
Z77	20 c. slate and chestnut	7·50
Z78	30 c. dull green and black	25·00
Z79	50 c. green and magenta	22·00
Z83	$5 purple and blue-green	£425

1907–11. *Wmk Mult Crown CA* (*Nos.* 91/9).

Z85	1 c. brown	3·75
Z86	2 c. green	3·25
Z87	4 c. carmine-red	2·25
Z88	6 c. orange-vermilion and purple	12·00
Z89	10 c. bright ultramarine	3·00
Z90	20 c. purple and sage-green	55·00
Z91	30 c. purple and orange-yellow	45·00
Z92	50 c. black/*green*	

1912–15. *Wmk Mult Crown CA* (*Nos.* 100/16).

Z 93	1 c. brown	4·50
Z 94	2 c. green	4·25
Z 95	4 c. red	2·25
Z 96	6 c. orange	3·50
Z 97	8 c. grey	18·00
Z 98	10 c. ultramarine	3·50
Z 99	12 c. purple/*yellow*	17·00
Z100	20 c. purple and sage-green	6·00
Z102	30 c. purple and orange-yellow	14·00
Z103	50 c. black/*green*	8·50
Z104	$1 purple and blue/*blue*	18·00
Z105	$3 green and purple	£110

POSTCARD STAMPS

1879. (*Nos.* P1/2).

ZP106	3 c. on 16 c. yellow	£475
ZP107	5 c. on 18 c. lilac	£500

POSTAL FISCAL STAMPS

1874–1902. *Wmk Crown CC.* (*a*) *P* 15½×15 (*Nos.* F1/3)

ZF109	$2 olive-green	£110
ZF110	$3 dull violet	£100

1891. (*No.* F9).

ZF116	$5 on $10 purple/*red*	£200

1897. (*No.* F10).

ZF118	$1 on $2 olive-green	

ANPING

Anping is the port for Tainan, on the island of Formosa, opened to British trade in 1860. A British Vice-consulate operated in the port and mail is known postmarked there between 1889 and 1895. Formosa passed under Japanese control in 1895 and British Treaty Port rights then lapsed.

Type **D** *used* 1889–95

Stamps of HONG KONG *cancelled at Anping between* 1889 *and* 1895 *with postmark detailed above.*

1882–91. *Wmk Crown CA* (*Nos.* 32/9).

Z120	2 c. carmine	£650
Z121	5 c. blue	£500
Z123	10 c. green	£650
Z124	10 c. purple/*red*	£800

1885. (*Nos.* 40/2).

Z126	20 c. on 30 c. orange-red	£650
Z127	50 c. on 48 c. yellowish brown	£900

CANTON

A British postal service was organised in Cantom from 1834, but was closed when the foreign communities were evacuated in August 1839. The city was one of the original Treaty Ports and a consular agency was opened there in 1844. The consulate closed during the riots of 1857, being replaced by a temporary postal agency at Whampoa, further down the river. When British forces reached Canton a further temporary agency was set up in 1859, but both closed in July 1863 when the consulate was re-established.

Type **A** ("C1") (*supplied* 1866) *used* 1875–84
Type **C** (*supplied* 1866) *used* 1870–1901
Type **D** *used* 1890–1922

Stamps of HONG KONG *cancelled at Canton between* 1870 *and* 1916 *with postmarks detailed above.*

1862. *No wmk* (*Nos.* 1/7).

Z135	18 c. lilac	£100

1863–71. *Wmk Crown CC* (*Nos.* 8/19).

Z136	2 c. brown	38·00
Z137	4 c. grey	40·00
Z138	6 c. lilac	48·00
Z139	8 c. orange	40·00
Z140	12 c. blue	19·00
Z142	24 c. green	50·00
Z143	30 c. vermilion	
Z144	30 c. mauve	17·00
Z145	48 c. rose	70·00
Z147	96 c. brownish grey	85·00

1876–77. (*Nos.* 20/1).

Z148	16 c. on 18 c. lilac	£300
Z149	28 c. on 30 c. mauve	£120

1877. *Wmk Crown CC* (*No.* 22).

Z150	16 c. yellow	£140

1880. (*Nos.* 23/7).

Z151	5 c. on 8 c. orange	£150
Z152	5 c. on 18 c. lilac	£120
Z153	10 c. on 12 c. blue	£110
Z154	10 c. on 16 c. yellow	£225
Z155	10 c. on 24 c. green	£140

1880. *Wmk Crown CC* (*Nos.* 28/31).

Z156	2 c. rose	40·00
Z157	5 c. blue	50·00
Z158	10 c. mauve	48·00

1882–96. *Wmk Crown CA* (*Nos.* 32/9).

Z159	2 c. rose-lake	
Z160	2 c. carmine	2·25
Z161	4 c. slate-grey	8·50
Z162	5 c. blue	4·25
Z163	10 c. dull mauve	22·00
Z164	10 c. green	7·50
Z165	10 c. purple/*red*	4·00
Z166	30 c. green	29·00

1885. (*Nos.* 40/2).

Z167	20 c. on 30 c. orange-red	10·00
Z168	50 c. on 48 c. yellowish brown	48·00
Z169	$1 on 96 c. grey-olive	85·00

1891. (*Nos.* 43/5, 48/50).

Z170	7 c. on 10 c. green	19·00
Z171	14 c. on 30 c. mauve	95·00
Z171*a*	20 c. on 30 c. green (No. 45)	£200
Z172	20 c. on 30 c. green (No. 48)	15·00
Z173	50 c. on 48 c. dull purple	17·00
Z174	$1 on 96 c. purple/*red*	45·00

1891. *50th Anniv of Colony* (*No.* 51).

Z175	2 c. carmine	£800

1898. (*No.* 52).

Z176	$1 on 96 c. black	£100

1898. (*No.* 55)

Z177	10 c. on 30 c. grey-green	

1900–01. *Wmk Crown CA* (*Nos.* 56/61).

Z178	2 c. dull green	3·50
Z179	4 c. carmine	3·25
Z180	5 c. yellow	25·00
Z181	10 c. ultramarine	3·25
Z182	12 c. blue	75·00
Z183	30 c. brown	48·00

1903. *Wmk Crown CA* (*Nos.* 62/76).

Z184	1 c. dull purple and brown	3·50
Z185	2 c. dull green	3·25
Z186	4 c. purple/*red*	2·25
Z187	5 c. dull green and brown-orange	16·00
Z188	8 c. slate and violet	7·00
Z189	10 c. purple and blue/*blue*	3·25
Z190	12 c. green and purple/*yellow*	11·00
Z191	20 c. slate and chestnut	6·00
Z192	30 c. dull green and black	35·00

1904–06. *Wmk Mult Crown CA* (*Nos.* 77/90).

Z199	2 c. dull green	3·25
Z200	4 c. purple/*red*	2·25
Z201	5 c. dull green and brown-orange	14·00
Z202	8 c. slate and violet	11·00
Z203	10 c. purple and blue/*blue*	3·00
Z204	12 c. green and purple/*yellow*	16·00
Z205	20 c. slate and chestnut	9·00
Z206	30 c. dull green and black	24·00
Z207	50 c. green and magenta	26·00
Z208	$1 purple and sage-green	45·00
Z212	$10 slate and orange/*blue*	£1300

1907–11. *Wmk Mult Crown CA* (*Nos.* 91/9).

Z213	1 c. brown	3·50
Z214	2 c. green	3·50
Z215	4 c. carmine-red	2·25
Z216	6 c. orange-vermilion and purple	13·00
Z217	10 c. bright ultramarine	3·00
Z218	20 c. purple and sage-green	60·00
Z219	30 c. purple and orange-yellow	42·00
Z220	50 c. black/*green*	35·00

1912–15. *Wmk Mult Crown CA* (*Nos.* 100/16).

Z222	1 c. brown	3·75
Z223	2 c. green	3·00
Z224	4 c. red	2·00
Z225	6 c. orange	3·25
Z226	8 c. grey	16·00
Z227	10 c. ultramarine	3·25
Z228	12 c. purple/*yellow*	13·00
Z229	20 c. purple and sage-green	4·75
Z231	30 c. purple and orange-yellow	13·00
Z232	50 c. black/*green*	4·25
Z235	$3 green and purple	£120

POSTCARD STAMPS

1879. (*Nos.* P1/2).

ZP236	3 c. on 16 c. yellow	£450
ZP237	5 c. on 18 c. lilac	£500

POSTAL FISCAL STAMPS

1874–1902. *Wmk Crown CC.* (*a*) *P* 15½×15 (*Nos.* F1/3)

ZF238	$2 olive-green	£140

1891. (*No.* F9).

ZF246	$5 on $10 purple/*red*	£300

1897. (*No.* F10).

ZF247	$1 on $2 olive-green	

CHEFOO

Chefoo was opened to British trade in 1860. Altho consulate was established in 1863 no organised postal a was provided until 1 January 1903 when one was opened premises of Curtis Brothers, a commercial firm.

Type **E** (*supplied* 1902) *used* 1903–20
Type **D** (*supplied* 1907) *used* 1907–13
Type **F** *used* 1916–22

Stamps of HONG KONG *cancelled at Chefoo between* 190 1916 *with postmarks detailed above.*

1882–96. *Wmk Crown CA* (*Nos.* 32/9).

Z249	5 c. blue	

1891. (*Nos.* 43/50)

Z250	20 c. on 30 c. grey-green (No. 48*a*)	

1898. (*No.* 52).

Z251	$1 on 96 c. black	

1900–01. *Wmk Crown CA* (*Nos.* 56/61).

Z252	2 c. dull green	
Z253	4 c. carmine	
Z254	5 c. yellow	
Z255	10 c. ultramarine	
Z257	30 c. brown	

1903. *Wmk Crown CA* (*Nos.* 62/76).

Z258	1 c. dull purple and brown	
Z259	2 c. dull green	
Z260	4 c. purple/*red*	
Z261	5 c. dull green and brown-orange	1
Z262	8 c. slate and violet	1
Z263	10 c. purple and blue/*blue*	
Z264	12 c. green and purple/*yellow*	2
Z268	$1 purple and sage-green	

1904–06. *Wmk Mult Crown CA* (*Nos.* 77/90)

Z273	2 c. dull green	
Z274	4 c. purple/*red*	
Z275	5 c. dull green and brown-orange	1
Z276	8 c. slate and violet	1
Z277	10 c. purple and blue/*blue*	
Z278	12 c. green and purple/*yellow*	2
Z279	20 c. slate and chestnut	1
Z280	30 c. dull green and black	3
Z281	50 c. green and magenta	4
Z283	$2 slate and scarlet	£
Z284	$3 slate and dull blue	£
Z285	$5 purple and blue-green	

1907–11. *Wmk Mult Crown CA* (*Nos.* 91/9).

Z287	1 c. brown	
Z288	2 c. green	
Z289	4 c. carmine-red	
Z290	6 c. orange-vermilion and purple	2
Z291	10 c. bright ultramarine	
Z292	20 c. purple and sage-green	6
Z293	30 c. purple and orange-yellow	4
Z295	$2 carmine-red and black	

1912–15. *Wmk Mult Crown CA* (*Nos.* 100/16).

Z296	1 c. brown	6
Z297	2 c. green	6
Z298	4 c. red	5
Z299	6 c. orange	10
Z301	10 c. ultramarine	6
Z302	12 c. purple/*yellow*	21
Z303	20 c. purple and sage-green	9
Z305	30 c. purple and orange-yellow	13
Z306	50 c. black/*green*	7
Z307	$1 purple and blue/*blue*	9
Z308	$2 carmine-red and grey-black	65
Z309	$3 green and purple	95
Z310	$5 green and red/*green*	£4
Z311	$10 purple and black/*red*	£

FOOCHOW

Foochow, originally known as Foochowfoo, was one of original Treaty Ports opened to British trade in 1842. A Brit consulate and postal agency was established in June 1844.

Type **A** ("F1") (*supplied* 1866) *used* 1873–84
Type **D** (inscr "FOOCHOWFOO") (*supplied* 1866) *u* 1867–1905
Type **D** (inscr "FOOCHOW") (*supplied* 1894) *used* 18 1917
Type **E** (inscr "B.P.O.") *used* 1906–10
Type **F** *used* 1915–22

Stamps of HONG KONG *cancelled at Foochow between* 18 *and* 1916 *with postmarks detailed above.*

1862. *No wmk* (*Nos.* 1/7).

Z312	18 c. lilac	£1

1863–71. *Wmk Crown CC* (*Nos.* 8/19).

Z313	2 c. brown	35·
Z314	4 c. grey	35·
Z315	6 c. lilac	45·
Z316	8 c. orange	38·
Z317	12 c. blue	17·
Z318	18 c. lilac	£6
Z319	24 c. green	65·
Z320	30 c. vermilion	
Z321	30 c. mauve	14·
Z322	48 c. rose	70·
Z324	96 c. brownish grey	80·

-77. (*Nos.* 20/1).
16 c. on 18 c. lilac £325
28 c. on 30 c. mauve £150

Wmk Crown CC (*No.* 22).
16 c. yellow £120

(*Nos.* 23/7).
5 c. on 8 c. orange £350
5 c. on 18 c. lilac £130
10 c. on 12 c. blue £130
10 c. on 16 c. yellow
10 c. on 24 c. green £170

Wmk Crown CC (*Nos.* 28/31).
2 c. rose 35·00
5 c. blue 60·00
10 c. mauve 42·00
48 c. brown £140

-96. *Wmk Crown CA* (*Nos.* 32/9).
a 2 c. rose-lake
2 c. carmine 2·00
3 4 c. slate-grey 5·50
5 c. blue 3·25
) 10 c. dull mauve 26·00
10 c. green 11·00
2 10 c. purple/*red* 3·75
3 30 c. green 32·00

. (*Nos.* 40/2).
4 20 c. on 30 c. orange-red 12·00
5 50 c. on 48 c. yellowish brown 45·00
6 $1 on 96 c. grey-olive 80·00

. (*Nos.* 43/4, 48/50).
7 7 c. on 10 c. green
8 14 c. on 30 c. mauve 85·00
9 20 c. on 30 c. green 18·00
) 50 c. on 48 c. dull purple 20·00
$1 on 96 c. purple/*red* 45·00

8. (*No.* 52).
3 $1 on 96 c. black 60·00

8. (*No.* 55).
4 10 c. on 30 c. green £180

0–01. *Wmk Crown CA* (*Nos.* 56/61).
5 2 c. dull green 3·25
6 4 c. carmine 3·75
7 5 c. yellow 14·00
8 10 c. ultramarine 3·25

3. *Wmk Crown CA* (*Nos.* 62/76).
1 1 c. dull purple and brown 4·00
2 2 c. dull green 3·25
3 4 c. purple/*red* 2·25
4 5 c. dull green and brown-orange 15·00
5 8 c. slate and violet 8·50
6 10 c. purple and blue/*blue* 3·50
7 12 c. green and purple/*yellow* 11·00
8 20 c. slate and chestnut 8·00
9 30 c. dull green and black 30·00
70 50 c. dull green and magenta 45·00

)4–06. *Wmk Mult Crown CA* (*Nos.* 77/90).
76 2 c. dull green 3·25
77 4 c. purple/*red* 2·25
78 5 c. dull green and brown-orange 10·00
79 8 c. slate and violet 8·00
80 10 c. purple and blue/*blue* 3·50
81 12 c. green and purple/*yellow* 15·00
82 20 c. slate and chestnut 7·50
83 30 c. dull green and black 25·00
84 50 c. green and magenta 23·00
85 $1 purple and sage-green 42·00

07–11. *Wmk Mult Crown CA* (*Nos.* 91/9).
90 1 c. brown 3·25
91 2 c. green 3·25
92 4 c. carmine-red 2·25
93 6 c. orange-vermilion and purple 13·00
94 10 c. bright ultramarine 3·00
95 20 c. purple and sage-green 60·00
96 30 c. purple and orange-yellow 42·00
97 50 c. black/*green* 32·00

12–15. *Wmk Mult Crown CA* (*Nos.* 100/16).
399 1 c. brown 3·50
400 2 c. green 3·50
401 4 c. red 2·25
402 6 c. orange 8·00
403 8 c. grey 17·00
404 10 c. ultramarine 3·25
406 20 c. purple and sage-green 4·75
407 25 c. purple and magenta (Type A)
408 30 c. purple and orange-yellow 8·00

POSTCARD STAMPS

379. (*Nos.* P1/2).
P413 3 c. on 16 c. yellow £500

POSTAL FISCAL STAMPS

874–1902. *Wmk Crown CC.* (*a*) *P* 15½×15 (*Nos.* F1/3)
F415 $2 olive-green £110
F416 $3 dull violet 95·00

HANKOW

Hankow, on the Yangtse River 600 miles from the sea, became a Treaty Port in 1860. A British consulate opened the following year, but no organised British postal agency was established until 1872.

Type **D** (*supplied* 1874) *used* 1874–1916
Type **B** ("D29") (*supplied* 1876) *used* 1878–83
Type **F** *used* 1916–22

Stamps of HONG KONG *cancelled at Hankow between* 1874 *and* 1916 *with postmarks detailed above.*

1862. *No wmk* (*Nos.* 1/7).
Z426 18 c. lilac £150

1863–71. *Wmk Crown CC* (*Nos.* 8/19).
Z427 2 c. brown 75·00
Z428 4 c. grey 75·00
Z429 6 c. lilac 90·00
Z430 8 c. orange 75·00
Z431 12 c. blue 27·00
Z432 18 c. lilac £650
Z433 24 c. green 90·00
Z435 30 c. mauve £100
Z436 48 c. rose £120
Z438 96 c. brownish grey

1876–77. (*Nos.* 20/1).
Z439 16 c. on 18 c. lilac £325
Z440 28 c. on 30 c. mauve £170

1877. *Wmk Crown CC* (*No.* 22).
Z441 16 c. yellow £150

1880. (*Nos.* 23/7).
Z442 5 c. on 8 c. orange £160
Z443 5 c. on 18 c. lilac £130
Z444 10 c. on 12 c. blue £140
Z445 10 c. on 16 c. yellow £275
Z446 10 c. on 24 c. green £160

1880. *Wmk Crown CC* (*Nos.* 28/31).
Z447 2 c. rose 60·00
Z448 5 c. blue 70·00
Z449 10 c. mauve 70·00
Z450 48 c. brown £190

1882–96. *Wmk Crown CA* (*Nos.* 32/9).
Z451 2 c. carmine 6·00
Z452 4 c. slate-grey 12·00
Z453 5 c. blue 6·50
Z454 10 c. dull mauve 48·00
Z455 10 c. green 8·00
Z456 10 c. purple/*red* 7·00
Z457 30 c. green 38·00

1885. (*Nos.* 40/2).
Z458 20 c. on 30 c. orange-red 21·00
Z459 50 c. on 48 c. yellowish brown 50·00
Z460 $1 on 96 c. grey-olive 95·00

1891. (*Nos.* 43/4, 48/50).
Z461 7 c. on 10 c. green 23·00
Z462 14 c. on 30 c. mauve 95·00
Z463 20 c. on 30 c. green 16·00
Z464 50 c. on 48 c. dull purple 16·00
Z465 $1 on 96 c. purple/*red* 45·00

1898. (*No.* 52).
Z467 $1 on 96 c. black 60·00

1898. (*No.* 55).
Z468 10 c. on 30 c. green £190

1900–01. *Wmk Crown CA* (*Nos.* 56/61).
Z469 2 c. dull green 4·00
Z470 4 c. carmine 4·00
Z471 5 c. yellow 17·00
Z472 10 c. ultramarine 5·00
Z473 12 c. blue 90·00
Z474 30 c. brown 50·00

1903. *Wmk Crown CA* (*Nos.* 62/76).
Z475 1 c. dull purple and brown 4·00
Z476 2 c. dull green 3·75
Z477 4 c. purple/*red* 3·25
Z478 5 c. dull green and brown-orange 14·00
Z479 8 c. slate and violet 11·00
Z480 10 c. purple and blue/*blue* 3·75
Z481 12 c. green and purple/*yellow* 13·00
Z482 20 c. slate and chestnut 9·00
Z483 30 c. dull green and black 30·00
Z484 50 c. dull green and magenta 50·00
Z485 $1 purple and sage-green 40·00

1904–06. *Wmk Mult Crown CA* (*Nos.* 77/90).
Z490 2 c. dull green 3·75
Z491 4 c. purple/*red* 3·25
Z492 5 c. dull green and brown-orange 14·00
Z493 8 c. slate and violet 8·00
Z494 10 c. purple and blue/*blue* 3·75
Z495 12 c. green and purple/*yellow* 16·00
Z496 20 c. slate and chestnut 14·00
Z497 30 c. dull green and black 25·00
Z498 50 c. green and magenta 20·00
Z499 $1 purple and sage-green 42·00

1907–11. *Wmk Mult Crown CA* (*Nos.* 91/9).
Z504 1 c. brown 3·75
Z505 2 c. green 3·75
Z506 4 c. carmine-red 2·50
Z507 6 c. orange-vermilion and purple 16·00
Z508 10 c. bright ultramarine 3·75
Z509 20 c. purple and sage-green 65·00
Z510 30 c. purple and orange-yellow 45·00

1912–15. *Wmk Mult Crown CA* (*Nos.* 100/16).
Z513 1 c. brown 4·25
Z514 2 c. green 4·25
Z515 4 c. red 3·25
Z516 6 c. orange 8·00
Z518 10 c. ultramarine 3·75
Z520 20 c. purple and sage-green 9·50
Z522 30 c. purple and orange-yellow 14·00
Z523 50 c. black/*green* 8·50
Z527 $5 green and red/*green* £375

POSTCARD STAMPS

1879. (*Nos.* P1/2).
ZP528 3 c. on 16 c. yellow £800

POSTAL FISCAL STAMPS

1874–1902. *Wmk Crown CC.* (*a*) *P* 15½×15 (*Nos.* F1/3)
ZF529 $2 olive-green £150
(*b*) *P* 14 (*Nos.* F4/6)
ZF532 $2 dull bluish green

1897. (*No.* F11)
ZF533 $1 on $2 dull bluish green £400

KIUNGCHOW (HOIHOW)

Kiungchow, a city on the island of Hainan, and its port of Hoihow was added to the Treaty Port system in 1860. A consular postal agency was opened at Kiungchow in 1876, being transferred to Hoihow in 1878. A second agency was opened at Kiungchow in 1879.

Type **B** ("D28") (*supplied* 1876) *used* 1879–83
Type **D** (inscr "KIUNG-CHOW") (*supplied* 1876) *used* 1879–81

A
28 JA85
KIUNG-CHOW

"REGISTERED KIUNG-CHOW" with "REGISTERED" removed (*originally supplied* 1876) *used* 1883–85
Type **D** (inscr "HOIHOW") *used* 1885–1922

Stamps of HONG KONG *cancelled at Kiungchow* (*Hoihow*) *between* 1879 *and* 1916 *with postmarks detailed above.*

1863–71. *Wmk Crown CC* (*Nos.* 8/19).
Z540 2 c. brown £750
Z541 4 c. grey £500
Z542 6 c. lilac £850
Z543 8 c. orange £550
Z544 12 c. blue £550
Z546 24 c. green £750
Z547 30 c. vermilion
Z548 30 c. mauve £700
Z549 48 c. rose £750
Z551 96 c. brownish grey £900

1876–77. (*Nos.* 20/1).
Z552 16 c. on 18 c. lilac £750
Z553 28 c. on 30 c. mauve £600

1877. (*No.* 22)
Z554 16 c. yellow £950

1880. (*Nos.* 23/7).
Z555 5 c. on 8 c. orange £550
Z556 5 c. on 18 c. lilac £550
Z557 10 c. on 12 c. blue £550
Z558 10 c. on 16 c. yellow £1000
Z559 10 c. on 24 c. green

1880. *Wmk Crown CC* (*Nos.* 28/31).
Z561 5 c. blue £475
Z562 10 c. mauve £650

1882–96. *Wmk Crown CA* (*Nos.* 32/9).
Z564 2 c. carmine 38·00
Z565 4 c. slate-grey 48·00
Z566 5 c. blue 38·00
Z567 10 c. dull mauve £400
Z568 10 c. green 45·00
Z569 10 c. purple/*red* 38·00
Z570 30 c. green 75·00

1885. (*Nos.* 40/2).
Z571 20 c. on 30 c. orange-red .. .. .. 80·00
Z572 50 c. on 48 c. yellowish brown .. .. .. 85·00
Z573 $1 on 96 c. grey-olive £140

1891. (*Nos.* 43/4, 48/50).
Z574 7 c. on 10 c. green £150
Z576 20 c. on 30 c. green .. .. .. 38·00
Z577 50 c. on 48 c. dull purple .. .. .. 48·00
Z578 $1 on 96 c. purple/*red* .. .. .. 95·00

1891. *50th Anniv of Colony* (*No.* 51).
Z579 2 c. carmine .. ..

1898. (*No.* 52).
Z580 $1 on 96 c. black £180

1898. (*No.* 55).
Z581 10 c. on 30 c. green £400

1900–01. *Wmk Crown CA* (*Nos.* 56/61).
Z582 2 c. dull green .. .. .. 50·00
Z583 4 c. carmine .. .. .. 25·00
Z584 5 c. yellow .. .. .. 55·00
Z585 10 c. ultramarine .. .. .. 28·00
Z587 30 c. brown £120

1903. *Wmk Crown CA* (*Nos.* 62/76).
Z588 1 c. dull purple and brown .. .. .. 19·00
Z589 2 c. dull green .. .. .. 19·00
Z590 4 c. purple/*red* .. .. .. 14·00
Z591 5 c. dull green and brown-orange .. .. 32·00
Z592 8 c. slate and violet .. .. .. 30·00
Z593 10 c. purple and blue/*blue* .. .. .. 16·00
Z594 12 c. green and purple/*yellow* .. .. 38·00
Z597 50 c. dull green and magenta .. ..
Z598 $1 purple and sage-green .. .. .. 85·00

1904–06. *Wmk Mult Crown CA* (*Nos.* 77/90).
Z603 2 c. dull green .. .. .. 17·00
Z604 4 c. purple/*red* .. .. .. 14·00
Z605 5 c. dull green and brown-orange .. .. 32·00
Z606 8 c. slate and violet .. .. .. 21·00
Z607 10 c. purple and blue/*blue* .. .. .. 15·00
Z608 12 c. green and purple/*yellow* .. .. 35·00
Z609 20 c. slate and chestnut .. .. .. 42·00
Z610 30 c. dull green and black .. .. .. 55·00

1907–11. *Wmk Mult Crown CA* (*Nos.* 91/9).
Z617 1 c. brown .. .. .. 17·00
Z618 2 c. green .. .. .. 16·00
Z619 4 c. carmine-red .. .. .. 14·00
Z620 6 c. orange-vermilion and purple .. .. 35·00
Z621 10 c. bright ultramarine .. .. .. 15·00
Z622 20 c. purple and sage-green .. .. .. 65·00

1912–15. *Wmk Mult Crown CA* (*Nos.* 100/16).
Z625 1 c. brown .. .. .. 16·00
Z626 2 c. green .. .. .. 15·00
Z627 4 c. red .. .. .. 14·00
Z628 6 c. orange .. .. .. 20·00
Z629 8 c. grey .. .. ..
Z630 10 c. ultramarine .. .. .. 14·00
Z631 12 c. purple/*yellow* .. .. .. 35·00
Z632 20 c. purple and sage-green .. .. .. 28·00
Z633 25 c. purple and magenta (Type A) .. .. 60·00
Z635 50 c. black/*green* .. .. .. 42·00
Z636 $1 purple and blue/*blue* .. .. .. 45·00

POSTAL FISCAL STAMPS

1874–1902. *Wmk Crown CC.* (*a*) *P* 15½×15 (*Nos.* F1/3)
ZF641 $2 olive-green £160
(*b*) *P* 14 (*Nos.* F4/6)
ZF644 $2 dull bluish green £325

1897. (*Nos.* F10/11)
ZF650 $1 on $2 olive-green £300

NINGPO

Ningpo was one of the 1842 Treaty Ports and a consular postal agency was established there in 1844.

Type **A** ("N1") (*supplied* 1866) *used* 1870–82
Type **C** (*supplied* 1866) *used* 1870–99
Type **D** *used* 1899–1922

Stamps of HONG KONG *cancelled at Ningpo between* 1866 *and* 1916 *with postmarks detailed above.*

1862. *No wmk* (*Nos.* 1/7).
Z652 18 c. lilac £300

1863–71. *Wmk Crown CC* (*Nos.* 8/19).
Z653 2 c. brown £150
Z654 4 c. grey £150
a. Perf 12½ .. .. ..
Z655 6 c. lilac £180
Z656 8 c. orange £140
Z657 12 c. blue £100
Z658 18 c. lilac .. .. ..
Z659 24 c. green £180
Z660 30 c. vermilion £190
Z661 30 c. mauve .. .. .. 90·00
Z662 48 c. rose £250
Z663 96 c. olive-bistre .. .. ..
Z664 96 c. brownish grey £300

1876–77. (*Nos.* 20/1).
Z665 16 c. on 18 c. lilac £400
Z666 28 c. on 30 c. mauve £200

1877. *Wmk Crown CC* (*No.* 22).
Z667 16 c. yellow £200

1880. (*Nos.* 23/7).
Z668 5 c. on 8 c. orange £250
Z669 5 c. on 18 c. lilac £225
Z670 10 c. on 12 c. blue £250
Z672 10 c. on 24 c. green £250

1880. *Wmk Crown CC* (*Nos.* 28/31).
Z674 5 c. blue £120
Z675 10 c. mauve £120
Z676 48 c. brown £400

1882–96. *Wmk Crown CA* (*Nos.* 32/9).
Z677 2 c. carmine .. .. .. 30·00
Z678 4 c. slate-grey .. .. .. 42·00
Z679 5 c. blue .. .. .. 30·00
Z680 10 c. dull mauve £120
Z681 10 c. green .. .. .. 32·00
Z682 10 c. purple/*red* .. .. .. 32·00
Z683 30 c. green .. .. .. 65·00

1885. (*Nos.* 40/2).
Z685 50 c. on 48 c. yellowish brown .. .. 75·00

1891. (*Nos.* 43/4, 48/50).
Z686 7 c. on 10 c. green .. .. .. 38·00
Z687 14 c. on 30 c. mauve .. .. ..
Z688 20 c. on 30 c. green .. .. .. 26·00
Z689 50 c. on 48 c. dull purple .. .. .. 42·00
Z690 $1 on 96 c. purple/*red* .. .. .. 75·00

1898. (*No.* 52).
Z692 $1 on 96 c. black .. .. .. 85·00

1898. (*No.* 55).
Z693 10 c. on 30 c. green £200

1900–01. *Wmk Crown CA* (*Nos.* 56/61).
Z694 2 c. dull green .. .. .. 17·00
Z695 4 c. carmine .. .. .. 16·00
Z697 10 c. ultramarine .. .. .. 17·00

1903. *Wmk Crown CA* (*Nos.* 62/76).
Z700 1 c. dull purple and brown .. .. .. 16·00
Z701 2 c. dull green .. .. .. 16·00
Z702 4 c. purple/*red* .. .. .. 12·00
Z703 5 c. dull green and brown-orange .. .. 30·00
Z704 8 c. slate and violet .. .. .. 18·00
Z705 10 c. purple and blue/*blue* .. .. .. 14·00
Z706 12 c. green and purple/*yellow* .. .. 38·00
Z709 50 c. dull green and magenta .. .. 55·00

1904–06. *Wmk Mult Crown CA* (*Nos.* 77/90).
Z715 2 c. dull green .. .. .. 16·00
Z716 4 c. purple/*red* .. .. .. 14·00
Z718 8 c. slate and violet .. .. .. 27·00
Z720 12 c. green and purple/*yellow* .. .. 38·00
Z721 20 c. slate and chestnut .. .. .. 38·00
Z722 30 c. dull green and black .. .. .. 48·00
Z724 $1 purple and sage-green .. .. .. 60·00

1907–11. *Wmk Mult Crown CA* (*Nos.* 91/9).
Z729 1 c. brown .. .. .. 13·00
Z730 2 c. green .. .. .. 13·00
Z731 4 c. carmine-red .. .. .. 11·00
Z733 10 c. bright ultramarine .. .. .. 12·00
Z734 20 c. purple and sage-green .. .. .. 75·00
Z735 30 c. purple and orange-yellow .. .. 55·00

1912–15. *Wmk Mult Crown CA* (*Nos.* 100/16).
Z738 1 c. brown .. .. .. 14·00
Z739 2 c. green .. .. .. 13·00
Z740 4 c. red .. .. .. 12·00
Z742 8 c. grey .. .. .. 38·00
Z743 10 c. ultramarine .. .. .. 13·00
Z745 20 c. purple and sage-green .. .. ..
Z747 30 c. purple and orange-yellow .. .. ..
Z749 $1 purple and blue/*blue* .. .. .. 38·00

POSTCARD STAMPS

1879. (*Nos.* P1/2).
ZP751 3 c. on 16 c. yellow £750

POSTAL FISCAL STAMPS

1874–1902. *Wmk Crown CC.* (*a*) *P* 15½×15 (*Nos.* F1/3)
ZF754 $2 olive-green £180

1881. (*No.* F7).
ZF760 12 c. on $10 rose-carmine .. .. ..

1897. (*No.* F10).
ZF763 $1 on $2 olive-green .. ..

SHANGHAI

Shanghai was one of the original Treaty Ports of 1842 packet agency was opened at the British consulate in 1844. It moved to a separate premises in 1861 and was upg to a Post Office in September 1867.

British military post offices operated in Shanghai from until 1940.

Type **D** (inscr "SHANGHAE" (*supplied* 1861) *used* 1861-

Sunburst *used* 1864–65
Type **A** ("S1") (*supplied* 1866) *used* 1866–85
Type **D** (inscr "SHANGHAI") (*supplied* 1885) *used* 1906
Type **G** (inscr "B.P.O." at foot) (*supplied* 1904) *used* 1904
Type **G** (inscr "Br.P.O." at foot) (*supplied* 1907) 1907–22
Type **E** (figures "I" to "VIII" at foot) *used* 1912–22

Stamps of HONG KONG *cancelled at Shanghai between and* 1916 *with postmarks detailed above.*

1862. *No wmk* (*Nos.* 1/7).
Z765 2 c. brown 9
Z766 8 c. yellow-buff 8
Z767 12 c. pale greenish blue 6
Z768 18 c. lilac 5
Z769 24 c. green .. .. ..
Z770 48 c. rose .. .. ..
Z771 96 c. brownish grey .. .. ..

1863–71. *Wmk Crown CC* (*Nos.* 8/19).
Z772 2 c. brown .. .. ..
Z773 4 c. grey .. .. ..
a. Perf 12½ .. .. ..
Z774 6 c. lilac 1
Z775 8 c. orange 1
Z776 12 c. blue .. .. ..
Z777 18 c. lilac .. .. .. £
Z778 24 c. green .. .. ..
Z779 30 c. vermilion 1
Z780 30 c. mauve .. .. ..
Z781 48 c. rose 2
Z782 96 c. olive-bistre .. .. .. £
Z783 96 c. brownish grey 4

1876–77. (*Nos.* 20/1).
Z784 16 c. on 18 c. lilac .. .. .. £
Z785 28 c. on 30 c. mauve 55

1877. *Wmk Crown CC* (*No.* 22).
Z786 16 c. yellow 70

1880. (*Nos.* 23/7).
Z787 5 c. on 8 c. orange 95
Z788 5 c. on 18 c. lilac 60
Z789 10 c. on 12 c. blue 55
Z790 10 c. on 16 c. yellow .. .. .. £
Z791 10 c. on 24 c. green 85

1880. *Wmk Crown CC* (*Nos.* 28/31).
Z792 2 c. rose 22
Z793 5 c. blue 38
Z794 10 c. mauve 16
Z795 48 c. brown £1

1882–96. *Wmk Crown CA* (*Nos.* 32/9).
Z795*a* 2 c. rose-lake .. .. ..
Z796 2 c. carmine 1
Z797 4 c. slate-grey 1
Z798 5 c. blue 1
Z799 10 c. dull mauve 13
Z800 10 c. green 1
Z801 10 c. purple/*red* 1
Z802 30 c. green 20

1885. (*Nos.* 40/2).
Z803 20 c. on 30 c. orange-red 6
Z804 50 c. on 48 c. yellowish brown .. .. 32·
Z805 $1 on 96 c. grey-olive .. .. 65·

1891. (*Nos.* 43/44, 46/50).
Z806 7 c. on 10 c. green .. .. .. 11·
Z807 14 c. on 30 c. mauve .. .. .. 60·
Z807*a* 50 c. on 48 c. dull purple (No. 46) £3
Z807*b* $1 on 96 c. purple/*red* (No. 47) £4
Z808 20 c. on 30 c. green .. .. .. 6·
Z809 50 c. on 48 c. dull purple (No. 49) .. .. 6·
Z810 $1 on 96 c. purple/*red* (No. 50) .. .. 24·

1898. (*No.* 52).
Z812 $1 on 96 c. black .. .. .. 30·

1898. (*No.* 55).
Z813 10 c. on 30 c. green .. .. .. 80·

-01. *Wmk Crown CA* (*Nos.* 56/61).
2 c. dull green .. 1·10
4 c. carmine .. 1·10
5 c. yellow .. 7·50
10 c. ultramarine .. 2·25
12 c. blue .. 60·00
30 c. brown .. 26·00

Wmk Crown CA (*Nos.* 62/76).
1 c. dull purple and brown .. 75
2 c. dull green .. 1·75
4 c. purple/*red* .. 60
5 c. dull green and brown-orange .. 10·00
8 c. slate and violet .. 1·75
10 c. purple and blue/*blue* .. 1·75
12 c. green and purple/*yellow* .. 5·00
20 c. slate and chestnut .. 4·00
30 c. dull green and black .. 24·00
50 c. dull green and magenta .. 38·00
$1 purple and sage-green .. 25·00
$3 slate and dull blue .. £375
$5 purple and blue-green .. £475
$10 slate and orange/*blue* .. £500

-06. *Wmk Mult Crown CA* (*Nos.* 77/90).
2 c. dull green .. 1·75
4 c. purple/*red* .. 60
5 c. dull green and brown-orange .. 6·50
8 c. slate and violet .. 2·50
10 c. purple and blue/*blue* .. 1·50
12 c. green and purple/*yellow* .. 7·00
20 c. slate and chestnut .. 2·75
30 c. dull green and black .. 20·00
50 c. green and magenta .. 9·50
$1 purple and sage-green .. 23·00
$2 slate and scarlet .. 95·00
$3 slate and dull blue .. £225
$5 purple and blue-green .. £350
$10 slate and orange/*blue* .. £850

-11. *Wmk Mult Crown CA* (*Nos.* 91/9).
9 1 c. brown .. 1·25
0 2 c. green .. 1·90
1 4 c. carmine-red .. 60
2 6 c. orange-vermilion and purple .. 4·25
3 10 c. bright ultramarine .. 60
4 20 c. purple and sage-green .. 45·00
5 30 c. purple and orange-yellow .. 24·00
6 50 c. black/*green* .. 17·00
7 $2 carmine-red and black .. £275

2–15. *Wmk Mult Crown CA* (*Nos.* 100/16).
8 1 c. brown .. 70
9 2 c. green .. 45
0 4 c. red .. 45
1 6 c. orange .. 1·10
2 8 c. grey .. 7·50
3 10 c. ultramarine .. 45
4 12 c. purple/*yellow* .. 7·00
5 20 c. purple and sage-green .. 1·10
7 30 c. purple and orange-yellow .. 6·00
8 50 c. black/*green* .. 2·25
9 $1 purple and blue/*blue* .. 3·00

POSTCARD STAMPS

9. (*Nos.* P1/2).
871 3 c. on 16 c. yellow .. £350
872 5 c. on 18 c. lilac .. £350

POSTAL FISCAL STAMPS

74–1902. *Wmk Crown CC.* (*a*) *P* 15½×15 (*Nos.* F1/5)
874 $2 olive-green .. 55·00
875 $3 dull violet .. 38·00
876 $10 rose-carmine .. £700

(*b*) *P* 14
877 $2 dull bluish green .. £250
878 $3 dull mauve .. £400

81. (*No.* F7).
880 12 c. on $10 rose-carmine .. £300

91. (*No.* F9).
882 $5 on $10 purple/*red* .. £120

97. (*No.* F10/11).
883 $1 on $2 olive-green .. £150
884 $1 on $2 dull bluish green .. £200

SWATOW

Swatow became a Treaty Port in 1860 and a consular packet gency was opened in the area made available for foreign firms uring the following year. In 1867 the original agency was ansferred to the Chinese city on the other side of the Han ver, but a second agency was subsequently opened in the reign concession during 1883.

Type **A** ("S2") (*supplied* 1866) *used* 1875–85
Type **C** (*supplied* 1866) *used* 1866–90
Type **D** (*supplied* 1883) *used* 1884–1922
Type **F** *used* 1916–22

Stamps of HONG KONG *cancelled at Swatow between* 1866 *and* 1916 *with postmarks detailed above.*

862. *No wmk* (*Nos.* 1/7).
885 18 c. lilac .. £180

1863–71. *Wmk Crown CC* (*Nos.* 8/19).
Z886 2 c. brown .. 90·00
Z887 4 c. grey .. 90·00
a. Perf 12½ ..
Z888 6 c. lilac .. £350
Z889 8 c. orange .. 95·00
Z890 12 c. blue .. 40·00
Z891 18 c. lilac .. £650
Z892 24 c. green .. 95·00
Z893 30 c. vermilion ..
Z894 30 c. mauve .. 40·00
Z895 48 c. rose .. £110
Z897 96 c. brownish grey .. £500

1876–77. (*Nos.* 20/1).
Z898 16 c. on 18 c. lilac .. £375
Z899 28 c. on 30 c. mauve .. £170

1877. *Wmk Crown CC* (*No.* 22).
Z900 16 c. yellow .. £350

1880. (*Nos.* 23/7).
Z901 5 c. on 8 c. orange .. £170
Z902 5 c. on 18 c. lilac .. £160
Z903 10 c. on 12 c. blue .. £170
Z904 10 c. on 16 c. yellow .. £325
Z905 10 c. on 24 c. green .. £225

1880. *Wmk Crown CC* (*Nos.* 28/31).
Z906 2 c. rose .. 80·00
Z907 5 c. blue .. 80·00
Z908 10 c. mauve .. 95·00

1882–96. *Wmk Crown CA* (*Nos.* 32/9).
Z910 2 c. carmine .. 4·75
Z911 4 c. slate-grey .. 14·00
Z912 5 c. blue .. 5·50
Z913 10 c. dull mauve .. 60·00
Z914 10 c. green .. 7·00
Z915 10 c. purple/*red* .. 4·75
Z916 30 c. green .. 35·00

1885. (*Nos.* 40/2).
Z917 20 c. on 30 c. orange-red .. 9·50

1891. (*Nos.* 43/4, 47/50).
Z919 7 c. on 10 c. green .. 18·00
Z920 14 c. on 30 c. mauve .. 85·00
Z921 $1 on 96 c. purple/*red* (No. 47) .. £450
Z922 20 c. on 30 c. green .. 16·00
Z923 50 c. on 48 c. dull purple .. 17·00
Z924 $1 on 96 c. purple/*red* (No. 50) .. 38·00

1891. *50th Anniv of Colony* (*No.* 51).
Z925 2 c. carmine .. £850

1898. (*No.* 52).
Z926 $1 on 96 c. black .. 50·00

1898. (*No.* 55).
Z927 10 c. on 30 c. green .. £160

1900–01. *Wmk Crown CA* (*Nos.* 56/61).
Z928 2 c. dull green .. 5·50
Z929 4 c. carmine .. 4·25
Z930 5 c. yellow .. 16·00
Z931 10 c. ultramarine .. 4·75
Z933 30 c. brown .. 40·00

1903. *Wmk Crown CA* (*Nos.* 62/76).
Z934 1 c. dull purple and brown .. 4·50
Z935 2 c. dull green .. 4·50
Z936 4 c. purple/*red* .. 3·50
Z937 5 c. dull green and brown-orange .. 13·00
Z938 8 c. slate and violet .. 8·00
Z939 10 c. purple and blue/*blue* .. 4·50
Z940 12 c. green and purple/*yellow* .. 11·00
Z941 20 c. slate and chestnut .. 6·50
Z942 30 c. dull green and black .. 30·00

1904–06. *Wmk Mult Crown CA* (*Nos.* 77/90).
Z949 2 c. dull green .. 4·50
Z950 4 c. purple/*red* .. 3·50
Z951 5 c. dull green and brown-orange .. 13·00
Z952 8 c. slate and violet .. 8·00
Z953 10 c. purple and blue/*blue* .. 4·25
Z954 12 c. green and purple/*yellow* .. 11·00
Z955 20 c. slate and chestnut .. 8·00
Z956 30 c. dull green and black .. 27·00
Z957 50 c. green and magenta .. 20·00
Z958 $1 purple and sage-green .. 45·00
Z959 $2 slate and scarlet .. £160
Z962 $10 slate and orange/*blue* .. £1000

1907–11. *Wmk Mult Crown CA* (*Nos.* 91/9).
Z963 1 c. brown .. 5·00
Z964 2 c. green .. 5·00
Z965 4 c. carmine-red .. 3·75
Z966 6 c. orange-vermilion and purple .. 9·50
Z967 10 c. bright ultramarine .. 4·25
Z969 30 c. purple and orange-yellow .. 42·00
Z970 50 c. black/*green* .. 27·00

1912–15. *Wmk Mult Crown CA* (*Nos.* 100/16).
Z972 1 c. brown .. 3·75
Z973 2 c. green .. 3·75
Z974 4 c. red .. 3·25
Z975 6 c. orange .. 5·00
Z976 8 c. grey .. 16·00
Z977 10 c. ultramarine .. 3·00
Z978 12 c. purple/*yellow* .. 9·50
Z979 20 c. purple and sage-green .. 4·50
Z980 25 c. purple and magenta (Type A) .. 32·00
Z981 30 c. purple and orange-yellow .. 14·00
Z982 50 c. black/*green* .. 7·00
Z983 $1 purple and blue/*blue* .. 13·00

POSTCARD STAMPS

1879. (*Nos.* P1/2).
ZP986 3 c. on 16 c. yellow .. £750

POSTAL FISCAL STAMPS

1874–1902. *Wmk Crown CC.* (*a*) *P* 15½×15 (*Nos.* F1/3)
ZF988 $2 olive-green .. 90·00
ZF989 $3 dull violet .. 80·00

(*b*) *P* 14
ZF991 $2 dull bluish green .. £300

TIENTSIN

Tientsin became a Treaty Port in 1860. A British consulate was established in 1861, but no formal postal agency was organised there until 1882. It was not, however, very successful and was closed during 1890. The British Post Office reopened on 1 October 1906 under the management of the Chinese Engineering and Mining Company.

British military post offices operated in Tientsin from 1927 until 1940.

Type **E** *used* 1906–13
Type **G** (*supplied* 1907) *used* 1907–22

Stamps of HONG KONG *cancelled at Tientsin between* 1906 *and* 1916 *with postmarks detailed above.*

1903. *Wmk Crown CA* (*Nos.* 62/76).
Z 998 1 c. dull purple and brown .. 8·50
Z 999 5 c. dull green and brown-orange .. 20·00
Z1000 8 c. slate and violet .. 8·00

1904–06. *Wmk Mult Crown CA* (*Nos.* 77/90).
Z1001 2 c. dull green .. 4·25
Z1002 4 c. purple/*red* .. 3·25
Z1003 5 c. dull green and brown-orange .. 11·00
Z1004 8 c. slate and violet .. 8·50
Z1005 10 c. purple and blue/*blue* .. 3·75
Z1006 12 c. green and purple/*yellow* .. 13·00
Z1007 20 c. slate and chestnut .. 8·50
Z1008 30 c. dull green and black .. 25·00
Z1009 50 c. green and magenta .. 19·00
Z1010 $1 purple and sage-green .. 35·00
Z1011 $2 slate and scarlet .. £150
Z1013 $5 purple and blue-green .. £450
Z1014 $10 slate and orange/*blue* .. £1000

1907–11. *Wmk Mult Crown CA* (*Nos.* 91/9).
Z1015 1 c. brown .. 4·25
Z1016 2 c. green .. 3·50
Z1017 4 c. carmine-red .. 2·75
Z1018 6 c. orange-vermilion and purple .. 13·00
Z1019 10 c. bright ultramarine .. 3·25
Z1020 20 c. purple and sage-green .. 60·00
Z1021 30 c. purple and orange-yellow .. 45·00
Z1022 50 c. black/*green* .. 35·00

1912–15. *Wmk Mult Crown CA* (*Nos.* 100/16).
Z1024 1 c. brown .. 3·50
Z1025 2 c. green .. 3·50
Z1026 4 c. red .. 2·50
Z1027 6 c. orange .. 4·75
Z1028 8 c. grey .. 20·00
Z1029 10 c. ultramarine .. 4·00
Z1031 20 c. purple and sage-green .. 6·50
Z1033 30 c. purple and orange-yellow .. 10·00
Z1034 50 c. black/*green* .. 6·00
Z1035 $1 purple and blue/*blue* .. 8·00
Z1037 $3 green and purple .. £110

WEI HAI WEI

The territory of Wei Hai Wei was leased from the Chinese by the British Government from 24 May 1898 having been previously occupied by the Japanese. At that time there were no organised postal services from the area, although a private local post did operate between the port and Chefoo from 8 December 1898 until 15 March 1899. A Chinese Imperial post office opened in March 1899 to be followed by a British postal agency on the offshore island of Liu Kung Tau on 1 September 1899. A second British agency opened at Port Edward on 1 April 1904.

Liu Kung Tau oval *used* 1899–1901
Type **D** (inscr "LIU KUNG TAU") (*supplied* 1899) *used* 1901–30

Stamps of HONG KONG *cancelled at Liu Kung Tau between* 1899 *and* 1916 *with postmarks detailed above.*

1863–71. *Wmk Crown CC* (*Nos.* 8/19).
Z1039 12 c. pale blue

1882–96. *Wmk Crown CA* (*Nos.* 32/9).
Z1040 2 c. carmine .. 35·00
Z1041 4 c. slate-grey .. 48·00
Z1042 5 c. blue .. 35·00
Z1043 10 c. purple/*red* .. 22·00
Z1044 30 c. green .. 42·00

1891. (*Nos.* 48/50).
Z1045 20 c. on 30 c. green .. 28·00
Z1046 50 c. on 48 c. dull purple .. 28·00

1898. (*No.* 52).
Z1047 $1 on 96 c. black .. 60·00

1900–01. *Wmk Crown CA* (*Nos.* 56/61).
Z1049 2 c. dull green .. 5·50
Z1050 4 c. carmine .. 5·50
Z1051 5 c. yellow .. 17·00
Z1052 10 c. ultramarine .. 5·50
Z1053 12 c. blue .. 80·00
Z1054 30 c. brown .. 48·00

1903. *Wmk Crown CA* (*Nos.* 62/76).
Z1055 1 c. dull purple and brown .. 4·75
Z1056 2 c. dull green .. 4·00
Z1057 4 c. purple/*red* .. 4·00
Z1058 5 c. dull green and brown-orange .. 13·00
Z1059 8 c. slate and violet .. 8·50
Z1060 10 c. purple and blue/*blue* .. 6·50
Z1061 12 c. green and purple/*yellow* .. 18·00
Z1062 20 c. slate and chestnut .. 8·50
Z1063 30 c. dull green and black .. 29·00
Z1064 50 c. dull green and magenta .. 55·00
Z1065 $1 purple and sage-green .. 42·00

1904–06. *Wmk Mult Crown CA* (*Nos.* 77/90).
Z1070 2 c. dull green .. 4·50
Z1071 4 c. purple/*red* .. 4·00
Z1073 8 c. slate and violet .. 7·50
Z1076 20 c. slate and chestnut
Z1078 50 c. green and magenta .. 38·00

1907–11. *Wmk Mult Crown CA* (*Nos.* 91/9).
Z1084 1 c. brown .. 4·50
Z1085 2 c. green .. 4·50
Z1086 4 c. carmine-red .. 3·75
Z1088 10 c. bright ultramarine .. 4·00
Z1089 20 c. purple and sage-green .. 60·00
Z1090 30 c. purple and orange-yellow .. 45·00
Z1091 50 c. black/*green* .. 38·00

1912–15. *Wmk Mult Crown CA* (*Nos.* 100/16).
Z1093 1 c. brown .. 4·75
Z1094 2 c. green .. 3·75
Z1095 4 c. red .. 3·50
Z1096 6 c. orange .. 7·00
Z1097 8 c. grey .. 19·00
Z1098 10 c. ultramarine .. 4·00
Z1104 $1 purple and blue/*blue* .. 17·00

POSTAL FISCAL STAMPS

1874–1902. *Wmk Crown CC.* (*b*) *P* 14 (*Nos.* F4/6)
Z1106 $2 dull bluish green .. £650

PORT EDWARD
13 JUL 1904
WEI-HAI-WEI

Port Edward rectangle used 1904–08
Type **D** (inscr "WEI-HAI-WEI" at top and "PORT EDWARD" at foot) (*supplied* 1907) used 1907–30

Stamps of HONG KONG *cancelled at Port Edward between* 1904 *and* 1916 *with postmarks detailed above.*

1900–01. *Wmk Crown CA* (*Nos.* 56/61).
Z1109 2 c. dull green .. 48·00
Z1110 10 c. ultramarine .. 50·00

1903. *Wmk Crown CA* (*Nos.* 62/76).
Z1111 1 c. dull purple and brown .. 17·00
Z1112 2 c. dull green .. 17·00
Z1113 4 c. purple/*red* .. 15·00
Z1114 5 c. dull green and brown-orange .. 22·00
Z1115 8 c. slate and violet .. 22·00
Z1116 10 c. purple and blue/*blue* .. 18·00
Z1117 12 c. green and purple/*yellow* .. 29·00
Z1118 20 c. slate and chestnut .. 45·00
Z1119 30 c. dull green and black .. 42·00
Z1120 50 c. dull green and magenta .. 50·00
Z1121 $1 purple and sage-green .. 48·00

1904–06. *Wmk Mult Crown CA* (*Nos.* 77/90).
Z1126 2 c. dull green .. 9·50
Z1127 4 c. purple/*red* .. 9·00
Z1128 5 c. dull green and brown-orange .. 15·00
Z1129 8 c. slate and violet .. 10·00
Z1132 20 c. slate and chestnut .. 45·00
Z1133 30 c. dull green and black .. 38·00
Z1134 50 c. green and magenta .. 42·00

1907–11. *Wmk Mult Crown CA* (*Nos.* 91/9).
Z1140 1 c. brown .. 9·50
Z1141 2 c. green .. 9·50
Z1142 4 c. carmine-red .. 6·50
Z1143 6 c. orange-vermilion and purple
Z1144 10 c. bright ultramarine .. 7·50

1912–15. *Wmk Mult Crown CA* (*Nos.* 100/16).
Z1151 1 c. brown .. 8·00
Z1152 2 c. green .. 6·50
Z1153 4 c. red .. 4·25
Z1155 8 c. grey .. 17·00
Z1156 10 c. ultramarine .. 4·25
Z1158 20 c. purple and sage-green .. 11·00
Z1161 50 c. black/*green* .. 11·00
Z1162 $1 purple and blue/*blue* .. 12·00

PRICES FOR STAMPS ON COVER	
Nos. 1/14	*from* × 50
Nos. 15/17	—
Nos. 18/28	*from* × 30

The overprinted stamps Nos. 1/17 were introduced on 1 January 1917 to prevent currency speculation in the Treaty Ports. They were used in the then-existing agencies of Amoy, Canton, Chefoo, Foochow, Hankow, Hoihow, Ningpo, Shanghai, Swatow, Tientsin and were also supplied to the British naval base of Wei Hai Wei.

CHINA

(1)

1917 (1 Jan)–**21.** *Stamps of Hong Kong,* 1912–21 (*wmk Mult Crown CA*), *optd with T* **1**, *at Somerset House.*

1	1 c. brown	3·00	1·50
	a. Black-brown	2·50	2·50
	b. Crown broken at right	£300	£350
	c. Wmk sideways	†	£2500
	w. Wmk inverted	†	—
2	2 c. green	4·00	30
3	4 c. carmine-red	3·75	30
4	6 c. orange	4·00	60
5	8 c. slate	10·00	1·25
6	10 c. ultramarine	9·50	30
	y. Wmk inverted and reversed	†	£350
7	12 c. purple/*yellow*	7·50	2·50
8	20 c. purple and sage-green	11·00	60
9	25 c. purple and magenta (A)	7·50	15·00
11	30 c. purple and orange-yellow	26·00	5·00
12	50 c. black/*blue-green* (*olive back*)	50·00	1·50
	a. Emerald surface (1917?)	35·00	8·50
	b. On emerald back (1919)	26·00	5·50
	c. On white back (1920)	£275	60·00
13	$1 reddish purple and bright blue/*blue*	65·00	2·50
	a. Grey-purple and blue/blue (1921)	65·00	7·00
14	$2 carmine-red and grey-black	£190	50·00
15	$3 green and purple	£400	£170
16	$5 green and red/*blue-green* (*olive back*)	£350	£225
17	$10 purple and black/*red*	£850	£425
1/17	*Set of* 16	£1800	£800
12s/17s	H/S "Specimen" *Set of* 6	£1700	

1922 (Mar)–**27.** *As last, but wmk Mult Script CA.*

18	1 c. brown	1·75	3·50
19	2 c. green	2·75	2·25
	w. Wmk inverted	£120	
20	4 c. carmine-rose	4·00	2·00
	a. Lower Chinese character at right broken at top	£160	£140
21	6 c. orange-yellow	3·75	4·25
22	8 c. grey	5·50	13·00
23	10 c. bright ultramarine	7·00	2·75
	w. Wmk inverted	£120	
24	20 c. purple and sage-green	11·00	5·00
25	25 c. purple and magenta (B)	17·00	60·00
	a. Broken flower	£400	
26	50 c. black/*emerald* (1927)	50·00	£150
	s. Handstamped "Specimen"	£225	
27	$1 purple and blue/*blue*	65·00	45·00
28	$2 carmine-red and grey-black	£190	£250
18/28	*Set of* 11	£325	£475

STAMP BOOKLETS

1917. *Black on red cover inscribed* "BRITISH POST OFFICE AGENCIES IN CHINA". *Stapled.*
SB1 $1 booklet containing eight 2 c., six 4 c. and six 10 c. (Nos. 2/3, 6)

1922. *Cover as No.* SB1. *Stapled.*
SB2 $1 booklet containing eight 2 c., six 4 c., and six 10 c. (Nos. 19/20, 23) .. £4000

The British P.O.'s in the Treaty Ports closed by agreement with the Chinese on 30 November 1922, but the above overprinted issues continued in use at the Wei Hai Wei offices until they in turn closed on 30 September 1930. Under the terms of the Convention signed with China the Royal Navy continued to use the base at Wei Hai Wei until the mid-1930s.

BRITISH POST OFFICES IN JAPAN

Under the terms of the Anglo-Japanese Treaty of Yedo, signed on 26 August 1858, five Japanese ports were opened to British trade. British consulates were established at Decima (Nagasaki), Kanagawa (Yokohama), Hiogo (Kobe) and Hakodadi (Hakodate). The postage stamps of Hong Kong became available at the Yokohama and Nagasaki consulates during October 1864 and at Hiogo in 1869, although cancellation of mail did not commence until 1866 at Yokohama and Nagasaki or 1876 at Hiogo. Japan became a member of the U.P.U. on 1 June 1877 and all of the British Postal Agencies were closed by the end of 1879.

For illustrations of postmark types see BRITISH POST OFFICES IN CHINA.

HAKODATE

A British consular office existed at Hakodate, but it was never issued with a c.d.s., obliterator or Hong Kong stamps. No British covers are recorded from this consulate prior to opening of the Japanese Post Office.

HIOGO

The Port of Hiogo (Kobe) was first opened to foreigne[rs on] 1 January 1868. The British Consular mail service at [Hiogo] commenced during 1869 to serve the foreigners at Hiogo, and Osaka. The cities of Hiogo and Kobe later merged to be the single city of Kobe. The consular office at Hiogo closed November 1879.

Type **B** ("D30") (*supplied* 1876) *used* 1876–79
Type **D** (*supplied* 1876) *used* 1876–79

Stamps of HONG KONG *cancelled at Hiogo between* 1876 1879 *with postmarks detailed above.*

1863–71. *Wmk Crown CC* (*Nos.* 8/19).
Z 1 2 c. brown .. £
Z 2 4 c. grey .. £
Z 3 6 c. lilac .. £
Z 4 8 c. orange .. £
Z 5 12 c. blue .. £
Z 6 18 c. lilac ..
Z 7 24 c. green .. £
Z 8 30 c. vermilion
Z 9 30 c. mauve .. £
Z10 48 c. rose .. £
Z12 96 c. brownish grey .. £

1877. (*Nos.* 20/1).
Z13 16 c. on 18 c. lilac

1877. *Wmk Crown CC* (*No.* 22).
Z15 16 c. yellow .. £

NAGASAKI

The British Consulate opened in Nagasaki on 14 June 1 but, with few British residents at the port, the consular found it inconvenient to carry out postal duties so that Nagasaki c.d.s. or "N2" cancellations exist. The postal ser was terminated on 30 September 1879.

Type **A** ("N2") (*supplied* 1866) *used* 1876–79
Type **D** (*supplied* 1866) *used* 1876–79

Stamps of HONG KONG *cancelled at Nagasaki between* 1 *and* 1879 *with postmarks detailed above.*

1862. *No wmk* (*Nos.* 1/8).
Z15*a* 18 c. lilac .. £1

1863–71. *Wmk Crown CC* (*Nos.* 8/19).
Z16 2 c. brown .. £1
Z17 4 c. grey .. £
Z18 6 c. lilac .. £
Z19 8 c. orange .. £
Z20 12 c. blue .. £
Z21 18 c. lilac .. £1
Z22 24 c. green .. £1
Z24 30 c. mauve .. £1
Z25 48 c. rose .. £1
Z27 96 c. brownish grey

1876–77. (*Nos.* 20/1).
Z28 16 c. on 18 c. lilac .. £1
Z29 28 c. on 30 c. mauve .. £

1877. *Wmk Crown CC* (*No.* 22).
Z30 16 c. yellow .. £1

YOKOHAMA

The British Consulate opened in Kanagawa on 21 July 18 but was relocated to Yokohama where it provided pos services from 1 July 1860 until a separate Post Office w established in July 1867. The British Post Office in Yokoha closed on 31 December 1879.

Type **A** ("Y1") (*supplied* 1866) *used* 1867–79
Type **D** (*supplied* 1866) *used* 1866–79

Stamps of HONG KONG *cancelled at Yokohama between* 18 *and* 1879 *with postmarks detailed above.*

1862. *No wmk* (*Nos.* 1/8).
Z30*a* 8 c. yellow-buff .. £1
Z31 18 c. lilac .. 85·

1863–71. *Wmk Crown CC* (*Nos.* 8/19).
Z32 2 c. brown .. 19·
Z33 4 c. grey .. 19·
a. Perf 12½ .. £5
Z34 6 c. lilac .. 25·
Z35 8 c. orange .. 25·
Z36 12 c. blue .. 19·
Z37 18 c. lilac .. £5
Z38 24 c. green .. 21·
Z39 30 c. vermilion .. 35·
Z40 30 c. mauve .. 19·
Z41 48 c. rose .. 40·
Z43 96 c. brownish grey .. 50·

1876–77. (*Nos.* 20/1).
Z44 16 c. on 18 c. lilac .. £27
Z45 28 c. on 30 c. mauve .. 80·0

1877. *Wmk Crown CC* (*No.* 22).
Z46 16 c. yellow .. £11

POSTAL FISCAL STAMPS

1874. *Wmk Crown CC. P* 15½×15 (*Nos.* F1/3).
ZF47 $2 olive-green .. 85·0
ZF48 $3 dull violet .. 80·0
ZF49 $10 rose-carmine .. £120

India

PRICES FOR STAMPS ON COVER TO 1945

Nos. S1/3	*from* × 2
No. 1	†
Nos. 2/26	*from* × 3
Nos. 27/30	—
Nos. 31/4	*from* × 8
Nos. 35/49	*from* × 3
Nos. 50	†
Nos. 51/3	*from* × 4
Nos. 54/65	*from* × 2
Nos. 66/8	*from* × 5
Nos. 69/74	*from* × 3
Nos. 73/277	*from* × 2
Nos. O1/14	*from* × 6
Nos. O15/18	—
No. O19	*from* × 5
Nos. O20/30*a*	*from* × 10
No. O30*b*	†
Nos. O31/133	*from* × 6
Nos. O135/150	*from* × 2

(Currency. 12 pies = 1 anna; 16 annas = 1 rupee)

ISSUE FOR SIND PROVINCE

1

: (1 July). "Scinde Dawk." *Embossed.*

1		½ a. white	£4500	£800
		½ a. blue	£12000	£3500
		½ a. scarlet	£65000	£8000

nese stamps were issued under the authority of Sir Bartle re, Commissioner in Sind.

o. S3 is on sealing wax (usually cracked). Perfect copies are rare.

is believed that examples in red were issued first followed, urn, by those in white and blue. The latter, which shows an a ring round the circumference, may have been produced by La Rue. The Scinde Dawks were withdrawn in October 1854.

EAST INDIA COMPANY ADMINISTRATION

2 (*Much reduced*)

3

The ½ a., 1 a. and 4 a. were lithographed in Calcutta at the office the Surveyor-General. The die was engraved by Mr Maniruddin elling uncertain). *Ungummed* paper watermarked as T **2** (the o. 4" paper) with the Arms of the East India Co in the sheet. The termark is sideways on the ½ a. and 1 a., and upright on the a. where the paper was trimmed so that only the central portion owing the oval and the arms was used. Imperforate.

54 (April).

3	½ a. vermilion		£800
	a. Deep vermilion		£1200

This stamp, with 9½ arches in the side border, was prepared for e and a supply was sent to Bombay, but was not officially issued. The vermilion shade is normally found on toned paper and the ep vermilion on white.

MINIMUM PRICE

he minimum price quote is 10p which represents handling charge rather than a basis for valuing ommon stamps. For further notes about prices see introductory pages.

ILLUSTRATIONS. Types 4/8 are shown twice actual size.

4

1854 (1 Oct)–**55.** *Die I.*

2	4	½ a. blue	55·00	14·00
		a. Printed on both sides	†	£8000
		b. Printed double	†	£6000
3		½ a. pale blue	85·00	19·00
4		½ a. deep blue	70·00	19·00
5		½ a. indigo	£250	65·00

We give the official date of validity. Stamps were on sale to the public from mid September. Actual usage at Toungoo, Burma, is known from mid August.

These stamps were printed between 5 May and 29 July 1854 (Printing 30 millions).

4*a*

Die II

6	4*a*	½ a. blue	50·00	75·00
7		½ a. indigo	60·00	85·00

The bulk were printed between 1 and 12 August 1854, with some extra sheets on or before 2 November (Printing about 2 millions).

5

Die III (1855)

8	5	½ a. pale blue	£750	38·00
8*a*		½ a. blue	£700	35·00
9		½ a. greenish blue	£1500	£160
10		½ a. deep blue	£950	70·00

These stamps were printed between 3 July and 25 August 1855 (Printing about 4¾ millions).

THE THREE DIES OF THE ½ ANNA

DIE I. *Chignon shading* mostly solid blobs of colour. *Corner ornaments*, solid blue stars with long points, always conspicuous. *Band below diadem* always heavily shaded. *Diadem and jewels.* The middle and right-hand jewels usually show a clearly defined cross. *Outer frame lines.* Stamps with white or faintly shaded chignons and weak frame lines are usually Die I (worn state).

DIE II. *Chignon* normally shows much less shading. A strong line of colour separates hair and chignon. *Corner ornaments.* The right blue star is characteristic (see illustration) but tends to disappear. It never obliterates the white cross. *Band below diadem.* As Die I but heavier, sometimes solid. *Diadem and jewels.* As Die I but usually fainter. *Outer frame lines.* Always strong and conspicuous.

DIE III. *Chignon shading* shows numerous fine lines, often blurred. *Corner ornaments* have a small hollow blue star with short points, which tends to disappear as in Die II. *Band below diadem,* shows light shading or hardly any shading. *Diadem and jewels.* Jewels usually marked with a solid squat star. The ornaments between the stars appear in the shape of a characteristic white "w". *Frame lines* variable.

The above notes give the general characteristics of the three Dies, but there are a few exceptions due to retouching, etc.

6 (*See note below No.* 14)

Die I

11	6	1 a. deep red	£375	45·00
12		1 a. red	£225	32·00

Printing of these stamps commenced on 26 July 1854, and continued into August (Printing, see note below No. 14).

7

*Die II: With more lines in the chignon than in Die I, and with white curved line where chignon joins head**

13	7	1 a. deep red	£150	48·00
14		1 a. dull red	42·00	35·00

*Very worn printings of Die II may be found with chignon nearly as white as in Die I.

In stamps of Die I, however, the small blob of red projecting from the hair into the chignon is always visible.

These stamps were printed in August and September 1854 (Total printing, Dies I and II together, about 7¾ millions).

8

Die III. With pointed bust (1855)

15	8	1 a. red	£900	£130
16		1 a. dull red	£1400	£180

These stamps were printed between 7 July and 25 August 1855 (Printing, about 1½ millions).

9

NOTE. Our catalogue prices for Four Annas stamps are for cut-square specimens, with clear margins and in good condition. Cut-to-shape copies are worth from 3% to 20% of these prices according to condition.

Dies of the Head:—

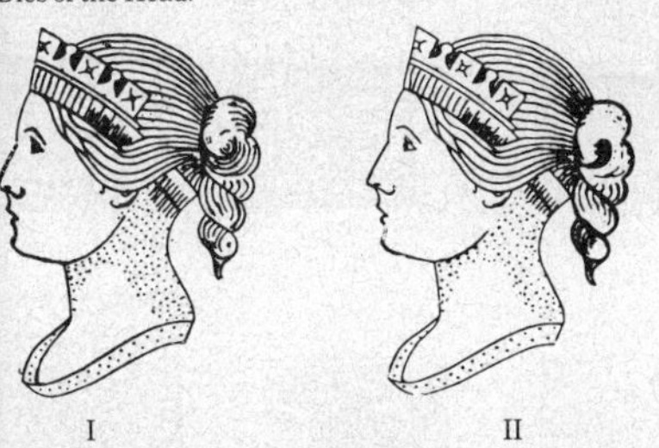

I II

I. Band of diadem and chignon strongly shaded.

II. Lines in band of diadem worn. Few lines in the upper part the chignon, which, however, shows a strong drawn comma-:e mark.

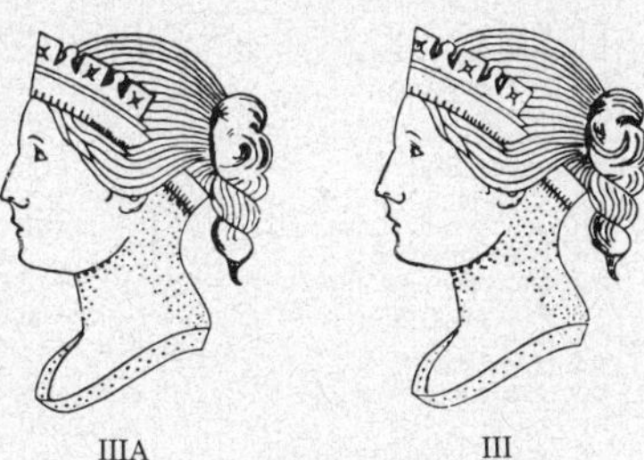

IIIA III

:IIIA. Upper part of chignon partly redrawn, showing two short, urved vertical lines in the NE corner. "Comma" has isappeared.

: III. Upper part of chignon completely redrawn, but band of iadem shows only a few short lines.

o Dies of the Frame:—

e I. Outer frame lines weak. Very small dots of colour, or none at all, in the "R" and "A's". The white lines to the right of "INDIA" are separated, by a line of colour, from the inner white circle.

)ie II. Outer frame lines strengthened. Dots in the "R" and "A's" strong. White lines to right of "INDIA" break into inner white circle.

(Des Capt. H. Thuillier)

1854 (15 Oct)–**55.** *W* **2** *upright, central portion only. Imperf.*
st Printing, Head Die I. Frame Die I. Stamps widely spaced and separated by blue wavy line.

			Un	*Used*	*Us pr*
17	**9**	4 a. indigo and red	£4250	£500	£1800
18		4 a. blue and pale red.. ..	£4250	£425	£1600
		a. Head inverted	†	£25000/ £85000	†

This printing was made between 13 and 28 Oct 1854 (Printing, 206,040).

Twenty-seven confirmed examples of No. 18a are now known, only three of which are cut-square. The range of prices quoted reflects the difference in value between a sound cut-to-shape stamp and the finest example known.

2nd Printing. Head Die II. Frame Die I. Stamps widely spaced and separated by blue wavy line.

19	**9**	4 a. blue and red	£4000	£275	£1000
		a. Blue (head) printed double	†	£6000	†
20		4 a. indigo and deep red ..	£4000	£325	£1200

This printing was made between 1 and 13 Dec 1854 (Printing, 393,960).

No. 19a is only known used cut-to-shape.

3rd Printing. Head Dies II, IIIA and III. Frame Dies I and II. Stamps, often in bright shades, widely spaced and separated by wavy line (1855).

21	**9**	4 a. blue and red (*shades*) (Head III, Frame I)	£9000	£1100	£3500
		a. Head II, Frame I	—	£1600	£5000
		b. Head IIIA, Frame I ..	—	£1600	£4750
		c. Head III, Frame II.. ..	—	—	£9500

This printing was made between 10 March and 2 April 1855 (Printing, 138,960).

4th Printing. Head Die III. Frame Die II. Stamps closely spaced 2 to 2½ mm without separating line (1855).

22	**9**	4 a. deep blue and red	£2750	£275	£850
23		4 a. blue and red	£2500	£225	£750
		a. Blue (head) printed double	†	£4500	†
24		4 a. pale blue and pale red ..	£2750	£300	£900

This printing was made between 3 April and 9 May 1855 (Printing, 540,960).

No. 23a is only known used cut-to-shape.

5th Printing. Head Die III. Frame Die II. Stamps spaced 4 to 6 mm without separating line (1855).

25	**9**	4 a. blue and rose-red	£4500	£400	£1600
26		4 a. deep blue and red	£4500	£400	£1600

This printing was made between 4 Oct and 3 Nov 1855 (Printing, 380,064).

Serrated perf about 18, or pin-perf

27	½ a. blue (Die I)	† £4000	—
28	1 a. red (Die I)	† £2250	—
29	1 a. red (Die II)	† £2000	—
30	4 a. blue and red (Die II)	† £9000	—

This is believed to be an unofficial perforation. Most of the known specimens bear Madras circle postmarks (C122 to C126), but some are known with Bombay postmarks. Beware of fakes.

BISECTS. The bisected stamps for issues between 1854 and 1860 were used exclusively in the Straits Settlements during shortages of certain values. Prices quoted are for those with Singapore "B 172" cancellations. Penang marks are considerably rarer.

10 11

(Plate made at Mint, Calcutta. Typo Stamp Office)

1854 (4 Oct). *Sheet wmk sideways, as W* **2** *but with* "No. 3" *at top left. Imperf.*

31	**10**	2 a. green (*shades*)	85·00	23·00
		a. Bisected (1 a.) (1857) (on cover)	†	£120000
34		2 a. emerald-green	£1000	

The 2 a. was also printed on paper with sheet watermark incorporating the words "STAMP OFFICE. One Anna", etc. (*Price £475 unused, £375 used*).

Apart from the rare emerald-green shade, there is a range of shades of No. 31 varying from bluish to yellowish green.

Many stamps show traces of lines external to the design shown in our illustration. Stamps with this frame on all four sides are scarce.

Many reprints of the ½, 1, 2, and 4 a. exist.

PRINTERS. All Indian stamps from No. 35 to 200 were typographed by De La Rue & Co.

1855 (Oct). *Blue glazed paper. No wmk. P* 14.

35	**11**	4 a. black	£450	14·00
		a. Imperf (pair)	£3000	£3000
		b. Bisected (2 a.) (1859) (on cover) ..	†	£7500
36		8 a. carmine (Die I)	£425	12·00
		a. Imperf (pair)	£1800	
		b. Bisected (4 a.) (1859) (on cover) ..	†	£50000

The first supply of the 4 a. was on white paper, but it is difficult to distinguish it from No. 45.

In the 8 a. the paper varies from deep blue to almost white.

For difference between Die I and Die II in the 8 a., see illustrations above No. 73.

1856–64. *No wmk. Paper yellowish to white. P* 14.

37	**11**	½ a. blue (Die I)	55·00	3·00
		a. Imperf (pair)	£325	£950
38		½ a. pale blue (Die I)	50·00	1·40
39		1 a. brown	48·00	2·00
		a. Imperf between (vert pair) ..		
		b. Imperf (pair)	£750	£1300
		c. Bisected (½ a.) (1859) (on cover)	†	£55000
40		1 a. deep brown	65·00	3·25
41		2 a. dull pink (1861)	£425	26·00
		a. Imperf (pair)	£1700	
42		2 a. yellow-buff (1859)	£190	26·00
		a. Imperf (pair)	£1000	£1800
43		2 a. yellow (1863)	£300	28·00
44		2 a. orange (1858)	£375	28·00
		a. Imperf (pair)		
45		4 a. black	£200	8·50
		a. Bisected diagonally (2 a.) (1859) (on cover)	†	£20000
		b. Imperf (pair)	£1800	£1800
46		4 a. grey-black	£180	4·75
47		4 a. green (1864)	£900	35·00
48		8 a. carmine (Die I)	£225	18·00
49		8 a. pale carmine (Die I)	£275	18·00
		a. Bisected (4 a.) (1859) (on cover) ..	†	£50000

Prepared for use, but not officially issued

50	**11**	2 a. yellow-green	£700	£800
		a. Imperf (pair)	£1700	

This stamp is known with trial obliterations, and a few are known postally used. It also exists *imperf*, but is not known used thus.

For difference between Die I and Die II in the ½ a., see illustrations above No. 73.

CROWN COLONY

On the 1 November 1858, Her Majesty Queen Victoria assumed the government of the territories in India "heretofore administered in trust by the Honourable East India Company".

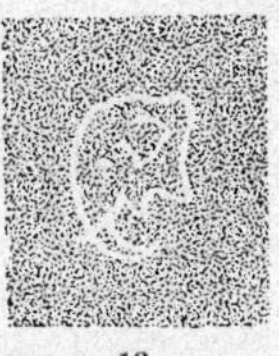

12 13

1860 (9 May). *No wmk. P* 14.

51	**12**	8 p. purple/*bluish*	£200	85·00
52		8 p. purple/*white*	38·00	4·50
		a. Bisected diagonally (4 p.) (1862) (on cover)	†	£55000
		b. Imperf (pair)	£2000	£3000
53		8 p. mauve	48·00	6·50

1865. *Paper yellowish to white. W* **13**. *P* 14.

54	**11**	½ a. blue (Die I)	9·50	50
		a. Imperf	†	£800
		w. Wmk inverted	—	16·00
55		½ a. pale blue (Die I)	9·50	50
56	**12**	8 p. purple	8·50	8·50
		w. Wmk inverted	30·00	
57		8 p. mauve	10·00	8·50
58	**11**	1 a. pale brown	5·00	60
59		1 a. deep brown	4·50	50
		w. Wmk inverted	42·00	21·00
60		1 a. chocolate	9·00	70
61		2 a. yellow	75·00	4·00
62		2 a. orange	45·00	1·40
		a. Imperf (pair)	†	£3000
63		2 a. brown-orange	21·00	2·00
		w. Wmk inverted	50·00	26·00
64		4 a. green	£325	19·00
		w. Wmk inverted	†	80·00
65		8 a. carmine (Die I)	£1000	75·00
		w. Wmk inverted	£1500	£150

The 8 p. mauve, No. 57, is found variously surcharged "NINE" or "NINE PIE" by local postmasters, to indicate that it was being sold for 9 pies, as was the case during 1874. Such surcharges were made without Government sanction. (*Price, from* £400 *unused*).

The stamps of India, wmk Elephant's Head, surcharged with a crown and value in "cents", were used in the Straits Settlements.

14 (15) (16)

POSTAGE POSTAGE

1866 (28 June). *Fiscal stamps as T* **14** *optd. Wmk Crown over* "INDIA". *P* 14 (*at sides only*). (*a*) *As T* **15**.

66	6 a. purple (G.)	£600	£110
	a. Overprint inverted	†	£9000

There are 20 different types of this overprint.

(*b*) *With T* **16**

68	6 a. purple (G.)	£1100	£140

17 18

Die I Die II

Two Dies of 4 a:—

Die I.—Mouth closed, line from corner of mouth downwards only. Pointed chin.

Die II.—Mouth slightly open; lips, chin, and throat defined by line of colour. Rounded chin.

1866 (Aug)–**78.** *W* **13**. *P* 14.

69	**17**	4 a. green (Die I)	60·00	2·75
70		4 a. deep green (Die I)	65·00	2·75
71		4 a. blue-green (Die II) (1878) ..	18·00	1·90
72	**18**	6 a. 8 p. slate (4.67)	35·00	18·00
		a. Imperf (pair)	£1700	

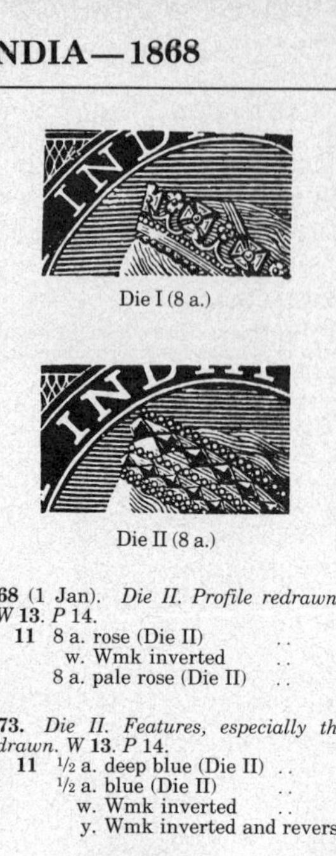

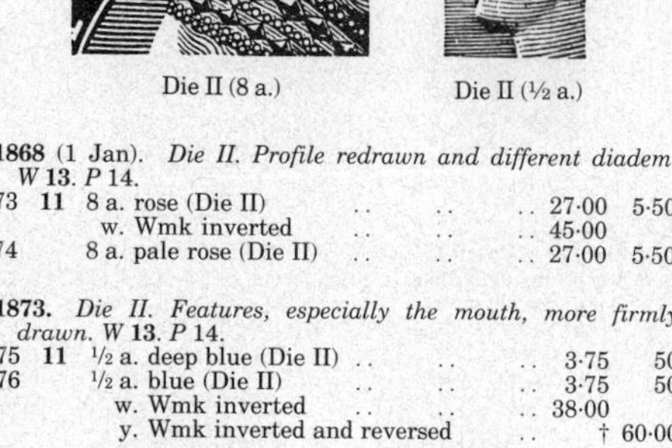

Die I (8 a.) (Die I (½ a.)

Die II (8 a.) Die II (½ a.)

1868 (1 Jan). *Die II. Profile redrawn and different diadem. W* **13**. *P* 14.

73	**11**	8 a. rose (Die II)	27·00	5·50
		w. Wmk inverted	45·00	
74		8 a. pale rose (Die II)	27·00	5·50

1873. *Die II. Features, especially the mouth, more firmly drawn. W* **13**. *P* 14.

75	**11**	½ a. deep blue (Die II)	3·75	50
76		½ a. blue (Die II)	3·75	50
		w. Wmk inverted	38·00	
		y. Wmk inverted and reversed	†	60·00

19

20

1874 (18 July–1 Sept). *W* **13**. *P* 14.

77	**19**	9 p. bright mauve (18.7.74)	12·00	12·00
78		9 p. pale mauve	12·00	12·00
79	**20**	1 r. slate (1.9.74)	35·00	22·00

21

22

1876 (19 Aug). *W* **13**. *P* 14.

80	**21**	6 a. olive-bistre	6·00	2·50
		w. Wmk inverted	55·00	
81		6 a. pale brown	5·00	1·50
82	**22**	12 a. Venetian red	7·50	19·00

EMPIRE

Queen Victoria assumed the title of Empress of India in 1877, and the inscription on the stamps was altered from "EAST INDIA" to "INDIA".

23 24 25 26 27 28 29 30 31 32 33 34

1882 (1 Jan)–**90.** *W* **34**. *P* 14.

84	**23**	½ a. deep blue-green (1883)	3·75	10
85		½ a. blue-green	3·75	10
		a. Double impression	£400	£500
		w. Wmk inverted	—	55·00
86	**24**	9 p. rose (1883)	1·00	1·75
87		9 p. aniline carmine	1·00	1·75
		w. Wmk inverted	—	55·00
88	**25**	1 a. brown-purple (1883)	3·75	30
89		1 a. plum	3·75	30
		w. Wmk inverted	—	55·00
90	**26**	1 a. 6 p. sepia	1·00	1·25
91	**27**	2 a. pale blue (1883)	3·75	30
92		2 a. blue	3·75	30
		a. Double impression	£800	£1100
93	**28**	3 a. orange	14·00	6·00
94		3 a. brown-orange (1890)	7·00	80
		w. Wmk inverted	—	65·00
95	**29**	4 a. olive-green (6.85)	14·00	80
96		4 a. slate-green	14·00	80
		w. Wmk inverted	—	45·00
97	**30**	4 a. 6 p. yellow-green (1.5.86)	17·00	4·50
98	**31**	8 a. dull mauve (1883)	20·00	2·00
99		8 a. magenta	20·00	2·00
100	**32**	12 a. purple/*red* (1.4.88)	6·50	3·25
		w. Wmk inverted	—	65·00
101	**33**	1 r. slate (1883)	12·00	5·00
		w. Wmk inverted	—	55·00
84/101		*Set of* 11	80·00	18·00
97s, 100s		Handstamped "Specimen" *Set of* 2	75·00	

No. 92a is from a sheet of 2 a. stamps with a very marked double impression issued in Karachi in early 1898.

2½ As.

(35)

36

37

1891 (1 Jan). *No.* 97 *surch with T* **35** *by Govt Press, Calcutta.*

102	**30**	2½ a. on 4½ a. yellow-green	2·75	60
		a. Surch double, one albino		

There are several varieties in this surcharge due to variations in the relative positions of the letters and figures.

1892 (Jan)–**97.** *W* **34**. *P* 14.

103	**36**	2 a. 6 p. yellow-green	2·00	40
104		2 a. 6 p. pale blue-green (1897)	2·75	80
105	**37**	1 r. green and rose	21·00	5·50
106		1 r. green and aniline carmine	9·00	2·00

38

1/4 1/4

(39) Slanting serif (Lower pane R.1/1)

40

USED HIGH VALUES. It is necessary to emphasise that used prices quoted for the following and all later high value stamps are for postally used copies.

(Head of Queen from portrait by von Angeli)

1895 (1 Sept). *W* **34**. *P* 14.

107	**38**	2 r. carmine and yellow-brown	35·00	11·00
107*a*		2 r. carmine and brown	40·00	13·00
108		3 r. brown and green	25·00	10·00
109		5 r. ultramarine and violet	38·00	25·00
107/9		*Set of* 3	90·00	40·00

1898 (1 Oct). *No.* 85 *surch with T* **39** *by Govt Press, Calcutta.*

110	**23**	¼ a. on ½ a. blue-green	10	50
		a. Surch double	£170	
		b. Double impression of stamp	£225	
		c. Slanting serif on "1"	20·00	

1899. *W* **34**. *P* 14.

111	**40**	3 p. aniline carmine	40	10

1900 (1 Oct)–**02.** *W* **34**. *P* 14.

112	**40**	3 p. grey	75	1·00
113	**23**	½ a. pale yellow-green	1·60	45
114		½ a. yellow-green	1·75	45
115	**25**	1 a. carmine	1·75	20
116	**27**	2 a. pale violet	3·25	1·50
117		2 a. mauve (1902)	7·00	2·25
118	**36**	2 a. 6 p. ultramarine	3·25	4·00
112/18		*Set of* 5	9·50	6·50

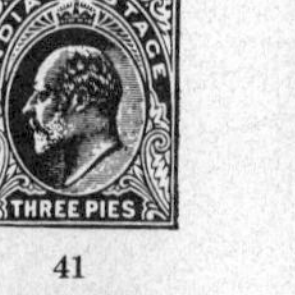

41

42

43

44 45

46

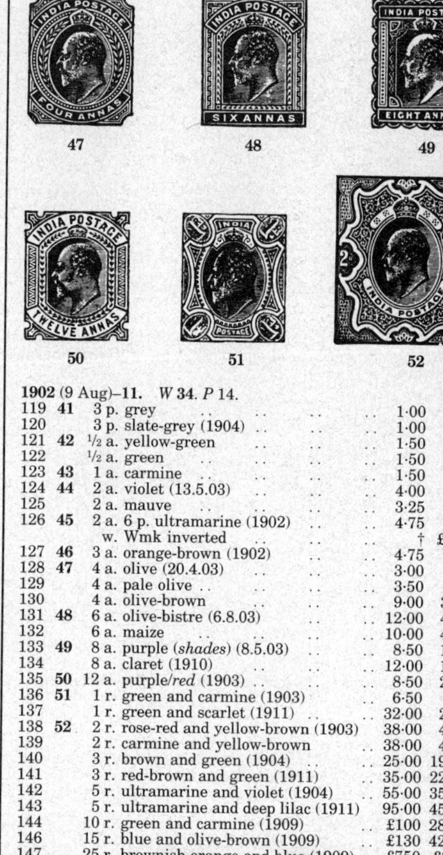

47 48 49 50 51 52

1902 (9 Aug)–**11.** *W* **34**. *P* 14.

119	**41**	3 p. grey	1·00	
120		3 p. slate-grey (1904)	1·00	
121	**42**	½ a. yellow-green	1·50	
122		½ a. green	1·50	
123	**43**	1 a. carmine	1·50	
124	**44**	2 a. violet (13.5.03)	4·00	
125		2 a. mauve	3·25	
126	**45**	2 a. 6 p. ultramarine (1902)	4·75	
		w. Wmk inverted	†	£1
127	**46**	3 a. orange-brown (1902)	4·75	
128	**47**	4 a. olive (20.4.03)	3·00	
129		4 a. pale olive	3·50	
130		4 a. olive-brown	9·00	3
131	**48**	6 a. olive-bistre (6.8.03)	12·00	4
132		6 a. maize	10·00	4
133	**49**	8 a. purple (*shades*) (8.5.03)	8·50	1
134		8 a. claret (1910)	12·00	1
135	**50**	12 a. purple/*red* (1903)	8·50	2
136	**51**	1 r. green and carmine (1903)	6·50	
137		1 r. green and scarlet (1911)	32·00	2
138	**52**	2 r. rose-red and yellow-brown (1903)	38·00	4
139		2 r. carmine and yellow-brown	38·00	4
140		3 r. brown and green (1904)	25·00	19
141		3 r. red-brown and green (1911)	35·00	22
142		5 r. ultramarine and violet (1904)	55·00	35
143		5 r. ultramarine and deep lilac (1911)	95·00	45
144		10 r. green and carmine (1909)	£100	28
146		15 r. blue and olive-brown (1909)	£130	42
147		25 r. brownish orange and blue (1909)	£750	£8
119/47		*Set of* 17	£1000	£8

No. 147 can often be found with telegraph cancellation; these c be supplied at one third of the price given above.

1905 (2 Feb). *No.* 122 *surch with T* **39**.

148	**42**	¼ on ½ a. green	55	
		a. Surch inverted	—	£8

It is doubtful if No. 148a exists unused with genuine surcharg

53

54

1906 (6 Dec)–**07.** *W* **34**. *P* 14.

149	**53**	½ a. green	3·00	1
150	**54**	1 a. carmine (7.1.07)	1·75	1

55 56 57 58* 59 60

61 62 63 64 65 66

67

"Rs" flaw in right value tablet (R.1/4)

. Two types of the 1½ a.; (A) As illustrated. (B) Inscribed "1½ As". "ONE AND A HALF ANNAS".

(Dec)–22. *W* 34. *P* 14.

55 3 p. grey (1912) .. .. 1·40 20
3 p. pale grey .. .. 1·50 20
3 p. bluish grey (1922) .. .. .. 2·00 50
w. Wmk inverted .. .. 12·00
3 p. slate .. .. 1·50 20
a. "Rs" flaw .. .. 13·00
3 p. violet-grey .. .. 2·50 50
56 ½ a. light green (1912) .. .. .. 1·50 15
½ a. emerald .. .. 1·75 15
½ a. bright green .. .. 1·75 15
57 1 a. rose-carmine .. .. 2·50 20
1 a. carmine .. .. 2·50 20
1 a. aniline carmine .. .. 2·25 15
1 a. pale rose-carmine (*chalk-surfaced paper*) (1918) .. .. .. 2·75 40
58 1½ a. chocolate (Type A) (1919) .. .. 3·00 30
1½ a. grey-brown (Type A) .. .. 7·50 2·50
1½ a. chocolate (Type B) (1921) .. .. 3·25 3·75
w. Wmk inverted .. .. 8·50
59 2 a. purple .. .. 3·25 40
2 a. reddish purple .. .. 4·75 30
2 a. deep mauve .. .. 3·75 40
w. Wmk inverted .. .. 17·00
2 a. bright reddish violet .. .. .. 4·50 50
60 2 a. 6 p. ultramarine (1912) .. .. 2·75 3·00
61 2 a. 6 p. ultramarine (1913) .. .. 2·75 20
62 3 a. orange .. .. 4·00 20
3 a. dull orange .. .. 6·00 45
63 4 a. deep olive (1912) .. .. .. 6·00 50
4 a. olive-green .. .. 6·00 50
w. Wmk inverted .. .. 17·00
64 6 a. yellow-bistre (1912) .. .. .. 4·00 1·00
6 a. brown-ochre .. .. 4·00 1·00
65 8 a. deep magenta (1912) .. .. .. 6·00 1·25
8 a. deep mauve .. .. 11·00 1·10
8 a. bright mauve .. .. 27·00 5·00
8 a. purple .. .. 14·00 1·50
66 12 a. carmine-lake (1912) .. .. .. 7·00 2·25
12 a. claret .. .. 15·00 2·50
67 1 r. red-brown & dp blue-green (1913) 13·00 2·00
w. Wmk inverted .. .. 38·00
1 r. brown and green (*shades*) .. .. 17·00 1·50
a 1 r. orange-brown & dp turquoise-grn 30·00 3·00
2 r. carmine and brown (1913) .. .. 21·00 1·75
w. Wmk inverted .. .. 50·00
5 r. ultramarine and violet (1913) .. 48·00 6·50
10 r. green and scarlet (1913) .. .. 70·00 12·00
15 r. blue and olive (1913) .. .. 90·00 24·00
25 r. orange and blue (1913) .. .. £160 35·00
/91 .. .. *Set of* 19 £350 75·00

Examples of the ½ a. printed double are now believed to be forgeries.

RGERIES.—Collectors are warned against forgeries of all the er surcharges of India, and particularly the errors.

NINE

PIES

(68)

21. *T* 57 *surch with T* 68.

2 9 p. on 1 a. rose-carmine 85 30
a. Error. "NINE NINE" .. .. .. 75·00 £130
b. Error. "PIES PIES" .. .. .. 75·00 £130
c. Surch double £150 £180
w. Wmk inverted .. .. † 48·00
3 9 p. on 1 a. carmine-pink .. .. .. 1·75 60
4 9 p. on 1 a. aniline carmine .. .. .. 8·00 3·00

In the initial setting of the surcharge No. 192a occurred on R. 13–16 of the fourth pane and No. 192b on R. 4/13–16 of the ird. For the second setting No. 192a was corrected. Examples No. 192b still occur but on R. 2/13–16 of the third pane. Later intings showed this corrected also.

22. *T* 56 *surch with T* 39.

5 ¼ a. on ½ a. bright green 50 35
a. Surch inverted .. .. 9·00
b. Surch omitted (in horiz pair with normal) £200
6 ¼ a. on ½ a. emerald .. .. .. 2·00 65

922–26. *W* 34. *P* 14.

7 57 1 a. chocolate 75 10
8 58 1½ a. rose-carmine (Type B) (1926) .. 3·00 30
9 61 2 a. 6 p. orange (1926) .. .. .. 5·00 2·75
00 62 3 a. ultramarine (1923) .. .. .. 12·00 60
97/200 .. .. *Set of* 4 18·00 3·25

69

70

71

PRINTERS. The following issues of postage and contemporary official stamps were all printed by the Security Printing Press, Nasik, *unless otherwise stated*.

1926–33. *Typo. W* 69. *P* 14.

201 55 3 p. slate 30 10
w. Wmk inverted .. .. 1·40 30
202 56 ½ a. green .. .. 1·25 10
w. Wmk inverted .. .. 1·50 30
203 57 1 a. chocolate 50 10
a. *Tête-bêche* (pair) (1932) .. .. 1·25 10·00
w. Wmk inverted 50 10
204 58 1½ a. rose-carmine (Type B) (1929) .. 1·60 10
w. Wmk inverted .. .. 1·75 30
205 59 2 a. bright purple .. .. 6·50 7·00
a. Stop under "s" in right value tablet (R. 4/16) .. .. .. 85·00
206 70 2 a. purple .. .. 1·40 10
a. *Tête-bêche* (pair) (1933) .. .. 9·00 38·00
w. Wmk inverted .. .. 1·60 30
207 61 2 a. 6 p. orange (1929) .. .. .. 1·40 10
w. Wmk inverted .. .. 1·60 40
208 62 3 a. ultramarine .. .. 8·00 1·00
209 3 a. blue (1928) .. .. 7·50 10
w. Wmk inverted .. .. 8·50 75
210 63 4 a. pale sage-green .. .. 1·50 10
w. Wmk inverted .. .. — 6·00
211 71 4 a. sage-green .. .. 6·00 10
w. Wmk inverted .. .. 11·00 40
212 65 8 a. reddish purple .. .. 4·00 10
w. Wmk inverted .. .. 6·00 40
213 66 12 a. claret .. .. 5·00 30
w. Wmk inverted .. .. 7·00 80
214 67 1 r. chocolate and green .. .. .. 5·00 45
a. Chocolate (head) omitted £3500
w. Wmk inverted .. .. 9·00 75
215 2 r. carmine and orange .. .. .. 11·00 80
w. Wmk inverted .. .. 12·00 1·50
216 5 r. ultramarine and purple .. .. 23·00 1·25
w. Wmk inverted .. .. 42·00 2·00
217 10 r. green and scarlet (1927) .. .. 45·00 3·00
w. Wmk inverted .. .. 80·00 5·00
218 15 r. blue and olive (1928) .. .. 40·00 30·00
w. Wmk inverted .. .. 24·00 30·00
219 25 r. orange and blue (1928) .. .. 90·00 35·00
w. Wmk inverted .. .. £120 40·00
201/19 .. .. *Set of* 18 £200 65·00

Examples of the ½ a. printed double are believed to be forgeries.

72 De Havilland D.H.66 Hercules

Missing tree-top (R. 11/6 of 8 a.)

Reversed serif on second "I" of "INDIA"

(Des R. Grant. Litho)

1929 (22 Oct). *Air. W* 69 (*sideways**). *P* 14.

220 72 2 a. deep blue-green .. .. .. 2·25 50
w. Wmk stars pointing left .. .. 1·75 60
221 3 a. blue .. .. 1·00 1·75
w. Wmk stars pointing left .. .. 1·75 1·75
222 4 a. olive-green .. .. .. 2·25 1·25
w. Wmk stars pointing left .. .. 3·00 1·25
223 6 a. bistre .. .. 2·25 1·00
w. Wmk stars pointing left .. .. 2·50 1·00
224 8 a. purple .. .. 2·75 1·00
a. Missing tree-top .. .. .. 90·00 60·00
b. Reversed serif .. .. .. £170 85·00
w. Wmk stars pointing left .. .. 3·25 1·00
225 12 a. rose-red .. .. 10·00 5·50
w. Wmk stars pointing left .. .. 12·00 5·50
220/5 .. .. *Set of* 6 18·00 10·00

*The normal sideways watermark shows the stars pointing right, *as seen from the back of the stamp.*

73 Purana Qila

(Des H. W. Barr. Litho)

1931 (9 Feb). *Inauguration of New Delhi. T* 73 *and similar horiz designs. W* 69 (*sideways**). *P* 13½×14.

226 ¼ a. olive-green and orange-brown .. 2·00 3·00
a. "F" for "P" in "PURANA" .. .. 90·00 95·00
w. Wmk stars pointing left .. .. 1·75 2·75
227 ½ a. violet and green .. .. .. 1·25 40
w. Wmk stars pointing left .. .. 2·00 40
228 1 a. mauve and chocolate .. .. 1·25 20
w. Wmk stars pointing left .. .. 2·50 25
229 2 a. green and blue .. .. .. 1·50 2·25
w. Wmk stars pointing left .. .. 2·00 1·25
230 3 a. chocolate and carmine .. .. 3·50 2·50
w. Wmk stars pointing left .. .. 2·50 2·50
231 1 r. violet and green .. .. .. 9·00 24·00
w. Wmk stars pointing left .. .. 8·00 24·00
226/31 .. .. *Set of* 6 14·50 28·00

Designs:—½ a. War Memorial Arch; 1 a. Council House; 2 a. The Viceroy's House; 3 a. Government of India Secretariat; 1 r. Dominion Columns and the Secretariat.

*The normal sideways watermark shows the stars pointing to the right, *as seen from the back of the stamp.*

79

80

81

82

83

9 p. litho. Heavier and longer lines on face. King's nose often shows 6 horizontal lines and always has lowest line long and thin.

9 p. typo. Lines lighter and shorter. Always 5 lines on King's nose with the lowest short and thick.

(T 82/3 des T. I. Archer. 9 p. litho or typo; 1 a. 3 p., 3 a. 6 p. litho; others typo)

1932–36. *W* 69. *P* 14.

232 79 ½ a. green (1934) .. .. 3·25 10
w. Wmk inverted .. .. — 50
233 80 9 p. deep green (*litho*) (22.4.32) .. 85 10
aw. Wmk inverted .. .. 1·50 50
233*b* 9 p. deep green (*typo*) (27.8.34) .. 1·10 10
234 81 1 a. chocolate (1934) .. .. .. 4·50 10
w. Wmk inverted .. .. — 50
235 82 1 a. 3 p. mauve (22.4.32) 50 10
w. Wmk inverted 50 30
236 70 2 a. vermilion .. .. 9·00 4·00
aw. Wmk inverted .. .. 9·00 5·50
236*b* 59 2 a. vermilion (1934) .. .. .. 3·75 50
236*c* 2 a. vermilion (*small die*) (1936) .. 4·75 30
cw. Wmk inverted .. .. — 5·50
237 62 3 a. carmine .. .. 4·50 10
w. Wmk inverted .. .. — 1·25
238 83 3 a. 6 p. ultramarine (22.4.32) .. 3·50 20
w. Wmk inverted .. .. 3·50 30
239 64 6 a. bistre (1935) .. .. .. 7·00 1·50
w. Wmk inverted .. .. — 11·00
232/9 .. .. *Set of* 9 32·00 5·50

No. 236*b* measures 19×22.6 mm and No. 236*c* 18.4×21.8 mm.

84 Gateway of India, Bombay

"Bird" flaw (R.9/3)

1935 (6 May). *Silver Jubilee. T* 84 *and similar horiz designs. Litho. W* 69 (*sideways**). *P* 13½×14.

240 ½ a. black and yellow-green 85 20
w. Wmk stars pointing left 75 15
241 9 p. black and grey-green 50 20
w. Wmk stars pointing left 50 30
242 1 a. black and brown 85 20
w. Wmk stars pointing left 60 10
243 1¼ a. black and bright violet 50 10
w. Wmk stars pointing left 90 15
244 2½ a. black and orange .. .. .. 2·50 1·60
w. Wmk stars pointing left .. .. 1·75 1·00

245		3½ a. black and dull ultramarine	3·75	4·00
		a. "Bird" flaw	£110	80·00
		w. Wmk stars pointing left	4·25	4·00
246		8 a. black and purple	3·50	3·25
		w. Wmk stars pointing left	5·50	3·75
240/6		*Set of* 7	10·00	8·00

Designs:—9 p. Victoria Memorial Calcutta; 1 a. Rameswaram Temple, Madras; 1¼ a. Jain Temple, Calcutta; 2½ a. Taj Mahal, Agra; 3½ a. Golden Temple, Amritsar; 8 a. Pagoda in Mandalay.

*The normal sideways watermark shows the stars pointing to the right, *as seen from the back of the stamp.*

91 King George VI

92 Dak Runner

93 King George VI

1937 (23 Aug)–**40.** *Typo. W* **69**. *P* 13½×14 *or* 14×13½ (*T* **93**).

247	**91**	3 p. slate (15.12.37)	75	10
248		½ a. red-brown (15.12.37)	3·00	10
		w. Wmk inverted		
249		9 p. green	7·00	20
		w. Wmk inverted		
250		1 a. carmine	1·25	10
		a. *Tête-bêche* (vert pair) (1940)	2·50	1·75
		w. Wmk inverted (from booklets)	1·25	1·25
251	**92**	2 a. vermilion (15.12.37)	4·00	30
		w. Wmk inverted		
252	–	2 a. 6 p. bright violet (15.12.37)	1·25	20
		w. Wmk inverted		
253	–	3 a. yellow-green (15.12.37)	5·50	30
		w. Wmk inverted		
254	–	3 a. 6 p. bright blue (15.12.37)	3·25	50
		w. Wmk inverted		
255	–	4 a. brown (15.12.37)	13·00	20
		w. Wmk inverted		
256	–	6 a. turquoise-green (15.12.37)	14·00	80
257	–	8 a. slate-violet (15.12.37)	7·50	50
		w. Wmk inverted		
258	–	12 a. lake (15.12.37)	18·00	1·10
		w. Wmk inverted		
259	**93**	1 r. grey and red-brown (15.12.37)	1·00	15
		w. Wmk inverted		
260		2 r. purple and brown (15.12.37)	4·00	30
		w. Wmk inverted	22·00	
261		5 r. green and blue (15.12.37)	19·00	50
		w. Wmk inverted	40·00	
262		10 r. purple and claret (15.12.37)	16·00	70
263		15 r. brown and green (15.12.37)	70·00	60·00
		w. Wmk inverted	95·00	80·00
264		25 r. slate-violet and purple (15.12.37)	£100	17·00
		w. Wmk inverted	—	£100
247/64		*Set of* 18	£250	75·00

Designs: *Horiz as T* **92**—2 a. 6 p. Dak bullock cart; 3 a. Dak tonga; 3 a. 6 p. Dak camel; 4 a. Mail train; 6 a. *Strathnaver* (liner); 8 a. Mail lorry; 12 a. Armstrong Whitworth A.W.27 Ensign I mail plane (small head).

No. 250a comes from surplus booklet sheets issued as normal stock following the rise in postal rates.

100a King George VI

101 King George VI **102**

103 Armstrong Whitworth A.W.27 Ensign I Mail Plane (large head)

(T **100a/102** des T. I. Archer. Typo (1½ a. and 3 a. litho also)).

1940–43. *W* **69**. *P* 13½×14.

265	**100a**	3 p. slate	30	10
		w. Wmk inverted		
266		½ a. purple (1.10.42)	1·00	10
		w. Wmk inverted		
267		9 p. green	1·00	10
		w. Wmk inverted		
268		1 a. carmine (1.4.43)	1·00	10
		w. Wmk inverted		
269	**101**	1 a. 3 p. yellow-brown	1·00	10
		aw. Wmk inverted		
269*b*		1½ a. dull violet (9.42)	1·25	10
		bw. Wmk inverted		
270		2 a. vermilion	1·50	10
		w. Wmk inverted		
271		3 a. bright violet (1942)	3·00	10
		w. Wmk inverted	—	10·00
272	**101**	3½ a. bright blue	1·00	20
		w. Wmk inverted		
273	**102**	4 a. brown	75	10
		w. Wmk inverted		
274		6 a. turquoise-green	3·50	10
275		8 a. slate-violet	1·50	30
		w. Wmk inverted		
276		12 a. lake	3·00	50
277	**103**	14 a. purple (15.10.40)	18·00	1·25
265/77		*Set of* 14	32·00	2·25

The 1½ a. and 3 a. were at first printed by lithography and were of finer execution and without Jubilee lines in the sheet margins. The two values exist with watermark inverted from both printing processes.

105 "Victory" and King George VI

3 PIES

(**106**)

1946 (2 Jan). *Victory. Litho. W* **69**. *P* 13.

278	**105**	9 p. yellow-green (8.2.46)	30	60
279		1½ a. dull violet	30	30
280		3½ a. bright blue	75	60
281		12 a. claret (8.2.46)	1·50	75
278/81		*Set of* 4	2·50	2·00

1946 (8 Aug). *Surch with T* **106**.

282	**101**	3 p. on 1 a. 3 p. yellow-brown	10	15

DOMINION

301 Asokan Capital (Inscr reads "Long Live India")

302 Indian National Flag

303 Douglas DC-4

(Des T. I. Archer. Litho)

1947 (21 Nov–15 Dec). *Independence. W* **69**. *P* 14 × 13½ (1½ *a.*) *or* 13½ × 14 (*others*).

301	**301**	1½ a. grey-green (15 Dec)	15	10
302	**302**	3½ a. orange-red, blue and green	30	1·60
		w. Wmk inverted	7·00	7·00
303	**303**	12 a. ultramarine (15 Dec)	1·50	2·00
301/3		*Set of* 3	1·75	3·25

304 Lockheed Constellation

(Des T. I. Archer. Litho)

1948 (29 May). *Air. Inauguration of India-U.K. Air Service. W* **69**. *P* 13½ × 14.

304	**304**	12 a. black and ultramarine	1·00	2·50

305 Mahatma Gandhi **306**

(Photo Courvoisier)

1948 (15 Aug). *First Anniv of Independence. P* 11½.

305	**305**	1½ a. brown	2·00	30
306		3½ a. violet	4·25	2·00
307		12 a. grey-green	6·00	1·25
308	**306**	10 r. purple-brown and lake	45·00	40·00
305/8		*Set of* 4	50·00	40·00

307 Ajanta Panel

308 Konarak Horse

309 Trir

310 Bodhisattva

311 Nataraja

312 Sanchi S East Gat

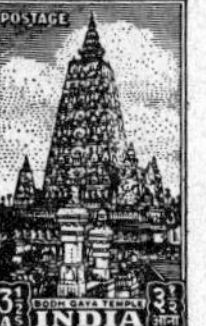

313 Bodh Gaya Temple

314 Bhuvanesvara

315 Gol Gumbad Bijapur

316 Kandarya Mahadeva Temple

317 Golden Temple, Amritsar

318 Victory Tower, Chittorgarh

319 Red Fort, Delhi

320 Taj Mahal, Agra

321 Qutb Minar, Delhi

322 Satrunjaya Temple, Palitana

(Des T. I. Archer and I. M. Das. Typo (low values), litho (rup values))

1949 (15 Aug). *W* **69** (*sideways* on* 6 *p.*, 1 *r. and* 10 *r.*). *P* 1 (3 *p. to* 2 *a.*), 13½ (3 *a. to* 12 *a.*), 14×13½ (1 *r. and* 10 *r.* 13½×14 (2 *r. and* 5 *r.*), 13 (15 *r.*).

309	**307**	3 p. slate-violet	15	1
		w. Wmk inverted		
310	**308**	6 p. purple-brown	25	1
		w. Wmk star pointing right	3·75	1·0
311	**309**	9 p. yellow-green	40	1
312	**310**	1 a. turquoise	60	1
		w. Wmk inverted		
313	**311**	2 a. carmine	80	1
		w. Wmk inverted	12·00	1·0
314	**312**	3 a. brown-orange	1·50	1
315	**313**	3½ a. bright blue	1·50	3·0
316	**314**	4 a. lake	4·00	2
		w. Wmk inverted	15·00	1·2
317	**315**	6 a. violet	1·50	1
		w. Wmk inverted	3·00	5
318	**316**	8 a. turquoise-green	1·50	1
		w. Wmk inverted	—	50·0

317 12 a. dull blue .. .. .. 1·50 20
w. Wmk inverted .. .. .. 7·50 1·00
318 1 r. dull violet and green .. .. 9·00 10
w. Wmk star pointing left .. 23·00 1·00
319 2 r. claret and violet .. .. 10·00 20
w. Wmk inverted .. .. .. 30·00 1·25
320 5 r. blue-green and red-brown .. 28·00 1·00
w. Wmk inverted .. .. .. 60·00 2·00
321 10 r. purple-brown and deep blue .. 48·00 6·00
a. *Purple-brown and blue* .. 95·00 3·75
aw. Wmk star pointing left ..
322 15 r. brown and claret .. .. 14·00 17·00
4 .. .. *Set of* 16 £110 23·00

e normal sideways watermark has the star pointing to the n the 6 p. value and to the right on the 1 r. and 10 r. (323*a*) *seen from the back of the stamp.*
T **310** with statue reversed see No. 333.

323 Globe and Asokan Capital

(10 Oct). *75th Anniv of U.P.U. Litho.* W **69**. *P* 13.
323 9 p. green .. .. .. 1·00 2·00
2 a. rose .. .. .. 1·00 2·00
3½ a. bright blue .. .. .. 1·50 2·25
12 a. brown-purple .. .. .. 2·00 2·50
3 .. .. *Set of* 4 5·00 8·00

REPUBLIC

324 Rejoicing Crowds

328 As T **310**, but statue reversed

(Des D. J. Keymer & Co. Litho)

0 (26 Jan). *Inauguration of Republic.* T **324** *and similar esigns.* W **69** *(sideways on* 3½ *a.). P* 13.
2 a. scarlet .. .. .. 1·00 40
w. Wmk inverted .. .. .. 15·00 1·75
3½ a. ultramarine .. .. .. 1·50 2·75
4 a. violet .. .. .. 1·50 65
12 a. maroon .. .. .. 3·25 2·25
w. Wmk inverted .. .. .. 17·00 4·75
/32 .. .. .. *Set of* 4 6·50 5·50

esigns: *Vert*—3½ a. Quill, ink-well and verse. *Horiz*—4 a. Ear orn and plough; 12 a. Spinning-wheel and cloth.

0 (15 July)–51. *Typo.* W **69**. *P* 14 (1 a.), 13½ *(others).*
328 1 a. turquoise .. .. 2·50 10
aw. Wmk inverted ..
b 313 2½ a. lake (30.4.51) .. .. 2·50 2·75
c 314 4 a. bright blue (30.4.51) .. .. 6·00 10
/c .. .. .. *Set of* 3 10·00 2·75

329 *Stegodon ganesa*

330 Torch

51 (13 Jan). *Centenary of Geological Survey of India. Litho.* W **69**. *P* 13.
4 **329** 2 a. black and claret .. .. .. 2·00 70

51 (4 Mar). *First Asian Games, New Delhi. Litho.* W **69** *(sideways). P* 14.
5 **330** 2 a. reddish purple and brown-orange .. 1·00 50
6 12 a. chocolate and light blue .. 4·00 1·25

STAMP BOOKLETS

904. *Black on green* (No. SB1) *or black on pink* (No. SB2) *covers. Stapled.*
B1 12¼ a. booklet containing twenty-four ½ a. (No. 121) in blocks of 6 .. .. £850
B2 12¼ a. booklet containing twelve 1 a. (No. 123) in blocks of 6 .. .. £850

906–11. *Black on green* (No. SB3), *black on pink* (No. SB4) *or black on green and pink* (No. SB5) *match book type covers inscr* "Post Office of India" *and royal cypher of King Edward VII. Stapled.*
B3 1 r. booklet containing thirty-two ½ a. (No. 149) in blocks of 4 .. .. £450
a. Without "Post Office of India" inscr .. £400
b. Ditto and showing royal cypher of King George V (1911) £375

SB4 1 r. booklet containing sixteen 1 a. (No. 150) in blocks of 4 (1907) £400
a. Without "Post Office of India" inscr .. £350
b. Ditto and showing royal cypher of King George V (1911) £375
SB5 1 r. booklet containing sixteen ½ a. and eight 1 a. (Nos. 149/50) in blocks of 4 (1907) .. £900
a. Without "Post Office of India" inscr .. £800
b. Ditto and showing royal cypher of King George V (1911) £750

1912–22. *Black on green* (Nos. SB6/7, SB12), *black on pink* (No. SB8), *black on green and pink* (No. SB9), *black on purple* (Nos. SB10) *or black on blue* (No. SB11) *match book type covers with foreign postage rates on back. Stapled.*
SB 6 1 r. booklet containing sixty-four 3 p. (No. 152) in blocks of 4 (blank back cover) .. £475
SB 7 1 r. booklet containing thirty-two ½ a. (No. 155) in blocks of 4 .. .. £180
a. Blank back cover £180
b. Advertisement contractor's notice on back cover £275
c. Advertisement on back (1922) .. £275
SB 8 1 r. booklet containing sixteen 1 a. (No. 159) in blocks of 4 .. .. £140
a. Blank back cover £140
b. Advertisements on front flap and back cover (1922) £180
SB 9 1 r. booklet containing sixteen ½ a. and eight 1 a. (Nos. 155, 159) in blocks of 4 (blank back cover) £130
SB10 1 r. 8 a. booklet containing sixteen 1½ a. (No. 163) in blocks of 4 (1919) £325
a. Blank back cover (1921) £325
SB11 2 r. booklet containing sixteen 2 a. (No. 169) in blocks of 4 (blank back cover) (1921) .. £400
a. Black on purple cover with postage rates on back (1922) £400
SB12 2 r. booklet containing sixteen 2 a. (No. 166) in blocks of 4 (1922) £400
a. Black on purple cover £400

1921. *Black on buff match book type cover. Stapled.*
SB13 1 r. 2 a. booklet containing twenty-four 9 p. on 1 a. (No. 192) in blocks of 4 .. .. £100

1922. *Black on brown* (No. SB14) *or black on green and pink* (No. SB15) *match book type covers with foreign postage rates on back. Stapled.*
SB14 1 r. booklet containing sixteen 1 a. (No. 197) in blocks of 4 .. .. £200
a. Advertisement on back £200
b. Advertisements on front flap and back cover
c. Black on lilac cover with blank back .. £200
ca. Advertisements on front flap and back cover £275
d. Black on pink cover with blank back .. £250
SB15 1 r. booklet containing sixteen ½ a. and eight 1 a. (Nos. 155, 197) in blocks of 4 (blank back cover) £425

1926–28. *Black on brown* (No. SB16) *or black on purple* (No. SB17) *match book type covers with foreign postage rates on back. Stapled.*
SB16 1 r. booklet containing sixteen 1 a. (No. 203) in blocks of 4 .. .. 85·00
SB17 2 r. booklet containing sixteen 2 a. (No. 205) in blocks of 4 .. .. £275
a. Containing No. 206 (1928) £325

1929. *Black on brown* (No. SB18) *or black on purple* (No. SB19) *separate leaf covers. Stitched.*
SB18 1 r. booklet containing sixteen 1 a. (No. 203) in blocks of 4 (blank back cover) .. 85·00
a. Advertisement contractor's notice on back cover .. .. 85·00
b. Advertisements on front flap and back cover £100
c. Advertisement on back cover .. £100
SB19 2 r. booklet containing sixteen 2 a. (No. 205) in blocks of 4 (foreign postage rates on back cover) £300
a. Advertisement contractor's notice on back cover £300
b. Containing No. 206 (foreign postage rates on back cover) £350
ba. Advertisement contractor's notice on back cover £350

1932. *Black on brown cover. Stitched.*
SB20 1 r. 4 a. booklet containing sixteen 1¼ a. (No. 235) in blocks of 4 .. .. £275

1934. *Black on buff cover. Stitched.*
SB21 1 r. booklet containing sixteen 1 a. (No. 234) in blocks of 4 .. .. £150

1937. *Black on red cover. Stamps with wmk upright or inverted. Stitched.*
SB22 1 r. booklet containing sixteen 1 a. (No. 250) in blocks of 4 .. .. £200

OFFICIAL STAMPS

Stamps overprinted "POSTAL SERVICE" or "I.P.N." were not used as postage stamps, and are therefore omitted.

Service.
(O 1)

(Optd by the Military Orphanage Press, Calcutta)

1866 (1 Aug)–**72.** *Optd with Type* O **1**. *P* 14. *(a) No wmk.*
O 1 **11** ½ a. blue .. .. — £225
O 2 ½ a. pale blue £950 £120
a. Opt inverted ..
O 3 1 a. brown .. .. — £160
O 4 1 a. deep brown .. .. — £120
O 5 8 a. carmine .. .. 19·00 45·00

(b) Wmk Elephant's Head, T **13**
O 6 **11** ½ a. blue .. .. £225 22·00
w. Wmk inverted .. .. † £110
O 7 ½ a. pale blue £225 1200
a. Opt inverted ..
b. No dot on "i" (No. 50 on pane) .. — £250
c. No stop (No. 77 on pane) .. — £200
O 8 **12** 8 p. purple (1.72) .. .. 19·00 50·00
a. No dot on "i" £225 £300
b. No stop £225
O 9 **11** 1 a. brown .. .. £200 15·00
O10 1 a. deep brown .. .. £200 38·00
a. No dot on "i" .. .. — £425
b. No stop .. .. — £350
O11 2 a. orange .. .. £170 75·00
O12 2 a. yellow .. .. £170 75·00
a. Opt inverted ..
b. Imperf ..
w. Wmk inverted £250
y. Wmk inverted and reversed .. † £250
O13 4 a. green .. .. £180 70·00
a. Opt inverted ..
O14 **17** 4 a. green (Die I) £950 £250

A variety with wide and more open capital "S" occurs six times in sheets of all values except No. O8. Price four times the normal.
Reprints exist of Nos. O6, O9 and O14; the latter is Die II instead of Die I.
Reprints of the overprint have also been made, in different setting, on the 8 pies, purple, no watermark.

O 2

O 6

O 3

O 4

(No. O15 surch at Calcutta, others optd at Madras)

1866 (Oct). *Fiscal stamps, Nos. O15/18 with top and bottom inscrs removed, surch or optd. Wmk Crown over* "INDIA".

(a) Surch as in Type O **2**. *Thick blue glazed paper. Imperf* × *perf* 14
O15 O **2** 2 a. purple £275 £225

(b) Optd "SERVICE POSTAGE" *in two lines as in Types* O **3**/**4** *and similar type. Imperf* × *perf* 14
O16 O **3** 2 a. purple (G.) £800 £400
O17 O **4** 4 a. purple (G.) £3250 £1100
O18 – 8 a. purple (G.) £3750 £3750
a. Optd on complete stamp (inscr "FOREIGN BILL") .. .. † £9500

(c) Optd "SERVICE POSTAGE" *in semi-circle. Wmk Large Crown. P* 15½ × 15
O19 O **6** ½ a. mauve/*lilac* (G.) .. .. £400 85·00
a. Opt double £2750

So-called reprints of Nos. O15 to O18 are known, but in these the surcharge differs entirely in the spacing, etc., of the words; they are more properly described as Government imitations. The imitations of No. O15 have surcharge in *black* or in *green*. No. O19 exists with reprinted overprint which has a full stop after "POSTAGE".

PRINTERS. The following stamps up to No. O108 were overprinted by De La Rue and thereafter Official stamps were printed or overprinted by the Security Printing Press at Nasik.

Service.
(O 7)

On H. S. M.
(O 8)

On H. S. M.
(O 9)

1867–73. *Optd with Type* O **7**. *Wmk Elephant's Head.* T **13**. *P* 14.
O20 **11** ½ a. blue (Die I) .. .. 30·00 50
w. Wmk inverted .. .. † 70·00
O21 ½ a. pale blue (Die I) .. .. 38·00 2·00
O22 ½ a. blue (Die II) (1873) .. .. £150 65·00
O23 1 a. brown .. .. 38·00 50
w. Wmk inverted .. .. † 85·00
O24 1 a. deep brown .. .. 40·00 2·25
O25 1 a. chocolate .. .. 45·00 2·25
O26 2 a. yellow .. .. 20·00 2·50
O27 2 a. orange .. .. 4·75 2·25
O28 **17** 4 a. pale green (Die I) .. .. 16·00 2·00
O29 4 a. green (Die I) .. .. 3·00 1·50
O30 **11** 8 a. rose (Die II) (1868) .. .. 3·25 1·50
O30*a* 8 a. pale rose (Die II) .. .. 3·25 1·50
aw. Wmk inverted .. .. 30·00 22·00

Prepared for use, but not issued
O30*b* **18** 6 a. 8 p. slate £275

1874–82. *Optd with Type* O **8**. (a) *In black.*
O31 **11** ½ a. blue (Die II) .. .. 9·00 20
O32 1 a. brown .. .. 14·00 20
O33 2 a. yellow .. .. 55·00 27·00
O33*a* 2 a. orange .. .. 40·00 17·00
O34 **17** 4 a. green (Die I) .. .. 14·00 3·00
O35 **11** 8 a. rose (Die II) .. .. 5·50 4·25

(b) *Optd in blue-black*
O36 **11** ½ a. blue (Die II) (1877) .. .. £300 42·00
O37 1 a. brown (1882) £500 £120

1883–99. *Wmk Star, T* **34**. *P* 14. *Optd with Type* O **9**.
O37*a* **40** 3 p. aniline carmine (1899) 20 10
O38 **23** ½ a. deep blue-green .. .. .. 1·25 10
a. Opt double .. .. .. † £1100
O39 ½ a. blue-green .. .. 1·00 10
O40 **25** 1 a. brown-purple .. .. 2·25 50
a. Opt inverted £350 £450
aw. Wmk inverted .. .. † £550
b. Opt double .. .. † £1200
c. Opt omitted (in horiz pair with normal) £1500
O41 1 a. plum 50 10
O42 **27** 2 a. pale blue .. .. 4·50 60
O43 2 a. blue .. .. 5·50 60
O44 **29** 4 a. olive-green .. .. 15·00 50
O44*a* 4 a. slate-green .. .. 15·00 50
O45 **31** 8 a. dull mauve .. .. 17·00 1·25
O46 8 a. magenta .. .. 8·50 50
O47 **37** 1 r. green and rose (1892) .. .. 45·00 4·00
O48 1 r. green and carmine (1892) .. .. 11·00 40
O37*a*/48 .. .. *Set of* 7 35·00 2·00

1900 *Colours changed. Optd with Type* O **9**.
O49 **23** ½ a. pale yellow-green .. .. .. 1·75 90
O49*a* ½ a. yellow-green .. .. .. 3·00 50
ab. Opt double £900
O50 **25** 1 a. carmine .. .. 2·50 10
a. Opt inverted .. .. † £1200
b. Opt double .. .. † £1300
O51 **27** 2 a. pale violet .. .. 30·00 1·50
O52 2 a. mauve .. .. 35·00 50
O49/52 .. .. *Set of* 3 32·00 1·00

1902–9. *Stamps of King Edward VII optd with Type* O **9**.
O54 **41** 3 p. grey (1903) .. .. .. 2·50 50
O55 3 p. slate-grey (1905) .. .. .. 2·50 50
a. No stop after "M" (R. 6/10) .. £160 £100
O56 **42** ½ a. green .. .. 1·25 30
O57 **43** 1 a. carmine .. .. 1·00 10
O58 **44** 2 a. violet .. .. 4·50 40
O59 2 a. mauve .. .. 3·25 10
O60 **47** 4 a. olive .. .. 12·00 30
O61 4 a. pale olive .. .. 12·00 30
O62 **48** 6 a. olive-bistre (1909) .. .. .. 1·50 15
O63 **49** 8 a. purple (*shades*) .. .. .. 6·00 1·00
O64 8 a. claret .. .. 8·00 85
O65 **51** 1 r. green and carmine (1905) .. .. 4·00 80
O54/65 .. .. *Set of* 8 28·00 2·75

1906. *New types. Optd with Type* O **9**.
O66 **53** ½ a. green .. .. 1·25 10
a. No stop after "M" (R. 6/10) .. 95·00 48·00
O67 **54** 1 a. carmine .. .. 2·00 10
a. No stop after "M" (R. 6/10) .. £150 75·00
b. Opt albino (in pair with normal) £1000

On

H. S.

M.

(O 9*a*)

1909. *Optd with Type* O **9***a*.
O68 **52** 2 r. carmine and yellow-brown .. .. 8·00 1·50
O68*a* 2 r. rose-red and yellow-brown .. .. 8·00 1·50
O69 5 r. ultramarine and violet .. .. 14·00 1·50
O70 10 r. green and carmine .. .. .. 27·00 13·00
O70*a* 10 r. green and scarlet .. .. .. 60·00 7·00
O71 15 r. blue and olive-brown .. .. 60·00 40·00
O72 25 r. brownish orange and blue .. .. £140 60·00
O68/72 .. .. *Set of* 5 £225 £100

NINE

SERVICE — (O 10) (14 mm)
SERVICE — (O 11) (21½ mm)
PIES — (O 12)

1912–13. *Stamps of King George V* (*wmk Single Star, T* **34**) *optd with Type* O **10** *or* O **11** (*rupee values*).
O73 **55** 3 p. grey 40 10
O73*a* 3 p. pale grey 30 10
O74 3 p. bluish grey 60 10
a. Opt omitted (in pair with normal)
O75 3 p. slate 40 30
a. "Rs" flaw .. ..
O75*b* 3 p. violet-grey .. .. 3·25 30
O76 **56** ½ a. light green 50 10
O77 ½ a. emerald 50 15
O78 ½ a. bright green 50 15
a. Opt double £100
O80 **57** 1 a. rose-carmine .. .. 1·00 10
O81 1 a. carmine .. .. 1·60 10
O82 1 a. aniline carmine .. .. .. 1·60 10
a. Opt double .. .. † £900
O83 **59** 2 a. purple 75 30
O83*a* 2 a. reddish purple 75 25
O84 2 a. deep mauve 75 30
O84*a* 2 a. bright reddish violet .. .. .. 2·25 25
O85 **63** 4 a. deep olive .. .. 1·00 10
O86 4 a. olive-green .. .. 1·00 10
O87 **64** 6 a. yellow-bistre .. .. 1·50 2·50
O88 6 a. brown-ochre .. .. 3·00 4·25
O89 **65** 8 a. deep magenta .. .. 2·25 1·25
O89*a* 8 a. deep mauve .. .. 2·25 1·25
O90 8 a. bright mauve .. .. 15·00 3·00
O91 **67** 1 r. red-brown & dp blue-green (1913) 3·00 1·75
O91*a* 1 r. brown and green .. .. .. 2·50 1·40
O92 2 r. rose-carmine and brown (1913) .. 3·50 5·00
O93 5 r. ultramarine and violet (1913) .. 15·00 19·00
O94 10 r. green and scarlet (1913) .. .. 48·00 48·00
O95 15 r. blue and olive (1913) .. .. 90·00 £100
O96 25 r. orange and blue (1913) £200 £160
O73/96 .. .. *Set of* 13 £325 £300

1921. *No.* O80 *surch with Type* O **12**.
O97 **57** 9 p. on 1 a. rose-carmine .. .. 1·25 75

1922. *No.* 197 *optd with Type* O **10**.
O98 **57** 1 a. chocolate .. .. 1·50 10

ONE
RUPEE

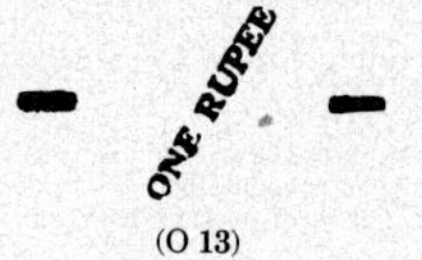

(O 13) (O 14)

1925. *Official stamps surcharged.*
(a) *Issue of* 1909, *as Type* O **13**
O 99 **52** 1 r. on 15 r. blue and olive .. .. 4·25 4·00
O100 1 r. on 25 r chestnut and blue .. .. 20·00 70·00
O101 2 r. on 10 r green and scarlet .. .. 3·75 4·25
O101*a* 2 r. on 10 r. green and carmine .. .. £200 50·00
(b) *Issue of* 1912, *with Type* O **14**
O102 **67** 1 r. on 15 r. blue and olive .. .. 19·00 75·00
O103 1 r. on 25 r. orange and blue .. .. 5·50 11·00
a. Surch inverted £600
(c) *Issue of* 1912, *as Type* O **13**
O104 **67** 2 r. on 10 r. green and scarlet £750
Examples of the above showing other surcharge errors are believed to be of clandestine origin.

(O 15) (O 16)

1926. *No.* O62 *surch with Type* O **15**.
O105 **48** 1 a. on 6 a. olive-bistre 30 30

1926. *Postage stamps of* 1911–22 (*wmk Single Star*), *surch as Type* O **16**.
O106 **58** 1 a. on 1½ a. chocolate (A) 20 10
O107 1 a. on 1½ a. chocolate (B) .. .. 2·25 4·50
a. Error. On 1 a. chocolate (197) .. £160
O108 **61** 1 a. on 2 a. 6 p. ultramarine 60 80
The surcharge on No. O108 has no bars at top.
Examples of Nos. O106/7 with inverted or double surcharges are believed to be of clandestine origin.

SERVICE — (O 17) (13½ mm)
SERVICE — (O 18) (19½ mm)

1926–31. *Stamps of King George V* (*wmk Multiple Star, T* **69**) *optd with Types* O **17** *or* O **18** (*rupee values*).
O109 **55** 3 p. slate (1.10.29) 15 10
w. Wmk inverted .. .. .. 1·40 60
O110 **56** ½ a. green (1931) .. .. .. 6·50 60
w. Wmk inverted .. .. .. — 1·75
O111 **57** 1 a. chocolate 15 10
w. Wmk inverted .. .. .. 1·75 60
O112 **70** 2 a. purple 30 10
w. Wmk inverted .. .. .. 1·25 50
O113 **71** 4 a. sage-green 50 20
w. Wmk inverted .. .. .. 2·00 70
O115 **65** 8 a. reddish purple 80 10
w. Wmk inverted 80 30
O116 **66** 12 a. claret (1927) .. .. .. 70 2·50
w. Wmk inverted .. .. .. — 3·50
O117 **67** 1 r. chocolate and green (1930) .. .. 3·00 1·00
w. Wmk inverted .. .. .. 2·75 1·50
O118 2 r. carmine and orange (1930) .. .. 7·00 8·00
w. Wmk inverted .. .. .. — 12·00
O120 10 r. green and scarlet (1931) .. .. 70·00 48·00
O109/20 .. .. *Set of* 10 80·00 55·00

1930. *As No.* O111, *but optd as Type* O **10** (*14 mm*).
O125 **57** 1 a. chocolate .. .. — 5·00
w. Wmk inverted .. .. .. 90·00 5·50

1932–36. *Stamps of King George V* (*wmk Mult Star, T* **69**) *optd with Type* O **17**.
O126 **79** ½ a. green (1935) .. .. .. 1·00 10
O127 **80** 9 p. deep green (*litho*) 30 15
aw. Wmk inverted .. .. ..
O127*b* 9 p. deep green (*typo*) .. .. .. 1·00 10
O127*c* **81** 1 a. chocolate (1936) .. .. .. 2·50
cw. Wmk inverted .. .. .. 3·25
O128 **82** 1 a. 3 p. mauve 30
w. Wmk inverted 60
O129 **70** 2 a. vermilion .. .. 1·00
w. Wmk inverted .. .. ..
O130 **59** 2 a. vermilion (1935) .. .. .. 2·00
O130*a* 2 a. vermilion (*small die*) (1936) .. 1·25
aw. Wmk inverted .. .. ..
O131 **61** 2 a. 6 p. orange (22.4.32) 50
w. Wmk inverted .. .. .. 1·75
O132 **63** 4 a. sage-green (1935) .. .. .. 1·50
w. Wmk inverted .. .. ..
O133 **64** 6 a. bistre (1936) .. .. .. 21·00 1
O126/33 *Set of* 9 .. .. .. 26·00 1

1937–39. *Stamps of King George VI optd as Types* O **17** *or* (*rupee values*).
O135 **91** ½ a. red-brown (1938) .. .. .. 17·00
O136 9 p. green (1937) .. .. .. 19·00
O137 1 a. carmine (1937) .. .. .. 3·50
O138 **93** 1 r. grey and red-brown (5.38) 50
O139 2 r. purple and brown (5.38) .. .. 1·50
w. Wmk inverted .. .. .. — 2
O140 5 r. green and blue (10.38) .. .. 2·50
w. Wmk inverted .. .. ..
O141 10 r. purple and claret (1939) .. .. 14·00
O135/41 .. .. *Set of* 7 50·00 1

(O 19)

O 20

1939 (May). *Stamp of King George V, surch with Type* O 1
O142 **82** 1 a. on 1¼ a. mauve .. .. .. 12·00
w. Wmk inverted .. .. ..

(Des T. I. Archer)

1939 (1 June)–**42**. *Typo. W* **69**. *P* 14.
O143 O **20** 3 p. slate 40
O144 ½ a. red-brown .. .. 4·50
O144*a* ½ a. purple (1942) 30
O145 9 p. green 30
O146 1 a. carmine 30
O146*a* 1 a. 3 p. yellow-brown (1941) .. .. 3·00
aw. Wmk inverted .. .. ..
O146*b* 1½ a. dull violet (1942) 65
O147 2 a. vermilion 60
O148 2½ a. bright violet 60
O149 4 a. brown 60
O150 8 a. slate-violet 90
O143/50 .. .. *Set of* 11 11·00 1

1948 (15 Aug). *First Anniv of Independence. Nos.* 305/8 *optd Type* O **17**.
O150*a* **305** 1½ a. brown .. .. .. 42·00 30
O150*b* 3½ a. violet £750 £4
O150*c* 12 a. grey-green £2000 £16
O150*d* **306** 10 r. purple-brown and lake .. £12000
Nos. O150*a*/*d* were only issued to the Governor-Genera Secretariat.

O 21 Asokan Capital O 22

(Des T. I. Archer)

1950 (2 Jan)–**51**. *Typo* (O **21**) *or litho* (O **22**). *W* **69**. *P* 14.
O151 O **21** 3 p. slate-violet (1.7.50) 10
O152 6 p. purple-brown (1.7.50) 20
O153 9 p. green (1.7.50) 70
O154 1 a. turquoise (1.7.50) .. .. .. 1·00
O155 2 a. carmine (1.7.50) .. .. .. 1·25
w. Wmk inverted .. .. ..
O156 3 a. red-orange (1.7.50) .. .. .. 4·00 2·0
O157 4 a. lake (1.7.50) .. .. .. 5·50 2
O158 4 a. ultramarine (1.10.51) 50 1
O159 6 a. bright violet (1.7.50) .. .. 4·00 5
O160 8 a. red-brown (1.7.50) .. .. .. 1·75 1
w. Wmk inverted .. .. .. 11·00
O161 O **22** 1 r. violet .. .. 3·00 1
w. Wmk inverted .. .. ..
O162 2 r. rose-carmine .. .. .. 1·00 7
O163 5 r. bluish green .. .. .. 2·00 2·0
O164 10 r. reddish brown .. .. .. 3·00 18·0
O151/64 .. .. *Set of* 14 25·00 21·0

INDIA USED ABROAD

In the years following 1858 the influence of the Indian Empire political, military and economic, extended beyond its border into neighbouring states, the Arabian Gulf, East Africa and th Far East. Such influence often led to the establishment of Indiar civil post offices in the countries concerned where unoverprinted stamps of India were used.

Such offices operated in the following countries. An * indicate that details will be found under that heading elsewhere in th catalogue.

ADEN*

Unoverprinted stamps of India used from 1854 until 1937.

BAHRAIN*

Unoverprinted stamps of India used from 1884 until 1933.

BRITISH EAST AFRICA (KENYA, UGANDA AND TANGANYIKA)*

›verprinted stamps of India used during August and ›mber 1890.

FRENCH INDIAN SETTLEMENTS

first Indian post office, at Chandernagore, was open by ›o be followed by offices in the other four Settlements. By ›reement with the French, dating from 1814, these offices ›ed mail destined for British India, Great Britain, the ›h Empire and most other foreign destinations except ›e and the French colonies. In later years the system was ›ded by a number of sub-offices and it continued to operate the French territories were absorbed into India on 2 May (Chandernagore) or 1 November 1954.

›andernagore. Open by 1784. Used numeral cancellations ›86" or "86".
›ub-offices:
Gondalpara (opened 1906)
Lakhiganj (opened 1909)
Temata (opened 1891)
›rikal. Open by 1794. Used numeral cancellations "C147", 147" or "6/M–21".
›ub-offices:
Ambagarattur (opened 1904)
Kottuchari (opened 1901)
Nedungaon (opened 1903)
Puraiyar Road (opened 1901)
Settur (opened 1905)
Tirumalrayapatnam (opened 1875 – used numeral cancellation "6/M-21/1")
Tiramilur (opened 1898)
›he. Open by 1795. Used numeral cancellations "C192" or ›9/M-14".
›ndicherry. Opened 1787. Used numeral cancellations "C111", "111" (also used elsewhere), "6/M-19" (also used ›lsewhere) or "6/M-20".
›ub-offices:
Ariyankuppam (opened 1904)
Bahoor (opened 1885)
Mudaliarpet (opened 1897)
Muthialpet (opened 1885)
Pondicherry Bazaar (opened 1902)
Pondicherry Railway Station (opened 1895)
Olugarai (opened 1907)
Vallinur (opened 1875) – used numeral cancellation "M-19/1"
Yanam. Opened 1876. Used numeral cancellation "5/M-4".

IRAN

›e British East India Company was active in the Arabian ›f from the early years of the 17th century with their first ›ory (trading centre) being established at Jask in 1619. After ›3 this commercial presence was converted into a political of the Indian Government culminating in the appointment Political Resident to Bushire in 1862.
›he first Indian post office in Iran (Persia) opened at Bushire 1 May 1864 with monthly mail services operating to the ›ident there and to the British Legation at Tehran. Further ›es in the other Gulf ports followed, but, unless otherwise ›ed below, all were closed on 1 April 1923.

Abadan. Opened 1917.
Ahwaz. Opened March 1915.
Bandar Abbas. Opened 1 April 1867. Used numeral cancellations "258", "22" or "1/K-5"
Bushire. Opened 1 May 1864. Used numeral cancellations "308", "26" (also used elsewhere) or "K-5".
Chabbar. Opened 20 August 1913.
Duzdab. Opened 1922. Closed 1927?
Henjam. Opened 21 June 1913
Jask. Opened 1 September 1880
Kuh-Malik-Siah-Ziarat. Opened January 1906. Closed 1924
Linga. Opened 1 April 1867. Used numeral cancellations "21" or "2/K-5".
Maidsan-i-Naphtun. Opened 1917. Closed 1920.
Mirjawa. Opened January 1921. Closed 1930.
Mohammera. Opened 19 July 1892.

IRAQ*

›noverprinted stamps of India used from 1868 until 1918.

KUWAIT*

›noverprinted stamps of India used from 1904 until 1923.

MALAYSIA (STRAITS SETTLEMENTS)*

Unoverprinted stamps of India used from 1854 until 1867.

MUSCAT*

Unoverprinted stamps of India used from 1864 until 1947.

NEPAL

A post office was opened in the British Residency at Kath›andu in 1816 following the end of the Gurkha War. Stamps of ›dia were used from 1854, initially with "B137", "137" or ›-37" numeral cancellations. The Residency Post Office ›ntinued to provide the overseas mail service after Nepal ›troduced its own issues in 1881.
In 1920 the Residency Post Office became the British Legation ›ost Office. On the independence of India in 1947 the service was ›ansferred to the Indian Embassy and continued to function ›ntil 1965.

PORTUGUESE INDIA

A British post office was open in Damaun by 1823 and Indian ›amps were used there until November 1883, some with "13" ›nd "3/B-19" numeral cancellations.
No other British post offices were opened in the Portuguese ›erritories, but from 1854 Indian stamps were sold by the local ›ost offices. Between 1871 and 1877 mail intended for, or passing ›rough, British India required combined franking of India and ›ortuguese India issues. After 1877 the two postal ›dministrations accepted the validity of each other's stamps.

SOMALILAND PROTECTORATE*

Unoverprinted stamps of India used from 1887 until 1903.

TIBET

The first Indian post office accompanied the Tibetan Frontier Commission in 1903. The Younghusband Military Expedition to Lhasa in the following year operated a number of Field Post Offices which were replaced by civil post offices at Gartok (opened 23 September 1906), Gyantse (opened March 1905), Pharijong (opened 1905) and Yatung (opened 1905). All Indian post offices in Tibet closed on 1 April 1955 except Gartok which, it is believed, did not operate after 1943. A temporary post office, C-622, operated at Gyantse between July 1954 and August 1955 following a flood disaster.

TRUCIAL STATES

Unoverprinted stamps of India used at Dubai from 1909 until 1947.

ZANZIBAR*

Unoverprinted stamps of India used from 1875 until 1895.

CHINA EXPEDITIONARY FORCE

Following the outbreak of the Boxer Rising in North China the Peking Legations were besieged by the rebels in June 1900. An international force, including an Indian Army division, was assembled for their relief. The Legations were relieved on 14 August 1900, but operations against the Boxers continued in North China with Allied garrisons at key cities and along the Peking–Tientsin–Shanhaikwan railway. The last Indian Army battalion, and accompanying Field Post Offices, did not leave North China until 1 November 1923.

Field Post Offices accompanied the Indian troops and commenced operations on 23 July 1900 using unoverprinted Indian postage and official stamps. The unoverprinted postage issues were replaced in mid-August by stamps overprinted "C.E.F." to prevent currency speculation. The use of unoverprinted official stamps continued as they were not valid for public postage.

PRICES FOR STAMPS ON COVER

Nos. C1/10	*from* × 15
No. C10*a*	†
Nos. C11/22	*from* × 8
Nos. C23/34	*from* × 20

C. E. F.
(C 1)

Stamps of India overprinted with Type* C 1, *in black

1900 (16 Aug). *Stamps of Queen Victoria.*

C 1	**40**	3 p. carmine	40	1·25
		a. No stop after "C" (R. 1/2)		
		b. No stop after "F"	£140	
		c. Opt double, one albino		
C 2	**23**	½ a. blue-green	75	30
		a. Opt double		
		b. No stop after "F"	£140	
C 3	**25**	1 a. plum	4·00	1·50
		a. No stop after "F"	£190	
C 4	**27**	2 a. pale blue	3·00	9·00
		a. No stop after "F"	£190	
C 5	**36**	2 a. 6 p. green	2·75	13·00
		a. No stop after "F"	£275	
C 6	**28**	3 a. orange	2·75	16·00
		a. Opt double, one albino	£120	
		b. No stop after "F"	£275	
C 7	**29**	4 a. olive-green	2·75	7·50
		a. Opt double, one albino	£120	
		b. No stop after "F"	£275	
C 8	**31**	8 a. magenta	2·75	18·00
		a. No stop after "F"	£325	
		b. Opt double, one albino	£120	
C 9	**32**	12 a. purple/*red*	16·00	16·00
		a. Opt double, one albino	£160	
		b. No stop after "F"	£400	
C10	**37**	1 r. green and carmine	21·00	21·00
		a. No stop after "F"	£400	
		b. Opt double, one albino	£180	
C1/10		*Set of* 10	50·00	90·00

Prepared, but not issued

C10*c*	**26**	1 a. 6 p. sepia	£200	

The missing stop after "F" variety occurs in the ninth row of the upper pane.

1904 (27 Feb).

C11	**25**	1 a. carmine	28·00	8·00

1905 (16 Sept)–**11.** *Stamps of King Edward VII.*

C12	**41**	3 p. grey (4.11)	5·00	6·50
		a. Opt double, one albino	£120	
		b. Opt triple, one albino	£375	
		c. Slate-grey	4·50	6·50
C13	**43**	1 a. carmine	7·50	70
		a. Opt double, one albino	£100	
C14	**44**	2 a. mauve (11.3.11)	14·00	2·50
		a. Opt double, one albino	£130	
C15	**45**	2 a. 6 p. ultramarine (11.3.11)	3·25	5·00
C16	**46**	3 a. orange-brown (11.3.11)	3·75	4·00
C17	**47**	4 a. olive-green (11.3.11)	8·50	11·00
C18	**49**	8 a. claret (11.3.11)	8·00	7·50
		a. Purple	60·00	55·00
C19	**50**	12 a. purple/*red* (1909)	11·00	19·00
		a. No stop after "E"	£475	
C20	**51**	1 r. green and carmine (11.3.11)	13·00	28·00
C12/20		*Set of* 9	65·00	75·00

1908 (Dec)–**09.** "POSTAGE & REVENUE".

C21	**53**	½ a. green (No. 149) (29.9.09)	1·75	1·50
		a. Opt double, one albino	£110	
C22	**54**	1 a. carmine (No. 150)	2·25	30
		a. Opt double, one albino	£150	

1914 (5 May)–**22.** *Stamps of King George V. Wmk Star.*

C23	**55**	3 p. grey (7.10.14)	4·50	26·00
		a. Opt double, one albino	£250	
C24	**56**	½ a. light green	3·50	6·00
C25	**57**	1 a. aniline carmine	4·00	4·00
C26	**58**	1½ a. chocolate (Type A) (9.3.21)	23·00	70·00
		a. Opt double, one albino	£160	
C27	**59**	2 a. purple (11.19)	17·00	60·00
		a. Opt triple	£425	
		b. Deep mauve	15·00	60·00
C28	**61**	2 a. 6 p. bright blue (2.19)	11·00	25·00
C29	**62**	3 a. orange (5.22)	25·00	£190
C30	**63**	4 a. olive-green (5.22)	22·00	£150
C32	**65**	8 a. deep mauve (12.21)	25·00	£325
C33	**66**	12 a. carmine-lake (8.20)	22·00	£110
C34	**67**	1 r. brown and green (10.21)	60·00	£275
C23/34		*Set of* 11	£190	£1100

Most dates quoted for Nos. C23/34 are those of the earliest recorded postmarks.

On No. C27a two of the overprints are only lightly inked.

BRITISH RAILWAY ADMINISTRATION

As a vital communications link the North China Railway (Peking – Tientsin – Shanhaikwan) was captured by Russian forces during operations against the Boxers. Control of the line was subsequently, in February 1901, assigned to the China Expeditionary Force and a British Railway Administration was set up to run it. By international agreement the line was to provide postal services for the other national contingents and also, to a lesser extent, for the civilian population. Travelling post offices were introduced and, on 20 April 1901, a late letter service for which an additional fee of 5 c. was charged.

Type **32** of China

B.R.A.
5
Five Cents
(BR **35**)

1901 (20 Apr). *No.* 108 *of China surch with Type* BR **35**.

BR133	**32**	5 c. on ½ c. brown (Bk.)	£325	£100
		a. Surch inverted	£8000	£2500
		b. Surch in green	£275	£140
		ba. Imperf between (horiz pair)	†	£16000

No. BR133 was used for the collection of the 5 c. late letter fee and was affixed to correspondence by a postal official at the railway station. It was cancelled with a violet circular postmark showing "RAILWAY POST OFFICE" at top and the name of the station (PEKING, TIENTSIN, TONGKU, TONGSHAN or SHANHAIKWAN) at foot. With the exception of official mail it could only be used in combination with Indian stamps overprinted "C.E.F.", stamps from the other allied contingents or of the Chinese Imperial Post (*Price used on cover*: No. BR133 *from* £250. No. BR133b *from* £300).

It is suggested that stamps overprinted in black were used at Tientsin and Tongku with those in green being available at Peking, Tongshan and Shanhaikwan.

The late fee charge was abolished on 20 May 1901 and No. BR133 was then withdrawn. The British Railway Administration continued to run the line, and its travelling post offices, until it was returned to its private owners in September 1902.

INDIAN EXPEDITIONARY FORCES 1914–21

Nos. E1/13 were for use of Indian forces sent overseas during the First World War and its aftermath. Examples were first used in France during September 1914. Other areas where the stamps were used included East Africa, Mesopotamia and Turkey. "I.E.F." overprints ceased to be valid for postage on 15 October 1921.

PRICES FOR STAMPS ON COVER

Nos. E1/13	*from* × 10

I. E. F.
(E 1)

1914 (Sept). *Stamps of India (King George V) optd with Type* E 1.

E 1	**55**	3 p. grey	15	30
		a. No stop after "F"	23·00	26·00
		b. No stop after "E"	£100	£100
		c. Opt double	42·00	30·00
E 2	**56**	½ a. light green	50	30
		a. No stop after "F"	70·00	70·00
		b. Opt double	£140	£250
E 3	**57**	1 a. aniline carmine	1·25	30
		a. No stop after "F"	32·00	35·00
E 4		1 a. carmine	4·00	4·00
E 5	**59**	2 a. purple	1·25	30
		a. No stop after "F"	50·00	65·00
		b. No stop after "E"	£225	£250
E 6	**61**	2 a. 6 p. ultramarine	1·50	3·50
		a. No stop after "F"	£160	£170
E 7	**62**	3 a. orange	1·00	1·50
		a. No stop after "F"	£150	£160
E 8	**63**	4 a. olive-green	1·00	1·50
		a. No stop after "F"	£225	£250
E 9	**65**	8 a. deep magenta	1·25	2·50
		a. No stop after "F"	£225	£250
E10		8 a. deep mauve	9·00	13·00
E11	**66**	12 a. carmine-lake	2·25	6·00
		a. No stop after "F"	£275	£275
		b. Opt double, one albino	55·00	
E12		12 a. claret		
E13	**67**	1 r. red-brown and deep blue-green	2·50	4·00
		a. Opt double, one albino	£100	
		b. Brown and green	3·50	5·00
E1/13		*Set of* 10	11·50	18·00

The "no stop after F" variety occurred on R. 4/12 of the upper pane, in one printing.

INDIAN NATIONAL ARMY

The following are stated to have been used in the Japanese occupied areas of India during the drive on Imphal. Issued by the Indian National Army.

Genuine examples are inscribed "PROVISIONAL GOVERNMENT OF FREE INDIA". Forgeries also exist inscribed "PROVISIONAL GOVT. OF FREE INDIA".

Typo in Rangoon. No gum. Perf 11½ or imperf. 1 p. violet, 1 p. maroon, 1 a. green *Price from £50 each unused*

JAPANESE OCCUPATION OF THE ANDAMAN AND NICOBAR ISLANDS

The Andaman Islands in the Bay of Bengal were occupied on the 23 March 1942 and the Nicobar Islands in July 1942. Civil administration was resumed in October 1945.

The following Indian stamps were surcharged with large figures preceded by a decimal point:—

Postage stamps—.3 on ½ a. (No. 248), .5 on 1 a. (No. 250), .10 on 2 a. (No. 236*b*), .30 on 6 a. (No. 274).

Official stamps—.10 on 1 a. 3 p. (No. O146*a*), .20 on 3 p. (No. O143), .20 in red on 3 p. (No. O143).

Prices from £500 each unused

INDIAN CONVENTION STATES

The following issues resulted from a series of postal conventions agreed between the Imperial Government and the state administrations of Patiala (1 October 1884), Gwalior, Jind and Nabha (1 July 1885), and Chamba and Faridkot (1 January 1887).

Under the terms of these conventions the British Indian Post Office supplied overprinted British India issues to the state administrations which, in turn, had to conform to a number of conditions covering the issue of stamps, rates of postage and the exchange of mail.

Such overprinted issues were valid for postage within the state of issue, to other "Convention States" and to destinations in British India.

Stamps of Chamba, Gwalior, Jind, Nabha and Patiala ceased to be valid for postage on 1 January 1951, when they were replaced by those of the Republic of India, valid from 1 April 1950.

RULERS OF INDIAN CONVENTION AND FEUDATORY STATES. Details of the rulers of the various states during the period when stamps were issued are now provided in a somewhat simplified form which omits reference to minor titles. Dates quoted are of the various reigns, extended to 1971 when the titles of the surviving rulers of the former princely states were abolished by the Indian Government.

During the absorption of the Convention and Feudatory States there was often an interim period during which the administration was handed over. In some instances it is only possible to quote the end of this interim period as the point of transfer.

Stamps of India overprinted

In the Queen Victoria issues we omit varieties due to broken type, including the numerous small "A" varieties which may have come about through damaged type. We do, however, list the small "G", small "R" and tall "R" in "GWALIOR" as these were definitely the result of the use of type of the wrong size.

Variations in the length of the words due to unequal spacing when setting are also omitted.

CHAMBA

PRICES FOR STAMPS ON COVER	
Nos. 1/27	*from* × 20
Nos. 28/120	*from* × 12
Nos. O1/86	*from* × 25

Raja Sham Singh, 1873–1904

CHAMBA STATE (1) CHAMBA (2)

1887 (1 Jan)–**95.** *Queen Victoria. Optd with T* **1**.

No.	Type	Description	Unused	Used
1	**23**	½ a. blue-green	15	45
		a. "CHMABA"	£325	£400
		b. "8TATE"	£650	
		c. Opt double	£600	
2	**25**	1 a. brown-purple	90	1·10
		a. "CHMABA"	£475	£500
		b. "8TATE"	£1000	
3		1 a. plum	1·50	1·10
4	**26**	1 a. 6 p. sepia (1895)	1·00	9·00
5	**27**	2 a. dull blue	1·40	1·60
		b. "CHMABA"	£1800	£1900
		c. "8TATE"	£1800	
6		2 a. ultramarine	1·10	1·25
7	**36**	2 a. 6 p. green (1895)	28·00	75·00
8	**28**	3 a. orange (1887)	6·00	16·00
9		3 a. brown-orange (1891)	1·00	3·75
		a. "CHMABA"	£4500	£4500
		b. Opt inverted		
10	**29**	4 a. olive-green	3·25	6·50
		a. "CHMABA"	£1400	£1600
		b. "8TATE"	£2750	
11		4 a. slate-green	3·75	4·75
		a. Opt double, one albino	55·00	
12	**21**	6 a. olive-bistre (1890)	2·75	13·00
		a. Opt treble, two albino	80·00	
13		6 a. bistre-brown	11·00	13·00
14	**31**	8 a. dull mauve (1887)	5·50	7·00
		a. "CHMABA"	£3750	£3750
15		8 a. magenta (1895)	5·00	13·00
16	**32**	12 a. purple/*red* (1890)	4·25	10·00
		a. "CHMABA"	£6500	
		b. First "T" in "STATE" inverted	£6500	
		c. Opt double, one albino	32·00	
17	**33**	1 r. slate (1887)	32·00	£100
		a. "CHMABA"	£9000	
18	**37**	1 r. green and carmine (1895)	5·50	11·00
		a. Opt double, one albino	45·00	
19	**38**	2 r. carmine and yellow-brown (1895)	80·00	£250
20		3 r. brown and green (1895)	80·00	£200
21		5 r. ultramarine and violet (1895)	90·00	£375
		a. Opt double, one albino	£160	
1/21		*Set of* 15	£300	£950

1900–4. *Colours changed.*

No.	Type	Description	Unused	Used
22	**40**	3 p. carmine	10	50
		a. Opt double, one albino	32·00	
23		3 p. grey (1904)	15	1·60
		a. Opt inverted	75·00	
24	**23**	½ a. pale yellow-green (1902)	1·00	2·00
25		½ a. yellow-green (1903)	25	70
26	**25**	1 a. carmine (1902)	10	30
27	**27**	2 a. pale violet (1903)	6·50	22·00
22/7		*Set of* 5	6·50	23·00

Raja Bhuri Singh, 1904–1919

1903–5. *King Edward VII. Optd with T* **1**.

No.	Type	Description	Unused	Used
28	**41**	3 p. pale grey	10	85
29		3 p. slate-grey (1905)	10	85
30	**42**	½ a. green	20	20
31	**43**	1 a. carmine	85	35
32	**44**	2 a. pale violet (1904)	1·00	
33		2 a. mauve	85	
34	**46**	3 a. orange-brown (1905)	2·25	
		a. Opt double, one albino	32·00	
35	**47**	4 a. olive (1904)	3·50	
36	**48**	6 a. olive-bistre (1905)	2·75	
		a. Opt double, one albino	32·00	
37	**49**	8 a. purple (*shades*) (1904)	3·50	
38		8 a. claret	7·00	2
39	**50**	12 a. purple/*red* (1905)	5·00	2
		a. Opt double, one albino	32·00	
40	**51**	1 r. green and carmine (1904)	5·50	1
		a. Opt double, one albino	42·00	
28/40		*Set of* 10	22·00	8

1907. *Nos. 149/50 of India optd with T* **1**.

No.	Type	Description	Unused	Used
41	**53**	½ a. green	60	
		a. Opt double, one albino	32·00	
42	**54**	1 a. carmine	75	

1913. *King George V optd with T* **1**.

No.	Type	Description	Unused	Used
43	**55**	3 p. grey	10	
		a. Pale grey	50	
		b. Bluish grey	50	
44	**56**	½ a. light green	30	
		a. Emerald	50	
		b. Bright green	75	
		w. Wmk inverted		
45	**57**	1 a. rose-carmine	4·25	
		a. Aniline carmine	60	
		ab. Opt double, one albino	30·00	
		b. Deep mauve	3·50	
		c. Bright reddish violet	5·00	
47	**59**	2 a. purple	2·00	7
		a. Reddish purple	2·50	7
48	**62**	3 a. orange	2·25	5
		a. Dull orange	—	4
49	**63**	4 a. olive	1·60	3
50	**64**	6 a. yellow-bistre	1·75	4
		a. Brown-ochre	2·75	3
51	**65**	8 a. deep magenta	3·00	9
		a. Deep mauve	3·50	8
		b. Bright mauve	6·00	
		c. Purple	6·00	
52	**66**	12 a. carmine-lake	2·75	10
		a. Claret	6·00	10
53	**67**	1 r. red-brown and deep blue-green	11·00	20
		a. Opt double, one albino	32·00	
		b. Brown and green	11·00	20
		c. Orange-brown & dp turquoise-green	15·00	
43/53		*Set of* 10	23·00	55

Raja Ram Singh, 1919–1935

1921. *No. 192 of India optd with T* **2.**

No.	Type	Description	Unused	Used
54	**57**	9 p. on 1 a. rose-carmine	1·00	17

1923–27. *Optd with T* **1**. *New values, etc.*

No.	Type	Description	Unused	Used
55	**57**	1 a. chocolate	1·40	3
56	**58**	1½ a. chocolate (Type A)	21·00	95
57		1½ a. chocolate (Type B) (1924)	1·10	4
58		1½ a. rose-carmine (Type B) (1927)	75	15
59	**61**	2 a. 6 p. ultramarine	60	3
60		2 a. 6 p. orange (1927)	1·25	13
61	**62**	3 a. ultramarine (1924)	2·25	16
55/61		*Set of* 7	25·00	£1

Nos. 58 and 60 with inverted overprint are of clandesti origin.

CHAMBA STATE (3) CHAMBA STATE (4)

1927–37. *King George V (Nasik printing, wmk Mult Sta Optd at Nasik with T* **3** *or* **4** *(1 r.).*

No.	Type	Description	Unused	Used
62	**55**	3 p. slate (1928)	10	1·
		w. Wmk inverted	2·75	
63	**56**	½ a. green (1928)	20	1·
		w. Wmk inverted	1·00	
64	**80**	9 p. deep green (*litho*) (1932)	2·00	11·
64*a*		9 p. deep green (*typo*)	6·00	13·
65	**57**	1 a. chocolate	1·60	
		w. Wmk inverted	3·00	
66	**82**	1 a. 3 p. mauve (1932)	1·10	4·
		w. Wmk inverted	3·00	4·
67	**58**	1½ a. rose-carmine (B) (1932)	4·50	4·
		w. Wmk inverted	4·25	4·
68	**70**	2 a. purple (1928)	1·25	1·
69	**61**	2 a. 6 p. orange (1932)	1·25	12·
		w. Wmk inverted	1·40	13·
70	**62**	3 a. bright blue (1928)	1·00	14·
71	**71**	4 a. sage-green (1928)	80	3·
72	**64**	6 a. bistre (*wmk inverted*) (1937)	26·00	£1
73	**65**	8 a. reddish purple (1928)	1·40	8·
		w. Wmk inverted	1·25	7·
74	**66**	12 a. claret (1928)	1·40	9·
75	**67**	1 r. chocolate and green (1928)	4·50	20·
		w. Wmk inverted	7·50	20·
62/75		*Set of* 14	42·00	£2

Raja Lakshman Singh, 1935–1971

1935–36. *New types and colours. Optd with T* **3**.

No.	Type	Description	Unused	Used
76	**79**	½ a. green	1·00	7·
77	**81**	1 a. chocolate	1·25	6
78	**59**	2 a. vermilion (No. 236*b*)	85	19·
79		2 a. vermilion (*small die, No.* 236*c*)	95·00	£11
80	**62**	3 a. carmine	1·90	8·0
81	**63**	4 a. sage-green (1936)	2·25	11·0
76/81		*Set of* 6	95·00	£14

CHAMBA STATE (5) CHAMBA (6) CHAMBA (7)

1938. *King George VI. Nos. 247/64 optd with T* **3** *(3 p. to 1 a.) T* **5** *(2 a. to 12 a.) or T* **4** *(rupee values).*

No.	Type	Description	Unused	Used
82	**91**	3 p. slate	5·00	9·5
83		½ a. red-brown	1·00	5·5
84		9 p. green	5·50	24·0
85		1 a. carmine	1·00	1·7

2 2 a. vermilion .. .. 3·75 8·50
- 2 a. 6 p. bright violet .. .. 4·50 18·00
- 3 a. yellow-green .. .. 5·00 18·00
- 3 a. 6 p. bright blue .. .. 5·00 21·00
- 4 a. brown .. .. 16·00 15·00
- 6 a. turquoise-green .. .. 15·00 45·00
- 8 a. slate-violet .. .. 16·00 38·00
- 12 a. lake .. .. 10·00 42·00
3 1 r. grey and red-brown .. .. .. 25·00 50·00
2 r. purple and brown .. .. 48·00 £225
5 r. green and blue .. .. 80·00 £350
10 r. purple and claret £130 £500
15 r. brown and green £160 £750
25 r. slate-violet and purple £225 £800
.. .. *Set of* 18 £700 £2500

-47. *Optd with T* **6** *(to 12 a), "CHAMBA" only, as in T* **5** *a.) or T* **7** *(rupee values). (a) Stamps of* 1937. *W* **69** *(inverted 15 r.).*

91 ½ a. red-brown .. .. 28·00 20·00
1 a. carmine .. .. 32·00 24·00
93 1 r. grey and red-brown .. .. .. 18·00 50·00
2 r. purple and brown .. .. 24·00 £190
5 r. green and blue .. .. 45·00 £200
10 r. purple and claret .. .. 65·00 £400
15 r. brown and green £140 £600
w. Wmk upright .. .. — £750
25 r. slate-violet and purple £140 £600
.. .. *Set of* 8 £450 £1800

(b) Stamps of 1940–43

100*a* 3 p. slate .. .. 70 3·75
½ a. purple (1943) .. .. 70 3·50
9 p. green .. .. 1·00 11·00
1 a. carmine (1943) .. .. 1·00 3·00
101 1½ a. dull violet (1943) .. .. 1·00 7·00
2 a. vermilion (1943) .. .. 3·75 7·50
3 a. bright violet .. .. 12·00 25·00
3½ a. bright blue .. .. 6·50 28·00
102 4 a. brown .. .. 8·00 8·50
6 a. turquoise-green .. .. 12·00 35·00
8 a. slate-violet .. .. 12·00 42·00
12 a. lake .. .. 18·00 55·00
103 14 a. purple (1947) .. .. 9·50 3·00
120 .. .. *Set of* 13 80·00 £200

e 3 a. exists printed by lithography or typography.

OFFICIAL STAMPS

SERVICE

CHAMBA STATE
(O 1)

7 (1 Jan)–98. *Queen Victoria. Optd with Type* O **1**.

23 ½ a. blue-green 10 10
a. "CHMABA" £190 £180
b. "SERV CE" .. ..
c. "8TATE" £650
d. Thin seriffed "I" in "SERVICE" .. £120
2 25 1 a. brown-purple .. .. 1·10 60
a. "CHMABA" £375 £350
b. "SERV CE" £2250
c. "8TATE" £1300
d. "SERVICE" double £1100 £1000
e. "SERVICE" double, one albino .. 42·00
3 1 a. plum 90 10
a. Thin seriffed "I" in "SERVICE" .. £140
4 27 2 a. dull blue .. .. 1·40 1·10
a. "CHMABA" £1000 £1300
5 2 a. ultramarine (1887) .. .. .. 1·00 1·40
a. Thin seriffed "I" in "SERVICE" .. £200
6 28 3 a. orange (1890) .. ..
7 3 a. brown-orange (1891) .. .. .. 1·90 9·00
a. "CHMABA" £2250 £2500
b. Thin seriffed "I" in "SERVICE" ..
c. Opt double, one albino .. ..
8 29 4 a. olive-green .. .. 2·00 3·75
a. "CHMABA" £1000 £1300
b. "SERV CE" £2750
c. "8TATE" £2750
9 4 a. slate-green .. .. 1·40 6·00
a. Thin seriffed "I" in "SERVICE" ..
10 21 6 a. olive-bistre (1890) .. .. .. 4·00 9·00
a. "SERVICE" double, one albino .. 42·00
1 6 a. bistre-brown .. ..
12 31 8 a. dull mauve (1887) .. .. .. 3·00 4·75
a. "CHMABA" £4500 £4500
13 8 a. magenta (1895) .. .. .. 1·00 1·75
a. Thin seriffed "I" in "SERVICE" .. £425
14 32 12 a. purple/*red* (1890) .. .. .. 7·50 32·00
a. "CHMABA" £5500
b. First "T" in "STATE" inverted .. £5500
c. Thin seriffed "I" in "SERVICE" ..
d. "SERVICE" double, one albino .. 42·00
e. "CHAMBA STATE" double, one albino .. ..
15 33 1 r. slate (1890) .. .. 13·00 95·00
a. "CHMABA" £4250
16 37 1 r. green and carmine (1898) .. .. 6·00 28·00
a. Thin seriffed "I" in "SERVICE" ..
1/16 .. .. *Set of* 10 32·00 £160

Printings up to and including that of December 1895 had the SERVICE" overprint applied to sheets of stamps already over-inted with Type 1. From the printing of September 1898 onwards oth "SERVICE" and "CHAMBA STATE" were overprinted at the ame time. Nos. O6, O8 and O12 only exist using the first method, nd No. O16 was only printed using the second.

The thin seriffed "I" in "SERVICE" variety occured on R. 19/12 f the September 1898 printing only.

902–4. *Colours changed. Optd as Type* O **1**.

17 40 3 p. grey (1904) 15 50
18 23 ½ a. pale yellow-green .. .. 20 2·75
19 ½ a. yellow-green .. .. 2·75 1·75
20 25 1 a. carmine 40 40
21 27 2 a. pale violet (1903) .. .. .. 9·00 25·00
17/21 .. .. *Set of* 4 9·00 25·00

1903–5. *King Edward VII. Stamps of India optd as Type* O **1**.

O22 **41** 3 p. pale grey 15 15
a. Opt double, one albino .. .. 27·00
O23 3 p. slate-grey (1905) 10 65
O24 **42** ½ a. yellow-green 25 10
O25 **43** 1 a. carmine 65 30
O26 **44** 2 a. pale violet (1904) .. .. .. 2·25 75
O27 2 a. mauve 90 50
O28 **47** 4 a. olive (1905) .. .. 3·50 14·00
O29 **49** 8 a. purple (1905) .. .. 4·00 13·00
O30 8 a. claret .. .. 7·00 19·00
a. Opt double, one albino .. .. 32·00
O31 **51** 1 r. green and carmine (1905) .. .. 1·75 8·50
O22/31 .. .. *Set of* 7 10·00 32·00

The 2 a. mauve King Edward VII, overprinted "On H.M.S.", was discovered in Calcutta, but was not sent to Chamba, and is an unissued variety (*Price un.* £35).

1907. *Nos.* 149/50 *of India, optd with Type* O **1**.

O32 **53** ½ a. green 25 75
a. Opt inverted £4000 £4000
b. Opt double, one albino .. .. 27·00
O33 **54** 1 a. carmine .. .. 2·00 1·40

The inverted overprint, No. O32a, was due to an inverted cliché on R. 20/1 which was corrected after a few sheets had been printed.

1913–23. *King George V Official stamps (wmk Single Star) optd with T* **1**.

O34 **55** 3 p. grey 20 40
a. Pale grey 30 40
b. Bluish grey 40 50
c. Slate 30 65
O36 **56** ½ a. light green 10 10
a. Emerald .. .. 1·25 30
b. Bright green .. .. 1·50 30
O38 **57** 1 a. aniline carmine 10 10
a. Rose-carmine .. .. 4·00 40
O40 **59** 2 a. purple (1914) .. .. 1·10 10·00
a. Reddish purple .. .. 5·00
b. Bright reddish violet (1923) .. .. 5·00 10·00
O41 **63** 4 a. olive .. .. 1·10 13·00
O42 **65** 8 a. deep magenta .. .. 1·75 14·00
a. Deep mauve .. .. 2·75 14·00
O43 **67** 1 r. red-brown & dp blue-green (1914) 4·00 23·00
a. Opt double, one albino .. .. 30·00
b. Brown and green .. .. .. 5·00 25·00
O34/43 .. .. *Set of* 7 7·50 55·00

No. O36 with inverted overprint and No. O38*a* with double or inverted overprint (on gummed side) are of clandestine origin.

1914. *King George V. Optd with Type* O **1**.

O44 **59** 2 a. purple .. .. 13·00
O45 **63** 4 a. olive .. .. 10·00

1921 *No.* O97 *of India optd with T* **2** *at top.*

O46 **57** 9 p. on 1 a. rose-carmine .. .. .. 15 6·00

1925. *As* 1913–14. *New colour.*

O47 **57** 1 a. chocolate .. .. 1·90 50

CHAMBA STATE SERVICE
(O 2)

CHAMBA STATE SERVICE
(O 3)

1927–39. *King George V (Nasik printing, wmk Mult Star), optd at Nasik with Type* O **2** *or* O **3** *(rupee values).*

O48 **55** 3 p. slate (1928) 50 30
w. Wmk inverted .. .. — 75
O49 **56** ½ a. green (1928) 35 15
O50 **80** 9 p. deep green (1932) .. .. .. 2·00 7·50
O51 **57** 1 a. chocolate 20 10
w. Wmk inverted .. .. — 40
O52 **82** 1 a. 3 p. mauve (1932) .. .. .. 5·00 60
w. Wmk inverted .. ..
O53 **70** 2 a. purple (1928) .. .. 1·25 60
O54 **71** 4 a. sage-green (1928) .. .. .. 1·10 1·50
O55 **65** 8 a. reddish purple (1930) .. .. .. 3·75 7·00
w. Wmk inverted .. .. 5·00
O56 **66** 12 a. claret (1928) .. .. 2·50 18·00
w. Wmk inverted .. .. 9·00
O57 **67** 1 r. chocolate and green (1930) .. .. 11·00 32·00
O58 2 r. carmine and orange (1939) .. .. 21·00 £180
O59 5 r. ultramarine and purple (1939) .. 40·00 £250
O60 10 r. green and scarlet (1939) .. .. 60·00 £250
O48/60 .. .. *Set of* 13 £130 £650

1935–39. *New types and colours. Optd with Type* O **2**.

O61 **79** ½ a. green .. .. 2·50 50
O62 **81** 1 a. chocolate .. .. 2·50 45
O63 **59** 2 a. vermilion .. .. 3·50 1·00
O64 2 a. vermilion (*small die*) (1939) .. .. 3·50 13·00
O65 **63** 4 a. sage-green (1936) .. .. .. 5·00 4·25
O61/5 .. .. *Set of* 5 15·00 17·00

1938–40. *King George VI. Optd with Type* O **2** *or* O **3** *(rupee values).*

O66 **91** 9 p. green .. .. 9·50 42·00
O67 1 a. carmine .. .. 8·00 2·00
O68 **93** 1 r. grey and red-brown (1940?) £350 £800
O69 2 r. purple and brown (1939) .. .. 38·00 £275
O70 5 r. green and blue (1939) .. .. 60·00 £350
O71 10 r. purple and claret (1939) .. .. 90·00 £600
O66/71 .. .. *Set of* 6 £500 £1800

CHAMBA SERVICE
(O 4)

1940–43. *(a) Official stamps optd with T* **6**.

O72 **O 20** 3 p. slate 70 70
O73 ½ a. red-brown .. .. 13·00 1·75
O74 ½ a. purple (1943) .. .. 70 2·00
O75 9 p. green .. .. 4·00 6·50
w. Wmk inverted .. .. 14·00 10·00
O76 1 a. carmine (1941) .. .. 70 1·50
O77 **O 20** 1 a. 3 p. yellow-brown (1941) .. .. 45·00 14·00
O78 1½ a. dull violet (1943) .. .. .. 4·25 5·50
O79 2 a. vermilion .. .. 4·25 5·00
O80 2½ a. bright violet (1941) .. .. .. 2·25 17·00
O81 4 a. brown .. .. 3·50 8·00
O82 8 a. slate-violet .. .. 11·00 45·00
w. Wmk inverted .. .. 10·00 45·00

(b) Postage stamps optd with Type O **4**.

O83 **93** 1 r. grey and red-brown (1942) .. .. 20·00 £160
O84 2 r. purple and brown (1942) .. .. 35·00 £225
O85 5 r. green and blue (1942) .. .. 60·00 £350
O86 10 r. purple and claret (1942) .. .. 80·00 £600
O72/86 .. .. *Set of* 15 £250 £1200

Chamba became part of Himachal Pradesh on 15 April 1948.

FARIDKOT

For earlier issues, see under INDIAN FEUDATORY STATES

PRICES FOR STAMPS ON COVER	
Nos. 1/17	*from* × 30
Nos. O1/15	*from* × 40

Raja Bikram Singh, 1874–1898

FARIDKOT STATE
(1)

1887 (1 Jan)–1900. *Queen Victoria. Optd with T* **1**.

1 **23** ½ a. deep green .. .. 1·00 1·00
a. "ARIDKOT" .. ..
b. "FAR DKOT" .. .. — £1300
c. Opt double, one albino .. .. 38·00
2 **25** 1 a. brown-purple .. .. 1·00 2·00
3 1 a. plum .. .. 1·25 1·25
4 **27** 2 a. blue .. .. 2·75 4·00
5 2 a. deep blue .. .. 2·75 5·00
6 **28** 3 a. orange .. .. 5·00 8·50
7 3 a. brown-orange (1893) .. .. .. 1·90 3·00
8 **29** 4 a. olive-green .. .. 5·50 13·00
a. "ARIDKOT" £1100
9 4 a. slate-green .. .. 6·00 17·00
10 **21** 6 a. olive-bistre .. .. 24·00 42·00
a. "ARIDKOT" £1600
b. Opt double, one albino .. .. 38·00
11 6 a. bistre-brown .. .. 1·75 12·00
12 **31** 8 a. dull mauve .. .. 9·50 30·00
a. "ARIDKOT" £2250
13 8 a. magenta .. .. 14·00 95·00
a. Opt double, one albino .. .. 32·00
14 **32** 12 a. purple/*red* (1900) .. .. .. 32·00 £350
15 **33** 1 r. slate .. .. 38·00 £325
a. "ARIDKOT" £2250
16 **37** 1 r. green and carmine (1893) .. .. 32·00 80·00
a. Opt double, one albino .. .. 55·00
1/16 .. .. *Set of* 10 £110 £750

The ½ a., 1 a., 2 a., 3 a., 4 a., 8 a. and 1 r. (No. 16) are known with broken "O" (looking like a "C") in "FARIDKOT".

Raja Balbir Singh, 1898–1906

1900. *Optd with T* 1.

17 **40** 3 p. carmine .. .. 90 38·00

OFFICIAL STAMPS

SERVICE

FARIDKOT STATE
(O 1)

1887 (1 Jan)–98. *Queen Victoria. Optd with Type* O **1**.

O 1 **23** ½ a. deep green 15 60
a. "SERV CE" £1600
b. "FAR DKOT" .. ..
c. Thin seriffed "I" in "SERVICE" .. £160
d. "FARIDKOT STATE" double, one albino .. .. 32·00
O 2 **25** 1 a. brown-purple .. .. 55 1·25
a. Thin seriffed "I" in "SERVICE" .. £170
b. Opt double, one albino .. .. 40·00
O 3 1 a. plum .. .. 1·00 1·25
a. "SERV CE" £2000
O 4 **27** 2 a. dull blue .. .. 1·75 7·50
a. "SERV CE" £2000
O 5 2 a. deep blue .. .. 1·00 10·00
O 6 **28** 3 a. orange .. .. 5·00 7·00
a. "SERVICE" double, one albino ..
O 7 3 a. brown-orange (12.98) .. .. .. 1·10 26·00
a. Thin seriffed "I" in "SERVICE" .. £425
O 8 **29** 4 a. olive-green .. .. 3·75 19·00
a. "SERV CE" £2000
b. "ARIDKOT" .. ..
c. "SERVICE" treble, two albino .. 65·00
O 9 4 a. slate-green .. .. 9·00 32·00
a. "SERVICE" double, one albino .. 32·00
O10 **21** 6 a. olive-bistre .. .. 26·00 70·00
a. "ARIDKOT" £1200
b. "SERVIC" £2000
c. "SERVICE" double, one albino .. 42·00
d. "FARIDKOT STATE" double, one albino .. .. 42·00
O11 6 a. bistre-brown .. .. 17·00 22·00
O12 **31** 8 a. dull mauve .. .. 5·00 22·00
a. "SERV CE" £2250
O13 8 a. magenta .. .. 13·00 95·00

O14 **33** 1 r. slate .. .. 42·00 £160
a. "SERVICE" double, one albino .. 65·00
O15 **37** 1 r. green and carmine (12.98) .. 75·00 £450
a. Thin seriffed "I" in "SERVICE" ..
O1/15 .. .. *Set of* 9 £130 £600

The ½ a., 1 a., 2 a., 3 a., 4 a., 8 a. and 1 r. (No. O15) are known with the broken "O".

Printings up to and including that of November 1895 had the "SERVICE" overprint applied to sheets already overprinted with Type 1. From December 1898 onwards "SERVICE" and "FARIDKOT STATE" were overprinted at one operation to provide fresh supplies of Nos. O1/3, O7 and O15.

The thin seriffed "I" variety occurs on the December 1898 overprinting only.

This State ceased to use overprinted stamps after 31 March 1901.

GWALIOR

PRICES FOR STAMPS ON COVER

Nos. 1/3	*from* × 10
Nos. 4/11	—
Nos. 12/66	*from* × 5
Nos. 67/128	*from* × 4
Nos. 129/37	*from* × 5
Nos. O1/94	*from* × 12

OVERPRINTS. From 1885 to 1926 these were applied by the Government of India Central Printing Press, Calcutta, and from 1927 at the Security Press, Nasik, *unless otherwise stated.*

Maharaja Jayaji Rao Sindhia, 1843–1886

गवालियर

GWALIOR
(1)

GWALIOR
गवालियर
(2)

GWALIOR
Small "G"

GWALIOR
Small "R"

GWALIOR
Tall "R"
(original state)

GWALIOR
Tall "R"
(damaged state)

OVERPRINT VARIETIES OF TYPE 2.

Small "G"—Occurs on R.7/11 from June 1900 printing of ½, 1, 2, 3, 4 a. and 3 p. (No. 38), and on an unknown position from May 1901 printing of 2, 3 and 5 r.

Small "R"—Occurs on R. 9/3 from June 1900 printing of 3 p. to 4 a. and on R.2/3 from May 1901 printing of 2, 3 and 5 r.

Tall "R" —Occurs on R.20/2 from printings between June 1900 and May 1907. The top of the letter is damaged on printings from February 1903 onwards.

1885 (1 July)–**97.** *Queen Victoria. I. Optd with T* **1**.

(*a*) *Space between two lines of overprint* 13 *mm. Hindi inscription* 13 *to* 14 *mm long* (May 1885)

1 **23** ½ a. blue-green .. .. .. £100 20·00
2 **25** 1 a. brown-purple .. .. .. 70·00 25·00
3 **27** 2 a. dull blue .. .. .. 60·00 12·00
1/3 .. .. *Set of* 3 £200 50·00

A variety exists of the ½ a. in which the space between the two lines of overprint is only 9½ mm but this is probably from a proof sheet.

(*b*) *Space between two lines of overprint* 15 *mm on* 4 *a. and* 6 *a. and* 16 *to* 17 *mm on other values* (June 1885). *Hindi inscription* 13 *to* 14 *mm long*

4 **23** ½ a. blue-green .. .. 40·00
a. Opt double, one albino .. .. 55·00
b. Hindi inscr 15 to 15½ mm long .. 90·00
ba. Opt double, one albino £130
c. Pair. Nos. 4/4b £500
5 **25** 1 a. brown-purple .. .. .. 45·00
a. Opt double, one albino .. .. 50·00
b. Hindi inscr 15 to 15½ mm long .. 90·00
ba. Opt double, one albino £100
c. Pair. Nos. 5/5b £500
6 **26** 1 a. 6 p. sepia .. .. 60·00
b. Hindi inscr 15 to 15½ mm long .. £160
c. Pair. Nos. 6/6b £600
7 **27** 2 a. dull blue .. .. 45·00
b. Hindi inscr 15 to 15½ mm long .. £100
c. Pair. Nos. 7/7b £375
8 **17** 4 a. green .. .. 65·00
b. Hindi inscr 15 to 15½ mm long .. £150
c. Pair. Nos. 8/8b £650
9 **21** 6 a. olive-bistre .. .. .. 65·00
a. Opt double, one albino .. .. 75·00
b. Hindi inscr 15 to 15½ mm long .. £160
ba. Opt double, one albino £180
c. Pair. Nos. 9/9b £650
10 **31** 8 a. dull mauve .. .. .. 60·00
b. Hindi inscr 15 to 15½ mm long .. £150
c. Pair. Nos. 10/10b £650
11 **33** 1 r. slate .. .. 60·00
b. Hindi inscr 15 to 15½ mm long .. £160
c. Pair. Nos. 11/11b £650
4/11 .. .. *Set of* 8 £400
4b/11b .. .. *Set of* 8 £950

The two types of overprint on these stamps occur in the same settings, with about a quarter of the stamps in each sheet showing the long inscription. Nos. 4/7 and 10/11 were overprinted in sheets of 240 and Nos. 8/9 in half-sheets of 160.

II. *Optd with T* **2**. *Hindi inscription* 13 *to* 14 *mm long*

(*a*) *In red* (Sept 1885)

12 **23** ½ a. blue-green 55 20
b. Hindi inscr 15 to 15½ mm long .. 90 55
c. Pair. Nos. 12/12b .. .. .. 10·00 13·00
13 **27** 2 a. dull blue .. .. .. 11·00 12·00
b. Hindi inscr 15 to 15½ mm long .. 26·00 28·00
c. Pair. Nos. 13/13b £300 £325
14 **17** 4 a. green .. .. .. 19·00 10·00
b. Hindi inscr 15 to 15½ mm long .. £160 85·00
c. Pair. Nos. 14/14b £500
15 **33** 1 r. slate .. .. .. 7·50 19·00
aw. Wmk inverted .. .. .. 16·00 28·00
b. Hindi inscr 15 to 15½ mm long .. 28·00 65·00
bw. Wmk inverted .. .. .. 42·00 85·00
c. Pair. Nos. 15/15b .. .. .. 60·00 £100
cw. Wmk inverted .. .. .. 80·00
12/15 .. .. *Set of* 4 32·00 38·00
12b/15b .. .. *Set of* 4 £190 £160

No. 14 was overprinted in half-sheets of 160, about 40 stamps having the Hindi inscription 15 to 15½ mm long. The remaining three values were from a setting of 240 containing 166 13 to 14 mm long and 74 15 to 15½ mm long.

Reprints have been made of Nos. 12 to 15, but the majority of the specimens have the word "REPRINT" overprinted upon them.

(*b*) *In black* (1885–97)

16 **23** ½ a. blue-green (1889) .. .. .. 1·00 1·40
a. Opt double
b. Opt double, one albino .. .. 20·00
c. Hindi inscr 15 to 15½ mm long .. 20 10
ca. Opt double
cb. Opt double, one albino .. .. 60·00
cc. "GWALICR" .. .. .. 85·00 £100
cd. Small "G" .. .. .. 60·00 48·00
ce. Small "R" .. .. .. 70·00
cf. Tall "R" .. .. .. 70·00 70·00
d. Pair. Nos. 16/16c .. .. .. 50·00 55·00
17 **24** 9 p. carmine (1891) .. .. .. 30·00 50·00
a. Opt double, one albino .. .. 50·00
c. Hindi inscr 15 to 15½ mm long .. 50·00 70·00
ca. Opt double, one albino .. .. 80·00
d. Pair. Nos. 17/17c £225
18 **25** 1 a. brown-purple 70 20
c. Hindi inscr 15 to 15½ mm long .. 1·90 35
d. Pair. Nos. 18/18c .. .. .. 13·00 14·00
19 1 a. plum (*Hindi inscr* 15 *to* 15½ *mm long*) .. .. .. 1·75 10
a. Small "G" .. .. .. 75·00 55·00
b. Small "R" .. .. .. 80·00
c. Tall "R" .. .. .. 90·00
20 **26** 1 a. 6 p. sepia .. .. .. 50 1·00
c. Hindi inscr 15 to 15½ mm long .. 1·00 40
d. Pair. Nos. 20/20c .. .. .. 13·00 16·00
21 **27** 2 a. dull blue .. .. .. 4·75 80
c. Hindi inscr 15 to 15½ mm long .. 60 10
ca. "R" omitted £450 £450
d. Pair. Nos. 21/21c £120
22 2 a. deep blue .. .. .. 6·50 1·60
c. Hindi inscr 15 to 15½ mm long .. 1·75 30
ca. Small "G" £140 £140
cb. Small "R" £190
cc. Tall "R" £200 £200
d. Pair. Nos. 22/22c £140
23 **36** 2 a. 6 p. yellow-green (*Hindi inscr* 15 *to* 15½ *mm long*) (1896) .. .. 5·50 16·00
a. "GWALICR" £500
24 **28** 3 a. orange .. .. .. 5·00 9·00
a. Opt double, one albino .. .. 42·00
c. Hindi inscr 15 to 15½ mm long .. 48·00 32·00
ca. Opt double, one albino
d. Pair. Nos. 24/24c £200
25 3 a. brown-orange .. .. .. 22·00 4·00
c. Hindi inscr 15 to 15½ mm long .. 1·50 15
ca. Opt double, one albino .. .. 32·00
cb. Small "G" £225 £225
cc. Small "R" £475
cd. Tall "R" £190 £190
d. Pair. Nos. 25/25c £180
26 **29** 4 a. olive-green (1889) .. .. .. 4·50 80
c. Hindi inscr 15 to 15½ mm long .. 9·00 3·00
d. Pair. Nos. 26/26c £120
27 4 a. slate-green .. .. .. 5·50 1·60
c. Hindi inscr 15 to 15½ mm long .. 2·50 60
ca. Opt double, one albino .. .. 55·00
cb. Small "G" £450 £300
cc. Small "R" £450
cd. Tall "R" £325 £300
d. Pair. Nos. 27/27c .. .. .. 35·00
28 **21** 6 a. olive-bistre .. .. .. 5·50 11·00
c. Hindi inscr 15 to 15½ mm long .. 2·75 11·00
d. Pair. Nos. 28/28c .. .. .. 48·00
29 6 a. bistre-brown .. .. .. 1·60 6·00
c. Hindi inscr 15 to 15½ mm long .. 3·25 8·00
d. Pair. Nos. 29/29c .. .. .. 21·00
30 **31** 8 a. dull mauve .. .. .. 8·50 32·00
c. Hindi inscr 15 to 15½ mm long .. 3·00 75
d. Pair. Nos. 30/30c £250
31 8 a. magenta (*Hindi inscr* 15 *to* 15½ *mm long*) (1897) .. .. .. 6·00 7·00
32 **32** 12 a. purple/*red* (1891) .. .. .. 3·00 8·00
c. Hindi inscr 15 to 15½ mm long .. 3·25 65
ca. Pair, one without opt £3000
cb. Tall "R" £900 £650
d. Pair. Nos. 32/32c .. .. .. 70·00
33 **33** 1 r. slate (1889) £100 £375
c. Hindi inscr 15 to 15½ mm long .. 2·50 1·10
d. Pair. Nos. 33/33c £425
34 **37** 1 r. green and carmine (*Hindi inscr* 15 *to* 15½ *mm long*) (1896) .. .. 3·00 2·75
a. Opt double, one albino .. .. 65·00
b. "GWALICR" £750 £900
35 **38** 2 r. carmine and yellow-brown (*Hindi inscr* 15 *to* 15½ *mm long*) (1896) .. 5·50 3·00
a. Small "G" £275 £180
b. Small "R" £300 £200
36 3 r. brown and green (*Hindi inscr* 15 *to* 15½ *mm long*) (1896) .. .. 7·50 3·50
a. Small "G" £300 £190
b. Small "R" £325 £225
37 **38** 5 r. ultramarine and violet (*Hindi inscr* 15 *to* 15½ *mm long*) (1896) .. .. 14·00
a. Small "G" £350
b. Small "R" £400
16/37 .. .. *Set of* 16 70·00

Printings to 1891 continued to use the setting showing types, but subsequently a new setting containing the l overprint only was used.

The ½ a., 1 a., 2 a. and 3 a. exist with space between "I "O" of "GWALIOR".

The "GWALICR" error occurs on R. 1/5 in the May printing only.

Maharaja Madhav Rao Sindhia, 1886–1925

1899–1911. (*a*) *Optd with T* **2** (B).

38 **40** 3 p. carmine 10
a. Opt inverted £800
b. Small "G" .. .. .. 55·00 5
d. Small "R" .. .. .. 65·00
e. Tall "R" .. .. .. 42·00
f. Opt double, one albino .. .. 32·00
39 3 p. grey (1904) .. .. .. 6·50 6
e. Tall "R" £225
f. Opt double, one albino .. .. 55·00
40 **23** ½ a. pale yellow-green (1901) 20
e. Tall "R" .. .. .. 85·00
f. Opt double, one albino .. .. 21·00
40*g* ½ a. yellow-green (1903) .. .. 2·75
ge. Tall "R" £130
41 **25** 1 a. carmine (1901) 70
e. Tall "R" .. .. .. 90·00
f. Opt double, one albino .. .. 38·00
42 **27** 2 a. pale violet (1903) .. .. .. 1·00
e. Tall "R" £140
43 **36** 2 a. 6 p. ultramarine (1903) .. .. 1·00
e. Tall "R" £180
38/43 .. .. *Set of* 6 8·50 65

(*b*) *Optd as T* **2**, *but* "GWALIOR" 13 *mm long. Opt spaced* 2¾ *mm*

44 **38** 3 r. brown and green (1911) .. .. £160 £
45 5 r. ultramarine and violet (1910) .. 55·00 55
a. Opt double, one albino .. .. 85·00

1903–11. *King Edward VII. Optd as T* **2**.

A. "GWALIOR" 14 *mm long. Overprint spaced* 1¾ *mm* (1903–

46A **41** 3 p. pale grey 60
e. Tall "R" .. .. .. 30·00 3.
f. Slate-grey (1905) 90
fe. Tall "R" .. .. .. 35·00 38
48A **42** ½ a. green 10
e. Tall "R" .. .. .. 28·00 32
49A **43** 1 a. carmine 10
e. Tall "R" .. .. .. 32·00 38
f. Opt double, one albino .. .. 32·00
50A **44** 2 a. pale violet (1904) 70
e. Tall "R" .. .. .. 80·00
f. Mauve .. .. .. 1·50
fe. Tall "R" .. .. .. 95·00 95
52A **45** 2 a. 6 p. ultramarine (1904) .. .. 17·00 65
e. Tall "R" £750
53A **46** 3 a. orange-brown (1904) .. .. 1·50
e. Tall "R" .. .. .. £130 £
54A **47** 4 a. olive .. .. .. 1·40
e. Tall "R" .. .. .. £170 £
f. Pale olive .. .. .. 7·00 2
fe. Tall "R" £275
56A **48** 6 a. olive-bistre (1904) .. .. 2·50 2
e. Tall "R" £800
57A **49** 8 a. purple (*shades*) (1905) .. .. 3·00 1
e. Tall "R" £350 £2
59A **50** 12 a. purple/*red* (1905) .. .. 2·75 15
e. Tall "R" £850
60A **51** 1 r. green and carmine (1905) .. .. 2·25 1
e. Tall "R" £750 £7
61A **52** 2 r. carmine and yellow-brown (1906) 30·00 42
a. Opt double, one albino .. .. 50·00
46A/61A .. .. *Set of* 12 55·00 £1

B. "GWALIOR" 13 *mm long. Overprint spaced* 2¾ *mm* (1908–11)

46B **41** 3 p. pale grey .. .. .. 1·50
f. Slate-grey .. .. .. 1·90
49B **43** 1 a. carmine .. .. .. 2·25
50/B 2 a. mauve .. .. .. 1·90
52B **45** 2 a. 6 p. ultramarine .. .. .. 1·00 6
53B **46** 3 a. orange-brown .. .. .. 2·50
54/B 4 a. pale olive .. .. .. 3·75
56B **48** 6 a. olive-bistre .. .. .. 4·25 1
57B **49** 8 a. purple (*shades*) .. .. .. 6·00 1
f. Claret .. .. .. 14·00 2
fa. Opt double, one albino .. .. 42·00
59B **50** 12 a. purple/*red* .. .. .. 3·75 3
f. Opt double, one albino .. .. 55·00
60B **51** 1 r. green and carmine .. .. .. 3·50 1
61B **52** 2 r. carmine and yellow-brown .. .. 9·00 11
a. Opt double, one albino .. .. 42·00
62B 3 r. brown and green (1910) .. .. 26·00 45
a. Red-brown and green .. .. 60·00 70
63B 5 r. ultramarine and violet (1911) .. 19·00 27
46B/63B .. .. *Set of* 13 75·00 85

1907–08. *Nos.* 149 *and* 150 *of India optd as T* **2**.

(*a*) "GWALIOR" 14 *mm long. Overprint spaced* 1¾ *mm*

64 **53** ½ a. green 10 7
e. Tall "R" .. .. .. 48·00 75

(*b*) "GWALIOR" 13 *mm long. Overprint spaced* 2¾ *mm* (1908

65 **53** ½ a. green 60
66 **54** 1 a. carmine .. .. 1·25

1912–14. *King George V. Optd as T* **2**.

67 **55** 3 p. grey 10 1
a. Opt double .. .. .. † £80
b. Pale grey 10 1
c. Bluish grey .. .. .. — 3
d. Slate 30 3
da. "Rs" flaw .. .. .. 26·00 30·0
68 **56** ½ a. light green 20 1
a. Emerald .. .. .. — 3
b. Bright green 50 1
ba. Opt inverted .. .. .. † £37

7 1 a. aniline carmine 25 10
a. Opt double .. .. 25·00
9 2 a. purple 40 10
a. Reddish purple 60 10
aw. Wmk inverted .. .. .. † 65·00
b. Deep mauve .. .. .. 1·00 30
c. Bright reddish violet .. .. 1·00 30
2 3 a. orange 50 15
a. Dull orange 50 15
3 4 a. olive (1913) 60 60
4 6 a. yellow-bistre .. .. .. 1·00 90
a. Brown-ochre .. .. .. 1·00 90
5 8 a. deep magenta (1913) .. .. 1·10 50
a. Deep mauve .. .. .. 2·00 30
b. Bright mauve .. .. .. 5·00 1·00
6 12 a. carmine-lake (1914) .. .. 1·25 2·50
a. Claret .. .. — 3·25
7 1 r. red-brown & deep blue-green (1913) 5·00 70
a. Opt double, one albino .. .. 20·00
b. Brown and green .. .. .. 3·50 40
ba. Opt double £650
c. Orange-brown & dp turquoise-green — 1·50
2 r. carmine-rose and brown (1913) .. 4·50 4·50
a. Opt double, one albino .. .. 50·00
5 r. ultramarine and violet (1913) .. 20·00 6·50
a. Opt double, one albino .. .. 70·00
.. .. *Set of* 12 30·00 14·50

GWALIOR
(3)

. *No.* 192 *of India optd with T* **3**.
57 9 p. on 1 a. rose-carmine 10 50
. 79 with inverted overprint is of clandestine origin.

–7. *Optd as T* **2**. *New colours and values.*
57 1 a. chocolate 50 10
a. Opt double, one albino .. .. 32·00
58 1½ a. chocolate (B) (1925) .. .. 1·40 50
1½ a. rose-carmine (B) (1927) 20 20
61 2 a. 6 p. ultramarine (1925) .. .. 1·50 1·75
2 a. 6 p. orange (1927) 35 50
62 3 a. ultramarine (1924) .. .. 1·10 60
.. .. *Set of* 6 4·50 3·25
. 82 with inverted overprint is of clandestine origin.

Maharaja George Jivaji Rao Sindhia, 1925–1961

GWALIOR
गवालियर
(4)

GWALIOR
गवालियर
(5)

–36. *King George V (Nasik printing, wmk Mult Star), optd at Nasik with T* **4** *or* **5** *(rupee values).*
55 3 p. slate (1932) 75 15
w. Wmk inverted .. .. .. 1·00 1·00
56 ½ a. green (1930) .. .. .. 1·50 10
w. Wmk inverted .. .. ..
80 9 p. deep green (*litho*) (1932) .. .. 1·75 20
aw. Wmk inverted .. .. .. 2·50 80
9p. deep green (*typo*) .. .. .. 2·75 50
57 1 a. chocolate 75 10
w. Wmk inverted .. .. .. — 75
82 1 a. 3 p. mauve (1936) 50 15
70 2 a. purple 75 30
w. Wmk inverted 75 30
62 3 a. bright blue .. .. .. 1·00 40
71 4 a. sage-green .. .. .. 1·00 1·00
w. Wmk inverted .. .. .. 1·75 2·25
65 8 a. reddish purple (*wmk inverted*) .. 1·25 1·10
66 12 a. claret .. .. 1·50 2·75
67 1 r. chocolate and green .. .. 2·00 3·00
w. Wmk inverted .. .. .. 3·50 3·00
2 r. carmine and orange .. .. 6·00 4·50
w. Wmk inverted .. .. .. 5·00 4·00
5 r. ultramarine and purple (*wmk inverted*) (1929) .. .. .. 16·00 22·00
10 r. green and scarlet (1930) .. .. 45·00 30·00
15 r. blue & olive (*wmk inverted*) (1930) 70·00 48·00
25 r. orange and blue (1930) £150 £120
101 .. .. *Set of* 16 £275 £200

5–36. *New types and colours. Optd with T* **4**.
79 ½ a. green (1936) 50 20
w. Wmk inverted .. .. .. 3·25 2·25
81 1 a. chocolate 10 10
59 2 a. vermilion (1936) .. .. .. 1·25 2·00
2/4 .. .. *Set of* 3 1·60 2·10

8–48. *King George VI. Nos.* 247/50, 253, 255/6, *and* 259/64 *optd with T* **4** *or* **5** *(rupee values).*
5 **91** 3 p. slate .. .. 5·00 10
6 ½ a. red-brown .. .. 5·50 10
7 9 p. green (1939) .. .. .. 35·00 3·00
8 1 a. carmine .. .. 5·00 15
9 – 3 a. yellow-green (1939) .. .. 13·00 3·25
0 – 4 a. brown .. .. 42·00 2·25
1 – 6 a. turquoise-green (1939) .. .. 2·50 7·50
2 **93** 1 r. grey and red-brown (1942) .. .. 7·00 1·50
3 2 r. purple and brown (1948) .. .. 35·00 8·00
4 5 r. green and blue (1948) .. .. 30·00 32·00
5 10 r. purple and claret (1948) .. .. 30·00 40·00
6 15 r. brown and green (1948) .. .. 90·00 £160
7 25 r. slate-violet and purple (1948) .. 80·00 £120
5/117 .. .. *Set of* 13 £350 £325

42–5. *King George VI. Optd with T* **4**.
8 **100*a*** 3 p. slate 45 10
w. Wmk inverted .. .. .. — 15·00
9 ½ a. purple (1943) 45 10
20 9 p. green 45 10
21 1 a. carmine (1943) 40 10
a. Opt double .. .. .. — £140
22 **101** 1½ a. dull violet .. .. .. 5·00 20
23 2 a. vermilion 65 20
24 3 a. bright violet .. .. .. 10·00 50
a. Opt double .. .. .. — £140

125 **102** 4 a. brown .. .. 1·25 20
126 6 a. turquoise-green (1945) .. .. 16·00 21·00
127 8 a. slate-violet (1944) .. .. 2·75 2·75
128 12 a. lake (1943) .. .. .. 4·50 18·00
118/28 .. .. *Set of* 11 38·00 38·00
The 1½ a. and 3 a. exist printed by lithography or typography.

GWALIOR
गवालियर
(6)

1949 (Apr). *King George VI. Optd with T* **6** *at the Alizah Printing Press, Gwalior.*
129 **100*a*** 3 p. slate 90 50
130 ½ a. purple 75 50
131 1 a. carmine 75 60
132 **101** 2 a. vermilion .. .. .. 17·00 2·00
133 3 a. bright violet .. .. .. 42·00 23·00
134 **102** 4 a. brown .. .. 3·50 2·75
135 6 a. turquoise-green .. .. .. 38·00 45·00
136 8 a. slate-violet .. .. .. 85·00 45·00
137 12 a. lake £325 £130
129/137 .. .. *Set of* 9 £450 £225

OFFICIAL STAMPS

गवालियर
सरविस
(O 1)

गवालियर
सरविस
(O 2)

1895–96. *Queen Victoria. Optd with Type* O **1**.
O 1 **23** ½ a. blue-green 10 10
a. Hindi characters transposed .. 24·00 28·00
b. 4th Hindi character omitted .. £425 40·00
c. Opt double .. .. † £850
O 2 **25** 1 a. brown-purple .. .. .. 7·50 1·00
O 3 1 a. plum 65 10
a. Hindi characters transposed .. 38·00 42·00
b. 4th Hindi character omitted .. — 65·00
O 4 **27** 2 a. dull blue .. .. 1·50 40
O 5 2 a. deep blue .. .. 1·10 40
a. Hindi characters transposed .. 60·00 80·00
b. 4th Hindi character omitted .. 80·00 £100
O 6 **29** 4 a. olive-green .. .. .. 1·75 75
a. Hindi characters transposed .. £500 £500
b. 4th Hindi character omitted .. £2000 £1300
O 7 4 a. slate-green .. .. .. 1·40 1·00
a. Hindi characters transposed .. £300
O 8 **31** 8 a. dull mauve .. .. .. 2·25 1·50
a. Opt double, one albino .. .. 32·00
O 9 8 a. magenta .. .. 1·40 1·25
a. Hindi characters transposed .. £1200 £1300
b. 4th Hindi character omitted ..
O10 **37** 1 r. green and carmine (1896) .. 4·50 3·00
a. Hindi characters transposed .. £2500
O1/10 .. .. *Set of* 6 8·25 5·00
In the errors listed above it is the last two Hindi characters that are transposed, so that the word reads "Sersiv". The error occurs on R.19/1 in the sheet from the early printings up to May 1896.

1901–04. *Colours changed.*
O23 **40** 3 p. carmine (1902) 30 20
O24 3 p. grey (1904) .. .. .. 1·25 1·90
O25 **23** ½ a. pale yellow-green .. .. 3·50 15
O26 ½ a. yellow-green 20 10
O27 **25** 1 a. carmine .. .. 3·75 10
O28 **27** 2 a. pale violet (1903) .. .. 60 1·50
O23/8 .. .. *Set of* 5 5·50 3·50

1903–08. *King Edward VII. Optd as Type* O **1**.
(*a*) *Overprint spaced* 10 *mm* (1903–5)
O29 **41** 3 p. pale grey 30 10
a. Slate-grey (1905) 30 10
O31 **42** ½ a. green .. .. 2·25 10
O32 **43** 1 a. carmine 40 10
O33 **44** 2 a. pale violet (1905) .. .. 1·75 50
a. Mauve .. .. 1·25 30
O35 **47** 4 a. olive (1905) .. .. .. 12·00 1·25
a. Opt double, one albino .. .. 45·00
O36 **49** 8 a. purple (1905) .. .. .. 3·50 70
a. Claret .. .. 12·00 4·00
ab. Opt double, one albino .. .. 35·00
O38 **51** 1 r. green and carmine (1905) .. 2·75 1·60
O29/38 .. .. *Set of* 7 20·00 3·75
(*b*) *Overprint spaced* 8 *mm* (1907–8)
O39 **41** 3 p. pale grey .. .. .. 3·75 15
a. Slate-grey .. .. .. 5·50 1·00
O41 **42** ½ a. green .. .. 1·75 15
O42 **43** 1 a. carmine 60 10
O43 **44** 2 a. mauve .. .. 11·00 75
O44 **47** 4 a. olive .. .. 3·00 85
O45 **49** 8 a. purple .. .. 3·25 3·75
O46 **51** 1 r. green and carmine (1908) .. 29·00 10·00
O39/46 .. .. *Set of* 7 48·00 13·50

1907–08. *Nos.* 149 *and* 150 *of India optd as Type* O **1**.
(*a*) *Overprint spaced* 10 *mm* (1908)
O47 **53** ½ a. green .. .. 5·50 10
O48 **54** 1 a. carmine .. .. 4·50 15
a. Opt double, one albino .. .. 32·00
(*b*) *Overprint spaced* 8 *mm* (1907)
O49 **53** ½ a. green 80 15
O50 **54** 1 a. carmine .. .. 48·00 3·00

1913–23. *King George V. Optd with* O **1**.
O51 **55** 3 p. grey 20 10
a. Pale grey 20 10
b. Bluish grey .. .. .. — 30
c. Slate 20 10
ca. "Rs" flaw .. .. 55·00
O52 **56** ½ a. light green 20 10
a. Opt double £100 £150
b. Emerald .. .. — 10
c. Bright green 20 10
O53 **57** 1 a. rose-carmine .. .. .. 8·00 50
a. Aniline carmine 30 10
ab. Opt double .. .. .. 65·00
O54 1 a. chocolate (1923) .. .. .. 2·75 15
O55 **59** 2 a. purple 60 30
a. Reddish purple .. .. .. 1·25 20
b. Deep mauve .. .. .. 1·50
c. Bright reddish violet 75 20
O56 **63** 4 a. olive 60 90
O57 **65** 8 a. deep magenta .. .. .. 90 1·25
a. Deep mauve .. .. .. 1·00 90
b. Bright mauve .. .. .. 1·50
O58 **67** 1 r. red-brown and deep blue-green .. 20·00 16·00
a. Opt double, one albino .. .. 55·00
b. Brown and green .. .. 16·00 15·00
c. Orange-brown & dp turquoise-grn 20·00 17·00
O51/8 .. .. *Set of* 8 19·00 16·00

1921. *No.* O97 *of India optd with T* **3**.
O59 **57** 9 p. on 1 a. rose-carmine 10 30

1927–35. *King George V (Nasik printing, wmk Mult Star), optd at Nasik as Type* O **1** *(but top line measures* 13 *mm instead of* 14 *mm) or with Type* O **2** *(rupee values).*
O61 **55** 3 p. slate 30 10
w. Wmk inverted 10 50
O62 **56** ½ a. green 10 15
w. Wmk inverted .. .. .. 2·25
O63 **80** 9 p. deep green (1932) 10 15
O64 **57** 1 a. chocolate 10 10
w. Wmk inverted .. .. .. 1·00 50
O65 **82** 1 a. 3 p. mauve (1933) 50 15
w. Wmk inverted .. .. .. 2·75
O66 **70** 2 a. purple 20 15
w. Wmk inverted .. .. .. 2·00
O67 **71** 4 a. sage-green 50 30
w. Wmk inverted .. .. .. — 1·25
O68 **65** 8 a. reddish purple (1928) 50 80
w. Wmk inverted .. .. .. 2·00 1·25
O69 **67** 1 r. chocolate and green .. .. 1·00 1·75
w. Wmk inverted .. .. .. 1·90 2·75
O70 2 r. carmine and orange (1935) .. 9·00 10·00
O71 5 r. ultramarine and purple (1932) .. 14·00 £150
w. Wmk inverted .. .. .. 15·00
O72 10 r. green and scarlet (1932) £100 £325
O61/72 .. .. *Set of* 12 £110 £450

1936–37. *New types. Optd as Type* O **1** (13 *mm*).
O73 **79** ½ a. green 15 15
w. Wmk inverted .. .. .. — 3·00
O74 **81** 1 a. chocolate 15 15
O75 **59** 2 a. vermilion 20 40
O76 2 a. vermilion (*small die*) .. .. 2·00 1·10
O77 **63** 4 a. sage-green (1937) 60 75
O73/7 .. .. *Set of* 5 2·75 2·25

1938. *King George VI. Optd as Type* O **1** (13 *mm*).
O78 **91** ½ a. red-brown .. .. .. 6·50 30
O79 1 a. carmine .. .. 1·10 20

गवालियर
(O 3)

1A———1A
(O 4)

1940–42. *Official stamps optd with Type* O **3**.
O80 **O 20** 3 p. slate 50 10
O81 ½ a. red-brown .. .. .. 3·00 25
O82 ½ a. purple (1942) 50 10
O83 9 p. green (1942) 70 60
O84 1 a. carmine .. .. 2·25 10
O85 1 a. 3 p. yellow-brown (1942) .. .. 32·00 1·75
w. Wmk inverted .. .. .. — 15·00
O86 1½ a. dull violet (1942) .. .. 1·00 30
O87 2 a. vermilion .. .. 1·00 30
O88 4 a. brown (1942) .. .. .. 1·25 1·75
O89 8 a. slate-violet (1942) .. .. 2·75 6·50
O80/9 .. .. *Set of* 10 40·00 10·50

1941. *Stamp of* 1932 *(King George V) optd with Type* O **1** *and surch with Type* O **4**.
O90 **82** 1 a. on 1 a. 3 p. mauve .. .. 21·00 2·75
w. Wmk inverted .. .. .. 25·00 5·50

1942–47. *King George VI. Optd with Type* O **2**.
O91 **93** 1 r. grey and red-brown .. .. 10·00 15·00
O92 2 r. purple and brown .. .. .. 18·00 75·00
O93 5 r. green and blue (1943) .. .. 30·00 £425
O94 10 r. purple and claret (1947) .. .. 80·00 £850
O91/4 .. .. *Set of* 4 £120 £1200

Gwalior became part of Madhya Bharat by 1 July 1948.

JIND

For earlier issues, see under INDIAN FEUDATORY STATES

PRICES FOR STAMPS ON COVER	
Nos. 1/4	*from* × 20
Nos. 5/16	—
Nos. 17/40	*from* × 15
Nos. 41/149	*from* × 8
Nos. O1/86	*from* × 15

Raja Raghubir Singh, 1864–1887

JHIND STATE (1) — JEEND STATE (2) — JHIND STATE (3)

1885 (1 July). *Queen Victoria. Optd with T* **1**.
1 **23** ½ a. blue-green .. 2·25 3·25
a. Opt inverted .. 85·00 95·00
2 **25** 1 a. brown-purple .. 26·00 35·00
a. Opt inverted .. £700 £750
3 **27** 2 a. dull blue .. 10·00 14·00
a. Opt inverted .. £500 £550
4 **17** 4 a. green .. 50·00 70·00
5 **31** 8 a. dull mauve .. £425
a. Opt inverted .. £9000
6 **33** 1 r. slate .. £425
a. Opt inverted .. £10000
1/6 .. *Set of* 6 £850

The overprint inverted errors occurred on R.10/8 in the setting of 120, although it is believed that one pane of the ½ a. had the overprint inverted on the entire pane. Examples of inverted overprints on the ½ a., 1 a. and 2 a. with the lines much less curved are thought to come from a trial printing.

All six values exist with reprinted overprint. This has the words "JHIND" and "STATE" 8 and 9 mm in length respectively, whereas in the originals the words are 9 and 9½ mm.

1885. *Optd with T* **2**.
7 **23** ½ a. blue-green (R.) .. 90·00
8 **25** 1 a. brown-purple .. 95·00
9 **27** 2 a. dull blue (R.) .. 95·00
10 **17** 4 a. green (R.) .. £130
a. Opt double, one albino .. £170
11 **31** 8 a. dull mauve .. £140
12 **33** 1 r. slate (R.) .. £150
7/12 .. *Set of* 6 £650

1886. *Optd with T* **3**, *in red.*
13 **23** ½ a. blue-green .. 24·00
a. "JEIND" for "JHIND" .. £950
14 **27** 2 a. dull blue .. 25·00
a. "JEIND" for "JHIND" .. £1200
b. Opt double, one albino .. 55·00
15 **17** 4 a. green .. 42·00
a. Opt double, one albino .. 48·00
b. Opt treble, two albino .. 75·00
16 **33** 1 r. slate .. 48·00
a. "JEIND" for "JHIND" .. £1700
13/16 .. *Set of* 4 £120

1886–99. *Optd with T* **3**.
17 **23** ½ a. blue-green .. 50 10
a. Opt inverted .. £200
18 **25** 1 a. brown-purple .. 1·00 20
a. "JEIND" for "JHIND" .. £450
b. Opt double, one albino .. 32·00
19 1 a. plum (1899) .. 2·50 1·00
20 **26** 1 a. 6 p. sepia (1896) .. 1·40 2·75
a. Opt double, one albino .. 38·00
21 **27** 2 a. dull blue .. 1·75 40
22 2 a. ultramarine .. 1·50 60
a. Opt double, one albino .. 38·00
23 **28** 3 a. brown-orange (1891) .. 1·75 60
24 **29** 4 a. olive-green .. 2·75 2·00
25 4 a. slate-green .. 3·50 3·00
26 **21** 6 a. olive-bistre (1891) .. 6·00 15·00
a. Opt double, one albino .. 32·00
27 6 a. bistre-brown .. 1·00 8·50
28 **31** 8 a. dull mauve .. 4·25 13·00
a. "JEIND" for "JHIND" .. £1600
29 8 a. magenta (1897) .. 6·50 20·00
a. Opt double, one albino .. 32·00
30 **32** 12 a. purple/*red* (1896) .. 4·75 19·00
a. Opt double, one albino .. 32·00
31 **33** 1 r. slate .. 8·00 38·00
32 **37** 1 r. green and carmine (1897) .. 8·00 42·00
33 **38** 2 r. carmine and yellow-brown (1896) .. £250 £700
34 3 r. brown and green (1896) .. £400 £700
35 5 r. ultramarine and violet (1896) .. £450 £700
17/35 .. *Set of* 14 £1000 £2000

Varieties exist in which the word "JHIND" measures 10½ mm and 9¾ mm instead of 10 mm. Such varieties are to be found on Nos. 17, 18, 21, 24, 28 and 31.

Raja (Maharaja from 1911) Ranbir Singh, 1887–1959

1900–4. *Colours changed.*
36 **40** 3 p. carmine .. 1·10 1·00
37 3 p. grey (1904) .. 15 2·75
38 **23** ½ a. pale yellow-green (1902) .. 3·00 4·50
39 ½ a. yellow-green (1903) .. 6·50 10·00
40 **25** 1 a. carmine (1902) .. 20 4·50
a. Opt double, one albino .. 27·00
36/40 .. *Set of* 4 4·00 11·50

1903–9. *King Edward VII. Optd with T* **3**.
41 **41** 3 p. pale grey .. 10 10
a. Opt double, one albino .. 16·00
42 3 p. slate-grey (1905) .. 20 50
43 **42** ½ a. green .. 60 1·50
44 **43** 1 a. carmine .. 2·25 1·40
45 **44** 2 a. pale violet .. 2·25 2·25
46 2 a. mauve (1906) .. 1·90 80
a. Opt double, one albino .. 27·00
47 **45** 2 a. 6 p. ultramarine (1909) .. 35 5·00
a. Opt double, one albino .. 21·00
48 **46** 3 a. orange-brown .. 40 40
a. Opt double .. £110 £200
49 **47** 4 a. olive .. 6·00 9·00
a. Opt double, one albino .. 42·00
50 4 a. pale olive .. 5·50 8·00
51 **48** 6 a. bistre (1905) .. 6·50 16·00
a. Opt double, one albino .. 32·00
52 **49** 8 a. purple (*shades*) .. 2·50 19·00
53 8 a. claret .. 11·00 25·00
54 **50** 12 a. purple/*red* (1905) .. 2·50 12·00
55 **51** 1 r. green and carmine (1905) .. 2·75 14·00
a. Opt double, one albino .. 42·00
41/55 .. *Set of* 11 23·00 70·00

1907–9. *Nos.* 149/50 *of India optd with T* **3**.
56 **53** ½ a. green .. 10 20
57 **54** 1 a. carmine (1909) .. 10 70

1913. *King George V. Optd with T* **3**.
58 **55** 3 p. grey .. 10 1·75
59 **56** ½ a. light green .. 10 75
60 **57** 1 a. aniline carmine .. 10 45
61 **59** 2 a. purple .. 15 4·00
62 **62** 3 a. orange .. 1·50 9·00
63 **64** 6 a. yellow-bistre .. 6·00 23·00
58/63 .. *Set of* 6 7·25 35·00

JIND STATE (4) — JIND STATE (5) — JIND STATE (6)

1914–27. *King George V. Optd with T* **4**.
64 **55** 3 p. grey .. 75 30
a. Pale grey .. 50 20
b. Bluish grey .. 1·00
c. Slate .. 1·00
65 **56** ½ a. light green .. 1·75 15
a. Emerald .. — 50
b. Bright green .. 1·75 30
66 **57** 1 a. aniline carmine .. 1·10 15
67 **58** 1½ a. chocolate (Type A) (1922) .. 1·10 3·75
a. Type B (1924) .. 35 1·50
69 **59** 2 a. purple .. 2·00 45
a. Reddish purple .. 5·00
b. Bright reddish violet (1922) .. 5·00 75
70 **61** 2 a. 6 p. ultramarine (1922) .. 35 4·00
71 **62** 3 a. orange .. 50 2·50
72 **63** 4 a. olive .. 1·60 7·00
73 **64** 6 a. yellow-bistre .. 2·25 13·00
a. Brown-ochre .. 1·75 11·00
74 **65** 8 a. deep magenta .. 3·75 8·50
a. Deep mauve (1925) .. 6·00 8·00
b. Bright mauve (1918) .. — 15·00
75 **66** 12 a. carmine-lake .. 2·25 12·00
76 **67** 1 r. red-brown and deep blue-green .. 7·50 15·00
a. Opt double, one albino .. 27·00
b. Brown and green .. 10·00
77 2 r. carmine and yellow-brown (1927) .. 5·50 95·00
78 5 r. ultramarine and violet (1927) .. 35·00 £190
64/78 .. *Set of* 15 60·00 £325

No. 71 with inverted overprint is of clandestine origin.

1922. *No.* 192 *of India optd "JIND" in block capitals.*
79 **57** 9 p. on 1 a. rose-carmine .. 1·25 13·00

1924–27. *Optd with T* **4**. *New colours.*
80 **57** 1 a. chocolate .. 3·75 1·60
81 **58** 1½ a. rose-carmine (Type B) (1927) .. 20 1·50
82 **61** 2 a. 6 p. orange (1927) .. 50 6·00
83 **62** 3 a. bright blue (1925) .. 1·75 3·50
80/3 .. *Set of* 4 5·50 11·50

Nos. 81/2 with inverted overprint are of clandestine origin.

1927–37. *King George V (Nasik printing, wmk Mult Star), optd at Nasik with T* **5** *or* **6** *(rupee values).*
84 **55** 3 p. slate .. 10 10
w. Wmk inverted .. 1·90
85 **56** ½ a. green (1929) .. 10 35
86 **80** 9 p. deep green (1932) .. 90 40
87 **57** 1 a. chocolate (1928) .. 15 10
w. Wmk inverted .. — 1·40
88 **82** 1 a. 3 p. mauve (1932) .. 20 30
89 **58** 1½ a. rose-carmine (Type B) (1930) .. 50 2·00
w. Wmk inverted .. 1·10 2·00
90 **70** 2 a. purple (1928) .. 1·50 40
w. Wmk inverted .. 1·50 40
91 **61** 2 a. 6 p. orange (1930) .. 80
w. Wmk inverted .. 1·00 8·00
92 **62** 3 a. bright blue (1930) .. 2·75 10·00
w. Wmk inverted .. 8·00
93 **83** 3 a. 6 p. ultramarine (1937) .. 2·50
w. Wmk inverted .. 60 14·00
94 **71** 4 a. sage-green (1928) .. 3·75 2·25
w. Wmk inverted .. 1·40 2·00
95 **64** 6 a. bistre (1937) .. 65 15·00
w. Wmk inverted .. 4·00
96 **65** 8 a. reddish purple (1930) .. 2·75 2·00
w. Wmk inverted .. 2·75
97 **66** 12 a. claret (1930) ..
w. Wmk inverted .. 4·00 16·00
98 **67** 1 r. chocolate and green (1930) .. 3·50 4·00
w. Wmk inverted ..
99 2 r. carmine and orange (1930) .. 28·00 £110
w. Wmk inverted .. 15·00
100 5 r. ultramarine and purple (1928) .. 11·00 35·00
w. Wmk inverted .. 40·00
101 10 r. green and carmine (1928) .. 13·00 18·00
102 15 r. blue & olive (*wmk inverted*) (1929) 65·00 £450
103 25 r. orange and blue (1929) .. 95·00 £550
84/103 .. *Set of* 20 £200 £1100

1934. *New types and colours. Optd with T* **5**.
104 **79** ½ a. green .. 30 25
105 **81** 1 a. chocolate .. 1·40 25
w. Wmk inverted .. — 3·00
106 **59** 2 a. vermilion .. 1·25 60
107 **62** 3 a. carmine .. 2·25 40
108 **63** 4 a. sage-green .. 3·00 1·00
104/8 .. *Set of* 5 7·50 2·25

1937–38. *King George VI. Nos.* 247/64 *optd with T* **5** *or T* **6** *(rupee values).*
109 **91** 3 p. slate .. 10·00 1·75
110 ½ a. red-brown .. 75 2·75
111 9 p. green (1937) .. 75 2·75
112 1 a. carmine (1937) .. 75 60
113 **92** 2 a. vermilion .. 1·75 13·00
114 – 2 a. 6 p. bright violet .. 1·25 14·00
115 – 3 a. yellow-green .. 6·00 13·00
116 – 3 a. 6 p. bright blue .. 2·75 14·00
117 – 4 a. brown .. 7·50 14·00
118 – 6 a. turquoise-green .. 4·50 18·00
119 – 8 a. slate-violet .. 3·50 1
120 – 12 a. lake .. 2·25 2
121 **93** 1 r. grey and red-brown .. 12·00 3
122 2 r. purple and brown .. 15·00 9
123 5 r. green and blue .. 25·00 7
124 10 r. purple and claret .. 45·00 6
125 15 r. brown and green .. £110 £
126 25 r. slate-violet and purple .. £400 £
109/26 .. *Set of* 18 £600 £1

JIND (7)

1941–43. *King George VI. Optd with T* **7**. (*a*) *Stamps of* 1
W 69 (*inverted on* 15 *r.*).
127 **91** 3 p. slate .. 12·00 1
128 ½ a. red-brown .. 1·00
129 9 p. green .. 10·00 1
130 1 a. carmine .. 1·00
131 **93** 1 r. grey and red-brown .. 8·00 2
132 2 r. purple and brown .. 16·00 2
133 5 r. green and blue .. 38·00 8
134 10 r. purple and claret .. 55·00 7
135 15 r. brown and green .. £120 £
136 25 r. slate-violet and purple .. 75·00 £
127/136 .. *Set of* 10 £300 £

(*b*) *Stamps of* 1940–43
137 **100*a*** 3 p. slate (1942) .. 50
138 ½ a. purple (1943) .. 50
139 9 p. green (1942) .. 60
140 1 a. carmine (1942) .. 65
141 **101** 1 a. 3 p. yellow-brown .. 1·00
142 1½ a. dull violet (1942) .. 6·50
143 2 a. vermilion .. 1·75
144 3 a. bright violet (1942) .. 16·00
145 3½ a. bright blue .. 8·50
146 **102** 4 a. brown .. 4·00
147 6 a. turquoise-green .. 5·00 1
148 8 a. slate-violet .. 2·50
149 12 a. lake .. 13·00 1
137/149 .. *Set of* 13 55·00 5

The 1½ a. and 3 a. exist printed by lithography or typograph

OFFICIAL STAMPS

SERVI

SERVICE (O 14) — SERVICE (O 15) — JHIN STAT (O 16

1885 (1 July). *Queen Victoria. Nos.* 1/3 *of Jind optd with T* **O 14**.
O1 **23** ½ a. blue-green .. 50
a. Opt Type **1** inverted .. 95·00 6
O2 **25** 1 a. brown-purple .. 30
a. Opt Type **1** inverted .. 12·00
O3 **27** 2 a. dull blue .. 32·00 4
a. Opt Type **1** inverted .. £900

The three values have had the overprint reprinted in the sa way as the ordinary stamps of 1885. See note after No. 6.

1885. *Nos.* 7/9 *of Jind optd with Type* **O 15**.
O7 **23** ½ a. blue-green (R.) .. 80·00
a. "JEEND STATE" double, one albino £110
O8 **25** 1 a. brown-purple .. 70·00
O9 **27** 2 a. dull blue (R.) .. 75·00
O7/9 .. *Set of* 3 £200

1886. *Optd with Type* **O 16**, *in red.*
O10 **23** ½ a. blue-green .. 13·00
a. "ERVICE" .. £3000
b. "JEIND" .. £600
c. "JHIND STATE" double, one albino 55·00
O11 **27** 2 a. dull blue .. 22·00
a. "ERVICE" .. £1800
b. "JEIND" .. £900
c. "SERVICE" double, one albino .. 38·00
d. "JHIND STATE" double, one albino 38·00

1886–1902. *Optd with Type* **O 16**.
O12 **23** ½ a. blue-green .. 75
a. "JHIND STATE" double, one albino 32·00
O13 **25** 1 a. brown-purple .. 19·00
a. "ERVICE" ..
b. "JEIND" .. £450
c. "SERVICE" double, one albino .. 23·00
O14 1 a. plum (1902) .. 8·50
O15 **27** 2 a. dull blue .. 1·90
a. "SERVICE" double, one albino .. 32·00
b. "SERVICE" treble, two albino .. 38·00
O16 2 a. ultramarine .. 50
a. "JHIND STATE" double, one albino 38·00
O17 **29** 4 a. olive-green (1892) .. 1·40
a. "JHIND STATE" double, one albino 30·00
O18 4 a. slate-green .. 1·50 1
O19 **31** 8 a. dull mauve (1892) .. 3·50 2
O20 8 a. magenta (1897) .. 3·00 5
a. "JHIND STATE" double, one albino 32·00
O21 **37** 1 r. green and carmine (1896) .. 6·00 32
a. "SERVICE" double, one albino .. 42·00
b. "JHIND STATE" treble, two albino 55·00
O12/21 .. *Set of* 6 18·00 32

Varieties mentioned in note after No. 35 exist on Nos. O12, O O17 and O20.

Printings up to and including that of October 1897 had "SERVICE" overprint. Type O 15, applied to sheets already ov printed with Type 3. From the printing of December 1899 onwa "SERVICE" and "JHIND STATE" were overprinted at one op ation, as Type O 16, to provide fresh supplies of Nos. O12, O14 a O21.

Colour changed. Optd with Type O **16**.
23 ½ a. yellow-green .. .. 1·40 20
a. "V" of "SERVICE" omitted .. 85·00 45·00
O22a normally shows a tiny trace of the "V" remaining. ples showing the letter completely missing are worth more.

-6. *King Edward VII stamps of India optd with Type* 6.
41 3 p. pale grey 10 10
3 p. slate-grey (1906) 25 10
42 ½ a. green .. .. 2·25 10
a. "HIND" £2250 £250
b. Opt double, one albino .. .. 26·00
43 1 a. carmine .. .. 1·10 10
a. "HIND" .. .. † £225
b. Opt double, one albino .. .. 26·00
44 2 a. pale violet .. .. 1·75 60
2 a. mauve 60 10
47 4 a. olive 40 45
a. Opt double, one albino .. .. 38·00
49 8 a. purple (*shades*) .. .. .. 7·50 5·00
8 a. claret .. .. 3·50 1·50
51 1 r. green and carmine (1906) .. 2·50 2·25
32 .. .. *Set of* 7 9·25 4·00

. *Nos. 149/50 of India optd with Type* O **16**.
53 ½ a. green 15 10
54 1 a. carmine 40 10

-27. *King George V. Official stamps of India optd with* 4.
55 3 p. grey 10 10
a. "JIND STATE" double, one albino 32·00
b. Pale grey 10 10
c. Bluish grey .. .. — 30
56 ½ a. light green 10 10
a. Emerald .. .. 1·00 30
b. Bright green 30 10
57 1 a. aniline carmine 45 10
a. Pale rose-carmine 90 10
59 2 a. purple 15 30
a. Reddish purple .. .. .. — 15
b. Deep mauve .. .. 1·00 30
63 4 a. olive 60 15
64 6 a. brown-ochre (1926) .. .. 70 2·25
65 8 a. deep magenta .. .. .. 50 1·00
a. Deep mauve .. .. 1·00 1·50
67 1 r. red-brown and deep blue-green .. 1·25 1·75
a. "JIND STATE" double, one albino 32·00
b. Brown and green (1923) .. .. 5·00
2 r. carmine and yellow-brown (1927) 14·00 60·00
5 r. ultramarine and violet (1927) .. 18·00 £170
'45 .. .. *Set of* 10 32·00 £200
o. O40 with double overprint is of clandestine origin.

. *As 1914-27. New colour.*
57 1 a. chocolate 60 10

ND STATE
ERVICE
(O 17)

JIND STATE
SERVICE
(O 18)

JIND
SERVICE
(O 19)

7-37. *King George V (Nasik printing, wmk Mult Star), optd with Types* O **17** *or* O **18** *(rupee values).*
55 3 p. slate (1928) 10 20
56 ½ a. green (1929) 10 90
80 9 p. deep green (*litho*) (1932) 50 15
9a 9 p. deep green (*typo*) .. .. .. — 75
57 1 a. chocolate 10 10
w. Wmk inverted 75
82 1 a. 3 p. mauve (1932) 40 15
w. Wmk inverted .. .. 1·00 50
2 **70** 2 a. purple (1929) 25 15
3 **61** 2 a. 6 p. orange (1937) .. .. .. 70 17·00
4 **71** 4 a. sage-green (1929) 35 25
w. Wmk inverted .. .. 1·10 75
5 **64** 6 a. bistre (1937) .. .. 1·25
w. Wmk inverted .. .. 2·50 14·00
6 **65** 8 a. reddish purple (1929) .. .. — 1·75
w. Wmk inverted .. .. 50 1·75
7 **66** 12 a. claret (1928) .. .. 1·25 12·00
8 **67** 1 r. chocolate and green (1928) .. 3·00 3·00
9 2 r. carmine and orange (1930) .. 35·00 28·00
w. Wmk inverted .. .. 28·00
0 5 r. ultramarine and purple (1929) .. 13·00 £180
1 10 r. green and carmine (1928) .. .. 29·00 £100
w. Wmk inverted .. .. 38·00
7/61 .. .. *Set of* 15 70·00 £325

34. *Optd with Type* O **17**.
2 **79** ½ a. green 20 15
3 **81** 1 a. chocolate 20 15
4 **59** 2 a. vermilion 30 15
w. Wmk inverted .. .. 50 1·25
5 **63** 4 a. sage-green .. .. 4·00 30
2/5 .. .. *Set of* 4 4·25 65

37-40. *King George VI. Optd with Types* O **17** *or* O **18** *(rupee values).*
66 **91** ½ a. red-brown (1938) .. .. .. 48·00 30
67 9 p. green .. .. 85 9·00
68 1 a. carmine 55 30
69 **93** 1 r. grey and red-brown (1940) .. .. 26·00 45·00
70 2 r. purple and brown (1940) .. .. 40·00 £180
71 5 r. green and blue (1940) .. .. 75·00 £325
72 10 r. purple and claret (1940) £200 £850
66/72 .. .. *Set of* 7 £350 £1300

39-43. (*a*) *Official stamps optd with T* **7**.
73 O **20** 3 p. slate 50 90
74 ½ a. red-brown .. .. 1·50 70
75 ½ a. purple (1943) 60 30
76 9 p. green .. .. 1·75 8·50
77 1 a. carmine .. .. 2·25 15
78 1½ a. dull violet (1942) .. .. .. 7·00 1·25
79 2 a. vermilion .. .. 3·25 30
w. Wmk inverted .. .. 8·00 2·50
80 2½ a. bright violet .. .. 2·50 7·00
81 4 a. brown .. .. 4·50 2·25
82 8 a. slate-violet .. .. 5·00 4·00

(*b*) *Postage stamps optd with Type* O **19**
O83 **93** 1 r. grey and red-brown (1942) .. .. 18·00 42·00
O84 2 r. purple and brown (1942) .. .. 32·00 £130
O85 5 r. green and blue (1942) .. .. 70·00 £325
O86 10 r. purple and claret (1942) £140 £400
O73/86 .. .. *Set of* 14 £250 £800

Jind was absorbed into the Patiala and East Punjab States Union by 20 August 1948.

NABHA

PRICES FOR STAMPS ON COVER	
Nos. 1/3	*from* × 15
Nos. 4/6	—
Nos. 10/36	*from* × 12
Nos. 37/117	*from* × 7
Nos. O1/68	*from* × 15

Raja Hira Singh, 1871–1911.

NABHA STATE
(1)

NABHA
STATE
(2)

1885 (1 July). *Queen Victoria. Optd with T* **1**.
1 **23** ½ a. blue-green .. .. 2·50 3·75
2 **25** 1 a. brown-purple .. .. 35·00 £130
3 **27** 2 a. dull blue .. .. 13·00 40·00
4 **17** 4 a. green .. .. 70·00 £170
5 **31** 8 a. dull mauve £300
6 **33** 1 r. slate £300
1/6 .. .. *Set of* 6 £650

All six values have had the overprint reprinted. On the reprints the words "NABHA" and "STATE" both measure 9¼ mm in length, whereas on the originals these words measure 11 and 10 mm respectively. The varieties with overprint double come from the reprints.

1885 (Nov)–**1900**. *Optd with T* **2**. (*a*) *In red.*
10 **23** ½ a. blue-green 20 50
11 **27** 2 a. dull blue .. .. 2·00 1·50
a. Opt double, one albino .. .. 42·00
12 **17** 4 a. green .. .. 30·00 £150
13 **33** 1 r. slate .. .. 95·00 £190
a. Opt double, one albino £130
10/13 .. .. *Set of* 4 £110 £300

(*b*) *In black* (Nov 1885–97)
14 **23** ½ a. blue-green (1888) 10 10
15 **24** 9 p. carmine (1892) .. .. .. 1·00 2·75
16 **25** 1 a. brown-purple .. .. 1·50 70
17 1 a. plum .. .. 1·25 60
18 **26** 1 a. 6 p. sepia (1891) .. .. .. 1·10 2·50
a. "ABHA" for "NABHA" £300
19 **27** 2 a. dull blue (1888) .. .. .. 2·00 1·25
20 2 a. ultramarine .. .. 1·60 1·00
21 **28** 3 a. orange (1889) .. .. 6·00 15·00
a. Opt double, one albino .. .. 27·00
22 3 a. brown-orange .. .. 2·50 1·40
23 **29** 4 a. olive-green (1888) .. .. .. 4·00 1·75
24 4 a. slate-green .. .. 4·00 1·75
25 **21** 6 a. olive-bistre (1889) .. .. .. 4·50 10·00
26 6 a. bistre-brown .. .. 1·60 2·25
27 **31** 8 a. dull mauve .. .. 1·75 1·60
a. Opt double, one albino .. .. 32·00
28 **32** 12 a. purple/*red* (1889) .. .. .. 3·00 3·50
a. Opt double, one albino .. .. 29·00
29 **33** 1 r. slate (1888) .. .. 8·50 40·00
30 **37** 1 r. green and carmine (1893) .. .. 8·00 3·75
a. "N BHA" for "NABHA" .. ..
b. Opt double, one albino .. .. 42·00
31 **38** 2 r. carmine and yellow-brown (1897) .. £100 £190
a. Opt double, one albino £170
32 3 r. brown and green (1897) £100 £250
33 5 r. ultramarine and violet (1897) .. £100 £375
14/33 .. .. *Set of* 15 £300 £800

(*c*) *New value. In black* (Nov 1900)
36 **40** 3 p. carmine 10 15

1903–09. *King Edward VII. Optd with T* **2**.
37 **41** 3 p. pale grey 40 15
a. "NAB STA" for "NABHA STATE" £850
b. Opt double, one albino .. .. 21·00
37*c* 3 p. slate-grey (1906) 40 15
38 **42** ½ a. green 55 35
a. "NABH" for "NABHA" £950
39 **43** 1 a. carmine .. .. 1·10 60
40 **44** 2 a. pale violet .. .. 1·00 2·00
40*a* 2 a. mauve .. .. 2·00 35
40*b* **45** 2 a. 6 p. ultramarine (1909) .. .. 18·00 85·00
ba. Opt double, one albino .. .. 32·00
41 **46** 3 a. orange-brown 50 30
a. Opt double, one albino .. .. 38·00
42 **47** 4 a. olive .. .. 2·00 1·75
43 **48** 6 a. olive-bistre .. .. 1·50 13·00
a. Opt double, one albino .. .. 22·00
44 **49** 8 a. purple .. .. 7·50 16·00
44*a* 8 a. claret .. .. 9·50 18·00
45 **50** 12 a. purple/*red* .. .. 3·00 18·00
46 **51** 1 r. green and carmine .. .. .. 7·50 10·00
37/46 .. .. *Set of* 11 38·00 £130

1907. *Nos. 149/50 of India optd with T* **2**.
47 **53** ½ a. green .. .. 1·00 1·25
48 **54** 1 a. carmine 50 70

Maharaja Ripudaman (Gurcharan) Singh, 1911–1928.

1913. *King George V. Optd with T* **2**.
49 **55** 3 p. grey 30 30
a. Pale grey 20 20
b. Bluish grey 75 30
c. Slate .. .. 1·00
50 **56** ½ a. light green 20 10
a. Emerald .. .. 1·00 50
b. Bright green 50 10
51 **57** 1 a. aniline carmine 85 10
52 **59** 2 a. purple 50 45
a. Reddish purple .. .. .. 1·00 45
b. Deep mauve .. .. 1·25
53 **62** 3 a. orange 50 35
a. Dull orange 50 35
54 **63** 4 a. olive .. .. 65 1·10
55 **64** 6 a. yellow-bistre .. .. 75 4·50
a. Brown-ochre .. .. 75 4·50
56 **65** 8 a. deep magenta .. .. 2·75 3·75
a. Deep mauve .. .. 2·25 3·00
b. Bright mauve .. .. 4·00
57 **66** 12 a. carmine-lake .. .. 1·75 19·00
58 **67** 1 r. red-brown and deep blue-green .. 7·50 3·50
a. Opt double, one albino .. .. 38·00
b. Brown and green .. .. .. 10·00 3·50
c. Orange-brown & dp turquoise-green 12·00
49/58 .. .. *Set of* 10 13·50 29·00

1924. *As 1913. New colour.*
59 **57** 1 a. chocolate .. .. 4·00 2·00
No. 59 with inverted or double overprint is of clandestine origin.

NABHA STATE
(3)

NABHA STATE
(4)

1927–36. *King George V (Nasik printing, wmk Mult Star), optd as T* **3** *or* **4** *(rupee values).*
60 **55** 3 p. slate (1932) .. .. 1·00 15
w. Wmk inverted .. .. 2·25 1·10
61 **56** ½ a. green (1928) 40 20
61*a* **80** 9 p. deep green (*litho*) (1934) .. .. 10·00 10·00
61*b* 9 p. deep green (*typo*) .. .. .. 1·75 1·10
62 **57** 1 a. chocolate .. .. 1·00 15
w. Wmk inverted .. ..
63 **82** 1 a. 3 p. mauve (1936) .. .. .. 1·25 4·50
w. Wmk inverted 75
64 **70** 2 a. purple (1932) .. .. 2·25 35
65 **61** 2 a. 6 p. orange (1932) .. .. .. 70 7·00
66 **62** 3 a. bright blue (1930) .. .. .. 2·00 1·00
67 **71** 4 a. sage-green (1932) .. .. .. 2·25 1·50
71 **67** 2 r. carmine and orange (1932) .. .. 24·00 85·00
72 5 r. ultramarine and purple (*wmk inverted*) (1932) .. .. 70·00 £250
60/72 .. .. *Set of* 11 95·00 £325

Maharaja Partab Singh, 1928–1971

1936–37. *New types and colours. Optd as T* **3**.
73 **79** ½ a. green 50 35
74 **81** 1 a. chocolate 35 30
75 **62** 3 a. carmine (1937) .. .. 4·00 11·00
76 **63** 4 a. slate-green (1937) .. .. .. 3·50 3·00
73/6 .. .. *Set of* 4 7·50 13·00

NABHA STATE
(5)

NABHA
(6)

1938. *King George VI. Nos. 247/64 optd as T* **3** *(3 p. to 1 a.), T* **5** *(2 a. to 12 a.) or T* **4** *(rupee values). W* **69** *(inverted on 15 r.).*
77 **91** 3 p. slate .. .. 6·50 40
78 ½ a. red-brown .. .. 4·50 75
79 9 p. green .. .. 18·00 3·75
80 1 a. carmine .. .. 2·00 45
81 **92** 2 a. vermilion .. .. 1·25 5·00
82 – 2 a. 6 p. bright violet .. .. .. 1·25 8·00
83 – 3 a. yellow-green .. .. 1·40 4·50
84 – 3 a. 6 p. bright blue .. .. .. 1·40 17·00
85 – 4 a. brown .. .. 6·50 6·50
86 – 6 a. turquoise-green .. .. .. 3·00 17·00
87 – 8 a. slate-violet .. .. 2·25 17·00
88 – 12 a. lake .. .. 2·50 17·00
89 **93** 1 r. grey and red-brown .. .. .. 11·00 24·00
90 2 r. purple and brown .. .. .. 24·00 80·00
91 5 r. green and blue .. .. 35·00 £160
92 10 r. purple and claret .. .. .. 55·00 £325
93 15 r. brown and green £160 £600
94 25 r. slate-violet and purple £140 £600
w. Wmk inverted £250 £700
77/94 .. .. *Set of* 18 £425 £1700

1941–45. *King George VI. Optd with T* **6**. (*a*) *Stamps of* 1937.
95 **91** 3 p. slate (1942) .. .. 30·00 3·50
96 ½ a. red-brown (1942) .. .. .. 70·00 4·50
97 9 p. green (1942) .. .. 10·00 11·00
98 1 a. carmine (1942) .. .. 10·00 2·50
95/8 .. .. *Set of* 4 £110 19·00

(*b*) *Stamps of* 1940-43
105 **100*a*** 3 p. slate (1942) 90 75
106 ½ a. purple (1943) .. .. 4·00 90
107 9 p. green (1942) .. .. 3·25 85
108 1 a. carmine (1945) .. .. 90 2·75
109 **101** 1 a. 3 p. yellow-brown .. .. .. 90 2·25
110 1½ a. dull violet (1942) .. .. .. 1·50 1·60
111 2 a. vermilion (1943) .. .. .. 1·10 3·50
112 3 a. bright violet (1943) .. .. .. 3·75 3·25
113 3½ a. bright blue (1944) .. .. .. 13·00 42·00
114 **102** 4 a. brown .. .. 1·75 75
115 6 a. turquoise-green (1943) .. .. 9·00 40·00
116 8 a. slate-violet (1943) .. .. .. 7·00 30·00
117 12 a. lake (1943) .. .. 4·50 42·00
105/117 .. .. *Set of* 13 45·00 £150
The 1½ a. exists printed by lithography or typography.

OFFICIAL STAMPS

SERVICE (O 8)

NABHA STATE (O 9)

1885 (1 July). *Nos. 1/3 of Nabha optd with Type* O **8**.
O1 **23** ½ a. blue-green 2·50 75
O2 **25** 1 a. brown-purple 30 15
a. Opt Type O 8 double † £1300
O3 **27** 2 a. dull blue 60·00 £120
O1/3 *Set of* 3 60·00 £120

The three values have had the overprint reprinted in the same way as the ordinary stamps of 1885.

1885 (Nov)–**97**. *Optd with Type* O **9**. (*a*) *In red*.
O 4 **23** ½ a. blue-green 5·50 4·00
O 5 **27** 2 a. deep blue 75 55

(*b*) *In black* (Nov 1885–97)
O 6 **23** ½ a. blue-green (1888) 10 10
a. "SERVICE." with stop £120 2·25
b. "S ATE" for "STATE"
c. "SERVICE" double, one albino 27·00
O 7 **25** 1 a. brown-purple 85 45
O 8 1 a. plum 75 25
a. "SERVICE." with stop 6·00 75
ab. "SERVICE." with stop, and "NABHA STATE" double † £250
O 9 **27** 2 a. dull blue (1888) 1·75 75
O10 2 a. ultramarine 2·25 1·10
O11 **28** 3 a. orange (1889) 20·00 65·00
O12 3 a. brown-orange 20·00 65·00
a. "NABHA STATE" double, one albino 42·00
O13 **29** 4 a. olive-green (1888) 2·25 85
O14 4 a. slate-green 2·25 85
O15 **21** 6 a. olive-bistre (1889) 15·00 24·00
a. "SERVICE" double, one albino 32·00
O16 6 a. bistre-brown £600
O17 **31** 8 a. dull mauve (1889) 1·75 70
O18 **32** 12 a. purple/*red* (1889) 6·00 16·00
a. "SERVICE" double, one albino 32·00
b. "NABHA STATE" double, one albino 32·00
O19 **33** 1 r. slate (1889) 30·00 £200
O20 **37** 1 r. green and carmine (1.97) 29·00 65·00
O6/20 *Set of* 10 95·00 £325

Printings up to and including that of August 1895 had the "SERVICE" overprint applied to sheets of stamps already overprinted with Type **2**. From the printing of January 1897 onwards the two parts of the overprint were applied at one operation. This method was only used for printings of the ½ a., 1 a. and 1 r. (O20).

1903–06. *King Edward VII stamps of India optd with Type* O **9**.
O24 **41** 3 p. pale grey (1906) 4·25 18·00
O25 3 p. slate-grey (1906) 80 11·00
a. Opt double, one albino 26·00
O26 **42** ½ a. green 50 20
O27 **43** 1 a. carmine 25 10
O28 **44** 2 a. pale violet 1·75 75
O29 2 a. mauve 1·50 40
a. Opt double, one albino 32·00
O30 **47** 4 a. olive 1·50 50
O32 **49** 8 a. purple (*shades*) 1·10 1·50
a. Opt double, one albino 26·00
O33 8 a. claret 7·50 3·50
O34 **51** 1 r. green and carmine 1·50 2·25
O24/34 *Set of* 7 6·00 14·00

1907. *Nos. 149/50 of India optd with Type* O **9**.
O35 **53** ½ a. green 20 50
a. Opt double, one albino 16·00
O36 **54** 1 a. carmine 25 30
a. Opt double, one albino 26·00

1913. *King George V. Optd with Type* O **9**.
O37 **63** 4 a. olive 10·00 50·00
O38 **67** 1 r. red-brown and deep blue-green 55·00 £350
a. Opt double, one albino £100

1913. *Official stamps of India optd with T* **2**.
O39 **55** 3 p. grey 75 8·50
a. Pale grey 50 6·50
b. Bluish grey 75 6·50
c. Slate 50 6·50
O40 **56** ½ a. light green 20 10
a. Emerald 50 10
b. Bright green 50 10
O41 **57** 1 a. aniline carmine 15 10
O42 **59** 2 a. purple 30 30
a. Reddish purple 1·00 15
b. Deep mauve 1·25
c. Bright reddish violet
O43 **63** 4 a. olive 40 50
O44 **65** 8 a. deep magenta 75 1·25
a. Deep mauve 2·25
b. Bright mauve 2·25
O46 **67** 1 r. red-brown and deep blue-green 3·75 2·50
a. Brown and green 5·00 2·50
O39/46 *Set of* 7 5·50 10·00

NABHA STATE SERVICE (O 10)

NABHA SERVICE (O 11)

1932–42?. *King George V (Nasik printing, wmk Mult Star), optd at Nasik with Type* O **10**.
O47 **55** 3 p. slate 10 15
O48 **81** 1 a. chocolate (1935) 15 15
O49 **63** 4 a. sage-green (1942?) 20·00 2·50
O50 **65** 8 a. reddish purple (1937) 1·00 2·00
O47/50 *Set of* 4 20·00 4·25

1938. *King George VI. Optd as Type* O **10**.
O53 **91** 9 p. green 2·50 3·00
O54 1 a. carmine 11·00 65

1940–43. (*a*) *Official stamps optd with T* **6**.
O55 O **20** 3 p. slate (1942) 80 90
O56 ½ a. red-brown (1942) 90 30
O57 ½ a. purple (1943) 3·50 60
O58 9 p. green 1·25 20
O59 1 a. carmine (1942) 60 20
O61 1½ a. dull violet (1942) 70 40
O62 2 a. vermilion (1942) 2·00 85
w. Wmk inverted 3·00 1·25
O64 4 a. brown (1942) 3·50 2·50
O65 8 a. slate-violet (1942) 5·50 15·00

(*b*) *Postage stamps optd with Type* O **11**.
O66 **93** 1 r. grey and red-brown (1942) 8·50 32·00
O67 2 r. purple and brown (1942) 26·00 £150
O68 5 r. green and blue (1942) £170 £500
O55/68 *Set of* 12 £200 £650

Nabha was absorbed into the Patiala and East Punjab States Union by 20 August 1948.

PATIALA

PRICES FOR STAMPS ON COVER	
Nos. 1/6	*from* × 10
Nos. 7/34	*from* × 6
Nos. 35/45	*from* × 8
Nos. 46/115	*from* × 4
Nos. O1/84	*from* × 15

Maharaja Rajindra Singh, 1876–1900

PUTTIALLA STATE (1)

PUTTIALLA STATE (2)

PATIALA STATE (3)

1884 (1 Oct). *Queen Victoria. Optd with T* **1**, *in red*.
1 **23** ½ a. blue-green 3·00 3·00
a. Opt double, one sideways £2000 £600
b. Opt double, one albino 55·00
2 **25** 1 a. brown-purple 42·00 45·00
a. Opt double
b. Optd in red and in black £650
3 **27** 2 a. dull blue 10·00 10·00
4 **17** 4 a. green 60·00 60·00
5 **31** 8 a. dull mauve £300 £750
a. Opt inverted £6500
b. Optd in red and in black 85·00 £300
ba. Ditto. Opts inverted £4250
c. Opt double, one albino £375
6 **33** 1 r. slate £130 £425
1/6 *Set of* 6 £500 £1200

Nos. 5a and 5ba each occur once in the setting of 120. The 8 a. value also exists with a trial overprint (showing the words more curved) reading downwards (*Price* £425 *unused*), which should not be confused with No. 5a.

1885. *Optd with T* **2**. (*a*) *In red*.
7 **23** ½ a. blue-green 2·00 20
a. "AUTTIALLA" 14·00 20·00
b. "STATE" only
c. Wide spacing between lines 4·75 5·00
8 **27** 2 a. dull blue 3·50 1·60
a. "AUTTIALLA" 30·00
b. Wide spacing between lines 16·00 16·00
ba. Ditto "AUTTIALLA" £400
9 **17** 4 a. green 2·75 2·50
a. Optd in red and in black £200
b. Wide spacing between lines £300
c. Opt double, one albino 35·00
10 **33** 1 r. slate 8·50 55·00
a. "AUTTIALLA" £400
b. Wide spacing between lines £300

(*b*) *In black*
11 **25** 1 a. brown-purple 25 25
a. Optd in red and in black 6·50 60·00
b. "AUTTIALLA" 65·00
ba. Ditto. Optd in red and in black £1400
c. Opt double £225 £250
d. Wide spacing between lines £160
12 **31** 8 a. dull mauve 14·00 32·00
a. "AUTTIALLA" £350
b. Opt double, one albino 60·00
c. Wide spacing between lines £300
7/12 *Set of* 6 28·00 80·00

The ½, 2 and 4 a. (T **29**), and 1 r. (all overprinted in black), are proofs.

All six values exist with reprinted overprints, and the error "AUTTIALLA STATE" has been reprinted in complete sheets on all values and in addition in black on the ½, 2, 4 a. and 1 r. Nearly all these however, are found with the word "REPRINT" overprinted upon them. On the genuine "AUTTIALLA" errors, which occur on R. 9/12 in the setting of 120, the word "STATE" is 8½ mm long; on the reprints only 7¾ mm.

Nos. 7c, 8b, 9b, 10b, 11d and 12c show 1¼ mm spacing between the two lines of overprint. The normal spacing is ¾ mm.

Nos. 7/8 and 10/12 exist with error "PUTTILLA", but their status is uncertain.

1891–96. *Optd with T* **3**.
13 **23** ½ a. blue-green (1892) 10 10
14 **24** 9 p. carmine 65 1·25
15 **25** 1 a. brown-purple 1·00 30
16 1 a. plum 1·40 70
a. "PATIALA" omitted £180 £350
b. "PA" omitted
c. "PATIA" omitted
d. "PATIAL" omitted
17 **26** 1 a. 6 p. sepia 85
18 **27** 2 a. dull blue (1896) 95
19 2 a. ultramarine 1·40
20 **28** 3 a. brown-orange 1·50
21 **29** 4 a. olive-green (1896) 1·90
a. "PATIALA" omitted £425
22 4 a. slate-green 1·90
23 **21** 6 a. bistre-brown 1·90
24 6 a. olive-bistre 2·00
a. Opt double, one albino 42·00
25 **31** 8 a. dull mauve
26 8 a. magenta (1896) 1·40
27 **32** 12 a. purple/*red* 1·50
28 **37** 1 r. green and carmine (1896) 4·00
29 **38** 2 r. carmine and yellow-brown (1895) £100
30 3 r. brown and green (1895) £140
a. Opt double, one albino £190
b. Opt treble, two albino £160
31 5 r. ultramarine and violet (1895) £180
13/31 *Set of* 14 £400 £

The errors on the 1 a. plum and 4 a. olive-green occu R.19/1 in the December 1898 printing. Nos. 16b/d are stages of the error before the entire word was omitted.

1899–1902. *Colours changed and new value. Optd with T*
32 **40** 3 p. carmine (1899) 10
a. Pair, one without opt £3000
b. Opt double, one albino 32·00
33 **23** ½ a. pale yellow-green 70
34 **25** 1 a. carmine 2·00
32/4 *Set of* 3 2·50

Maharaja Bhupindra Singh, 1900–1938

1903–06. *King Edward VII. Optd with T* **3**.
35 **41** 3 p. pale grey 10
a. Additional albino opt of Jind Type **3** £225
b. "S" in "STATE" sideways (R.20/1) £900
36 3 p. slate-grey (1906) 10
37 **42** ½ a. green 85
38 **43** 1 a. carmine 10
a. Horiz pair, one without opt £900
39 **44** 2 a. pale violet 1·10
a. Mauve 7·00
40 **46** 3 a. orange-brown 60
41 **47** 4 a. olive (1905) 2·75
42 **48** 6 a. olive-bistre (1905) 2·75
43 **49** 8 a. purple (1906) 3·25
44 **50** 12 a. purple/*red* (1906) 4·75
45 **51** 1 r. green and carmine (1905) 2·75
35/45 *Set of* 10 18·00

1912. *Nos. 149/50 of India optd with T* **3**.
46 **53** ½ a. green 10
47 **54** 1 a. carmine 1·25

1912–26. *King George V. Optd with T* **3**.
48 **55** 3 p. grey 25
a. Pale grey 50
b. Bluish grey 1·00
c. Slate 1·00
ca. "Rs" flaw 25·00
49 **56** ½ a. light green 50
a. Emerald 75
b. Bright green 50
50 **57** 1 a. aniline carmine 1·10
51 **58** 1½ a. chocolate (Type A) (1922) 30
52 **59** 2 a. purple 75
a. Reddish purple 1·25
b. Deep mauve 1·25
c. Bright reddish violet 1·25
53 **62** 3 a. orange 1·50
54 **63** 4 a. olive 2·50
55 **64** 6 a. yellow-bistre 1·10
a. Brown-ochre (1921) 3·00
56 **65** 8 a. deep magenta 2·25
a. Purple (1921) 3·50
57 **66** 12 a. carmine-lake 2·75
58 **67** 1 r. red-brown and deep blue-green 5·00
a. Opt double, one albino 32·00
b. Brown and green (1924) 7·50
59 2 r. carmine and yellow-brown (1926) 11·00
60 5 r. ultramarine and violet (1926) 26·00

1923–6. *As 1912–26. New colours.*
61 **57** 1 a. chocolate 2·75
62 **62** 3 a. ultramarine (1926) 2·50
48/62 *Set of* 15 55·00

PATIALA STATE (4)

PATIALA STATE (5)

1928–34. *King George V (Nasik printing, wmk Mult Star) o at Nasik with T* **4** *or* **5** *(rupee values).*
63 **55** 3 p. slate (1932) 1·25
w. Wmk inverted 2·25
64 **56** ½ a. green 25
w. Wmk inverted 1·50
65 **80** 9 p. deep green (*litho*) (1934) 1·00
65*a* 9 p. deep green (*typo*) 1·25
66 **57** 1 a. chocolate 75
w. Wmk inverted 2·50
67 **82** 1 a. 3 p. mauve (1932) 2·50
w. Wmk inverted 2·75
68 **70** 2 a. purple 1·25
w. Wmk inverted 2·25
69 **61** 2 a. 6 p. orange (1934) 3·75
w. Wmk inverted 2·75
70 **62** 3 a. bright blue (1929) 2·25
71 **71** 4 a. sage-green 3·00
w. Wmk inverted 5·00
72 **65** 8 a. reddish purple (1933) 4·00
73 **67** 1 r. chocolate and green (1929) 6·00
w. Wmk inverted —
74 2 r. carmine and orange 19·00
w. Wmk inverted 9·00
63/74 *Set of* 12 32·00

37. *Optd with T* **4**.
) ½ a. blue-green (1937) 75 30
1 a. chocolate (1936) .. .. .. 1·10 20
) 2 a. vermilion (No. 236*b*) (1936) .. .. 40 1·00
2 3 a. carmine .. .. 6·50 5·00
w. Wmk inverted .. .. 5·50 6·00
3 4 a. sage-green .. .. 1·50 1·50
.. .. *Set of* 5 8·25 7·25

ALA STATE (6) PATIALA (7) PATIALA (8)

8. *King George VI. Nos.* 247/64 *optd with T* **4** (3 *p. to* 1 *a.*), (2 *a. to* 12 *a.*), *or T* **5** (*rupee values*).
1 3 p. slate .. .. 28·00 35
½ a. red-brown .. .. 8·00 40
9 p. green (1937) .. .. 3·00 75
1 a. carmine (1937) .. .. 2·00 20
2 2 a. vermilion .. .. 1·50 6·50
– 2 a. 6 p. bright violet .. .. 3·75 14·00
– 3 a. yellow-green .. .. 3·00 6·00
– 3 a. 6 p. bright blue .. .. 4·25 18·00
– 4 a. brown .. .. 19·00 11·00
– 6 a. turquoise-green .. .. 19·00 40·00
– 8 a. slate-violet .. .. 19·00 28·00
– 12 a. lake .. .. 21·00 45·00
3 1 r. grey and red-brown .. .. .. 20·00 38·00
2 r. purple and brown .. .. 24·00 80·00
5 r. green and blue .. .. 30·00 £170
10 r. purple and claret .. .. 45·00 £275
15 r. brown and green .. .. 90·00 £425
25 r. slate-violet and purple £120 £500
.. .. *Set of* 18 £425 £1500

Maharaja Yadavindra Singh, 1938–1971

-6. *King George VI. Optd with T* **7** *or* **8** (*rupee value*).

(*a*) *Stamps of* 1937
91 3 p. slate .. .. 9·50 1·25
½ a. red-brown .. .. 6·50 75
9 p. green .. .. £160 4·00
w. Wmk inverted .. ..
1 a. carmine .. .. 21·00 1·25
93 1 r. grey and red-brown (1946) .. 10·00 70·00
02 .. .. *Set of* 5 £190 70·00

(*b*) *Stamps of* 1940–43
100*a* 3 p. slate (1942) .. .. 2·50 15
½ a. purple (1943) .. .. 2·50 15
a. Pair, one without opt £4500
9 p. green (1942) .. .. 1·00 15
a. Vert pair, one without opt .. £2750
1 a. carmine (1944) .. .. .. 1·00 10
101 1 a. 3 p. yellow-brown .. .. .. 1·60 2·25
1½ a. violet (1942) .. .. 9·00 2·25
2 a. vermilion (1944) .. .. .. 8·00 35
3 a. bright violet (1944) .. .. .. 6·50 1·50
3½ a. bright blue (1944) .. .. .. 17·00 26·00
102 4 a. brown (1944) .. .. 6·50 2·00
6 a. turquoise-green (1944) .. .. 2·50 18·00
8 a. slate-violet (1944) .. .. .. 3·00 9·00
12 a. lake (1945) .. .. 11·00 55·00
15 .. .. *Set of* 13 65·00 £100
ne 1½ a. exists printed by lithography or typography.

OFFICIAL STAMPS

SERVICE (O 2) SERVICE (O 3)

4 (1 Oct). *Nos.* 1/3 *of Patiala optd with Type* O **2**, *in black.*
23 ½ a. blue-green .. .. 9·00 20
25 1 a. brown-purple 60 10
a. Opt Type **1** inverted £1500 £275
b. Opt Type **1** double .. .. .. † £100
c. "SERVICE" double £1500 £500
d. "SERVICE" inverted .. .. .. † £1500
w. Wmk inverted .. .. † £250
27 2 a. dull blue £4250 £100
ssays of No. O3 exist on which "STATE" measures 10 mm g (normal 9 mm) and the words of the Type **1** overprint are re curved. These are rare (*Price* £850 *unused*).

5–90. (*a*) *No.* 7 *of Patiala optd with Type* O **2**, *in black.*
23 ½ a. blue-green 40 10
a. "SERVICE" double .. .. .. † £600
b. "AUTTIALLA" .. .. .. 60·00 16·00
ba. "AUTTIALLA", and "SERVICE" double .. .. † £4500

(*b*) *No.* 11 *of Patiala optd with Type* O **2**, *in black*
25 1 a. brown-purple 30 10
a. "SERVICE" double £1400
b. "SERVICE" double, one inverted .. † £500
c. "AUTTIALLA" .. .. £600 45·00
d. "PUTTIALLA STATE" double † £1000

(*c*) *As No.* 7 *of Patiala, but optd in black, and No.* 8, *optd with Type* O **3**
23 ½ a. blue-green (Bk.) (1890) .. .. 1·40 10
27 2 a. dull blue (R.) 30 20
a. "SERVICE" double, one inverted .. 30·00 £170
Stamps as Nos. O4/5, but with Type O **3** (in red on the ½ a.), re prepared for use but not issued, although some were roneously overprinted "REPRINT". No. O7 with overprint in ack is a proof. The ½ a "AUTTIALLA" has been reprinted in mplete sheets, and can be found with "AUTTIALLA" double. No. O7 exists with error "PUTTILLA", but its status is ncertain.

ERVICE

ATIALA STATE (O 4) PATIALA STATE SERVICE (O 5) PATIALA STATE SERVICE (O 6)

1891 (Nov)–**1900**. *Optd with Type* O **4**, *in black.*
O 8 **23** ½ a. blue-green (9.95) 10 10
a. "SERVICE" inverted .. .. .. 55·00
b. "I" of "SERVICE" omitted £850
c. Second "T" of "STATE" omitted .. £450 £400
O 9 **25** 1 a. plum (10.1900) .. .. 4·00 10
a. "SERVICE" inverted .. .. .. 60·00
O10 **27** 2 a. dull blue (12.98) .. .. 4·00 1·40
a. Deep blue .. .. 3·25 1·75
b. "SERVICE" inverted .. .. .. 60·00 £170
c. Thin seriffed "I" in "SERVICE" .. £160
O12 **28** 3 a. brown-orange .. .. 50 1·75
a. "I" of "SERVICE" omitted .. ..
O13 **29** 4 a. olive-green 60 70
a. Slate-green (9.95) 60 20
b. "I" of "SERVICE" omitted ..
O15 **21** 6 a. bistre-brown .. .. 1·25 35
a. Olive-bistre £1100
O16 **31** 8 a. dull mauve .. .. 1·90 80
a. Magenta (12.98) .. .. .. 1·40 1·00
b. "I" of "SERVICE" omitted £3000
c. Thin seriffed "I" in "SERVICE" .. £325
O18 **32** 12 a. purple/*red* 50 50
a. "I" of "SERVICE" omitted £4500
O19 **33** 1 r. slate .. .. 1·00 55
a. "I" of "SERVICE" omitted
O8/19 .. .. *Set of* 9 11·50 5·25

Stamps from the first printing of November 1891 (Nos. O12/13, O15/16, O18/19) had the "SERVICE" overprint, as Type O **3**, applied to sheets already overprinted with Type **3**. Subsequent printings of Nos. O8/10*a*, O13*a* and O16*a* had both overprints applied at one operation as shown on Type O **4**.

The errors with "SERVICE" inverted occur from a trial printing, in two operations, during 1894, which was probably not issued. Some of the "I" omitted varieties may also come from the same trial printing.

1902 (Jan)–**03**. *Optd with Type* O **4**.
O20 **25** 1 a. carmine 15 10
O21 **37** 1 r. green and carmine (5.03) .. .. 5·00 9·00

1903–10. *King Edward VII stamps of India optd with Type* O **4**.
O22 **41** 3 p. pale grey 10 10
a. Slate-grey (1909) 15 15
O24 **42** ½ a. green 10 10
O25 **43** 1 a. carmine 10 10
O26 **44** 2 a. pale violet (1905) 30 25
a. Mauve 20 10
O28 **46** 3 a. orange-brown .. .. 2·50 1·75
O29 **47** 4 a. olive (1905) .. .. 1·00 20
a. Opt double, one albino .. .. 42·00
O30 **49** 8 a. purple (*shades*) 60 55
a. Claret (1910) .. .. 3·00 1·40
O32 **51** 1 r. green and carmine (1906) 70 70
O22/32 .. .. *Set of* 8 4·75 3·25

1907. *Nos.* 149/50 *of India optd with Type* O **4**.
O33 **53** ½ a. green 20 20
O34 **54** 1 a. carmine 20 10

1913–26. *King George V. Official stamps of India optd with T* **3**.
O35 **55** 3 p. grey 10 20
a. Pale grey 30 30
b. Slate (1926) 30 30
O36 **56** ½ a. light green 10 10
a. Emerald .. .. 1·50 50
b. Bright green 30 30
O37 **57** 1 a. aniline carmine 10 10
O38 1 a. chocolate (1925) .. .. 6·00 1·00
O39 **59** 2 a. purple 50 30
a. Reddish purple .. .. — 1·00
b. Deep mauve .. .. 1·00 30
O40 **63** 4 a. olive 40 30
O41 **64** 6 a. brown-ochre (1926) .. .. .. 1·00 1·75
O42 **65** 8 a. deep magenta 55 70
O43 **67** 1 r. red-brown and deep blue-green .. 1·40 1·40
O44 2 r. carmine and yellow-brown (1926) 14·00 38·00
O45 5 r. ultramarine and violet (1926) .. 9·00 20·00
O35/45 .. .. *Set of* 11 30·00 55·00

1927–36. *King George V (Nasik printing, wmk Mult Star), optd at Nasik with* Type O **5** *or Type* O **6** (*rupee values*).
O47 **55** 3 p. slate 10 10
a. Blue opt .. .. 1·25 1·10
w. Wmk inverted .. .. 2·00 1·00
O48 **56** ½ a. green (1932) 65 55
w. Wmk inverted .. .. — 2·50
O49 **57** 1 a. chocolate 15 10
w. Wmk inverted .. .. 1·10 50
O50 **82** 1 a. 3 p. mauve (1932) 30 10
w. Wmk inverted .. .. 2·75 20
O51 **70** 2 a. purple 20 30
O52 2 a. vermilion (1933) 30 35
O53 **61** 2 a. 6 p. orange (1933) .. .. .. 1·75 35
w. Wmk inverted 60 80
O54 **71** 4 a. sage-green (1935) 50 30
w. Wmk inverted .. .. 2·00 1·10
O55 **65** 8 a. reddish purple (1929) .. .. .. 1·00 65
w. Wmk inverted .. .. 1·00 80
O56 **67** 1 r. chocolate and green (1929) .. .. 4·00 2·00
w. Wmk inverted .. .. 2·75 2·25
O57 2 r. carmine and orange (1936) .. .. 8·50 30·00
O47/57 .. .. *Set of* 11 13·50 32·00

1935–9. *New types. Optd with Type* O **5**.
O58 **79** ½ a. green (1936) 10 10
O59 **81** 1 a. chocolate (1936) 30 30
O60 **59** 2 a. vermilion 15 30
O61 2 a. vermilion (*small die*) (1939) .. .. 14·00 3·00
O62 **63** 4 a. sage-green (1936) .. .. .. 1·50 75
O58/62 .. .. *Set of* 5 14·50 4·00

1937–39. *King George VI. Optd with Types* O **5** *or* O **6** (*rupee values*).
O63 **91** ½ a. red-brown (1938) 75 20
O64 9 p. green (1938) .. .. 13·00 55·00
O65 1 a. carmine 75 20
O66 **93** 1 r. grey and red-brown (1939) .. .. 1·00 4·50
O67 2 r. purple and brown (1939) .. .. 4·50 5·00
O68 5 r. green and blue (1939) .. .. .. 15·00 50·00
O63/8 .. .. *Set of* 6 32·00 £100

1A 1A (O 7) 1A SERVICE 1A (O 8) PATIALA SERVICE (O 9)

1939–40. *Stamp of* 1932 (*King George V*).

(*a*) *Optd with Types* O **5** *and* O **7**
O69 **82** 1 a. on 1 a. 3 p. mauve .. .. .. 7·00 1·60
w. Wmk inverted .. .. 7·00 2·25

(*b*) *Optd with T* **4** *and* O **8**
O70 **82** 1 a. on 1 a. 3 p. mauve (1940) .. .. 5·50 2·00
w. Wmk inverted .. .. 6·00 2·50

"SERVICE" measures 9¼ mm on No. O69 but only 8¾ mm on O70.

1939–44. (*a*) *Official stamps optd with T* **7**.
O71 **O 20** 3 p. slate (1940) 75 10
O72 ½ a. red-brown .. .. 4·25 10
w. Wmk inverted .. .. — 10·00
O73 ½ a. purple (1942) 50 10
O74 9 p. green 50 30
w. Wmk inverted .. ..
O75 1 a. carmine .. .. 1·75 10
O76 1 a. 3 p. yellow-brown (1941) .. .. 1·00 25
O77 1½ a. dull violet (1944) .. .. .. 4·25 65
O78 2 a. vermilion (1940) .. .. .. 6·00 30
w. Wmk inverted .. .. 11·00
O79 2½ a. bright violet (1940) .. .. .. 2·00 75
O80 4 a. brown (1943) .. .. 1·25 1·75
O81 8 a. slate-violet (1944) .. .. .. 2·50 4·50

(*b*) *Postage stamps optd with Type* O **9**.
O82 **93** 1 r. grey and red-brown (1943) .. .. 5·00 8·00
O83 2 r. purple and brown (1944) .. .. 12·00 50·00
O84 5 r. green and blue (1944) .. .. .. 20·00 75·00
O71/84 .. .. *Set of* 14 55·00 £120

Patiala became part of the Patiala and East Punjab States Union by 20 August 1948.

INDIAN FEUDATORY STATES

These stamps were only valid for use within their respective states, *unless otherwise indicated.*

Postage stamps of the Indian States, current at that date, were replaced by those of the Republic of India on 1 April 1950.

Unless otherwise stated, all became obsolete on 1 May 1950 (with the exception of the "Anchal" stamps of Travancore-Cochin, which remained current until 1 July 1951 or Sept 1951 for the Official issues).

ALWAR

PRICES FOR STAMPS ON COVER

Nos. 1/2	*from* × 25
No. 3	*from* × 50
No. 4	—
No. 5	*from* × 50

Maharao Raja (Maharaja from 1889) Mangal Singh, 1874–1892.

1 (1 a.).

1877. *Litho. Rouletted.*

1 1 ¼ a. steel blue .. .. 13·00 7·00
a. Bright greenish blue .. .. .. 7·00 7·00
b. Ultramarine .. .. 3·75 1·00
c. Grey-blue (shades) .. .. .. 3·00 90
2 1 a. pale yellowish brown .. .. .. 7·00 4·50
a. Brown (shades) .. .. .. 2·75 1·25
b. Chocolate .. .. 9·00 8·00
c. Pale reddish brown .. .. .. 2·25 1·00

Maharaja Jai Singh, 1892–1937

1899–1901. *Redrawn. P 12. (a) Wide margins between stamps.*

3 1 ¼ a. slate-blue .. .. 6·50 2·50
a. Imperf between (horiz pair) .. £300 £350
b. Imperf between (vert pair) £550 £600
4 ¼ a. emerald-green £550

(b) Narrower margins (1901)

5 1 ¼ a. emerald-green .. .. .. 3·25 2·25
a. Imperf between (horiz pair) .. £190 £225
b. Imperf between (vert pair) £200 £225
c. Imperf horiz (vert pair) £200
d. Imperf (pair) £275
e. Pale yellow-green .. .. .. 5·50 2·25
ea. Imperf (pair) £450
eb. Imperf between (horiz pair) .. † £450

In the redrawn type only the bottom outer frameline is thick, whereas in the original 1877 issue the left-hand frameline is also thick, as shown in Type **1**.

The stamps of Alwar became obsolete on 1 July 1902.

BAHAWALPUR

See after **PAKISTAN**

BAMRA

PRICES FOR STAMPS ON COVER

Nos. 1/6	—
Nos. 8/40	*from* × 25

Raja Sudhal Deo, 1869–1903

GUM. The stamps of Bamra were issued without gum.

1 (¼ a.) 1*a* 2 (½ a.)

3 (1 a.) 4 (2 a.) 5 (4 a.)

6 (8 a.)

(illustrations actual size)

(Typo Jagannata Ballabh Press, Deogarh)

1888. *Imperf.*

1 1 ¼ a. black/*yellow* £325
a. "g" inverted (R.5/1) £3500
b. Last native character inverted .. £3500
c. Last native character as Type 1*a* .. £3500
2 2 ½ a. black/*rose* .. .. .. 70·00
a. "g" inverted (R.5/1) £1500
3 3 1 a. black/*blue* .. .. .. 45·00
a. "g" inverted (R.5/1) £1300
b. Scroll inverted (R.8/4) £1100
4 4 2 a. black/*green* .. .. .. 65·00 £225
a. "a" omitted (R.8/3) £1500
b. Scroll inverted (R.8/4) £1300
5 5 4 a. black/*yellow* .. .. .. 55·00 £225
a. "a" omitted (R.8/3) £1400
b. Scroll inverted (R.8/4) £1200
6 6 8 a. black/*rose* .. .. .. 38·00
a. "a" omitted (R.8/3) £1200
b. Horiz pair, one printed on back .. £600
c. Scroll inverted (R.8/4) £1000

These stamps were all printed from the same plate of 96 stamps, 12 × 8, but for some values only part of the plate was used. There are 96 varieties of the ½, 4 and 8 a., 72 of the 1 a., 80 of the 2 a. and not less than 88 of the ¼ a.

The scroll ornament can be found pointing to either the right or the left.

There are two forms of the third native character. In the first five horizontal rows it is as in T 1 and in the last three rows as in T 4.

These stamps have been reprinted: the ¼ a. and ½ a. in blocks of 8 varieties (all showing scroll pointing to right), and all the values in blocks of 20 varieties (all showing scroll pointing to left). On the reprints the fourth character is of a quite different shape.

8

1890 (July)–93. *Black on coloured paper. Nos. 24/5 and 39/40 show face value as "One Rupee". (a) "Postage" with capital "P".*

8 8 ¼ a. on *rose-lilac* .. .. .. 3·50 4·50
a. "Eeudatory" (R. 2/4) .. .. 15·00 23·00
b. "Quatrer" (R. 1/3) .. .. .. 15·00 23·00
c. Inverted "e" in "Postage" (R. 2/3) .. 15·00 23·00
9 ¼ a. on *bright rose* .. .. .. 1·50 2·25
10 ¼ a. on *reddish purple* .. .. .. 1·60 2·00
a. First "a" in "anna" inverted (R. 3/3) 35·00 40·00
b. "AMRA" inverted (R. 4/4) .. .. 50·00 50·00
c. "M" and second "A" in "BAMRA" inverted (R. 4/4) .. .. .. 65·00 65·00
11 ½ a. on *dull green* .. .. .. 2·00 2·50
a. "Eeudatory" (R. 2/4) .. .. 42·00 50·00
12 ½ a. on *blue-green* .. .. .. 3·75 3·50
13 1 a. on *bistre-yellow* .. .. .. 3·75 2·50
a. "Eeudatory" (R. 2/4) .. .. 90·00 95·00
14 1 a. on *orange-yellow* .. .. .. 32·00 32·00
a. "annas" for "anna" £120 £120
15 2 a. on *rose-lilac* .. .. .. 14·00 23·00
a. "Eeudatory" (R. 2/4) £130 £170
16 2 a. on *bright rose* .. .. .. 3·50 4·00
17 2 a. on *dull rose* .. .. .. 9·00 6·00
18 4 a. on *rose-lilac* £600 £750
a. "Eeudatory" (R. 2/4) £3750
19 4 a. on *dull rose* .. .. .. 7·50 4·50
a. "Eeudatory" (R. 2/4) £800 £800
b. "BAMBA" (R. 2/1) £800 £800
20 4 a. on *bright rose* .. .. .. 5·00 7·00
20*a* 4 a. on *deep pink* .. .. .. 12·00 10·00
21 8 a. on *rose-lilac* .. .. .. 18·00 45·00
a. "Foudatory" and "Postagc" (R. 1/2) £160 £225
b. "BAMBA" (R. 2/1) £160 £225
22 8 a. on *bright rose* .. .. .. 11·00 14·00
23 8 a. on *dull rose* .. .. .. 21·00 12·00
24 1 r. on *rose-lilac* .. .. .. 42·00 75·00
a. "Eeudatory" (R. 2/4) £375 £450
b. "BAMBA" (R. 2/1) £300 £350
c. "Postagc" (R. 1/2) £300 £350
25 1 r. on *bright rose* .. .. .. 15·00 18·00
a. Small "r" in "rupee" £180 £180

(b) "postage" with small "p" (1891–93)

26 8 ¼ a. on *bright rose* .. .. .. 1·50 2·25
27 ¼ a. on *reddish purple* .. .. .. 1·60 2·00
28 ½ a. on *dull green* .. .. .. 2·75 3·00
a. First "a" in "anna" inverted (R. 3/3) 26·00 26·00
29 ½ a. on *blue-green* .. .. .. 3·75 3·50
a. First "a" in "anna" inverted (R. 3/3) 28·00 28·00
30 1 a. on *bistre-yellow* .. .. .. 3·25 2·50
31 1 a. on *orange-yellow* .. .. .. 32·00 32·00
32 2 a. on *bright rose* .. .. .. 3·50 4·00
33 2 a. on *dull rose* .. .. .. 9·00 6·00
34 4 a. on *dull rose* .. .. .. 9·00 4·50
35 4 a. on *bright rose* .. .. .. 5·50 7·50
35*a* 4 a. on *deep pink* .. .. .. 15·00 12·00
36 8 a. on *rose-lilac* .. .. .. 40·00 75·00
37 8 a. on *bright rose* .. .. .. 14·00 16·00
38 8 a. on *dull rose* .. .. .. 21·00 12·00
39 1 r. on *rose-lilac* .. .. .. 60·00 £100
40 1 r. on *bright rose* .. .. .. 21·00 22·00
a. Small "r" in "rupee" £225 £225
b. Small "r" in "rupee" and native characters in the order 2, 3, 1, 4, 5 (R. 4/4) £1400 £1400

There are 10 settings of Type **8**. The first setting (of 20 (4×5)) has capital "P" throughout. The remaining settings (of 16 (4×4)) have capital "P" and small "p" mixed.

For the first setting the 8 a. and 1 r. values were printed within the same block, the ten lefthand stamps being 8 a. values and the ten righthand stamps 1 r.

The various stamps were distributed between the settings as follows:

Setting I—Nos. 8/c, 11/a, 13/a, 15/a, 18/19a, 21, 24/a.
Setting II—Nos. 19, 19b, 21/b, 24, 24b/c, 34, 36, 39
Setting III—Nos. 9, 11, 13, 16, 26, 28, 30, 32
Setting IV—Nos. 20, 22, 25, 35, 37, 40
Setting V—Nos. 10, 10b/c, 20*a*, 27, 35*a*
Setting VI—Nos. 11, 12, 28, 28a, 29/a
Setting VII—Nos. 10/a, 12, 17, 19, 23, 25a, 27, 29, 33/4, 38, 40a/b
Setting VIII—Nos. 17, 33
Setting IX—Nos. 10/a, 12, 14/a, 17, 19, 23, 27, 29, 31, 33/4, 38
Setting X—Nos. 19, 34

There are 4 sizes of the central ornament, which represents an elephant's trunk holding a stick:—*(a)* 4 mm long; *(b)* 5 mm; *(c)* 6½ mm; *(d)* 11 mm. These ornaments are found pointing to right or left, either upright or inverted.

Ornaments *(a)* are found in all settings; *(b)* in all settings from Settings III to X; *(c)* in Settings I and II; and *(d)* only in Setting I.

The stamps of Bamra have been obsolete since 1 January 1895.

BARWANI

PRICES FOR STAMPS ON COVER

Nos. 1/2	*from* × 3
Nos. 3/43	*from* × 5

PROCESS. All Barwani stamps are typographed from c and are in sheets of 4, *unless otherwise indicated.*

Issues to about 1930 were printed by the Barwani State Pr Press, and subsequently by the *Times of India* Press, Bon

GUM. Nos. 1/31 were issued without gum.

BOOKLET PANES. Those stamps which were printed in s of 4 were issued in stamp booklets, binding holes appearing i side margin.

Rana Ranjit Singh, 1894–1930

1

2

3

1921 (Mar?). *Clear impression. Medium wove paper. P round.*

1 1 ¼ a. blue-green (dull *to* deep) £110
2 ½ a. dull blue £200
a. Imperf (pair) .. .. — £

No. 1 also exists perforated on two sides only.

1921 (June?). *Blurred impression. Soft wove paper. P 7 on tu three sides.*

3 1 ¼ a. green *(shades)* .. .. .. 19·00 9
4 ½ a. ultramarine (dull *to* pale) .. .. 17·00

NOTE. As the small sheets of Barwani stamps were often perforated all round, many of the earlier stamps are perforate two or three sides only. Owing to the elementary metho printing, the colours vary greatly in depth, even within a si sheet.

1921. *Clear impression. Vertically laid bâtonné paper. Imperf*

5 1 ¼ a. green *(shades)* .. .. .. 18·00 5
6 ½ a. green *(shades)* .. .. .. 4·00
a. Perf 11 at top or bottom only .. 3·00

It is suggested that No. 5 may be an error due to printing f the wrong plate.

1922 (?). *Clear impression. Thickish glazed wove paper. P 7 on or three sides.*

7 1 ¼ a. dull blue .. .. 75·00

1922. *Smooth, soft medium wove paper. P 7 on two or three sid*

(a) Clear impression

8 1 ¼ a. deep grey-blue .. .. .. 32·00 8(

(b) Poor impression

9 1 ¼ a. steel blue .. .. 17·00

Examples of No. 9 exist with perforations on all four sides.

1922. *P 11 on two or three sides.*

(a) Thick, glazed white wove paper

10 2 1 a. vermilion *(shades)* .. .. .. 2·25 19
a. Imperf between (vert pair) £225
b. Doubly printed £750
11 2 a. purple *(to violet)* .. .. .. 2·25 22
a. Doubly printed £275
b. Imperf between (horiz pair) £170 £2
c. Imperf between (vert pair) £170

(b) Thick, toned wove paper

12 2 2 a. purple .. .. 13·00 45

1922. *Poor impression. Thin, poor wove paper. Pin-perf 8½ on t or three sides.*

13 1 ¼ a. grey (*to* grey-blue) .. .. .. 1·60 40
a. Imperf (pair) £275
b. Imperf between (vert pair) £120

1923. *Thin, smooth, unglazed wove paper. P 11 on two or th sides.*

14 1 ½ a. green (pale *to* deep) .. .. .. 1·25 18
a. Imperf between (vert pair) £425
15 2 1 a. brown-red £2500 £2

1923. *Poor impression. Thick, soft wove paper. P 7.*

16 1 ½ a. green (pale *to* deep) .. .. .. 25·00

No. 16 also exists perforated on two or three sides.

1923 (Mar?). *Poor quality wove paper. P 7 on two or three sides.*

17 1 ¼ a. black .. .. 65·00 £2
a. Imperf between (horiz pair) £1700

1923 (May?). *Horizontally laid bâtonné paper. P 12.*

18 1 ¼ a. rose *(shades)* .. .. .. 1·25 11·
a. Imperf between (vert pair) £375
ab. Imperf between (horiz pair) £700
b. Pin perf 6 .. .. £120 60·(
c. Perf compound of 12 and 6 .. .. 45·00 60·(
d. Perf 7 .. .. £450
da. On wove paper £1600

No. 18 was issued in sheets of 12 (3 panes of 4) and was printe on paper showing a sheet watermark of Britannia and a doubl lined inscription. No. 18d was only issued in booklet panes of

Vertically laid bâtonné paper. P 11.
¼ a. blue (*pale to deep*) .. .. .. 1·00 11·00
a. *Tête-bêche* (horiz pair) £1800
19 was issued in sheets of 8 and was printed on paper with a vatermark of a shell and an inscription "SHELL" in double-apitals.

Very poor impression. Thin, brittle wove paper. P 7.
¼ a. milky blue (*shades*).. .. .. 9·00 30·00
½ a. yellow-green (*shades*) .. .. 10·00 50·00
a. Imperf between (horiz pair) .. £800
3 4 a. orange-brown .. .. .. 65·00 £325
a. Imperf between (horiz pair) .. £1300
.. .. *Set of* 3 75·00 £375

Thick wove paper. Sewing machine perf 6–10.
4 a. yellow-brown .. .. .. 85·00
a. Imperf between (horiz pair) .. £1700
b. Perf 7 .. .. 20·00 £180
c. *Orange-brown* £110 £350

-32 (?). *Thick glazed paper.* (a) *P* 7.
¼ a. deep bright blue .. .. .. 11·00
½ a. bright yellow-green .. .. 22·00
(b) *P* 10½ (*rough*) (Nov 1928)
¼ a. ultramarine .. .. .. 4·00
a. *Tête-bêche* (horiz pair) .. .. 9·00
b. Horiz pair, one stamp printed on reverse £1000
½ a. apple-green .. .. .. 4·75
a. *Tête-bêche* (vert pair) .. .. 9·00
(c) *P* 11 (*clean-cut*) (1929–32?)
¼ a. bright blue .. .. 2·25 11·00
a. *Indigo* .. .. 1·75 11·00
ab. Imperf between (horiz pair) .. 70·00
ac. Imperf between (horiz strip of 4) .. £300
b. *Deep dull blue* .. .. .. 1·50 11·00
ba. Imperf between (vert pair) .. £200
c. *Ultramarine* .. .. .. 2·00 12·00
½ a. myrtle-green .. .. .. 2·75 12·00
a. Imperf between (horiz pair) .. £180
b. *Turquoise-green* .. .. .. 3·50 14·00
ba. Imperf between (vert pair) .. £425 £475
2 1 a. rose-carmine (1931) .. .. 11·00 32·00
a. Imperf between (vert pair) .. † £1200
3 4 a. salmon (*to orange*) (1931) .. .. 55·00 £150
a. Imperf between (horiz pair) .. £1600
.. .. *Set of* 4 65·00 £180
). 26 was printed in sheets of 8 (4 × 2) with the two centre pairs *bêche* while No. 27 in similar sheets, had the two horizontal *tête-bêche*. Both sheets are always found with one long side rforate.
os. 28/31 were printed in sheets of 8 the two lower values cing either 4 × 2 or 2 × 4 and the two higher values 4 × 2 only. *ête-bêche* pairs were included in these printings. It is believed a small printing of No. 31 was produced in sheets of 4, but ils are uncertain.

Rana Devi Singh, 1930–1971

4 Rana Devi Singh 5

2 (Oct)–47. *Medium to thick wove paper.*
Close setting (2½–4½ *mm*). *P* 11, 12 *or compound* (1932–41)
4 ¼ a. slate .. .. 1·50 17·00
½ a. blue-green .. .. .. 2·00 17·00
1 a. brown .. .. 2·25 16·00
a. Imperf between (horiz pair) .. £1400
2 a. purple (*shades*) .. .. .. 3·50 27·00
4 a. olive-green .. .. .. 6·00 30·00
./6A .. .. *Set of* 5 14·00 95·00
B. *Wide setting* (6–7 *mm*). *P* 11 (1945–47)
4 ¼ a. slate .. .. 4·25 22·00
½ a. blue-green .. .. .. 3·50 17·00
1 a. brown .. .. 9·00 17·00
b. *Chocolate.* Perf 8½ (1947) .. 12·50 38·00
B 2 a. rose-carmine £170 £400
4 a. olive-green .. .. .. 21·00 35·00
'he measurements given in the heading indicate the vertical cing between impressions. There are eight settings of this eresting issue: four "Close" where the overall stamp nensions from centre to centre of perfs vary in width from ½ to 23 mm and in height from 25 to 27½ mm; three "Wide", th 23–23½ mm and height 29–30 mm and one "Medium" ½×31 mm) (No. 34B*b* only).

3–47. *P* 11.
Close setting (3–4½ *mm*). *Thick, cream-surfaced wove paper* (1933 *and* 1941 (*No.* 38A*a*)
1 ¼ a. black .. .. 3·50 48·00
½ a. blue-green .. .. .. 10·00 25·00
a. *Yellowish green* (1941) .. .. 8·50 22·00
2 1 a. brown (*shades*) .. .. .. 16·00 23·00
3 4 a. sage-green .. .. .. 26·00 70·00
B. *Wide setting* (7–10 *mm*). *Medium to thick wove paper* (1939–47)
B 1 ¼ a. black (1945) .. .. .. 3·00 27·00
aB ½ a. yellowish green (1945) .. .. 4·50 28·00
B 2 1 a. brown (*shades*) .. .. .. 11·00 22·00
a. Perf 8½ (5 mm) (1947) .. 11·00 35·00
B 2 a. bright purple .. .. .. 80·00 £190
B 2 a. rose-carmine (1945) .. .. 22·00 85·00
B 3 4 a. sage-green (1941) .. .. 26·00 48·00
a. *Pale sage-green* (1939) .. .. 11·00 35·00
'here were two "Close" settings (over-all stamp size 25×29 ı) and five "Wide" settings with over-all sizes 26½–31½ × -36½ mm. There was also one "Medium" setting (26½×31 ı) but this was confined to the 1 a. perf 8½, No. 39a.

1938. *P* 11.
43 5 1 a. brown .. .. 27·00 50·00
Stamps printed in red with designs similar to Types **3** and **5** were intended for fiscal use.

STAMP BOOKLETS

Nos. 1/17, 18d/da and 20/5 are believed to have been issued in sewn or stapled booklets, usually containing thirty-two examples of one value in blocks of 4. All these early booklets had plain covers, often in shades of brown. Few complete booklets have survived from this period.

Nos. 32/47, produced by the *Times of India* Press in a series of nine printings between 1932 and 1947, were only issued in booklet form. Booklets from the 1932, 1933, 1937 and 1939 printings had plain card or paper covers in various colours, usually containing eight blocks of 4, except for the 1933 printing, which contained twenty blocks of 4. Booklets from the 1945 printing had plain white tissue covers from the same stock as the interleaving. All booklets were stapled at left.

The following booklets, from a printing in 1941 and a series of three printings in 1947, had printed covers, produced by a handstamp in the case of Nos. SB14/15.

1941. *Buff, green* (*No.* SB3) *or blue* (*No.* SB7) *card covers inscribed* "BARWANI STATE POSTAGE STAMPS", *booklet value in brackets and number and value of stamps thus* "(Rs 4) 32 2 Annas". *Panes of* 4 *with margin at left only. Stapled.*

(*a*) *Booklets* 59×55 *mm*
SB1 8 a. booklet containing thirty-two ¼ a. (No. 32A) £300
SB2 1 r. booklet containing thirty-two ½ a. (No. 33A) £475
SB3 2 r. booklet containing thirty-two 1 a. (No. 34A) £550
SB4 4 r. booklet containing thirty-two 2 a. (No. 35A) £325
SB5 8 r. booklet containing thirty-two 4 a. (No. 36A) £450
(*b*) *Booklets* 63×60 *mm* (*No.* SB6) *or* 73×72 *mm* (*No.* SB7)
SB6 1 r. booklet containing thirty-two ½ a. (No. 38A*a*) £650
SB7 8 r. booklet containing thirty-two 4 a. (No. 42B) £900

1947. *Grey tissue covers inscribed* "32 STAMPS VALUE....' *Panes of* 4 *with margins all round. Stapled at left.*
(*a*) *Booklets* 70×95 *mm.*
SB 8 1 r. booklet containing thirty-two ½ a. (No. 33B) £600
SB 9 2 r. booklet containing thirty-two 1 a. (No. 34B) £850
SB10 8 r. booklet containing thirty-two 4 a. (No. 36B) £950
(*b*) *Booklets* 76×95 *mm*
SB11 8 a. booklet containing thirty-two ¼ a. (No. 37B) £750
SB12 4 r. booklet containing thirty-two 2 a. (No. 41B) £800
SB13 8 r. booklet containing thirty-two 4 a. (No. 42B*a*) £450

1947. *Buff paper covers with violet handstamp inscribed* "32 STAMPS VALUE Rs 2/-". *Panes of* 4 *with margins all round, Sewn with twine at left.*
SB14 2 r. booklets (71×69 *mm*) containing thirty-two 1 a. (No. 34B*b*) £450
SB15 2 r. booklet (71×73 *mm*) containing thirty-two 1 a. (No. 39B*a*) £375

1947. *Grey tissue covers inscribed* "32 STAMPS VALUE As 8". *Panes of* 4 *with margins all round. Stapled at left.*
SB16 8 a. booklet (70×75 *mm*) containing thirty-two ¼ a. (No. 32B) £170
SB17 8 a. booklet (85×75 *mm*) containing thirty-two ¼ a. (No. 37B) £190

Barwani became part of Madhya Bharat by 1 July 1948

BHOPAL

PRICES FOR STAMPS ON COVER	
Nos. 1/100	*from* × 10
Nos. O301/57	*from* × 15

The correct English inscription on these stamps is "H.H. NAWAB SHAH JAHAN BEGAM". In the case of Nos. 22 and 23 the normal stamps are spelt "BEGAN" and specimens with "BEGAM" are "errors".

As the stamps were printed from lithographic stones on which each unit was drawn separately by hand, numerous errors of spelling occurred. These are constant on all sheets and are listed. Some of our illustrations inadvertently include errors of spelling.

ILLUSTRATIONS. Types **1**/**3***a* and **6**/**12***a* are shown actual size.

EMBOSSING. Nos. 1/99 were only valid for postage when embossed with the device, in Urdu, of the ruling Begam. On T **1**/**3** and **6** to **12***a*. this was intended to fill the central part of the design. Almost all varieties can be found with the embossing inverted or sideways, as well as upright.

Shah Jahan

Sultan Jahan

(*actual size*)

The various basic types were often in concurrent use but for greater convenience the following list is arranged according to types instead of being in strict chronological order.

GUM. Nos. 1/99 were issued without gum.

Nawab Shah Jahan Begam, 16 November 1868–15 June 1901

1 (¼ a.)

1872. *Litho.* (*a*) *Double frame. Sheets of* 20 (5 × 4)
1 1 ¼ a. black £425 £325
a. "BFGAM" (R.3/1) £1300 £1100
b. "BEGAN" (R.2/2, R.4/4) £750 £650
c. "EGAM" (R.4/5) £1300 £1100
2 ½ a. red .. .. 15·00 32·00
a. "BFGAM" (R.3/1) .. .. .. 60·00 £110
b. "BEGAN" (R.2/2, R.4/4) .. .. 40·00 75·00
c. "EGAM" (R.4/5) .. .. .. 60·00 £110

2 (½ a.)

(*b*) *Single frame. Sheets of* 20 (4 × 5)
3 2 ¼ a. black .. .. † £4500
4 ½ a. red .. .. 25·00 45·00
a. "NWAB" (R.2/2) £120 £180

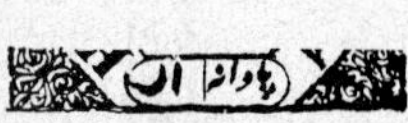
3 (¼ a.) **3***a* (¼ a.)

1878 (Jan). *All lettered* "EEGAM" *for* "BEGAM". *Sheets of* 20 (4 × 5).
(*a*) *Plate* 1. *Frame lines extend horiz and vert between stamps throughout sheet*
5 3 ¼ a. black .. .. 6·00 10·00
(*b*) *Plate* 2. *Frame lines normal*
5*a* 3*a* ¼ a. black .. .. 6·00 12·00
Apart from the frame line difference between Types **3** and **3***a* the stamps can also be distinguished by the differences in the value tablets, notably the thin vertical line in the centre in Type **3***a* compared with the slightly diagonal and heavier line in Type **3**.

4 (¼ a.) **5** (½ a.)

1878 (June?)–**79**. *Value in parenthesis* (*Nos.* 6/7). *Sheets of* 32 (4 × 8). *Imperf.*
6 4 ¼ a. green (1879) .. .. .. 10·00 17·00
7 ¼ a. green (*perf*) (1879) .. .. .. 8·00 12·00
8 5 ½ a. red .. .. 5·00 10·00
a. "JAHN" (R.5/2) .. .. .. 26·00
b. "NWAB" (R.3/2, R.4/2) .. .. 16·00
c. "EEGAM" (R.1/3) .. .. .. 26·00
9 ½ a. brown .. .. 22·00 32·00
a. "JAHN" (R.5/2) £130
b. "NWAB" (R.3/2, R.4/2) .. .. 80·00
c. "EEGAM" (R.1/3) £130
The ¼ a. shows the "N" of "NAWAB" reversed on R.6/4 and the "N" of "JAHAN" reversed on R.1/2–4 and R.2/2–4.

1880. *T* **5** *redrawn; value not in parenthesis. Sheets of* 32 (4 × 8)
(*a*) *Imperf*
10 ¼ a. blue-green .. .. 6·50
a. "NAWA" (R.2/2–4) .. .. .. 22·00
b. "CHAH" (R.8/3) .. .. .. 60·00
11 ½ a. brown-red .. .. 14·00 17·00
(*b*) *Perf*
12 ¼ a. blue-green .. .. 8·00
a. "NAWA" (R.2/2–4) .. .. .. 32·00
b. "CHAH" (R.8/3) .. .. .. 85·00
13 ½ a. brown-red .. .. 12·00
The ¼ a. shows the "N" of "NAWAB" reversed on R.8/4.
Nos. 12/13 sometimes come with gum.

1884. *T* **5** *again redrawn. Sheets of* 32 (4 × 8), *some with value in parenthesis, others not. Perf.*

14 ¼ a. greenish blue .. .. 3·75 10·00
a. "ANAWAB" (R.8/1–4) .. .. .. 12·00

In this plate there is a slanting dash under and to left of the letters "JA" of "JAHAN," instead of a character like a large comma, as on all previous varieties of this design. With the exception of R.1/1 all stamps in the sheet show "N" of "JAHAN" reversed.

1895. *T* **5** *again redrawn. Sheets of* 8 (2 × 4). *Laid paper.*

15 ¼ a. red (*imperf*) .. .. 4·50 1·75
16 ¼ a. red (*perf*) .. .. — £550

In these cases where the same design has been redrawn several times, and each time in a number of varieties of type, it is not easy to distinguish the various issues. Nos. 6 and 7 may be distinguished from Nos. 10 and 12 by the presence or absence of the parenthesis marks (); 8, 9 and 11 differ principally in colour; 8 and 15 are very much alike, but differ in the value as well as in paper.

6 (1 a.)

1881. *Sheets of* 24 (4 × 6). *Imperf.*

17 **6** ¼ a. black .. .. 4·50 15·00
a. "NWAB" (R.6/2–4) .. .. .. 11·00
18 ½ a. red .. .. 3·75 10·00
a. "NWAB" (R.6/2–4) .. .. .. 9·00
19 1 a. brown .. .. 3·25 11·00
a. "NWAB" (R.6/2–4) .. .. .. 7·00
20 2 a. blue .. .. 1·75 11·00
a. "NWAB" (R.6/2–4) .. .. .. 4·50
21 4 a. buff .. .. 13·00 42·00
a. "NWAB" (R.6/2–4) .. .. .. 35·00
17/21 .. .. *Set of* 5 24·00 80·00

In this issue all values were produced from the same drawing, and therefore show exactly the same varieties of type. The value at foot in this and all the following issues is given in only one form.

7 (½ a.)

1886. *Similar to T* **6** *but normally lettered (incorrectly)* "BEGAN"; *larger lettering. Sheets of* 32 (4 × 8). (*a*) *Imperf.*

22 **7** ½ a. pale red .. .. 1·60 8·00
a. "BEGAM" (R.2/1) .. .. .. 9·00
b. "NWAB" (R.3/4) .. .. .. 9·00

(*b*) *Perf*

23 **7** ½ a. pale red £300
a. "BEGAM" (R.2/1) £650
b. "NWAB" (R.3/4) £650

8 (4 a.)

1886. *T* **8**. *T* **6** *redrawn. Sheets of* 24 (4 × 6). *The* "M" *of* "BEGAM" *is an inverted* "W". *The width of the stamps is rather greater than the height.* (*a*) *Wove paper. Imperf.*

24 **8** 4 a. yellow £750
a. "EEGAM" (R.2/3–4, R.3/3–4, R.4/2, R.4/4, R.6/1) £900

(*b*) *Laid paper*

25 **8** 4 a. yellow (*imperf*) .. .. .. 7·50
a. "EEGAM" (R.2/3–4, R.3/3–4, R.4/2, R.4/4, R.6/1) .. .. .. 10·00
26 4 a. yellow (*perf*) .. .. 2·75 14·00
a. "EEGAM" (R.2/3–4, R.3/3–4, R.4/2, R.4/4, R.6/1) .. .. .. 5·00 18·00

1889. *T* **6** *again redrawn. Sheets of* 32 (4×8) *lettered* "BEGAN."

27 ¼ a. black (*perf*) .. .. 1·00 3·75
a. "EEGAN" (R.7/3) .. .. .. 11·00 22·00
b. Imperf between (horiz pair) £200
28 ¼ a. black (*imperf*) .. .. 1·10 3·50
a. "EEGAN" (R.7/3) .. .. .. 13·00 22·00

9 (¼ a.)

1889–90. *T* **9**. *T* **6** *again redrawn. Sheets of* 24 (4 × 6), *all with* "M" *like an inverted* "W". *Wove paper.* (*a*) *Imperf.*

29 **9** ¼ a. black .. .. 1·50 1·10
30 1 a. brown .. .. 1·10 3·50
a. "EEGAM" (R.2/3) .. .. .. 10·00 18·00
b. "BBGAM" (R.3/1) .. .. .. 10·00 18·00
31 2 a. blue .. .. 1·00 1·25
a. "BBEGAM" (R.1/2) .. .. .. 6·50 10·00
b. "NAWAH" (R.4/2) .. .. .. 6·50 10·00
32 4 a. orange-yellow .. .. 1·40 2·75
29/32 .. .. *Set of* 4 4·50 7·75

(*b*) *Perf*

33 **9** ¼ a. black .. .. 1·75 2·75
34 1 a. brown .. .. 3·50 4·75
a. "EEGAM" (R.2/3) .. .. .. 20·00 26·00
b. "BBGAM" (R.3/1) .. .. .. 20·00 26·00
35 2 a. blue .. .. 1·10 2·00
a. "BBEGAM" (R.1/2) .. .. .. 6·50 13·00
b. "NAWAH" (R.4/2) .. .. .. 6·50 13·00
36 4 a. orange-yellow .. .. 1·90 5·00
33/6 .. .. *Set of* 4 7·50 13·00

Nos. 32 and 36 are nearly square, in many cases rather larger in height than in width.

1891. *As last, but sheets of* 32 (4 × 8).

37 **9** ½ a. red (*imperf*) .. .. 1·25 2·75
38 ½ a. red (*perf*) .. .. 1·00 3·75

1894–98. *T* **6** *again redrawn*; (*a*) *Sheets of* 24 (4 × 6), *almost all showing a character inside the octagon below, as in T* **9**. *Wove paper.*

39 1 a. deep brown (*imperf*) .. .. .. 5·50 2·75
a. Red-brown .. .. 28·00
b. Printed both sides .. .. .. — £425
41 1 a. deep brown (*perf*) .. .. .. 4·75 2·75

10 (1 a.)

(*b*) *As Nos.* 39/41, *but printed from a new stone showing the lines blurred and shaky. Wove paper. Imperf* (1898)

42 **10** 1 a. purple-brown .. .. 2·50 3·25
a. "NAWAH" (R.4/1) .. .. .. 14·00 19·00
43 1 a. purple-brown/*buff* .. .. .. 2·50 3·25
a. "NAWAH" (R.4/1) .. .. .. 14·00 19·00
b. Printed on both sides .. ..

The above are known without embossing.

11 (¼ a.)

1895. *Sheets of* 8 (2 × 4), *lettered* "EEGAM". *White laid paper.*

44 **11** ¼ a. black (*imperf*) .. .. .. 2·50 1·90
a. "A" inserted (R.4/2) .. .. .. 6·50 5·00
45 ¼ a. black (*perf*) .. .. 75·00 35·00
a. "NAW B" (R.4/2) £250 £150

On the perf stamp the second "A" in "NAWAB" was missing on R.4/2 in the setting. This letter was later inserted for the imperf printing varying progressively from small to large.

12 (½ a.)

1895. *Narrow label at bottom. Sheets of* 8 (2 × 4), *lettered for* "H H". *Laid paper.*

46 **12** ½ a. black (*imperf*) .. .. .. 1·00

12*a*

1895. *Sheets of* 8 (2 × 4). *Laid paper.*

47 **12*a*** ½ a. red (*imperf*) .. .. 1·25

No. 47 is a combination of Types **1** and **6**, having the double frame to the octagon and the value in one form only.

13 (¼ a.)

(**14** (¼ a.)

1884. *Sheets of* 32 (4 × 8). *Perf.*

48 **13** ¼ a. blue-green £130
a. "JAN" (R.2/1–2, R.3/1, R3/3–4, R.4/1–3, R.5/1–3) £130
b. "BEGM" (R.2/3–4) £350
c. "NWAB" and "JAN" (R.3/2) .. £600
ca. "NWAB" and "JN" (R.5/4) £600
d. "SHAHAN" (R.4/4) £600
e. "JAHA" (R.6/2–4) £275

1895. *T* **14**, *double-lined frame round each stamp. Shee* 6 (2 × 3), *lettered* "JAN". *Laid paper.*

49 **14** ¼ a. bright green (*imperf*) .. .. 4·00

15 (½ a.)

16 (¼ a.)

1884. *Sheets of* 32 (4 × 8). *Laid paper.*

50 **15** ¼ a. blue-green (*imperf*) £100
a. "NWAB" (R.1/1) £300
b. "SAH" (R.1/4) £300
c. "NAWA" and "JANAN" (R.3/2) .. £300
51 ¼ a. blue-green (*perf*) 65
a. "NWAB" (R.1/1) .. .. .. 3·25
b. "SAH" (R.1/4) .. .. .. 3·25
c. "NAWA" and "JANAN" (R.3/2) .. 3·25
d. Imperf between (vert pair) £200
52 ½ a. black (*imperf*) .. .. .. 1·75
a. "NWAB" (R.1/1) .. .. .. 7·50
b. "SAH" (R.1/4) .. .. .. 7·50
c. "NAWA" and "JANAN" (R.3/2) .. 7·50
53 ½ a. black (*perf*) 50
a. "NWAB" (R.1/1) .. .. .. 3·00
b. "SAH" (R.1/4) .. .. .. 3·00
c. "NAWA" and "JANAN" (R.3/2) .. 3·00

The ¼ a. of this issue is in *blue-green*, or *greenish blue*. B values were printed from the same stone, the value alone be altered. There are therefore the same varieties of each. These the only stamps of this design on laid paper.

Both values show the "N" of "NAWAB" reversed on R.1/ R.2/1–4, R.3/1–4 and the "N" of "JAHAN" reversed on R.1/ R.2/1–4, R.3/4.

1886. *T* **15** *redrawn. Sheets of* 32 (4 × 8). *Wove paper.*

54 ¼ a. green (*imperf*) 45 2
a. "NAWA" (R.6/3–4) .. .. .. 1·50
b. "NWAB" (R.1/1) .. .. .. 2·50
c. "NWABA" (R.7/4) .. .. .. 2·50
d. "NAWAA" (R.6/2) .. .. .. 2·50
e. "BEGAAM" and "NWABA" (R.7/3) .. 2·50
55 ¼ a. green (*perf*) .. .. 1·90 3
a. "NAWA" (R.6/3–4) .. .. .. 6·50
b. "NWAB" (R.1/1) .. .. .. 10·00
c. "NWABA" (R.7/4) .. .. .. 10·00
d. "NAWAA" (R.6/2) .. .. .. 10·00
e. "BEGAAM" and "NWABA" (R.7/3) .. 10·00
f. Imperf between (horiz pair) £130
56 ½ a. red (*imperf*) 50 1
a. "SAH" (R.1/4) .. .. .. 3·50
b. "NAWABA" (R.6/3–4) .. .. .. 2·75

The ¼ a. varies from *yellow-green* to *deep green*.

All examples of the ¼ a. value show the "N" of "NAWA reversed. On the same value the "N" of "JAHAN" is reversed on positions except R.3/2, R.4/1, R.4/3. On the ½ a. both "N"s a always reversed.

T 15 again redrawn. Sheets of 32 (4 × 8), *letters in upper* …*les smaller.* "N" of "NAWAB" *correct. Wove paper.*

/4 a. deep green (*imperf*) .. .. 60 1·25
 a. "SAH" (R.6/2) .. .. 3·75 5·00
 b. "NAWA" (R.4/4) .. .. 3·75 5·00
/4 a. deep green (*perf*) .. .. 1·00 1·75
 a. "SAH" (R.6/2) .. .. 4·50
 b. "NAWA" (R.4/4) .. .. 4·50
 c. Imperf between (vert pair) £180

…s. 50 to 58 have the dash under the letter "JA" as in No. 14.

T 15 again redrawn. Sheets of 32 (4 × 8), *lettered* "NWAB." …*ve paper. (a) Imperf.*

½ a. red .. .. 1·25 75
 a. "SAH" (R.2/4) .. .. 3·75

(*b*) *P* 3 *to* 4½, *or about* 7

½ a. red .. .. 60 1·10
 a. "SAH" (R.2/4) .. .. 4·50

…s. 59 and 60 have the comma under "JA". The "N" of "JAHAN" …ersed on R.1/1–3, R.2/1–2.

T 15 again redrawn; letters in corners larger than in 1888, …*ue in very small characters. Sheets of* 32 (4 × 8), *all with* "G" *in* …*-hand lower corner. Wove paper.*

¼ a. green (*imperf*) 80 80
 a. "NAWAH" (R.4/4) .. .. 5·50 6·00
 b. Value in brackets (R.1/1) .. .. 5·50 6·00
¼ a. green (*perf*) .. .. 2·00 1·50
 a. "NAWAH" (R.4/4) .. .. 9·00 9·00
 b. Value in brackets (R.1/1) .. .. 9·00 9·00

…s. 61 and 62 have neither the dash nor the comma under …

. *T* **16**; *oval narrower, stops after* "H.H.", *space after* …AWAB". *The line down the centre is under the first* "H" *of* …HAH" *or between* "HA" *instead of being under the second* "H" …*between* "AH". *Sheets of* 32 (4 × 8). *Wove paper. Imperf.*

16 ¼ a. bright green 40 40
 a. "SHAN" (R.1/1) .. .. 3·00
 ¼ a. pale green 40 35
 a. "SHAN" (R.1/1) .. .. 3·00
 ¼ a. black 30 30
 a. "SHAN" (R.1/1) .. .. 3·00

. *T* **15** *redrawn. Sheets of* 32 (4 × 8), *the first* "A" *of* "NAWAB" …*ways absent. Numerous defective and malformed letters. Wove* …*per. Imperf.*

½ a. black .. .. 3·25 4·25
 a. "NWASBAHJANNI" (R.2/4) .. .. 17·00 20·00
 b. "SBAH" (R.3/3, R.4/3–4, R.5/1–2, R.6/4) 8·00 10·00
 c. "SBAN" (R.8/2) .. .. 17·00 20·00
 d. "NWIB" (R.3/2) .. .. 17·00 20·00
 e. "BEIAM" (R.4/4) .. .. 17·00 20·00
 f. "SHH" (R.6/3) .. .. 17·00 20·00
 g. "SBAH" and "BBGAM" (R.3/4) .. 17·00 20·00
 h. "BBGAM" (R.1/3) .. .. 17·00 20·00

17 (8 a.)

18 (¼ a.)

…0. *T* **17**. *Sheets of* 10 (2 × 5). *Single-line frame to each stamp.*

(*a*) *Wove paper*

17 8 a. slate-green (*imperf*) .. .. .. 40·00 75·00
 a. "HAH" (R.3/1, R.4/1, R.5/1) .. 55·00
 b. "JABAN" (R.2/2) .. .. 55·00
 8 a. slate-green (*perf*) .. .. .. 40·00 75·00
 a. "HAH" (R.3/1, R.4/1, R.5/1) .. 55·00
 b. "JABAN" (R.2/2) .. .. 55·00

(*b*) *Thin laid paper*

17 8 a. green-black (*imperf*) .. .. .. 48·00 95·00
 a. "HAH" (R.3/1, R.4/1, R.5/1) .. 65·00
 b. "JABAN" (R.2/2) .. .. 65·00
 8 a. green-black (*perf*) .. .. .. 48·00 95·00
 a. "HAH" (R.3/1, R.4/1, R.5/1) .. 70·00
 b. "JABAN" (R.2/2) .. .. 70·00

…The "N" of "NAWAB" is reversed on R.5/2 and the "N" of …AHAN" on R.1/1–2, R.2/2, R.3/2, R.4/2 and R.5/2.

…93. *T* **17** *redrawn. No frame to each stamp, but a frame to the sheet. Sheets of* 10 (2 × 5). (*a*) *Wove paper.*

 8 a. green-black (*imperf*) .. .. .. 18·00 18·00
 8 a. green-black (*perf*) .. .. .. 23·00 29·00

(*b*) *Thin laid paper. Imperf*

 8 a. green-black £140 £160

…98. *Printed from a new stone. Lettering irregular. Sheets of* 10 (2×5). *Wove paper. Imperf.*

 8 a. green-black .. .. 32·00 45·00
 a. Reversed "E" in "BEGAM" (R.1/2, R.3/2) 70·00
 8 a. black .. .. 32·00 45·00
 a. Reversed "E" in "BEGAM" (R.1/2, R.3/2) 70·00

…896–1901. *Sheets of* 32 (4×8). (*a*) *Wove paper. Imperf.*

… **18** ¼ a. black 85 85

(*b*) *Printed from a new stone, lines shaky* (1899)

… **18** ¼ a. black .. .. 1·90 1·90

(*c*) *The same, on thick wove paper* (1901)

… **18** ¼ a. black £500 £500

Nawab Sultan Jahan Begam, 16 June 1901–17 May 1926

19 (¼ a.)

20

1902. *T* **19**. *With the octagonal embossed device of the previous issues. Sheets of* 16 (4 × 4) ¼ *a. or* 8 (2 × 4) *others. Thin, yellowish wove paper. Imperf.*

79 **19** ¼ a. rose .. .. 3·75 6·00
80 ¼ a. rose-red .. .. 1·75 3·75
81 ½ a. black .. .. 2·50 4·50
 a. Printed both sides £500
82 1 a. brown .. .. 4·00 11·00
83 1 a. red-brown .. .. 3·25 9·50
84 2 a. blue .. .. 5·50 9·50
85 4 a. orange .. .. 45·00 75·00
86 4 a. yellow .. .. 30·00 60·00
87 8 a. lilac .. .. 75·00 £130
88 1 r. rose £190 £275
79/88 .. .. *Set of* 7 £275 £425

1903. *With a circular embossed device. Sheets of* 16 (4×4) ¼ *a.* (*two plates*) *or* 8 (2×4) (*others*). *Wove paper.*

89 **19** ¼ a. rose-red .. .. 80 3·50
 a. Laid paper .. .. 60 5·00
90 ¼ a. red .. .. 70 3·25
 a. Laid paper .. .. 30 4·25
91 ½ a. black .. .. 65 4·00
 a. Laid paper .. .. 70 5·50
92 1 a. brown .. .. 1·10 4·75
 a. Laid paper .. .. 75·00
93 1 a. red-brown .. .. 4·00
 a. Laid paper .. ..
94 2 a. blue .. .. 4·00 18·00
 a. Laid paper £130 £150
95 4 a. orange (*laid paper*) £190 £190
96 4 a. yellow .. .. 14·00 40·00
 a. Laid paper .. .. 95·00 90·00
97 8 a. lilac .. .. 38·00 95·00
 a. Laid paper £1100
98 1 r. rose .. .. 55·00 £130
 a. Laid paper £950
89/98 .. .. *Set of* 7 £100 £250

1903. *No.* 71 *optd with initial of the new Begam, either* 6 *or* 11 *mm long, in red.*

99 8 a. green-black .. .. 90·00 90·00
 a. Opt inverted £225 £225

Some of the previous stamps remained on sale (and probably in use) after the issue of the series of 1902, and some of these were afterwards put on sale with the new form of embossing; fresh plates were made of some of the old designs, in imitation of the earlier issues, and impressions from these were also sold with the new embossed device. We no longer list these doubtful items.

(Recess Perkins, Bacon & Co)

1908. *P* 13½.

100 **20** 1 a. green .. .. 3·00 3·00
 a. Printed both sides £100
 b. Imperf (pair) .. ..

The ordinary postage stamps of Bhopal became obsolete on 1 July 1908.

OFFICIAL STAMPS

SERVICE (O 1) **SERVICE** (O 2)

(Recess and optd Perkins, Bacon)

1908–11. *As T* **20**, *but inscribed* "H.H. BEGUM'S SERVICE" *at left. No wmk. P* 13 *to* 14. *Overprinted.* (*a*) *With Type* O **1**.

O301 ½ a. yellow-green .. .. 2·00 10
 a. Imperf (pair) £100
 b. Pair, one without overprint .. £425
 c. Opt double, one inverted £110
 ca. Ditto. Imperf (pair) £130
 d. Opt inverted £120 £120
 e. Imperf between (horiz pair) .. £500
O302 1 a. carmine-red .. .. 3·75 35
 a. Opt inverted .. .. 75·00 75·00
 b. Imperf (pair) .. .. 90·00
 c. Red .. .. 4·50 10
O303 2 a. ultramarine .. .. 22·00 10
 a. Imperf (pair) .. .. 55·00
O304 4 a. brown (1911) .. .. 9·50 30
O301/4 .. .. *Set of* 4 32·00 55

(*b*) *With Type* O **2**

O305 ½ a. yellow-green .. .. 4·75 40
O306 1 a. carmine-red .. .. 7·00 90
O307 2 a. ultramarine .. .. 3·00 40
 a. Opt inverted .. .. 25·00
O308 4 a. brown (1911) .. .. 70·00 70
 a. Opt inverted .. .. 20·00 65·00
 b. Opt double .. .. 90·00
 c. Imperf (pair) .. .. 80·00
 d. Imperf (pair) and opt inverted .. 80·00
O305/8 .. .. *Set of* 4 75·00 2·00

The two overprints differ in the shape of the letters, noticeably in the "R".

MINIMUM PRICE

The minimum price quote is 10p which represents a handling charge rather than a basis for valuing common stamps. For further notes about prices see introductory pages.

Nawab Mohammad Hamidullah. Khan
17 May 1926 to transfer of administration to India, 1 June 1949

SERVICE

(O 3)

(O 4)

(Des T. I. Archer. Litho Indian Govt Ptg Wks, Nasik)

1930 (1 July)–**31**. *Type* O **4** (25½ × 30½ *mm*) *optd with Type* O **3**. *P* 14.

O309 O **4** ½ a. sage-green (1931) .. .. 8·00 1·25
O310 1 a. carmine-red .. .. .. 9·00 15
O311 2 a. ultramarine .. .. .. 8·50 45
O312 4 a. chocolate .. .. 8·00 80
O309/12 .. .. *Set of* 4 30·00 2·25

The ½ a., 2 a. and 4 a. are inscribed "POSTAGE" at left.

(Litho Perkins, Bacon)

1932–34. *As Type* O **4** (21 × 25 *mm*), *but inscr* "POSTAGE" *at left. Optd with Type* O **1**. (*a*) "BHOPAL STATE" *at right. P* 13.

O313 ¼ a. orange .. .. 2·50 50
 a. Perf 11½ (1933) .. .. .. 4·50 20
 b. Perf 14 (1934) .. .. 11·00 30
 c. Perf 13½ (1934) .. .. .. 12·00 30
 ca. Vert pair, one without opt .. £110

(*b*) "BHOPAL GOVT" *at right. P* 13½

O314 ½ a. yellow-green .. .. 4·50 10
O315 1 a. carmine-red .. .. 8·00 15
 a. Vert pair, one without opt .. £200
O316 2 a. ultramarine .. .. 8·00 45
O317 4 a. chocolate .. .. 6·50 1·00
 a. Perf 14 (1934) .. .. 13·00 40
O313/17 .. .. *Set of* 5 27·00 1·10

No. O317 is comb-perforated and No. O317a line-perforated.

¼A (O 5) THREE PIES (O 6) ONE ANNA (O 7)

1935–36. *Nos.* O314, O316 *and* O317 *surch as Types* O **5** *to* O **7**.

O318 O **5** ¼ a. on ½ a. yellow-green (R.) .. 21·00 12·00
 a. Surch inverted .. .. .. £140 75·00
 b. Vert pair. Nos. O318/19 .. 32·00 19·00
 ba. Ditto. Surch inverted £300 £150
O319 O **6** 3 p. on ½ a. yellow-green (R.) .. 2·50 3·00
 a. "THEEE PIES" (R. 7/10) .. 60·00 45·00
 b. "THRFE" for "THREE" (R. 10/6) 60·00 45·00
 c. Surch inverted .. .. .. 60·00 38·00
O320 O **5** ¼ a. on 2 a. ultramarine (R.) .. 22·00 15·00
 a. Surch inverted .. .. .. £140 60·00
 b. Vert pair. Nos. O320/1 .. 32·00 21·00
 ba. Ditto. Surch inverted £300 £140
O321 O **6** 3 p. on 2 a. ultramarine (R.) .. 3·75 3·25
 a. Surch inverted .. .. .. 60·00 35·00
 b. "THEEE PIES" (R. 7/10) .. 65·00 42·00
 ba. Ditto. Surch inverted £425 £375
 c. "THRFE" for "THREE" (R. 10/6) 65·00 42·00
 ca. Ditto. Surch inverted £425 £375
O322 O **5** ¼ a. on 4 a. chocolate (R.) £700 £225
 a. Vert pair. Nos O322 and O324 £1000 £400
O323 ¼ a. on 4 a. chocolate (No. O317a) (Blk.) (25.5.36) .. .. .. 55·00 20·00
 a. Vert pair. Nos. O323 and O325 80·00 35·00
O324 O **6** 3 p. on 4 a. chocolate (R.) .. .. 85·00 42·00
 a. "THEEE PIES" (R. 7/10) .. £425 £350
 c. "THRFE" for "THREE" (R. 10/6) £425 £350
O325 3 p. on 4 a. chocolate (No. O317a) (Blk.) (25.5.36) .. .. .. 2·50 2·75
 a. "THRER" for "THREE" (R. 8/2) £275 £160
 b. "FHREE" for "THREE" (R. 3/10, 10/1) £300 £225
 c. "PISE" for "PIES" (R. 10/10) .. £450 £325
 d. "PIFS" for "PIES" (R. 7/9) .. £275 £180
O326 O **7** 1 a. on ½ a. yellow-green (V.) .. 3·25 1·50
 a. Surch inverted .. .. .. 65·00 40·00
 b. First "N" in "ANNA" inverted (R. 4/5) .. .. 75·00 50·00
 ba. Ditto. Surch inverted £425 £350
O327 1 a. on 2 a. ultramarine (R.) .. 2·25 1·75
 a. Surch inverted .. .. .. 70·00 38·00
 b. First "N" in "ANNA" inverted (R. 4/5) .. .. 60·00 50·00
 ba. Ditto. Surch inverted £425 £350
O327*d* 1 a. on 2 a. ultramarine (V.) .. 42·00 42·00
 da. Surch inverted .. .. .. 85·00 85·00
 db. First "N" in "ANNA" inverted (R. 4/5) £425 £425
 dc. Ditto. Surch inverted £700 £700
O328 1 a. on 2 a. ultram (Blk.) (25.5.36) 70 1·10
 a. "ANNO" £1100
O329 1 a. on 4 a. chocolate (B.) .. .. 4·25 4·50
 a. First "N" in "ANNA" inverted (R. 4/5) .. .. 80·00 65·00
 b. Perf 14 .. .. 8·00 3·75
 ba. Ditto. First "N" in "ANNA" inverted (R. 4/5) .. .. .. £170 85·00

Nos. O318 to O325 are arranged in composite sheets of 100 (10 × 10). The two upper horizontal rows of each value are surcharged as Type O **5** and the next five rows as Type O **6**. The remaining three rows are also surcharged as Type O **6** but in a slightly narrower setting.

The surcharge on No. O323 differs from Type O **5** in the shape of the figures and letter.

O 8

(Des T. I. Archer. Litho Indian Govt Ptg Wks, Nasik (No. O330). Typo Bhopal Govt Ptg Wks (others))

1935–39. *As Type* O **8**.

(*a*) *Litho. Inscr* "BHOPAL GOVT POSTAGE". *Optd* "SERVICE" (13½ *mm*). *P* 13½
O330 1 a. 3 p. blue and claret 3·50 50

(*b*) *Typo. Inscr* "BHOPAL STATE POSTAGE". *Optd* "SERVICE" (11 *mm*). *P* 12
O331 1 a. 6 p. blue and claret (1937) 1·75 50
a. Imperf between (pair) £140 £150
b. Opt omitted £120 90·00
c. Opt double, one inverted £325 £325
d. Imperf (pair) † £120
e. Blue printing double † £110
O332 1 a. 6 p. claret (1939) 4·75 1·00
a. Imperf between (pair) £140 £150
b. Opt omitted — £275
c. Opt double, one inverted — £275
d. Opt double — £275

PRINTERS. From No. O333 all issues were printed by the Bhopal Govt Ptg Wks in typography.

O **9**

O **10** The Moti Mahal

1936 (July)–**38.** *Optd* "SERVICE". *P* 12.
O333 O **9** ¼ a. orange (Br.) 90 30
a. Imperf between (vert pair) £130
ab. Imperf between (horiz pair) † £225
b. Opt inverted £275 £190
c. Black opt 8·00 75
ca. Opt inverted † £275
cb. Opt double † £250
O334 ¼ a. yellow (Br.) (1938) 2·50 85
O335 1 a. scarlet 1·50 10
a. Imperf between (horiz pair) £100 95·00
b. Imperf between (vert pair) † £190
c. Imperf between (block of four) £275 £275
d. Imperf vert (horiz pair) † £110

1936–49. *As Type* O **10** (*various palaces*). *P* 12.

(*a*) *Optd* "SERVICE" (13½ *mm*)
O336 ½ a. purple-brown and yellow-green 70 60
a. Imperf between (vert pair) † £150
ab. Imperf between (horiz pair) † £150
b. Opt double £225 £150
c. Frame double £110 15·00
d. Purple-brown and green (1938) 70 30

(*b*) *Optd* "SERVICE" (11 *mm*)
O337 2 a. brown and blue (1937) 1·60 40
a. Imperf between (vert pair) † £225
ab. Imperf between (horiz pair) † £160
b. Opt inverted £250 £250
c. Opt omitted £300
d. Pair, one without opt £425
e. As d. but opt inverted £650
O338 2 a. green and violet (1938) 7·50 30
a. Imperf between (vert pair) † £160
b. Imperf between (vert strip of 3) £110 £120
c. Frame double † £170
d. Centre double † £180
O339 4 a. blue and brown (1937) 3·25 50
a. Imperf between (horiz pair) † £425
b. Opt omitted † £200
c. Opt double † £130
d. Centre double † £250
e. Blue and reddish brown (1938) 3·25 55
ea. Frame double † £170
O340 8 a. bright purple and blue (1938) 4·00 1·25
a. Imperf between (vert pair) † £275
b. Opt omitted † £110
c. Opt double † £130
d. Imperf vert (horiz pair) and opt omitted † £200
e. Imperf (pair) and opt omitted † £200
O341 1 r. blue and reddish purple (Br.) (1938) 14·00 6·00
a. Imperf horiz (vert pair) † £900
b. Opt in black (1942) 14·00 4·50
ba. Light blue and bright purple 35·00 28·00
bb. Laid paper £475 £500
O336/41 *Set of* 6 28·00 6·25

(*c*) *Optd* "SERVICE" (11½ *mm*) *with serifs*
O342 1 r. dull blue and bright purple (Blk.) (1949) 40·00 65·00
a. "SREVICE" for "SERVICE" (R. 6/6) £130 £170
b. "SERVICE" omitted £600

(*d*) *Optd* "SERVICE" (13½ *mm*) *with serifs*
O343 8 a. bright purple and blue (1949) 65·00 90·00
a. "SERAICE" for "SERVICE" (R. 6/5) £300 £400
b. Fig "1" for "I" in "SERVICE" (R. 7/1) £300 £400

The ½ a. is inscr "BHOPAL GOVT" below the arms, other values have "BHOPAL STATE".

Designs:—(37½ × 22½ *mm*) 2 a. The Moti Masjid; 4 a. Taj Mahal and Be-Nazir Palaces. (39 × 24 *mm*)–8 a. Ahmadabad Palace. (45½ × 27½ *mm*)—1 r. Rait Ghat.

O **11** Tiger

O **13** The Moti Mahal

1940. *As Type* O **11** (*animals*). *P* 12.
O344 ¼ a. bright blue 3·25 1·10
O345 1 a. bright purple (Spotted Deer) 17·00 1·40

1941. *As Type* O **8** *but coloured centre inscr* "SERVICE"; *bottom frame inscr* "BHOPAL STATE POSTAGE". *P* 12.
O346 1 a. 3 p. emerald-green 1·00 1·00
a. Imperf between (pair) £375 £375

1944–47. *As Type* O **13** (*various palaces*). *P* 12.
O347 ½ a. green 85 70
a. Imperf (pair) † 75·00
b. Imperf between (vert pair) † £140
c. Doubly printed † £110
O348 2 a. violet 7·00 3·00
a. Imperf (pair) † 75·00
c. Bright purple (1945) 1·90 2·75
d. Mauve (1947) 11·00 14·00
e. Error. Chocolate (imperf) £160 £160
O349 4 a. chocolate 4·25 1·40
a. Imperf (pair) † 90·00
b. Imperf vert (horiz pair) † £170
c. Doubly printed † £130
O347/9 *Set of* 3 6·50 4·25

Design inscr "BHOPAL STATE":—2 a. The Moti Masjid; 4 a. Be-Nazir Palaces.

O **14** Arms of Bhopal

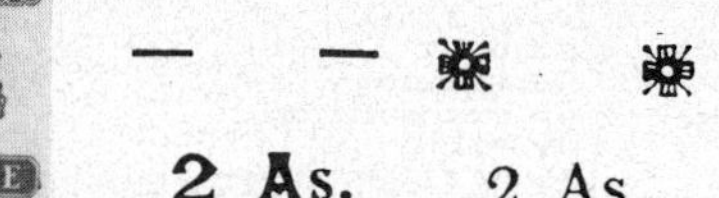

(O **15**) (O **16**)

1944–49. *P* 12.
O350 O **14** 3 p. bright blue 65 50
a. Imperf between (vert pair) 90·00 95·00
b. Imperf between (horiz pair) † £180
c. Stamp doubly printed 45·00
O351 9 p. chestnut (*shades*) (1945) 8·00 2·50
a. Imperf (pair) † £140
b. Orange-brown 2·00 2·75
O352 1 a. purple (1945) 4·25 1·10
a. Imperf horiz (vert pair) † £275
b. Violet (1946) 7·00 2·25
O353 1½ a. claret (1945) 1·25 50
a. Imperf between (horiz pair) † £250
b. Imperf between (vert pair)
O354 3 a. yellow 8·50 9·00
a. Imperf (pair) † £140
b. Imperf horiz (vert pair) † £190
c. Imperf vert (horiz pair)
d. Orange-brown (1949) 80·00 70·00
O355 6 a. carmine (1945) 12·00 35·00
a. Imperf (pair) † £160
b. Imperf horiz (vert pair) † £190
c. Imperf vert (horiz pair) † £190
O350/5 *Set of* 6 26·00 42·00

1949 (July). *Surch with Type* O **15**. *P* 12.
O356 O **14** 2 a. on 1½ a. claret 2·50 5·50
a. Stop omitted 12·00 21·00
b. Imperf (pair) £170 £190
ba. Stop omitted (pair) £450 £475
c. "2" omitted (in pair with normal) £600

The "stop omitted" variety occurs on positions 60 and 69 in the sheet of 81.

1949. *Surch with Type* O **16**. *Imperf*.
O357 O **14** 2 a. on 1½ a. claret £650 £650
a. Perf 12 £650 £650

Three different types of "2" occur in the setting of Type O **16**.

BHOR

PRICES FOR STAMPS ON COVER

Nos. 1/2	*from* × 40
No. 3	*from* × 6

GUM. The stamps of Bhor were issued without gum.

Pandit Shankar Rao, 1871–1922

1

2

1879. *Handstamped. Very thick to thin native paper. Imperf.*
1 **1** ½ a. carmine (*shades*) 2·00 3·75
a. *Tête-bêche* (pair) £600
2 **2** 1 a. carmine (*shades*) 4·00 5·50

3

1901. *Typo. Wove paper. Imperf.*
3 **3** ½ a. red 11·00 3

BIJAWAR

PRICES FOR STAMPS ON COVER

The stamps of Bijawar are very rare used on cover.

Maharaja Sarwant Singh, 1899–1941

1

2

(Typo Lakshmi Art Ptg Works, Bombay)

1935 (1 July)–**36.** (*a*) *P* 11.
1 **1** 3 p. brown 4·75 3
a. Imperf (pair) 6·50
b. Imperf between (vert pair) 85·00
c. Imperf horiz (vert pair) 50·00
2 6 p. carmine 4·50 3
a. Imperf (pair) 85·00
b. Imperf between (vert pair) 80·00
c. Imperf between (horiz pair) 85·00 £1
d. Imperf horiz (vert pair) 85·00
3 9 p. violet 5·50 4
a. Imperf (pair) £140
b. Imperf between (vert pair) 85·00
c. Imperf between (horiz pair) 80·00
d. Imperf horiz (vert pair) 80·00
4 1 a. blue 6·00 4
a. Imperf (pair) 85·00
b. Imperf between (vert pair) 85·00
c. Imperf between (horiz pair) £120
d. Imperf horiz (vert pair) 85·00
e. Imperf vert (horiz strip of 3) £140
5 2 a. deep green 6·00 4
a. Imperf (pair) £100
b. Imperf horiz (vert pair) 11·00
c. Imperf between (vert pair) 35·00
d. Imperf between (horiz pair) 50·00 80
1/5 *Set of* 5 24·00 19·

(*b*) *Roul* 7 (1936)
6 **1** 3 p. brown 3·50 3
a. Printed on gummed side £400
7 6 p. carmine 4·75 17·
8 9 p. violet 5·50 85·
9 1 a. blue 7·50 90·
10 2 a. deep green 8·50 95·
6/10 *Set of* 5 27·00 £2

1937 (May). *Typo. P* 9.
11 **2** 4 a. orange 9·50 65·
a. Imperf between (vert pair) £140
b. Imperf (pair) £200
12 6 a. lemon 10·00 65·
a. Imperf between (vert pair) £140
b. Imperf (pair) £200
13 8 a. emerald-green 11·00 80·
a. Imperf (pair) £225
14 12 a. greenish blue 11·00 80·
a. Imperf (pair) £250
15 1 r. bright violet 32·00 £1
a. "1 Rs" for "1 R" (R. 1/2) 48·00 £3
b. Imperf (pair) £300
ba. "1 Rs" for "1 R" (R. 1/2) £850
11/15 *Set of* 5 65·00 £3

The stamps of Bijawar were withdrawn in 1941.

BUNDI

PRICES FOR STAMPS ON COVER

No. 1	*from* × 2
No. 2	*from* × 4
Nos. 3/53	*from* × 10
Nos. 54/63	*from* × 5
Nos. 64/78	*from* × 2
Nos. 79/92	*from* × 10
Nos. O1/52	*from* × 15
Nos. O53/9	*from* × 20

GUM. Nos. 1/17 were issued without gum.

ILLUSTRATIONS. Types **1/10** and **12/19** are shown actual size.

In Nos. 1 to 17 characters denoting the value are below th dagger, except in Nos. 2a, 11 and 17.

All Bundi stamps until 1914 are imperforate.

Maharao Raja Raghubir Singh, 1889–1927

1

(May). *Each stamp with a distinct frame and the stamps connected by the framing lines. Three vertical lines on* *ger. Laid or wove paper.*

1 ½ a. slate-grey £5500 £1600
  a. Last two letters of value below the rest .. .. † £3750

2 (Block of four stamps)

(Dec). *Stamps joined together, with no space between* *em. Two vertical lines on dagger. Thin wove paper.*

2 ½ a. slate-grey .. .. 32·00 35·00
  a. Value at top, name below £170 £200
  b. Right upper ornament omitted .. £1500 £1500
  c. Last two letters of value below the rest £1100 £1100
  d. Left lower ornament omitted .. £1500 £1500

3

3 (Nov). *Dagger shorter, lines thicker. Stamps separate. Laid* *per.*

3 ½ a. slate-grey .. .. 3·50 7·50
  a. Last two letters of value below the rest £300 £400

4 (1 anna)

5 (2 annas)

6 (2 annas)

97–98. *No shading in centre of blade of dagger. The stamps have spaces between them, but are connected by the framing lines, both vertically and horizontally. Laid paper.*

Blade of dagger comparatively narrow, and either triangular, as in T **4** *and* **6**, *or with the left-hand corner not touching the bar behind it, as in T* **5** (1897-98)

4 1 a. Indian red .. .. 8·50 20·00
5 1 a. red .. .. 7·50 13·00
  2 a. green .. .. 11·00 18·00
6 2 a. yellow-green .. .. .. 9·00 21·00
5 4 a. green .. .. 45·00 65·00
  8 a. Indian red .. .. 80·00 £170
  1 r. yellow/*red* £200 £350
0 .. .. *Set of* 5 £300 £550

7

II. *Blade varying in shape, but as a rule not touching the bar; value above and name below the dagger, instead of the reverse* (Jan 1898)

11 **7** 4 a. emerald-green .. .. .. 28·00
  a. Yellow-green .. .. .. 19·00 45·00

8 (½ anna)

9 (8 annas)

III. *Blade wider and (except on the ½ a.) almost diamond shaped; it nearly always touches the bar* (1898–1900)

12 **8** ½ a. slate-grey (5.2.98) .. .. .. 3·25 3·50
13 **9** 1 a. Indian red (7.98) .. .. .. 2·25 2·25
14 2 a. pale green (9.11.98) .. .. 7·00 10·00
  a. First two characters of value (= two) omitted £1200 £1200
15 8 a. Indian red (7.98) .. .. .. 8·50 11·00
16 1 r. yellow/*blue* (7.98) .. .. .. 22·00 38·00
  a. On wove paper .. .. .. 11·00 19·00
12/16a .. .. *Set of* 5 29·00 42·00

10

IV. *Inscriptions as on No.* 11; *point of dagger to left* (9.11.98)

17 **10** 4 a. green .. .. 18·00 23·00
  a. Yellow-green .. .. .. 10·00 15·00

All the above stamps are lithographed in large sheets, containing as many varieties of type as there are stamps in the sheets.

11 Raja protecting Sacred Cows

Type **11** was produced from separate clichés printed as a block of four. The same clichés were used for all values, but not necessarily in the same order within the block. The Devanagri inscriptions, "RAJ BUNDI" at top and the face value at bottom, were inserted into the basic clichés as required so that various differences exist within the 58 settings which have been identified.

The denominations may be identified from the following illustrations. The ½ a., 3 a. and rupee values can be easily distinguished by their colours.

Bottom tablets:—

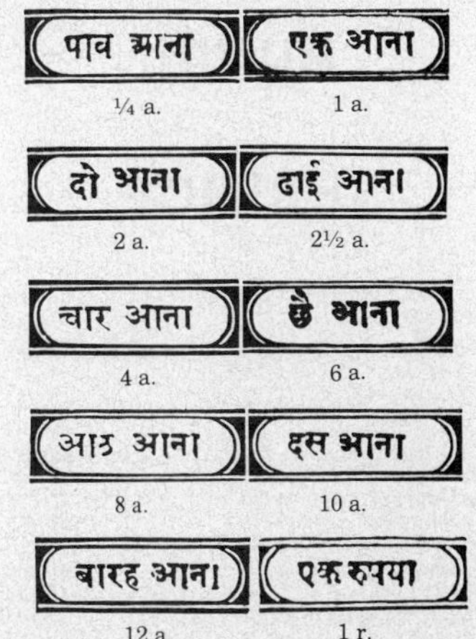

¼ a. 1 a. 2 a. 2½ a. 4 a. 6 a. 8 a. 10 a. 12 a. 1 r.

The nine versions of the inscriptions are as follows:

A B

Top tablet

Type A. Top tablet has inscription in two separate words with a curved line over the first character in the second. The second word has three characters. Bottom tablet has short line above the first character in the second word.

Type B. Top tablet as Type A, but without the curved line over the first character in the second word. Bottom tablet as Type A.

C

Type C. Top tablet as Type B, but with large loop beneath the first character in the second word. This loop is usually joined to the main character, but is sometimes detached as in the illustration. Bottom tablet as Type A.

D Top tablet

E Bottom tablet

Type D. Top tablet in thinner lettering with the inscription shown as one word of six characters. The fourth character has a curved line above it, as in Type A, and a loop beneath, as in Type C. Bottom tablet as Type A, but thinner letters.

Type E. Top tablet as Type C. Bottom tablet shows a redrawn first character to the second word. This has the line at top extending over the entire character.

F

Bottom tablet

Type F. Top tablet as Type B. Bottom tablet as Type E, but first character in second word differs.

G H

Type G. Top tablet as Type C, but without dot over first character in second word. There are now four characters in the second word. Bottom tablet as Type E.

Type H. Top tablet as Type G, but with characters larger and bolder. Bottom tablet as Type E, but with characters larger and bolder.

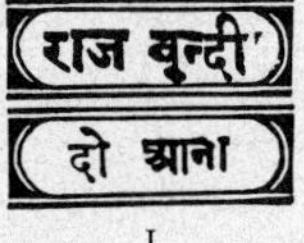

I

Type I. Top tablet as Type H. Bottom tablet as Type E.

Some settings contained more than one inscription type within the block of four so that *se-tenant* examples are known of Type B with Type C (¼, 1, 2, 4, 8, 10 and 12 a.), Type C with Type E (¼, ½ and 4 a.) and Type E with Type F (½ and 4 a.). Type F only exists from this mixed setting.

1914 (Oct)–**41**. *T* **11**. *Typo. Ungummed paper except for Nos.* 73/8.

I. *Rouletted in colour*

(*a*) *Inscriptions as Type A. Thin wove paper* (1916–23)

18 ½ a. black .. .. 2·25 10·00
19 1 a. vermilion .. .. 4·00 19·00
20 2 a. emerald .. .. 4·00 30·00
  a. Deep green (coarse ptg on medium wove paper) (1923) .. .. 3·00 9·00
21 2½ a. chrome-yellow (*shades*) (1917) .. .. 7·00 30·00
22 3 a. chestnut (1917) .. .. 17·00 32·00

23 4 a. yellow-green .. 19·00
24 6 a. cobalt (1917) .. 19·00 80·00
25 1 r. reddish violet (1917) .. 21·00 85·00

A special printing of the 1 a. took place in late 1917 in connection with the "OUR DAY" Red Cross Society Fund. This had the "RAJ BUNDI" inscription in the bottom tablet with the face value below it. The top tablet carried four Devanagri characters for "OUR DAY". No evidence has been found to suggest that this 1 a. stamp was used for postal purposes (*Price, £170 unused*).

(*b*) *Inscriptions as Type* B. *Thin wove or pelure paper* (1914–23)

25*a* ¼ a. cobalt (1916) .. 3·00 18·00
26 ¼ a. ultramarine (*shades*) (1917) .. 1·90 4·25
a. Indigo (1923) .. 3·25 7·50
b. Error. Black (1923)
27 ½ a. black .. 2·75 6·00
28 1 a. vermilion (1915) .. 3·25 9·50
a. Carmine (1923) .. 8·00 10·00
b. Red (*shades*) (1923) .. 5·00 10·00
29 2 a. emerald (*shades*) (1915) .. 5·00 16·00
30 2½ a. olive-yellow (1917) .. 5·00 21·00
31 3 a. chestnut (1917) .. 4·75 30·00
32 4 a. apple-green (1915) .. 3·50 32·00
32*a* 4 a. olive-yellow (1917) .. £130 £150
33 6 a. pale ultramarine (*shades*) (1917) .. 11·00 80·00
a. Deep ultramarine (1917) .. 7·00
34 8 a. orange (1915) .. 7·50 85·00
35 10 a. olive-sepia (1917) .. £225 £500
36 12 a. sage-green (1917) .. £550
36*a* 1 r. lilac (*shades*) (1915) .. 24·00

(*c*) *Inscriptions as Type* C. *Thin to medium wove paper* (1917–41)

37 ¼ a. ultramarine (*shades*) (1923) .. 5·50 6·50
a. Indigo (1923) .. 6·00 8·00
b. Error. Black (1923)
c. Cobalt (*medium wove paper*) (1937) .. 17·00 17·00
38 ½ a. black .. 1·40 4·50
39 1 a. orange-red .. 15·00 20·00
a. Carmine (1923) .. 13·00 18·00
b. Deep red (*medium wove paper*) (1936) .. 17·00 17·00
40 2 a. emerald .. 8·50 21·00
a. Sage-green .. 7·00 21·00
41 4 a. yellow-green (*shades*) .. 40·00 90·00
a. Olive-yellow .. 95·00 £140
b. Bright apple-green (*medium wove paper*) (1936) .. £400 £225
42 8 a. reddish orange .. 9·00 55·00
43 10 a. brown-olive .. 16·00 80·00
a. Olive-sepia .. 38·00 £110
b. Yellow-brown .. 65·00
44 12 a. sage-green .. 9·50 85·00
45 1 r. lilac .. 23·00 £120
46 2 r. red-brown and black .. 60·00 £225
a. Chocolate and black (*medium wove paper*) (1936) .. 60·00 £250
47 3 r. blue and red-brown .. 90·00 £250
a. Grey-blue and chocolate (*medium wove paper*) (1941) .. £100
ab. Chocolate (inscriptions) inverted .. £9000
48 4 r. emerald and scarlet .. £190 £325
49 5 r. scarlet and emerald .. £200 £350

(*d*) *Inscriptions as Type* D. *Thin wove paper* (1918?)

50 2½ a. buff (*shades*) .. 12·00 42·00
51 3 a. red-brown .. 22·00 25·00
a. Semi-circle and dot omitted from 4th character .. 38·00 42·00
52 10 a. bistre .. 28·00 90·00
a. 4th character turned to left instead of downwards .. 48·00
53 12 a. grey-olive .. 35·00 95·00
a. 4th character turned to left instead of downwards .. 65·00
b. Blackish green .. 55·00
ba. 4th character turned to left instead of downwards .. 85·00

(*e*) *Inscriptions as Type* E. (i) *Medium wove paper* (1930–37)

54 ¼ a. deep slate .. 16·00 21·00
54*a* ¼ a. indigo (*thin wove paper*) (1935) .. 16·00 21·00
b. Cobalt (1937) .. 16·00 16·00
55 ½ a. black .. 11·00 11·00
56 1 a. carmine-red .. 21·00 27·00
57 3 a. chocolate (*shades*) (1936) .. 11·00 28·00
58 4 a. yellow-olive (1935) .. £450 £190
a. Bright apple-green (1936) .. £450 £190
ab. No tail to 4th character .. £650 £325

(ii) *Very thick wove paper* (1930–32)

59 ¼ a. indigo (1932) .. 18·00 23·00
60 ½ a. black .. 80·00 85·00
61 1 a. bright scarlet (1931) .. 18·00 21·00
a. Carmine-red .. 65·00 75·00

(iii) *Thin horizontally laid paper* (1935)

62 ¼ a. indigo .. 4·50 17·00
63 1 a. scarlet-vermilion .. 8·50 23·00

Nos. 62 and 63 exist in *tête-bêche* blocks of four on the same or opposite sides of the paper.

(*f*) *Inscriptions as Type* F. *Medium wove paper* (1935)

63*a* ½ a. black .. 80·00
63*b* 4 a. yellow-olive .. £750 £450

(*g*) *Inscriptions as Type* G. (i) *Horizontally laid paper* (1935)

64 ½ a. black .. 85·00 85·00
a. Vert laid paper .. 80·00 80·00
65 1 a. scarlet .. 70·00 50·00
66 4 a. bright green .. 20·00 38·00

(ii) *Medium wove paper* (1936)

66*a* ½ a. black .. 4·00 24·00
66*b* 4 a. yellow-green .. £1000 £500

(*h*) *Inscriptions as Type* H. *Medium wove paper* (1935–41)

67 ¼ a. ultramarine .. 1·75 7·00
68 ½ a. black (1938) .. 75·00 75·00
69 1 a. deep red .. 7·00 32·00
a. Rosine (1938) .. 17·00 35·00
70 4 a. emerald (1938) .. 18·00 27·00
71 4 r. yellow-green and vermilion (1941) .. £180
72 5 r. vermilion and yellow-green (1941) .. £250

No. 70 shows the currency spelt as "ANE" with the last letter missing and an accent over the Devanagri "N".

II. *P* 11.

(*a*) *Inscriptions as Type* H. *Medium wove paper with gum* (1939–41)

73 ¼ a. ultramarine .. 25·00 38·00
a. Greenish blue (1941) .. 1·75 48·00
74 ½ a. black .. 30·00 30·00
75 1 a. scarlet-vermilion (1940) .. £120 60·00
a. Rose (1940) .. 12·00 50·00
76 2 a. yellow-green (1941) .. 16·00 75·00

(*b*) *Inscriptions as Type* I. *Medium wove paper with gum* (1940)

77 ½ a. black .. £120 95·00
78 2 a. bright apple-green .. 50·00 50·00

FISCAL USE. Collectors are warned that the low values of the later settings of Type **11** were extensively used for fiscal purposes. Stamps which have been fraudulently cleaned of pen-cancels, regummed or provided with forged postmarks are frequently met with. Particular care should be exercised with examples of Nos. 58/*a*, 64/5, 68/70, 74/5*a* and 77.

Maharao Raja Ishwari Singh, 1927–1945

20

1941–44. *Typo. P* 11.

79 **20** 3 p. bright blue .. 2·00 3·00
80 6 p. deep blue .. 3·50 5·00
81 1 a. orange-red .. 3·75 6·50
82 2 a. chestnut .. 5·50 14·00
a. Deep brown (*no gum*) (1944) .. 14·00 16·00
83 4 a. bright green .. 11·00 40·00
84 8 a. dull green .. 12·00 £140
85 1 r. deep blue .. 32·00 £200
79/85 .. *Set of* 7 60·00 £375

The first printing only of Nos. 79/85 is usual with gum; all further printings, including No. 82*a*, are without gum.

Maharao Raja Bahadur Singh, 1945–1971

21 Maharao Raja Bahadur Singh **22** Bundi

(Typo *Times of India* Press, Bombay)

1947. *P* 11.

86 **21** ¼ a. blue-green .. 1·60 28·00
87 ½ a. violet .. 1·60 27·00
88 1 a. yellow-green .. 1·60 26·00
89 – 2 a. vermilion .. 1·60 50·00
90 – 4 a. orange .. 1·60 75·00
91 **22** 8 a. ultramarine .. 2·00
92 1 r. chocolate .. 14·00
86/92 .. *Set of* 7 22·00

On the 2 and 4 a. the Maharao is in Indian dress.

OFFICIAL STAMPS

PRICES. Prices for Nos. O1/52 are for unused examples. Used stamps are generally worth a small premium over the prices quoted.

बूंदी BUNDI

सरविस SERVICE

(O 1) (O 2)

BUNDI

SERVICE

(O 3)

1915–41. *T* **11** *handstamped as Types* O 1/3. *Ungummed paper except Nos.* O47/52.

A. *Optd with Type* O 1. B. *Optd with Type* O 2. C. *Optd with Type* O 3.

I. *Rouletted in colour*

A B C

(*a*) *Inscriptions as Type* A. *Thin wove paper.*

O 1 ½ a. black .. £300 † †
a. Red opt .. £275 † †
O 1*b* 2 a. emerald .. 2·75 £250 †
ba. Deep green (*coarse ptg on medium wove paper*) .. 6·50 13·00 £200
bb. Red opt .. 12·00 13·00 †
O 2 2½ a. chrome-yellow (*shades*) .. 2·75 14·00 £200
a. Red opt .. £150 £170 †

A B

O 3 3 a. chestnut .. 3·00 20·00
a. Green opt .. £140 †
b. Red opt .. £180 £180
O 4 6 a. cobalt .. 24·00 26·00
a. Red opt .. £200 £225
O 5 1 r. reddish violet .. 42·00 42·00
a. Red opt .. £275 £300

(*b*) *Inscriptions as Type* B. *Thin wove or pelure paper*

O 6 ¼ a. ultramarine (*shades*) .. 1·60 1·75
a. Red opt .. 1·25 4·00
O 7 ½ a. black .. 7·50 6·00
a. Red opt .. 4·25 11·00
O 8 1 a. vermilion .. 4·00 †
a. Red opt .. — †
b. Carmine .. 23·00 12·00
c. Red (*shades*) .. — 7·00
O 9 2 a. emerald (*shades*) .. 25·00 32·00
a. Red opt .. — £100
O 9*b* 3 a. chestnut (R.) .. — †
O10 4 a. apple-green .. 12·00 60·00
a. Red opt .. £225 †
O10*b* 4 a. olive-yellow .. £200 £225
ba. Red opt .. — £425
O11 6 a. pale ultramarine (*shades*) .. 13·00 £170
a. Red opt .. £225 £225
b. Deep ultramarine .. 55·00 70·00
ba. Red opt .. £180 £160
O12 8 a. orange .. 45·00 60·00
a. Red opt .. £250 †
O13 10 a. olive-sepia .. £170 £225
a. Red opt .. £500 £550
O14 12 a. sage-green .. £140 £375
a. Red opt .. † †
O14*b* 1 r. lilac .. £300 †

(*c*) *Inscriptions as Type* C. *Thin to medium wove paper.*

O15 ¼ a. ultramarine (*shades*) .. 2·75 3·25
a. Red opt .. 1·00 5·00
b. Green opt .. 3·00 38·00
c. Cobalt (*medium wove paper*) .. 50·00 48·00
ca. Red opt .. 38·00 16·00
O16 ½ a. black .. 7·50 3·00
a. Red opt .. 75 8·00
b. Green opt .. 3·00 †
O17 1 a. orange-red .. 1·25 —
a. Carmine .. 22·00 8·00
b. Deep red (*medium wove paper*) .. 32·00 42·00
ba. Red opt .. † £120
O18 2 a. emerald .. 5·00 14·00
a. Red opt .. † 85·00
b. Sage-green .. 8·50 13·00
O19 4 a. yellow-green (*shades*) .. 9·00 65·00
b. Red opt .. — †
c. Olive-yellow .. £110 £100
ca. Red opt .. £300 £300
O20 8 a. reddish orange .. 15·00 24·00
a. Red opt .. £200 £325
O21 10 a. brown-olive .. 45·00 75·00
a. Red opt .. £350 £350
O22 12 a. sage-green .. 40·00 85·00
a. Red opt .. £450 †
O23 1 r. lilac .. £120 †
a. Red opt .. £300 †
O24 2 r. red-brown and black .. £375 £180
a. Red opt .. † £800
b. Chocolate and black (*medium wove paper*) .. £550 £550
O25 3 r. blue and red-brown .. £350 £200
a. Red opt .. £800 †
b. Grey-blue & chocolate (*medium wove paper*) .. £800 £800
ba. Red opt .. £850 †
O26 4 r. emerald and scarlet .. £300 £300
O27 5 r. scarlet and emerald .. £300 £300

(*d*) *Inscriptions as Type* D. *Thin wove paper*

O28 2½ a. buff (*shades*) .. 15·00 18·00
b. Red opt .. £170 —
O29 3 a. red-brown .. 29·00 24·00
a. Variety as No. 51a .. 48·00 45·00
b. Red opt .. † £300
O30 10 a. bistre .. 40·00 75·00
a. Variety as No. 52a .. 65·00 £130
b. Red opt .. £350 £450
O31 12 a. grey-olive .. 55·00 85·00
a. Variety as No. 53a .. 85·00 £140
b. Red opt .. £350 £425
ba. Variety as No. 53a .. £450 †

(*e*) *Inscriptions as Type* E. (i) *Medium wove paper*

O32 ¼ a. deep slate .. 30·00 15·00
a. Red opt .. 27·00 35·00
O32*b* ¼ a. indigo (*thin wove paper*) .. 28·00 32·00
ba. Red opt .. 28·00 30·00
bb. Green opt .. 75·00 80·00
c. Cobalt .. 55·00 55·00
ca. Red opt .. 35·00 30·00
O33 ½ a. black .. 35·00 12·00
a. Red opt .. 22·00 10·00
b. Green opt .. £275 £180
O34 1 a. carmine-red .. 30·00 30·00
O35 3 a. chocolate (*shades*) .. £180 £120
a. Red opt .. £400 £400
O35*b* 4 a. yellow-olive .. † £425
ba. Bright apple-green .. £750 †

(ii) *Very thick wove paper*

O36 ¼ a. indigo .. 9·00 12·00
a. Red opt .. 20·00 42·00
b. Green opt .. 90·00 †
O37 ½ a. black .. 90·00 £100
O38 1 a. bright scarlet .. 13·00 13·00
a. Carmine-red .. 95·00 70·00

(iii) *Thin horizontally laid paper*

O39 ¼ a. indigo .. 75·00 85·00
a. Red opt .. 5·00 8·00
O40 1 a. scarlet-vermilion .. 35·00 22·00
a. Red opt .. £250 £275

Nos. O39/40a exist in *tête-bêche* blocks of four on the same or opposite sides of the paper.

	A	B	C
(f) Inscriptions as Type F. Medium wove paper			
½ a. black	—	—	†
ba. Red opt	£275	£375	†
4 a. yellow-olive	†	£600	†
g) Inscriptions as Type G. (i) Horizontally laid paper			
½ a. black (red opt)	£120	£120	†
a. Vert laid paper	£140	£140	†
ab. Red opt	£170	60·00	£325
4 a. bright green	£200	£180	†
a. Red opt	£225	£300	†
(ii) Medium wove paper			
½ a. black	£190	£200	†
ba. Red opt	£275	£275	†
(h) Inscriptions as Type H. Medium wove paper			
¼ a. ultramarine	25·00	75·00	†
a. Red opt	£170	£275	†
½ a. black	90·00	£140	†
a. Red opt	75·00	†	£400
1 a. rosine	£170	£150	£375
4 a. emerald	£150	£170	£350
a. Red opt	£375	†	£400

1. *(a) Inscriptions as Type H. Medium wove paper with gum*

	A	B	C
¼ a. ultramarine	45·00	70·00	£110
a. Red opt	70·00	90·00	†
b. Greenish blue	70·00	70·00	£180
c. Ditto. Red opt	£170	†	†
½ a. black	45·00	60·00	£300
a. Red opt	90·00	£225	£160
1 a. scarlet-vermilion	£200	£250	£425
a. Stamp doubly printed	†	†	£850
b. Rose	£130	£120	£325
2 a. yellow-green	£375	£160	£225
) Inscriptions as Type I. Medium wove paper with gum			
½ a. black	£110	£225	£375
a. Red opt	£300	£375	†
2 a. bright apple-green	£350	£375	£600

ntil 1941 it was the general practice to carry official mail free ome of the above undoubtedly exist postally used.

. *Nos. 79 to 85 optd* "SERVICE".

20	3 p. bright blue (R.)	5·50	10·00
	6 p. deep blue (R.)	13·00	10·00
	1 a. orange-red	13·00	7·50
	2 a. brown	10·00	8·50
	4 a. bright green	30·00	75·00
	8 a. dull green	£120	£375
	1 r. deep blue (R.)	£140	£400
9	*Set of* 7	£300	£800

wo different types of "R" occur in the "SERVICE" overprint. ive positions in the sheet of 12 the "R" shows a larger loop a pointed diagonal leg.

undi became part of the Rajasthan Union by 15 April 1948.

BUSSAHIR (BASHAHR)

PRICES FOR STAMPS ON COVER

Nos. 1/21	*from* × 8
Nos. 22/23	*from* × 2
Nos. 24/43	*from* × 8

Raja Shamsher Singh, 1850–1914

1 2 3 4 5 6 7 8 (9)

e initials are those of the Tika Raghunath Singh, son of the then Raja, who was the organiser and former director of the State Post Office.

itho at the Bussahir Press by Maulvi Karam Bakhsh, Rampur)

95 (20 June). *Laid paper. Optd with* T **9** *in pale greenish blue* B.), *rose* (R.), *mauve* (M.) *or lake* (L.). *With or without gum.*

(a) Imperf.

1	¼ a. pink (M.) (1.9.95)	£1200	
	a. Monogram in rose	£1600	
2	½ a. grey (R.)	£350	
	a. Monogram in mauve		
3	1 a. vermilion (M.)	£140	
4	2 a. orange-yellow (M.)	45·00	£140
	a. Monogram in rose	90·00	
	b. Monogram in lake	60·00	
	c. Monogram in blue	£150	
5	4 a. slate-violet (M.)	85·00	
	a. Monogram in rose	£110	
	b. Monogram in lake	95·00	
	c. Without monogram	£225	
6 6	8 a. red-brown (M.)	85·00	£150
	a. Monogram in blue	£110	
	b. Monogram in lake		
	c. Without monogram	£190	
	d. Thick paper	£100	
7 7	12 a. green (L.)	£190	
	a. Monogram in mauve		
8 8	1 r. ultramarine (R.)	75·00	
	a. Monogram in mauve	£140	
	b. Monogram in lake	£110	
	c. Without monogram	£225	
	(b) Perf with a sewing machine; gauge and size of holes varying between 7 and 11½		
9 1	¼ a. pink (B.)	42·00	85·00
	a. Monogram in mauve	—	£130
	b. Without monogram	£225	£110
10 2	½ a. grey (R.)	18·00	90·00
	a. Without monogram	£450	
11 3	1 a. vermilion (M.)	19·00	75·00
	a. Without monogram		
12 4	2 a. orange-yellow (B.)	28·00	80·00
	a. Monogram in rose		
	b. Monogram in mauve	80·00	
	c. Without monogram	—	£170
13 5	4 a. slate-violet (B.)	19·00	85·00
	a. Monogram in rose	27·00	95·00
	b. Monogram in mauve	38·00	
	c. Without monogram	40·00	
14 6	8 a. red-brown (M.)	20·00	90·00
	a. Monogram in blue	45·00	£130
	b. Monogram in rose	70·00	
	c. Without monogram	£100	
15 7	12 a. green (R.)	60·00	£110
	a. Monogram in mauve	£100	
	b. Monogram in lake	95·00	
	c. Without monogram	£150	
16 8	1 r. ultramarine (R.)	32·00	90·00
	a. Monogram in mauve	90·00	
	b. Without monogram	£190	£300
9/16	*Set of* 8	£200	£650

1899. *As 1895, but pin-perf or rouletted.*

17 3	1 a. vermilion (M.)	£150	£170
18 4	2 a. orange-yellow (M.)	45·00	£110
	a. Monogram in lake	50·00	
	b. Monogram in rose	70·00	
	c. Monogram in blue	£100	
	d. Without monogram	£275	
19 5	4 a. slate-violet (L.)	£190	
	a. Monogram in blue		
	b. Monogram in rose	£250	
	c. Monogram in mauve	£250	
20 7	12 a. green (R.)	£375	£425
21 8	1 r. ultramarine (R.)	£375	

Nos. 1 to 21 were in sheets of 24. They seem to have been overprinted and perforated as required. Those first issued for use were perforated, but they were subsequently supplied imperf, both to collectors and for use. Nos. 17 to 21 were some of the last supplies. No rule seems to have been observed as to the colour of the overprinted monogram; pale blue, rose and mauve were used from the first. The pale blue varies to greenish blue or blue-green, and appears quite green on the yellow stamps. The lake is possibly a mixture of the mauve and the rose—it is a quite distinct colour and apparently later than the others. Specimens without overprint are either remainders left in the Treasury or copies that have escaped accidentally; they have been found sticking to the backs of others that bore the overprint.

Varieties may also be found doubly overprinted, in two different colours.

10 11 12

T **11**. Lines of shading above and at bottom left and right of shield.
T **12**. White dots above shield and ornaments in bottom corners.

13 14 15 16

(Printed at the Bussahir Press by Maulvi Karam Bakhsh)

1896–97. *Wove paper. Optd with monogram* "R.S.", T **9**, *in rose. Recess singly from line-engraved dies. With or without gum. Various perfs.*

22 10	¼ a. deep violet (1897)	—	£750
23 11	½ a. grey-blue	£550	£190
23*a*	½ a. deep blue (1897)	—	£275

No. 23 exists sewing-machine perf about 10 and also perf 14½–16. Nos. 22 and 23*a* are pin-perf.

1896–1900. *As Nos. 22/3, but lithographed in sheets of various sizes. No gum.*

(a) Imperf

24 10	¼ a. slate-violet (R.)	5·00	
	a. Monogram in mauve	7·00	
	b. Monogram in blue	9·00	
	c. Monogram in lake	14·00	
25 11	½ a. blue (*shades*) (R.)	6·00	14·00
	a. Monogram in mauve	6·50	14·00
	b. Monogram in lake	7·00	
	c. Without monogram		
	d. Laid paper (B.)	85·00	
	da. Monogram in lake		
26 13	1 a. olive (*shades*) (R.)	12·00	28·00
	a. Monogram in mauve	30·00	
	b. Monogram in lake	29·00	
	(b) Pin-perf or rouletted		
27 10	¼ a. slate-violet (R.)	15·00	14·00
	a. Monogram in lake	18·00	17·00
	b. Monogram in mauve	—	26·00
28 11	½ a. blue (*shades*) (R.)	9·50	26·00
	a. Monogram in mauve	13·00	27·00
	b. Monogram in lake	25·00	35·00
	c. Monogram in blue		
	d. Laid paper (M.)		
29 13	1 a. olive (*shades*) (R.)	18·00	
	a. Monogram in mauve	38·00	38·00
	b. Monogram in lake	40·00	40·00
30 14	2 a. orange-yellow (B.)	£425	£450

Originally printings of the ¼ a. and ½ a. were in sheets of 8 (stone I), but this was subsequently increased to 24 (4×6). The 1 a. and 2 a. were always in sheets of 4.

Nos. 25d/da were printed from stone I and care is needed to distinguish this laid paper printing from some of the reprints on similar paper. Stamps from stone I are without marginal lines and are very clear impressions; reprints from stone IV have thick marginal lines and, in those shades similar to No. 25, show indistinct impressions.

1900–01. *¼ a., 1 a, colours changed; ½ a. redrawn type; 2 a. with dash before "STATE" and characters in lower left label; 4 a. new value. No gum.*

(a) Imperf

31	10	¼ a. vermilion (M.)	3·50	7·50
		a. Monogram in blue	4·00	7·00
		b. Without monogram		
31*c*	12	½ a. blue (M.)	8·00	20·00
		ca. Monogram in rose	25·00	
		cb. Without monogram	40·00	
32	13	1 a. vermilion (M.)	3·50	10·00
		a. Monogram in blue	6·00	7·50
		b. Monogram in lake		
		c. Without monogram	35·00	
33	15	2 a. ochre (M.) (9.00)	35·00	75·00
34		2 a. yellow (M.) (11.00)	35·00	
		a. Monogram in blue	38·00	80·00
		b. Without monogram	60·00	
35		2 a. orange (B.) (1.01)	42·00	75·00
		a. Monogram in mauve	42·00	70·00
		b. Without monogram	50·00	
36	16	4 a. claret (R.)	38·00	90·00
		a. Monogram in mauve	48·00	£100
		b. Monogram in blue	65·00	£110
		c. Without monogram	29·00	
		(b) Pin-perf or rouletted		
37	10	¼ a. vermilion (M.)	3·00	7·50
		a. Monogram in blue	3·75	
		b. Without monogram		
37*c*	12	½ a. blue (M.)	38·00	48·00
38	13	1 a. vermilion (M.)	4·50	10·00
		a. Monogram in blue	8·00	8·50
39		1 a. brown-red (M.) (3.01)	—	£190
40	15	2 a. ochre (M.) (9.00)	45·00	
		a. Monogram in blue		
41		2 a. yellow (M.) (11.00)	35·00	60·00
		a. Monogram in rose	50·00	80·00
		b. Monogram in blue	60·00	90·00
42		2 a. orange (M.) (1.01)	45·00	55·00
		a. Monogram in blue	65·00	70·00
		b. Without monogram	—	£150
43	16	4 a. claret (R.)	48·00	
		a. Monogram in blue	55·00	£120
		b. Monogram in mauve	80·00	

The ¼ a., ½ a. and 1 a. are in sheets of 24; the 2 a. in sheets of 50 differing throughout in the dash and the characters added at lower left; the 4 a. in sheets of 28.

(17)

The stamps formerly catalogued with large overprint "R.N.S." (T **17**) are now believed never to have been issued for use.

Remainders are also found with overprint "P.S.", the initials of Padam Singh who succeeded Raghunath Singh in the direction of the Post Office, and with the original monogram "R.S." in a damaged state, giving it the appearance of a double-lined "R."

The stamps of Bussahir have been obsolete since 1 April 1901. Numerous remainders were sold after this date, and all values were later reprinted in the colours of the originals, or in fancy colours, from the original stones, or from new ones. Printings were also made from new types, similar to those of the second issue of the 8 a., 12 a., and 1 r. values, in sheets of 8.

Reprints are frequently found on laid paper.

Collectors are warned against obliterated copies bearing the Rampur postmark with date "19 MA 1900." Many thousand remainders and reprints were thus obliterated for export after the closing of the State Post Office.

CHARKHARI

PRICES FOR STAMPS ON COVER

Nos. 1/4	*from* × 2
Nos. 5/26	*from* × 20
Nos. 27/44	*from* × 3
Nos. 45/53	*from* × 100
Nos. 54/5	*from* × 5
No. 56	*from* × 2

Maharaja Malkhan Singh, 1880–1908

1

1/4 1/2 1 2 4

1/4 1/2 1 2 4

The top row shows the figures of value used in the stamps of 1894-97, and the bottom row those for the 1904 issue. In the 4 a. the figure slopes slightly to the right in the first issue, and to the left in the second.

1894. *Typo from a single die. No gum. Imperf.*
1 1 1/4 anna, rose £1000 £700
2 1 annas, dull green £1600 £2250
3 2 annas, dull green £2000
4 4 annas, dull green £1200
Nos. 1/2 are known pin-perforated.

1897. *Inscr "ANNA". No gum. Imperf.*
5 1 1/4 a. magenta .. .. 42·00 50·00
a. Purple .. .. 3·00 3·00
b. Violet .. .. 3·00 3·00
6 1/2 a. purple .. .. 2·50 3·50
a. Violet .. .. 2·50 3·00
7 1 1 a. blue-green .. .. 4·75 7·00
a. Turquoise-blue .. .. 4·00 4·50
b. Indigo .. .. 12·00 19·00
8 2 a. blue-green .. .. 8·00 14·00
a. Turquoise-blue .. .. 7·00 8·00
b. Indigo .. .. 13·00 22·00
9 4 a. blue-green .. .. 9·00 16·00
a. Turquoise-blue .. .. 6·00 9·50
b. Indigo .. .. 23·00 38·00
ba. Figure of value sideways £110
5/9 .. .. *Set of* 5 20·00 25·00
Minor varieties may be found with the first "A" in "ANNA" not printed.
All values are known on various coloured papers, but these are proofs or trial impressions.

1904. *Numerals changed as illustrated above. No gum.*
10 1 1/4 a. violet .. .. 1·75 2·50
11 1/2 a. violet .. .. 3·25 3·50
12 1 a. green .. .. 5·00 12·00
13 2 a. green .. .. 23·00 23·00
14 4 a. green .. .. 15·00 27·00
10/14 .. .. *Set of* 5 45·00 60·00
Stamps of this issue can be found showing part of the paper-maker's watermark. "Mercantile Script Extra Strong John Haddon & Co.".

Maharaja Jujhar Singh, 1908–1914

2 (Right-hand sword over left)

Type I

Type II

Type I. "P" of "POSTAGE" in same size as other letters. "E" small with long upper and lower arms. White dot often appears on one or both of the sword hilts.
Type II. "P" larger than the other letters. "E" large with short upper and lower arms. No dots occur on the hilts.

1909–19. *Litho in Calcutta. Wove paper. P* 11. (*a*) *Type* I.
15 2 1 p. chestnut .. .. 38·00 45·00
a. Pale chestnut .. .. 3·25 38·00
b. Orange-brown .. .. 3·25 38·00
16 1 p. turquoise-blue 60 45
a. Imperf between (horiz pair) .. £150
b. Greenish blue (1911) .. .. .. 90 1·00
c. Pale turquoise-green .. .. .. 1·50 70
17 1/2 a. vermilion .. .. 2·00 1·00
a. Imperf (pair) £750
b. Deep rose-red .. .. 90 1·25
18 1 a. sage-green .. .. 2·00 2·25
a. Yellow-olive .. .. 1·75 1·60
19 2 a. grey-blue .. .. 3·00 3·25
a. Dull violet-blue .. .. 3·00 3·50
20 4 a. deep green .. .. 3·50 4·75
21 8 a. brown-red .. .. 7·50 16·00
22 1 r. pale chestnut .. .. 13·00 30·00
15*a*/22 .. .. *Set of* 8 30·00 85·00

(*b*) *Type* II
24 2 1 p. turquoise-blue .. .. 3·00 3·25
25 1/2 a. vermilion .. .. 1·25 1·50
b. Deep rose-red .. .. 4·25 4·25
26 1 a. yellow-olive (1919) .. .. .. 3·00 3·00
a. Sage-green .. .. 1·60 1·60
24/6 .. .. *Set of* 3 5·25 5·75
No. 15, from the original printing, shows an upstroke to the "1", not present on other brown printings of this value.
See also Nos. 31/44.

3

"ᒧI" below Swords. Right sword overlaps left. Double frame lines.

4

"JI" below Swords. Left sword overlaps right. Single frame line.

1912–17. *Handstamped. Wove paper. No gum. Imperf.*
27 3 1 p. violet .. .. £450 75·00
a. Dull purple .. .. — 85·00
28 4 1 p. violet (1917) .. .. 7·00 5·00
a. Dull purple .. .. 14·00 5·50
b. *Tête-bêche* (pair) .. .. .. 75·00 75·00
c. Laid paper .. .. — £350
d. Pair, one stamp sideways .. .. — £120

Maharaja Ganga Singh, 1914–1920

Maharaja Arimardan Singh, 1920–1942

5 (*actual size* 63 × 25 *mm*)

6 (Left-hand sword over right)

1921. *Handstamped. No gum.* (*a*) *Wove paper. Imperf.*
29 5 1 a. violet .. .. 70·00 80·00
a. Dull purple .. .. 85·00 90·00

(*b*) *Laid paper. P* 11
30 5 1 a. violet .. .. 65·00 £120
a. Imperf £160 £170

(Typo State Ptg Press, Charkhari)

1930–45. *Wove paper. No gum. Imperf.*
31 6 1 p. deep blue .. .. 35 13·00
a. Vert pair, top ptd inverted on back, bottom normal upright .. .. 13·00
b. *Tête-bêche* (vert pair) £225
c. Perf 11×imperf (horiz pair) (1939) 45·00 45·00
d. Bluish slate .. .. .. 22·00
e. Laid paper (1944) .. .. .. — £300
32 1 p. dull *to* light green (*pelure*) (1943) .. 45·00 £160
33 1 p. violet (1943) .. .. .. 16·00 £120
a. *Tête-bêche* (vert pair) .. .. 50·00
34 1/2 a. deep olive .. .. 1·25 13·00
35 1/2 a. red-brown (1940) .. .. .. 5·00 22·00
a. *Tête-bêche* (vert pair) £375
36 1/2 a. black (*pelure*) (1943) .. .. 50·00 £140
37 1/2 a. red (*shades*) (1943) .. .. 19·00 35·00
a. *Tête-bêche* (vert pair) .. .. 38·00
b. Laid paper (1944) .. .. .. — £275
38 1/2 a. grey-brown .. .. 60·00 75·00
39 1 a. green .. .. 75 13·00
a. Emerald (1938) .. .. .. 32·00 50·00
40 1 a. chocolate (1940) .. .. .. 7·00 22·00
a. *Tête-bêche* (vert pair) .. .. 75·00
b. Lake-brown .. .. .. — 42·00
41 1 a. red (1940) .. .. 85·00 55·00
a. Carmine .. .. — 55·00
b. Laid paper (1944) .. .. .. — £300
42 2 a. light blue .. .. 1·25 16·00
a. *Tête-bêche* (vert pair) .. .. 9·50
43 2 a. greenish grey (1941?) .. .. 42·00 50·00
a. *Tête-bêche* (vert pair) .. .. 80·00
b. Laid paper (1944) .. .. .. — £325
c. Greyish green .. .. .. 70·00 £130
43*d* 2 a. yellow-green (1945) .. .. — £550
44 4 a. carmine .. .. 3·00 19·00
a. *Tête-bêche* (vert pair) .. .. 14·00
There are two different versions of No. 37a, one with the stamps *tête-bêche* base to base and the other showing them top to top.

7 Imlia Palace

1/2 As.

(8)

(Typo Batliboi Litho Works, Bombay)

1931 (25 June). *T* 7 *and similar designs. P* 11, 11½, 12 *or compound.*
45 1/2 a. blue-green .. .. 1·10 10
a. Imperf between (horiz pair) .. .. 35·00 11·00
b. Imperf between (vert pair) .. .. 35·00 35·00
c. Imperf horiz (vert pair) .. .. 35·00
46 1 a. blackish brown .. .. .. 1·40 10
a. Imperf between (horiz pair) .. .. 11·00 8·00
b. Imperf between (vert pair) .. .. 12·00 8·00
c. Imperf horiz (vert pair) .. .. 12·00
47 2 a. violet .. .. 1·00 10
a. Imperf between (horiz pair) .. .. 30·00 25·00
b. Imperf between (vert pair) .. .. 30·00 25·00
c. Imperf horiz (vert pair) .. .. 22·00
d. Doubly printed .. .. .. 8·50
48 4 a. olive-green .. .. 1·10 15
a. Imperf between (vert pair) .. .. 55·00 55·00
49 8 a. magenta .. .. 1·40 10
a. Imperf between (horiz pair) .. .. 38·00 25·00
b. Imperf between (vert pair) .. .. 38·00 38·00
c. Imperf horiz (vert pair) .. .. 38·00 13·00
50 1 r. green and rose .. .. .. 2·00 20
a. Imperf between (vert pair) £100 £100
b. Green (centre) omitted .. .. — £120
51 2 r. red and brown .. .. 3·50
a. Imperf horiz (vert pair) .. .. .. 85·00
52 3 r. chocolate and blue-green .. .. .. 9·00
a. Imperf between (horiz pair) .. .. —
b. *Tête-bêche* (pair) £170
c. Chocolate (centre) omitted .. .. 21·00
53 5 r. turquoise and purple .. .. .. 8·50
a. Imperf between (horiz pair) £150
b. Centre inverted .. .. .. 55·00
c. Centre doubly printed .. .. —
45/53 .. .. *Set of* 9 26·00
Designs:—1/2 a. The Lake; 2 a. Industrial School; 4 a. Bir[d] view of City; 8 a. The Fort; 1 r. Guest House. 2 r. Palace Ga[te] Temples at Rainpur; 5 r. Goverdhan Temple.
This issue was the subject of speculative manipulation, stocks being thrown on the market cancelled-to-order a[t] low prices and unused at less than face value. The issue w[as] authorized one but was eventually withdrawn by the authorities.

1939 (Dec)–**40.** *Nos.* 21/2 *surch as T* 8.
54 2 1/2 a. on 8 a. brown-red (1940) .. .. 26·00
a. No space between "1/2" and "As" .. 32·00
b. Surch inverted £275
c. "1" of "1/2" inverted £250
55 1 a. on 1 r. chestnut (1940) .. .. 80·00
a. Surch inverted £300
56 "1 ANNA" on 1 r. chestnut £550

Maharaja Jaiendra Singh, 1942–1971

Charkhari became part of Vindhya Pradesh by 1 May 1[948].

COCHIN

(6 puttans = 5 annas. 12 pies = 1 anna; 16 annas = 1 rup[ee])

Stamps of Cochin were also valid on mail poste[d in] Travancore.

PRICES FOR STAMPS ON COVER	
Nos. 1/3	*from* × 30
Nos. 4/5	*from* × 10
Nos. 6/6*b*	*from* × 3
Nos. 7/9	*from* × 20
Nos. 11/22	*from* × 15
Nos. 26/128	*from* × 8
Nos. O1/105	*from* × 15

Raja Kerala Varma I, 1888–1895

1

2

(Dies eng P. Orr & Sons, Madras; typo Cochin Govt, Ernakula[m])

1892 (13 Apr). *No wmk, or wmk large Umbrella in the sh[eet]. P* 12.
1 1 1/2 put. buff .. .. 2·50
a. Orange-buff .. .. 2·50
b. Yellow .. .. 2·50
c. Imperf (pair) .. .. ..
2 1 put. purple .. .. 2·75
a. Imperf between (vert pair) .. .. † £2[..]
3 2 2 put. deep violet .. .. 2·00
1/3 .. .. *Set of* 3 6·50

1893. *Laid paper. P* 12.
4 1 1/2 put. orange-buff £475
a. Orange .. .. —
b. Yellow .. .. —

WATERMARKS. Prior to the 1911–23 issue, printed [by] Perkins, Bacon & Co, little attention was paid to the positio[n of] the watermark. Inverted and sideways watermarks [are] frequently found in the 1898 and 1902–03 issues.

1894. *Wmk a small Umbrella on each stamp. P* 12.
5 1 1/2 put. buff .. .. 4·50
a. Orange .. .. 1·60
ab. Imperf (pair) .. .. ..
b. Yellow .. .. 3·75
6 1 put. purple .. .. 6·00
7 2 2 put. deep violet .. .. 3·50
a. Imperf (pair) .. .. ..
b. Doubly printed .. .. .. † £12[..]
c. Printed both sides .. .. ..
d. *Tête-bêche* (pair) £3250
5/7 .. .. *Set of* 3 10·00
The paper watermarked with a small umbrella is more tra[nslucent] than that of the previous issue. The wmk is not easy [to] distinguish.
The 1 put. in deep violet was a special printing for fiscal u[se] only.

Raja Rama Varma I, 1895-1914

1896 (End). *Similar to T* 1, *but* 28×33 *mm. P* 12.
(*a*) *Wmk Arms and inscription in sheet*
8 1 put. violet .. .. 75·00 75·[00]
(*b*) *Wmk Conch Shell to each stamp*
9 1 put. deep violet .. .. 19·00 32·[00]
Nos. 8/9 were intended for fiscal use, but are also known use[d] for postal purposes.

3

4

5

6

Thin yellowish paper. Wmk small Umbrella on each stamp.
h or without gum. P 12.
3 pies, blue . . . . 1·40 1·10
a. Imperf between (horiz pair) . . £500
b. Imperf between (vert pair) . . £600
c. Doubly printed . . £600
½ put. green . . 1·50 90
a. Imperf between (horiz pair) . .
b. Stamp sideways (in pair) . .
1 put. pink . . 3·50 1·75
a. *Tête-bêche* (pair) . . £2750 £2000
b. Laid paper . . † £1600
ba. Laid paper. *Tête-bêche* (pair) . . † £6500
c. *Red* . . 2·50 1·60
d. *Carmine-red* . . 3·50 1·90
2 put. deep violet . . 3·00 2·00
a. Imperf between (vert pair) . . £475
b. Imperf between (vert strip of 3) . . £600
. . *Set of* 4 7·50 5·00

–03. *Thick white paper. Wmk small Umbrella on each*
mp. With or without gum. P 12.
3 3 pies, blue . . 70 10
a. Doubly printed . . — £275
b. Imperf between (horiz pair) . . † £600
4 ½ put. green . . 1·10 40
a. Stamp sideways (in pair) . . £700 £700
b. Doubly printed . . — £275
5 1 put. pink (1903) . . 1·75 10
a. *Tête-bêche* (pair) . . † £3000
6 2 put. deep violet . . 2·50 50
a. Doubly printed . . £750 £300
. . *Set of* 4 5·00 1·00

2 2 2
(7) (7*a*) (7*b*)

9. *T* 3 (*paper and perf of* 1903), *surch with T* 7. *Wmk is*
ways sideways. No gum.
3 2 on 3 pies, rosy mauve . . 15 50
a. Surch Type **7** inverted . . 80·00 80·00
b. Surch Type **7*a*** . . £600 £350
c. Surch Type **7*b*** . .
d. Stamps *tête-bêche* . . £120 £140
e. Stamps and surchs *tête-bêche* . . £160 £180
arieties a, d and e were caused by the inversion of one stamp
. 7) in the plate and the consequent inversion of the
esponding surcharge to correct the error.
ypes **7*a*** and **7*b*** were applied by handstamp to correct the
ssion of the surcharge on R. 3/2 in different settings. Other
ets show a handstamped version of Type **7**.

8 Raja Rama Varma I

8*a*

(Recess Perkins, Bacon & Co)

1–13. *Currency in pies and annas. W* **8*a***. *P* 14.
8 2 p. brown . . 30 10
a. Imperf (pair) . .
3 p. blue . . 60 10
a. Perf 14×12½ . . 27·00 2·50
w. Wmk inverted . . — 55·00
4 p. green . . 1·50 10
aw. Wmk inverted . .
b 4 p. apple-green . . 2·50 40
bw. Wmk inverted . .
9 p. carmine . . 1·10 10
a. Wmk sideways . .
1 a. brown-orange . . 2·75 10
1½ a. purple . . 5·50 45
2 a. grey (1913) . . 7·50 40
3 a. vermilion (1913) . . 35·00 35·00
/33 . . *Set of* 8 48·00 35·00
No. 27a is line perforated. No. 27 exists perforated 14 either
om comb or line machines. The other values only come from
e comb machine.

Raja (Maharaja from 1921) Rama Varma II, 1914–1932

9 Raja Rama Varma II **10**

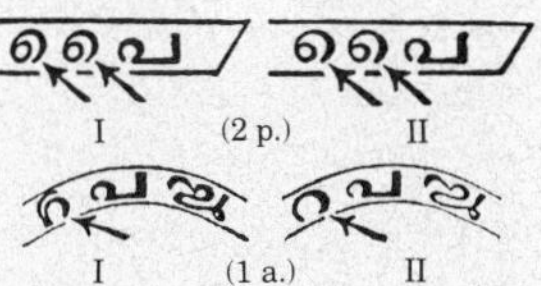
I (2 p.) II
I (1 a.) II

(Recess Perkins, Bacon & Co)

1916–30. *W* **8*a***. *P* 13½ *to* 14.
35 **10** 2 p. brown (Die I) (*a*) (*b*) (*c*) . . 6·00 10
a. Imperf (pair) . . £500
b. Die II (*b*) (*c*) (1930) . . 1·60 10
36 4 p. green (*a*) (*b*) . . 1·00 10
37 6 p. red-brown (*a*) (*b*) (*c*) (1922) . . 2·50 10
a. Wmk inverted . . — 80·00
38 8 p. sepia (*b*) (1923) . . 1·50 10
39 9 p. carmine (*a*) . . 16·00 25
40 10 p. blue (*b*) (1923) . . 2·75 10
41 **9** 1 a. orange (Die I) (*a*) . . 12·00 1·25
a. Die II (*a*) (*b*) (1922) . . 8·50 30
42 **10** 1½ a. purple (*b*) (1923) . . 2·25 20
43 2 a. grey (*a*) (*b*) (*d*) . . 4·25 10
44 2¼ a. yellow-green (*a*) (*d*) (1922) . . 4·25 3·25
45 3 a. vermilion (*a*) (*b*) . . 11·00 35
35/45 . . *Set of* 11 50·00 4·50
Four different perforating heads were used for this issue: (*a*) comb 13.9; (*b*) comb 13.6; (*c*) line 13.8; (*d*) line 14.2. Values on which each perforation occur are shown above. Stamps with perforation (*a*) are on hand-made paper, while the other perforations are on softer machine-made paper with a horizontal mesh.

2 2 2

Two pies **Two pies** **Two pies**
(11) (12) (13)

2 2

Two Pies **Two Pies**
(14) (15)

1922–29. *T* **8** (*P* 14), *surch with T* **11/15**.
46 **11** 2 p. on 3 p. blue . . 40 30
a. Surch double . . £325 £325
47 **12** 2 p. on 3 p. blue . . 2·50 90
a. Surch double . . £550
b. "Pies" for "pies" (R. 4/8) . . 40·00 20·00
ba. Surch double . .
c. Perf 12½ at foot . .
48 **13** 2 p. on 3 p. blue (6.24) . . 3·50 35
a. "Pies" for "pies" (R. 4/8) . . 50·00 16·00
b. Perf 14×12½ . . 14·00 16·00
ba. Ditto. "Pies" for "pies" (R. 4/8) . . £225 £250
49 **14** 2 p. on 3 p. blue (1929) . . 6·00 6·50
a. Surch double . . £325
b. Surch with Type **15** . . 65·00 £100
ba. Ditto. Surch double . . £1400
There are four settings of these overprints. The first (July 1922) consisted of 39 stamps with Type **11**, and 9 with Type **12**, and in Type **11** the centre of the "2" is above the "o" of "Two". In the second setting (May 1924) there were 36 of Type **11** and 12 of Type **12**, and the centre of the figure is above the space between "Two" and "Pies". The third setting (June 1924) consists of stamps with Type **13** only.
The fourth setting (1929) was also in sheets of 48, No. 49b being the first stamp in the fourth row.
No. 47c is from the bottom row of a sheet and was re-perforated 12½ line at foot as the bottom line of 14 perforations were too far from the design.

ONE ANNA
ഒരു അണ
ANCHAL & REVENUE
(16)

Three Pies
൩ **3**
മൂന്നു പൈ
(17)

1928. *Surch with T* **16**.
50 **10** 1 a. on 2¼ a. yellow-green (*a*) . . 5·00 12·00
a. "REVENUF" for "REVENUE" . . 48·00 75·00
b. Surch double . .

1932–33. *Surch as T* **17**. *W* **8*a***. *P* 13½.
51 **10** 3 p. on 4 p. green (*b*) . . 1·10 90
a. "r" in "Three" inverted . . † £250
52 3 p. on 8 p. sepia (*b*) . . 1·25 2·50
53 9 p. on 10 p. blue (*b*) . . 1·50 3·00
51/3 . . *Set of* 3 3·50 5·75

Maharaja Rama Varma III, 1932–1941

18 Maharaja Rama Varma III

(Recess Perkins, Bacon & Co)

1933–38. *T* **18** (*but frame and inscription of* 1 *a. as T* **9**). *W* **8*a***. *P* 13 × 13½.
54 **18** 2 p. brown (1936) . . 60 30
55 4 p. green . . 60 10
56 6 p. red-brown . . 70 10
57 – 1 a. brown-orange . . 70 10
58 **18** 1 a. 8 p. carmine . . 3·00 4·50
59 2 a. grey (1938) . . 4·50 75
60 2¼ a. yellow-green . . 1·50 15
61 3 a. vermilion (1938) . . 5·00 1·60
62 3 a. 4 p. violet . . 1·50 1·40
63 6 a. 8 p. sepia . . 1·75 10·00
64 10 a. blue . . 3·00 12·00
54/64 . . *Set of* 11 20·00 28·00
For stamps in this design, but lithographed, see Nos. 67/71.

1934. *Surcharged as T* **14**. *W* **8*a***. *P* 13½.
65 **10** 6 p. on 8 p. sepia (R.) (*b*) . . 75 60
66 6 p. on 10 p. blue (R.) (*b*) . . 1·75 2·00

"DOUBLE PRINTS". The errors previously listed under this description are now identified as blanket offsets, a type of variety outside the scope of this catalogue. Examples occur on issues from 1938 onwards.

SPACING OF OVERPRINTS AND SURCHARGES. The typeset overprints and surcharges issued from 1939 onwards show considerable differences in spacing. Except for specialists, however, these differences have little significance as they occur within the same settings and do not represent separate printings.

(Litho The Associated Printers, Madras)

1938. *W* **8*a***. *P* 11.
67 **18** 2 p. brown . . 1·00 40
aw. Wmk inverted . . — 65·00
b. Perf 13×13½ . . 5·50 60
68 4 p. green . . 1·00 25
aw. Wmk inverted . .
b. Perf 13×13½ . . 8·00 15·00
69 6 p. red-brown . . 2·25 10
aw. Wmk inverted . . † —
b. Perf 13×13½ . . † £2500
70 1 a. brown-orange . . 65·00 80·00
aw. Wmk inverted . .
b. Perf 13×13½ . . 80·00 95·00
71 2¼ a. sage-green . . 6·00 15
a. Perf 13×13½ . . 13·00 5·00
67/71 . . *Set of* 5 65·00 80·00
Most examples of Nos. 70/b were used fiscally. Collectors are warned against examples which have been cleaned and regummed or provided with forged postmarks.

ANCHAL (19) **ANCHAL** (19*a*) **THREE PIES** (20)

SURCHARGED **ANCHAL**

ONE ANNA
THREE PIES
(21)
ANCHAL

NINE PIES
(22)
ANCHAL

NINE PIES
(23)

SURCHARGED
NINE PIES
(24)

1939 (Jan). *Nos.* 57 *and* 70 *optd with T* **19/a**.
72 **18** 1 a. brown-orange (*recess*) (T **19**) . . 2·50 75
w. Wmk inverted . . † £100
73 1 a. brown-orange (*litho*) (T **19**) . . £250 85
aw. Wmk inverted . . † —
b. Perf 13×13½ . . — £275
74 1 a. brown-orange (*litho*) (T **19*a***) . . 75 1·60
a. Perf 13×13½ . . 11·00 50
In 1939 it was decided that there would be separate 1 a. stamps for revenue and postal purposes. The "ANCHAL" overprints were applied to stamps intended for postal purposes.

1942–44. T **18** *variously optd or surch.*

I. *Recess-printed stamp. No.* 58

75		3 p. on 1 a. 8 p. carmine (T **20**)	£160	75·00
76		3 p. on 1 a. 8 p. carmine (T **21**)	3·25	7·50
77		6 p. on 1 a. 8 p. carmine (T **20**)	3·00	19·00
78		1 a. 3 p. on 1 a. 8 p. carmine (T **21**)	1·00	30

II. *Lithographed stamps. Nos.* 68, 70 *and* 70b

79		3 p. on 4 p. (T **21**)	6·00	4·00
		a. Perf 13×13½	14·00	4·00
80		6 p. on 1 a. (T **22**)	£275	£180
		a. "SIX PIES" double	†	£800
81		6 p. on 1 a. (T **23**)	£225	£160
		a. Perf 13×13½	£100	55·00
82		9 p. on 1 a. (T **22**)	£100	£110
83		9 p. on 1 a. (T **23**) (*p* 13×13½)	£225	35·00
84		9 p. on 1 a. (T **24**) (*p* 13×13½)	16·00	5·50

Maharaja Kerala Varma II, 1941–1943

26 Maharaja Kerala Varma II

27 (*The actual measurement of this wmk is* 6¼ × 3⅝ *in.*)

(Litho The Associated Printers, Madras)

1943. *Frame of* 1 *a. inscr* "ANCHAL & REVENUE". *P* 13×13½. (*a*) *W* **8***a*.

85	**26**	2 p. grey-brown	1·40	2·25
		a. Perf 11	†	£1700
85*b*		4 p. green	£550	£275
85*c*		1 a. brown-orange	90·00	£100
85/*c*		*Set of* 3	£600	£350

(*b*) *W* **27**

86	**26**	2 p. grey-brown	25·00	2·25
		a. Perf 11	†	£2250
87		4 p. green	7·00	18·00
		a. Perf 11	3·00	3·75
88		6 p. red-brown	1·25	10
		a. Perf 11	8·00	1·40
89		9 p. ultramarine (*p* 11)	27·00	1·00
		a. Imperf between (horiz pair)	£1500	
90		1 a. brown-orange	£200	£160
		a. Perf 11	21·00	42·00
91		2¼ a. yellow-green	21·00	2·25
		a. Perf 11	27·00	8·50

Part of W **27** appears on many stamps in each sheet, while others are entirely without wmk.

Although inscribed "ANCHAL (= Postage) & REVENUE" most examples of Nos. 85*c* and 90/*a* were used fiscally. Collectors are warned against examples which have been cleaned and regummed or provided with forged postmarks.

Maharaja Ravi Varma 1943-1946

1943. T **26** *variously optd or surch. P* 13×13½. (*a*) *W* **8***a*

92		3 p. on 4 p. (T **21**)	60·00	18·00
92*a*		9 p. on 1 a. (T **23**)	4·75	2·25
92*b*		9 p. on 1 a. (T **24**)	4·50	2·50
92*c*		1 a. 3 p. on 1 a. (T **21**)	—	£2750

(*b*) *W* **27**

93		2 p. on 6 p. (T **20**)	75	3·00
		a. Perf 11	85	2·75
94		3 p. on 4 p. (T **20**) (*p* 11)	2·75	10
95		3 p. on 4 p. (T **21**)	4·00	10
96		3 p. on 6 p. (T **20**)	85	20
		a. Perf 11	85	75
97		4 p. on 6 p. (T **20**)	3·50	9·50

No. 92*c* is believed to be an error; a sheet of No. 85*b* having been included in a stock of No. O52 intended to become No. O66.

28 Maharaja Ravi Varma **29**

I II

(Litho The Associated Printers, Madras)

1944–48. *W* **27**. *No gum.* (*a*) *Type* I. *P* 11.

98	**28**	9 p. ultramarine (1944)	12·00	2·25

(*b*) *Type* II. *P* 13

98*a*	**28**	9 p. ultramarine (1946)	8·00	14·00
		ab. Perf 13 × 13½	32·00	3·25
99		1 a. 3 p. magenta (1948)	5·00	8·50
		a. Perf 13 × 13½	£180	40·00
100		1 a. 9 p. ultramarine (*shades*) (1948)	8·00	13·00
98*a*/100		*Set of* 3	19·00	22·00

Nos. 98*a*/100 are line-perforated, Nos. 98ab and 99a comb-perforated.

Maharaja Kerala Varma III, 1946–48

(Litho The Associated Printers, Madras)

1946–48. *Frame of* 1 *a. inscr* "ANCHAL & REVENUE". *W* **27**. *No gum* (*except for stamps perf* 11). *P* 13.

101	**29**	2 p. chocolate	1·75	10
		a. Imperf horiz (vert pair)	£1500	£1500
		c. Perf 11	8·00	60
		d. Perf 11×13	£375	£140
102		3 p. carmine	50	15
103		4 p. grey-green	£1800	80·00
104		6 p. red-brown (1947)	20·00	3·50
		a. Perf 11	£160	3·50
105		9 p. ultramarine	50	10
		a. Imperf between (horiz pair)	†	£1600
106		1 a. orange (1948)	6·50	26·00
		a. Perf 11	£500	
107		2 a. black	85·00	8·00
		a. Perf 11	£120	6·50
108		3 a. vermilion	55·00	60
101/8		*Set of* 8	£1900	£100

Although inscribed "ANCHAL (=Postage) & REVENUE" most examples of No. 106 were used fiscally.

The 1 a. 3 p. magenta, 1 a. 9 p. ultramarine and 2¼ a. yellow-green in Type **29** subsequently appeared surcharged or overprinted for official use. Examples of the 1 a. 3 p. magenta exist without overprint, but may have not been issued in this state (*Price* £200 *unused*).

30 Maharaja Kerala Varma III

Tail to turban flaw (R. 1/7)

(Litho The Associated Printers, Madras)

1948–50. *W* **27** (*upright or inverted*). *P* 11.

109	**30**	2 p. grey-brown	1·75	15
		a. Imperf vert (horiz pair)	—	£1500
110		3 p. carmine	75	15
		a. Imperf between (vert pair)	—	£1300
111		4 p. green	12·00	2·00
		a. Imperf vert (horiz pair)	£275	£325
112		6 p. chestnut	14·00	20
		a. Imperf vert (horiz pair)	£800	
113		9 p. ultramarine	2·50	20
114		2 a. black	45·00	75
115		3 a. orange-red	55·00	75
		a. Imperf vert (horiz pair)	£1800	
116		3 a. 4 p. violet (1950)	70·00	£350
		a. Tail to turban flaw	£250	£600
109/16		*Set of* 8	£180	£350

Maharaja Rama Varma IV, 1948–1964

31 Chinese Nets **32** Dutch Palace

(Litho The Associated Printers, Madras)

1949. *W* **27**. *P* 11.

117	**31**	2 a. black	3·75	6·00
		a. Imperf vert (horiz pair)	£425	
118	**32**	2¼ a. green	2·75	5·50
		a. Imperf vert (horiz pair)	£425	

A used example of a 2¼ a. value in a slightly different design exists showing a larger portrait of the ruler, the conch shell at upper right pointing to the right and with shading below "DUTCH PALACE". This may have come from a proof sheet subsequently used for postal purposes.

SIX PIES

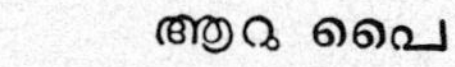

(**33**)

Normal

Error

Due to similarities between two Malayalam characters values of the 1948 provisional issue exist with an error i[n the] second word of the Malayalam surcharge. On Nos. 119, 12[..] O103 this occurs twice in the setting of 48. No. 125 shows examples and No. O104b one. Most instances are as illust[rated] above, but in two instances on the setting for No. 125 the [error] occurs on the second character.

1949. *Surch as T* **33**. (i) *On* 1944–48 *issue. P* 13.

119	**28**	6 p. on 1 a. 3 p. magenta	3·50	
		a. Incorrect character	26·00	
120		1 a. on 1 a. 9 p. ultramarine (R.)	90	

(ii) *On* 1946–48 *issue*

121	**29**	3 p. on 9 p. ultramarine	8·50	
122		6 p. on 1 a. 3 p. magenta	12·00	
		a. Surch double	†	
		b. Incorrect character	80·00	
123		1 a. on 1 a. 9 p. ultramarine (R.)	3·00	
		a. Surch in black	†	£
		b. Black surch with smaller native characters 7½ mm instead of 10 mm long	†	£

(iii) *On* 1948–50 *issue*

124	**30**	3 p. on 9 p. ultramarine	1·75	
		a. Larger native characters 20 mm instead of 16½ mm long	2·50	
		ab. Imperf between (vert pair)	†	£1
		b. Surch double	£425	
		c. Surch both sides	£350	
125		3 p. on 9 p. ultramarine (R.)	3·25	
		a. Incorrect character	19·00	
126		6 p. on 9 p. ultramarine (R.)	1·00	
119/26		*Set of* 8	27·00	

The 9 p. ultramarine (T **29**) with 6 p. surcharge (T **33**) in [..] was prepared for use but not issued (*Price* £200 *unused*)

1949. *Surch as T* **20**. *W* **27**. *P* 13.

127	**29**	6 p. on 1 a. orange	55·00	
128		9 p. on 1 a. orange	75·00	

OFFICIAL STAMPS

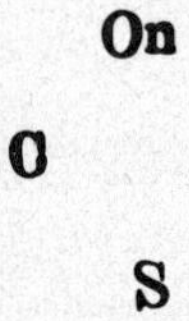

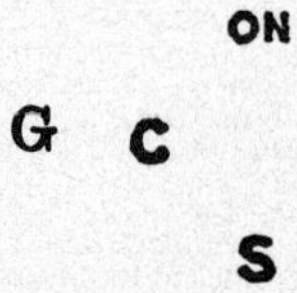

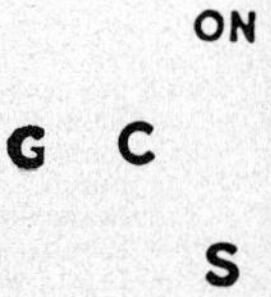

(O **1**) (O **2** Small "ON") (O **3** "G" with[out] serif)

1913. *Optd with Type* O **1** (3 *p.*) *or* O **2** (*others*).

O1	**8**	3 p. blue (R.)	£120	
		a. Black opt	†	£1(
		b. Inverted "S"	—	48
		c. Opt double	†	£5
O2		4 p. green (*wmk sideways*)	8·50	
		a. Opt inverted	—	£
O3		9 p. carmine	90·00	
		a. Wmk sideways	15·00	
		w. Wmk inverted	†	80
O4		1½ a. purple	38·00	
		a. Opt double	£500	£5
O5		2 a. grey	13·00	
O6		3 a. vermilion	48·00	
O7		6 a. violet	40·00	2
O8		12 a. ultramarine	38·00	6
O9		1½ r. deep green	30·00	55
O1/9		*Set of* 9	£325	60

1919–33. *Optd as Type* O **3**.

O10	**10**	4 p. green (*a*) (*b*)	3·75	
		a. Opt double	—	£4
O11		6 p. red-brown (*a*) (*b*) (1922)	7·00	
		a. Opt double	—	£3
		w. Wmk inverted	†	
O12		8 p. sepia (*b*) (1923)	11·00	
O13		9 p. carmine (*a*) (*b*)	48·00	
O14		10 p. blue (*b*) (1923)	12·00	
O15		1½ a. purple (*a*) (*b*) (1921)	5·50	
O16		2 a. grey (*b*) (1923)	40·00	
O17		2¼ a. yellow-green (*a*) (*b*) (1922)	12·00	
		a. Opt double	†	£3
O18		3 a. vermilion (*a*) (*b*) (*c*)	15·00	
		a. Opt inverted	†	£3
O19		6 a. violet (*a*) (*b*) (1924)	32·00	
O19*a*		12 a. ultramarine (*a*) (*b*) (1929)	15·00	3
O19*b*		1½ r. deep green (*a*) (*b*) (1933)	22·00	95
O10/19*b*		*Set of* 12	£200	95

All values exist showing a straight-backed "C" variety o[n] R. 4/1.

8

ON ON

C G C G

ht pies S S

27½ mm high)
(O **5** Straight back to "C")
(O **6** Circular "O"; "N" without serifs)

(Jan)–**24.** *T* **8** *and* **10** *surch with Type* O **4**.
8 p. on 9 p. carmine (No. O3) .. .. £325 1·60
a. "Pies" for "pies" (R. 4/8) .. .. £900 55·00
b. Wmk sideways £130 20
ba. "Pies" for "pies" (R. 4/8) .. .. £375 18·00
c. Surch double .. .. .. † £350
8 p. on 9 p. carm (*a*) (*b*) (No. O13) (11.24) 70·00 10
a. "Pies" for "pies" (R. 4/8) .. .. £180 12·00
b. Surch double .. .. .. † £275
c. Opt Type O **3** double .. .. † £275
rieties with smaller "i" or "t" in "Eight" and small "i" in "Pies" so known from a number of positions in the setting.

(Apr). *T* **10** *surch as Type* O **4**.
10 p. on 9 p. carmine (*b*) (No. O13) .. 65·00 65
b. Surch double .. .. .. † £300
c. Surch 25 mm high (*a*) £170 90
ca. Surch double .. .. .. † £325

T **8** *surch as Type* O **4**.
10 p. on 9 p. carmine (No. O3a) .. .. £850 9·50
a. Surch double .. .. .. † £400
b. Wmk upright .. .. .. — 45·00

–**31.** *Optd with Type* O **5**.
10 4 p. green (*b*) (1931) .. .. .. 22·00 1·40
a. Inverted "S" .. .. .. £160 13·00
6 p. red-brown (*b*) (*c*) (*d*) (1930) .. 13·00 10
a. Inverted "S" .. .. .. 90·00 4·25
8 p. sepia (*b*) (1930) .. .. .. 7·00 10
a. Inverted "S" .. .. .. 55·00 4·75
10 p. blue (*b*) .. .. 6·00 10
a. Inverted "S" .. .. .. 55·00 5·00
2 a. grey (*b*) (1930) .. .. .. 26·00 15
a. Inverted "S" .. .. .. £130 7·50
3 a. vermilion (*b*) (1930) .. .. 8·00 15
a. Inverted "S" .. .. .. 85·00 8·00
6 a. violet (*b*) (*d*) (1930) .. .. 75·00 3·00
a. Inverted "S" .. .. .. £450 80·00
30 .. .. *Set of* 7 £140 4·25

Pie3

No. O32b

3. *Nos.* O26/7 *surch as T* **14**, *in red.*
10 6 p. on 8 p. sepia (*b*) .. .. .. 2·00 10
a. Inverted "S" .. .. .. 18·00 4·25
b. "3" for "s" in "Pies" .. ..
6 p. on 10 p. blue (*b*) .. .. .. 4·00 10
a. Inverted "S" .. .. .. 38·00 3·75
he inverted "S" varieties occur on R.2/1 of one setting of this rprint only.

3–38. *Recess-printed stamps of* 1933–38 *optd.*

(*a*) *With Type* O **5**
4 **18** 4 p. green .. .. 2·25 10
5 6 p. red-brown (1934) .. .. .. 2·50 10
6 1 a. brown-orange .. .. .. 11·00 10
7 1 a. 8 p. carmine .. .. .. 1·50 30
8 2 a. grey .. .. 11·00 10
9 2¼ a. yellow-green .. .. .. 4·00 10
0 3 a. vermilion .. .. .. 40·00 10
1 3 a. 4 p. violet .. .. .. 1·50 15
2 6 a. 8 p. sepia .. .. .. 1·50 20
3 10 a. blue .. .. 1·50 70
4/43 .. .. *Set of* 10 70·00 1·75

(*b*) *With Type* O **6** (*typo*)
4 **18** 1 a. brown-orange (1937) .. .. .. 38·00 60
5 2 a. grey-black (1938) .. .. .. 21·00 1·40
6 3 a. vermilion (1938) .. .. .. 11·00 1·40
4/6 .. .. *Set of* 3 65·00 3·00

ON C G S
(O **7** Curved back to "c")

ON C G S
(O **8**)

ON C G S
O **9** Circular "O"; N with serifs)

ON C G S
(O **10** Oval "O")

ON C G S
(O **11**)

1938–44. *Lithographed stamps of* 1938. *W* **8a**, *optd.*

(*a*) *With Type* O **7** *or* O **8** (1 *a*). *P* 11
O47 **18** 4 p. green .. .. 25·00 1·75
a. Inverted "S" .. .. .. 30·00 1·75
b. Perf 13×13½ .. .. .. 21·00 2·00
O48 6 p. red-brown .. .. .. 22·00 40
a. Inverted "S" .. .. .. 25·00 50
O49 1 a. brown-orange .. .. .. £250 2·50
O50 2 a. grey-black .. .. .. 18·00 70
a. Inverted "S" .. .. .. 19·00 80

(*b*) *With Type* O **9** (*litho*) *or* O **10** (6 *p.*)
O51 **18** 6 p. red-brown (*p* 13×13½) .. .. 9·00 2·75
O52 1 a. brown-orange .. .. .. 1·00 10
O53 3 a. vermilion .. .. .. 3·00 1·00

(*c*) *With Type* O **11**
O53*a* **18** 6 p. red-brown £750 £325

The inverted "S" varieties, Nos. O47a, O48a and O50a, occur 21 times in the setting of 48.

1942–43. *Unissued stamps optd with Type* O **10**. *Litho. W* **27**. *P* 11.
O54 **18** 4 p. green .. .. 65·00 14·00
a. Perf 13×13½ .. .. .. 2·25 70
O55 6 p. red-brown .. .. .. £100 11·00
a. Perf 13×13½ .. .. .. 19·00 90
ab. Optd both sides .. .. .. † £110
O56 1 a. brown-orange .. .. .. 16·00 5·00
a. Perf 13×13½ .. .. .. 1·60 4·25
ab. Optd both sides .. .. .. † £110
O56*b* 2 a. grey-black (1943) .. .. .. 50·00 80
ba. Opt omitted .. .. .. † £1200
O56*c* 2¼ a. sage-green (1943) .. .. £1000 5·00
O56*d* 3 a. vermilion (1943) .. .. .. 14·00 4·50

1943. *Official stamps variously surch with T* **20** *or* **21**.

(i) *On* 1½ *a. purple, of* 1919–33
O57 **10** 9 p. on 1½ a. (*b*) (T **20**) .. .. .. £400 20·00

(ii) *On recess-printed* 1 *a.* 8 *p. carmine of* 1933–44 (*Type* O **5** *opt*)
O58 3 p. on 1 a. 8 p. (T **21**) .. .. .. 5·50 1·25
O59 9 p. on 1 a. 8 p. (T **20**) .. .. .. £100 26·00
O60 1 a. 9 p. on 1 a. 8 p. (T **20**) .. .. 2·50 1·60
O61 1 a. 9 p. on 1 a. 8 p. (T **21**) 80 30

(iii) *On lithographed stamps of* 1938–44. *P* 11. (*a*) *W* **8a**
O62 **18** 3 p. on 4 p. (Types O **7** and **20**) (*p* 13×13½) .. .. 21·00 6·00
a. Surch double £325 £150
O63 3 p. on 4 p. (Types O **7** and **21**) (*p* 13×13½) .. .. 95·00 45·00
O64 3 p. on 1 a. (Types O **9** and **20**) .. 2·00 2·75
O65 9 p. on 1 a. (Types O **9** and **20**) .. £200 45·00
O66 1 a. 3 p. on 1 a. (Types O **9** and **21**) .. £275 90·00

(*b*) *W* **27**
O67 **18** 3 p. on 4 p. (Types O **10** and **20**) (*p* 13×13½) .. .. 75·00 45·00
O67*a* 3 p. on 4 p. (Types O **10** and **21**) (*p* 13×13½) £600
O67*b* 3 p. on 1 a. (Types O **10** and **20**) .. £110 60·00
ba. Perf 13×13½ .. .. .. 85·00 60·00

1944. *Optd with Type* O **10**. *W* **27**. *P* 13×13½.
O68 **26** 4 p. green .. .. 22·00 3·50
a. Perf 11 .. .. £120 5·50
b. Perf 13 .. .. £300 65·00
O69 6 p. red-brown .. .. .. 1·50 10
a. Opt double .. .. .. — 60·00
b. Perf 11 .. .. 70 10
ba. Opt double .. .. .. — 60·00
c. Perf 13 .. .. 7·00 2·25
O70 1 a. brown-orange .. .. .. £1800 45·00
O71 2 a. black .. .. 3·75 45
O72 2¼ a. yellow-green .. .. .. 2·50 70
a. Optd both sides .. .. .. † £110
O73 3 a. vermilion .. .. .. 6·00 50
a. Perf 11 .. .. 6·00 40

Stamps perforated 13 × 13½ are from a comb machine; those perforated 13 from a line perforator.

1944. *Optd with Type* O **10** *and variously surch as Types* **20** *and* **21**. *W* **27**.
O74 **26** 3 p. on 4 p. (T **20**) .. .. .. 2·50 10
a. Perf 11 .. .. 6·50 60
ab. Optd Type O **10** on both sides .. † £120
O75 3 p. on 4 p. (T **21**) .. .. .. 4·50 30
a. Perf 11 .. .. £375 £160
O76 3 p. on 1 a. (T **20**) .. .. .. 16·00 4·00
O77 9 p. on 6 p. (T **20**) .. .. .. 7·00 2·00
a. Stamp printed both sides .. .. † £300
O78 9 p. on 6 p. (T **21**) .. .. .. 3·50 30
O79 1 a. 3 p. on 1 a. (T **20**) .. .. 6·00 1·25
O80 1 a. 3 p. on 1 a. (T **21**) .. .. 3·25 10
O74/80 .. .. *Set of* 7 38·00 7·25

1946–47. *Stamps of* 1944–48 (*Head Type II*) *optd with Type* O **10**. *P* 13.
O81 **28** 9 p. ultramarine .. .. .. 2·75 10
a. Stamp printed both sides .. .. † £400
b. Perf 13×13½ .. .. .. 3·75 10
O82 1 a. 3 p. magenta (1947) .. .. 1·60 20
a. Opt double .. .. .. 19·00 12·00
b. Optd on both sides .. ..
ba. Optd both sides, opt double and inverted on reverse .. .. 50·00
O83 1 a. 9 p. ultramarine (1947) 40 90
a. Opt double .. .. ..
b. Pair, one without opt .. .. † £1100
O81/3 .. .. *Set of* 3 4·25 1·10

1948. *Stamps of* 1946–48 *and unissued values optd with Type* O **2**. *P* 13.
O84 **29** 3 p. carmine .. .. .. 1·00 10
a. Stamp printed both sides .. .. † —
O85 4 p. grey-green .. .. .. 25·00 4·75
O86 6 p. red-brown .. .. .. 6·00 70
O87 9 p. ultramarine 75 10
O88 1 a. 3 p. magenta .. .. .. 2·50 50
O89 1 a. 9 p. ultramarine .. .. .. 2·00 40
O90 2 a. black .. .. 13·00 3·00
O91 2¼ a. yellow-green .. .. .. 18·00 3·00
O84/91 .. .. *Set of* 8 60·00 11·50

1949. *Stamps of* 1948–50 *and unissued values optd with Type* O **7**.
O92 **30** 3 p. carmine .. .. 1·25 15
a. "C" for "G" in opt .. .. 12·00 3·00
O93 4 p. green .. .. 1·10 30
a. Imperf between (horiz pair) .. † £1100
b. Imperf between (vert pair) .. † £1100
c. Optd on both sides .. .. 65·00 65·00
d. "C" for "G" in opt .. .. 12·00 4·50
O94 6 p. chestnut .. .. 2·50 10
a. Imperf between (vert pair) .. † £1300
b. "C" for "G" in opt .. .. 22·00 2·75
O95 9 p. ultramarine .. .. .. 2·50 10
a. "C" for "G" in opt .. .. 18·00 3·75
O96 2 a. black .. .. 1·25 15
a. "C" for "G" in opt .. .. 16·00 4·25
O97 2¼ a. yellow-green .. .. .. 2·75 4·75
a. "C" for "G" in opt .. .. 25·00 38·00
O98 3 a. orange-red .. .. .. 1·10 50
a. "C" for "G" in opt .. .. 16·00 9·00
O99 3 a. 4 p. violet .. .. .. 32·00 29·00
a. "C" for "G" in opt £275 £300
b. Tail to turban flaw £225
O92/9 .. .. *Set of* 8 38·00 29·00

The "C" for "G" variety occurs on R. 1/4. Nos. O92/9, O103/4 and O104b also exist with a flat back to "G" which occurs twice in each sheet on R. 1/5 and R. 2/8.

No. O93 exists with watermark sideways, but can usually only be identified when in multiples.

1949. *Official stamps surch as T* **33**. (i) *On* 1944 *issue.*
O100 **28** 1 a. on 1 a. 9 p. ultramarine (R.) .. 60 60

(ii) *On* 1948 *issue*
O101 **29** 1 a. on 1 a. 9 p. ultramarine (R.) .. 19·00 14·00

(iii) *On* 1949 *issue*
O103 **30** 6 p. on 3 p. carmine .. .. .. 1·00 60
a. Imperf between (vert pair) .. † £800
b. Surch double .. .. .. † £275
c. "C" for "G" in opt .. .. 11·00 10·00
d. Incorrect character .. .. 11·00 10·00
O104 9 p. on 4 p. green (18 *mm long*) .. 75 1·75
a. Imperf between (horiz pair) .. £650 £750
b. Larger native characters, 22 mm long .. .. 1·10 80
ba. Ditto. Imperf between (horiz pair) £650 £650
bb. Incorrect character .. .. 17·00 13·00
c. "C" for "G" in opt .. .. 14·00 20·00
ca. Ditto. Larger native characters, 22 mm long .. .. .. 17·00 13·00
O100/4 .. .. *Set of* 4 20·00 14·00

No. O104 exists with watermark sideways, but can usually only be identified when in multiples.

1949. *No.* 124*a*, *but with lines of surch* 17½ *mm apart, optd* "SERVICE".
O105 **30** 3 p. on 9 p. ultramarine 60 55
a. Imperf between (horiz pair) .. † £1300

From 1 July 1949 Cochin formed part of the new state of Travancore-Cochin. Existing stocks of Cochin issues continued to be used in conjunction with stamps of Travancore surcharged in Indian currency.

DHAR

PRICES FOR STAMPS ON COVER

Nos. 1/4	*from* × 50
No. 5	*from* × 30
No. 6	—
Nos. 7/9	*from* × 50
No. 10	—

Raja (Maharaja from 1877) Anand Rao Puar III, 1857–1898

1

2

अर्धा बलड. No. 1c
अर्धा लबड. No. 1d
आर्धा डबल. No. 2

1897–1900. *Type-set. Colour-fugitive paper. With oval handstamp in black. No gum. Imperf.*
1 **1** ½ p. black/*red* (three characters at bottom left) .. .. 2·25 2·75
a. Handstamp omitted £250
b. Line below upper inscription (R. 2/2) 55·00 55·00
c. Character transposed (R. 2/3) .. 23·00 23·00
d. Character transposed (R. 2/5) .. 55·00
2 ½ p. black/*red* (four characters at bottom left) .. .. 2·25 3·00
a. Handstamp omitted £180
3 ¼ a. black/*orange* .. .. .. 2·25 3·25
a. Handstamp omitted £225
4 ½ a. black/*magenta* .. .. .. 3·50 4·25
a. Handstamp omitted £225 £190
b. Line below upper inscription (R. 2/2) £100 £110
5 1 a. black/*green* .. .. .. 7·00 12·00
a. Handstamp omitted £400
b. Printed both sides £750
c. Line below upper inscription (R. 2/2) £180 £190
6 2 a. black/*yellow* .. .. .. 24·00 38·00
e. Top right corner ornament transposed with one from top of frame (R. 2/5) £100 £130
1/6 .. .. *Set of* 6 38·00 55·00

Nos. 1/6 were each issued in sheets of 10 (5 × 2), but may, on the evidence of a single sheet of the ½ pice value, have been printed in sheets of 20 containing two of the ½ value sheets *tête-bêche*.

Research has identified individual characteristics for stamps printed from each position in the sheet.

The same research suggests that the type remained assembled during the entire period of production, being amended as necessary to provide the different values. Seven main settings have been identified with changes sometimes occurring during their use which form sub-settings.

The distribution of stamps between the main settings was as follows:

Setting I—½ p.
Setting II—½ a., 1 a.
Setting III—1 a.
Setting IV—½ p., ½ a., 1 a.
Setting V—½ p.
Setting VI—½ p. (No. 2), ¼ a.
Setting VII—2 a.

The listed constant errors all occurred during Setting IV.

In No. 1c the three characters forming the second word in the lower inscription are transposed to the order (2) (3) (1) and in No. 1d to the order (3) (2) (1).

On Nos. 1b, 4b and 5c the line which normally appears above the upper inscription is transposed so that it appears below the characters.

All values show many other constant varieties including mistakes in the corner and border ornaments, and also both constant and non-constant missing lines, dots and characters.

Examples of complete forgeries and faked varieties on genuine stamps exist.

Raja (Maharaja from 1918) Udaji Rao Puar II, 1898–1926

(Typo at Bombay)

1898–1900. *P* 11 *to* 12.
7 **2** ½ a. carmine .. .. 3·25 6·00
a. Imperf (pair) .. .. .. 38·00
b. Deep rose .. .. 2·75 5·50
8 1 a. claret .. .. 3·00 6·00
9 1 a. reddish violet .. .. .. 3·50 12·00
a. Imperf between (horiz pair) .. £400
b. Imperf (pair) £100
10 2 a. deep green .. .. 5·50 20·00
7/10 .. .. *Set of* 4 13·50 40·00

The stamps of Dhar have been obsolete since 31 March 1901.

DUNGARPUR

PRICES FOR STAMPS ON COVER
Nos. 1/15 *from* × 2

Maharawal Lakshman Singh, 1918–1971

1 State Arms

(Litho Shri Lakshman Bijaya Printing Press, Dungarpur)

1933–47. *P* 11.
1 **1** ¼ a. bistre-yellow .. .. — £150
2 ¼ a. rose (1935) .. .. — £425
3 ¼ a. red-brown (1937) .. .. — £275
4 1 a. pale turquoise-blue .. .. .. — £120
5 1 a. rose (1938) .. .. — £1400
6 1 a. 3 p. deep reddish violet (1935) .. .. — £180
7 2 a. deep dull green (1947) .. .. .. — £250
8 4 a. rose-red (1934) .. .. — £450

Nos. 2 and 5 are known in a *se-tenant* strip of 3, the centre stamp being the 1 a. value.

2 3 4

Maharawal Lakshman Singh

Three dies of ½ a. (*shown actual size*):

Die I. Size 21×25½ mm. Large portrait (head 5 mm and turban 7½ mm wide), correctly aligned (sheets of 12 and left-hand stamps in subsequent blocks of four *se-tenant* horizontally with Die II)

Die II. Size 20×24½ mm. Large portrait (head 4¾ mm and turban 7 mm wide), but with less detail at foot and with distinct tilt to left (right-hand stamps in sheets of four horizontally *se-tenant* with Die I)

Die III. Size 21×25½ mm. Small portrait (head 4½ mm and turban 6½ mm wide) (sheets of 4)

(Typo L.V. Indap & Co, Bombay)

1939–46. *T* **2** (*various frames*) *and* **3/4**. *Various perfs.*
9 **2** ¼ a. orange (*p* 12, 11, 10½ *or* 10) .. £750 60·00
10 ½ a. verm (Die I) (*p* 12, 11 *or* 10½) (1940) £200 45·00
a. Die II (*p* 10½) (1944) .. .. £200 55·00
ab. Horiz pair. Die I and Die II .. £450 £140
b. Die III (*p* 10) (1945) .. .. £275 45·00
c. Imperf between (vert pair) .. † £2000
11 1 a. deep blue (*p* 12, 11, 10½ *or* 10) .. £200 35·00
12 **3** 1 a. 3 p. brt mauve (*p* 10½ *or* 10) (1944) £750 £170
13 **4** 1½ a. deep violet (*p* 10) (1946) £800 £170
14 **2** 2 a. brt green (*p* 12, *pin* perf 11½) (1943) £950 £325
15 4 a. brown (*p* 12, 10½ *or* 10) (1940) .. £750 £140

Stamps perforated 12, 11 and 10½ were printed in sheets of 12 (4×3) which were imperforate along the top, bottom and, sometimes, at right so that examples exist with one or two adjacent sides imperforate. Stamps perforated 10 were printed in sheets of 4 either imperforate at top, bottom and right-hand side or fully perforated.

Dungarpur became part of Rajasthan by 15 April 1948.

DUTTIA (DATIA)

PRICES FOR STAMPS ON COVER
Nos. 1/15 —
Nos. 16/40 *from* × 20

All the stamps of Duttia were impressed with a circular handstamp (as a rule in *blue*) before issue.

This handstamp shows the figure of Ganesh in the centre, surrounded by an inscription in Devanagari reading "DATIYA STET POSTAJ 1893". Stamps could not be used for postage without this control mark.

PROCESS. Nos. 1/15 were type-set and printed singly. Nos. 16/40 were typo from plates comprising 8 or more clichés.

GUM. The stamps of Duttia (*except No.* 25c) were issued without gum.

Maharaja Bhawani Singh, 1857–1907

Rectangular labels each showing a double hand-drawn frame (in black for the 1 a. and in red for the others), face value in black and the Ganesh handstamp are known on thin cream (½ a.), rose (1 a.), orange (2 a.) or pale yellow (4 a.) paper. These are considered by some specialists to be the first stamps of Duttia, possibly issued during 1893, but the evidence for this is inconclusive.

1 (2 a.) 2 (½ a.) 3 (4 a.)
Ganesh

1894?. *Rosettes in lower corners. Control handstamp in blue. Imperf.*
1 **1** ½ a. black/*green* £7000
2 2 a. grey-blue/*yellow* £2500
a. Handstamp in black £2250

Only two examples of No. 1 have been reported. In both instances the Devanagari inscription was originally 8 a., but was amended in manuscript to ½ a.

1896. *Control handstamp in blue. Imperf.*
3 **2** 1 a. red £2250
a. Handstamp in black £2250

1896. *Control handstamp in blue. Imperf.*
4 **3** ¼ a. black/*orange* £3000
a. Without handstamp £2000
5 ½ a. black/*blue-green* £3750
a. Without handstamp £2000
6 2 a. black/*yellow* £1900
a. Without handstamp £5000
7 4 a. black/*rose* £1300

Two types of centre:

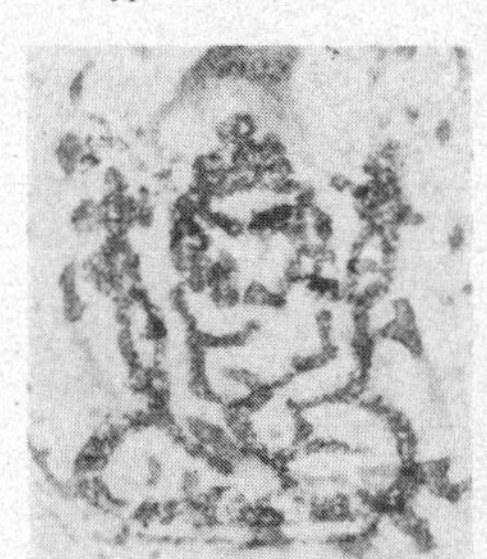

I II

Type I. Small Ganesh. Height 13 mm. Width of statue 11 mm. Width of pedestal 8 mm.

Type II. Large Ganesh. Height 13½ mm. Width of statu[e] 11½ mm. Width of pedestal 11½ mm. "Flag" in god's right hand; "angle" above left. All stamps show dot at top right corner.

1897–98. *Imperf.*
8 **2** ½ a. black/*green* (I) (value in one group) 48·00
a. *Tête-bêche* (horiz pair) £900
b. Value in two groups .. .. 18·00
ba. *Tête-bêche* (vert pair) £950
bb. Type II (1898) .. .. .. 19·00
9 1 a. black/*white* (I) .. .. .. 70·00
a. *Tête-bêche* (horiz pair) £950
b. Laid paper .. .. 16·00
ba. *Tête-bêche* (vert pair) £900
c. Type II (1898) .. .. .. 75·00
ca. Laid paper .. .. 19·00
10 2 a. black/*yellow* (I) .. .. .. 24·00
a. *On lemon* .. .. 30·00
b. Type II (1898) .. .. .. 27·00
11 4 a. black/*rose* (I) .. .. .. 20·00
a. *Tête-bêche* (horiz pair) £250
b. *Tête-bêche* (vert pair) £150
c. Doubly printed £1600
d. Type II (1898) .. .. .. 22·00

A used example of the 4 a. is known showing black roule[tte] at foot.

4 (½ a.) 5 (¼ a.)

1897. *Name spelt* "DATIA." *Imperf.*
12 **4** ½ a. black/*green* .. .. 70·00
13 1 a. black/*white* £140
14 2 a. black/*yellow* .. .. 80·00
a. *Tête-bêche* (vert pair) £3000
15 4 a. black/*rose* .. .. 75·00
a. *Tête-bêche* (vert pair) £3000
12/15 .. .. *Set of* 4 £325

1899–1906.

(*a*) *Rouletted in colour or in black, horizontally and at end o[f] rows*
16 **5** ¼ a. vermilion .. .. 3·25
a. Rose-red .. .. 2·25
b. Pale rose .. .. 2·25
c. Lake .. .. 3·75
d. Carmine .. .. 3·50
e. Brownish red .. .. 8·00
ea. *Tête-bêche* (pair) £3000
17 ½ a. black/*blue-green* .. .. .. 2·50
a. On deep green .. .. .. 4·75
b. On yellow-green (pelure) .. .. 4·75
c. On dull green (1906) .. .. 2·75
18 1 a. black/*white* .. .. 2·75
19 2 a. black/*lemon-yellow* .. .. .. 8·00
a. On orange-yellow .. .. .. 10·00
b. On buff-yellow .. .. .. 2·50
ba. Handstamp in black .. .. .. 9·00
bb. Without handstamp £190
c. On pale yellow (1906) .. .. 2·75
20 4 a. black/*deep rose* .. .. .. 3·25
a. *Tête-bêche* (pair) .. .. ..
b. Handstamp in black .. .. .. 12·00
c. Without handstamp £170

(*b*) *Rouletted in colour between horizontal rows, but imperf a[t] top and bottom and at ends of rows*
20*d* **5** ¼ a. brownish red .. .. 35·00
21 1 a. black/*white* .. .. 13·00
a. Without handstamp £450

One setting of 16 (8×2) of the ¼ a. value (No. 16*e*) showed a[n] inverted cliché at R. 1/2.

5. *Without rouletting.*
¼ a. red .. .. 3·00 24·00
a. Without handstamp £300
½ a. black/*green* .. .. 15·00
1 a. black (1905) .. .. 11·00 28·00

Maharaja Govind Singh, 1907–1955

P 13½. Stamps very wide apart.
¼ a. carmine .. .. 5·50 38·00
a. Imperf horiz (vert pair) £225
b. Imperf between (horiz pair) .. £250
c. Stamps closer together (with gum) .. 7·00 26·00
d. As c. Imperf vert (horiz pair) .. £110
1 a. black £750
25e was mainly used for fiscal purposes (*Price on piece,* but one example has been seen used on a registered ard.

Printed close together. (a) Coloured roulette×imperf
½ a. black/*green* .. .. 7·00

Printed wide apart. P 13½×coloured roulette (¼ a.) or 13½×imperf (½ a.)
¼ a. carmine .. .. 5·50 28·00
½ a. black/*dull green* .. .. .. 12·00 32·00

Colours changed. Control handstamp in blue (Nos. 33) or black (No. 34). Imperf.
¼ a. deep blue .. .. 5·50 19·00
½ a. green .. .. 5·50 21·00
a. Without handstamp .. .. † £600
1 a. purple .. .. 5·00 22·00
a. *Tête-bêche* (vert pair) .. .. 24·00
ab. Without handstamp £600
2 a. brown .. .. 13·00 26·00
2 a. lilac .. .. 5·00 25·00
a. Handstamp in black .. .. 23·00
b. Without handstamp £140
4 a. Venetian red (date?) .. .. 75·00
a. Without handstamp £500

Colours changed. (a) Imperf.
5 ½ a. blue .. .. 3·25 14·00
1 a. pink .. .. 3·00 16·00
a. Handstamp in black .. .. 6·50
b. Without handstamp £150

(b) P 11½
5 ¼ a. black .. .. 4·00 19·00

Rouletted.
5 ¼ a. blue .. .. 2·25 10·00
a. Roul × perf 7 .. .. 35·00 35·00
b. Imperf between (vert pair) .. £500
c. Without handstamp £110
d. Handstamp in black .. .. 6·00
½ a. pink .. .. 3·00 15·00
a. Roul × perf 7 .. .. £150
b. Without handstamp £150

Rough perf about 7.
5 ½ a. dull red .. .. 11·00 28·00
a. Handstamp in black .. .. 32·00
b. Without handstamp £170

ne stamps of Duttia have been obsolete since 1 April 1921.

FARIDKOT

PRICES FOR STAMPS ON COVER

Nos. N1/4	*from* × 10
Nos. N5/6	*from* × 50
Nos. N7/8	—

M. The stamps of Faridkot (Nos. N1/8) were issued without n.

Raja Bikram Singh, 1874-1898

1 (1 folus = ¼ a.) N 2 (1 paisa = ¼ a.) N 3

9-86. *Rough, handstamped impression. Imperf.*

(a) Native thick laid paper
N 1 1 f. ultramarine .. .. .. 35·00 40·00
N 2 1 p. ultramarine .. .. .. 95·00 £100

(b) Ordinary laid paper
N 1 1 f. ultramarine .. .. .. 14·00 16·00
N 2 1 p. ultramarine .. .. .. 60·00 80·00

(c) Wove paper, thick to thinnish
N 1 1 f. ultramarine .. .. .. 1·75 3·25
a. *Tête-bêche* (pair) £250
N 2 1 p. ultramarine .. .. .. 3·00 7·50
a. Pair, one stamp sideways £1000

(d) Thin wove whity brown paper
7 N 2 1 p. ultramarine .. .. .. 28·00 30·00

Faridkot signed a postal convention with the Imperial overnment which led to the provision of India issues erprinted "FARIDKOT STATE" from 1 January 1887. These e listed in the Convention States section.

Although the previous issues were no longer valid for postal urposes the state authorities continued to sell them to ollectors for many years after 1887. Initially remaining stocks Nos. N1/7 were on offer, but these were soon supplemented by ype N 1 handstamped in other colours, examples of a ½ a., andstamped in various colours, which had originally been repared in 1877 and by a replacement 1 p., as Type N 3, (*Price* ·25 *unused, tête-bêche pair,* £200, *unused*) which had not done postal duty before the convention came into force. The sale of such items was clearly an important source of revenue as the 1 f. as Type N 1, yet another version of the 1 p. and the ½ a. subsequently appeared printed in sheets by lithography for sale to stamp collectors.

HYDERABAD

PRICES FOR STAMPS ON COVER

Nos. 1/3	*from* × 10
Nos. 4/12	—
Nos. 13/60	*from* × 5
Nos. O1/53	*from* × 10

The official title of the State in English was The Dominions of the Nizam and in Urdu "Sarkar-i-Asafia" (State of the successors of Asaf). This Urdu inscription appears in many of the designs.

Nawab Mir Mahbub Ali Khan Asaf Jah VI, 1869–1911

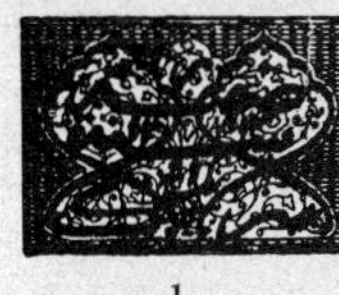
1

2

(Eng Mr. Rapkin. Plates by Nissen & Parker, London. Recess Mint, Hyderabad)

1869 (8 Sept). *P 11½.*
1 1 1 a. olive-green .. .. 15·00 6·50
a. Imperf between (horiz pair) .. £120
b. Imperf horiz (vert pair) £400 £110
c. Imperf (pair) £325 £325

Reprints in the colour of the issue, and also in fancy colours, were made in 1880 on white wove paper, perforated 12½. Fakes of No. 1c are known created by the removal of the outer perforations from examples of Nos. 1a/b.

1870 (16 May). *Locally engraved; 240 varieties of each value; wove paper. Recess. P 11½.*
2 2 ½ a. brown .. .. 4·00 4·00
3 2 a. sage-green .. .. 45·00 40·00

Stamps exist showing traces of lines in the paper, but they do not appear to be printed on true laid paper.

Reprints of both values were made in 1880 on white wove paper, perforated 12½: the ½ a. in grey-brown, yellow-brown, sea-green, dull blue and carmine and the 2 a. in bright green and in blue-green.

3

A Normal 2 a. B Variety

In A the coloured lines surrounding each of the four labels join a coloured circle round their inner edge, in B this circle is missing.

C 3 a. D

C. Normal
D. Character ʌ omitted

Left side of central inscription omitted (Pl 4 R. 2/11)

Dot at top of central inscription omitted

Second dot in bottom label omitted

Centre dot in bottom label omitted

(Plates by Bradbury, Wilkinson & Co. Recess Mint, Hyderabad)

1871–1909. *(a) No wmk. (i) Rough perf 11½*
4 3 ½ a. red-brown .. .. 18·00 19·00
5 1 a. purple-brown £110 £120
6 2 a. green (A) £800
7 3 a. ochre-brown .. .. 32·00 42·00
8 4 a. slate £140 £150
9 8 a. deep brown .. ..
10 12 a. dull blue £275

(ii) Pin perf 8–9
11 3 ½ a. red-brown .. .. — £375
12 1 a. drab £325 £160

(iii) P 12½
13 3 ½ a. orange-brown .. .. .. 1·75 10
a. Imperf vert (horiz pair) .. .. † 85·00
ab. Imperf horiz (vert pair) .. .. † £500
b. *Orange* .. .. .. 2·25 10
c. *Red-brown* .. .. .. 1·75 10
d. *Brick-red* .. .. .. 1·60 10
da. Imperf vert (horiz pair) .. .. † 85·00
db Doubly printed .. .. † £160
e. *Rose-red* .. .. .. 2·00 20
ea. Doubly printed .. .. † £200
f. Error. Magenta .. .. 48·00 8·00
g. Left side of central inscription omitted £200 65·00
h. Dot at top of central inscription omitted .. .. 48·00 2·25
14 1 a. purple-brown .. .. .. 4·50 4·50
a. Doubly printed £425
b. *Drab* 90 15
ba. Imperf (pair) .. .. .. — £275
bb. Doubly printed £200
c. *Grey-black* .. .. .. 1·50 10
d. *Black* (1909) .. .. .. 1·50 10
da. Doubly printed £425 £225
db. Imperf vert (horiz pair) .. .. † £600
dc. Imperf horiz (vert pair) .. .. † £600
e. Dot at top of central inscription omitted .. .. — £120
f. Second dot in bottom label omitted 80·00 32·00
15 2 a. green (A) .. .. .. 2·75 15
a. *Deep green* (A) .. .. .. 3·00 40
b. *Blue-green* (A) .. .. .. 2·75 40
ba. *Blue-green* (B) .. .. .. £180 65·00
c. *Pale green* (A) .. .. .. 2·75 15
ca. *Pale green* (B) .. .. .. £180 75·00
d. *Sage-green* (A) (1909) .. .. 2·50 35
da. *Sage-green* (B) .. .. .. £130 45·00
e. Dot at top of central inscription omitted .. .. £225 95·00
f. Centre dot in bottom panel omitted £110 40·00
16 3 a. ochre-brown (C) .. .. .. 1·90 1·10
a. Character omitted (D) .. .. £170 70·00
b. *Chestnut* (C) .. .. .. 1·40 85
ba. Character omitted (D) .. .. £120 55·00
17 4 a. slate .. .. 5·00 2·00
a. Imperf horiz (vert pair) £650 £650
b. *Greenish grey* .. .. .. 3·75 1·75
ba. Imperf vert (horiz pair) £1000
c. *Olive-green* .. .. .. 3·50 1·00
18 8 a. deep brown .. .. .. 1·50 2·50
a. Imperf vert (horiz pair) £700
19 12 a. pale ultramarine .. .. .. 3·00 5·00
a. *Grey-green* .. .. .. 3·00 3·25
13/19 .. .. .. *Set of* 7 13·00 7·25

(b) W 7. P 12½
19*b* 3 1 a. black (1909) .. .. .. 90·00 10·00
19*c* 2 a. sage-green (A) (1909) .. .. — 85·00
19*d* 12 a. bluish grey (1909?) £850

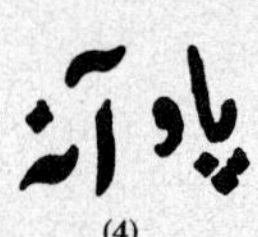
(4)

5

1898. *Surch with T* **4.** *P* 12½.
20 3 ¼ a. on ½ a. orange-brown 50 85
a. Surch inverted .. .. .. 30·00 22·00
b. Pair, one without surcharge .. £450
c. Left side of central inscription omitted £120

(Des Khusrat Ullah. Recess Mint, Hyderabad)

1900 (20 Sept). *P* 12½.
21 5 ¼ a. deep blue .. .. 4·50 3·00
a. Pale blue .. .. 4·50 3·00

6

7

(Plates by Allan G. Wyon, London. Recess Mint, Hyderabad)

1905 (7 Aug). *W* **7.** *P* 12½.
22 6 ¼ a. dull blue .. .. 1·25 45
a. Imperf (pair) .. .. .. 28·00 75·00
b. Dull ultramarine .. .. .. 5·00 80
ba. Perf 11 × 12½ .. .. .. 22·00 22·00
c. Pale blue-green .. .. .. 18·00 2·00
23 ½ a. orange .. .. 4·50 35
a. Perf 11 .. ..
b. Vermilion .. .. 2·25 25
ba. Imperf (pair) .. .. .. 26·00 75·00
c. Yellow .. .. 65·00 16·00

1908–11. *W* **7.** *P* 12½.
24 6 ¼ a. grey 50 10
a. Imperf between (horiz pair) .. £225 £225
b. Imperf between (vert pair) .. † £225
c. Perf 11½, 12 .. .. .. 2·00 35
d. Perf 11 .. .. 50·00 20·00
25 ½ a. green .. .. 2·25 10
a. Imperf between (vert pair) .. £200
b. Perf 11½, 12 .. .. .. 4·00 10
c. Perf 13½ .. .. 85·00 35·00
d. Pale green .. .. 2·25 20
da. Perf 11½, 12 .. .. .. 4·00 10
e. Blue-green .. .. 5·00 90
26 1 a. carmine .. .. 1·40 10
a. Perf 11½, 12 .. .. .. 4·50 50
b. Perf 11 .. .. 25·00 8·50
c. Double impression (*perf* 12½×11) ..
27 2 a. lilac .. .. 1·10 30
a. Perf 11½, 12 .. .. .. 3·50 1·10
b. Perf 11 .. .. 2·50 55
c. Perf 13½ .. .. 1·40 15
ca. Imperf between (horiz pair) .. † £350
cb. Rose-lilac .. .. 1·25 10
28 3 a. brown-orange (1909) .. .. 1·25 40
a. Perf 11½, 12 .. .. .. 8·00 2·00
b. Perf 11 .. .. 1·10 60
c. Perf 13½ .. .. 1·50 30
29 4 a. olive-green (1909) .. .. 1·10 45
a. Perf 11½, 12 .. .. .. 6·50 4·00
b. Perf 11 .. .. 30·00 9·00
ba. Imperf between (pair) £450 £450
c. Perf 13½ .. .. 1·00 30
30 8 a. purple (1911) .. .. .. 3·00 4·00
a. Perf 11½, 12 .. .. ..
b. Perf 11 .. .. 1·75 3·00
c. Perf 13½ .. .. 1·10 40
31 12 a. blue-green (1911) .. .. 85·00 50·00
a. Perf 11½, 12 .. .. .. 12·00 15·00
b. Perf 11 .. ..
c. Perf 13½ .. .. 3·50 2·00
24/31c .. .. *Set of* 8 11·00 3·00
The above perforations also exist compound.

Nawab Mir Osman Ali Khan Asaf Jah VII, 1911–1967

1912. *New plates engraved by Bradbury, Wilkinson & Co. W* **7.** *P* 12½.
32 6 ¼ a. grey-black .. .. 1·40 10
a. Imperf horiz (vert pair) .. .. † £200
b. Perf 11½, 12 .. .. .. 60 35
c. Perf 11 .. .. 80 15
ca. Imperf between (horiz pair) .. † £200
cb. Imperf between (vert pair) .. † £200
d. Perf 13½ 40 10
33 ¼ a. brown-purple (*shades*) (*p* 13½) .. 60 10
a. Imperf horiz (vert pair) .. .. † £200
34 ½ a. deep green 50 10
a. Imperf between (pair) .. .. † £225
b. Imperf (pair). Laid paper .. .. 80·00 60·00
c. Perf 11½, 12 .. .. .. 6·50 55
d. Perf 11 .. .. 8·00 10
e. Perf 13½ .. ..
The above perforations also exist compound.

In Wyon's ¼ a. stamp the fraction of value is closer to the end of the label than in the B.W. issue. In the Wyon ¼ a. and ½ a. the value in English and the label below are further apart than in the B.W.

Wyon's ¼ a. measures 19½ × 20 mm and the ½ a. 19½ × 20½ mm; both stamps from the Bradbury plates measure 19¾ × 21½ mm.

8 Symbols

9

1915. *Inscr* "Post & Receipt". *W* **7.** *P* 13½.
35 8 ½ a. green 70 10
a. Imperf between (pair) .. .. 65·00 70·00
b. Emerald-green .. .. .. 3·00 10
c. Perf 12½ .. .. 6·00 35
ca. Imperf between (pair) .. ..
d. Perf 11 .. .. 60 10
da. Imperf between (pair) .. .. † £180
db. Imperf vert (horiz pair) .. .. † £180
e. Imperf (pair) .. .. .. £130 85·00
36 1 a. carmine .. .. 1·00 10
a. Imperf between (pair) £170
b. Scarlet .. .. 1·00 10
ba. Imperf between (horiz pair) .. † £180
bb. Imperf between (vert pair) .. † £180
c. Perf 12½ .. .. 13·00 85
ca. Imperf between (pair) .. ..
cc. Scarlet .. ..
d. Perf 11 .. .. 1·00 20
da. Scarlet .. .. — 19·00
e. Imperf (pair) £170 £160
The above perforations also exist compound.
For ½ a. claret, see No. 58.

1927 (1 Feb). *As W* **7**, *but larger and sideways. P* 13½.
37 9 1 r. yellow .. .. 9·00 11·00

10 (4 pies)

11 (8 pies)

1930 (6 May). *Surch as T* **10** *and* **11.** *W* **7.** *P* 13½.
38 6 4 p. on ¼ a. grey-black (R.) .. .. 60·00 16·00
a. Perf 11 .. .. † £200
b. Perf 12½ .. .. † 80·00
39 4 p. on ¼ a. brown-purple (R.) .. 25 10
a. Imperf between (pair) £425 £425
b. Surch double .. .. .. † £180
c. Perf 11 .. .. † £400
d. Black surch £425 £425
40 8 8 p. on ½ a. green (R.) 25 10
a. Imperf between (horiz pair) .. † £190
b. Perf 11 .. .. £275 £140
c. Perf 12½ .. .. † £275

12 Symbols

13 The Char Minar

14 Bidar College

(Plates by De La Rue. Recess Stamps Office, Hyderabad)

1931 (12 Nov)–**47.** *T* **12** *to* **14** (*and similar types*). *W* **7.** *Wove paper. P* 13½.
41 12 4 p. black 30 10
a. Laid paper (1947) .. .. .. 2·50 5·00
b. Imperf (pair) .. .. .. 48·00 75·00
42 8 p. green 50 10
a. Imperf between (vert pair) .. — £550
b. Imperf (pair) .. .. .. 60·00 90·00
c. Laid paper (1947) .. .. .. 3·00 4·50
43 13 1 a. brown (*shades*) 50 10
a. Imperf between (horiz pair) .. — £550
b. Perf 11 .. .. † £750
44 – 2 a. violet (*shades*) .. .. .. 2·50 10
a. Imperf (pair) £130 £180
45 – 4 a. ultramarine .. .. .. 1·40 50
a. Imperf (pair) £140 £225
46 – 8 a. orange .. .. 4·50 3·00
a. Yellow-orange (1944) .. .. 65·00 30·00
47 14 12 a. scarlet .. .. 4·50 9·50
48 – 1 r. yellow .. .. 4·50 3·50
41/8 .. .. *Set of* 8 17·00 15·00
Designs (*as T* **14**): *Horiz*—2 a. High Court of Justice; 4 a. Osman Sagar Reservoir. *Vert*—8 a. Entrance to Ajanta Caves; 1 r. Victory Tower, Daulatabad.

Nos. 41a and 42c have a large sheet watermark "THE NIZAM's GOVERNMENT HYDERABAD DECCAN" and arms within a circle, but this does not appear on all stamps.

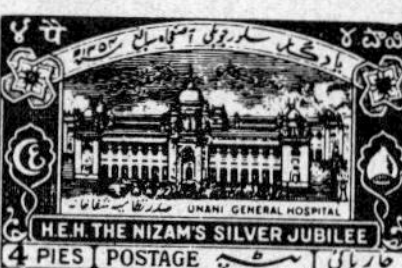
15 Unani General Hospital

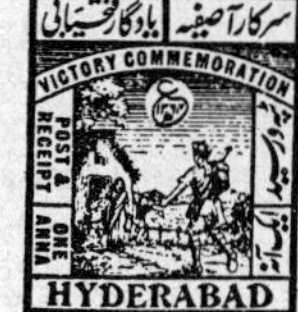
16 Family Reunion

(Litho Indian Security Printing Press, Nasik)

1937 (13 Feb). *Various horiz designs as T* **15**, *inscr* "H.E.H. NIZAM'S SILVER JUBILEE". *P* 14.
49 4 p. slate and violet 60
50 8 p. slate and brown 90
51 1 a. slate and orange-yellow 90
52 2 a. slate and green .. .. 1·10
49/52 .. .. *Set of* 4 3·25
Designs:—8 p. Osmania General Hospital; 1 a. Osmania Uni[versity]; 2 a. Osmania Jubilee Hall.

(Des T. I. Archer. Typo)

1945 (6 Dec). *Victory. W* **7** (*very faint*). *Wove paper. P* 13½.
53 16 1 a. blue 10
a. Imperf between (vert pair) £500
b. Laid paper 70
No. 53b shows the sheet watermark described beneath [Nos.] 41/8

17 Town Hall

18 Power House, Hyderaba[d]

(Des. T. I. Archer. Litho Government Press)

1947 (17 Feb). *Reformed Legislature. P* 13½.
54 17 1 a. black .. .. 1·00 1
a. Imperf between (pair) .. .. — £[…]

(Des T. I. Archer. Typo)

1947–49. *As T* **18** (*inscr* "H. E. H. THE NIZAM'S GO[VT] POSTAGE"). *W* **7.** *P* 13½.
55 1 a. 4 p. green .. .. 1·00 1
56 3 a. greenish blue .. .. 1·25 2
a. Bluish green .. .. 1·75 3
57 6 a. sepia .. .. 3·25 12
a. Red-brown (1949) .. .. .. 18·00 27
ab. Imperf (pair) £110
55/7 .. .. *Set of* 3 5·00 15·
Designs:—3 a. Kaktyai Arch, Warangal Fort; 6 a. Golkur[nda] Fort.

1947. *As* 1915 *issue but colour changed. P* 13½.
58 8 ½ a. claret .. .. 1·75
a. Imperf between (horizontal pair) .. — £2
b. Imperf between (vert pair) .. .. — £5
An Independence commemorative set of four, 4 p., 8 p., 1 and 2 a., was prepared in 1948, but not issued.

1948. *As T* **12** ("POSTAGE" *at foot*). *Recess. W* **7.** *P* 13½.
59 6 p. claret .. .. 7·00 6·
Following intervention by the forces of the Dominion of Ind[ia] during September 1948 the Hyderabad postal system was tak[en] over by the Dominion authorities, operating as an agency of t[he] India Post Office.

1949. *T* **12** ("POSTAGE" *at top*). *Litho. W* **7.** *P* 13½.
60 12 2 p. bistre-brown .. .. 1·00 2·
a. Imperf between (horizontal pair) .. † £6
b. Imperf (pair) £200 £4
No. 60 was produced from a transfer taken from a plate of t[he] 4 p., No. 41, with each impression amended individually.

OFFICIAL STAMPS

Official stamps became valid for postage within India from 191[…]

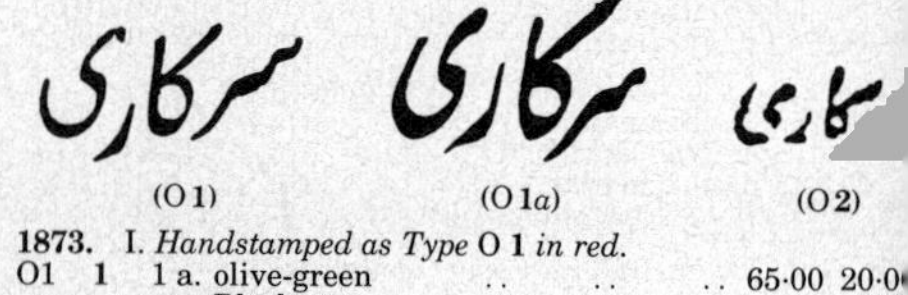
(O 1) (O 1*a*) (O 2)

1873. I. *Handstamped as Type* O **1** *in red.*
O1 1 1 a. olive-green .. .. .. 65·00 20·0
a. Black opt .. .. — £20
O2 2 ½ a. brown .. .. — £42
a. Black opt .. .. — £42
O3 2 a. sage-green .. .. — £42
a. Black opt .. .. — £14
At least ten different handstamps as Type O 1 were used t[o] produce Nos. O1/17. These differ in the size, shape and spacing of the characters. The prices quoted are for the cheapes[t] versions where more than one is known to exist on a particula[r] stamp.

Imitations of these overprints on genuine stamps and or reprints are found horizontally or vertically in various shades o[f] red, in magenta and in black.

II. *T* **3** *handstamped as Type* O **1** *in red.*

(*a*) *Rough perf* 11½

No.	Description	Mint	Used
	½ a. red-brown		
	a. Black opt	—	£600
	1 a. purple-brown	—	£800
	a. Black opt	£130	£160
	2 a. green (A)		
	a. Black opt	—	£800
	4 a. slate	—	£900
	a. Black opt		
	8 a. deep brown		
	a. Black opt	£900	£900
	12 a. dull blue	—	£900

(*b*) *Pin perf* 8–9

No.	Description	Mint	Used
	1 a. drab (*black opt*)	6·50	85·00
	ca. Second dot in bottom label omitted	£140	

(*c*) *P* 12½

No.	Description	Mint	Used
	½ a. red-brown	10·00	3·50
	a. Black opt	7·00	2·50
	ab. Left side of central inscription omitted	—	£140
	ac. Dot at top of central inscription omitted	—	40·00
	1 a. purple-brown	80·00	55·00
	a. Black opt	—	22·00
	1 a. drab	15·00	16·00
	a. Black opt	1·50	1·60
	ab. Second dot in bottom label omitted	80·00	80·00
	2 a. green (*to* deep) (A)	28·00	24·00
	a. Black opt	3·25	4·25
	ab. Inner circle missing (B)	£180	
	ac. Centre dot in bottom label omitted	£100	£100
	3 a. ochre-brown	£100	£100
	a. Black opt	26·00	20·00
	4 a. slate	48·00	30·00
	a. Black opt	13·00	13·00
	8 a. deep brown	48·00	90·00
	a. Imperf vert (horiz pair)	£600	
	b. Black opt	35·00	28·00
	12 a. blue	75·00	£100
	a. Black opt	40·00	60·00

ne use of Official Stamps (Sarkari) was discontinued in 1878, was resumed in 1909, when the current stamps were overted from a new die.

9–11. *Optd with Type* O **1***a*. (*a*) *On Type* **3**. *P* 12½.

No.	Description	Mint	Used
	½ a. orange-brown	80·00	4·00
	a. Opt inverted	†	£375
	1 a. black	65·00	10
	a. Second dot in bottom label omitted	—	6·00
	2 a. sage-green (A)	75·00	30
	a. Optd on No. 15da (B)	—	10·00
	b. Stamp doubly printed	†	£150
	c. Centre dot in bottom label omitted	—	7·00
)*d*	3 a. ochre-brown	3·50	1·25
	da. Character omitted (D)	—	£300
)*e*	4 a. olive-green	£300	3·75
	ea. Perf 11½, 12	—	£250
)*f*	8 a. deep brown	—	30·00
0*g*	12 a. grey-green	—	65·00

(*b*) *On Type* **6** (*Wyon ptgs*). *P* 12½

No.	Description	Mint	Used
	½ a. orange	—	1·75
	a. Vermilion	£100	15
	b. Opt inverted	†	£300
	c. Imperf between (vert pair)	†	£300
2	½ a. green	15·00	10
	a. Pale green	15·00	10
	b. Opt inverted	†	60·00
	c. Imperf between (vert pair)	†	£200
	d. Imperf between (horiz pair)	†	£190
	e. Stamp doubly printed	†	£130
	f. Perf 11½, 12	13·00	30
	fa. Pale green	13·00	30
	fb. Opt inverted	†	60·00
	g. Perf 11		
	ga. Pale green		
	h. Perf 13½	—	60·00
3	1 a. carmine	40·00	15
	a. Opt double	£170	
	b. Perf 11½, 12	50·00	30
	ba. Stamp doubly printed	—	£130
	c. Perf 11	—	5·50
24	2 a. lilac	45·00	30
	a. Perf 11½, 12	80·00	4·25
	b. Perf 11	£375	
25	3 a. brown-orange	£100	10·00
	a. Opt inverted	†	£150
	b. Perf 11½, 12	£170	22·00
	c. Perf 11	£375	35·00
	d. Perf 13½	—	65·00
26	4 a. olive-green (1911)	26·00	30
	a. Perf 11½, 12	80·00	3·25
	b. Perf 11	—	16·00
27	8 a. purple (1911)	13·00	1·75
	a. Perf 11½, 12	85·00	6·00
	b. Perf 11	£375	£110
28	12 a. blue-green (1911)	9·00	1·50
	a. Imperf between (horiz pair)	†	£750
	b. Perf 11½, 12	24·00	2·50
	c. Perf 11		

(*c*) *On Type* **6** (*Bradbury Wilkinson ptgs*). *P* 11

No.	Description	Mint	Used
28*d*	**6** ½ a. deep green	£375	

911–12. *Optd with Type* O **2**. (*a*) *Type* **6** (*Wyon printings*). *P* 13½ (*8 a, 12 a.*) *or* 12½ (*others*).

No.	Description	Mint	Used
)29	¼ a. grey	45·00	1·00
	a. Perf 11½, 12	20·00	30
	ab. Imperf between (vert pair)	†	£250
	b. Perf 11	75·00	30·00
	c. Perf 13½		
)30	½ a. pale green	32·00	1·10
	a. Perf 11½, 12	—	30
	b. Perf 13½		
)31	1 a. carmine	1·00	15
	a. Opt inverted	—	38·00
	b. Imperf horiz (vert pair)	†	£250
	c. Perf 11½, 12	5·50	15
	d. Perf 11	1·00	15
	e. Perf 13½		
O32	2 a. lilac	5·50	90
	a. Perf 11½, 12	19·00	2·25
	b. Perf 11	1·00	30
	c. Perf 13½	5·00	10
	ca. Imperf between (horiz pair)	†	£350
	cb. Rose-lilac	1·75	10
O33	3 a. brown-orange	17·00	2·50
	a. Opt inverted	†	70·00
	b. Perf 11½, 12	10·00	2·00
	ba. Opt inverted	†	75·00
	c. Perf 11	25·00	2·75
	ca. Opt inverted	†	70·00
	d. Perf 13½	16·00	40
	da. Opt inverted	†	60·00
O34	4 a. olive-green	12·00	1·60
	a. Opt inverted	—	70·00
	b. Perf 11½, 12	4·50	2·25
	ba. Opt inverted	—	75·00
	c. Perf 11	2·25	1·10
	d. Perf 13½	2·50	10
	da. Opt inverted	†	70·00
O35	8 a. purple	3·50	20
	a. Perf 11½, 12		
	b. Perf 11	£300	40·00
	c. Perf 12½	—	£325
O36	12 a. blue-green	13·00	75
	a. Perf 11½, 12		
	b. Perf 11		
	c. Perf 12½		

(*b*) *Type* **6** (*Bradbury, Wilkinson printings*). *P* 12½

No.	Description	Mint	Used
O37	¼ a. grey-black	2·75	40
	a. Opt inverted	†	55·00
	b. Pair, one without opt		
	c. Imperf between (vert pair)	†	£190
	d. Perf 11½, 12	6·00	1·00
	da. Opt inverted	†	55·00
	db. Pair, one without opt		
	e. Perf 11	85	35
	ea. Opt sideways	†	55·00
	f. Perf 13½	2·75	10
	fa. Opt inverted	†	60·00
	fb. Pair, one without opt	†	£120
	fc. Imperf between (horiz pair)	†	£180
O38	¼ a. brown-purple (*shades*) (*p* 13½)	2·00	10
	a. Imperf horiz (vert pair)	†	£190
	b. Imperf between (horiz pair)	†	£200
	c. Perf 11		
O39	½ a. deep green	2·75	15
	a. Opt inverted	—	22·00
	b. Perf 11½, 12	7·50	1·25
	ba. Pair, one without opt	†	£120
	c. Perf 11	2·25	10
	ca. Opt inverted	—	25·00
	cb. Imperf horiz (vert pair)	†	£200
	d. Perf 13½	1·75	10
	da. Imperf between (horiz pair)	†	£170
	db. Yellow-green	—	50

1917–20. *T* **8** *optd with Type* O **2**. *P* 13½.

No.	Description	Mint	Used
O40	½ a. green	1·75	10
	a. Opt inverted	†	20·00
	b. Pair, one without opt	†	90·00
	c. Imperf between (horiz pair)	†	£130
	d. Imperf between (vert pair)	†	£180
	e. Emerald-green	3·00	40
	f. Perf 12½	—	3·50
	g. Perf 11	6·00	30
	ga. Opt inverted	†	22·00
	gb. Pair, one without opt		
O41	1 a. carmine	3·00	10
	a. Opt inverted	†	25·00
	b. Opt double	†	75·00
	c. Imperf horiz (vert pair)	†	£180
	d. Stamp printed double		
	e. Scarlet (1920)	1·00	10
	ea. Stamp printed double	†	£140
	eb. Imperf between (horiz pair)	†	£200
	ec. Imperf between (vert pair)	†	£160
	ed. Imperf horiz (vert pair)	†	£180
	f. Perf 12½	—	3·50
	g. Perf 11	9·00	15
	ga. Opt inverted	†	16·00
	gb. Scarlet (1920)	—	22·00

1930–34. *T* **6** *and* **8** *optd as Type* O **2** *and surch at top of stamp, in red, as T* **10** *or* **11**.

No.	Description	Mint	Used
O42	4 p. on ¼ a. grey-black (O37*f*) (1934)	£250	17·00
O43	4 p. on ¼ a. brown-purple (O38)	80	10
	b. Imperf between (horiz pair)	†	£180
	c. Imperf between (vert pair)	†	£180
	d. Imperf horiz (vert pair)	†	£180
	e. Red surch double	†	85·00
	f. Black opt double	†	£180
O44	8 p. on ½ a. green (O40)	75	10
	c. Imperf between (horiz pair)	†	£170
	ca. Imperf between (vert pair)	†	£180
	d. Red surch double	†	85·00
	e. Stamp doubly printed	†	£170
	f. Black opt double	†	£180
O45	8 p. on ½ a. yellow-green (O39*db*)	35·00	45·00

For Nos. O42/5 the red surcharge was intended to appear on the upper part of the stamp, above the official overprint, Type O **2**, but surcharge and overprint are not infrequently found superimposed on one another.

1934–44. *Nos.* 41/8 *optd with Type* O **2**.

No.	Description	Mint	Used
O46	4 p. black	1·25	10
	a. Imperf (pair)	65·00	
	b. Imperf between (vert pair)	£500	£500
	c. Imperf between (horiz pair)	—	£500
O47	8 p. green	60	10
	a. Opt inverted	†	£150
	b. Imperf between (horiz pair)	—	£500
	c. Opt double	†	£120
	d. Imperf (pair)	£120	£150
O48	1 a. brown	80	10
	a. Imperf between (vert pair)	£400	£400
	b. Imperf between (horiz pair)	—	£400
	c. Imperf (pair)	£140	£180
	d. Opt double	—	£160
O49	2 a. violet	4·50	10
	a. Imperf vert (horiz pair)	†	£950
O50	4 a. ultramarine	1·90	20
	a. Opt double	†	£400
	b. Imperf between (vert pair)	†	£1100
O51	8 a. orange (1935)	9·00	60
	a. Yellow-orange (1944)	—	38·00
O52	12 a. scarlet (1935)	6·50	1·50
O53	1 r. yellow (1935)	15·00	2·00
O46/53	*Set of* 8	35·00	4·25

1947. *No.* 58 *optd with Type* O **2**.

No.	Description	Mint	Used
O54	**8** ½ a. claret	9·00	6·00

1949. *No.* 60 *optd with Type* O **2**.

No.	Description	Mint	Used
O55	**12** 2 p. bistre-brown	7·00	8·00

1950. *No.* 59 *optd with Type* O **2**.

No.	Description	Mint	Used
O56	6 p. claret	9·00	19·00

IDAR

PRICES FOR STAMPS ON COVER

Nos. 1/2*b*	*from* × 2
Nos. 3/6	*from* × 3
Nos. F1/5	*from* × 2

Maharaja Himmat Singh, 1931–1960

1 Maharaja Himmat Singh **2**

(Typo M. N. Kothari & Sons, Bombay)

1932 (1 Oct)–**43.** *P* 11. (*a*) *White panels.*

No.	Type	Description	Mint	Used
1	**1**	½ a. light green	—	27·00
		a. Pale yellow-green (*thick paper*) (1939)	15·00	19·00
		b. Emerald (1941)	14·00	19·00
		ba. Imperf between (pair)	£1000	
		c. Yellow-green (1943)	12·00	17·00
		ca. Imperf between (horiz pair)	£950	

(*b*) *Coloured panels*

No.	Type	Description	Mint	Used
2	**1**	½ a. pale yellow-green (*thick paper*) (1939)	26·00	24·00
		a. Emerald (1941)	19·00	20·00
		b. Yellow-green (1943)	11·00	19·00

In No. 2 the whole design is composed of half-tone dots. In No. 1 the dots are confined to the oval portrait.

(Typo P. G. Mehta & Co, Hitmatnagar)

1944 (21 Oct). *P* 12.

No.	Type	Description	Mint	Used
3	**2**	½ a. blue-green	2·75	55·00
		a. Imperf between (vert pair)	£250	
		b. Yellow-green	2·50	55·00
		ba. Imperf between (vert pair)	12·00	
4		1 a. violet	2·75	48·00
		a. Imperf (pair)	£200	
		b. Imperf vert (horiz pair)	£225	
5		2 a. blue	3·00	80·00
		a. Imperf between (vert pair)	75·00	
		b. Imperf between (horiz pair)	£200	
6		4 a. vermilion	3·25	85·00
		a. Doubly printed	£600	
3/6		*Set of* 4	10·50	£225

Nos. 1 to 6 are from booklet panes of 4 stamps, producing single stamps with one or two adjacent sides imperf.

The 4 a. violet is believed to be a colour trial.

POSTAL FISCAL STAMPS

F 1 F 2

1936 (?). *Typo. P* 11½ *on two or three sides.*

No.	Type	Description	Mint	Used
F1	**F 1**	1 a. reddish lilac and bright green	—	£500

1940 (?)–**45.** *Typo. P* 12 *on two or three sides.*

No.	Type	Description	Mint	Used
F2	–	1 a. violet	—	£110
		a. Perf 11	70·00	£110
F3	**F 2**	1 a. violet (1943)	—	£110
F4		1¼ a. on 1 a. violet	£100	£225
F5		1¼ a. yellow-green (1945)	14·00	
		a. Imperf between (vert pair)	32·00	
		b. Blue-green (1945)	55·00	£110

No. F2 shows the portrait as Type **1**. Used prices are for examples with postal cancellations. No. F4 shows a handstamped surcharge in Gujerati.

Idar became part of Bombay Province on 10 June 1948.

INDORE

(HOLKAR STATE)

PRICES FOR STAMPS ON COVER	
Nos. 1/15	*from* × 20
Nos. 16/43	*from* × 6
Nos. S1/7	*from* × 40

Maharaja Tukoji Rao Holkar II, 1843–1886

1 Maharaja Tukoji Rao Holkar II

(Litho Waterlow & Sons)

1886 (6 Jan). *P* 15. (*a*) *Thick white paper.*
1 1 ½ a. bright mauve .. .. 8·50 9·00
(*b*) *Thin white or yellowish paper*
2 1 ½ a. pale mauve .. .. 2·25 1·60
a. Dull mauve .. .. 2·50 1·90

Maharaja Shivaji Rao Holkar, 1886–1903

2 Type I

2*a* Type II

TYPES 2 AND 2a. In addition to the difference in the topline character (marked by arrow), the two Types can be distinguished by the difference in the angles of the 6-pointed stars and the appearance of the lettering. In Type I the top characters are smaller and more cramped than the bottom; in Type II both are in the same style and similarly spaced.

1889 (Sept). *Handstamped. No gum. Imperf.*
3 2 ½ a. black/*pink* .. .. 30·00 30·00
4 2*a* ½ a. black/*pink* .. .. 2·50 3·25
a. *Tête-bêche* (pair) £190

3 Maharaja Shivaji Rao Holkar

4 Maharaja Tukoji Holkar III

5

(Recess Waterlow)

1889–92. *Medium wove paper. P* 14 *to* 15.
5 3 ¼ a. orange (9.2.92) 75 60
a. Imperf between (horiz pair) .. .. † £550
b. Very thick wove paper .. .. .. 1·50 75
c. Yellow .. .. 1·25 80
6 ½ a. dull violet .. .. 1·50 60
a. Brown-purple .. .. 1·10 15
b. Imperf between (vert pair) £500
7 1 a. green (7.2.92) .. .. 1·10 50
a. Imperf between (vert pair) £750
b. Very thick wove paper .. .. .. 75·00
8 2 a. vermilion (7.2.92) .. .. .. 4·00 1·00
a. Very thick wove paper .. .. .. 5·00 3·00
5/8 .. .. *Set of* 4 6·25 1·75

Maharaja Tukoji Rao Holkar III, 1903–1926

(Recess Perkins, Bacon & Co)

1904–20. *P* 13½, 14.
9 4 ¼ a. orange 40 10
10 5 ½ a. lake (1909) .. .. 8·50 10
a. Brown-lake (*shades*) .. .. .. 10·00 15
b. Imperf (pair) .. .. 17·00
11 1 a. green .. .. 1·60 10
a. Imperf (pair) £120
b. Perf 12½ (1920) .. .. † 90·00
12 2 a. brown .. .. 9·00 50
a. Imperf (pair) .. .. 75·00
13 3 a. violet .. .. 15·00 6·00
14 4 a. ultramarine .. .. 12·00 2·25
a. Dull blue .. .. 5·00 1·10
9/14 .. .. *Set of* 6 35·00 7·00

पाव आना.

(6)

7 Maharaja Yeshwant Rao Holkar II

1905 (June). *No. 6a surch* "QUARTER ANNA" *in Devanagari, as T* **6**.
15 3 ¼ a. on ½ a. brown-purple .. .. .. 4·00 18·00

On 1 March 1908 the Indore State postal service was amalgamated with the Indian Imperial system. Under the terms of the agreement stamps showing the Maharaja would still be used for official mail sent to addresses within the state. Initially Nos. 9/14 were used for this purpose, the "SERVICE" overprints, Nos. S1/7, being withdrawn.

Maharaja Yeshwant Rao Holkar II, 1926–1961

(Recess Perkins, Bacon & Co)

1927–37. *P* 13 *to* 14.
16 7 ¼ a. orange (*a*) (*d*) (*e*) 30 10
17 ½ a. claret (*a*) (*d*) (*e*) 80 10
18 1 a. green (*a*) (*d*) (*e*) .. .. .. 1·50 10
19 1¼ a. green (*c*) (*d*) (1933) .. .. .. 2·00 35
20 2 a. sepia (*a*) .. .. 4·25 1·40
21 2 a. bluish green (*d*) (1936) .. .. 12·00 1·00
a. Imperf (pair) .. .. 25·00 £120
22 3 a. deep violet (*a*) .. .. 1·50 9·00
23 3 a. Prussian blue (*d*) (1935?) .. .. 16·00
a. Imperf (pair) .. .. 30·00 £300
24 3½ a. violet (*d*) (1934) .. .. .. 6·00 10·00
a. Imperf (pair) .. .. 50·00 £300
25 4 a. ultramarine (*a*) .. .. 3·50 3·50
26 4 a. yellow-brown (*d*) (1937) .. .. 24·00 1·50
a. Imperf (pair) .. .. 30·00 £200
27 8 a. slate-grey (*a*) .. .. 5·50 4·50
28 8 a. red-orange (*d*) (1937) .. .. .. 18·00 19·00
29 12 a. carmine (*d*) (1934) .. .. .. 5·00 10·00
30 – 1 r. black and light blue (*b*) .. .. 8·00 14·00
31 – 2 r. black and carmine (*b*) .. .. 40·00 40·00
32 – 5 r. black & brown-orange (*b*) .. .. 65·00 70·00

Nos. 30/32 are as Type **7**, but larger, size 23 × 28 mm.

Five different perforating heads were used for this issue: (*a*) comb 13·6; (*b*) comb 13·9; (*c*) line 13·2; (*d*) line 13·8; (*e*) line 14·2. Values on which each perforation occur are indicated above.

Nos. 21a, 23a, 24a and 26a were specifically ordered by the state government in 1933 and are known used for postage *circa* 1938–42. A plate proof of the 1 r. in green and carmine is also known postally used (*Price of pair £35, unused, £350 used*).

Nos. 16/19 and 28/32 also exist as imperforate plate proofs, but these were never sent to India.

(8)

9

1940 (1 Aug). *Surch in words as T* **8** *by* Times of India *Press, Bombay.*
33 7 ¼ a. on 5 r. black and brown-orange (*b*) 11·00 1·25
a. Surch double (Blk. + G.) .. .. † £400
34 ½ a. on 2 r. black and carmine (*b*) .. 14·00 2·00
35 1 a. on 1¼ a. green (*c*) (*d*) (*e*) .. .. 13·00 50
b. Surch inverted (*d*) .. .. .. 90·00
c. Surch double (*c*) £325
33/5 .. .. *Set of* 3 35·00 3·25

(Typo "*Times of India*" Press, Bombay)

1941–46. *P* 11.
36 9 ¼ a. red-orange .. .. 2·00 10
37 ½ a. claret .. .. 2·00 10
38 1 a. green .. .. 9·00 10
39 1¼ a. yellow-green .. .. 14·00 75
a. Imperf (pair) £200
40 2 a. turquoise-blue .. .. 11·00 1·00
41 4 a. yellow-brown (1946) .. .. .. 12·00 10·00
Larger size (23 × 28 *mm*)
42 2 r. black and carmine (1943) .. .. 10·00 £120
43 5 r. black and yellow-orange (1943) .. 10·00 £160
36/43 .. .. *Set of* 8 65·00 £250

OFFICIAL STAMPS

SERVICE

(S 1)

SERVICE

(S 2)

1904–6. (*a*) *Optd with Type* S 1.
S1 4 ¼ a. orange (1906) 20 60
S2 5 ½ a. lake 15 10
a. Opt inverted .. .. 20·00 28·00
b. Opt double .. .. 18·00
c. Imperf (pair) .. .. 55·00
d. Brown-lake 15 10
da. Opt inverted .. .. 18·00
e. Pair, one without opt £450
S3 1 a. green 15 20
S4 2 a. brown (1905) 30 30
a. Vert pair, one without opt £700
S5 3 a. violet (1906) .. .. 2·00 2·25
a. Imperf (pair) £325
S6 4 a. ultramarine (1905) .. .. .. 3·50 1·50
(*b*) *Optd with Type* S 2
S7 5 ½ a. lake 10 60
a. Opt double £350
S1/7 .. .. *Set of* 7 5·75 5·00

Types S 1 and S 2 differ chiefly in the shape of the letter "R".

Indore became part of Madhya Bharat by 1 July 1948

JAIPUR

PRICES FOR STAMPS ON COVER	
No. 1	*from* × 3
No. 2	*from* × 2
Nos. 3/5	*from* × 10
Nos. 6/70	*from* × 4
Nos. 71/80	*from* × 6
Nos. O1/34	*from* × 8

Maharaja Sawai Madho Singh II, 1880–1922

1

1*a*

2

Chariot of the Sun God, Surya

Type **1** – Value at sides in small letters and charact "HALF ANNA", shown as one word except R. 1/1 and 1/3, measuring between 13½ and mm. Sheets of 12 (4×3) with stamps 2 to 2½ apart.

Type **1***a* – Value in large letters and characters. "HA ANNA", always with a gap between the two wor measuring between 14½ and 15½ mm. Sheets 24 (4×6) with stamps 3 to 4 mm apart.

Type **2** – Value in large letters and characters. "HA ANNA" measuring 16 to 17 mm. Both s inscriptions start below the inner frame li Sheets of 24 (4×6) with stamps 1½ to 2 mm apa

(Litho Durbar Press, Jaipur)

1904 (14 July). *Roughly perf* 14.
1 1 ½ a. pale blue .. .. 95·00 £1
a. Ultramarine £130 £1
b. Imperf, *ultramarine* £350
2 1*a* ½ a. grey-blue £1400 £2
a. Imperf £350 £5
b. Ultramarine .. .. — £3
3 2 ½ a. pale blue .. .. 2·75 5
a. Deep blue .. .. 3·00 5
b. Ultramarine .. .. 3·25 5
c. Imperf £350 £3
4 1 1 a. dull red .. .. 4·50 13·
a. Scarlet .. .. 4·50 13·
5 2 a. pale green .. .. 3·75 11·
a. Emerald-green .. .. .. 4·00

Nos. 1b, 2a and 3c are on gummed paper. Imperforate pla proofs also exist for Nos. 1/5, but these are ungummed.

3 Chariot of the Sun God, Surya

(Recess Perkins, Bacon & Co)

1904. *P* 12.
6 3 ½ a. blue .. .. 4·00 7·0
a. Perf 12½ .. .. 22·00 16·0
b. Perf comp of 12 and 12½ .. .. 15·00 17·0
7 1 a. brown-red .. .. 50·00 50·0
a. Perf 12½ £120 £12
b. Perf comp of 12 and 12½ £120 £12
c. Carmine .. .. 2·25 4·2
ca. Imperf between (vert pair) £450 £65
cb. Perf comp of 12 and 12½ .. .. 10·00 15·0
8 2 a. deep green .. .. 5·50 11·0
a. Perf 12½ .. .. £130 90·0
b. Perf comp of 12 and 12½ .. .. 25·00 32·0

Nos. 6b, 7b, 7cb and 8b occur on the bottom two rows of sheet otherwise perforated 12.

1905–8. *Wmk* "JAs WRIGLEY & SON Ld. 219" "SPECIAI POSTAGE PAPER LONDON" *or* "PERKINS BACON & Cc Ld LONDON" *in sheet. P* 13½.
9 3 ¼ a. olive-yellow (1906) 65 6
10 ½ a. blue (1906) .. .. 2·00 1·9
a. Indigo 75 4
11 1 a. brown-red (1906) .. .. .. 4·75 4·2
a. Bright red (1908) .. .. .. 2·25 4
12 2 a. deep green (1906) .. .. .. 1·25 75
13 4 a. chestnut .. .. 5·00 2·00
14 8 a. bright violet .. .. 3·00 2·75
15 1 r. yellow .. .. 16·00 16·00
a. Orange-yellow .. .. .. 15·00 16·00
b. Yellow-ochre .. .. .. 19·00 25·00
9/15 .. .. *Set of* 7 25·00 20·00

4 Chariot of the Sun God, Surya

३ आना

(5)

(Typo Jaipur State Press)

Thin wove paper. No gum. Imperf.

¼ a. green .. .. 2·00 2·75
a. Printed double .. .. .. 6·50
ab. Ditto, one inverted .. .. ..
b. "¼" inverted in right upper corner (R. 1/2) .. .. .. 5·00
c. No stop after "STATE" (R. 3/1) .. 5·00
¼ a. greenish yellow 30 70
a. Printed double .. .. .. 2·00
b. "¼" inverted in right upper corner (R. 1/2) .. .. .. 1·50
c. No stop after "STATE" (R. 3/1) .. 1·50
½ a. ultramarine 30 70
a. Printed double .. .. .. 2·00
b. No stop after "STATE" (R. 3/1) .. 75
c. Large "J" in "JAIPUR" (R. 1/2) .. 75
d. "⅓" for "½" at lower left (R. 3/1) .. 1·50
e. "1½ a." at lower right (R. 3/2) .. 1·50
½ a. grey-blue .. .. 1·75 1·75
a. No stop after "STATE" (R. 3/1) .. 3·00
b. Large "J" in "JAIPUR" (R. 1/2) .. 3·00
c. "⅓" for "½" at lower left (R. 3/1) .. 3·50
d. "1½ a." at lower right (R. 3/2) .. 4·00
1 a. rose-red 45 75
a. Printed double £190
2 a. greyish green .. .. .. 2·25 5·50
a. Deep green .. .. .. 2·00 5·50
ab. Printed double £200

sued in sheets of 6 (2×3). There are three recognised ngs. Nos. 18d/e and 19c/d come from Setting B, and Nos. c, 17b/c, 18b/c and 19a/b from Setting C.
ne sheet of the ¼ a. is known in blue.

(Typo Jaipur State Press)

2–22. *Paper-maker's wmk* "DORLING & CO. LONDON" *i sheet. P* 11.

3 ¼ a. pale olive-yellow 40 90
a. Imperf horiz (vert pair) £200 £200
b. Imperf vert (horiz pair) .. .. — £160
¼ a. olive .. .. 45 1·10
a. Imperf between (horiz pair) .. £190
b. Imperf vert (horiz pair) £200
c. Imperf horiz (vert pair) £200
d. *Tête-bêche* (pair) £350
¼ a bistre .. .. 30 1·10
a. Imperf between (horiz pair) .. £190
b. Imperf between (vert pair) .. .. † £275
c. Imperf horiz (vert pair) .. .. † £275
d. Doubly printed .. .. .. † —
½ a. pale ultramarine .. .. .. 1·10 50
a. Imperf vert (horiz pair) .. .. † £400
b. Blue .. .. 1·25 45
ba. Imperf between (horiz pair) .. £325
1 a. carmine (1918) .. .. .. 3·75 3·75
a. Imperf between (vert pair) .. .. † £550
b. Imperf horiz (vert pair) .. .. † £550
1 a. rose-red .. .. 2·50 7·50
a. Imperf between (vert pair) .. £600
1 a. scarlet (1922) .. .. .. 2·25 2·00
a. Imperf between (vert pair) .. £600 £600
2 a. green (1918) .. .. .. 3·50 3·00
4 a. chocolate .. .. 3·75 6·50
4 a. pale brown .. .. 4·25 7·50
a. Imperf vert (horiz pair) £450
'31 .. .. *Set of* 5 10·00 11·50

Maharaja Sawai Man Singh II 1922–1970

26. *Surch with T* 5.

3 3 a. on 8 a. bright violet (R.) .. .. 1·40 1·90
a. Surch inverted £170 £140
3 a. on 1 r. yellow (R.) .. .. .. 2·25 4·25
a. Surch inverted £400 £170
c. Yellow-ochre .. .. .. 6·50 8·50

28. *As* 1913–18 *issue. Wmk* "DORLING & CO. LONDON" (*½ a., 1 a., 2 a.*) *or* "OVERLAND BANK" (*all values*) *in sheet. No gum. P* 12.

3 ½ a. ultramarine .. .. .. 3·00 4·00
a. Perf comp of 12 and 11 .. .. 13·00 8·00
1 a. rose-red .. .. 23·00 17·00
a. Imperf between (vert pair) .. £450
1 a. scarlet .. .. 38·00 12·00
a. Perf comp of 12 and 11 .. .. 50·00 25·00
2 a. green .. .. 70·00 26·00
a. Perf comp of 12 and 11 .. .. £170 55·00
8 a. bright violet .. .. ..
1 r. orange-vermilion £250 £375

The "OVERLAND BANK" paper has a coarser texture. The ½ a. nd 2 a. values also exist on this paper perforated 11, but such amps are difficult to distinguish from examples of Nos. 25 and 29.

6 Chariot of the Sun God, Surya

7 Maharaja Sawai Man Singh II

8 Sowar in Armour

(Des T. I. Archer. Litho Indian Security Printing Press, Nasik)

1931 (14 Mar). *Investiture of Maharaja. T* **6/8** *and similar designs. No wmk. P* 14.

40 ¼ a. black and deep lake .. .. .. 1·50 1·75
41 ½ a. black and violet 30 10
42 1 a. black and blue .. .. .. 6·00 6·50
43 2 a. black and buff .. .. .. 4·50 6·50
44 2½ a. black and carmine .. .. .. 28·00 45·00
45 3 a. black and myrtle .. .. .. 10·00 40·00
46 4 a. black and olive-green .. .. 12·00 45·00
47 6 a. black and deep blue .. .. .. 6·00 42·00
48 8 a. black and chocolate .. .. .. 12·00 65·00
49 1 r. black and pale olive .. .. .. 26·00 £180
50 2 r. black and yellow-green .. .. 24·00 £225
51 5 r. black and purple .. .. .. 38·00 £250
40/51 .. .. *Set of* 12 £150 £800

Designs: *Vert*—1 a. Elephant and state banner; 2½ a. Common Peafowl; 8 a. Sireh-Deorhi Gate. *Horiz*—3 a. Bullock carriage; 4 a. Elephant carriage; 6 a. Albert Museum; 1 r. Chandra Mahal; 2 r. Amber Palace; 5 r. Maharajas Jai Singh and Man Singh.

Eighteen of these sets were issued for presentation purposes with a special overprint "INVESTITURE-MARCH 14,1931" in red (*Price for set of* 12 £3000, *unused* £4000, *used*).

10 Maharaja Sawai Man Singh II

One Rupee

(11)

(Des T. I. Archer. Litho Indian Security Printing Press, Nasik)

1932–46. *P* 14. (*a*) *Inscr* "POSTAGE & REVENUE".

52 **10** 1 a. black and blue .. .. .. 1·00 60
53 2 a. black and buff .. .. .. 2·25 1·40
54 4 a. black and grey-green .. .. 3·25 6·50
55 8 a. black and chocolate .. .. .. 4·50 9·50
56 1 r. black and yellow-bistre .. .. 18·00 80·00
57 2 r. black and yellow-green .. .. 75·00 £325
52/7 .. .. *Set of* 6 95·00 £375

(*b*) *Inscr* "POSTAGE"

58 **7** ¼ a. black and brown-lake 30 15
59 ¾ a. black and brown-red (1943?) .. 5·00 3·00
60 1 a. black and blue (1943?) .. .. 6·50 2·50
61 2 a. black and buff (1943?) .. .. 6·00 3·25
62 2½ a. black and carmine .. .. .. 2·75 2·00
63 3 a. black and green .. .. .. 2·00 45
64 4 a. black and grey-green (1943?) .. 24·00 90·00
65 6 a. black and deep blue .. .. 3·00 22·00
a. Black and pale blue (1946) .. .. 7·50 50·00
66 8 a. black and chocolate (1946) .. .. 16·00 85·00
67 1 r. black and yellow-bistre (1946) .. 20·00 £120
58/67 .. .. *Set of* 10 75·00 £300

1936. *Nos.* 57 *and* 51 *surch with T* **11**.

68 **10** 1 r. on 2 r. black and yellow-green (R.) 7·00 75·00
69 – 1 r. on 5 r. black and purple .. .. 7·00 60·00

पाव आना

(12)

13 Maharaja and Amber Palace

1938 (Dec). *No.* 41 *surch* "QUARTER ANNA" *in Devanagari, T* **12**.

70 **7** ¼ a. on ½ a. black and violet (R.) .. 10·00 13·00

(Recess D.L.R.)

1947 (Dec)–**48.** *Silver Jubilee of Maharaja's Accession to Throne. Various designs as T* **13**. *P* 13½×14.

71 ¼ a. red-brown and green (5.48) .. .. 85 3·25
72 ½ a. green and violet .. .. .. 30 3·00
73 ¾ a. black and lake (5.48) .. .. .. 90 3·75
74 1 a. red-brown and ultramarine .. .. 50 3·00
75 2 a. violet and scarlet .. .. .. 50 3·25
76 3 a. green and black (5.48) .. .. 1·10 4·25
77 4 a. ultramarine and brown .. .. 50 3·00
78 8 a. vermilion and brown .. .. .. 60 4·00
79 1 r. purple and green (5.48) .. .. 1·60 23·00
71/9 .. .. *Set of* 9 6·25 45·00

Designs:—¼ a. Palace Gate; ¾ a. Map of Jaipur; 1 a. Observatory; 2 a. Wind Palace; 3 a. Coat of Arms; 4 a. Amber Fort Gate; 8 a. Chariot of the Sun; 1 r. Maharaja's portrait between State flags.

3 PIES

(14)

1947 (Dec). *No.* 41 *surch with T* **14**.

80 **7** 3 p. on ½ a. black and violet (R.) .. 14·00 22·00
a. "PIE" for "PIES" .. .. .. 42·00 80·00
b. Bars at left vertical .. .. .. 55·00 90·00
c. Surch inverted .. .. .. 40·00 32·00
d. Surch inverted and "PIE" for "PIES" £170 £160
e. Surch double, one inverted .. .. 55·00 45·00
f. As variety e, but inverted surch showing "PIE" for "PIES" £350 £325

There were three settings of Type **14**, each applied to quarter sheets of 30 (6×5). No. 80a occurs in two of these settings on R.5/5 and one of these settings also shows No. 80b on R.6/1.

OFFICIAL STAMPS

SERVICE (O 1) SERVICE (O 2)

1928 (13 Nov)–**31.** *T* **3** *typographed. No gum* (*except for Nos. O6/a*). *P* 11, 12, *or compound. Wmk* "DORLING & CO. LONDON" (*4 a.*) *or* "OVERLAND BANK" (*others*). (*a*) *Optd with Type* O **1**.

O 1 ¼ a. olive .. .. 1·25 1·60
a. Bistre .. .. 1·50 1·60
O 2 ½ a. pale ultramarine (Blk.) 65 20
a. Imperf between (horiz pair) £275 £275
b. Imperf between (vert pair) .. .. † £500
c. Opt inverted .. .. .. † £325
d. Opt double (R. and Blk.) .. .. † £400
O 3 ½ a. pale ultramarine (R.) (13.10.30) .. 2·50 25
a. Imperf horiz (vert pair) £500
b. Stamp doubly printed .. .. † £375
O 3c 1 a. rose-red 70 25
d. Imperf between (horiz pair) .. .. † £500
O 4 1 a. scarlet .. .. 1·00 50
a. Opt inverted £600 £600
b. Imperf between (horiz pair) .. .. † £550
O 5 2 a. green 65 40
a. Imperf between (vert pair) .. .. † £650
b. Imperf between (horiz pair) £650 £650
O 6 4 a. pale brown (with gum) .. .. 3·75 1·75
a. Chocolate (with gum) .. .. 2·00 1·75
O 7 8 a. bright violet (R.) (13.10.30) .. 16·00 50·00
O 8 1 r. orange-vermilion .. .. .. 32·00 £225

(*b*) *Optd with Type* O **2**

O 9 ½ a. ultramarine (Blk.) (11.2.31) .. £200 15
a. Imperf vert (horiz pair) .. .. † £600
O10 ½ a. ultramarine (R.) (15.10.30) £170 15
a. Imperf between (vert pair) .. .. † £600
O11 8 a. bright violet (11.2.31) £400 £180
O12 1 r. orange-vermilion (11.2.31) £350 £250

SERVICE (O 3) आध आना (O 4)

1931–7. *Nos.* 41/3 *and* 46 *optd at Nasik with Type* O **3**, *in red.*

O13 **7** ½ a. black and violet 30 10
O14 – 1 a. black and blue .. .. .. £225 1·75
O15 **8** 2 a. black and buff (1936) .. .. 2·50 4·75
O16 – 4 a. black and olive-green (1937) .. 27·00 24·00
O13/16 .. .. *Set of* 4 £225 28·00

1932. *No.* O5 *surch with Type* O **4**.

O17 **3** ½ a. on 2 a. green .. .. .. £140 1·25

1932–7. *Nos.* 52/6 *optd at Nasik with Type* O **3**, *in red.*

O18 **10** 1 a. black and blue .. .. .. 2·50 10
O19 2 a. black and buff .. .. .. 3·00 10
O20 4 a. black and grey-green (1937) .. £250 6·50
O21 8 a. black and chocolate .. .. .. 6·50 1·10
O22 1 r. black and yellow-bistre .. .. 17·00 18·00
O18/22 .. .. *Set of* 5 £250 23·00

1936–46. *Stamps of* 1932–46, *inscr* "POSTAGE".

(*a*) *Optd at Nasik with Type* O **3**, *in red*

O23 **7** ¼ a. black and brown-lake (1936) .. 40 10
O24 ¾ a. black and brown-red (1944) .. 1·50 50
O25 1 a. black and blue (1941?) .. .. 4·00 30
O26 2 a. black and buff (date?) .. .. 4·00 2·00
O27 2½ a. black and carmine (1946) .. 7·50 80·00
O28 4 a. black and grey-green (1942) .. 4·00 3·75
O29 8 a. black and chocolate (1943) .. 4·00 5·50
O30 1 r. black and yellow-bistre (date?) .. 50·00
O23/9 .. .. *Set of* 7 23·00 85·00

(*b*) *Optd locally as Type* O **2** (*16 mm long*), *in black*

O31 **7** ¼ a. black and red-brown (1936) .. 70·00 55·00

9 PIES

(O 5)

1947. *No.* O25 *surch with Type* O **5**, *in red.*

O32 **7** 9 p. on 1 a. black and blue .. .. 3·00 2·50

1947 (Dec). *No.* O13 *surch as T* **14**, *but* "3 PIES" *placed higher.*

O33 **7** 3 p. on ½ a. black and violet (R.) .. 4·50 10·00
a. Surch double, one inverted .. .. 38·00 38·00
ab. "PIE" for "PIES" in inverted surcharge £200 £225
c. Surch inverted .. .. .. — £1200

1948 (Dec). *No.* O13 *surch* "THREE-QUARTER ANNA" *in Devanagari, as T* **12**, *but with two bars on each side.*

O34 **7** ¾ a. on ½ a. black and violet (R.) .. 14·00 14·00
a. Surch double £1200 £1200

There are three different types of surcharge in the setting of 30, which vary in one or other of the Devanagari characters.

Jaipur became part of Rajasthan by 7 April 1949.

JAMMU AND KASHMIR

PRICES FOR STAMPS ON COVER

Nos. 1/73	*from* × 3
Nos. 74/84	*from* × 2
No. 85	—
Nos. 86/9	*from* × 2
Nos. 90/101	*from* × 10
Nos. 101*b*/23	*from* × 5
Nos. 124/36	*from* × 10
Nos. 138/9	*from* × 100
Nos. 140/61*a*	*from* × 15
Nos. 162/8	*from* × 5
No. O1	*from* × 2
Nos. O2/4	*from* × 4
No. O5	—
Nos. O6/14	*from* × 30
Nos. O15/18	—

ILLUSTRATIONS. Designs of Jammu and Kashmir are illustrated actual size.

Maharaja Ranbir Singh, 1857–1885

1 (½ a.) **2** (1 a.)

3 (4 a.)

Characters denoting the value (on the circular stamps only) are approximately as shown in the central circles of the stamps illustrated above.

These characters were taken from Punjabi merchants' notation and were not familiar to most of the inhabitants of the state. Type **1** was certainly the ½ anna value, but there has long been controversy over the correct face values of Types **2** and **3**.

The study of surviving material suggests that, to some extent, this confusion involved contemporary post office officials. Although covers posted at Jammu, where the stamps were in use for twelve years, show Type **2** used as the 1 a. value and Type **3** as the 4 a., those originating from Srinagar (Kashmir) during 1866–68 show both Types **2** and **3** used as 1 a. stamps.

In the following listing we have followed contemporary usage at Jammu and this reflects the prevailing opinion amongst modern authorities.

GUM. The stamps of Jammu and Kashmir were issued without gum.

PRICES. Prices for the circular stamps, Nos. 1/49, are for cut-square examples. Cut-to-shape examples are worth from 10% to 20% of these prices, according to condition.

A. *Handstamped in watercolours*

1866 (23 Mar). *Native paper, thick to thin, usually having the appearance of laid paper and tinted grey or brown. For Jammu and Kashmir.*

No.	Type	Description	Unused	Used
1	**1**	½ a. grey-black	£160	75·00
2	**2**	1 a. grey-black	£1200	£1000
4		1 a. royal blue	£550	£375
4*a*	**1**	½ a. ultramarine	£2250	£2250
5	**2**	1 a. ultramarine	£350	80·00
6	**3**	4 a. ultramarine	£650	£325

1867–76. *Reissued for use in Jammu only.*

No.	Type	Description	Unused	Used
6*a*	**3**	4 a. grey-black	£1300	
7		4 a. indigo	£1500	£850
8		4 a. red (1869)	55·00	95·00
9		4 a. orange-red (1872)	£150	£200
10		4 a. orange (1872)		
11		4 a. carmine-red (1876)	£700	

1874–76. *Special Printings.*

No.	Type	Description	Unused	Used
12	**1**	½ a. red	70·00	£275
12*a*		½ a. orange-red	£500	£550
13	**2**	1 a. red	£140	£200
13*a*		1 a. orange-red	£500	£550
13*b*		1 a. orange	£650	
14	**1**	½ a. deep black	17·00	£150
		a. *Tête-bêche* (pair)	£375	
15	**2**	1 a. deep black	£225	
16	**3**	4 a. deep black	£200	
17	**1**	½ a. bright blue (1876)	£250	£325
18	**2**	1 a. bright blue (1876)	90·00	£275
19	**3**	4 a. bright blue (1876)	£150	
20	**1**	½ a. emerald-green	75·00	£190
21	**2**	1 a. emerald-green	80·00	£190
22	**3**	4 a. emerald-green	£180	£325
23	**1**	½ a. yellow	£475	£600
24	**2**	1 a. yellow	£650	
25	**3**	4 a. yellow	£375	
25*a*		4 a. deep blue-black (1876)	£1000	£600

These special printings were available for use, but little used.

B. *Handstamped in oil colours. Heavy blurred prints*

1877 (June)–**78.** (*a*) *Native paper.*

No.	Type	Description	Unused	Used
26	**1**	½ a. red	26·00	45·00
27	**2**	1 a. red	30·00	£150
28	**3**	4 a. red	£190	£400
29	**1**	½ a. black	26·00	45·00
32		½ a. slate-blue	£110	£180
34	**2**	1 a. slate-blue	22·00	£200
35	**1**	½ a. sage-green	£110	
36	**2**	1 a. sage-green	£120	
37	**3**	4 a. sage-green	£120	

(*b*) *European laid paper, medium to thick*

No.	Type	Description	Unused	Used
38	**1**	½ a. red	—	£700
39	**3**	4 a. red	£325	£350
41	**1**	½ a. black	20·00	45·00
		a. Printed both sides	£600	
		b. *Tête-bêche* (pair)	£300	
44		½ a. slate-blue	35·00	£200
45	**2**	1 a. slate-blue	45·00	£300
46	**3**	4 a. slate-blue	£600	£600
47		4 a. sage-green	£1000	
48	**1**	½ a. yellow	£110	

(*c*) *Thick yellowish wove paper*

No.	Type	Description	Unused	Used
49	**1**	½ a. red (1878)	—	£800

Forgeries exist of the ½ a. and 1 a. in types which were at one time supposed to be authentic.

Reprints and imitations (of which some of each were found in the official remainder stock) exist in a great variety of fancy colours, both on native paper, usually thinner and smoother than that of the originals, and on various thin European *wove* papers, on which the originals were never printed.

The imitations, which do not agree in type with the above illustrations, are also to be found on *laid* paper.

All the reprints, etc. are in oil colours or printer's ink. The originals in oil colour are usually blurred, particularly when on native paper. The reprints, etc. are usually clear.

FOR USE IN JAMMU

½ a. ½ a.

1 a. **4** ½ a.

T **4** to **11** have a star at the top of the oval band; the characters denoting the value are in the upper part of the inner oval. All are dated 1923, corresponding with A.D. 1866.

T **4.** *Printed in blocks of four, three varieties of ½ anna and one of 1 anna.*

1867 (Sept). *In watercolour on native paper.*

No.	Description	Unused	Used
52	½ a. grey-black	£650	£200
53	1 a. grey-black	£1900	£850
54	½ a. indigo	£275	£200
55	1 a. indigo	£550	£275
56	½ a. deep ultramarine	£200	£140
57	1 a. deep ultramarine	£500	£275
58	½ a. deep violet-blue	£140	75·00
59	1 a. deep violet-blue	£500	£275

1868 (May)–**72.** *In watercolour on native paper.*

No.	Description	Unused	Used
60	½ a. red (*shades*)	5·00	2·50
61	1 a. red (*shades*)	12·00	8·00
62	½ a. orange-red	£170	55·00
63	1 a. orange-red	£550	£200
64	½ a. orange (1872)	90·00	95·00
65	1 a. orange (1872)	£1600	£1000

1874–6. *Special printings; in watercolour on native paper.*

No.	Description	Unused	Used
66	½ a. bright blue (1876)	£1000	£250
67	1 a. bright blue (1876)	£325	£350
68	½ a. emerald-green	£1300	£800
69	1 a. emerald-green	£2250	£1400
69*a*	½ a. jet-black	£110	£140
69*b*	1 a. jet-black	£1300	£1100

1877 (June)–**78.** *In oil colour.* (*a*) *Native paper.*

No.	Description	Unused	Used
70	½ a. red	9·00	5·50
71	1 a. red	26·00	19·00
72	½ a. brown-red (1878)	—	32·00
73	1 a. brown-red (1878)	—	95·00
74	½ a. black	†	£750
75	1 a. black	†	£1700
76	½ a. deep blue-black	†	£1200
77	1 a. deep blue-black	†	£3250

(*b*) *Laid paper (medium or thick)*

No.	Description	Unused	Used
78	½ a. red	—	£800

(*c*) *Thick wove paper*

No.	Description	Unused	Used
79	½ a. red	†	£375
80	1 a. red		

(*d*) *Thin laid, bâtonné paper*

No.	Description	Unused	Used
84	½ a. red	†	£1100
85	1 a. red	£3250	

The circular and rectangular stamps listed under the heading "Special Printings' did not supersede those in *red*, which was the normal colour for Jammu down to 1878. It is not known for what reason other colours were used during that period, but stamps were printed in 1874 or 1875 and were certainly put use. The rectangular stamps were again printed in *black* (jet-b as against the greyish black of the 1867 printings) at that time impressions of the two periods can also be distinguished by obliterations, which until 1868 were in *magenta* and after th *black*.

There are reprints of these, in *oil* colour, *brown-red* and *b* *blue*, on native paper; they are very clearly printed, which is no case with the originals in *oil* colour.

4*a*

1877 (Sept). *Provisional. Seal obliterator of Jammu ha stamped in red watercolour on pieces of native paper, and u as a ½ anna stamp.*

No.	Type	Description	Unused	Used
86	**4*a***	(½ a.) rose-red	—	£1

FOR USE IN KASHMIR

5

1866 (Sept(?). *Printed from a single die. Native laid paper.*

No.	Type	Description	Unused	Used
87	**5**	½ a. black	£2250	£3

Forgeries of this stamp are commonly found, copied from illustration in *Le Timbre-Poste.*

6 (½ a.) **7** (1 a.)

1867 (Apr). *Native laid paper.*

No.	Type	Description	Unused	Used
88	**6**	½ a. black	£1000	£1
89	**7**	1 a. black	£1800	£3

Printed in sheets of 25 (5×5), the four top rows being ½ a. a the bottom row 1 a.

8 (¼ a.) **9** (2 a.)

10 (4 a.) **11** (8 a.)

1867–77. *Native laid paper.*

No.	Type	Description	Unused	Used
90	**8**	¼ a. black	2·25	2·5
91	**6**	½ a. ultramarine (6.67)	2·25	1·2
		a. Bisected (¼ a.) (on cover) (1877)	†	£500
92		½ a. violet-blue (1870)	4·00	2·5
93	**7**	1 a. ultramarine (6.67)	£3000	£120
94		1 a. orange (7.67)	8·00	8·5
95		1 a. brown-orange (1868)	10·00	8·0
96		1 a. orange-vermilion (1876)	12·00	8·50
97	**9**	2 a. yellow	11·00	13·00
98		2 a. buff	17·00	14·00
99	**10**	4 a. emerald-green	28·00	28·00
		a. *Tête-bêche* (pair)	£900	
100		4 a. sage-green	£250	£120
100*a*		4 a. myrtle-green	£600	£600
101	**11**	8 a. red (1868)	30·00	28·00
		a. *Tête-bêche* (pair)	£900	

Of the above, the ½ a. and 1 a. were printed from the same plate of 25 as Nos. 88/9, the ¼ a. and 2 a. from a new plate of 10 (5×2), the top row being ¼ a. and the lower 2 a., and the 4 a. and 8 a. from single dies. Varieties at one time catalogued upon European papers were apparently never put into circulation, though some of them were printed while these stamps were still in use.

Nos. 86 to 101 are in watercolour.

No. 91a was used at Srinagar, in conjunction with an India ½ a., and was cancelled "KASHMIR 5/L-6".

FOR USE IN JAMMU AND KASHMIR

e following issues there are 15 varieties on the sheets of the ¼ a. and ½ a.; 20 varieties of the 1 a. and 2 a. and 8 varieties a. and 8 a. The value is in the lower part of the central oval.

12 (¼ a.)

13 (½ a.)

14 (1 a.)

15 (2 a.)

16 (4 a.)

17 (8 a.)

3 (May)–79. *Provisional printings.*

I. *Ordinary white laid paper, of varying thickness*

(*a*) *Rough perf* 10 *to* 12 (i) *or* 13 *to* 16 (ii)

b **12** ¼ a. red (i)
13 ½ a. red (i) .. 12·00 14·00
14 1 a. red (i) .. £1000
13 ½ a. slate-violet (i) .. 70·00 50·00
a **14** 1 a. violet (ii)
b **15** 2 a. violet (i) .. £1400

(*b*) *Imperf*

13 ½ a. slate-violet (*shades*) .. 14·00 12·00
14 1 a. slate-purple .. 20·00 21·00
1 a. mauve .. 30·00 30·00
15 2 a. violet .. 21·00 21·00
2 a. bright mauve .. 28·00 26·00
2 a. slate-blue .. 42·00 42·00
2 a. dull blue .. 80·00 85·00
12 ¼ a. red .. 19·00 14·00
13 ½ a. red .. 8·00 8·00
14 1 a. red .. 7·50 8·00
15 2 a. red .. 65·00 65·00
16 4 a. red .. £160 £140

II. *Medium wove paper.* (*a*) *Rough perf* 10 *to* 12

7 **13** ½ a. red .. — £190

(*b*) *Imperf*

7b **12** ¼ a. red
8 **13** ½ a. red .. 13·00 7·00
9 **14** 1 a. red .. 12·00 8·00
0 **15** 2 a. red .. 65·00

III. *Thick wove paper. Imperf*

1 **13** ½ a. red .. 23·00 45·00
2 **14** 1 a. red .. 42·00 18·00
3 **15** 2 a. red .. 16·00 19·00

Of the above stamps those in red were intended for use in mmu and those in shades of violet and blue for use in ashmir.

79. *Definitive issue. Thin wove paper, fine to coarse.*

(*a*) *Rough perf* 10 *to* 12

24 **13** ½ a. red .. £225 £150

(*b*) *Imperf*

25 **12** ¼ a. red .. 3·00 3·25
26 **13** ½ a. red .. 60 65
a. Bisected (¼ a.) on postcard .. † £3000
27 **14** 1 a. red .. 2·50 3·00
28 **15** 2 a. red .. 3·25 4·00
29 **16** 4 a. red .. 7·50 7·50
30 **17** 8 a. red .. 7·50 8·50

The plates were transferred from Jammu to Srinagar in early 881 when further printings in red and all orange stamps were roduced.

880 (Mar). *Provisional printing in watercolour on thin bâtonné paper. Imperf.*

30*a* **12** ¼ a. ultramarine .. £800 £475

881–83. *As Nos.* 124 *to* 130. *Colour changed.*

(*a*) *Rough perf* 10 *to* 12

30*b* **13** ½ a. orange

(*b*) *Imperf*

31 **12** ¼ a. orange .. 8·50 10·00
32 **13** ½ a. orange .. 19·00 13·00
33 **14** 1 a. orange .. 18·00 9·50
a. Bisected (½ a.) (on cover) .. † £3250

134 **15** 2 a. orange .. 15·00 9·50
135 **16** 4 a. orange .. 30·00 42·00
136 **17** 8 a. orange .. 60·00 65·00

Nos. 126*a* and 133*a* were used at Leh between April and July 1883.

Nos. 125/30 and 132/6 were re-issued between 1890 and 1894 and used concurrently with the stamps which follow. Such re-issues can be identified by the "three circle" cancellations, introduced in December 1890.

18 (⅛ a.)

1883–94. *New colours. Thin wove papers, toned, coarse to fine, or fine white* (1889). *Imperf.*

138 **18** ⅛ a. yellow-brown .. 90 1·25
139 ⅛ a. yellow .. 90 1·25
140 **12** ¼ a. sepia .. 75 55
141 ¼ a. brown .. 70 55
a. Double impression .. £1100
142 ¼ a. pale brown .. 70 55
a. Error. Green .. 55·00
143 **13** ½ a. dull blue .. 5·00
144 ½ a. bright blue .. 42·00
145 ½ a. vermilion .. 1·10 50
146 ½ a. rose .. 1·10 75
147 ½ a. orange-red .. 1·10 50
148 **14** 1 a. greenish grey .. 85 65
149 1 a. bright green .. 95 95
a. Double impression
150 1 a. dull green .. 85 65
151 1 a. blue-green .. 1·25
152 **15** 2 a. red/*yellow* .. 1·60 1·10
153 2 a. red/*yellow-green* .. 2·50 3·00
154 2 a. red/*deep green* .. 12·00 12·00
155 **16** 4 a. deep green .. 3·00 3·75
156 4 a. green .. 3·25 3·00
157 4 a. pale green .. 3·25 3·25
158 4 a. sage-green .. 3·50
159 **17** 8 a. pale blue .. 6·00 8·00
159*a* 8 a. deep blue .. 9·00 10·00
160 8 a. bright blue .. 8·00 9·50
161 8 a. indigo-blue .. 10·00 11·00
161*a* 8 a. slate-lilac .. 10·00 16·00

Well-executed forgeries of the ¼ a. to 8 a. have come from India, mostly postmarked; they may be detected by the type, which does not agree with any variety on the genuine sheets, and also, in the low values, by the margins being filled in with colour, all but a thin white frame round the stamp. The forgeries of the 8 a. are in sheets of eight like the originals.

Other forgeries of nearly all values also exist, showing all varieties of type. All values are on thin, coarse wove paper.

In February 1890, a forgery, in watercolour, of the ½ a. orange on thin wove or on thin laid paper appeared, and many have been found genuinely used during 1890 and 1891 (*Price* £3).

Nos. 143 and 144 were never issued.

Examples of the ¼ a. brown, ½ a. orange-red and 1 a. green on wove paper exist with clean-cut perf 12.

There is a reference in the Jammu and Kashmir State Administration Report covering 1890–91 to the re-introduction of perforating and the machine-gumming of paper at the Jammu printing works.

The few known examples, the ¼ a. being only recorded used, the others unused or used, would appear to date from this period, but there is, as yet, no direct confirmation as to their status.

Maharaja Partap Singh, 1885–1925

1887–94. *Thin creamy laid paper. Imperf.*

162 **18** ⅛ a. yellow .. 42·00 50·00
163 **12** ¼ a. brown .. 9·00 6·00
164 **13** ½ a. brown-red (March 1887) .. — 60·00
165 ½ a. orange-red .. 7·00 4·75
166 **14** 1 a. grey-green .. £100 £100
168 **17** 8 a. blue (*Printed in watercolour*) .. £150 £150
a. On wove paper .. £100 £100

19

T **19** represents a ¼ a. stamp, which exists in sheets of twelve varieties, in *red* and *black*, on thin wove and laid papers, also in *red* on native paper, but which does not appear ever to have been issued for use. It was first seen in 1886.

The ¼ a. *brown* and the 4 a. *green* both exist on ordinary white laid paper and the ½ a. *red* on native paper. None of these are known to have been in use.

OFFICIAL STAMPS

1878. I. *White laid paper.* (*a*) *Rough perf* 10 *to* 12.

O1 **13** ½ a. black .. — £1300

(*b*) *Imperf*

O2 **13** ½ a. black .. 95·00 90·00
O3 **14** 1 a. black .. 60·00 60·00
O4 **15** 2 a. black .. 55·00 50·00

II. *Medium wove paper. Imperf*

O5 **14** 1 a. black .. £225

1880–94. *Thin wove papers, toned, coarse to fine, or fine white* (1889). *Imperf.*

O 6 **12** ¼ a. black .. 80 90
a. Double print .. £190
O 7 **13** ½ a. black .. 15 30
a. Printed both sides .. £425
O 8 **14** 1 a. black .. 20 60
O 9 **15** 2 a. black .. 30 45
O10 **16** 4 a. black .. 35 90
O11 **17** 8 a. black .. 1·40 1·10

1887–94. *Thin creamy laid paper. Imperf.*

O12 **12** ¼ a. black .. 5·50 5·50
O13 **13** ½ a. black .. 3·25 3·50
O14 **14** 1 a. black .. 1·60 2·25
O15 **15** 2 a. black .. 12·00
O16 **16** 4 a. black .. 50·00 55·00
O17 **17** 8 a. black .. 28·00 45·00

1889. *Stout white wove paper. Imperf.*

O18 **12** ¼ a. black .. £180 £110

The stamps of Jammu and Kashmir have been obsolete since 1 November 1894.

JASDAN

PRICES FOR STAMPS ON COVER

Nos. 1/2	*from* × 2
No. 3	*from* × 3
Nos. 4/6	*from* × 4

Darbar Ala Khachar, 1919–1971

1 Sun

(Typo L. V. Indap & Co, Bombay)

1942 (15 Mar)–**47.** *Stamps from booklet panes. Various perfs.*

1 **1** 1 a. deep myrtle-green (*p* 10½×*imperf*) .. £700 £450
2 1 a. light green (*p* 12×*imperf*) .. £425 £450
3 1 a. light green (*p* 10½×*imperf*) (1943) .. £110 £140
4 1 a. pale yellow-green (*p* 8½×*imperf*) .. 15·00 £110
5 1 a. dull yellow-green (*p* 10) (1946) .. 20·00 £130
6 1 a. bluish green (*p* 9) (1947) .. 16·00 £110

Nos. 1/4 were issued in panes of four with the stamps imperforate on one or two sides; Nos. 5/6 were in panes of eight perforated all round.

A 1 a. rose with the arms of Jasdan in the centre is a fiscal stamp.

Jasdan was merged with the United State of Kathiawar (later Saurashtra) by 15 April 1948.

JHALAWAR

PRICES FOR STAMPS ON COVER

Nos. 1/2	*from* × 25

Maharaj Rana Zalim Singh, 1875–1896

(Figure of an Apsara, "RHEMBA", a dancing nymph of the Hindu Paradise)

1 (1 paisa) **2** (¼ anna)

1886–90. *Typo in horizontal strips of* 12. *Laid paper. No gum.*

1 **1** 1 p. yellow-green .. 3·75 9·50
a. Blue-green .. 85·00 38·00
2 **2** ¼ a. green (*shades*) .. 90 1·90

The stamps formerly listed as on wove paper are from sheets on laid paper, with the laid paper lines almost invisible.

The Maharaj Rana was deposed in 1896 and much of the state's territory transferred to Kotah on 1 January 1899.

Raj (Maharaj from 1918) Rana Bhawani Singh, 1899–1929

The stamps of Jhalawar have been obsolete since 1 November 1900.

JIND

PRICES FOR STAMPS ON COVER
Nos. J1/34 *from* × 100

ILLUSTRATIONS. Designs of Jind are illustrated actual size.

Raja Raghubir Singh, 1864–1887

J 1 (½ a.)

J 2 (1 a.)

J 3 (2 a.)

J 4 (4 a.)

J 5 (8 a.)

(Litho Jind State Rajah's Press, Sungroor)

1874. *Thin yellowish paper. Imperf.*

No.	Type	Description	Unused	Used
J1	J 1	½ a. blue	6·00	2·75
		a. No frame to value. (Retouched all over)	£275	£150
J2	J 2	1 a. rosy mauve	7·00	6·00
J3	J 3	2 a. yellow	1·00	3·25
J4		2 a. brown-buff	£160	90·00
J5	J 4	4 a. green	18·00	6·00
J6	J 5	8 a. dull purple	£475	£130
J6*a*		8 a. bluish violet	£170	75·00
J7		8 a. slate-blue	£140	65·00

Nos. J1/7 were produced from two sets of stones. Those from the first set had rather blurred impressions, but those from the second are clearer with a conspicuous white frame around the value. Nos. J4 and J6*a*/13 were only printed from the second set.

1876. *Bluish laid card-paper. No gum. Imperf.*

No.	Type	Description	Unused	Used
J 8	J 1	½ a. blue	75	3·25
J 9	J 2	1 a. purple	1·50	7·50
J10	J 3	2 a. brown	2·75	10·00
J11	J 4	4 a. green	1·75	10·00
J11*a*	J 5	8 a. bluish violet	8·00	20·00
J12		8 a. slate-blue	7·00	10·00
J13		8 a. steel-blue	9·00	15·00

Stocks of the ½ a. (No. J8) and 2 a. (No. J4) were perforated 12 in 1885 for use as fiscal stamps.

J 6 (¼ a.)

J 7 (½ a.)

J 8 (1 a.)

J 9 (2 a.)

J 10 (4 a.)

J 11 (8 a.)

(Litho Jind State Rajah's Press, Sungroor)

1882–85. *Types* J **6** *to* J **11**. 25 *varieties of each value. No gum.*

A. *Imperf* (1882–4). (*a*) *Thin yellowish wove paper.*

No.	Description	Unused	Used
J15	¼ a. buff (*shades*)	30	1·50
J16	¼ a. red-brown	30	1·25
	a. Doubly printed	42·00	
J17	½ a. lemon	1·00	1·75
J18	½ a. buff	1·90	1·50
J19	½ a. brown-buff	80	60
J20	1 a. brown (*shades*)	1·75	3·25
J21	2 a. blue	1·75	7·00
J22	2 a. deep blue	2·50	1·00
J23	4 a. sage-green	1·50	90
J24	4 a. blue-green	1·75	2·75
J25	8 a. red	5·50	4·50

(*b*) *Various thick laid papers*

No.	Description	Unused	Used
J26	¼ a. brown-buff	1·25	
J27	½ a. lemon	1·25	
J28	½ a. brown-buff		
J29	1 a. brown	1·25	2·50
J30	2 a. blue	18·00	21·00
J31	8 a. red	2·50	9·50

(*c*) *Thick white wove paper*

No.	Description	Unused	Used
J32	¼ a. brown-buff	13·00	
J33	½ a. brown-buff	27·00	
J34	1 a. brown	4·00	
J35	8 a. red	4·75	9·00

B. *Perf* 12 (1885). (*a*) *Thin yellowish wove paper*

No.	Description	Unused	Used
J36	¼ a. buff (*shades*)	75	2·75
	a. Doubly printed	85·00	
J37	¼ a. red-brown	3·50	
J38	½ a. lemon	£110	£110
J39	½ a. buff	60	3·75
J40	½ a. brown-buff	3·00	4·50
J41	1 a. brown (*shades*)	2·50	4·75
J42	2 a. blue	3·50	9·00
J43	2 a. deep blue	2·75	6·00
J44	4 a. sage-green	5·00	9·00
J45	4 a. blue-green	2·00	
	a. Imperf vert (horiz pair)	£500	
J46	8 a. red	9·50	

(*b*) *Various thick laid papers*

No.	Description	Unused	Used
J47	¼ a. brown-buff	6·00	
J48	½ a. lemon	95·00	22·00
J49	1 a. brown	1·50	
J50	2 a. blue	20·00	23·00
J51	8 a. red	2·50	7·50

(*c*) *Thick white wove paper*

No.	Description	Unused	Used
J52	1 a. brown		
J53	8 a. red	9·50	

The perforated stamps ceased to be used for postal purposes in July 1885, but were used as fiscals to at least the mid-1920s. Other varieties exist, but they must either be fiscals or reprints, and it is not quite certain that all those listed above were issued as early as 1885.

Jind became a Convention State and from 1 July 1885 used overprinted Indian stamps.

KISHANGARH

PRICES FOR STAMPS ON COVER

Nos. 1/3	—
Nos. 4/91	*from* × 8
Nos. O1/32	*from* × 30

GUM. The stamps of Kishangarh were issued without gum, *except for* Nos. 42/50 and O 17/24.

Maharaja Sardul Singh, 1879–1900

1

1899–1900. *Medium wove paper. Typo from a plate of* 8 (4×2).

No.	Type	Description	Unused	Used
1	1	1 a. green (*imperf*)	22·00	55·00
2		1 a. green (*pin-perf*) (1900)	70·00	

1900. *Thin white wove paper. Printed from a single die. Imperf.*

No.	Type	Description	Unused	Used
3	1	1 a. blue	£400	

ILLUSTRATIONS. Types **2** to **10*a*** are shown actual size.

2 (¼ a.)

3 (½ a.)

4 (1 a.)

5 (2 a.)
Maharaja Sardul Singh

6 (4 a.)

7 (1 r.)

8 (2 r.)

9 (5 r.)

1899 (Sept)–**1901.** *Thin white wove paper.* (*a*) *Imperf.*

No.	Type	Description	Unused	Used
4	2	¼ a. green (1900)	£500	£
5		¼ a. carmine	6·50	
		a. Rose-pink	1·00	1
6		¼ a. magenta	5·00	5
		a. Doubly printed	80·00	
7	3	½ a. lilac (1900)	£110	£
8		½ a. red (1899)	£1900	£1
9		½ a. green (1899)	28·00	32
10		½ a. pale yellow-olive	42·00	42
11		½ a. slate-blue (1900)	35·00	35
		b. Deep blue	6·50	7
		c. Light blue	1·60	1
		ca. Pair, one stamp sideways	£1000	
12	4	1 a. slate	4·50	5
		a. Laid paper	40·00	
12*b*		1 a. pink	55·00	£1
13		1 a. mauve	6·00	5
		a. Laid paper	32·00	
14		1 a. brown-lilac	1·10	1
		a. Laid paper	28·00	
15	5	2 a. dull orange	4·50	4·
		a. Laid paper	£425	£3
16	6	4 a. chocolate	6·00	
		a. Lake-brown	6·00	9·
		b. Chestnut	6·00	9·
		c. Laid paper (*shades*)	60·00	60·
17	7	1 r. dull green	18·00	30·
18		1 r. brown-lilac	20·00	25·
19	8	2 r. brown-red	70·00	90·
		a. Laid paper	55·00	
20	9	5 r. mauve	60·00	70·
		a. Laid paper	60·00	

(*b*) *Pin-perf* 12½ *or* 14 (*from* Nov 1899)

No.	Type	Description	Unused	Used
21	2	¼ a. green	£200	£3
		a Imperf between (pair)	£1000	
22		¼ a. carmine	4·25	5·
		a. Rose-pink	25	4
		ab. *Tête-bêche* (horiz pair)	£750	
		b. Rose		
23		¼ a. magenta	5·00	7·
		a. Bright purple		
		ab. Doubly printed		
24	3	½ a. green	18·00	23·
		a. Imperf between (pair)	£160	
25		½ a. pale yellow-olive	13·00	16·
		a. Imperf vert (horiz pair)	£160	
		b. Imperf between (horiz pair)	†	£3
26		½ a. deep blue	1·90	3·2
		a. Light blue	85	5
		ab. Doubly printed	£100	£10
27	4	1 a. slate	4·75	3·2
		a. Laid paper	35·00	18·0
27*b*		1 a. pink	65·00	£18
28		1 a. mauve	85	1·6
		a. Laid paper	35·00	13·0
29		1 a. brown-lilac	75	1·0
		a. Laid paper	32·00	13·0
30	5	2 a. dull orange	4·00	5·0
		a. Laid paper	£500	
31	6	4 a. chocolate	2·00	5·5
		a. Lake-brown	2·50	5·5
		b. Chestnut	3·50	6·0
		c. Laid paper (*shades*)	48·00	45·0
32	7	1 r. dull green	10·00	15·0
		a. Laid paper	70·00	
33		1 r. pale olive-yellow	£650	
34	8	2 r. brown-red	32·00	48·0
		a. Laid paper	40·00	
35	9	5 r. mauve	32·00	48·0
		a. Laid paper	60·00	

All the above, both imperf and pin-perf, were printed singly sometimes on paper with spaces marked in pencil. They exist in vertical *tête-bêche* pairs imperf between from the centre of the sheet. *Prices from* 3 × *normal, unused.* No. 22ab is an error.

AL STAMPS. Many of the following issues were produced erent colours for fiscal purposes. Such usage is indicated initials "M.C.", punched hole or violet Stamp Office amp.

Maharaja Madan Singh, 1900–1926

10 (¼ a.)

10*a* (1 r.)

Toned wove paper. Pin-perf.

10 ¼ a. dull pink .. .. 8·00 6·00
4 1 a. violet .. .. 40·00 27·00
10*a* 1 r. dull green .. .. 14·00 16·00
.. .. *Set of* 3 55·00 45·00

s. 36/8 were printed in sheets of 24. Sheets of the 1 r. were ys torn to remove R. 5/4 where the cliché is believed to have defective.

e 1 a. (No. 37) differs from T 4 in having an inscription in e characters below the words "ONE ANNA".

11 (½ a.)

12 Maharaja Sardul Singh

. *Litho. Thick white wove glazed paper. Imperf.*

11 ½ a. pink .. .. 9·50 3·00
a. Printed both sides .. .. .. † £1000
12 2 a. dull yellow .. .. 3·00 6·00

12*a* (8 a.)

. *Printed singly. Thin paper. Pin-perf.*

12*a* 8 a. grey .. .. 5·00 7·50
a. *Tête-bêche* (vert pair) .. .. 26·00
b. Doubly printed £110

13 Maharaja Madan Singh 14

(Recess Perkins Bacon & Co)

04–10. *With gum. P* 12½.

13 ¼ a. carmine 45 55
a. Perf 13½ (1910) 55 55
b. Perf 12×12½ .. .. .. 85·00
½ a. chestnut .. .. 1·75 85
a. Perf 13½ (1906) 60 30
1 a. blue .. .. 4·00 2·75
a. Perf 13½ (1906) .. .. .. 1·75 1·50
2 a. orange-yellow .. .. .. 15·00 7·00
a. Perf 13½ (1907) .. .. .. 17·00 14·00
4 a. brown .. .. 19·00 17·00
a. Perf 13½ (1907) .. .. .. 13·00 16·00
b. Perf 12 .. .. 50·00 42·00
8 a. violet (1905) .. .. .. 7·00 19·00
1 r. green .. .. 24·00 32·00
2 r. olive-yellow .. .. .. 24·00 £120
5 r. purple-brown .. .. .. 23·00 £150
/50 .. .. *Set of* 9 95·00 £325

Stamps in other colours, all perforated 13½, were produced by rkins Bacon as business samples.

912. *Printed from half-tone blocks. No ornaments to left and right of value in English; large ornaments on either side of value in Hindi. Small stop after "STATE". (a) Thin wove paper. Rouletted.*

1 14 2 a. deep violet ("TWO ANNA") .. 3·25 7·50
a. *Tête-bêche* (vert pair) .. .. 8·50
b. Imperf (pair) £350

No. 51 is printed in four rows, each inverted in respect to that bove and below it.

(b) *Thick white chalk-surfaced paper. Imperf.*

2 14 2 a. lilac ("TWO ANNA") £1300 £650

(c) *Thick white chalk-surfaced paper. Rouletted in colour (Medallion only in half-tone)*

3 14 ¼ a. ultramarine .. .. .. 15·00 15·00

1913. *No ornaments on either side of value in English. Small ornaments in bottom label. With stop after "STATE". Thick white chalk-surfaced paper. Rouletted.*

54 14 2 a. purple ("TWO ANNAS") .. .. 2·50 5·00

15

पाव ग्रना

No. 59e. This occurs on R. 3/3 on one setting only

2 TWO ANNAS 2 — No. 60. Small figures

2 TWO ANNAS 2 — No. 60b. Large figures

(Typo Diamond Soap Works, Kishangarh)

1913 (Aug). *Thick surfaced paper. Half-tone centre. Type-set inscriptions. Rouletted. Inscr* "KISHANGARH".

59 15 ¼ a. pale blue 30 90
a. Imperf (pair) .. .. .. 7·00
b. Roul × imperf (horiz pair) .. 25·00
ba. Imperf between (horiz pair) .. 42·00
c. "OUARTER" (R. 4/4) .. .. 5·00 7·00
ca. As last, imperf (pair) .. .. 28·00
cb. As last, roul × imperf .. .. 55·00
d. "KISHANGAHR" (R. 2/3) .. .. 5·00 7·00
da. As last, imperf (pair) .. .. 28·00
db. As last, roul × imperf .. .. 55·00
dc. As last, imperf between (horiz pair) 85·00
e. Character omitted .. .. 7·00 7·00
ea. As last, imperf (pair) .. .. 32·00
60 2 a. purple .. .. 7·00 18·00
a. "KISHANGAHR" (R. 2/3) .. .. 50·00 90·00
b. Large figures "2" .. .. .. 32·00 55·00

1913–16. *Stamps printed far apart, horizontally and vertically, otherwise as No.* 54, *except as noted below.*

63 14 ¼ a. blue 20 45
64 ½ a. green (1915) .. .. .. 20 1·00
a. Printed both sides £200
b. Imperf (pair) £150 £150
c. *Emerald-green* (1916) .. .. 1·75 4·00
65 1 a. red .. .. 1·00 2·50
a. Without stop* .. .. .. 1·25 4·50
ab. Imperf (pair) £180
66 2 a. purple ("TWO ANNAS") (1915) .. 6·00 7·00
67 4 a. bright blue .. .. .. 6·00 8·00
68 8 a. brown .. .. 7·00 38·00
69 1 r. mauve .. .. 16·00 £100
a. Imperf (pair) £275
70 2 r. deep green .. .. .. 80·00 £225
71 5 r. brown .. .. 50·00 £350
63/71 .. .. *Set of* 9 £150 £650

*For this issue, ornaments were added on either side of the English value (except in the ¼ a.) and the inscription in the right label was without stop, except in the case of No. 65.

In Nos. 70 and 71 the value is expressed as "RUPIES" instead of "RUPEES".

Initial printings of the ¼ a., 1 a. and 4 a. values were in sheets of 20 containing two panes of 10 separated by a central gutter margin. Stamps from these sheets measure 20×25½ mm and have heavier screening dots on the perforation margins than on the designs. Subsequent printings of these stamps, and of other values in the set, were from single pane sheets of 20 on which the designs measured 19½×23¾ mm and with the screening dots uniform across the sheet.

Maharaja Yagyanarayan Singh, 1926–1939

16 Maharaja Yagyanarayan Singh 17

1928–36. *Thick surfaced paper. Typo. Pin-perf.*

72 16 ¼ a. light blue .. .. 80 2·00
73 ½ a. yellow-green .. .. .. 2·50 1·40
a. *Deep green* .. .. .. 3·00 3·00
ab. Imperf (pair) .. .. .. 80·00 80·00
ac. Imperf between (vert or horiz pair) 95·00 95·00
74 17 1 a. carmine .. .. 75 1·50
a. Imperf (pair) £150 £100
75 2 a. purple .. .. 3·00 8·50
75*a* 2 a. magenta (1936) .. .. .. 6·00 12·00
ab. Imperf (pair) £225
76 16 4 a. chestnut .. .. 1·40 1·75
a. Imperf (pair)
77 8 a. violet .. .. 3·50 25·00
78 1 r. light green .. .. .. 13·00 50·00
79 2 r. lemon-yellow (1929) .. .. 27·00 £160
80 5 r. claret (1929) .. .. .. 32·00 £180
a. Imperf (pair) £110
72/80 .. .. *Set of* 9 75·00 £375

The 4 a. to 5 r. are slightly larger than, but otherwise similar to, the ¼ a. and ½ a. The 8 a. has a dotted background covering the whole design.

Maharaja Sumar Singh, 1939–1971

1943–47. *As last, but thick, soft, unsurfaced paper. Poor impression. Typo. Pin-perf.*

81 16 ¼ a. pale dull blue (1945) .. .. 4·00 9·00
a. Imperf (pair) .. .. .. 32·00
82 ¼ a. greenish blue (1947) .. .. 1·75 7·50
a. Imperf (pair) .. .. .. 28·00
83 16 ½ a. deep green (1944) .. .. .. 1·00 2·25
a. Imperf (pair) .. .. .. 25·00 25·00
b. Imperf between (vert or horiz pair) 42·00
84 ½ a. yellow-green (1946) .. .. 5·00 7·50
a. Imperf (pair) .. .. .. 28·00 28·00
b. Imperf between (vert or horiz pair) 42·00
85 17 1 a. carmine-red (1944) .. .. 7·50 3·00
a. Double print £300
b. Imperf (pair) .. .. .. 30·00 30·00
c. Imperf between (vert or horiz pair) 42·00
d. *Red-orange* (1947) .. .. .. 60·00 26·00
da. Imperf (pair) .. .. .. £100 80·00
86 2 a. bright magenta .. .. .. 8·50 13·00
a. Imperf (pair) .. .. .. 60·00 65·00
87 2 a. maroon (1947) .. .. .. 70·00 16·00
a. Imperf (pair) .. .. .. 45·00 45·00
b. Imperf between (vert or horiz pair) 80·00
88 16 4 a. brown (1944) .. .. .. 24·00 17·00
a. Imperf (pair) .. .. ..
89 8 a. violet (1945) .. .. .. 45·00 £110
90 1 r. green (1945) .. .. .. 50·00 £120
a. Imperf (pair) £180 £275
90*b* 2 r. yellow (date?) .. .. ..
ba. Imperf (pair) £425
91 5 r. claret (1945) £475 £500
a. Imperf (pair) £325

OFFICIAL STAMPS

ON
K S
D

(O 1)

1918. *Handstamped with Type* O 1.

(a) *Stamps of* 1899–1901. (i) *Imperf*

O 1 2 ¼ a. green .. .. — £160
O 2 ¼ a. rose-pink .. .. — 6·00
a. Pair, one without opt .. .. — 70·00
O 3 4 1 a. mauve .. .. — 55·00
O 3*a* 1 a. brown-lilac .. .. .. 42·00 5·50
ab. Pair, one without opt .. .. £160 70·00
O 4 6 4 a. chocolate .. .. .. — 90·00

(ii) *Pin-perf*

O 5 2 ¼ a. green .. .. — £120
O 6 ¼ a. rose-pink .. .. .. 2·25 60
a. Pair, one without opt .. .. 80·00 38·00
b. Stamp doubly printed .. .. 90·00 60·00
O 7 3 ½ a. light blue .. .. .. £140 35·00
O 8 4 1 a. mauve .. .. 38·00 1·50
O 9 1 a. brown-lilac .. .. .. 35·00 1·50
O10 5 2 a. dull orange .. .. .. — £120
O11 6 4 a. chocolate .. .. .. 45·00 16·00
a. Pair, one without opt .. .. — 75·00
O12 7 1 r. dull green .. .. .. £140 95·00
O13 8 2 r. brown-red .. .. .. — £750
O14 9 5 r. mauve .. .. — £1500

(b) *Stamp of* 1901

O14*a* 10*a* 1 r. dull green .. .. .. — £600

(c) *Stamps of* 1903 *and* 1904

O15 12 2 a. dull yellow .. .. .. 65·00 5·00
a. Stamp printed both sides .. .. † £750
b. Red opt £325 £180
O16 12*a* 8 a. grey .. .. 65·00 22·00
a. Red opt .. .. — £180

(d) *Stamps of* 1904–5. *P* 13½ (¼ *a. to* 4 *a.*) *or* 12½ (*others*)

O17 13 ¼ a. carmine .. .. — £250
O18 ½ a. chestnut 75 35
a. Pair, one without opt .. .. — 45·00
O19 1 a. blue .. .. 7·00 4·00
a. Red opt .. .. 23·00 7·00
b. Pair, one without opt .. .. — 60·00
O20 2 a. orange-yellow .. .. .. — £800
O21 4 a. brown .. .. 50·00 18·00
a. Red opt .. .. 65·00 32·00
O22 8 a. violet £275 £170
a. Red opt .. .. — £180
O23 1 r. green £550 £500
a. Red opt .. .. — £475
O24 5 r. purple-brown .. .. ..

(e) *Stamps of* 1913

O25 15 ¼ a. pale blue .. .. .. 6·00
a. Imperf (pair) .. .. .. 85·00
b. Roul×imperf (horiz pair) £140
c. "OUARTER" .. .. .. 22·00
ca. As last, imperf (pair) £130
d. "KISHANGAHR" .. .. .. 22·00
da. As last, imperf (pair) £130
e. Character omitted .. .. .. 22·00
ea. As last, imperf (pair) £130
O26 14 2 a. purple (No. 54) .. .. .. — 90·00
a. Red opt .. .. £130 20·00
O27 15 2 a. purple £400 £425
a. "KISHANGAHR" £750
b. Large figures "2" £550 £600

(f) *Stamps of* 1913–16

O28 14 ¼ a. blue 50 50
a. Red opt .. .. 2·00 1·75
O29 ½ a. green 75 75
a. Pair, one without opt .. .. — 60·00
b. Red opt .. .. 3·25 1·60
ba. Pair, one without opt .. .. — £120
O30 1 a. red .. .. 9·50 4·50
a. Without stop .. .. .. 1·00 1·00
b. Pair, one without opt £110
c. Red opt .. .. £120 75·00
O31 2 a. purple .. .. 6·00 4·00
a. Red opt .. .. £120 65·00
b. Pair, one without opt .. .. — 65·00
O32 4 a. bright blue .. .. .. 20·00 15·00
a. Red opt .. .. — 30·00

O33 14 8 a. brown .. .. £100 40·00
a. Red opt .. .. .. — 85·00
O34 1 r. mauve £300 £300
O35 2 r. deep green .. .. ..
O36 5 r. brown £1300

This overprint is found inverted as often as it is upright; and many other "errors" exist.

Kishangarh became part of Rajasthan by 15 April 1948.

LAS BELA

PRICES FOR STAMPS ON COVER
Nos. 1/12 *from* × 8

Mir Kamal Khan, 1896–1926

1

2

(Litho Thacker & Co, Bombay)

1897–98. *Thick paper. P* 11½.
1 1 ½ a. black on *white* .. .. .. 20·00 13·00

1898–1900. *P* 11½.
2 1 ½ a. black on *greyish blue* (1898) .. 13·00 8·00
3 ½ a. black on *greenish grey* (1899) .. 11·00 7·00
a. "BFLA" for "BELA" £150
b. Imperf between (horiz strip of 3) ..
4 ½ a. black on *thin white surfaced paper* (1899) .. .. .. 23·00 35·00
5 ½ a. black on *slate* (1900) .. .. 25·00 38·00
a. Imperf between (horiz pair) £750

1901–2. *P* 11½.
6 1 ½ a. black on *pale grey* .. .. .. 10·00 8·00
a. "BFLA" for "BELA" £110 £150
7 ½ a. black on *pale green* (1902) .. .. 18·00 19·00
8 2 1 a. black on *orange* .. .. .. 15·00 17·00

There are at least 14 settings of the above ½ a. stamps, the sheets varying from 16 to 30 stamps.

No. 6a occurred on R.3/2 of the July 1901 printing in sheets of 16 (4×4).

1904 (Feb–Nov). *Stamps printed wider apart. P* 11½.
11 1 ½ a. black on *pale blue* .. .. .. 10·00 6·50
a. Imperf between (pair) £650
b. Imperf between (horiz strip of 3) .. £900
c. Perf 12½ (Nov) .. .. .. 13·00 8·00
12 ½ a. black on *pale green* .. .. .. 10·00 6·50
c. Perf 12½ (Nov) .. .. .. 13·00 8·00

There are five plates of the above two stamps, each consisting of 18 (3×6) varieties.

All the coloured papers of the ½ a. show coloured fibres, similar to those in granite paper.

The stamps of Las Bela have been obsolete since 1 April 1907.

MORVI

PRICES FOR STAMPS ON COVER
Nos. 1/17 *from* × 6
Nos. 18/19 *from* × 3

Thakur (Maharaja from 1926) Lakhdirji, 1922–48

1

2

3

Maharaja Lakhdirji

1931 (1 April). *Typo. P* 12.

(*a*) *Printed in blocks of four. Stamps 10 mm apart (Nos. 1/2) or 6½ mm apart (No. 3). Perf on two or three sides*
1 1 3 p. deep red .. .. 3·00 14·00
2 ½ a. blue .. .. 23·00 32·00
3 2 a. yellow-brown .. .. .. 85·00
1/3 .. .. *Set of* 3 £100

(*b*) *Printed in two blocks of four. Stamps 5½ mm apart. Perf on four sides*
4 1 3 p. bright scarlet .. .. .. 5·00 18·00
a. Error. Dull blue .. .. .. 4·00 18·00
b. Ditto. Double print £600
c. Ditto. Printed on gummed side .. £600
5 ½ a. dull blue .. .. 2·50 11·00
a. Chalk-surfaced paper .. .. 2·25 11·00
6 1 a. brown-red .. .. .. 3·25 21·00
7 2 a. yellow-brown .. .. .. 4·00 28·00
4/7 .. .. *Set of* 4 13·00 70·00

Nos. 1/3 were supplied to post offices in panes of four sewn into bundles with interleaving.

1932–33. *Horizontal background lines wider apart and portrait smaller than in T* 1. *Typo. P* 11.
8 2 3 p. carmine-rose (*shades*) .. .. 2·75 8·50
9 6 p. green .. .. 4·75 11·00
a. Imperf between (horiz pair) .. £1800
b. Emerald-green .. .. .. 3·50 8·50
10 1 a. ultramarine (*to deep*) .. .. 2·75 9·00
a. Imperf between (vert pair) £1400
11 2 a. bright violet (1933) .. .. .. 10·00 28·00
a. Imperf between (vert pair) £1400
8/11 .. .. *Set of* 4 17·00 48·00

1934. *Typo. London ptg. P* 14.
12 3 3 p. carmine .. .. 2·00 2·00
13 6 p. emerald-green .. .. .. 1·00 4·50
14 1 a. purple-brown .. .. .. 1·10 9·00
a. Imperf between (horiz pair) .. † £1300
15 2 a. bright violet .. .. .. 2·50 18·00
12/15 .. .. *Set of* 4 6·00 30·00

1935–48. *Typo. Morvi Press ptg. Rough perf* 11.
16 3 3 p. scarlet (*shades*) .. .. .. 85 2·75
a. Imperf between (horiz pair) .. £1300
17 6 p. grey-green .. .. 75 2·00
a. Emerald-green .. .. .. 6·50 24·00
18 1 a. brown .. .. 12·00 14·00
a. Pale yellow-brown .. .. .. 16·00 25·00
b. Chocolate .. .. 22·00 30·00
19 2 a. dull violet (*to deep*) .. .. 2·50 15·00
16/19 .. .. *Set of* 4 14·50 30·00

Nos. 17*a*, 18*a* and 18*b* were issued between 1944 and 1948.

Maharaja Mahendra Singh, 1948–1957

Morvi was merged with the United State of Kathiawar (later Saurashtra) by 15 April 1948.

NANDGAON

PRICES FOR STAMPS ON COVER
The stamps of Nandgaon are very rare used on cover.

GUM. The stamps of Nandgaon were issued without gum.

Raja Mahant Balram Das, 1883–1897

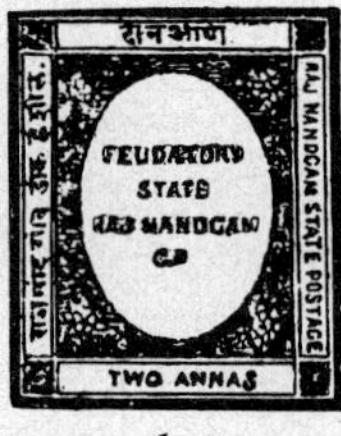

1

2 (½ a.)

(Litho at Poona)

1891. *Imperf.*
1 1 ½ a. blue .. .. 4·50 £130
a. Dull blue .. .. 4·75
2 2 a. rose .. .. 20·00 £400

The few covers in existence franked with Nos. 1/2 have undated manuscript cancellations, but other forms are known on loose examples.

The state was under Imperial administration from January 1888 to November 1891 and it is possible that Nos. 1/2 may have appeared in late 1887.

Last character in top line omitted

(Typo Balram Press, Raj-Nandgaon)

1893 (1 Jan)–**94.** *Printed in sheets of* 16 (4×4). *Imperf.*

(*a*) *Stamps printed wide apart (8 to 10 mm) without wavy lines between them. Thin, toned wove paper*
3 2 ½ a. dull *to* deep green .. .. .. 9·50 65·00
4 2 a. red .. .. 8·50 65·00
b. Dull rose .. .. 8·50 65·00

(*b*) *Stamps printed closer together (4 to 7 mm) with wavy lines between them. Thin, white wove paper* (1894)
5 2 ½ a. green .. .. 22·00 50·00
a. Last character in top line omitted (R. 4/3) .. .. 85·00
6 1 a. rose .. .. 45·00 £100
ba. Laid paper £200

There were three settings of Type 2 with a number of sep[arate] printings made from the third:
Setting I – Nos. 3, 4, 4a, 4*b*, O2
Setting II – Nos. 5, 5b, 6, 6a, 6b
Setting III – Nos. 5, 6ba, O3, O3*a*, O4, O4a, O5 subsequent reprints

The same clichés were used for all values with the face [value] inscriptions changed. These exist in two different sizes with[...] occurring on the ½ a., the small on the 1 a. and the large o[n the] 2 a. except for No. O5 which has the small type.

The ordinary postage stamps of Nandgaon became obsole[te on] 1 July 1894.

OFFICIAL STAMPS

(O 1)
("M.B.D." = Mahant Balram Das)

1893. *Handstamped with ruler's initials in oval. Type* O 1 *in purple.*
O1 1 ½ a. blue £350
O2 2 a. rose £700

1894. *Handstamped with Type* O 1 *in purple.*

(*a*) *Stamps printed wide apart (8 to 10 mm) without wavy li[nes] between them. Thin, toned wove paper*
O3 2 2 a. red .. .. 22·00 £

(*b*) *Stamps printed closer together (4 to 7 mm) with wavy li[nes] between them. Thin, white wove paper*
O4 2 ½ a. yellow-green .. .. 4·75 8
a. Sage-green .. .. 6·50
O5 1 a. rose (*shades*) .. .. 7·50 28
a. Thin laid paper .. .. .. 10·00 70
O6 2 a. rose (*shades*) .. .. 7·00 18

Further printings took place in 1895 after the Official stam[ps] were withdrawn from postal use on 31 December 1894. Th[ese] were all on thin, white wove paper with the ½ a. and 2 a. [in] slightly different shades and the 1 a. in brown or ultramarin[e].

There is a forgery of the handstamp, Type O 1, which sho[ws] 8 mm between the two ornaments below the initials instead [of] the normal 4 mm.

NAWANAGAR

PRICES FOR STAMPS ON COVER

No. 1	*from* × 20
No. 2	*from* × 8
Nos. 3/4	*from* × 3
No. 5	—
Nos. 6/12	—
Nos. 13/15	*from* × 100
Nos. 16/18	—

GUM. The stamps of Nawanagar were issued without gum.

Jam Vibhaji 1882–1895

1 (1 docra)

2 (2 docra)

3 (3 docra)

1877. *Typo in sheets of* 32 (4×8 *or* 8×4). *Laid paper.* (*a*) *Impe[rf]*
1 1 1 doc. blue (*shades*) .. .. 50 22·[00]
a. *Tête-bêche* (pair) £1000
b. Doubly printed .. .. 80·00

(*b*) *Perf* 12½ (*line*)
2 1 1 doc. slate-blue .. .. 60·00 £10[0]
a. Perf 11 (harrow) .. .. .. 65·00
ab. *Tête-bêche* (pair) £1300

The inverted clichés which cause the *tête-bêche* pairs com[e] from different settings and occur on R. 3/2 (No. 1a) or R. 4/4 (No. 2ab) of sheets of 32 (4×8).

1877. *T* 2 *and* 3. *Type-set in black. Wove paper. Thic[k] horizontal and vertical frame lines. Stamp 19 mm wide.*
3 1 doc. *deep mauve* .. .. £3000 £17[00]
a. Stamp 14½–15 mm wide .. .. † £27[5]
b. Stamp 16 mm wide .. .. .. † £20[0]
4 2 doc. *green* .. .. £3000 £150[0]
5 3 doc. *yellow* .. .. £3000 £150[0]

1880. *As last, but thin frame lines, as illustrated. Stamp* 15 *t[o]* 18 *mm wide.*
6 1 doc. *deep mauve* .. .. 2·50 7·5[0]
a. On rose .. .. 2·50
ab. Stamp 14 mm wide .. .. .. 2·50 5·5[0]
7 1 doc. *magenta* (*stamp 14 mm wide*) .. 2·50
8 2 doc. *yellow-green* .. .. 3·25 9·5[0]
a. On blue-green .. .. 6·00
b. Error. Yellow £325
c. Stamp 14 mm wide .. .. .. 3·25 8·0[0]
ca. On blue-green .. .. 7·50

No.	Type	Description	Unused	Used
		doc. *orange-yellow*	8·50	
		a. *On yellow*	3·75	14·00
		ab. On laid paper	90·00	
		b. Stamp 14 mm wide. *On yellow*	4·50	9·00
		ba. On laid paper	42·00	

re are several different settings of each value of this

8b occurs in the sheet of the 3 doc. value from one setting

4 (1 docra)

Typo in sheets of 36. *P* 12. (*a*) *Thick paper.*

No.	Type	Description	Unused	Used
		1 doc. black	2·25	
		a. Imperf (pair)	£500	
		3 doc. orange	2·50	
		(*b*) *Thick laid paper*		
		1 doc. black	£500	
		(*c*) *Thin wove paper*		
		1 doc. black *to* grey	90	4·25
		a. Imperf between (pair)	£450	
		b. Imperf (pair)	£425	
		c. Imperf horiz (vert pair)	£600	
		d. Imperf between (horiz strip of 6)	£1200	
		2 doc. green	1·10	4·75
		a. Imperf (pair)	£450	
		b. Imperf between (vert pair)	£475	
		3 doc. orange-yellow	1·50	8·50
		a. Imperf between (pair)	£475	
		b. *Orange*	1·10	8·00
		ba. Imperf (pair)	£450	
		bb. Imperf vert (horiz pair)	£475	
		bc. Imperf between (horiz pair)	£475	
		(*d*) *Thin, soft wove paper*		
	4	1 doc. black		
		2 doc. deep green	2·50	
		3 doc. brown-orange	3·50	

ancellations for postal purposes were intaglio seals, applied black. Other forms of cancellation were only used on ainders.

ne stamps of Nawanagar became obsolete on 1 January 5.

NEPAL

epal being an independent state, its stamps will be found listed art 21 (*South-East Asia*) of this catalogue.

ORCHHA

PRICES FOR STAMPS ON COVER

Nos. 1/2	—
Nos. 3/7	*from* × 8
Nos. 8/30	*from* × 50
Nos. 31/45	*from* × 4

set of four stamps, ½ a. red, 1 a. violet, 2 a. yellow and 4 a. p blue-green, in a design similar to T **2**, was prepared in 1897 h State authority but not put into use. These exist both perforate and pin-perforated. (*Price for set of* 4, *£16 unused or* o.)

Maharaja Partab Singh, 1874–1930

1

2

(T **1/2** litho Shri Pratap Prabhakar)

13. *Background to arms unshaded. Very blurred impression. Wove paper. No gum. Imperf.*

No.	Type	Description	Unused	Used
	1	½ a. green	30·00	80·00
		1 a. red	19·00	

14–35. *Background shaded with short horizontal lines. Clearer impression. Wove paper. No gum. Imperf.*

No.	Type	Description	Unused	Used
	2	¼ a. bright ultramarine	1·50	3·50
		a. *Grey-blue*	40	3·25
		b. *Deep blue*	1·60	3·25
		ba. Laid paper	£550	
		½ a. green (*shades*)	55	4·25
		a. *Dull green*	1·50	4·50
		b. *Apple-green*	2·25	3·75
		1 a. scarlet	2·50	7·00
		a. Laid paper	—	£375
		b. *Indian red*	1·75	9·00
		c. *Carmine*	2·50	4·50
		ca. Laid paper (1935)	£200	£250
		2 a. red-brown (1916)	4·50	21·00
		a. *Light brown*	11·00	21·00
		b. *Chestnut*	18·00	22·00
		4 a. ochre (1917)	9·50	28·00
		a. *Yellow-orange*	8·00	28·00
		b. *Yellow*	8·00	25·00
/7		*Set of* 5	13·50	50·00

There are two sizes of T **2** in the setting of 8 (4 × 2). In each value tamps from the upper row are slightly taller than those from the ower.

Maharaja Vir Singh II, 1930–1956

3 Maharaja Vir Singh II **4**

(Typo Lakshmi Art Ptg Wks, Bombay)

1935 (1 Apr). *Thick, chalk-surfaced wove paper. P* 9½, 10, 10×9½, 11, 11×9½, 11½, 11½×11, 11½×12, 12 *or* 12×11.

No.	Type	Description	Unused	Used
8	**3**	¼ a. purple and slate	1·50	2·50
		a. Imperf between (vert pair)		
		b. Ordinary paper	35	2·00
		ba. Imperf between (vert pair)	11·00	
		bb. Imperf vert (horiz pair)	65·00	
		bc. Imperf horiz (vert pair)	65·00	
9		½ a. olive-grey and emerald	50	1·25
		a. Imperf (pair)	75·00	
10		¾ a. magenta and deep myrtle-green	50	1·40
		a. Imperf (pair)	75·00	
11		1 a. myrtle-green and purple-brown	50	1·25
		a. Imperf (pair)	65·00	70·00
		b. Imperf horiz (vert pair)		
		c. Imperf vert (horiz pair)		
12		1¼ a. slate and mauve	45	1·25
		a. Imperf (pair)	75·00	£225
		b. Imperf between (horiz pair)	75·00	
		c. Frame doubly printed	75·00	
13		1½ a. brown and scarlet	45	1·25
		a. Imperf between (vert pair)	75·00	
		b. Imperf between (horiz pair)	75·00	
14		2 a. blue and red-orange	45	1·25
		a. Imperf (pair)	13·00	
		b. Imperf between (horiz pair)	75·00	
15		2½ a. olive-brown and dull orange	65	1·40
		a. Imperf (pair)	13·00	
		b. Imperf between (horiz pair)	75·00	
16		3 a. bright blue and magenta	65	1·40
		a. Imperf between (horiz pair)	75·00	£100
		b. Imperf (pair)	75·00	
17		4 a. deep reddish purple and sage-green	65	3·25
		a. Imperf (pair)	9·00	
		b. Imperf between (vert pair)	75·00	
		c. Imperf vert (horiz pair)	75·00	
18		6 a. black and pale ochre	70	3·25
		a. Imperf (pair)	9·00	
19		8 a. brown and purple	1·75	3·75
		a. Imperf (pair)	9·00	
		b. Imperf between (vert pair)	85·00	
20		12 a. bright emerald and bright purple	1·00	4·00
		a. Imperf (pair)	9·00	
		b. Imperf between (vert pair)	85·00	
21		12 a. pale greenish blue and bright purple	24·00	55·00
22		1 r. chocolate and myrtle-green	80	4·75
		a. Imperf (pair)	9·50	
		b. Imperf between (horiz pair)	75·00	
23	**4**	1 r. chocolate and myrtle-green	6·00	15·00
		a. Imperf (pair)	85·00	
		b. Imperf between (horiz pair)	£100	
24	**3**	2 r. purple-brown and bistre-yellow	2·75	12·00
		a. Imperf (pair)	9·50	
25		3 r. black and greenish blue	1·50	12·00
		a. Imperf (pair)	9·50	
26		4 r. black and brown	2·75	13·00
		a. Imperf (pair)	9·50	
27		5 r. bright blue and plum	3·00	14·00
		a. Imperf (pair)	9·50	
28		10 r. bronze-green and cerise	7·00	21·00
		a. Imperf (pair)	13·00	
		b. Imperf between (horiz pair)	95·00	
29		15 r. black and bronze-green	12·00	48·00
		a. Imperf (pair)	13·00	
30		25 r. red-orange and blue	16·00	55·00
		a. Imperf (pair)	16·00	
8/20, 22/30		*Set of* 22	55·00	£200

Values to 5 r. except the 1 a., are inscribed "POSTAGE", and the remaining values "POSTAGE & REVENUE".

The central portrait of Type **3** is taken from a half-tone block and consists of large square dots. The portrait of Type **4** has a background of lines.

Owing to a lack of proper State control considerable quantities of these stamps circulated at below face value and the issue was subsequently withdrawn, supplies being exchanged for the 1939–42 issue. We are, however, now satisfied that the lower values at least did genuine postal duty until 1939.

Used prices are for stamps cancelled-to-order, postally used examples being worth considerably more.

5 Maharaja Vir Singh II **6**

(Litho Indian Security Printing Press, Nasik)

1939–42? *P* 13½ × 14 (*T* **5**) *or* 14 × 13½ (*T* **6**).

No.	Type	Description	Unused	Used
31	**5**	¼ a. chocolate	3·25	55·00
32		½ a. yellow-green	3·50	45·00
33		¾ a. bright blue	3·50	75·00
34		1 a. scarlet	3·50	15·00
35		1¼ a. blue	3·50	75·00
36		1½ a. mauve	3·75	90·00
37		2 a. vermilion	3·50	55·00
38		2½ a. turquoise-green	3·50	£160
39		3 a. slate-violet	4·75	85·00
40	**5**	4 a. slate	6·00	23·00
41		8 a. magenta	9·50	£160
42	**6**	1 r. grey-green	17·00	
43		2 r. bright violet	35·00	£425
44		5 r. yellow-orange	£100	
45		10 r. turquoise-green (1942)	£400	
46		15 r. slate-lilac (date ?)	£8500	
47		25 r. claret (date ?)	£6000	

Orchha became part of Vindhya Pradesh by 1 May 1948.

POONCH

PRICES FOR STAMPS ON COVER

No. 1	*from* × 3
Nos. 1*a*/2	*from* × 2
Nos. 3/63	*from* × 10
Nos. O1/10	*from* × 30

Poonch was ruled by a junior branch of the Jammu and Kashmir princely family and, by treaty, was subject to the "advice and consent" of the Maharaja of that state.

The Poonch postal service operated an office at Kahuta in the Punjab which acted as the office of exchange between the state post and that of British India.

GUM. The stamps of Poonch were issued without gum, except for some examples of Nos. 7/10.

The stamps of Poonch are all imperforate, and handstamped in watercolours.

ILLUSTRATIONS. Designs of Poonch are illustrated actual size.

Raja Moti Singh, 1852–1892

1

2

1876. *T* **1** (22 × 21 *mm*). *Yellowish white, wove paper.*

No.	Type	Description	Unused	Used
1		6 p. red	£6000	£110

1877. *As T* **1** (19 × 17 *mm*). *Same paper.*

No.	Type	Description	Unused	Used
1*a*		½ a. red	£7000	£3250

1879. *T* **2** (21 × 19 *mm*). *Same paper.*

No.	Type	Description	Unused	Used
2		½ a. red	—	£3250

3 (½ a.)

4 (1 a.)

5 (2 a.)

6 (4 a.)

1880. *Yellowish white, wove paper.*

No.	Type	Description	Unused	Used
3	**3**	½ a. red	38·00	16·00
4	**4**	1 a. red	75·00	42·00
5	**5**	2 a. red	£130	90·00
6	**6**	4 a. red	£140	£100

1884. *Toned wove bâtonné paper.*

No.	Type	Description	Unused	Used
7	**3**	½ a. red	4·00	4·00
8	**4**	1 a. red	16·00	
9	**5**	2 a. red	15·00	18·00
10	**6**	4 a. red	30·00	30·00

These are sometimes found gummed.

7 (1 pice)

1884–87. *Various papers.* (*a*) *White laid bâtonné or ribbed bâtonné.*

No.	Type	Description	Unused	Used
11	**7**	1 p. red	16·00	18·00
		a. Pair, one stamp sideways	£170	
12	**3**	½ a. red	2·00	2·75
		a. *Tête-bêche* (pair)	£2000	
13	**4**	1 a. red	2·75	
14	**5**	2 a. red	7·00	8·50
15	**6**	4 a. red	9·00	

(b) Thick white laid paper

22 7 1 p. red .. .. 42·00
23 3 ½ a. red .. .. 60·00
24 4 1 a. red .. .. 60·00
25 5 2 a. red .. .. 60·00
26 6 4 a. red .. .. 75·00

(c) Yellow wove bâtonné

27 7 1 p. red .. .. 3·00 3·00
a. Pair, one stamp sideways .. 30·00
28 3 ½ a. red .. .. 3·50 4·50
29 4 1 a. red .. .. 32·00
30 5 2 a. red .. .. 6·50 8·50
31 6 4 a. red .. .. 3·50 3·75

(d) Orange-buff wove bâtonné

32 7 1 p. red .. .. 2·00 2·50
a. Pair, one stamp sideways .. 22·00 27·00
b. *Tête-bêche* (pair) .. .. .. 35·00
33 3 ½ a. red .. .. 19·00
34 5 2 a. red .. .. 70·00
35 6 4 a. red .. .. 16·00

(e) Yellow laid paper

36 7 1 p. red .. .. 1·50 2·75
a. Pair, one stamp sideways .. 18·00
b. *Tête-bêche* (pair) .. .. .. 25·00
37 3 ½ a. red .. .. 2·50
38 4 1 a. red .. .. 35·00
39 5 2 a. red .. .. 42·00 42·00
40 6 4 a. red .. .. 32·00

(f) Yellow laid bâtonné

41 7 1 p. red .. .. 9·00 7·00

(g) Buff laid or ribbed bâtonné paper thicker than (d)

42 4 1 a. red .. .. 50·00
43 6 4 a. red .. .. 55·00

(h) Blue-green laid paper (1887)

44 3 ½ a. red .. .. 32·00
45 4 1 a. red .. .. 2·25 4·00
46 5 2 a. red .. .. 26·00
47 6 4 a. red .. .. 48·00

(i) Yellow-green laid paper

48 3 ½ a. red .. ..

(j) Blue-green wove bâtonné

49 7 1 p. red .. .. 35·00 32·00
49*a* 3 ½ a. red £800
50 4 1 a. red .. .. 1·50 2·75

(k) Lavender wove bâtonné

51 4 1 a. red .. .. 70·00
52 5 2 a. red .. .. 1·75 2·75
a Pair, one stamp sideways £2000

(l) Blue wove bâtonné

53 7 1 p. red .. .. 2·00 1·75
a. Pair, one stamp sideways .. .. 22·00
b. *Tête-bêche* (pair) .. .. .. 32·00
54 4 1 a. red £350

(m) Various coloured papers

55 7 1 p. red/*grey-blue laid* .. .. .. 7·00 4·25
56 1 p. red/*lilac laid* .. .. .. 45·00 48·00
a. Pair, one stamp sideways £275 £275
b. *Tête-bêche* (pair) £250

1888. *Printed in aniline rose on various papers.*

57 7 1 p. on *blue wove bâtonné* .. .. 3·75
a. *Tête-bêche* (pair) .. .. .. 65·00
58 1 p. on *buff laid* .. .. .. 11·00
a. *Tête-bêche* (pair) £100
59 3 ½ a. on *white laid* .. .. .. 17·00
60 4 1 a. on *green laid* .. .. .. 13·00 14·00
61 1 a. on *green wove bâtonné* .. .. 7·50 7·50
62 5 2 a. on *lavender wove bâtonné* .. .. 6·50 6·50
63 6 4 a. on *yellow laid* .. .. .. 13·00 14·00
a. Pair, one stamp sideways £600
b. *Tête-bêche* (pair) £600

OFFICIAL STAMPS

Raja Baldeo Singh, 1892–1918

1887. *(a) White laid bâtonné paper.*

O 1 7 1 p. black .. .. 1·90 2·00
a. Pair, one stamp sideways .. .. 13·00 15·00
b. *Tête-bêche* (pair) .. .. .. 16·00
O 2 3 ½ a. black .. .. 2·25 3·00
O 3 4 1 a. black .. .. 2·00 2·25
O 4 5 2 a. black .. .. 3·25 3·25
O 5 6 4 a. black .. .. 5·00 8·50

(b) White or toned wove bâtonné paper

O 6 7 1 p. black .. .. 1·90
a. Pair, one stamp sideways .. .. 27·00
b. *Tête-bêche* (pair) .. .. .. 38·00
O 7 3 ½ a. black .. .. 2·25 2·75
a. Pair, one stamp sideways £1500
O 8 4 1 a. black .. .. 15·00 14·00
O 9 5 2 a. black .. .. 6·50 6·50
O10 6 4 a. black .. .. 10·00

RAJASTHAN

Rajasthan was formed in 1948–49 from a number of States in Rajputana; these included Bundi, Jaipur and Kishangarh, whose posts continued to function more or less separately until ordered by the Indian Government to close on 1 April 1950.

PRICES FOR STAMPS ON COVER

Nos. 1/7	*from* × 15
Nos. 8/10	—
Nos. 11/12	*from* × 5
Nos. 13/14	—
Nos. 15/25	*from* × 4
Nos. 26/42	*from* × 3
No. 43	*from* × 5
Nos. 44/60	*from* × 3
No. 61	*from* × 5
Nos. 62/5	—

BUNDI

(1)

1948–49. *Nos. 86/92 of Bundi. (a) Handstamped with T* **1**.

A. *In black.* B. *In violet.* C. *In blue*

		A	B	C
1	¼ a. blue-green	5·50	4·75	26·00
	a. Pair, one without opt	£225	†	†
2	½ a. violet	4·00	3·25	30·00
	a. Pair, one without opt	£250	£225	†
3	1 a. yellow-green	4·75	11·00	32·00
	a. Pair, one without opt	†	£225	†
4	2 a. vermilion	8·50	22·00	—
5	4 a. orange	32·00	25·00	80·00
6	8 a. ultramarine	5·00	7·00	50·00
7	1 r. chocolate	—	£170	65·00

The above prices are for unused, used stamps being worth about six times the unused prices. Most of these handstamps are known, sideways, inverted or double.

(b) Machine-printed as T **1** *in black*

8 ¼ a. blue-green .. ..
9 ½ a. violet .. ..
10 1 a. yellow-green .. ..
11 2 a. vermilion .. .. 4·75 60·00
a. Opt inverted £250
12 4 a. orange .. .. 2·50 60·00
a. Opt double £225
13 8 a. ultramarine .. .. .. 20·00
a. Opt inverted £475
b. Opt double £375
14 1 r. chocolate .. .. .. 7·50

JAIPUR

राजस्थान

RAJASTHAN

(2)

1950 (26 Jan). *T* **7** *of Jaipur optd with T* **2**.

15 ¼ a. black and brown-lake (No. 58) (B.) .. 4·50 15·00
16 ½ a. black and violet (No. 41) (R.) .. 3·25 16·00
17 ¾ a. black and brown-red (No. 59) (Blue-blk.) 7·00 18·00
a. Opt in pale blue .. .. .. 14·00 35·00
18 1 a. black and blue (No. 60) (R.) .. 4·00 32·00
19 2 a. black and buff (No. 61) (R.) .. 7·50 42·00
20 2½ a. black and carmine (No. 62) (B.) .. 8·00 20·00
21 3 a. black and green (No. 63) (R.) .. 8·50 48·00
22 4 a. black and grey-green (No. 64) (R.) .. 8·50 55·00
23 6 a. black and pale blue (No. 65*a*) (R.) .. 9·00 80·00
24 8 a. black and chocolate (No. 66) (R.) .. 13·00 £110
25 1 r. black and yellow-bistre (No. 67) (R.) .. 15·00 £160
15/25 .. .. *Set of* 11 80·00 £550

KISHANGARH

1948 (Oct)–**49**. *Various stamps of Kishangarh handstamped with T* **1** *in red.*

(a) On stamps of 1899–1901

26 ¼ a. rose-pink (No. 5*a*) (B.) £170
26*a* ¼ a. rose-pink (No. 22*a*) .. .. — £160
27 ½ a. deep blue (No. 26) £300
29 1 a. brown-lilac (No. 29) .. .. 14·00 38·00
b. Imperf (pair) .. .. .. 40·00 80·00
c. Violet handstamp .. .. — £250
d. Black handstamp .. .. — £300
30 4 a. chocolate (No. 31) .. .. 65·00 85·00
a. Violet handstamp .. .. — £375
31 1 r. dull green (No. 32) £190 £200
31*a* 2 r. brown-red (No. 34) £250
32 5 r. mauve (No. 35) £225 £225

(b) On stamps of 1904–10

33 13 ½ a. chestnut .. .. .. — £110
33*a* 1 a. blue .. .. — £150
34 4 a. brown .. .. 13·00
a. Blue handstamp £180
35 12*a* 8 a. grey .. .. 85·00 £130
36 13 8 a. violet .. .. 11·00
37 1 r. green .. .. 12·00
38 2 r. olive-yellow .. .. .. 19·00
39 5 r. purple-brown .. .. .. 24·00
a. Blue handstamp £325

(c) On stamps of 1912–16

40 14 ½ a. green (No. 64) .. .. .. — £160
41 1 a. red .. .. — £160
42 2 a. deep violet (No. 51) £300
43 2 a. purple (No. 66) .. .. .. 3·00 7·00
44 4 a. bright blue .. .. .. — £375
45 8 a. brown .. .. 5·00
a. Pair, one without handstamp .. £300
46 1 r. mauve .. .. 10·00
47 2 r. deep green .. .. .. 10·00
48 5 r. brown £275

(d) On stamps of 1928–36

49 16 ½ a. yellow-green £100
49*a* 2 a. magenta .. .. —
50 4 a. chestnut £160
51 8 a. violet .. .. 6·00
a. Pair, one without handstamp .. £275
52 1 r. light green .. .. .. 21·00
53 2 r. lemon-yellow .. .. .. 16·00
54 5 r. claret .. .. 16·00

(e) On stamps of 1943–47

55 16 ¼ a. pale dull blue .. .. .. 75·00
56 ¼ a. greenish blue .. .. .. 38·00
a. Imperf (pair) £170
57 ½ a. deep green .. .. .. 26·00
a. Violet handstamp .. .. .. —
57*b* ½ a. yellow-green .. .. .. 38·00
ba. Imperf (pair) £170
bb. Blue handstamp .. .. .. —
58 17 1 a. carmine-red .. .. .. 45·00
a. Violet handstamp .. .. .. —
58*b* 1 a. orange-red (*imperf*) £110
ba. Blue handstamp £120
59 2 a. bright magenta £120
60 2 a. maroon (*imperf*) £140
61 16 4 a. brown .. .. 2·00
62 8 a. violet .. .. 15·00
63 1 r. green .. .. 6·50
64 2 r. yellow .. .. 90·00
65 5 r. claret .. .. 50·00

A 1 a. value in deep violet-blue was issued for reve purposes, but is known postally used (*Price* £60 *used*).

RAJPIPLA

PRICES FOR STAMPS ON COVER

No. 1	*from* × 30
Nos. 2/3	–

Maharana Ganbhir Singh, 1860–1897

The Rajpipla state post was opened to the public sometime the late 1870s. Adhesive stamps were preceded by pos stationery lettersheets which were first reported in 1879.

1 (1 pice)

2 (2 a.)

3 (4 a.)

1880. *Litho. With or without gum* (1 *p.*) *or no gum* (*other P* 11 (1 *p.*) *or* 12½.

1 1 1 p. blue (1 June) .. .. .. 2·50 26·
2 2 2 a. green .. .. 24·00 75·
a. Imperf between (pair) £550 £5
3 3 4 a. red .. .. 13·00 45·
1/3 .. .. *Set of* 3 35·00 £1

No. 1 was produced in sheets of 64 (8×8) and the high values in sheets of 20 (5×4).

These stamps became obsolete in 1886 when the Imperi postal service absorbed the Rajpipla state post.

SHAHPURA

PRICES FOR STAMPS ON COVER

Nos. 1/4	*from* × 2
No. F1	*from* × 2

DATES. Those quoted are of first known use.

Rajadhiraj Nahar Singh, 1870–1932

RAJ SHAHPURA Postage 1 pice	RAJ SHAHPURA 1 pice
1	2

1914–17. *Typo.*

1 1 1 p. carmine/*bluish grey* (*p* 11) .. .. — £50
2 1 p. carmine/*drab* (*imperf*) (1917) .. .. — £75

Some examples of No. 1 are imperforate on one side or on tw adjacent sides.

1920–28. *Typo. Imperf.*

3 2 1 p. carmine/*drab* (1928) .. .. .. — £100
4 1 a. black/*pink* .. .. — £120

POSTAL FISCAL

Rajadhiraj Umaid Singh, 1932–1947

Rajadhiraj Sudarshan Deo, 1947–1971

F 1

47. *Typo. P* 11, 11½ *or* 12.
1 1 a. red (*shades*) .. .. .. 65·00 £200
a. Pin-perf 7 (1947) ..

. F1/a were used for both fiscal and postal purposes. script cancellations must be assumed to be fiscal, unless on showing other evidence of postal use. The design was first for fiscal purposes in 1898.

hpura became part of Rajasthan by 15 April 1948.

SIRMOOR

PRICES FOR STAMPS ON COVER

The stamps of Sirmoor are very rare used on cover.

Raja Shamsher Parkash, 1886–1898

1 (1 pice)

2

3 Raja Shamsher Parkash

(June)–80. *Litho. P* 11½.
1 1 p. pale green .. .. 10·00 £250
1 p. blue (on *laid* paper) (1880) .. .. 4·00 £150
a. Imperf between (pair) £325
b. Imperf (pair) £325

(Litho at Calcutta)

2. *Thick wove paper. P* 11½.
2 1 p. yellow-green 75 80
a. Imperf between (vert pair) .. .. 70·00
b. *Deep green* 65 70
ba. Imperf between (vert pair) .. .. 70·00 70·00
1 p. blue 75 75
a. Imperf between (vert pair) .. .. 60·00 60·00
b. Imperf between (horiz pair) .. .. 60·00 60·00
c. Imperf vert (horiz pair) .. .. 60·00
d. Imperf (pair) .. .. 75·00

hese were originally made as reprints, about 1891, to supply ectors, but there being very little demand for them they were into use. The design was copied (including the perforations) n an illustration in a dealer's catalogue.

A

B

C

D

here were seven printings of stamps as Type **3**, all in sheets 0 (10×7) and made up from groups of transfers which can be ced through minor varieties.
rintings I to V and VII of the 3 p. and 6 p. are as Types A and both with large white dots evenly spaced between the ends of upper and lower inscriptions).
rinting VI is as Type B (small white dots and less space) and pe D (large white dots unevenly positioned between the scriptions).

(Litho Waterlow)

85–96. *P* 14 *to* 15.
3 3 p. chocolate (A) 55 30
a. Brown (B) (1896) 30 35
3 p. orange (A) (1888) .. .. .. 1·50 20
a. Type B (1896) 30 20
ab. Imperf (pair) £550
6 p. blue-green (C) .. .. 4·25 2·75
a. Green (C) (1888) 95 50
b. Bright green (C) (1891) .. .. 60·00 60·00
c. Deep green (C) (1894) 50 25
d. Yellowish green (D) (1896) .. .. 40 1·50
1 a. bright blue .. .. 2·50 2·75
a. Dull blue (1891) .. .. .. 6·50 4·50
b. Steel-blue (1891) .. .. .. 85·00 85·00
c. Grey-blue (1894) .. .. .. 2·25 1·00
d. Slate-blue (1896) .. .. .. 50 1·75
2 a. pink .. .. 4·25 10·00
a. Carmine (1894) .. .. .. 3·50 3·00
b. Rose-red (1896) .. .. .. 3·25 4·00

Composition of the various printings was as follows:
Printing I – Nos. 5, 7, 8 and 9
Printing II – Nos. 6 and 7*a*
Printing III – Nos. 6, 7*b* and 8*a*
Printing IV – Nos. 5, 6, 7*a*, and 8*b*
Printing V – Nos. 6, 7*c*, 8*c* and 9*a*
Printing VI – Nos. 5*a*, 6a, 7*d*, 8*d* and 9*b*
Printing VII – Only exists overprinted "On S. S. S." (Nos. 78/81).

NEW INFORMATION

he editor is always interested to correspond with eople who have new information that will improve or correct the Catalogue.

4 Indian Elephant

5 Raja Shamsher Parkash

(Recess Waterlow & Sons)

1894–99. *P* 12 *to* 15 *and compounds.*
22 4 3 p. orange-brown .. .. 2·00 30
23 6 p. green 75 30
a. Imperf between (vert pair) £1400
24 1 a. blue .. .. 3·25 1·25
25 2 a. rose .. .. 1·75 1·00
26 3 a. yellow-green .. .. 17·00 30·00
27 4 a. deep green .. .. 9·00 16·00
28 8 a. deep blue .. .. 13·00 21·00
29 1 r. vermilion .. .. 27·00 48·00
22/9 .. .. *Set of* 8 65·00 £100

Raja Surindra Bikram Parkash, 1898–1911

(Recess Waterlow & Sons)

1899. *P* 13 *to* 15.
30 5 3 a. yellow-green .. .. 2·00 21·00
31 4 a. deep green .. .. 2·75 15·00
32 8 a. deep blue .. .. 4·50 12·00
33 1 r. vermilion .. .. 9·00 38·00
30/3 .. .. *Set of* 4 16·50 80·00

OFFICIAL STAMPS

NOTE. The varieties occurring in the machine-printed "On S.S.S." overprints may, of course, also be found in the inverted and double overprints, and many of them are known thus.

Roman figures denote printings of the basic stamps (Nos. 7/21). Where more than one printing was overprinted the prices quoted are for the commonest.

I. MACHINE-PRINTED

On
S. S.
S.
(11)

1890. *Optd with T* **11**. (*a*) *In black.*
50 3 6 p. green (C) £900 £900
a. Stop before first "S" .. ..
51 2 a. pink .. .. 50·00 £150
a. Stop before first "S" £130

(*b*) *In red*
52 3 6 p. green (C) .. .. 18·00 2·50
a. Stop before first "S" .. .. .. 55·00 25·00
53 1 a. bright blue .. .. 42·00 13·00
a. Stop before first "S" .. .. .. £110 60·00
b. Opt inverted £1000 £550

(*c*) *Doubly optd in red and in black*
53*c* 3 6 p. green (C) £950 £950
ca. Stop before first "S" £2250 £2250

Nos. 50, 52 and 53*c* are from Printing II and the remainder from Printing I.

On
S. S.
S.
(12)

On
S. S.
S.
(13)

1891. *Optd with T* **12**. (*a*) *In black.*
54 3 3 p. orange (A) .. .. 2·25 35·00
a. Opt inverted £425
55 6 p. green (C) .. .. 1·50 1·50
a. Opt double £170
b. No stop after lower "S" .. .. .. 22·00 22·00
c. Raised stop before lower "S" £150 £110
56 1 a. bright blue £275 £350
57 2 a. pink .. .. 13·00 50·00

(*b*) *In red*
58 3 6 p. green (C) .. .. 27·00 3·00
a. Opt inverted £200 £170
b. Opt double £200 £180
59 1 a. bright blue .. .. 20·00 27·00
a. Opt inverted .. .. † £450
b. Opt double .. .. † £450
c. No stop after lower "S" £160 £170

(*c*) *In black and red*
59*d* 3 6 p. green (C) £950

Nos. 54/5, 58 and 59*d* are from Printing II and the others from Printing I.

1892–97. *Optd with T* **13**. (*a*) *In black.*
60 3 3 p. orange (A) 60 50
a. Type B .. .. 3·00 60
b. Opt inverted £225
c. First "S" inverted and stop raised .. 5·00 5·00
d. No stop after lower "S" .. .. .. 5·00 5·00
e. Raised stop after second "S" .. .. 35·00 16·00
f. Vertical pair, Types **12** and **13** .. £110
61 6 p. green (C) .. .. 6·00 1·25
a. Deep green (C) .. .. 1·60 50
b. First "S" inverted and stop raised .. 32·00 14·00
c. Raised stop after second "S" .. .. 32·00 12·00
d. No stop after lower "S" .. .. .. 42·00 17·00
e. Opt double £550
62 1 a. steel-blue .. ..
a. Grey-blue .. .. 8·00 1·00
b. Opt double £350
c. First "S" inverted and stop raised .. 32·00 10·00
d. No stop after lower "S" .. .. .. £140 50·00
e. Raised stop after second "S" .. .. 55·00 12·00
63 2 a. pink .. .. 10·00 16·00
a. Carmine .. .. 7·00 7·00
b. Opt inverted £700 £700
c. First "S" inverted and stop raised .. 35·00 35·00
d. No stop after lower "S" .. .. .. 35·00 35·00
e. Raised stop after second "S" £150 £150

(*b*) *In red*
64 3 6 p. green (C) .. .. 3·50 50
a. Bright green (C) .. .. .. 7·50 1·00
b. Opt inverted .. .. £110 90·00
c. First "S" inverted and stop raised .. 20·00 5·00
d. Vertical pair, Types **12** and **13** .. £110 £110
65 1 a. bright blue .. .. 15·00 3·00
a. Steel-blue .. .. 11·00 1·00
b. Opt inverted £225 £170
c. Opt double £275
d. First "S" inverted and stop raised .. 32·00 8·00
e. No stop after lower "S" .. .. .. 32·00 8·00

(*c*) *Doubly overprinted in black and red*
65*f* 3 6 p. bright green (C) .. .. .. — £900
fa. Green (C). Red opt inverted .. .. † £1300

The printings used for this issue were as follows:
Printing I – Nos. 63 and 65
Printing II – Nos. 60, 64 and 65*fa*
Printing III – Nos. 60, 64*a* and 65*f*
Printing IV – Nos. 61, 62, 64 and 65*a*
Printing V – Nos. 60, 61*a*, 62*a* and 63*a*
Printing VI – No. 60a

There are seven settings of this overprint, the first of which was a composite setting of 20 (10×2), with examples of Type **12** in the upper row. The inverted "S" and the missing stop occur in the 3rd and 6th settings with the latter also including the raised stop after second "S".

On
S. S.
S.
(14)

On
S. S.
S.
(15)

1896–97. *Optd as T* **14**.
66 3 3 p. orange (B) (1897) .. .. .. 9·00 1·25
a. Comma after first "S" .. .. .. 45·00 30·00
b. Opt inverted .. .. ..
c. Opt double .. .. † £500
67 6 p. deep green (C) .. .. 5·50 60
a. Yellowish green (D) .. .. .. — 2·25
b. Comma after first "S" .. .. .. 45·00 18·00
c. Comma after lower "S" .. .. .. £150 18·00
d. "S" at right inverted .. .. .. £150 42·00
68 1 a. grey-blue .. .. 7·00 1·25
a. Comma after first "S" .. .. .. 60·00 22·00
b. Comma after lower "S" .. .. .. £170 22·00
c. "S" at right inverted .. .. .. — 45·00
69 2 a. carmine (1897) .. .. 17·00 14·00
a. Comma after first "S" £120 £120

Nos. 66 and 67*a* are from Printing VI and the remainder from Printing V.

There are four settings of this overprint, (1) 23 mm high, includes the comma after lower "S"; (2) and (3) 25 mm high, with variety, comma after first "S"; (4) 25 mm high, with variety, "S" at right inverted.

1898 (Nov). *Optd with T* **15**.
70 3 6 p. deep green (C) .. .. £170 7·50
a. Yellowish green (D) .. .. .. £160 6·00
b. Small "S" at right .. .. .. £275 25·00
c. Comma after lower "S" .. .. .. — 50·00
d. Lower "S" inverted and stop raised .. — 50·00
71 1 a. grey-blue .. .. £180 14·00
a. Small "S" at right .. .. .. £300 40·00
b. Small "S" without stop .. .. .. — £180

No. 70*a* is from Printing VI and the others Printing V.

There are two settings of this overprint. Nos. 70b and 71a/b occur in the first setting, and Nos. 70c/d in the second setting.

On
S. S.
S.
(16)

On
S. S.
S.
(17)

1899 (July). *Optd with T* **16**.
72 **3** 3 p. orange (B) .. .. £225 6·50
73 6 p. deep green (C) .. .. — 19·00
No. 72 is from Printing VI and No. 73 from Printing V.

1899 (Dec)–**1900**. *Optd as T* **17**.
74 **3** 3 p. orange (B) .. .. — 6·00
a. Raised stop after lower "S" .. .. † 55·00
b. Comma after first "S" .. .. † £180
c. No stop after first "S" .. .. † £110
75 6 p. deep green (C) .. .. .. — 6·00
a. Yellowish green (D) .. .. .. † 7·00
b. Raised stop after lower "S" .. .. † 55·00
c. Comma after first "S" .. .. † £170
76 1 a. bright blue .. .. † £140
a. Grey-blue .. .. † 8·00
b. Slate-blue .. .. — 9·50
c. Raised stop after lower "S" .. .. † 85·00
d. Comma after first "S" .. .. † £190
e. No stop after first "S" .. .. † £110
77 2 a. carmine .. .. — £110
a. Raised stop after lower "S" .. .. † £425
There are two settings of this overprint: (1) 22 mm high, with raised stop variety; (2) 23 mm high, with "comma" and "no stop" varieties.
The printings used for this issue were as follows:
Printing I – No. 76
Printing V – Nos. 75, 76*a* and 77
Printing VI – Nos. 74, 75*a* and 76*b*

On On
S. S. S S
S. S
(18) (19)

(Optd by Waterlow & Sons)

1900. *Optd with T* **18**.
78 **3** 3 p. orange .. .. 2·75 6·00
79 6 p. green 50 45
80 1 a. blue 35 50
81 2 a. carmine .. .. 3·25 60·00
Nos. 78/81 were from Printing VII which was not issued without the overprint.

II. HANDSTAMPED

The words "On" and each letter "S" struck separately (except for Type **22** which was applied at one operation).

1894. *Handstamped with T* **19**. (*a*) *In black.*
82 **3** 3 p. orange (A) .. .. 3·00 3·75
a. "On" only .. .. 65·00
83 6 p. green (C) .. .. 5·00 6·00
a. Deep green (C) .. .. 9·00 12·00
b. "On" only .. .. 65·00 65·00
84 1 a. bright blue .. .. 42·00 32·00
a. Dull blue .. .. 14·00 16·00
b. Steel-blue .. ..
c. Grey-blue .. .. 14·00 13·00
d. "On" only .. .. — 90·00
85 2 a. carmine .. .. 18·00 18·00
a. "On" only £100

(*b*) *In red*
86 **3** 6 p. green (C) £100 £110
86*a* 1 a. grey-blue £325 £325
The printings used for this issue were as follows:
Printing I – No. 84
Printing III – No. 84*a*
Printing IV – Nos. 83, 84*b* and 86
Printing V – Nos. 82, 83*a*, 84*c*, 85 and 86*a*

1896. *Handstamped with letters similar to those of T* **13**, *with stops, but irregular.*
87 **3** 3 p. orange (A) .. .. 80·00 65·00
a. Type B .. ..
88 6 p. green (C) .. ..
a. Deep green (C) .. .. 70·00 60·00
b. "On" omitted £140
88*c* 1 a. grey-blue .. .. 95·00 95·00
89 2 a. carmine £160
Printings used for this issue were as follows:
Printing II – No. 88
Printing III – No. 87
Printing IV – No. 88
Printing V – Nos. 87, 88*a*, 88*c* and 89
Printing VI – No. 87a

1897. *Handstamped with letters similar to those of T* **14**, *with stops, but irregular.*
90 **3** 3 p. orange (B) .. .. 8·50 18·00
91 6 p. deep green (C) .. .. 50·00 60·00
a. "On" only .. .. — £100
92 1 a. grey-blue £225 £225
a. "On" only .. .. — £100
93 2 a. carmine £100 £100
No. 90 was from Printing VI and the remainder from Printing V.

1897. *Handstamped with letters similar to those of T* **16**, *with stops, but irregular.*
93*a* **3** 6 p. deep green (C) £130 £100
No. 93*a* is from Printing V.

ON On
S S S S
S S
(20) (21)

1896. (*a*) *Handstamped with T* **20**.
94 **3** 3 p. orange (A) .. .. 55·00 60·00
95 2 a. carmine .. .. 60·00 65·00

(*b*) *Handstamped with T* **21**
96 **3** 3 p. orange (A) £150 £160
97 6 p. bright green (C) .. ..
98 1 a. bright blue £200
a. Dull blue .. ..
98*b* 2 a. carmine £225
No. 98 comes from Printing I, No. 98*a* from Printing III, No. 97 possibly from Printing IV and the remainder from Printing V.

On On
S S S S
S S
(22) (23)

(*c*) *Handstamped with T* **22**
99 **3** 3 p. orange (B) £120
100 6 p. deep green £180
101 1 a. grey-blue £225
101*a* 2 a. carmine £325
No. 99 is from Printing VI and the others from Printing V.

1899. *Handstamped with T* **23**.
102 **3** 3 p. orange (A) .. .. — £140
a. Type B .. .. 21·00 7·00
103 6 p. green (C) .. ..
a. Deep green (C) .. .. 23·00 15·00
b. Yellowish green (D) .. .. .. 15·00 16·00
104 1 a. bright blue .. .. — 95·00
a. Grey-blue .. .. 45·00 40·00
105 2 a. pink .. ..
a. Carmine .. .. 45·00 22·00
b. Rose-red .. .. 55·00 38·00
c. "On" only .. .. — £130
Printings used for this issue were as follows:
Printing I – Nos. 104 and 105
Printing IV – Nos. 102 and 103
Printing V – Nos. 102, 103*a*, 104*a* and 105*a*
Printing VI – Nos. 102a, 103*b* and 105*b*

On
S S
S
(24)

1901 (?). *Handstamped with T* **24**.
105*d* **3** 6 p. yellowish green (D) .. .. .. — £350
From Printing VI

III. MIXED MACHINE-PRINTED AND HANDSTAMPED

1896. (i) *Handstamped "On" as in T* **19**, *and machine-printed opt T* **13** *complete.*
106 **3** 6 p. green (C) .. .. — £425
(ii) *Handstamped opt as T* **14**, *and machine-printed opt T* **13** *complete*
107 **3** 6 p. deep green (C) .. ..
No. 106 is from Printing IV and No. 107 from Printing V.
Various other types of these handstamps are known to exist, but in the absence of evidence of their authenticity we do not list them. It is stated that stamps of T **4** were never officially overprinted.

The stamps of Sirmoor have been obsolete since 1 April 1902.

PRICES OF SETS

Set prices are given for many issues, generally those containing three stamps or more. Definitive sets include one of each value or major colour change, but do not cover different perforations, die types or minor shades. Where a choice is possible the set prices are based on the cheapest versions of the stamps included in the listings.

SORUTH

PRICES FOR STAMPS ON COVER

Nos. 1/2	*from* × 5
Nos. 4/4*a*	—
Nos. 5/8	*from* × 1
No. 8*a*	*from* × 3
No. 9	*from* × 1
Nos. 10/11	*from* × 5
No. 11*e*	*from* × 1
No. 12	*from* × 4
No. 13	*from* × 5
Nos. 14/15	*from* × 3
Nos. 16/24	*from* × 20
Nos. 33/6	*from* × 50
Nos. 37/8	*from* × 10
Nos. 40/1	*from* × 50
Nos. 42/57	*from* × 10
Nos. O1/13	*from* × 20
No. 58	*from* × 15
No. 59	*from* × 6
No. 60	*from* × 10
No. 61	*from* × 6
Nos. O14/22	*from* × 10

The name "Saurashtra", corrupted to "Sorath" or "Soru was originally used for all the territory later known Kathiawar. Strictly speaking the name should have b applied only to a portion of Kathiawar including the stat Junagadh. As collectors have known these issues under heading of "Soruth" for so long, we retain the name.

GUM. Nos. 1/47 of Soruth were issued without gum.

JUNAGADH

Nawab Mahabat Khan II, 1851–1882

(Currency 40 dokras or 16 annas = 1 koree)

1
(="Saurashtra Post 1864–65")

1864 (Nov). *Handstamped in water-colour. Imperf.*
1 **1** (1 a.) black/*azure to grey* (laid) £650 55
2 (1 a.) black/*azure to grey* (wove) .. .. — £1
4 (1 a.) black/*cream* (laid) .. .. † £11
4*a* (1 a.) black/*cream* (wove) .. .. — £7

ILLUSTRATIONS. Types **2** to **11** are shown actual size.

2 (1 a.) (Devanagri numeral)

3 (1 a.) (Gujarati numeral)

4 (4 a.) (Devanagri numeral)

5 (4 a.) (Gujarati numeral)

Differences in first character of bottom line on Nos. 8/*a*:

Type A "u" (error)

Type B "ka" (correct)

(Type-set Nitiprakash Ptg Press, Junagadh)

1868 (June)–**75**. *Designs as T* **2** *to* **5**. *Imperf.*

A. *Inscriptions in Gujarati characters. Wove paper*
5 1 a. black/*yellowish* .. .. † £650

B. *Inscriptions in Devanagri characters* (*as in the illustrations*)

I. *Accents over first letters in top and bottom lines. Wove paper*
6 1 a. red/*green* .. .. † £200
7 1 a. red/*blue* .. .. † £200
8 1 a. black/*pink* (first character in bottom line as Type A) .. .. .. † £95
8*a* 1 a. black/*pink* (first character in bottom line as Type B) £750 £11
9 2 a. black/*yellow* (1869) .. .. .. † £325

II. *Accents over second letters in top and bottom lines*

(*a*) *Wove paper*

1 a. black/*pink* (1869) .. .. £400 50·00
a. Printed both sides .. .. .. † —
b. First two characters in last word of bottom line omitted (R. 4/1) .. — £500

(*b*) *Laid paper*

1 a. black/*azure* (1870) .. .. 70·00 8·00
a. Final character in both top and bottom lines omitted (R. 1/1) .. .. — £140
b. First two characters in last word of bottom line omitted (R. 4/1) .. — £100
c. Doubly printed .. .. .. † £650
d. *Se-tenant* pair. Nos. 11/12 .. .. £275 £100
1 a. black/*white* .. .. † £3000
1 a. black/*azure* (1870) .. .. £160 17·00
a. Printed both sides .. .. .. † £750
b. Final character in bottom line omitted (R. 1/1) .. .. — £100
c. Accent omitted from last word in bottom line (R. 5/2, 5/4) .. .. — 80·00
d. Large numeral (R. 4/1) £500 £140
e. First character in middle line omitted (R. 2/4) .. .. — £250
f. Central two characters in middle line omitted (R. 2/4) .. .. .. — £425
1 a. red/*white* (1875) .. .. .. 17·00 18·00
a. First two characters in bottom line omitted (R. 5/1) .. .. .. 80·00 £100
5 4 a. black/*white* £200 £375
a. First two characters in last word of bottom line omitted (R. 4/1) .. £900
b. Final character in bottom line omitted (R. 5/2) £1600
4 4 a. black/*white* £110 £180
a. Final character in bottom line omitted (R. 1/1) £450

e settings of Nos. 5/7 are unknown.
s. 10/15, and probably Nos. 8/9, were printed in sheets of 20). The same type was used throughout, but changes rred as the loose type was amended.
ecialists now recognise four main settings for the 1 a., one of h was amended for the 2 a. and another for the 4 a. There ub-settings within some of these groups:

1 a. Setting I (pink wove paper) (No. 8)
Setting II (pink wove paper) (No. 8*a*)
Setting III (pink wove paper) (No. 10)
Setting IV (Devanagri numerals only) (pink wove paper) (Nos. 10/b)
Setting IVA (Devanagri numerals only) (azure vertical laid paper) (Nos. 11, 11b)
Setting IVB (Devanagri and Gujarati numerals mixed) (azure horizontal laid paper) (Nos. 11/a, 11d, 12)
Setting IVC (Devanagri and Gujarati numerals mixed) (azure or white vertical laid paper) (Nos. 11, 11c/d, 11e, 12/b, 12e/f)
Setting IVD (Devanagri and Gujarati numerals mixed) (azure vertical laid paper) (Nos. 11, 11d, 12, 12d)
Setting IVE (Gujarati numerals only) (white vertical laid paper) (Nos. 13/a)

2 a. Setting I (probably derived from 1 a. Setting II) (yellow wove paper) (No. 9)

4 a. Setting IA (Gujarati numerals only) (white vertical laid paper) (Nos. 14/a)
Setting IB (Devanagri numerals only) (white horizontal laid paper) (No. 15)
Setting 1C (Devanagri numerals only) (white vertical laid paper) (Nos. 15/a)
Setting ID (only Gujarati numerals so far identified) (white vertical laid paper) (Nos. 14, 14b)

ettings IVA/D of the 1 a. were subsequently adapted to form ings IA/D of the 4 a.
he two known examples of No. 8 both come from the top row ne sheet. Marginal inscriptions indicate that No. 8*a* is from a arate setting.
)fficial imitations, consisting of 1 a. carmine-red on white ve and white laid, 1 a. black on blue wove, 4 a. black on white ve, 4 a. black on blue wove, 4 a. red on white laid—all oerforate; 1 a. carmine-red on white laid, 1 a. black on blue ve, 4 a. black on white laid and blue wove—all perforated 12, re made in 1890. Entire sheets of originals have 20 stamps <5), the imitations only 4 or 16.

6

7

(Typo Nitiprakash Ptg Press, Junagadh)

78 (16 Jan)–**86**. *Laid paper with the lines wide apart. Imperf.*
6 1 a. green 60 30
a. Printed both sides £475 £500
b. Laid lines close together (1886) .. 60 30
7 4 a. vermilion .. .. 2·00 1·40
a. Printed both sides £550
b. Scarlet/bluish .. .. .. 3·00 2·50
4 a. brown .. .. 9·00

Nawab Bahadur Khan III, 1882–1892

86. P 12. (*a*) *On toned laid paper with the lines close together*
6 1 a. green 30 15
a. Imperf vert (horiz pair) £100
b. Doubly printed .. .. .. † £400
c. Error. Blue £600 £600
d. On bluish white laid paper .. .. 2·75 3·75
da. Imperf between (pair) £160
e. Emerald-green .. .. .. 2·50 1·25
7 4 a. red .. .. 1·40 75
a. On bluish white laid paper .. .. 8·50 13·00
b. Carmine .. .. 2·75 2·25
4 a. brown .. .. 7·00

(*b*) *Wove paper*

22 6 1 a. green .. .. 1·75 65
a. Imperf (pair) .. .. 60·00 80·00
b. Error. Blue .. .. — £600
c. Imperf horiz (vert pair) £120
23 7 4 a. red .. .. 3·75 8·00
a. Imperf (pair) £150 £180
24 4 a. brown .. .. 12·00

There is a very wide range of colours in both values. The laid paper, on which imperforate printings continued to appear until 1912, is found both vertical and horizontal.

The 1 a. was originally issued in sheets of 15 (5×3), but later appeared in sheets of 20 (5×4) with marginal inscriptions. Stamps were sometimes printed in double sheets showing two impressions of the plate printed *tête-bêche* on the same or opposite sides of the paper.

The 4 a. was in horizontal strips of 5. No. 20 exists as a sheet of 10 (5×2), with two impressions of the plate printed *tête-bêche*, and No. 23 in a similar sized sheet but with both impressions upright.

Nawab Rasul Khan 1892–1911
Nawab Mahabat Khan III, 1911–1959

(Indian currency)

Three pies.
ત્રણ પાઈ.
(8)

One anna.
એક આનો.
(9)

1913 (1 Jan). *Surch in Indian currency with T* **8** *or* **9**. *P* 12.

(*a*) *On toned wove paper*

33 6 3 p. on 1 a. emerald-green 15 20
a. Imperf (pair) £350
b. Imperf between (horiz pair) £300
34 7 1 a. on 4 a. red .. .. 1·75 4·75
a. Imperf (pair) £600
b. Capital "A" in "Anna" .. .. .. 6·00
c. Surch inverted £700
d. Imperf between (horiz pair) .. ..

(*b*) *On white wove paper*

35 6 3 p. on 1 a. emerald-green 15 20
a. Imperf between (pair) .. ..
b. Surch inverted .. .. .. 35·00 20·00
c. Surch double .. .. .. † —
36 7 1 a. on 4 a. carmine .. .. .. 1·60 4·75
a. Imperf (pair) .. .. ..
b. Surch both sides £750
c. Capital "A" in "Anna" .. .. 13·00

(*c*) *On white laid paper*

37 6 3 p. on 1 a. emerald-green .. .. 75·00 30·00
a. Imperf (pair) .. .. .. — £375
b. Larger English surch (21 mm long with capital "p" in "Pies") inverted .. † £1500
38 7 1 a. on 4 a. red .. .. 7·50 42·00
a. Capital "A" in "Anna" £225
b. Surch inverted £700
c. Surch double £700
d. Surch double, one inverted £700

The 1 a. surcharge with capital "A" in "Anna" comes from a separate setting.

10

11

(Dies eng Thacker & Co, Bombay. Typo Junagadh State Press)

1914 (1 Sept). *New plates. T* **6/7** *redrawn as T* **10/11**. *Wove paper. P* 12.
40 10 3 p. green 75 35
a. Imperf (pair) .. .. 5·50 18·00
b. Imperf vert (horiz pair) .. .. 75·00
c. Laid paper .. .. 3·00 1·50
ca. Imperf (pair) .. .. 14·00 26·00
d. Error. Red (imperf) .. .. .. † £1700
41 11 1 a. red .. .. 80 1·40
a. Imperf (pair) .. .. 19·00 70·00
b. Imperf between (pair) £400
c. Laid paper £300 £110

12 Nawab Mahabat Khan III 13

(Dies eng Popatlal Bhimji Pandya. Typo Junagadh State Press)

1923 (1 Sept). *Blurred impression. Laid paper. Pin-perf* 12.
42 12 1 a. red .. .. 3·00 8·00
Sheets of 16 stamps (8×2).

This setting was later printed on wove paper, but single examples cannot readily be distinguished from No. 46b.

ત્રણ પાઇ
(14)

ત્રણ પાઈ
(14*a*)

1923 (1 Sept). *Surch with T* **14**.
43 12 3 p. on 1 a. red .. .. 3·50 7·00
a. Surch with T **14*a*** .. .. .. 4·00 11·00

Four stamps in the setting have surch. T 14*a*, i.e. with top of last character curved to right.

1923 (Oct). *Blurred impression. Wove paper. Pin-perf* 12, *small holes.*
44 13 3 p. mauve 35 45
Sheets of 16 (4×4).

1924. *Clear impression. Wove paper. P* 12, *large holes.*
45 13 3 p. mauve (1.24) .. .. .. 1·25 35
46 12 1 a. red (4.24) .. .. 6·00 6·50
a. Imperf (pair) .. .. 48·00
b. Pin perf .. .. 3·00 3·25

The first plate of the 3 p., which printed No. 44, produced unsatisfactory impressions, so it was replaced by a second plate, producing two panes of 16 (4×4), from which No. 45 comes. Sheets printed from the first plate had very large margins.

The 1 a. is also from a new plate, giving a clearer impression. Sheets of 16 stamps (4×4).

1929. *Clear impressions. Laid paper. P* 12, *large holes.*
47 13 3 p. mauve .. .. 4·25 3·25
a. Imperf (pair) .. .. 3·00 25·00
b. Perf 11 .. .. 7·50 6·00
ba. Imperf between (horiz pair) .. 3·00 22·00
Sheets of two panes of 16 (4×4).
The laid paper shows several sheet watermarks.
No. 47ba was intentional to create a 6 p. franking required by a rate change in October 1929.

15 Junagadh City

16 Gir Lion

17 Nawab Mahabat Khan III

18 Kathi Horse

(Des Amir Sheikh Mahamadbhai. Litho Indian Security Printing Press, Nasik)

1929 (1 Oct). *Inscr* "POSTAGE". *P* 14.
49 15 3 p. black and blackish green 80 10
50 16 ½ a. black and deep blue .. .. 5·00 10
51 17 1 a. black and carmine .. .. 4·00 1·00
52 18 2 a. black and dull orange .. .. 10·00 1·90
a. Grey and dull yellow .. .. 27·00 1·90
53 15 3 a. black and carmine .. .. 4·00 7·50
54 16 4 a. black and purple .. .. 13·00 21·00
55 18 8 a. black and yellow-green .. .. 10·00 20·00
56 17 1 r. black and pale blue .. .. 5·50 21·00
49/56 .. .. *Set of* 8 48·00 65·00

1935 (1 Jan). *As T* **17**, *but inscr* "POSTAGE AND REVENUE". *P* 14.
57 17 1 a. black and carmine .. .. .. 5·00 1·00

OFFICIAL STAMPS

SARKARI
(O 1)

1929 (1 Oct). *Optd with Type* O **1**, *in vermilion, at Nasik.*
O1 15 3 p. black and blackish green .. .. 1·00 15
a. Red opt 75 10
O2 16 ½ a. black and deep blue .. .. 2·00 10
a. Red opt .. .. 3·00 40
O3 17 1 a. black and carmine (No. 51) .. 2·75 35
a. Red opt .. .. 1·75 15
O4 18 2 a. black and dull orange .. .. 2·50 80
a. Grey and dull yellow .. .. 18·00 60
b. Red opt .. .. 24·00 2·75
O5 15 3 a. black and carmine 75 30
a. Red opt .. .. 16·00 1·50
O6 16 4 a. black and purple .. .. .. 2·75 45
a. Red opt .. .. 20·00 2·50
O7 18 8 a. black and yellow-green .. .. 2·50 2·00
O8 17 1 r. black and pale blue .. .. 2·50 16·00
O1/8 .. .. *Set of* 8 14·00 18·00

SARKARI
(O 2)

SARKARI
(O 3)

1932 (Jan)–**35**. *Optd with Type* O **2**, *in red, at Junagadh State Press.*
O 9 15 3 a. black and carmine .. .. .. 19·00 15·00
a. Optd with Type O **3** (1.35) .. .. 75·00 7·00
O10 16 4 a. black and purple .. .. .. 26·00 16·00
O11 18 8 a. black and yellow-green .. .. 28·00 18·00
O12 17 1 r. black and pale blue .. .. 23·00 70·00
a. Optd with Type O **3** (1.35) £110 £110

1938. *No. 57 optd with Type* O 1, *in vermilion.*
O13 **17** 1 a. black and carmine .. .. .. 13·00 2·00
a. Brown-red opt .. .. .. 10·00 1·50

The state was occupied by Indian troops on 9 November 1947 following the flight of the Nawab to Pakistan.

UNITED STATE OF SAURASHTRA

The administration of Junagadh state was assumed by the Government of India on 9 November 1947. An Executive Council took office on 1 June 1948.

Under the new Constitution of India the United State of Saurashtra was formed on 15 February 1948, comprising 221 former states and estates of Kathiawar, including Jasdan, Morvi, Nawanagar and Wadhwan, but excluding Junagadh. A referendum was held by the Executive Council of Junagadh which then joined the United State on 20 January 1949. It is believed that the following issues were only used in Junagadh.

The following issues were surcharged at the Junagadh State Press.

POSTAGE & REVENUE

ONE ANNA

(19)

Postage & Revenue

ONE ANNA

(20)

1949. *Stamps of* 1929 *surch. (a) With T* **19** *in red.*
58 **16** 1 a. on ½ a. black and deep blue (5.49) 9·50 4·75
a. Surch double .. .. .. † £450
b. "AFNA" for "ANNA" and inverted "N" in "REVENUE" £1800
c. Larger first "A" in "ANNA" (R. 2/5) 80·00 60·00
(b) With T **20** *in green*
59 **18** 1 a. on 2 a. grey and dull yellow (2.49) .. 11·00 22·00
a. "evenue" omitted .. .. .. — £475

No. 58b may have occurred on R. 2/5 with No. 58c being caused by its correction.

A number of other varieties occur on No. 58, including: small "V" in "REVENUE" (R. 2/3); small "N" in "REVENUE" (R. 2/4, 3/4); small "E" in "POSTAGE" (R. 3/2); thick "A" in "POSTAGE" (R. 4/4); inverted "N" in "REVENUE" and small second "A" in "ANNA" (R. 4/5); small "O" in "ONE" (R. 5/1); small "V" and "U" in "REVENUE" (R. 6/3); small "N" in "ONE" (R. 7/2).

In No. 59 no stop after "ANNA" is known on R. 1/4, 4/2, 7/4 and 8/3 and small "N" in "ONE" on R. 2/4.

21

(Typo Waterlow)

1949 (Sept). *Court Fee stamps of Bhavnagar state optd* "SAURASHTRA" *and further optd* "U.S.S. REVENUE & POSTAGE" *as in T* **21**, *in black. P* 11.
60 **21** 1 a. purple .. .. .. 9·00 9·50
a. "POSTAGE" omitted (R. 1/2) .. £250 £180
b. Opt double £250 £300

The Court Fee stamps were in sheets of 80 (8×10) and were overprinted in a setting of 40 applied twice to each sheet.

Minor varieties include small "S" in "POSTAGE" (R. 2/1 of the setting); small "N" in "REVENUE" (R. 2/7); small "U" in "REVENUE" (R. 3/2); small "V" in "REVENUE" (R. 3/8, 5/5); and small "O" in "POSTAGE" (R. 4/7).

Various missing stop varieties also occur.

POSTAGE & REVENUE
ONE ANNA

(22)

1950 (2 Mar). *Stamp of* 1929 *surch with T* **22**.
61 **15** 1 a. on 3 p. black and blackish green .. 50·00 55·00
a. "P" of "POSTAGE" omitted (R. 8/1) £600 £600
b. "O" of "ONE" omitted (R. 6/1) .. £750

Other minor varieties include small second "A" in "ANNA" (R. 1/2); small "S" in "POSTAGE" with small "V" in "REVENUE" (R. 3/4, 6/1) and small "V" in "REVENUE" (R. 2/3, 3/1).

OFFICIAL STAMPS

1948 (July–Dec). *Nos.* O4/O7 *surch* "ONE ANNA" (2¼ *mm high) by Junagadh State Press.*
O14 **18** 1 a. on 2 a. grey & dull yellow (B.) .. £6000 23·00
O15 **15** 1 a. on 3 a. black and carmine (Aug) .. £1800 50·00
a. Surch double .. .. .. † £1800
O16 **16** 1 a. on 4 a. black and purple (Dec) .. £300 45·00
a. "ANNE" for "ANNA" (R. 5/4) .. £2250 £375
b. "ANNN" for "ANNA" (R. 7/5) .. £2250 £375
O17 **18** 1 a. on 8 a. black & yellow-green (Dec) £275 35·00
a. "ANNE" for "ANNA" (R. 5/4) .. £2250 £275
b. "ANNN" for "ANNA" (R. 7/5) .. £2250 £275

Numerous minor varieties of fount occur in this surcharge.

1948 (Nov). *Handstamped* "ONE ANNA" (4 *mm high*).
O18 **17** 1 a. on 1 r. (No. O8) .. .. .. £1200 35·00
O19 1 a. on 1 r. (No. O12a) .. .. £475 38·00
a. Optd on No. O12 .. .. .. — 60·00

A used copy of No. O12a is known surcharged in black as on Nos. O14/17. This may have come from a proof sheet.

1949 (Jan). *Postage stamps optd with Type* O **3**, *in red.*
O20 **15** 3 p. black and blackish green .. .. £250 12·00
O21 **16** ½ a. black and deep blue .. .. £550 12·00
O22 **18** 1 a. on 2 a. grey and dull yellow (No. 59) 70·00 21·00

Various wrong fount letters occur in the above surcharges.

MANUSCRIPT OVERPRINTS. Nos. 49, 50, 57, 58, 59 and 60 are known with manuscript overprints reading "Service" or "SARKARI" (in English or Gujerati script), usually in red. Such provisionals were used at Gadhda and Una between June and December 1949 (*Price from £95 each, used on piece*).

The United State of Saurashtra postal service was incorporated into that of India on 30 March 1950.

TRAVANCORE

PRICES FOR STAMPS ON COVER	
Nos. 1/77	*from* × 10
Nos. O1/108	*from* × 15

(16 cash = 1 chuckram; 28 chuckrams = 1 rupee)

"Anchel" or "Anchal" = Post Office Department.

The stamps of Travancore were valid on mail posted to Cochin.

PRINTERS. All stamps of Travancore were printed by the Stamp Manufactory, Trivandrum, *unless otherwise stated.*

PRINTING METHODS. The dies were engraved on brass from which electrotypes were made and locked together in a forme for printing the stamps. As individual electrotypes became worn they were replaced by new ones and their positions in the forme were sometimes changed. This makes it difficult to plate the early issues. From 1901 plates were made which are characterised by a frame (or "Jubilee" line) round the margins of the sheets.

Up to the 6 cash of 1910 the dies were engraved by Dharmalingham Asari.

SHADES. We list only the main groups of shades but there are many others in view of the large number of printings and the use of fugitive inks. Sometimes shade variation is noticeable within the same sheet.

Maharaja Rama Varma X, 1885–1924

1 Conch or Chank Shell

1888 (16 Oct). *As T* **1**, *but each value differs slightly. Laid paper. P* 12.
1 **1** 1 ch. ultramarine (*shades*) .. .. 3·75 3·00
2 2 ch. red .. .. 3·50 8·50
3 4 ch. green .. .. 15·00 12·00
1/3 .. .. *Set of* 3 20·00 21·00

The paper bears a large sheet watermark showing a large conch shell surmounted by "GOVERNMENT" in large outline letters, in an arch with "OF TRAVANCORE" at foot in a straight line. Many stamps in the sheet are without watermark.

These stamps on laid paper in abnormal colours are proofs.

2

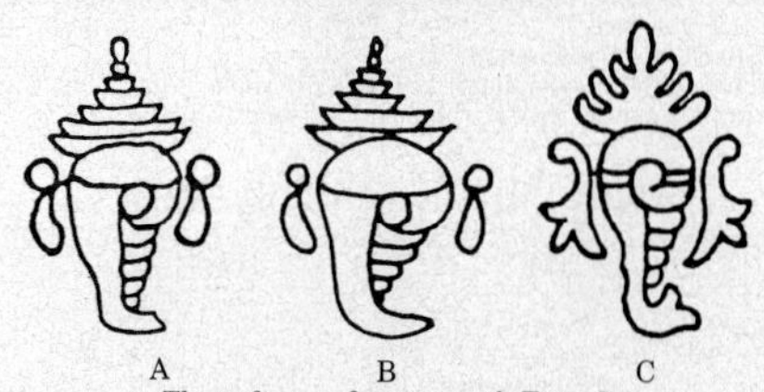

A B C

Three forms of watermark Type **2**.
(as seen from the back of the stamp)

WATERMARKS AND PAPERS.

Type A appeared upright on early printings of the 1, 2 and values on odd-sized sheets which did not fit the number of s Later it was always sideways with 15 mm between the she standard-sized sheets of 84 (14 × 6) containing 60 shells (1C It therefore never appears centred on the stamps and it occ hand-made papers only.

Type B is similar in shape but can easily be distinguished a invariably upright, with 11 mm between the shells, and i centred on the stamps. It also occurs only on handmade pap was introduced in 1904 and from 1914, when Type A brought back into use, it was employed concurrently 1924.

Type C is quite different in shape and occurs on machine- papers. There are two versions. The first, in use from 19 1939, has 84 shells 11 mm apart and is always uprigh well centred. The second, introduced in 1929 and believ to have been used after 1930, has 60 shells (12×5) 1 apart and is invariably badly centred so that some stan the sheet are without watermark. This second vers normally found upright, but a few sideways water varieties are known and listed as Nos. 35g, 37c, O31j and We do not distinguish between the two versions of Typ the lists, but stamps known to exist in the second versic indicated in footnotes. The machine-made paper is gen smoother and of more even texture.

NO WATERMARK VARIETIES. Some of these were forr listed but we have now decided to omit them as they do not occ full sheets. They arise in the following circumstances: (*a*) on s with wmk A; (*b*) on sheets with the wide-spaced form of wmk C (*c*) on late printings of the pictorial issues of 1939–46. They are collected in pairs, with and without watermark.

DATES OF ISSUE. In the absence of more definite inform the dates quoted usually refer to the first reported date of new p ings on different watermarks but many were not noted at the and the dates of these are indicated by a query. Dated postm on single stamps are difficult to find.

3

4

5

6

7 8

1889–1904. *Wove paper. Wmk* A (*upright or sideways*). *P* (*sometimes rough*).
4 **1** ½ ch. slate-lilac (1894) .. .. .. 2·25
a. Doubly printed .. .. .. † £
b. Reddish lilac 60
ba. Imperf between (vert pair) .. .. £225 £
bb. Doubly printed .. .. .. † £
c. Purple (1899) .. .. .. 1·25
ca. Doubly printed .. .. .. † £
d. Dull purple (1904) .. .. .. 1·50
5 **5** ¾ ch. black (14.3.01) .. .. .. 3·00
6 **1** 1 ch. ultramarine .. .. 1·50
a. *Tête-bêche* (pair) £2000 £2
b. Doubly printed .. .. .. † £
c. Imperf vert (horiz pair) .. .. † £
d. Imperf between (vert pair) .. .. † £
e. Pale ultramarine (1892) .. .. 2·75
f. Violet-blue (1901) .. .. .. 3·25
7 2 ch. salmon (1890) .. .. .. 4·00 1
a. Rose (1891) .. .. 3·50
ab. Imperf (pair) .. .. .. † £4
b. Pale pink (1899) .. .. .. 3·00
ba. Imperf between (vert pair) £140
bb. Doubly printed £200
c. Red (1904) .. .. 3·00
ca. Imperf between (horiz pair) £300 £3
8 4 ch. green .. .. 3·25
a. Yellow-green (1901) .. .. .. 2·50
b. Dull green (1904) .. .. .. 6·50 1
ba. Doubly printed .. .. .. † £3

Nos. 6, 6*d*, 7 and 8 occur with the watermark upright and si ways. No. 7*a* is known only with the watermark upright. T remainder exist only with the watermark sideways.

The sheet sizes were as follows:
½ ch. 56 (14 × 4) except for No. 4*d* which was 84 (14 × 6), initia without border, later with border.
¾ ch. 84 (14 × 6) with border.
1 ch. No. 6, 80 (10 × 8) and later 84 (14 × 6) without border a then with border; No. 6*d*, 96 (16 × 6); No. 6*e*, 84 (14 × 6) wi border.
2 ch. No. 7, 80 (10 × 8); No. 7*a*, 70 (10 × 7); Nos. 7*b*, 7*c*, 60 (10 ×
4 ch. No. 8, 60 (10 × 6); Nos. 8*a*/*b*, 84 (14 × 6) with border.

After 1904 all stamps in Types **3** to **8** were in standard-si sheets of 84 (14 × 6) with border.

For later printings watermarked Type A, see Nos. 23/30.

1904–20. *Wmk* B, *upright* (*centred*). *P* 12, *sometimes rough.*
9 **3** 4 ca. pink (11.08) 30
a. Imperf between (vert pair) .. £200 £2
10 **1** 6 ca. chestnut (2.10) 30
a. Imperf between (horiz pair) .. † £2
11 ½ ch. reddish lilac .. .. .. 1·10
a. Reddish violet (6.10) .. .. 1·00
b. Lilac .. .. 1·25 3
c. "CHUCRRAM" (R. 5/6) .. .. 5·50 3·2
d. Imperf horiz (vert pair) .. † £15

4 10 ca. pink (1920) .. .. .. 26·00 5·50
5 ¾ ch. black .. .. 1·50 25
1 1 ch. bright blue .. ..
a. Blue .. .. 3·25 30
b. Deep blue .. .. 3·25 30
c. Indigo (8.10) 75 10
d. *Chalky blue* (1912) .. .. .. 4·00 60
1¼ ch. claret (*shades*) (10.14) .. 55 55
a. Imperf between (horiz pair) .. £225 £225
2 ch. salmon .. .. 18·00 6·00
a. Red (8.10) 60 10
6 3 ch. violet (11.3.11) .. .. .. 2·75 20
a. Imperf between (vert pair) .. £200 £200
b. Imperf between (vert strip of 3) .. † £275
1 4 ch. dull green .. .. 10·00 3·50
a. Slate-green .. .. 1·60 35
7 7 ch. claret (1916) .. .. .. 2·00 50
a. Error. Carmine-red .. .. — 50·00
8 14 ch. orange-yellow (1916) .. .. 2·75 1·50
a. Imperf vert (horiz strip of 3) .. £450

¼ (9) 1 C (10)

Surch as T **9**. *Wmk* B.
1 ¼ on ½ ch. reddish lilac 30 30
a. Reddish violet 30 20
b. Lilac 50 30
c. "CHUCRRAM" (R.5/6) .. 3·50 3·25
d. Surch inverted .. .. 45·00 28·00
⅜ on ½ ch. reddish lilac 20 35
a. Reddish violet 20 35
b. Lilac 20 35
c. "CHUCRRAM" (R.5/6) .. 3·25 3·50
d. Surch inverted .. .. — 40·00
e. Surch double .. ..
f. "8" omitted .. .. — 40·00

–22. *Reversion to wmk A (sideways). P* 12 (*sometimes* ugh).
3 4 ca. pink (1915) .. .. .. 8·00 60
4 5 ca. olive-bistre (30.10.21) 80 10
a. Imperf between (horiz pair) .. 45·00 50·00
b. Imperf between (horiz strip of 3) .. 90·00 95·00
c. "TRAVANCOPE" .. .. .. — 8·00
1 6 ca. orange-brown (2.15) .. .. 5·50 40
½ ch. reddish violet (12.14) .. .. 2·50 40
a. "CHUCRRAM" (R. 5/6) .. 9·50 3·75
b. Imperf between (horiz pair) .. £160
4 10 ca. pink (26.10.21) 40 10
1 1 ch. grey-blue (5.22) .. .. .. 9·00 1·75
a. Deep blue .. .. 9·00 1·75
1¼ ch. claret (12.19) .. .. .. 11·00 35
a. Imperf between (horiz pair) .. † £250
6 3 ch. reddish lilac (8.22) .. .. 11·00 1·50

1 (Mar). *Surch as T* **10**. *Wmk* A.
3 1 c. on 4 ca. pink 15 20
a. Surch inverted .. .. .. 20·00 9·50
1 5 c. on 1 ch. grey-blue (R.) .. .. 1·00 10
a. Deep blue .. .. .. 1·00 10
b. Stamp printed both sides ..
c. Imperf between (vert pair) .. † £200
d. Surch inverted .. .. .. 13·00 8·50
e. Surch double .. .. .. 45·00 35·00
f. On wmk B. *Deep blue* .. .. 20·00 20·00
fa. Surch inverted .. .. .. † £150

BINO OVERPRINT VARIETIES. Stamps with overprint ble, one albino are frequently found in the provisional and cial issues of Travancore, and are only worth a small mium over the normal prices.

Maharaja Bala Rama Varma XI, 1924–1971

24–39. *Wmk* C. *Machine-made paper. P* 12.
4 5 ca. olive-bistre (18.6.25) .. .. 11·00 2·75
a. Imperf between (horiz pair) .. £140
b. "TRAVANCOPE" .. .. — 13·00
5 ca. chocolate (1930) .. .. 2·75 20
a. Imperf between (horiz pair) .. 38·00
b. Imperf between (vert pair) .. † £130
1 6 ca. brown-red (3.24) .. .. 4·25 10
a. Imperf between (horiz pair) .. 22·00 24·00
b. Imperf between (vert pair) .. 95·00 95·00
c. Printed both sides .. .. 50·00
d. Perf 12½ .. .. .. 4·25 50
e. Perf comp of 12 and 12½ .. 6·00 4·00
f. Perf 12½×11 .. .. — 85·00
g. Wmk sideways .. .. — 16·00
½ ch. reddish violet (date?) .. .. 4·25 4·25
a. "CHUCRRAM" (R. 5/6) .. 32·00
4 10 ca. pink (8.24) .. .. .. 2·25 10
a. Imperf between (horiz pair) .. 75·00 75·00
b. Imperf between (vert pair) .. 22·00 25·00
c. Wmk sideways (16.9.28) .. — 6·50
5 ¾ ch. black (4.10.32) .. .. .. 9·00 50
¾ ch. mauve (16.11.32) 35 10
a. Imperf between (horiz pair) .. † £140
b. Perf 12½ (8.37) .. .. 9·00 70
ba. Imperf between (horiz pair) .. £130
c. Perf comp of 12 and 12½ .. 13·00 5·00
ca. Imperf between (horiz pair) .. £150
¾ ch. reddish violet (1939) .. .. 3·00 70
a. Perf 12½ .. .. .. 4·50 50
b. Perf comp 12 and 12½ .. 7·50 2·25
c. Perf 11 .. .. .. — 85·00
d. Perf comp of 12 and 11 .. — 85·00
1 1 ch. slate-blue (8.26) .. .. 2·75 30
a. Indigo .. .. 4·00 20
b. Imperf between (horiz pair) .. † £180
c. Imperf between (vert pair) .. † £180
d. Perf 12½ .. .. .. 10·00 1·10

42 1 1½ ch. rose (1932) .. .. .. 2·75 10
a. Imperf between (horiz strip of 3) £180
b. Perf 12½ .. .. .. 22·00 2·75
c. Perf comp of 12 and 12½ .. — 28·00
43 2 ch. carmine-red (4.6.29) .. .. 3·00 30
44 6 3 ch. violet (4.25) .. .. .. 6·50 15
a. Imperf between (vert pair) .. 90·00 90·00
b. Perf 12½ .. .. .. — 11·00
c. Perf comp of 12 and 12½ .. — 26·00
45 1 4 ch. grey-green (5.4.34) .. .. 5·00 45
46 7 7 ch. claret (1925) .. .. .. 9·00 1·75
a. Doubly printed .. .. .. † £350
b. Carmine-red (date?) .. .. 65·00 55·00
c. Brown-purple (1932) .. .. 15·00 4·25
ca. Perf 12½ .. .. .. 8·50 15·00
cb. Perf comb of 12 and 12½ .. 7·50 15·00
46*d* 8 14 ch. orange-yellow (date?) .. .. 40·00
da. Perf 12½ £180

It is believed that the 12½ perforation and the perf 12 and 12½ compound were introduced in 1937 and that the 11 perforation came later, probably in 1939.

The 5 ca. chocolate, 6 ca., 10 ca. and 3 ch. also exist on the wide-spaced watermark (60 shells to the sheet of 84).

11 Sri Padmanabha Shrine

12 State Chariot

13 Maharaja Bala Rama Varma XI

(Des M. R. Madhawan Unnithan. Plates by Calcutta Chromotype Co. Typo Stamp Manufactory, Trivandrum)

1931 (6 Nov). *Coronation. Cream or white paper. Wmk* C. *P* 11½, 12.
47 11 6 ca. black and green .. .. .. 1·25 1·25
a. Imperf between (horiz pair) .. £180 £200
48 12 10 ca. black and ultramarine .. .. 1·10 60
a. Imperf between (vert pair) .. † £400
49 13 3 ch. black and purple .. .. 2·50 2·25
47/9 .. .. *Set of* 3 4·50 3·75

1 C (14) 1 C (15)

16 Maharaja Bala Rama Varma XI and Subramania Shrine

1932 (14 Jan). (i) *Surch as T* **14**. (*a*) *Wmk A* (*sideways*).
50 1 1 c. on 1¼ ch. claret 15 50
a. Imperf between (horiz pair) .. 95·00
b. Surch inverted .. .. .. 4·25 7·00
c. Surch double .. .. .. 28·00 28·00
d. Pair, one without surch .. .. 90·00 £100
e. "c" omitted .. .. .. 45·00 45·00
51 2 c. on 1¼ ch. claret 15 15
a. Surch inverted .. .. .. 4·25 7·00
b. Surch double .. .. .. 26·00
c. Surch double, one inverted .. 55·00
d. Surch treble .. .. .. 60·00
e. Surch treble, one inverted .. 70·00 70·00
f. Pair, one without surch .. .. 95·00 £100
g. "2" omitted .. .. .. 45·00 45·00
h. "c" omitted .. .. .. 45·00 45·00
i. Imperf between (horiz pair) .. 95·00
j. Imperf between (vert pair) .. £100

(*b*) *Wmk B* (*upright*)
52 1 1 c. on 1¼ ch. claret .. .. .. 75 1·00
a. Surch inverted .. .. .. 20·00
b. Surch double .. .. .. 38·00
53 2 c. on 1¼ ch. claret .. .. .. 6·50 6·50
a. Imperf between (horiz pair) .. £120

(*c*) *Wmk C*
54 1 1 c. on 1¼ ch. claret .. .. .. 14·00 16·00
a. Surch inverted .. .. .. 50·00 55·00
55 2 c. on 1¼ ch. claret .. .. .. 23·00 17·00

(ii) *Surch as T* **10**. *Wmk B*
56 1 2 c. on 1¼ ch. claret .. .. .. 4·00 14·00

1932 (5 Mar) *Surch as T* **15**. *Wmk* C.
57 4 1 c. on 5 ca. chocolate 15 15
a. Imperf between (horiz pair) .. £110
b. Surch inverted .. .. .. 7·50 10·00
c. Surch inverted on back only .. 65·00
d. Pair, one without surch .. .. 90·00
e. "1" omitted .. .. .. 38·00
f. "C" omitted .. .. .. — 38·00
g. "TRAVANCOPE" .. .. .. 8·50
58 1 c. on 5 ca. slate-purple .. .. 1·25 15
a. Surch inverted .. .. .. † £180
b. "1" inverted .. .. .. 75·00 75·00
59 2 c. on 10 ca. pink 15 15
a. Imperf between (horiz pair) .. £100
b. Surch inverted .. .. .. 5·00 8·00
c. Surch double .. .. .. 19·00 21·00
d. Surch double, one inverted .. .. 60·00 60·00
e. Surch double, both inverted .. 42·00

No. 58 was not issued without the surcharge.

(Plates by Indian Security Printing Press, Nasik. Typo Stamp Manufactory, Trivandrum)

1937 (29 Mar). *Temple Entry Proclamation. T* **16** *and similar horiz designs. Wmk* C. *P* 12.
60 6 ca. carmine .. .. 1·00 1·00
a. Imperf between (horiz strip of 3) .. £450
b. Perf 12½ .. .. 1·25 1·50
c. Compound perf .. .. .. 27·00 27·00
61 12 ca. bright blue .. .. 2·00 30
a. Perf 12½ .. .. 2·50 70
ab. Imperf between (vert pair) £425
b. Compound perf .. .. .. 42·00
62 1½ ch. yellow-green .. .. .. 1·50 1·00
a. Imperf between (vert pair) £350
b. Perf 12½ .. .. 22·00 5·50
c. Compound perf .. .. ..
63 3 ch. violet .. .. 3·25 1·75
a. Perf 12½ .. .. 4·00 2·25
60/3 .. .. *Set of* 4 7·00 3·75

Designs:—Maharaja's portrait and temples—12 ca. Sri Padmanabha; 1½ ch. Mahadeva; 3 ch. Kanyakumari.

COMPOUND PERFS. This term covers stamps perf compound of 12½ and 11, 12 and 11 or 12 and 12½, and where two or more combinations exist the prices are for the commonest. Such compounds can occur on values which do not exist perf 12 all round.

17 Lake Ashtamudi

18 Maharaja Bala Rama Varma XI

(Des Nilakantha Pellai. Plates by Indian Security Printing Press, Nasik. Typo Stamp Manufactory, Trivandrum)

1939 (9 Nov). *Maharaja's 27th Birthday. T* **17**/**18** *and similar designs. Wmk* C. *P* 12½.
64 1 ch. yellow-green .. .. 4·00 10
a. Imperf between (horiz pair) .. .. 20·00
b. Perf 11 .. .. 8·00 10
ba. Imperf between (vert pair) .. .. 35·00 40·00
bb. Imperf between (vert strip of 3) .. 20·00 35·00
c. Perf 12 .. .. 16·00 1·00
ca. Imperf between (horiz pair) .. .. 20·00
cb. Imperf between (vert pair) .. .. 35·00
d. Compound perf .. .. .. 19·00 2·00
da. Imperf between (vert pair) .. .. 95·00
65 1½ ch. scarlet .. .. 2·50 2·50
a. Doubly printed £225
b. Imperf between (horiz pair) .. .. 27·00
c. Imperf between (vert pair) .. .. 21·00
d. Perf 11 .. .. 3·25 18·00
da. Imperf horiz (vert pair) .. .. 8·00
e. Perf 12 .. .. 26·00 3·50
f. Perf 13½ .. .. 14·00 50·00
g. Compound perf .. .. .. 38·00 4·75
h. Imperf (pair) .. .. .. 30·00
66 2 ch. orange .. .. 4·50 1·10
a. Perf 11 .. .. 14·00 40
b. Perf 12 .. .. 80·00 3·75
c. Compound perf .. .. .. 80·00 5·00
67 3 ch. brown .. .. 5·50 10
a. Doubly printed .. .. .. — £110
b. Imperf between (horiz pair) .. .. 35·00 48·00
c. Perf 11 .. .. 17·00 30
ca. Doubly printed .. .. .. 42·00 50·00
d. Perf 12 .. .. 30·00 2·75
da. Imperf between (vert pair) £110 £120
e. Compound perf .. .. .. 27·00 1·00
68 4 ch. red .. .. 4·50 40
a. Perf 11 .. .. 28·00 50
b. Perf 12 .. .. 25·00 5·50
c. Compound perf £130 £100
69 7 ch. pale blue .. .. 8·00 14·00
a. Perf 11 .. .. 65·00 24·00
ab. Blue .. .. 65·00 22·00
b. Compound perf .. .. .. 80·00 28·00
70 14 ch. turquoise-green .. .. .. 7·00 45·00
a. Perf 11 .. .. 8·50 80·00
64/70 .. .. *Set of* 7 32·00 55·00

Designs: *Vert as T* **18**—1½ ch., 3 ch. Portraits of Maharaja in different frames. *Horiz as T* **17**—4 ch. Sri Padmanabha Shrine; 7 ch. Cape Comorin; 14 ch. Pachipari Reservoir.

19 Maharaja and Aruvikara Falls

2 CASH (20)

(Des Nilakantha Pellai. Plates by Indian Security Printing Press, Nasik. Typo Stamp Manufactory, Trivandrum)

1941 (20 Oct). *Maharaja's 29th Birthday. T* **19** *and similar horiz design. Wmk* C. *P* 12½.
71 6 ca. blackish violet .. .. .. 5·50 10
a. Perf 11 .. .. 5·50 10
ab. Imperf between (vert pair) .. .. 20·00
ac. Imperf horiz (vert pair) .. .. 38·00 50·00
b. Perf 12 .. .. 18·00 1·00
ba. Imperf between (horiz pair) .. .. 24·00
bb. Imperf between (vert pair) .. .. 38·00
bc. Imperf between (vert strip of 3) .. 22·00
c. Compound perf .. .. .. 5·50 80

72 ¾ ch. brown .. .. 5·50 20
a. Perf 11 .. .. 7·50 20
ab. Imperf between (horiz pair) £120
ac. Imperf between (vert pair) .. .. 28·00 38·00
ad. Imperf between (vert strip of 3) .. 24·00
ae. Block of four imperf between (horiz and vert) £160
b. Perf 12 .. .. 42·00 7·50
c. Compound perf .. .. 9·50 1·10
Design:—¾ ch. Maharaja and Marthanda Varma Bridge, Alwaye.

1943 (17 Sept). *Nos.* 65, 71 (*colour changed*) *and* 72 *surch as T* **20**. *P* 12½.
73 2 ca. on 1½ ch. scarlet .. .. 1·40 60
a. Imperf between (vert pair) .. .. 35·00
b. "2" omitted £200 £200
c. "CA" omitted £325
d. "ASH" omitted £325
e. Perf 11 .. .. 30 20
ea. "CA" omitted £325
f. Compound perf 55 85
fa. Imperf between (vert pair) £110
fb. "2" omitted £225
74 4 ca. on ¾ ch. brown .. .. 3·25 1·10
a. Perf 11 .. .. 3·50 30
b. Perf 12 .. .. — £100
c. Compound perf .. .. 4·00 1·00
75 8 ca. on 6 ca. scarlet .. .. 4·00 10
a. Perf 11 .. .. 3·00 10
ab. Imperf between (horiz pair) .. .. 32·00
b. Perf 12 .. .. — 70·00
c. Compound perf .. .. 12·00 6·00
73/5 .. .. *Set of* 3 6·00 55

21 Maharaja Bala Rama Varma XI

SPECIAL (22)

(Des Nilakantha Pellai. Plates by Indian Security Printing Press, Nasik. Typo Stamp Manufactory, Trivandrum)

1946 (24 Oct). *Maharaja's 34th Birthday. Wmk* C. *P* 12½.
76 **21** 8 ca. carmine .. .. 21·00 3·00
a. Perf 11 .. .. 65 1·00
b. Perf 12 .. .. 30·00 2·50
ba. Imperf between (horiz pair) .. .. 30·00 45·00
bb. Imperf between (horiz strip of 3) 48·00
c. Compound perf .. .. ..

1946. *No.* O103 *revalidated for ordinary postage with opt T* **22**, *in orange. P* 12½.
77 **19** 6 ca. blackish violet .. .. .. 6·00 2·25
a. Perf 11 .. .. .. 30·00 5·00
b. Compound perf .. .. .. 6·00 5·00

OFFICIAL STAMPS

GUM. Soon after 1911 the Official stamps were issued without gum. Thus only the initial printings of the 1, 2, 3 and 4 ch. values were gummed. As Nos. O38/9, O41/2 and O95 were overprinted on stamps intended for normal postage these, also, have gum.

PRINTINGS. Sometimes special printings of postage stamps were made specifically for overprinting for Official use, thus accounting for Official stamps appearing with watermarks or in shades not listed in the postage issues.

SETTINGS. These are based on the study of complete sheets of 84, and the measurements given are those of the majority of stamps on the sheet. Examples are known showing different measurements as each overprint was set individually in loose type, but these are not included in the listings.

On S. S — On S S

(O 1) (O 2)
Rounded "O"

1911 (16 Aug)–**30**. *Contemporary stamps optd with Type* O **1** (13 *mm wide*). *P* 12, *sometimes rough.* (*a*) *Wmk* B (*upright*) (16.8.11–21).
O 1 **3** 4 ca. pink (1916) 20 10
a. Opt inverted .. .. .. † 70·00
b. Opt double .. .. .. £100 80·00
c. "S S" inverted .. .. .. 30·00 16·00
d. Imperf (pair) £200 £200
e. Stamp doubly printed .. .. † £200
f. Left "S" inverted .. .. — 15·00
O 2 **1** 6 ca. chestnut (date ?) .. .. 30·00 30·00
O 3 ½ ch. reddish lilac (R.) (1919) .. 70 35
a. "CHUCRRAM" (R. 5/6) .. .. 8·50 4·50
O 4 **4** 10 ca. pink (1921) .. .. .. 15·00 2·75
a. "O" inverted .. .. .. 42·00 8·50
b. Left "S" inverted .. .. 42·00 8·50
c. Right "S" inverted .. .. 42·00 8·50
d. Opt inverted .. .. .. † 95·00
O 5 **1** 1 ch. chalky blue (R.) 65 10
a. Imperf between (vert pair) .. † £170
b. Opt inverted .. .. .. 7·00 4·25
c. Opt double .. .. .. 60·00 50·00
d. "nO" for "On" .. .. .. 75·00 75·00
e. "O" inverted .. .. .. 6·50 2·00
f. Left "S" inverted .. .. 7·00 2·25
g. Right "S" inverted .. .. 7·50 2·50
h. "S S" inverted .. .. .. — 42·00
O 6 **1** 2 ch. red 35 10
a. Opt inverted .. .. .. 8·00 8·00
b. "O" inverted .. .. .. 7·50 1·25
c. Left "S" inverted .. .. 7·50 1·25
d. Right "S" inverted .. .. 8·50 1·75
O 7 2 ch. red (B.) (date ?) .. .. .. — 90·00
O 8 **6** 3 ch. violet 35 10
a. Imperf between (vert pair) .. £160 £160
b. Imperf vert (horiz pair) £140
c. Opt inverted .. .. .. 10·00 10·00
d. Opt double .. .. .. 75·00 65·00
e. Right "S" inverted .. .. 4·50 1·00
f. Right "S" omitted .. .. 95·00 95·00
g. Left "S" omitted .. .. 95·00 95·00
O 9 3 ch. violet (B.) (date ?) .. .. £130 65·00
O10 **1** 4 ch. slate-green 55 10
a. Imperf between (horiz pair) .. — £200
b. Opt inverted .. .. .. 42·00 13·00
c. Opt double .. .. .. 95·00 85·00
d. "O" inverted .. .. .. 9·00 2·40
e. Left "S" inverted .. .. 10·00 3·00
f. Right "S" inverted .. .. 11·00 3·50
g. Left "S" omitted .. .. 95·00 95·00
O11 4 ch. slate-green (B.) (1921) .. .. — 50·00
a. "O" inverted .. .. .. — £120
b. Left "S" inverted .. .. — £120
c. Right "S" inverted .. .. — £120

(*b*) *Wmk* A (*sideways*) (1919–25)
O12 **3** 4 ca. pink .. .. 3·75 15
a. Imperf (pair) £250 £250
b. Opt inverted .. .. .. 55·00 17·00
c. "O" inverted .. .. .. 30·00 8·50
d. Left "S" inverted .. .. 35·00 10·00
e. Right "S" inverted .. .. 35·00 10·00
O13 4 ca. pink (B.) (1921) .. .. 38·00 75
a. "O" inverted .. .. .. — 20·00
O14 **4** 5 ca. olive-bistre (1921) 60 10
a. Opt inverted .. .. .. 12·00 9·00
b. "O" inverted .. .. .. 5·00 1·50
c. Left "S" inverted .. .. 5·00 1·50
d. Right "S" inverted .. .. 5·00 1·50
O15 **1** 6 ca. orange-brown (1921) 30 10
a. Imperf between (vert pair) .. † £170
b. Opt inverted .. .. .. 10·00 8·50
c. Opt double .. .. .. 60·00 60·00
d. "O" inverted .. .. .. 6·00 1·60
e. Left "S" inverted .. .. 5·50 1·40
f. Right "S" inverted .. .. 6·00 1·60
O16 6 ca. orange-brown (B.) (1921) .. 8·50 1·50
a. Opt inverted .. .. .. 95·00 95·00
b. "O" inverted .. .. .. 42·00 14·00
c. Left "S" inverted .. .. 42·00 14·00
d. Right "S" inverted .. .. 42·00 14·00
O17 ½ ch. reddish violet (R.) (date?) .. 1·10 20
a. Reddish lilac (date?) .. .. 1·10 20
b. Imperf between (horiz pair) .. £120 £120
c. Imperf between (vert pair) .. 55·00 55·00
d. Stamp doubly printed .. .. 48·00
e. Opt inverted .. .. .. 9·00 3·00
f. Opt double, both inverted .. £120
g. "CHUCRRAM" (R. 5/6) .. .. 6·50 2·75
h. "On" omitted .. .. .. — £110
i. Right "S" inverted .. .. — 24·00
j. Right "S" omitted .. .. — £110
O18 **4** 10 ca. pink (3.21) 65 10
a. Scarlet (1925?) .. .. — 9·50
b. Opt inverted .. .. .. — 18·00
c. Opt double .. .. .. 85·00 70·00
d. "O" inverted .. .. .. 8·50 2·50
e. Left "S" inverted .. .. 7·00 1·75
f. Right "S" inverted .. .. 8·50 2·50
g. Imperf between (horiz pair) .. — £130
O19 10 ca. pink (B.) (date?) .. .. 65·00 16·00
a. Opt inverted .. .. .. — 80·00
b. "O" inverted .. .. .. — 48·00
O20 **1** 1 ch. grey-blue (R.) (date?) .. .. 4·25 60
a. Deep blue .. .. .. 4·50 80
b. "O" inverted .. .. .. 32·00 8·00
c. Left "S" inverted .. .. 35·00 9·00
d. "On" omitted .. .. ..
e. Opt inverted .. .. .. † 55·00
O21 1¼ ch. claret (12.19) 40 10
a. Stamp doubly printed .. .. — £225
b. Opt inverted .. .. .. 9·00 8·00
c. Opt double .. .. .. 45·00
d. "O" inverted .. .. .. 10·00 2·00
e. Left "S" inverted .. .. 13·00 3·50
f. Right "S" inverted .. .. 13·00 3·50
g. Error. Carmine .. .. .. 50·00
O22 1¼ ch. claret (B.) (1921) .. .. — 65·00
a. "O" inverted .. .. .. — £140
b. Left "S" inverted .. .. — £140
c. Right "S" inverted .. .. — £140

(*c*) *Wmk* C (1925–30)
O23 **4** 5 ca. olive-bistre (1926) 40 40
a. Imperf between (horiz pair) .. £170 £170
b. Opt inverted .. .. .. 16·00 13·00
c. "O" inverted (R. 1/7) .. .. 4·75 2·75
d. Left "S" inverted (R. 6/1, 6/8) .. 4·50 2·50
e. Right "S" inverted (R. 6/7) .. 4·75 2·75
O23*f* 5 ca. chocolate (1930) .. .. 45·00
fa. Opt inverted .. .. .. — £100
O24 10 ca. pink (1926) .. .. .. 3·75 15
a. Imperf between (vert pair) .. — £160
b. Opt inverted .. .. .. 60·00 60·00
c. "O" inverted (R. 1/7) .. .. 22·00 2·75
d. Left "S" inverted (R. 6/1, 6/8) .. 20·00 2·50
e. Right "S" inverted (R. 6/7) .. 22·00 2·75
f. Stamp doubly printed .. ..
g. Opt double .. .. .. † 95·00
O25 **1** 1¼ ch. claret (1926) .. .. 13·00 40
a. "O" inverted (R. 1/7) .. .. 45·00 5·50
b. Left "S" inverted (R. 6/1, 6/8) .. 42·00 5·00
c. Right "S" inverted (R. 6/7) .. 45·00 5·50
d. Opt double .. .. .. † 95·00
O26 **7** 7 ch. claret .. .. .. 1·50 30
a. "O" inverted (R. 1/7) .. .. 15·00 3·75
b. Left "S" inverted (R. 6/1, 6/8) .. 14·00 3·50
c. Right "S" inverted (R. 6/7) .. 15·00 3·75
d. Error. Carmine-red .. .. 60·00
O27 **8** 14 ch. orange-yellow .. .. .. 2·25
a. "O" inverted (R. 1/7) .. .. 15·00
b. Left "S" inverted (R. 6/1, 6/8) .. 14·00
c. Right "S" inverted (R. 6/7) .. 15·00

1926–30. *Contemporary stamps optd with Type* O **2** (16 *wide*). *Wmk* C. *P* 12.
O28 **4** 5 ca. olive-bistre .. .. .. 2·50
a. Right "S" inverted .. .. 14·00
b. Left "S" inverted .. .. 17·00
O29 5 ca. chocolate (1930) 25
a. Imperf between (vert pair) .. †
b. Opt inverted .. .. .. 18·00
c. "O" inverted .. .. .. 3·50
d. Left "S" inverted .. .. 3·50
O30 **1** 6 ca. brown-red (date?) .. .. 4·75
a. "O" inverted .. .. .. 21·00
b. Left "S" inverted .. .. 24·00
c. Opt double .. .. .. †
O31 **4** 10 ca. pink 30
a. Imperf between (horiz pair) .. 60·00
b. Imperf between (vert pair) .. 48·00
c. Imperf vert (horiz strip of 3) .. †
d. Opt inverted .. .. .. 9·00
e. "Ou" for "On" .. .. .. 42·00
f. "O" inverted .. .. .. 4·25
g. Left "S" inverted .. .. 3·75
h. Right "S" inverted .. .. 3·75
i. Left "S" omitted .. .. .. 40·00
j. Wmk sideways .. .. .. 20·00
O32 **1** 1¼ ch. claret (*shades*) .. .. .. 1·60
a. Imperf between (horiz pair) .. 85·00
b. Imperf between (vert pair) .. 95·00
c. Opt inverted .. .. .. 22·00
d. "O" inverted .. .. .. 18·00
e. Left "S" inverted .. .. 18·00
f. Right "S" inverted .. .. 18·00
g. Left "S" omitted £110
h. Right "S" omitted £110
i. Wmk sideways .. .. .. —
O33 **6** 3 ch. violet .. .. 8·00
a. Opt inverted .. .. .. †
b. "O" inverted .. .. .. 40·00
c. "O" omitted .. .. .. 90·00
d. "Ou" for "On" £120
e. Left "S" inverted .. .. — 3
O34 **7** 7 ch. claret (date?) £110
O35 **8** 14 ch. orange-yellow .. .. .. 42·00
a. Imperf between (vert pair) .. £425
b. "O" inverted £100

The 5 ca. olive-bistre, 3 ch. and 7 ch. exist only with the no[rmal] watermark spaced 11 mm; the 5 ca. chocolate and 14 ch. exist with the wide 15 mm spacing; the 6 ca., 10 ca. and 1¼ ch. exi[st in] both forms.

On S S — On S S — On S

(O 3) (O 4) (O 5)
Italic "S S"

1930. *Wmk* C. *P* 12. (*a*) *Optd with Type* O **3**.
O36 **4** 10 ca. pink .. .. £190 £
O37 **1** 1¼ ch. carmine-rose .. .. .. 3·25

(*b*) *Optd with Type* O **4**
O38 **5** ¾ ch. black (R.) 35
a. Left "S" omitted .. .. .. 85·00
b. Right "S" omitted .. .. 85·00
c. Large roman "S" at left .. .. — 8

(*c*) *Optd with Type* O **5**
O39 **5** ¾ ch. black (R.) 35
a. Opt inverted .. .. .. † £
b. "n" omitted .. .. .. 90·00 9
O40 **1** 4 ch. slate-green (R.) .. .. .. 28·00 13

On S S — On S S — On S

(O 6) (O 7) (O 8)
Oval "O"

1930–39(?). *Contemporary stamps overprinted. P* 12.

(*a*) *With Type* O **6** (16 *mm high*) (i) *Wmk* A
O41 **3** 4 ca. pink .. .. 21·00 40
a. Large right "S" as Type O **2** (R. 6/14) .. .. .. 95·00 £1

(ii) *Wmk* B
O42 **3** 4 ca. pink .. .. 20·00 45·
a. Large right "S" as Type O **2** (R. 6/14) .. .. .. 95·00 £1

(iii) *Wmk* C
O43 **1** 6 ca. brown-red (1932) 35
a. Opt inverted .. .. .. 20·00
b. Opt double .. .. .. 45·00 45·
c. "O" inverted (R. 5/11–12) .. .. 8·00 5·
O44 **4** 10 ca. pink .. .. 2·00 1·
O45 **5** ¾ ch. mauve (1933) .. .. .. 3·50
a. Imperf between (horiz pair) .. 90·00 65·
b. Imperf between (horiz strip of 3) † £1
c. Imperf between (vert pair) .. † 95·
d. Stamp doubly printed .. .. † £1
e. Perf 12½ .. .. 7·00 4
f. Perf comp of 12 and 12½ .. 15·00 1·7
g. Right "S" inverted .. .. — 22·
O46 **1** 1¼ ch. carmine-rose .. .. .. 11·00 1·7
a. Opt double .. .. .. £100 80·
b. Large right "S" as Type O **2** (R. 6/14) .. .. .. £100 50·
O47 4 ch. grey-green .. .. .. 1·60 4·5

1 4 ch. grey-green (R.) (27.10.30) .. 70 20
a. Imperf between (horiz pair) .. £110 £110
b. Opt double .. .. .. 25·00 25·00
c. "O" inverted .. .. .. 30·00 18·00
d. Large right "S" as Type O **2** (R. 6/14) .. .. .. 42·00 28·00
e. Imperf between (vert pair) .. £110
8 14 ch. orange-yellow (1931) .. .. 7·50 1·75
a. Imperf between (vert pair) .. † £140
: the 1½ ch. and 3 ch., and for Nos. O43 and O48/9 but perf see Nos. O66/70 (new setting combining Types O **6** and

(*b*) *With Type* O **7** (14 *mm high*). *Wmk* C
3 4 ca. pink .. .. 12·00 28·00
a. "O" inverted .. .. .. 45·00 75·00
4 5 ca. chocolate (1932) .. .. 19·00 9·00
a. Opt inverted .. .. .. 65·00 65·00
1 6 ca. brown-red 20 10
a. Imperf between (vert pair) .. 50·00 50·00
b. Opt inverted .. .. .. 26·00
c. Opt double .. .. .. † 65·00
d. "nO" for "On" £110 £110
e. Right "S" inverted .. .. 20·00 14·00
f. Left "S" omitted .. .. — 75·00
g. Large "n" as Type O **5** (R. 1/1, 1/14) .. .. .. 20·00 12·00
h. Large italic left "S" as Type O **5** 22·00 13·00
i. Perf 12½ .. .. .. — 7·50
j. Perf compound of 12 and 12½ .. — 17·00
½ ch. reddish violet (1932) 30 15
a. "CHUCRRAM" (R. 5/6) .. .. 7·50 5·50
b. "Ou" for "On" .. .. .. 55·00 55·00
c. Left "S" omitted .. .. — £100
d. "O" of "On" omitted £150
½ ch. reddish violet (R.) (1935) .. 20 10
a. Imperf between (vert pair) .. £110 £110
b. "CHUCRRAM" (R. 5/6) .. .. 3·25 3·00
c. Left "S" inverted .. .. 22·00 20·00
4 10 ca. pink (date ?) .. .. .. 3·75 1·75
a. Imperf between (horiz pair) .. 12·00 18·00
b. Imperf between (vert pair) .. 10·00 17·00
c. "O" inverted .. .. .. 32·00 20·00
d. Right "S" inverted .. .. 32·00 20·00
5 ¾ ch. mauve (1933?) 30 15
a. Imperf between (vert pair) .. † £120
b. "Ou" for "On" .. .. .. 60·00 60·00
c. "O" inverted .. .. .. 22·00 19·00
d. Right "S" inverted .. .. — 19·00
e. Opt double .. .. .. † £110
f. Perf comp of 12 and 12½ .. 24·00 15·00
1 1 ch. deep blue (R.) (1935) .. .. 1·75 35
a. Slate-blue .. .. .. 1·00 20
b. Imperf between (horiz pair) .. £100 £100
c. Imperf between (vert pair) .. 25·00 35·00
d. Perf 12½ .. .. .. 8·00 3·25
e. Perf comp of 12 and 12½ .. 18·00 6·50
1¼ ch. claret .. .. 1·25 1·40
1½ ch. rose (1933) 40 10
a. Imperf between (vert pair) .. † £130
b. Opt double .. .. .. 70·00 70·00
c. "O" inverted .. .. .. 4·50 2·50
e. Large "n" as Type O **5** (R. 1/1, 1/14) .. .. .. 50·00 22·00
f. Large italic left "S" as Type O **5** 55·00 22·00
g. Left "S" inverted .. .. — 22·00
h. Perf 12½ .. .. .. — 10·00
i. Perf comp of 12 and 12½ .. — 19·00
ia. Stamp doubly printed .. .. — £170
) 6 3 ch. reddish violet (1933) .. .. 1·25 60
a. "O" inverted .. .. .. 18·00 7·50
b. Opt double .. .. .. † 90·00
3 ch. violet (R.) (1934) 70 10
a. Imperf between (horiz pair) .. 80·00 42·00
b. Imperf between (vert pair) .. 60·00 40·00
c. Opt inverted .. .. .. † 48·00
d. "O" inverted .. .. .. 19·00 12·00
e. Perf 12½ .. .. .. — 2·00
ea. Imperf between (vert pair) .. † £160
f. Perf comp of 12 and 12½ .. — 12·00
fa. Imperf between (horiz pair) .. † £160
g. "Ou" for "On" .. .. .. — 75·00
2 1 4 ch. grey-green (1934) .. .. — £250
3 4 ch. grey-green (R.) (1935?) .. .. 1·00 20
a. "Ou" for "On" (R. 1/1) .. .. 55·00 42·00
4 7 7 ch. claret (*shades*) .. .. .. 1·10 30
a. Imperf between (vert pair) .. 27·00 35·00
b. "O" inverted .. .. .. 42·00 20·00
c. Left "S" inverted .. .. 45·00 22·00
d. Perf 12½ .. .. .. — 7·50
e. Perf comp of 12 and 12½ .. — 8·00
ea. Imperf between (vert pair) .. † 95·00
eb. Imperf between (vert strip of 3) £130 £130
5 8 14 ch. orange (1933) .. .. .. 1·75 40
a. Imperf between (horiz pair) .. 32·00 45·00
b. Imperf between (vert pair) .. £130
c. Opt inverted .. .. .. † £325

:) *New setting combining Type* O **8** (18 *mm high*) *in top row with Type* O **6** (16 *mm high*) *for remainder. Wmk* C (dates?)

A. *Type* O **8**.
6A 1 6 ca. brown-red .. .. .. 7·00 3·50
a. Perf 12½ .. .. .. 7·00 3·50
7A 1½ ch. rose .. .. 35·00 5·00
a. Perf 12½ .. .. .. 42·00 8·50
8A 6 3 ch. violet (R.) .. .. .. 50·00 8·50
a. Perf 12½ .. .. .. 65·00 18·00
b. Perf comp of 12 and 12½ .. 90·00 22·00
9A 1 4 ch. grey-green (R.) .. .. 45·00 22·00
a. Perf 12½ .. .. .. 50·00 18·00
70A 8 14 ch. orange-yellow .. .. 48·00 14·00
a. Perf 12½ .. .. .. 50·00 15·00

B. *Type* O **6**
66Ba 1 6 ca. brown-red (*p* 12½) .. .. 3·00 90
ab. Imperf between (vert pair) .. 95·00 95·00
ac. "O" inverted .. .. .. 16·00 8·50
g. Perf comp of 12 and 12½ .. — 17·00
67B 1½ ch. rose .. .. 9·00 35
a. Perf 12½ .. .. .. 14·00 50
ab. "O" inverted .. .. .. 48·00 17·00
c. Perf comp of 12 and 12½ .. — 20·00
68B 6 3 ch. violet (R.) .. .. .. 9·50 1·00
a. Perf 12½ .. .. .. 17·00 1·00
b. Perf comp of 12 and 12½ .. 25·00 5·50

O69Ba 1 4 ch. grey-green (R.) (*p* 12½) .. 6·50 2·50
ab. Imperf between (horiz pair) .. † £170
ac. "O" inverted .. .. .. 80·00 35·00
O70Ba 8 14 ch. orange-yellow (*p* 12½) .. 12·00 1·00

Nos. O66/70A/B in vertical *se-tenant* pairs are very scarce.

As with the postage issues it is believed that the 12½ and compound perforations were issued between 1937 and 1939.

1 ch
8 c
(O **9**)

1 ch
Wrong fount "1 c" (R.6/7)

1932. *Official stamps surch as T* **14** *or with Type* O **9**. *P* 12.

(*a*) *With opt Type* O **1** (i) *Wmk* A
O71 4 6 c. on 5 ca. olive-bistre .. .. 42·00 19·00
a. "O" inverted .. .. .. £140 60·00
b. Left "S" inverted .. .. £130 55·00
c. Right "S" inverted .. .. £140 60·00

(ii) *Wmk* C
O72 4 6 c. on 5 ca. olive-bistre .. .. 22·00 8·00
a. "O" inverted .. .. .. 55·00 20·00
b. Left "S" inverted .. .. 50·00 18·00
c. Right "S" inverted .. .. 55·00 20·00
O73 12 c. on 10 ca. pink £120

(*b*) *With opt Type* O **2**. *Wmk C*
O74 4 6 c. on 5 ca. olive-bistre .. .. 1·60 1·10
a. Opt and surch inverted .. 45·00
b. Surch inverted .. .. .. 60·00
c. Left "S" inverted .. .. 13·00 4·75
d. Right "S" inverted .. .. 13·00 4·75
e. "6" omitted .. .. .. — 75·00
O75 6 c. on 5 ca. chocolate 20 25
a. Surch inverted .. .. .. 9·00 9·50
b. Surch double £100
c. Surch double, one inverted .. 95·00
d. "O" inverted .. .. .. 4·00 4·00
e. Left "S" inverted .. .. 4·00 4·00
f. Pair, one without surch .. £250
O76 12 c. on 10 ca. pink .. .. 1·50 50
a. Opt inverted .. .. .. 12·00 13·00
b. Surch inverted .. .. .. 7·00 7·00
c. Opt and surch inverted .. 32·00 32·00
d. Pair, one without surch .. £300
e. "O" inverted .. .. .. 6·50 3·25
f. Left "S" inverted .. .. 6·50 3·25
g. "Ou" for "On" .. .. .. 80·00 80·00
h. Right "S" inverted .. .. 6·50 3·25
i. "c" omitted (R. 6/1) .. .. 50·00 50·00
O77 1 1 ch. 8 c. on 1¼ ch. claret .. .. 2·25 1·00
a. Surch inverted .. .. .. † 80·00
b. "O" inverted .. .. .. 9·50 4·25
c. Left "S" inverted .. .. 9·50 4·25
d. Right "S" inverted .. .. 9·50 4·25
e. Wrong fount "1 c" .. .. 24·00 18·00

(*c*) *With opt Type* O **3**. *Wmk* C
O78 4 12 c. on 10 ca. pink .. .. † £325
O79 1 1 ch. 8 c. on 1¼ ch. carmine-rose .. 55·00 35·00
a. "n" omitted £200
b. Wrong fount "1 c" £190 £140

(*d*) *With opt Type* O **6**. *Wmk* C
O80 4 12 c. on 10 ca. pink .. .. 90·00 22·00
O81 1 1 ch. 8 c. on 1¼ ch. carmine-rose .. £100 18·00
a. Wrong fount "1 c" .. .. £275 80·00
b. "h" omitted .. .. ..
c. Brown-red .. .. .. — 18·00

(*e*) *With opt Type* O **7**. *Wmk* C
O82 4 6 c. on 5 ca. chocolate 20 30
a. Opt inverted .. .. .. 70·00 70·00
b. Surch inverted .. .. .. 11·00 12·00
c. Right "S" omitted £100 £100
d. Two quads for right "S" .. £450
e. Right "S" inverted .. .. 25·00
O83 12 c. on 10 ca. pink 20 15
a. Opt inverted .. .. .. 7·50 7·50
b. Surch inverted .. .. .. 6·00 6·00
c. Opt and surch inverted .. 32·00 32·00
d. Opt double .. .. .. † 85·00
e. "O" inverted .. .. .. 15·00 15·00
f. Right "S" inverted .. .. 16·00 16·00
g. "On" omitted .. .. .. — 95·00
h. "n" omitted .. .. .. — 95·00
i. "c" omitted (R. 6/1) .. .. 30·00 30·00
j. Surch double .. .. .. † 90·00
O84 1 1 ch. 8 c. on 1¼ ch. claret 35 25
a. Imperf between (vert pair) .. † £250
b. Opt omitted .. .. .. † £425
c. Surch inverted .. .. .. 14·00 14·00
d. Surch double .. .. .. 65·00
e. "O" inverted .. .. .. 4·50 2·75
f. Wrong fount "1 c" .. .. 18·00 15·00

SERVICE
(O **10**)
13 mm ("R" with curved tail)

SERVICE
(O **11**)
13½ mm ("R" with straight tail)

SERVICE
8 CASH
(O **12**)

1939–41. *Nos.* 35 *and* 40 *with type-set opt, Type* O **10**. *P* 12½.
O85 1 6 ca. brown-red (1941) 80 30
a. Perf 11 .. .. .. 1·40 75
b. Perf 12 .. .. .. 70 30
c. Compound perf .. .. 70 1·10
O86 5 ¾ ch. reddish violet .. .. £100 55·00
a. Perf 12 .. .. .. 22·00 1·40
b. Compound perf .. .. 95·00 55·00

1939 (9 Nov). *Maharaja's 27th Birthday. Nos.* 64/70 *with type-set opt, Type* O **10**. *P* 12½.
O87 1 ch. yellow-green .. .. .. 4·50 25
O88 1½ ch. scarlet .. .. .. 4·50 75
a. "SESVICE" .. .. .. 80·00 26·00
b. Perf 12 .. .. .. 35·00 6·50
ba. "SESVICE" .. .. .. — £110
bb. Imperf between (horiz pair) .. † £150
c. Compound perf .. .. 11·00 1·75
O89 2 ch. orange .. .. .. 4·50 5·00
a. "SESVICE" .. .. .. 95·00 £110
b. Compound perf .. .. 80·00 80·00
O90 3 ch. brown .. .. .. 3·75 20
a. "SESVICE" .. .. .. 70·00 21·00
b. Perf 12 .. .. .. 20·00 45
ba. "SESVICE" .. .. .. £180 42·00
c. Compound perf .. .. 8·50 3·25
O91 4 ch. red .. .. .. 9·00 3·50
O92 7 ch. pale blue .. .. .. 10·00 2·25
O93 14 ch. turquoise-green .. .. 13·00 3·50
O87/93 .. .. *Set of* 7 45·00 14·00

1940 (?)–**45.** *Nos.* 40*a and* 42*b optd with Type* O **11** *from stereos. P* 12½.
O94 5 ¾ ch. reddish violet .. .. 12·00 20
a. Imperf between (horiz pair) .. £120
b. Perf 11 .. .. .. 55·00 1·10
c. Perf 12 .. .. .. 18·00 20
d. Compound perf .. .. 45·00 75
O95 1 1½ ch. rose (1945) .. .. 13·00 8·00
a. Perf 12 .. .. .. 4·50 1·00
b. Compound perf .. .. 20·00 12·00

1942 (?). *Nos.* 64/70 *optd with Type* O **11** *from stereos. P* 12½.
O 96 1 ch. yellow-green .. .. .. 1·00 10
a. Imperf between (vert pair) .. 45·00 48·00
b. Opt inverted .. .. .. † 40·00
c. Opt double .. .. .. 21·00
d. Perf 11 .. .. .. 75 10
da. Imperf between (vert pair) .. 28·00
db. Opt double .. .. .. 95·00 95·00
e. Perf 12 .. .. .. 3·00 50
ea. Imperf between (vert pair) .. 85·00 85·00
eb. Stamp doubly printed £120
ec. Opt inverted .. .. .. † 95·00
ed. Opt double .. .. .. 23·00
f. Compound perf .. .. 6·50 1·00
fa. Imperf between (vert pair) .. † £130
O 97 1½ ch. scarlet .. .. .. 3·25 10
a. Imperf between (horiz pair) .. 55·00
b. Perf 11 .. .. .. 1·25 15
ba. Imperf between (vert pair) .. 95·00 95·00
bb. Imperf between (vert strip of 3) 70·00
bc. Imperf between (horiz pair) .. † £100
c. Perf 12 .. .. .. 4·75 50
ca. Imperf between (vert strip of 3) £130
d. Compound perf .. .. 2·50 30
e. Imperf (pair) .. .. .. 26·00
O 98 2 ch. orange .. .. .. 1·25 30
a. Perf 11 .. .. .. 7·50 1·10
ab. Imperf between (vert pair) ..
b. Perf 12 .. .. .. 80·00 80·00
ba. Imperf between (vert pair) .. £325 £325
c. Compound perf .. .. 80·00 80·00
O 99 3 ch. brown 85 10
a. Imperf between (vert pair) ..
b. Perf 11 .. .. .. 2·25 10
c. Perf 12 .. .. .. 4·50 1·50
ca. Imperf between (vert pair) .. £250 £250
d. Compound perf .. .. 16·00 75
O100 4 ch. red .. .. .. 2·25 75
a. Perf 11 .. .. .. 3·00 45
b. Perf 12 .. .. .. 15·00 3·75
c. Compound perf .. .. 60·00 21·00
O101 7 ch. pale blue .. .. .. 6·50 35
a. Perf 11 .. .. .. 4·75 3·75
b. Perf 12 .. .. .. 19·00 7·50
c. Compound perf .. .. 16·00 4·50
d. Blue (*p* 11) .. .. .. 10·00 5·00
da. Perf 12 .. .. .. 7·50 4·75
db. Compound perf .. .. 23·00 16·00
O102 14 ch. turquoise-green .. .. 11·00 70
a. Perf 11 .. .. .. 11·00 1·50
b. Perf 12 .. .. .. 8·50 2·40
c. Compound perf .. .. 55·00 6·50
O96/102 .. .. *Set of* 7 18·00 1·90

1942. *Maharaja's 29th Birthday. Nos* 71/2 *optd with Type* O **11**. *P* 12½.
O103 6 ca. blackish violet 40 50
a. Perf 11 .. .. .. 70 1·00
b. Perf 12 .. .. .. 55·00 5·50
c. Compound perf .. .. 1·50 1·00
O104 ¾ ch. brown .. .. .. 3·75 10
a. Imperf between (vert pair) .. † £300
b. Perf 11 .. .. .. 6·00 10
c. Perf 12 .. .. .. 55·00 2·00
d. Compound perf .. .. 7·50 85

1943. *Surch with Type* O **12**. *P* 12½.
O105 19 8 ca. on 6 ca. scarlet .. .. 2·00 20
a. Perf 11 .. .. .. 1·25 10
ab. Surch inverted .. .. † £800
b. Compound perf .. .. 6·00 1·25

1945. *Nos.* 73/4 *optd with Type* O **11**. *P* 12½.
O106 2 ca. on 1½ ch. scarlet 50 60
a. Perf 11 .. .. .. 45 15
ab. Pair, one without surch .. £250
b. Compound perf .. .. 70 1·00
ba. "2" omitted £250 £250
c. Perf 12 .. .. ..
O107 4 ca. on ¾ ch. brown .. .. 2·75 30
a. Perf 11 .. .. .. 1·50 20
b. Compound perf .. .. 1·40 1·00

1947. *Maharaja's 34th Birthday. Optd with Type* O **11.**

O108 **21** 8 ca. carmine — 2·25 70
a. Imperf between (horiz pair) — 38·00
ab. Imperf between (vert pair) — † £140
b. Opt double — † £190
c. Perf 12½ — 3·50 1·10
ca. Stamp doubly printed — 30·00
d. Perf 12 — 3·50 1·40
da. Stamp doubly printed — 40·00

From 1 July 1949 Travancore formed part of the new State of Travancore-Cochin and stamps of Travancore surcharged in Indian currency were used.

TRAVANCORE-COCHIN

On 1 July 1949 the United State of Travancore and Cochin was formed ("U.S.T.C.") and the name was changed to State of Travancore-Cochin ("T.C.") by the new constitution of India on 26 January 1950.

PRICES FOR STAMPS ON COVER	
Nos. 1/13	*from* × 8
Nos. O1/17	*from* × 15

NO WATERMARK VARIETIES. These were formerly listed but we have now decided to omit them as they do not occur in full sheets. They are best collected in pairs, with and without watermarks.

COMPOUND PERFS. The notes above Type **17** of Travancore also apply here.

VALIDITY OF STAMPS. From 6 June 1950 the stamps of Travancore-Cochin were valid on mail from both Indian and state post offices to destinations in India and abroad.

ONE ANNA
ഒരണ
(1)

2 p. on 6 ca.

രണ്ടു പൈസ   രണ്ടു പൈസ

Normal — 1st character of 2nd group as 1st character of 1st group (Rt pane R.14/2)

1949 (1 July). *Stamps of Travancore surch in* "PIES" *or* "ANNAS" *as T* **1**. *P* 12½.

1 **19** 2 p. on 6 ca. blackish violet (R.) — 2·25 1·00
a. Surch inverted — 38·00
b. Character error — £120 80·00
c. "O" inverted (Rt pane R. 13/1) — 28·00 15·00
d. Perf 11 — 1·40 30
da. Imperf between (vert pair) — £130 £130
db. Pair, one without surch — 90·00
dc. Character error — £110 80·00
dd. "O" inverted (Rt pane R. 13/1) — 30·00 15·00
e. Perf 12 — 40 20
ea. Imperf between (horiz pair) — 50·00
eb. Imperf between (vert pair) — 5·00 14·00
ec. Surch inverted — 85·00
ed. Character error — £120 80·00
ee. Imperf between (vert strip of 3) — 35·00
ef. Block of four imperf between (horiz and vert) — 50·00
eg. "O" inverted (Rt pane R. 13/1) — 27·00 14·00
f. Perf 14 — † £450
g. Imperf (pair) — 8·50
h. Compound perf — — 32·00

2 **21** 4 p. on 8 ca. carmine — 1·10 30
a. Surch inverted — 40·00
b. "S" inverted — 85·00 42·00
c. Perf 11 — 1·75 30
ca. Imperf between (vert pair) — £140 £140
cb. Surch inverted — 85·00
cc. Pair, one without surch — £100
cd. "FOUP" for "FOUR" — £140 95·00
ce. "S" inverted — 85·00 42·00
d. Perf 12 — 50 30
da. Imperf between (vert pair) — 17·00
db. Pair, one without surch — 95·00
dc. "FOUP" for "FOUR" — £110 85·00
dd. "S" inverted — 85·00 48·00
de. Surch inverted — £100
e. Imperf (pair) — 70·00
f. Compound perf — — 32·00
g. Perf 13½ — † £475

3 **17** ½ a. on 1 ch. yellow-green — 3·00 30
a. "NANA" for "ANNA" (Lt pane R.3/3) — £130 85·00
b. Inverted "H" in "HALF" — — 85·00
c. Imperf between (vert pair) — † £120
d. Perf 11 — 2·00 20
da. Imperf between (vert pair) — 27·00
db. Surch inverted — † £160
dc. "NANA" for "ANNA" (Lt pane R.3/3) — £160 95·00
dd. Inverted "H" in "HALF" — — 85·00
e. Perf 12 — 65 40
ea. Imperf between (horiz pair) — 45·00 48·00
eb. Imperf between (vert pair) — 5·00 12·00
ec. Surch inverted — 5·00
ed. "NANA" for "ANNA" (Lt pane R.3/3) — £180 £110
ee. Block of four imperf between (horiz and vert) — 42·00
f. Perf 14 — † £400
g. Imperf (pair) — 9·00 19·00
h. Compound perf — — 29·00

4 **18** 1 a. on 2 ch. orange — 3·00 30
a. Perf 11 — 55 30
ab. Surch double — 50·00
b. Perf 12 — 3·00 50
ba. Imperf between (horiz pair) — 7·00
bb. Imperf between (vert pair) — 4·25 11·00
bc. Block of four imperf between (horiz and vert) — 45·00
c. Perf 13½ — £150 2·00
d. Imperf (pair) — 8·50
e. Compound perf — 35·00 23·00

5 – 2 a. on 4 ch. red (68) — 2·75 60
a. Surch inverted — † £225
b. "O" inverted — 35·00 16·00
c. Perf 11 — 2·75 60
ca. "O" inverted — — 18·00
d. Perf 12 — 2·25 55
da. "O" inverted — 40·00 18·00
e. Compound perf — 40·00 26·00

6 **18** 3 a. on 7 ch. pale blue (69) — 10·00 4·50
a. Perf 11 — 4·50 2·50
ab. Blue — 50·00 4·50
ac. "3" omitted — † £450
b. Perf 12 — 9·00 2·75
c. Compound perf — — 55·00
ca. Blue — — 75·00

7 – 6 a. on 14 ch. turquoise-green (70) — 13·00 22·00
a. Accent omitted from native surch (Rt pane R.13/4) — £200 £225
b. Perf 11 — 11·00 18·00
ba. Accent omitted from native surch (Rt pane R.13/4) — £200 £225
c. Perf 12 — 13·00 19·00
ca. Accent omitted from native surch (Rt pane R. 13/4) — £225 £250
d. Compound perf — 29·00 32·00
da. Accent omitted from native surch (Rt pane R.13/4) — £325
e. Imperf (pair)

1/7 — *Set of* 7 18·00 20·00

There are two settings of the ½ a. surcharge. In one the first native character is under the second downstroke of the "H" and in the other it is under the first downstroke of the "A" of "HALF". They occur on stamps perf 12½, 11 and 12 equally commonly and also on the Official stamps.

U. S. T. C. (2)   **T.-C.** (3)   **SIX PIES** (4)

1949. *No.* 106 *of Cochin optd with T* **2**.

8 **29** 1 a. orange — 4·50 50·00
a. No stop after "S" (R. 1/6) — 75·00
b. Raised stop after "T" (R. 4/1) — 75·00

1950 (1 Apr). *No.* 106 *of Cochin optd with T* **3**.

9 **29** 1 a. orange — 5·50 48·00
a. No stop after "T" — 50·00
b. Opt inverted — £190
ba. No stop after "T" — £1500

The no stop variety occurs on No. 5 in the sheet and again on No. 8 in conjunction with a short hyphen.

1950 (1 Apr). *No.* 9 *surch as T* **4**.

10 **29** 6 p. on 1 a. orange — 3·25 40·00
a. No stop after "T" (R. 1/5) — 19·00
b. Error. Surch on No. 8 — 15·00
ba. No stop after "S" — £200
bb. Raised stop after "T" — £200

11 9 p. on 1 a. orange — 2·50 35·00
a. No stop after "T" (R. 1/5) — 17·00
b. Error. Surch on No. 8 — £160
ba. No stop after "S" — £600
bb. Raised stop after "T" — £600

5 Conch or Chank Shell

6 Palm Trees

(Litho Indian Security Printing Press, Nasik)

1950 (24 Oct). *W* **69** *of India. P* 14.

12 **5** 2 p. rose-carmine — 2·00 2·00
13 **6** 4 p. ultramarine — 2·75 13·00

The ordinary issues of Travancore-Cochin became obsolete on 1 July 1951.

OFFICIAL STAMPS

VALIDITY. Travancore-Cochin official stamps were valid for use throughout India from 30 September 1950.

SERVICE (O 1)   **SERVICE** (O 2)

1949 (1 July)–**51.** *Stamps of Travancore surch with va[lue as]* *T* **1** *and optd* "SERVICE". *No gum. P* 12½. (*a*) *With Ty[pe]*

(i) *Wmk C of Travancore*

O 1 **19** 2 p. on 6 ca. blackish violet (R.) — 1·00
a. Imperf between (vert pair) — £140
b. Character error (Rt pane R. 14/2) — 38·00
c. "O" inverted — 22·00
d. Pair, one without surch — £130
e. Perf 11 — 70
ea. Imperf between (vert pair) — £140
eb. Character error (Rt pane R. 14/2) — 42·00
ec. "O" inverted — 22·00
f. Perf 12 — 35
fa. Imperf between (horiz pair) — 8·50
fb. Imperf between (vert pair) — 6·00
fc. Character error (Rt pane R. 14/2) — 38·00
fd. "O" inverted — 22·00
fe. Block of four imperf between (horiz and vert) — 26·00
g. Imperf (pair) — 8·50
ga. Character error (Rt pane R. 14/2) — £190

O 2 **21** 4 p. on 8 ca. carmine — 2·50
a. "FOUB" for "FOUR" (Lt pane R. 2/3) — £170
b. Perf 11 — 2·50
ba. "FOUB" for "FOUR" (Lt pane R. 2/3) — 90·00
c. Perf 12 — 2·50
ca. "FOUB" for "FOUR" (Lt pane R. 2/3) — £100
d. Compound perf — 18·00

O 3 **17** ½ a. on 1 ch. yellow-green — 50
a. Pair, one without surch — 75·00
b. Surch inverted — 26·00
c. "NANA" for "ANNA" (Lt pane R. 3/3) — £190
d. Perf 11 — 1·00
da. Pair, one without surch — £120
db. Surch inverted — 55·00
dc. "NANA" for "ANNA" (Lt pane R. 3/3) — £180
e. Perf 12 — 8·50
ea. "NANA" for "ANNA" (Lt pane R. 3/3) — £350
eb. Pair, one without surch — 95·00
ec. Surch inverted on back only — £200
f. Compound perf — — 2

O 4 **18** 1 a. on 2 ch. orange — 18·00
a. Surch inverted — 90·00
b. Pair, one without surch — £500
c. Perf 11 — 16·00
ca. Pair, one without surch — £600

O 5 – 2 a. on 4 ch. red (68) — 1·25
b. Perf 11 — 4·50
ba. Surch inverted — £600
bb. "O" inverted — — 3
c. Perf 12 — 5·50
ca. "O" inverted — — 6
cb. Pair, one without surch — £225
d. Compound perf — — 2
e. Imperf (pair) — 12·00

O 6 – 3 a. on 7 ch. pale blue (69) — 4·50
a. Imperf between (vert pair) — 18·00
b. Blue — 35·00
c. Perf 11 — 2·40
ca. Blue — 35·00
d. Perf 12 — 3·00
da. Imperf between (horiz pair) — 17·00
db. Imperf between (vert pair) — 8·50
dc. Block of four imperf between (horiz and vert) — 38·00
dd. Blue — 35·00
e. Imperf (pair) — 11·00

O 7 – 6 a. on 14 ch. turquoise-green (70) — 13·00
a. Imperf between (vert pair) — 30·00
b. Perf 11 — 11·00
c. Perf 12 — 45·00
ca. Imperf between (horiz pair) — 27·00
cb. Imperf between (vert pair) — 32·00
cc. Block of four imperf between (horiz and vert) — 60·00
d. Imperf (pair) — 14·00

O1/7 — *Set of* 7 32·00 13

(ii) *W* **27** *of Cochin*

O 8 **19** 2 p. on 6 ca. blackish violet (R.) — 30
a. Type O **1** double — 18·00
b. Perf 11 — 50 1
c. Perf 12 — 55 1

O 9 – 2 a. on 4 ch. red (68) — 1·50 1
a. Perf 11 — 60
ab. Imperf between (vert pair) — £200 £
b. Compound perf — 50·00 30

(*b*) *With Type* O **2**

(i) *Wmk C of Travancore*

O10 **21** 4 p. on 8 ca. carmine — 40
a. "FOUB" for "FOUR" (Lt pane R.2/3) — £100 38
b. 2nd "E" of "SERVICE" in wrong fount — — 48
c. "S" in "PIES" inverted — — 50
d. Imperf between (vert pair) — † £1
e. Perf 11 — 30
ea. Imperf between (horiz pair) — 4·50
eb. Imperf between (vert pair) — 32·00
ec. "FOUB" for "FOUR" (Lt pane R.2/3) — 95·00 32·
ed. 2nd "E" of "SERVICE" in wrong fount — £100 55·
ee. "S" in "PIES" inverted — — 65·
ef. Block of four imperf between (horiz and vert) — 35·00
f. Perf 12 — 30
fa. Imperf between (horiz pair) — 5·00
fb. Imperf between (vert pair) — 2·00
fc. Block of four imperf between (horiz and vert) — 13·00 23·
fd. "FOUB" for "FOUR" (Lt pane R.2/3) — £110 40·
ff. 2nd "E" of "SERVICE" in wrong fount — £110 48·
fg. "FOUK" for "FOUR" — † £42
g. Perf 13½ — 3·75 1·2
h. Compound perf — 8·00 8·
i. Imperf (pair) — 6·00
ia. 2nd "E" of "SERVICE" in wrong fount — £150

7 ½ a. on 1 ch. yellow-green 60 20
a. "AANA" for "ANNA" (Rt pane R.13/1) .. .. £150 60·00
b. Perf 11 .. .. 30 20
ba. Imperf between (horiz pair) .. 60·00 60·00
bb. Imperf between (vert pair) .. 9·00
bc. Block of four imperf between (horiz and vert) .. .. 50·00
bd. "AANA" for "ANNA" (Rt pane R.13/1) .. .. 75·00 40·00
c. Perf 12 .. .. 85 15
ca. Imperf between (horiz pair) .. 3·50
cb. Imperf between (vert pair) .. 3·50 9·00
cc. "AANA" for "ANNA" (Rt pane R.13/1) .. .. 95·00 55·00
cd. Block of four imperf between (horiz and vert) .. .. 23·00
d. Compound perf .. .. .. 21·00 15·00
da. "AANA" for "ANNA" (Rt pane R.13/1) .. .. — £170
e. Imperf (pair) .. .. .. 6·50 16·00
18 1 a. on 2 ch. orange 40 30
a. Imperf between (vert pair) .. † £130
ab. Imperf between (horiz pair) .. † £130
b. Perf 11 .. .. 2·75 50
ba. Imperf between (horiz pair) .. 6·50 16·00
bb. Imperf between (vert pair) .. 80·00 80·00
c. Perf 12 .. .. 40 20
ca. Imperf between (horiz pair) .. 7·00
cb. Imperf between (vert pair) .. 3·75 10·00
cc. Block of four imperf between (horiz and vert) .. .. 21·00
d. Compound perf .. .. .. 25·00 17·00
e. Imperf (pair) .. .. .. 14·00
– 2 a. on 4 ch. red (68) .. .. .. 3·00 80
a. "O" inverted (Lt pane R. 14/3) .. 70·00 38·00
b. Perf 11 .. .. 1·50 1·10
ba. "O" inverted (Lt pane R. 14/3) .. 60·00 38·00
c. Perf 12 .. .. 8·50 1·10
ca. Imperf between (vert pair) .. £130 £140
cb. "O" inverted (Lt pane R. 14/3) .. £110 38·00
cc. Pair, one without surch .. .. † £650
d. Compound perf .. .. .. 23·00 13·00
– 3 a. on 7 ch. pale blue (69) .. .. 6·50 1·10
a. "S" inverted in "SERVICE" (Lt pane R.6/3) .. .. 75·00 32·00
b. First "E" inverted (Lt pane R.7/4) £170 £130
c. "C" inverted (Lt pane R.4/1 and 5/1) 90·00 75·00
d. Second "E" inverted (Lt pane R.3/2) £160 £120
e. Perf 11 .. .. 1·50 1·10
ea. "S" inverted in "SERVICE" (Lt pane R.6/3) .. .. 50·00 32·00
f. Perf 12 .. .. 3·75 1·60
fa. "S" inverted in "SERVICE" (Lt pane R.6/3) .. .. £130 80·00
g. Compound perf .. .. .. — 42·00
h. Imperf (pair) .. .. .. 40·00
– 6 a. on 14 ch. turquoise-green (70) .. 1·50 3·25
a. Accent omitted from native surch 16·00 13·00
b. "S" inverted in "SERVICE" (Lt pane R.6/3) .. .. 70·00 42·00
c. Perf 11 .. .. 12·00 3·25
ca. Accent omitted from native surch 60·00 22·00
cb. "S" inverted in "SERVICE" (Lt pane R.6/3) .. .. £130 50·00
d. Perf 12 .. .. 42·00 4·50
da. Accent omitted from native surch £130 30·00
db. "S" inverted in "SERVICE" (Lt pane R.6/3) .. .. £275 65·00
e. Compound perf .. .. .. 75·00 75·00
15 .. .. .. *Set of* 6 5·00 5·00

(ii) *W* **27** *of Cochin*

17 ½ a. on 1 ch. yellow-green .. .. 1·50 65
a. Perf 11 .. .. 40 40
b. Perf 12 .. .. 17·00 9·00
c. Compound perf .. .. .. 11·00 3·00
18 1 a. on 2 ch. orange .. .. .. 1·00 65
a. Perf 11 .. .. 50 40
b. Perf 12 .. .. 11·00 4·00
c. Perf 13½ .. .. 2·00 1·00
d. Compound perf .. .. .. 5·00 3·00

os. O2, O10, O12 and O17 have the value at top in English and ottom in native characters with "SERVICE" in between. All ers have "SERVICE" below the surcharge.

ype O 2 was overprinted at one operation with the harges.

os. O10b, O10ed, O10ff and O10ia, show the second "E" of RVICE" with serifs matching those on the surcharge. The ety occurred on Right pane R. 10/6 and R. 11/6, but was soon ected.

he "accent omitted" varieties on No. O15 occur on Left pane /1, 11/4 and Right pane R. 1/4, 12/4, 14/1 and 13/4.

he Official stamps became obsolete in September 1951.

WADHWAN

PRICES FOR STAMPS ON COVER	
No. 1	*from* × 30
No. 2	—
Nos. 3/6	*from* × 30

Thakur Bal Singh, 1885–1910

1

1888–94. *Litho.* (a) *Thin toned wove paper*
1 1 ½ pice, black (I, III) (*p* 12½ *large holes*) .. 16·00 50·00
a. Imperf between (vert pair) (I) ..
b. Pin-perf 6½ irregular (I) .. .. 90·00
c. Compound of 12½ and pin-perf 6½ (I) £160
2 ½ pice, black (II) (*p* 12½ *irregular small holes*) .. .. 38·00

(b) *Medium toned wove paper*
3 1 ½ pice, black (III) (*p* 12½) .. .. .. 10·00 40·00
4 ½ pice, black (V) (*p* 12) .. .. .. 9·00 10·00

(c) *Thick off-white or toned wove paper*
5 1 ½ pice, black (IV, VI) (*p* 12) (7.92) .. .. 7·00 7·50
a. Perf compound of 12 and 11 (IV) .. 17·00 42·00
6 ½ pice, black (VII) (*fine impression*) (*p* 12) (1894) .. .. 7·50 20·00

Sheets from the Stone IV printing had at least one horizontal line of perforations gauging 11, normally between the bottom two rows of the sheet.

These stamps were lithographed from seven different stones taken from a single die. Brief details of the individual stones are as follows:

Stone I	– No. 1. Sheet size not known, but possibly 28 (4×7). Sheet margins imperforate
Stone II	– No. 2. Sheets of 42 (7×6) with imperforate margins
Stone III	– Nos. 1 (thin paper) and 3 (medium paper). Sheets of 40 (4×10) with imperforate margins
Stone IV	– Nos. 5/a. Sheets of 32 (4×8) with imperforate margins at top and right
Stone V	– No. 4. Sheets of 20 (4×5) with imperforate margins at top, right and bottom
Stone VI	– No. 5. Sheets of 30 (5×6) with all margins perforated
Stone VII	– No. 6. Sheets of 32 (4×8) with all margins perforated. Much finer impression than the other stones

Stamps from stones I and II come with or without the dot before "STATE". Those from the later stones always show the dot. The shading on the pennant above the shield can also be used in stone identification. Stamps from stones I to III show heavy shading on the pennant, but this is less evident on stone IV and reduced further to a short line or dot on stones V to VII. There is a ")" hairline after "HALF" on the majority of stamps from Stone III.

The stamps of Wadhwan became obsolete on 1 January 1895.

Ionian Islands

The British occupation of the Ionian Islands was completed in 1814 and the archipelago was placed under the protection of Great Britain by the Treaty of Paris of 9 November 1815. The United States of the Ionian Islands were given local self-government, which included responsibility for the postal services. Crowned-circle handstamps were, however, supplied in 1844, although it is believed these were intended for use on prepaid mail to foreign destinations.

Examples of the Great Britain 1855 1d. red-brown stamp are known used at Corfu, cancelled as No. CC2, but it is believed that these originate from mail sent by the British garrison.

For illustrations of the handstamp types see BRITISH POST OFFICES ABROAD notes, following GREAT BRITAIN.

CEPHALONIA

CROWNED-CIRCLE HANDSTAMPS

CC1 CC 1 CEPHALONIA (19.4.1844) .. *Price on cover* £1000

CORFU

CROWNED-CIRCLE HANDSTAMPS

CC2 CC 1 CORFU (19.4.1844) .. .. *Price on cover* £500
CC3 CC 1 CORFU (G. or B.) (1844) .. *Price on cover* —

ZANTE

CROWNED-CIRCLE HANDSTAMPS

CC4 CC 1 ZANTE (G. or B.) (19.4.1844) .. *Price on cover* £1000

Nos. CC1/2 were later, *circa* 1860/1, struck in green (Cephalonia) or red (Corfu).

It is believed that examples of No. CC4 in black are from an unauthorised use of this handstamp which is now on display in the local museum. A similar handstamp, but without "PAID AT" was introduced in 1861.

PRICES FOR STAMPS ON COVER	
Nos. 1/3	*from* × 10

PERKINS BACON "CANCELLED". For notes on these handstamps, showing "CANCELLED" between horizontal bars forming an oval, see Catalogue Introduction.

1

(Eng C. Jeens. Recess Perkins, Bacon & Co)

1859 (15 June). *Imperf.*
1 1 (½d.) orge (no wmk) (H/S "CANCELLED" in oval £5000) .. .. .. 80·00 £500
2 (1d.) blue (wmk "2" (H/S "CANCELLED" in oval £5000) .. .. .. 20·00 £180
3 (2d.) carm (wmk "1") (H/S "CANCELLED" in oval £4500) .. .. .. 15·00 £180

On 30 May 1864, the islands were ceded to Greece, and these stamps became obsolete.

Great care should be exercised in buying used stamps, on or off cover, as forged postmarks are plentiful.

Iraq

Indian post offices were opened at Baghdad and Basra, then part of the Turkish Empire, on 1 January 1868. Unoverprinted stamps of India were used, Baghdad being allocated numeral cancellations "356", "18" and "K-6", and Basra (also spelt Bussorah, Busreh, Busrah, Busra) "357", "19" and "1/K-6".

Both offices closed on 30 September 1914, but Basra re-opened in December 1914 when Indian stamps overprinted "I.E.F." were used.

(Currency. 16 annas = 1 rupee)

I. ISSUES FOR BAGHDAD

PRICES FOR STAMPS ON COVER	
Nos 1/25	*from* × 6

BRITISH OCCUPATION

British and Indian troops occupied the port of Basra on 22 November 1914 to protect the oil pipeline. They then advanced up the rivers, and after a hard campaign took Baghdad from the Turks on 11 March 1917.

IN BRITISH BAGHDAD OCCUPATION
2 Ans
(1)

1917 (1 Sept). *Stamps of Turkey, surch as T* **1** *in three operations.*

(*a*) *Pictorial designs of* 1914. *T* **32**, *etc., and* **31**

1 **32** ¼ a. on 2 pa. claret (Obelisk) £100 £120
a. "IN BRITISH" omitted £5500
2 **34** ¼ a. on 5 pa. dull purple (Leander's Tower) 75·00 80·00
a. Value omitted £5000
3 **36** ½ a. on 10 pa. green (Lighthouse garden) £550 £650
4 **31** ½ a. on 10 pa. green (Mosque of Selim) .. £900 £1100
5 **37** 1 a. on 20 pa. red (Castle) £325 £350
a. "BAGHDAD" double £1300
6 **38** 2 a. on 1 pi. bright blue (Mosque) .. £130 £160

(*b*) *As* (*a*), *but overprinted with small five-pointed Star*

7 **37** 1 a. on 20 pa. red (B.) £180 £200
a. "OCCUPATION" omitted £4500
b. "BAGHDAD" double £1300
8 **38** 2 a. on 1 pi. bright blue (R.) £2750 £3500

(*c*) *Postal Jubilee stamps* (*Old G.P.O.*). *P* 12½

9 **60** ½ a. on 10 pa. carmine £350 £375
a. Perf 13½ £750 £800
10 1 a. on 20 pa. blue £3250
a. Value omitted £6500
b. Perf 13½ £800 £950
11 2 a. on 1 pi. black and violet £160 £170
a. "BAGHDAD" omitted £4500
b. Perf 13½ .. .. .. 75·00 85·00

(*d*) *T* **30** (*G.P.O., Constantinople*) *with opt T* **26**.

12 **30** 2 a. on 1 pi. ultramarine £300 £425
a. "IN BRITISH" omitted £6000

(*e*) *Stamps optd with six-pointed Star and Arabic date* "1331" *within Crescent. T* **53** (*except No.* 16, *which has five-pointed Star and Arabic* "1332", *T* **57**)

13 **30** ½ a. on 10 pa. green (R.) .. .. 75·00 80·00
14 1 a. on 20 pa. rose £325 £350
a. Value omitted £3750 £3750
b. Optd with T **26** (Arabic letter "B") also £4500 £4500
15 **23** 1 a. on 20 pa. rose (No. 554a) £375 £400
a. Value omitted £6000
16 **21** 1 a. on 20 pa. carmine (No. 732) .. £3000 £3750
17 **30** 2 a. on 1 pi. ultramarine (R.) .. .. 85·00 £100
a. "BAGHDAD" omitted .. .. † —
18 **21** 2 a. on 1 pi. dull blue (No. 543) (R.) .. £140 £150
a. "OCCUPATION" omitted £6000

(*f*) *Stamps with similar opt, but date between Star and Crescent* (*Nos.* 19 *and* 22, *T* **54**; *others T* **55**, *five-pointed Star*)

19 **23** ½ a. on 10 pa. grey-green (No. 609a) (R.) 90·00 95·00
a. "OCCUPATION" omitted £4750
20 **60** ½ a. on 10 pa. carmine (*p* 12½) (B.) .. £130 £140
a. Perf 13½ £275 £300
21 **30** 1 a. on 20 pa. rose .. .. .. 85·00 £110
22 **28** 1 a. on 20 pa. rose (Plate II) (No. 617) .. £325 £375
23 **15** 1 a. on 10 pa. on 20 pa. claret (No. 630) £160 £160
a. "OCCUPATION" omitted £5000 £5000
24 **30** 2 a. on 1 pi. ultramarine (R.) £140 £150
a. "OCCUPATION" omitted £5000
b. "BAGHDAD" omitted £5000
25 **28** 2 a. on 1 pi. ultramarine (Pl. II) (No. 645) £1200 £1400

The last group (*f*) have the Crescent obliterated by hand in violet-black ink, as this included the inscription, "Tax for the relief of children of martyrs".

II. ISSUES FOR MOSUL

PRICES FOR STAMPS ON COVER
Nos. 1/8 *from* × 40

BRITISH OCCUPATION

A British and Indian force occupied Mosul on 1 November 1918.

As the status of the vilayet was disputed stocks of "IRAQ IN BRITISH OCCUPATION" surcharges were withdrawn in early 1919 and replaced by Nos. 1/8.

POSTAGE

I.E.F. 'D'

1 Anna (1) **4** I **4** II

Two types of tougra in central design:
(a) Large "tougra" or sign-manual of El Ghazi 7 mm high.
(b) Smaller "tougra" of Sultan Rechad 5½ mm high.

Two types of 4 a. surcharge:
I. Normal "4". Apostrophes on D 3½ mm apart.
II. Small "4" Apostrophes on D 4½ mm apart.

1919 (28 Jan). *Turkish Fiscal stamps surch as T* **1** *by Govt Press, Baghdad. P* 11½ (½ *a.*), 12 (1 *a.*), *or* 12½ (*others*).

1 ½ a. on 1 pi. green and red .. .. 2·25 1·90
2 1 a. on 20 pa. black/*red* (*a*) .. .. 1·40 1·75
a. Imperf between (horiz pair) £600
b. Surch double £500
c. "A" of "Anna" omitted £200
3 1 a. on 20 pa. black/*red* (*b*) .. .. 4·00 3·00
b. Surch double £600
4 2½ a. on 1 pi. mauve and yellow (*b*) .. 1·50 1·50
a. No bar to fraction (R. 2/4) .. 30·00 42·00
b. Surch double £650
5 3 a. on 20 pa. green (*a*) .. .. 1·60 4·00
6 3 a. on 20 pa. green and orange (*b*) .. 32·00 50·00
7 4 a. on 1 pi. deep violet (*a*) (I) .. .. 3·00 3·50
a. "4" omitted £1400
c. Surch double £800
7*d* 4 a. on 1 pi. deep violet (*a*) (II) .. .. 9·50 12·00
da. Surch double, one with "4" omitted .. £2250

8 8 a. on 10 pa. lake (*a*) .. .. .. 4·00 5·00
a. Surch inverted £600 £700
b. Surch double £500 £600
c. No apostrophe after "D" (R. 1/5) .. 24·00 35·00
d. Surch inverted. No apostrophe after "D" .. ..
e. "na" of "Anna" omitted £250
f. Error. 8 a. on 1 pi. deep violet .. £1700

No. 4a occurs on some sheets only. No. 8c comes from the first setting only.

Nos. 1/8 were replaced by "IRAQ IN BRITISH OCCUPATION" surcharges during 1921.

In December 1925 the League of Nations awarded the vilayet of Mosul to Iraq.

III. ISSUES FOR IRAQ

PRICES FOR STAMPS ON COVER
Nos. 1/18 *from* × 4
Nos. 41/154 *from* × 2
Nos. O19/171 *from* × 2

BRITISH OCCUPATION

IN BRITISH **IRAQ** **1An.** **OCCUPATION**
(1) A B

1918 (1 Sept)–**21**. *Turkish pictorial issue of* 1914, *surch as T* **1** *by Bradbury Wilkinson. P* 12.

(*a*) *No wmk. Tougra as* A (1 Sept 1918–20)

1 **34** ¼ a. on 5 pa. dull purple .. .. 50 1·00
2 **36** ½ a. on 10 pa. green 50 20
3 **37** 1 a. on 20 pa. red 50 10
4 **34** 1½ a. on 5 pa. dull purple (1920) .. .. 3·50 50
5 **38** 2½ a. on 1 pi. bright blue .. .. 1·25 1·40
a. Surch inverted £3500
6 **39** 3 a. on 1½ pi. grey and rose .. .. 1·25 25
a. Surch double (Bk. + R.) £1500 £2250
7 **40** 4 a. on 1¾ pi. red-brown and grey .. 1·50 25
a. Centre inverted .. .. † £15000
8 **41** 6 a. on 2 pi. black and green .. .. 1·60 1·25
9 **42** 8 a. on 2½ pi. green and orange .. 1·25 60
a. Surch inverted .. .. † £9000
10 **43** 12 a. on 5 pi. deep lilac .. .. 1·75 4·00
11 **44** 1 r. on 10 pi. red-brown .. .. 2·25 1·40
12 **45** 2 r. on 25 pi. yellow-green .. .. 7·50 2·50
13 **46** 5 r. on 50 pi. rose .. .. 20·00 21·00
14 **47** 10 r. on 100 pi. indigo .. .. 48·00 17·00
1/14 .. .. .. *Set of* 14 80·00 45·00
1s/14s (*ex* 1½ a. on 5 pa.) Perf "Specimen" *Set of* 13 £250

(*b*) *No wmk. Tougra as* B (*one device instead of two*) (1921)

15 **44** 1 r. on 10 pi. red-brown .. .. £100 24·00

(*c*) *Wmk Mult Script CA* (*sideways on* ½ *a.*, 1½ *a.*) (1921)

16 **36** ½ a. on 10 pa. green .. .. 1·50 2·00
17 **34** 1½ a. on 5 pa. dull purple .. .. 1·50 1·00
18 **45** 2 r. on 25 pi. yellow-green .. .. 13·00 11·00
16/18 .. .. .. *Set of* 3 14·50 12·50
16s/18s Optd "Specimen" .. *Set of* 3 55·00

Designs: *Horiz*—5 pa. Leander's Tower; 10 pa. Lighthouse-garden, Stamboul; 20 pa. Castle of Europe; 1 pi. Mosque of Sultan Ahmed; 1½ pi. Martyrs of Liberty Monument; 1¾ pi. Fountains of Suleiman; 2 pi. Cruiser *Hamidiye*; 2½ pi. Candilli, Bosphorus; 5 pi. Former Ministry of War; 10 pi. Sweet Waters of Europe; 25 pi. Suleiman Mosque; 50 pi. Bosphorus at Rumeli Hisar; 100 pi. Sultan Ahmed's Fountain.

The original settings of Nos. 1/18 showed the surcharge 27 mm wide, except for the 2½ a. (24 mm), 4 a. (26½ mm), 6 a. (32 mm), 8 a. (30½ mm), 12 a. (33 mm), 1 r. (31½ mm), 2 r. (30 mm) and 5 r. (32 mm). The 6 a., 8 a. and 5 r. also exist from a subsequent setting on which the surcharge was 27½ mm wide.

Nos. 2, 3, 5, 6 and 7/9 are known bisected and used on philatelic covers. All such covers have Makinah or F.P.O. 339 cancellations.

During January 1923 an outbreak of cholera in Baghdad led to the temporary use for postal purposes of the above issue overprinted "REVENUE".

LEAGUE OF NATIONS MANDATE

On 25 April 1920 the Supreme Council of the Allies assigned to the United Kingdom a mandate under the League of Nations to administer Iraq.

The Emir Faisal, King of Syria in 1920, was proclaimed King of Iraq on 23 August 1921.

King Faisal I
23 August 1921–8 September 1933

2 Sunni Mosque, Muadhdham

3 Winged Cherub

4 Allegory of Date Palm

(Des Miss Edith Cheesman (½ a., 1 a., 4 a., 6 a., 8 a., 2 r., 10 r.), Mrs. C. Garbett (Miss M. Maynard) (others). Typo or recess (others) Bradbury, Wilkinson)

1923 (1 June)–**25**. *T* **2/4** *and similar designs. Wmk Mult CA* (*sideways on* 2 *a.*, 3 *a.*, 4 *a.*, 8 *a.*, 5 *r.*). *P* 12.

41 **2** ½ a. olive-green 75
42 – 1 a. brown .. .. .. 1·75
43 **3** 1½ a. lake 80
44 – 2 a. orange-buff 80
45 – 3 a. grey-blue (1923) 85
46 – 4 a. violet .. .. .. 2·50
47 – 6 a. greenish blue .. .. .. 1·00
48 – 8 a. olive-bistre .. .. .. 2·75
49 **4** 1 r. brown and blue-green .. .. 3·75
50 **2** 2 r. black .. .. .. 13·00
51 2 r. olive-bistre (1925) .. .. 35·00
52 – 5 r. orange .. .. .. 26·00
53 – 10 r. lake .. .. .. 32·00
41/53 .. .. .. *Set of* 13 £110
41s/53s Optd "Specimen" *Set of* 13 £225

Designs: *Horiz* (*as T* **2**)—1 a. Gufas on the Tigris. (30×24 —2 a. Bull from Babylonian wall-sculpture, 6 a., 10 r. S Mosque, Kadhimain. (34×24 *mm*)—3 a. Arch of Ctesiphon. (*as T* **3**)—4 a., 8 a., 5 r. Tribal Standard, Dulaim Camel C

With the exception of Nos. 49 and 50, later printings of stamps and of No. 78 are on a thinner paper.

10

11
King Faisal I

12

(Recess Bradbury, Wilkinson)

1927 (1 Apr). *Wmk Mult Script CA. P* 12.

78 **10** 1 r. red-brown .. .. .. 7·00
s. Optd "Specimen" .. .. 30·00

See note below No. 53.

(Recess Bradbury Wilkinson)

1931 (17 Feb). *Wmk Mult Script CA* (*sideways on* 1 *r. to* 2 *P* 12.

80 **11** ½ a. green .. .. .. 1·50
81 1 a. red-brown .. .. .. 1·50
82 1½ a. scarlet .. .. .. 1·50
83 2 a. orange .. .. .. 1·25
84 3 a. blue .. .. .. 1·25
85 4 a. slate-purple .. .. .. 1·25
86 6 a. greenish blue .. .. .. 1·50
87 8 a. deep green .. .. .. 1·50
88 **12** 1 r. chocolate .. .. .. 3·25
89 2 r. yellow-brown .. .. .. 5·50
90 5 r. orange .. .. .. 18·00 3
91 10 r. scarlet .. .. .. 60·00 8
92 **10** 25 r. violet .. .. .. £500 £
80/91 .. .. .. *Set of* 12 85·00 £
80s/92s Perf "Specimen" .. *Set of* 13 £500

(New Currency. 1000 fils = 1 dinar)

10 Fils ١٠ فلس (13) **½ Dinar** ١/٢ دينار (14)

Fils فلس Normal "SIN" **Fils** فلص Error "SAD" (R. 8/16 of second setting)

(Surcharged at Govt Ptg Wks, Baghdad)

1932 (1 Apr). *Nos.* 80/92 *and* 46 *surch in* "Fils" *or* "Dinar" *T* **13** *or* **14**.

106 **11** 2 f. on ½ a. green (R.) 50
107 3 f. on ½ a. green 50
a. Surch double £140
b. Surch inverted £140
c. Arabic letter "SAD" instead of "SIN" .. .. .. 20·00 20
108 4 f. on 1 a. red-brown (G.) .. .. 2·25
109 5 f. on 1 a. red-brown 75
a. Inverted Arabic "5" (R. 8/11) .. 27·00 32
b. Surch inverted £250
110 8 f. on 1½ a. scarlet 50
a. Surch inverted £140
111 10 f. on 2 a. orange 50
a. Inverted Arabic "1" (R. 8/13) .. 18·00 18
b. No space between "10" and "Fils" .. 50
112 15 f. on 3 a. blue .. .. .. 1·50 1
113 20 f. on 4 a. slate-purple .. .. 1·75 1
a. Surch inverted £250

25 f. on 4 a. violet (No. 46) 2·75 3·75
a. "Flis" for "Fils" (R. 2/1, 10/8, 10/15) £300 £350
b. Inverted Arabic "5" (R. 10/7, 10/14) £350 £450
c. Vars a and b in *se-tenant* pair £700
d. Error. 20 f. on 4 a. violet (R. 10/1, 10/9) £1200
1 30 f. on 6 a. greenish blue 2·00 60
a. Error. 80 f. on 6 a. greenish blue £1000
40 f. on 8 a. deep green 2·50 3·25
2 75 f. on 1 r. chocolate 2·00 3·25
a. Inverted Arabic "5" 32·00 42·00
100 f. on 2 r. yellow-brown 5·50 3·75
200 f. on 5 r. orange 13·00 20·00
½ d. on 10 r. scarlet 50·00 75·00
a. No bar in English "½" £600 £650
b. Scarlet-vermilion 50·00 85·00
0 1 d. on 25 r. violet 85·00 £150
21 *Set of* 16 £150 £225

. 106/13 and 115/16 were in sheets of 160 (16×10), No. 114 s of 150 (15×10) and Nos. 117/21 sheets of 100 (10×10). were three settings of the surcharge for the 3 f. and two gs for the 5, 10, 25, 40, 100 and 200 f. Nos. 109a and 111a from the first setting and Nos. 107c, 111b and 114a/b come the second.

109a can be easily identified as it shows the point of the c numeral at the foot of the surcharge.

10 f. stamps from the second setting are as No. 111b except . 4/7–8 and 15–16 where the spacing is the same as for the setting (Type **13**).

. 114d shows "20" instead of "25". Many examples of this were removed from the sheets before issue. The Arabic "25" was unaltered.

. 115a shows the error in the English face value only.

. 117a occurs on R. 1/2, 1/7 and a third position in the first cal row not yet identified.

. 120a occurs on R. 10/1, one position in the first horizontal and another in the second.

. 120b was a special printing of No. 91 which does not exist rcharged.

15

(9 May). *T* **10** *to* **12**, *but with values altered to* "FILS" *or* INAR" *as in T* **15**. *Wmk Mult Script CA* (*sideways on* 50 *f. to* .). *P* 12.

11 2 f. ultramarine 50 20
3 f. green 50 10
4 f. brown-purple 50 10
5 f. grey-green 50 10
8 f. scarlet 1·50 10
10 f. yellow 1·50 10
15 f. blue 1·50 10
20 f. orange 1·75 50
25 f. mauve 1·75 50
30 f. bronze-green 2·25 15
40 f. violet 1·50 70
12 50 f. brown 1·50 20
75 f. dull ultramarine 2·50 2·75
100 f. deep green 3·75 70
200 f. scarlet 13·00 3·25
10 ½ d. deep blue 38·00 32·00
1 d. claret 75·00 75·00
54 *Set of* 17 £130 £100
/54s Perf "Specimen" *Set of* 17 £190

OFFICIAL STAMPS

ON STATE SERVICE

(O **2**)

) (16 May)–**23.** *As Nos.* 1/18, *but surch includes additional* *ording* "ON STATE SERVICE" *as Type* O **2** *in black.*

(*a*) *No wmk. Tougra as* A

36 ½ a. on 10 pa. blue-green 4·75 1·75
37 1 a. on 20 pa. red 1·50 60
34 1½ a. on 5 pa. purple-brown 12·00 2·50
2 **38** 2½ a. on 1 pi. blue 2·25 2·50
3 **39** 3 a. on 1½ pi. black and rose 14·00 80
4 **40** 4 a. on 1¾ pi. red-brown and grey-blue 16·00 3·00
5 **41** 6 a. on 2 pi. black and green 13·00 4·75
6 **42** 8 a. on 2½ pi. yellow-green & orge-brn 13·00 2·75
7 **43** 12 a. on 5 pi. purple 9·00 6·00
8 **44** 1 r. on 10 pi. red-brown 12·00 5·50
9 **45** 2 r. on 25 pi. olive-green 19·00 11·00
0 **46** 5 r. on 50 pi. rose-carmine 35·00 26·00
1 **47** 10 r. on 100 pi. slate-blue 50·00 75·00
9/31 *Set of* 13 £180 £130

(*b*) *No wmk. Tougra as* B (*No.* 15) (1922)

2 **44** 1 r. on 10 pi. red-brown 22·00 7·00

) *Wmk Mult Script CA* (*sideways on* ½ *a. to* 8 *a.*) (1921–23)

3 **36** ½ a. on 10 pa. green 1·00 1·00
4 **37** 1 a. on 20 pa. red 3·00 1·00
5 **34** 1½ a. on 5 pa. purple-brown 2·75 65
6 **40** 4 a. on 1¾ pi. red-brown and grey-blue 2·00 1·40
7 **41** 6 a. on 2 pi. black and green (10.3.23) 14·00 80·00
8 **42** 8 a. on 2½ pi. yellow-green & orge-brn 3·25 2·00
9 **43** 12 a. on 5 pi. purple (10.3.23) 17·00 65·00
0 **45** 2 r. on 25 pi. olive-green (10.3.23) 50·00 80·00
3/40 *Set of* 8 80·00 £200
3s/40s Optd "Specimen" *Set of* 8 £130

Nos. O25/6, O30 and O37/8 only exist from the setting with surcharge 27½ mm wide.

ON STATE SERVICE

(O **6**)

ON
STATE
SERVICE

(O **7**)

23. *Optd with Types* O **6** (*horiz designs*) *or* O **7** (*vert designs*).

54 **2** ½ a. olive-green 1·50 85
55 – 1 a. brown 1·75 20
O56 **3** 1½ a. lake 1·75 1·00
O57 – 2 a. orange-buff 2·00 30
O58 – 3 a. grey-blue 2·50 1·00
O59 – 4 a. violet 4·25 70
O60 – 6 a. greenish blue 3·75 1·25
O61 – 8 a. olive-bistre 4·00 2·25
O62 **4** 1 r. brown and blue-green 7·00 1·50
O63 **2** 2 r. black (R.) 20·00 8·00
O64 – 5 r. orange 48·00 28·00
O65 – 10 r. lake 70·00 48·00
O54/65 *Set of* 12 £140 80·00
O54s/65s Optd "Specimen" *Set of* 12 £200

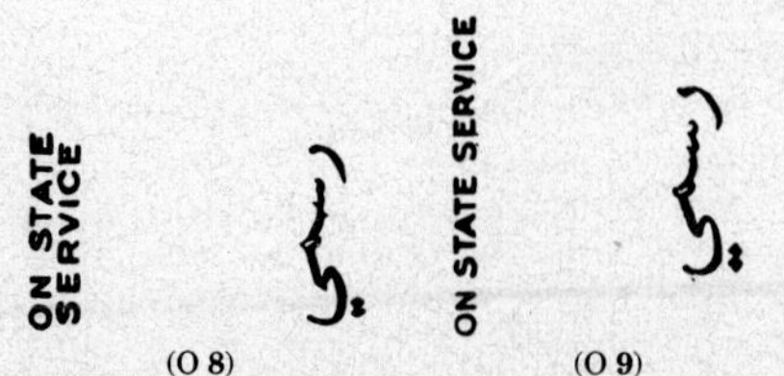

(O **8**) (O **9**)

1924–25. *Optd with Types* O **8** (*horiz designs*) *or* O **9** (*vert designs*).

O66 **2** ½ a. olive-green 1·25 10
O67 – 1 a. brown 1·00 10
O68 **3** 1½ a. lake 1·00 30
O69 – 2 a. orange-buff 1·50 10
O70 – 3 a. grey-blue 2·00 10
O71 – 4 a. violet 4·00 30
O72 – 6 a. greenish blue 1·75 20
O73 – 8 a. olive-bistre 3·75 35
O74 **4** 1 r. brown and blue-green 9·50 1·25
O75 **2** 2 r. olive-bistre (1925) 30·00 3·75
O76 – 5 r. orange 50·00 42·00
O77 – 10 r. lake 70·00 42·00
O66/77 *Set of* 12 £160 80·00
O66s/77s Optd "Specimen" *Set of* 12 £200

1927 (1 Apr). *Optd with Type* O **9**.

O79 **10** 1 r. red-brown 6·00 1·75
s. Optd "Specimen" 30·00

ON STATE SERVICE

ON STATE SERVICE رسمي

(O **12**)

رسمي

(O **13**)

1931. *Optd.* (*a*) *As Type* O **12**.

O 93 **11** ½ a. green 65 2·75
O 94 1 a. red-brown 80 10
O 95 1½ a. scarlet 4·50 19·00
O 96 2 a. orange 80 10
O 97 3 a. blue 85 1·25
O 98 4 a. slate-purple 1·00 1·50
O 99 6 a. greenish blue 4·50 17·00
O100 8 a. deep green 4·75 17·00

(*b*) *As Type* O **13**, *horizontally*

O101 **12** 1 r. chocolate 14·00 16·00
O102 2 r. yellow-brown 22·00 60·00
O103 5 r. orange 42·00 £110
O104 10 r. scarlet 75·00 £170

(*c*) *As Type* O **13**, *vertically upwards*

O105 **10** 25 r. violet £550 £700
O93/104 *Set of* 12 £150 £375
O93s/105s Perf "Specimen" *Set of* 13 £500

1932 (1 Apr). *Official issues of* 1924–25 *and* 1931 *surch in* "FILS" *or* "DINAR", *as T* **13** *or* **14**.

O122 **11** 3 f. on ½ a. green 3·50 3·50
a. Pair, one without surch £250
O123 4 f. on 1 a. red-brown (G.) 2·50 10
O124 5 f. on 1 a. red-brown 2·50 10
a. Inverted Arabic "5" (R. 8/11) 40·00 28·00
O125 **3** 8 f. on 1½ a. lake (No. O68) 4·50 50
O126 **11** 10 f. on 2 a. orange 2·75 10
a. Inverted Arabic "1" (R. 8/13) 32·00 25·00
b. "10" omitted † £1500
c. No space between "10" and "Fils" 2·75 10
O127 15 f. on 3 a. blue 4·25 1·50
O128 20 f. on 4 a. slate-purple 4·25 2·00
O129 25 f. on 4 a. slate-purple 4·50 2·00
O130 – 30 f. on 6 a. greenish blue (No. O72) 4·50 1·75
O131 **11** 40 f. on 8 a. deep green 4·00 3·50
a. "Flis" for "Fils" (R. 7/5, 7/13) £200 £275
O132 **12** 50 f. on 1 r. chocolate 4·50 3·50
a. Inverted Arabic "5" (R. 1/2) 65·00 75·00
O133 75 f. on 1 r. chocolate 6·00 6·00
a. Inverted Arabic "5" 45·00 55·00
O134 **2** 100 f. on 2 r. olive-bistre (surch at top) 15·00 3·50
a. Surch at foot 17·00 10·00
O135 – 200 f. on 5 r. orange (No. O76) 23·00 23·00
O136 – ½ d. on 10 r. lake (No. O77) 60·00 80·00
a. No bar in English "½" (R. 2/10) £650 £750
O137 **10** 1 d. on 25 r. violet 95·00 £160
O122/37 *Set of* 16 £200 £250

Nos. O122/4, O126/9 and O131 were in sheets of 160 (16×10), Nos. O130, O134 and O136 150 (10×15), No. O135 150 (15×10) and Nos. O125, O132/3 and O137 in sheets of 100 (10×10). There was a second setting of the surcharge for the 3 f. (equivalent to the third postage setting), 10 f. to 25 f., 40 f. to 100 f. and 1 d. Nos. O126c, O131a and O134a come from the second setting.

All 100 f. stamps from the second setting are as No. O134a.

For notes on other varieties see below No. 121.

1932 (9 May). *Optd.* (*a*) *As Type* O **12**.

O155 **11** 2 f. ultramarine 1·50 10
O156 3 f. green 1·50 10
O157 4 f. brown-purple 1·50 10
O158 5 f. grey-green 1·50 10
O159 8 f. scarlet 1·50 10
O160 10 f. yellow 2·25 10
O161 15 f. blue 2·50 10
O162 20 f. orange 2·50 15
O163 25 f. mauve 2·50 15
O164 30 f. bronze-green 3·50 20
O165 40 f. violet 4·50 30

(*b*) *As Type* O **13**, *horizontally*

O166 **12** 50 f. brown 3·25 20
O167 75 f. dull ultramarine 2·50 1·00
O168 100 f. deep green 11·00 2·00
O169 200 f. scarlet 20·00 6·50

(*c*) *As Type* O **13**, *vertically upwards*

O170 **10** ½ d. deep blue 12·00 24·00
O171 1 d. claret 55·00 85·00
O155/71 *Set of* 17 £110 £110
O155s/71s Perf "Specimen" *Set of* 17 £300

The British Mandate was given up on 3 October 1932 and Iraq became an independent kingdom. Later issues will be found listed in Part 19 (*Middle East*) of this catalogue.

Ireland (Republic)

All the issues of Ireland are listed together here, in this section of the Gibbons Catalogue, purely as a matter of convenience to collectors.

PRICES FOR STAMPS ON COVER TO 1945

Nos. 1/15	*from* × 5
Nos. 17/21	*from* × 3
Nos. 26/9*a*	*from* × 5
Nos. 30/43	*from* × 4
Nos. 44/6	—
Nos. 47/63	*from* × 5
Nos. 64/6	*from* × 3
Nos. 67/70	*from* × 6
Nos. 71/82	*from* × 2
Nos. 83/8	*from* × 3
Nos. 89/98	*from* × 2
Nos. 99/104	*from* × 3
Nos. 105/37	*from* × 2
Nos. D1/4	*from* × 7
Nos. D5/14	*from* × 6

PROVISIONAL GOVERNMENT

16 January—6 December 1922

Stamps of Great Britain overprinted. T 104/8, W 100; T 109, W 110

Rialtas Sealadaċ na hÉireann 1922
(1)

Rialtas Sealadaċ na hÉireann 1922.
(2)

Rialtas Sealadaċ na hÉireann 1922
(3)

("Provisional Government of Ireland, 1922")

1922 (17 Feb–July). *T* **104** *to* **108** (*W* **100**) *and* **109** *of Great Britain overprinted in black.*

(*a*) *With T* **1**, *by Dollard Printing House Ltd. Optd in black**

1	**105**	½d. green	1·50	40
		a. Opt inverted	£400	£550
2	**104**	1d. scarlet	1·50	35
		a. Opt inverted	£250	£300
		b. Opt double, both inverted, one albino	£350	
		c. Opt double	†	—
		w. Wmk inverted	—	£150
3		1d. carmine-red	3·25	60
4		2½d. bright blue	2·00	5·00
		a. Red opt (1 Apr)	1·25	3·75
5	**106**	3d. bluish violet	4·25	3·75
6		4d. grey-green	4·00	11·00
		a. Red opt (1 Apr)	8·50	15·00
		b. Carmine opt (July)	40·00	65·00
7	**107**	5d. yellow-brown	4·25	8·50
		x. Wmk reversed	—	£200
8	**108**	9d. agate	11·00	22·00
		a. Opt double, one albino		
		b. Red opt (1 Apr)	14·00	18·00
		c. Carmine opt (July)	80·00	85·00
9		10d. turquoise-blue	8·50	45·00
1/9		*Set of* 8	32·00	80·00

*All values except 2½d. and 4d. are known with greyish black overprint, but these are difficult to distinguish.

The carmine overprints on the 4d. and 9d. may have been produced by Alex Thom & Co. Ltd. There was a further overprinting of the 2½d. at the same time, but this is difficult to distinguish.

The ½d. with red overprint is a trial or proof printing (*Price* £150).

Bogus inverted T **1** overprints exist on the 2d., 4d., 9d and 1s. values.

(*b*) *With T* **2**, *by Alex Thom & Co Ltd.*

10	**105**	1½d. red-brown	1·60	1·25
		a. Error. "PENCF"	£350	£275
		w. Wmk inverted	—	£120
		x. Wmk reversed	—	£120
12	**106**	2d. orange (Die I)	3·00	50
		a. Opt inverted	£180	£250
		w. Wmk inverted	—	£100
		x. Wmk reversed	—	£120
13		2d. orange (Die II)	3·00	50
		a. Opt inverted	£300	£400
		w. Wmk inverted	—	£120
14	**107**	6d. reddish pur (*chalk-surfaced paper*)	11·00	16·00
15	**108**	1s. bistre-brown	11·00	9·00
10/15		*Set of* 5	26·00	24·00

Varieties occur throughout the T **2** overprint in the relative positions of the lines of the overprint, the "R" of "Rialtas" being over either the "Se" or "S" of "Sealadac" or intermediately.

(*c*) *With T* **3** *by Dollard Printing House Ltd*

17	**109**	2s. 6d. chocolate-brown	35·00	65·00
18		2s. 6d. reddish brown	50·00	75·00
19		5s. rose-red	60·00	£120
21		10s. dull grey-blue	£120	£250
17/21		*Set of* 3	£190	£400

1922 (19 June–Aug). *Optd as T* **2**, *in black, by Harrison & Sons, for use in horiz and vert coils.*

26	**105**	½d. green	2·25	12·00
27	**104**	1d. scarlet	2·75	6·50
28	**105**	1½d. red-brown (21.6)	4·00	38·00
29	**106**	2d. bright orange (Die I)	18·00	30·00
29*a*		2d. bright orange (Die II) (August)	19·00	27·00
		ay. Wmk inverted and reversed	—	£200
26/9*a*		*Set of* 5	40·00	£100

The Harrison overprint measures 15×17 mm (maximum) against the 14½×16 mm of T **2** (Thom printing) and is a much bolder black than the latter, while the individual letters are taller, the "i" of "Rialtas" being specially outstanding as it extends below the foot of the "R".

The "R" of "Rialtas" is always over the "Se" of "Sealadac".

1922. *Optd by Thom.*

(*a*) *As T* **2** *but bolder, in dull to shiny blue-black or red* (June–Nov)

30	**105**	½d. green	2·25	80
31	**104**	1d. scarlet	1·75	50
		a. "Q" for "O" (No. 357ab)	£1200	£1100
		b. Reversed "Q" for "O" (No. 357ac)	£350	£250
32	**105**	1½d. red-brown	3·50	3·50
33	**106**	2d. orange (Die I)	18·00	1·50
34		2d. orange (Die II)	2·75	50
		y. Wmk inverted and reversed	£120	£120
35	**104**	2½d. blue (R.)	6·00	19·00
36	**106**	3d. violet	3·00	2·00
		y. Wmk inverted and reversed	75·00	75·00
37		4d. grey-green (R.)	3·25	5·50
38	**107**	5d. yellow-brown	4·25	9·00
39		6d. reddish pur (*chalk-surfaced paper*)	8·00	3·25
		w. Wmk inverted	75·00	50·00
40	**108**	9d. agate (R.)	12·00	17·00
41		9d. olive-green (R.)	5·00	35·00
42		10d. turquoise-blue	26·00	55·00
43		1s. bistre-brown	9·00	12·00
30/43		*Set of* 14	85·00	£140

Both 2d. stamps exist with the overprint inverted but there remains some doubt as to whether they were issued.

These Thom printings are distinguishable from the Harrison printings by the size of the overprint, and from the previous Thom printings by the intensity and colour of the overprint, the latter being best seen when the stamp is looked through with a strong light behind it.

(*b*) *As with T* **3**, *but bolder, in shiny blue-black* (Oct–Dec)

44	**109**	2s. 6d. chocolate-brown	£180	£250
45		5s. rose-red	£170	£275
46		10s. dull grey-blue	£850	£1000
44/6		*Set of* 3	£1100	£1400

The above differ from Nos. 17/21 not only in the bolder impression and colour of the ink but also in the "h" and "é" of "héireann" which are closer together and horizontally aligned.

Rialtas Sealadaċ na hÉireann 1922.
(4)

Saorstát Éireann 1922
(5 Wide date)
("Irish Free State 1922")

1922 (21 Nov–Dec). *Optd by Thom with T* **4** (*wider setting*) *in shiny blue-black.*

47	**105**	½d. green	1·00	1·75
		a. Opt in jet-black	£100	90·00
48	**104**	1d. scarlet	4·75	2·50
49	**105**	1½d. red-brown (4 December)	3·00	10·00
50	**106**	2d. orange (Die II)	9·00	7·00
51	**108**	1s. olive-bistre (4 December)	45·00	55·00
47/51		*Set of* 5	55·00	70·00

The overprint T **4** measures 15¾ × 16 mm (maximum).

IRISH FREE STATE

6 December 1922—29 December 1937

1922 (Dec)–**23.**

(*a*) *Optd by Thom with T* **5**, *in dull to shiny blue-black or red*

52	**105**	½d. green	1·25	30
		a. No accent in "Saorstat"	£1000	£900
		b. Accent inserted by hand	85·00	95·00
53	**104**	1d. scarlet	1·00	50
		aa. No accent in "Saorstat"	£7000	£5000
		a. No accent and final "t" missing	£6000	£4500
		b. Accent inserted by hand	£130	£150
		c. Accent and "t" inserted	£225	£250
		d. Reversed "Q" for "O" (No. 357ac)	£300	£250
54	**105**	1½d. red-brown	3·50	8·50
55	**106**	2d. orange (Die II)	1·50	1·00
56	**104**	2½d. bright blue (R.) (6.1.23)	6·50	8·00
		a. No accent	£140	£170
57	**106**	3d. bluish violet (6.1.23)	3·75	11·00
		a. No accent	£250	£275
58		4d. grey-green (R.) (16.1.23)	3·25	6·50
		a. No accent	£150	£170
59	**107**	5d. yellow-brown	3·50	4·75
60		6d. reddish pur (*chalk-surfaced paper*)	2·00	2·00
		a. Accent inserted by hand	£700	£700
		y. Wmk inverted and reversed	60·00	35·00
61	**108**	9d. olive-green (R.)	3·25	5·50
		a. No accent	£250	£275
62		10d. turquoise-blue	16·00	55·00
63		1s. bistre-brown	7·00	11·00
		a. No accent	£5500	£6500
		b. Accent inserted by hand	£600	£650
64	**109**	2s. 6d. chocolate-brown	35·00	55·00
		a. Major Re-entry	£850	£950
		b. No accent	£350	£400
		c. Accent reversed	£425	£475
65		5s. rose-red	65·00	£120
		a. No accent	£450	£500
		b. Accent reversed	£550	£600
66		10s. dull grey-blue	£140	£275
		a. No accent	£2000	£2500
		b. Accent reversed	£2750	£3500
52/66		*Set of* 15	£250	£500

The accents inserted by hand are in dull black. The re accents are grave (thus "à") instead of acute ("á"). A variet "S" of "Saorstat" directly over "é" of "éireann", instead of may be found in all values except the 2½d. and 4d. In the 5s. and 10s. it is very slightly to the left in the "S" over "é" v bringing the "á" of "Saorstat" directly above the last "éireann".

(*b*) *Optd with T* **5**, *in dull or shiny blue-black, by Harrison, in horiz or vert coils* (7.3.23)

67	½d. green	1·75	
	a. Long "1" in "1922"	20·00	
	y. Wmk inverted and reversed		
68	1d. scarlet	4·00	
	a. Long "1" in "1922"	75·00	
69	1½d. red-brown	6·00	
	a. Long "1" in "1922"	85·00	
70	2d. orange (Die II)	7·00	
	a. Long "I" in "1922"	29·00	
	w. Wmk inverted	—	
67/70	*Set of* 4	17·00	

In the Harrison overprint the characters are rather bolde those of the Thom overprint, and the foot of the "1" of "19 usually rounded instead of square. The long "1" in "1922" has at foot. The second "e" of "éireann" appears to be slightly rais

PRINTERS. The following and all subsequent issues to N were printed at the Government Printing Works, Dublin, *u otherwise stated.*

6 "Sword of Light"

7 Map of Ireland

8 Arms of Ir

9 Celtic Cross

10

(Des J. J. O'Reilly, T **6**; J. Ingram, T **7**; Miss M. Girling, T **8** Miss L. Williams, T **9**. Typo. Plates made by Royal Mint, Lon

1922 (6 Dec)–**34.** *W* **10**. *P* 15×14.

71	**6**	½d. bright green (20.4.23)	1·00	
		a. Imperf × perf 14, wmk sideways (11.34)	20·00	4
		w. Wmk inverted	30·00	1
72	**7**	1d. carmine (23.2.23)	1·00	
		aw. Wmk inverted		
		b. Perf 15 × imperf (single perf) (1933)	85·00	£
		c. Perf 15 × imperf (7.34)	12·00	4
		cw. Wmk inverted		
		d. Booklet pane. Three stamps plus three printed labels (21.8.31)	£225	
		dw. Wmk inverted		
73		1½d. claret (2.2.23)	1·60	2
		w. Wmk inverted		
74		2d. grey-green (6.12.22)	1·50	
		a. Imperf × perf 14, wmk sideways (11.34)	38·00	70
		b. Perf 15 × imperf (1934)	£8500	£1
		w. Wmk inverted	20·00	5
		y. Wmk inverted and reversed	30·00	7
75	**8**	2½d. red-brown (7.9.23)	4·00	4
		w. Wmk inverted	50·00	8
76	**9**	3d. ultramarine (16.3.23)	2·00	
		w. Wmk inverted	65·00	12
77	**8**	4d. slate-blue (28.9.23)	2·00	3
		w. Wmk inverted	75·00	25
78	**6**	5d. deep violet (11.5.23)	8·00	9
		w. Wmk inverted		
79		6d. claret (21.12.23)	4·50	3
		w. Wmk inverted	£110	25
80	**8**	9d. deep violet (26.10.23)	13·00	8
		w. Wmk inverted		
81	**9**	10d. brown (11.5.23)	9·00	18
		w. Wmk inverted		
82	**6**	1s. light blue (15.6.23)	17·00	5
		w. Wmk inverted		
71/82		*Set of* 12	55·00	50

No. 72b is imperf vertically except for a single perf at each corner. It was issued for use in automatic machines.

See also Nos. 111/22.

Saorstát Éireann 1922
(**11** Narrow Date)

12 Daniel O'Connell

1925 (Aug)–**28.** *T* **109** *of Great Britain (Bradbury, Wilkins printing) optd at the Government Printing Works, Dublin or Harrison and Sons.* (*a*) *With T* **11** *in black or grey-black* (25.8.2

83	2s. 6d. chocolate-brown	38·00	80·
	a. Wide and narrow date (pair) (1927)	£250	
84	5s. rose-red	50·00	£1
	a. Wide and narrow date (pair) (1927)	£400	
85	10s. dull grey-blue	£110	£2
	a. Wide and narrow date (pair) (1927)	£1000	
83/5	*Set of* 3	£180	£4

The varieties with wide and narrow date *se-tenant* are from wh is known as the "composite setting," in which some stamps show

...le date, as T 5, while in others the figures were close together, ...' 11.

...le specimens of this printing with wide date may be ...guished from Nos. 64 to 66 by the colour of the ink, which is ...r grey-black in the composite setting and blue-black in the ... printing.

... type of the "composite" overprint usually shows distinct ...f wear.

(*b*) *As T 5* (*wide date*) *in black* (1927–28)
2s. 6d. chocolate-brown (9.12.27) .. .. 42·00 48·00
a. Circumflex accent over "a" £200 £250
b. No accent over "a" £350 £375
c. Flat accent on "a" £300 £350
5s. rose-red (2.28) .. .. .. 60·00 80·00
a. Circumflex accent over "a" £325 £375
c. Flat accent on "a" £400 £450
10s. dull grey-blue (15.2.28) £150 £170
a. Circumflex accent over "a" £800 £900
c. Flat accent on "a" £900 £1000
.. .. *Set of* 3 £225 £250

...s printing can be distinguished from the Thom overprints in ...lack, by the clear, heavy impression (in deep black) which shows in relief on the back of the stamp.

... variety showing a circumflex accent over the "a" occurred ...9/2. The overprint in this position finally deteriorated to ...an extent that some examples of the 2s. 6d. were without ... (No. 86b). A new cliché was then introduced with the ... virtually flat and which also showed damage to the "a" ...he crossbar of the "t".

(Des L. Whelan. Typo)

... (22 June). *Catholic Emancipation Centenary.* W 10. ...5 × 14.
12 2d. grey-green 50 45
3d. blue .. .. 4·00 8·50
9d. bright violet .. .. 4·00 4·00
.. .. *Set of* 3 7·50 11·50

13 Shannon Barrage

14 Reaper

(Des E. L. Lawrenson. Typo)

... (15 Oct). *Completion of Shannon Hydro-Electric Scheme.* ...10. *P* 15 × 14.
13 2d. agate .. .. 1·00 55

(T **14** and **15** des G. Atkinson. Typo)

... (12 June). *Bicentenary of the Royal Dublin Society.* W 10. ...15 × 14.
14 2d. blue 65 30

...he Cross of Cong

16 Adoration of the Cross

17 Hurler

...2 (12 May). *International Eucharistic Congress.* W 10. ...15×14.
15 2d. grey-green .. .. 1·00 30
w. Wmk inverted .. .. ..
3d. blue .. .. 2·25 5·00

(T **16** to **19** des R. J. King. Typo)

...3 (18 Sept). *"Holy Year".* W **10**. *P* 15 × 14.
16 2d. grey-green .. .. 1·25 15
3d. blue .. .. 2·50 2·00

...4 (27 July). *Golden Jubilee of the Gaelic Athletic Association.* ...*V* **10**. *P* 15 × 14.
17 2d. green .. .. 1·00 55

...5 (Mar–July). *T* **109** *of Great Britain* (*Waterlow printings*) ...*ptd as T* **5** (*wide date*), *at the Government Printing Works, ...ublin.*
109 2s. 6d. chocolate (No. 450) .. .. 45·00 48·00
a. Flat accent on "a" (R. 9/2) £225 £200
5s. bright rose-red (No. 451) .. .. 80·00 80·00
a. Flat accent on "a" (R. 9/2) £300 £250
10s. indigo (No. 452) £275 £275
a. Flat accent on "a" (R. 9/2) £900 £750
...'101 .. .. *Set of* 3 £350 £350

18 St. Patrick

19 Ireland and New Constitution

1937 (8 Sept). W **10**. *P* 14×15.
102 **18** 2s. 6d. emerald-green .. .. .. £140 65·00
w. Wmk inverted £600 £225
103 5s. maroon £180 £120
w. Wmk inverted £500 £225
104 10s. deep blue .. .. £140 50·00
w. Wmk inverted .. .. ..
102/4 .. .. *Set of* 3 £425 £200
See also Nos. 123/5.

EIRE

29 December 1937—17 April 1949

1937 (29 Dec). *Constitution Day.* W **10**. *P* 15×14.
105 **19** 2d. claret .. .. 1·00 20
w. Wmk inverted .. .. .. — £180
106 3d. blue .. .. 4·00 3·75
For similar stamps see Nos. 176/7.

20 Father Mathew

(Des S. Keating. Typo)

1938 (1 July). *Centenary of Temperance Crusade.* W **10**. *P* 15×14.
107 **20** 2d. agate .. .. 1·50 30
w. Wmk inverted .. .. ..
108 3d. blue .. .. 9·00 6·00

21 George Washington, American Eagle and Irish Harp

22

(Des G. Atkinson. Typo)

1939 (1 Mar). *150th Anniv of U.S. Constitution and Installation of First U.S. President.* W **10**. *P* 15 × 14.
109 **21** 2d. scarlet .. .. 1·75 65
110 3d. blue .. .. 3·25 4·25

SIZE OF WATERMARK. T **22** can be found in various sizes from about 8 to 10 mm high. This is due to the use of two different dandy rolls supplied by different firms and to the effects of paper shrinkage and other factors such as pressure and machine speed.

White line above left value tablet joining horizontal line to ornament (R. 3/7)

1940–68. *Typo.* W **22**. *P* 15×14 *or* 14×15 (2s. 6d. *to* 10s.).
111 **6** ½d. bright green (24.11.40) .. .. 2·00 40
w. Wmk inverted .. .. 50·00 6·50
112 **7** 1d. carmine (26.10.40) 30 10
aw. Wmk inverted .. .. 2·00 30
b. From coils. Perf 14×imperf (9.40) 60·00 65·00
c. From coils. Perf 15×imperf (20.3.46) .. .. .. 35·00 15·00
cw. Wmk inverted .. .. 35·00 15·00
d. Booklet pane. Three stamps plus three printed labels £1500
dw. Wmk inverted .. ..
113 1½d. claret (1.40) .. .. .. 14·00 30
w. Wmk inverted .. .. 35·00 8·00
114 2d. grey-green (1.40) 30 10
w. Wmk inverted .. .. 2·50 1·00
115 **8** 2½d. red-brown (3.41) .. .. 9·00 15
w. Wmk inverted .. .. 20·00 4·25
116 **9** 3d. blue (12.40) 60 10
w. Wmk inverted .. .. 3·75 60
117 **8** 4d. slate-blue (12.40) 55 10
w. Wmk inverted .. .. 15·00 2·75
118 **6** 5d. deep violet (7.40) 65 10
w. Wmk inverted .. .. 27·00 1·50
119 6d. claret (3.42) .. .. .. 2·25 50
aw. Wmk inverted .. .. 22·00 3·25
b. Chalk-surfaced paper (1967) .. 1·25 20
bw. Wmk inverted .. .. 13·00 2·50
119*c* 8d. scarlet (12.9.49) 80 80
cw. Wmk inverted .. .. 35·00 10·00
120 **8** 9d. deep violet (7.40) .. .. 1·50 80
w. Wmk inverted .. .. 10·00 2·00
121 **9** 10d. brown (7.40) 60 80
aw. Wmk inverted .. .. 11·00 3·75
121*b* 11d. rose (12.9.49) .. .. 1·50 2·25
122 **6** 1s. light blue (6.40) .. .. 65·00 17·00
w. Wmk inverted £650 £160
123 **18** 2s. 6d. emerald-green (10.2.43) .. 40·00 1·25
aw. Wmk inverted .. .. 95·00 22·00
b. Chalk-surfaced paper (1968?) .. 1·50 2·25
bw. Wmk inverted .. .. 30·00 4·00
124 **18** 5s. maroon (15.12.42) .. .. 40·00 3·00
a. Line flaw .. .. ..
bw. Wmk inverted .. .. £180 38·00
c. Chalk-surfaced paper (1968?) .. 13·00 4·25
ca. Purple .. .. .. 6·00 8·00
cb. Line flaw .. .. .. 95·00
cw. Wmk inverted .. .. 35·00 9·00
125 10s. deep blue (7.45) .. .. 60·00 6·00
aw. Wmk inverted .. .. £200 80·00
b. Chalk-surfaced paper (1968) .. 19·00 12·00
ba. Blue .. .. .. 7·00 16·00
bw. Wmk inverted .. .. £140 65·00
111/25 .. .. *Set of* 17 £100 30·00

There is a wide range of shades and also variation in paper used in this issue.

See also Nos. 227/8.

1941
I gCuimhne
Aiséirghe
1916

(**23** *Trans* "In memory of the rising of 1916")

24 Volunteer and G.P.O., Dublin

1941 (12 Apr). *25th Anniv of Easter Rising* (1916). *Provisional issue. T* **7** *and* **9** (*2d. in new colour*), *optd with T* **23**.
126 **7** 2d. orange (G.) .. .. 1·00 50
127 **9** 3d. blue (V.) .. .. 24·00 9·50

(Des V. Brown. Typo)

1941 (27 Oct). *25th Anniv of Easter Rising* (1916). *Definitive issue.* W **22**. *P* 15 × 14.
128 **24** 2½d. blue-black .. .. 1·25 60

25 Dr. Douglas Hyde

26 Sir William Rowan Hamilton

27 Bro. Michael O'Clery

(Des S. O'Sullivan. Typo)

1943 (31 July). *50th Anniv of Founding of Gaelic League.* W **22**. *P* 15 × 14.
129 **25** ½d. green 40 30
130 2½d. claret .. .. 1·25 10

(Des S. O'Sullivan from a bust by Hogan. Typo)

1943 (13 Nov). *Centenary of Announcement of Discovery of Quaternions.* W **22**. *P* 15 × 14.
131 **26** ½d. green 40 40
w. Wmk inverted .. .. ..
132 2½d. brown .. .. 1·75 10

(Des R. J. King. Typo)

1944 (30 June). *Tercentenary of Death of Michael O'Clery. (Commemorating the "Annals of the Four Masters").* W **22** (*sideways**). *P* 14×15.
133 **27** ½d. emerald-green 10 10
w. Wmk facing right 55 20
134 1s. red-brown 70 10
w. Wmk facing right .. .. 2·50 65

*The normal sideways watermark shows the top of the e facing left, *as seen from the back of the stamp.*

Although issued as commemoratives these two stamps were kept in use as part of the current issue, replacing Nos. 111 and 122.

28 Edmund Ignatius Rice

29 "Youth Sowing Seeds of Freedom"

(Des S. O'Sullivan. Typo)

1944 (29 Aug). *Death Centenary of Edmund Rice (founder of Irish Christian Brothers).* W **22**. *P* 15 × 14.
135 **28** 2½d. slate 85 45
w. Wmk inverted .. .. ..

(Des R. J. King. Typo)

1945 (15 Sept). *Centenary of Death of Thomas Davis (founder of Young Ireland Movement).* W **22**. *P* 15 × 14.
136 **29** 2½d. blue .. .. 1·00 25
w. Wmk inverted .. .. .. — £130
137 6d. claret .. .. 6·00 3·75

30 "Country and Homestead"

(Des R. J. King. Typo)

1946 (16 Sept). *Birth Centenaries of Davitt and Parnell (land reformers).* W **22**. *P* 15 × 14.
138 **30** 2½d. scarlet .. .. 1·50 20
139 3d. blue .. .. 2·75 3·50

31 Angel Victor over Rock of Cashel

(Des R. J. King. Recess Waterlow (1d. to 1s. 3d. until 1961), D.L.R. (8d., 1s. 3d. from 1961 and 1s. 5d.))

1948 (7 Apr)–**65.** *Air. T* **31** *and similar horiz designs. W* **22.** *P* 15 (1s. 5d.) *or* 15 × 14 (*others*).

No.	Type	Description	Unused	Used
140	**31**	1d. chocolate (4.4.49)	1·50	3·50
141	–	3d. blue	3·00	2·25
142	–	6d. magenta	80	1·50
		aw. Wmk inverted		
142*b*	–	8d. lake-brown (13.12.54)	6·00	7·00
143	–	1s. green (4.4.49)	80	1·50
143*a*	**31**	1s. 3d. red-orange (13.12.54)	7·50	1·25
		aw. Wmk inverted	£550	£250
143*b*		1s. 5d. deep ultramarine (1.4.65)	2·75	1·00
140/3*b*		*Set of* 7	20·00	16·00

Designs:—3d., 8d. Lough Derg; 6d. Croagh Patrick; 1s. Glendalough.

35 Theobald Wolfe Tone

(Des K. Uhlemann. Typo)

1948 (19 Nov). *150th Anniv of Insurrection. W* **22.** *P* 15×14.

No.	Type	Description	Unused	Used
144	**35**	2½d. reddish purple	1·00	10
		w. Wmk inverted		
145		3d. violet	3·25	3·25

REPUBLIC OF IRELAND

18 April 1949

36 Leinster House and Arms of Provinces   **37** J. C. Mangan

(Des Muriel Brandt. Typo)

1949 (21 Nov). *International Recognition of Republic. W* **22.** *P* 15 × 14.

No.	Type	Description	Unused	Used
146	**36**	2½d. reddish brown	1·50	10
147		3d. bright blue	5·50	4·25

(Des R. J. King. Typo)

1949 (5 Dec). *Death Centenary of James Clarence Mangan (poet). W* **22.** *P* 15 × 14.

No.	Type	Description	Unused	Used
148	**37**	1d. green	1·50	20
		w. Wmk inverted		

38 Statue of St. Peter, Rome

(Recess Waterlow & Sons)

1950 (11 Sept). *Holy Year. W* **22.** *P* 12½.

No.	Type	Description	Unused	Used
149	**38**	2½d. violet	1·00	40
150		3d. blue	8·00	9·50
151		9d. brown	8·00	11·00
149/51		*Set of* 3	15·00	19·00

STAMP BOOKLETS

Nos. SB1 to SB24 are stitched. Subsequent booklets have their panes attached by the selvedge, *unless otherwise stated.*

B **1** Harp and Monogram

B **2** Harp and "EIRE"

1931 (21 Aug)–**40.** *Black on red cover as Type* B **1**.

SB1 2s. booklet containing six ½d., six 2d. (Nos. 71, 74), each in block of 6, and nine 1d. (No. 72) in block of 6 and pane of 3 stamps and 3 labels (No. 72d or 72dw) . . . *From* £2000

Edition Nos.:—31–1, 31–2, 32–3, 33–4, 33–5, 34–6, 34–7, 35–8, 35–9, 36–10, 36–11, 37–12, 37–13, 37–14, 15–38, 16–38, 17–38,

a. Cover as Type B 2

Edition Nos.:—18–39, 19–39, 20–39, 21–40, 22–40

1940. *Black on red cover as Type* B **2**.

SB2 2s. booklet containing six ½d., six 2d. (Nos. 71, 74), each in block of 6, and nine 1d. (No. 72) in block of 6 and pane of 3 stamps and 3 labels (No. 112d or 112dw) . . £6500

Edition No.:—22–40

1940. *Black on red cover as Type* B **2**.

SB3 2s. booklet containing six ½d., six 2d. (Nos. 111, 114), each in block of 6, and nine 1d. (No. 112) in block of 6 and pane of 3 stamps and 3 labels (No. 112d or 112dw) . . £6500

Edition No.:—23–40

1941–44. *Black on red cover as Type* B **2**.

SB4 2s. booklet containing twelve ½d., six 1d. and six 2d. (Nos. 111/12, 114) in blocks of 6 . . £750

Edition Nos.:—24–41, 25–42, 26–44

B **3**

1945. *Black on red cover as Type* B **3**.

SB5 2s. booklet containing twelve ½d., six 1d. and six 2d. (Nos. 111/12, 114) in blocks of 6 . . £650

Edition No.:—27–45

1946. *Black on buff cover as Type* B **2**.

SB6 2s. booklet containing twelve ½d., six 1d. and six 2d. (Nos. 111/12, 114) in blocks of 6 . . £475

Edition No.:—28–46

1946–47. *Black on buff cover as Type* B **2**.

SB7 2s. booklet containing twelve ½d., six 1d. and six 2d. (Nos. 133, 112, 114) in blocks of 6 . . *From* £225

Edition Nos.:—29–46, 30–47

B **4** Harp only

1948–50. *Black on red cover as Type* B **4**.

SB8 2s. 6d. booklet containing six ½d., twelve 1d. and six 2½d. (Nos. 133, 112, 115) in blocks of 6 . . £130

Edition Nos.:—31–48, 32–49, 33–50

1951–53. *Black on buff cover as Type* B **4**.

SB9 2s. 6d. booklet containing six ½d., twelve 1d. and six 2½d. (Nos. 133, 112, 115) in blocks of 6 . . 50·00

Edition Nos.:—34–51, 35–52, 36–53

POSTAGE DUE STAMPS

From 1922 to 1925 Great Britain postage due stamps in both script and block watermarks were used without overprint.

D **1**

(Des Ruby McConnell. Typo Govt Printing Works, Dub

1925 (20 Feb). *W* **10.** *P* 14×15.

No.	Type	Description	Unused	Used
D1	D **1**	½d. emerald-green		12·00
D2		1d. carmine		15·00
		a. Wmk sideways		£600
		w. Wmk inverted		£275
D3		2d. deep green		30·00
		a. Wmk sideways		45·00
		w. Wmk inverted		80·00
D4		6d. plum		6·00
D1/4		*Set of* 4		55·00

1940–70. *W* **22.** *P* 14×15.

No.	Type	Description	Unused	Used
D 5	D **1**	½d. emerald-green (1942)		35·00
		w. Wmk inverted		£300
D 6		1d. carmine (1941)		1·50
		w. Wmk inverted		65·00
D 7		1½d. vermilion (1953)		2·00
		w. Wmk inverted		16·00
D 8		2d. deep green (1940)		2·75
		w. Wmk inverted		22·00
D 9		3d. blue (10.11.52)		2·50
		w. Wmk inverted		6·00
D10		5d. blue-violet (3.3.43)		4·50
		w. Wmk inverted		6·50
D11		6d. plum (21.3.60)		3·25
		a. Wmk sideways (1968)		1·00
D12		8d. orange (30.10.62)		8·50
		w. Wmk inverted		17·00
D13		10d. bright purple (27.1.65)		8·50
D14		1s. apple-green (10.2.69)		6·00
		a. Wmk sideways (1970)		70·00
D5/14		*Set of* 10		65·00

Jamaica

ecords show that the first local Postmaster for Jamaica on a lar basis was appointed as early as 1671, although a reason- organised service did not evolve until 1687–8. In the early s of the 18th century overseas mail was carried by the British ets, but between 1704 and 1711 this service was run on a mercial basis by Edmund Dummer. Following the collapse of Dummer scheme Jamaica was virtually without a Post Office l 1720 and it was not until 1755 that overseas mail was again ied by British packets.

amps of Great Britain were used in Jamaica from 8 May 3, initially on overseas mail only, but their use was extended ail sent to Jamaican addresses from 1 February 1859. The nd assumed responsibility for the postal service on 1 August 0 and the use of Great Britain stamps then ceased.

KINGSTON

Z 1

mps of GREAT BRITAIN *cancelled* "A 01" *as Type* Z **1**.
8 *to* 1860.

	1d. rose-red (1857), *perf* 16	£225
	1d. rose-red (1857), *perf* 14	32·00
	4d. rose-carmine *or* rose (1857)	38·00
	6d. lilac (1856)	38·00
	1s. green (1856)	£110

Z 2

amps of GREAT BRITAIN *cancelled* "A 01" *as Type* Z **2**.
59 *to* 1860.

7	1d. rose-red (1857), *perf* 14	£170
9	4d. rose-carmine *or* rose (1857)	38·00
0	6d. lilac (1856)	38·00
1	1s. green (1856)	£275

Z 3

amps of GREAT BRITAIN *cancelled* "A 01" *as Type* Z **3**.
859 *to* 1860.

12	1d. rose-red (1857), *perf* 14	£200
14	4d. rose-carmine *or* rose (1857)	£120
	a. Thick glazed paper	£400
15	6d. lilac (1856)	£120
16	1s. green (1856)	

Cancellation "A 01" was later used by the London, Foreign ranch Office.

OTHER JAMAICA POST OFFICES

British stamps were issued to several District post offices etween 8 May 1858 and 1 March 1859 (i.e. before the Obliterators 27–A 78 were issued). These can only be distinguished (off the over) when they have the Town's date-stamp on them. They are orth about three times the price of those with an obliteration umber.

Stamps of GREAT BRITAIN *cancelled* "A 27" *to* "A 78" *as Type* Z **1**
859 *to* 1860.

"A 27". ALEXANDRIA

Z17	1d. rose-red (1857), *perf* 14	£425
Z17*a*	2d. blue (1855) Large Crown, *perf* 14 (Plate 6)	£475
Z18	4d. rose (1857)	£160
Z19	6d. lilac (1856)	£375

"A 28". ANNOTTO BAY

Z20	1d. rose-red (1857), *perf* 14	£300
Z21	4d. rose (1857)	75·00
Z22	6d. lilac (1856)	£225

"A 29". BATH

Z23	1d. rose-red (1857), *perf* 14	£120
Z24	4d. rose (1857)	85·00
Z25	6d. lilac (1856)	£400

"A 30". BLACK RIVER

Z26	1d. rose-red (1857), *perf* 14	£120
Z27	4d. rose (1857)	55·00
Z28	6d. lilac (1856)	£120

"A 31". BROWN'S TOWN

Z29	1d. rose-red (1857), *perf* 14	£160
Z30	4d. rose (1857)	£160
Z31	6d. lilac (1856)	£160

"A 32". BUFF BAY

Z32	1d. rose-red (1857), *perf* 14	£120
Z33	4d. rose (1857)	£150
Z34	6d. lilac (1856)	£120

"A 33". CHAPELTON

Z35	1d. rose-red (1857), *perf* 14	£160
Z36	4d. rose (1857)	£100
Z37	6d. lilac (1856)	£160

"A 34". CLAREMONT

Z38	1d. rose-red (1857), *perf* 14	£300
Z39	4d. rose (1857)	£150
Z40	6d. lilac (1856)	£300

"A 35". CLARENDON

Z41	1d. rose-red (1857), *perf* 14	£250
Z42	4d. rose (1857)	£100
Z43	6d. lilac (1856)	£160

"A 36". DRY HARBOUR

Z44	1d. rose-red (1857), *perf* 14	£375
Z45	4d. rose (1857)	£300
Z46	6d. lilac (1856)	£250

"A 37". DUNCANS

Z47	1d. rose-red (1857), *perf* 14	
Z48	4d. rose (1857)	£375
Z49	6d. lilac (1856)	£250

"A 38". EWARTON

A 38 was allocated to EWARTON but this office was closed towards the end of 1858 before the postmark arrived. A 38 was re-issued to Falmouth in 1862.

"A 39". FALMOUTH

Z53	1d. rose-red (1857), *perf* 14	85·00
Z54	4d. rose (1857)	48·00
Z55	6d. lilac (1856)	60·00
Z56	1s. green (1856)	£500

"A 40". FLINT RIVER

Z57	1d. rose-red (1857), *perf* 14	£150
Z58	4d. rose (1857)	£100
Z59	6d. lilac (1856)	£150
Z60	1s. green (1856)	£500

"A 41". GAYLE

Z61	1d. rose-red (1857), *perf* 14	£450
Z62	4d. rose (1857)	£120
Z63	6d. lilac (1856)	£130
Z64	1s. green (1856)	£250

"A 42". GOLDEN SPRING

Z65	1d. rose-red (1857), *perf* 14	£170
Z66	4d. rose (1857)	£150
Z67	6d. lilac (1856)	£400
Z68	1s. green (1856)	£500

"A 43". GORDON TOWN

Z69	1d. rose-red (1857), *perf* 14	
Z70	4d. rose (1857)	
Z71	6d. lilac (1856)	£450

"A 44". GOSHEN

Z72	1d. rose-red (1857), *perf* 14	£120
Z73	4d. rose (1857)	£110
Z74	6d. lilac (1856)	55·00

"A 45". GRANGE HILL

Z75	1d. rose-red (1857), *perf* 14	£150
Z76	4d. rose (1857)	48·00
Z77	6d. lilac (1856)	60·00
Z77*a*	1s. green (1856)	£425

"A 46". GREEN ISLAND

Z78	1d. rose-red (1857), *perf* 14	£300
Z79	4d. rose (1857)	£150
Z80	6d. lilac (1856)	£250
Z81	1s. green (1856)	£500

"A 47". HIGHGATE

Z82	1d. rose-red (1857), *perf* 14	£170
Z83	4d. rose (1857)	£110
Z84	6d. lilac (1856)	£170

"A 48". HOPE BAY

Z85	1d. rose-red (1857), *perf* 14	£400
Z86	4d. rose (1857)	£150
Z87	6d. lilac (1856)	£400

"A 49". LILLIPUT

Z88	1d. rose-red (1857), *perf* 14	£150
Z89	4d. rose (1857)	£150
Z90	6d. lilac (1856)	75·00

"A 50". LITTLE RIVER

A 50 was allocated for use at LITTLE RIVER but this office was closed late in 1858, before the obliterator could be issued. Issued to Malvern in 1862.

"A 51". LUCEA

Z91	1d. rose-red (1857), *perf* 14	£225
Z92	4d. rose (1857)	55·00
Z93	6d. lilac (1856)	£150

"A 52". MANCHIONEAL

Z94	1d. rose-red (1857), *perf* 14	£300
Z95	4d. rose (1857)	£160
Z96	6d. lilac (1856)	

"A 53". MANDEVILLE

Z97	1d. rose-red (1857), *perf* 14	£160
Z98	4d. rose (1857)	55·00
Z99	6d. lilac (1856)	£140

"A 54". MAY HILL

Z100	1d. rose-red (1857), *perf* 14	85·00
Z101	4d. rose (1857)	80·00
Z102	6d. lilac (1856)	55·00

"A 55". MILE GULLY

Z103	1d. rose-red (1857), *perf* 14	£250
Z104	4d. rose (1857)	£150
Z105	6d. lilac (1856)	£150

"A 56". MONEAGUE

Z106	1d. rose-red (1857), *perf* 14	£150
Z107	4d. rose (1857)	£190
Z108	6d. lilac (1856)	£400

"A 57". MONTEGO BAY

Z109	1d. rose-red (1857), *perf* 14	£160
Z110	4d. rose (1857)	48·00
Z111	6d. lilac (1856)	55·00
Z112	1s. green (1856)	£500

"A 58". MONTPELIER

Z113	1d. rose-red (1857), *perf* 14	
Z114	4d. rose (1857)	
Z115	6d. lilac (1856)	£650

"A 59". MORANT BAY

Z116	1d. rose-red (1857), *perf* 14	£300
Z117	4d. rose (1857)	55·00
Z118	6d. lilac (1856)	60·00

"A 60". OCHO RIOS

Z119	1d. rose-red (1857), *perf* 14	
Z120	4d. rose (1857)	80·00
Z121	6d. lilac (1856)	£140

"A 61". OLD HARBOUR

Z122	1d. rose-red (1857), *perf* 14	£150
Z123	4d. rose (1857)	£110
Z124	6d. lilac (1856)	£110

"A 62". PLANTAIN GARDEN RIVER

Z125	1d. rose-red (1857), *perf* 14	£110
Z126	4d. rose (1857)	80·00
Z127	6d. lilac (1856)	£110

"A 63". PEAR TREE GROVE

No genuine specimen of A 63 has been found on a British stamp.

"A 64". PORT ANTONIO

Z131	1d. rose-red (1857), *perf* 14	£375
Z132	4d. rose (1857)	£225
Z133	6d. lilac (1856)	£225

"A 65". PORT MORANT

Z134	1d. rose-red (1857), *perf* 14	£225
Z135	4d. rose (1857)	85·00
Z136	6d. lilac (1856)	£225

"A 66". PORT MARIA

Z137	1d. rose-red (1857), *perf* 14	£150
Z138	4d. rose (1857)	60·00
Z139	6d. lilac (1856)	£225

"A 67". PORT ROYAL

Z140	1d. rose-red (1857), *perf* 14	£300
Z140*a*	2d. blue (1858) (plate 9)	
Z141	4d. rose (1857)	£300
Z142	6d. lilac (1856)	£300

"A 68". PORUS

Z143	1d. rose-red (1857), *perf* 14	£150
Z144	4d. rose (1857)	75·00
Z145	6d. lilac (1856)	£300

"A 69". RAMBLE

Z146	1d. rose-red (1857), *perf* 14	£150
Z147	4d. rose (1857)	£150
	a. Thick glazed paper	£400
Z149	6d. lilac (1856)	£225

"A 70". RIO BUENO

Z150	1d. rose-red (1857), *perf* 14	
Z151	4d. rose (1857)	£140
Z152	6d. lilac (1856)	90·00

"A 71". RODNEY HALL

Z153	1d. rose-red (1857), *perf* 14	£120
Z154	4d. rose (1857)	85·00
Z155	6d. lilac (1856)	£110

"A 72". ST. DAVID

Z156	1d. rose-red (1857), *perf* 14	£150
Z157	4d. rose (1857)	£300
Z158	6d. lilac (1856)	

"A 73". ST. ANN'S BAY

Z159	1d. rose-red (1857), *perf* 14	£150
Z160	4d. rose (1857)	80·00
Z161	6d. lilac (1856)	£150

"A 74". SALT GUT

Z162	1d. rose-red (1857), *perf* 14	£140
Z163	4d. rose (1857)	
Z164	6d. lilac (1856)	£150

"A 75". SAVANNAH-LA-MAR

Z165	1d. rose-red (1857), *perf* 14	85·00
Z166	4d. rose (1857)	50·00
Z167	6d. lilac (1856)	£150
Z168	1s. green (1856)	£450

"A 76". SPANISH TOWN

Z169	1d. rose-red (1857), *perf* 14	95·00
Z170	4d. rose (1857)	48·00
Z171	6d. lilac (1856)	85·00
Z172	1s. green (1856)	£325

"A 77". STEWART TOWN

Z173	1d. rose-red (1857), *perf* 14	£400
Z174	4d. rose (1857)	£250
Z175	6d. lilac (1856)	£150

"A 78". VERE

Z176 1d. rose-red (1857), *perf* 14 — £225
Z177 4d. rose (1857) — 75·00
Z178 6d. lilac (1856) — 50·00
Z179 1s. green (1856) — £500

PRICES FOR STAMPS ON COVER

Nos. 1/6	*from* × 4
Nos. 7/15	*from* × 6
Nos. 16/26	*from* × 8
Nos. 27/9	*from* × 6
No. 30	*from* × 5
Nos. 31/2	*from* × 15
Nos. 33/6	*from* × 5
Nos. 37/56	*from* × 3
No. 57	*from* × 4
Nos. 58/67	*from* × 3
Nos. 68/77	*from* × 6
Nos. 78/89	*from* × 3
Nos. 90/103	*from* × 4
Nos. 104/7	*from* × 5
Nos. 108/17	*from* × 3
Nos. 118/20	*from* × 5
Nos. 121/33*a*	*from* × 4
Nos. 134/40	*from* × 8
Nos. F1/9	*from* × 3
Nos. O1/5	*from* × 30

CROWN COLONY

PRINTERS. Until 1923, all the stamps of Jamaica were typographed by De La Rue & Co, Ltd, London, *unless otherwise stated.*

The official dates of issue are given, where known, but where definite information is not available the dates are those of earliest known use, etc.

1 2 3 4 5 6 7 A

1860 (23 Nov)–**70.** *W* **7**. *P* 14.

1 **1** 1d. pale blue — 60·00 15·00
a. Pale greenish blue — 65·00 19·00
b. Blue — 50·00 12·00
c. Deep blue (1865) — 95·00 28·00
d. Bisected (½d.) (20.11.61) (on cover) — † £650
w. Wmk inverted — £100 40·00
2 **2** 2d. rose — £190 48·00
a. Deep rose — £120 48·00
w. Wmk inverted — — 60·00
3 **3** 3d. green (10.9.63) — £130 25·00
w. Wmk inverted — £160 40·00
4 **4** 4d. brown-orange — £200 45·00
a. Red-orange — £200 22·00
w. Wmk inverted
5 **5** 6d. dull lilac — £180 18·00
a. Grey-purple — £275 32·00
b. Deep purple (1870) — £800 45·00
w. Wmk inverted — — 75·00
6 **6** 1s. yellow-brown — £450 24·00
a. Purple-brown (1862) — £500 23·00
b. Dull brown (1868) — £180 27·00
c. "$" for "S" in "SHILLING" (A) — £1700 £600
w. Wmk inverted — — 50·00

The diagonal bisection of the 1d. was authorised by a P.O. notice dated 20 November 1861 to pay the ½d. rate for newspapers or book post. Specimens are only of value when on original envelope or wrapper. The authority was withdrawn as from 1 December 1872. Fakes are frequently met with. Other bisections were unauthorised.

The so-called "dollar variety" of the 1s. occurs once in each sheet of stamps in all shades and in later colours, etc, on the second stamp in the second row of the left upper pane. The prices quoted above are for the dull brown shade, the prices for the other shades being proportionate to their normal value.

All values except the 3d. are known imperf, mint only.

There are two types of watermark in the 3d. and 1s., one being short and squat and the other elongated.

MINIMUM PRICE

The minimum price quote is 10p which represents a handling charge rather than a basis for valuing common stamps. For further notes about prices see introductory pages.

8

9

10

1870–83. *Wmk Crown CC.* (*a*) *P* 14.

7 **8** ½d. claret (29.10.72) — 14·00 3·50
a. Deep claret (1883) — 16·00 5·50
w. Wmk inverted — — 28·00
8 **1** 1d. blue (4.73) — 55·00 75
a. Deep blue — 60·00 1·50
w. Wmk inverted — £120 23·00
9 **2** 2d. rose (4.70) — 55·00 70
a. Deep rose — 70·00 1·00
w. Wmk inverted — 80·00 23·00
10 **3** 3d. green (1.3.70) — 90·00 8·50
w. Wmk inverted — — 50·00
11 **4** 4d. brown-orange (1872) — £170 11·00
a. Red-orange (1883) — £350 6·00
w. Wmk inverted — — 45·00
12 **5** 6d. mauve (10.3.71) — 60·00 5·50
w. Wmk inverted — — 35·00
13 **6** 1s. dull brown (*to deep*) (23.2.73) — 25·00 8·50
a. "$" for "S" in "SHILLING" (A) — £1100 £600
w. Wmk inverted — — 50·00

(*b*) *P* 12½

14 **9** 2s. Venetian red (27.8.75) — 40·00 16·00
w. Wmk inverted — 60·00 70·00
15 **10** 5s. lilac (27.8.75) — 90·00 £130
w. Wmk inverted — £110 £180
7/15 — *Set of* 9 £550 £160

The ½d., 1d., 4d., 2s. and 5s. are known imperforate.

1883–97. *Wmk Crown CA. P* 14.

16 **8** ½d. yellow-green (2.85) — 2·50 1·00
a. Green — 1·00 10
w. Wmk inverted — — 23·00
x. Wmk reversed — — 35·00
17 **1** 1d. blue (1884) — £300 4·50
18 1d. rose (*to deep*) (3.3.85) — 55·00 85
a. Carmine (1886) — 28·00 60
w. Wmk inverted — — 35·00
19 **2** 2d. rose (*to deep*) (17.3.84) — £200 4·00
w. Wmk inverted — — 45·00
20 2d. grey (1885) — 80·00 3·00
a. Slate (1886) — 60·00 50
w. Wmk inverted — — 23·00
21 **3** 3d. sage-green (11.86) — 4·00 1·00
a. Pale olive-green — 2·50 1·25
22 **4** 4d. red-orange* (9.3.83) — £350 22·00
aw. Wmk inverted
b. Red-brown (*shades*) (1885) — 2·00 35
bw. Wmk inverted — 55·00 23·00
23 **5** 6d. deep yellow (4.10.90) — 20·00 6·50
a. Orange-yellow — 4·00 3·50
24 **6** 1s. brown (*to deep*) (3.97) — 5·00 6·00
a. "$" for "S" in "SHILLING" (A) — £750 £450
b. Chocolate — 15·00 12·00
25 **9** 2s. Venetian red (2.97) — 27·00 20·00
26 **10** 5s. lilac (2.97) — 48·00 65·00
16/26 — *Set of* 11 £600 95·00
16s, 18s, 20s/3s Optd "Specimen" — *Set of* 6 £450

*No. 22 is the same colour as No. 11*a*.

The 1d. carmine, 2d. slate, and 2s. are known imperf. All values to the 6d. inclusive are known perf 12. These are proofs.

11

TWO PENCE
HALF-PENNY

(12)

1889 (8 Mar)–**91.** *Value tablet in second colour. Wmk Crown CA. P* 14.

27 **11** 1d. purple and mauve — 2·75 20
w. Wmk inverted — — 23·00
28 2d. green — 20·00 3·50
a. Deep green (*brown gum*) — 4·50 6·00
aw. Wmk inverted — 60·00
29 2½d. dull purple and blue (25.2.91) — 4·75 50
w. Wmk inverted — 60·00
27/9 — *Set of* 3 11·00 3·75
27s/9s Optd "Specimen" — *Set of* 3 £100

A very wide range of shades may be found in the 1d. The headplate was printed in many shades of purple, and the duty-plate in various shades of mauve and purple and also in carmine, etc. There are fewer shades for the other values and they are not so pronounced.

1890 (4 June)–**91.** *No. 22b surch with T* **12** *by C. Vendryes, Kingston.*

30 **4** 2½d. on 4d. red-brown — 27·00 8·50
a. Spacing between lines of surch 1½ mm (2.91) — 32·00 17·00
b. Surch double — £325 £225
c. "PFNNY" for "PENNY" — 75·00 65·00
ca. Ditto and broken "K" for "Y" — £130 £110
w. Wmk inverted — 65·00 32·00

This provisional was issued pending receipt of No. 29 which is listed above for convenience of reference.

Three settings exist. (1) Ten varieties arranged in a single vertical row and repeated six times in the pane. (2) Twelve varieties, in two horizontal rows of six, repeated five times, alternate rows show 1 and 1½ mm spacing between lines of surcharge. (3) Three varieties, arranged horizontally and repeated twenty times. All these settings can be reconstructed by examination of the spacing and relative position of the words of the surcharge and of the broken letters, etc, which are numerous.

A variety reading "PFNNK", with the "K" unbroken, is a forgery.

Surcharges misplaced either horizontally or vertically are with, the normal position being central at the foot of the s with "HALF-PENNY" covering the old value.

13 Llandovery Falls, Jamaica (photo by Dr. J. Johnston)

14 Arms of Jamaica

(Recess D.L.R.)

1900 (1 May)–**01.** *Wmk Crown CC* (*sideways**). *P* 14.

31 **13** 1d. red — 2·00
w. Wmk Crown to left of CC — 2·25
x. Wmk reversed — — 3
y. Wmk sideways inverted and reversed
32 1d. slate-black and red (25.9.01) — 3·00
a. Blued paper — £110
b. Imperf between (vert pair) — £7000
w. Wmk Crown to left of CC — 10·00 1
x. Wmk reversed — — 3
y. Wmk sideways inverted and reversed
31s/2s Optd "Specimen" — *Set of* 2 £130

*The normal sideways wmk shows Crown to right of CC, *seen from the back of the stamp.*

Many shades exist of both centre and frame of the bi-coloured which was, of course, printed from two plates and the design sh minor differences from that of the 1d. red which was printed fro single plate.

(Typo D.L.R.)

1903 (16 Nov)–**04.** *Wmk Crown CA. P* 14.

33 **14** ½d. grey and dull green — 1·50
a. "SER.ET" for "SERVIET" — 40·00 45
w. Wmk inverted — 30·00 30
34 1d. grey and carmine (24.2.04) — 1·75
a. "SER.ET" for "SERVIET" — 32·00 35
35 2½d. grey and ultramarine — 2·75
a. "SER.ET" for "SERVIET" — 60·00 75
36 5d. grey and yellow (1.3.04) — 15·00 23
a. "SER.ET" for "SERVIET" — £600 £8
w. Wmk inverted — 75·00
33/6 — *Set of* 4 19·00 23
33s/6s Optd "Specimen" — *Set of* 4 75·00

The "SER.ET" variety occurs on R. 4/2 of the left upper pa It was corrected by De La Rue in July 1905.

The centres of the above and later bi-coloured stamps in t Arms type vary in colour from grey to grey-black.

15 Arms type redrawn **16**

1905–11. *Wmk Mult Crown CA. P* 14. (*a*) *Arms typ Chalk-surfaced paper.*

37 **14** ½d. grey and dull green (20.11.05) — 5·50
a. "SER.ET" for "SERVIET" — 32·00 40·
w. Wmk inverted
38 **15** ½d. yell-grn (*ordinary paper*) (8.11.06) — 7·50
a. Dull green — 3·75
b. Deep green — 4·50
39 **14** 1d. grey and carmine (20.11.05) — 18·00
w. Wmk inverted — — 80·
40 **16** 1d. carmine (*ordinary paper*) (1.10.06) — 1·25
w. Wmk inverted — 30·00
41 **14** 2½d. grey and ultramarine (12.11.07) — 3·00 3·2
42 2½d. pale ultramarine (*ordinary paper*) (21.9.10) — 2·50 1·2
a. Deep ultramarine — 2·50 1·7
43 5d. grey and orange-yellow (24.4.07) — 55·00 60·
a. "SER.ET" for "SERVIET" — £750 £10
44 6d. dull and bright purple (18.8.11) — 13·00 12·
45 5s. grey and violet (11.05) — 42·00 30·
37/45 — *Set of* 9 £130 95·
38s, 40s, 42s, 44s/5s Optd "Specimen" — *Set of* 5 £140

See note below No. 36 concerning grey centres.

(*b*) *Queen Victoria types. Ordinary paper*

46 **3** 3d. olive-green (3.8.05) — 6·00 3·
a. Sage-green (1907) — 5·00 3·
47 3d. purple/*yellow* (10.3.10) — 4·50 3·5
a. Chalk-surfaced paper. *Pale purple/yellow* (11.7.10) — 2·00 1·5
aw. Wmk inverted — 42·00 42·0
48 **4** 4d. red-brown (6.6.08) — 70·00 65·0
49 4d. black/*yellow* (*chalk-surfaced paper*) (21.9.10) — 7·50 40·0
50 4d. red/*yellow* (3.10.11) — 1·50 8·0
51 **5** 6d. dull orange (27.6.06) — 15·00 25·0
a. Golden yellow (9.09) — 25·00 48·0
52 6d. lilac (19.11.09) — 27·00 40·0
a. Chalk-surfaced paper. *Purple* (7.10) — 10·00 17·0
53 **6** 1s. brown (11.06) — 19·00 24·0
a. Deep brown — 27·00 35·0
b. "$" for "S" in "SHILLING" (A) — £900 £100
54 1s. black/*green* (*chalk-surfaced paper*) (21.9.10) — 4·25 8·5
a. "$" for "S" in "SHILLING" (A) — £800 £100
55 **9** 2s. Venetian red (11.08) — £100 £15
56 2s. pur/*bl* (*chalk-surfaced paper*) (21.9.10) — 6·50 3·5
46/56 — *Set of* 11 £190 £30
47s, 49s/50s, 52s, 54s, 56s Optd "Specimen" *Set of* 6 £170

No. 38 exists in coils constructed from normal sheets.

17

18

(T **17/18** typo D.L.R.)

(3 Feb). *Wmk Mult Crown CA. P* 14.
17 2d. grey .. .. 3·00 13·00
s. Optd "Specimen" .. .. .. 35·00

–20. *Wmk Mult Crown CA. Chalk-surfaced paper (3d. to .). P* 14.
18 1d. carmine-red (5.12.12) .. .. 1·50 10
a. Scarlet (1916) .. .. .. 1·75 70
1½d. brown-orange (13.7.16) .. .. 1·00 60
a. Yellow-orange .. .. .. 13·00 1·00
b. Wmk sideways .. .. .. † £1500
2d. grey (2.8.12) .. .. .. 2·00 1·75
a. Slate-grey .. .. 1·25 3·00
2½d. blue (13.2.13) .. .. .. 1·50 15
a. Deep bright blue .. .. .. 65 1·00
3d. purple/*yellow* (6.3.12) 50 45
a. White back (2.4.13) 55 40
b. On lemon (25.9.16) .. .. 3·75 1·50
bs. Optd "Specimen" .. .. .. 32·00
w. Wmk inverted .. .. ..
4d. black and red/*yellow* (4.4.13) .. 50 3·50
a. White back (7.5.14) .. .. 75 4·00
b. On lemon (1916) .. .. .. 23·00 19·00
bs. Optd "Specimen" .. .. .. 32·00
c. On pale yellow (1919) .. .. 22·00 15·00
6d. dull and bright purple (14.11.12) .. 4·50 9·00
a. Dull purple and bright mauve (1915) 75 1·00
b. Dull purple & bright magenta (1920) 3·50 2·25
1s. black/*green* (2.8.12) .. .. .. 2·25 2·00
a. White back (4.1.15) .. .. 1·00 4·75
b. On blue-green, olive back (1920) .. 2·25 5·50
2s. purple and bright blue/*blue* (10.1.19) 13·00 25·00
5s. green and red/*yellow* (5.9.19) .. 55·00 90·00
a. On pale yellow (1920) .. .. 55·00 90·00
b. On orange-buff (1920) £120 £160
67 .. .. *Set of* 10 65·00 £110
/67s Optd "Specimen" .. .. *Set of* 10 £190

No. 58 exists in coils constructed from normal sheets.
The paper of No. 67 is a bright yellow and the gum rough and l. No. 67*a* is on practically the normal creamy "pale yellow" per, and the gum is smooth and shiny. The paper of No. 67*b* proaches the "coffee" colour of the true "orange-buff", and the ours of both head and frame are paler, the latter being of a mine tone.
For the ½d. and 6d. with Script wmk see Nos. 89*a*/90.

ED CROSS LABELS. A voluntary organization, the Jamaica ar Stamp League later the Jamaica Patriotic Stamp League, was unded in November 1915 by Mr. Lewis Ashenheim, a Kingston licitor. The aims of the League were to support the British Red oss, collect funds for the purchase of aircraft for the Royal Flying rps and the relief of Polish Jews.
One fund-raising method used was the sale, from 1 December 15, of ½d. charity labels. These labels, which were available om post offices, depicted a bi-plane above a cross and were printed red by Dennison Manufacturing Company, Framingham, S.A., the stamps being perforated 12 except for those along the ges of the sheet which have one side imperforate.
From 22 December 1915 supplies of the labels were overprinted AMAICA" in red, the colour of this overprint being changed to ack from 15 January 1916. Copies sold from 11 March 1916 rried an additional "Half-Penny" surcharge, also in black.
Such labels had no postal validity when used by the general ublic, but, by special order of the Governor, were accepted for the ayment of postage on the League's official mail. To obtain this ncession the envelopes were to be inscribed "Red Cross Business" "Jamaica Patriotic Stamp League" and the labels used endorsed ith Mr. Ashenheim's signature. Such covers are rare.

WAR STAMP. (19) — WAR STAMP. (20) — WAR STAMP. (21)

(T 19/21 optd Govt Printing Office, Kingston)

916 (1 Apr–Sept). *Optd with T* 19.
15 ½d. yellow-green 10 35
a. No stop after "STAMP" (R. 18/2) .. 10·00 24·00
b. Opt double £100 £120
c. Opt inverted .. .. 85·00 £100
d. Space between "W" and "A" (R. 20/1) 10·00 24·00
e. Blue-green 10 60
ea. No stop after "STAMP" (R. 3/11 or 11/1) .. .. 10·00 24·00
eb. Space between "W" and "A" (R. 20/1) 13·00 28·00
w. Wmk inverted .. .. ..
9 18 3d. purple/*yellow* (white back) .. .. 10·00 25·00
a. On lemon (6.16) .. .. .. 1·00 17·00
ab. No stop after "STAMP" (R. 8/6 or 9/6) 23·00 75·00
b. On pale yellow (9.16) .. .. 8·50 24·00

Minor varieties: ½d. (i) Small "P"; (ii) "WARISTAMP" (raised uad between words); (iii) Two stops after "STAMP". 3d. WARISTAMP". There were several settings of the overprint ised for each value. Where two positions are quoted for a variety hese did not occur on the same sheet.

NOTE. The above and succeeding stamps with "WAR STAMP" overprint were issued for payment of a special war tax on letters and postcards or on parcels. Ordinary unoverprinted stamps could also be used for this purpose.

1916 (Sept–Dec). *Optd with T* 20.
70 15 ½d. blue-green (*shades*) (2.10.16) .. 10 30
a. No stop after "STAMP" (R. 5/7) .. 10·00 32·00
b. Opt omitted (in pair with normal) £1700 £1600
c. "R" inserted by hand (R. 11/10) .. £650 £600
w. Wmk inverted .. .. .. 35·00

71 18 1½d. orange (1.9.16) 10 15
aa. Wmk sideways .. .. .. † £1700
a. No stop after "STAMP" (R. 4/12, 8/6, 10/10, 11/1, 18/12, 19/12) .. .. 5·00 7·50
b. "S" in "STAMP" omitted (R. 6/12) (Dec) £120 £130
c. "S" inserted by hand £250
d. "R" in "WAR" omitted (R. 1/10) .. £1100 £1000
e. "R" inserted by hand £650 £550
f. Inverted "d" for "P" £200 £160
w. Wmk inverted .. .. .. 15·00 15·00
72 3d. purple/*lemon* (2.10.16) .. .. 1·00 1·00
aa. Opt inverted £275
a. No stop after "STAMP" (R. 5/7) .. 27·00 55·00
b. "S" in "STAMP" omitted (R. 6/12) (Dec) £375 £350
c. "S" inserted by hand £180 £180
e. On yellow (12.16) .. .. .. 6·00 9·00
ea. "S" in "STAMP" omitted (R. 6/12) £500 £450
eb. "S" inserted by hand £325 £250

Nos. 70c, 71c, 71e, 72c and 72eb show the missing "R" or "S" inserted by handstamp. The 3d. is known with this "S" handstamp inverted or double.
Minor varieties, such as raised quads, small stop, double stop, spaced letters and letters of different sizes, also exist in this overprint. The setting was altered several times.

1917 (March). *Optd with T* 21.
73 15 ½d. blue-green (*shades*) (25.3.17) .. 50 30
a. No stop after "STAMP" (R. 2/5, 8/11, 8/12) .. .. 7·50 20·00
b. Stop inserted and "P" impressed a second time (R. 7/6) £180
c. Optd on back only £160
d. Opt inverted .. .. .. 10·00 32·00
74 18 1½d. orange (3.3.17) 20 10
aa. Wmk sideways .. .. .. † £1500
a. No stop after "STAMP" (R. 2/5, 8/11, 8/12) .. .. 3·00 17·00
b. Stop inserted and "P" impressed a second time (R. 7/6) £225
c. Opt double .. .. 80·00 85·00
d. Opt inverted .. .. .. 80·00 75·00
e. "WAP STAMP" (R. 6/2) .. ..
w. Wmk inverted .. .. .. 15·00 20·00
75 3d. purple/*yellow* (3.3.17) .. .. 50 1·40
a. No stop after "STAMP" (R. 2/5, 8/11, 8/12) .. .. 14·00 32·00
b. Stop inserted and "P" impressed a second time (R. 7/6) £200
c. Opt inverted £140
d. Opt sideways (reading up) £300
da. Opt omitted (in horiz pair with No. 75d) £2250

No. 75da shows the left-hand stamp as No. 75d and the right-hand stamp without overprint.
There are numerous minor varieties in this overprint with the setting being altered several times.

WAR STAMP

(22)

1919 (4 Oct)–**20**. *Optd with T* 22 *in red by D.L.R.*
76 15 ½d. green 20 15
77 18 3d. purple/*yellow* .. .. .. 3·00 3·00
a. Pale purple/buff (3.1.20) .. .. 2·50 1·25
b. Deep purple/buff (1920) .. .. 6·00 6·00
76s/7s Optd "Specimen" .. .. *Set of* 2 70·00

We list the most distinct variations in the 3d. The buff tone of the paper varies considerably in depth.

23 Jamaica Exhibition 1891

24 Arawak Woman preparing Cassava

25 War Contingent embarking, 1915

26 King's House, Spanish Town

Re-entry. Nos. 80a, 93a

The greater part of the design is re-entered, the hull showing in very solid colour and the people appear very blurred. There are also minor re-entries on stamps above (R. 7/4 and 6/4).

27 Return of War Contingent, 1919

A B

28 Landing of Columbus, 1494

29 Cathedral, Spanish Town

34

(Typo (½d., 1d.), recess (others) D.L.R.)

1919–21. *T* 23/29, 34 *and similar vert designs. Wmk Mult Crown CA (sideways* on 1d., 1½d. and 10s.). Chalk-surfaced paper (½d., 1d.). P* 14.
78 23 ½d. green and olive-green (12.11.20) 1·00 1·00
w. Wmk inverted .. .. ..
x. Wmk reversed .. .. ..
y. Wmk inverted and reversed ..
79 24 1d. carmine and orange (3.10.21) .. 1·75 1·75
w. Wmk Crown to left of CA ..
80 25 1½d. green (*shades*) (4.7.19) .. .. 40 1·00
a. Major re-entry (R. 8/4) .. .. 65·00
b. "C" of "CA" missing from wmk .. † £225
c. "A" of "CA" missing from wmk .. † —
w. Wmk Crown to left of CA .. 20·00
y. Wmk sideways inverted and reversed .. .. .. — 32·00
81 26 2d. indigo and green (18.2.21) .. 1·00 4·00
w. Wmk inverted .. .. .. 35·00
y. Wmk inverted and reversed .. 35·00
82 27 2½d. deep blue and blue (A) (18.2.21) 13·00 3·00
a. Blue-black and deep blue .. 1·50 1·75
b. "C" of "CA" missing from wmk .. — £200
c. "A" of "CA" missing from wmk .. £200
w. Wmk inverted .. .. .. 25·00
x. Wmk reversed .. .. .. 30·00
y. Wmk inverted and reversed .. 30·00
83 28 3d. myrtle-green and blue (8.4.21) .. 1·50 2·50
w. Wmk inverted .. .. .. 30·00 32·00
84 29 4d. brown and deep green (21.1.21) 2·50 9·00
w. Wmk inverted .. .. ..
x. Wmk reversed .. .. ..
85 – 1s. orange-yell & red-orge (10.12.20) 3·75 5·50
a. Frame inverted £20000 £14000
b. "C" of "CA" missing from wmk .. £300
c. "A" of "CA" missing from wmk ..
w. Wmk inverted .. .. ..
x. Wmk reversed .. .. ..
86 – 2s. light blue and brown (10.12.20) 13·00 26·00
b. "C" of "CA" missing from wmk .. £600
c. "A" of "CA" missing from wmk ..
w. Wmk inverted .. .. .. 32·00 40·00
x. Wmk reversed .. .. ..
y. Wmk inverted and reversed ..
87 – 3s. violet-blue and orange (10.12.20) 20·00 80·00
88 – 5s. blue and yellow-orange (15.4.21) 55·00 80·00
a. Blue and pale dull orange .. 48·00 75·00
w. Wmk inverted .. .. ..
x. Wmk reversed .. .. ..
89 – 10s. myrtle-green (6.5.20) .. .. 75·00 £150
78/89 .. .. .. *Set of* 12 £150 £325
78s/89s Optd "Specimen" .. *Set of* 12 £250

Designs: *Vert*—1s. Statue of Queen Victoria, Kingston; 2s. Admiral Rodney Memorial, Spanish Town; 3s. Sir Charles Metcalfe Statue, Kingston; 5s. Jamaican scenery.
*The normal sideways wmk on Nos. 79/80 shows Crown to right of CA, *as seen from the back of the stamp.*
The 2½d. of the above series showed the Union Jack at left, incorrectly, as indicated in illustration A. In the issue on paper with Script wmk the design was corrected (Illustration B).
An example of the "C" omitted has been reported on an example of No. 88 overprinted "Specimen".
A 6d. stamp showing the reading of the Declaration of Freedom from Slavery in 1836 was prepared and sent out in April 1921, but for political reasons was not issued and the stock was destroyed. Copies overprinted "Specimen" are known on both the Mult CA and Script CA papers, and are worth £650 each. Price without "Specimen" on Script CA £16000.

COVER PRICES

Cover factors are quoted at the beginning of each country for most issues to 1945. An explanation of the system can be found on page x. The factors quoted do not, however, apply to philatelic covers.

"Bow" flaw (R.18/12)

1921 (21 Oct)–**27.** *Wmk Mult Script CA. Chalk-surfaced paper (6d.). P* 14.

89*a*	**18**	½d. green (3.11.27)	1·75	10
		ab. Bow flaw	45·00	24·00
		as. Optd "Specimen"	45·00	
90		6d. dull purple and bright magenta ..	7·50	4·00
		s. Optd "Specimen"	38·00	

35 "POSTAGE & REVENUE" added

36 "Port Royal in 1853" (A. Duperly)

(Printing as before; the 6d. recess-printed)

1921–29. *As Nos.* 78/89. *Wmk Mult Script CA* (*sideways* on 1d. and* 1½*d.*). *Chalk-surfaced paper* (½*d.,* 1*d.*). *P* 14.

91	**23**	½d. green and olive-green (5.2.22) ..	50	50
		a. Green and deep olive-green ..	30	50
		w. Wmk inverted	25·00	25·00
92	**35**	1d. carmine and orange (5.12.22) ..	1·50	10
		w. Wmk Crown to right of CA ..	15·00	15·00
		x. Wmk reversed	—	35·00
93	**25**	1½d. green (*shades*) (2.2.21) ..	75	45
		a. Major re-entry (R. 8/4)	65·00	
		w. Wmk Crown to left of CA ..	—	20·00
		x. Wmk reversed	20·00	20·00
		y. Wmk sideways inverted and reversed	—	40·00
94	**26**	2d. indigo and green (4.11.21) ..	6·50	80
		a. Indigo and grey-green (1925) ..	9·00	1·00
		w. Wmk inverted	†	—
95	**27**	2½d. deep blue and blue (B) (4.11.21)	5·50	1·75
		a. Dull blue and blue (B)	6·00	60
		w. Wmk inverted	25·00	25·00
		x. Wmk reversed		
		y. Wmk inverted and reversed ..		
96	**28**	3d. myrtle-green and blue (6.3.22) ..	2·50	70
		a. Green and pale blue	1·25	15
		x. Wmk reversed		
97	**29**	4d. brown and deep green (5.12.21) ..	1·00	30
		a. Chocolate and dull green ..	1·00	30
		w. Wmk inverted	25·00	
		x. Wmk reversed	35·00	
98	**36**	6d. black and blue (5.12.22)	12·00	2·00
		a. Grey and dull blue	12·00	1·50
99	–	1s. orange and red-orange (4.11.21) ..	1·75	80
		a. Orange-yellow and brown-orange	1·75	65
		w. Wmk inverted		
		x. Wmk reversed	—	£100
100	–	2s. light blue and brown (5.2.22) ..	3·25	65
		w. Wmk inverted	30·00	30·00
101	–	3s. violet-blue and orange (23.8.21) ..	11·00	9·00
102	–	5s. blue and yellow-brown (8.11.23) ..	28·00	25·00
		a. Blue and pale dull orange ..	55·00	65·00
		b. Blue and yellow-orange (1927) ..	26·00	23·00
		c. Blue and pale bistre-brown (1929)	27·00	22·00
		w. Wmk inverted	—	£130
		x. Wmk reversed		
103	**34**	10s. myrtle-green (3.22)	50·00	70·00
91/103		.. .. *Set of* 13	£110	95·00
91s/103s Optd "Specimen"		.. *Set of* 13	£250	

*The normal sideways wmk shows Crown to left of CA on No. 92 or Crown to right of CA on No. 93, *both as seen from the back of the stamp.*

The frame of No. 102*a* is the same colour as that of No. 88*a*.

The designs of all values of the pictorial series, with the exception of the 5s. and 10s. (which originated with the Governor, Sir Leslie Probyn), were selected by Mr. F. C. Cundall, F.S.A. The 1d. and 5s. were drawn by Miss Cundall, the 3d. by Mrs. Cundall, and the 10s. by De La Rue & Co. The 6d. is from a lithograph. The other designs are from photographs, the frames of all being the work of Miss Cundall and Miss Wood.

37

38

39

(Centres from photos by Miss V. F. Taylor. Frames des F. C. Cundall, F.S.A., and drawn by Miss Cundall. Recess B.W.)

1923 (1 Nov). *Child Welfare. Wmk Mult Script CA. P* 12.

104	**37**	½d. +½d. black and green	60	5·50
105	**38**	1d. +½d. black and scarlet	1·75	10·00
106	**39**	2½d. +½d. black and blue	8·50	18·00
104/6		.. .. *Set of* 3	9·50	30·00
104s/6s Optd "Specimen"		.. *Set of* 3	£120	

Sold at a premium of ½d. for the Child Welfare League, these stamps were on sale annually from 1 November to 31 January, until 31 January 1927, when their sale ceased, the remainders being destroyed on 21 February 1927.

40

41

42

Die I

Die II

(Recess D.L.R.)

1929–32. *Wmk Mult Script CA. P* 14.

108	**40**	1d. scarlet (Die I) (15.3.29)	2·00	20
		a. Die II (1932)	4·00	10
109	**41**	1½d. chocolate (18.1.29)	2·00	15
110	**42**	9d. maroon (5.3.29)	3·25	1·00
108/10		.. .. *Set of* 3	6·50	1·10
108s/10s Perf "Specimen"		.. *Set of* 3	75·00	

In Die I the shading below JAMAICA is formed of thickened parallel lines, and in Die II of diagonal cross-hatching.

43 Coco Palms at Don Christopher's Cove

44 Wag Water River, St. Andrew

45 Priestman's River, Portland

(Dies eng and recess Waterlow)

1932. *Wmk Mult Script CA* (*sideways on* 2*d. and* 2½*d.*). *P* 12½.

111	**43**	2d. black and green (4.11.32)	11·00	2·75
		a. Imperf between (vert pair) ..	£5500	
112	**44**	2½d. turquoise-blue & ultram (5.3.32)	2·25	1·50
		a. Imperf between (vert pair) ..	£11000	£11000
113	**45**	6d. grey-black and purple (4.2.32) ..	10·00	1·25
111/13		.. .. *Set of* 3	21·00	5·00
111s/13s Perf "Specimen"		.. *Set of* 3	80·00	

1935 (6 May). *Silver Jubilee. As Nos.* 91/4 *of Antigua, but ptd by B.W. P* 11×12.

114	1d. deep blue and scarlet	40	15
	b. Short extra flagstaff	£800	
	d. Flagstaff on right-hand turret ..	75·00	
	e. Double flagstaff	75·00	
115	1½d. ultramarine and grey-black	60	1·50
	a. Extra flagstaff	80·00	£110
	b. Short extra flagstaff	85·00	
	c. Lightning conductor	75·00	
116	6d. green and indigo	5·50	13·00
	a. Extra flagstaff	£180	£225
	b. Short extra flagstaff	£190	
	c. Lightning conductor	£160	
117	1s. slate and purple	4·50	8·00
	a. Extra flagstaff	£250	£300
	b. Short extra flagstaff	£300	
	c. Lightning conductor	£200	
114/17	.. .. *Set of* 4	10·00	20·00
114s/17s Perf "Specimen"	.. *Set of* 4	75·00	

For illustrations of plate varieties see Omnibus section following Zanzibar.

1937 (12 May). *Coronation. As Nos.* 95/7 *of Antigua, but printed by D.L.R. P* 14.

118	1d. scarlet	30	15
119	1½d. grey-black	50	30
120	2½d. bright blue	85	70
118/20	.. .. *Set of* 3	1·50	1·00
118s/20s Perf "Specimen"	.. *Set of* 3	55·00	

NEW INFORMATION

The editor is always interested to correspond with people who have new information that will improve or correct the Catalogue.

48 King George VI

49 Coco Palms at Don Christopher's Cove

50 Bananas

51 Citrus Grove

52 Kingston Harbour

53 Sugar Industry

54 Bamboo Walk

55 King George VI

56 Tobacco Growing and Cigar Making

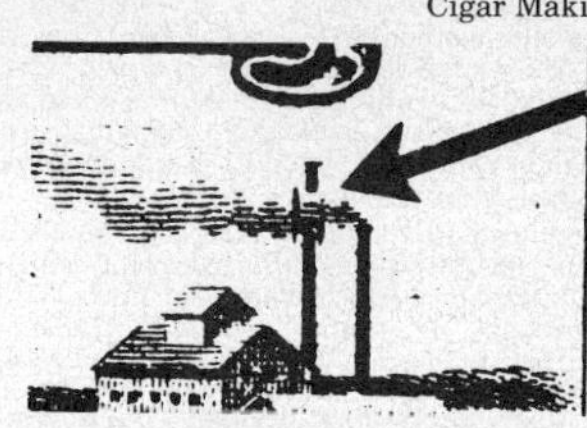

Repaired chimney (Centre plate 1 R. 11/1)

(Recess D.L.R. (T **48**, 5s. and 10s.), Waterlow (others))

1938 (10 Oct)–**52.** *T* **48/56** *and as Nos.* 88, 112/13, *but wi[th] inset portrait of King George VI, as in T* **49**. *Wmk Mult Scrip[t] CA. P* 13½×14 (½*d.,* 1*d.,* 1½*d.*), 14 (5*s.,* 10*s.*) *or* 12½ (*others*)

121	**48**	½d. blue-green (10.10.38)	1·75	1
		a. Wmk sideways	†	£400
121*b*		½d. orange (25.10.51)	70	3
122		1d. scarlet	1·25	1
122*a*		1d. blue-green (25.10.51)	1·25	1
123		1½d. brown	1·25	1
124	**49**	2d. grey and green (10.12.38) ..	1·25	8
		a. Perf 13×13½ (1939)	2·75	5
		ab. "C" of "CA" missing from wmk ..	£750	
		b. Perf 12½×13 (1951)	1·25	1
125	**44**	2½d. greenish blue & ultram (10.12.38)	3·00	1·7
126	**50**	3d. ultramarine and green (10.12.38)	75	1·5
		a. "A" of "CA" missing from wmk ..	£750	
126*b*		3d. greenish blue and ultram (15.8.49)	1·25	1·2
126*c*		3d. green and scarlet (1.7.52) ..	2·25	3
127	**51**	4d. brown and green (10.12.38) ..	50	1
128	**45**	6d. grey and purple (10.12.38) ..	3·50	3
		a. Perf 13½×13 (10.10.50) ..	2·25	1
129	**52**	9d. lake (10.12.38)	50	5
		a. "A" of "CA" missing from wmk ..		
130	**53**	1s. green and purple-brown (10.12.38)	6·00	2
		a. Repaired chimney	£475	£10
131	**54**	2s. blue and chocolate (10.12.38) ..	20·00	1·0
132	–	5s. slate-blue & yellow-orge (10.12.38)	14·00	3·75
		a. Perf 14, line (1941)	£3000	£190
		b. Perf 13 (24.10.49)	6·50	3·00
		ba. Blue and orange (10.10.50) ..	6·50	3·00
133	**55**	10s. myrtle-green (10.12.38)	11·00	8·00
		aa. Perf 13 (10.10.50)	9·00	7·00
133*a*	**56**	£1 chocolate and violet (15.8.49) ..	27·00	26·00
121/33*a*		.. .. *Set of* 18	70·00	38·00
121s/33s Perf "Specimen"		.. *Set of* 13	£200	

No. 130a occurred in conjunction with Frame plate 2 on printings between 1943 and 1951.

No. 132a shows the emergency use of a line perforation machine, giving an irregular gauge of 14–14.15, after the De La Rue works were damaged in December 1940. The normal comb measures 13.8×13.7.

Nos. 121 and 122 exist in coils constructed from normal sheets.

Labuan
see North Borneo

Lagos
see Nigeria

Leeward Islands

he Federal Colony of the Leeward Islands was constituted in 1 formalising links between Antigua, British Virgin Islands, minica, Montserrat and St. Kitts-Nevis which stretched back he 1670s. Issues for the individual islands were superseded those inscribed "LEEWARD ISLANDS", but were in current use with them from 1903. Dominica was transferred he Windward Islands on 31 December 1939.

PRICES FOR STAMPS ON COVER TO 1945

Nos. 1/8	*from* × 10
Nos. 9/16	*from* × 12
Nos. 17/19	*from* × 8
Nos. 20/8	*from* × 5
Nos. 29/35	*from* × 4
Nos. 36/45	*from* × 5
Nos. 46/57	*from* × 4
Nos. 58/87	*from* × 5
Nos. 88/91	*from* × 6
Nos. 92/4	*from* × 10
Nos. 95/114	*from* × 5

RINTERS. All the stamps of Leeward Islands were typographed De La Rue & Co, Ltd, London, *except where otherwise stated.*

1

2

90 (31 Oct). *Name and value in second colour. Wmk Crown CA. P* 14.

No.	Type	Description		
	1	½d. dull mauve and green	3·50	1·25
		1d. dull mauve and rose	3·50	20
		2½d. dull mauve and blue	4·00	20
		w. Wmk inverted	£275	£160
		4d. dull mauve and orange	4·50	7·50
		6d. dull mauve and brown	11·00	12·00
		7d. dull mauve and slate	3·50	11·00
	2	1s. green and carmine	17·00	45·00
		5s. green and blue	£120	£250
'8		*Set of* 8	£150	£300
s/8s		Optd "Specimen" *Set of* 8	£200	

The colours of this issue are fugitive.

(3)

One Penny

(4)

One Penny

(5)

897 (22 July). *Queen Victoria's Diamond Jubilee. Handstamped with T* **3**.

No.	Type	Description		
9	1	½d. dull mauve and green	3·25	11·00
		a. Opt double	£1200	
.0		1d. dull mauve and rose	3·75	11·00
		a. Opt double	£1000	
		b. Opt triple	£3250	
.1		2½d. dull mauve and blue	4·25	11·00
		a. Opt double	£1200	
.2		4d. dull mauve and orange	32·00	70·00
		a. Opt double	£1200	
13		6d. dull mauve and brown	48·00	90·00
		a. Opt double	£1400	
14		7d. dull mauve and slate	48·00	90·00
		a. Opt double	£1400	
15	2	1s. green and carmine	£120	£190
		a. Opt double	£1800	
16		5s. green and blue	£450	£750
		a. Opt double	£5000	
9/16		*Set of* 8	£600	£1100

Beware of forgeries.

1902 (11 Aug). *Nos. 4/6 surch locally.*

No.	Type	Description		
17	4	1d. on 4d. dull mauve and orange	2·25	4·75
		a. Pair, one with tall narrow "O" in "One"	30·00	70·00
		b. Surch double		
18		1d. on 6d. dull mauve and brown	3·25	11·00
		a. Pair, one with tall narrow "O" in "One"	45·00	£120
19	5	1d. on 7d. dull mauve and slate	2·75	5·50
17/19		*Set of* 3	7·50	19·00

The tall narrow "O" variety occurred on R. 1/1, 5/3, 5/5 and 7/4.

6

7

8

LEEWARD ISLANDS

Wide "A" (R. 6/1 of both panes. Replaced in 1912)

LEEWARD ISLANDS

Dropped "R" (R.1/1 of both panes from Pl 2 (1st ptg only))

1902 (1 Sept–Oct). *Wmk Crown CA. P* 14.

No.	Type	Description		
20	6	½d. dull purple and green	5·50	1·00
21		1d. dull purple and carmine	7·00	20
22	7	2d. dull purple and ochre (Oct)	2·75	4·25
23	6	2½d. dull purple and ultramarine	5·00	2·25
		a. Wide "A" in "LEEWARD"	£190	£150
24	7	3d. dull purple and black (Oct)	3·75	7·50
25	6	6d. dull purple and brown	2·50	8·00
26	8	1s. green and carmine	3·25	19·00
		a. Dropped "R" in "LEEWARD"	£275	£475
27	7	2s. 6d. green and black (Oct)	27·00	65·00
28	8	5s. green and blue	48·00	70·00
20/8		*Set of* 9	95·00	£160
20s/8s		Optd "Specimen" *Set of* 9	£140	

1905 (Apr)–**08**. *Wmk Mult Crown CA. Ordinary paper* (*½d., 3d.*) *or chalk-surfaced paper* (*others*).

No.	Type	Description		
29	6	½d. dull purple and green (2.06)	3·50	2·00
		a. Chalk-surfaced paper (25.7.08)	17·00	11·00
30		1d. dull purple and carmine (29.8.06)	8·50	80
31	7	2d. dull purple and ochre (25.7.08)	4·50	12·00
32	6	2½d. dull purple and ultramarine (23.7.06)	60·00	32·00
		a. Wide "A" in "LEEWARD"	£550	£325
33	7	3d. dull purple and black	8·50	35·00
		a. Chalk-surfaced paper (18.4.08)	35·00	65·00
34	6	6d. dull purple and brown (15.7.08)	40·00	65·00
35	8	1s. green and carmine (15.7.08)	42·00	95·00
29/35		*Set of* 7	£150	£225

1907 (14 Apr)–**11**. *Wmk Mult Crown CA. Chalk-surfaced paper* (*3d. to 5s.*). *P* 14.

No.	Type	Description		
36	7	¼d. brown ((7.8.09)	2·75	1·75
37	6	½d. dull green	3·25	1·25
38		1d. bright red (7.07)	10·00	80
		a. *Rose-carmine* (1910)	35·00	3·00
39	7	2d. grey (3.8.11)	3·50	7·50
40	6	2½d. bright blue (5.07)	6·00	4·25
		a. Wide "A" in "LEEWARD"	£200	£170
41	7	3d. purple/*yellow* (28.10.10)	3·50	7·50
42	6	6d. dull and bright purple (3.8.11)	8·00	7·00
43	8	1s. black/*green* (3.8.11)	4·50	21·00
44	7	2s. 6d. black and red/*blue* (15.9.11)	40·00	48·00
45	8	5s. green and red/*yellow* (21.11.10)	42·00	65·00
36/45		*Set of* 10	£110	£150
36s/45s		Optd "Specimen" *Set of* 10	£200	

10

11

12

13

1912 (23 Oct)–**22**. *Die* I (*¼d. to 3d., 6d., 1s., 2s. 6d., 5s.*) *or Die* II (*4d., 2s.*). *Wmk Mult Crown CA. Chalk-surfaced paper* (*3d. to 5s.*). *P* 14.

No.	Type	Description		
46	10	¼d. brown	1·75	1·00
		a. *Pale brown*	3·50	2·00
47	11	½d. yellow-green (12.12)	5·50	2·00
		a. *Deep green* (1916)	4·50	1·50
48		1d. red	5·00	1·00
		a. *Bright scarlet* (8.15)	6·00	1·00
49	10	2d. slate-grey (9.1.13)	4·00	5·50
50	11	2½d. bright blue	3·25	7·00
		a. *Deep bright blue* (1914)	3·75	4·00
51	10	3d. purple/*yellow* (9.1.13)	1·75	10·00
		a. *White back* (11.13)	55·00	£110
		as. Optd "Specimen"	42·00	
		b. *On lemon* (11.14)	4·50	16·00
		c. *On buff* (1920)	35·00	50·00
		cs. Optd "Specimen"	42·00	
		d. *On orange-buff* (1920)	3·75	12·00
		dw. Wmk inverted	£250	
52		4d. blk & red/*pale yell* (Die II) (12.5.22)	3·75	22·00
53	11	6d. dull and bright purple (9.1.13)	3·00	8·00
54	12	1s. black/*green* (9.1.13)	3·00	8·00
		a. *White back* (11.13)	45·00	35·00
		as. Optd "Specimen"	45·00	
		b. *On blue-green, olive back* (1917)	7·00	8·00
		bs. Optd "Specimen"	45·00	
55	10	2s. purple & blue/*blue* (Die II) (12.5.22)	8·50	50·00
56		2s. 6d. black and red/*blue* (11.13)	12·00	38·00
57	12	5s. green and red/*yellow* (9.14)	48·00	85·00
		a. *White back* (11.13)	42·00	75·00
		as. Optd "Specimen"	48·00	
		b. *On lemon* (1915)	22·00	60·00
		c. *On orange-buff* (1920)	90·00	£150
46/57*b*		*Set of* 12	65·00	£180
46s/57s		Optd "Specimen" *Set of* 12	£275	

Nos. 51a, 54a and 57 were only on sale from Montserrat.

HIGH VALUE KEY TYPES. The reign of King Edward VII saw the appearance of the first in a new series of "key type" designs, initially on the issues of Malaya—Straits Settlements and Nyasaland, to be used for high value denominations where a smaller design was felt to be inappropriate. The system was extended during the reign of King George V, using the portrait as Leeward Islands Type **13**, to cover Bermuda, Ceylon, Leeward Islands, Malaya—Straits Settlements, Malta and Nyasaland. A number of these territories continued to use the key type concept for high value King George VI stamps and one, Leeward Islands, for stamps of Queen Elizabeth II.

In each instance the King George V issues were printed in sheets of 60 (12×5) on various coloured papers. The system utilised a common "head" plate used with individual "duty" plates which printed the territory name and face value.

Two major plate flaws occur on the King George V head plate: the break on scroll on R. 1/12 and the broken crown and scroll on R. 2/12. Both of these occur in different states, having been repaired and then damaged once again, perhaps on several occasions. The prices quoted in the listings are for examples approximately as illustrated.

Break in scroll (R. 1/12)

Broken crown and scroll (R. 2/12)

"D I" shaved at foot 1d. R. 7/3 of left pane (all ptgs between Sept 1947 and July 1949. 1s. R. 9/6 of right pane (all ptgs between 1932 and 1938)

1921 (Oct)–**32**. *Wmk Mult Script CA or Mult Crown CA* (£1). *Chalk-surfaced paper* (*3d. to* £1). *P* 14.

(*a*) *Die II* (1921–29)

No.	Type	Description		
58	10	¼d. brown (1.4.22)	2·25	1·00
59	11	½d. blue-green	1·00	75
60		1d. carmine-red	2·25	55
61		1d. bright violet (21.8.22)	2·25	1·00
62		1d. bright scarlet (1929)	6·50	2·25
63	10	1½d. carmine-red (10.9.26)	3·25	2·00
64		1½d. red-brown (1929)	1·25	10
65		2d. slate-grey (6.22)	2·00	80
		x. Wmk reversed		

66 **11** 2½d. orange-yellow (22.9.23) .. .. 6·50 50·00
67 2½d. bright blue (1.3.27) .. .. 3·25 1·25
68 **10** 3d. light ultramarine (22.9.23) .. 4·25 26·00
a. Deep ultramarine (1925) .. .. 50·00 50·00
69 3d. purple/*yellow* (1.7.27) .. .. 1·25 6·50
70 4d. black and red/*pale yellow* (2.24) .. 3·00 21·00
71 5d. dull purple and olive-green (12.5.22) 2·50 4·25
72 **11** 6d. dull and bright purple (17.7.23) .. 10·00 27·00
73 **12** 1s. black/*emerald* (17.7.23) .. .. 6·50 8·00
74 **10** 2s. purple and blue/*blue* (12.5.22) .. 16·00 42·00
a. Red-purple and blue/blue (1926) .. 7·50 45·00
aw. Wmk inverted £225
75 2s. 6d. black and red/*blue* (17.7.23) .. 6·50 23·00
76 3s. bright green and violet (12.5.22) .. 12·00 24·00
77 4s. black and red (12.5.22) .. .. 12·00 42·00
78 **12** 5s. green and red/*pale yellow* (17.7.23) 38·00 65·00
79 **13** 10s. green and red/*green* (1928) .. 55·00 75·00
a. Break in scroll £160
b. Broken crown and scroll £160
80 £1 purple and black/*red* (1928) .. £225 £250
a. Break in scroll £375
b. Broken crown and scroll £375
58/80 .. .. *Set of* 22 £350 £600
58s/80s Optd or Perf (£1) "Specimen" .. *Set of* 23 £550

(*b*) *Reversion to Die* I (*Plate* 23) (1931–32)
81 **10** ¼d. brown .. .. .. 4·50 16·00
82 **11** ½d. blue-green .. .. .. 27·00 28·00
83 1d. bright scarlet .. .. .. 18·00 50
84 **10** 1½d. red-brown .. .. .. 3·75 2·75
85 **11** 2½d. bright blue .. .. .. 6·50 3·50
86 6d. dull and bright purple .. .. 16·00 75·00
87 **12** 1s. black/*emerald* .. .. .. 48·00 75·00
a. "D I" flaw £350
b. "A" of "CA" missing from wmk .. — £2000
81/7 .. .. *Set of* 7 £110 £180

No. 60 may not have been used locally before January 1923.
No. 68*a* was issued in St. Kitts-Nevis.
Nos. 59, 62 and 82/3 exist in coils, constructed from normal sheets.
Nos. 81/7 result from the use, in error, of Die I which had previously been "retired" in late 1920, to produce Plate 23.

1935 (6 May). *Silver Jubilee. As Nos.* 91/4 *of Antigua, but printed by Waterlow. P* 11×12.
88 1d. deep blue and scarlet .. .. .. 1·60 1·50
89 1½d. ultramarine and grey .. .. 2·25 70
90 2½d. brown and deep blue .. .. 2·25 3·50
91 1s. slate and purple .. .. .. 7·00 15·00
k. Kite and vertical log £225
l. Kite and horizontal log £250
88/91 .. .. *Set of* 4 11·50 19·00
88s/91s Perf "Specimen" .. *Set of* 4 80·00

For illustrations of plate varieties see Omnibus section following Zanzibar.

1937 (12 May). *Coronation. As Nos.* 95/7 *of Antigua, but printed by D.L.R.*
92 1d. scarlet 30 15
93 1½d. buff 40 35
94 2½d. bright blue 40 60
92/4 .. .. *Set of* 3 1·00 1·00
92s/4s Perf "Specimen" .. .. *Set of* 3 60·00

14

15

(Die A) (Die B)

In Die B the figure "1" has a broader top and more projecting serif.

"ISI.ANDS" flaw (R. 1/2 of right pane) (Pl. 2 ptgs from November 1942 until corrected in July 1949)

Broken second "E" in "LEEWARD" (R. 4/1 of right pane) (Pl. 3 ptgs from August 1942 until corrected in June 1949) (A similar variety occurs on 5s.)

Broken top right scroll (R. 5/11) (1942 ptg of 10s. only. Corrected on £1 value from same period)

Broken lower right scroll (R. 5/12. 1942 ptgs only)

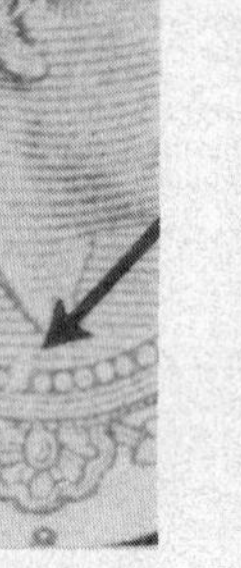
Missing pearl (R. 5/1. 1944 ptgs only)

Gash in chin (R. 2/5. 1942 ptgs only)

1938 (25 Nov)–**51.** *T* **14** (*and similar type, but shaded value tablet,* ½*d.,* 1*d.,* 2½*d.,* 6*d.*) *and* **15** (10*s.,* £1). *Chalk-surfaced paper* (3*d. to* £1). *P* 14.

(*a*) *Wmk Mult Script CA*
95 ¼d. brown .. .. 60 1·50
a. Chalk-surfaced paper. *Dp brn* (13.6.49) 30 1·75
96 ½d. emerald 70 70
a. "ISLANDS" flaw .. .. .. 55·00
97 ½d. slate-grey (*chalk-surfaced paper*) (1.7.49) .. .. 30 1·50
98 1d. scarlet (Die A) .. .. .. 9·50 2·50
99 1d. scarlet (*shades*) (Die B) (1940) .. 2·25 1·75
a. "D I" flaw (9.47) £170
b. Carmine (9.42) .. .. .. 1·50 5·50
c. Red (13.9.48) .. .. .. 6·00 3·25
ca. "D I" flaw £170
100 1d. bl-grn (*chalk-surfaced paper*) (1.7.49) 55 15
a. "D I" flaw £140
101 1½d. chestnut .. .. 1·00 50
102 1½d. yellow-orange and black (*chalk-surfaced paper*) (1.7.49) 85 40
103 2d. olive-grey .. .. 3·00 1·00
a. Slate-grey (11.42) .. .. .. 5·50 3·00
104 2d. scarlet (*chalk-surfaced paper*) (1.7.49) 1·40 1·25
105 2½d. bright blue .. .. 13·00 2·50
a. Light bright blue (11.42) .. .. 80 1·25
106 2½d. black and purple (*chalk-surfaced paper*) (1.7.49) 55 15
107 3d. orange .. .. 35·00 2·75
a. Ordinary paper. *Pale orange* (11.42) 50 85
108 3d. bright blue (1.7.49) 65 15
109 6d. deep dull purple and bright purple 23·00 4·75
a. Ordinary paper (8.42) .. .. 5·50 2·25
ab. Broken "E" £250
b. Purple and deep magenta (29.9.47) .. 5·50 3·00
ba. Broken "E" £250
110 1s. black/*emerald* .. .. .. 16·00 2·00
a. "D I" flaw £375
b. Ordinary paper (3.42) .. .. 4·25 1·00
ba. Grey and black/emerald (8.42) .. 18·00 4·00
bb. Black and grey/emerald (11.42) .. £130 11·00
111 2s. reddish purple and blue/*blue* .. 21·00 2·50
a. Ordinary paper (3.42) .. .. 10·00 2·00
ab. Deep purple and blue/blue (29.9.47) 11·00 2·50
112 5s. green and red/*yellow* .. .. 48·00 15·00
a. Broken "E" (R. 3/4 of left pane) .. £650
b. Ordinary paper (12.43) .. .. 32·00 14·00
ba. Broken "E" (R. 3/4 of left pane) .. £550
c. Bright green and red/yellow (24.10.51) 55·00 50·00
113 10s. bluish green and deep red/*green* .. £200 £120
a. Ordinary paper. *Pale green and dull red/green* (26.6.44*) £475 £250
ad. Broken top right scroll £3000
ae. Broken lower right scroll £3000 £3000
af. Gash in chin £3000 £3000
b. Ordinary paper. *Green and red/green* (22.2.45*) .. .. .. £150 65·00
c. Ordinary paper. *Deep green and deep vermilion/green* (15.10.47*) .. .. £120 70·00
ca. Missing pearl £1200

(*b*) *Wmk Mult Crown CA*
114 £1 brown-purple and black/*red* £325 £250
a. Purple and black/carmine (21.9.42*) .. 85·00 45·00
ae. Broken lower right scroll £1100 £600
af. Gash in chin £1100 £600
b. Brown-purple & black/salmon (5.2.45*) 35·00 24·00
ba. Missing pearl £1000 £700
c. Perf 13. *Violet & black/scarlet* (4.1.52*) 32·00 38·00
ca. Wmk sideways £3000
cw. Wmk inverted £2250
95/114*b* .. .. .. *Set of* 19 £190 £100
95s/114s Perf "Specimen" .. .. *Set of* 13 £500

*Dates quoted for Nos. 113a/14c are earliest known postmark dates. Nos. 113a and 114a were despatched to the Leeward Islands in March 1942, Nos. 113b and 114*b* in December 1943, No. 113*c* in June 1944 and No. 114*c* on 13 December 1951.
Nos. 96, 98/9 and 99b exist in coils constructed from normal sheets.
Printings of the 10s. in March 1942 (No. 113*a*) and of the £1 in February and October 1942 (No. 114*a*) were made by Williams Lea & Co. Ltd. following bomb damage to the De La Rue works in 1940.
For illustrations of Nos. 99a, 99ca, 100a and 110a see above No. 58.

1946 (1 Nov). *Victory. As Nos.* 110/11 *of Antigua.*
115 1½d. brown 15 30
116 3d. red-orange 15 30
115s/16s Perf "Specimen" .. *Set of* 2 55·00

1949 (2 Jan). *Royal Silver Wedding. As Nos.* 112/13 *of Antigua.*
117 2½d. ultramarine 10 10
118 5s. green .. .. 4·00 3·00

1949 (10 Oct). *75th Anniv of Universal Postal Union. As* 114/17 *of Antigua.*
119 2½d. blue-black 10
120 3d. deep blue .. .. 1·25
121 6d. magenta 15
122 1s. blue-green 15
119/22 .. .. *Set of* 4 1·40

(New Currency. 100 cents = 1 B.W.I. dollar)

1951 (16 Feb). *Inauguration of B.W.I. University College. Nos.* 118/19 *of Antigua.*
123 3 c. orange and black 30
124 12 c. rose-carmine and reddish violet .. 70

Long Island

PRICES FOR STAMPS ON COVER

Most covers from Long Island are philatelic, but these re worth from × 2 (Nos. 1/3) or from × 5 (Nos. 4/36).

ne Turkish island of Chustan (or Keustan) in the Gulf of rna was occupied by the Royal Navy during April 1916 and amed Long Island.

he following stamps were provided by the Civil Administrator, t-Cmdr H. Pirie-Gordon, for the postal service inaugurated on ay 1916.

ED STAMPS. Stamps of Long Island were cancelled by d-drawn circular date stamps in blue crayon for the thend post office ("N") or in red crayon for Nikola post office).

ANTITIES ISSUED. The figures quoted do not include the ainders subsequently recorded as having been destroyed.

(1)

2

16 (7 May). *Turkish fiscal stamps surch by typewriter as in T 1. No wmk. P 12.*

	½d. on 20 pa. green and buff (new value in red, remainder of surch in black)	£2250	£4000
	1d. on 10 pa. carmine and buff	£2500	£4000
	2½d. on 1 pi. violet and buff (R.)	£2250	£4000

Quantities issued: ½d. 25; 1d. 20; 2½d. 25.

16 (7 May). *Typewritten as T 2 in various colours of ribbon and carbon. Each stamp initialled by the Civil Administrator. No gum. Imperf.*

On pale green paper with horizontal grey lines. No wmk. heets of 12 (4×3) or 16 (4×4) with stamps initialled in red ink.

	½d. black	£1100	£900
	a. "G.R.I." double	£1900	
	b. "7" for "&"	£3000	
	½d. blue	£900	
	a. "G.R.I." double	£1900	
	b. "7" for "&"	£3000	
	½d. mauve	£425	£500
	a. "G.R.I." double	£1000	
	b. "7" for "&"	£2250	

Quantity issued: 140 in all.

) *On thin horiz laid paper with sheet wmk of* "Silver Linen" *in double-lined letters. Sheets of 20 (4×5) or 16 (some ptgs of 1s.) with stamps initialled in red ink.*

7	½d. black	£400	£500
	a. "postage" for "Postage"	£1700	
	b. "7" for "&"	£1700	
8	½d. blue	£600	£650
	b. "7" for "&"	£1700	
9	½d. mauve	£190	£250
	a. "postage" for "Postage"	£1000	
	b. "7" for "&"	£1200	
0	1d. black	£160	£300
	a. "7" for "&"	£1200	
	b. "Rvevue" for "Revenue"	£1200	
	g. "Postagg" for "Postage"	£1700	
1	1d. blue	£225	£375
	a. "7" for "&"	£1700	
	c. "postage" for "Postage"	£1700	
	e. "G.R?I." for "G.R.I."	£1700	
	f. "ONR" for "ONE"	£1000	
2	1d. mauve	£120	£225
	a. "7" for "&"	£1300	
	b. "Rvevue" for "Revenue"	£1700	
	c. "postage" for "Postage"	£1700	
	e. "G.R?I?" for "G.R.I."	†	£1800
	f. "ONR" for "ONE"	£750	£1000
	g. "Postagg" for "Postage"	£1200	
3	1d. red	£140	£250
	a. "7" for "&"	£1200	
	c. "postage" for "Postage"	£1700	
	f. "ONR" for "ONE"	£1000	£1100
4	2½d. black	£800	
5	2½d. blue	£800	£1000
6	2½d. mauve	£1500	£1000
7	6d. black (inscr "SIX PENCE")	£1000	£1400
	a. "SIXPENCE" (one word)	£2000	
	b. Without red ink initials	†	£1700
19	6d. mauve (inscr "SIX PENCE")	£375	£800
	a. "SIXPENCE" (one word)	£1500	
20	1s. black	£120	£325
	a. "ISLANA" for "ISLAND"	£1700	
	b. "Postge" for "Postage"	£950	£1400
	c. "Rebenue" for "Revenue"	£1700	
21	1s. blue	£1000	
22	1s. mauve	£110	£400
	a. "ISLANA" for "ISLAND"	£1200	
	b. "Postge" for "Postage"	£1700	
	c. "Rebenue" for "Revenue"	£1700	

Quantities issued (all colours); ½d. 237; 1d. 881; 2½d. 80; 6d. 89; 1s. 383.

(c) *On thin wove paper. No wmk. Sheets of 24 with stamps initialled in indelible pencil.*

23	½d. black	£300	£400
25	½d. mauve	£550	
26	1d. black	£350	£450
27	1d. red	£4500	£900
30	2d. black	£180	£450
	b. Error. 1d. and 2d. *se-tenant*	£3750	
	c. Initialled in red ink	£850	£950
31	2d. mauve	£180	£300
	a. Error. 1d. and 2d. *se-tenant*	£3500	
32	2½d. black	£400	£500
33	2½d. blue	£1000	
34	2½d. mauve	£900	£900
35	6d. black	£190	£450
	a. "Rvenne &" for "Revenue"	£1600	
	b. Error. 2d. and 6d. *se-tenant*, also "ISLND" for "ISLAND"	£3750	£3750
	c. "PENCC"	£1300	
36	6d. blue	£700	
	a. "Rvenne &" for "Revenue"	£2000	
	b. Error. 2d. and 6d. *se-tenant*, also "ISLND" for "ISLAND"	£4000	
	c. "PENCC"	£1700	

Quantities issued (all colours); ½d. 114; 1d. 120; 2d. 249; 2½d. 115; 6d. 200.

TOP SHEETS AND CARBONS. It is believed that the production sequence of the typewritten stamps was as follows:

½d. on pale green (Nos. 4/6)
- Two black top sheets of 12 (4×3) and one of 16 (4×4)
- Two blue carbon sheets of 12 (4×3) and one of 16 (4×4)
- Five mauve carbon sheets of 12, two from one top sheet and three from the other
- Varieties: "7" for "&" occurs on an unknown position from one of the sheets of 12 and "G.R.I." double occurs on R. 3/2-4 of the other

½d. on laid paper (Nos. 7/9) in sheets of 20 (4×5)
- Three black top sheets
- Three blue carbon sheets
- Eight mauve carbon sheets, two or three from each top sheet
- Varieties: "postage" occurs on R. 3/2 of one top sheet and "7" for "&" on R. 4/2 of another

1d. on laid paper (Nos. 10/13) in sheets of 20 (4×5)
- Eleven red top sheets
- Fifteen black carbon sheets, three each from five of the top sheets
- Six blue carbon sheets, one each from six of the top sheets
- Twenty-two mauve carbon sheets, probably two from each top sheet
- Varieties: "7" for "&" on R. 3/3, "postage" on R. 3/3, "Rvevue" on R. 1/3 and "Postagg" on R. 2/4, all from different top sheets. The position of "G.R?I?" is not known. "ONR" occurs from three different top sheets on R. 5/1, R. 5/2 & 4 or R. 4/1 and 5/2

2½d. on laid paper (Nos. 14/16) in sheets of 20 (4×5)
- One black top sheet
- One blue carbon sheet
- Two mauve carbon sheets

6d. on laid paper (Nos. 17/19) in sheets of 20 (4×5)
- One black top sheet
- One blue carbon sheet*
- Three mauve carbon sheets
- Variety: "SIXPENCE" occurs on R. 1/2-3

1s. on laid paper (Nos. 20/2)
- Five black top sheets, four of 20 (4×5) and one of 16 (4×4)
- Nine black carbon sheets, three each from two of the top sheets of 20 and three from the top sheet of 16
- Two blue carbon sheets, one each from two of the top sheets of 20
- Twelve mauve carbon sheets, nine from various top sheets of 20 and three from the top sheet of 16
- Varieties: "ISLANA" occurs on R. 1/2 of one of the sheets of 20 and "Postge" on R. 1/3 of the sheet of 16. "Rebenue" comes from one of the other sheets of 20

½d. on wove paper (Nos. 23/5) in sheets of 24 (4×6)
- One black top sheet
- Three black carbon sheets
- One blue carbon sheet*
- One mauve carbon sheet

1d. on wove paper (Nos. 26/7) in sheets of 24 (4×6)
- One red top sheet
- Three black carbon sheets
- One blue carbon sheet*
- One mauve carbon sheet*

2d. on wove paper (Nos. 30/1) in sheets of 24 (4×6)
- Two black top sheets
- Six black carbon sheets, three from each top sheet. One initialled in red ink
- Four mauve carbon sheets, two from each top sheet
- Variety: the "1d." error occurs on R. 5/2 from one top sheet

2½d. on wove paper (Nos. 32/4) in sheets of 24 (4×6)
- One black top sheet
- Three black carbon sheets
- One blue carbon sheet
- One mauve carbon sheet

6d. on wove paper (Nos. 35/6) in sheets of 24 (4×6)
- Two black top sheets
- Six black carbon sheets, three from each top sheet
- Two blue carbon sheets, one from each top sheet
- Varieties: the "2d." error occurs on R. 5/3 from one top sheet which also showed "PENCC" on R. 3/2, and "Rvenne &" on R. 4/1 of the other

*These carbons are described in written records, but their existence has yet to be confirmed by actual examples.

Madagascar

PRICES FOR STAMPS ON COVER

Nos. 1/47	—
Nos. 50/6	*from* × 50
Nos. 57/62	*from* × 30

BRITISH CONSULAR MAIL

After May 1883 mail from the British community at Antananarivo, the capital, was sent by runner to the British Consulate at Tamatave for forwarding via the French Post Office.

In March of the following year the British Vice-Consul at Antananarivo, Mr. W. C. Pickersgill, reorganised this service and issued stamps for use on both local and overseas mail. Such stamps were only gummed at one of the top corners. This was to facilitate their removal from overseas mail where they were replaced by Mauritius stamps (at Port Louis) or by French issues (at the Vice-Consulate) for transmission via Tamatave and Reunion. Local mail usually had the stamps removed also, being marked with a "PAID" or a Vice-Consular handstamp, although a few covers have survived intact.

CONDITION. Due to the type of paper used, stamps of the British Consular Mail are usually found with slight faults, especially thins. Our prices are for average examples, really fine stamps being worth a premium.

USED STAMPS. Postmarks are not usually found on these issues. Cancellations usually take the form of a manuscript line or cross in crayon, ink or pencil or as five parallel horizontal bars in black or red, approximately 15 mm long. Examples of Nos. 1/3, 5/8 and 11 showing a red diagonal line are believed to be cancelled-to-order.

1

2

1884 (Mar). *Typo locally. Rouletted vertically in colour. No gum, except on one upper corner. With circular consular handstamp reading* "BRITISH VICE-CONSULATE ANTANANARIVO" *around Royal arms in black.*

(a) *Inscr* "LETTER".

1	1	6d. (½ oz) magenta	£400	£425
		a. Violet handstamp	£1800	
2		1s. (1 oz) magenta	£375	
3		1s. 6d. (1½ oz) magenta	£400	
4		2s. (2 oz) magenta	£600	

(b) *Inscr* "POSTAL PACKET"

5	1	1d. (1 oz) magenta	£400	£350
		a. Without handstamp	£4000	£4000
6		2d. (2 oz) magenta	£275	£250
7		3d. (3 oz) magenta	£275	£250
8		4d. (1 oz amended in ms to "4 oz") magenta	£650	£600
		a. Without manuscript amendment	£3250	£3250
		ab. Violet handstamp	£1100	
		ac. Without handstamp	£4000	£4000

Nos. 1/8 were printed in horizontal strips of four, each strip containing two impressions of the setting. Each strip usually contained two stamps with normal stops after "B.C.M." and two with a hollow stop after "B" (1d., 2d., 3d., 4d., 6d. and 2s.) or after "M" (1s. and 1s. 6d.), although the 2d. has also been seen with a hollow stop after "M" and the 6d. with hollow stops after both "B" and "C".

Several values are known with the handstamp either inverted or double.

1886. *Manuscript provisionals.*

(a) *No. 2 with* "SHILLING" *erased and* "PENNY" *written above in red ink*

9 1 1d. on 1s. (1 oz) magenta

(b) *No. 2 surch* "4½d." *and* "W.C.P." *in red ink with a line through the original value*

10 1 4½d. on 1s. (1 oz) magenta

1886. *As No. 1, but colour changed. Handstamped with circular* "BRITISH VICE-CONSULATE ANTANANARIVO" *in black.*

11	1	6d. (½ oz) rose-red	£550	£500

1886. *As No. 8, but handstamped* "BRITISH CONSULAR MAIL ANTANANARIVO" *in black.*

12	1	4d. (1 oz) magenta	£1600	
		a. Violet handstamp	£3750	

1886. *Typo locally. "POSTAGE" and value in words printed in black. Rouletted vertically in colour. No gum, except on one upper corner.*

I. "POSTAGE" 29½ *mm long. Stops after* "POSTAGE" *and value*

(*a*) *Handstamped* "BRITISH VICE-CONSULATE ANTANANARIVO" *in black*

No.	Type			
14	2	1d. rose	£100	£130
		a. Violet handstamp	£275	
15		1½d. rose	£1200	£1000
		a. Violet handstamp	£850	£750
16		2d. rose	£140	
		a. Violet handstamp	£275	
17		3d. rose	£1200	£950
		a. Violet handstamp	£350	£325
18		4½d. rose	£850	£500
		a. Violet handstamp	£450	£300
19		8d. rose	£2250	£2250
		a. Violet handstamp	£1000	£1000
20		9d. rose	£2750	£2500
		a. Violet handstamp	£950	

(*b*) *Handstamped* "BRITISH CONSULAR MAIL ANTANANARIVO" *in black*

No.	Type			
21	2	1d. rose	70·00	
22		1½d. rose	70·00	
23		2d. rose	90·00	
24		3d. rose	85·00	£120
		a. Handstamp in red	†	£8000
25		4½d. rose	85·00	£120
		a. Handstamp in red	†	£4750
26		8d. rose	£100	
		a. Handstamp in violet	£1200	
27		9d. rose	£110	£160
		a. Without handstamp	£2750	
		b. Handstamp in violet	£250	

II. "POSTAGE" 29½ *mm long. No stops after* "POSTAGE" *or value*

(*a*) *Handstamped* "BRITISH VICE-CONSULATE ANTANANARIVO" *in violet*

No.	Type			
28	2	1d. rose	£850	
29		1½d. rose	£1600	
30		3d. rose	£1000	
31		4½d. rose	£1500	
32		6d. rose	£1200	

(*b*) *Handstamped* "BRITISH CONSULAR MAIL ANTANANARIVO" *in black*

No.	Type			
33		1d. rose	70·00	£100
		a. Without handstamp	£1800	
		b. Violet handstamp	85·00	
34		1½d. rose	65·00	95·00
		a. Without handstamp	£1900	
		b. Violet handstamp	£130	
35		2d. rose	65·00	95·00
		b. Violet handstamp	£140	
36		3d. rose	70·00	£100
		a. Without handstamp	£2750	
		b. Violet handstamp	£120	
37		4½d. rose	70·00	£100
		a. Without handstamp	£2750	
		b. Violet handstamp	£120	
38		6d. rose	70·00	£100
		a. Without handstamp	£3000	
		b. Violet handstamp	£300	

III. "POSTAGE" 24½ *mm long. No stop after* "POSTAGE", *but stop after value.*

(*a*) *Handstamped* "BRITISH VICE-CONSULATE ANTANANARIVO" *in violet*

No.	Type			
39	2	4d. rose	£400	
40		8d. rose	£500	
40*a*		1s. rose		
41		1s. 6d. rose	£3500	
42		2s. rose	£2000	
		a. Handstamp in black		

(*b*) *Handstamped* "BRITISH CONSULAR MAIL ANTANANARIVO" *in black*

No.	Type			
43		4d. rose	£180	
		a. Without handstamp	£2250	
		b. Violet handstamp	£375	
44		8d. rose	£600	
		a. Without handstamp	£2250	
		b. Violet handstamp	£500	
45		1s. rose	£450	
		a. Without handstamp	£2250	
		b. Violet handstamp	£1200	
46		1s. 6d. rose	£500	
		a. Without handstamp	£3000	
		b. Violet handstamp	£1200	
47		2s. rose	£600	
		a. Without handstamp	£3000	
		b. Violet handstamp	£1500	

The above were also printed in horizontal strips of four.

The stamps of the British Consular Mail were suppressed in 1887, but the postal service continued with the charges paid in cash.

BRITISH INLAND MAIL

In January 1895 the Malagasy government agreed that a syndicate of British merchants at Antananarivo, including the Vice-Consul, should operate an inland postal service during the war with France. Mail was sent by runner to the port of Vatomandry and forwarded via Durban where Natal stamps were added.

Nos. 50/62 were cancelled with dated circular postmarks inscribed "BRITISH MAIL".

4

5 Malagasy Runners

(Typeset London Missionary Society Press, Antananarivo)

1895 (Jan). *Rouletted in black.* (*a*) *Thick laid paper.*

No.	Type			
50	4	4d. black	25·00	13·00
		a. "FUOR" for "FOUR"	—	£900

(*b*) *In black on coloured wove paper*

No.	Type			
51	4	1d. *blue-grey*	25·00	12·00
52		6d. *pale yellow*	25·00	12·00
53		8d. *salmon*	25·00	12·00
54		1s. *fawn*	38·00	12·00
55		2s. *bright rose*	40·00	14·00
		a. Italic "2" at left	£130	60·00
56		4s. *grey*	55·00	12·00
50/6		*Set of* 7	£200	75·00

There are six types of each value, printed in blocks of 6 (2×3) separated by gutters, four times on each sheet; the upper and lower blocks being *tête-bêche*.

Nos. 50a and 55a occur in the sixth position in their respective blocks. No. 50a was soon corrected.

(Typo John Haddon & Co, London)

1895 (Mar). *The inscription in the lower label varies for each value. P* 12.

No.	Type			
57	5	2d. blue	5·00	42·00
		a. Imperf between (pair)	£400	
58		4d. rose	5·50	42·00
		a. Imperf between (pair)	£250	
59		6d. green	6·50	42·00
		a. Imperf between (pair)	£500	
60		1s. slate-blue	6·50	50·00
		a. Imperf between (pair)	£400	
61		2s. chocolate	13·00	65·00
		a. Imperf between (pair)	£425	
62		4s. bright purple	22·00	85·00
		a. Imperf between (pair)	£1300	
57/62		*Set of* 6	50·00	£300

This post was suppressed when the French entered Antananarivo on 30 September 1895.

Malaya

The Federation of Malaya was formed on 1 February 1948 by the former Straits Settlements of Malacca and Penang, the four Federated Malay States and the five Unfederated States. It did not, however, issue any stamps until it became an independent member of the Commonwealth in 1957.

The philatelic history of the component parts of the federation is most complex.

The method adopted is to show the general issues for the area first, before dealing with the issues for the individual States. The section is divided as follows:

I. STRAITS SETTLEMENTS
II. FEDERATED MALAY STATES
III. MALAYAN POSTAL UNION
IV. MALAYA (BRITISH MILITARY ADMINISTRATION)
V. MALAYAN STATES—Johore, Kedah, Kelantan, Malacca, Negri Sembilan (with Sungei Ujong), Pahang, Penang, Perak, Perlis, Selangor, Trengganu
VI. SIAMESE POSTS IN NORTHERN MALAYA 1887–1909
VII. JAPANESE OCCUPATION OF MALAYA 1942–45
VIII. THAI OCCUPATION OF MALAYA 1943–45

I. STRAITS SETTLEMENTS

The three original Settlements, Malacca, Penang (with Province Wellesley) and Singapore (with Christmas Island), were formed into a Crown Colony on 1 April 1867. The Cocos (Keeling) Islands were transferred to Straits Settlements on 7 February 1886. Labuan was attached to the Colony in 1896, becoming the fourth Settlement in 1906, but was transferred to North Borneo in 1946.

The first known prestamp cover with postal markings from Penang (Prince of Wales Island) is dated March 1806 and from Malacca, under British civil administration, February 1841. The civil post office at Singapore opened on 1 February 1823.

The stamps of India were used at all three post offices from late in 1854 until the Straits Settlements became a separate colony on 1 September 1867.

The Indian stamps were initially cancelled by dumb obliterators and their use in the Straits Settlements can only be identified from complete covers. In 1856 cancellations of the standard Indian octagonal type were issued, numbered "B 109" for Malacca, "B 147" for Penang and "B 172" for Singapore.

CURRENCY. Before 1867 official accounts of the East India Company administration for the Straits Settlements were kept in rupees, although the vast majority of commercial transactions used Spanish American silver dollars, supplies of which reached Malaya via the Philippines.

This confusing situation was rapidly amended when the Straits Settlements became a Crown Colony on 1 April 1867 and Spanish American dollars were declared to be the only legal currency. In 1874 American trade dollars and Japanese yen were also accepted, but in 1890 recognition of the Spanish American dollars was restricted to those from the Mexican mints. A shortage of silver coinage led to the introduction of silver British trade dollars in 1895 which also circulated in Hong Kong and Labuan.

Dollar banknotes first appeared in 1899, but Mexican d[ollars] were not finally replaced until the issue of silver St[raits] Settlements dollars in 1903, the gold value of which was [fixed at] 2s. 4d. in January 1906.

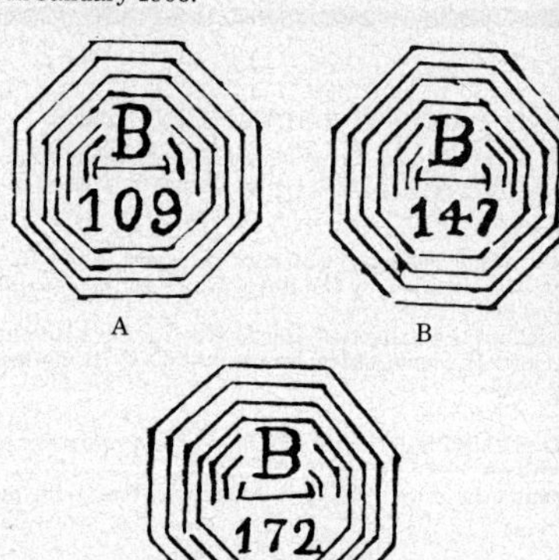

A B

C

The Penang and Singapore octagonals were replaced b[y a] duplex type, consisting of a double-ringed datestamp an[d a] diamond-shaped obliterator containing the office number [in] 1863 and 1865 respectively.

D

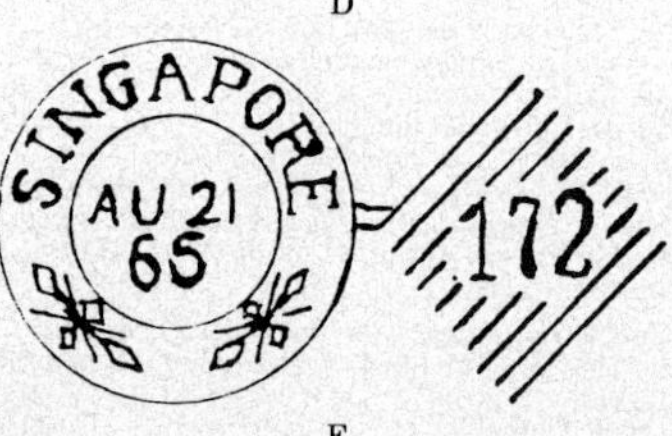

E

PRICES. Catalogue prices in this section are for stamps wi[th] clearly legible, if partial, examples of the postmarks.

EAST INDIA COMPANY ADMINISTRATION

MALACCA

Stamps of INDIA *cancelled with Type* A.

1854. (*Nos.* 2/34).

No.		
Z1	½ a. blue (Die I)	£12
Z2	1 a. red (Die I)	£9
Z3	1 a. dull red (Die II)	£10
Z4	2 a. green	£14
Z4*a*	4 a. blue and pale red (Head Die I) (*cut-to-shape*)	£15
Z5	4 a. blue and red (Head Die II) (*cut-to-shape*)	£15
Z5*a*	4 a. blue and red (Head Die III) (*cut-to-shape*)	£15

1855. (*Nos.* 35/6).

No.		
Z6	8 a. carmine (Die I)/*blue glazed*	£37

1856–64. (*Nos.* 37/49).

No.		
Z7	½ a. pale blue (Die I)	£22
Z8	1 a. brown	£16
Z8*a*	2 a. dull pink	£25
Z9	2 a. yellow-buff	£17
Z10	2 a. yellow	£18
Z11	4 a. green	£35
Z12	8 a. carmine (Die I)	£22

1860. (*Nos.* 51/3).

No.		
Z13	8 p. purple/*bluish*	£66
Z14	8 p. purple/*white*	£30

1865. (*Nos.* 54/65).

No.		
Z15	4 a. green	£35

PENANG

Stamps of INDIA *cancelled with Type* B.

1854. (*Nos.* 2/34).

No.		
Z20	½ a. blue (Die I)	£35
Z21	1 a. red (Die I)	£16
Z22	2 a. green	£22
Z23	4 a. blue and pale red (Head Die I)	£130
Z24	4 a. blue and red (Head Die II)	£130
Z25	4 a. blue and red (Head Die III)	£90

1855. (*Nos.* 35/6).

No.		
Z26	4 a. black/*blue glazed*	75·00
Z27	8 a. carmine (Die I)/*blue glazed*	65·00
	a. Bisected (4 a.) (1860) (on cover)	£55000

–64. (*Nos*. 37/49).
½ a. pale blue (Die I) .. .. 70·00
1 a. brown .. .. 42·00
2 a. dull pink .. .. 60·00
2 a. yellow-buff .. .. 55·00
2 a. yellow .. .. 55·00
2 a. orange .. .. 55·00
4 a. black .. .. 42·00
8 a. carmine (Die I) .. .. 50·00

. (*Nos*. 51/3).
8 p. purple/*white* £120

nps of INDIA *cancelled with Type* D.

4. (*Nos*. 2/34).
1 a. red (Die I) £2250

–64. (*Nos*. 37/49).
½ a. pale blue (Die I) £160
1 a. brown .. .. 42·00
2 a. yellow .. .. 50·00
4 a. black .. .. 45·00
4 a. green £130
8 a. carmine (Die I) .. .. 48·00

0. (*Nos*. 51/3).
8 p. purple/*white* .. .. 75·00
8 p. mauve .. .. 75·00

5. (*Nos*. 54/65).
8 p. purple .. ..
1 a. deep brown .. .. 42·00
2 a. yellow .. .. 50·00
4 a. green £140
8 a. carmine (Die I) .. ..

6–67. (*Nos*. 69/72)
4 a. green (Die I) £140

SINGAPORE

mps of INDIA *cancelled with Type* C.

54. (*Nos*. 2/34).
0 ½ a. blue (Die I) £170
1 1 a. red (Die I) £100
2 1 a. dull red (Die II) £140
3 1 a. red (Die III) £1000
4 2 a. green .. .. 80·00
a. Bisected (1 a.) (1857) (on cover) £120000
5 4 a. blue and pale red (Head Die I) £1000
6 4 a. blue and red (Head Die II) £1100
7 4 a. blue and red (Head Die III) £700

55. (*Nos*. 35/6).
8 4 a. black/*blue glazed* .. .. 35·00
a. Bisected (2 a.) (1859) (on cover) £7500
9 8 a. carmine/*blue glazed* .. .. .. 38·00
a. Bisected (4 a.) (1859) (on cover) £50000

56–66. (*Nos*. 37/49).
70 ½ a. pale blue (Die I) .. .. 35·00
71 1 a. brown .. .. 23·00
a. Bisected (½ a.) (1859) (on cover) £55000
72 2 a. dull pink .. .. 40·00
73 2 a. yellow-buff .. .. 32·00
74 2 a. yellow .. .. 5·00
75 2 a. orange .. .. 40·00
76 4 a. black .. .. 23·00
a. Bisected (2 a.) (1859) (on cover) £20000
77 4 a. green £100
78 8 a. carmine (Die I) .. .. 30·00
a. Bisected (4 a.) (1866) (on cover) £50000

860–61. (*Nos*. 51/3).
79 8 p. purple/*bluish* £475
80 8 p. purple/*white* .. .. 60·00
a. Bisected diagonally (4 p.) (1861) (on cover) £55000
81 8 p. mauve .. .. 60·00

865. (*Nos*. 54/65).
82 ½ a. blue (Die I) .. .. 42·00
83 8 p. purple £100
84 1 a. deep brown .. .. 32·00
85 2 a. yellow .. .. 38·00
86 2 a. orange .. .. 38·00
87 4 a. green £100
88 8 a. carmine (Die I) £275

1866–67. (*Nos*. 69/72).
Z89 4 a. green (Die I) £110
Z90 6 a. 8 p. slate £225

OFFICIAL STAMPS

1866–67. (*Nos*. O6/14).
Z91 ½ a. pale blue £325
Z92 2 a. yellow £450

Stamps of INDIA *cancelled with Type* E.

1856–64. (*Nos*. 37/49).
Z100 1 a. brown £225
Z101 2 a. yellow £300
Z102 4 a. black £300
Z103 8 a. carmine (Die I) £300

1860. (*Nos*. 51/3).
Z104 8 p. purple/*white* £325

1865. (*Nos*. 54/65).
Z105 2 a. yellow £275
Z106 2 a. orange £275
Z107 4 a. green £350

PRICES FOR STAMPS ON COVER

Nos. 1/9	*from* × 15
No. 10	—
Nos. 11/19	*from* × 8
Nos. 20/1	*from* × 20
Nos. 22/39	*from* × 10
Nos. 41/6	*from* × 20
No. 47	—
Nos. 48/9	*from* × 10
Nos. 50/62	*from* × 20
Nos. 63/71	*from* × 15
No. 72	—
Nos. 73/8	*from* × 20
No. 80	*from* × 30
Nos. 82/5	*from* × 10
Nos. 86/7	*from* × 20
Nos. 88/94	*from* × 15
Nos. 95/105	*from* × 8
Nos. 106/9	*from* × 20
Nos. 110/21	*from* × 6
No. 122	—
Nos. 123/6	*from* × 5
Nos. 127/38	*from* × 4
Nos. 139/40	—
Nos. 141/51	*from* × 15
Nos. 152/67	*from* × 4
Nos. 168/9	—
Nos. 193/212	*from* × 3
Nos. 213/15	—
Nos. 216/17	*from* × 10
Nos. 218/40a	*from* × 3
Nos. 240*b*/*d*	—
Nos. 241/55	*from* × 15
Nos. 256/9	*from* × 4
Nos. 260/98	*from* × 3
Nos. D1/6	*from* × 20

PRINTERS. All Straits Settlements issues were printed in typography by De La Rue & Co, Ltd, London, *unless otherwise stated*.

USED PRICES. The prices quoted for Nos. 1/9 are for fine used examples. Those showing parts of commercial "chops" are worth less.

CROWN COLONY

(Currency. 100 cents = 1 Spanish American dollar)

THREE-HALF CENTS (1) 32 CENTS (2)

1867 (1 Sept). *Nos. 54, 59, 61, 69 and 73 of India surch as T* **1** *or* **2** *(24 c., 32 c.) by De La Rue. W* **13** *(Elephant's head) of India. P* 14.
1 1½ c. on ½ a. blue (Die I) (R.) .. .. 80·00 £190
2 2 c. on 1 a. deep brown (R.) .. .. £100 75·00
3 3 c. on 1 a. deep brown (B.) .. .. £110 80·00
4 4 c. on 1 a. deep brown (Bk.) £200 £250
5 6 c. on 2 a. yellow (P.) £500 £200
6 8 c. on 2 a. yellow (G.) .. .. £160 42·00
7 12 c. on 4 a. green (R.) £850 £300
a. Surch double £1600
8 24 c. on 8 a. rose (Die II) (B.) .. .. £350 80·00
9 32 c. on 2 a. yellow (Bk.) .. .. £300 85·00

The 32 c. was re-issued for postal use in 1884.
No. 7a. is only known unused.

1869 (?). *No. 1 with "THREE HALF" deleted and "2" written above, in black manuscript.*
10 2 on 1½ c. on ½ a. blue £8000 £3750

This stamp has been known from very early days and was apparently used at Penang, but nothing is known of its history.

5

6

7

8

9

1867 (Dec)–**72.** *Ornaments in corners differ for each value. Wmk Crown CC. P* 14.
11 **5** 2 c. brown (6.68) .. .. 24·00 3·75
a. Yellow-brown .. .. 25·00 3·75
b. Deep brown .. .. 70·00 10·00
w. Wmk inverted .. ..
12 4 c. rose (7.68) .. .. 38·00 6·50
a. Deep rose .. .. 50·00 8·50
w. Wmk inverted £110
13 6 c. dull lilac (1.68) .. .. 70·00 14·00
a. Bright lilac .. .. 75·00 14·00
14 **6** 8 c. orange-yellow .. .. £120 8·50
a. Orange .. .. £120 9·50
w. Wmk inverted .. .. £225 90·00
15 12 c. blue .. .. 90·00 6·50
a. Ultramarine .. .. 95·00 9·00
w. Wmk inverted .. ..
16 **7** 24 c. blue-green .. .. 95·00 5·00
a. Yellow-green .. .. £200 21·00
w. Wmk inverted .. ..
17 **8** 30 c. claret (12.72) .. .. £180 11·00
w. Wmk inverted .. ..
18 **9** 32 c. pale red .. .. £400 65·00
w. Wmk inverted .. .. † £180
19 96 c. grey .. .. £225 40·00
a. Perf 12½ (6.71) £1900 £225

Five Cents. (10) Seven Cents. (11)

1879 (May). *Nos. 14a and* 18 *surch with T* **10** *and* **11**.
20 **6** 5 c. on 8 c. orange .. .. 85·00 £130
a. No stop after "Cents" £650 £700
b. "F i" spaced £700 £750
21 **9** 7 c. on 32 c. pale red .. .. 90·00 £120
a. No stop after "Cents" £800 £850

The no stop error occured once in the setting.

10 cents. (12)

10 (*a*) 10 (*b*) 10 (*c*) 10 (*d*)
10 (*e*) 10 (*f*) 10 (*g*) 10 (*h*)
10 (*i*) 10 (*j*) 10 (*jj*) 10 (*k*) 10 (*l*)

(*a*) "1" thin curved serif and thin foot, "0" narrow.
(*b*) "1" thick curved serif and thick foot; "0" broad. Both numerals heavy.
(*c*) "1" as (*a*); "0" as (*b*)
(*d*) "1" as (*a*) but thicker; "0" as (*a*)
(*e*) As (*a*) but sides of "0" thicker.
(*f*) "1" as (*d*); "0" as (*e*)
(*g*) As (*a*) but "0" narrower.
(*h*) "1" thin, curved serif and thick foot; "0" as (*g*)
(*i*) "1" as (*b*); "0" as (*a*)
(*j*) "1" as (*d*); "0" as (*g*) but raised.
(*jj*) "1" as (*a*) but shorter, and with shorter serif and thicker foot; "0" as (*g*) but level with "1".
(*k*) "1" as (*jj*); "0" as (*a*)
(*l*) "1" straight serif; "0" as (*g*)

1880 (Mar). *No.* 17 *surch with T* **12** *(showing numerals (a) to (jj))*.
22 10 c. on 30 c. claret (*a*) .. .. £275 65·00
23 10 c. on 30 c. claret (*b*) .. .. £250 60·00
24 10 c. on 30 c. claret (*c*) £2750 £500
25 10 c. on 30 c. claret (*d*) £1200 £170
26 10 c. on 30 c. claret (*e*) £4000 £900
27 10 c. on 30 c. claret (*f*) £4000 £900
28 10 c. on 30 c. claret (*g*) £1600 £350
29 10 c. on 30 c. claret (*h*) £4000 £900
30 10 c. on 30 c. claret (*i*) £4000 £900
31 10 c. on 30 c. claret (*j*) £4000 £900
32 10 c. on 30 c. claret (*jj*) £4000 £900

Nos. 22/32 come from the same setting of 60 (6 × 10) containing twenty examples of No. 22 (R.1/1-2, 1/4, 1/6, 2/1-6, 3/1, 3/3, 3/5, 4/1, 4/3-4, 10/1, 10/3-5), twenty-two of No. 23 (R.4/6, 5/1-6, 6/1-6, 7/1, 8/2-4, 9/1-5), six of No. 25 (R.1/5, 3/2, 3/4, 4/2, 4/5, 10/2), four of No. 28 (R.7/2-5), two of No. 24 (R.9/6, 10/6) and one each of Nos. 26 (R.3/6), 27 (R.1/3), 29 (R.7/6), 30 (R.8/1), 31 (R.8/6) and 32 (R.8/5).

No. 23 is known with large stop after "cents" and also with stop low.

1880 (Apr). *No.* 17 *surch as T* **12**, *but without "cents.", showing numerals (a) to (c), (g) to (i), (k) and (l)*.
33 10 on 30 c. claret (*a*) .. .. £140 48·00
w. Wmk inverted .. .. † £140
34 10 on 30 c. claret (*b*) .. .. £150 48·00
w. Wmk inverted .. .. † £140
35 10 on 30 c. claret (*c*) £450 £110
w. Wmk inverted .. .. † £300
36 10 on 30 c. claret (*g*) £1000 £275
aw. Wmk inverted .. .. † £600
36*b* 10 on 30 c. claret (*h*) .. .. † —
37 10 on 30 c. claret (*i*) £2750 £700
38 10 on 30 c. claret (*k*) £2750 £700
39 10 on 30 c. claret (*l*) £2750 £700

Nos. 33/9 were surcharged from an amended setting of 60 (6×10) of which 59 positions have been identified. Of those known No. 33 occurs on twenty-four (R.6/1–6, 7/1–6, 8/1–6, 9/1–2, 9/6, 10/1–3), No. 34 on twenty-one (R.1/2–6, 2/1–6, 3/1–6, 4/3–5, 5/6), No. 35 on eight (R.1/1, 4/2, 4/6, 5/1–5), No. 36 on three (R.9/3–5) and Nos. 37 (R.10/6), 38 (R.10/4) and 39 (R.10/5) on one each. R.4/1 remains unidentified.

The existence of No. 36*b*, known as a single example from the 6th vertical column, and a stamp in the Royal Collection with "1" as (*b*) and "0" as (*g*) suggests that there may have been another setting.

5 cents. (13) **5** cents. (14) **5** cents. (15)

Aug). *No. 14a surch with T* **13** *to* **15**.
13 5 c. on 8 c. orange £100 £130
14 5 c. on 8 c. orange .. .. .. 95·00 £120
15 5 c. on 8 c. orange £350 £425
charged in a setting of 60 (6 × 10) with T **13** on rows one to
T **14** on rows five to nine and T **15** on row ten.

10 cents. (16) **5** cents. (17)

81. *Nos.* 13, 15*a and* 17 *surch with T* **16**.
10 c. on 6 c. lilac (11.81) .. .. 50·00 6·00
a. Surch double .. .. — £1800
10 c. on 12 c. ultramarine (1.81) .. .. 55·00 16·00
a. Blue .. .. 42·00 9·00
10 c. on 30 c. claret (12.80) .. .. .. £325 85·00
econd printing of the 10 c. on 6 c. has the surcharge heavier
ne "10" usually more to the left or right of "cents".

(Jan). *No.* 12 *surch with T* **17**.
5 c. on 4 c. rose £225 £250

18

19

(Jan). *Wmk Crown CC. P* 14.
18 5 c. purple-brown .. .. .. 75·00 80·00
19 10 c. slate .. .. £325 65·00
s. Optd "Specimen" £325

2. *Wmk Crown CA. P* 14.
5 2 c. brown (Aug) .. .. .. £200 40·00
4 c. rose (April) .. .. .. 95·00 4·75
6 8 c. orange (Sept) .. .. .. 3·00 1·00
w. Wmk inverted .. .. ..
19 10 c. slate (Oct) .. .. 4·00 1·25
w. Wmk inverted .. .. ..
or the 4 c. in deep carmine see No. 98.

TWO CENTS 20*a* "S" wide — TWO CENTS 20*b* "E" and "S" wide — TWO CENTS 20*c* "N" wide

TWO CENTS 20*d* All letters narrow — TWO CENTS 20*e* "EN" and "S" wide — TWO CENTS 20*f* "E" wide

83 (Apr). *Nos.* 52 *and* 18 *surch with T* **20***a/f*.
20*a* 2 c. on 8 c. orange .. .. .. £170 90·00
20*b* 2 c. on 8 c. orange .. .. .. £170 90·00
20*c* 2 c. on 8 c. orange .. .. .. £170 90·00
20*d* 2 c. on 8 c. orange .. .. .. 95·00 60·00
a. Surch double £2250 £950
20*e* 2 c. on 8 c. orange £500 £300
20*a* 2 c. on 32 c. pale red £500 £150
20*f* 2 c. on 32 c. pale red £550 £160
a. Surch double .. .. ..
The 8 c. was surcharged using one of two triplet settings, ther 54 + 55 + 56 or 57 + 57 + 57, applied to rows 2 to 10. A ngle handstamp, either No. 57 or No. 58, was then used to mplete row 1. The 32 c. was surcharged in the same way with a iplet of 59 + 60 + 59 and a single handstamp as No. 60.

2 Cents. (21) **4** Cents (22) **8** Cents (23)

883 (June–July). *Nos.* 51 *and* 15 *surch with T* **21**.
1 2 c. on 4 c. rose .. .. .. 75·00 85·00
a. "s" of "Cents" inverted £1000 £1100
2 2 c. on 12 c. blue (July) £200 £110
a. "s" of "Cents" inverted £2750 £1500
The inverted "S" error occurred once in the setting of 60.

Broken oval above "O" of "POSTAGE" (Lower right pane R. 10/5)

1883 (July)–**91.** *Wmk Crown CA. P* 14.
63 5 2 c. pale rose .. .. .. 35·00 3·25
a. Bright rose (1889) .. .. 5·50 85
64 4 c. pale brown .. .. .. 21·00 1·25
a. Broken oval .. .. .. £180 40·00
b. Deep brown .. .. .. 32·00 3·25
ba. Broken oval .. .. .. £300 65·00
c. Olive-bistre £350 £275
ca. Broken oval .. .. ..
w. Wmk inverted .. .. .. 90·00 65·00
65 18 5 c. blue (8.83) .. .. .. 10·00 1·00
66 5 6 c. lilac (11.84) .. .. .. 25·00 9·00
a. Violet .. .. .. 2·00 3·00
aw. Wmk inverted .. .. ..
67 6 12 c. brown-purple .. .. .. 65·00 9·50
68 7 24 c. yellow-green (2.84) .. .. 70·00 5·50
a. Blue-green .. .. .. 4·00 3·75
69 8 30 c. claret (9.91) .. .. .. 8·00 8·00
w. Wmk inverted .. .. .. 75·00 60·00
70 9 32 c. orange-vermilion (1.87) .. .. 7·00 2·50
w. Wmk inverted .. .. .. 50·00 50·00
71 96 c. olive-grey (8.88) .. .. .. 75·00 45·00
63*a*/71 .. .. *Set of* 9 £180 65·00
63s/5s, 67s Optd "Specimen" .. *Set of* 4 £700
For the 4 c. in deep carmine and 12 c. in claret see Nos. 98 and 102.

1884 (Feb–Aug). *Nos.* 65, 15 *and* 67 *surch with T* **22** *or* **23**.
72 18 4 c. on 5 c. blue (Aug) £2500 £3250
73 4 c. on 5 c. blue (R.) (Aug) .. .. 95·00 85·00
74 6 8 c. on 12 c. blue £300 £120
w. Wmk inverted .. .. † £350
75 8 c. on 12 c. brown-purple (Aug) .. £250 £120
a. Inverted "8" .. .. .. † —
b. "s" of "Cents" low (R. 5/1) .. £1400 £850

1884 (Aug). *No.* 65 *surch with T* **20***d/f*.
76 20*d* 2 c. on 5 c. blue £100 £110
77 20*e* 2 c. on 5 c. blue £100 £110
a. Pair, with and without surch ..
b. Surch double .. .. ..
78 20*f* 2 c. on 5 c. blue £100 £110
Surcharged as a triplet, 77 + 76 + 78. On No. 76 "TS" are dropped below the line.

8 (24) **3** CENTS (25) THREE CENTS (26)

1884 (Sept). *No.* 75 *additionally surch with large numeral as T* **24** *in red*.
80 6 8 on 8 c. on 12 c. dull purple £200 £225
a. Surch T **24** double £3750
b. Surch T **23** in blue £5000
c. "s" of "Cents" low £1200
Examples as No. 75, but with Type **23** in blue, were further surcharged in error.
A similar "4" surcharge in red on No. 73 exists from a trial printing of which seven examples are known, all used on an official's correspondence (*Price* £11000 *used*).

1885. *No.* 65 *and T* **9** *in new colour, wmk Crown CA, surch with T* **25** *or* **26**.
82 25 3 c. on 5 c. blue (Sept) £100 £200
a. Surch double £1700
83 26 3 c. on 32 c. pale magenta (Dec) .. 3·25 3·75
a. Deep magenta .. .. .. 1·25 1·00
s. Optd "Specimen" £170
The surcharge on No. 82 was applied locally by a triplet setting. No. 83 was surcharged by De La Rue in complete panes.

3 cents (27) **2** Cents (28)

1886 (Apr). *No.* 48 *surch with T* **27**.
84 18 3 c. on 5 c. purple-brown £170 £180
The surcharge on No. 84 was applied by a triplet setting.

1887 (July). *No.* 65 *surch with T* **28**.
85 18 2 c. on 5 c. blue.. .. .. 20·00 55·00
a. "C" of "Cents" omitted .. .. — £2500
b. Surch double £1000 £900
The surcharge on No. 85 was applied by a triplet setting.

10 CENTS (29) THIRTY CENTS (30)

1891 (Nov). *Nos.* 68 *and* 70 *surch with T* **29** *and* **30**.
86 7 10 c. on 24 c. yellow-green .. .. 2·75 1·25
a. Narrow "0" in "10" (R. 4/6) .. 28·00 28·00
w. Wmk inverted .. .. .. 42·00 48·00
87 9 30 c. on 32 c. orange-vermilion .. .. 6·50 3·50
w. Wmk inverted .. .. ..
The "R" of "THIRTY" and "N" of "CENTS" are found wide or narrow and in all possible combinations.

ONE CENT (31) ONE CENT (32)

1892. *Stamps of* 1882–91 (*wmk Crown CA*) *surch with T* **31**.
88 1 c. on 2 c. bright rose (Mar) .. .. 2·00 3·75
89 1 c. on 4 c. brown (Apr) .. .. 5·00 5·50
a. Surch double £950
b. Broken oval .. .. .. 90·00 95·00
w. Wmk inverted .. .. ..
90 1 c. on 6 c. lilac (Feb) .. .. 1·40 4·75
a. Surch double, one inverted £1100 £1000
w. Wmk inverted .. .. ..
91 1 c. on 8 c. orange (Jan) .. .. 1·00 1·25
92 1 c. on 12 c. brown-purple (Mar) .. 5·00 9·00
88/92 .. .. .. *Set of* 5 13·00 22·00
The three settings used for Nos. 88/92 contained various combinations of the following varieties: "ON" of "ONE" and "N" of "CENT" wide; "O" wide, "N" of "ONE" narrow and "N" of "CENT" wide; "O" narrow and both letters "N" wide; "ON" narrow, and "N" of "CENT" wide; "O" wide and both letters "N" narrow; "ON" wide and "N" of "CENT" narrow; "ON" and "N" of "CENT" narrow; "O" narrow "N" of "ONE" wide and "N" of "CENT" narrow. Antique "N" and "E" letters also occur.

1892–94. *Colours changed. Wmk Crown CA. P* 14. *Surch with T* **32** *and* **26** *by De La Rue*.
93 6 1 c. on 8 c. green (3.92) .. .. 1·00 1·50
94 9 3 c. on 32 c. carmine-rose (6.94) .. 2·25 70
a. Surch omitted £3250
93s/4s Optd "Specimen" .. .. *Set of* 2 85·00
No. 94a comes from a sheet found at Singapore on which all stamps in the upper left pane had the surcharge omitted. Five vertical inter-panneau pairs still exist with the surcharge omitted on the upper stamps (*Price* £24000 *unused*). The only used example of the error is on cover.

33

34

4 cents. (35)

1892 (Mar)–**99.** *Wmk Crown CA. P* 14.
95 33 1 c. green (9.92) .. .. .. 2·50 70
a. Malformed "S" .. .. .. £200 85·00
b. Repaired "S" .. .. .. £180 75·00
96 3 c. carmine-rose (2.95) .. .. 11·00 40
a. Malformed "S" .. .. .. £275 95·00
97 3 c. brown (3.99) .. .. .. 5·00 60
a. Repaired "S" .. .. .. £225 95·00
b. Yellow-brown .. .. .. 3·50 60
98 5 4 c. deep carmine (7.99) .. .. 4·00 1·25
a. Broken oval .. .. .. 85·00 48·00
99 18 5 c. brown (6.94) .. .. .. 3·75 1·00
100 5 c. magenta (7.99) .. .. .. 2·25 2·00
101 6 8 c. ultramarine (6.94) .. .. 4·50 50
a. Bright blue .. .. .. 7·00 80
102 12 c. claret (3.94) .. .. .. 9·00 8·50
103 33 25 c. purple-brown and green .. .. 22·00 6·50
a. Malformed "S" £475 £225
b. Repaired "S" £425 £200
c. Dull purple and green .. .. 21·00 6·00
104 50 c. olive-green and carmine .. .. 20·00 2·50
a. Repaired "S" £475 £180
105 34 $5 orange and carmine (10.98) .. £300 £250
a. Repaired "S" £2250 £2250
95/105 .. .. .. *Set of* 11 £350 £250
95s/101s, 103s/5s Optd "Specimen" *Set of* 10 £400

1898 (26 Dec). *T* **18** *and* **6** *surch with T* **35** *at Singapore*.
106 4 c. on 5 c. brown (No. 99) .. .. 2·75 4·75
107 4 c. on 5 c. blue (No. 65) .. .. 2·75 12·00
a. Surch double .. .. .. — £1200
108 4 c. on 8 c. ultramarine (No. 101) .. 1·25 2·75
a. Surch double £950 £850
b. Bright blue (No. 101*a*) .. .. 80 1·00
106/8*b* .. .. .. *Set of* 3 5·50 16·00
Nos. 107 and 108*b* exist with stop spaced 1½ mm from the "S" (R. 10/6).

FOUR CENTS (36)

37

38

1899 (Mar). *T* **18** (*wmk Crown CA. P* 14), *surch with T* **36** *by De La Rue*.
109 4 c. on 5 c. carmine 75 30
a. Surch omitted £22000
s. Optd "Specimen" .. .. .. 42·00
x. Wmk reversed .. .. .. 65·00
No. 109a is only known unused.

1902 (Apr)–**03.** *Wmk Crown CA. P* 14.
110 **37** 1 c. grey-green (7.02) .. .. .. 2·25 3·00
a. Pale green .. .. .. 4·25 3·25
111 3 c. dull purple and orange .. .. 3·50 20
w. Wmk inverted .. .. .. — £170
112 4 c. purple/*red* (9.02) .. .. .. 4·75 30
113 **38** 5 c. dull purple (8.02) .. .. .. 5·50 85
114 8 c. purple/*blue* .. .. .. 3·25 20
115 10 c. purple and black/*yellow* (9.02) .. 23·00 1·50
116 **37** 25 c. dull purple and green (8.02) .. 11·00 6·00
117 **38** 30 c. grey and carmine (7.02) .. .. 18·00 8·00
118 **37** 50 c. deep green and carmine (9.02) .. 20·00 20·00
a. Dull green and carmine .. .. 23·00 23·00
119 **38** $1 dull green and black (9.02) .. 22·00 60·00
120 **37** $2 dull purple and black (9.02) .. 65·00 70·00
121 **38** $5 dull green & brown-orange (10.02) £190 £160
122 **37** $100 purple and green/*yellow* (3.03) .. £8000
s. Optd "Specimen" £350
110/21 .. .. *Set of* 12 £325 £300
110s/21s Optd "Specimen" .. *Set of* 12 £325

(Currency 100 cents = 1 Straits, later Malayan, dollar)

39

40

41

42

(Des N. Trotter and W. Egerton)

1903 (Dec)–**04.** *Wmk Crown CA. P* 14.
123 **39** 1 c. grey-green .. .. 1·00 8·00
124 **40** 3 c. dull purple (1.04) .. .. .. 11·00 4·50
125 **41** 4 c. purple/*red* (4.04) .. .. .. 3·75 30
126 **42** 8 c. purple/*blue* (7.04) .. .. .. 45·00 1·25
123/6 .. .. *Set of* 4 55·00 12·50
123s/6s Optd "Specimen" .. *Set of* 4 £130

1904 (Aug)–**10.** *Wmk Multiple Crown CA. Ordinary paper* (1 c. *to* $1 *and* $5) *or chalk-surfaced paper* ($2, $25, $100). *P* 14.
127 **39** 1 c. deep green (9.04) .. .. .. 2·50 10
a. Chalk-surfaced paper (12.05) .. 9·00 1·50
w. Wmk inverted .. .. .. 80·00 45·00
128 **40** 3 c. dull purple .. .. .. 2·25 30
a. Chalk-surfaced paper (8.06) .. 8·50 1·50
aw. Wmk inverted .. .. .. 80·00 55·00
b. Plum (2.08) .. .. .. 6·50 1·75
129 **41** 4 c. purple/*red* (6.05) .. .. .. 7·50 75
a. Chalk-surfaced paper (10.05) .. 8·00 1·25
aw. Wmk inverted .. .. .. 50·00
130 **38** 5 c. dull purple (12.06) .. .. 8·50 2·25
a. Chalk-surfaced paper (12.06) .. 12·00 7·00
131 **42** 8 c. purple/*blue* (8.05) .. .. 28·00 1·50
a. Chalk-surfaced paper (12.05) .. 19·00 2·75
132 **38** 10 c. purple and black/*yellow* (8.05) .. 6·00 80
a. Chalk-surfaced paper (11.05) .. 12·00 2·75
133 **37** 25 c. dull purple and green (1.05) .. 28·00 19·00
a. Chalk-surfaced paper (11.05) .. 35·00 19·00
134 **38** 30 c. grey and carmine (3.05) .. .. 48·00 2·50
a. Chalk-surfaced paper (3.06) .. 50·00 2·75
135 **37** 50 c. dull green and carmine (10.05) .. 55·00 15·00
a. Chalk-surfaced paper (11.06) .. 29·00 15·00
136 **38** $1 dull green and black (3.05) .. 55·00 21·00
a. Chalk-surfaced paper (3.06) .. 45·00 18·00
137 **37** $2 dull purple and black (10.05) .. 95·00 85·00
138 **38** $5 dull green & brown-orange (10.05) £180 £160
a. Chalk-surfaced paper (1.08) .. £160 £140
139 **37** $25 grey-green and black (7.06) .. £1300 £1300
s. Optd "Specimen" £170
140 $100 purple and green/*yellow* (6.10) .. £9000
127/38 .. .. *Set of* 12 £400 £250

STRAITS
SETTLEMENTS.
(43)

Straits Settlements.
(44)

STRAITS
SETTLEMENTS.

FOUR CENTS.
(45)

1906 (20 Dec)–**07.** *T* 18 *of Labuan* (*Nos.* 117 *etc.*) *optd with T* 43 *or* 44 (10 *c.*), *or additionally surch with T* 45, *in black* (*No.* 145), *claret* (*No.* 151) *or brown-red* (*others*) *at Singapore. P* 13½–14.
141 1 c. black and purple (*p* 14½–15) .. 60·00 £160
a. Perf 14 .. .. £225 £350
b. Line through "B" £475
142 2 c. black and green £250 £325
a. Perf 14½–15 .. .. .. £160 £275
b. Perf 13½–14 comp 12–13 .. — £950
c. Line through "B" £800
143 3 c. black and sepia (1.07) .. .. 20·00 85·00
a. Line through "B" £250
144 4 c. on 12 c. black and yellow .. .. 2·00 6·00
a. No stop after "CENTS" (R. 1/8, 6/8) £225
b. Line through "B" £120
145 4 c. on 16 c. green and brown (Blk.) .. 4·00 8·00
a. "STRAITS SETTLEMENTS" in both brown-red and black £650 £700
b. Ditto. In vert pair with normal .. £4250
c. Line through "B" £130
146 4 c. on 18 c. black and pale brown .. 2·75 6·50
a. No stop after "CENTS" (R.1/8, 6/8) .. £225
b. "FOUR CENTS" and bar double .. £6500
c. "FOUR CENTS" and bar 1½ mm below normal position (pair with normal) £950
d. Line through "B" £120
147 8 c. black and vermilion .. .. .. 2·50 8·00
a. Line through "B" £120
148 10 c. brown and slate .. .. .. 6·50 6·50
a. No stop after "Settlements" (R. 1/4, 6/4) £275
b. Line through "B" £170
149 25 c. green and greenish blue (1.07) .. 12·00 38·00
a. Perf 14½–15 .. .. .. 80·00 £120
b. Perf 13½–14 comp 14½–15 .. .. £300
c. Line through "B" £225
150 50 c. dull purple and lilac (1.07) .. 14·00 70·00
a. Line through "B" £300
151 $1 claret and orange (Claret) (1.07) .. 42·00 £110
a. Perf 14½–15 .. .. .. £475
b. Line through "B" £475
141/51 .. .. *Set of* 11 £275 £700

Nos. 141/51 were overprinted by a setting of 50 (10×5) applied twice to the sheets of 100. The "FOUR CENTS" surcharges were applied separately by a similar setting.

No. 145a shows impressions of Type **43** in both brown-red and black. It is known from one complete sheet and the top half of another.

No. 146b occurred on row 5 from one sheet only. No. 146*c* occurred on R.4/10 and 9/10 of the first printing.

The line through "B" flaw occurs on R.5/10 of the basic stamp. For illustration see Labuan.

46

47

1906 (Sept)–**12.** *Wmk Mult Crown CA. Ordinary paper* (1 *c. to* 10 *c.*) *or chalk-surfaced paper* (21 *c. to* $500). *P* 14.
152 **39** 1 c. blue-green (3.10) .. .. .. 23·00 1·10
153 **40** 3 c. red (6.08) .. .. 2·00 10
154 **41** 4 c. red (7.07) .. .. 5·50 2·50
155 4 c. dull purple (2.08) .. .. .. 5·50 10
a. Chalk-surfaced paper (1.12) .. 11·00 2·25
156 4 c. claret (9.11) .. .. 1·75 80
157 **38** 5 c. orange (4.09) .. .. 2·75 1·50
158 **42** 8 c. blue .. .. 3·50 50
159 **38** 10 c. purple/*yellow* (7.08) .. .. .. 5·50 1·00
a. Chalk-surfaced paper (5.12) .. 14·00 6·00
160 **46** 21 c. dull purple and claret (11.10) .. 6·50 32·00
161 **37** 25 c. dull and bright purple (7.09) .. 12·00 6·00
162 **38** 30 c. purple and orange-yellow (11.09) 35·00 3·75
163 **46** 45 c. black/*green* (11.10) .. .. 2·50 4·00
164 **37** 50 c. black/*green* (4.10) .. .. .. 5·00 4·50
165 **38** $1 black and red/*blue* (10.10) .. 13·00 4·75
166 **37** $2 green and red/*yellow* (12.09) .. 24·00 23·00
167 **38** $5 green and red/*green* (11.09) .. £110 75·00
w. Wmk inverted £800
168 **47** $25 purple and blue/*blue* (5.11) .. £1200 £950
s. Optd "Specimen" £250
169 $500 purple and orange (5.10) £70000
s. Optd "Specimen" £1000
152/67 .. .. *Set of* 16 £225 £150
153s/67s Optd "Specimen" .. *Set of* 15 £400

Beware of dangerous forgeries of No. 169.

48

49

50

51

52

53

54

1912–23. *$25, $100 and $500 as T* **47**, *but with head of King George V. Die I* (5, 10, 25, 30, 50 *c.*, $1, $2, $5). *Wmk Mult Crown CA. Ordinary paper* (*Nos.* 193/6, 198/201, 203) *or chalk-surfaced paper* (*others*). *P* 14.
193 **48** 1 c. green (9.12) .. .. 6·00 1·25
a. Pale green (1.14) .. .. .. 6·00 1·25
b. Blue-green (1917) .. .. .. 6·50 1·75
bw. Wmk inverted .. .. .. † £250
194 1 c. black (2.19) .. .. 1·00 1·00
195 **52** 2 c. green (10.19) 75 50
196 **49** 3 c. red (2.13) .. .. 2·75
a. Scarlet (2.17) .. .. 2·25
197 **50** 4 c. dull purple (3.13) .. .. .. 1·50
a. Wmk sideways .. .. .. †
198 4 c. rose-scarlet (2.19) .. .. .. 1·75
a. Carmine .. .. 1·75
199 **51** 5 c. orange (8.12) .. .. 1·50
a. Yellow-orange .. .. 2·75
200 **52** 6 c. dull claret (3.20) .. .. .. 1·75
a. Deep claret .. .. 6·00
aw. Wmk inverted £250
201 8 c. ultramarine (3.13) .. .. .. 1·25
202 **51** 10 c. purple/*yellow* (9.12) .. .. .. 1·50
a. White back (1913) .. .. .. 1·50
as. Optd "Specimen" .. .. .. 45·00
b. On lemon (1916) .. .. .. 16·00
bs. Optd "Specimen" .. .. .. 65·00
c. Wmk sideways .. .. .. † £
203 10 c. deep bright blue (1918) .. .. 5·50
a. Bright blue (1919) .. .. .. 4·00
204 **53** 21 c. dull and bright purple (11.13) .. 4·50
205 **54** 25 c. dull purple and mauve (7.14) .. 9·50
aw. Wmk inverted .. .. .. 85·00
b. Dull purple and violet (1919) .. 60·00
207 **51** 30 c. dull purple and orange (12.14) .. 8·00
208 **53** 45 c. black/*green* (*white back*) (12.14) 6·50
a. On blue-green, olive back (7.18) 3·25
as. Optd "Specimen" .. .. .. 48·00
b. On emerald back (6.22) .. .. 3·25
209 **54** 50 c. black/*green* (7.14) .. .. .. 5·50
a. On blue-green, olive back (1918) 18·00
b. On emerald back (1921) .. .. 12·00
c. Die II. *On emerald back* (1922) .. 3·00
cs. Optd "Specimen" .. .. .. 45·00
210 **51** $1 black and red/*blue* (10.14) .. 9·00
w. Wmk inverted £100
211 **54** $2 grn & red/*yell, white back* (1914) 7·50
a. Green and red/yellow (1915) .. 10·00
as. Optd "Specimen" .. .. .. 48·00
b. On orange-buff (1921) .. .. 50·00
c. On pale yellow (1921) .. .. 55·00
212 **51** $5 grn & red/*grn, white back* (11.13) 70·00
a. Green and red/green (1915) .. 75·00
as. Optd "Specimen" .. .. .. 65·00
b. On blue-green, olive back (1918) £130
c. On emerald back (1920) £160
d. Die II. *On emerald back* (1923) .. 90·00
ds. Optd "Specimen" .. .. .. 85·00
213 – $25 purple and blue/*blue* £1000
a. Break in scroll £1800
b. Broken crown and scroll £1800
s. Optd "Specimen" £190
214 – $100 black and carmine/*blue* (8.12) .. £4500
a. Break in scroll £7000
b. Broken crown and scroll £7000
s. Optd "Specimen" £425
215 – $500 purple and orange-brown (8.12) £35000
a. Break in scroll £45000
b. Broken crown and scroll £45000
s. Optd "Specimen" £1100
193/212 .. .. *Set of* 19 £120
193s/212s Optd "Specimen" .. *Set of* 19 £600

The 6 c. is similar to T **52**, but the head is in a beaded oval a[...] T **53**. The 2 c., 6 c. (and 12 c. below) have figures of value [...] circular ground while in the 8 c. this is of oval shape.

For illustrations of the varieties on Nos. 213/15 see above [...] 58 of Leeward Islands.

RED CROSS
2c.
(55)

MALAYA-
BORNEO
EXHIBITION.
(56)

1917 (1 May). *Surch with T* **55**.
216 **49** 2 c. on 3 c. scarlet .. .. .. 2·00 24·
a. No stop (R. 2/3) £225 £4
217 **50** 2 c. on 4 c. dull purple .. .. .. 2·75 24·
a. No stop (R. 2/3) £250 £4

Nos. 216a and 217a occur in the first setting only.

Type I

Type II

The duty plate for the 25 c. value was replaced in 1926. [...] Type II the solid shading forming the back of the figure extends to the top of the curve; the upturned end of the foot [...] the 2 is short; two background lines above figure 5; c close to STRAITS SETTLEMENTS in taller letters.

1921–33. *Wmk Mult Script CA. Ordinary paper* (1 *c. to* 6 *c*[...] 10 *c.* (*No.* 230), 12 *c.*) *or chalk-surfaced paper* (*others*). *P* 14.
218 **48** 1 c. black (3.22) 50 1
219 **52** 2 c. green (5.21) 50 1
w. Wmk inverted .. .. .. 28·00
x. Wmk reversed .. .. .. †
y. Wmk inverted and reversed
220 2 c. brown (12.25) .. .. 7·00 2·5
221 **49** 3 c. green (9.23) .. .. 1·50 8
w. Wmk inverted .. .. .. 28·00
222 **50** 4 c. carmine-red (9.21) .. .. .. 2·00 4·0
223 4 c. bright violet (8.24) 60 1
w. Wmk inverted .. .. .. 28·00
224 4 c. orange (8.29) .. .. 1·00 1
225 **51** 5 c. orange (Die I) (5.21) .. .. .. 1·50 1
a. Wmk sideways .. .. .. † £190
bw. Wmk inverted .. .. .. 28·00
bx. Wmk reversed .. .. .. †
c. Die II (1922) .. .. 2·25 1·2
226 5 c. brown (Die II) (1932) .. .. .. 2·50 1
a. Die I (1933) .. .. 5·00 1

52 6 c. dull claret (10.22) .. .. .. 2·00 15
w. Wmk inverted .. .. 28·00 35·00
6 c. rose-pink (2.25) .. .. .. 19·00 9·50
6 c. scarlet (1.27) .. .. .. 2·50 10
51 10 c. bright blue (Die I) (1921) .. 1·75 2·25
w. Wmk inverted .. .. .. 28·00
10 c. purple/*pale yellow* (Die I) (1923) 2·50 6·00
a. Die II (11.26) .. .. .. 2·00 30
b. *Purple/brt yellow* (Die II) (1932) 7·50 1·75
ba. Die I (1933) .. .. .. 5·50 10
52 12 c. bright blue (1.22) .. .. 1·00 20
w. Wmk inverted .. .. .. 28·00
53 21 c. dull and bright purple (2.23) .. 6·00 48·00
54 25 c. dull purple and mauve (Die I, Type I) (1921) .. .. .. 28·00 70·00
a. Die II, Type I (1923) .. .. 15·00 3·75
b. Die II, Type II (1927) .. .. 5·00 1·75
51 30 c. dull purple & orange (Die I) (1921) 22·00 32·00
a. Die II (1922) .. .. .. 2·00 1·25
53 35 c. dull purple & orange-yellow (8.22) 12·00 6·00
a. *Dull purple and orange* .. 3·50 5·50
35 c. scarlet and purple (4.31) .. 10·00 7·00
54 50 c. black/*emerald* (9.25) .. .. 1·75 40
51 $1 black and red/*blue* (Die II) (1921) 6·00 65
54 $2 grn & red/*pale yell* (Die II) (1923) 10·00 8·00
51 $5 green and red/*green* (Die II) (1926) 85·00 32·00
– $25 purple and blue/*blue* (5.23) .. £600 £120
ba. Break in scroll £1100
bb. Broken crown and scroll .. £1100
bs. Optd "Specimen" £160
– $100 black and carmine/*blue* (5.23) .. £3500 £1500
ca. Break in scroll £5000
cb. Broken crown and scroll .. £5000
cs. Optd "Specimen" £350
– $500 purple and orange-brown (4.23) £28000
da. Break in scroll £32000
db. Broken crown and scroll £35000
ds. Optd "Specimen" £950
40a .. .. *Set of* 24 £160 £110
/40as (*ex* 6 c. rose-pink) Optd or Perf (Nos. 4s, 226s, 237s) "Specimen" .. *Set of* 23 £600

os. 240*b*/*d* are as Type **47**, but with portrait of George V.
ne 2 c. green was reissued in 1927, and exists with cimen" overprint 15.5×1.75 mm instead of the 14.5×2.5 of the original issue (*Price*, £60).
n 8 c. in carmine was prepared but not issued (Optd cimen" £350).
ne paper of Nos. 231*b*/ba is the normal *pale yellow* at the , but with a bright yellow surface.
1926 new Key and Duty plates were made of 100 (10×10) ead of the usual 60 (6×10).
or illustrations of the varieties on Nos. 240*b*/*d* see above No. f Leeward Islands.

TINGS OF TYPE 56. Nos. 241/55 were produced using a eset block of 12 (6×2) overprints from which ten stereos were en to provide a forme for the complete sheet of 120. Two such nes were prepared of which the second was only used for a ited number of Straits Settlements sheets in addition to the ah and Trengganu issues.
everal constant varieties occur on the original typeset block 2 and so appear ten times on sheets printed from both ings I and II. These include:
Oval last "O" in "BORNEO" (R. 1/3 of typeset block of 12)
Raised stop after "EXHIBITION" (R. 2/2 of typeset block of 12)
Small second "A" in "MALAYA" (R. 2/6 of typeset block of 12).
he two formes also produced constant varieties in each ing which include:
etting I
No hyphen (Left pane. R. 7/1 or 9/2)
No stop (Left and right panes. Either on R. 10/4 (right pane) or, for some sheets, on other stamps from even numbered horizontal rows in the 4th vertical column (both panes))
Third "I" in "EXHIBITION" omitted (R. 8/5, 10/5 (left pane)). This must have occurred very late in the use of this setting and is only found on the 5 c. and 10 c.)
etting II
No stop (Left pane. R. 1/5)
"EXH.BITION" (Left pane. Stamps from even numbered horizontal rows in the 3rd vertical column)

22 (Apr). *Malaya–Borneo Exhibition, Singapore. Optd with T* **56**.
(*a*) *Wmk Mult Crown CA* (*Nos.* 195, 198/9, 201, 205, 208*a*, 210, 211*b and* 212*b*)

1 52 2 c. green .. .. 28·00 75·00
b. Oval last "O" in "BORNEO" .. 50·00 £110
c. Raised stop after "EXHIBITION" 50·00 £110
d. Small second "A" in "MALAYA" .. 50·00 £110
e. No hyphen £150
f. No stop .. .. 60·00 £120
2 50 4 c. rose-scarlet .. .. .. 7·50 23·00
b. Oval last "O" in "BORNEO" .. 15·00 40·00
c. Raised stop after "EXHIBITION" 15·00 40·00
d. Small second "A" in "MALAYA" .. 15·00 40·00
e. No hyphen .. .. .. 50·00
f. No stop .. .. 18·00 45·00
h. "EXH.BITION" .. .. .. 50·00
43 51 5 c. orange .. .. 5·00 19·00
b. Oval last "O" in "BORNEO" .. 10·00 32·00
c. Raised stop after "EXHIBITION" 10·00 32·00
d. Small second "A" in "MALAYA" .. 10·00 32·00
e. No hyphen .. .. .. 35·00
f. No stop .. .. 12·00 38·00
g. Third "I" in "EXHIBITION" omitted
h. "EXH.BITION" .. .. .. 35·00
44 52 8 c. ultramarine .. .. .. 1·75 7·00
b. Oval last "O" in "BORNEO" .. 4·50 13·00
c. Raised stop after "EXHIBITION" 4·50 13·00
d. Small second "A" in "MALAYA" .. 4·50 13·00
e. No hyphen .. .. .. 25·00
f. No stop .. .. 5·00 14·00
h. "EXH.BITION" .. .. .. 25·00
45 54 25 c. dull purple and mauve .. 3·25 28·00
b. Oval last "O" in "BORNEO" .. 8·00 50·00
c. Raised stop after "EXHIBITION" 8·00 50·00
d. Small second "A" in "MALAYA" .. 8·00 50·00
e. No hyphen .. .. .. 32·00
f. No stop .. .. 9·00 60·00
h. "EXH.BITION" .. .. .. 32·00

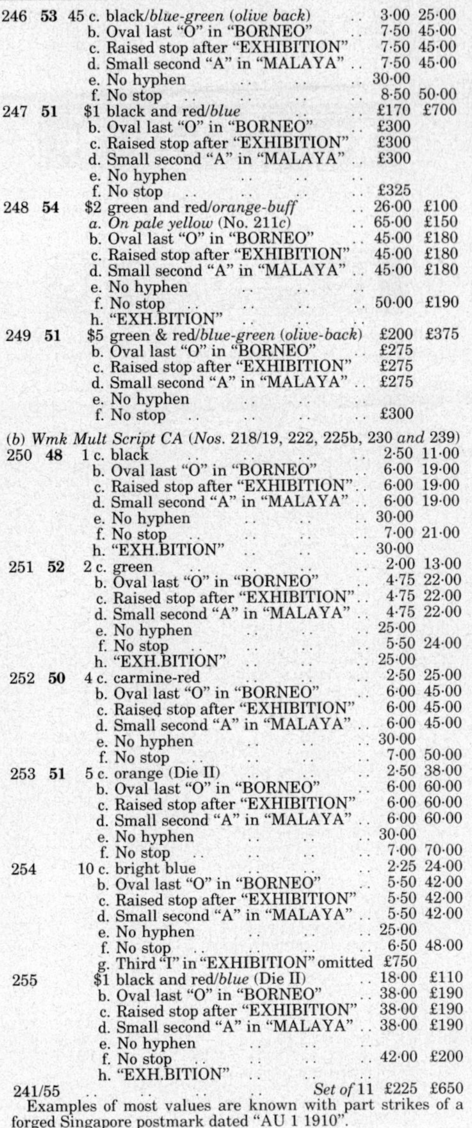

246 53 45 c. black/*blue-green* (*olive back*) .. 3·00 25·00
b. Oval last "O" in "BORNEO" .. 7·50 45·00
c. Raised stop after "EXHIBITION" 7·50 45·00
d. Small second "A" in "MALAYA" .. 7·50 45·00
e. No hyphen .. .. .. 30·00
f. No stop .. .. 8·50 50·00
247 51 $1 black and red/*blue* £170 £700
b. Oval last "O" in "BORNEO" .. £300
c. Raised stop after "EXHIBITION" £300
d. Small second "A" in "MALAYA" .. £300
e. No hyphen .. .. ..
f. No stop £325
248 54 $2 green and red/*orange-buff* .. 26·00 £100
a. On pale yellow (No. 211*c*) .. 65·00 £150
b. Oval last "O" in "BORNEO" .. 45·00 £180
c. Raised stop after "EXHIBITION" 45·00 £180
d. Small second "A" in "MALAYA" .. 45·00 £180
e. No hyphen .. .. ..
f. No stop .. .. 50·00 £190
h. "EXH.BITION" .. .. ..
249 51 $5 green & red/*blue-green* (*olive-back*) £200 £375
b. Oval last "O" in "BORNEO" .. £275
c. Raised stop after "EXHIBITION" £275
d. Small second "A" in "MALAYA" .. £275
e. No hyphen .. .. ..
f. No stop £300

(*b*) *Wmk Mult Script CA* (*Nos.* 218/19, 222, 225*b*, 230 *and* 239)

250 48 1 c. black .. .. 2·50 11·00
b. Oval last "O" in "BORNEO" .. 6·00 19·00
c. Raised stop after "EXHIBITION" .. 6·00 19·00
d. Small second "A" in "MALAYA" .. 6·00 19·00
e. No hyphen .. .. .. 30·00
f. No stop .. .. 7·00 21·00
h. "EXH.BITION" .. .. .. 30·00
251 52 2 c. green .. .. 2·00 13·00
b. Oval last "O" in "BORNEO" .. 4·75 22·00
c. Raised stop after "EXHIBITION" .. 4·75 22·00
d. Small second "A" in "MALAYA" .. 4·75 22·00
e. No hyphen .. .. .. 25·00
f. No stop .. .. 5·50 24·00
h. "EXH.BITION" .. .. .. 25·00
252 50 4 c. carmine-red .. .. .. 2·50 25·00
b. Oval last "O" in "BORNEO" .. 6·00 45·00
c. Raised stop after "EXHIBITION" 6·00 45·00
d. Small second "A" in "MALAYA" .. 6·00 45·00
e. No hyphen .. .. .. 30·00
f. No stop .. .. 7·00 50·00
253 51 5 c. orange (Die II) .. .. 2·50 38·00
b. Oval last "O" in "BORNEO" .. 6·00 60·00
c. Raised stop after "EXHIBITION" 6·00 60·00
d. Small second "A" in "MALAYA" .. 6·00 60·00
e. No hyphen .. .. .. 30·00
f. No stop .. .. 7·00 70·00
254 10 c. bright blue .. .. .. 2·25 24·00
b. Oval last "O" in "BORNEO" .. 5·50 42·00
c. Raised stop after "EXHIBITION" 5·50 42·00
d. Small second "A" in "MALAYA" .. 5·50 42·00
e. No hyphen .. .. .. 25·00
f. No stop .. .. 6·50 48·00
g. Third "I" in "EXHIBITION" omitted £750
255 $1 black and red/*blue* (Die II) .. 18·00 £110
b. Oval last "O" in "BORNEO" .. 38·00 £190
c. Raised stop after "EXHIBITION" 38·00 £190
d. Small second "A" in "MALAYA" .. 38·00 £190
e. No hyphen .. .. ..
f. No stop .. .. 42·00 £200
h. "EXH.BITION" .. .. ..
241/55 .. .. *Set of* 11 £225 £650

Examples of most values are known with part strikes of a forged Singapore postmark dated "AU 1 1910".

1935 (6 May). *Silver Jubilee. As Nos.* 91/4 *of Antigua, but ptd by Waterlow & Sons. P* 11×12.

256 5 c. ultramarine and grey .. .. 3·00 30
257 8 c. green and indigo .. .. 3·00 3·25
258 12 c. brown and deep blue .. .. 3·00 3·50
j. Damaged turret £200
259 25 c. slate and purple .. .. 3·25 5·00
256/9 .. .. *Set of* 4 11·00 11·00
256s/9s Perf "Specimen" .. .. *Set of* 4 £130

For illustration of plate variety see Omnibus section following Zanzibar.

57

58

1936 (1 Jan)–**37**. *Chalk-surfaced paper. Wmk Mult Script CA. P* 14.

260 57 1 c. black (1.1.37) .. .. .. 1·00 20
261 2 c. green (1.2.36) .. .. .. 1·00 70
262 4 c. orange (15.6.36) .. .. 2·00 70
263 5 c. brown (1.8.36) 75 30
264 6 c. scarlet (1.2.36) .. .. 1·25 1·10
265 8 c. grey .. .. 1·25 70
266 10 c. dull purple (1.7.36) .. .. 1·50 60
267 12 c. bright ultramarine (1.9.36) .. 2·00 2·50
268 25 c. dull purple and scarlet (1.2.36) 1·25 50
269 30 c. dull purple and orange .. 1·25 3·25
270 40 c. scarlet and dull purple .. 1·25 2·50
271 50 c. black/*emerald* (1.9.36) .. 4·50 1·25
272 $1 black and red/*blue* (1.7.36) .. 19·00 1·50
273 $2 green and scarlet (1.4.36) .. 38·00 10·00
274 $5 green and red/*emerald* (1.1.37) 80·00 10·00
260/74 .. .. *Set of* 15 £140 32·00
260s/74s Perf "Specimen" .. *Set of* 15 £275

1937 (12 May). *Coronation. As Nos.* 95/7 *of Antigua, but printed by D.L.R.*

275 4 c. orange 30 10
276 8 c. grey-black 70 10
277 12 c. bright blue .. .. .. 1·25 60
275/7 .. .. *Set of* 3 2·00 65
275s/7s Perf "Specimen" .. *Set of* 3 80·00

1937–41. *Chalk-surfaced paper. Wmk Mult Script CA. P* 14 *or* 15×14 (15 *c.*). (*a*) *Die I* (*printed at two operations*).

278 58 1 c. black (1.1.38) .. .. .. 5·00 10
279 2 c. green (6.12.37) .. .. .. 18·00 10
280 4 c. orange (1.1.38) .. .. .. 15·00 20
281 5 c. brown (19.11.37) .. .. .. 20·00 30
282 6 c. scarlet (10.1.38) .. .. .. 11·00 50
283 8 c. grey (26.1.38) .. .. .. 40·00 10
284 10 c. dull purple (8.11.37) .. .. 8·00 10
285 12 c. ultramarine (10.1.38) .. .. 8·00 50
286 25 c. dull purple and scarlet (11.12.37) .. 42·00 1·10
287 30 c. dull purple and orange (1.12.37) .. 25·00 2·00
288 40 c. scarlet and dull purple (20.12.37) .. 11·00 2·25
289 50 c. black/*emerald* (26.1.38) .. .. 10·00 10
290 $1 black and red/*blue* (26.1.38) .. 15·00 20
291 $2 green and scarlet (26.1.38) .. .. 32·00 4·75
292 $5 green and red/*emerald* (26.1.38) .. 25·00 3·50

(*b*) *Die II* (*printed at one operation*)

293 58 2 c. green (28.12.38) .. .. .. 50·00 40
294 2 c. orange (6.10.41) .. .. .. 2·00 10·00
295 3 c. green (*ordinary paper*) (5.9.41) .. 4·25 4·00
296 4 c. orange (29.10.38) .. .. .. 75·00 10
297 5 c. brown (18.2.39) .. .. .. 28·00 10
298 15 c. ultram (*ordinary paper*) (6.10.41) 6·00 10·00
278/98 .. .. *Set of* 18 £275 35·00
278s/92s, 294s/5s, 298s Perf "Specimen" *Set of* 18 £375

Die I. Lines of background outside central oval touch the oval and the foliage of the palm tree is usually joined to the oval frame. The downward-pointing palm frond, opposite the King's eye, has two points.

Die II. Lines of background are separated from the oval by a white line and the foliage of the palm trees does not touch the outer frame. The palm frond has only one point.

Nos. 295 and 298 were printed by Harrison and Sons following bomb damage to the De La Rue works on 29 December 1940.

The 6 c. grey, 8 c. scarlet and $5 purple and orange were only issued with the BMA overprint, but the 8 c. without overprint is known although in this state it was never issued (*Price* £14).

STAMP BOOKLETS

1914–19. *Black on blue* (*No.* SB1) *or grey* (*No.* SB1*b*) *covers. Stapled.*

SB1 $1 booklet containing twenty-five 4 c. dull purple (No. 197) in two blocks of 12 and one single
a. Containing 4 c. rose-scarlet (No. 198) (1919)
SB1*b* $1 booklet containing four 1 c., sixteen 3 c. and twelve 4 c. (Nos. 193, 196/7) in blocks of four

1921. *Black on blue cover. Stapled.*

SB2 $1 booklet containing twenty-five 4 c. (No. 222) in two blocks of 12 and one single .. ..
a. Contents as SB2, but four blocks of 6 and one single .. ..

1922. *Black on red cover. Stapled.*

SB3 $1 booklet containing 5 c. (No. 225) in block of 8 and 6 c. (No. 227) in block of 10 .. .. £1000

1925–29. *Black on red cover. Stapled.*

SB4 $1.20, booklet containing thirty 4 c. bright violet (No. 223) in blocks of 10 .. .. ..
a. Containing 4 c. orange (No. 224) (1929) ..

1927. *Black on grey* (*No.* SB5), *green* (*No.* SB6) *or blue* (*No.* SB7) *covers. Stapled.*

SB5 $1 booklet containing 4 c. and 6 c. (Nos. 223, 229) in blocks of 10 .. ..
SB6 $1.20, booklet containing twenty 6 c. (No. 229) in blocks of 10 .. ..
SB7 $1.20, booklet containing 2 c., 4 c. and 6 c. (Nos. 219, 223, 229) in blocks of 10 .. ..

1933. *Black on buff cover. Stapled.*

SB8 $1 booklet containing twenty 5 c. (No. 226a) in blocks of 10 .. ..

1936. *Stapled.*

SB9 $1 booklet containing twenty 5 c. (No. 263) in blocks of 10 .. ..
SB10 $1.30, booklet containing 5 c. and 8 c. (Nos. 263, 265) in blocks of 10 .. ..

1938. *Black on buff* (*No.* SB11) *or black on green* (*No.* SB12) *covers. Stapled.*

SB11 $1 booklet containing twenty 5 c. (No. 281) in blocks of 10 .. .. £1300
SB12 $1.30, booklet containing 5 c. and 8 c. (Nos. 281, 283) in blocks of 10 and pane of airmail labels £1600

POSTAGE DUE STAMPS

D 1

1924 (1 Jan)–**26**. *Wmk Mult Script CA. P* 14.

D1 D 1 1 c. violet .. .. 5·00 6·50
D2 2 c. black .. .. 3·25 1·25
D3 4 c. green (5.26) .. .. .. 2·00 4·75
D4 8 c. scarlet .. .. 4·50 55
D5 10 c. orange .. .. 6·00 85
D6 12 c. bright blue .. .. .. 7·00 65
D1/6 .. .. *Set of* 6 25·00 13·00
D1s/6s .. .. *Set of* 6 £200

For later issues of Postage Due stamps, see MALAYAN POSTAL UNION.

The Straits Settlements were occupied by the Japanese in 1942. After the Second World War the stamps of MALAYA (BRITISH MILITARY ADMINISTRATION) were used. In 1946 Singapore became a separate Crown Colony and Labuan was transferred to North Borneo. Separate stamps were issued for Malacca and Penang, which both joined the Malayan Federation on 1 February 1948.

II. FEDERATED MALAY STATES

On 1 July 1896, the States of Negri Sembilan, Pahang, Perak and Selangor were organised on a federal basis to be known as the Federated Malay States. For the time being each State continued with individual issues, but stamps for the use of the Federation replaced these in 1900.

PRICES FOR STAMPS ON COVER

Nos. 1/13	*from* × 12
No. 14	—
Nos. 15/22	*from* × 10
Nos. 23/5	*from* × 3
No. 26	—
Nos. 27/50	*from* × 6
No. 51	—
Nos. 52/81	*from* × 5
No. 82	—
Nos. D1/6	*from* × 10

PRINTERS. All issues of the Federated Malay States were printed in typography by De La Rue & Co, Ltd, London, *unless otherwise stated.*

FEDERATED MALAY STATES (1)   FEDERATED MALAY STATES (2)

1900. *Optd with T* **1** *(cent values) or* **2** *(dollar values).*

(*a*) *Stamps of Negri Sembilan* (*T* **3**)

1 1 c. dull purple and green .. 2·50 5·50
2 2 c. dull purple and brown .. 27·00 60·00
3 3 c. dull purple and black .. 2·00 4·00
4 5 c. dull purple and olive-yellow .. 65·00 £160
5 10 c. dull purple and orange .. 5·50 23·00
6 20 c. green and olive .. 80·00 95·00
7 25 c. green and carmine .. £200 £325
8 50 c. green and black .. 85·00 £120
1/8 .. *Set of* 8 £425 £700
1s/8s Optd "Specimen" .. *Set of* 8 £170

(*b*) *Stamps of Perak* (*T* **44** *and* **45**)

9 5 c. dull purple and olive-yellow .. 13·00 55·00
10 10 c. dull purple and orange .. 65·00 65·00
11 $1 green and pale green .. £160 £200
 w. Wmk inverted .. £750
12 $2 green and carmine .. £130 £200
13 $5 green and ultramarine .. £325 £475
14 $25 green and orange .. £7000
 s. Optd "Specimen" .. £300
11s/13s Optd "Specimen" .. *Set of* 3 £130

The Negri Sembilan 3 c. dull purple and black does not exist without overprint Type **1**.

The stamps of STRAITS SETTLEMENTS were used in Federated Malay States from 16 July 1900 until replaced by the 1900–1 issue.

3

4

1900–1. *P* 14. (*a*) *T* **3**. *Wmk Crown CA, sideways* (1901).

15 1 c. black and green .. 5·00 5·00
 a. Grey and green .. 2·50 55
 b. Grey-brown and green .. 8·00 30
16 3 c. black and brown .. 7·50 3·25
 a. Grey and brown .. 4·25 35
 b. Grey-brown and brown .. 3·25 20
17 4 c. black and carmine .. 14·00 4·50
 a. Grey and carmine .. 4·75 3·25
 b. Grey-brown and carmine .. 18·00 2·00
18 5 c. green and carmine/*yellow* .. 2·00 2·50
19 8 c. black and ultramarine .. 42·00 15·00
 a. Grey and ultramarine .. 20·00 4·50
 b. Grey-brown and ultramarine .. 26·00 3·75
20 10 c. black and claret .. 90·00 25·00
 a. Grey and claret .. 70·00 6·50
 b. Black and purple .. £110 25·00
 c. Grey and purple .. 80·00 9·00
 d. Grey-brown and purple .. 85·00 6·00
21 20 c. mauve and black .. 17·00 8·50
22 50 c. black and orange-brown .. £130 £110
 a. Grey and orange-brown .. 90·00 45·00
 b. Grey-brown and orange-brown .. 85·00 40·00
15/22 .. *Set of* 8 £180 55·00
15s/22s Optd "Specimen" .. *Set of* 8 £160

Later printings in 1903–4 show the two upper lines of shading in the background at the corner nearest to the "S" of "STATE" blurred and running into one another, whereas in earlier printings these lines are distinct. Two plates were used for printing the central design of T 3. In Plate 1 the lines of background are regular throughout, but in Plate 2 they are lighter around the head and back of the tiger. The 5 c. was the only value with single wmk to be printed from Plate 2. Stamps with multiple wmk were printed for a short time from Plate 1, and show the two blurred lines of background near "S" of "STATE," but the majority of these stamps were printed from Plate 2 and later plates.

(*b*) *T* **4**. *Wmk Crown CC* (1900)

23 $1 green and pale green .. £100 £110
24 $2 green and carmine .. £120 £130
25 $5 green and bright ultramarine .. £190 £225
 a. Green and pale ultramarine .. £190 £200
26 $25 green and orange .. £1900 £1100
 s. Optd "Specimen" .. £190
23s/5s Optd "Specimen" .. *Set of* 3 £120

Two dies for 1 c. green and 4 c. scarlet

Die I. "Head" and duty plates. Thick frame line below "MALAY" and in the 1 c. the "c" is thin whilst in the 4 c. it is thick.

Die II. Single working plate. Thin frame line below "MALAY" and in the 1 c. the "c" is thicker whilst in the 4 c. it is thinner.

1904 (Aug)–**22.** *T* **3** *and T* **4** (*dollar values*). *Wmk Mult Crown CA* (*sideways* on T* **3**). *Ordinary paper* (1 c. *to* 50 c.) *or chalk-surfaced paper* ($1 *to* $25).

27 1 c. grey and green (8.04) .. 65·00 8·50
 a. Grey-brown and green .. 27·00 70
28 1 c. green (Die I) (8.7.06) .. 11·00 30
29 1 c. green (Die II) (1908) .. 3·50 20
 a. Yellow-green .. 16·00 1·25
 aw. Wmk Crown to right of CA .. 38·00 9·00
 b. Blue-green .. 21·00 1·25
30 1 c. deep brown (21.1.19) .. 2·25 90
31 2 c. green (18.2.19) .. 1·50 30
 w. Wmk Crown to right of CA .. 38·00 11·00
32 3 c. grey and brown (10.04) .. 55·00 1·00
 a. Grey-brown and brown (12.05) .. 35·00 1·25
 ab. Chalk-surfaced paper .. 35·00 2·50
33 3 c. brown (11.7.06) .. 7·00 15
34 3 c. carmine (2.2.09) .. 2·25 10
 aw. Wmk Crown to right of CA .. 5·50 40
 b. Scarlet (1.17) .. 13·00 40
 bw. Wmk Crown to right of CA .. 23·00 4·25
35 3 c. grey (29.10.18) .. 1·50 20
 w. Wmk Crown to right of CA .. 32·00 11·00
36 4 c. grey and scarlet (10.10.04) .. 38·00 3·00
 a. Chalk-surfaced paper. *Grey and rose* .. 14·00 1·50
 b. Grey-brown and scarlet .. 35·00 2·75
 c. Black and scarlet .. 22·00 2·25
 d. Black and rose .. 4·00 50
 dw. Wmk Crown to right of CA .. 6·50 50
 e. Black and deep rose (*aniline*) (1909) .. 45·00 5·00
 f. Jet black and rose (1914) .. 21·00 1·75
37 4 c. scarlet (Die I) (11.2.19) .. 2·50 4·00
38 4 c. scarlet (Die II) (15.4.19) .. 1·50 15
 aw. Wmk Crown to right of CA .. 38·00 5·00
 b. Wmk upright (2.22) .. † £350
39 5 c. green and carmine/*yellow* (5.06) .. 7·50 1·50
 aw. Wmk Crown to right of CA .. 48·00 18·00
 b. Chalk-surfaced paper .. 22·00 3·75
 c. Deep green and carmine/yellow .. 7·50 2·00
 d. On orange-buff (1921) .. 13·00 5·50
 e. On pale yellow (4.22) .. 8·00 3·75
40 6 c. orange (11.2.19) .. 2·50 2·00
41 8 c. grey and ultramarine (2.05) .. 60·00 18·00
 aw. Wmk Crown to right of CA ..
 b. Grey-brown and ultramarine (12.05) .. 17·00 3·75
 ba. Chalk-surfaced paper .. 45·00 12·00
 bb. Wmk upright (3.07) .. 6·00 4·50
42 8 c. ultramarine (8.3.10) .. 13·00 1·00
 aw. Wmk Crown to right of CA .. 60·00 25·00
 b. Deep blue (1918) .. 16·00 1·25
43 10 c. grey-brown and claret (10.10.04) .. 60·00 5·00
 a. Chalk-surfaced paper (1905) .. 75·00 7·00
 b. Black and claret .. 21·00 50
 bw. Wmk Crown to right of CA .. 35·00 1·25
 c. Grey-brown and purple (1905) .. 60·00 3·00
 d. Black and purple .. 21·00 2·50
 e. Jet-black and bright purple (1914) .. 70·00 4·75
44 10 c. deep blue (3.6.19) .. 6·50 1·50
 a. Bright blue .. 6·50 1·00
 ab. Wmk inverted .. † —
 aw. Wmk Crown to right of CA .. 45·00 20·00
45 20 c. mauve and black (3.05) .. 8·00 85
 a. Chalk-surfaced paper .. 11·00 2·50
 w. Wmk Crown to right of CA .. 55·00 20·00
46 35 c. scarlet/*pale yellow* (25.8.22) .. 5·50 12·00
47 50 c. grey and orange (3.05) .. 65·00 7·00
 aw. Wmk Crown to right of CA .. £150 50·00
 b. Wmk inverted .. † —
 c. Grey-brown and orange-brown (1906) 42·00 7·00
 caw. Wmk Crown to right of CA .. † —
 cb. Chalk-surfaced paper. *Grey-brown and orange-brown* .. 50·00 6·50
 cc. Grey and orange-brown .. 55·00 6·50
 cd. Black and orange-brown .. 75·00 13·00
 ce. Jet-black and orange-brown (1914) .. £100 16·00
48 $1 grey-green and green (11.07) .. 60·00 40·00
 a. Green and pale green .. 80·00 40·00
 aw. Wmk inverted ..
49 $2 green and carmine (4.12.07) .. 75·00 £110
 a. Printed on the gummed side ..
 w. Wmk inverted ..
50 $5 green and blue (1.08) .. £140 £130
51 $25 green and orange (12.09) .. £1100 £700
27/50 .. *Set of* 22 £425 £275
28s, 30s/1s, 33s/5s, 37s, 40s, 42s, 44s, 46s Optd "Specimen" .. *Set of* 11 £375

*The normal sideways watermark shows Crown to left of CA, *as seen from the back of the stamp.*

Nos. 29/*b*, 30, 31, 33, 34/*b* and 35 were printed from single working plates and all the rest from double plates.

Most examples of No. 47*b* have fiscal cancellations, but at least one is known postally used.

1922–34. *Wmk Mult Script CA* (*sideways* on T* **3**). *Ordinary paper* (1 *c. to* 10 *c.* (*No.* 66), 12 *c.*, 35 *c.* (*No.* 72)) *or chalk-surfaced paper* (*others*).

52 **3** 1 c. deep brown (1.8.22) .. 1·50 3·00
 w. Wmk Crown to right of CA .. 38·00 38·00
53 1 c. black (12.6.23) .. 75 20
54 2 c. brown (5.8.25) .. 6·00 4·75
55 2 c. green (15.6.26) .. 2·75 10
56 **3** 3 c. grey (27.12.22) .. 1·75
 w. Wmk Crown to right of CA .. 45·00
57 3 c. green (22.1.24) .. 1·25
58 3 c. brown (31.5.27) .. 1·25
59 4 c. carmine-red (Die II) (27.11.23) .. 3·50
 w. Wmk Crown to right of CA .. 30·00
60 4 c. orange (9.11.26) .. 1·25
 a. No watermark .. £300
61 5 c. mauve/*pale yellow* (17.3.22) .. 1·00
 w. Wmk Crown to right of CA .. 38·00
62 5 c. brown (1.3.32) .. 3·25
63 6 c. orange (2.5.22) .. 1·00
 w. Wmk Crown to right of CA ..
64 6 c. scarlet (9.11.26) .. 1·25
 a. Wmk upright ..
65 10 c. bright blue (23.10.23) .. 1·25
 w. Wmk Crown to right of CA ..
66 10 c. black and blue (18.1.24†) .. 2·00
67 10 c. purple/*pale yellow* (14.7.31) .. 3·75
68 12 c. ultramarine (12.9.22) .. 1·25
 w. Wmk Crown to right of CA .. 45·00
69 20 c. dull purple & black (*chalk-surfaced paper*) (3.4.23) .. 4·00
 a. Ordinary paper (29.12.26) .. 27·00
 b. Wmk inverted .. †
70 25 c. purple and bright magenta (3.9.29) 2·75
71 30 c. purple and orange-yellow (3.9.29) 3·25
72 35 c. scarlet/*pale yellow* (6.11.28) .. 3·25
73 35 c. scarlet and purple (29.9.31) .. 13·00
74 50 c. black and orange (24.4.24) .. 13·00
 aw. Wmk Crown to right of CA .. 95·00
 b. Black and orange-brown .. 27·00
75 50 c. black/*green* (16.6.31) .. 4·00
76 **4** $1 pale green and green (2.2.26) .. 21·00
 a. Grey-green and emerald (5.10.26) 15·00
77 **3** $1 black and red/*blue* (10.3.31) .. 12·00
78 **4** $2 green and carmine (17.8.26) .. 18·00
79 **3** $2 green and red/*yellow* (6.2.34) .. 38·00
80 **4** $5 green and blue (24.2.25) .. 90·00
 w. Wmk inverted .. £750
81 **3** $5 green and red/*green* (7.34) .. £140
82 **4** $25 green and orange (14.2.28) .. £800
 s. Optd "Specimen" .. £140
52/81 .. *Set of* 30 £350
52s/81s Optd or Perf (No. 81s) "Specimen" *Set of* 30 £750

*The normal sideways watermark shows Crown to left of *as seen from the back of the stamp.*

†No. 66 was released in London by the Crown Agents s months earlier but this is the official date of issue in the Sta

Nos. 52, 56 and 59 were printed from single working pla and the rest from double plates.

No. 55 exists in coils constructed from normal sheets.

The 5 c. mauve on white Script paper is the result of soak early printings of No. 61 in water.

STAMP BOOKLETS

1909. *Black on pink* (*Nos.* SB1/2) *or black on buff* (*No.* S *covers. Stapled.*

SB1 25 c. booklet containing twenty-four 1 c. (No. 29) in blocks of 6 .. £2
 a. Black on green cover (1917)
 b. Black on blue cover .. £2
SB2 73 c. booklet containing twenty-four 3 c. (No. 34) in blocks of 6 .. £1
 a. Black on red cover (1917)
 b. Black on blue cover .. £1
SB3 97 c. booklet containing twenty-four 4 c. (No. 36*d*) in blocks of 6 .. £2

1919. *Black on green* (*No.* SB4) *or black on pink* (*No.* S *covers. Stapled.*

SB4 49 c. booklet containing twenty-four 2 c. (No. 31) £5
 in blocks of 6
SB5 97 c. booklet containing twenty-four 4 c. (No. 37) in blocks of 6 .. £1

1922. *Black on buff cover* (*No.* SB7). *Stapled.*

SB6 $1. 21, booklet containing twenty-four 5 c. (No. 61) in blocks of 6 ..
SB7 $1. 45, booklet containing twenty-four 6 c. (No. 63) in blocks of 6 .. £20

1926. *As Nos.* SB4, SB3 *and* SB7, *but sold at face value witho premium. Black on green* (*No.* SB8), *black on pink* (*No.* SB *or black on buff* (*No.* SB10) *covers. Stapled.*

SB8 48 c. booklet containing twenty-four 2 c. (No. 55) in blocks of 6 ..
SB9 96 c. booklet containing twenty-four 4 c. (No. 60) in blocks of 6 .. £20
SB10 $1.44 booklet containing twenty-four 6 c. (No. 64) in blocks of 6 .. £20

1926. *Black on grey cover. Stapled.*

SB11 $1 booklet containing 4 c. and 6 c. (Nos. 60, 64) each in block of 10 ..

1927. *Black on bluish green cover. Stapled.*

SB12 $1.50, booklet containing 2 c., 3 c., 4 c. and 6 c. (Nos. 55, 58, 60, 64) each in block of 10 .. £20

1927–30. *Black on red* (*No.* SB13), *black on green* (*No.* SB1 *or black on blue* (*No.* SB15) *covers. Stapled.*

SB13 $1.20, booklet containing thirty 4 c. (No. 60) in blocks of 10 .. £200
 a. Black on orange cover (1930)
SB14 $1.20, booklet containing twenty 6 c. (No. 64) in blocks of 10 (1928) ..
SB15 $1.20, booklet containing 2 c., 4 c. and 6 c. (Nos. 55, 60, 64) each in block of 10 (1928) ..
 a. Black on white cover (1930)

1934. *Black on buff cover. Stapled.*

SB16 $1 booklet containing twenty 5 c. (No. 62) in blocks of 10 .. £225

POSTAGE DUE STAMPS

D 1

(Typo Waterlow)

1 Dec)–**26**. *Wmk Mult Script CA (sideways*). P* 15×14.
D 1 1 c. violet .. .. 4·75 25·00
w. Wmk Crown to left of CA (1926) 12·00 19·00
2 c. black .. .. 1·75 3·50
w. Wmk Crown to left of CA (1926) 4·00 3·25
4 c. green (*wmk Crown to left of CA*) (27.4.26) .. .. 2·25 5·00
8 c. red .. .. 5·50 25·00
w. Wmk Crown to left of CA (1926) .. 13·00 18·00
10 c. orange .. .. 9·00 17·00
w. Wmk Crown to left of CA (1926) 18·00 14·00
12 c. blue .. .. 9·00 24·00
w. Wmk Crown to left of CA (1926) .. 15·00 14·00
.. .. *Set of* 6 29·00 65·00
s Optd "Specimen" .. .. *Set of* 6 £150
e normal sideways watermark shows Crown to right of *s seen from the back of the stamp.*

e issues of the Federated Malay States were replaced by s for the individual States from 1935 onwards.

III. MALAYAN POSTAL UNION

e Malayan Postal Union was organised in 1934 and, initially, ed the Straits Settlements and the Federated Malay States. ps of the Straits Settlements together with issues for the indi- l States continued to be used, but Malayan Postal Union ge due stamps were introduced in 1936.
lowing the end of the Second World War the use of these ge dues spread throughout Malaya and to Singapore.

PRICES FOR STAMPS ON COVER TO 1945	
Nos. D1/6	*from* × 10
Nos. D7/13	*from* × 4

POSTAGE DUE STAMPS

D 1

10

cents

(D 2)

(Typo Waterlow until 1961, then D.L.R.)

(June)–**38**. *Wmk Mult Script CA. P* 15×14.
D 1 1 c. slate-purple (4.38) .. .. 4·00 70
4 c. green (9.36) .. .. 15·00 1·00
8 c. scarlet .. .. 7·50 3·50
10 c. yellow-orange .. .. 10·00 30
12 c. pale ultramarine (9.36) .. .. 12·00 14·00
50 c. black (1.38) .. .. 28·00 6·00
6 .. .. *Set of* 6 70·00 23·00
/6s .. .. *Set of* 6 £150
or use in Negri Sembilan, Pahang, Perak, Selangor and Straits lements including Singapore.

5–**49**. *New values and colours. Wmk Mult Script CA.* 15×14.
7 D 1 1 c. purple .. .. 3·25 2·00
8 3 c. green .. .. 6·00 7·50
9 5 c. scarlet .. .. 6·00 5·00
0 8 c. yellow-orange (1949) .. .. 16·00 16·00
s. Perf "Specimen" .. .. 75·00
1 9 c. yellow-orange .. .. .. 50·00 48·00
2 15 c. pale ultramarine .. .. £150 35·00
3 20 c. blue (1948) .. .. .. 8·00 5·00
s. Perf "Specimen" .. .. 75·00
/13 .. .. *Set of* 7 £200 £110

1 (8 Aug)–**63**. *Wmk Mult Script CA. P* 14.
4 D 1 1 c. violet (21.8.52) .. .. .. 70 1·60
5 2 c. deep slate-blue (16.11.53) .. .. 1·25 2·25
a. Perf 12½ (15.11.60) .. .. 60 13·00
ab. Chalk-surfaced paper (10.7.62) 75 7·00
ac. Ditto. Imperf horiz (vert pair) .. † £10000
6 3 c. deep green (21.8.52) .. .. 24·00 12·00
7 4 c. sepia (16.11.53) .. .. .. 70 5·50
a. Perf 12½ (15.11.60) .. .. 80 17·00
ab. Chalk-surfaced paper. *Bistre-brown* (10.7.62) .. .. .. 80 14·00
8 5 c. vermilion .. .. .. 48·00 12·00
9 8 c. yellow-orange .. .. .. 2·25 4·50
0 12 c. bright purple (1.2.54) .. .. 1·25 6·00
a. Perf 12½. Chalk-surfaced paper (10.7.62) .. .. .. 2·00 23·00
1 20 c. blue .. .. 4·75 6·50
a. Perf 12½. *Deep blue* (10.12.57) 7·00 26·00
ab. Chalk-surfaced paper (15.10.63) 3·50 35·00
4/21 .. .. *Set of* 8 70·00 45·00
Nos. D7 to D21ab were for use in the Federation and ngapore.

IV. MALAYA (BRITISH MILITARY ADMINISTRATION)

Following the Japanese surrender on 2 September 1945 British troops landed in Malaya which was placed under a British Military Administration. The Director of Posts was ashore at Singapore on 6 September and had reached Kuala Lumpur by 13 September. Postal services in Singapore and Johore resumed on 17 September and had spread to the remainder of the country by 5 October. No stamps were initially available so all mail up to 1 oz. was carried free until the first overprinted stamps appeared on 19 October.

De La Rue had overprinted available stocks of pre-war Straits Settlements stamps earlier in 1945 and initial supplies of these London overprints were placed on sale from 19 October (Nos. 1, 2a, 4, 6a, 7 and 8a) with the 15 c. and 25 c. (Nos. 11 and 13a) issued later. A second consignment contained dollar values including the $5 purple and orange. Duplicate plates were subsequently sent to the Government Printing Office at Kuala Lumpur, where the overprinting of surviving local stocks of the 1 c., 5 c., 10 c., 15 c. (overprinted in black) and $5 black and red on emerald took place, and to Australia for those shipments which had been diverted there in 1941.

The stamps were used throughout all Malay States and in Singapore. From 1948 this general issue was gradually replaced by individual issues for each state. The last usage was in Kelantan where B M A overprints were not withdrawn until 10 July 1951.

BMA
MALAYA

(1)

1945 (19 Oct)–**48**. *T* **58** *of Straits Settlements from Die I (double-plate printing) or Die II (single-plate printing) optd with T* **1**. *Wmk Mult Script CA. Chalk-surfaced paper. P* 14 *or* 15×14 (*No.* 11).
1 1 c. black (I) (R.) .. .. 3·00 40
a. Ordinary paper 10 30
2 2 c. orange (II) (8.7.47) .. .. .. 4·50 60
a. Ordinary paper (19.10.45) 20 10
w. Wmk inverted .. .. .. † £1400
3 2 c. orange (I) (*ordinary paper*) (9.46) .. 18·00 3·50
4 3 c. yellow-green (II) (*ordinary paper*) .. 30 50
a. Blue-green (27.1.47) .. .. .. 3·75 3·50
b. Chalk-surfaced paper. *Blue-grn* (8.7.47) 12·00 1·00
5 5 c. brown (II) (24.10.45) .. .. .. 70 1·00
6 6 c. grey (II) (22.3.48) .. .. .. 15·00 3·00
a. Ordinary paper (19.10.45) 30 20
7 8 c. scarlet (II) (*ordinary paper*) 30 10
8 10 c. purple (I) (12.45) .. .. .. 3·75 70
a. Ordinary paper (19.10.45) 50 10
b. Slate-purple (12.45) .. .. .. 3·25 30
c. Magenta (22.3.48) .. .. .. 6·50 70
9 10 c. purple (II) (28.7.48) .. .. .. 18·00 2·50
10 12 c. bright ultramarine (I) (11.45) .. 1·75 5·00
11 15 c. brt ultram (II) (*ordinary paper*) (11.45) 2·50 8·50
12 15 c. bright ultramarine (II) (R.) (22.3.48) 24·00 90
a. Ordinary paper (12.45) 75 20
b. Blue (27.11.47) .. .. .. 48·00 85
ba. Ordinary paper (8.7.47) .. .. £100 13·00
13 25 c. dull purple and scarlet (I) (22.3.48) .. 11·00 1·50
a. Ordinary paper (12.45) .. .. 1·40 30
ab. Opt double £4500
14 50 c. black/*emerald* (I) (R.) (12.45) .. .. 25·00 2·25
a. Ordinary paper 75 10
15 $1 black and red (I) (*ordinary paper*) (12.45) 2·00 10
16 $2 green & scar (I) (*ordinary paper*) (12.45) 2·75 75
17 $5 green and red/*emerald* (I) (11.45) .. 85·00 90·00
18 $5 pur & orge (I) (*ordinary paper*) (12.45) 3·75 3·00
1/18 .. .. *Set of* 15 90·00 90·00
1s/11s, 13s/16s, 18s Perf "Specimen" .. *Set of* 14 £400

The 8 c. grey with "BMA" opt was prepared but not officially issued (*Price £275 unused*).

Nos. 3 and 9 do not exist without the overprint.

Initial printings on ordinary paper were produced by Harrison and Sons in 1941 following bomb damage to the De La Rue works on 29 December 1940.

No. 8 with reddish purple medallion and dull purple frame is from a 1947 printing with the head in fugitive ink which discolours with moisture.

Postal forgeries of the 50 c. value exist made by dyeing examples of the 1 c. and then altering the face value to 50 c.

In 1946 8 c. and 15 c. stamps in the Crown Colony Victory design were prepared for the Malayan Union, but not issued. Examples of the 8 c. carmine from this issue exist from unofficial leakages (*Price £275 unused*).

V. MALAYAN STATES

PRINTERS. All Malayan States stamps were printed in typography by De La Rue and Co, Ltd, London, *unless otherwise stated.*

JOHORE

A British adviser was appointed to Johore in 1914. The state joined the Federation of Malaya on 1 February 1948.

Until 1 January 1899 mail for addresses outside Malaya had the external postage paid by stamps of the STRAITS SETTLEMENTS.

PRICES FOR STAMPS ON COVER TO 1945	
Nos. 1/2	—
Nos. 3/5	*from* × 15
No. 6	*from* × 20
Nos. 7/8	—
Nos. 9/15	*from* × 25
No. 16	—
Nos. 17/20	*from* × 15
Nos. 21/31	*from* × 10
Nos. 32/8	*from* × 15
Nos. 39/53	*from* × 8
Nos. 54/60	*from* × 6
Nos. 61/74	*from* × 8
Nos. 75/7	—
Nos. 78/87	*from* × 8
No. 88	*from* × 10
Nos. 89/102	*from* × 6
Nos. 103/25	*from* × 5
Nos. 126/8	—
Nos. 129/30	*from* × 6
Nos. D1/5	*from* × 5

(1)

1876 (July). *No.* 11 *of Straits Settlements handstamped with T* 1.
1 2 c. brown £9500 £4000
No. 1 is known with the handstamp double.

From September 1878 to August 1884 no overprinted stamps were supplied by Singapore to Johore.

JOHORE
(2)

JOHORE
(3) ("H" and "E" wide. "J" raised. Opt 16 mm long)

JOHORE
(4) ("H" wide, "E" narrow. Opt 16 mm long)

JOHORE
(5) ("H" and "E" wide. Opt 16¾ mm long)

JOHORE.
(6)

JOHORE
(7)

JOHORE
(8)

1884 (June)–**86**. *No.* 63 *of Straits Settlements optd with T* **2/8**.
2 2 2 c. pale rose £4000
3 3 2 c. pale rose (8.84) £1200 £500
a. Opt double £2750
4 4 2 c. pale rose (8.84) £1500 £600
a. Opt double .. ..
5 5 2 c. pale rose (8.84) £1200 £500
a. Opt double .. .. — £1500
6 6 2 c. pale rose (3.85) £150 £160
a. Opt double .. ..
7 7 2 c. pale rose (1885) £2250
8 8 2 c. pale rose (4.86) .. .. .. 75·00 90·00
Nos. 3 to 7 were from triplet settings, either 3+4+5 or three examples of the same overprint. Nos. 2 and 8 are probably single unit handstamps.

JOHOR
(9) (All letters narrow)

JOHOR
(10)

JOHOR
(11) ("H" wide)

.JOHOR
(12)

JOHOR
(13)

JOHOR.
(14)

JOHOR
(15)

JOHOR
(16)

1884 (Aug)–**91**. *Nos.* 63/a *of Straits Settlements optd with T* **9/16**.
9 9 2 c. pale rose .. .. 8·50 15·00
a. Opt double £700
10 10 2 c. pale rose (10.84) .. .. .. 8·50 5·50
a. Thin, narrow "J" (R. 6/6) .. .. £120 90·00
b. Opt double £700
c. Bright rose (1890) .. .. .. 8·50 9·00
ca. Thin, narrow "J" (R. 6/6) £140 £150
cb. Opt double £800
11 11 2 c. pale rose (2.85) .. .. .. 80·00 80·00
12 12 2 c. pale rose (1886) .. .. .. 48·00 48·00
a. Opt double £750
13 13 2 c. pale rose (1886) .. .. .. 35·00 38·00
14 14 2 c. pale rose (1888) .. .. .. £110 50·00
a. Thin, narrow "J" £550 £325
b. Opt double £700
15 15 2 c. bright rose (9.90) .. .. .. 12·00 12·00
16 16 2 c. bright rose (1891) £7500

Settings:
No. 9 — various triplets with the length of the overprint varying from 12 to 15 mm
No. 10 — triplet or 60 (6×10)
No. 11 — triplet 11 + 9 + 9
No. 12 — triplet
No. 13 — triplet
No. 14 — 30 (3×10)
No. 15 — 60 (6×10)
No. 16 — not known. As no used examples are known it is possible that this stamp was not issued.

JOHOR
Two
CENTS
(17)

JOHOR
Two
CENTS
(18)

JOHOR Two CENTS (19) JOHOR Two CENTS (20)

1891 (May). *No.* 68 *of Straits Settlements surch as T* **17/20**.
17 **17** 2 c. on 24 c. green .. .. .. 23·00 35·00
a. "CENST" (R. 5/4) £800 £425
w. Wmk inverted £120 £120
18 **18** 2 c. on 24 c. green £110 £110
a. Thin, narrow "J" (R. 6/6) £325 £325
19 **19** 2 c. on 24 c. green .. .. .. 35·00 50·00
20 **20** 2 c. on 24 c. green £100 £100

Nos. 17/20 come from the same setting of 60. Type **17** occurs on horizontal rows 1 to 5, Type **18** on row 6, Type **19** on rows 7, 8 and 9 and Type **20** on row 10.

21 Sultan Aboubakar

3 cents. (22)

KEMAHKOTAAN (23)

1891 (16 Nov)–**94**. *No wmk. P* 14.
21 **21** 1 c. dull purple and mauve (7.94) .. 50 50
22 2 c. dull purple and yellow .. .. 50 1·50
23 3 c. dull purple and carmine (7.94) .. 55 50
24 4 c. dull purple and black .. .. 2·75 14·00
25 5 c. dull purple and green .. .. 7·00 20·00
26 6 c. dull purple and blue .. .. 8·00 20·00
27 $1 green and carmine .. .. .. 70·00 £150
21/7 .. .. *Set of* 7 80·00 £190

1894 (Mar). *Surch with T* **22**.
28 **21** 3 c. on 4 c. dull purple and black .. 2·25 50
a. No stop (R. 5/11) .. .. .. 65·00 55·00
29 3 c. on 5 c. dull purple and green .. 1·00 2·75
a. No stop (R. 5/11) .. .. .. 85·00 £110
b. "3 cents." spaced 3½ mm from bar £120 85·00
30 3 c. on 6 c. dull purple and blue .. 2·50 3·25
a. No stop (R. 5/11) £120 £140
31 3 c. on $1 green and carmine .. .. 10·00 55·00
a. No stop (R. 5/11) £325 £550
28/31 .. .. *Set of* 4 14·00 55·00

No. 29b shows the surcharge spaced 3½ mm from the bar instead of the normal 7½ mm. It appears to come from a separate setting as a cancelled-to-order block of eight is known.

1896 (Mar). *Coronation of Sultan Ibrahim. Optd with T* **23**.
32 **21** 1 c. dull purple and mauve 50 85
a. "KETAHKOTAAN" .. .. .. 3·25 5·00
33 2 c. dull purple and yellow .. .. 50 1·00
a. "KETAHKOTAAN" .. .. .. 3·00 6·00
34 3 c. dull purple and carmine .. .. 55 1·00
a. "KETAHKOTAAN" .. .. .. 7·50 9·00
35 4 c. dull purple and black .. .. 80 2·25
a. "KETAHKOTAAN" .. .. .. 2·75 8·50
36 5 c. dull purple and green .. .. 5·50 7·50
a. "KETAHKOTAAN" .. .. .. 3·25 7·50
37 6 c. dull purple and blue .. .. 3·50 6·00
a. "KETAHKOTAAN" .. .. .. 5·00 7·50
38 $1 green and carmine .. .. .. 45·00 £100
a. "KETAHKOTAAN" .. .. .. 30·00 £140
32/8 .. .. *Set of* 7 50·00 £110
32a/8a .. .. *Set of* 7 50·00 £160

Stamps overprinted "KETAHKOTAAN" (= We mourn) come from the first overprinting. The overprint was subsequently changed to the intended "KEMAHKOTAAN" (= Coronation), but both were issued together some months after the Coronation of Sultan Ibrahim had taken place.

24 Sultan Ibrahim 25

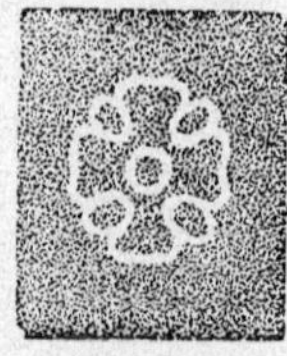

26 27

1896 (26 Aug)–**99**. *W* **27**. *P* 14.
39 **24** 1 c. green 80 55
40 2 c. green and blue 50 30
41 3 c. green and purple .. .. .. 3·25 2·00
a. Green and dull claret .. .. 3·25 2·00
42 4 c. green and carmine 50 70
43 4 c. yellow and red (1899) .. .. 1·00 75
44 5 c. green and brown .. .. .. 1·50 1·60
45 6 c. green and yellow .. .. .. 1·50 2·75
46 **25** 10 c. green and black (1898) .. .. 7·00 45·00
47 25 c. green and mauve (1898) .. .. 9·00 40·00
48 50 c. green and carmine (1898) .. .. 15·00 42·00
49 **24** $1 dull purple and green (1898) .. 28·00 70·00
50 **26** $2 dull purple and carmine (1898) .. 30·00 75·00
51 $3 dull purple and blue (1898) .. 30·00 £100
52 $4 dull purple and brown (1898) .. 30·00 80·00
53 $5 dull purple and yellow (1898) .. 65·00 £120
39/53 .. .. *Set of* 15 £200 £500

3 cents. (28) 10 cents. (29)

1903 (Apr). *Surch with T* **28** *or* **29**.
54 **24** 3 c. on 4 c. yellow and red .. .. 60 1·10
a. Original value uncancelled .. .. 3·75 16·00
55 10 c. on 4 c. green and carmine .. .. 2·50 8·00
a. Tall "1" in "10" (R. 9/12) .. .. 75·00 £120
b. Original value uncancelled .. .. 20·00 65·00
ba. As b, with tall "1" in "10" (R. 9/12) £850 £1100

The bars on these stamps were ruled by hand with pen and ink.

50 Cents. (30) One Dollar (31)

1903 (Oct). *Surch with T* **30** *or* **31**.
56 **26** 50 c. on $3 dull purple and blue .. .. 29·00 80·00
57 $1 on $2 dull purple and carmine .. 60·00 £110
a. "e" of "One" inverted (R. 7/9) .. £1300

10 CENTS. (32)

1904. *Surch as T* **32**.
58 **24** 10 c. on 4 c. yellow and red (Apr) .. 20·00 40·00
a. Surcharge double £6500
59 10 c. on 4 c. green and carmine (Aug) .. 9·00 40·00
60 **26** 50 c. on $5 dull purple and yellow (May) 65·00 £150
58/60 .. .. *Set of* 3 85·00 £200

33 34 35 Sultan Sir Ibrahim

1904 (Sept)–**10**. *W* **27**. *Ordinary paper. P* 14.
61 **33** 1 c. dull purple and green .. .. 2·00 40
a. Chalk-surfaced paper (10.10) .. 4·75 6·00
62 2 c. dull purple and orange .. .. 2·50 3·25
a. Chalk-surfaced paper (10.10) .. 6·00 9·00
63 3 c. dull purple and olive-black .. .. 3·75 60
64 4 c. dull purple and carmine .. .. 8·00 3·00
65 5 c. dull purple and sage-green .. .. 2·00 2·75
66 **35** 8 c. dull purple and blue .. .. 4·00 9·00
67 **34** 10 c. dull purple and black .. .. 48·00 11·00
a. Chalk-surfaced paper (1910) .. 70·00 70·00
68 25 c. dull purple and green .. .. 7·50 35·00
69 50 c. dull purple and red .. .. 45·00 15·00
70 **33** $1 green and mauve .. .. .. 13·00 50·00
71 **35** $2 green and carmine .. .. .. 20·00 48·00
72 $3 green and blue .. .. .. 24·00 75·00
73 $4 green and brown .. .. .. 24·00 £100
74 $5 green and orange .. .. .. 38·00 85·00
75 **34** $10 green and black .. .. .. 55·00 £150
76 $50 green and ultramarine £170 £250
77 $100 green and scarlet £325 £475
61/75 .. .. *Set of* 15 £275 £500

1910–19. *Wmk Mult Rosettes (vertical). Chalk-surfaced paper. P* 14.
78 **33** 1 c. dull purple and green (1912) .. 85 15
79 2 c. dull purple and orange (1912) .. 5·50 65
80 3 c. dull purple and olive-black (1912) .. 8·00 65
a. Wmk horizontal (1910) .. .. 10·00 17·00
81 4 c. dull purple and carmine (1912) .. 7·00 1·00
a. Wmk horizontal (1910) .. .. 20·00 45·00
82 5 c. dull purple and sage-green (1912) .. 4·00 1·50
83 **35** 8 c. dull purple and blue (1912) .. .. 4·00 5·50
84 **34** 10 c. dull purple and black (1912) .. 48·00 3·00
a. Wmk horizontal (1911) .. .. 23·00 60·00
85 25 c. dull purple and green (1912) .. 8·00 30·00
86 50 c. dull purple and red (1919) .. .. 50·00 £110
87 **33** $1 green and mauve (1918) .. .. 80·00 95·00
78/87 .. .. *Set of* 10 £170 £225

3 CENTS.

(36)

37 Sultan Sir Ibrahim and Sultana

1912 (Mar). *No.* 66 *surch with T* **36**.
88 3 c. on 8 c. dull purple and blue .. .. 2·75 6·00
a. "T" of "CENTS" omitted £1200
b. Bars double .. ..

No. 88b shows the bars printed twice with the upper pair partly erased.

1918–20. *Wmk Mult Crown CA. Chalk-surfaced paper.*
89 **33** 2 c. dull purple and green (1919) .. 50
w. Wmk inverted .. .. .. †
90 2 c. purple and orange (1919) .. 70
91 4 c. dull purple and red .. .. 1·00
92 5 c. dull purple and sage-green (1920) 2·00
w. Wmk inverted £130
93 **34** 10 c. dull purple and blue .. .. 2·00
94 21 c. dull purple and orange (1919) .. 2·25
95 25 c. dull purple and green (1920) .. 8·00
96 50 c. dull purple and red (1920) .. 22·00
97 **33** $1 green and mauve .. .. 12·00
98 **35** $2 green and carmine .. .. 21·00
99 $3 green and blue .. .. .. 45·00
100 $4 green and brown .. .. 45·00
101 $5 green and orange .. .. 80·00
102 **34** $10 green and black £180
89/102 .. .. *Set of* 14 £375
89s/102s Optd "Specimen" .. *Set of* 14 £400

1922–40. *Wmk Mult Script CA. Chalk-surfaced paper. P*
103 **33** 1 c. dull purple and black 30
104 2 c. purple and sepia (1924) 85
105 2 c. green (1928) 40
106 3 c. green (1925) .. .. .. 1·75
107 3 c. purple and sepia (1928) .. .. 1·10
108 4 c. purple and carmine (1924) .. 2·50
109 5 c. dull purple and sage-green .. 50
w. Wmk inverted .. .. ..
110 6 c. dull purple and claret 50
111 **34** 10 c. dull purple and blue .. .. 16·00
112 10 c. dull purple and yellow 50
113 **33** 12 c. dull purple and blue .. .. 1·00
114 12 c. ultramarine (1940) .. .. 38·00
115 **34** 21 c. dull purple and orange (1928) .. 2·00
116 25 c. dull purple and myrtle .. .. 2·75
117 **35** 30 c. dull purple and orange (1936) .. 6·00
118 40 c. dull purple and brown (1936) .. 6·00
119 **34** 50 c. dull purple and red .. .. 3·25
120 **33** $1 green and mauve .. .. 3·25
121 **35** $2 green and carmine (1923) .. 6·00
122 $3 green and blue (1925) .. .. 48·00
123 $4 green and brown (1926) .. .. 80·00
w. Wmk inverted
124 $5 green and orange .. .. 55·00
125 **34** $10 green and black (1924) £170
126 $50 green and ultramarine £600
s. Optd "Specimen" £150
127 $100 green and scarlet £1400
s. Optd "Specimen" £250
128 **35** $500 blue and red (1926) £17000
s. Optd "Specimen" £750
103/25 .. .. *Set of* 23 £400
103s/25s Optd or Perf (12 c ultram, 30 c,. 40 c.) "Specimen" .. .. *Set of* 23 £550

It is believed that printings of various values were mad 1941 by Williams, Lea & Co. Ltd. following bomb damage to De La Rue works on 29 December 1940. Of the ten va involved examples of the 10 c. and $2 have been reported use Johore during 1942.

(Recess Waterlow)

1935 (15 May). *50th Anniv of Treaty Relations with G Britain. Wmk Mult Script CA (sideways). P* 12½.
129 **37** 8 c. bright violet and slate .. .. 3·00
s. Perf "Specimen" .. .. .. 42·00

38 Sultan Sir Ibrahim **39**

(Recess D.L.R.)

1940 (Feb). *Wmk Mult Script CA. P* 13½.
130 **38** 8 c. black and pale blue .. .. 15·00
s. Perf "Specimen" .. .. .. 42·00

1948 (1 Dec). *Royal Silver Wedding. As Nos.* 112/13 *Antigua.*
131 10 c. violet 20
132 $5 green .. .. 24·00 35·

1949 (2 May)–**55**. *Wmk Mult Script CA. Chalk-surfaced pap P* 17½ × 18.
133 **39** 1 c. black 50
134 2 c. orange 20
a. Orange-yellow (22.1.52) 50
135 3 c. green 50
a. Yellow-green (22.1.52) .. .. 10·00
136 4 c. brown 30
136*a* 5 c. bright purple (1.9.52) 30
137 6 c. grey 30
a. Pale grey (22.1.52) 50
ac. Error. St. Edward's Crown W **9***b* .. £1200
138 8 c. scarlet .. .. 3·25
138*a* 8 c. green (1.9.52) .. .. .. 3·50
139 10 c. magenta 60
aa. Imperf (pair) £1700
139*a* 12 c. scarlet (1.9.52) .. .. .. 3·50
140 15 c. ultramarine .. .. .. 2·75
141 20 c. black and green 50
141*a* 20 c. bright blue (1.9.52) .. .. 1·00
142 25 c. purple and orange .. .. .. 1·00
142*a* 30 c. scarlet and purple (5.9.55) .. 1·75
142*b* 35 c. scarlet and purple (1.9.52) .. 4·00
143 40 c. red and purple .. .. .. 4·00
144 50 c. black and blue .. .. .. 2·00
145 $1 blue and purple .. .. .. 4·50
146 $2 green and scarlet .. .. .. 14·00
147 $5 green and brown .. .. .. 40·00
133/47 .. .. *Set of* 21 75·00 35·

[1949 (1]0 Oct). *75th Anniv of U.P.U. As Nos. 114/17 of Antigua.*
10 c. purple 30 20
15 c. deep blue 1·25 1·00
25 c. orange 65 2·50
50 c. blue-black 1·25 5·50
Set of 4 3·00 5·50

STAMP BOOKLETS

Black on white card. Interleaved with tissue. Stapled.
$2 booklet containing ten 1 c. and 2 c. (Nos. 103, 105), twenty 4 c. (No. 108), each in blocks of 10 and eighteen 5 c. (No. 109) in blocks of 6

Black on pink cover. Stapled.
$1 booklet containing 2 c., 3 c. and 5 c. (Nos. 105, 107, 109) in blocks of 10

Black on buff cover. Stapled.
$1 booklet containing ten 1 c. and 5 c. (Nos. 103, 109) and twenty 2 c. (Nos. 105) in blocks of 10

POSTAGE DUE STAMPS

D 1

(Typo Waterlow)

[1938 (]1 Jan). *Wmk Mult Script CA. P 12½.*
D 1 1 c. carmine 12·00 38·00
4 c. green 40·00 40·00
8 c. orange 48·00 £140
10 c. brown 48·00 48·00
12 c. purple 55·00 £130
Set of 5 £180 £350
[D1s/5]s Perf "Specimen" *Set of 5* £130

KEDAH

[Su]zerainty over Kedah was transferred by Thailand to Great [Brit]ain on 15 July 1909. A Treaty of Friendship between Great [Brit]ain and Kedah was signed on 1 November 1923.
[Th]e state joined the Federation of Malaya on 1 February [1948].

For stamps of THAILAND used in Kedah between 1887 [an]d 1909 see SIAMESE POSTS IN NORTHERN [M]ALAYA section.
Issues of the FEDERATED MALAY STATES were used [in] Kedah from 16 July 1909 until 15 June 1912.

PRICES FOR STAMPS ON COVER TO 1945

Nos. 1/14	*from* × 15
Nos. 15/23	*from* × 10
Nos. 24/40	*from* × 8
Nos. 41/8	*from* × 12
Nos. 49/51	—
Nos. 52/9	*from* × 4
Nos. 60/8	*from* × 3
Nos. 68*a*/9	*from* × 4

1 Sheaf of Rice

2 Malay ploughing

3 Council Chamber, Alor Star

(Recess D.L.R.)

[19]12 (16 June). *Wmk Mult Crown CA (sideways* on 10 c. to $5). P 14.*
1 1 1 c. black and green 60 25
2 3 c. black and red 3·50 30
3 4 c. rose and grey 10·00 25
4 5 c. green and chestnut 2·25 3·00
5 8 c. black and ultramarine 3·25 3·50
6 2 10 c. blue and sepia 1·75 90
w. Wmk Crown to left of CA † —
7 20 c. black and green 4·25 4·00
x. Wmk reversed £130
8 30 c. black and rose 2·50 11·00
9 40 c. black and purple 3·50 14·00
10 50 c. brown and blue 9·00 13·00
11 3 $1 black and red/*yellow* 14·00 19·00
w. Wmk Crown to left of CA 38·00
x. Wmk reversed £200
y. Wmk Crown to left of CA and reversed

12 3 $2 green and brown 20·00 85·00
13 $3 black and blue/*blue* 65·00 £160
a. "A" of "CA" missing from wmk £1200
14 $5 black and red 65·00 £150
1/14 *Set of 14* £180 £425
1s/14s Optd "Specimen" *Set of 14* £300

*The normal sideways watermark shows the Crown to right of CA, *as seen from the back of the stamp.*

Due to an increase in postal rates 1 c. and 4 c. stamps of STRAITS SETTLEMENTS were used in Kedah for some months from March 1919.

(i)

(ii)

DOUBLE AND SINGLE PLATES. (i) Printed from separate plates for frame and centre, with dotted shading extending close to the central sheaf. Soft impression of centre with little clear detail.
(ii) Printed from single plate, with white space around sheaf. Centre more deeply etched with sharp image.

1919 (June)–**21**. *New colours and values. Wmk Mult Crown CA (sideways* on 21 c., 25 c.). P 14.*
15 1 1 c. brown (i) (18.8.19) 55 50
w. Wmk inverted 80·00
y. Wmk inverted and reversed † £180
18 2 c. green (ii) 50 20
19 3 c. deep purple (i) (1920) 65 80
x. Wmk reversed
y. Wmk inverted and reversed 70·00 90·00
20 4 c. rose (i) 3·25 20
21 4 c. red (ii) (18.8.19) 3·25 65
w. Wmk inverted
22 2 21 c. mauve and purple (18.8.19) 5·50 55·00
w. Wmk Crown to left of CA £100
x. Wmk reversed
y. Wmk Crown to left of CA and reversed £180
23 25 c. blue and purple (1921) 1·75 22·00
a. "A" of "CA" missing from wmk £400
15/23 *Set of 6* 10·50 70·00
15s/23s Optd "Specimen" *Set of 6* £140

*The normal sideways watermark shows Crown to right of CA, *as seen from the back of the stamp.*

(4) (5)

(Surch by Ribeiro & Co, Penang)

1919 (Mar). *Surch as T 4.*
24 3 50 c. on $2 green and brown 60·00 70·00
a. "C" of "CENTS" inserted by handstamp (R. 6/4) £1100 £1200
25 $1 on $3 black and blue/*blue* 20·00 90·00

Nos. 24/5 were surcharged from settings of 30 (5×6).

Two types of centre plate for Type 2 wmkd Mult Script CA:

Type I (Plate 1) (produced by electrotyping)

Type II (Plate 2) (produced by transfer die)

A new common centre plate, 2, was prepared from the original die in 1926. Stamps from Plate 2, produced using a transfer die, show considerably more detail of the ground and have the oxen, ploughman's hat and his clothing much more deeply cut as illustrated in Type II above.

1921–32. *Wmk Mult Script CA (sideways* on 10 c. to $5). P 14.*
26 1 1 c. brown (ii) 60 20
w. Wmk inverted † £180
y. Wmk inverted and reversed † £180
27 2 c. dull green (ii) (Type I) 1·25 20
28 3 c. deep purple (ii) 80 70
w. Wmk inverted £225
29 4 c. deep carmine (ii) 5·00 20
30 2 10 c. blue and sepia (I) 2·75 75
ay. Wmk Crown to left of CA and reversed 70·00
b. Type II (*wmk Crown to left of CA*) (1927) 38·00 3·25
by. Wmk Crown to right of CA and reversed £275 £180
31 20 c. black and yellow-green (I) 4·00 2·00
32 21 c. mauve and purple (I) 2·00 13·00
33 25 c. blue and purple (I) 2·25 7·50
a. Type II (*wmk Crown to left of CA*) (1932) 60·00 4·00
34 30 c. black and rose (I) (1922) 3·00 8·50
a. Type II (*wmk Crown to left of CA*) (1927) 35·00 3·00
35 40 c. black and purple (I) 4·25 45·00
aw. Wmk Crown to left of CA (1924) 27·00 40·00
b. Type II (*wmk Crown to left of CA*) (1932) 60·00 20·00
36 50 c. brown and grey-blue (I) 2·25 12·00
aw. Wmk Crown to left of CA (1924) 25·00 15·00
b. Type II (*wmk Crown to left of CA*) (1932) 70·00 5·50
37 3 $1 black and red/*yellow* (1924) 60·00 65·00
w. Wmk Crown to left of CA 6·50 8·00
38 $2 myrtle and brown 13·00 95·00
w. Wmk Crown to left of CA (1924) 25·00 85·00
39 $3 black and blue/*blue* 65·00 90·00
w. Wmk Crown to left of CA (1924) 80·00 80·00
40 $5 black and deep carmine 75·00 £150
w. Wmk Crown to left of CA (1926) 85·00 £150
26/40 *Set of 15* £170 £350
26s/40s Optd "Specimen" *Set of 15* £300

*The normal sideways watermark shows Crown to right of CA, *as seen from the back of the stamp.*

Nos. 26/40 were produced by De La Rue using the "wet" method of recess-printing during which the stamps contracted when they were dried before gumming. From 1933 the firm adopted the "dry" method, using pre-gummed paper, with the result that stamps were up to 0.5 mm larger in size. Of the low values as Type **1** in this series only the 2 c. was still current when the "dry" method was introduced.

Stamps as Type **1** can be found perforated either comb or line. The 1 c. and 4 c. come comb only, the 3 c. line only and the 2 c. either way.

Examples of Nos. 37/40 are known with part strikes of a forged Sungei Patang postmark dated "14 JY 1920".

For the 2 c. Type II see No. 69.

OVERPRINT SETTINGS FOR NOS. 41/51. The low values in Type **1** were overprinted using Setting II as detailed under Straits Settlements. The three listed constant varieties from the original typeset block of 12 occur in the same positions for these Kedah stamps as does the No Stop variety from R. 1/5 of the left pane.

For the higher values in Type **2**, which were in sheets of 60 (5×12), a further setting was prepared using the first four vertical rows of the typeset block with each horizontal row completed by a single random impression of the overprint. This means that, in addition to their positions in the truncated typeset block, the Oval last "O" additionally occurs on R. 11/5 and the Raised stop on R. 5/5 of the sheet. In this setting, as for the low values, "BORNEO" was 14 mm long.

Further supplies were subsequently required of the 21, 25 and 50 c. values and these were produced using a completely different setting of 20 (5×4), applied three times to each sheet, on which "BORNEO" was 15–15½ mm long.

1922 (Apr). *Malaya-Borneo Exhibition, Singapore. Optd as T 5 at Singapore.*

I. "BORNEO" 14 *mm long*

(*a*) *Wmk Mult Crown CA (Nos. 10, 18 and 22/3)*
41 1 2 c. green (ii) 3·50 22·00
b. Oval last "O" in "BORNEO" 7·50 40·00
c. Raised stop after "EXHIBITION" 7·50 40·00
d. Small second "A" in "MALAYA" 7·50 40·00
f. No stop 32·00
42 2 21 c. mauve and purple 25·00 80·00
b. Oval last "O" in "BORNEO" 45·00 £120
c. Raised stop after "EXHIBITION" 45·00 £120
43 25 c. blue and purple 25·00 80·00
a. Opt inverted £950
b. Oval last "O" in "BORNEO" 45·00 £120
c. Raised stop after "EXHIBITION" 45·00 £120
44 50 c. brown and blue 25·00 95·00
b. Oval last "O" in "BORNEO" 45·00 £140
c. Raised stop after "EXHIBITION" 45·00 £140

(*b*) *Wmk Mult Script CA (Nos. 26 and 28/30)*
45 1 1 c. brown (ii) 2·75 15·00
b. Oval last "O" in "BORNEO" 6·00 26·00
c. Raised stop after "EXHIBITION" 6·00 26·00
d. Small second "A" in "MALAYA" 6·00 26·00
f. No stop 27·00
46 3 c. deep purple (ii) 3·00 38·00
b. Oval last "O" in "BORNEO" 6·50 60·00
c. Raised stop after "EXHIBITION" 6·50 60·00
d. Small second "A" in "MALAYA" 6·50 60·00
f. No stop 30·00
47 4 c. deep carmine (ii) 3·00 25·00
b. Oval last "O" in "BORNEO" 6·50 42·00
c. Raised stop after "EXHIBITION" 6·50 42·00
d. Small second "A" in "MALAYA" 6·50 42·00
f. No stop 30·00
48 2 10 c. blue and sepia (I) 4·50 40·00
b. Oval last "O" in "BORNEO" 9·00 65·00
c. Raised stop after "EXHIBITION" 9·00 65·00
41/8 *Set of 8* 80·00 £350

II. "BORNEO" 15–15½ *mm long. Wmk Mult Crown CA (Nos. 10 and 22/3)*
49 2 21 c. mauve and purple 21·00 95·00
50 25 c. blue and purple 22·00 £110
51 50 c. brown and blue 48·00 £160
49/51 *Set of 3* 80·00 £325

Examples of all values are known with part strikes of the forged postmark mentioned after Nos. 26/40.

1922–40. *New colours, etc. Wmk Mult Script CA* (*sideways* on 12, 35 c.*). *P* 14.
52 **1** 1 c. black (ii) (Type I) 50 10
53 3 c. green (ii) (1924) .. .. .. 1·75 90
54 4 c. violet (ii) (1926) .. .. .. 1·00 10
55 5 c. yellow (ii) .. .. 1·50 10
w. Wmk inverted .. .. .. 75·00
x. Wmk reversed .. .. .. † £150
y. Wmk inverted and reversed .. † £150
56 6 c. carmine (ii) (1926) .. .. .. 1·25 65
a. Carmine-red (1940) .. .. 12·00 48·00
57 8 c. grey-black (ii) (10.36) .. .. 10·00 10
58 **2** 12 c. black and indigo (II) (1926) .. 2·75 4·00
59 35 c. purple (II) (1926) .. .. 5·50 26·00
52/9 .. .. *Set of* 8 22·00 28·00
52s/9s Optd or Perf (8 c.) "Specimen" .. *Set of* 8 £200

*The normal sideways watermark shows Crown to left of CA, *as seen from the back of the stamp.*

With the exception of the 6 c. and 8 c. the printing plates for the Type **1** values listed above were, as for the previous issue, produced by electrotyping with the face values added to the plates by pantograph. The plates for the 6 c. and 8 c. values were constructed by the more modern method of using a transfer die to enter each impression.

Printings after November 1933 were normally produced by the "dry" method as described beneath Nos. 26/40. There were late "wet" printings of the 1 c. (No. 68*a*) and 2 c. (No. 27) in August 1938. The 3 c. only exists from a "wet" printing, the 6 c. (No. 56*a*) and 8 c. from dry printings and the remainder from either method.

Stamps as Type **1** can be found perforated either comb or line. The 3 c. and 6 c. (No. 56) come comb only, the 6 c. (No. 56*a*) and 8 c. line only and the 1, 4 and 5 c. either way.

For the 1 c. Type II see No. 68*a*.

6 Sultan Abdul Hamid Halimshah

(Recess Waterlow)

1937 (30 June). *Wmk Mult Script CA. P* 12½.
60 **6** 10 c. ultramarine and sepia .. .. 4·00 1·00
61 12 c. black and violet .. .. 32·00 12·00
a. "A" of "CA" missing from wmk ..
62 25 c. ultramarine and purple .. .. 7·50 4·50
63 30 c. green and scarlet .. .. 8·00 10·00
64 40 c. black and purple .. .. 4·00 16·00
65 50 c. brown and blue .. .. 6·00 4·50
66 $1 black and green .. .. 4·00 10·00
67 $2 green and brown .. .. £120 80·00
68 $5 black and scarlet .. .. 32·00 £150
60/8 .. .. .. *Set of* 9 £190 £250
60s/8s Perf "Specimen" .. .. *Set of* 9 £200

I II I II

1938 (May)–**40.** *As Nos. 52 and 27, but face values redrawn as Types* II.
68*a* **1** 1 c. black .. .. 90·00 3·00
69 2 c. bright green (1940) .. .. .. £180 6·50

1 c. Type II. Figures "1" have square-cut corners instead of rounded, and larger top serif. Larger "C". Line perf. Produced from a new electrotyped Plate 2 with different engraved face values. Printings exist from either the "wet" or "dry" methods.

2 c. Type II. Figures "2" have circular instead of oval drops and the letters "c" are thin and tall instead of thick and rounded. Produced from a new plate, made from a transfer die, and printed by the "dry" method.

1948 (1 Dec). *Royal Silver Wedding. As Nos.* 112/13 *of Antigua.*
70 10 c. violet 20 20
71 $5 carmine .. .. 25·00 32·00

1949 (10 Oct). *75th Anniv of U.P.U. As Nos.* 114/17 *of Antigua.*
72 10 c. purple 25 30
73 15 c. deep blue .. .. 1·50 1·50
74 25 c. orange .. .. 65 1·50
75 50 c. blue-black .. .. .. 1·00 2·25
72/5 .. .. *Set of* 4 3·00 5·00

7 Sheaf of Rice

8 Sultan Badlishah

1950 (1 June)–**55.** *Wmk Mult Script CA. Chalk-surfaced paper. P* 17½ × 18.
76 **7** 1 c. black 50 30
77 2 c. orange 50 15
78 3 c. green .. .. 2·00 1·00
79 4 c. brown 75 10
79*a* 5 c. bright purple (1.9.52) .. .. 1·25 2·00
ab. Bright mauve (24.9.53) .. .. 1·25 1·00
80 6 c. grey 70 15
81 8 c. scarlet .. .. 1·75 2·50
81*a* 8 c. green (1.9.52) .. .. .. 1·00 1·75
ab. Deep green (24.9.53) .. .. 10·00 9·50
82 **7** 10 c. magenta 70 10
82*a* 12 c. scarlet (1.9.52) .. .. .. 85 2·50
83 15 c. ultramarine .. .. .. 1·25 35
84 20 c. black and green .. .. .. 1·25 2·50
84*a* 20 c. bright blue (1.9.52) .. .. .. 1·00 10
85 **8** 25 c. purple and orange .. .. .. 1·50 30
85*a* 30 c. scarlet and purple (5.9.55) .. .. 2·00 1·25
85*b* 35 c. scarlet and purple (1.9.52) .. .. 1·00 1·50
86 40 c. red and purple .. .. .. 2·75 6·00
87 50 c. black and blue .. .. .. 2·25 35
88 $1 blue and purple .. .. .. 3·00 3·50
89 $2 green and scarlet .. .. .. 20·00 23·00
90 $5 green and brown .. .. .. 42·00 38·00
76/90 .. .. *Set of* 21 75·00 75·00

KELANTAN

Suzerainty over Kelantan was transferred by Thailand to Great Britain on 15 July 1909. A British adviser was appointed in 1923.

The state joined the Federation of Malaya on 1 February 1948.

For stamps of THAILAND used in Kelantan between 1895 and 1909 see SIAMESE POSTS IN NORTHERN MALAYA section.

From 1909 until the introduction of Kelantan stamps in 1911 the issues of the FEDERATED MALAY STATES to $2 were in use.

PRICES FOR STAMPS ON COVER TO 1945

Nos. 1/11	*from* × 30
No. 12	—
Nos. 14/23	*from* × 30
Nos. 30/8	*from* × 15
Nos. 39/*a*	*from* × 10
Nos. 40/8	*from* × 30
Nos. 49/52	*from* × 20
No. 53	*from* × 3
No. 54	—

1

MALAYA
BORNEO
EXHIBITION
(2)

1911 (Jan)–**15.** *Wmk Mult Crown CA. Ordinary paper* (1 *c. to* 10 *c.*) *or chalk-surfaced paper* (30 *c. to* $25). *P* 14.
1 **1** 1 c. yellow-green .. .. .. 4·00 90
a. Blue-green .. .. .. 3·50 30
2 3 c. red .. .. 4·00 15
3 4 c. black and red .. .. .. 1·50 15
4 5 c. green and red/*yellow* .. .. 9·00 85
w. Wmk inverted .. .. .. † £400
5 8 c. ultramarine .. .. .. 5·50 1·00
6 10 c. black and mauve .. .. .. 30·00 75
7 30 c. dull purple and red .. .. .. 10·00 2·50
a. Purple and carmine .. .. 27·00 14·00
8 50 c. black and orange .. .. .. 7·50 2·50
9 $1 green and emerald .. .. .. 45·00 48·00
9*a* $1 green and brown (5.15) .. .. 40·00 2·00
10 $2 green and carmine .. .. .. 1·50 4·00
11 $5 green and blue .. .. .. 4·00 7·50
12 $25 green and orange .. .. .. 40·00 80·00
1/12 .. .. .. *Set of* 13 £180 £130
1s/12s Optd "Specimen" .. .. *Set of* 13 £275

1921 (5 May)–**28.** *Wmk Mult Script CA. Ordinary paper* (1 *c. to* 10 *c.*) *or chalk-surfaced paper* (30 *c. to* $1). *P* 14.
14 **1** 1 c. dull green (7.21) .. .. .. 4·25 60
15 1 c. black (24.2.23) 50 50
16 2 c. brown (29.7.22) .. .. .. 5·50 3·75
16*a* 2 c. green (24.7.26) .. .. .. 2·50 40
16*b* 3 c. brown (5.3.27) .. .. .. 3·75 1·00
ba. "C" of "CA" missing from wmk ..
17 4 c. black and red (15.7.22) .. .. 1·75 10
18 5 c. green and red/*pale yellow* (12.22) .. 1·00 10
19 6 c. claret (29.7.22) .. .. .. 3·00 1·50
19*a* 6 c. scarlet (26.5.28) .. .. .. 4·00 5·50
20 10 c. black and mauve .. .. .. 2·50 10
21 30 c. purple and carmine (24.7.26) .. 4·00 5·50
22 50 c. black and orange (21.3.25) .. .. 6·50 45·00
23 $1 green and brown (9.2.24) .. .. 28·00 75·00
14/23 .. .. .. *Set of* 13 60·00 £120
14s/23s Optd "Specimen" .. .. *Set of* 13 £350

Examples of Nos. 22/3 are known showing part strikes of a forged Kota Bharu postmark dated "27 JUL 11".

For the 4 c., 5 c. and 6 c. surcharged, see issues under "Japanese Occupation".

OVERPRINT SETTINGS FOR NOS. 30/8. All values were overprinted using a triplet of three slightly different types. It is not known if this was applied to the sheets three stamps at a time or if a forme to overprint a pane of 60 was constructed from it.

On the normal setting "MALAYA" is 14 mm long. The 5 c. only is also known with "MALAYA" 15 mm from a different triplet setting. It has been suggested that this was a trial overprint on one sheet which was subsequently included in postal stocks.

1922 (31 Mar). *Malaya–Borneo Exhibition, Singapore. Optd with T* **2** ("MALAYA" 14 *mm long*) *by Govt Survey Office, Khota Bharu.*

(*a*) *Wmk Mult Crown CA*
30 **1** 4 c. black and red .. .. .. 4·00 42·00
a. Opt double £2500
31 5 c. green and red/*pale yellow* .. .. 4·75 42·00
a. "MALAYA" 15 mm long .. ..
32 30 c. dull purple and red .. .. .. 4·75 60·00
33 **1** 50 c. black and orange .. .. .. 7·50
34 $1 green and brown .. .. .. 25·00
35 $2 green and carmine .. .. .. 55·00
36 $5 green and blue £150

(*b*) *Wmk Mult Script CA*
37 **1** 1 c. green .. .. 2·75
a. Opt double £2500
38 10 c. black and mauve .. .. .. 5·00
30/8 .. .. *Set of* 9 £225

Nos. 30a and 37a show all three lines of the overprint c

Examples of all values are known showing part strikes forged postmark mentioned below Nos. 14/23.

3 Sultan Ismail **4**

(Recess Harrison (No. 39) or D.L.R. (No. 39a))

1928–35. *Wmk Mult Script CA. P* 12.
39 **3** $1 blue .. .. 11·00
a. Perf 14 (1935) .. .. .. 35·00
s. Perf "Specimen" .. .. .. 65·00

(Recess B.W.)

1937 (July)–**40.** *Wmk Mult Script CA. P* 12.
40 **4** 1 c. grey-olive and yellow 50
41 2 c. green .. .. 3·25
42 4 c. scarlet .. .. 5·50
43 5 c. red-brown .. .. 4·75
44 6 c. lake (10.37) .. .. .. 11·00
45 8 c. grey-olive .. .. 4·75
46 10 c. purple (10.37) .. .. .. 22·00
47 12 c. blue .. .. 3·50
48 25 c. vermilion and violet .. .. .. 5·00
49 30 c. violet and scarlet (10.37) .. .. 40·00
50 40 c. orange and blue-green .. .. 8·50
51 50 c. grey-olive and orange (10.37) .. 60·00
52 $1 violet and blue-green (10.37) .. 48·00
53 $2 red-brown and scarlet (3.40) .. £190
54 $5 vermilion and lake (3.40) £350
40/54 .. .. .. *Set of* 15 £700
40s/54s Perf "Specimen" .. .. *Set of* 15 £400

For above issue surcharged see issues under "Japa Occupation".

1948 (1 Dec). *Royal Silver Wedding. As Nos.* 112/1 *Antigua.*
55 10 c. violet 60
56 $5 carmine .. .. 24·00 4

1949 (10 Oct). *75th Anniv of U.P.U. As Nos.* 114/17 *of Anti*
57 10 c. purple 25
58 15 c. deep blue .. .. 1·50
59 25 c. orange 40
60 50 c. blue-black 60
57/60 .. .. *Set of* 4 2·50

Due to the exhaustion of certain B.M.A. values th stamps of PERAK were used in Kelantan from Novembe 1950 until the issue of Nos. 61/81.

5 Sultan Ibrahim

Normal No. 62a
Tiny stop (R. 1/2)

1951 (11 July)–**55.** *Chalk-surfaced paper. Wmk Mult Sc CA. P* 17½ × 18.
61 **5** 1 c. black 50
62 2 c. orange .. .. 1·25
a. Tiny stop .. .. 25·00
b. Orange-yellow (11.5.55) .. .. 3·00 1
63 3 c. green .. .. 4·00 1
64 4 c. brown 75
65 5 c. bright purple (1.9.52) 75
a. Bright mauve (9.12.53) .. .. 2·25
66 6 c. grey 75
67 8 c. scarlet .. .. 2·00 3
68 8 c. green (1.9.52) 75 1
69 10 c. magenta 50
70 12 c. scarlet (1.9.52) .. .. .. 1·50 2
71 15 c. ultramarine .. .. 4·00
72 20 c. black and green 50 6
73 20 c. bright blue (1.9.52) 80
74 25 c. purple and orange .. .. .. 1·50
75 30 c. scarlet and purple (5.9.55) .. .. 1·25 1·
76 35 c. scarlet and purple (1.9.52) .. .. 90 1·
77 40 c. red and purple .. .. .. 7·00 13
78 50 c. black and blue .. .. .. 3·00
79 $1 blue and purple .. .. .. 7·50 4
80 $2 green and scarlet .. .. .. 24·00 23·
81 $5 green and brown .. .. .. 48·00 40·
a. Green and sepia (8.12.53) .. .. 85·00 90·
61/81 .. .. *Set of* 21 £100 85·

STAMP BOOKLETS

(June). *Black on white* (*No.* SB1) *or black on grey* (*No.* 2) *covers. Stapled.*
36 c. booklet containing thirty-six 1 c. (No. 15) in blocks of 6 .. .. £2250
96 c. booklet containing twenty-four 4 c. (No. 17) in blocks of 6 .. .. £2250

(Dec). *Black on white* (*No.* SB3) *or on grey* (*No.* SB4) *ers. Stapled.*
40 c. booklet containing forty 1 c. (No. 15) in blocks of 10 .. .. £2250
80 c. booklet containing twenty 4 c. (No. 17) in blocks of 10 .. .. £2250

MALACCA

ne of the Straits Settlements which joined the Federation of aya on 1 February 1948.

8 (1 Dec). *Royal Silver Wedding. As Nos.* 112/13 *of ntigua.*
10 c. violet .. .. 30 1·50
$5 brown .. .. 26·00 35·00

9 (1 Mar)–**52**. *As T* **58** *of Straits Settlements, but inscr* MALACCA" *at foot. Wmk Mult Script CA. Chalk-surfaced per. P* 17½ × 18.
1 c. black 30 70
2 c. orange 80 45
3 c. green .. .. 30 1·75
4 c. brown 30 10
5 c. bright purple (1.9.52) .. .. .. 60 1·50
6 c. grey 75 85
8 c. scarlet .. .. 75 5·50
8 c. green (1.9.52) .. .. 85 4·50
10 c. purple 30 10
12 c. scarlet (1.9.52) .. .. 1·00 4·75
15 c. ultramarine .. .. 1·50 60
20 c. black and green .. .. 50 6·00
20 c. bright blue (1.9.52) .. .. .. 2·50 2·50
25 c. purple and orange 50 70
35 c. scarlet and purple (1.9.52) .. .. 1·00 3·00
40 c. red and purple .. .. 1·25 11·00
50 c. black and blue .. .. 1·00 1·25
$1 blue and purple .. .. 8·00 19·00
$2 green and scarlet .. .. 20·00 21·00
$5 green and brown .. .. 42·00 35·00
7 .. .. *Set of* 20 70·00 £110

9 (10 Oct). *75th Anniv of U.P.U. As Nos.* 114/17 *of Antigua.*
10 c. purple 20 50
15 c. deep blue .. .. 1·40 1·75
25 c. orange .. .. 30 3·75
50 c. blue-black .. .. 60 4·00
21 .. .. *Set of* 4 2·25 9·00

NEGRI SEMBILAN

A federation of smaller states reconstituted in 1886. Sungei ong, taken under British protection in 1874, was absorbed to Negri Sembilan by Treaty of 8 August 1895. The Negri mbilan federation joined the Federated Malay States in 1896.

A. SUNGEI UJONG

Until 1 January 1899, when the Federated Malay States joined the U.P.U., mail for addresses outside Malaya was franked with the stamps of the STRAITS SETTLEMENTS.

PRICES FOR STAMPS ON COVER	
Nos. 1/14	—
Nos. 15/27	*from* × 25
Nos. 28/36	*from* × 8
Nos. 37/49	*from* × 10
Nos. 50/5	*from* × 25

(1)

878. *No.* 11 *of Straits Settlements handstamped with T* **1**.
2 c. brown £1900 £2250
This overprint on India No. 54 is bogus.

SUNGEI (2) (Narrow letters) SUNGEI (3) ("N" wide) SUNGEI (4) ("S" wide)

UJONG (5) ("N" wide) UJONG (6) (Narrow letters, "UJ" close together) UJONG (7) Narrow letters, evenly spaced)

1881. *No.* 11 *of Straits Settlements optd with T* **2/7**.
2 **2+5** 2 c. brown £3250 £2500
3 **3+5** 2 c. brown £2000 £1700
4 **2+6** 2 c. brown £225
a. Opt Type **6** double £1500
5 **4+6** 2 c. brown £700
6 **2+7** 2 c. brown £325

The two lines of this surcharge were applied as separate operations. On Nos. 2/3 "SUNGEI" was printed as a triplet, probably 2+3+3, "UJONG" being added by a single unit handstamp. Nos. 4 and 5 come from a similar triplet, 4+4+5, completed by another single unit handstamp. No. 6 comes from a single type triplet with the second line added as a triplet instead of by a single unit handstamp.

The 10 c. slate overprinted Types **2** + **7** is bogus.

SUNGEI (**8**) ("N" and "E" wide) SUNGEI (**9**) ("SUN" and "E" wide) SUNGEI (**10**) ("SUN" wide)

SUNGEI (**11**) ("S" wide) SUNGEI (**12**) (Narrow letters)

UJONG (**13**) ("U" and "NG" wide) UJONG (**14**) (Narrow letters)

1881. *No.* 11 *of Straits Settlements optd with T* **8/14**.
7 **8+13** 2 c. brown £200
8 **9+13** 2 c. brown £225
9 **10+13** 2 c. brown £200
10 **11+14** 2 c. brown £225
a. "S" inverted £2750
11 **12+14** 2 c. brown £150

Nos. 7/11 also had the two lines of the overprint applied at separate operations. "SUNGEI" as a triplet, either 7+8+9 or 10+11+11, and "UJONG" as a single unit.

S.U.
(**15**)

1882. *Nos.* 50/1 *of Straits Settlements optd as T* **15**.
12 2 c. brown (with stops) £250
13 2 c. brown (without stops) £250 £300
14 4 c. rose (with stops) £2500 £2500

Each of the above was applied by a triplet setting.

Examples of Straits Settlements No. 11 with a similar overprint, including stops, are trials which were not issued.

SUNGEI (**16**) ("S" and "E" wide) SUNGEI (**17**) ("E" wide) UJONG (**18**) ("N" wide)

1882 (Dec)–**84**. *Nos.* 12, 50, 52/3 *and* 63 *of Straits Settlements optd with T* **11/12**, **14** *and* **16/18**.
15 **12+14** 2 c. brown £500 £325
16 **11+14** 2 c. brown £750 £450
17 **12+14** 2 c. pale rose (1884) £160 £180
18 **11+14** 2 c. pale rose (1884) £160 £180
a. Opt Type **14** double .. ..
19 **16+14** 2 c. pale rose (1884) .. .. 90·00 £100
20 **17+14** 2 c. pale rose (1884) £100 £120
21 **12+18** 2 c. pale rose (1884) £100 £120
a. Opt Type **18** double £750
22 **12+14** 4 c. rose £1100 £1200
23 **11+14** 4 c. rose £1900 £2000
24 **12+14** 8 c. orange £1300 £1000
25 **11+14** 8 c. orange £2250 £1700
26 **12+14** 10 c. slate £450 £450
27 **11+14** 10 c. slate £700 £700

Nos. 15/27 had the two lines of the overprint applied by separate triplets. Settings so far identified are Nos. 15+16+15, 17+18+19, 19+20+21, 22+23+22, 24+25+24 and 26+27+26.

The 4 c. rose overprinted Types **16** + **14** is now believed to be a trial.

UJONG. (**19**) (With stop. Narrow letters) UJONG. (**20**) (With stop "N" wide) UJONG (**21**) (Without stop. Narrow letters)

1883–84. *Nos.* 50 *and* 63/4 *of Straits Settlements optd with T* **12**, **16/17** *and* **19/21**.
28 **12+19** 2 c. brown .. .. 42·00 95·00
29 **16+19** 2 c. brown .. .. 42·00 95·00
30 **12+20** 2 c. brown .. .. 42·00 95·00
31 **16+21** 2 c. pale rose (1884) .. .. 85·00 90·00
32 **17+21** 2 c. pale rose (1884) .. .. 85·00 90·00
33 **12+21** 2 c. pale rose (1884) .. .. 85·00 90·00
34 **16+21** 4 c. brown (1884) £225 £300
a. Opt Type **16** double .. ..
b. Opt Type **21** double £1500
35 **17+21** 4 c. brown (1884) £225 £300
36 **12+21** 4 c. brown (1884) £225 £300
a. Opt Type **21** double £3750

Nos. 28/36 had the two lines of the overprint applied by separate triplets. Settings were Nos. 28+29+30, 31+32+33 and 34+35+36.

The 8 c. orange overprinted Types **12**+**19** is now believed to be a trial (*Price* £750 *unused*).

Sungei Ujong (**22**) SUNGEI UJONG (**23**) SUNGEI UJONG (**24**)

SUNGEI UJONG (**25**) SUNGEI UJONG (**26**) SUNGEI UJONG (**27**)

SUNGEI UJONG (**28**) SUNGEI UJONG. (**29**) SUNGEI UJONG (**30**)

1885–90. *Nos.* 63/*a of Straits Settlements optd with T* **22/30**.
37 **22** 2 c. pale rose .. .. 75·00 85·00
a. Opt double £550 £550
38 **23** 2 c. pale rose .. .. 26·00 60·00
a. Opt double £550
39 **24** 2 c. pale rose (1886) .. .. .. 95·00 £110
40 **25** 2 c. pale rose (1886) £120 £130
a. Opt double .. ..
41 **26** 2 c. pale rose (1886) .. .. .. 75·00 85·00
a. Opt double .. ..
42 **27** 2 c. pale rose (1887) .. .. .. 9·50 27·00
43 **28** 2 c. pale rose (1889) .. .. .. 6·00 9·00
a. Narrow "E" (2 mm wide) (R. 3/4 and 4/3) .. .. 70·00
c. Opt double £1300
d. Bright rose (1890) .. .. .. 8·50 7·50
da. Narrow "E" (2 mm wide) (R. 3/4 and 4/3) .. .. 80·00
db. Antique "N" in "UJONG" (R. 10/6) £120
44 **29** 2 c. pale rose (1889) .. .. .. 85·00 70·00
a. "UNJOG" (R. 7/3) £3750 £2750
45 **30** 2 c. bright rose (1890) .. .. .. 27·00 13·00
a. Antique "G" in "SUNGEI" (R. 6/1) .. £225
b. Antique "G" in "UJONG" (R. 8/3) .. £225
c. Pale rose .. ..

All the above overprints had both lines applied at the same operation. Nos. 37/42 were from different triplet settings. The first printing of Type **28** was from a triplet (No. 43) but this was followed by two further settings of 60 (6×10), the first containing No. 43a and the second Nos. 43*d*/db. Nos. 44/5 were both from settings of 60.

SUNGEI UJONG Two CENTS (**31**) SUNGEI UJONG Two CENTS (**32**) SUNGEI UJONG *Two* CENTS (**33**)

SUNGEI UJONG *Two* CENTS (**34**)

1891. *No.* 68 *of Straits Settlements surch with T* **31/4**.
46 **31** 2 c. on 24 c. green £600 £650
47 **32** 2 c. on 24 c. green £225 £250
w. Wmk inverted £400 £425
48 **33** 2 c. on 24 c. green £600 £650
49 **34** 2 c. on 24 c. green £130 £150
a. Antique "G" in "SUNGEI" (R. 6/1) .. £800
b. Antique "G" in "UJONG" (R. 8/3) .. £800
w. Wmk inverted £275 £300

Nos. 46/9 come from the same setting of 60 on which "SUNGEI UJONG" was from the same type as No. 45. No. 46 occurs in row 1. No. 47 from rows 2 to 4, No. 48 from row 5 and No. 49 from rows 6 to 10.

35

3 CENTS
(**36**)

37

1891 (Nov)–**94**. *Wmk Crown CA. P* 14.
50 **35** 2 c. rose .. .. 28·00 27·00
51 2 c. orange (12.94) .. .. 1·75 4·25
52 5 c. blue (3.93) .. .. 5·00 6·00
50/2 .. .. *Set of* 3 32·00 35·00
50s/2s Optd "Specimen" .. .. *Set of* 3 60·00

1894 (Dec). *Surch as T* **36** *by De La Rue. Wmk Mult Crown CA. P* 14.
53 **35** 1 c. on 5 c. green .. .. 1·00 70
54 3 c. on 5 c. rose .. .. 2·50 4·75

1895 (Oct). *Wmk Crown CA. P* 14.
55 **37** 3 c. dull purple and carmine .. .. 8·00 2·50
53s/5s Optd "Specimen" .. .. *Set of* 3 60·00

B. NEGRI SEMBILAN

Stamps of the STRAITS SETTLEMENTS were used in Negri Sembilan during 1891, until replaced by the stamps listed below. Until the Federated Malay States joined the U.P.U. On 1 January 1899 Straits Settlements stamps continued to be used for mail to addresses outside Malaya.

PRICES FOR STAMPS ON COVER TO 1945

No. 1	*from* × 200
Nos. 2/4	*from* × 10
Nos. 5/14	*from* × 8
Nos. 15/20	*from* × 10
Nos. 21/49	*from* × 4

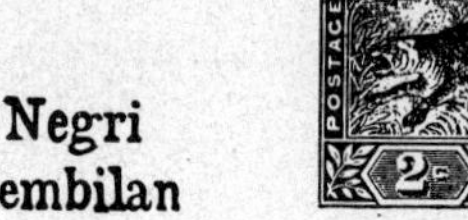

(1) 2 3

1891 (Aug?). *No. 63a of Straits Settlements optd with T* **1**.
1 2 c. bright rose .. .. 3·00 4·75

N.SEMBILAN

Short "N" in "SEMBILAN" (Top left pane R. 8/3)

1891 (Nov)–**94**. *Wmk Crown CA. P* 14.
2 **2** 1 c. green (6.93) .. .. 3·00 1·00
3 2 c. rose .. .. 3·25 6·50
a. Short "N" .. .. 75·00
4 5 c. blue (11.94) .. .. 30·00 40·00
2/4 .. .. *Set of* 3 32·00 42·00
2s/4s Optd "Specimen" .. .. *Set of* 3 70·00

1895–99. *Wmk Crown CA. P* 14.
5 **3** 1 c. dull purple and green (1899) .. 7·50 4·00
6 2 c. dull purple and brown (1898) .. 35·00 £110
7 3 c. dull purple and carmine .. 11·00 1·00
8 5 c. dull purple and orange-yellow (1897) 7·50 6·50
9 8 c. dull purple and ultramarine (1898) .. 29·00 16·00
10 10 c. dull purple and orange (1897) .. 27·00 14·00
11 15 c. green and violet (1896) .. 40·00 75·00
12 20 c. green and olive (1897) .. 55·00 38·00
13 25 c. green and carmine (1896) .. 70·00 90·00
14 50 c. green and black (1896) .. 65·00 65·00
5/14 .. .. .. *Set of* 10 £300 £375
5s/14s Optd "Specimen" .. *Set of* 10 £180

Four cents.

Four cents.

(4) (5)

1898 (Dec)–**1900**. (*a*) *Surch as T* **4**.
15 **3** 1 c. on 15 c. green and violet (1900) .. 85·00 £180
a. Raised stop (R. 5/1 and R. 10/1 of each pane) £375 £650
16 **2** 4 c. on 1 c. green .. .. .. 1·75 15·00
17 **3** 4 c. on 3 c. dull purple and carmine .. 3·00 15·00
a. Horiz pair, one without surch .. £3750 £3000
b. Surch double £1600 £1000
ba. Ditto. "Four cents" albino .. † £1000
c. Surch inverted £1300 £1100
d. "cents" repeated at left £1600 £1500
e. "Four" repeated at right £1600 £1500
f. Without bar £750 £600
g. Bar double .. .. .. † £750
18 **2** 4 c. on 5 c. blue .. .. .. 1·25 15·00

On Nos. 15 and 17 the bar is at the top of the stamp.

The surcharges were applied as a setting of 30 (6×5).

(*b*) *Surch as T* **5**
19 **3** 4 c. on 8 c. dull purple & ultram (G.) (12.98) 3·50 4·25
a. Vert pair, one without surch .. £3750 £2750
b. Surch double £1700
c. Surch double (G.+R.) £750 £750
20 4 c. on 8 c. dull purple & ultramarine (Bk.) £1000 £1100

Care should be taken in distinguishing the true black surcharge, No. 20, from very deep shades of the green surcharge, No. 19.

Pending the arrival of the permanent Federated Malay States issue the stamps of SELANGOR, FEDERATED MALAY STATES provisional overprints, STRAITS SETTLEMENTS and PERAK were used at various times between October 1899 and April 1901.

The general issues for FEDERATED MALAY STATES were used in Negri Sembilan from 29 April 1901 until 1935.

6 Arms of Negri Sembilan 7

1935 (2 Dec)–**41**. *Wmk Mult Script CA. Ordinary paper* (6 c. *grey*, 15 c.) *or chalk-surfaced paper* (*others*). *P* 14.
21 **6** 1 c. black (1.1.36) .. .. .. 1·00 20
22 2 c. green (1.1.36) .. .. .. 1·00 20
23 2 c. orange (11.12.41) .. .. .. 4·25 65·00
24 3 c. green (21.8.41) .. .. .. 8·00 8·00
a. Ordinary paper .. .. .. 17·00 8·00
25 4 c. orange .. .. 1·00 10
26 5 c. brown (5.12.35) .. .. .. 1·75 10
27 6 c. scarlet (1.1.37) .. .. .. 13·00 2·50
a. Stop omitted at right (R. 10/4) .. £325 90·00
28 **6** 6 c. grey (18.12.41) .. .. .. 4·75 75·00
a. Stop omitted at right (R. 10/4) .. £140 £500
29 8 c. grey .. .. 2·00 10
30 10 c. dull purple (1.1.36) 70 10
31 12 c. bright ultramarine (1.1.36) .. .. 1·40 50
32 15 c. ultramarine (1.10.41) .. .. 10·00 50·00
33 25 c. dull purple and scarlet (1.4.36) .. 1·00 70
34 30 c. dull purple and orange (1.1.36) .. 3·50 2·00
35 40 c. scarlet and dull purple .. .. 1·25 2·00
36 50 c. black/*emerald* (1.2.36) .. .. 3·75 2·25
37 $1 black and red/*blue* (1.4.36) .. .. 3·00 3·25
38 $2 green and scarlet (16.5.36) .. .. 29·00 16·00
39 $5 green and red/*emerald* (16.5.36) .. 17·00 50·00
21/39 .. .. *Set of* 19 90·00 £250
21s/39s Perf "Specimen" .. *Set of* 19 £300

The stamps issued in 1941 were printed by Harrison and Sons following bomb damage to the De La Rue works on 29 December 1940. The used prices quoted for Nos. 23, 28 and 32 are for examples with clearly identifiable 1941 cancellations.

An 8 c. scarlet was issued but only with opt during Japanese Occupation of Malaya. Unoverprinted specimens result from leakages.

During shortages in 1941 stamps of STRAITS SETTLEMENTS (2 c.), SELANGOR (2 c., 8 c.), PERAK (2 c., 25 c., 50 c.) and PAHANG (8 c.) were issued in Negri Sembilan.

1948 (1 Dec). *Royal Silver Wedding. As Nos.* 112/13 *of Antigua.*
40 10 c. violet 15 50
41 $5 green .. .. 18·00 28·00

1949 (1 Apr)–**55**. *Chalk-surfaced paper. Wmk Mult Script CA. P* 17½ × 18.
42 **7** 1 c. black 20 10
43 2 c. orange 20 10
44 3 c. green 20 30
45 4 c. brown 20 10
46 5 c. bright purple (1.9.52) 30 50
a. Bright mauve (25.8.53) 30 45
47 6 c. grey 50 10
a. Pale grey (25.8.53) .. .. .. 4·00 80
48 8 c. scarlet 50 75
49 8 c. green (1.9.52) .. .. .. 1·75 1·60
50 10 c. purple 20 10
51 12 c. scarlet (1.9.52) .. .. .. 1·75 2·75
52 15 c. ultramarine .. .. 3·00 10
53 20 c. black and green 50 75
54 20 c. bright blue (1.9.52) .. .. .. 1·00 10
55 25 c. purple and orange 50 10
56 30 c. scarlet and purple (5.9.55) .. .. 1·25 2·50
57 35 c. scarlet and purple (1.9.52) .. .. 1·00 1·00
58 40 c. red and purple .. .. .. 1·25 4·75
59 50 c. black and blue .. .. .. 1·25 20
60 $1 blue and purple .. .. .. 3·50 2·25
61 $2 green and scarlet .. .. .. 12·00 16·00
62 $5 green and brown .. .. .. 50·00 38·00
42/62 .. .. *Set of* 21 70·00 60·00

1949 (10 Oct). *75th Anniv of U.P.U. As Nos.* 114/17 *of Antigua.*
63 10 c. purple 20 10
64 15 c. deep blue .. .. 1·10 2·25
65 25 c. orange .. .. 30 2·25
66 50 c. blue-black .. .. 60 2·75
63/6 .. .. *Set of* 4 2·00 6·50

STAMP BOOKLETS

1935. *Stapled.*
SB1 $1 booklet containing twenty 5 c. (No. 26) in blocks of 10 .. ..
SB2 $1.30, booklet containing 5 c. and 8 c. (Nos. 26, 29), each in block of 10 .. ..

PAHANG

The first British Resident was appointed in 1888. Pahang joined the Federated Malay States in 1896.

Until 1 January 1899, when the Federated Malay States joined the U.P.U., mail for addresses outside Malaya was franked with stamps of the STRAITS SETTLEMENTS.

PRICES FOR STAMPS ON COVER TO 1945

No. 1	*from* × 50
Nos. 2/3	—
No. 4	*from* × 100
No. 5	—
No. 6	*from* × 100
Nos. 7/10	*from* × 8
Nos. 11/13	*from* × 25
Nos. 14/16	*from* × 20
Nos. 17/*a*	—
Nos. 18/*d*	*from* × 6
Nos. 19/24	*from* × 8
No. 25	*from* × 20
Nos. 26/7	—
No. 28	*from* × 15
Nos. 29/46	*from* × 6

PAHANG PAHANG PAHANG

(1) (2) (2*a*) (Antique letters)

1889 (Jan). *Nos. 52/3 and 63 of Straits Settlements optd with T* **1**.
1 2 c. pale rose .. .. 85·00 50·00
2 8 c. orange £1700 £1400
3 10 c. slate £225 £250

All three values were overprinted from a triplet setting, but the 2 c. also exists from a similar setting of 30 or 60.

1889. *No. 63 of Straits Settlements optd with T* **2**.
4 2 c. pale rose .. .. 10·00
a. Bright rose .. .. 4·00
ab. Opt Type **2a**. Antique letters £700

No. 4 was overprinted from a setting of 60. No. 4ab us occurs on R. 10/1, but has also been found on R. 8/1 as the r of revision of the setting.

PAHANG PAHANG

(3) (4)

1890. *No. 63a of Straits Settlements optd.*
5 **3** 2 c. bright rose .. .. .. £3750 £
6 **4** 2 c. bright rose .. .. .. 85·00
w. Wmk inverted .. .. ..

No. 5 may have been overprinted from a triplet setting. was from a setting of 60.

PAHANG Two CENTS PAHANG Two CENTS

(5) (6)

PAHANG Two CENTS PAHANG Two CENTS

(7) (8)

1891. *No. 68 of Straits Settlements surch with T* **5/8**.
7 **5** 2 c. on 24 c. green .. .. .. £130 £
8 **6** 2 c. on 24 c. green .. .. .. £600 £
9 **7** 2 c. on 24 c. green .. .. .. £200 £
10 **8** 2 c. on 24 c. green .. .. .. £600 £

Nos. 7/10 come from one setting used to surcharge the pa of sixty. No. 7 occurs in rows 1 to 5, No. 8 on row 6, No. 9 on r 7 to 9 and No. 10 on row 10.

9 10

1891 (Nov)–**95**. *Wmk Crown CA. P* 14.
11 **9** 1 c. green (3.95) .. .. 3·75 3
12 2 c. rose .. .. 4·50 3
13 5 c. blue (6.93) .. .. 9·50 38
11/13 .. .. *Set of* 3 16·00 40
11s/13s Optd "Specimen" .. *Set of* 3 65·00

Following an increase of postage rates on 1 March 189 1 cent stamps of STRAITS SETTLEMENTS were used i Pahang until the autumn of the following year.

1895–99. *Wmk Crown CA. P* 14.
14 **10** 3 c. dull purple and carmine .. .. 6·00 2·7
15 4 c. dull purple and carmine (1899) .. 17·00 12·0
16 5 c. dull purple and olive-yellow (1897) .. 22·00 21·0
14/16 .. .. *Set of* 3 40·00 32·0
14s/16s Optd "Specimen" .. *Set of* 3 65·00

1897 (2 Aug). *No. 13 bisected, surch in red manuscript Kuala Lipis and initialled "JFO". (a) Bisected horizontally.*
17 2 c. on half 5 c. blue (surch "2" and bar across "5") .. .. — £16
17*a* 3 c. on half of 5 c. blue (surch "3") .. £4500 £16

(*b*) *Bisected diagonally*
18 2 c. on half of 5 c. blue (surch "2" and bar across "5") £1300 £37
a. Unsevered pair. Nos. 18 and 18d .. £9000 £37
b. *Se-tenant* pair. Nos. 18 and 18d .. £3750 £9
c. Surch in black manuscript £7500 £27
18*d* 3 c. on half of 5 c. blue (surch "3") .. £1300 £37
dc. Surch in black manuscript £7500 £27

The initials are those of John Fortescue Owen, the Distric Treasurer at Kuala Lipis.

Nos. 17 and 18 only occur on the bottom half of the 5 c. an Nos. 17*a* and 18*d* on the top half. No. 18a is a complete exampl of No. 13 showing the two surcharges. No. 18b is a *se-tenant* pa of bisects from adjoining stamps.

Pahang. Pahang.

(11) (12)

1898–99. (*a*) *Nos. 72/5 of Perak optd with T* **11**.
19 10 c. dull purple and orange (3.98) .. .. 16·00 25·0
20 25 c. green and carmine .. .. .. 85·00 £14
21 50 c. dull purple and greenish black .. £300 £32
22 50 c. green and black (1899) £200 £22

(*b*) *Nos. 76 and 79 of Perak optd with T* **12**
23 $1 green and pale green £325 £35
24 $5 green and ultramarine £950 £120

Pahang
Four cents

(13)

Four cents.

(14)

(*a*) *No.* 71 *of Perak surch with T* **13**.
4 c. on 8 c. dull purple and ultramarine .. 2·50 5·50
a. Surch inverted £2250 £1200
b. Surch double £700

T **13** *on plain paper (no stamp), but issued for postage. Imperf.*
4 c. black .. .. — £2500
5 c. black £1700
26 also exists pin-perforated.

No. 16 *surch with T* **14**.
4 c. on 5 c. dull purple and olive-yellow .. 13·00 50·00

ending the arrival of the permanent Federated Malay tes issue the stamps of SELANGOR, FEDERATED LAY STATES provisional overprints and PERAK were d at various times between November 1899 and July 2.
he general issues for the FEDERATED MALAY ATES were used in Pahang from July 1902 until 1935.

15 Sultan Sir Abu Bakar

16 Sultan Sir Abu Bakar

5 (2 Dec)–**41**. *Chalk-surfaced paper. Wmk Mult Script CA.* 14.
15 1 c. black (1.1.36) 15 40
2 c. green (1.1.36) 60 50
3 c. green (21.8.41) .. .. .. 15·00 15·00
a. Ordinary paper .. .. .. 28·00 4·25
4 c. orange 50 50
5 c. brown (5.12.35) 60 10
6 c. scarlet (1.1.37) .. .. .. 9·50 2·25
8 c. grey 60 10
8 c. scarlet (11.12.41) .. .. .. 2·00 45·00
10 c. dull purple (1.1.36) 60 10
12 c. bright ultramarine (1.1.36) .. 1·25 1·75
15 c. ultram (*ordinary paper*) (1.10.41) .. 8·50 50·00
25 c. dull purple and scarlet (1.4.36) .. 80 1·75
30 c. dull purple and orange (1.1.36) .. 80 1·10
40 c. scarlet and dull purple .. .. 75 2·50
50 c. black/*emerald* (1.2.36) .. .. 2·75 1·75
$1 black and red/*blue* (1.4.36) .. .. 2·00 8·00
$2 green and scarlet (16.5.36) .. .. 18·00 26·00
$5 green and red/*emerald* (16.5.36) .. 7·00 55·00
6 .. .. *Set of* 18 60·00 £180
46s Perf "Specimen" .. .. *Set of* 18 £275
he stamps issued during 1941 were printed by Harrison and s following bomb damage to the De La Rue works on ecember 1940. The used prices quoted for Nos. 36 and 39 for examples with clearly identifiable 1941 cancellations.
2 c. orange and a 6 c. grey were prepared but not officially ed. (*Price mint £4 each*).

During shortages in 1941 stamps of STRAITS SETTLE-IENTS (2 c.), SELANGOR (2 c., 8 c.) and PERAK (2 c.) were ssued in Pahang.

8 (1 Dec). *Royal Silver Wedding. As Nos.* 112/13 *of Antigua.*
10 c. violet 15 60
$5 green .. .. 22·00 40·00

9 (10 Oct). *75th Anniv of U.P.U. As Nos.* 114/17 *of Antigua.*
10 c. purple 30 20
15 c. deep blue 90 85
25 c. orange .. .. 35 1·10
50 c. blue-black .. .. 70 2·00
52 .. .. *Set of* 4 2·00 3·75

0 (1 June)–**56**. *Wmk Mult Script CA. Chalk-surfaced paper. P* 17½×18.
16 1 c. black 10 10
2 c. orange 20 10
3 c. green 30 80
4 c. brown 80 10
a. Chocolate (24.3.54) .. .. 6·00 1·75
5 c. bright purple (1.9.52) 50 70
a. Bright mauve (10.9.53) 50 15
6 c. grey 30 30
8 c. scarlet .. .. .. 50 1·50
8 c. green (1.9.52) 85 75
10 c. magenta 25 10
12 c. scarlet (1.9.52) .. .. .. 85 1·25
15 c. ultramarine 75 10
20 c. black and green .. .. .. 50 2·75
20 c. bright blue (1.9.52) .. .. 1·00 10
a. Ultramarine (8.3.56) .. .. 4·75 2·75
25 c. purple and orange 50 10
30 c. scarlet and brown-purple (5.9.55) .. 1·25 35
a. Scarlet and purple (8.3.56) .. .. 13·00 3·75

68 **16** 35 c. scarlet and purple (1.9.52) 60 25
69 40 c. red and purple .. .. .. 1·50 7·50
70 50 c. black and blue .. .. .. 1·50 10
71 $1 blue and purple .. .. .. 2·75 2·75
72 $2 green and scarlet .. .. .. 13·00 21·00
73 $5 green and brown .. .. .. 55·00 60·00
a. Green and sepia (24.3.54) .. .. 90·00 90·00
53/73 .. .. *Set of* 21 70·00 85·00

STAMP BOOKLETS

1935. *Black on buff covers. Stapled.*
SB1 $1 booklet containing twenty 5 c. (No. 33) in blocks of 10 .. ..
SB2 $1.30, booklet containing 5 c. and 8 c. (Nos. 33, 35) each in block of 10 and pane of airmail labels £2500

PENANG

One of the Straits Settlements which joined the Federation of Malaya on 1 February 1948.

1948 (1 Dec). *Royal Silver Wedding. As Nos.* 112/13 *of Antigua.*
1 10 c. violet 30 20
2 $5 brown .. .. 30·00 28·00

1949 (21 Feb)–**52**. *As T* **58** *of Straits Settlements, but inscr* "PENANG" *at foot. Wmk Mult Script CA. Chalk-surfaced paper. P* 17½ × 18.
3 1 c. black 20 10
4 2 c. orange 85 10
5 3 c. green 20 50
6 4 c. brown 20 10
7 5 c. bright purple (1.9.52) .. .. .. 1·50 2·25
8 6 c. grey 30 20
9 8 c. scarlet .. .. 60 3·00
10 8 c. green (1.9.52) .. .. 1·25 1·25
11 10 c. purple 20 10
12 12 c. scarlet (1.9.52) .. .. 1·50 4·00
13 15 c. ultramarine 50 30
14 20 c. black and green .. .. 50 1·00
15 20 c. bright blue (1.9.52) 55 75
16 25 c. purple and orange .. .. .. 1·50 20
17 35 c. scarlet and purple (1.9.52) 60 80
18 40 c. red and purple .. .. 85 9·00
19 50 c. black and blue .. .. 1·50 20
20 $1 blue and purple .. .. 14·00 1·75
21 $2 green and scarlet .. .. 19·00 1·75
22 $5 green and brown .. .. 48·00 3·00
3/22 .. .. *Set of* 20 85·00 26·00

1949 (10 Oct). *75th Anniv of U.P.U. As Nos.* 114/17 *of Antigua.*
23 10 c. purple 20 10
24 15 c. deep blue .. .. 1·50 1·75
25 25 c. orange .. .. 45 2·00
26 50 c. blue-black .. .. 1·50 2·75
23/6 .. .. *Set of* 4 3·25 6·00

PERAK

Perak accepted a British Resident in 1874, although he was later murdered.
The state joined the Federated Malay States in 1896.

The stamps of the STRAITS SETTLEMENTS were used in Perak during 1877/8.
Until 1 January 1899, when the Federated Malay States joined the U.P.U., mail for addresses outside Malaya was franked with stamps of the STRAITS SETTLEMENTS.

PRICES FOR STAMPS ON COVER TO 1945

No. 1	—
Nos. 2/9	*from* × 60
Nos. 10/13	*from* × 30
Nos. 14/16	*from* × 8
Nos. 17/22	*from* × 20
No. 23	—
Nos. 24/5	—
Nos. 26/8	*from* × 15
No. 29	*from* × 75
No. 30	*from* × 20
Nos. 31/2	—
Nos. 33/40	*from* × 15
Nos. 43/60	*from* × 6
Nos. 61/5	*from* × 20
Nos. 66/79	*from* × 12
No. 80	—
Nos. 81/7	*from* × 8
Nos. 88/102	*from* × 4
Nos. 103/21	*from* × 3

The Official stamps of Perak are rare used on cover.

(1)

1878. *No.* 11 *of Straits Settlements handstamped with T* **1**.
1 2 c. brown £1300 £950

PERAK (2) (14½ mm long)
PERAK (3) (11 mm long)
PERAK (4) (10¼ mm long)

PERAK (5) (17 mm long)
PERAK (6) ("RA" narrow)
PERAK (7) ("R" narrow)
PERAK (8) ("P" and "K" wide)
PERAK (9) (12 to 13½ mm long)

1880–81. *No.* 11 (*wmk Crown CC*) *of Straits Settlements optd with T* **2/9**.
2 **2** 2 c. brown £1100 £550
3 **3** 2 c. brown £900 £450
4 **4** 2 c. brown £500 £400
5 **5** 2 c. brown (1881) .. .. 26·00 50·00
6 **6** 2 c. brown (1881) £160 £170
7 **7** 2 c. brown (1881) £110 £130
8 **8** 2 c. brown (1881) £375 £350
9 **9** 2 c. brown (1881) £110 £120
Of the above No. 2 is from a single unit overprint, No. 5 from a setting of sixty and the remainder from settings applied as horizontal strips of three. Nos. 6/8 come from mixed triplets, either 6 + 7 + 7 or 7 + 7 + 8. No. 4 is believed to come from a single unit overprint in addition to a triplet.

PERAK (10) ("A" wide)
PERAK (11) ("E" wide)

1882–83. *Nos.* 50 (*wmk Crown CA*) *and* 63 *of Straits Settlements optd with T* **9/11**.
10 **9** 2 c. brown .. .. 19·00 42·00
a. Opt double £550
11 2 c. pale rose (1883) .. .. .. 20·00 38·00
a. Opt double £600
12 **10** 2 c. pale rose (1883) .. .. .. 20·00 55·00
13 **11** 2 c. pale rose (1883) .. .. .. 20·00 45·00
a. Opt double £600
The above were all overprinted as triplet settings. Those for the 2 c. rose were 11 + 12 + 13, 13 + 11 + 11 and 13 + 11 + 12.

2 CENTS PERAK (12)
2 CENTS (13)

1883 (July). *No.* 51 (*wmk Crown CA*) *of Straits Settlements surch.*

(*a*) *Surch with T* **12**
14 2 c. on 4 c. rose £2250
a. On Straits Settlements No. 12 (wmk Crown CC) £7000

(*b*) *Optd as T* **9** *or* **11** *and surch with T* **13**
15 **11** 2 c. on 4 c. rose £900 £375
16 **9** 2 c. on 4 c. rose £550 £250
It is believed that No. 14 occurred on the top row of the sheet with the remaining nine rows surcharged with a triplet containing 15 + 16 + 16.
Only one unused example, with defects, of No. 14a is recorded.

PERAK (14) ("E" wide)
PERAK (15) ("E" narrow)
PERAK (16) (12½–13 mm long)
PERAK (17) (12–12½ mm long)
PERAK (18) (10½ mm long)
PERAK (19) (10 mm long)
PERAK (20) (13 mm long)

1884–91. *Nos.* 63/*a of Straits Settlements optd with T* **14/20**.
17 **14** 2 c. pale rose .. .. 2·00 1·60
a. Opt double £550 £550
b. Opt inverted £350 £450
c. Bright rose .. .. 3·00 1·25
18 **15** 2 c. pale rose .. .. 60·00 60·00
b. Opt inverted £1200 £1300
c. Opt triple £1200
d. Bright rose .. ..
19 **16** 2 c. pale rose (1886) .. .. .. 1·40 5·50
a. Optd "FERAK" £300 £350
20 **17** 2 c. pale rose (1886) .. .. .. 4·00 19·00
a. Opt double £1300
21 **18** 2 c. pale rose (1886) .. .. .. 90·00 £100
a. Bright rose .. ..
22 **19** 2 c. bright rose (1890) .. .. .. 12·00 40·00
23 **20** 2 c. bright rose (1891) £2500
Settings:
Nos. 17/18 – triplets (either 17 + 17 + 17 or 18 + 17 + 17)
– 30 (3 × 10) (containing twenty-eight as No. 17 and two as No. 18)
– 60 (6 × 10) (containing either fifty-seven as No. 17 and three as No. 18 or all as No. 17)
No. 19 – 60 (6 × 10) (No. 19a occurs on one position of the setting, it is often found amended in manuscript)
No. 20 – triplet
No. 21 – triplet
No. 22 – 60 (6 × 10)
No. 23 – not known

1 CENT

(21)

1886. *No.* 17 *surch with T* **21**.
24 **14** 1 c. on 2 c. pale rose £2000 £2000

ONE CENT PERAK (22)
ONE CENT PERAK. (23)
ONE CFNT PERAK. (24) ("N" wide in "ONE" and "CENT")

1886. *No.* 63 *of Straits Settlements surch with T* **22/4**.
25 **22** 1 c. on 2 c. pale rose £500 £550
26 **23** 1 c. on 2 c. pale rose .. .. .. 55·00 75·00
a. Surch double £800
27 **24** 1 c. on 2 c. pale rose .. .. .. 85·00 £100

Nos. 26/7 are from a triplet setting, 26 + 27 + 26, used on the top nine rows of the sheet. No. 25 may have been used on the bottom row.

1 CENT PERAK (25)
One CENT PERAK (26)
ONE CENT PERAK (27)

1886. *No.* 63 *of Straits Settlements surch with T* **25**.
28 1 c. on 2 c. pale rose £100 £110
a. Surch double £1500

No. 28 comes from a triplet setting.

1886. *No.* 63 *of Straits Settlements surch with T* **26**.
29 1 c. on 2 c. pale rose .. .. .. 1·50 8·00
a. "One" inverted £2500
b. Surch double £1000

No. 29 comes from a triplet setting. It is believed that No. 29a occurred when the type was dropped and "One" replaced upside down.

1887. *No.* 63 *of Straits Settlements surch with T* **27** *in blue*.
30 1 c. on 2 c. pale rose .. .. .. 35·00 48·00
a. Optd in black £1600 £1100

No. 30 was printed from a setting of 60.

1 CENT PERAK (28)
1 CENT PERAK (29)

1887. *No.* 63 *of Straits Settlements surch with T* **28**.
31 1 c. on 2 c. pale rose £450 £475

No. 31 comes from a triplet setting

1887. *No.* 63 *of Straits Settlements surch with T* **29**.
32 1 c. on 2 c. pale rose £1500 £1600

The size of setting used for No. 32 is not known.

One CENT PERAK (30)
One CENT PERAK (31)
One CENT PERAK (32)
One CENT PERAK (33)
One CENT PERAK (34)
One CENT PERAK (35)
One CENT PERAK (36)
One CENT PERAK (37)

1887–89. *No.* 63 *of Straits Settlements surch with T* **30/7**.
33 **30** 1 c. on 2 c. pale rose .. .. .. 1·25 4·00
a. Surch double £1000
b. Bright rose .. .. .. 1·50 2·00
34 **31** 1 c. on 2 c. pale rose (1889) £110 £130
b. Bright rose .. .. ..
35 **32** 1 c. on 2 c. pale rose (1889) .. .. 9·00 29·00
a. "PREAK" (R. 6/1) £450 £500
b. Bright rose .. .. 13·00 29·00
ba. "PREAK" (R. 6/1) £600 £700
w. Wmk inverted £130
36 **33** 1 c. on 2 c. pale rose (1889) .. .. 4·75 9·50
b. Bright rose .. .. 4·25 9·50
37 **34** 1 c. on 2 c. pale rose (1889) .. .. 6·00 13·00
b. Bright rose .. .. 4·25 13·00
38 **35** 1 c. on 2 c. bright rose (1889) £550 £700
39 **36** 1 c. on 2 c. bright rose (1889) £250 £300
40 **37** 1 c. on 2 c. pale rose (1889) .. .. 12·00 27·00
b. Bright rose .. .. 12·00 26·00

Settings. No. 33 originally appeared as a triplet, then as a block of 30 (3 × 10) and, finally, as part of a series of composite settings of 60. Specialists recognise four such composite settings:

Setting I contained No. 33 in Rows 1 to 4, R. 5/1 to 5/5 and Row 7; No. 34 on R. 5/6, 6/1 and 6/2; No. 35 on R. 6/3–6; No. 36 on Row 8; No. 37 on Rows 9 and 10.

Setting II was similar, but had the example of No. 33 on R. 3/5 replaced by No. 38 and those on R. 7/4 and R. 7/6 by No. 39.

Setting III contained No. 33 in Rows 1 to 5; No. 35 in Row 6 with the "PREAK" error on the first position; No. 36 in Row 7; No. 37 in Rows 8 and 9; No. 40 in Row 10.

Setting IV was similar, but showed the "PREAK" error on R. 6/1 corrected.

ONE CENT. (38)
ONE CENT (39)

1889–90. *No.* 17 *surch with T* **38/9**.
41 **38** 1 c. on 2 c. bright rose £190 £130
42 **39** 1 c. on 2 c. bright rose (1890) .. .. — £250

PERAK Two CENTS (40)
PERAK One CENT (41)

1891. *Nos.* 63*a*, 66 *and* 68 *of Straits Settlements surch.*

(*a*) *As T* **30**, **32/4** *and* **37**, *but with* "PERAK" *at top and a bar through the original value*
43 **30** 1 c. on 6 c. lilac .. .. 42·00 25·00
44 **32** 1 c. on 6 c. lilac £150 £140
45 **33** 1 c. on 6 c. lilac £150 £140
46 **34** 1 c. on 6 c. lilac .. .. 70·00 65·00
47 **37** 1 c. on 6 c. lilac £150 £140

(*b*) *With T* **40** *and as T* **32/4** *and* **37** *but with* "PERAK" *at top, all with a bar through the original value*
48 **40** 2 c. on 24 c. green .. .. 12·00 9·00
49 **32** 2 c. on 24 c. green .. .. 80·00 55·00
50 **33** 2 c. on 24 c. green .. .. 80·00 55·00
51 **34** 2 c. on 24 c. green .. .. 45·00 25·00
52 **37** 2 c. on 24 c. green .. .. 80·00 55·00

(*c*) *With T* **41** *and as T* **30**, **34** *and* **37**, *but with* "PERAK" *at top.*
(i) *Without bar over original value*
53 **30** 1 c. on 2 c. bright rose £160
a. Narrow "O" in "One" (R. 3/3) .. £1800
54 **41** 1 c. on 2 c. bright rose £750
55 **34** 1 c. on 2 c. bright rose £300
56 **37** 1 c. on 2 c. bright rose £750

(ii) *With bar through original value*
57 **30** 1 c. on 2 c. bright rose .. .. .. 1·00 5·50
a. Narrow "O" in "One" (R. 3/3) .. 20·00 50·00
58 **41** 1 c. on 2 c. bright rose .. .. .. 5·00 22·00
59 **34** 1 c. on 2 c. bright rose .. .. .. 1·10 7·50
60 **37** 1 c. on 2 c. bright rose .. .. .. 5·00 22·00

Settings. Nos. 43/7 were arranged as Setting IV described under Nos. 33/40.

Nos. 48/52 were similar except that Type **40** replaced Type **30** on the first five rows.

The first printing of the 1 c. on 2 c. was without a bar through the original face value. Both printings, Nos. 53/60, were from the same setting with Type **30** on Rows 1 to 5, **41** on Row 6, **34** on Rows 7 to 9 and **37** on Row 10.

42

3 CENTS

(43)

1892 (1 Jan)–**95**. *Wmk Crown CA. P* 14.
61 **42** 1 c. green .. .. 2·25 15
62 2 c. rose .. .. 1·75 30
63 2 c. orange (9.9.95) .. .. 50 3·25
64 5 c. blue .. .. 3·25 7·50
61/4 .. .. *Set of* 4 7·00 10·00
61s/4s Optd "Specimen" .. .. *Set of* 4 75·00

1895 (26 Apr). *Surch with T* **43**. *Wmk Crown CA. P* 14.
65 **42** 3 c. on 5 c. rose .. .. 2·00 1·75
s. Optd "Specimen" .. .. .. 25·00

44

45

1895 (2 Sept)–**99**. *P* 14. (*a*) *Wmk Crown CA.*
66 **44** 1 c. dull purple and green .. .. .. 1·50 50
67 2 c. dull purple and brown .. .. 1·50 50
68 3 c. dull purple and carmine .. .. 1·75 50
69 4 c. dull purple and carmine (1899) .. 9·00 4·75
70 5 c. dull purple and olive-yellow .. .. 3·00 55
71 8 c. dull purple and ultramarine .. .. 42·00 65
72 10 c. dull purple and orange .. .. 10·00 50
73 25 c. green and carmine (1897) .. .. £120 12·00
74 50 c. dull purple and greenish black .. 42·00 29·00
75 50 c. green and black (2.99) £150 £150

(*b*) *Wmk Crown CC*
76 **45** $1 green and pale green (1896) £130 £140
77 $2 green and carmine (1896) £225 £250
78 $3 green and ochre (1898) £275 £325
79 $5 green and ultramarine (1896) £500 £475
80 $25 green and orange (1899?) £7000 £2500
s. Optd "Specimen" £180
66/76 .. .. *Set of* 11 £450 £300
66s/79s Optd "Specimen" .. .. *Set of* 14 £350

Pending the arrival of the permanent Federated Malay States issue the stamps of FEDERATED MALAY STATES provisional overprints, SELANGOR and STRAITS SETTLEMENTS were used at various times between June 1900 and February 1901.

The general issues for the FEDERATED MALAY STATES were used in Perak from 1901 until 1935.

One Cent. (46)
ONE CENT. (47)
Three Cent. (48)
Three Cent. (49)

1900. *Stamps of* 1895–99 *surch.*
81 **46** 1 c. on 2 c. dull purple & brown (13 July*) 40
a. Antique "e" in "One" (R. 5/2) .. 50·00
b. Antique "e" in "Cent" (R. 9/4) .. 50·00
82 **47** 1 c. on 4 c. dull purple and carmine .. 65
a. Surch double £950
83 **46** 1 c. on 5 c. dull purple & ol-yell (30 June*) 1·00
a. Antique "e" in "One" (R. 5/2) .. 70·00
b. Antique "e" in "Cent" (R. 9/4) .. 70·00
84 **48** 3 c. on 8 c. dull purple & ultram (26 Sept*) 3·00
a. Antique "e" in "Cent" (R. 9/4) .. £130
b. No stop after "Cent" (R. 9/5) .. £130
c. Surch double £425
85 3 c. on 50 c. green and black (31 Aug*) .. 1·50
a. Antique "e" in "Cent" (R. 9/4) .. 95·00
b. No stop after "Cent" (R. 9/5) .. 95·00
86 **49** 3 c. on $1 green and pale green (21 Oct*) 55·00
a. Thinner "t" in "Cent" £300
b. Surch double £1300
87 3 c. on $2 green and carmine (24 Oct*) .. 28·00 8
81/7 .. .. *Set of* 7 80·00

*Earliest known postmark date.

With exception of No. 86a, whose sheet position is not kno the remaining surcharge varieties all occur in the left-h pane. On No. 86a the "t" is in a different font which is thin than normal with a different curve to the foot.

No. 86b is also known showing the thinner "t" in "Ce variety. (*Price* £3500 *unused*).

50 Sultan Iskandar **51**

1935 (2 Dec)–**37**. *Chalk-surfaced paper. Wmk Mult Script* (*P* 14.
88 **50** 1 c. black (1.1.36) 50
89 2 c. green (1.1.36) 50
90 4 c. orange 65
91 5 c. brown (5.12.35) 50
92 6 c. scarlet (1.1.37) .. .. .. 11·00 4
93 8 c. grey 65
94 10 c. dull purple (1.1.36) 50
95 12 c. bright ultramarine (1.1.36) .. .. 90 1·
96 25 c. dull purple and scarlet (1.4.36) .. 1·25 1·
97 30 c. dull purple and orange (1.1.36) .. 1·50 1·
98 40 c. scarlet and dull purple .. .. 3·25 4·
99 50 c. black/*emerald* (1.2.36) .. .. 3·75 1·
100 $1 black and red/*blue* (1.4.36) .. .. 2·50 1·
101 $2 green and scarlet (16.5.36) .. .. 16·00 8·
102 $5 green and red/*emerald* (16.5.36) .. 75·00 30·
88/102 .. .. *Set of* 15 £110 48·
88s/102s Perf "Specimen" .. *Set of* 15 £200

No. 91 exists in coils constructed from normal sheets in 193

1938 (2 May)–**41**. *Wmk Mult Script CA. Chalk-surfaced pape P* 14.
103 **51** 1 c. black (4.39) .. .. .. 7·00
104 2 c. green (13.1.39) .. .. .. 3·00
105 2 c. orange (30.10.41) .. .. .. 2·50 6·
a. Ordinary paper .. .. .. 3·25 16·
106 3 c. green (21.8.41) .. .. .. 2·00 4·
107 4 c. orange (5.39) .. .. .. 35·00
108 5 c. brown (1.2.39) .. .. .. 4·75
109 6 c. scarlet (12.39) .. .. .. 27·00
110 8 c. grey (1.12.38) .. .. .. 23·00
111 8 c. scarlet (18.12.41) .. .. .. 1·00 65·0
112 10 c. dull purple (17.10.38) .. .. 24·00
113 12 c. bright ultramarine (17.10.38) .. 20·00 1·5
114 15 c. brt ultram (*ordinary paper*) (8.41) 2·75 13·0
115 25 c. dull purple and scarlet (12.39) .. 60·00 4·2
116 30 c. dull purple and orange (17.10.38) 9·50 3·0
117 40 c. scarlet and dull purple .. .. 50·00 2·0
118 50 c. black/*emerald* (17.10.38) .. .. 29·00 7
119 $1 black and red/*blue* (7.40) .. .. £130 16·0
120 $2 green and scarlet (9.40) .. .. £140 60·0
121 $5 green and red/*emerald* (1.41) .. £200 £27
103/21 .. .. *Set of* 19 £700 £40
103s/21s Perf "Specimen" .. *Set of* 19 £300

No. 108 exists in coils constructed from normal sheets.

The stamps issued during 1941 were printed by Harrison an Sons following bomb damage to the De La Rue works o 29 December 1940. The used price quoted for No. 111 is for a example with clearly identifiable 1941 cancellation.

During shortages in 1941 stamps of STRAITS SETTLEMENTS (2 c.), SELANGOR (2 c., 3 c.) and PAHANG (8 c.) were issued in Perak.

1948 (1 Dec). *Royal Silver Wedding. As Nos.* 112/13 *o Antigua.*
122 10 c. violet 15 1
123 $5 green .. .. 20·00 26·0

www.stanleygibbons.com

Collections and Ranges

Auction catalogue of mixed lots, specialised collections an
one country lots.
Available on subscription at £30.00 per year.
(This price includes Postbid) *

Postbid

Postal Auction catalogue of all world range
of single items and sets.
Available on subscription at £30.00 per year.
(This price includes Collections and Ranges.) *

Mail Order lists

We produce regular lists of our top
50 selling countries.
Available free of charge. *

Bookshelf

Rare philatelic literature list.
Available at £5.00 per copy.*

* **All these publications are available to download FREE of charge on www.stanleygibbons.com**

† All these subscriptions are refundable against the value of orders from these lists, higher in value than the subscription cost.

Valid until 30 June 2003

Please send this information back to Stanley Gibbons by:

Fax	**Email**
020 7836 7342	**info@stanleygibbons.co.uk**

Or for your security, Freepost this coupon in an envelope to:

Stanley Gibbons Publications
FREEPOST
BH 252, 5/7 Parkside,
Christchurch Road, Ringwood,
Hampshire BH24 3BR

(10 Oct). *75th Anniv of U.P.U. As Nos. 114/17 of Antigua.*

10 c. purple . . 15 10
15 c. deep blue . . 1·00 1·50
25 c. orange . . 30 1·00
50 c. blue-black . . 1·25 3·25
. . *Set of* 4 2·40 5·25

52 Sultan Yussuf 'Izzuddin Shah

(17 Aug)–**56**. *Chalk-surfaced paper. Wmk Mult Script* . *P* 17½×18.

52 1 c. black . . 10 10
2 c. orange . . 20 10
3 c. green . . 2·50 10
a. *Yellowish green* (15.11.51) . . 7·00 4·50
4 c. brown . . 50 10
a. *Yellow-brown* (20.6.56) . . 4·75 10
5 c. bright purple (1.9.52) . . 50 1·50
a. *Bright mauve* (10.11.54) . . 1·25 1·50
6 c. grey . . 20 10
8 c. scarlet . . 65 1·75
8 c. green (1.9.52) . . 1·00 85
10 c. purple . . 20 10
a. *Brown-purple* (20.6.56) . . 4·50 30
12 c. scarlet (1.9.52) . . 1·00 3·25
15 c. ultramarine . . 75 10
20 c. black and green . . 75 50
20 c. bright blue (1.9.52) . . 75 10
25 c. purple and orange . . 50 10
30 c. scarlet and purple (5.9.55) . . 1·50 20
35 c. scarlet and purple (1.9.52) . . 85 25
40 c. red and purple . . 1·75 4·75
50 c. black and blue . . 1·75 10
$1 blue and purple . . 7·00 65
$2 green and scarlet . . 13·00 5·50
$5 green and brown . . 38·00 11·00
48 . . *Set of* 21 65·00 26·00

STAMP BOOKLETS

5.

$1 booklet containing twenty 5 c. (No. 91) in blocks of 10 . .
$1.30, booklet containing 5 c. and 8 c. (Nos. 91, 93), each in block of 10 . .

8.

$1 booklet containing twenty 5 c. (No. 108) in blocks of 10 . .
$1.30, booklet containing 5 c. and 8 c. (Nos. 108, 110), each in block of 10 . .

OFFICIAL STAMPS

P.G.S. (O 1) Service. (O 2)

9 (1 Nov). *Stamps of Straits Settlements optd Type* O **1**. *Wmk Crown CC (Nos.* O6 *and* O8*) or Crown CA (others).*

2 c. bright rose . . 3·00 4·00
a. Opt double . . £750 £750
b. Wide space between "G" and "S" . . 48·00 60·00
c. No stop after "S" . . 48·00 60·00
4 c. brown . . 9·00 18·00
a. Wide space between "G" and "S" . . 70·00 85·00
b. No stop after "S" . . £110 £130
w. Wmk inverted . . 70·00
6 c. lilac . . 20·00 40·00
a. Wide space between "G" and "S" . . £100 £140
8 c. orange . . 27·00 65·00
a. Wide space between "G" and "S" . . £130 £180
10 c. slate . . 75·00 75·00
a. Wide space between "G" and "S" . . £250 £250
12 c. blue (CC) . . £180 £200
a. Wide space between "G" and "S" . . £600
12 c. brown-purple (CA) . . £200 £275
a. Wide space between "G" and "S" . . £700
24 c. green (CC) . . £650 £750
a. Wide space between "G" and "S" . . £1900
24 c. green (CA) . . £160 £180
a. Wide space between "G" and "S" . . £550

Nos. O1/9 were overprinted from a setting of 30 (3 × 10). The riety "wide space between G and S" occurs on R. 10/3 and R. 10/6 the original printing. A later printing of the 2 c. and 4 c. values d this variety corrected, but was without a stop after "S" on 10/1 and R. 10/4.

94 (1 June). *No. 64 optd with Type* O **2**.

10 5 c. blue . . 60·00 1·00
a. Overprint inverted . . £750 £450

97. *No. 70 optd with Type* O **2**.

11 5 c. dull purple and olive-yellow . . 1·75 50
a. Overprint double . . £475 £400

PERLIS

Suzerainty over Perlis was transferred by Thailand to Great ritain in 1909. A Treaty of Friendship between Great Britain d Perlis was signed on 28 April 1930.

The State joined the Federation of Malaya on 1 February 948.

For stamps of THAILAND used in Perlis between 1894 and 1909 see SIAMESE POSTS IN NORTHERN MALAYA section.

Issues of the FEDERATED MALAY STATES were in use from 10 July 1909 until 1912 and these were replaced by the stamps of KEDAH between 1912 and 1941.

1948 (1 Dec). *Royal Silver Wedding. As Nos.* 112/13 *of Antigua.*

1 10 c. violet . . 30 2·25
2 $5 brown . . 28·00 42·00

1949 (10 Oct). *75th Anniv of U.P.U. As Nos.* 114/17 *of Antigua.*

3 10 c. purple . . 30 85
4 15 c. deep blue . . 1·25 3·00
5 25 c. orange . . 45 2·00
6 50 c. blue-black . . 1·00 3·75
3/6 . . *Set of* 4 2·75 8·50

1 Raja Syed Putra

1951 (26 Mar)–**55**. *Chalk-surfaced paper. Wmk Mult Script CA. P* 17½ × 18.

7 **1** 1 c. black . . 20 1·00
8 2 c. orange . . 75 50
9 3 c. green . . 1·50 2·75
10 4 c. brown . . 1·25 30
11 5 c. bright purple (1.9.52) . . 50 3·00
12 6 c. grey . . 1·50 1·25
13 8 c. scarlet . . 2·25 4·75
14 8 c. green (1.9.52) . . 75 2·75
15 10 c. purple . . 50 30
a. Error. St. Edward's Crown W **9b** . . £3500
16 12 c. scarlet (1.9.52) . . 75 2·50
17 15 c. ultramarine . . 2·50 3·50
18 20 c. black and green . . 1·75 6·00
19 20 c. bright blue (1.9.52) . . 1·00 70
20 25 c. purple amd orange . . 1·75 1·75
21 30 c. scarlet and purple (5.9.55) . . 1·75 8·50
22 35 c. scarlet and purple (1.9.52) . . 75 4·00
23 40 c. red and purple . . 2·00 16·00
24 50 c. black and blue . . 3·25 4·25
25 $1 blue and purple . . 7·50 18·00
26 $2 green and scarlet . . 14·00 27·00
27 $5 green and brown . . 50·00 70·00
7/27 . . *Set of* 21 85·00 £160

SELANGOR

The first British Resident was appointed in 1874. Selangor joined the Federated Malay States in 1896.

The stamps of the STRAITS SETTLEMENTS were used in Selangor from 1879 until 1881.

Until 1 January 1899, when the Federated Malay States joined the U.P.U., mail for addresses outside Malaya was franked with stamps of the STRAITS SETTLEMENTS.

PRICES FOR STAMPS ON COVER TO 1945

Nos. 1/8	—
Nos. 9/19	*from* × 10
Nos. 20/30	*from* × 12
Nos. 31/3	*from* × 25
Nos. 34/6	*from* × 20
Nos. 37/8	*from* × 15
Nos. 38*a*/40	—
Nos. 41/2	*from* × 8
No. 43	—
Nos. 44/8	*from* × 8
Nos. 49/53	*from* × 30
Nos. 54/66	*from* × 10
Nos. 66*a*/7	*from* × 4
Nos. 68/85	*from* × 3
Nos. 86/7	*from* × 4

The Straits Settlements 1867 2 c. brown with Crown CC watermark (No. 11) has been known since 1881 overprinted in black with a crescent and star over a capital S, all within an oval, similar in style to the overprints listed for Perak and Sungei Ujong.

The status of this item remains unclear, but it may well represent the first issue of distinctive stamps for Selangor. This overprint should not be confused with a somewhat similar cancellation used on Selangor stamps of the same period. This cancellation differs in having a circular frame with the capital S shown above the crescent and star. It is usually struck in red.

A similar overprint in red on the Straits Settlements 2 c. brown with Crown CA watermark also exists and may have been produced for sale to collectors (*Price* £275, *unused*).

SELANGOR (1) ("S" inverted and narrow letters)
SELANGOR (2) ("S" wide)
SELANGOR (3) (narrow letters)
SELANGOR (4) ("N" wide)
SELANGOR (5) ("SE" and "AN" wide)
SELANGOR (6) ("SEL" and "N" wide)
SELANGOR (7) ("SELAN" wide)

1881–82. *No.* 11 *(wmk Crown CC) of Straits Settlements optd with T* **1**/**7**.

1 **1** 2 c. brown . . £400 £425
2 **2** 2 c. brown . . £150 £160
3 **3** 2 c. brown . . 95·00 95·00
4 **4** 2 c. brown . . † £2000
5 **5** 2 c. brown (1882) . . £180 £190
6 **6** 2 c. brown (1882) . . £180 £190
7 **7** 2 c. brown (1882) . . £180 £190

Nos. 1/3 and 5/7 have been identified as coming from triplet settings, either Nos. 1 + 2 + 3, 2 + 3 + 3 or 5 + 6 + 7. The setting for No. 4 is unknown.

S. (8)

1882. *No.* 50 *(wmk Crown CA) of Straits Settlements optd with T* **8**.

8 **8** 2 c. brown . . — £2500

SELANGOR (9) ("SEL" and "NG" wide)
SELANGOR (10) ("E" and "ANG" wide)
SELANGOR (11) ("ELANG" wide)
SELANGOR (12) ("S" and "L" wide)
SELANGOR (13) ("S" and "A" wide)
SELANGOR (14) ("E" wide)
SELANGOR (15) ("EL" wide)
SELANGOR (16) ("SE" and "N" wide)
SELANGOR (17) ("S" and "N" wide)

1882–83. *No.* 50 *(wmk Crown CA) of Straits Settlements optd with T* **2**/**3** *and* **9**/**17**.

9 **9** 2 c. brown . . £200 £200
10 **10** 2 c. brown . . £200 £200
11 **11** 2 c. brown . . £200 £200
12 **2** 2 c. brown (1883) . . £130 £100
13 **3** 2 c. brown (1883) . . £225 £100
14 **12** 2 c. brown (1883) . . — £2000
15 **13** 2 c. brown (1883) . . £425 £375
16 **14** 2 c. brown (1883) . . £300 £225
17 **15** 2 c. brown (1883) . . £300 £225
18 **16** 2 c. brown (1883) . . £140 £130
a. Opt double . . £850
19 **17** 2 c. brown (1883) . . £140 £130

The above were all printed from triplet settings. Those so far identified are Nos. 9 + 10 + 11, 12 (with defective "G") + 13 + 13, 15 + 16 + 17 and 18 + 12 + 19. No. 14 occurs as the first position of a triplet, but the second and third units are not yet known.

SELANGOR (18) ("E" and "A" wide)
SELANGOR (19) ("A" wide)
SELANGOR (20) ("L" wide)
SELANGOR (21) ("L" narrow)
SELANGOR (22) ("A" narrow)
SELANGOR (23) (wide letters)

1883–85. *No.* 63 *of Straits Settlements optd with T* **2**, **4**, **12**, **14**/**15** *and* **18**/**23**.

20 **12** 2 c. pale rose . . £160 £130
21 **14** 2 c. pale rose . . £100 85·00
a. Opt double . .
22 **4** 2 c. pale rose (1884) . . £160 £130
23 **15** 2 c. pale rose (1884) . . 90·00 80·00
a. Opt double . . £750
b. Opt triple . .
24 **2** 2 c. pale rose (1884) . . £100 80·00
25 **18** 2 c. pale rose (1884) . . £100 80·00
26 **19** 2 c. pale rose (1884) . . £275 £150
27 **20** 2 c. pale rose (1884) . . £350 £180
28 **21** 2 c. pale rose (1885) . . 85·00 80·00
29 **22** 2 c. pale rose (1885) . . £150 £120
30 **23** 2 c. pale rose (1885) . . £325 £170

The above come from triplet settings with Nos. 20 + 21 + 21, 22 + 22 + 23, 23 + 26 (with defective "A") + 26, 24 + 25 + 23 and 28 + 29 + 28 so far identified. The triplets for Nos. 27 and 30 are not known.

SELANGOR (24) *Selangor* (25) SELANGOR (26)

SELANGOR (27) SELANGOR (28) SELANGOR (29) SELANGOR (30)

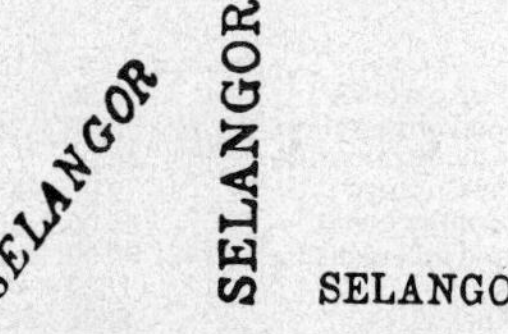

(31) (32)

SELANGOR (33) *SELANGOR* (34)

1885–91. *Nos. 63/a of Straits Settlements optd with T* **24/34**.
31 **24** 2 c. pale rose .. .. 8·00 18·00
a. Opt double £800 £700
32 **25** 2 c. pale rose £900 £950
33 **26** 2 c. pale rose .. .. 30·00 32·00
34 **27** 2 c. pale rose (1886) .. .. 50·00 50·00
a. Opt double .. .. † £650
35 **28** 2 c. pale rose (horiz opt without stop) (1887) .. .. 7·50 2·50
a. Opt double £650
b. Bright rose .. .. 7·50 2·25
36 2 c. pale rose (horiz opt with stop) (1887) 70·00 55·00
a. Bright rose .. ..
37 **29** 2 c. pale rose (1889) .. .. £160 75·00
38 **30** 2 c. pale rose (vert opt) (1889) .. .. 60·00 6·00
a. Bright rose .. ..
38*b* 2 c. bright rose (horiz opt) (1889) .. £3250
39 **31** 2 c. pale rose (diagonal opt) (1889) .. £1600
40 **32** 2 c. pale rose (1889) .. .. .. £375 25·00
41 **28** 2 c. brt rose (vert opt without stop) (1890) 14·00 25·00
42 **33** 2 c. bright rose (1890) .. .. .. £110 3·00
43 **34** 2 c. bright rose (1891) £325 £150

Settings:
Nos. 31/4 – each in triplet containing three examples of the same stamp
No. 35 – triplet or 60 (6×10)
No. 36 – 60 (6×10)
Nos. 37/8 – 60 (6×10) containing both overprints in an unknown combination, but with No. 38 predominating
Nos. 38*b*/9 – not known
Nos. 40/3 – each in 60 (6×10)

SELANGOR Two CENTS (35) SELANGOR Two CENTS (36) SELANGOR Two CENTS (37)

SELANGOR Two CENTS (38) SELANGOR Two CENTS (39)

1891. *No. 68 of Straits Settlements, surch with T* **35/9**, *each with bar obliterating old value.*
44 **35** 2 c. on 24 c. green .. .. .. 23·00 65·00
45 **36** 2 c. on 24 c. green £150 £200
46 **37** 2 c. on 24 c. green £150 £200
47 **38** 2 c. on 24 c. green .. .. .. 80·00 £120
a. "SELANGCR" .. .. ..
48 **39** 2 c. on 24 c. green £150 £200

Nos. 44/8 come from the one setting used to surcharge the panes of sixty. No. 44 occurs in rows 1 to 5, No. 45 on row 6, No. 46 on row 7, No. 47 on rows 8 and 9, and No. 48 on row 10.

The error, No. 47a, occurs in the first printing only and is No. 45 (R.8/3) on the pane.

40

3 CENTS (41)

1891 (Nov)–**95.** *Wmk Crown CA. P* 14.
49 **40** 1 c. green (5.93) .. .. .. 1·00 25
50 2 c. rose .. .. 3·50 1·00
51 2 c. orange (27.5.95) .. .. .. 2·25 60
52 5 c. blue (8.92) .. .. 21·00 4·50
49/52 .. .. *Set of* 4 25·00 5·75
49s/52s Optd "Specimen" .. *Set of* 4 80·00

1894 (Dec). *Surch with T* **41**. *Wmk Crown CA. P* 14.
53 **40** 3 c. on 5 c. rose .. .. .. 2·25 50
s. Optd "Specimen" .. .. .. 30·00

42

43

SELANGOR

Dented frame above "A" of "SELANGOR" (left pane R. 4/5)

1895–99. *Wmk Crown CA or Crown CC (dollar values). P* 14.
54 **42** 3 c. dull purple and carmine .. .. 6·00 30
55 5 c. dull purple and olive-yellow .. 2·75 30
56 8 c. dull purple and ultramarine (1898) 48·00 7·00
57 10 c. dull purple and orange .. .. 9·00 1·50
58 25 c. green and carmine (1896) .. .. 80·00 50·00
59 50 c. dull purple and greenish black (1896) 50·00 22·00
a. Dented frame £325
60 50 c. green and black (1898) £350 £110
a. Dented frame .. ..
61 **43** $1 green and yellow-green .. .. .. 48·00 £120
62 $2 green and carmine (1897) £180 £180
63 $3 green and ochre (1897) £425 £325
64 $5 green and blue £200 £250
65 $10 green and purple (1899) £550 £650
s. Optd "Specimen" £100
66 $25 green and orange (1899?) £2500
s. Optd "Specimen" £200
54/62 .. .. *Set of* 9 £700 £450
54s/64s Optd "Specimen" .. *Set of* 11 £275

Pending the arrival of the permanent Federated Malay States issue the stamps of STRAITS SETTLEMENTS and PERAK were used at various times between July 1900 and March 1901.

The general issues for the FEDERATED MALAY STATES were used in Selangor from 1901 until 1935.

One cent. (44) Three cents. (45)

1900 (Oct). *Nos. 55 and 59 surch with T* **44** *or* **45**.
66*a* **42** 1 c. on 5 c. dull purple & ol-yell (31 Oct*) 60·00 £120
66*b* 1 c. on 50 c. green and black (22 Oct*) 1·75 19·00
bc. "cent" repeated at left £1800
bd. Dented frame .. .. .. 75·00
67 3 c. on 50 c. green and black (30 Oct*) 4·00 19·00
a. Antique "t" in "cents" £250 £350
b. Dented frame £190

*Earliest known postmark date.

It is believed that these stamps were surcharged from settings of 30, repeated four times to complete the sheet of 120.

No. 66bc occurred on two separate vertical strips of five stamps where two impressions of the setting overlapped.

The position in the setting of No. 67a is not known.

46 Mosque at Palace, Klang 47 Sultan Suleiman

(Des E. J. McNaughton)

1935 (2 Dec)–**41.** *Wmk Mult Script CA (sideways on T* **46**). *Chalk-surfaced paper. P 14 or* 14×14½ *(No. 70).*
68 **46** 1 c. black (1.1.36) 30 10
69 2 c. green (1.1.36) 90 10
70 2 c. orange (*ordinary paper*) (*p* 14×14½) (21.8.41) .. .. 3·50 75
a. Perf 14. Ordinary paper (9.41) .. 20·00 5·00
71 3 c. green (21.8.41) .. .. .. 16·00 2·75
a. Ordinary paper .. .. .. 1·25 7·50
72 4 c. orange 50 10
73 5 c. brown (5.12.35) 70 10
74 6 c. scarlet (1.1.37) .. .. .. 5·50 10
75 8 c. grey 60 10
76 10 c. dull purple (1.1.36) 60 10
77 12 c. bright ultramarine (1.1.36) .. .. 1·00 10
78 15 c. brt ultram (*ordinary paper*) (1.10.41) 12·00 32·00
79 25 c. dull purple and scarlet (1.4.36) .. 1·00 60
80 30 c. dull purple and orange (1.1.36) .. 1·00 85
81 40 c. scarlet and dull purple .. .. 1·25 1·25
82 50 c. black/*emerald* (1.2.36) .. .. 1·00 15
83 **47** $1 black and rose/*blue* (1.4.36) .. 7·00 90
84 $2 green and scarlet (16.5.36) .. .. 22·00 8·00
85 $5 green and red/*emerald* (16.5.36) .. 60·00 23·00
68/85 .. .. *Set of* 18 £110 60·00
68s/85s Perf "Specimen" .. *Set of* 18 £275

The stamps issued during 1941 were printed by Harrison and Sons following bomb damage to the De La Rue works on 29 December 1940.

Supplies of an unissued 8 c. scarlet were diverted to Australia in 1941. Examples circulating result from leakages of this supply (*Price* £500).

48 Sultan Hisamud-din Alam Shah 49

1941. *Wmk Mult Script CA. Chalk-surfaced paper. P* 14.
86 **48** $1 black and red/*blue* (15.4.41) .. .. 13·00 6·00
87 $2 green and scarlet (7.7.41) .. .. 48·00 27·00
s. Perf "Specimen" .. .. 70·00

A $5 green and red on emerald, T **48**, was issued overprinted during the Japanese occupation of Malaya. Unoverprinted examples are known, but were not issued (*Price* £110).

During shortages in 1941 stamps of STRAITS SETTLEMENTS (2 c.) and PERAK (25 c.) were issued in Selangor.

1948 (1 Dec). *Royal Silver Wedding. As Nos. 112/13 of Antigua.*
88 10 c. violet 20 10
89 $5 green .. .. 24·00 14·00

1949 (12 Sept)–**55.** *Wmk Mult Script CA. Chalk-surfa paper. P* 17½×18.
90 **49** 1 c. black 10
91 2 c. orange 10
92 3 c. green 75
93 4 c. brown 20
94 5 c. bright purple (1.9.52) 30
a. Bright mauve (17.9.53) 30
95 6 c. grey 20
96 8 c. scarlet 35
97 8 c. green (1.9.52) 65 1
98 10 c. purple 10
99 12 c. scarlet (1.9.52) 80 2
w. Wmk inverted £250
100 15 c. ultramarine .. .. .. 2·75
101 20 c. black and green .. .. .. 1·00
102 20 c. bright blue (1.9.52) 80
103 25 c. purple and orange .. .. 1·50
104 30 c. scarlet and purple (5.9.55) .. 1·50 1
105 35 c. scarlet and purple (1.9.52) .. 70 1
106 40 c. scarlet and purple .. .. 5·00 4
107 50 c. black and blue .. .. .. 1·25
108 $1 blue and purple .. .. .. 2·75
109 $2 green and scarlet .. .. .. 11·00
110 $5 green and brown .. .. .. 45·00 1
90/110 .. .. *Set of* 21 65·00 14

1949 (10 Oct). *75th Anniv of U.P.U. As Nos.* 114/17 *of Antig*
111 10 c. purple 30
112 15 c. deep blue .. .. 1·50 1
113 25 c. orange 35 2
114 50 c. blue-black .. .. 1·00 2
111/14 .. .. *Set of* 4 2·75 6

STAMP BOOKLETS

1935. *Stapled.*
SB1 $1 booklet containing twenty 5 c. (No. 73) in blocks of 10 .. ..
SB2 $1.30, booklet containing 5 c. and 8 c. (Nos. 73, 75), each in block of 10 .. .. ..

TRENGGANU

Suzerainty over Trengganu was transferred by Thailand Great Britain in 1909. A British adviser was appointed in 191

The state joined the Federation of Malaya on 1 February 194

PRICES FOR STAMPS ON COVER TO 1945	
Nos. 1/17	*from* × 12
No. 18	—
Nos. 19/22	*from* × 10
Nos. 23/33	*from* × 12
Nos. 34/6	—
Nos. 37/47	*from* × 15
Nos. 48/60	*from* × 6
Nos. D1/4	—

RED CROSS 2c.

1 Sultan Zain ul ab din 2 (3)

1910 (14 Dec)–**19.** *Wmk Mult Crown CA. Ordinary paper* (1 c *to* 10 c.) *or chalk-surfaced paper* (20 c. *to* $25). *P* 14.
1 **1** 1 c. blue-green .. .. 1·00 1·0
a. Green .. .. 2·25 1·0
2 2 c. brown and purple (1915) 70 9
3 3 c. carmine-red .. .. 2·25 2·2
4 4 c. orange .. .. 3·50 5·5
5 4 c. red-brown and green (1915) .. 2·00 3·7
5*a* 4 c. carmine-red (1919) .. .. .. 1·25 1·7
6 5 c. grey .. .. 1·25 3·2
7 5 c. grey and brown (1915) .. .. 2·25 2·0
8 8 c. ultramarine .. .. 1·25 9·0
9 10 c. purple/*yellow* .. .. .. 5·00 13·0
a. On pale yellow .. .. .. 3·25 5·0
10 10 c. green and red/*yellow* (1915) .. 1·25 2·2
11 20 c. dull and bright purple .. .. 3·50 4·2
12 25 c. green and dull purple (1915) .. 6·50 28·0
13 30 c. dull purple and black (1915) .. 6·50 50·0
14 50 c. black/*green* .. .. .. 4·50 7·5
15 $1 black and carmine/*blue* .. .. 16·00 20·0
16 $3 green and red/*green* (1915) £130 £27
17 **2** $5 green and dull purple (1912) .. £140 £40
18 $25 rose-carmine and green (1912) .. £900
s. Optd "Specimen" £190
1/17 .. .. *Set of* 18 £275 £75
1s/17s Optd "Specimen" .. *Set of* 18 £475

The 8 c. is known used bisected at Kretai in December 1918. Such use was not officially authorised.

1917 (June)–**18.** *Surch with T* **3**.
19 **1** 2 c. on 3 c. carmine-red .. .. .. 50 6·00
a. Comma after "2 c." .. .. .. 8·50 35·00
b. "SS" in "CROSS" inverted £325 £400
c. "CSOSS" for "CROSS" .. .. 90·00 £180
d. "2" in thick block type .. .. 20·00 55·00
e. Surch inverted £750 £800
f. Pair, one without surch £2750 £2250
g. "RED CROSS" omitted £275
h. "RED CROSS" twice £350
i. "2 c." omitted £275
j. "2 c." twice £325

2 c. on 4 c. orange .. .. .. 1·25 13·00
a. Comma after "2 c." .. .. .. 16·00 60·00
b. "SS" in "CROSS" inverted £1600 £1100
c. "CSOSS" for "CROSS" £170 £375
d. Surch double £900
e. "RED CROSS" omitted £325
f. "RED CROSS" twice £475
g. "2 c." omitted £325
h. "2 c." twice £425
2 c. on 4 c. red-brown and green (1918) 2·50 32·00
a. Pair, one without surch £1800
2 c. on 8 c. ultramarine (1917) .. .. 80 26·00
a. Comma after "2 c." .. .. .. 11·00 80·00
b. "SS" in "CROSS" inverted £700
c. "CSOSS" for "CROSS" £150 £400
d. "RED CROSS" omitted £325
e. "RED CROSS" twice £425
f. "2 c." omitted £325
g. "2 c." twice £400

surcharges on Nos. 19/22 were arranged in settings of 18 applied three times to cover the top nine rows of the sheet the tenth row completed by a further impression so that CROSS" from the centre row of the setting appears on the n sheet margin. Specialists recognise six different settings:

tting I — Shows comma after "2" on both R.1/3 and 1/5, "SS" inverted on R.1/6 and "CSOSS" for "CROSS" on R.2/1. Used for 4 c. orange and 8 c.
tting Ia — Inverted "SS" on R.1/6 corrected. Other varieties as Setting I. Used for 3 c., 4 c. orange and 8 c.
tting II — "CSOSS" on R.2/1 corrected. Comma varieties as Setting I. Used for 3 c., 4 c. orange and 8 c.
tting III — Both comma varieties now corrected. Used for 3 c., both 4 c. and 8 c.
tting IIIa — "SS" inverted on R.2/5. Used for 3 c. only
tting IV — Thick block "2" on R. 2/2. Inverted "SS" on R. 2/5 corrected. Used for 3 c. only.

s. 19g/j, 20e/h and 22d/g result from the misplacement of urcharge.

During a temporary shortage between March and August 21 2 c., 4 c. and 6 c. stamps of the STRAITS SETTLE-ENTS were authorised for use in Trengganu.

2 CENTS

4 Sultan Suleiman 5 (6)

1–41. *Chalk-surfaced paper. P 14. (a) Wmk Mult Crown A.*
4 $1 purple and blue/*blue* .. .. .. 12·00 21·00
$3 green and red/*emerald* .. .. 90·00 £200
5 $5 green and red/*pale yellow* .. .. 95·00 £300
5 .. .. *Set of* 3 £180 £475
5s Optd "Specimen" .. .. *Set of* 3 £110

(b) Wmk Mult Script CA
4 1 c. black (1926) .. .. .. 1·25 1·25
a. Ordinary paper (1941) .. .. — 21·00
2 c. green .. .. 1·25 1·60
a. Ordinary paper (1941) .. .. — 21·00
3 c. green (1926) .. .. .. 2·00 1·00
3 c. reddish brown (1938) .. .. 22·00 12·00
a. Ordinary paper. *Chestnut* (1941) .. — 17·00
4 c. rose-red .. .. 1·25 75
a. Ordinary paper. *Scarlet-verm* (1941) — 21·00
5 c. grey and deep brown .. .. 2·00 5·00
5 c. purple/*yellow* (1926) .. .. 1·75 1·25
a. Deep reddish purple/brt yellow (1939) £225 5·00
6 c. orange (1924) .. .. .. 3·25 30
a. Ordinary paper (1941) .. .. — 25·00
8 c. grey (1938) .. .. 25·00 5·00
a. Ordinary paper (1941) .. .. — 19·00
10 c. bright blue .. .. 2·00 1·00
12 c. bright ultramarine (1926) .. .. 4·25 4·50
20 c. dull purple and orange .. .. 2·00 1·50
25 c. green and deep purple .. .. 2·25 3·00
30 c. dull purple and black .. .. 3·25 3·25
35 c. carmine/*yellow* (1926) .. .. 4·75 8·00
50 c. green and bright carmine .. .. 5·50 2·75
$1 purple and blue/*blue* (1929) .. 9·00 3·75
$3 green and lake/*green* (1926) .. 60·00 £140
a. Green and brown-red/green (1938) .. £130
5 $5 green and red/*yellow* (1938) .. £250 £1500
$25 purple and blue £650 £1100
s. Optd "Specimen" £120
$50 green and yellow £1600 £2750
s. Optd "Specimen" £225
$100 green and scarlet £5000 £6000
s. Optd "Specimen" £450
/44 .. .. *Set of* 19 £350 £1600
s/44s Optd or Perf (3 c., 8 c., $1, $5) "Specimen" *Set of* 19 £650

The used price quoted for No. 44 is for an example with an entifiable cancellation from 1938–41.

Printings of the 2 c. yellow-orange, 3 c. blue-green, 4 c. rple/*yellow*, 6 c. slate-grey, 8 c. rose, 15 c. ultramarine and $1 ack and red/*blue* on ordinary paper were despatched to alaya in late 1941, but did not arrive before the Japanese cupation. Unused examples are known of the 2, 3, 6, 8 and c. (*Prices*, 3 c. £300, *others* £140 *each, unused*).

VERPRINT SETTINGS FOR NOS. 48/58. The low values Types **1** and **4** were overprinted using Setting II as detailed ider Straits Settlements. The three listed constant varieties om the original typeset block of 12 occur in the same positions r these Trengganu stamps as does the No stop variety from 1/5 of the left pane.

A separate setting, believed to be of 30 (6×5), was required for the $5 in the larger design. This was constructed by duplicating the second horizontal row of the original typeset block five times so that the raised stop after "EXHIBITION" variety occurs on all stamps in the second vertical row and the small second "A" in "MALAYA" on all stamps in the sixth.

1922 (Apr). *Malaya–Borneo Exhibition, Singapore. Optd as T* **56** *of Straits Settlements at Singapore.*
48 4 2 c. green .. .. 3·75 26·00
b. Oval last "O" in "BORNEO" .. 7·50 45·00
c. Raised stop after "EXHIBITION" .. 7·50 45·00
d. Small second "A" in "MALAYA" .. 7·50 45·00
f. No stop .. ..
49 4 c. rose-red .. .. 6·50 30·00
b. Oval last "O" in "BORNEO" .. 12·00 50·00
c. Raised stop after "EXHIBITION" .. 12·00 50·00
d. Small second "A" in "MALAYA" .. 12·00 50·00
f. No stop .. ..
50 1 5 c. grey and brown .. .. .. 3·25 35·00
b. Oval last "O" in "BORNEO" .. 6·50 55·00
c. Raised stop after "EXHIBITION" .. 6·50 55·00
d. Small second "A" in "MALAYA" .. 6·50 55·00
f. No stop .. ..
51 10 c. green and red/*yellow* .. .. 4·25 30·00
b. Oval last "O" in "BORNEO" .. 8·50 50·00
c. Raised stop after "EXHIBITION" .. 8·50 50·00
d. Small second "A" in "MALAYA" .. 8·50 50·00
f. No stop .. ..
52 20 c. dull and bright purple .. .. 4·25 35·00
b. Oval last "O" in "BORNEO" .. 8·50 55·00
c. Raised stop after "EXHIBITION" .. 8·50 55·00
d. Small second "A" in "MALAYA" .. 8·50 55·00
f. No stop .. ..
53 25 c. green and dull purple .. .. 4·00 35·00
b. Oval last "O" in "BORNEO" .. 8·00 55·00
c. Raised stop after "EXHIBITION" .. 8·00 55·00
d. Small second "A" in "MALAYA" .. 8·00 55·00
f. No stop .. ..
54 30 c. dull purple and black .. .. 4·25 35·00
b. Oval last "O" in "BORNEO" .. 8·50 55·00
c. Raised stop after "EXHIBITION" .. 8·50 55·00
d. Small second "A" in "MALAYA" .. 8·50 55·00
f. No stop .. ..
55 50 c. black/*green* .. .. .. 4·25 35·00
b. Oval last "O" in "BORNEO" .. 8·50 55·00
c. Raised stop after "EXHIBITION" .. 8·50 55·00
d. Small second "A" in "MALAYA" .. 8·50 55·00
f. No stop .. ..
56 $1 black and carmine/*blue* .. .. 12·00 70·00
b. Oval last "O" in "BORNEO" .. 21·00 £110
c. Raised stop after "EXHIBITION" .. 21·00 £110
d. Small second "A" in "MALAYA" .. 21·00 £110
f. No stop .. ..
57 $3 green and red/*green* £130 £375
b. Oval last "O" in "BORNEO" .. £190 £500
c. Raised stop after "EXHIBITION" .. £190 £500
d. Small second "A" in "MALAYA" .. £190 £500
f. No stop .. ..
58 2 $5 green and dull purple £250 £650
c. Raised stop after "EXHIBITION" .. £325 £750
d. Small second "A" in "MALAYA" .. £325 £750
48/58 .. .. *Set of* 11 £375 £1200

1941 (1 May). *Nos. 32a and 35 surch as T* **6**.
59 4 2 c. on 5 c. deep reddish purple/*brt yellow* 6·50 3·50
60 8 c. on 10 c. bright blue .. .. .. 7·00 3·50

1948 (2 Dec). *Royal Silver Wedding. As Nos. 112/13 of Antigua.*
61 10 c. violet .. .. 15 1·00
62 $5 carmine .. .. 22·00 35·00

1949 (10 Oct). *75th Anniv of U.P.U. As Nos. 114/17 of Antigua.*
63 10 c. purple 30 50
64 15 c. deep blue .. .. 1·10 2·50
65 25 c. orange .. .. 40 2·25
66 50 c. blue-black .. .. 1·00 3·00
a. "C" of "CA" missing from wmk ..
63/6 .. .. *Set of* 4 2·50 7·50

7 Sultan Ismail

1949 (27 Dec)–**55**. *Wmk Mult Script CA. Chalk-surfaced paper. P* $17^1/_2$×18.
67 7 1 c. black 10 30
68 2 c. orange 20 30
69 3 c. green .. .. 70 2·50
70 4 c. brown 20 30
71 5 c. bright purple (1.9.52) .. .. 30 1·25
72 6 c. grey 75 30
73 8 c. scarlet .. .. 30 2·00
74 8 c. green (1.9.52) .. .. .. 65 1·00
a. Deep green (11.8.53) .. .. 6·50 7·00
75 10 c. purple 30 10
76 12 c. scarlet (1.9.52) .. .. .. 65 2·00
77 15 c. ultramarine .. .. .. 1·25 30
78 20 c. black and green .. .. .. 1·75 2·50
79 20 c. bright blue (1.9.52) 80 30
80 25 c. purple and orange .. .. 1·25 1·50
81 30 c. scarlet and purple (5.9.55) .. 1·25 1·50
82 35 c. scarlet and purple (1.9.52) .. 70 1·75
83 40 c. red and purple .. .. .. 4·25 13·00
84 50 c. black and blue .. .. .. 1·50 1·75
85 $1 blue and purple .. .. .. 6·00 6·50
86 $2 green and scarlet .. .. .. 24·00 20·00
87 $5 green and brown .. .. .. 50·00 48·00
67/87 .. .. *Set of* 21 85·00 95·00

POSTAGE DUE STAMPS

D 1

1937 (10 Aug). *Wmk Mult Script CA (sideways). P* 14.
D1 D 1 1 c. scarlet .. .. 7·50 55·00
D2 4 c. green .. .. 9·50 60·00
D3 8 c. yellow .. .. 55·00 £325
D4 10 c. brown .. .. £110 95·00
D1/4 .. .. *Set of* 4 £160 £475
D1s/4s Perf "Specimen" .. .. *Set of* 4 £130

VI. SIAMESE POSTS IN NORTHERN MALAYA 1887–1909

The Thai monarchy exercised suzerainty over the northern states of the Malay Peninsula from the 16th century onwards. The extent of Thai involvement in the internal affairs of Kedah, Kelantan, Perlis and Trengganu was very variable, being dependent on the strength, or otherwise, of the Bangkok administration and the degree of co-operation of the local rulers.

The Thai public postal service, which had been inaugurated in 1883, gradually extended into the north of the Malay Peninsula from 1887 onwards and post offices were established in Kedah, Kelantan and Perlis. There is some evidence that Sultan Zainal Abidin III of Trengganu successfully blocked the use of Siamese stamps in his state.

Types of Thailand (Siam)

1

2

9

๑ อัฐ 1
(12)

๒ อัฐ 2
(17)

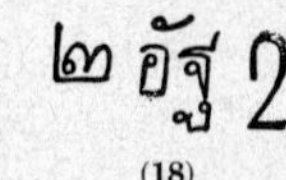

(18)

4 atts
(24)

4 atts
(25)

1 Atts.

ราคา ๑ อัฐ
(27)

2 Atts.
(28)

2
(33)

1 Att.

1 Att.

ราคา ๑ อัฐ
(34)

ราคา ๑ อัฐ
(35)

1 Att.
(36)

2 Atts.

10 Atts.

ราคา ๒ อัฐ
(37)

2 Atts.
(38)

ราคา ๑๐ อัฐ
(39)

4 Atts.
(40)

4 Atts.
(41)

1 Att.

ราคา ๑ อัฐ
(42)

2 Atts.
(44)

3 Atts.
(45)

4 Atts.
(46)

2 Atts.
(48*a*)

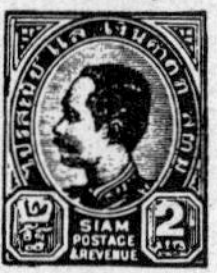

49

50

1 Att.

(51)

(56)

9 Atts

(59)

The following types of postmark were used on Siamese stamps from the Malay tributary states:

Type A. Single ring with date at foot (examples from 1900 show the year in manuscript)

Type B. Single ring with date in centre

Type C. Double ring. Bilingual

Type D. Double ring. English at top and ornament at foot

Type E. Double ring. English at top and bottom

PRICES are for stamps showing a large part of the postmark with the inscription clearly visible.

KEDAH

The Siamese post office at Alor Star was opened during 1887 with the first known postmark being dated 27 October. Further post offices at Kuala Muda (3 Oct 1907), Kulim (7 July 1907) and Langkawi (16 Feb 1908) followed.

A straight-line obliteration showing "KEDAH" between short vertical dashes is not believed to be genuine.

Alor Star

Stamps of SIAM *cancelled as Type* A *inscribed* "KEDAH".

1883. (*Nos.* 1/5).
Z2 **1** 1 att. rose-carmine £225
Z3 1 sio. red £425
Z4 **2** 1 sik. yellow £425

1887–91. (*Nos.* 11/18).
Z 6 **9** 1 a. green .. .. 80·00
Z 7 2 a. green and carmine .. .. .. 70·00
Z 8 3 a. green and blue .. .. 90·00
Z 9 4 a. green and brown .. .. .. 80·00
Z10 8 a. green and yellow .. .. .. 80·00
Z11 12 a. purple and carmine .. .. .. 70·00
Z12 24 a. purple and blue .. .. 80·00
Z13 64 a. purple and brown £130

1889–91. *Surch as T* **12** (*Nos.* Z15, Z19), *T* **17** (*No.* Z21) *or T* **18** (*No.* Z22) (*Nos.* 20/30).
Z15 **9** 1 a. on 2 a. green and carmine .. .. 90·00
Z19 1 a. on 3 a. green and blue £100
Z21 2 a. on 3 a. green and blue £130
Z22 2 a. on 3 a. green and blue £160

1892. *Surch as T* **24/5** (*with or without stop*) *and Siamese handstamp* (*Nos.* 33/6).
Z28 **9** 4 a. on 24 a. purple and blue (Type **24**) .. 90·00
Z29 4 a. on 24 a. purple and blue (Type **25**) .. £110
Z30 4 a. on 24 a. purple and blue (Type **24** with stop) £110
Z31 4 a. on 24 a. purple and blue (Type **25** with stop) £110

1894. *Surch as T* **27** *with variations of English figures as T* **28** *and* **33** (*Nos.* 37/44).
Z34 **9** 2 a. on 64 a. purple and brown (Type **28**) .. 90·00
Z39 2 a. on 64 a. purple and brown (Type **33**) .. 90·00

1894. *Surch with T* **34** (*No.* 45).
Z41 **9** 1 a. on 64 a. purple and brown £110

1894–95. *Surch as T* **35** *with variations of English figures as T* **36/9** (*Nos.* 46/50).
Z42 **9** 1 a. on 64 a. purple and brown (Type **35**) .. 90·00
Z43 1 a. on 64 a. purple and brown (Type **36**) .. 90·00
Z44 2 a. on 64 a. purple and brown (Type **37**) .. 90·00
Z45 2 a. on 64 a. purple and brown (Type **38**) .. 90·00
Z46 10 a. on 24 a. purple and blue (Type **39**) .. 90·00

1896. *Surch as T* **39** (*Siamese*) *and T* **40** (*English*) (*No.* 51).
Z47 **9** 4 a. on 12 a. purple and carmine .. .. 90·00

1897. *Surch as T* **39** (*Siamese*) *and T* **41** (*English*) (*No.* 52).
Z48 **9** 4 a. on 12 a. purple and carmine .. .. 90·00

1898–99. *Surch as T* **42** *with variations of English section as T* **44/6** (*Nos.* 53/62).
Z49 **9** 1 a. on 12 a. purple and carmine (Type **42**–11½ mm long) £120
Z52 2 a. on 64 a. purple and brown (Type **44**) .. £100
Z53 3 a. on 12 a. purple and carmine (Type **45**–13½ mm long) .. .. 90·00
Z54 3 a. on 12 a. purple and carmine (Type **45**–11½ to 11¾ mm long) .. .. 90·00
Z55 4 a. on 12 a. purple & carm (Type **46**–8 mm long) 90·00
Z56 4 a. on 12 a. purple and carmine (Type **46**–8½ to 9 mm long) .. .. 90·00

1899. *Surch in Siamese and English with T* **48a** (*Nos.* 63/6).
Z62 **9** 2 a. on 64 a. purple and brown £100

1899–1904. (*Nos.* 67/81).
Z63 **49** 1 a. olive-green (wide Siamese characters in face value) .. .. 90·00
Z64 2 a. grass-green .. .. 70·00
Z65 3 a. red and blue .. .. 75·00
Z66 4 a. carmine .. .. 70·00
Z67 8 a. deep green and orange .. .. .. 70·00
Z69 12 a. brown-purple and carmine £110
Z70 24 a. brown-purple and blue £160
Z71 64 a. brown-purple and chestnut £130

1899. (*Nos.* 82/6).
Z72 **50** 1 a. green £275
Z73 2 a. green and red £425

Stamps of SIAM *cancelled as Type* B *inscr* "KEDAH" (*from* March 1901).

1887–91. (*Nos.* 11/18).
Z74 **9** 12 a. purple and carmine .. .. .. 70·00
Z75 24 a. purple and brown .. .. .. 70·00

1898–99. *Surch with T* **42** *with variations of English section as T* **45/6** (*Nos.* 53/62).
Z76 **9** 1 a. on 12 a. pur & carm (Type **42**–11½ mm long) 90·00
Z81 3 a. on 12 a. purple and carmine (Type **45**–11½ to 11¾ mm long) .. .. 70·00
Z83 4 a. on 12 a. purple and carmine (Type **46**–8½ to 9 mm long) .. .. 70·00
Z84 4 a. on 24 a. purple and blue (Type **46**) .. 75·00

1899–1904. (*Nos.* 67/81).
Z86 **49** 1 a. olive-green (wide Siamese characters in face value) .. .. 70·00
a. Narrow Siamese characters in face value 65·00
Z87 2 a. grass-green .. .. 55·00
Z88 2 a. scarlet and pale blue .. .. .. 55·00
Z89 3 a. red and blue .. .. 65·00
Z90 3 a. deep green .. .. 65·00
Z91 4 a. carmine .. .. 55·00
Z92 4 a. chocolate and pink .. .. .. 60·00
Z93 8 a. deep green and orange .. .. .. 55·00
Z94 10 a. ultramarine .. .. 55·00
Z95 12 a. brown-purple and carmine .. .. 65·00
Z96 24 a. brown-purple and blue £130
Z97 64 a. brown-purple and chestnut £120

1905–09. (*Nos.* 92/105).
Z102 **53** 1 a. green and orange .. .. ..
Z103 2 a. grey and deep violet .. .. ..
Z104 3 a. green .. ..
Z105 4 a. pale red and sepia .. .. ..
Z106 5 a. carmine .. ..
Z107 8 a. olive-bistre and dull black .. ..
Z108 12 a. blue .. ..
Z109 24 a. red-brown .. ..
Z110 1 t. bistre and deep blue .. .. ..

Stamps of SIAM *cancelled as Type* C *inscr* "Kedah" *at foot* July 1907).

1887–91. (*Nos.* 11/18).
Z111 **9** 12 a. purple and carmine 8

1899–1904. (*Nos.* 67/81).
Z112 **49** 1 a. olive-green (wide Siamese characters in face value) 6
a. Narrow Siamese characters in face value 6
Z113 2 a. scarlet and pale blue 5
Z114 3 a. red and blue 6
Z116 8 a. deep green and orange 6
Z117 10 a. ultramarine 6
Z118 12 a. brown-purple and carmine 6

1905–09. (*Nos.* 95/105).
Z128 **53** 1 a. green and orange 5
Z129 2 a. grey and deep violet 5
Z130 3 a. green 6
Z131 4 a. pale red and sepia 5
Z132 4 a. scarlet 5
Z133 5 a. carmine 6
Z134 8 a. olive-bistre and dull black 5
Z135 9 a. blue 5
Z136 18 a. red-brown 9
Z137 24 a. red-brown .. .. £
Z138 1 t. bistre and deep blue .. .. .. £

1907. *Surch with T* **56** (*No.* 109).
Z139 **9** 1 a. on 24 a. purple and blue 6

Kuala Muda

Stamps of SIAM *cancelled as Type* B *inscr* "KUALA MU (*from* Oct 1907).

1887–91. (*Nos.* 11/18).
Z143 **9** 12 a. purple and carmine .. .. .. £

1899–1904. (*Nos.* 67/81).
Z144 **49** 2 a. scarlet and pale blue .. .. .. £
Z145 24 a. brown-purple and blue .. .. .. £

1905–09. (*Nos.* 92/105).
Z146 **53** 1 a. green and orange .. .. .. £
Z147 2 a. grey and deep violet .. .. .. £
Z148 3 a. green .. .. £
Z150 5 a. carmine .. .. £
Z151 8 a. olive-bistre and dull black .. .. £

Stamps of SIAM *cancelled as Type* C *inscr* "Kwala Muda" *at* (*from* 1907).

1887–91. (*Nos.* 11/18).
Z155 **9** 12 a. purple and carmine £1

1899–1904. (*Nos.* 67/81).
Z156 **49** 8 a. deep green and orange £1
Z157 10 a. ultramarine £1

1905–09. (*Nos.* 92/105).
Z158 **53** 1 a. green and orange £1
Z159 2 a. grey and deep violet £1
Z160 3 a. green £1
Z161 4 a. pale red and sepia £1
Z162 4 a. scarlet £1
Z163 5 a. carmine £2
Z164 8 a. olive-bistre and dull black £1
Z165 9 a. blue £1
Z166 24 a. red-brown £3

1907. *Surch with T* **56** (*No.* 109).
Z167 **9** 1 a. on 24 a. purple and blue £1

Kulim

Stamps of SIAM *cancelled as Type* D *inscr* "KULIM" (*from* Ju 1907).

1887–91. (*Nos.* 11/18).
Z173 **9** 12 a. purple and carmine £32

1899–1904. (*Nos.* 67/81).
Z174 **49** 8 a. deep green and orange £32

1905–09. (*Nos.* 92/105).
Z175 **53** 1 a. green and orange £35
Z176 2 a. grey and deep violet £35
Z177 3 a. green £37
Z178 4 a. pale red and sepia £32
Z179 4 a. scarlet £32
Z180 5 a. carmine £35
Z181 8 a. olive-bistre and dull black £32
Z182 9 a. blue £32

Surch with T **56**. (*No.* 109).
9 1 a. on 24 a. purple and blue £325

s of SIAM *cancelled as Type* C *inscr* "Kulim" *at foot* (*from* 1908).

91. (*Nos.* 11/18).
9 12 a. purple and carmine £130

1904. (*Nos.* 67/81).
49 8 a. deep green and orange £130
10 a. ultramarine £140

09. (*Nos.* 92/105).
53 4 a. pale red and sepia £130
4 a. scarlet £130
5 a. carmine £140
9 a. blue £140
24 a. red-brown £325
1 t. bistre and deep blue £325

Surch with T **56** (*No.* 109).
9 1 a. on 24 a. purple and blue £140

Langkawi

ps of SIAM *cancelled as Type* D *inscr* "LANGKAWI" (*from* b 1908).

–1904. (*Nos.* 67/81).
49 8 a. deep green and orange £325
10 a. ultramarine £325

–09. (*Nos.* 92/105).
53 3 a. green £350
4 a. pale red and sepia £325
8 a. olive-bistre and dull black £325

ps of SIAM *cancelled as Type* C *inscr* "Langkawi" *at foot* om Nov 1908).

–91. (*Nos.* 11/18).
9 12 a. purple and carmine £140

–1904. (*Nos.* 67/81)
49 1 a. olive-green (Type B) £150
8 a. green and orange £140

5–09. (*Nos.* 92/105).
2 **53** 2 a. grey and deep violet £140
3 3 a. green £190
4 4 a. pale red and sepia £140
5 4 a. scarlet £150
6 8 a. olive-bistre and dull black £140
8 24 a. red-brown £375
9 1 t. bistre and deep blue £375

7. *Surch with T* **56** (*No.* 109).
0 **9** 1 a. on 24 a. purple and blue £150

KELANTAN

he first Siamese post office in Kelantan opened at Kota aru in 1895. It appears that in the early years this office only epted letters franked with stamps for delivery within antan.

he initial cancellation, of which no complete example has n discovered, showed Thai characters only. Partial examples ve been reported on the 1887–91 8 a. and 1896 4 a. on 12 a.

he operations of the Duff Development Company in lantan from 1903 led to a considerable expansion of the postal vice based on the company's river steamers. A further post ice opened at Batu Mengkebang in 1908, but may have been ceded by manuscript endorsements of "B.M." and date known m early 1907 onwards.

Kota Bharu

amps of SIAM *cancelled as Type* B *inscr* "KALANTAN" (*from* March 1898).

87–91. (*Nos.* 11/18).
37 **9** 2 a. green and carmine 90·00
38 3 a. green and blue 95·00
39 4 a. green and brown 95·00
40 8 a. green and yellow 95·00
41 12 a. purple and carmine 85·00
42 24 a. purple and blue 90·00

94. *Surch as T* **27** *with variation of English figures as T* **33** (*Nos.* 37/44).
51 **9** 2 a. on 64 a. purple and brown £130

94–95. *Surch as T* **35** *with variation of English figures as T* **36** (*Nos.* 46/50).
255 **9** 1 a. on 64 a. purple and brown £110

96. *Surch as T* **39** (*Siamese*) *and T* **40** (*English*) (*No.* 51).
259 **9** 4 a. on 12 a. purple and carmine £110

897. *Surch as T* **39** (*Siamese*) *and T* **41** (*English*) (*No.* 52).
260 **9** 4 a. on 12 a. purple and carmine £110

898–99. *Surch as T* **42** *with variation of English section as T* **46** (*Nos.* 53/62).
267 **9** 4 a. on 12 a. purple and carmine (8 mm long) £110

1899–1904. (*Nos.* 67/81).
Z275 **49** 1 a. olive-green (wide Siamese characters in face value) 90·00
Z276 2 a. grass-green 85·00
Z277 2 a. scarlet and pale blue 85·00
Z278 3 a. red and blue 95·00
Z279 4 a. carmine 85·00
Z280 4 a. chocolate and pink 95·00
Z281 8 a. deep green and orange 85·00
Z282 10 a. ultramarine 90·00
Z283 12 a. brown-purple and carmine 90·00
Z284 64 a. brown-purple and chestnut £190

1905–09. (*Nos.* 92/105).
Z293 **53** 1 a. green and orange 85·00
Z294 2 a. grey and deep violet 85·00
Z296 4 a. pale red and sepia 85·00
Z297 4 a. scarlet 85·00
Z298 5 a. carmine £100
Z299 8 a. olive-bistre and dull black 85·00
Z300 12 a. blue £100
Z301 24 a. red-brown £275
Z302 1 t. bistre and deep blue £275

1907. *Surch with T* **56** (*No.* 109).
Z303 **9** 1 a. on 24 a. purple and blue £110

Stamps of SIAM *cancelled as Type* E *inscr* "Kota Bahru/ Kelantan" (*from* July 1908).

1887–91. (*Nos.* 11/18).
Z307 **9** 12 a. purple and carmine 85·00
Z308 24 a. purple and blue £110

1899–1904. (*Nos.* 67/81).
Z309 **49** 8 a. deep green and orange 90·00
Z310 64 a. brown-purple and chestnut £130

1905–09. (*Nos.* 92/105).
Z311 **53** 1 a. green and orange 90·00
Z312 2 a. grey and deep violet 90·00
Z313 2 a. pale yellow-green 90·00
Z314 4 a. pale red and sepia 90·00
Z315 4 a. scarlet 90·00
Z316 8 a. olive-bistre and dull black 85·00
Z317 9 a. blue 95·00
Z318 18 a. red-brown £150

1907. *Surch with T* **56** (*No.* 109).
Z320 **9** 1 a. on 24 a. purple and blue 90·00

1908. *Surch as T* **59** (*Nos.* 110/12).
Z326 **9** 2 a. on 24 a. purple and blue £130
Z327 **53** 4 a. on 5 a. carmine £160
Z328 **49** 9 a. on 10 a. ultramarine £100

Batu Mengkebang

Stamps of SIAM *cancelled as Type* E *inscr* "Batu Menkebang/ Kelantan" (*from* July 1908).

1887–91. (*Nos.* 11/18).
Z329 **9** 12 a. purple and carmine £150

1899–1904. (*Nos.* 67/81).
Z330 **49** 8 a. deep green and orange £160

1905–09. (*Nos.* 92/105).
Z331 **53** 1 a. green and orange £150
Z332 2 a. grey and deep violet £150
Z333 2 a. pale yellow-green £160
Z334 4 a. pale red and sepia £160
Z335 4 a. scarlet £150
Z336 8 a. olive-bistre and dull black £130
Z337 9 a. blue £130
Z338 12 a. blue £190
Z339 24 a. red-brown £325
Z340 1 t. bistre and deep blue £350

1907. *Surch with T* **56** (*No.* 109)
Z341 **9** 1 a. on 24 a. purple and blue £130

1908. *Surch as T* **59** (*Nos.* 110/12).
Z347 **49** 9 a. on 10 a. ultramarine £190

PERLIS

The Siamese post office at Kangar is recorded as opening during 1894. It is believed that the initial cancellation showed Thai characters only, but no complete example has so far been discovered.

Stamps of SIAM *cancelled as Type* B *inscr* "PERLIS" (*from* July 1904).

1887–91. (*Nos.* 11/18).
Z349 **9** 12 a. purple and carmine £150
Z350 24 a. purple and blue £200

1897. *Surch as T* **39** (*Siamese*) *and T* **41** (*English*) (*No.* 52).
Z351 **9** 4 a. on 12 a. purple and carmine £275

1899–1904. (*Nos.* 67/81).
Z352 **49** 1 a. olive-green (wide Siamese characters in face value) £180
Z353 2 a. grass-green £160
Z354 2 a. scarlet and pale blue £160
Z355 3 a. red and blue £250
Z356 4 a. carmine £160
Z357 4 a. chocolate and pink £160
Z358 8 a. deep green and orange £160
Z359 10 a. ultramarine £160
Z360 12 a. brown-purple and carmine £150
Z361 24 a. brown-purple and blue £300

1905–09. (*Nos.* 97/105).
Z370 **53** 1 a. green and orange £150
Z371 2 a. grey and deep violet £150
Z372 3 a. green £160
Z373 4 a. pale red and sepia £150
Z374 5 a. carmine £160
Z375 8 a. olive-bistre and dull black £150
Z376 12 a. blue £170
Z377 24 a. red-brown £250

Stamps of SIAM *cancelled as Type* C *inscr* "Perlis" *at foot* (*from* Sept. 1907).

1887–91. (*Nos.* 11/18).
Z379 **9** 12 a. purple and carmine £170

1899–1904. (*Nos.* 67/81).
Z380 **49** 1 a. olive-green (narrow Siamese characters in face value) £180
Z381 8 a. deep green and orange £170
Z382 10 a. ultramarine £180

1905–09. (*Nos.* 92/105).
Z383 **53** 1 a. green and orange £180
Z384 2 a. grey and deep violet £170
Z385 3 a. green £180
Z386 4 a. pale red and sepia £170
Z387 4 a. scarlet £180
Z388 5 a. carmine £180
Z389 8 a. olive-bistre and dull black £180
Z390 9 a. blue £170
Z391 24 a. red-brown £300

1907. *Surch with T* **56** (*No.* 109).
Z392 **9** 1 a. on 24 a. purple and blue £180

Siam transferred suzerainty over the four northern Malay states to Great Britain on 15 July 1909. Use of Siamese stamps in Kelantan and Perlis appears to have extended into early August 1909.

VII. JAPANESE OCCUPATION OF MALAYA

PRICES FOR STAMPS ON COVER

Nos. J1/55	*from* × 10
Nos. J56/76	*from* × 12
Nos. J77/89	*from* × 20
Nos. J90/1	*from* × 15
Nos. J92/115	*from* × 6
Nos. J116/18	—
Nos. J119/32	*from* × 12
Nos. J133/45	*from* × 10
Nos. J146/223	*from* × 6
Nos. J224/58	*from* × 12
No. J259	*from* × 15
Nos. J260/96	*from* × 12
Nos. J297/310	*from* × 20
Nos. J311/17	—
Nos. JD1/10	*from* × 30
Nos. JD11/16	*from* × 12
Nos. JD17/20	*from* × 30
Nos. JD21/7	*from* × 20
Nos. JD28/33	*from* × 30
Nos. JD34/41	*from* × 60

Japanese forces invaded Malaya on 8 December 1941 with the initial landings taking place at Kota Bharu on the east coast. Penang fell, to a force which crossed the border from Thailand, on 19 December, Kuala Lumpur on 11 January 1942 and the conquest of the Malay penisula was completed by the capture of Singapore on 15 February.

During the Japanese Occupation various small Dutch East Indies islands near Singapore were administered as part of Malaya. Stamps of the Japanese Occupation of Malaya were issued to the post offices of Dabo Singkep, Puloe Samboe, Tanjong Balei, Tanjong Batu, Tanjong Pinang and Terempa between 1942 and 1945. The overprinted issues were also used by a number of districts in Atjeh (Northern Sumatra) whose postal services were administered from Singapore until the end of March 1943.

Malayan post offices were also opened in October 1943 to serve camps of civilians working on railway construction and maintenance in Thailand. Overprinted stamps of the Japanese Occupation of Malaya were used at these offices between October 1943 and the end of the year after which mail from the camps was carried free. Their postmarks were inscribed in Japanese Katakana characters, and, uniquely, showed the Japanese postal symbol.

JOHORE

The postal service in Johore was reconstituted in mid-April 1942 using Nos. J146/60 and subsequently other general issues. Stamps of Johore overprinted "DAI NIPPON 2602" were, however, only used for fiscal purposes. Overprinted Johore postage due stamps were not issued for use elsewhere in Malaya.

POSTAGE DUE STAMPS

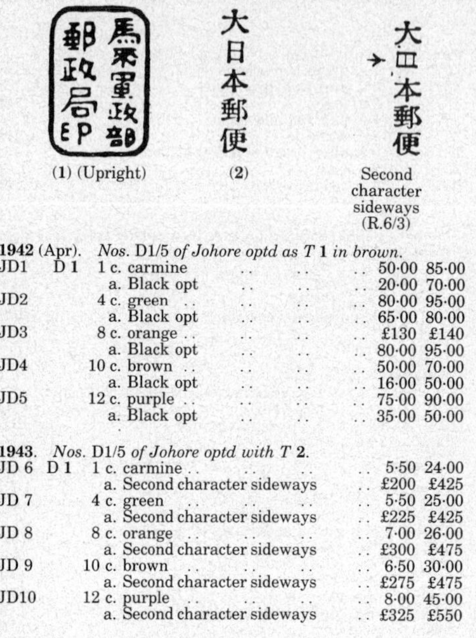

(1) (Upright) (2) Second character sideways (R.6/3)

1942 (Apr). *Nos.* D1/5 *of Johore optd as T* **1** *in brown.*
JD1 **D 1** 1 c. carmine .. .. .. 50·00 85·00
a. Black opt .. .. .. 20·00 70·00
JD2 4 c. green .. .. .. 80·00 95·00
a. Black opt .. .. .. 65·00 80·00
JD3 8 c. orange £130 £140
a. Black opt .. .. .. 80·00 95·00
JD4 10 c. brown .. .. .. 50·00 70·00
a. Black opt .. .. .. 16·00 50·00
JD5 12 c. purple .. .. .. 75·00 90·00
a. Black opt .. .. .. 35·00 50·00

1943. *Nos.* D1/5 *of Johore optd with T* **2**.
JD 6 **D 1** 1 c. carmine .. .. .. 5·50 24·00
a. Second character sideways .. £200 £425
JD 7 4 c. green .. .. .. 5·50 25·00
a. Second character sideways .. £225 £425
JD 8 8 c. orange .. .. .. 7·00 26·00
a. Second character sideways .. £300 £475
JD 9 10 c. brown .. .. .. 6·50 30·00
a. Second character sideways .. £275 £475
JD10 12 c. purple .. .. .. 8·00 45·00
a. Second character sideways .. £325 £550

KEDAH

Postal services resumed by 31 January 1942 using unoverprinted Kedah values from 1 c. to 8 c. which were accepted for postage until 13 May 1942.

During the Japanese occupation Perlis was administered as part of Kedah.

DAI NIPPON 2602 (3) DAI NIPPON 2602 (4)

1942 (13 May)–**43**. *Stamps of Kedah (Script wmk) optd with T* **3** *(1 c. to 8 c.) or* **4** *(10 c. to $5), both in red.*
J 1 **1** 1 c. black (No. 68*a*) .. .. 4·25 7·50
J 2 2 c. bright green (No. 69) .. .. 25·00 30·00
J 3 4 c. violet .. .. .. 4·00 4·00
J 4 5 c. yellow .. .. .. 3·75 4·00
a. Black opt (1943) £200 £225
J 5 6 c. carmine (No. 56) (Blk.) .. 3·00 10·00
J 6 8 c. grey-black .. .. .. 3·25 2·00
J 7 **6** 10 c. ultramarine and sepia .. .. 10·00 10·00
J 8 12 c. black and violet .. .. 25·00 35·00
J 9 25 c. ultramarine and purple .. .. 7·50 11·00
a. Black opt (1943) £250 £250
J10 30 c. green and scarlet .. .. 65·00 80·00
J11 40 c. black and purple .. .. 32·00 48·00
J12 50 c. brown and blue .. .. 32·00 50·00
J13 $1 black and green £140 £150
a. Opt inverted £650 £650
J14 $2 green and brown £170 £170
J15 $5 black and scarlet .. .. 65·00 85·00
a. Black opt (1943) £850 £850

Nos. J1/15 were gradually replaced by issues intended for use throughout Malaya. Kedah and Perlis were ceded to Thailand by the Japanese on 19 October 1943.

KELANTAN

Postal services resumed on 1 June 1942. Stamps used in Kelantan were overprinted with the personal seals of Sunagawa, the Japanese Governor, and of Handa, the Assistant Governor.

(5) Sunagawa Seal

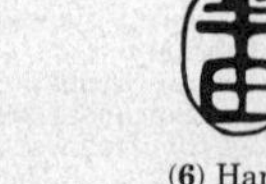

(6) Handa Seal

40 CENTS (7) $1.00 (8)

1 Cents (9)

1942 (June). *Stamps of Kelantan surch*

(*a*) *As T* **7** *or* **8** *(dollar values). Optd with T* **5** *in red*
J16 **4** 1 c. on 50 c. grey-olive and orange .. £225 £180
J17 2 c. on 40 c. orange and blue-green .. £550 £300
J18 4 c. on 30 c. violet and scarlet .. £1700 £1200
J19 5 c. on 12 c. blue (R.) £225 £190
J20 6 c. on 25 c. vermilion and violet .. £275 £190
J21 8 c. on 5 c. red-brown (R.) £350 £140
J22 10 c. on 6 c. lake .. .. 75·00 £120
a. "CENST" for "CENTS" .. £3000
J23 12 c. on 8 c. grey-olive (R.) .. .. 48·00 £110
J24 25 c. on 10 c. purple (R.) £1200 £1300
J25 30 c. on 4 c. scarlet £1800 £2000
J26 40 c. on 2 c. green (R.) .. .. 55·00 85·00
a. Surch double (B.+R.) £1800
J27 50 c. on 1 c. grey-olive and yellow .. £1400 £1300
J28 **1** $1 on 4 c. black and red (R., bars Blk.) 50·00 80·00
J29 $2 on 5 c. green and red/*yellow* .. 50·00 80·00
J30 $5 on 6 c. scarlet .. .. 50·00 80·00
a. Surch double £375

(*b*) *As T* **7**. *Optd with T* **6** *in red*
J31 **4** 12 c. on 8 c. grey-olive £160 £250
a. Type **6** omitted (in horiz pair with normal) £1800

(*c*) *As T* **9**. *Optd with T* **5** *in red.*
J32 **4** 1 c. on 50 c. grey-olive and orange .. £150 95·00
a. "Cente" for "Cents" (R. 5/1) .. £1400 £1100
J33 2 c. on 40 c. orange and blue-green .. £130 95·00
a. "Cente" for "Cents" (R. 5/1) .. £1300
J34 5 c. on 12 c. blue (R.) £130 £120
a. "Cente" for "Cents" (R. 5/1) .. £1300
J35 8 c. on 5 c. red-brown (R.) .. .. £110 75·00
a. "Cente" for "Cents" (R. 5/1) .. £1100 £950
J36 10 c. on 6 c. lake £300 £325
a. "Cente" for "Cents" (R. 5/1) .. £2250

(*d*) *As T* **9**. *Optd with T* **6** *in red.*
J41 **4** 1 c. on 50 c. grey-olive and orange .. 95·00 £140
a. "Cente" for "Cents" (R. 5/1) .. £1200
J42 2 c. on 40 c. orange and blue-green .. £100 £150
a. "Cente" for "Cents" (R. 5/1) .. £1200
J43 8 c. on 5 c. red-brown (R.) .. .. 65·00 £130
a. "Cente" for "Cents" (R. 5/1) .. £1000
J44 10 c. on 6 c. lake .. .. .. 85·00 £150
a. "Cente" for "Cents" (R. 5/1) .. £1200

As stamps of the above series became exhausted the equivalent values from the series intended for use throughout Malaya were introduced. Stamps as Nos. J28/30, J32/3 and J35/6, but without Type **5** or **6**, are from remainders sent to Singapore or Kuala Lumpur after the state had been ceded to Thailand (*Price from* £16 *each unused*). Nos. J19, J21, J23 and J25/6 have also been seen without Type **5** (*Price from* £60 *each unused*).

The 12 c. on 8 c., 30 c. on 4 c., 40 c. on 2 c. and 50 c. on 1 c. surcharged with Type **9**, formerly listed as Nos. J37/40, are now believed to exist only as remainders without the Type **5** red handstamp (*Price from* £20 *each, unused*).

Kelantan was ceded to Thailand by the Japanese on 19 October 1943.

MALACCA

Postal services from Malacca resumed on 21 April 1942, but there were no stamps available for two days.

PRICES. Those quoted are for single stamps. Blocks of four showing the complete handstamp are worth from five times the price of a single stamp.

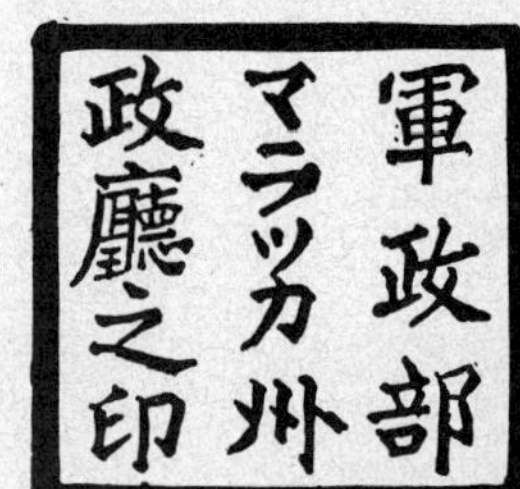

(**10**) "Military Administration Malacca State Government Seal"

1942 (23 Apr). *Stamps of Straits Settlements handstamped as T* **10**, *in red, each impression covering four stamps.*

Single Un. Used
J45 **58** 1 c. black .. .. .. 80·00 65·00
J46 2 c. orange .. .. .. 55·00 65·00
J47 3 c. green .. .. .. 55·00 70·00
J48 5 c. brown £120 £130
J49 8 c. grey £170 £110
J50 10 c. dull purple .. .. .. 80·00 90·00
J51 12 c. ultramarine .. .. .. 90·00 £100
J52 15 c. ultramarine .. .. .. 70·00 85·00
J53 40 c. scarlet and dull purple £550 £600
J54 50 c. black/*emerald* £850 £850
J55 $1 black and red/*blue* £900 £850

The 30 c., $2 and $5 also exist with this overprint, but these values were not available to the public. (*Price for set of* 3 £4250 *unused*)

POSTAGE DUE STAMPS

1942 (23 Apr). *Postage Due stamps of Malayan Postal Union handstamped as T* **10**, *in red, each impression covering four stamps.*
JD11 **D 1** 1 c. slate-purple £200 £180
JD12 4 c. green £225 £225
JD13 8 c. scarlet £1900 £1500
JD14 10 c. yellow-orange £425 £375
JD15 12 c. ultramarine £600 £500
JD16 50 c. black £1800 £1400

Nos. J45/55 and JD11/16 were replaced during May 1942 by the overprinted issues intended for use throughout Malaya.

PENANG

Postal services on Penang Island resumed on 30 March using Straits Settlements stamps overprinted by Japanese of the Government Accountant, Mr. A. Okugawa, and assistant, Mr. Itchiburi.

(**11**) Okugawa Seal (**12**) Itchiburi Seal DAI NI 260 PENAN (**13**)

1942 (30 Mar). *Straits Settlements stamps optd.*

(*a*) *As T* **11** *(three forms of the seal)*
J56 **58** 1 c. black .. .. .. 9·50
J57 2 c. orange .. .. .. 24·00
J58 3 c. green .. .. .. 20·00
J59 5 c. brown .. .. .. 24·00
J60 8 c. grey .. .. .. 26·00
J61 10 c. dull purple .. .. .. 50·00
J62 12 c. ultramarine .. .. .. 28·00
J63 15 c. ultramarine .. .. .. 45·00
J64 40 c. scarlet and dull purple .. .. 90·00
J65 50 c. black/*emerald* £200
J66 $1 black and red/*blue* £200
J67 $2 green and scarlet £600
J68 $5 green and red/*emerald* £1700

(*b*) *With T* **12**
J69 **58** 1 c. black £140
J70 2 c. orange £130
J71 3 c. green .. .. .. 95·00
J72 5 c. brown £1600
J73 8 c. grey .. .. .. 75·00
J74 10 c. dull purple £120
J75 12 c. ultramarine .. .. .. 90·00
J76 15 c. ultramarine £100

Straits Settlements stamps overprinted with a similar impression, but circular and containing four characters, believed to be fiscal issues.

1942 (15 Apr). *Straits Settlements stamps optd with T* **13** *Penang Premier Press.*
J77 **58** 1 c. black (R.) .. .. .. 3·25
a. Opt inverted £375
b. Opt double £300
J78 2 c. orange .. .. .. 4·25
a. "PE" for "PENANG" £100 8
b. Opt inverted £150
c. Opt double £375
J79 3 c. green (R.) .. .. .. 4·25
a. Opt double, one inverted £350
J80 5 c. brown (R.) .. .. .. 2·50
a. "N PPON" £180
b. Opt double £350
J81 8 c. grey (R.) .. .. .. 2·25
a. "N PPON" .. .. .. 50·00 55
b. Opt double, one inverted £375
J82 10 c. dull purple (R.) .. .. 1·50
a. Opt double £375
b. Opt double, one inverted £400
J83 12 c. ultramarine (R.) .. .. 3·25 12
a. "N PPON" £450
b. Opt double £375
c. Opt double, one inverted £475
J84 15 c. ultramarine (R.) .. .. 1·75
a. "N PPON" £100
b. Opt inverted £400
c. Opt double £475
J85 40 c. scarlet and dull purple .. .. 4·25 12
J86 50 c. black/*emerald* (R.) .. .. 3·75 22
J87 $1 black and red/*blue* .. .. 6·00 28
a. Opt inverted £850
J88 $2 green and scarlet .. .. 50·00 80
J89 $5 green and red/*emerald* £475

Nos. J77/89 were replaced by the overprinted issues intended for use throughout Malaya.

SELANGOR

Postal services resumed in the Kuala Lumpur area on 3 April 1942 and gradually extended to the remainder of the state. Stamps of the general overprinted issue were used, but the following commemorative set was only available in Selangor.

SELANGOR EXHIBITION DAI NIPPON 2602 MALAYA

(**14**)

1942 (3 Nov). *Selangor Agri-horticultural Exhibition. Nos* 294 *and* 283 *of Straits Settlements optd with T* **14**.
J90 **58** 2 c. orange .. .. .. 12·00 24·
a. "C" for "G" in "SELANGOR" (R. 1/9) £325
b. Opt inverted £300
J91 8 c. grey .. .. .. 13·00 24·
a. "C" for "G" in "SELANGOR" (R. 1/9) £325
b. Opt inverted £300

NEW INFORMATION

The editor is always interested to correspond with people who have new information that will improve or correct the Catalogue.

SINGAPORE

first post offices re-opened in Singapore on 16 March

(**15**) "Malaya Military Government Division Postal Services Bureau Seal"

(Handstamped at Singapore)

(16 Mar). *Stamps of Straits Settlements optd with T* **15** *in*

58 1 c. black .. .. 13·00 17·00
2 c. orange .. .. 13·00 13·00
a. Pair, one without handstamp .. £1300
3 c. green .. .. 50·00 70·00
8 c. grey .. .. 22·00 18·00
15 c. ultramarine .. .. 15·00 15·00

e overprint Type **15** has a double-lined frame, although the ines are not always apparent, as in the illustration. Three s were used, differing slightly in the shape of the acters, but forgeries also exist. It is distinguishable from **1**, used for the general issues, by its extra width, suring approximately 14 mm against 12½ mm.
e 6, 10, 30, 40, 50 c., $2 and $5 also exist with this print, but were not sold to the public.
s. J92/6 were replaced on the 3 May 1942 by the stamps printed with Type **1** which were intended for use through- Malaya.

TRENGGANU

ostal services resumed in Trengganu on 5 March 1942 using verprinted stamps up to the 35 c. value. These remained in until September 1942.

2 (Sept). *Stamps of Trengganu (Script wmk) optd as T* **1** *at uala Lumpur.*

4 1 c. black (No. 26a) .. .. .. 90·00 90·00
a. Chalk-surfaced paper (No. 26) .. — £110
b. Red opt £180 £200
c. Brown opt (chalk-surfaced paper) .. £450 £275
8 2 c. green (No. 27a) £140 £140
a. Chalk-surfaced paper (No. 27) .. — £170
b. Red opt £250 £275
c. Brown opt £500 £325
9 2 c. on 5 c. deep reddish purple/*bright yellow* (No. 59) .. .. 50·00 50·00
a. Red opt .. .. 48·00 70·00
0 3 c. chestnut (No. 29a) .. .. .. 85·00 80·00
a. Brown opt £600 £450
1 4 c. scarlet-vermilion (No. 30a) £150 £140
2 5 c. dp reddish purple/*brt yell* (No. 32a) 10·00 19·00
a. *Purple/yellow* (No. 32) .. .. 90·00 £100
b. Red opt .. .. 23·00
3 6 c. orange (No. 33a) .. .. .. 9·00 25·00
a. Red opt £120
b. Brown opt £500 £500
4 8 c. grey (No. 34a) .. .. 9·00 13·00
a. Chalk-surfaced paper (No. 34) .. £110
b. Brown to red opt .. .. 55·00 70·00
5 8 c. on 10 c. bright blue (No. 60) .. 13·00 42·00
a. Red opt .. .. 21·00
6 10 c. bright blue .. .. 19·00 32·00
a. Red opt £120
b. Brown opt £500 £500
7 12 c. bright ultramarine .. .. .. 8·00 35·00
a. Red opt .. .. 27·00 55·00
8 20 c. dull purple and orange .. .. 8·50 30·00
a. Red opt .. .. 21·00
9 25 c. green and deep purple .. .. 7·50 38·00
a. Red opt .. .. 22·00
b. Brown opt £550 £550
10 30 c. dull purple and black .. .. 8·00 30·00
a. Red opt .. .. 27·00 55·00
11 35 c. carmine/*yellow* .. .. .. 23·00 42·00
a. Red opt .. .. 26·00
12 50 c. green and bright carmine .. .. 70·00 85·00
13 $1 purple and blue/*blue* £2750 £2750
14 $3 green & brown-red/*green* (No. 43a) 55·00 95·00
a. *Green and lake/green* (No. 43) .. £140
b. Red opt .. .. 65·00
15 5 $5 green and red/*yellow* £130 £180
16 $25 purple and blue £1100
a. Red opt £3750
17 $50 green and yellow £10000
18 $100 green and scarlet £1300

DAI NIPPON

2602

MALAYA

(**16**)

942 (Sept). *Stamps of Trengganu (Script wmk) optd with T* **16**.

119 4 1 c. black (No. 26a) .. .. .. 12·00 12·00
120 2 c. green (No. 27a) £170 £190
121 2 c. on 5 c. deep reddish purple/*bright yellow* (No. 59) .. .. .. 6·00 8·00
122 3 c. chestnut (No. 29a) .. .. .. 11·00 20·00
123 4 c. scarlet-vermilion (No. 30a) .. .. 10·00 11·00
124 5 c. dp reddish purple/*brt yell* (No. 32a) 5·50 13·00
125 6 c. orange (No. 33a) .. .. .. 5·00 13·00
126 8 c. grey (No. 34a) .. .. .. 75·00 27·00
127 8 c. on 10 c. bright blue (No. 60) .. 5·50 10·00
128 12 c. bright ultramarine .. .. .. 5·00 23·00
129 20 c. dull purple and orange .. .. 12·00 14·00
130 25 c. green and deep purple .. .. 7·00 30·00
131 30 c. dull purple and black .. .. 7·50 27·00
132 $3 green & brown-red/*green* (No. 43a) 70·00 £130

1943. *Stamps of Trengganu (Script wmk) optd with T* **2**.

J133 4 1 c. black .. .. 10·00 16·00
J134 2 c. green (No. 27a) .. .. .. 9·00 26·00
J135 2 c. on 5 c. bright reddish purple/*bright yellow* (No. 59) .. .. .. 6·00 18·00
J136 5 c. brt reddish purple/*brt yell* (No. 32*a*) 7·50 26·00
J137 6 c. orange (No. 33a) .. .. .. 8·50 29·00
J138 8 c. grey (No. 34a) .. .. .. 60·00 90·00
J139 8 c. on 10 c. bright blue (No. 60) .. 21·00 45·00
J140 10 c. bright blue .. .. 85·00 £200
J141 12 c. bright ultramarine .. .. .. 13·00 40·00
J142 20 c. dull purple and orange .. .. 17·00 40·00
J143 25 c. green and deep purple .. .. 13·00 42·00
J144 30 c. dull purple and black .. .. 18·00 45·00
J145 35 c. carmine/*yellow* .. .. .. 18·00 48·00

POSTAGE DUE STAMPS

1942 (Sept). *Nos. D1/4 of Trengganu optd with T* **1** *sideways.*

JD17 D 1 1 c. scarlet .. .. 50·00 85·00
JD18 4 c. green .. .. 80·00 £110
a. Brown opt .. .. 50·00 90·00
JD19 8 c. yellow .. .. 14·00 50·00
JD20 10 c. brown .. .. 14·00 50·00

The Trengganu 8 c. postage due also exists overprinted with Type **16**, but this was not issued (*Price* £500 *unused*).

Trengganu was ceded to Thailand by the Japanese on 19 October 1943.

GENERAL ISSUES

The following stamps were produced for use throughout Malaya, except for Trengganu.

1942 (3 Apr). *Stamps optd as T* **1**. *(a) On Straits Settlements.*

J146 58 1 c. black (R.) .. .. 3·25 3·25
a. Black opt £350 £350
b. Violet opt £700 £550
J147 2 c. green (V.) £2250 £1800
J148 2 c. orange (R.) .. .. 3·00 2·25
a. Black opt £110 £120
b. Violet opt £190 £190
c. Brown opt £700 £600
J149 3 c. green (R.) .. .. 2·75 2·25
a. Black opt £300 £325
b. Violet opt £700 £650
J150 5 c. brown (R.) .. .. 22·00 28·00
a. Black opt £500 £500
J151 8 c. grey (R.) .. .. 3·75 2·25
a. Black opt £250 £250
J152 10 c. dull purple (R.) .. .. .. 42·00 42·00
a. Brown opt £750 £650
J153 12 c. ultramarine (R.) .. .. .. 75·00 £110
J154 15 c. ultramarine (R.) .. .. .. 3·50 3·75
a. Violet opt £550 £500
J155 30 c. dull purple and orange (R.) .. £1700 £1700
J156 40 c. scarlet and dull purple (R.) .. 80·00 90·00
a. Brown opt £550 £375
J157 50 c. black/*emerald* (R.) .. .. 45·00 48·00
J158 $1 black and red/*blue* (R.) .. .. 75·00 75·00
J159 $2 green and scarlet (R.) £130 £160
J160 $5 green and red/*emerald* (R.) .. £170 £190

(b) On Negri Sembilan

J161 6 1 c. black (R.) .. .. 19·00 13·00
a. Violet opt .. .. 22·00 20·00
b. Brown opt .. .. 13·00 17·00
c. Black opt .. .. 50·00 38·00
d. Pair. Nos. J161/a £275
e. Pair. Nos. J161 and J161b
J162 2 c. orange (R.) .. .. 24·00 17·00
a. Violet opt .. .. 45·00 27·00
b. Black opt .. .. 32·00 28·00
c. Brown opt .. .. 60·00 48·00
J163 3 c. green (R.) .. .. 30·00 20·00
a. Violet opt .. .. 23·00 29·00
c. Brown opt .. .. £100 50·00
d. Black opt .. .. 48·00 42·00
J164 5 c. brown .. .. 32·00 21·00
a. Pair, one without opt £1400
b. Brown opt .. .. 17·00 15·00
c. Red opt .. .. 15·00 11·00
d. Violet opt .. .. 50·00 38·00
e. Pair. Nos. J164c/d £300
J165 6 c. grey £140 £120
a. Brown opt £325 £325
J166 8 c. scarlet .. .. 95·00 85·00
J167 10 c. dull purple £150 £150
a. Red opt £250 £200
b. Brown opt £375 £300
J168 12 c. bright ultramarine (Br.) £1100 £1100
J169 15 c. ultramarine (R.) .. .. .. 19·00 8·00
a. Violet opt .. .. 65·00 28·00
b. Brown opt .. .. 27·00 12·00
J170 25 c. dull purple and scarlet .. .. 28·00 38·00
a. Red opt .. .. 60·00 75·00
b. Brown opt £350 £300
J171 30 c. dull purple and orange £180 £150
a. Brown opt £850 £750
J172 40 c. scarlet and dull purple £900 £900
a. Brown opt £800 £800
J173 50 c. black/*emerald* £650 £650
J174 $1 black and red/*blue* £190 £200
a. Red opt £160 £180
b. Brown opt £400 £400
J175 $5 green and red/*emerald* £500 £600
a. Red opt £750 £850

(c) On Pahang

J176 15 1 c. black .. .. 50·00 40·00
a. Red opt .. .. 50·00 42·00
b. Violet opt £325 £250
c. Brown opt £200 £190
J177 3 c. green £275 £250
a. Red opt £225 £275
b. Violet opt £650 £475
J178 5 c. brown .. .. 13·00 11·00
a. Red opt £170 £110
b. Brown opt £200 £110
c. Violet opt £425 £250
J179 8 c. grey £600 £475
J180 8 c. scarlet .. .. 20·00 8·00
a. Red opt .. .. £100 50·00
b. Violet opt .. .. £100 55·00
c. Brown opt .. .. £110 65·00
d. Pair. Nos. J180/a £350
J181 15 10 c. dull purple £225 £120
a. Red opt £225 £200
b. Brown opt £375 £250
J182 12 c. bright ultramarine £1500 £1500
a. Red opt £1200 £1200
J183 15 c. ultramarine £120 £110
a. Red opt £275 £250
b. Violet opt £600 £475
c. Brown opt £450 £325
J184 25 c. dull purple and scarlet .. .. 20·00 29·00
J185 30 c. dull purple and orange .. .. 12·00 28·00
a. Red opt £140 £170
J186 40 c. scarlet and dull purple .. .. 18·00 32·00
a. Brown opt £325 £275
b. Red opt .. .. 80·00 85·00
J187 50 c. black/*emerald* £650 £650
a. Red opt £700 £700
J188 $1 black and red/*blue* (R.) £130 £150
a. Black opt £300 £300
b. Brown opt £600 £600
J189 $5 green and red/*emerald* £650 £800
a. Red opt £900 £1000

(d) On Perak

J190 51 1 c. black .. .. 50·00 35·00
a. Violet opt £180 £100
b. Brown opt .. .. 80·00 80·00
J191 2 c. orange .. .. 29·00 20·00
a. Violet opt .. .. 70·00 70·00
b. Red opt .. .. 60·00 40·00
c. Brown opt .. .. 55·00 55·00
J192 3 c. green .. .. 26·00 28·00
a. Violet opt £425 £300
b. Brown opt £180 £150
c. Red opt £325 £250
J193 5 c. brown .. .. 7·00 6·00
a. Pair, one without opt £1000
b. Brown opt .. .. 35·00 26·00
c. Violet opt £200 £200
d. Red opt £225 £200
J194 8 c. grey .. .. 65·00 45·00
a. Red opt £350 £225
b. Brown opt £350 £250
J195 8 c. scarlet .. .. 32·00 38·00
a. Violet opt £450 £275
J196 10 c. dull purple .. .. 26·00 24·00
a. Red opt £325 £225
J197 12 c. bright ultramarine £225 £225
J198 15 c. ultramarine .. .. 24·00 32·00
a. Red opt £225 £200
b. Violet opt £350 £275
c. Brown opt £350 £275
J199 25 c. dull purple and scarlet .. .. 14·00 25·00
J200 30 c. dull purple and orange .. .. 17·00 32·00
a. Pair, one without opt £1500
b. Brown opt £475 £375
c. Red opt .. .. 32·00 55·00
J201 40 c. scarlet and dull purple £325 £325
a. Brown opt £500 £425
J202 50 c. black/*emerald* .. .. .. 38·00 50·00
a. Red opt .. .. 50·00 60·00
b. Brown opt £375 £350
J203 $1 black and red/*blue* £400 £400
a. Brown opt £450 £375
J204 $2 green and scarlet £2500 £2500
J205 $5 green and red/*emerald* £475
a. Brown opt £1500

(e) On Selangor

J206 46 1 c. black, S .. .. 12·00 24·00
a. Red opt, SU .. .. 42·00 38·00
b. Violet opt, SU .. .. .. 40·00 38·00
J207 2 c. green, SU £1100 £1100
a. Violet opt, SU £1400 £1200
J208 2 c. orange (*p* 14×14½), S .. .. 80·00 55·00
a. Red opt, U £180 £160
b. Violet opt, U £225 £150
c. Brown opt, S .. .. 70·00 80·00
J209 2 c. orange (*p* 14), S .. .. .. £100 80·00
a. Red opt, U £190 £170
b. Violet opt, U £300 £160
c. Brown opt, S .. .. — £160
J210 3 c. green, SU .. .. 23·00 15·00
a. Red opt, SU .. .. 18·00 15·00
b. Violet opt, SU .. .. .. 65·00 50·00
c. Brown opt, SU .. .. .. 18·00 15·00
J211 5 c. brown, SU .. .. 6·00 5·50
a. Red opt, SU .. .. 12·00 16·00
b. Violet opt, SU .. .. .. 21·00 22·00
c. Brown opt, SU .. .. .. 90·00 80·00
J212 6 c. scarlet, S £350 £350
a. Red opt, S £200 £250
b. Brown opt, S £650 £650
J213 8 c. grey, S .. .. 17·00 17·00
a. Red opt, SU .. .. 55·00 40·00
b. Violet opt, U .. .. 35·00 35·00
c. Brown opt, S .. .. £140 70·00
J214 10 c. dull purple, S .. .. .. 13·00 21·00
a. Red opt, S .. .. 70·00 60·00
b. Brown opt, S .. .. £130 75·00
J215 12 c. bright ultramarine, S .. .. 60·00 65·00
a. Red opt, S £120 £130
b. Brown opt, S £110 £120
J216 15 c. ultramarine, S .. .. .. 16·00 22·00
a. Red opt, SU .. .. 55·00 55·00
b. Violet opt, U .. .. £140 95·00
c. Brown opt, S .. .. 85·00 65·00
J217 25 c. dull purple and scarlet, S .. .. 75·00 95·00
a. Red opt, S .. .. 60·00 80·00
J218 30 c. dull purple and orange, S .. .. 11·00 24·00
a. Brown opt, S £375 £250
J219 40 c. scarlet and dull purple, S £140 £140
a. Brown opt, S £325 £200
J220 50 c. black/*emerald*, S £120 £130
a. Red opt, S £120 £130
b. Brown opt, S £400 £375
J221 48 $1 black and red/*blue* .. .. .. 30·00 45·00
a. Red opt £120 £150
J222 $2 green and scarlet .. .. .. 35·00 60·00
a. Pair, one without opt £1400
b. Red opt £500 £550
J223 $5 green and red/*emerald* .. .. 65·00 90·00

Nos. J161a and J163a exist with the handstamped overprint sideways.

On T **46** the overprint is normally sideways (with "top" to either right or left), but on T **48** it is always upright.

S= Sideways
U= Upright
SU= Sideways or upright (our prices being for the cheaper).

Specialists recognise nine slightly different chops as Type 1. Initial supplies with the overprint in red were produced at Singapore. Later overprintings took place at Kuala Lumpur in violet, red or brown and, finally, black. No. J155 was from the Kuala Lumpur printing only. Except where noted these overprints were used widely in Malaya and, in some instances, Sumatra.

The following stamps also exist with this overprint, but were not available to the public:
Straits Settlements (in red) 6, 25 c.
Kelantan (in black) 10 c.
Negri Sembilan 2 c. green (Blk. or Brn.), 4 c. (Blk.), 6 c. scarlet (Blk.), 8 c. grey (Blk.), 12 c. (Blk.), $2 (Blk. or Brn.)
Pahang (in black, 2 c. also in brown) 2, 4, 6 c., $2
Perak 2 c. green (R.), 6 c. (Blk.)
Selangor 4 c. (Blk.)

1942 (May). *Optd with T* **16**. (*a*) *On Straits Settlements.*
J224 **58** 2 c. orange .. 1·40 50
a. Opt inverted .. 9·00 17·00
b. Opt double, one inverted .. 48·00 60·00
J225 3 c. green .. 50·00 65·00
J226 8 c. grey .. 4·00 2·00
a. Opt inverted .. 13·00 27·00
J227 15 c. blue .. 11·00 7·50

(*b*) *On Negri Sembilan*
J228 **6** 1 c. black .. 1·75 60
a. Opt inverted .. 9·00 25·00
b. Opt double, one inverted .. 35·00 50·00
J229 2 c. orange .. 5·00 50
J230 3 c. green .. 3·50 50
J231 5 c. brown .. 1·00 2·00
J232 6 c. grey .. 3·00 1·50
a. Opt inverted .. — £1200
b. Stop omitted at right (R. 10/4) .. 85·00 90·00
J233 8 c. scarlet .. 4·00 1·25
J234 10 c. dull purple .. 3·00 2·50
J235 15 c. ultramarine .. 13·00 2·50
J236 25 c. dull purple and scarlet .. 3·00 12·00
J237 30 c. dull purple and orange .. 6·00 3·00
J238 $1 black and red/*blue* .. 80·00 95·00

(*c*) *On Pahang*
J239 **15** 1 c. black .. 2·00 2·25
a. Opt omitted (in pair with normal) £500
J240 5 c. brown .. 1·25 70
J241 8 c. scarlet .. 25·00 2·50
a. Opt omitted (in pair with normal) £1200
J242 10 c. dull purple .. 9·00 6·50
J243 12 c. bright ultramarine .. 1·50 10·00
J244 25 c. dull purple and scarlet .. 3·75 16·00
J245 30 c. dull purple and orange .. 1·90 8·00

(*d*) *On Perak*
J246 **51** 2 c. orange .. 2·00 1·50
a. Opt inverted .. 35·00 35·00
J247 3 c. green .. 85 85
a. Opt inverted .. 12·00 23·00
b. Opt omitted (in pair with normal) £500
J248 8 c. scarlet .. 60 40
a. Opt inverted .. 4·50 7·00
b. Opt double, one inverted .. £225 £250
c. Opt omitted (in horiz pair with normal) .. £400
J249 10 c. dull purple .. 13·00 6·00
J250 15 c. ultramarine .. 5·00 2·00
J251 50 c. black/*emerald* .. 2·25 3·50
J252 $1 black and red/*blue* .. £375 £425
J253 $5 green and red/*emerald* .. 35·00 70·00
a. Opt inverted .. £275 £350

(*e*) *On Selangor*
J254 **46** 3 c. green .. 1·00 2·50
J255 12 c. bright ultramarine .. 1·10 10·00
J256 15 c. ultramarine .. 4·25 1·50
J257 40 c. scarlet and dull purple .. 2·00 3·50
J258 **48** $2 green and scarlet .. 10·00 35·00

On T **46** the overprint is sideways, with "top" to left or right.

The following stamps also exist with this overprint, but were not available to the public.
Perak 1, 5, 30 c. (*Price for set of* 3 £350 *unused*).
Selangor 1, 5, 10, 30 c., $1, $5 (*Price for set of* 6 £600 *unused*).

DAI NIPPON
2602
MALAYA
2 Cents
(17)

DAI NIPPON
YUBIN
2 Cents
(18)
"Japanese Postal Service"

1942 (Nov). *No.* 108 *of Perak surch with T* **17**.
J259 **51** 2 c. on 5 c. brown .. 1·25 2·25

1942 (Nov). *Perak stamps surch or opt only, as in T* **18**.
J260 **51** 1 c. black .. 4·00 8·50
a. Opt inverted .. 19·00 40·00
J261 2 c. on 5 c. brown .. 2·00 6·50
a. "DAI NIPPON YUBIN" inverted 17·00 38·00
b. Ditto and "2 Cents" omitted .. 45·00 65·00
J262 8 c. scarlet .. 4·00 2·25
a. Opt inverted .. 11·00 24·00

A similar overprint exists on the Selangor 3 c. but this was not available to the public (*Price* £350 *unused*).

On 8 December 1942 contemporary Japanese 3, 5, 8 and 25 s. stamps were issued without overprint in Malaya and the 1, 2, 4, 6, 7, 10, 30 and 50 s. and 1 y. values followed on 15 February 1943.

大日本郵便
(19)

6cts.
(20)

6 cts.
(21)

2 Cents
(22)

6 cts.
(23)

$1.00
(24)

1942 (4 Dec)–**44**. *Stamps of various Malayan territories optd "Japanese Postal Service" in Kanji characters as T* **2** *or* **19**, *some additionally surch as T* **20** *to* **24**.

(*a*) *Stamps of Straits Settlements optd with T* **2**
J263 **58** 8 c. grey (Blk.) (1943) .. 1·40 50
a. Opt inverted .. 42·00 55·00
b. Opt omitted (in pair with normal) £800
c. Red opt .. 1·75 2·25
J264 12 c. ultramarine (1943) .. 1·00 8·50
J265 40 c. scarlet and dull purple (1943) .. 1·25 3·50

(*b*) *Stamps of Negri Sembilan optd with T* **2** *or surch also*
J266 **6** 1 c. black .. 30 1·50
a. Opt inverted .. 9·50 26·00
b. Sideways second character .. 29·00 30·00
ba. Opt inverted with sideways second character .. £700
J267 2 c. on 5 c. brown (surch as T **20**) .. 70 70
J268 6 c. on 5 c. brown (surch T **21**) (1943) 40 1·00
a. Opt Type **2** and surch as Type **21** both inverted .. £225 £225
J269 25 c. dull purple and scarlet (1943) .. 1·10 12·00

(*c*) *Stamp of Pahang optd with T* **2** *and surch also*
J270 **15** 6 c. on 5 c. brown (surch T **20**) (1943) 50 75
J271 6 c. on 5 c. brown (surch T **21**) (1943) 1·00 1·75

(*d*) *Stamps of Perak optd with T* **2** *or surch also*
J272 **51** 1 c. black .. 1·00 70
a. Sideways second character .. £200 £225
J273 2 c. on 5 c. brown (surch as T **20**) .. 50 50
a. Opt Type **2** and surch Type **20** both inverted .. 18·00 32·00
b. Opt Type **2** inverted .. 18·00 32·00
c. Sideways second character .. 50·00 50·00
J274 2 c. on 5 c. brown (surch T **22**) .. 60 50
a. Surch Type **22** inverted .. 18·00 32·00
b. Opt Type **2** and surch Type **22** both inverted .. 18·00 32·00
c. Sideways second character .. 25·00 32·00
ca. Surch Type **22** inverted .. £1100
cb. Opt Type **2** with sideways second character and surch Type **22** both inverted .. £1100
d. Inverted "s" in Type **22** (R. 3/5) .. 50·00
J275 5 c. brown .. 55 55
a. Opt inverted .. 28·00 38·00
b. Sideways second character .. £450 £375
J276 8 c. scarlet .. 55 1·00
a. Opt inverted .. 15·00 27·00
b. Sideways second character .. 50·00 65·00
ba. Opt inverted with sideways second character .. £700
J277 10 c. dull purple (1943) .. 60 50
J278 30 c. dull purple and orange (1943) .. 2·75 4·50
J279 50 c. black/*emerald* (1943) .. 3·25 16·00
J280 $5 green and red/*emerald* (1943) .. 55·00 90·00

(*e*) *Stamps of Selangor optd with T* **2** (*sideways on T* **46**)
J281 **46** 1 c. black (1943) .. 1·00 1·75
J282 3 c. green .. 40 45
a. Sideways second character .. 17·00 25·00
J283 12 c. bright ultramarine .. 45 1·60
a. Sideways second character .. 40·00 55·00
J284 15 c. ultramarine .. 3·25 3·25
a. Sideways second character .. 48·00 50·00
J285 **48** $1 black and red/*blue* .. 3·00 18·00
a. Opt inverted .. £225 £225
b. Sideways second character .. £350 £375
J286 $2 green and scarlet (1943) .. 10·00 42·00
J287 $5 green and red/*emerald* (1943) .. 22·00 80·00
a. Opt inverted .. £225 £275

(*f*) *Stamps of Selangor optd with T* **19** *or surch also*
J288 **46** 1 c. black (R.) (1943) .. 35 50
J289 2 c. on 5 c. brown (surch as T **21**) (R.) (1943) .. 30 50
J290 3 c. on 5 c. brown (surch as T **21**) (1943) 30 3·50
a. "s" in "cts." inverted (R. 4/3) .. 28·00 50·00
b. Comma after "cts" (R. 9/3) .. 28·00 50·00
J291 5 c. brown (R.) (1944) .. 1·00 3·50
J292 6 c. on 5 c. brown (surch T **21**) (1944) 30 1·25
J293 6 c. on 5 c. brown (surch T **23**) (1944) 30 70
a. "6" inverted (R. 7/8) .. £850
b. Surch and opt double .. £400
J294 15 c. ultramarine .. 4·00 4·00
J295 $1 on 10 c. dull purple (surch T **24**) (18.12.1944) .. 30 1·00
J296 $1.50 on 30 c. dull purple and orange (surch T **24**) (18.12.1944) .. 30 1·00

The error showing the second character in Type **2** sideways occurred on R. 6/3 in the first of four settings only.

The 2 c. orange, 3 c. and 8 c. grey of Perak also exist overprinted with Type **2**, but these stamps were not available to the public (*Price for set of* 3 £100 *unused*).

Examples of No. J275 are known postally used from the Shan States (part of pre-war Burma).

25 Tapping Rubber

26 Fruit

27 Japanese Shrine, Singapore

(Litho Kolff & Co, Batavia)

1943 (29 Apr–30 Oct). *T* **25/7** *and similar designs. P* 12½.
J297 **25** 1 c. grey-green (30 Oct) .. 65 55
J298 **26** 2 c. pale emerald (1 June) .. 65 20
J299 **25** 3 c. drab (30 Oct) .. 30 20
J300 – 4 c. carmine-rose .. 1·50 20
J301 – 8 c. dull blue .. 30 20
J302 – 10 c. brown-purple (30 Oct) .. 30 20
J303 **27** 15 c. violet (30 Oct) .. 60 2·75
J304 – 30 c. olive-green (30 Oct) .. 75 35
J305 – 50 c. blue (30 Oct) .. 2·50
J306 – 70 c. blue (30 Oct) .. 16·00
J297/306 .. *Set of* 10 21·00

Designs: *Vert*—4 c. Tin dredger; 8 c. War Memorial, Batok, Singapore; 10 c. Fishing village; 30 c. Sago palms; Straits of Johore. *Horiz*—70 c. Malay Mosque, Kuala Lum

The 2 c. and 4 c. values exist, printed by typography, in shades either imperforate or rouletted. It is suggested that may have been available in Singapore at the very end o Japanese Occupation.

28 Ploughman

29 Rice-planting

1943 (1 Sept). *Savings Campaign. Litho. P* 12½.
J307 **28** 8 c. violet .. 9·50
J308 15 c. scarlet .. 6·50

(Des Hon Chin. Litho)

1944 (15 Feb). *"Re-birth" of Malaya. P* 12½.
J309 **29** 8 c. rose-red .. 12·00
J310 15 c. magenta .. 4·00

大日本
マライ郵便
50 セント
(30)

大日本
マライ郵便
1 ドル
(31)

大日本
マライ郵
1½ ドル
(32)

1944 (16 Dec). *Stamps intended for use on Red Cross lett Surch with T* **30/2** *in red.* (*a*) *On Straits Settlements.*
J311 **58** 50 c. on 50 c. black/*emerald* .. 10·00 2
J312 $1 on $1 black and red/*blue* .. 18·00 3
J313 $1.50 on $2 green and scarlet .. 28·00 7

(*b*) *On Johore*
J314 **29** 50 c. on 50 c. dull purple and red .. 7·00 2
J315 $1.50 on $2 green and carmine .. 4·00 1

(*c*) *On Selangor*
J316 **48** $1 on $1 black and red/*blue* .. 3·50 1
J317 $1.50 on $2 green and scarlet .. 5·00 2

Nos. J311/17 were issued in Singapore but were withdra after one day, probably because supplies of Nos. J295/6 we received and issued on the 18 December.

A similar 6 c. surcharge exists on the Straits Settlements 5 but this was not available to the public (*Price* £450 *unused*).

STAMP BOOKLETS

1942. *Nos.* SB3/4 *of Perak and* SB2 *of Selangor with cov optd with T* **1**.
SB1 $1 booklet containing twenty 5 c. (No. J193) in blocks of 10 .. £22
SB2 $1.30, booklet containing 5 c. and 8 c. (Nos. J193/4), each in block of 10 .. £22
SB3 $1.30, booklet containing 5 c. and 8 c. (Nos. J211 and J213), each in block of 10 .. £22

POSTAGE DUE STAMPS

Postage Due stamps of the Malayan Postal Union ove printed.

1942 (3 Apr). *Handstamped as T* **1** *in black.*
JD21 **D 1** 1 c. slate-purple .. 12·00 23·
a. Red opt .. £100 £1
b. Brown opt .. £100 £1
JD22 3 c. green .. 55·00 60·
a. Red opt .. £160 £1
JD23 4 c. green .. 40·00 29·
a. Red opt .. 50·00 48·
b. Brown opt .. £120 £1
JD24 8 c. scarlet .. 75·00 65·
a. Red opt .. £120 £1
b. Brown opt .. £140 £1
JD25 10 c. yellow-orange .. 23·00 38·
a. Red opt .. £120 £1
b. Brown opt .. 60·00 65·
JD26 12 c. ultramarine .. 23·00 48·
a. Red opt .. £140 £1
JD27 50 c. black .. 55·00 75·
a. Red opt .. £325 £35

1942. *Optd with T* **16**.
JD28 **D 1** 1 c. slate-purple .. 1·75 8·5
JD29 3 c. green .. 12·00 18·0
JD30 4 c. green .. 12·00 11·0
JD31 8 c. scarlet .. 16·00 15·0
JD32 10 c. yellow-orange .. 1·75 12·0
JD33 12 c. ultramarine .. 1·75 26·0

The 9 c. and 15 c. also exist with this overprint, but these wer not issued (*Price* £475 *each unused*).

1943–45. *Optd with T* **2**.
JD34 **D 1** 1 c. slate-purple .. 1·25 3·0
JD35 3 c. green .. 1·25 3·0
a. Opt omitted (in pair with normal) .. £650
JD36 4 c. green .. 45·00 40·0
JD37 5 c. scarlet .. 1·50 4·0
JD38 9 c. yellow-orange .. 80 6·0
a. Opt inverted .. 20·00 28·0
JD39 10 c. yellow-orange .. 1·25 6·5
a. Opt inverted .. 55·00 55·0
JD40 12 c. ultramarine .. 1·50 12·0
JD41 15 c. ultramarine .. 1·50 6·5

VIII. THAI OCCUPATION OF MALAYA

mps issued for use in the Malay States of Kedah (renamed ·i), Kelantan, Perlis and Trengganu, ceded by Japan to and on 19 October 1943. British rule was restored on 9 ntan), 18 (Perlis), 22 (Kedah) and 24 September 1945 gganu). Nos. TM1/6 continued to be used for postage until ced by the overprinted B.M.A. Malaya issues on 10 October

PRICES FOR STAMPS ON COVER	
Nos. TK1/5	*from* × 30
Nos. TM1/6	*from* × 25
Nos. TT1/35	—

KELANTAN

TK 1

(Typo Kelantan Ptg Dept, Khota Baru)

 (15 Nov). *Handstamped with State arms in violet. No m. P* 11.

TK 1 1 c. black £200 £300
2 c. black £250 £250
a. Handstamp omitted £700
4 c. black £250 £300
a. Handstamp omitted £850
8 c. black £250 £250
a. Handstamp omitted £550
10 c. black £300 £400

os. TK1/5 were printed in sheets of 84 (12×7) and have t watermarks in the form of "STANDARD" in block capitals curved "CROWN" above and "AGENTS" below in double-l capitals. This watermark occurs four times in the sheet. eets were imperforate at top and left so that stamps exist erforate at top, left or at top and left.

enuine examples have a solid star at the top centre of the s, as shown in Type TK 1. Examples with a hollow outline in this position are forgeries.

milar stamps, but with red handstamps, were for fiscal use.

GENERAL ISSUE

TM 1 War Memorial

(Litho Defence Ministry, Bangkok)

4 (15 Jan–4 Mar). *Thick opaque, or thin semi-transparent aper. Gummed or ungummed. P* $12^1/_2$.

1 TM 1 1 c. yellow (4 Mar) .. .. .. 30·00 32·00
2 2 c. red-brown .. .. .. 12·00 20·00
a. Imperf (pair) £850
b. Perf $12^1/_2$×11 .. .. .. 20·00 20·00
3 3 c. green (4 Mar) .. .. .. 20·00 38·00
a. Perf $12^1/_2$×11 .. .. .. 30·00 42·00
4 4 c. purple (4 Mar) .. .. .. 14·00 28·00
a. Perf $12^1/_2$×11 .. .. .. 20·00 35·00
5 8 c. carmine (4 Mar) .. .. .. 14·00 20·00
a. Perf $12^1/_2$×11 .. .. .. 20·00 20·00
6 15 c. blue (4 Mar) .. .. .. 38·00 60·00
a. Perf $12^1/_2$×11 .. .. .. 42·00 60·00

5 c. and 10 c. stamps in this design were prepared, but never ued.

TRENGGANU

TRENGGANU

(TT 1)

(Overprinted at Trengganu Survey Office)

44 (1 Oct). *Various stamps optd with Type* TT 1.

(*a*) *On Trengganu without Japanese opt*

T1 4 1 c. black (26a) .. .. ..
T2 30 c. dull purple and black (39) ..

) *On Trengganu stamps optd as T* 1 *of Japanese Occupation*

T2*a* 4 1 c. black (J97) .. .. .. — £1200
T3 8 c. grey (J104) £475 £350

(*c*) *On stamps optd with T* **16** *of Japanese Occupation.*

(i) *Pahang*

T 4 **15** 12 c. bright ultramarine (J243) .. £375 £120

(ii) *Trengganu*

T 5 4 2 c. on 5 c. deep reddish purple/*bright yellow* (J121)* £450 £450
T 6 8 c. on 10 c. brt blue (J127) (inverted) £375 £375
T 7 12 c. brt ultramarine (J128) (inverted) £375 £375

"This is spelt "TRENGANU" with one "G".

(*d*) *On stamps optd with T* 2 *of Japanese Occupation.*

(i) *Straits Settlements*

T 8 **58** 12 c. ultramarine (J264) £400 £400
T 9 40 c. scarlet and dull purple (J265) .. £400 £400

(ii) *Negri Sembilan*

T 9*a* **6** 25 c. dull purple and scarlet (J269) .. — £1200

(iii) *Pahang*

TT10 **15** 6 c. on 5 c. brown (J271) .. ..

(iv) *Perak*

TT11 **51** 1 c. black (J272) .. .. ..
TT12 10 c. dull purple (J277) .. ..
TT13 30 c. dull purple and orange (J278) .. £700 £400
TT13*a* 50 c. black/*emerald* (J279) .. .. — £1200

(v) *Selangor*

TT14 **46** 3 c. green (J282) £300 £300
TT15 12 c. brt ultramarine (J283) (L. to R.) £180 £110
TT16 12 c. brt ultramarine (J283) (R. to L.) £180 £110
a. Sideways second character .. £1800 £1800

(*e*) *On Selangor stamps optd with T* **19** *of Japanese Occupation*

TT16*b* **46** 1 c. black (J288) .. .. .. — £1200
TT17 2 c. on 5 c. brown (J289) £400 £400
TT18 3 c. on 5 c. brown (J290) £400 £400

(*f*) *On pictorials of* 1943 (*Nos.* J297/306)

TT19 **25** 1 c. grey-green £300 £275
TT20 **26** 2 c. pale emerald £300 £150
TT21 **25** 3 c. drab £180 £120
TT22 – 4 c. carmine-rose £275 £150
TT23 – 8 c. dull blue £450 £425
TT24 – 10 c. brown-purple £900 £600
TT25 **27** 15 c. violet £275 £150
TT26 – 30 c. olive-green £400 £130
TT27 – 50 c. blue £400 £250
TT28 – 70 c. blue £800 £600

(*g*) *On Savings Campaign stamps* (*Nos.* J307/8)

TT29 **28** 8 c. violet £450 £450
TT30 15 c. scarlet £325 £160

(*h*) *On stamps of Japan*

TT31 – 3 s. green (No. 319) .. ..
TT32 – 5 s. claret (No. 396) £400 £325
TT33 – 25 c. brown and chocolate (No. 329) £250 £110
TT34 – 30 c. blue-green (No. 330) £400 £160

(i) *On Trengganu Postage Due stamp optd with T* 1 *of Japanese Occupation*

TT35 D 1 1 c. scarlet (JD17) £1600 £1600

Maldive Islands

PRICES FOR STAMPS ON COVER TO 1945	
Nos. 1/6	*from* × 10
Nos. 7/10	*from* × 50
Nos. 11/20	*from* × 20

BRITISH PROTECTORATE

(Currency. 100 cents = 1 Ceylon rupee)

MALDIVES

(1)

2 Minaret, Juma Mosque, Malé

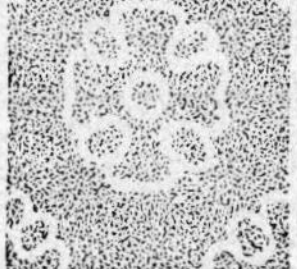

3

1906 (9 Sept). *Nos.* 277/9, 280a *and* 283/4 *of Sri Lanka (Ceylon) optd with T* 1. *Wmk Mult Crown CA. P* 14.

1 **44** 2 c. red-brown .. .. 15·00 35·00
2 **45** 3 c. green .. .. 18·00 35·00
3 4 c. orange and ultramarine .. .. 32·00 70·00
4 **46** 5 c. dull purple .. .. 4·00 6·50
5 **48** 15 c. blue .. .. 60·00 £120
6 25 c. bistre .. .. 70·00 £130
1/6 .. .. *Set of* 6 £180 £350

Supplies of Nos. 1/6 were exhausted by March 1907 and the stamps of CEYLON were used until 1909. Overseas mail to destinations other than Ceylon or India continued to be franked with Ceylon stamps until 1967 when Maldive Islands joined the U.P.U.

(Recess D.L.R.)

1909 (May). *T* **2** ($18^1/_2$×$22^1/_2$ *mm*). *W* **3**. *P* 14×$13^1/_2$ (2 *c*., 5 *c*.) *or* $13^1/_2$×14 (3 *c*., 10 *c*.).

7 **2** 2 c. orange-brown .. .. .. 2·25 2·75
a. Perf $13^1/_2$×14 .. .. .. 2·50 90
8 3 c. deep myrtle 50 70
9 5 c. purple 50 35
10 10 c. carmine .. .. 7·50 80
7/10 .. .. *Set of* 4 9·50 2·50

These stamps perforated 14×$13^1/_2$ (14×13.7) are from a line machine and those perforated $13^1/_2$×14 (13.7×13.9) from a comb machine.

4

(Photo Harrison)

1933. *T* **2** *redrawn* (*reduced to* 18×$21^1/_2$ *mm*). *W* **4**. *P* 15×14.

A. *Wmk upright*

11A **2** 2 c. grey .. .. 2·75 2·00
12A 3 c. red-brown .. .. 70 2·75
14A 5 c. mauve .. .. 21·00 10·00
15A 6 c. scarlet .. .. 1·50 5·50
16A 10 c. green 85 55
17A 15 c. black .. .. 6·50 14·00
18A 25 c. brown .. .. 6·50 14·00
19A 50 c. purple .. .. 6·50 14·00
20A 1 r. deep blue .. .. 11·00 11·00
11A/20A .. .. *Set of* 9 50·00 65·00

B. *Wmk sideways*

11B **2** 2 c. grey .. .. 4·00 4·00
12B 3 c. red-brown .. .. 3·50 1·75
13B 5 c. claret .. .. 32·00 32·00
15B 6 c. scarlet .. .. 6·00 5·50
16B 10 c. green .. .. 3·25 3·75
17B 15 c. black .. .. 11·00 15·00
18B 25 c. brown .. .. 11·00 15·00
19B 50 c. purple .. .. 11·00 15·00
20B 1 r. deep blue .. .. 12·00 3·25
11B/20B .. .. *Set of* 9 85·00 85·00

(New Currency. 100 larees=1 rupee)

5 Palm Tree and Dhow

(Recess B.W.)

1950 (24 Dec). *P* 13.

21 **5** 2 l. olive-green .. .. 1·50 80
22 3 l. blue .. .. 8·50 50
23 5 l. emerald-green .. .. 8·50 50

24 5 6 l. red-brown 70 50
25 10 l. scarlet 70 50
26 15 l. orange 70 50
27 25 l. purple 70 60
28 50 l. violet .. .. 70 1·25
29 1 r. chocolate .. .. 8·50 26·00
21/9 .. .. *Set of* 9 27·00 28·00

7 Fish

8 Native Products

(Recess B.W.)

1952. *P* 13.
30 7 3 l. blue .. .. 1·40 30
31 8 5 l. emerald .. .. 50 1·40

Malta

Early records of the postal services under the British Occupation are fragmentary, but it is known that an Island Postmaster was appointed in 1802. A British Packet Agency was established in 1806 and it later became customary for the same individual to hold the two appointments together. The inland posts continued to be the responsibility of the local administration, but the overseas mails formed part of the British G.P.O. system.

The stamps of Great Britain were used on overseas mails from September 1857. Previously during the period of the Crimean War letters franked with Great Britain stamps from the Crimea were cancelled at Malta with a wavy line obliterator. Such postmarks are known between April 1855 and September 1856.

The British G.P.O. relinquished control of the overseas posts on 31 December 1884 when Great Britain stamps were replaced by those of Malta.

Z 1

M

Z 2

1855–56. *Stamps of* GREAT BRITAIN *cancelled with wavy lines obliteration, Type* Z **1**.
Z1 1d. red-brown (1854), Die I, *wmk* Small Crown, *perf* 16 .. .. £800
Z2 1d. red-brown (1855), Die II, *wmk* Small Crown, *perf* 14 .. .. £800
a. Very blued paper
Z3 1d. red-brown (1855), Die II, *wmk* Large Crown, *perf* 16 .. .. £800
Z3*a* 1d. red-brown (1855), Die II, *wmk* Large Crown, *perf* 14 .. .. £800
Z4 2d. blue (1855), *wmk* Large Crown, *perf* 14 Plate No. 5 .. ..
Z5 6d. (1854) embossed £4000
Z6 1s. (1847) embossed £4500

It is now established that this obliterator was sent to Malta and used on mail in transit emanating from the Crimea.

1857 (18 Aug)–**59.** *Stamps of* GREAT BRITAIN *cancelled* "M", *Type* Z **2**.
Z 7 1d. red-brown (1841) £1400
Z 8 1d. red-brown, Die I, *wmk* Small Crown, *perf* 16 .. £100
Z 9 1d. red-brown, Die II, *wmk* Small Crown, *perf* 16 £800
Z10 1d. red-brown, Die II (1855), *wmk* Small Crown, *perf* 14 .. .. £170
Z11 1d. red-brown, Die II (1855), *wmk* Large Crown, *perf* 14 .. .. 70·00
Z12 1d. rose-red (1857), *wmk* Large Crown, *perf* 14 .. 20·00
Z13 2d. blue (1841), *imperf* £2500
Z14 2d. blue (1854) *wmk* Small Crown, *perf* 16 .. £650
Plate No. 4.
Z15 2d. blue (1855), *wmk* Large Crown, *perf* 14 *From* 50·00
Plate Nos. 5, 6.
Z16 2d. blue (1858), *wmk* Large Crown, *perf* 16 .. £250
Plate No. 6.
Z17 2d. blue (1858) (Plate Nos. 7, 8, 9) .. .. *From* 35·00
Z18 4d. rose (1857) .. .. 35·00
a. Thick glazed paper £170
Z19 6d. violet (1854), embossed £3000
Z20 6d. lilac (1856) .. .. 40·00
a. Thick paper £190
Z21 6d. lilac (1856) (blued *paper*) £850
Z22 1s. green (1856) £120
a. Thick paper £170

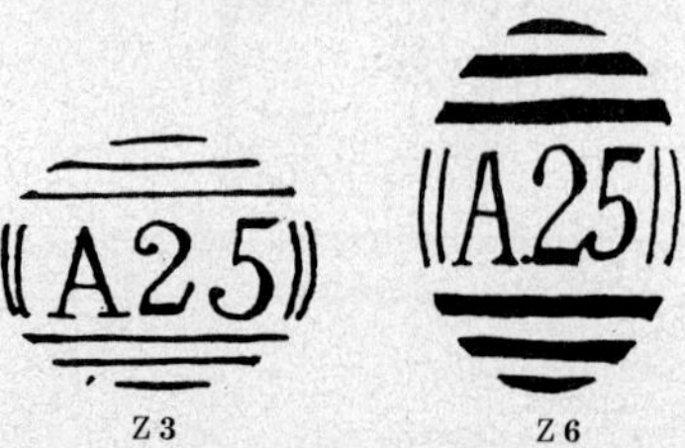

Z 3 Z 6

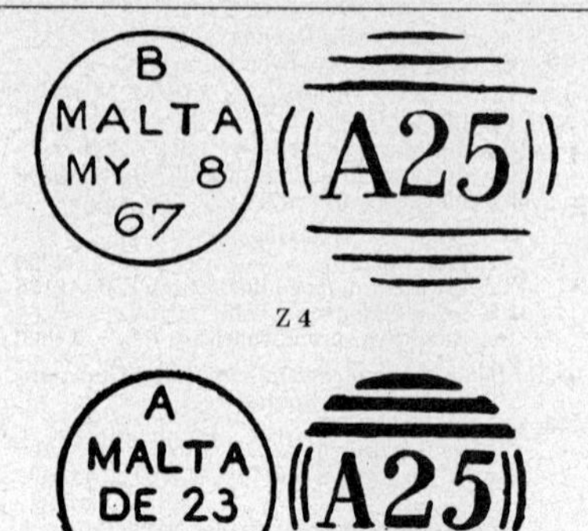

Z 4

Z 5

MALTA C NO 14 83 A25

Z 7

1859–84. *Stamps of* GREAT BRITAIN *cancelled* "A 25" *as in Types* Z **3**/**7**.
Z23 ½d. rose-red (1870–79) .. .. .. *From* 19·00
Plate Nos. 4, 5, 6, 8, 9, 10, 11, 12, 13, 14, 15, 19, 20.
Z24 1d. red-brown (1841), *imperf* £2250
Z25 1d. red-brown (1854), *wmk* Small Crown, *perf* 16 £250
Z26 1d. red-brown (1855), *wmk* Large Crown, *perf* 14 60·00
Z27 1d. rose-red (1857), *wmk* Large Crown, *perf* 14 7·50
Z28 1d. rose-red (1861), Alphabet IV £450
Z30 1d. rose-red (1864–79) .. .. .. *From* 12·00
Plate Nos, 71, 72, 73, 74, 76, 78, 79, 80, 81, 82, 83, 84, 85, 86, 87, 88, 89, 90, 91, 92, 93, 94, 95, 96, 97, 98, 99, 100, 101, 102, 103, 104, 105, 106, 107, 108, 109, 110, 111, 112, 113, 114, 115, 116, 117, 118, 119, 120, 121, 122, 123, 124, 125, 127, 129, 130, 131, 132, 133, 134, 135, 136, 137, 138, 139, 140, 141, 142, 143, 144, 145, 146, 147, 148, 149, 150, 151, 152, 153, 154, 155, 156, 157, 158, 159, 160, 161, 162, 163, 164, 165, 166, 167, 168, 169, 170, 171, 172, 173, 174, 175, 176, 177, 178, 179, 180, 181, 182, 183, 184, 185, 186, 187, 188, 189, 190, 191, 192, 193, 194, 195, 196, 197, 198, 199, 200, 201, 202, 203, 204, 205, 206, 207, 208, 209, 210, 211, 212, 213, 214, 215, 216, 217, 218, 219, 220, 221, 222, 223, 224.
Z31 1½d. lake-red (1870–79) (Plate Nos. 1, 3) .. *From* £350
Z32 2d. blue (1841), *imperf* £3500
Z33 2d. blue (1855) *wmk* Large Crown *perf* 14 .. 60·00
Z34 2d. blue (1858–69) .. .. *From* 15·00
Plate Nos. 7, 8, 9, 12, 13, 14, 15.
Z35 2½d. rosy mauve (1875) (blued *paper*) *From* 65·00
Plate Nos. 1, 2.
Z36 2½d. rosy mauve (1875–76) (Plate Nos. 1, 2, 3) *From* 30·00
Z37 2½d. rosy mauve (*Error of Lettering*) £2250
Z38 2½d. rosy mauve (1876–79) .. .. *From* 16·00
Plate Nos. 3, 4, 5, 6, 7, 8, 9, 10, 11, 12, 13, 14, 15, 16, 17.
Z39 2½d. blue (1880–81) (Plate Nos. 17, 18, 19, 20) *From* 10·00
Z40 2½d. blue (1881) (Plate Nos. 21, 22, 23) .. *From* 7·00
Z41 3d. carmine-rose (1862) £100
Z42 3d. rose (1865) (Plate No. 4) .. .. .. 60·00
Z43 3d. rose (1867–73) .. .. .. *From* 20·00
Plate Nos. 4, 5, 6, 7, 8, 9, 10.
Z44 3d. rose (1873–76) .. .. .. *From* 26·00
Plate Nos. 11, 12, 14, 15, 16, 17, 18, 19, 20.
Z45 3d. rose (1881) (Plate Nos. 20, 21) .. .. *From* £850
Z46 3d. on 3d. lilac (1883) £450
Z47 4d. rose (or rose-carmine) (1857) .. .. 27·00
a. Thick glazed paper £110
Z48 4d. red (1862) (Plate Nos. 3, 4) .. .. *From* 30·00
Z49 4d. vermilion (1865–73) .. .. .. *From* 16·00
Plate Nos. 7, 8, 9, 10, 11, 12, 13, 14.
Z50 4d. vermilion (1876) (Plate No. 15) £160
Z51 4d. sage-green (1877) (Plate Nos. 15, 16) .. *From* 85·00
Z52 4d. grey-brown (1880) *wmk* Large Garter .. £120
Plate No. 17.
Z53 4d. grey-brown (1880) *wmk* Crown .. *From* 38·00
Plate Nos. 17, 18.
Z54 6d. violet (1854), embossed £2000
Z55 6d. lilac (1856) .. .. 35·00
a. Thick paper .. ..
Z56 6d. lilac (1862) (Plate Nos. 3, 4) .. .. *From* 30·00
Z57 6d. lilac (1865–67) (Plate Nos. 5, 6) .. *From* 28·00
Z58 6d. lilac (1865–67) (*Wmk error*) £1200
Z59 6d. lilac (1867) (Plate No. 6) .. .. .. 32·00
Z60 6d. violet (1867–70) (Plate Nos. 6, 8, 9) .. *From* 25·00
Z61 6d. buff (1872–73) (Plate Nos. 11, 12) .. *From* £100
Z62 6d. chestnut (1872) (Plate No. 11) .. .. 30·00
Z63 6d. grey (1873) (Plate No. 12) .. .. .. 75·00
Z64 6d. grey (1873–80) .. .. .. *From* 26·00
Plate Nos. 13, 14, 15, 16, 17.
Z65 6d. grey (1881–82) (Plate Nos. 17, 18) .. *From* 45·00
Z66 6d. on 6d. lilac (1883) £110
Z67 8d. orange (1876) £275
Z68 9d. straw (1862) £550
Z69 9d. bistre (1862) £500
Z70 9d. straw (1865) £500
Z71 9d. straw (1867) £650
Z72 10d. red-brown (1867) £130
Z73 1s. (1847), embossed £2250
Z74 1s. green (1856) .. ..
Z75 1s. green (1856) (thick *paper*) .. .. ..
Z76 1s. green (1862) .. ..
Z77 1s. green ("K" *variety*) .. ..
Z78 1s. green (1865) (Plate No. 4) .. .. ..
Z79 1s. green (1867–73) (Plate Nos. 4, 5, 6, 7) . *From*
Z80 1s. green (1873–77) .. .. .. *From*
Plate Nos. 8, 9, 10, 11, 12, 13.
Z81 1s. orange-brown (1880) (Plate No. 13) .. ..
Z82 1s. orange-brown (1881) (Plate Nos. 13, 14) *From*
Z83 2s. blue (*shades*) (1867) .. .. .. *From*
Z84 2s. brown (1880) .. .. £
Z85 5s. rose (1867–74) (Plate Nos. 1, 2) .. *From*
Z86 5s. rose (1882) (Plate No. 4), blue *paper* .. .. £
Z87 5s. rose (1882) (Plate No. 4), white *paper* .. .. £
Z88 10s. grey-green (1878) .. .. £

1880.
Z89 ½d. deep green 1
Z90 ½d. pale green .. ..
Z91 1d. Venetian red .. ..
Z92 1½d. Venetian red .. ..
Z93 2d. pale rose 3
Z94 2d. deep rose 3
Z95 5d. indigo 5

1881.
Z96 1d. lilac (14 *dots*) .. ..
Z97 1d. lilac (16 *dots*) .. ..

1883–84.
Z 98 ½d. slate-blue 1
Z 99 1½d. lilac .. ..
Z100 2d. lilac 6
Z101 2½d. lilac 1
Z102 3d. lilac .. ..
Z103 4d. dull green .. .. £
Z104 5d. dull green .. .. £
Z105 6d. dull green .. ..
Z106 9d. dull green .. ..
Z107 1s. dull green .. ..
Z108 5s. rose (*blued paper*) £1
Z109 5s. rose (*white paper*) .. .. .. £

POSTAL FISCALS

Z109*a* 1d. reddish lilac (Type F **8**) (1867) *wmk* Anchor
Z110 1d. purple (Type F **12**) (1871) *wmk* Anchor .. £
Z111 1d. purple (Type F **12**) (1881) *wmk* Orb .. £

PRICES FOR STAMPS ON COVER TO 1945

Nos. 1/3	*from* × 4
Nos. 4/19	*from* × 5
Nos. 20/9	*from* × 6
No. 30	—
Nos. 31/3	*from* × 4
Nos. 34/7	*from* × 10
Nos. 38/88	*from* × 4
Nos. 92/3	*from* × 5
Nos. 97/103	*from* × 3
Nos. 104/5	—
Nos. 106/20	*from* × 3
No. 121	—
Nos. 122/38	*from* × 3
Nos. 139/40	—
Nos. 141/72	*from* × 4
Nos. 173/209	*from* × 3
Nos. 210/31	*from* × 2
Nos. D1/10	*from* × 30
Nos. D11/20	*from* × 15

CROWN COLONY

PRINTERS. Nos. 1/156. Printed by De La Rue; typographed exc *where otherwise stated.*

1

Type 1

The first Government local post was established on 10 Jun 1853 and, as an experiment, mail was carried free of charg During 1859 the Council of Government decided that a rate c ½d. per ½ ounce should be charged for this service and stamps i Type I were ordered for this purpose. Both the new rate and th stamps were introduced on 1 December 1860. Until 1 Januar 1885 the ½d. stamps were intended for the local service onl mail for abroad being handled by the British Post Office o Malta, using G.B. stamps.

Specialists now recognise 29 printings in shades of yellow ar one in green during the period to 1884. These printings can l linked to the changes in watermark and perforation as follows:

Ptg 1—Blued paper without wmk. P 14.
Ptgs 2 and 3—White paper without wmk. P 14.
Ptgs 4 to 9, 11, 13 to 19, 22 to 24—Crown CC wmk. P 14.
Ptg 10—Crown CC wmk. P 12½ (rough).
Ptg 12—Crown CC wmk. P 12½ (clean-cut).
Ptgs 20 and 21—Crown CC wmk. P 14 × 12½.
Ptgs 25 to 28, 30—Crown CA wmk. P 14.
Ptg 29—In green (No. 20).

(Des E. Fuchs)

1860 (1 Dec)–**63.** *No wmk. P* 14. (*a*) *Blued paper.*
1 ½d. buff (1.12.60) £850 £425

(b) Thin, hard white paper

ʼ2d. brown-orange (11.61) £800 £325
ʼ2d. buff (1.63) £550 £275
a. Pale buff £550 £275

1 is printed in fugitive ink. It is known imperforate but ıot issued in that state (*Price* £9000 *unused*).
e printing on No. 2 gives a very blurred and muddy ession; on Nos. 3/3*a* the impression is clear.
ecks of carmine can often be detected with a magnifying glass os. 2/3*a*, and also on No. 4. Examples also exist on which parts design are in pure rose, due to defective mixing of the ink.

-81. *Wmk Crown CC. (a) P* 14.
½d. buff (6.63) .. .. .. 80·00 50·00
w. Wmk inverted £250 £250
x. Wmk reversed £650
½d. bright orange (11.64) £400 £110
w. Wmk inverted .. .. .. † £475
½d. orange-brown (4.67) .. .. £300 80·00
½d. dull orange (4.70) .. .. £180 65·00
w. Wmk inverted .. .. .. † £325
x. Wmk reversed £600
½d. orange-buff (5.72) .. .. £130 55·00
½d. golden yellow (aniline) (10.74) .. £250 £300
½d. yellow-buff (9.75) .. .. 60·00 55·00
½d. pale buff (3.77) .. .. £150 55·00
w. Wmk inverted .. .. .. † £375
½d. bright orange-yellow (4.80) .. £140 75·00
½d. yellow (4.81) .. .. .. 85·00 50·00
w. Wmk inverted .. .. .. † £325

(b) P 12½ rough (No. 14) or clean-cut (No. 15)

½d. buff-brown (11.68) .. .. £110 90·00
½d. yellow-orange (5.71) £250 £150

(c) P 14×12½

½d. yellow-buff (7.78) .. .. £150 85·00
½d. yellow (2.79) .. .. .. £170 90·00

ɛamples of No. 4 from the 1863 printing are on thin, surfaced er; later printings in the same shade were on unsurfaced paper.
ıe ink used for No. 5 is mineral and, unlike that on No. 9, does stain the paper.
ome variations of shade on No. 6 may be described as chestnut. ink of No. 6 is clear and never muddy, although some examples over-inked. Deeper shades of No. 4, with which examples of 6 might be confused, have muddy ink.
is believed that there are no surviving pairs of the buff-wn imperforate between variety previously listed.
ıe Royal Collection contains an unused horizontal pair of the ow-buff perforated 12½×14.

2 (Mar)–84. *Wmk Crown CA. P* 14.
½d. orange-yellow .. .. .. 30·00 35·00
½d. red-orange (9.84) .. .. .. 17·00 48·00

2

3

4 5

85 (1 Jan)–90. *Wmk Crown CA. P* 14.
) 1 ½d. green .. .. .. 2·00 50
w. Wmk inverted .. .. .. 90·00 75·00
2 1d. rose .. .. .. 85·00 26·00
1d. carmine (*shades*) (1890) .. 3·00 35
w. Wmk inverted .. .. .. † £850
3 3 2d. grey .. .. .. 5·00 1·50
4 4 2½d. dull blue .. .. .. 55·00 2·50
5 2½d. bright blue .. .. .. 35·00 1·00
6 2½d. ultramarine .. .. .. 35·00 1·00
7 3 4d. brown .. .. .. 11·00 3·00
a. Imperf (pair) £4750 £4750
3 1s. violet .. .. .. 35·00 9·00
9 1s. pale violet (1890) .. .. 55·00 19·00
w. Wmk inverted £500 £200
)/9 .. .. .. *Set of* 6 80·00 14·00
)s/8s Optd "Specimen" .. *Set of* 6 £2250

Although not valid for postage until 1 January 1885 these amps were available at the G.P.O., Valletta from 27 December 884.
Three unused examples of the ½d. green, No. 20, are known ıne perforated 12. It is believed that these originated from proof ooks, the stamp not being issued for use with this perforation.
The Royal Collection includes an example of the 1d. carmine rinted on the gummed side.

886 (1 Jan). *Wmk Crown CC. P* 14.
0 5 5s. rose .. .. .. £110 80·00
s. Optd "Specimen" £450
w. Wmk inverted £140 £110

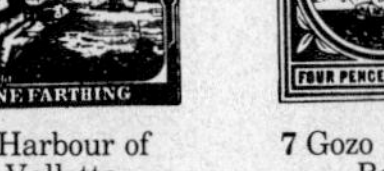
6 Harbour of Valletta

7 Gozo Fishing Boat
8 Galley of Knights of St. John

9 Emblematic figure of Malta

10 Shipwreck of St. Paul

(T **6/10** recess)

1899 (4 Feb)–**1901.** *P* 14. *(a) Wmk Crown CA (sideways* on ¼d).*
31 **6** ¼d. brown (4.1.01) .. .. .. 3·00 2·50
a. Red-brown .. .. .. 1·50 40
w. Wmk Crown to left of CA .. 2·50 75
x. Wmk sideways reversed .. .. 35·00 20·00
y. Wmk Crown to left of CA and reversed .. .. .. 45·00 25·00
32 **7** 4½d. sepia .. .. .. 15·00 10·00
33 **8** 5d. vermilion .. .. .. 32·00 15·00
x. Wmk reversed £130 £130

(b) Wmk Crown CC

34 **9** 2s. 6d. olive-grey .. .. .. 40·00 12·00
35 **10** 10s. blue-black .. .. .. 90·00 65·00
x. Wmk reversed .. .. .. — £325
y. Wmk inverted and reversed .. £300 £225
31/5 .. .. .. *Set of* 5 £160 90·00
31s/5s Optd "Specimen" .. *Set of* 5 £225

*The normal sideways watermark shows Crown to right of CA, *as seen from the back of the stamp.*

One Penny
(11)

12

1902 (4 July). *Nos. 24 and 25 surch locally at Govt Ptg Office with T* 11.
36 1d. on 2½d. dull blue .. .. .. 1·00 1·25
a. Surch double .. .. .. — £3750
b. "One Pnney" (R. 9/2) .. .. 28·00 55·00
ba. Surch double, with "One Pnney"
s. Optd "Specimen" .. .. 70·00
37 1d. on 2½d. bright blue .. .. 1·00 1·75
a. "One Pnney" (R. 9/2) .. .. 30·00 55·00

(Des E. Fuchs)

1903 (12 Mar)–**04.** *Wmk Crown CA. P* 14.
38 **12** ½d. green .. .. .. 8·00 85
39 1d. blackish brown and red (7.5.03) .. 15·00 40
40 2d. purple and grey .. .. 27·00 6·00
41 2½d. maroon and blue (9.03) .. 16·00 4·50
42 3d. grey and purple (26.3.03) .. 1·75 50
43 4d. blackish brown and brown (19.5.04) 25·00 15·00
44 1s. grey and violet (6.4.03) .. 16·00 7·00
38/44 .. .. .. *Set of* 7 £100 30·00
38s/44s Optd "Specimen" .. *Set of* 7 £130

1904–14. *Wmk Mult Crown CA (sideways* on ¼d.). P* 14.
45 **6** ¼d. red-brown (10.10.05) .. .. 3·50 50
a. Deep brown (2.4.10†) .. .. 2·25 10
aw. Wmk Crown to left of CA .. 6·50 1·50
ax. Wmk reversed
ay. Wmk Crown to left of CA and reversed
47 **12** ½d. green (6.11.04) .. .. 3·75 30
aw. Wmk inverted
b. Deep green (1909) .. .. 3·75 10
bw. Wmk inverted
48 1d. black and red (24.4.05) .. .. 14·00 20
49 1d. red (2.4.07) .. .. .. 2·25 10
50 2d. purple and grey (22.2.05) .. 8·00 2·25
51 2d. grey (4.10.11) .. .. .. 3·25 5·50
52 2½d. maroon and blue (10.04) .. 15·00 60
53 2½d. bright blue (15.1.11) .. .. 5·50 2·75
54 4d. black and brown (1.4.06) .. 11·00 5·50
w. Wmk inverted
55 4d. black and red/*yellow* (21.11.11) .. 4·00 3·50
57 **7** 4½d. brown (27.2.05) .. .. 25·00 5·50
w. Wmk inverted £180 £160
58 4½d. orange (16.3.12†) .. .. 4·50 3·50
59 **8** 5d. vermilion (20.2.05) .. .. 26·00 5·00
60 5d. pale sage-green (1909) .. 4·25 3·50
a. Deep sage-green (1914) .. .. 11·00 14·00
61 **12** 1s. grey and violet (14.12.04) .. 48·00 2·00
62 1s. black/*green* (15.3.11) .. .. 7·50 2·75
63 5s. green and red/*yellow* (22.3.11) .. 65·00 75·00
45/63 .. .. .. *Set of* 17 £225 £100
45as, 47bs, 49s, 51s, 53s, 55s, 58s, 60s, 62s/3s Optd "Specimen" .. *Set of* 10 £300

*The normal sideways watermark shows Crown to right of CA, *as seen from the back of the stamp.*
†These are the earliest known dates of use.

13

14

15

1914–21. *Wmk Mult Crown CA. Ordinary paper (¼d. to 2½d., 2s. 6d.) or chalk-surfaced paper (others). P* 14.
69 **13** ¼d. brown (2.1.14) .. .. .. 1·00 10
a. Deep brown (1919) .. .. 1·00 60
x. Wmk reversed .. .. .. † £425
71 ½d. green (20.1.14) .. .. .. 2·25 30
aa. Wmk sideways .. .. .. † £3750
a. Deep green (1919) .. .. 2·25 60
aw. Wmk inverted .. .. .. † £180
73 1d. carmine-red (15.4.14) .. .. 1·50 10
a. Scarlet (1915) .. .. .. 1·50 40
w. Wmk inverted .. .. .. † £180
75 2d. grey (12.8.14) .. .. .. 7·00 3·00
aw. Wmk inverted .. .. .. † £425
b. Deep slate (1919) .. .. 8·00 11·00
77 2½d. bright blue (11.3.14) .. .. 2·25 50
w. Wmk inverted .. .. .. † £120
78 **14** 3d. purple/*yellow* (1.5.20) .. .. 2·50 8·00
a. On orange-buff .. .. .. 48·00 40·00
79 **6** 4d. black (21.8.15) .. .. .. 15·00 3·25
a. Grey-black (28.10.16) .. .. 25·00 8·00
80 **13** 6d. dull and bright purple (10.3.14) .. 11·00 16·00
a. Dull purple and magenta (1918) .. 14·00 16·00
w. Wmk inverted
81 **14** 1s. black/*green (white back)* (2.1.14) .. 13·00 24·00
a. On green, green back (1915) .. 12·00 14·00
ab. Wmk sideways .. .. .. † £1800
as. Optd "Specimen" .. .. 45·00
b. On blue-green, olive back (1918) .. 19·00 21·00
c. On emerald surface (1920) .. 8·50 21·00
d. On emerald back (1921) .. .. 28·00 60·00
86 **15** 2s. purple and bright blue/*blue* (15.4.14) 50·00 29·00
a. Break in scroll £225
b. Broken crown and scroll £275
c. Dull purple and blue/blue (1921) .. 75·00 50·00
ca. Break in scroll £300
cb. Broken crown and scroll £350
87 **9** 2s. 6d. olive-green (1919) .. .. 55·00 75·00
a. Olive-grey (1920) .. .. 60·00 95·00
88 **15** 5s. green and red/*yellow* (21.3.17) .. 80·00 95·00
a. Break in scroll £350
b. Broken crown and scroll £400
69/88 .. .. .. *Set of* 12 £200 £200
69s/88s (*ex* 2s. 6d.) Optd "Specimen" *Set of* 11 £400

The design of Nos. 79/*a* differs in various details from that of Type **6**.
We have only seen one copy of No. 71aa; it is in used condition.
A 3d. purple on yellow on white back, Type **14**, was prepared for use but not issued. It exists overprinted "Specimen" (*Price* £250).
An example of the 2s. 6d. olive-grey with bottom margin attached exists with the "A" omitted from "CA" in the watermark on the margin.
For illustrations of the varieties on Nos. 86 and 88 see above No. 58 of Leeward Islands.

WAR TAX
(16)

17

18

1917–18. *Optd with T* **16** *by De La Rue.*
92 **13** ½d. deep green (14.12.17*) .. .. 1·00 15
w. Wmk inverted £375
93 **12** 3d. grey and purple (15.2.18*) .. 1·50 7·50
92s/3s Optd "Specimen" .. *Set of* 2 £130

*These are the earliest known dates of use.

(T **17** recess)

1919 (6 Mar). *Wmk Mult Crown CA. P* 14.
96 **17** 10s. black £2500 £3500
s. Optd "Specimen" £750

Dark flaw on scroll (R. 2/4 1st state)

Lines omitted from scroll (R. 2/4 2nd state)

1921 (16 Feb)–**22.** *Wmk Mult Script CA. Chalk-surfaced paper (6d., 2s.) or ordinary paper (others). P* 14.
97 **13** ¼d. brown (12.1.22) .. .. .. 1·75 26·00
98 ½d. green (19.1.22) .. .. .. 2·00 18·00
99 1d. scarlet (24.12.21) .. .. 2·00 1·60
w. Wmk inverted £425 £150
100 **18** 2d. grey .. .. .. 3·50 1·75
101 **13** 2½d. bright blue (15.1.22) .. .. 3·00 26·00
102 6d. dull purple & brt purple (19.1.22) 29·00 70·00
103 **15** 2s. purple and blue/*blue* (19.1.22) .. 60·00 £190
a. Break in scroll £200
b. Broken crown and scroll £200
c. Dark flaw on scroll £1600
d. Lines omitted from scroll £350
104 **17** 10s. black (19.1.22) £325 £600
97/104 .. .. .. *Set of* 8 £375 £850
97s/104s Optd "Specimen" .. *Set of* 8 £400

For illustrations of other varieties on No. 103 see above No. 58 of Leeward Islands.
Examples of all values are known showing a forged G.P.O. Malta postmark dated "MY 10 22".

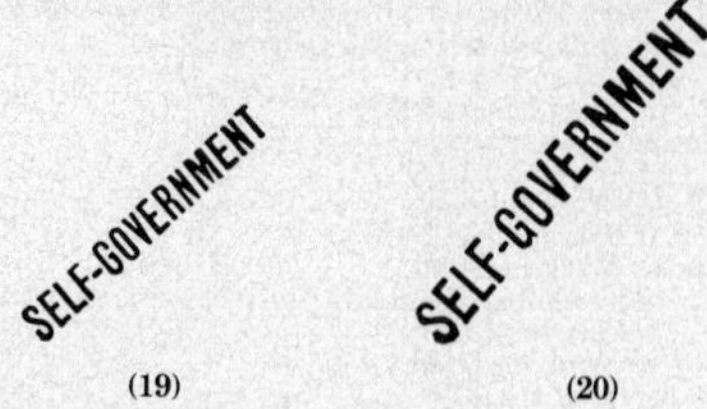

(19) (20)

1922 (12 Jan–Apr). *Optd with T* **19** *or T* **20** (*large stamps*), *at Govt Printing Office, Valletta.* (*a*) *On No.* 35. *Wmk Crown CC.*

No.	Type	Description	Unused	Used
105	**10**	10s. blue-black (R.)	£180	£325

(*b*) *On Nos.* 71, 77, 78*a*, 80, 81*d*, 86*c*, 87*a and* 88. *Wmk Mult Crown CA*

No.	Type	Description	Unused	Used
106	**13**	½d. green	1·00	1·75
		w. Wmk inverted	70·00	
107		2½d. bright blue	8·00	27·00
108	**14**	3d. purple/*orange-buff*	2·50	15·00
109	**13**	6d. dull and bright purple	2·50	15·00
		x. Wmk reversed	†	£600
110	**14**	1s. black/*emerald*	3·50	15·00
111	**15**	2s. purple and blue/*blue* (R.)	£200	£450
		a. Break in scroll	£600	
		b. Broken crown and scroll	£600	
112	**9**	2s. 6d. olive-grey	22·00	42·00
		a. "C" of "CA" missing from wmk	£850	
113	**15**	5s. green and red/*yellow*	50·00	80·00
		a. Break in scroll	£225	
		b. Broken crown and scroll	£225	
		c. Lines omitted from scroll	£300	
106/13		*Set of* 8	£250	£550

(*c*) *On Nos.* 97/104. *Wmk Mult Script CA*

No.	Type	Description	Unused	Used
114	**13**	¼d. brown	30	75
		w. Wmk inverted		
115		½d. green (29.4)	2·00	6·00
116		1d. scarlet	1·00	20
117	**18**	2d. grey	2·25	45
118	**13**	2½d. bright blue (15.1)	1·10	1·00
119		6d. dull and bright purple (19.4)	9·00	28·00
120	**15**	2s. purple and blue/*blue* (R.) (25.1)	40·00	85·00
		a. Break in scroll	£180	
		b. Broken crown and scroll	£180	
		c. Lines omitted from scroll	£300	
121	**17**	10s. black (R.) (9.3)	£120	£180
114/21		*Set of* 8	£160	£275

Examples of all values are known showing a forged G.P.O. Malta postmark dated "MY 10 22".

One Farthing

(21)

22

23

1922 (15 Apr). *No.* 100 *surch with T* **21**, *at Govt Printing Office, Valletta.*

No.	Type	Description	Unused	Used
122	**18**	¼d. on 2d. grey	85	30

(Des C. Dingli (T **22**) and G. Vella (**23**))

1922 (1 Aug)–**26**. *Wmk Mult Script CA* (*sideways* on T* **22**, *except No.* 140). *P* 14. (*a*) *Typo. Chalk-surfaced paper.*

No.	Type	Description	Unused	Used
123	**22**	¼d. brown (22.8.22)	2·25	60
		a. Chocolate-brown	3·00	70
		w. Wmk Crown to right of CA	—	55·00
124		½d. green	2·00	15
		w. Wmk Crown to right of CA	—	55·00
125		1d. orange and purple	2·75	20
		w. Wmk Crown to right of CA	—	42·00
126		1d. bright violet (25.4.24)	2·75	80
127		1½d. brown-red (1.10.23)	3·25	15
128		2d. bistre-brown & turquoise (28.8.22)	2·75	1·25
		w. Wmk Crown to right of CA	—	80·00
129		2½d. ultramarine (16.2.26)	2·25	6·50
130		3d. cobalt (28.8.22)	3·25	1·00
		a. Bright ultramarine	3·25	1·50
131		3d. black/*yellow* (16.2.26)	2·75	11·00
132		4d. yellow and bright blue (28.8.22)	1·75	2·25
		w. Wmk Crown to right of CA	£120	
133		6d. olive-green and reddish violet	3·25	2·25
134	**23**	1s. indigo and sepia	5·50	2·50
135		2s. brown and blue	9·00	8·50
136		2s. 6d. brt magenta & black (28.8.22)	10·00	15·00
137		5s. orange-yell & brt ultram (28.8.22)	21·00	38·00
138		10s. slate-grey and brown (28.8.22)	55·00	£150

(*b*) *Recess*

No.	Type	Description	Unused	Used
139	**22**	£1 black and carmine-red (*wmk sideways*) (28.8.22)	£120	£300
140		£1 black and bright carmine (*wmk upright*) (14.5.25)	90·00	£275
123/40		*Set of* 17	£190	£450
123s/39s Optd "Specimen"		*Set of* 17	£450	

*The normal sideways watermark shows Crown to left of CA, *as seen from the back of the stamp.*

Two pence halfpenny

(24)

POSTAGE

(25)

1925. *Surch with T* **24**, *at Govt Printing Office, Valletta.*

No.	Type	Description	Unused	Used
141	**22**	2½d. on 3d. cobalt (3 Dec)	1·75	3·50
142		2½d. on 3d. bright ultramarine (9 Dec)	1·75	3·50

1926 (1 Apr). *Optd with T* **25** *at Govt Printing Office, Valletta.*

No.	Type	Description	Unused	Used
143	**22**	¼d. brown	70	3·50
144		½d. green	70	15
		w. Wmk Crown to right of CA	60·00	
145		1d. bright violet	1·00	25
146		1½d. brown-red	1·00	60
147		2d. bistre-brown and turquoise	75	60
148		2½d. ultramarine	1·25	80
149		3d. black/*yellow*	75	80
		a. Opt inverted	£170	£475
150		4d. yellow and bright blue	5·50	15·00
151		6d. olive-green and violet	2·75	3·00
152	**23**	1s. indigo and sepia	5·50	9·50
153		2s. brown and blue	48·00	£140
154		2s. 6d. bright magenta and black	11·00	29·00
155		5s. orange-yellow & brt ultramarine	9·00	30·00
156		10s. slate-grey and brown	7·00	16·00
143/56		*Set of* 14	85·00	£225

26

27 Valletta Harbour

28 St. Publius

33 St. Paul

(T **26** typo, others recess Waterlow)

1926 (6 Apr)–**27.** *T* **26/8**, **33** *and similar designs. Inscr* "POSTAGE". *Wmk Mult Script CA. P* 15×14 (*T* **26**) *or* 12½ (*others*).

No.	Type	Description	Unused	Used
157	**26**	¼d. brown	80	15
158		½d. yellow-green (5.8.26)	60	15
		a. Printed on the gummed side	£600	
		w. Wmk inverted		
159		1d. rose-red (1.4.27)	3·00	90
160		1½d. chestnut (7.10.26)	2·00	10
161		2d. greenish grey (1.4.27)	4·50	8·50
162		2½d. blue (1.4.27)	4·00	1·00
162*a*		3d. violet (1.4.27)	4·25	2·25
163		4d. black and red	3·25	8·50
164		4½d. lavender and ochre	3·50	2·75
165		6d. violet and scarlet (5.5.26)	4·25	3·25
166	**27**	1s. black	6·50	3·50
167	**28**	1s. 6d. black and green	6·50	13·00
168	–	2s. black and purple	6·50	15·00
169	–	2s. 6d. black and vermilion	15·00	48·00
170	–	3s. black and blue	17·00	30·00
171	–	5s. black and green (5.5.26)	22·00	60·00
172	**33**	10s. black and carmine (9.2.27)	55·00	£100
157/72		*Set of* 17	£130	£250
157s/72s Optd "Specimen"		*Set of* 17	£275	

Designs: *Vert*—2s. 6d. Gozo fishing boat; 3s. Neptune; *Horiz*—2s. Mdina (Notabile); 5s. Neolithic temple, Mnajdra.

AIR MAIL

(34)

POSTAGE AND REVENUE

(35)

POSTAGE AND REVENUE.

(36)

1928 (1 Apr). *Air. Optd with T* **34**.

No.	Type	Description	Unused	Used
173	**26**	6d. violet and scarlet	1·50	1·00

1928 (1 Oct–5 Dec). *As Nos.* 157/72, *optd.*

No.	Type	Description	Unused	Used
174	**35**	¼d. brown	1·50	10
175		½d. yellow-green	1·50	10
176		1d. rose-red	1·75	3·25
177		1d. chestnut (5.12.28)	4·50	10
178		1½d. chestnut	1·75	85
179		1½d. rose-red (5.12.28)	4·25	10
180		2d. greenish grey	4·25	9·00
181		2½d. blue	2·00	10
182		3d. violet	2·00	70
183		4d. black and red	2·00	1·75
184		4½d. lavender and ochre	2·25	1·00
185		6d. violet and scarlet	2·25	1·50
186	**36**	1s. black (R.)	5·50	2·50
187		1s. 6d. black and green (R.)	6·50	9·50
188		2s. black and purple (R.)	24·00	50·00
189		2s. 6d. black and vermilion (R.)	17·00	23·00
190		3s. black and blue (R.)	19·00	30·00
191		5s. black and green (R.)	28·00	65·00
192		10s. black and carmine (R.)	55·00	90·00
174/92		*Set of* 19	£150	£250
174s/92s Optd "Specimen"		*Set of* 19	£300	

1930 (20 Oct). *As Nos.* 157/172, *but inscr* "POSTAGE (&) REVENUE".

No.	Type	Description	Unused	Used
193		¼d. brown	60	10
194		½d. yellow-green	60	10
195		1d. chestnut	60	10
196		1½d. rose-red	70	10
197		2d. greenish grey	1·25	50
198		2½d. blue	2·00	10
199		3d. violet	1·50	20
200		4d. black and red	1·25	3·75
201		4½d. lavender and ochre	3·25	1·25
202		6d. violet and scarlet	2·50	1·25
203		1s. black	10·00	13·00
204		1s. 6d. black and green	8·00	18·00
205		2s. black and purple	10·00	
206		2s. 6d. black and vermilion	17·00	
207		3s. black and blue	26·00	
208		5s. black and green	30·00	
209		10s. black and carmine	65·00	
193/209		*Set of* 17	£150	
193s/209s Perf "Specimen"		*Set of* 17	£275	

1935 (6 May). *Silver Jubilee. As Nos.* 91/4 *of Antigua, printed by B.W. P* 11×12.

No.	Type	Description	Unused	Used
210		½d. black and green	50	
		a. Extra flagstaff	22·00	
		b. Short extra flagstaff	38·00	
		c. Lightning conductor	30·00	
211		2½d. brown and deep blue	2·50	
		a. Extra flagstaff	£130	
		b. Short extra flagstaff	£140	
		c. Lightning conductor	£100	
212		6d. light blue and olive-green	7·00	
		a. Extra flagstaff	£180	
		b. Short extra flagstaff	£200	
		c. Lightning conductor	£140	
213		1s. slate and purple	11·00	
		a. Extra flagstaff	£425	
		b. Short extra flagstaff	£350	
		c. Lightning conductor	£250	
210/13		*Set of* 4	19·00	
210s/13s Perf "Specimen"		*Set of* 4	£130	

For illustrations of plate varieties see Omnibus sect following Zanzibar.

Sheets from the second printing of the ½d., 6d. and 1s. November 1935 had the extra flagstaff partially erased from stamp with a sharp point.

1937 (12 May). *Coronation. As Nos.* 95/7 *of Antigua, printed by D.L.R. P* 14.

No.	Type	Description	Unused	Used
214		½d. green	10	
215		1½d. scarlet	80	
		a. Brown-lake	£550	
216		2½d. bright blue	80	
214/16		*Set of* 3	1·50	
214s/16s Perf "Specimen"		*Set of* 3	60·00	

37 Grand Harbour, Valletta

38 H.M.S. *St. Angelo*

39 Verdala Palace

40 Hypogeum, Hal Saflieni

Broken cross (Right pane R. 5/7)

Extra windows (R. 2/7) (corrected in 1945)

Damaged value tablet (R. 4/9)

Semaphore flaw (R. 2/7)

(Recess Waterlow)

1938 (17 Feb*)–**43.** *T* **37/40** *and similar designs. Wmk Mult Script CA* (*sideways on No.* 217). *P* 12½.

No.	Type	Description	Unused	Used
217	**37**	¼d. brown	10	10
218	**38**	½d. green	1·75	30
218*a*		½d. red-brown (8.3.43)	55	30
219	**39**	1d. red-brown	4·25	40
219*a*		1d. green (8.3.43)	60	10
220	**40**	1½d. scarlet	1·00	30
		a. Broken cross	85·00	60·00
220*b*		1½d. slate-black (8.3.43)	30	15
		ba. Broken cross	55·00	50·00
221	–	2d. slate-black	40	2·00
		a. Extra windows	40·00	
221*b*	–	2d. scarlet (8.3.43)	40	30
		ba. Extra windows	40·00	
222	–	2½d. greyish blue	75	60
222*a*	–	2½d. dull violet (8.3.43)	60	10
223	–	3d. dull violet	55	80
223*a*	–	3d. blue (8.3.43)	30	20

– 4½d. olive-green and yellow-brown .. 50 30
– 6d. olive-green and scarlet 75 30
– 1s. black 75 30
– 1s. 6d. black and olive-green .. 7·00 4·00
– 2s. green and deep blue .. .. 4·50 4·00
– 2s. 6d. black and scarlet .. .. 8·00 5·50
a. Damaged value tablet £170 £120
– 5s. black and green .. .. 4·50 6·50
a. Semaphore flaw .. .. 65·00
– 10s. black and carmine .. .. 15·00 15·00
1 .. .. *Set of* 21 45·00 35·00
31s Perf "Specimen" .. *Set of* 21 £350

signs: *Horiz* (*as T* **39**)—2d. Victoria and citadel, Gozo; 2½d. sle Adam entering Mdina; 4½d. Ruins at Mnajdra; 1s. 6d. ıblius; 2s. Mdina Cathedral; 2s. 6d. Statue of Neptune, *Vert* **40**)—3d. St. John's Co-Cathedral; 6d. Statue of Manoel de na; 1s. Maltese girl wearing faldetta; 5s. Palace Square, tta; 10s. St. Paul.

his is the local date of issue but the stamps were released in on on 15 February.

(3 Dec). *Victory. As Nos.* 110/11 *of Antigua, but inscr* ALTA" *between Maltese Cross and George Cross.*
1d. green 15 10
w. Wmk inverted £500
3d. blue 20 50
/3s Perf "Specimen" .. .. *Set of* 2 50·00

SELF-GOVERNMENT

(52) "NT" joined (R. 4/10)

Halation flaw (Pl 2 R. 2/5) (ptg of 8 Jan 1953)

Cracked plate (Pl 2 R. 5/1) (ptg of 8 Jan 1953)

(Optd by Waterlow)

48 (25 Nov)–**53.** *New Constitution. As Nos.* 217/31 *but optd* s *T* **52**; *reading up on ½d. and 5s., down on other values, and* maller on ¼d. value.*
4 **37** ¼d. brown 30 20
5 **38** ½d. red-brown 30 10
a. "NT" joined .. .. .. 19·00
6 **39** 1d. green 30 10
6*a* 1d. grey (R.) (8.1.53) 30 10
7 **40** 1½d. blue-black (R.) .. .. .. 1·25 10
a. Broken cross .. .. .. 70·00 40·00
7*b* 1½d. green (8.1.53) 30 10
ba. Albino opt .. .. .. † £10000
8 – 2d. scarlet .. .. 1·25 10
a. Extra windows .. .. .. 45·00
8*b* – 2d. yellow-ochre (8.1.53) 30 10
ba. Halation flaw £120
bc. Cracked plate £110
9 – 2½d. dull violet (R.) 80 10
9*a* – 2½d. scarlet-vermilion (8.1.53) .. 50 1·25
0 – 3d. blue (R.) .. .. .. 1·00 15
0*a* – 3d. dull violet (R.) (8.1.53) 50 15
1 – 4½d. olive-green and yellow-brown .. 2·00 1·50
1*a* – 4½d. olive-grn & dp ultram (R.) (8.1.53) 50 90
2 – 6d. olive-green and scarlet .. .. 2·25 15
3 – 1s. black .. .. 2·25 40
4 – 1s. 6d. black and olive-green .. 2·50 45
5 – 2s. green and deep blue (R.) .. 5·00 2·00
46 – 2s. 6d. black and scarlet .. .. 12·00 2·50
a. Damaged value tablet £375
47 – 5s. black and green (R.) .. .. 17·00 3·50
a. "NT" joined £180 £100
b. Semaphore flaw .. .. .. — £1800
48 – 10s. black and carmine .. .. 17·00 21·00
34/48 .. .. *Set of* 21 55·00 30·00

949 (4 Jan). *Royal Silver Wedding. As Nos.* 112/13 *of Antigua, but inscr* "MALTA" *between Maltese Cross and George Cross and with* £1 *ptd in recess.*
49 1d. green 50 10
50 £1 indigo .. .. 38·00 35·00

949 (10 Oct). *75th Anniv of U.P.U. As Nos.* 114/17 *of Antigua, but inscr* "MALTA" *in recess.*
51 2½d. violet 30 10
52 3d. deep blue .. .. 2·75 50
53 6d. carmine-red 50 50
54 1s. blue-black .. .. 50 2·00
51/4 .. .. *Set of* 4 3·50 2·75

MINIMUM PRICE

The minimum price quote is 10p which represents a handling charge rather than a basis for valuing common stamps. For further notes about prices see introductory pages.

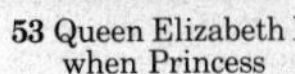

53 Queen Elizabeth II when Princess

54 "Our Lady of Mount Carmel" (attrib Palladino)

(T **53/4**. Recess B.W.)

1950 (1 Dec). *Visit of Princess Elizabeth to Malta. Wmk Mult Script CA. P* 12 × 11½.
255 **53** 1d. green 10 10
256 3d. blue 20 10
257 1s. black 55 90
255/7 .. .. *Set of* 3 70 1·00

1951 (12 July). *Seventh Centenary of the Scapular. Wmk Mult Script CA. P* 12 × 11½.
258 **54** 1d. green 10 10
259 3d. violet 25 10
260 1s. black 75 50
258/60 .. .. *Set of* 3 1·00 60

POSTAGE DUE STAMPS

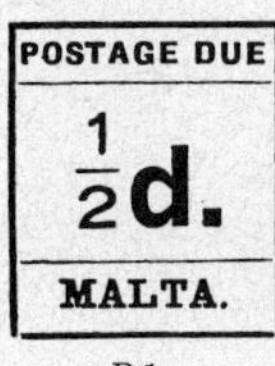

D 1

D 2

1925 (16 Apr). *Type-set by Govt Printing Office, Valletta. Imperf.*
D 1 **D 1** ½d. black .. .. 1·25 6·00
a. *Tête-bêche* (horiz pair) .. .. 5·00 17·00
D 2 1d. black .. .. 3·25 3·00
a. *Tête-bêche* (horiz pair) .. .. 10·00 12·00
D 3 1½d. black .. .. 3·00 3·75
a. *Tête-bêche* (horiz pair) .. .. 10·00 15·00
D 4 2d. black .. .. 6·00 12·00
a. *Tête-bêche* (horiz pair) .. .. 15·00 35·00
D 5 2½d. black .. .. 2·75 2·75
a. "2" of "½" omitted £800 £1200
b. *Tête-bêche* (horiz pair) .. .. 12·00 15·00
D 6 3d. black/*grey* .. .. .. 9·00 13·00
a. *Tête-bêche* (horiz pair) .. .. 30·00 45·00
D 7 4d black/*buff* .. .. .. 5·00 9·50
a. *Tête-bêche* (horiz pair) .. .. 17·00 38·00
D 8 6d. black/*buff* .. .. .. 5·00 15·00
a. *Tête-bêche* (horiz pair) .. .. 17·00 50·00
D 9 1s. black/*buff* .. .. .. 7·50 20·00
a. *Tête-bêche* (horiz pair) .. .. 25·00 60·00
D10 1s. 6d. black/*buff* .. .. .. 14·00 55·00
a. *Tête-bêche* (horiz pair) .. .. 40·00 £140
D1/10 .. .. *Set of* 10 50·00 £120

Nos. D1/10 were each issued in sheets containing 4 panes (6×7) printed separately, the impressions in the two right-hand panes being inverted. Fourteen horizontal *tête-bêche* pairs occur from the junction of the left and right-hand panes.

No. D5a occurred on R. 4/4 of the last 2½d. pane position to be printed. Forgeries exist, but can be detected by comparison with a normal example under ultra-violet light. They are often found in pair with normal, showing forged cancellations of "VALLETTA AP20 25" or "G.P.O" MY 7 25".

(Typo B.W.)

1925 (20 July). *Wmk Mult Script CA (sideways). P* 12.
D11 **D 2** ½d. green .. .. 1·25 60
D12 1d. violet .. .. 1·25 45
D13 1½d. brown .. .. 1·50 80
D14 2d. grey .. .. 11·00 1·00
D15 2½d. orange .. .. 2·00 1·25
x. Wmk reversed .. .. .. 80·00
D16 3d. blue .. .. 3·50 1·25
D17 4d. olive-green .. .. .. 12·00 16·00
D18 6d. purple .. .. 3·00 3·75
D19 1s. black .. .. 6·50 10·00
D20 1s. 6d. carmine .. .. .. 8·50 27·00
D11/20 .. .. *Set of* 10 45·00 55·00
D11s/20s Optd "Specimen" .. *Set of* 10 £200

Mauritius

GREAT BRITAIN STAMPS USED IN MAURITIUS. We no longer list the Great Britain stamps with obliteration "B 53" as there is no evidence that British stamps were available from the Mauritius Post Office.

See under SEYCHELLES for stamps of Mauritius used at Victoria with "B 64" cancellations between 1861 and 1890.

A similar "B 65" cancellation was used on the island of Rodrigues, a dependency of Mauritius, from 11 December 1861 onwards.

PRICES FOR STAMPS ON COVER TO 1945

Nos. 1/5	*from* × 2
Nos. 6/9	*from* × 3
Nos. 10/15	*from* × 4
Nos. 16/25	*from* × 5
Nos. 26/9	*from* × 3
Nos. 30/1	*from* —
Nos. 32/5	*from* × 4
Nos. 36/44	*from* × 5
Nos. 46/72	*from* × 3
Nos. 76/82	*from* × 5
Nos. 83/91	*from* × 6
Nos. 92/100	*from* × 4
Nos. 101/11	*from* × 3
Nos. 117/24	*from* × 8
Nos. 127/32	*from* × 7
No. 133	*from* × 4
Nos. 134/5	*from* × 10
No. 136	*from* × 8
Nos. 137/56	*from* × 6
Nos. 157/63	*from* × 5
Nos. 164/221	*from* × 3
No. 222	—
Nos. 223/41	*from* × 3
Nos. 242/4	*from* × 10
Nos. 245/8	*from* × 3
Nos. 249/63	*from* × 2
Nos. E1/6	*from* × 10
Nos. D1/7	*from* × 40
Nos. R1/3	*from* × 15

CROWN COLONY

Nos. 1/25*b* and 36/44 were printed in Mauritius.

1 ("POST OFFICE")

2 ("POST PAID")

(Engraved on copper by J. O. Barnard)

1847 (21 Sept). *Head of Queen on groundwork of diagonal and perpendicular lines. Imperf.*
1 **1** 1d. orange-red .. .. .. — £450000
2 2d. deep blue .. .. .. — £550000

A single plate contained one example of each value.

It is generally agreed that fifteen examples of No. 1 have survived (including two unused) and twelve of No. 2 (including four unused). Most are now in permanent museum collections.

NOTE. Our prices for early Mauritius are for stamps in very fine condition. Exceptional copies are worth more, poorer copies considerably less.

(Engraved on copper by J. O. Barnard)

1848 (June)–**59.** *Imperf.*

A. *Earliest impressions. Design deep, sharp and clear. Diagonal lines predominate. Thick paper (Period of use:* 1*d.* 1853–54, 2*d.* 1848–49)
3 **2** 1d. orange-vermilion/*yellowish* £35000 £13000
4 2d. indigo-blue/*grey to bluish* £30000 £15000
a. "PENOE" for "PENCE" (R. 3/1) .. £60000 £23000
5 2d. deep blue/*grey to bluish* £30000 £15000
a. "PENOE" for "PENCE" (R. 3/1) .. £60000 £26000

B. *Early impressions. Design sharp and clear but some lines slightly weakened. Paper not so thick, grey to yellowish white or bluish (Period of use:* 1*d.* 1853–55, 2*d.* 1849–54).
6 **2** 1d. vermilion £15000 £5500
7 1d. orange-vermilion £16000 £5000
8 2d. blue £17000 £6000
a. "PENOE" for "PENCE" (R. 3/1) .. £27000 £9500
9 2d. deep blue £21000 £6500

C. *Intermediate impressions. White patches appear where design has worn. Paper yellowish white, grey or bluish, of poorish quality (Period of use:* 1*d and* 2*d.* 1854–57)
10 **2** 1d. bright vermilion £7500 £2000
11 1d. dull vermilion £7500 £2000
12 1d. red £7500 £2000
13 2d. deep blue £10000 £3000
14 2d. blue £7500 £2250
a. "PENOE" for "PENCE" (R. 3/1) *from* £13000 £4750
15 2d. light blue £7500 £2250

D. *Worn impressions. Much of design worn away but some diagonal lines distinct. Paper yellowish, grey or bluish, of poorish quality (Period of use: 1d. 1857–59, 2d. 1855–58)*

No.	Type	Description	Unused	Used
16	2	1d. red/*yellowish or grey*	£2500	£425
17		1d. red-brown/*yellowish or grey*	£2500	£425
18		1d. red/*bluish*	£1800	£375
		a. Doubly printed		
19		1d. red-brown/*bluish*	£1800	£375
20		2d. blue (*shades*)/*yellowish or grey*	£2750	£800
		a. "PENOE" for "PENCE" (R. 3/1) .. *from*	—	£1300
21		2d. grey-blue/*yellowish or grey*	£3000	£750
22		2d. blue (*shades*)/*bluish*	£2750	£750
		a. Doubly printed		

E. *Latest impressions. Almost none of design showing except part of Queen's head and frame. Paper yellowish, grey or bluish, of poorish quality (Period of use: 1d. 1859, 2d. 1856–58)*

No.	Type	Description	Unused	Used
23	2	1d. red	£1500	£375
24		1d. red-brown	£1500	£375
25		2d. grey-blue/*bluish*	£2000	£500
		a. "PENOE" for "PENCE" (R. 3/1)	£3750	£900

Earliest known use of the 2d. value is on 19 June 1848, but the 1d. value is not known used before 27 September 1853.

There were separate plates for the 1d. and 2d. values, each of 12 (3×4).

3

(4)

5

(Eng G. Fairman. Recess P.B.)

1858*. *Surch with T* **4**. *Imperf.*

No.	Type	Description	Unused	Used
26	3	4d. green	£750	£375

*Although originally gazetted for use from 8 April 1854, research into the archives indicates that No. 26 was not actually issued until 1858, when the stamps were mentioned in an ordinance of 30 April. The earliest dated postmark known is 27 March 1858.

PERKINS BACON "CANCELLED". For notes on these handstamps, showing "CANCELLED" between horizontal bars forming an oval, see Catalogue Introduction.

1858–62. *No value expressed. Imperf.*

No.	Type	Description	Unused	Used
27	3	(4d.) green	£425	£200
28		(6d.) vermilion	29·00	50·00
29		(9d.) dull magenta (1859)	£550	£200
		a. Reissued as (1d.) value (11.62)	†	£160

Prepared for use but not issued

No.	Type	Description	Unused	Used
30	3	(No value), red-brown	13·00	
31		(No value), blue (H/S "CANCELLED" in oval £5000)	3·25	

Use of the dull magenta as a 1d. value can be confirmed by the presence of the "B 53" cancellation which was first introduced in 1861.

Remainders of Nos. 30/1, overprinted "L.P.E. 1890" in red, were perforated at the London Philatelic Exhibition and sold as souvenirs.

(Recess P.B.)

1859–61. *Imperf.*

No.	Type	Description	Unused	Used
32	5	6d. bl (H/S "CANCELLED" in oval £7000)	£600	35·00
33		6d. dull purple-slate (1861)	20·00	38·00
34		1s. vermilion (H/S "CANCELLED" in oval £4000)	£2000	45·00
35		1s. yellow-green (1861)	£475	£110

The 1859 printings had the colours transposed by mistake.

6

7

8

(Engraved on copper by J. Lapirot)

1859 (Mar–Nov). *Imperf. (a) Early impressions.*

No.	Type	Description	Unused	Used
36	6	2d. deep blue	£5000	£1800
37		2d. blue	£4000	£1600

(b) Intermediate prints. Lines of background, etc, partly worn away (July)

No.	Type	Description	Unused	Used
38	6	2d. blue	£2500	£600

(c) Worn impressions, bluish-paper (Oct)

No.	Type	Description	Unused	Used
39	6	2d. blue	£1200	£400

(d) Retouched impression (Nov)

No.	Type	Description	Unused	Used
39a	6	2d. blue	†	—
		ab. "MAURITUIS" (R.2/4)	†	£100000
		ac. "MAURITUS" (R.3/1)	†	£100000

Nos. 36/9a were printed from a plate of 12 (4×3). The plate became worn through use, and was eventually extensively re-engraved. Only two pairs (one on cover) have been recorded from this retouched impression. The errors made in the re-engraving of the inscriptions probably resulted in it being withdrawn from use.

(1848 plate re-engraved by R. Sherwin)

1859 (Oct). *Bluish paper. Imperf.*

No.	Type	Description	Unused	Used
40	7	2d. deep blue	£100000	£4000

The 1d. plate was also re-engraved, but was not put into use. Reprints in black were made in 1877 from both 1d. and 2d. re-engraved plates. Coloured autotype illustrations were prepared from these reprints and 600 were included in the R.P.S.L. handbook on *British Africa* in 1900. Further reprints in black were made in 1911 after the plates had been presented to the R.P.S.L. and defaced.

(Lithographed by L. A. Dardenne)

1859 (12 Dec). *White laid paper. Imperf.*

No.	Type	Description	Unused	Used
41	8	1d. deep red	£6000	£1500
41a		1d. red	£4500	£850
42		1d. dull vermilion	£3500	£750
43		2d. slate-blue	£3750	£700
43a		2d. blue	£1900	£475
44		2d. pale blue	£1800	£375
		a. Heavy retouch on neck	—	£1100
		b. Retouched below "TWO"	—	£600

The neck retouch shows a prominent curved white line running from the base of the chignon to the nape of the neck. No. 44b shows several diagonal lines in the margin below "TWO".

9

10

(Typo D.L.R.)

1860 (7 Apr)–**63.** *No wmk. P* 14.

No.	Type	Description	Unused	Used
46	9	1d. purple-brown	£160	18·00
47		2d. blue	£200	32·00
48		4d. rose	£200	25·00
49		6d. green (1862)	£600	£110
50		6d. slate (1863)	£200	80·00
51		9d. dull purple	95·00	38·00
52		1s. buff (1862)	£225	75·00
53		1s. green (1863)	£550	£150

1862. *Intermediate perf* 14 *to* 16.

No.	Type	Description	Unused	Used
54	5	6d. slate	18·00	48·00
		a. Imperf between (horiz pair)	£5000	
55		1s. deep green	£1800	£325

1863–72. *Wmk Crown CC. P* 14.

No.	Type	Description	Unused	Used
56	9	1d. purple-brown	60·00	9·50
		w. Wmk inverted	85·00	23·00
		y. Wmk inverted and reversed		
57		1d. brown	75·00	6·00
58		1d. bistre (1872)	95·00	8·00
		w. Wmk inverted		
59		2d. pale blue	70·00	7·50
		w. Wmk inverted	£100	23·00
		x. Wmk reversed		
		y. Wmk inverted and reversed		
60		2d. bright blue	70·00	7·50
		a. Imperf (pair)	£1300	£1800
61		3d. deep red	£120	22·00
61a		3d. dull red	45·00	9·00
		aw. Wmk inverted	95·00	28·00
62		4d. rose	80·00	3·25
		w. Wmk inverted	£120	17·00
63		6d. dull violet	£180	25·00
		w. Wmk inverted		
		x. Wmk reversed		
64		6d. yellow-green (1865)	£130	11·00
65		6d. blue-green	£110	4·50
		w. Wmk inverted	£170	28·00
		y. Wmk inverted and reversed		
66		9d. yellow-green (1872)	£110	£190
		w. Wmk inverted		
67	10	10d. maroon (1872)	£200	32·00
		w. Wmk inverted		
68	9	1s. yellow	£170	19·00
		w. Wmk inverted	£200	40·00
69		1s. blue (1866)	£130	18·00
		w. Wmk inverted	—	42·00
		x. Wmk reversed		
70		1s. orange (1872)	£160	12·00
		w. Wmk inverted	—	40·00
		y. Wmk inverted and reversed		
71		5s. rosy mauve	£150	50·00
		w. Wmk inverted	£300	
72		5s. bright mauve (1865)	£190	50·00
		w. Wmk inverted	£275	

HALF PENNY

(11)

½ d
HALF PENNY

(12)

1876. *(a) Nos.* 51 *and* 67 *surch with T* **11** *locally.*

No.	Type	Description	Unused	Used
76	9	½d. on 9d. dull purple	7·50	11·00
		a. Surch inverted	£425	
		b. Surch double	—	£1300
77	10	½d. on 10d. maroon	1·75	16·00
		y. Wmk inverted and reversed		

(b) Prepared for use, but not issued. No. 51 *surch with T* **12**.

No.	Type	Description	Unused	Used
78	9	½d. on 9d. dull purple (R.)	£1500	
		a. "PRNNY"		
		b. Black surch	£2000	

HALF PENNY

(13)

One Penny

(14)

One Shilling

(15)

Shill

Wrong fount "S"

1877 (Apr–Dec). *Nos.* 62, 67 *(colour changed) and* 71/2 *surch T* **13** *by D.L.R. or T* **14/15** *locally.*

No.	Type	Description	Unused	Used
79	10	½d. on 10d. rose	3·50	28·00
		w. Wmk inverted		
80	9	1d. on 4d. rose-carmine (6 Dec)	8·00	12·00
		w. Wmk inverted	—	50·00
81	9	1s. on 5s. rosy mauve (6 Dec)		£225
		w. Wmk inverted		£300
82		1s. on 5s. bright mauve (6 Dec)		£200
		a. Wrong fount "S"		
		w. Wmk inverted		

(New Currency. 100 cents = 1 rupee)

"CANCELLED" OVERPRINTS. Following the chan[ge] of currency in 1878 various issues with face values [in] sterling were overprinted "CANCELLED" in serifed ty[pe] and sold as remainders. The stamps involved were Nos. [5]6/62, 65, 67/8, 71/2, 76, 78/b, 79 and 81/2.

Examples of such overprints on stamps between Nos. [56] and 72 are worth about the same as the prices quoted [for] used, on Nos. 78/b they are worth 7% of the unused pri[ce], on No. 79 65% and on Nos. 81/2 20%.

2 CENTS

(16)

2 Rs. 50 C.

(17)

1878 (3 Jan). *Surch as T* **16** *or* **17** *(No. 91). Wmk Crown [CC.] P* 14.

No.	Type	Description	Unused	Used
83	10	2 c. dull rose (lower label blank)	6·50	
		w. Wmk inverted	—	3[illegible]
84	9	4 c. on 1d. bistre	10·00	[illegible]
85		8 c. on 2d. blue	65·00	[illegible]
		w. Wmk inverted		
86		13 c. on 3d. orange-red	9·00	2[illegible]
87		17 c. on 4d. rose	£150	[illegible]
88		25 c. on 6d. slate-blue	£180	[illegible]
89		38 c. on 9d. pale violet	18·00	5[illegible]
90		50 c. on 1s. green	85·00	[illegible]
		w. Wmk inverted		
91		2 r. 50 on 5s. bright mauve	12·00	14[illegible]
83/91		*Set of* 9	£475	£[illegible]

18

19

20

21

22

23

24

25

26

(Typo D.L.R.)

1879 (Mar)–**80.** *Wmk Crown CC. P* 14.

No.	Type	Description	Unused	Used
92	18	2 c. Venetian red (1.80)	35·00	13·[illegible]
93	19	4 c. orange	60·00	3·5[illegible]
		w. Wmk inverted		
94	20	8 c. blue (1.80)	15·00	2·2[illegible]
		w. Wmk inverted	—	80·[illegible]
95	21	13 c. slate (1.80)	£120	£16[illegible]
96	22	17 c. rose (1.80)	50·00	4·7[illegible]
		w. Wmk inverted	—	£11[illegible]
97	23	25 c. olive-yellow	£275	8·0[illegible]
98	24	38 c. bright purple (1.80)	£150	£20[illegible]
99	25	50 c. green (1.80)	3·75	2·7[illegible]
		w. Wmk inverted	80·00	
100	26	2 r. 50, brown-purple (1.80)	30·00	55·0[illegible]
92/100		*Set of* 9	£650	£40[illegible]

27

(Typo D.L.R.)

1883–94. *Wmk Crown CA. P* 14.

No.	Type	Description	Unused	Used
101	18	1 c. pale violet (1893)	1·75	50
102		2 c. Venetian red	30·00	4·75
103		2 c. green (1885)	2·25	60
104	19	4 c. orange	70·00	2·50
		w. Wmk inverted		
105		4 c. carmine (1885)	2·75	60
		w. Wmk inverted		
106	20	8 c. blue (1891)	2·00	90
		w. Wmk inverted		
		x. Wmk reversed		
107	27	15 c. chestnut (1893)	4·00	1·25
		w. Wmk inverted	—	80·00
108		15 c. blue (1894)	5·50	90
109		16 c. chestnut (1885)	4·00	1·00

23 25 c. olive-yellow .. .. 4·75 1·75
w. Wmk inverted .. .. ..
25 50 c. orange (1887) .. .. .. 28·00 8·00
w. Wmk inverted .. .. ..
11 .. .. *Set of* 11 £140 20·00
, 103s, 105s, 107s/9s, 111s Optd "Specimen" *Set of* 7 £400

16 CENTS (28) 16 CENTS (28*a*)

3 (26 Feb). *No. 96 surch with T* **28/*a*** *locally*
22 16 c. on 17 c. rose (surch T **28** –14½ mm long) .. .. £130 50·00
a. Surch double .. .. .. † £1600
b. Horiz pair. Nos. 112/13 .. .. £400
16 c. on 17 c. rose (surch T **28** –15½ mm long) .. .. £140 50·00
16 c. on 17 c. rose (surch T **28*a***) .. £275 £100
These stamps were surcharged using two different settings, h of which produced three horizontal rows at a time.
The length of the surcharge in the first setting (Type **28**) is er 14½ mm or 15½ mm and these exist in horizontal *tenant* pairs. In Type **28** the height of the surcharge is 3.25 . On the second setting (Type **28*a***) the type differs, especially numerals and "S", with the surcharge measuring 15–15½ n long and 3 mm high.

TEEN CENTS (29) 2 CENTS (30) 2 CENTS (31)

3 (14 July). *Surch with T* **29** *by D.L.R. Wmk Crown CA.* P 14.
5 22 16 c. on 17 c. rose .. .. .. 70·00 1·00
w. Wmk inverted .. .. ..

85 (11 May). *No. 98 surch with T* **30** *locally.*
6 24 2 c. on 38 c. bright purple .. .. 90·00 35·00
a. Without bar .. .. .. — £140
b. Surch inverted £500 £475
c. Surch double £600

87 (6 July). *No. 95 surch with T* **31** *locally.*
7 21 2 c. on 13 c. slate (R.) .. .. .. 42·00 75·00
a. Surch inverted £140 £160
b. Surch double .. .. .. — £500
c. Surch double, one on back of stamp £600

TWO CENTS (32) TWO CENTS (33)

891 (10–16 Sept). *Nos.* 88, 96, 98 *and* 105 *surch locally as T* **32** (*Nos.* 118/19, 121) *or T* **33** (*No.* 120).
18 19 2 c. on 4 c. carmine (No. 105) (12 Sept) 1·50 60
a. Surch inverted .. .. .. 70·00
b. Surch double .. .. .. 75·00 70·00
c. Surch double, one inverted .. .. 75·00 70·00
19 22 2 c. on 17 c. rose (No. 96) (16 Sept) .. 90·00 95·00
a. Surch inverted £300
b. Surch double £550 £550
20 9 2 c. on 38 c. on 9d. pale violet (No. 89) (16 Sept) .. .. 2·50 3·50
a. Surch inverted £275
b. Surch double £500 £500
c. Surch double, one inverted £120 £130
21 24 2 c. on 38 c. bright purple (No. 98) .. 3·00 4·25
a. Surch inverted £600
b. Surch double £140 £150
c. Surch double, one inverted £140 £150
Minor varieties are also known with portions of the surcharge missing, due to defective printing.

ONE CENT (34) ONE CENT (35)

1893 (1–7 Jan). *Surch with T* **34** *by D.L.R. or T* **35** *locally. Wmk Crown CA. P* 14.
123 **18** 1 c. on 2 c. pale violet .. .. .. 1·25 50
s. Optd "Specimen" .. .. .. 28·00
124 **27** 1 c. on 16 c. chestnut (7 Jan) .. .. 1·25 2·75
w. Wmk inverted .. .. .. 35·00

36 37

(Typo D.L.R.)

1895–9. *Wmk Crown CA. P* 14.
127 **36** 1 c. dull purple and ultramarine (8.7.97) 75 1·50
128 2 c. dull purple and orange (8.7.97) .. 2·25 50
129 3 c. dull purple and deep purple .. 70 50
130 4 c. dull purple and emerald (8.7.97) .. 3·75 50
131 6 c. green and rose-red (1899) .. 4·50 4·00
132 18 c. green and ultramarine (8.7.97) .. 8·00 3·50
127/32 .. .. .. *Set of* 6 18·00 9·50
127s/32s Optd "Specimen" *Set of* 6 90·00

(Des L. Duvergé. Typo D.L.R.)

1898 (15 Apr). *Diamond Jubilee. Wmk CA over Crown (sideways). P* 14.
133 **37** 36 c. orange and ultramarine .. .. 11·00 16·00
s. Optd "Specimen" .. .. .. 45·00

6 CENTS (38) 15 CENTS (39)

1899 (23–28 May). *Nos.* 132/3 *surcharged with T* **38/9** *locally.*
134 **36** 6 c. on 18 c. green and ultramarine (R.) 1·00 1·00
a. Surch inverted £350 £200
135 **37** 15 c. on 36 c. orge & ultram (B.) (28 May) 1·40 1·75
a. Bar of surch omitted £275
The space between "6" and "CENTS" varies from 2½ to 4 mm.

40 Admiral Mahé de Labourdonnais, Governor of Mauritius, 1735–46

4 Cents (41)

(Recess D.L.R.)

1899 (13 Dec). *Birth Bicentenary of Labourdonnais. Wmk Crown CC. P* 14.
136 **40** 15 c. ultramarine .. .. .. 10·00 3·25
s. Optd "Specimen" .. .. .. 70·00
w. Wmk inverted .. .. .. 60·00

1900. *No.* 109 *surch with T* **41** *locally.*
137 **27** 4 c. on 16 c. chestnut .. .. .. 2·50 11·00

42

12 CENTS (43)

(Typo D.L.R.)

1900–05. *Wmk Crown CC* (1 r.) *or Crown CA* (*others*) (*sideways on* 2 r. 50, 5 r.). *Ordinary paper. P* 14.
138 **36** 1 c. grey and black (1901) 50 10
139 2 c. dull purple and bright purple (4.01) 75 20
140 3 c. green and carmine/*yellow* (1902) 3·75 1·25
141 4 c. purple and carmine/*yellow* .. 1·50 40
w. Wmk inverted .. .. ..
142 4 c. grey-green and violet (1903) .. 75 2·00
w. Wmk inverted .. .. ..
143 4 c. black and carmine/*blue* (14.10.04) 6·00 60
w. Wmk inverted .. .. .. 15·00 15·00
144 5 c. dull purple & brt pur/*buff* (8.10.02) 6·50 50·00
145 5 c. dull purple and black/*buff* (2.03) 2·50 2·50
146 6 c. purple and carmine/*red* (1902) 1·75 80
w. Wmk inverted .. .. .. 20·00 15·00
147 8 c. green and black/*buff* (16.7.02) 2·00 7·00
148 12 c. grey-black and carmine (16.7.02) 1·75 2·25
149 15 c. green and orange .. .. 11·00 6·00
w. Wmk inverted .. .. ..
150 15 c. black and blue/*blue* (1905) .. 48·00 1·25
151 25 c. green and carmine/*green* (1902) .. 9·00 21·00
a. Chalk-surfaced paper .. .. 3·25 12·00
152 50 c. dull green & dp green/*yellow* (1902) 16·00 35·00
153 **42** 1 r. grey-black and carmine (1902) .. 48·00 48·00
w. Wmk inverted .. .. .. 90·00
154 2 r. 50, green and black/*blue* (1902) .. 17·00 80·00
155 5 r. purple and carmine/*red* (1902) .. 60·00 80·00
138/55 .. .. .. *Set of* 18 £200 £300
138s/55s Optd "Specimen" .. *Set of* 18 £300
Examples of Nos. 144 and 151/5 are known showing a forged Port Louis postmark dated "SP 29 10".

1902. *No.* 132 *surch with T* **43**.
156 **36** 12 c. on 18 c. green and ultramarine .. 2·00 5·00
The bar cancelling the original value seems in some cases to be one thick bar and in others two thin ones.

Postage & Revenue. (44)

1902 (7 July). *Various stamps optd with T* **44** *locally.*
157 **36** 4 c. purple and carmine/*yellow* (No. 141) 1·25 20
158 6 c. green and rose-red (No. 131) .. 1·00 2·75
159 15 c. green and orange (No. 149) .. 2·25 50
160 **23** 25 c. olive-yellow (No. 110) .. .. 2·25 2·50
161 **25** 50 c. green (No. 99) .. .. .. 3·75 2·50
162 **26** 2 r. 50, brown-purple (No. 100) .. 80·00 £110
157/62 .. .. .. *Set of* 6 80·00 £110
Nos. 157/62 were overprinted to make surplus stocks of postage stamps available for revenue (fiscal) purposes also.

1902 (22 Sept). *No.* 133 *surch as T* **43**, *but with longer bar.*
163 **37** 12 c. on 36 c. orange and ultramarine .. 1·25 1·25
a. Surch inverted £425 £325
The note below No. 156 also applies to No. 163.
Forged double surcharge errors show a straight, instead of a curved, serif to the "1" of "12".

1904–7. *Wmk Mult Crown CA. Ordinary paper* (2 c., 4 c., 6 c.) *or chalk-surfaced paper* (*others*). *P* 14.
164 **36** 1 c. grey and black (1907) .. .. 8·00 3·50
165 2 c. dull and bright purple (1905) .. 19·00 3·00
a. Chalk-surfaced paper .. .. 19·00 1·75
166 3 c. green and carmine/*yellow* .. 21·00 9·00
167 4 c. black and carmine/*blue* .. .. 12·00 1·50
a. Chalk-surfaced paper .. .. 2·50 10
168 6 c. purple and carmine/*red* .. .. 7·00 30
a. Chalk-surfaced paper .. .. 2·50 10
171 15 c. black and blue/*blue* (1907) .. 4·00 35
174 50 c. green and deep green/*yellow* .. 1·75 2·25
175 **42** 1 r. grey-black and carmine (1907) .. 20·00 45·00
164/75 .. .. .. *Set of* 8 70·00 55·00

46 47

(Typo D.L.R.)

1910 (17 Jan). *Wmk Mult Crown CA. Ordinary paper* (1 c. to 15 c.) *or chalk-surfaced paper* (25 c. to 10 r.). *P* 14.
181 **46** 1 c. black .. .. 2·75 30
182 2 c. brown .. .. 2·75 10
183 3 c. green .. .. 3·00 10
a. "A" of "CA" missing from wmk .. † —
w. Wmk inverted .. .. .. 23·00
184 4 c. pale yellow-green and carmine .. 3·50 10
w. Wmk inverted .. .. .. — 35·00
185 **47** 5 c. grey and carmine .. .. 2·75 3·00
186 **46** 6 c. carmine-red .. .. .. 2·25 20
a. Pale red .. .. 2·75 1·00
ab. "A" of "CA" missing from wmk .. † —
187 8 c. orange .. .. 3·00 1·25
188 **47** 12 c. greyish slate .. .. .. 2·00 2·75
189 **46** 15 c. blue .. .. 17·00 20
190 **47** 25 c. black and red/*yellow* .. .. 2·00 12·00
191 50 c. dull purple and black .. .. 2·00 18·00
192 1 r. black/*green* .. .. .. 6·50 12·00
193 2 r. 50, black and red/*blue* .. .. 13·00 70·00
194 5 r. green and red/*yellow* .. .. 26·00 95·00
195 10 r. green and red/*green* .. .. 85·00 £180
181/95 .. .. .. *Set of* 15 £150 £350
181s/95s Optd "Specimen" *Set of* 15 £275
On Nos. 188, 190 and 195 the value labels are as in T **49**.

48 49

(Typo D.L.R.)

1913–22. *Die I. Wmk Mult Crown CA. Ordinary paper* (5 c., 12 c.) *or chalk-surfaced paper* (*others*). *P* 14.
196 **48** 5 c. grey and carmine (1913) .. .. 1·75 4·00
a. Slate-grey and carmine .. .. 10·00 10·00
198 **49** 12 c. greyish slate (1914) .. .. 4·00 1·00
199 25 c. black and red/*yellow* (1913) .. 40 1·40
a. White back (1914) .. .. .. 50 14·00
aw. Wmk inverted and reversed .. 28·00
b. On orange-buff (1920) .. .. 32·00 60·00
c. On pale yellow (1921) .. .. 32·00 40·00
cs. Optd "Specimen" .. .. .. 32·00
cw. Wmk inverted .. .. .. 85·00
d. Die II. *On pale yellow* (1921) .. 60 17·00
ds. Optd "Specimen" .. .. .. 30·00
200 **48** 50 c. dull purple and black (1920) .. 38·00 70·00
201 1 r. black/*blue-green* (*olive back*) (1917) 3·25 17·00
a. On emerald (*olive back*) (1921) .. 7·50 48·00
b. Die II. *On emerald* (*emerald back*) (1921) .. .. 2·25 6·50
bs. Optd "Specimen" .. .. .. 32·00
202 2 r. 50, black and red/*blue* (1916) .. 18·00 48·00
203 5 r. green and red/*orange-buff* (1921) 75·00 £120
a. On pale yellow (1921) .. .. 65·00 £120
b. Die II. *On pale yellow* (1922) .. 45·00 £140
204 **49** 10 r. grn & red/*grn* (*bl-grn back*) (1913) 60·00 £130
a. On blue-green (*olive back*) (1919) £750
b. On emerald (*olive back*) (1921) .. 70·00 £130
c. On emerald (*emerald back*) (1921) 40·00 £120
d. Die II. *On emerald* (*emerald back*) (1922) .. .. 26·00 95·00
ds. Optd "Specimen" .. .. .. 38·00
196/204 .. .. .. *Set of* 8 £120 £325
196s/202s, 203as, 204s Optd "Specimen" *Set of* 8 £180
Examples of Nos. 200/4d are known showing part strikes of the forged Port Louis postmark mentioned after Nos. 238/55.

1921–26. *Wmk Mult Script CA. Chalk-surfaced paper* (50 r.). *P* 14.
205 **46** 1 c. black .. .. 1·00 1·00
w. Wmk inverted .. .. .. 21·00
206 2 c. brown .. .. 1·00 10
w. Wmk inverted .. .. ..
207 2 c. purple/*yellow* (1926) 75 20
w. Wmk inverted .. .. .. 17·00
208 3 c. green (1926) .. .. .. 2·75 1·00
209 4 c. pale olive-green and carmine .. 1·50 1·75
x. Wmk reversed .. .. ..
210 4 c. green (1922) .. .. .. 1·00 10
w. Wmk inverted .. .. ..
x. Wmk reversed .. .. ..

211 **46** 4 c. brown (1926) .. 2·75 1·50
212 6 c. carmine .. 12·00 6·50
x. Wmk reversed .. 60·00
213 6 c. bright mauve (1922) .. 1·25 10
214 8 c. orange (1925) .. 2·25 17·00
215 10 c. grey (1922) .. 2·00 3·25
216 10 c. carmine-red (1926) .. 3·75 1·50
217 12 c. carmine-red (1922) .. 1·50 40
218 12 c. grey (1926) .. 1·75 3·50
219 15 c. blue .. 5·50 4·75
ax. Wmk reversed .. 60·00
b. Cobalt (1926) .. 75 25
220 20 c. blue (1922) .. 2·00 80
221 20 c. purple (1926) .. 8·50 10·00
222 – 50 r. dull purple and green (1924) .. £700 £1300
s. Optd "Specimen" .. £190
205/21 .. *Set of* 17 42·00 42·00
205s/21s Optd "Specimen" .. *Set of* 17 £300

No. 222 is as Type **46**, but measures 25×35 mm.

Normal

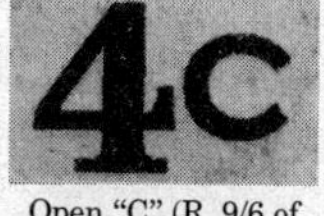

Open "C" (R. 9/6 of right pane)

MAURITIUS
12c
A

B

Two types of duty plate in the 12 c. In Type B the letters of "MAURITIUS" are larger; the extremities of the downstroke and the tail of the "2" are pointed, instead of square, and the "c" is larger.

1921–34. *Die II. Wmk Mult Script CA. Chalk-surfaced paper* (25 *c. to* 10 *r.*). *P* 14.

223 **49** 1 c. black (1926) .. 80 1·25
224 2 c. brown (1926) .. 70 10
225 3 c. green (1926) .. 70 40
226 4 c. sage-green and carmine (1926) .. 60 30
a. Open "C" .. 35·00
b. Die I (1932) .. 6·00 38·00
ba. Open "C" .. 90·00
226*c* 4 c. green (Die I) (1932) .. 5·50 45
ca. Open "C" .. 80·00
227 **48** 5 c. grey and carmine (1922) .. 90 10
a. Die I (1932) .. 6·00 6·00
228 **49** 6 c. sepia (1927) .. 1·25 60
229 8 c. orange (1926) .. 75 10·00
230 10 c. carmine-red (1926) .. 1·25 20
a. Die I (1932) .. 6·00 8·00
231 12 c. grey (Type A) (1922) .. 1·40 13·00
232 12 c. carmine-red (Type A) (1922) .. 30 3·50
232*a* 12 c. pale grey (Type A) (1926) .. 1·40 12·00
as. Optd "Specimen" .. 35·00
232*b* 12 c. grey (Type B) (1934) .. 4·25 20
233 15 c. Prussian blue (1926) .. 1·00 20
234 20 c. purple (1926) .. 55 40
235 20 c. Prussian blue (Die I) (1932) .. 9·50 90
a. Die II (1934) .. 12·00 40
236 25 c. black and red/*pale yellow* (1922) .. 30 15
a. Die I (1932) .. 2·75 30·00
237 **48** 50 c. dull purple and black (1921) .. 7·50 3·50
238 1 r. black/*emerald* (1924) .. 3·50 50
a. Die I (1932) .. 16·00 29·00
239 2 r. 50, black and red/*blue* (1922) .. 20·00 6·00
240 5 r. green and red/*yellow* (1924) .. 28·00 65·00
241 **49** 10 r. green and red/*emerald* (1924) .. 70·00 £170
223/41 .. *Set of* 20 £130 £225
223s/41s Optd or Perf (Nos. 226cs, 235s) "Specimen" .. *Set of* 20 £375

3
Cents
(50)

51

1925 (25 Nov). *Nos.* 210, 217 *and* 220 *surch locally as T* **50**.

242 **46** 3 c. on 4 c. green .. 2·50 3·75
243 10 c. on 12 c. carmine-red .. 30 30
244 15 c. on 20 c. blue .. 55 20
242/4 .. *Set of* 3 3·00 3·75
242s/4s Optd "Specimen" .. *Set of* 3 75·00

1935 (6 May). *Silver Jubilee. As Nos.* 91/4 *of Antigua. P* 13½×14.

245 5 c. ultramarine and grey .. 50 10
f. Diagonal line by turret .. 42·00 25·00
g. Dot to left of chapel .. 80·00 50·00
h. Dot by flagstaff .. 80·00 50·00
246 12 c. green and indigo .. 4·50 10
f. Diagonal line by turret .. 85·00 40·00
g. Dot to left of chapel .. £150 60·00
247 20 c. brown and deep blue .. 5·50 20
f. Diagonal line by turret .. £100 50·00
g. Dot to left of chapel .. £160 70·00
248 1 r. slate and purple .. 29·00 42·00
h. Dot by flagstaff .. £375
245/8 .. *Set of* 4 35·00 42·00
245s/8s Perf "Specimen" .. *Set of* 4 85·00

For illustrations of plate varieties see Omnibus section following Zanzibar.

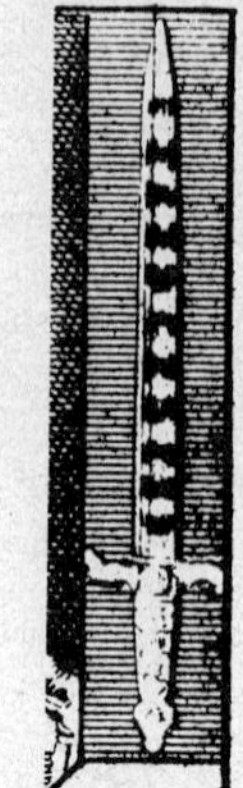
Line through sword (R. 2/2)

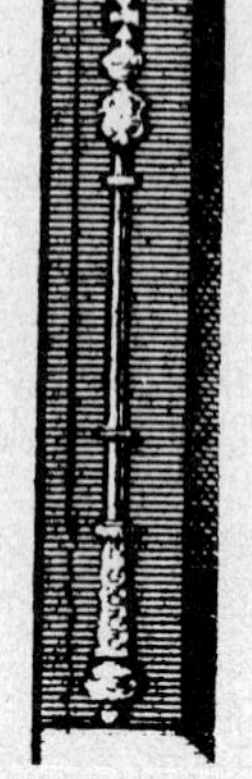
Line by sceptre (R. 5/3)

1937 (12 May). *Coronation. As Nos.* 95/7 *of Antigua, but printed by D.L.R. P* 14.

249 5 c. violet .. 40 10
250 12 c. scarlet .. 40 1·50
251 20 c. bright blue .. 40 10
a. Line through sword .. 60·00 35·00
b. Line by sceptre .. 60·00 35·00
249/51 .. *Set of* 3 1·10 1·50
249s/51s Perf "Specimen" .. *Set of* 3 55·00

Sliced "S" at right (R. 2/2, 3/2, right pane)

Sliced "S" at top (R. 4/1, left pane and R. 8/4, right pane)

Broken frame under "A" of "MAURITIUS" (R. 9/3 left pane, Key Plate 2)

"IJ" flaw (R. 3/6 of right pane)

Battered "A" (R. 6/1 of right pane)

(Typo D.L.R.)

1938–49. *T* **51** *and similar types. Wmk Mult Script CA. Chalk-surfaced paper* (25 *c. to* 10 *r.*). *P* 14.

252 2 c. olive-grey (9.3.38) .. 30 10
a. Perf 15×14 (1942) .. 1·00 10
253 3 c. reddish purple and scarlet (27.10.38) 2·00 1·75
a. Sliced "S" at right .. 80·00
b. Reddish lilac and red (4.43) .. 3·00 3·00
ba. Sliced "S" at right .. £110
254 4 c. dull green (26.2.38) .. 3·00 1·75
a. Open "C" .. 95·00
b. Deep dull green (4.43) .. 1·50 1·75
ba. Open "C" .. 70·00
255 5 c. slate-lilac (23.2.38) .. 8·00 70
a. Pale lilac (shades) (4.43) .. 2·75 20
b. Perf 15×14 (1942) .. 50·00 10
256 10 c. rose-red (9.3.38) .. 2·25 20
a. Sliced "S" at top .. £100
b. Deep reddish rose (shades) (4.43) .. 2·25 10
ba. Sliced "S" at top .. £100
c. Perf 15×14. *Pale reddish rose* (1942) 27·00 1·00
ca. Sliced "S" at top .. £325
257 12 c. salmon (*shades*) (26.2.38) .. 1·00 20
a. Perf 15×14 (1942) .. 50·00 75
258 20 c. blue (26.2.38) .. 1·00 10
a. Broken frame .. £160
259 25 c. brown-purple (2.3.38) .. 10·00 20
a. "IJ" flaw .. £225
b. Ordinary paper (8.4.43) .. 5·00 10
ba. "IJ" flaw .. £140
260 1 r. grey-brown (2.3.38) .. 25·00 1·50
a. Battered "A" .. £350
b. Ordinary paper (8.4.43) .. 17·00 1·00
ba. Battered "A" .. £275
c. Drab (4.49) .. 27·00 4·25
ca. Battered "A" .. £350
261 2 r. 50, pale violet (2.3.38) .. 38·00 12·00
a. Ordinary paper (8.4.43) .. 28·00 12·00
b. Slate-violet (4.48) .. 48·00 26·00
262 5 r. olive-green (2.3.38) .. 48·00 22·00
a. Ordinary paper. *Sage-green* (8.4.43) 27·00 22·00
263 10 r. reddish purple (*shades*) (2.3.38) .. 42·00 30·00
a. Ordinary paper (8.4.43) .. 11·00 23·00
252/63a .. *Set of* 12 85·00 55·00
252s/63s Perf "Specimen" .. *Set of* 12 £190

The stamps perf 15 × 14 were printed by Bradbury, Wilkinson from De La Rue plates and issued only in the colony in 1942. De La Rue printings of the 2 c. to 20 c. in 1943–45 were on thin, whiter paper. 1943–45 printings of the 25 c. to 10 r. were on unsurfaced paper.

1946 (20 Nov). *Victory. As Nos.* 110/11 *of Antigua.*

264 5 c. lilac .. 10 10
265 20 c. blue .. 10 10
264s/5s Perf "Specimen" .. *Set of* 2 50·00

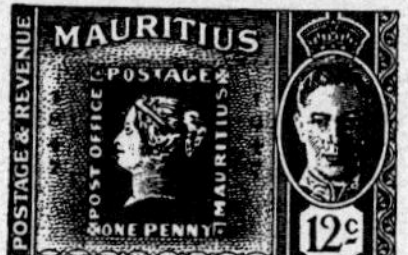

52 1d. "Post Office" Mauritius and King George VI

(Recess B.W.)

1948 (22 Mar). *Centenary of First British Colonial Post Stamp. Wmk Mult Script CA. P* 11½×11.

266 **52** 5 c. orange and magenta .. 10
267 12 c. orange and green .. 15
268 – 20 c. blue and light blue .. 15
269 – 1 r. blue and red-brown .. 15
266/9 .. *Set of* 4 50
266s/9s Perf "Specimen" .. *Set of* 4 95·00

Design:–20 c., 1 r. As T **52** but showing 2d. "Post Offi Mauritius.

1948 (25 Oct). *Royal Silver Wedding. As Nos.* 112/13 *Antigua.*

270 5 c. violet .. 10
271 10 r. magenta .. 9·50 22·

1949 (10 Oct). *75th Aniv of U.P.U. As Nos.* 114/17 *of Antigu*

272 12 c. carmine .. 40
273 20 c. deep blue .. 1·75 1·
274 35 c. purple .. 40
275 1 r. sepia .. 40
272/5 .. *Set of* 4 2·75 3·

53 Labourdonnais Sugar Factory

55 Aloe Plant

(Photo Harrison)

1950 (1 July). *T* **53, 55** *and similar designs. Wmk Mult Script CA Chalk surfaced paper. P* 13½ × 14½ (*horiz*), 14½ × 13½ (*vert*

276 1 c. bright purple .. 10 5
277 2 c. rose-carmine .. 15 1
278 3 c. yellow-green .. 60 2·5
279 4 c. green .. 20 1·2
280 5 c. blue .. 15 1
281 10 c. scarlet .. 30 7
282 12 c. olive-green .. 1·25 2·0
283 20 c. ultramarine .. 60 1
284 25 c. brown-purple .. 1·50 4
285 35 c. violet .. 30 1
286 50 c. emerald-green .. 2·25 5
287 1 r. sepia .. 4·25 1
288 2 r. 50, orange .. 12·00 7·5
289 5 r. red-brown .. 14·00 14·0
290 10 r. dull blue .. 14·00 19·0
276/290 .. *Set of* 15 45·00 42·0

Designs: *Horiz*—2 c. Grand Port; 5 c. Rempart Mountain; 10 c Transporting cane; 12 c. Mauritius Dodo and map; 35 c Government House, Reduit; 1 r. Timor Deer; 2 r. 50, Port Louis; 5 r. Beach scene; 10 r. Arms of Mauritius. *Vert*—4 c. Tamarind Falls; 20 c. Legend of Paul and Virginie (inscr "VIRGINIA"); 25 c. Labourdonnais statue; 50 c. Pieter Both Mountain.

The latitude is incorrectly shown on No. 282. This was corrected before the same design was used for No. 302*a*.

EXPRESS DELIVERY STAMPS

EXPRESS
DELIVERY
15c.
(E 1)

EXPRESS
DELIVERY
(INLAND)
15c.
(E 2)

EXPRESS
DELIVERY
(INLAND)
15 c.
(E 3)

EXPRESS
DELIVERY
(INLAND)
15 c
(E 4)

Type E **2**. "(INLAND)" was inserted at a second printing on stamps already surcharged with Type E **1** (No. E1).
Type E **3**. New setting made at one printing. More space above and below "(INLAND)".
Type E **4**. New setting with smaller "15 c" and no stop.

1903 (10 Aug)–**04**. *No.* 136 *surch locally in red.*

E1 E **1** 15 c. on 15 c. ultramarine .. 7·50 21·00
E2 E **2** 15 c. on 15 c. ultramarine (28.3.04) .. 35·00 45·00
a. "A" inverted .. £1000 £750
b. "(INLAND)" inverted .. † £2000

E 3 15 c. on 15 c. ultramarine (4.04) .. 7·50 3·00
a. Surch inverted £700 £450
aw. Surch and wmk inverted .. — £450
b. Surch double, both inverted .. £1200 £1200
c. Imperf between (vert pair) .. £3000
w. Wmk inverted .. .. ..
E 4 15 c. on 15 c. ultramarine (1904) .. £400 £400
a. Surch inverted .. .. .. — £1100
b. Surch double .. .. .. — £2500
c. Surch double, both inverted ..
d. "c" omitted .. .. .. — £1700

(FOREIGN)
EXPRESS
DELIVERY
18 CENTS
(E 5)

T 42 (*without value in label*), *surch with Type* E 5 *locally.*
Wmk Crown CC. P 14.
18 c. green .. .. 1·50 22·00
a. Exclamation mark for "I" in "FOREIGN" £450

T 42 (*without value in label*) *surch with Type* E 3 *locally.*
15 c. grey-green (R.) .. .. 3·50 3·50
a. Surch inverted £600 £550
b. Surch double £425 £450
c. Surch double, one "LNIAND" £500 £500

POSTAGE DUE STAMPS

D 1

(Typo Waterlow)

-54. *Wmk Mult Script CA. P* 15 × 14.
D 1 2 c. black .. .. 1·25 50
4 c. violet 50 65
6 c. scarlet 60 80
10 c. green 70 80
20 c. bright blue .. .. 50 1·25
50 c. deep magenta (1.3.54) .. .. 55 15·00
1 r. orange (1.3.54) .. .. .. 70 15·00
7 .. .. *Set of* 7 4·25 30·00
/5s Perf "Specimen" .. .. *Set of* 5 70·00
tamps in a similar design on Block CA paper were issued
ween 1966 and 1972.

FISCALS USED FOR POSTAGE

NLAND
EVENUE
(F 1)

INLAND
(F 2)

REVENUE

F 3

9. T 19, *wmk Crown CA, optd. P* 14.
F 1 4 c. carmine .. .. 13·00 5·00
F 2 4 c. lilac .. .. 3·00 11·00

(Typo D.L.R.)

6. *Wmk Crown CA. P* 14.
F 3 4 c. dull purple .. .. 23·00 35·00

Montserrat

A local post office operated on Montserrat from 1702, although the first recorded postal marking does not occur until 1791. A branch of the British G.P.O. was established at Plymouth, the island capital, in 1852.

The stamps of Great Britain were used from 1858 until the overseas postal service reverted to local control on 1 April 1860.

In the interim period between 1860 and the introduction of Montserrat stamps in 1876 No. CC1 and a similar "uncrowned" handstamp were again used.

PLYMOUTH

CROWNED-CIRCLE HANDSTAMPS

C 1

CC1 C 1 MONTSERRAT (R.) (15.7.1852) *Price on cover* £2750
No. CC1 was used as an emergency measure, struck in black, during 1886.

Stamps of GREAT BRITAIN *cancelled* "A 08" *as Type* Z 1 *of Jamaica.*

1858 (8 May) *to* **1860.**
Z1 1d. rose-red (1857), *perf* 14 .. .. £1100
Z2 4d. rose (1857) .. ..
Z3 6d. lilac (1856) £450
Z4 1s. green (1856) £1200

PRICES FOR STAMPS ON COVER TO 1945	
Nos. 1/2	*from* × 40
No. 3	†
Nos. 4/5	*from* × 8
Nos. 6/13	*from* × 12
Nos. 14/22	*from* × 4
No. 23	—
Nos. 24/33	*from* × 4
Nos. 35/47	*from* × 3
No. 48	—
Nos. 49/59	*from* × 3
Nos. 60/2	*from* × 15
Nos. 63/83	*from* × 3
Nos. 84/93	*from* × 4
Nos. 94/7	*from* × 3
Nos. 98/100	*from* × 8
Nos. 101/12	*from* × 5

1

(2)

3 (Die I)

(T 1 recess D.L.R.)

1876 (Sept)–**83.** *Stamps of Antigua optd with T* 2. *Wmk Crown CC. P* 14.
1 1 1d. red .. .. 24·00 15·00
a. Bisected (½d.) (1883) (on cover) .. † £1400
b. Inverted "S" £1000 £750
w. Wmk inverted .. .. 50·00
x. Wmk reversed .. .. 28·00 20·00
y. Wmk inverted and reversed .. .. 45·00
2 6d. green .. .. 60·00 40·00
a. Trisected (used as 2d.) (12.83) .. † £5000
b. Inverted "S" £1400 £1000
x. Wmk reversed .. .. — 75·00
3 6d. blue-green £1000
a. Inverted "S" £6000

Nos. 1/3 were overprinted either from a setting of 120 (12×10) or from a setting of 60 (6×10) applied twice to each sheet. This setting of 60 had an inverted "S" on R. 2/3. The same setting was subsequently used for some sheets of Nos. 6 and 8.

No. 1 was bisected and used for a ½d. in 1883. This bisected stamp is found surcharged with a small "½" in *black* and also in *red*; both were unofficial and they did not emanate from the Montserrat P.O.

The 6d. in blue-green is only known unused.

(T 3 typo D.L.R.)

1880 (Jan). *Wmk Crown CC. P* 14.
4 3 2½d. red-brown £250 £180
5 4d. blue .. .. £140 40·00
w. Wmk inverted .. .. — £110
x. Wmk reversed £275

1883 (Mar). *Wmk Crown CA. P* 12.
6 1 1d. red .. .. 70·00 55·00
a. Inverted "S" £1800 £1300
b. Bisected (½d.) (on cover) .. .. † £1600
x. Wmk reversed .. .. — 80·00

Top left triangle detached
(Pl 2 R.3/3 of right pane)

1884–85. *Wmk Crown CA. P* 14.
7 3 ½d. dull green .. .. 1·00 7·00
a. Top left triangle detached .. 55·00
8 1 1d. red .. .. 16·00 18·00
a. Inverted "S" £850 £850
bx. Wmk reversed .. .. — 25·00
c. *Rose-red* (1885) .. .. 17·00 14·00
ca. Bisected vert (½d.) (on cover) .. † £1300
cb. Inverted "S" £950 £950
cx. Wmk reversed .. .. 20·00 20·00
9 3 2½d. red-brown .. .. £225 65·00
10 2½d. ultramarine (1885) .. .. 20·00 18·00
a. Top left triangle detached .. £300
w. Wmk inverted .. .. 85·00
11 4d. blue £1800 £250
12 4d. mauve (1885) .. .. 4·50 3·00
a. Top left triangle detached .. £140
10s, 12s Optd "Specimen" .. *Set of* 2 £325

The stamps for Montserrat were superseded by the general issue for Leeward Islands in November 1890, but the following issues were in concurrent use with the stamps inscribed "LEEWARD ISLANDS" until 1 July 1956, when Leeward Islands stamps were withdrawn and invalidated.

4 Device of the Colony

5

(Typo D.L.R.)

1903 (Aug). (*a*) *Wmk Crown CA. P* 14.
14 4 ½d. grey-green and green .. .. 75 14·00
15 1d. grey-black and red 75 40
w. Wmk inverted .. .. ..
16 2d. grey and brown .. .. .. 5·50 28·00
17 2½d. grey and blue .. .. .. 1·50 1·75
18 3d. dull orange and deep purple .. 4·25 29·00
19 6d. dull purple and olive .. .. 4·75 45·00
20 1s. green and bright purple .. .. 10·00 17·00
21 2s. green and brown-orange .. .. 25·00 17·00
22 2s. 6d. green and black .. .. .. 18·00 32·00
(*b*) *Wmk Crown CC. P* 14
23 5 5s. black and scarlet .. .. .. 95·00 £150
14/23 .. .. *Set of* 10 £150 £300
14s/23s Optd "Specimen" .. *Set of* 10 £160

1904–08. *Wmk Mult Crown CA. Ordinary paper* (½*d.*, 2*d.*, 3*d.*, 6*d.*) *or chalk-surfaced paper* (*others*). *P* 14.
24 4 ½d. grey-green and green .. .. 4·25 2·00
a. Chalk-surfaced paper (3.06) .. 80 1·25
25 1d. grey-black and red (11.07) .. 14·00 24·00
26 2d. grey and brown .. .. .. 1·00 5·00
a. Chalk-surfaced paper (5.06) .. 2·25 1·25
27 2½d. grey and blue (12.05) .. .. 2·50 6·50
28 3d. dull orange and deep purple .. 7·00 7·00
a. Chalk-surfaced paper (5.08) .. 9·00 2·50
29 6d. dull purple and olive .. .. 4·25 22·00
a. Chalk-surfaced paper (5.08) .. 9·00 5·50
30 1s. green and bright purple (5.08) .. 10·00 7·00
31 2s. green and orange (5.08) .. .. 30·00 42·00
32 2s. 6d. green and black (5.08) .. 42·00 48·00
33 5 5s. black and red (9.07) .. .. 90·00 £110
24/33 .. .. *Set of* 10 £180 £225

1908 (June)–**14.** *Wmk Mult Crown CA. Ordinary paper* (½*d. to* 2½*d.*) *or chalk-surfaced paper* (3*d. to* 5*s.*). *P* 14.
35 4 ½d. deep green (4.10) .. .. .. 7·00 1·00
36 1d. rose-red .. .. 1·40 30
38 2d. greyish slate (9.09) .. .. .. 1·75 15·00
39 2½d. blue .. .. 2·25 3·50
40 3d. purple/*yellow* (9.09) .. .. .. 1·00 18·00
a. White back (1.14) (Optd S. £25) .. 4·00 28·00
43 6d. dull and deep purple (9.09) .. 6·50 50·00
a. Dull and bright purple (1914) .. 10·00 50·00
44 1s. black/*green* (9.09) .. .. .. 8·50 45·00
45 2s. purple and bright blue/*blue* (9.09) 28·00 55·00
46 2s. 6d. black and red/*blue* (9.09) .. 30·00 70·00
47 5 5s. red and green/*yellow* (9.09) .. 50·00 70·00
35/47 .. .. *Set of* 10 £120 £275
35s/47s Optd "Specimen" .. *Set of* 10 £190

Examples of most values are known showing forged Montserrat postmarks dated "OC 16 1909" or "NO 26 1910".

7

8

WAR STAMP

(9)

(T 7/8 typo D.L.R.)

1914. *Wmk Mult Crown CA. Chalk-surfaced paper. P 14.*
48 7 5s. red and green/*yellow* .. .. .. 60·00 90·00
s. Optd "Specimen" .. .. .. 75·00

1916 (10 Oct)–**22.** *Wmk Mult Crown CA. Ordinary paper* (½*d. to* 2½*d.*) *or chalk-surfaced paper* (3*d. to* 5*s.*). *P* 14.
49 8 ½d. green .. 30 2·50
50 1d. scarlet .. 75 75
a. Carmine-red .. 18·00 6·00
51 2d. grey .. 2·00 4·00
52 2½d. bright blue .. 1·50 17·00
53 3d. purple/*yellow* .. 1·25 8·00
a. On pale yellow (13.7.22) .. 75 12·00
as. Optd "Specimen" .. 22·00
54 4d. grey-black & red/*pale yell* (13.7.22) 5·50 35·00
55 6d. dull and deep purple .. 2·75 20·00
56 1s. black/*blue-green* (*olive back*) .. 3·00 21·00
57 2s. purple and blue/*blue* .. 14·00 28·00
58 2s. 6d. black and red/*blue* .. 22·00 50·00
59 5s. green and red/*yellow* .. 38·00 50·00
49/59 .. *Set of* 11 75·00 £200
49s/59s Optd "Specimen" .. *Set of* 11 £160

1917 (8 Oct)–**18.** *No. 49 optd with T* 9.
60 8 ½d. green (R.) .. 10 1·50
a. Short opt (right pane R. 10/1) .. 10·00
y. Wmk inverted and reversed .. 50·00
61 ½d. green (Blk.) (5.18) .. 50 2·50
a. Short opt (right pane R. 10/1) .. 13·00
b. Deep green (10.18) .. 15 1·75
ba. "C" and "A" missing from wmk
bb. Short opt (right pane R. 10/1) .. 10·00
w. Wmk inverted

Nos. 60a, 61a, and 61bb show the overprint 2 mm high instead of 2½ mm.

No. 61ba shows the "C" omitted from one impression and the "A" missing from the next.

1919 (6 Mar). *T* **8**. *Special printing in orange. Value and "WAR STAMP" as T* **9** *inserted in black at one printing.*
62 1½d. black and orange .. 10 30
60s/2s Optd "Specimen" .. *Set of* 3 80·00

1922 (13 July)–**29.** *Wmk Mult Script CA. Ordinary paper* (¼*d. to* 3*d.* (*No.* 73) *or chalk-surfaced paper* (*others*). *P* 14.
63 8 ¼d. brown .. 15 5·50
64 ½d. green (5.4.23) .. 30 30
65 1d. bright violet (5.4.23) .. 30 60
66 1d. carmine (1929) .. 75 1·50
67 1½d. orange-yellow .. 1·75 9·50
68 1½d. carmine (5.4.23) .. 30 3·50
69 1½d. red-brown (1929) .. 1·50 50
70 2d. grey .. 50 2·00
71 2½d. deep bright blue .. 8·00 16·00
a. Pale bright blue (17.8.26) .. 60 90
as. Optd "Specimen" .. 30·00
72 2½d. orange-yellow (5.4.23) .. 1·25 19·00
73 3d. dull blue (5.4.23) .. 60 16·00
74 3d. purple/*yellow* (2.1.27) .. 1·10 4·75
75 4d. black and red/*pale yellow* .. 60 12·00
76 5d. dull purple and olive .. 3·50 10·00
77 6d. pale and bright purple (5.4.23) .. 3·00 7·50
78 1s. black/*emerald* (5.4.23) .. 3·00 7·00
79 2s. purple and blue/*blue* .. 7·00 14·00
80 2s. 6d. black and red/*blue* (5.4.23) .. 12·00 50·00
81 3s. green and violet .. 12·00 18·00
82 4s. black and scarlet .. 15·00 38·00
83 5s. green and red/*pale yellow* (6.23) .. 26·00 40·00
63/83 .. *Set of* 21 75·00 £225
63s/83s Optd or Perf (Nos. 66s, 69s) "Specimen" *Set of* 21 £275

10 Plymouth

(Recess D.L.R.)

1932 (18 Apr). *300th Anniv of Settlement of Montserrat. Wmk Mult Script CA. P* 14.
84 10 ½d. green .. 75 6·50
85 1d. scarlet .. 75 5·50
86 1½d. red-brown .. 1·25 2·50
87 2d. grey .. 1·50 16·00
88 2½d. ultramarine .. 1·25 15·00
89 3d. orange .. 1·50 16·00
90 6d. violet .. 2·25 27·00
91 1s. olive-brown .. 12·00 35·00
92 2s. 6d. purple .. 48·00 70·00
93 5s. chocolate .. £100 £160
84/93 .. *Set of* 10 £150 £325
84s/93s Perf "Specimen" .. *Set of* 10 £225

Examples of all values are known showing a forged G.P.O. Plymouth postmark dated "MY 13 32".

1935 (6 May). *Silver Jubilee. As Nos. 91/4 of Antigua, but ptd by Waterlow & Sons. P* 11×12.
94 1d. deep blue and scarlet .. 85 3·25
95 1½d. ultramarine and grey .. 1·50 2·75
96 2½d. brown and deep blue .. 2·25 3·25
97 1s. slate and purple .. 3·00 14·00
94/7 .. *Set of* 4 7·00 21·00
94s/7s Perf "Specimen" .. *Set of* 4 75·00

1937 (12 May). *Coronation. As Nos.* 95/7 *of Antigua, but printed by D.L.R. P* 14.
98 1d. scarlet .. 30 75
99 1½d. yellow-brown .. 40 30
100 2½d. bright blue .. 40 90
98/100 .. *Set of* 3 1·00 1·75
98s/100s Perf "Specimen" .. *Set of* 3 50·00

11 Carr's Bay

12 Sea Island Cotton

13 Botanic Station

(Recess D.L.R.)

1938 (2 Aug)–**48.** *Wmk Mult Script CA. P* 12 (10*s.*, £1) *or* 13 (*others*).
101 11 ½d. blue-green .. 3·00 1·50
a. Perf 14 (1942) .. 15 20
102 12 1d. carmine .. 3·00 40
a. Perf 14 (1943) .. 50 30
103 1½d. purple .. 12·00 50
a. Perf 14 (1942) .. 50 50
ab. "A" of "CA" missing from wmk
104 13 2d. orange .. 12·00 60
a. Perf 14 (1942) .. 1·00 70
105 12 2½d. ultramarine .. 1·00 60
a. Perf 14 (1943) .. 50 30
106 11 3d. brown .. 2·50 50
a. Perf 14. *Red-brown* (1942) .. 1·75 40
ab. Deep brown (1943) .. 1·75 4·50
107 13 6d. violet .. 11·00 80
a. Perf 14 (1943) .. 2·50 60
108 11 1s. lake .. 12·00 70
a. Perf 14 (1942) .. 2·25 30
109 13 2s. 6d. slate-blue .. 24·00 80
a. Perf 14 (1943) .. 17·00 2·50
110 11 5s. rose-carmine .. 30·00 8·00
a. Perf 14 (1942) .. 21·00 3·00
111 13 10s. pale blue (1.4.48) .. 13·00 18·00
112 11 £1 black (1.4.48) .. 13·00 27·00
101a/12 .. *Set of* 12 65·00 48·00
101s/12s Perf "Specimen" .. *Set of* 12 £250

Nos. 101/2 exist in coils constructed from normal sheets.

1946 (1 Nov). *Victory. As Nos.* 110/11 *of Antigua.*
113 1½d. purple .. 10 10
114 3d. chocolate .. 10 10
113s/14s Perf "Specimen" .. *Set of* 2 55·00

1949 (3 Jan). *Royal Silver Wedding. As Nos.* 112/13 *of Antigua.*
115 2½d. ultramarine .. 10 10
116 5s. carmine .. 4·75 8·50

1949 (10 Oct). *75th Anniv of U.P.U. As Nos.* 114/17 *of Antigua.*
117 2½d. ultramarine .. 15 50
118 3d. brown .. 1·50 50
119 6d. purple .. 30 50
120 1s. purple .. 30 50
117/20 .. *Set of* 4 2·00 1·75

(New Currency. 100 cents = 1 West Indies, later Eastern Caribbean dollar)

1951 (16 Feb). *Inauguration of B.W.I. University College. As Nos.* 118/19 *of Antigua.*
121 3 c. black and purple .. 20 60
122 12 c. black and violet .. 20 60

14 Government House

18 Badge of Presidency

(Recess B.W.)

1951 (17 Sept). *T* **14**, **18** *and similar horiz designs. Wmk Mult Script CA. P* 11½ × 11.
123 14 1 c. black .. 10 2·00
124 – 2 c. green .. 15 70
125 – 3 c. orange-brown .. 30 70
126 – 4 c. carmine .. 30 70
127 – 5 c. reddish violet .. 30 70
128 18 6 c. olive-brown .. 30 30
129 – 8 c. deep blue .. 50 20
130 – 12 c. blue and chocolate .. 50 30
131 – 24 c. carmine and yellow-green .. 1·25 30
132 – 60 c. black and carmine .. 6·00 2·75
133 – $1.20, yellow-green and blue .. 6·00 6·00
134 – $2.40, black and green .. 6·00 12·00
135 18 $4.80, black and purple .. 16·00 16·00
123/135 .. *Set of* 13 32·00 38·00

Designs:—2 c., $1.20, Sea Island cotton: cultivation; 3 c. Map of colony; 4, 24 c. Picking tomatoes; 5, 12 c. St. Anthony's Church; 8, 60 c. Sea Island cotton: ginning; $2.40, Government House.

Morocco Agencies

(British Post Offices)

With the growth of trade and commerce during th century European powers opened post offices or postal ag in various ports along the Moroccan coast from the early onwards. French and, in the north, Spanish influence even became predominant, leading to the protectorates of 191 British, who had inaugurated a regular postal service be Gibraltar and Tangier or Tetuan in May 1778, establishe first postal agency in 1857. German offices followed arou turn of the century.

Before 1892 there was no indigenous postal service and towns where there was no foreign agency were served number of private local posts which continued to flourish 1900. In November 1892 the Sultan of Morocco establish Cherifian postal service, but this was little used until aft reorganization at the end of 1911. The Sultan's post absorbed by the French postal service on 1 October 1913. I of the local posts and of the Sultan's post can occasiona found used on cover in combination with stamps of Gibral the Morocco Agencies.

In 1857 the first British postal agency was establish Tangier within the precincts of the Legation and was run b official interpreter. From 1 March 1858 all letters for Britain sent via the British mail packets from Gibr required franking with Great Britain stamps.

In 1872 the Tangier office was relocated away from Legation and the interpreter was appointed British P Agent. At the same time the agency was placed under the co of the Gibraltar postmaster. When the colonial posts be independent of the British G.P.O. on 1 January 1886 Gibr retained responsibility for the Morocco Agencies. Fu offices, each under the control of the local Vice-Consul, opened from 1886 onwards.

I. GIBRALTAR USED IN MOROCCO

Details of the various agencies are given below. Type C "A26" killer, is very similar to postmarks used at Gibr during this period. In addition to the town name postmark Types A, B and D from Fez, Mazagan, Saffi and Tetuan were inscribed "MOROCCO".

Postmark Types used on Gibraltar issues.

Type A
Circular datestamp

Type C
"A26" killer

Type B
Duplex cancellation

Type D
Registered oval

BISECTS. The 10 c., 40 c. and 50 c. values of the 18 surcharges and of the 1889–96 issue are known bisected ar used for half their value from various of the Morocco Agencie These bisects were never authorised by the Gibraltar Po Office.

CASABLANCA

The British postal agency opened on 1 January 1887 and wa initially supplied with ½d., 4d. and 6d. stamps from th Gibraltar 1886 overprinted on Bermuda issue and 1d., 2d. an 2½d. values from the 1886–87 set.

Stamps of GIBRALTAR *cancelled with Types* A (*without code o code* "C"), B (*without code or code* "A") *or* D.

1886. *Optd on Bermuda* (*Nos.* 1/7).
Z1 ½d. dull green .. 65·0
Z2 4d. orange-brown .. £30
Z3 6d. deep lilac .. £30

–87. *Queen Victoria £sd issue* (Nos. 8/14).

No.	Description	Price
	½d. dull green	29·00
	1d. rose	32·00
	2d. brown-purple	70·00
	2½d. blue	42·00
	4d. orange-brown	£100
	1s. bistre	£300

. *Surch in Spanish currency* (Nos. 15/21).

No.	Description	Price
	5 c. on ½d. green	48·00
	10 c. on 1d. rose	40·00
	25 c. on 2d. brown-purple	60·00
	25 c. on 2½d. bright blue	38·00
	40 c. on 4d. orange-brown	£110
	50 c. on 6d. bright lilac	£100
	75 c. on 1s. bistre	£130

9–96. *Queen Victoria Spanish currency issue* (Nos. 22/33).

No.	Description	Price
	5 c. green	13·00
	10 c. carmine	13·00
	20 c. olive-green and brown	30·00
	25 c. ultramarine	13·00
	40 c. orange-brown	35·00
	50 c. bright lilac	27·00
	75 c. olive-green	80·00
	1 p. bistre	70·00
	1 p. bistre and ultramarine	35·00
	2 p. black and carmine	50·00

FEZ

he British postal agency in this inland town opened on February 1892 and was initially supplied with stamps up to 50 c. value from the Gibraltar 1889–96 issue.

mps of GIBRALTAR *cancelled with Types* A (*without code*) r D.

89–96. *Queen Victoria Spanish currency issue* (Nos. 22/33).

No.	Description	Price
	5 c. green	28·00
2	10 c. carmine	30·00
3	20 c. olive-green and brown	55·00
5	25 c. ultramarine	42·00
6	40 c. orange-brown	75·00
7	50 c. bright lilac	55·00

LARAICHE

The British postal agency at Laraiche opened in March 36, although the first postmark, an "A26" killer, was not pplied until May.

amps of GIBRALTAR *cancelled with Types* B (*without code*) or D.

86. *Optd on Bermuda* (Nos. 1/7).

No.	Description	Price
9	½d. dull green	
0	1d. rose-red	
1	2½d. ultramarine	

386–87. *Queen Victoria £sd issue* (Nos. 8/14).

No.	Description	Price
42	½d. dull green	90·00
43	1d. rose	85·00
45	2½d. blue	90·00

389. *Surch in Spanish currency* (Nos. 15/21).

No.	Description	Price
47	5 c. on ½d. green	60·00
48	10 c. on 1d. rose	
49	25 c. on 2½d. bright blue	

It is believed that the other surcharges in this series were ot supplied to Laraiche.

389–96. *Queen Victoria Spanish currency issue* (Nos. 22/33).

No.	Description	Price
50	5 c. green	30·00
51	10 c. carmine	40·00
52	20 c. olive-green and brown	
54	25 c. ultramarine	40·00
55	40 c. orange-brown	
56	50 c. bright-lilac	80·00
57	1 p. bistre and ultramarine	

MAZAGAN

This was the main port for the inland city of Marrakesh. The British postal agency opened on 1 March 1888 and was nitially supplied with stamps from the Gibraltar 1886–87 eries.

Stamps of GIBRALTAR *cancelled with Types* A (*codes* "A" *or* "C") *or* D (*without code, code* "A" *or code* "C").

1886–87. *Queen Victoria £sd issue* (Nos. 8/14).

No.	Description	Price
Z58	½d. dull green	30·00
Z59	1d. rose	30·00
Z60	2d. brown-purple	
Z61	2½d. blue	38·00
Z62	4d. orange-brown	£110
Z63	6d. lilac	£130

1889. *Surch in Spanish currency* (Nos. 15/21).

No.	Description	Price
Z64	5 c. on ½d. green	
Z65	10 c. on 1d. rose	
Z66	25 c. on 2½d. bright blue	

It is believed that the other surcharges in this series were not supplied to Mazagan.

1889–96. *Queen Victoria Spanish currency issue* (Nos. 22/33).

No.	Description	Price
Z67	5 c. green	19·00
Z68	10 c. carmine	17·00
Z69	20 c. olive-green and brown	50·00
Z70	25 c. ultramarine	42·00
Z71	40 c. orange-brown	75·00
Z72	50 c. bright lilac	
Z74	1 p. bistre and ultramarine	
Z75	2 p. black and carmine	

MOGADOR

The British postal agency at this port opened on 1 April 1887 and was initially supplied with stamps from the Gibraltar 1886–87 series.

Stamps of GIBRALTAR *cancelled with Types* A (*code* "C"), B (*code* "C") *or* D.

1886–87. *Queen Victoria £sd issue* (Nos. 8/14).

No.	Description	Price
Z76	½d. dull green	29·00
Z77	1d. rose	38·00
Z78	2d. brown-purple	70·00
Z79	2½d. blue	38·00

1889. *Surch in Spanish currency* (Nos. 15/21).

No.	Description	Price
Z80	5 c. on ½d. green	48·00
Z81	10 c. on 1d. rose	48·00
Z82	25 c. on 2½d. bright blue	48·00

It is believed that the other surcharges in this series were not supplied to Mogador.

1889–96. *Queen Victoria Spanish currency issue* (Nos. 22/33).

No.	Description	Price
Z83	5 c. green	13·00
Z84	10 c. carmine	15·00
Z85	20 c. olive-green and brown	
Z87	25 c. ultramarine	19·00
Z88	40 c. orange-brown	32·00
Z89	50 c. bright lilac	32·00

RABAT

The British postal agency at this port on the north-west coast of Morocco opened in March 1886, although the first cancellation, an "A26" killer, was not supplied until May. The initial stock of stamps was from the Gibraltar 1886 overprinted on Bermuda issue.

Stamps of GIBRALTAR *cancelled with Types* B (*code* "O") *or* D.

1886. *Optd on Bermuda* (Nos. 1/7).

No.	Description	Price
Z92	½d. dull green	
Z93	1d. rose-red	
Z94	2½d. ultramarine	£130

1886–87. *Queen Victoria £sd issue* (Nos. 8/14).

No.	Description	Price
Z 95	½d. dull green	29·00
Z 96	1d. rose	29·00
Z 97	2d. brown-purple	70·00
Z 98	2½d. blue	40·00
Z101	1s. bistre	£350

1889. *Surch in Spanish currency* (Nos. 15/21).

No.	Description	Price
Z102	5 c. on ½d. green	48·00
Z103	10 c. on 1d. rose	42·00
Z104	25 c. on 2½d. bright blue	48·00

It is believed that the other surcharges in this series were not supplied to Rabat.

1889–96. *Queen Victoria Spanish currency issue* (Nos. 22/33).

No.	Description	Price
Z105	5 c. green	18·00
Z106	10 c. carmine	18·00
Z107	20 c. olive-green and brown	40·00
Z108	25 c. ultramarine	19·00
Z109	40 c. orange-brown	45·00
Z110	50 c. bright lilac	40·00

SAFFI

The British postal agency at this port opened on 1 July 1891 and was supplied with stamps from the Gibraltar 1889–96 series.

Stamps of GIBRALTAR *cancelled with Types* B (*code* "C") *or* D (*code* "C").

1889–96. *Queen Victoria Spanish currency issue* (Nos. 22/33).

No.	Description	Price
Z111	5 c. green	19·00
Z112	10 c. carmine	19·00
Z113	20 c. olive-green and brown	45·00
Z115	25 c. ultramarine	21·00
Z116	40 c. orange-brown	75·00
Z117	50 c. bright lilac	55·00
Z118	1 p. bistre and ultramarine	60·00
Z119	2 p. black and carmine	70·00

TANGIER

The British postal agency in Tangier opened on 1 April 1857 and from 1 March of the following year letters from it sent via the packet service to Great Britain required franking with Great Britain stamps.

No identifiable postmark was supplied to Tangier until 1872 and all earlier mail was cancelled with one of the Gibraltar marks. In April 1872 a postmark as Type A was supplied on which the "N" of "TANGIER" was reversed. A corrected version, with code letter "A", followed in 1878, but both were used as origin or arrival marks and the Great Britain stamps continued to be cancelled with Gibraltar obliterators. The Type A postmarks generally fell into disuse after 1880 and very few identifiable marks occur on mail from Tangier until the introduction of Gibraltar stamps on 1 January 1886.

Stamps of GIBRALTAR *cancelled with Types* A (*codes* "A" *or* "C"), B (*code* "A") *or* D.

1886. *Optd on Bermuda* (Nos. 1/7).

No.	Description	Price
Z120	½d. dull green	42·00
Z121	1d. rose-red	65·00
Z122	2d. purple-brown	£140
Z123	2½d. ultramarine	42·00
Z124	4d. orange-brown	£170
Z125	6d. deep lilac	£225
Z126	1s. yellow-brown	£500

1886–87. *Queen Victoria £sd issue* (Nos. 8/14).

No.	Description	Price
Z127	½d. dull green	18·00
Z128	1d. rose	18·00
Z129	2d. brown-purple	48·00
Z130	2½d. blue	27·00
Z131	4d. orange-brown	80·00
Z132	6d. lilac	£120
Z133	1s. bistre	£275

1889. *Surch in Spanish currency* (Nos. 15/21).

No.	Description	Price
Z134	5 c. on ½d. green	29·00
Z135	10 c. on 1d. rose	20·00
Z136	25 c. on 2d. brown-purple	38·00
Z137	25 c. on 2½d. bright blue	29·00
Z138	40 c. on 4d. orange-brown	95·00
Z139	50 c. on 6d. bright lilac	90·00
Z140	75 c. on 1s. bistre	£120

1889–96. *Queen Victoria Spanish currency issue* (Nos. 22/33).

No.	Description	Price
Z141	5 c. green	5·00
Z142	10 c. carmine	5·00
Z143	20 c. olive-green and brown	21·00
Z144	20 c. olive-green	55·00
Z145	25 c. ultramarine	8·00
Z146	40 c. orange-brown	13·00
Z147	50 c. bright lilac	12·00
Z148	75 c. olive-green	50·00
Z149	1 p. bistre	60·00
Z150	1 p. bistre and ultramarine	20·00
Z151	2 p. black and carmine	40·00
Z152	5 p. slate-grey	£110

TETUAN

The British postal agency in this northern town opened on 1 April 1890 and was supplied with stamps from the Gibraltar 1889–96 series.

Stamps of GIBRALTAR *cancelled with Types* A (*code* "C"), B (*code* "C" *often inverted*) *or* D (*code* "C").

1889–96. *Queen Victoria Spanish currency issue* (Nos. 22/33).

No.	Description	Price
Z153	5 c. green	24·00
Z154	10 c. carmine	28·00
Z155	20 c. olive-green and brown	50·00
Z157	25 c. ultramarine	32·00
Z158	40 c. orange-brown	60·00
Z159	50 c. bright lilac	60·00
Z161	1 p. bistre and ultramarine	

PRICES FOR STAMPS ON COVER TO 1945

Nos.	Price
Nos. 1/16	*from* × 7
Nos. 17/30	*from* × 3
Nos. 31/74	*from* × 3
Nos. 75/6	*from* × 4
Nos. 112/24	*from* × 4
No. 125	—
Nos. 126/35	*from* × 5
Nos. 136/42	*from* × 2
Nos. 143/59	*from* × 3
Nos. 160/75	*from* × 8
Nos. 191/9	*from* × 5
Nos. 200/1	*from* × 3
Nos. 202/11	*from* × 4
Nos. 212/15	*from* × 5
Nos. 216/24	*from* × 8
Nos. 225/6	*from* × 2
Nos. 227/30	*from* × 8
Nos. 231/52	*from* × 6

The above prices apply to stamps used on cover from Morocco. Examples of Nos. 31/76 and 231/52 used on cover in Great Britain after 1950 have little value.

II. GIBRALTAR ISSUES OVERPRINTED

With the reversion of Gibraltar to sterling in 1898 it became necessary to provide separate issues for the Morocco Agencies which continued to use Spanish currency.

The following were used in all the British postal agencies.

Morocco Agencies (1) **Morocco Agencies** (2)

Agencies Inverted "V" for "A" (Right-hand pane R.6/6)

Agencies Long tail to "S" (Right-hand pane R.8/2)

Broken "M" (Pl 2 R. 4/5)

Flat top to "C" (Pl 2 R. 4/4)

1898 (1 June)–**1900.** *Nos.* 22/8 *and* 31/2 (*Queen Victoria*) *of Gibraltar optd with T* **1** (*wide* "M" *and ear of* "g" *projecting upwards*), *in black at* Gibraltar Chronicle *office.*

No.	Description	Unused	Used
1	5 c. green	2·00	2·00
	a. Inverted "V" for "A"	25·00	28·00
	b. Long tail to "S"	28·00	30·00
	c. Broken "M" in "CENTIMOS"	38·00	
2	10 c. carmine	3·00	50
	b. Bisected (5 c.) (on cover)	†	£1100
	c. Inverted "V" for "A"	£225	£275
	d. Long tail to "S"	£225	
	e. Lines of opt 5 mm apart (6.00)	4·00	2·50
	ea. Opt double	£500	

3 20 c. olive-green and brown .. .. 5·50 1·50
a. Inverted "V" for "A" .. .. .. 38·00 38·00
b. Long tail to "S" .. .. .. 42·00 42·00
3c 20 c. olive-green .. .. .. 6·50 5·50
ca. Opt double £450 £550
cb. Inverted "V" for "A" .. .. .. 45·00 50·00
cc. Long tail to "S" .. .. .. 48·00 55·00
cd. Flat top to "C" in "CENTIMOS" .. 65·00
4 25 c. ultramarine .. .. .. 3·25 60
a. Inverted "V" for "A" £100 £120
b. Long tail to "S" £110 £130
5 40 c. orange-brown (2.6.98) .. .. .. 4·50 3·25
a. Inverted "V" for "A" £150 £180
b. Long tail to "S" £160 £190
c. Blue opt (7.98) .. .. .. 40·00 32·00
6 50 c. bright lilac (2.6.98) .. .. .. 16·00 23·00
a. Inverted "V" for "A" £250 £300
b. Long tail to "S" £275 £300
c. Blue opt (7.98) .. .. .. 11·00 12·00
7 1 p. bistre and ultramarine (2.6.98) .. 14·00 27·00
a. Inverted "V" for "A" £190 £300
b. Long tail to "S" £200 £300
c. Blue opt (7.98) £140 £180
8 2 p. black and carmine (4.6.98) .. .. 17·00 27·00
a. Inverted "V" for "A" £225 £300
b. Long tail to "S" £250 £300
1/8 .. .. *Set of* 8 55·00 65·00

The blue overprint can be easily distinguished by looking through the stamp in front of a strong light.

The listed varieties of overprint occur from the first setting. They were corrected on the second setting of July 1898, which **produced Nos. 5c, 6c, 7c and further supplies of No. 8. The corrected type was subsequently used to produce additional stocks of Nos. 1/2. Numerous more minor varieties exist from** these settings.

No. 2e comes from two further printings in 1900 using a third setting on which the two lines of the overprint were 5 mm apart instead of the 4 mm space used previously.

Agencies — "CD" sideways flaw (Left-hand pane R.1/5)
Morocco — Broad top to "M" (Left-hand pane R.7/3)
Agencies — Hyphen between "nc" (Right-hand pane R.3/5)

1899 (Feb)–**1902.** *Nos. 22/3, 25/8 and 31/2 (Queen Victoria) of Gibraltar optd with T* **2** *(narrow "M" and ear of "g" horizontal), in black by D.L.R., London.*
9 5 c. green (4.99) 50 50
a. "CD" sideways .. .. .. 11·00 11·00
b. Broad top to "M" .. .. .. 8·00 8·00
c. Hyphen between "nc" .. .. .. 8·00 8·00
d. Broken "M" in "CENTIMOS" .. .. 20·00
10 10 c. carmine .. .. 1·25 30
a. "CD" sideways .. .. .. 11·00 11·00
b. Broad top to "M" .. .. .. 8·00 8·00
c. Hyphen between "nc" .. .. .. 8·00 8·00
d. Opt double £700 £700
11 20 c. olive-green (5.02) .. .. .. 4·50 70
b. Broad top to "M" .. .. .. 26·00 26·00
c. Hyphen between "nc" .. .. .. 26·00 26·00
d. Flat top to "C" in "CENTIMOS" .. 45·00
12 25 c. ultramarine (10.99) .. .. .. 7·50 90
a. "CD" sideways .. .. .. 38·00 38·00
b. Broad top to "M" .. .. .. 32·00 32·00
c. Hyphen between "nc" .. .. .. 32·00 32·00
13 40 c. orange-brown (3.02) .. .. .. 38·00 27·00
b. Broad top to "M" £190 £190
c. Hyphen between "nc" £190 £190
14 50 c. bright lilac (4.99) .. .. .. 8·00 3·50
b. Broad top to "M" .. .. .. 90·00 £110
c. Hyphen between "nc" .. .. .. 90·00 £110
15 1 p. bistre and ultramarine (4.99) .. .. 24·00 38·00
b. Broad top to "M" £130 £170
c. Hyphen between "nc" £130 £170
16 2 p. black and carmine (3.01) .. .. 48·00 48·00
b. Broad top to "M" £250 £325
c. Hyphen between "nc" £250 £325
9/16 .. .. *Set of* 8 £120 £110
9s/16s Optd "Specimen" .. .. *Set of* 8 £190

1903–5. *As Nos. 46/51 (King Edward VII) of Gibraltar, but with value in Spanish currency, optd with T* **2**. *Wmk Crown CA. P 14.*
17 5 c. grey-green and green (1.03) .. .. 7·50 2·75
a. "CD" sideways .. .. .. 40·00 38·00
b. Broad top to "M" .. .. .. 38·00 35·00
c. Hyphen between "nc" .. .. .. 38·00 35·00
18 10 c. dull purple/*red* (8.03) .. .. .. 7·00 30
a. "CD" sideways .. .. .. 38·00 32·00
b. Broad top to "M" .. .. .. 35·00 32·00
c. Hyphen between "nc" .. .. .. 35·00 32·00
w. Wmk inverted .. .. .. 30·00
19 20 c. grey-green and carmine (9.04) .. .. 13·00 45·00
a. "CD" sideways .. .. .. 80·00 £150
b. Broad top to "M" .. .. .. 75·00 £150
c. Hyphen between "nc" .. .. .. 75·00 £150
20 25 c. purple and black/*blue* (1.7.03) .. .. 7·00 20
a. "CD" sideways .. .. .. 42·00 38·00
b. Broad top to "M" .. .. .. 40·00 38·00
c. Hyphen between "nc" .. .. .. 40·00 38·00
21 50 c. purple and violet (3.7.05) .. .. 90·00 £160
a. "CD" sideways £300 £550
b. Broad top to "M" £300 £550
c. Hyphen between "nc" £300 £550
22 1 p. black and carmine (19.11.05) .. .. 45·00 £150
a. "CD" sideways £225 £475
b. Broad top to "M" £225 £475
c. Hyphen between "nc" £225 £475
23 2 p. black and blue (19.11.05) .. .. 50·00 £120
a. "CD" sideways £250 £450
b. Broad top to "M" £250 £450
c. Hyphen between "nc" £250 £450
17/23 .. .. *Set of* 7 £190 £425
17s/23s Optd "Specimen" .. .. *Set of* 7 £190

Examples of Nos. 19 and 21/3 are known showing a forged Registered Mazagan postmark dated "15 SP 10".

1905 (Jan)–**06.** *As Nos. 17/23 but wmk Mult Crown CA. Ordinary paper (5, 10, 20 c.) or chalk-surfaced paper (others).*
24 5 c. grey-green and green (4.05) .. .. 6·50 2·75
a. "CD" sideways .. .. .. 38·00 38·00
b. Broad top to "M" .. .. .. 38·00 38·00
c. Hyphen between "nc" £650 £700
d. Chalk-surfaced paper (1.06) .. .. 6·50 3·75
da. "CD" sideways .. .. .. 38·00 38·00
db. Broad top to "M" .. .. .. 38·00 38·00
25 10 c. dull purple/*red* .. .. .. 8·00 1·25
a. "CD" sideways .. .. .. 38·00 26·00
b. Broad top to "M" .. .. .. 38·00 26·00
cw. Wmk inverted .. .. .. 25·00 20·00
d. Chalk-surfaced paper (12.05) .. .. 3·00 1·25
da. "CD" sideways .. .. .. 25·00 25·00
db. Broad top to "M" .. .. .. 25·00 25·00
26 20 c. grey-green and carmine (1.06) .. .. 3·75 27·00
a. "CD" sideways .. .. .. 38·00 £110
b. Broad top to "M" .. .. .. 38·00 £110
27 25 c. purple and black/*blue* (6.06) .. .. 35·00 7·50
a. "CD" sideways £225 £130
b. Broad top to "M" £225 £130
28 50 c. purple and violet (7.06) .. .. 6·50 40·00
a. "CD" sideways £130 £200
b. Broad top to "M" £130 £200
29 1 p. black and carmine (11.05) .. .. 26·00 75·00
a. "CD" sideways £180 £300
b. Broad top to "M" £180 £300
30 2 p. black and blue (11.05) .. .. 15·00 35·00
a. "CD" sideways £160 £225
b. Broad top to "M" £160 £225
24/30 .. .. *Set of* 7 85·00 £170

Examples of Nos. 26 and 28/30 are known showing a forged Registered Mazagan postmark dated "15 SP 10".

Control of the British postal agencies in Morocco returned to the G.P.O., London, from 1 January 1907.

All the following issues are overprinted on Great Britain

III. BRITISH CURRENCY

Stamps overprinted "MOROCCO AGENCIES" only were primarily intended for use on parcels (and later, air-mail correspondence), and were on sale at British P.Os throughout Morocco including Tangier, until 1937.

PRICES. Our prices for used stamps with these overprints are for specimens used in Morocco. These stamps were valid for postal purposes in Great Britain from the summer of 1950 onwards. Examples with G.B. postmarks are worth 50 per cent of the used prices quoted.

MOROCCO AGENCIES (4) MOROCCO AGENCIES (5) MOROCCO AGENCIES (6)

1907 (30 Apr)–**13.** *King Edward VII optd as T* **4** *or* **5** *(2s. 6d.).*
(a) De La Rue printings. Ordinary paper (½d., 1d., 4d. (No. 35) or chalk-surfaced paper (others)
31 ½d. pale yellowish green (1.6.07) .. .. 2·25 8·00
32 1d. scarlet (5.5.07) .. .. .. 8·50 4·50
33 2d. pale grey-green and carmine-red .. 7·50 4·75
34 4d. green and chocolate-brown (29.10.07) 3·75 3·50
35 4d. pale orange (3.12) .. .. .. 9·50 9·50
a. Orange-red .. .. .. 9·50 9·50
36 6d. pale dull purple (5.5.07) .. .. 14·00 17·00
a. Dull purple .. .. .. 14·00 17·00
37 1s. dull green and carmine (5.5.07) .. 26·00 17·00
38 2s. 6d. pale dull purple (5.5.07) .. .. 65·00 £110
a. Dull purple .. .. .. 65·00 £110
31/8 .. .. *Set of* 8 £120 £160
37s/8s Optd "Specimen" .. .. *Set of* 2 £140

(b) Harrison printing. Ordinary paper
40 4d. bright orange (No. 286) (1913) .. 18·00 21·00

(c) Somerset House printing. Ordinary paper
41 2s. 6d. dull greyish purple (No. 315) (1913) 90·00 £160

1914–31. *King George V.*
(a) W **100** *(Simple Cypher). Optd with T* **4**
42 ½d. green .. .. 2·50 50
43 1d. scarlet 85 20
44 1½d. red-brown (1921) .. .. .. 2·75 12·00
45 2d. orange (Die I) .. .. .. 3·00 50
46 3d. bluish violet (1921) .. .. .. 1·25 35
47 4d. grey-green (1921) .. .. .. 3·00 1·25
48 6d. reddish purple (*chalk-surfaced paper*) (1921) .. .. .. 4·75 14·00
49 1s. bistre-brown (1917) .. .. .. 5·50 1·25
a. Opt triple, two albino £110

(b) W **110** *(Single Cypher). Optd with T* **6**.
50 2s. 6d. sepia-brown (*Waterlow ptg*) (No. 400) (1914) .. .. .. 42·00 55·00
a. Re-entry (R. 2/1) £750 £750
b. Opt double, one albino £160
51 2s. 6d. yellow-brown (*D.L.R. ptg*) (No. 406) (1917) .. .. .. 45·00 28·00
a. Opt double £1600 £1100
b. Pale brown (No. 407) .. .. .. 35·00 50·00
53 2s. 6d. chocolate-brown (*B.W. ptg*) (No. 414) 35·00 25·00
a. Opt double, one albino* £160
54 5s. rose-red (*B.W. ptg*) (No. 416) (1931) 50·00 90·00
a. Opt triple, two albino £200
42/54 .. .. *Set of* 10 95·00 £130
49s/50s, 54s Optd "Specimen" .. *Set of* 3 £200

*The albino overprint is quite clear, with the "MOROCCO" appearing just below "AGENCIES" of the normal overprint and a little to the right as seen from the back. There is also a second faint albino impression just below the normal overprint.

MOROCCO AGENCIES (7) S (A) MOROCCO AGENCIES (8) S (B)

Type 7: Opt 14 mm long; ends of "s" cut off diagonally.
Type 8: Opt 15½ mm long; ends of "s" cut off horizontally

1925–36. *King George V (W* **111** *(Block Cypher)) optd wit[h] (4d.) or* **7** *(others).*
55 ½d. green .. .. 1·00
aw. Wmk inverted .. .. .. 75·00
b. Optd with Type **8** .. .. .. 6·00
56 1½d. chestnut (1931) .. .. .. 11·00
57 2d. orange .. .. 2·00
58 2½d. blue .. .. 2·00
a. Optd with Type **8** £100
59 4d. grey-green (1.36) .. .. .. 6·00
60 6d. purple (1931) .. .. .. 2·00
a. Opt double, one albino £100
b. Optd with Type **8** .. .. .. 1·00
61 1s. bistre-brown .. .. .. 15·00
as. Optd "Specimen" .. .. .. 60·00
b. Optd with Type **8** .. .. .. 50·00 5
55/61 .. .. *Set of* 7 35·00 5

1935 (8 May). *Silver Jubilee (Nos. 453/6) optd "MOROC[CO] AGENCIES" only, as in T* **17**.
62 ½d. green (B.) .. .. 1·25
63 1d. scarlet (B.) .. .. 1·25
64 1½d. red-brown (B.) .. .. .. 2·25
65 2½d. blue (R.) .. .. 2·50
62/5 .. .. *Set of* 4 6·50 2

1935–37. *King George V. (a) Harrison photo ptgs (Nos. 44[0] and 449). W* **111** *(Block Cypher). Optd with T* **8**.
66 1d. scarlet (4.35) .. .. .. 3·25 1
67 1½d. red-brown (28.4.36) .. .. .. 3·25 14
68 2d. orange (1.5.36) .. .. .. 1·00 6
69 2½d. ultramarine (11.2.36) .. .. .. 1·75 4
70 3d. violet (2.3.36) 50
71 4d. deep grey-green (14.5.36) 50
72 1s. bistre-brown (31.8.36) 80 2
s. Optd "Specimen" .. .. .. 60·00

(b) Waterlow re-engraved ptgs. W **110** *(Single Cypher) opt[d] with T* **6**
73 2s. 6d. chocolate-brown (No. 450) .. 40·00 50
s. Optd "Specimen" .. .. .. 70·00
74 5s. bright rose-red (No. 451) (2.3.37) .. 23·00 95
66/74 .. .. *Set of* 9 65·00 £1

1936 (26 Oct)–**37.** *King Edward VIII, optd "MOROC[CO] AGENCIES" only, as in T* **18** *with "MOROCCO" 14¼ m[m] long.*
75 1d. scarlet 10
a. "MOROCCO" 15¼ mm long (5.1.37) .. 6·00 14
76 2½d. bright blue 10
a. "MOROCCO" 15¼ mm long (5.1.37) .. 1·00 4

The first two printings of both values showed all the stamp[s] with the short overprint, Nos. 75/6.

On 5 January 1937 a further printing of both values w[as] placed on sale in London which had the 24 stamps from t[he] bottom two horizontal rows (Rows 19 and 20) with the lo[ng] overprint, Nos. 75a/6a. Subsequent printings increased t[he] number of long overprints in the sheet to 25 by the addition [of] R. 8/9, and, finally, to 31 (R. 1/7, R. 7/1, R. 8/1, R. 13/3, 4 and 1[0], R. 14/6, but without R. 8/9).

For the 1d. value all sheets from cylinder 2 show the fir[st] setting. Sheets from cylinder 6 were also used for the first, a[nd] for all subsequent settings. The 2½d. value was overprinted [on] sheets from cylinder 2 throughout.

From 3 June 1937 unoverprinted stamps of Great Britai[n] were supplied to the post offices at Tangier and Tetuan (Spanis[h] Zone) as local stocks of issues overprinted "MOROCC[O] AGENCIES" were exhausted.

Type E Type F

Stamps of GREAT BRITAIN *cancelled as Types* E *or* F *a[t] Tangier.*

1937. *King George V.*
Z170 1½d. red-brown (No. 441)
Z171 2d. orange (No. 442) .. .. .. 12·0
Z172 3d. violet (No. 444) .. .. .. 12·0
Z173 4d. deep grey-green (No. 445) .. .. 9·0
Z174 6d. purple (No. 426*a*) .. .. .. 9·0
Z175 1s. bistre-brown (No. 449) .. .. 32·0
Z176 2s. 6d. chocolate-brown (No. 450) .. 70·0
Z177 5s. bright rose-red (No. 451) .. ..

1937–39. *King George VI (Nos. 462/75).*
Z178 ½d. green .. .. 13·00
Z179 1d. scarlet .. .. 13·00
Z180 1½d. red-brown .. .. .. 11·00
Z181 2d. orange .. .. 11·00
Z182 2½d. ultramarine .. .. .. 8·50
Z183 3d. violet .. .. 8·50
Z184 4d. grey-green .. .. .. 8·50
Z185 5d. brown .. .. 11·00
Z186 6d. purple .. .. 5·50
Z187 7d. emerald-green .. .. .. 9·00
Z188 8d. bright carmine .. .. .. 17·00
Z189 9d. deep olive-green .. .. .. 12·00
Z190 10d. turquoise-blue .. .. .. 17·00
Z191 1s. bistre-brown .. .. .. 5·50

1939–42. *King George VI (Nos. 476/8a).*
Z192 2s. 6d. brown .. .. .. 42·00
Z193 2s. 6d. yellow-green .. .. .. 13·00
Z194 5s. red .. .. 19·00
Z195 10s. dark blue .. .. .. 80·00
Z196 10s. ultramarine .. .. .. 35·00

-42. *King George VI pale colours* (*Nos.* 485/90).
1/2d. pale green .. .. 8·50
1d. pale scarlet .. .. 8·50
11/2d. pale red-brown .. .. 8·50
2d. pale orange .. .. 8·50
21/2d. light ultramarine .. .. 7·50
3d. pale violet .. .. 5·50

Victory (*Nos.* 491/2).
21/2d. ultramarine .. .. 7·50
3d. violet .. .. 7·50

Type G

-ps *of* GREAT BRITAIN *cancelled as Type G at Tetuan.*

. *King George V.*
3 4d. deep grey-green (No. 445) .. .. 20·00
) 6d. purple (No. 426*a*) .. ..
) 1s. bistre-brown (No. 449) .. .. ..

7–39. *King George VI* (*Nos.* 465/75)
1 2d. orange .. .. 17·00
2 21/2d. ultramarine .. ..
3 3d. violet .. ..
4 4d. grey-green .. .. 17·00
5 6d. purple .. .. 11·00
6 9d. deep olive-green .. ..
7 1s. bistre-brown .. .. 11·00

9–42. *King George VI* (*Nos.* 476/7).
8 2s. 6d. brown .. ..
9 2s. 6d. yellow-green .. .. 35·00
20 5s. red .. .. 45·00

1. *King George VI pale colours* (*Nos.* 485/90).
21 1/2d. pale green .. ..
22 2d. pale orange .. ..
23 21/2d. light ultramarine .. ..
24 3d. pale violet .. .. 11·00

Other unoverprinted stamps of Great Britain are known with -rocco Agencies postmarks during this period, but it is -ieved that only Nos. Z170/224 were sold by the local post -ices.

The use of unoverprinted stamps in Tangier ceased with the -ue of Nos. 261/75 on 1 January 1949. Stamps overprinted -OROCCO AGENCIES" replaced the unoverprinted values at -tuan on 16 August 1949.

MOROCCO AGENCIES
(9)

MOROCCO AGENCIES
(10)

-49 (16 Aug). *King George VI, optd with T* **9** *or* **10** (2*s.* 6*d.*, 5*s.*).
1/2d. pale green .. .. 1·75 7·00
1d. pale scarlet .. .. 2·75 9·00
11/2d. pale red-brown .. .. 2·75 8·50
2d. pale orange .. .. 3·00 9·00
21/2d. light ultramarine .. .. 3·25 10·00
3 3d. pale violet .. .. 1·50 1·60
3 4d. grey-green .. .. 50 1·25
4 5d. brown .. .. 3·00 15·00
5 6d. purple .. .. 1·50 1·25
6 7d. emerald-green .. .. 50 16·00
7 8d. bright carmine .. .. 3·00 6·50
8 9d. deep olive-green .. .. 50 11·00
9 10d. turquoise-blue .. .. 50 6·00
0 11d. plum .. .. 70 6·50
1 1s. bistre-brown .. .. 2·75 6·00
2 2s. 6d. yellow-green .. .. 13·00 35·00
3 5s. red .. .. 28·00 60·00
7/93 .. .. *Set of* 17 60·00 £180

-951 (3 May). *King George VI* (*Nos.* 503/7, 509/10), *optd with T* **9** *or* **10** (2*s.* 6*d.*, 5*s.*).
94 1/2d. pale orange .. .. 1·75 65
95 1d. light ultramarine .. .. 1·75 1·00
96 11/2d. pale green .. .. 1·75 2·00
97 2d. pale red-brown .. .. 1·75 3·50
98 21/2d. pale scarlet .. .. 1·75 3·50
99 2s. 6d. yellow-green (H.M.S. *Victory*) .. 12·00 19·00
100 5s. red (Dover) .. .. 12·00 20·00
-4/100 .. .. *Set of* 7 29·00 45·00

IV. SPANISH CURRENCY

Stamps surcharged in Spanish currency were sold at British P.Os. throughout Morocco until the establishment of the French Zone and the Tangier International Zone, when their use was confined to the Spanish Zone.

During this period further British postal agencies were opened at Alcazar (1907–1916), Fez–Mellah (Jewish quarter) 1909), Marrakesh (1909), Marrakesh–Mellah (Jewish quarter) 1909–17) and Mequinez (1907–1916).

MOROCCO AGENCIES
5 CENTIMOS
(11)

MOROCCO AGENCIES
6 PESETAS
(12)

1907 (1 Jan)–**12.** *King Edward VII surch as T* **11** (5 *c. to* 1 *p.*) *or* **12** (3 *p. to* 12 *p.*).

(*a*) *De La Rue printings. Ordinary paper* (*Nos.* 112/13, 116, 118, 122/3) *or chalk-surfaced paper* (*others*)
112 5 c. on 1/2d. pale yellowish green .. .. 5·00 20
a. Yellowish green .. .. .. 5·00 20
113 10 c. on 1d. scarlet .. .. .. 8·50 10
a. Bright scarlet .. .. .. 8·50 10
114 15 c. on 11/2d. pale dull purple and green .. 3·50 50
a. Slate-purple and bluish green .. 2·25 20
b. "1" of "15" omitted £4000
115 20 c. on 2d. pale grey-green and carmine-red 1·50 20
a. Pale grey-green and scarlet .. .. 2·00 50
116 25 c. on 21/2d. ultramarine .. .. .. 2·00 20
a. Pale ultramarine .. .. .. 1·50 20
117 40 c. on 4d. green & chocolate-brn (29.10.07) 1·00 2·50
a. Deep green and chocolate-brown .. 1·75 1·75
118 40 c. on 4d. pale orange (12.5.10) .. .. 1·75 90
a. Orange-red .. .. .. 1·00 60
119 50 c. on 5d. dull purple and ultramarine .. 3·25 2·50
a. Slate-purple and ultramarine .. 1·50 2·25
120 1 p. on 10d. dull purple and carmine .. 22·00 11·00
a. Slate-purple and carmine .. .. 19·00 10·00
b. No cross on crown .. .. ..
121 3 p. on 2s. 6d. pale dull purple .. .. 20·00 25·00
a. Dull purple .. .. .. 20·00 25·00
122 6 p. on 5s. bright carmine .. .. 35·00 45·00
a. Deep bright carmine .. .. .. 35·00 45·00
123 12 p. on 10s. ultramarine (30.4.07) .. 75·00 75·00
112/23 .. .. .. *Set of* 12 £150 £140
117s, 123s Optd "Specimen" .. *Set of* 2 £140

(*b*) *Harrison printing. Ordinary paper*
124 25 c. on 21/2d. bright blue (No. 283) (1912) 29·00 23·00
a. Dull blue .. .. 25·00 23·00

(*c*) *Somerset House printing. Ordinary paper*
125 12 p. on 10s. blue (No. 319) (1912) .. £160 £225

No. 114b occurred on stamps from the first vertical row of one sheet.

1912. *King George V* (*W* **49** (*Imperial Crown*)) *surch as T* **11.**
126 5 c. on 1/2d. green (No. 339) .. .. 3·00 20
127 10 c. on 1d. scarlet (No. 342) .. .. 1·00 10
a. No cross on crown .. .. .. £110 55·00

MOROCCO AGENCIES
3 CENTIMOS
(13)

MOROCCO 10 AGENCIES CENTIMOS
(14)

MOROCCO AGENCIES
15 CENTIMOS
(15)

MOROCCO AGENCIES
6 PESETAS
(16)

1914–26. *King George V.* (*a*) *W* **100** (*Simple Cypher*). *Surch as T* **11** (5 *c.*), **13** (3 *c. and* 40 *c.*)*, **15** (15 *c.*) *and* **14** (*remainder*).
128 3 c. on 1/2d. green (1917) .. .. .. 70 3·75
129 5 c. on 1/2d. green 50 10
130 10 c. on 1d. scarlet 80 10
y. Wmk inverted and reversed .. ..
131 15 c. on 11/2d. red-brown (1915) 80 10
a. Surch double, one albino .. .. 80·00
132 20 c. on 2d. orange (Die I) 70 25
a. Surch double, one albino .. .. 80·00
133 25 c. on 21/2d. blue (*shades*) .. .. 1·50 25
a. Surch double, one albino .. .. 60·00
w. Wmk inverted .. .. ..
134 40 c. on 4d. grey-green (1917) .. .. 2·25 4·00
a. Surch double, one albino .. ..
135 1 p. on 10d. turquoise-blue .. .. 2·25 5·50
a. Surch double, one albino .. .. 80·00

*The surcharge on Nos. 134, 148 and 158 is as T **13** for the value and T **15** for "MOROCCO AGENCIES".

(*b*) *W* **110** (*Single Cypher*). *Surch as T* **16.** (i) *Waterlow printings*
136 6 p. on 5s. rose-carmine .. .. 29·00 48·00
a. Surch double, one albino £130
b. Surch triple, two albino £140
137 6 p. on 5s. pale rose-carmine £130 £180
a. Surch double, one albino £180
138 12 p. on 10s. indigo-blue (R.) £110 £160
a. Surch double, one albino £225
b. Surch triple, two albino .. ..
136s, 138s Optd "Specimen" .. *Set of* 2 £180

(ii) *De La Rue printings*
139 3 p. on 2s. 6d. grey-brown (1918) .. 38·00 £110
a. Surch double, one albino .. ..
140 3 p. on 2s. 6d. yellow-brown .. .. 29·00 £140
a. Surch double, one albino .. ..
141 12 p. on 10s. blue (R.) £110 £160
a. Surch double, one albino £275

(iii) *Bradbury Wilkinson printings*
142 3 p. on 2s. 6d. chocolate-brown (1926) .. 23·00 75·00
128/42 .. .. .. *Set of* 11 £150 £275

1925–31. *King George V* (*W* **111** (*Block Cypher*)), *surch as T* **11, 13, 14** *or* **15.**
143 5 c. on 1/2d. green (1931) .. .. .. 2·50 12·00
144 10 c. on 1d. scarlet (1929) .. .. .. 18·00 23·00
145 15 c. on 11/2d. red-brown .. .. .. 7·50 21·00
146 20 c. on 2d. orange (1931) .. .. .. 3·00 7·50
a. Surch double, one albino .. .. 85·00
147 25 c. on 21/2d. blue .. .. 1·75 1·75
a. Surch double, one albino .. .. 60·00
w. Wmk inverted .. .. .. 50·00
148 40 c. on 4d. grey-green (1930) .. .. 1·75 1·75
a. Surch double, one albino .. ..
143/8 .. .. *Set of* 6 30·00 60·00

MOROCCO AGENCIES
10 CENTIMOS
(17)

MOROCCO 10 AGENCIES
CENTIMOS
(18)

1935 (8 May). *Silver Jubilee* (*Nos.* 453/6). *Surch as T* **17.**
149 5 c. on 1/2d. green (B.) .. .. .. 1·00 80
150 10 c. on 1d. scarlet (B.) .. .. .. 2·75 2·25
a. Pair, one with "CENTIMES" £1200 £1400
151 15 c. on 11/2d. red-brown (B.) .. .. 5·50 16·00
152 25 c. on 21/2d. blue (R.) .. .. .. 3·50 2·25
149/52 .. .. .. *Set of* 4 11·50 19·00

No. 150a occurred on R. 5/4 of a small second printing made in June 1935. The error can only be identified when *se-tenant* with a normal No. 150. Beware of forgeries.

1935–37. *King George V Harrison photo ptgs* (*Nos.* 439/43, 445 *and* 448). *W* **111** (*Block Cypher*). *Surch as T* **11, 13, 14** *or* **15.**
153 5 c. on 1/2d. green (9.6.36) .. .. 85 16·00
154 10 c. on 1d. scarlet (11.36) .. .. 2·50 7·50
155 15 c. on 11/2d. red-brown (4.35) .. .. 4·75 3·25
156 20 c. on 2d. orange (26.10.36) 50 25
157 25 c. on 21/2d. ultramarine (8.9.36) .. .. 1·25 3·75
158 40 c. on 4d. deep grey-green (18.5.37) .. 50 3·00
159 1 p. on 10d. turquoise-blue (14.4.37) .. 4·50 30
153/9 .. .. .. *Set of* 7 13·50 30·00

1936 (26 Oct)–**37.** *King Edward VIII surch as T* **18** *with* "MOROCCO" 141/4 *mm long.*
160 5 c. on 1/2d. green 10 10
161 10 c. on 1d. scarlet .. .. .. 50 1·75
a. "MOROCCO" 151/4 mm long (5.1.37) 3·50 11·00
162 15 c. on 11/2d. red-brown 10 15
163 25 c. on 21/2d. bright blue 10 10
160/3 .. .. .. *Set of* 4 65 1·75

The first three printings of the 10 c. on 1d. (from cyls 4, 5 and 6) showed all stamps with the short surcharge (No. 161).

On 5 January 1937 a further printing was placed on sale in London which had 49 stamps in the sheet (R. 1/2 to 11, R. 2/1, 5 and 6, 8 and 9, R. 3/5, R. 4/5, R. 5/4 and 5, 10, R. 6/6 and 7, R. 7/8, R. 8/8, R. 9/8, R. 11/7, 9, R. 13/2 to 5, 7 and 8, R. 14/1, 7, R.15/7, 11, R. 16/5, 10, R. 17/4, 10 and 11, R. 18/1, R. 19/2, R. 20/1 and 2, 3, 7, 9) with long surcharge (No. 161a). The next printing increased the number of long surcharges in the sheet to 50 (R. 10/2), but the final version, although retaining 50 long surcharges, showed them on R. 1/2 to 11, R. 17/5 to 8 and the entire rows 18, 19 and 20. The first two printings with long surcharges were from cylinder 6 and the last from cylinder 13.

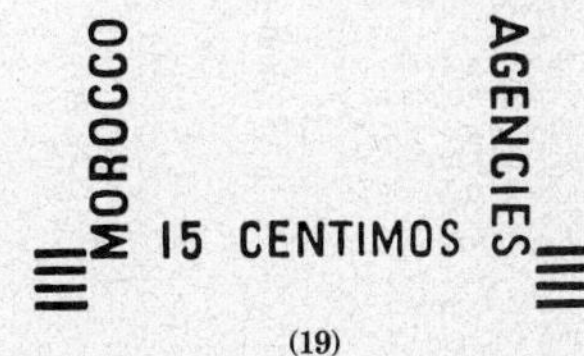

(19)

1937 (13 May). *Coronation* (*No.* 461), *surch as T* **19.**
164 15 c. on 11/2d. maroon (B.) 50 30

MOROCCO AGENCIES
10 CENTIMOS
(20)

MOROCCO AGENCIES
10 CENTIMOS
(21)

1937 (June)–**52.** *King George VI* (*Nos.* 462/4, 466, 468, 471 *and* 474), *surch as T* **20.**
165 5 c. on 1/2d. green (B.) 75 15
166 10 c. on 1d. scarlet 60 10
167 15 c. on 11/2d. red-brown (B.) (4.8.37) .. 65 25
168 25 c. on 21/2d. ultramarine 85 50
169 40 c. on 4d. grey-green (9.40) .. .. 28·00 11·00
170 70 c. on 7d. emerald-green (9.40) .. .. 75 9·50
171 1 p. on 10d. turquoise-blue (16.6.52) .. 1·50 3·50
165/71 .. .. .. *Set of* 7 30·00 22·00

1940 (6 May). *Centenary of First Adhesive Postage Stamps* (*Nos.* 479/81 *and* 483), *surch as T* **21.**
172 5 c. on 1/2d. green (B.) .. .. .. 30 1·75
173 10 c. on 1d. scarlet .. .. .. 2·75 2·00
174 15 c. on 11/2d. red-brown (B.) .. .. 40 2·00
175 25 c. on 21/2d. ultramarine 40 60
172/5 .. .. .. *Set of* 4 3·50 5·50

25
CENTIMOS

MOROCCO AGENCIES

(22)

45 PESETAS
MOROCCO AGENCIES

(23)

1948 (26 Apr). *Silver Wedding (Nos. 493/4), surch with T* **22** *or* **23**.
176 25 c. on 2½d. ultramarine 75 15
177 45 p. on £1 blue .. .. 17·00 22·00

1948 (29 July). *Olympic Games (Nos. 495/8), variously surch as T* **22**.
178 25 c. on 2½d. ultramarine 40 60
179 30 c. on 3d. violet 40 60
180 60 c. on 6d. bright purple 40 60
181 1 p. 20 c. on 1s. brown 55 60
a. Surch double £750
178/81 .. .. *Set of* 4 1·60 2·25

1951 (3 May)–**52**. *King George VI (Nos. 503/5 and 507/8), surch as T* **20**.
182 5 c. on ½d. pale orange .. .. .. 2·00 3·25
183 10 c. on 1d. light ultramarine .. .. 3·25 6·00
184 15 c. on 1½d. pale green .. .. .. 1·75 14·00
185 25 c. on 2½d. pale scarlet .. .. .. 1·75 6·50
186 40 c. on 4d. light ultramarine (26.5.52) .. 60 9·00
182/6 .. .. *Set of* 5 8·50 35·00

V. FRENCH CURRENCY

For use in the British postal agencies at Casablanca (closed 14.8.37), Fez (closed 8.1.38), Fez–Mellah (closed after 1930), Marrakesh (closed 14.8.37), Mazagan (closed 14.8.37), Mogador (closed 31.10.33), Rabat (closed 8.1.38) and Saffi (closed 14.8.37).

MOROCCO
AGENCIES

25
CENTIMES

(24)

MOROCCO
AGENCIES

1 FRANC

(25)

1917–24. *King George V (W* **100** *(Simple Cypher)), surch as T* **24** *or* **25** *(1 f.).*
191 3 c. on ½d. green (R.) .. .. .. 80 2·50
192 5 c. on ½d. green 30 20
193 10 c. on 1d. scarlet .. .. .. 3·25 20
194 15 c. on 1½d. red-brown .. .. .. 2·50 20
195 25 c. on 2½d. blue .. .. 2·00 20
196 40 c. on 4d. slate-green .. .. .. 2·50 1·00
197 50 c. on 5d. yellow-brown (1923) .. .. 80 2·75
198 75 c. on 9d. olive-green (1924) .. .. 1·00 75
199 1 f. on 10d. turquoise-blue .. .. 6·00 2·25
a. Surch double, one albino .. .. 85·00
191/9 .. .. *Set of* 9 17·00 9·00

1924–32. *King George V (B. W. ptg). W* **110** *(Single Cypher), surch as T* **25**, *but closer vertical spacing.*
200 3 f. on 2s. 6d. chocolate-brown .. .. 7·50 1·50
a. Major re-entry (R. 1/2) £375 £375
b. Surch double, one albino .. ..
c. *Reddish brown* .. .. .. 13·00 10·00
201 6 f. on 5s. rose-red (1932) .. .. 38·00 42·00
200s/1s Optd "Specimen" .. *Set of* 2 £120

1925–34. *King George V (W* **111** *(Block Cypher)), surch as T* **24** *or* **25** *(1 f.).*
202 5 c. on ½d. green .. .. 30 6·50
203 10 c. on 1d. scarlet .. .. 30 1·25
204 15 c. on 1½d. red-brown .. .. .. 85 1·75
205 25 c. on 2½d. blue 70 50
206 40 c. on 4d. grey-green 50 80
a. Surch double, one albino .. .. 65·00
207 50 c. on 5d. yellow-brown 85 10
w. Wmk inverted .. .. .. 75·00
208 75 c. on 9d. olive-green .. .. .. 2·00 15
w. Wmk inverted .. .. ..
209 90 c. on 9d. olive-green .. .. .. 13·00 6·00
210 1 f. on 10d. turquoise-blue .. .. 1·00 10
a. Surch double, one albino £100
211 1 f. 50 on 1s. bistre-brown .. .. 8·50 2·25
s. Optd "Specimen" .. .. .. 50·00
202/11 .. .. *Set of* 10 25·00 17·00

1935 (8 May). *Silver Jubilee (Nos. 453/6), surch as T* **17**, *but in French currency.*
212 5 c. on ½d. green (B.) 15 15
213 10 c. on 1d. scarlet (B.) .. .. .. 2·25 50
214 15 c. on 1½d. red-brown (B.) 30 50
215 25 c. on 2½d. blue (R.) 30 25
212/15 .. .. *Set of* 4 2·75 1·25

1935–37. *King George V (Harrison photo ptgs. W* **111** *(Block Cypher)), surch as T* **24** *or* **25** *(1 f.).*
216 5 c. on ½d. green (10.35) .. .. 50 4·25
217 10 c. on 1d. scarlet (2.3.36) 35 30
218 15 c. on 1½d. red-brown .. .. .. 4·00 4·75
219 25 c. on 2½d. ultramarine (25.9.36) .. 30 15
220 40 c. on 4d. deep grey-green (2.12.36) .. 30 15
221 50 c. on 5d. yellow-brown (15.9.36) .. 30 15
222 90 c. on 9d. deep olive-green (15.2.37) .. 35 1·25
223 1 f. on 10d. turquoise-blue (10.2.37) .. 30 30
224 1 f. 50 on 1s. bistre-brown (20.7.37) .. 50 2·75
s. Optd "Specimen" .. .. .. 50·00

1935–36. *King George V (Waterlow re-engraved ptgs. W* **100** *(Single Cypher)), surch as T* **25**, *but closer vertical spacing.*
225 3 f. on 2s. 6d. chocolate-brown (No. 450) 4·75 12·00
226 6 f. on 5s. bright rose-red (No. 451) (17.6.36) .. .. 6·00 21·00
216/26 .. .. *Set of* 11 16·00 42·00
225s/6s Optd "Specimen" .. *Set of* 2 £120

1936 (26 Oct). *King Edward VIII, surch as T* **18**, *but in French currency.*
227 5 c. in ½d. green 10 15
a. Bar through "POSTAGE" £475
228 15 c. on 1½d. red-brown 10 15

No. 227a involved R. 18/10 to 12 on a total of eight sheets. The bar, probably a printers rule, became progressively longer so that on four of the sheets it extends over all three stamps. Price quoted is for an example with the bar through the entire word.

1937 (13 May). *Coronation (No. 461), surch as T* **19**, *but in French currency.*
229 15 c. on 1½d. maroon (B.) 30 20

1937 (June). *King George VI, surch as T* **20**, *but in French currency.*
230 5 c. on ½d. green (B.) .. .. .. 1·25 1·75

Stamps surcharged in French currency were withdrawn from sale on 8 January 1938.

VI. TANGIER INTERNATIONAL ZONE

By an agreement between Great Britain, France and Spain Tangier was declared an international zone in 1924. Stamps overprinted "Morocco Agencies" or surcharged in Spanish currency were used there until replaced by Nos. 231/4.

PRICES. Our note *re* U.K. usage (at beginning of Section III) also applies to "TANGIER" optd stamps.

TANGIER

(26)

TANGIER TANGIER

(27)

1927. *King George V (W* **111** *(Block Cypher)), optd with T* **26**.
231 ½d. green .. .. 2·25 20
a. Opt double, one albino .. ..
232 1d. scarlet .. .. 2·50 20
a. Inverted "Q" for "O" (R. 20/3) .. £800
233 1½d. chestnut .. .. 4·25 3·00
234 2d. orange .. .. 3·25 20
a. Opt double, one albino .. .. 80·00
231/4 .. .. *Set of* 4 11·00 3·25

1934 (Dec)–**35**. *King George V (Harrison photo ptgs. W* **111** *(Block Cypher)), optd with T* **26**.
235 ½d. green (2.35) .. .. 1·00 1·50
236 1d. scarlet .. .. 3·00 1·50
237 1½d. red-brown 50 20
235/7 .. .. *Set of* 3 4·00 2·75

1935 (8 May). *Silver Jubilee (Nos. 453/5), optd with T* **27**.
238 ½d. green (B.) .. .. 1·00 3·50
239 1d. scarlet .. .. 13·50 13·00
240 1½d. red-brown (B.) .. .. .. 1·25 50
238/40 .. .. *Set of* 3 14·00 15·00

1936 (26 Oct). *King Edward VIII, optd with T* **26**.
241 ½d. green 10 15
242 1d. scarlet 10 10
243 1½d. red-brown 15 10
241/3 .. .. *Set of* 3 30 30

TANGIER TANGIER

(28)

TANGIER

(29)

1937 (13 May). *Coronation (No. 461), optd with T* **28**.
244 1½d. maroon (B.) 50 30

1937. *King George VI (Nos. 462/4), optd with T* **29**.
245 ½d. green (B.) (June) .. .. .. 1·75 60
246 1d. scarlet (June) .. .. .. 4·50 30
247 1½d. red-brown (B.) (4 Aug) .. .. 1·50 10
245/7 .. .. *Set of* 3 7·00 90

TANGIER

(30)

TANGIER

(31)

1940 (6 May). *Centenary of First Adhesive Postage Stamps (Nos. 479/81), optd with T* **30**.
248 ½d. green (B.) .. .. 30 3·75
249 1d. scarlet 45 50
250 1½d. red-brown (B.) .. .. .. 2·00 4·00
248/50 .. .. *Set of* 3 2·50 7·50

1944. *King George VI pale colours (Nos. 485/6), optd with T* **29**.
251 ½d. pale green (B.) .. .. .. 8·00 3·00
252 1d. pale scarlet .. .. 8·00 2·25

1946 (11 June). *Victory (Nos. 491/2), optd as T* **31**.
253 2½d. ultramarine 30 30
254 3d. violet .. .. 30 1·25

The opt on No. 254 is smaller (23×2½ mm).

1948 (26 Apr). *Royal Silver Wedding (Nos. 493/4), optd T* **30**.
255 2½d. ultramarine 50
a. Opt omitted (in vert pair with stamp optd at top) £3000
256 £1 blue .. .. 25·00

No. 255a comes from a sheet on which the overpr misplaced downwards resulting in the complete absence opt from the six stamps of the top row. On the rest of the the opt falls at the top of each stamp instead of at the foot £250, *unused*).

1948 (29 July). *Olympic Games (Nos. 495/8), optd with T*
257 2½d. ultramarine 75
258 3d. violet 75
259 6d. bright purple 75
260 1s. brown 75
257/60 .. .. *Set of* 4 2·75

1949 (1 Jan). *King George VI, optd with T* **29**.
261 2d. pale orange .. .. 4·00
262 2½d. light ultramarine .. .. .. 1·00
263 3d. pale violet 50
264 4d. grey-green .. .. 9·50
265 5d. brown .. .. 3·50
266 6d. purple 50
267 7d. emerald-green .. .. .. 1·00
268 8d. bright carmine .. .. .. 3·50
269 9d. deep olive-green .. .. .. 1·00
270 10d. turquoise-blue .. .. .. 1·00
271 11d. plum .. .. 1·00
272 1s. bistre-brown .. .. 1·00
273 2s. 6d. yellow-green .. .. .. 4·50
274 5s. red .. .. 13·00
275 10s. ultramarine .. .. 38·00
261/75 .. .. *Set of* 15 70·00

1949 (10 Oct). *75th Anniv of U.P.U. (Nos. 499/502), optd T* **30**.
276 2½d. ultramarine 50
277 3d. violet 50
278 6d. bright purple 50
279 1s. brown 50
276/9 .. .. *Set of* 4 1·75

1950 (2 Oct)–**51**. *King George VI, optd with T* **29** *or* **30** *(shi values).*
280 ½d. pale orange (3.5.51) 60
281 1d. light ultramarine (3.5.51) 70
282 1½d. pale green (3.5.51) 70
283 2d. pale red-brown (3.5.51) 70
284 2½d. pale scarlet (3.5.51) 70
285 4d. light ultramarine .. .. .. 2·50
286 2s. 6d. yell-grn (H.M.S. *Victory*) (3.5.51) 8·00
287 5s. red (Dover) (3.5.51) .. .. .. 14·00
288 10s. ultramarine (St. George) (3.5.51) .. 19·00
280/8 .. .. *Set of* 9 42·00

Muscat

ı independent Arab Sultanate in Eastern Arabia with an
ın postal administration.

ıe Indian post office at Muscat town is officially recorded as ıg opened on 1 May 1864. Stamps of India were provided for se, most surviving examples being of the ½ a. value, although rs to the 8 a. are known.

ıe office was initially included in the Bombay Postal Circle and irst postmark, so far only recorded on stampless covers, was a le circle, 21½ mm in diameter, broken at the top by SCAT" and with the date in two lines across the centre. This followed by a cancellation showing the post office number, ", within a diamond of 13, later 16, bars. It is believed that this used in conjunction with a single ring date stamp inscribed JSCAT".

1864 Diamond

ı 1869 the office was transferred to the Sind Circle, assigned a v number, "23", and issued with a duplex cancellation. Major rganisation of the postal service in 1873 resulted in Muscat oming office "K-4". For ten years from 1873 the cancellations do , very confusingly, carry any indication of the year of use.

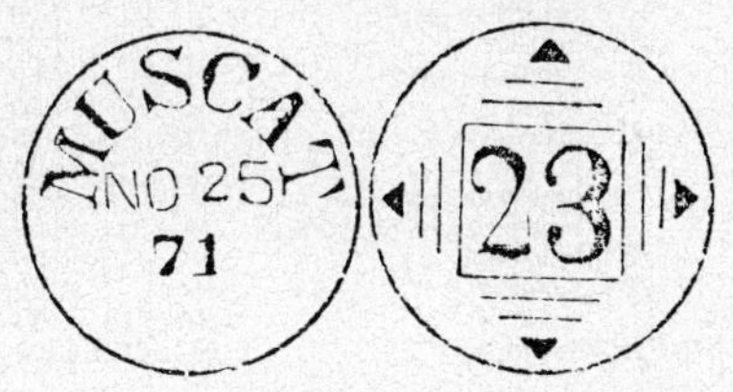

1869 Duplex

1873 Duplex

Muscat rejoined the Bombay Circle in 1879 and was issued with cancellation showing a "B" within a square of horizontal bars. ıe date stamp used at this time was unique in that it carried the ıscription "MASKAT", although the spelling reverted to the more ısual form by 1882. The square cancellation had been replaced by similar circular mark by 1884.

Subsequent postmarks were of various circular types, all ıscribed "MUSCAT".

There was only one Indian post office in Muscat, but a further ffice did exist, from 12 April 1868, at the Muscat dependency of ıadur, a port on the Mekran coast of Baluchistan.

No cancellations have been reported from Guadur before its ransfer to the Sind Circle in 1869. Cancellations are all similar in tyle to those for Muscat, Guadur being initially assigned number 24", although an office in Southern India is also known to have sed this numeral. The 1869 duplex is interesting in that it is nscribed "GWADUR". Under the 1873 reorganisation the office ecame "4/K-1", this postmark using the "GUADUR" spelling.

1869 Duplex

PRICES FOR STAMPS ON COVER

Nos. 1/15	*from* ×50
Nos. O1/10	*from* ×75

(Currency 12 pies = 1 anna; 16 annas = 1 Indian rupee)

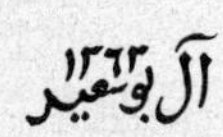

(1)

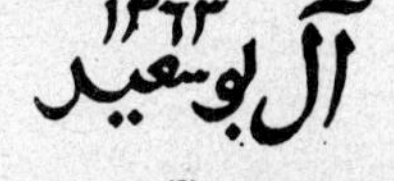

(2)

1944 (20 Nov). *Bicentenary of Al-Busaid Dynasty. Nos.* 259/60, 265/8 *and* 269*a*/77 (*King George VI*) *of India optd* ("AL BUSAID 1363" *in Arabic script*) *as T* **1** *or* **2** (*rupee values*).

No.	Description	Unused	Used
1	3 p. slate	30	5·00
	w. Wmk inverted	5·00	
2	½ a. purple	30	5·00
3	9 p. green	30	5·00
4	1 a. carmine	30	5·00
5	1½ a. dull violet	30	5·00
6	2 a. vermilion	30	5·00
	w. Wmk inverted		
7	3 a. bright violet	50	5·00
	w. Wmk inverted	5·00	
8	3½ a. bright blue	50	5·00
9	4 a. brown	50	5·00
10	6 a. turquoise-green	65	5·00
11	8 a. slate-violet	65	5·00
12	12 a. lake	80	5·00
13	14 a. purple	2·75	7·00
14	1 r. grey and red-brown	85	9·00
15	2 r. purple and brown	2·00	15·00
1/15	*Set of* 15	10·00	80·00

OFFICIAL STAMPS

1944 (20 Nov). *Bicentenary of Al-Busaid Dynasty. Nos.* O138, O143, O144*a*/6 *and* 146*b*/50 *of India optd as T* **1** *or* **2** (1 *r.*).

No.	Description	Unused	Used
O 1	3 p. slate	50	9·50
O 2	½ a. purple	50	9·50
O 3	9 p. green	50	9·50
O 4	1 a. carmine	50	9·50
O 5	1½ a. dull violet	50	9·50
O 6	2 a. vermilion	50	9·50
O 7	2½ a. bright violet	2·25	9·50
O 8	4 a. brown	1·00	9·50
O 9	8 a. slate-violet	2·50	11·00
O10	1 r. grey and red-brown	2·25	19·00
O1/10	*Set of* 10	10·00	95·00

From December 1947 there was a Pakistani postal administration and stamps of Pakistan were used until 31 March 1948. The subsequent British administration operated from 1 April 1948 to 29 April 1966 when the stamps of the BRITISH POSTAL AGENCIES IN EASTERN ARABIA were used. Guadur, however, continued to use the stamps of Pakistan until the dependency was finally ceded to that country in 1956.

Nauru
see after Australia

Nevis
see St. Kitts-Nevis

New Brunswick
see Canada

Newfoundland
see Canada

New Guinea
see after Australia

New Hebrides

Stamps of NEW SOUTH WALES were used by various Postal Agencies in the New Hebrides from August 1891 onwards. From late 1892 the N.S.W. agency at Port Vila was run by the Australian New Hebrides Company who, from 1897, issued local 1d. and 2d. stamps for the carriage of mail on the Company's ships. These can be found used in combination with N.S.W. issues. Similar Postal Agencies supplying the stamps of NEW CALEDONIA were opened from 1903 onwards. The use of New South Wales and New Caledonia stamps was prohibited after 1 December 1908.

PRICES FOR STAMPS ON COVER TO 1945

Nos. 1/8 (F1/5)	*from* × 10
No. 9	*from* × 2
Nos. 10/16 (F6/10)	*from* × 8
Nos. 18/28 (F11/32)	*from* × 6
Nos. 30/4 (F33/7)	*from* × 4
No. 35 (F32*a*)	—
Nos. 36/9	*from* × 3
Nos. 40/2 (F38/41)	*from* × 4
Nos. 43/51 (F42/52)	*from* × 5
Nos. 52/63 (F53/64)	*from* × 3
Nos. D1/10 (FD53/69)	*from* × 8

ANGLO-FRENCH CONDOMINIUM

The New Hebrides, an island group in the south-west Pacific, were recognised as an area of joint Anglo-French influence in 1878. The position was regularised by the Convention of 20 October 1906 which created a Condominium, the two nations having equal rights and shares in the administration of the islands.

Stamps inscribed in English or French were issued concurrently and had equal validity throughout the islands. A common currency was reflected in the face values from 1938.

Where common designs were used the main differences between stamps inscribed in English and those in French are as follows:

(a) Inscriptions in English or French.

(b) Position of cyphers. French issues normally have "RF" to the right or above the British royal cypher.

(c) French issues are without watermark, *unless otherwise stated.*

Inscriptions in English

Inscriptions in French

I. STAMPS INSCRIBED IN ENGLISH

NEW HEBRIDES. CONDOMINIUM.	NEW HEBRIDES CONDOMINIUM
(1)	(2)

1908 (29 Oct). *T* **23** *and* **24** *of Fiji optd with T* **1** *by Govt Printing Establishment, Suva. On the bicoloured stamps the word* "FIJI" *obliterated by a bar in the colour of the word. P* 14.

(*a*) *Wmk Multiple Crown CA. Ordinary paper* (½*d.*, 1*d.*) *or chalk-surfaced paper* (1*s.*)

No.	Description	Unused	Used
1	½d. green and pale green (No. 115)	3·25	14·00
1*a*	½d. green (No. 118)	40	7·00
2	1d. red	50	40
	a. Opt omitted (in vert pair with normal)	£5500	
3	1s. green and carmine	19·00	3·75

(*b*) *Wmk Crown CA*

No.	Description	Unused	Used
4	½d. green and grey-green	50·00	80·00
5	2d. dull purple and orange	60	70
6	2½d. dull purple and blue/*blue*	60	70
7	5d. dull purple and green	80	2·00
8	6d. dull purple and carmine	70	1·25
9	1s. green and carmine	£150	£225
1/9	*Set of* 9	£180	£275

1910 (15 Dec). *Types as last optd with T* **2** *by D.L.R. Wmk Multiple Crown CA. Ordinary paper* (½*d. to* 2½*d.*) *or chalk-surfaced paper* (5*d.*, 6*d.*, 1*s.*). *P* 14.

No.	Description	Unused	Used
10	½d. green	3·50	24·00
11	1d. red	10·00	8·50
12	2d. grey	60	3·00
13	2½d. bright blue	65	3·75
14	5d. dull purple and olive-green	1·25	5·50
15	6d. dull and deep purple	1·00	5·00
16	1s. black/*green* (R.)	1·00	7·50
10/16	*Set of* 7	16·00	50·00
10s/16s Optd "Specimen"	*Set of* 7	£250	

3 Weapons and Idols

1d.

(4)

(Des J. Giraud. Recess D.L.R.)

1911 (25 July). *Wmk Mult Crown CA. P* 14.

No.	Type	Description	Unused	Used
18	**3**	½d. green	85	1·75
19		1d. red	3·75	2·00
20		2d. grey	8·00	4·00
21		2½d. ultramarine	3·00	5·50
24		5d. sage-green	4·50	7·00
25		6d. purple	3·00	5·00
26		1s. black/*green*	2·75	13·00
27		2s. purple/*blue*	21·00	22·00
28		5s. green/*yellow*	35·00	48·00
18/28		*Set of* 9	70·00	95·00
18s/28s Optd "Specimen"		*Set of* 9	£180	

1920 (June)–**21.** *Surch with T* **4** *at Govt Printing Establishment, Suva.*

(*a*) *On Nos.* 24 *and* 26/8

30 **3** 1d. on 5d. sage-green (10.3.21) 7·00 60·00
a. Surch inverted £1800
31 1d. on 1s. black/*green* 1·25 13·00
32 1d. on 2s. purple/*blue* 1·00 10·00
33 1d. on 5s. green/*yellow* 1·00 10·00

(*b*) *On No.* F16

34 **3** 2d. on 40 c. red/*yellow* 1·00 16·00

(*c*) *On No.* F27

35 **3** 2d. on 40 c. red/*yellow* £120 £475

1921 (Sept–Oct). *Wmk Mult Script CA. P* 14.
36 **3** 1d. scarlet 2·50 14·00
37 2d. slate-grey 4·25 35·00
39 6d. purple 14·00 70·00
36/9 *Set of* 3 19·00 £110
36s/9s Optd "Specimen" *Set of* 3 70·00

1924 (1 May). *Surch as T* **4**, *at Suva.*
40 **3** 1d. on ½d. green (No. 18) 4·00 22·00
41 3d. on 1d. scarlet (No. 36) 4·00 11·00
42 5d. on 2½d. ultramarine (No. 21) 7·50 21·00
a. Surch inverted £1600
40/2 *Set of* 3 14·00 48·00

5

(Recess D.L.R.)

1925 (June). *Wmk Mult Script CA. P* 14.
43 **5** ½d. (5 c.) black 1·25 11·00
44 1d. (10 c.) green 1·00 11·00
45 2d. (20 c.) slate-grey 1·75 2·50
46 2½d. (25 c.) brown 1·00 13·00
47 5d. (50 c.) ultramarine 3·00 2·50
48 6d. (60 c.) purple 3·50 11·00
49 1s. (1.25 fr.) black/*emerald* 3·25 19·00
50 2s. (2.50 fr.) purple/*blue* 6·00 22·00
51 5s. (6.25 fr.) green/*yellow* 6·00 25·00
43/51 *Set of* 9 23·00 £100
43s/51s Optd "Specimen" *Set of* 9 £180

(New Currency. 100 gold centimes = 1 gold franc)

The currency used for the face values of issues to 1977 was an artificial, rather than an actual, monetary unit. The actual currencies in use were Australian dollars and the local franc.

6 Lopevi Is and Outrigger Canoe

(Des J. Kerhor. Eng J. G. Hall. Recess B.W.)

1938 (1 June). *Gold Currency. Wmk Mult Script CA. P* 12.
52 **6** 5 c. blue-green 2·50 3·50
53 10 c. orange 1·25 1·75
54 15 c. bright violet 3·00 3·50
55 20 c. scarlet 1·60 2·25
56 25 c. reddish brown 1·60 2·25
57 30 c. blue 1·90 2·00
58 40 c. grey-olive 4·50 5·00
59 50 c. purple 1·60 2·00
60 1 f. red/*green* 4·00 8·00
61 2 f. blue/*green* 30·00 17·00
62 5 f. red/*yellow* 70·00 48·00
63 10 f. violet/*blue* £200 75·00
52/63 *Set of* 12 £300 £150
52s/63s Perf "Specimen" *Set of* 12 £225

(Recess Waterlow)

1949 (10 Oct). *75th Anniv of U.P.U. As No.* 117 *of Antigua. Wmk Mult Script CA. P* 13½×14.
64 10 c. red-orange 30 50
65 15 c. violet 30 50
66 30 c. ultramarine 30 50
67 50 c. purple 40 50
64/7 *Set of* 4 1·10 1·75

7 Outrigger Sailing Canoes

(Des C. Hertenberger (1 f. to 5 f.), R. Serres (others). Recess Waterlow)

1953 (30 Apr). *T* **7** *and similar horiz designs. Wmk Mult Script CA. P* 12½.
68 5 c. green 60 10
69 10 c. scarlet 60 10
70 15 c. yellow-ochre 60 10
71 20 c. ultramarine 60 10
72 25 c. olive 60 10
73 30 c. brown 60 10
74 40 c. blackish brown 60 10
75 50 c. violet 1·00 10
76 1 f. orange 5·00 70
77 2 f. reddish purple 5·00 8·00
78 5 f. scarlet 7·00 26·00
68/78 *Set of* 11 20·00 32·00

Designs:—5 to 20 c. Type **7**; 25 to 50 c. Native carving; 1 to 5 f. Two natives outside hut.

POSTAGE DUE STAMPS

POSTAGE DUE (D 1) **POSTAGE DUE** (D 2) **POSTAGE DUE** (D 3)

1925 (June). *Optd with Type* D **1**, *by D.L.R.*
D1 **5** 1d. (10 c.) green 35·00 1·00
D2 2d. (20 c.) slate-grey 40·00 1·00
D3 3d. (30 c.) red 40·00 2·50
D4 5d. (50 c.) ultramarine 45·00 4·50
D5 10d. (1 f.) carmine/*blue* 50·00 5·50
D1/5 *Set of* 5 £190 13·00
D1s/5s Optd "Specimen" *Set of* 5 £190

1938 (1 June). *Optd with Type* D **2**, *by B.W.*
D 6 **6** 5 c. blue-green 22·00 32·00
D 7 10 c. orange 22·00 32·00
D 8 20 c. scarlet 28·00 50·00
D 9 40 c. grey-olive 35·00 60·00
D10 1 f. red/*green* 45·00 70·00
D6/10 *Set of* 5 £140 £225
D6s/10s Perf "Specimen" *Set of* 5 £120

1953 (30 Apr). *Nos.* 68/9, 71, 74 *and* 76 *optd with Type* D **3**, *by Waterlow.*
D11 5 c. green 4·00 11·00
D12 10 c. scarlet 1·75 8·00
D13 20 c. ultramarine 5·00 17·00
D14 40 c. blackish brown 7·00 27·00
D15 1 f. orange 4·50 27·00
D11/15 *Set of* 5 20·00 80·00

II. STAMPS INSCRIBED IN FRENCH

(Currency. 100 centimes = 1 French franc)

NOUVELLES HEBRIDES (F 1) **NOUVELLES-HEBRIDES** (F 2)

1908 (21 Nov). *T* **15/17** *of New Caledonia optd with Types* F **1** *or* F **2** (1 *f.*), *by Govt Ptg Wks, Paris.*
F1 5 c. green 4·50 4·25
F2 10 c. carmine 5·50 3·50
F3 25 c. blue/*greenish* (R.) 5·75 2·25
F4 50 c. red/*orange* 7·00 4·75
F5 1 f. blue/*green* (R.) 17·00 20·00
F1/5 *Set of* 5 35·00 30·00

CONDOMINIUM (F 3) **10c.** (F 4)

1910 (Aug)–**11.** *Nos.* F1/5 *further optd with Type* F **3**, *or larger* (1 *f.*), *by Govt Ptg Wks, Paris.*
F 6 5 c. green 2·00 3·00
F 7 10 c. carmine 2·00 1·25
F 8 25 c. blue/*greenish* (R.) (1911) 2·25 3·75
F 9 50 c. red/*orange* (1911) 6·50 9·75
F10 1 f. blue/*green* (R.) 14·00 22·00
F6/10 *Set of* 5 24·00 35·00

All the above were released in Paris on 16 March 1910. The 5 c., 10 c. and 1 f. were issued in New Hebrides in August but the 25 c. and 50 c. were not received until 1911 after the issue of the definitive stamps and they were placed in reserve, although some may have been issued on request.

1911 (12 July). *Wmk Mult Crown CA. P* 14.
F11 **3** 5 c. green 1·00 2·75
F12 10 c. carmine 50 75
F13 20 c. greyish slate 1·00 2·25
F14 25 c. ultramarine 2·50 7·00
F15 30 c. brown/*yellow* 6·50 5·25
F16 40 c. red/*yellow* 1·40 3·75
F17 50 c. sage-green 2·00 3·50
F18 75 c. orange 7·00 23·00
F19 1 f. red/*blue* 2·50 3·00
F20 2 f. violet 8·50 22·00
F21 5 f. red/*green* 12·00 35·00
F11/21 *Set of* 11 40·00 95·00

1913. *As last but wmk* "R F" *in sheet or without wmk.*
F22 **3** 5 c. green 1·25 4·50
F23 10 c. carmine 95 3·25
F24 20 c. greyish slate 95 2·40
F25 25 c. ultramarine 1·25 5·50
F26 30 c. brown/*yellow* 1·90 10·00
F27 40 c. red/*yellow* 22·00 70·00
F28 50 c. sage-green 9·00 27·00
F29 75 c. orange 9·00 40·00
F30 1 f. red/*blue* 6·00 9·75
F31 2 f. violet 9·00 35·00
F32 5 f. red/*green* 22·00 48·00
F22/32 *Set of* 11 75·00 £225

The above were placed on sale in Paris on 29 April 1912.

1920–21. *Surch as Type* F **4**, *at Govt Printing Establishment, Suva, Fiji.* (*a*) *On stamps of* 1908–11 (*June* 1920).
F32*a* 5 c. on 50 c. red/*orange* (F4) £425 £425
F33 5 c. on 50 c. red/*orange* (F9) 2·40 9·00
F33*a* 10 c. on 25 c. blue/*greenish* (F8) 50 1·50

(*b*) *On stamps of* 1911–13 (10.3.21)

F34 **3** 5 c. on 40 c. red/*yellow* (F27) 27·00 90·00
F35 20 c. on 30 c. brown/*yellow* (F15) 11·00 65·00
F36 20 c. on 30 c. brown/*yellow* (F26) 6·50 70·00

(*c*) *On Inscr in English* (10.3.21)

F37 **3** 10 c. on 5d. sage-green (24) 11·00 48·00

1924 (1 May). *Stamps of* 1911–13 *surch as Type* F **4**, *at Suva*
F38 **3** 10 c. on 5 c. green (F22) 1·00
F39 30 c. on 10 c. carmine (F23) 1·00
F40 50 c. on 25 c. ultramarine (F14) 28·00
F41 50 c. on 25 c. ultramarine (F25) 2·50
F38/41 *Set of* 4 29·00

F **5**

France Libre (F **6**)

(Recess D.L.R.)

1925 (June). *Wmk* "R F" *in sheet or without wmk. P* 14.
F42 F **5** 5 c. (½d.) black 75 1
F43 10 c. (1d.) green 1·00
F44 20 c. (2d.) greyish slate 1·75
F45 25 c. (2½d.) brown 1·50
F46 30 c. (3d.) red 1·50
F47 40 c. (4d.) red/*yellow* 1·50
F48 50 c. (5d.) ultramarine 1·50
F49 75 c. (7½d.) yellow-brown 1·50 1
F50 1 f. (10d.) carmine/*blue* 1·50
F51 2 f. (1/8) violet 2·50 2
F52 5 f. (4s.) carmine/*green* 3·50 2
F42/52 *Set of* 11 17·00 9
F42s/52s Optd "Specimen" *Set of* 11 £250

In July 1929 a batch of mail was carried by aircraft from I Vila to the French cruiser *Tourville* for sorting and forwardin Nouméa, New Caledonia. Stamps of the above issue (includ those with English inscriptions) were affixed to covers and ha stamped "PAR AVION" before cancellation.

(New Currency. 100 gold centimes = 1 gold franc)

1938 (1 June). *Gold Currency. Wmk* "R F" *in sheet or with wmk. P* 12.
F53 **6** 5 c. blue-green 1·90 4
F54 10 c. orange 1·60
F55 15 c. bright violet 1·25 3
F56 20 c. scarlet 1·60 2
F57 25 c. reddish brown 4·50 3
F58 30 c. blue 4·00 3
F59 40 c. grey-olive 1·25 7
F60 50 c. purple 1·25 2
F61 1 f. lake/*pale green* (*shades*) 1·60 4
F62 2 f. blue/*pale green* (*shades*) 26·00 28
F63 5 f. red/*yellow* 50·00 45
F64 10 f. violet/*blue* £120 90
F53/64 *Set of* 12 £190 £1
F53s/64s Perf "Specimen" *Set of* 12 £300

1941 (15 Apr). *Adherence to General de Gaulle. Optd with Ty* F **6**, *at Nouméa, New Caledonia.*
F65 **6** 5 c. blue-green 2·00 22·
F66 10 c. orange 3·00 21·
F67 15 c. bright violet 5·00 32·
F68 20 c. scarlet 16·00 28·
F69 25 c. reddish brown 19·00 35·
F70 30 c. blue 19·00 30·
F71 40 c. grey-olive 17·00 35·
F72 50 c. purple 17·00 30·
F73 1 f. lake/*pale green* 18·00 30·
F74 2 f. blue/*pale green* 16·00 32·
F75 5 f. red/*yellow* 16·00 32·
F76 10 f. violet/*blue* 16·00 32·
F65/76 *Set of* 12 £150 £3

1949 (10 Oct). *75th Anniv of U.P.U. As Nos.* 64/7. *Wmk* "R F" *sheet or without wmk. P* 13½.
F77 10 c. red-orange 2·25 4·
F78 15 c. violet 3·50 7
F79 30 c. ultramarine 5·00 10·
F80 50 c. purple 6·00 12·
F77/80 *Set of* 4 15·00 30·

1953 (30 Apr). *As Nos.* 68/78. *Wmk* "R F" *in sheet or without wmk P* 12½.
F81 **7** 5 c. green 1·50 2·1
F82 10 c. scarlet 2·00 2·1
F83 15 c. yellow-ochre 2·00 2·2
F84 20 c. ultramarine 2·00 2·1
F85 – 25 c. olive 1·25 2·1
F86 – 30 c. brown 1·25 2·2
F87 – 40 c. blackish brown 1·25 2·4
F88 – 50 c. violet 1·25 1·9
F89 – 1 f. orange 7·50 6·0
F90 – 2 f. reddish purple 15·00 45·0
F91 – 5 f. scarlet 18·00 85·0
F81/91 *Set of* 11 48·00 £14

POSTAGE DUE STAMPS

CHIFFRE TAXE (FD 1) **CHIFFRE TAXE** (FD 2) **TIMBRE-TAXE** (FD 3)

1925 (June). *Optd with Type* FD **1**, *by D.L.R.*
FD53 F **5** 10 c. (1d.) green 48·00 2·75
FD54 20 c. (2d.) greyish slate 55·00 2·75
FD55 30 c. (3d.) red 55·00 2·75
FD56 50 c. (5d.) ultramarine 45·00 2·75
FD57 1 f. (10d.) carmine/*blue* 45·00 2·75
FD53/7 *Set of* 5 £225 12·00
FD53s/7s Optd "Specimen" *Set of* 5 £225

Although on sale in Paris, the Postmaster would not issue any in unused condition for about a year and most copies are cancelled-to-order.

1938 (1 June). *Optd with Type* FD **2**, *by Bradbury, Wilkinson.*
FD65 **6** 5 c. blue-green 14·00 45·00
FD66 10 c. orange 17·00 45·00
FD67 20 c. scarlet 23·00 50·00
FD68 40 c. grey-olive 48·00 £100
FD69 1 f. lake/*pale green* 48·00 £120
FD65/9 *Set of* 5 £130 £325
FD65s/9s Perf "Specimen" *Set of* 5 £200

15 Apr). *Nos.* FD65/9 *optd with Type* F **6** *at Nouméa, New* *edonia.*

6	5 c. blue-green	11·00	30·00
	10 c. orange	11·00	30·00
	20 c. scarlet	11·00	30·00
	40 c. grey-olive	15·00	30·00
	1 f. lake/*pale green*	14·00	30·00
'81	.. .. *Set of* 5	55·00	£130

30 Apr). *Optd with Type* FD **3**, *by Waterlow.*

7	5 c. green	7·00	18·00
	10 c. scarlet	5·00	17·00
	20 c. ultramarine	18·00	27·00
–	40 c. blackish brown	11·00	25·00
–	1 f. orange	17·00	48·00
/6	.. .. *Set of* 5	50·00	£120

New Republic
see South Africa

New South Wales
see Australia

New Zealand

From 1831 mail from New Zealand was sent to Sydney, New South Wales, routed through an unofficial postmaster at Kororareka.

The first official post office opened at Kororareka in January 1840 to be followed by others at Auckland, Britannia, Coromandel Harbour, Hokianga, Port Nicholson, Russell and Waimate during the same year. New South Wales relinquished control of the postal service when New Zealand became a separate colony on 3 May 1841.

The British G.P.O. was responsible for the operation of the overseas mails from 11 October 1841 until the postal service once again passed under colonial control on 18 November 1848.

CC 1

CC 2

AUCKLAND

CROWNED-CIRCLE HANDSTAMPS

CC1 CC 1 AUCKLAND NEW ZEALAND (R.) (31.10.1846) .. .. *Price on cover* £275

NELSON

CROWNED-CIRCLE HANDSTAMPS

CC2 CC 1 NELSON NEW ZEALAND (R.) (31.10.1846) *Price on cover* £950

NEW PLYMOUTH

CROWNED-CIRCLE HANDSTAMPS

CC3 CC 1 NEW PLYMOUTH NEW ZEALAND (R. *or* Black) (31.10.1846) .. *Price on cover* £1800

CC3*a* CC **2** NEW PLYMOUTH NEW ZEALAND (R. *or* Black) (1854) .. *Price on cover* £2250

OTAGO

CROWNED-CIRCLE HANDSTAMPS

CC4 CC **2** OTAGO NEW ZEALAND (R.) (1851) *Price on cover* £1800

PETRE

CROWNED-CIRCLE HANDSTAMPS

CC5 CC 1 PETRE NEW ZEALAND (R.) (31.10.1846) *Price on cover* £1200

PORT VICTORIA

CROWNED-CIRCLE HANDSTAMPS

CC6 CC **2** PORT VICTORIA NEW ZEALAND (R.) (1851) .. .. .. *Price on cover* £1000

RUSSELL

CROWNED-CIRCLE HANDSTAMPS

CC7 CC 1 RUSSELL NEW ZEALAND (R.) (31.10.1846) *Price on cover* £3000

WELLINGTON

CROWNED-CIRCLE HANDSTAMPS

CC8 CC 1 WELLINGTON NEW ZEALAND (R.) (31.10.1846) .. .. *Price on cover* £300

A similar mark for Christchurch as Type CC **2** is only known struck, in black, as a cancellation after the introduction of adhesive stamps.

No. CC3*a* is a locally-cut replacement with the office name around the circumference, but a straight "PAID AT" in the centre.

PRICES FOR STAMPS ON COVER TO 1945

Nos. 1/125	*from* × 2
Nos. 126/36	*from* × 3
Nos. 137/9	*from* × 2
No. 140	—
No. 141	*from* × 2
No. 142	—
Nos. 143/8	*from* × 2
Nos. 149/51	*from* × 10
Nos. 152/84	*from* × 2
Nos. 185/6	—
Nos. 187/203	*from* × 3
Nos. 205/7*e*	—
Nos. 208/13	*from* × 2
Nos. 214/16*j*	—
Nos. 217/58	*from* × 3
No. 259	—
Nos. 260/9	*from* × 3
No. 270	—
Nos. 271/6	*from* × 3
Nos. 277/307	*from* × 2
Nos. 308/16	*from* × 3
No. 317	—
Nos. 318/28	*from* × 3
Nos. 329/48	—
No. 349	*from* × 5
Nos. 350/1	—
No. 352	*from* × 5
Nos. 353/69	—
Nos. 370/86	*from* × 2
No. 387	*from* × 4
Nos. 388/99	*from* × 3
Nos. 400/666	*from* × 2
Nos. E1/5	*from* × 5
No. E6	*from* × 10
Nos. D1/8	*from* × 3
Nos. D9/16	*from* × 5
Nos. D17/20	*from* × 3
Nos. D21/47	*from* × 6
Nos. O1/24	*from* × 12
Nos. O59/66	*from* × 4
Nos. O67/8	—
Nos. O69/81	*from* × 5
Nos. O82/7	—
Nos. O88/93	*from* × 20
Nos. O94/9	*from* × 12
Nos. O100/11	*from* × 5
Nos. O112/13	—
Nos. O115/19	*from* × 15
Nos. O120/33	*from* × 10
Nos. O134/51	*from* × 4
Nos. P1/7	*from* × 8
Nos. L1/9	*from* × 10
Nos. L9*a*/12	—
Nos. L13/20	*from* × 15
Nos. L21/3	—
Nos. L24/41	*from* × 12
No. F1	—
No. F2	*from* × 5
Nos. F3/144	—
Nos. F145/58	*from* × 3
Nos. F159/68	—
Nos. F169/79	*from* × 3
Nos. F180/6	—
Nos. F187/90	*from* × 2
Nos. F191/203	*from* × 3
Nos. F204/11	—
Nos. F212/18	*from* × 2
Nos. A1/3	*from* × 2

CROWN COLONY

PERKINS BACON "CANCELLED". For notes on these handstamps, showing "CANCELLED" between horizontal bars forming an oval, see Catalogue Introduction.

1

2

(Eng by Humphreys. Recess P.B.)

1855 (18 July). *Wmk Large Star*, W w **1**. *Imperf.*

1	**1**	1d. dull carmine (*white paper*) (H/S "CANCELLED" in oval £15000) ..	£32000	£9500
2		2d. dull blue (*blued paper*) (H/S "CANCELLED" in oval £10000) ..	£14000	£550
3		1s. pale yellow-green (*blued paper*) (H/S "CANCELLED" in oval £10000) ..	£25000	£5000
		a. Bisected (6d.) (on cover)	†	£32000

The 2d. and 1s. on white paper formerly listed are now known to be stamps printed on blued paper which have had the bluing washed out.

Nos. 3a and 6a were used at Dunedin between March 1857, when the rate for ½ oz. letters to Great Britain was reduced to 6d., and August 1859. All known examples are bisected vertically.

(Printed by J. Richardson, Auckland, N.Z.)

1855 (Dec). *First printing. Wmk Large Star. White paper. Imperf.*

3*b*	**1**	1d. orange	£18000	

1855 (Dec)–**57**. *No wmk. Blue paper. Imperf.*

4	**1**	1d. red	£7500	£1600
5		2d. blue (3.56)	£2750	£300
		a. Without value		
6		1s. green (9.57)	£23000	£3500
		a. Bisected (6d.) (on cover)	†	£21000

These stamps on blue paper may occasionally be found watermarked double-lined letters, being portions of the paper-maker's name.

Jan). *Wmk Large Star. White paper similar to the issue of* 1855.
1d. dull orange .. .. † £14000

s stamp is in the precise shade of the 1d. of the 1858 printing hardson on *no wmk* white paper. An unsevered pair is known Dunedin cancellation on a cover front showing an and arrival postmark of 19.1.1857.

63. *Hard or soft white paper. No wmk. (a) Imperf.*

1d. dull orange (1858) £1800 £550
2d. deep ultramarine (1858) £1700 £800
2d. pale blue £800 £180
2d. blue (12.57) £800 £180
2d. dull deep blue £1200 £275
6d. bistre-brown (8.59) £2500 £500
6d. brown £1500 £300
6d. pale brown £1500 £300
6d. chestnut £2750 £550
1s. dull emerald-green (1858) .. £11000 £1300
1s. blue-green £10000 £1300

(*b*) *Pin-roulette, about 10 at Nelson* (1860)

1 1d. dull orange .. .. .. † £4500
2d. blue .. .. † £3000
6d. brown .. .. † £3750
1s. dull emerald-green .. .. † £5500
1s. blue-green .. .. .. † £5500

(*c*) *Serrated perf about 16 or 18 at Nelson* (1862)

1 1d. dull orange .. .. .. † £4000
2d. blue .. .. † £3000
6d. brown .. .. † £2750
6d. chestnut .. .. † £5500
1s. blue-green .. .. .. † £5000

(*d*) *Rouletted 7 at Auckland* (April 1859)

1 1d. dull orange £6000 £4000
2d. blue £6000 £2750
6d. brown £5500 £2250
a. Imperf between (pair) £14000 £9000
1s. dull emerald-green .. .. † £3500
1s. blue-green .. .. .. † £3500

(*e*) *P 13 at Dunedin* (1863)

1 1d. dull orange .. .. .. † £4500
2d. pale blue £3250 £2000
6d. pale brown .. .. .. † £5000

(*f*) "H" *roulette 16 at Nelson*

1 2d. blue .. .. † £3500
6d. brown .. .. † £3750

(*g*) "Y" *roulette 18 at Nelson*

1 1d. dull orange .. .. .. † £4250
2d. blue .. .. † £3250
6d. brown .. .. † £3750
6d. chestnut .. .. † £3750
1s. blue-green .. .. .. † £6000

(*h*) *Oblique roulette 13 at Wellington*

1 1d. dull orange .. .. .. † £4500

he various separations detailed above were all applied by d to imperfe rate sheets. The results were often poorly cut badly aligned. Nos. 32*a*/*b* and 32*c*/*g* were produced using ette wheels fitted with cutting edges in the shape of "H" or

(Printed by John Davies at the G.P.O., Auckland, N.Z.)

2 (Feb–Dec). *Wmk Large Star.* (*a*) *Imperf.*

1 1d. orange-vermilion £500 £190
1d. vermilion £425 £190
1d. carmine-vermilion £375 £225
2d. deep blue (Plate I) .. .. .. £375 70·00
a. Double print .. .. .. — £2500
2d. slate-blue (Plate I) £1500 £180
2d. milky blue (Plate I, worn) .. .. — £225
2d. pale blue (Plate I, worn) .. .. £325 70·00
2d. blue (*to deep*) (Plate I, very worn) .. £300 70·00
3d. brown-lilac (Dec 1862) £325 £130
6d. black-brown £950 £100
6d. brown .. .. £850 90·00
6d. red-brown .. .. .. £750 90·00
1s. green £1000 £225
1s. yellow-green £950 £250
1s. deep green £1100 £300

The 2d. in a distinctive deep bright blue on white paper wmkd. rge Star is believed by experts to have been printed by chardson in 1861 or 1862. This also exists doubly printed and th serrated perf.

No. 37 shows traces of plate wear to the right of the Queen's ad. This is more pronounced on Nos. 37*a*/8 and quite extensive No. 39.

(*b*) *Rouletted 7 at Auckland* (5.62)

1 1d. orange-vermilion £3750 £750
1d. vermilion £2250 £750
a 1d. carmine-vermilion £3750 £900
2d. deep blue £2250 £425
2d. slate-blue £3250 £750
2d. pale blue £1800 £550
3d. brown-lilac £2250 £700
6d. black-brown £2500 £450
6d. brown £2250 £550
6d. red-brown £2250 £450
1s. green £2500 £700
1s. yellow-green £3500 £700
1s. deep green £3500 £800

(*c*) *Serrated perf 16 or 18 at Nelson* (8.62)

1 1d. orange-vermilion £7000 £1600
2d. deep blue .. .. † £1000
a. Imperf between (pair) £8500 £3750
2d. slate-blue .. ..
3d. brown-lilac £3250 £1500
6d. black-brown .. .. † £1600
6d. brown .. .. † £1800
1s. yellow-green .. .. .. † £3000

(*d*) *Pin-perf 10 at Nelson* (8.62)

1 2d. deep blue .. .. † £2250
6d. black-brown .. .. .. † £3250

(*e*) "H" *roulette 16 at Nelson*

7a 1 2d. deep blue (Plate I) .. .. .. † £1800
7b 6d. black-brown .. .. .. † £1800
7c 1s. green .. .. — £2750

(*f*) "Y" *roulette 18 at Nelson*

67*d* 1 1d. orange-vermilion .. .. .. † £1700
67*e* 2d. deep blue (Plate I) .. .. .. † £1700
67*f* 2d. slate-blue (Plate I) .. .. .. † £1700
67*g* 3d. brown-lilac .. .. .. † £2000
67*h* 6d. black-brown .. .. .. † £1700
67*i* 6d. brown .. .. † £1700
67*j* 1s. yellow-green .. .. .. † £2750

(*g*) *Oblique roulette 13 at Wellington*

67*k* 1 2d. deep blue (Plate I) .. .. .. † £1800
67*l* 2d. slate-blue (Plate I) .. .. ..
67*m* 3d. brown-lilac .. .. .. † £2250
67*n* 6d. black-brown .. .. .. † £1800

(*h*) *Square roulette 14 at Auckland*

67*o* 1 1d. orange-vermilion .. .. .. † £1700
67*p* 2d. deep blue (Plate I) .. .. .. † £1700
67*q* 3d. brown-lilac .. .. .. † £2250
67*r* 6d. black-brown .. .. .. † £1800

(*i*) *Serrated perf 13 at Dunedin*

67*s* 1 1d. orange-vermilion .. .. .. † £2000
67*t* 2d. deep blue (Plate I) .. .. .. † £1700
67*u* 3d. brown-lilac £3000 £1600
67*v* 6d. black-brown .. .. .. † £1700
67*w* 1s. yellow-green .. .. .. † £3000

The dates put to above varieties are the earliest that have been met with.

1862. *Wmk Large Star. P 13* (*at Dunedin*).

68 1 1d. orange-vermilion £1100 £275
a. Imperf between (horiz pair) .. .. † £6000
69 1d. carmine-vermilion £1100 £275
70 2d. deep blue (Plate I) .. .. £325 75·00
71 2d. slate-blue (Plate I) .. .. † £600
72 2d. blue (Plate I) .. .. .. £250 55·00
72*a* 2d. milky blue (Plate I) .. .. — £500
73 2d. pale blue (Plate I) .. .. £250 55·00
74 3d. brown-lilac £1100 £350
75 6d. black-brown £950 £180
a. Imperf between (horiz pair) .. ..
76 6d. brown £800 £100
77 6d. red-brown .. .. .. £750 85·00
78 1s. dull green £1100 £325
79 1s. deep green £1200 £300
80 1s. yellow-green £1200 £275

See also Nos. 110/25 and the note that follows these.

1862–63. *Pelure paper. No wmk.* (*a*) *Imperf.*

81 1 1d. orange-vermilion (1863) £6500 £1900
82 2d. ultramarine £3500 £800
83 2d. pale ultramarine £3250 £750
84 3d. lilac .. .. £28000 †
85 6d. black-brown £1600 £250
86 1s. deep green £7000 £950

The 3d. is known only unused.

(*b*) *Rouletted 7 at Auckland*

87 1 1d. orange-vermilion .. .. .. † £4500
88 6d. black-brown £2250 £475
89 1s. deep green £8000 £1500

(*c*) *P 13 at Dunedin*

90 1 1d. orange-vermilion £10000 £3000
91 2d. ultramarine £4500 £700
92 2d. pale ultramarine £4500 £700
93 6d. black-brown £3500 £400
94 1s. deep green £8000 £1400

(*d*) *Serrated perf 16 at Nelson*

95 1 6d. black-brown .. .. .. — £4250

(*e*) *Serrated perf 13 at Dunedin*

95*a* 9 1d. orange-vermilion .. .. .. † £6500

1863 (early). *Thick soft white paper. No wmk.* (*a*) *Imperf.*

96 1 2d. dull deep blue (*shades*) £2250 £800

(*b*) *P 13*

96*a* 1 2d. dull deep blue (*shades*) £1600 £475

These stamps show slight beginnings of wear of the printing plate in the background to right of the Queen's ear, as one looks at the stamps. By the early part of 1864, the wear of the plate had spread, more or less, all over the background of the circle containing the head. The major portion of the stamps of this printing appears to have been consigned to Dunedin and to have been there perforated 13.

1864. *Wmk* "N Z", W **2**. (*a*) *Imperf.*

97 1 1d. carmine-vermilion £700 £250
98 2d. pale blue (Plate I worn) £800 £225
99 6d. red-brown £3000 £600
100 1s. green £1000 £250

(*b*) *Rouletted 7 at Auckland*

101 1 1d. carmine-vermilion £4500 £2750
102 2d. pale blue (Plate I worn) £1400 £750
103 6d. red-brown £4500 £2750
104 1s. green £2750 £1000

(*c*) *P 13 at Dunedin*

104*a* 1 1d. carmine-vermilion £7000 £4750
105 2d. pale blue (Plate I worn) £550 £160
106 1s. green £1200 £450
a. Imperf between (horiz pair) .. £8500

(*d*) "Y" *roulette 18 at Nelson*

106*b* 1 1d. carmine-vermilion .. .. .. — £4750

(*e*) *P 12½ at Auckland*

106*c* 1 1d. carmine-vermilion £7000 £4250
107 2d. pale blue (Plate I worn) .. .. £225 50·00
108 6d. red-brown .. .. .. £250 38·00
109 1s. yellow-green £4500 £2250

1864–67. *Wmk Large Star. P 12½* (*at Auckland*).

110 1 1d. carmine-vermilion (1864) .. .. £120 27·00
111 1d. pale orange-vermilion .. .. £150 27·00
a. Imperf (pair) £2500 £1600
112 1d. orange .. .. £350 75·00
113 2d. pale blue (Plate I worn) (1864) .. £150 21·00
114 2d. deep blue (Plate II) (1866) .. £120 18·00
a. Imperf vert (horiz pair) .. .. † £3000
115 2d. blue (Plate II) .. .. .. £120 18·00
a. Retouched (Plate II) (1867) .. .. £190 45·00
c. Imperf (pair) (Plate II) £1600 £1400
d. Retouched. Imperf (pair) £2500 £2750
116 3d. brown-lilac (1864) £1500 £600
117 1 3d. lilac .. .. 95·00 28·00
a. Imperf (pair) £3000 £1600
118 3d. deep mauve .. .. .. £425 65·00
a. Imperf (pair) £3000 £1600
119 4d. deep rose (1865) £2250 £250
120 4d. yellow (1865) .. .. .. £150 95·00
121 4d. orange £1700 £900
122 6d. red-brown (1864) .. .. .. £170 24·00
122*a* 6d. brown .. .. £190 35·00
b. Imperf (pair) £1500 £1600
123 1s. deep green (1864) £650 £275
124 1s. green £325 £110
125 1s. yellow-green .. .. .. £150 85·00

The above issue is sometimes difficult to distinguish from Nos. 68/80 because the vertical perforations usually gauge 12¾ and sometimes a full 13. However stamps of this issue invariably gauge 12½ horizontally, whereas the 1862 stamps measure a full 13.

Nos. 111a, 115c/d, 117a, 118a and 122b were issued during problems with the perforation machine which occurred in 1866–67, 1869–70 and 1871–73. Imperforate sheets of the 1s. were also released, but these stamps are very similar to Nos. 44/6.

The new plate of the 2d. showed signs of deterioration during 1866 and thirty positions in rows 13 and 16 to 20 were retouched by a local engraver.

The 1d., 2d. and 6d. were officially reprinted imperforate, without gum, in 1884 for presentation purposes. They can be distinguished from the errors listed by their shades which are pale orange, dull blue and dull chocolate-brown respectively, and by the worn state of the plates from which they were printed (*Prices £65 each unused*).

1871. *Wmk Large Star.* (*a*) *P 10.*

126 1 1d. brown £475 £100

(*b*) *P 12½ × 10*

127 1 1d. deep brown .. .. † £2500

(*c*) *P 10 × 12½*

128 1 1d. brown .. .. £170 45·00
a. Perf 12½ comp 10 (1 side) £400 £140
129 2d. deep blue (Plate II) .. .. .. † £7000
a. Perf 10* .. .. † £12000
130 2d. vermilion .. .. £170 30·00
a. Retouched .. .. £275 48·00
b. Perf 12½ comp 10 (1 side) £1200 £400
c. Perf 10* .. .. † £12000
131 6d. deep blue £1500 £650
a. *Blue* £1000 £500
b. Imperf between (vert pair) .. .. — £5000
c. Perf 12½ comp 10 (1 side) £850 £425
ca. Imperf vert (horiz pair) .. .. † —

(*d*) *P 12½*

132 1 1d. red-brown .. .. £110 32·00
a. *Brown* (*shades, worn plate*) .. .. £110 32·00
b. Imperf horiz (vert pair) .. .. — £3500
133 2d. orange .. .. £100 25·00
a. Retouched .. .. £160 45·00
134 2d. vermilion .. .. £130 28·00
a. Retouched .. .. £200 55·00
135 6d. blue .. .. £160 50·00
136 6d. pale blue .. .. £120 50·00

*Only one used copy each of Nos. 129a and 130c have been reported.

1872. *No wmk. P 12½.*

137 1 1d. brown £550 £130
a. Watermarked (script letters)* .. £3250 £2250
b. Watermarked (double-lined capitals)* £1600 £550
138 2d. vermilion .. .. 90·00 48·00
a. Retouched .. .. £160 70·00
b. Watermarked (script letters)* .. £3000 £1300
c. Watermarked (double-lined capitals)* £1500 £750
139 4d. orange-yellow £140 £650
a. Watermarked (double-lined capitals)* £200

*In or about 1872 1d., 2d. and 4d. stamps were printed on paper showing sheet watermarks of either "W. T. & Co." (Wiggins Teape & Co.) in script letters or "T. H. Saunders" in double-lined capitals; portions of these letters are occasionally found on stamps.

1872. *Wmk* "N Z", W **2**. *P 12½.*

140 1 1d. brown .. .. † £4000
141 2d. vermilion £650 £250
a. Retouched £900 £350

1872. *Wmk Lozenges, with* "INVICTA" *in double-lined capitals four times in the sheet. P 12½.*

142 1 2d. vermilion £2750 £500
a. Retouched £4000 £750

NEW ZEALAND
NEWSPAPER POSTAGE

3 4

(Des John Davies. Die eng on wood in Melbourne. Printed from electrotypes at Govt Ptg Office, Wellington)

1873 (1 Jan). (*a*) *Wmk* "NZ", W **2**.

143 3 ½d. pale dull rose (*p* 10) .. .. 75·00 40·00
144 ½d. pale dull rose (*p* 12½) .. .. £180 65·00
145 ½d. pale dull rose (*p* 12½×10) .. .. £110 65·00
a. Perf 10×12½ .. .. .. £130 75·00

(*b*) *No wmk*

146 3 ½d. pale dull rose (*p* 10) .. .. £110 50·00
147 ½d. pale dull rose (*p* 12½) .. .. £200 75·00
148 ½d. pale dull rose (*p* 12½×10) .. .. £150 70·00
a. Perf 10×12½ .. .. .. £180 85·00

As the paper used for Nos. 143/5 was originally intended for fiscal stamps which were more than twice as large, about one-third of the impressions fall on portions of the sheet showing no watermark, giving rise to varieties Nos. 146/8. In later printings of No. 151 a few stamps in each sheet are without watermark. These can be distinguished from No. 147 by the shade.

1875 (Jan). *Wmk Star, W* **4**.

149	**3**	½d. pale dull rose (*p* 12½)	15·00	2·00
		a. Imperf horiz (vert pair)	£700	£400
		b. Imperf between (horiz pair)	†	£600
		c. Perf compound of 12½ and 10	†	—
150		½d. dull pale rose (*p nearly* 12)	60·00	11·00

1892 (May). *Wmk* "*NZ and Star*". *W* **12***b*. *P* 12½.

151	**3**	½d. bright rose (*shades*)	9·00	1·00
		a. No wmk	15·00	8·50
		w. Wmk inverted	50·00	30·00
		x. Wmk reversed	—	90·00

5

6

7

8

9

10

11

12

12*a* 6 mm

12*b* 7 mm

12*c* 4 mm

(T **5**/**10** eng De La Rue. T **11** and **12** des, eng & plates by W. R. Bock. Typo Govt Ptg Office, Wellington)

1874 (2 Jan)–**78**. *W* **12***a*. A. *White paper*. (*a*) *P* 12½.

152	**5**	1d. lilac	50·00	4·25
		a. Imperf	£400	
		w. Wmk inverted	†	40·00
		x. Wmk reversed	†	90·00
153	**6**	2d. rose	50·00	2·75
154	**7**	3d. brown	£100	55·00
155	**8**	4d. maroon	£275	65·00
		w. Wmk inverted	£475	95·00
156	**9**	6d. blue	£180	10·00
		w. Wmk inverted	—	50·00
		x. Wmk reversed		
157	**10**	1s. green	£550	28·00
		w. Wmk inverted	—	£250
		(*b*) *Perf nearly* 12		
158	**6**	2d. rose (1878)	£600	£180
		(*c*) *Perf compound of* 12½ *and* 10		
159	**5**	1d. lilac	£150	40·00
		w. Wmk inverted	—	60·00
160	**6**	2d. rose	£200	80·00
		w. Wmk inverted	—	£100
161	**7**	3d. brown	£160	65·00
162	**8**	4d. maroon	£400	£110
163	**9**	6d. blue	£225	45·00
		w. Wmk inverted	—	75·00
164	**10**	1s. green	£550	£110
		a. Imperf between (vert pair)	†	£4000
		bw. Wmk inverted	†	£250
		(*d*) *Perf nearly* 12×12½		
164*c*	**5**	1d. lilac (1875)	£650	£250
165	**6**	2d. rose (1878)	£650	£190
		B. *Blued paper*. (*a*) *P* 12½		
166	**5**	1d. lilac	90·00	30·00
167	**6**	2d. rose	£110	30·00
		w. Wmk inverted	—	50·00
		x. Wmk reversed	†	75·00
168	**7**	3d. brown	£225	85·00
169	**8**	4d. maroon	£425	£110
170	**9**	6d. blue	£325	50·00
171	**10**	1s. green	£1000	£190
		(*b*) *Perf compound of* 12½ *and* 10		
172	**5**	1d. lilac	£190	55·00
173	**6**	2d. rose	£550	85·00
174	**7**	3d. brown	£250	80·00
175	**8**	4d. maroon	£500	£130
176	**9**	6d. blue	£325	95·00
177	**10**	1s. green	£1000	£225

1875. *Wmk Large Star, W w* **1**. *P* 12½.

178	**5**	1d. deep lilac	£700	£110
179	**6**	2d. rose	£300	19·00

1878. *W* **12***a*. *P* 12×11½ (*comb*).

180	**5**	1d. mauve-lilac	40·00	3·50
181	**6**	2d. rose	40·00	2·00
182	**8**	4d. maroon	£140	40·00
183	**9**	6d. blue	80·00	10·00
184	**10**	1s. green	£120	35·00
		w. Wmk inverted	†	£300
185	**11**	2s. deep rose (1 July)	£325	£275
186	**12**	5s. grey (1 July)	£350	£275

This perforation is made by a horizontal "comb" machine, giving a gauge of 12 horizontally and about 11¾ vertically. Single specimens can be found apparently gauging 11½ all round or 12 all round, but these are all from the same machine. The perforation described above as "nearly 12" was from a single-line machine.

13 14 15

16 17 18

19 20 21

22

Description of Watermarks

*W***12***a*. 6 mm between "N Z" and star; broad irregular star; comparatively wide "N"; "N Z" 11½ mm wide.

*W***12***b*. 7 mm between "N Z" and star; narrower star; narrow "N"; "N Z" 10 mm wide.

*W***12***c*. 4 mm between "N Z" and star; narrow star; wide "N"; "N Z" 11½ mm wide.

Description of Papers

1882–88. Smooth paper with horizontal mesh. *W* **12***a*.
1888–98. Smooth paper with vertical mesh. *W* **12***b*.
1890–91. Smooth paper with vertical mesh. *W* **12***c*.
1898. Thin yellowish toned, coarse paper with clear vertical mesh. *W* **12***b*. Perf 11 only.

In 1899–1900 stamps appeared on medium to thick white coarse paper but we do not differentiate these (except where identifiable by shade) as they are more difficult to distinguish.

PAPER MESH. This shows on the back of the stamp as a series of parallel grooves, either vertical or horizontal. It is caused by the use of a wire gauze conveyor-belt during paper-making.

Description of Dies

1d.

Die 1

Die 2

Die 3

1882. Die 1. Background shading complete and heavy.
1886. Die 2. Background lines thinner. Two lines of shading weak or missing left of Queen's forehead.
1889. Die 3. Shading on head reduced; ornament in crown left of chignon clearer, with unshaded "arrow" more prominent.

2d.

Die 1

Die 2

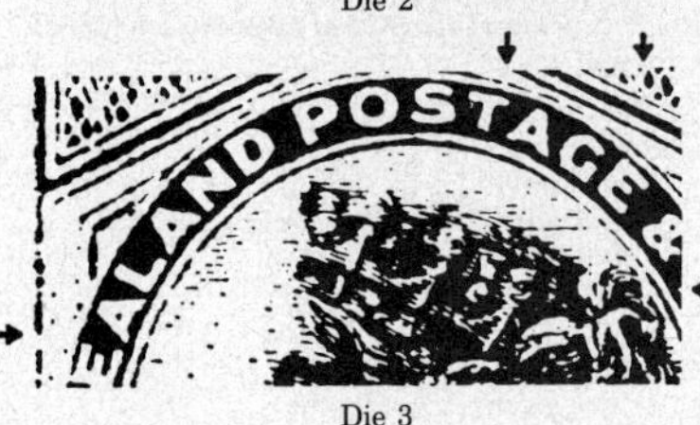

Die 3

1882. Die 1. Background shading complete and heavy.
1886. Die 2. Weak line of shading left of forehead and mi shading lines below "TA".
1889. Die 3. As Die 2 but with comma-like white notch in below "&".

6d.

Die 1

Die 2

1882. Die 1. Shading heavy. Top of head merges into shac Second ornament from the right on the cr shows a line in its left portion.
1892. Die 2. Background lines thinner, Shading on head n regular with clear line of demarcation betw head and background shading. Second ornam from the right in the crown has small dots i left portion. Most examples also show a brea the back line of the neck immediately above base.

STAMPS WITH ADVERTISEMENTS. During Novem 1891 the New Zealand Post Office invited tenders for printing of advertisements on the reverse of the current 1d 1s. stamps. The contract was awarded to Messrs Mi Truebridge & Reich and the first sheets with advertisements the reverse appeared in February 1893.

Different advertisements were applied to the backs of individual stamps within the sheets of 240 (four panes of 60

On the first setting those in a vertical format were inverte relation to the stamps and each of the horizontal advertiseme had its base at the left-hand side of the stamp when seen fr the back. For the second and third settings the vert advertisements were the same way up as the stamps and bases of those in the horizontal format were at the right as se from the back. The third setting only differs from the second the order of the individual advertisements.

The experiment was not, however, a success and the contr was cancelled at the end of 1893.

(Des F. W. Sears (½d.), A. E. Cousins (2½d.), A. W. Jones (5 others adapted from 1874 issue by W. H. Norris. Dies eng A. Cousins (½d., 2½d., 5d.), W. R. Bock (others). Typo Govt Office)

1882–1900. *Inscr* "POSTAGE & REVENUE".

A. *W* **12***a*. *Paper with horiz mesh* (1.4.82–86). (*a*) *P* 12×11½

187	**14**	1d. rose *to* rose-red (Die 1)	35·00	5·
		a. Imperf (pair)	£400	
		b. Imperf between (vert pair)	£425	
		cw. Wmk inverted		
		d. Die 2. *Pale rose to carm-rose* (1886)	30·00	5·
		dw. Wmk inverted	†	25·
		dx. Wmk reversed	60·00	25·
188	**15**	2d. lilac *to* lilac-purple (Die 1)	45·00	4·
		a. Imperf (pair)	£425	
		b. Imperf between (vert pair)	£425	
		cw. Wmk inverted	60·00	12·
		d. Die 2. *Lilac* (1886)	50·00	7·
189	**17**	3d. yellow (1884)	50·00	6·
190	**18**	4d. blue-green	70·00	5·
191	**20**	6d. brown (Die 1)	80·00	3·
		w. Wmk inverted	£150	25·

21 8d. blue (1885) .. .. .. 70·00 45·00
22 1s. red-brown .. .. .. 85·00 12·00

(b) P 12½ (1884?)

14 1d. rose *to* rose-red (Die 1) .. .. £170 85·00

B. W **12***b*. *Paper with vert mesh* (1888–95)

(a) P 12×11½ (1888–95)

13 ½d. black (1.4.95) .. .. .. 27·00 75·00
14 1d. rose *to* rosine (Die 2) .. .. 40·00 3·50
aw. Wmk inverted .. .. .. £150 15·00
b. Die 3. *Rose to carmine* (1889) .. 40·00 3·50
bb. Red-brn advert (1st setting) (2.93) 50·00 12·00
bc. Red advert (1st setting) (3.93) .. 50·00 12·00
bd. Blue advert (2nd setting) (4.93) .. 65·00 35·00
be. Mauve advert (2nd setting) (5.93) 45·00 7·00
bf. Green advert (2nd setting) (6.93)
bg. Brn-red advert (3rd setting) (9.93) 45·00 7·00
bw. Wmk inverted .. .. .. 60·00 15·00
bx. Wmk reversed .. .. .. 70·00 20·00
15 2d. lilac (Die 2) .. .. .. 45·00 4·50
a. Die 3. *Lilac to purple* (1889) .. 45·00 4·50
ab. Red advert (1st setting) (3.93) .. 60·00 16·00
ac. Mauve advert (2nd setting) (5.93) 50·00 16·00
ad. Sepia advert (2nd setting) (5.93) 50·00 22·00
ae. Green advert (2nd setting) (6.93) — 75·00
af. Brn-red advert (3rd setting) (9.93) 50·00 16·00
aw. Wmk inverted .. .. .. 60·00 8·00
16 2½d. pale blue (1891) .. .. 60·00 5·50
a. Brn-red advert (2nd setting) (4.93) 70·00 16·00
ax. Wmk reversed .. .. .. £110 30·00
b. Ultramarine (green advert. 2nd setting) (6.93) .. .. 70·00 18·00
17 3d. yellow .. .. .. 42·00 6·50
a. Brn-red advert (2nd setting) (4.93) 70·00 18·00
b. Sepia advert (2nd setting) (5.93)
18 4d. green *to* bluish green .. .. 50·00 3·00
a. Sepia advert (2nd setting) (5.93) 65·00 12·00
aw. Wmk inverted .. .. .. † —
19 5d. olive-black (1.2.91) .. .. 45·00 9·50
a. Imperf (pair) £400
b. Brn-pur advert (3rd setting) (9.93) 60·00 30·00
20 6d. brown (Die 1) .. .. .. 70·00 2·50
a. Die 2 (1892) .. .. .. £110 50·00
ab. Sepia advert (2nd setting) (5.93)
ac. Brn-red advert (3rd setting) (9.93) £150 70·00
ax. Wmk reversed .. .. .. † —
21 8d. blue .. .. .. 65·00 45·00
22 1s. red-brown .. .. .. 80·00 6·00
a. Black advert (2nd setting) (5.93) £300 £150
b. Brn-pur advert (3rd setting) (9.93) £110 16·00
w. Wmk inverted .. .. .. £120 15·00

(b) P 12×12½ (1888–91)

14 1d. rose (Die 2) .. .. .. £190 85·00
a. Die 3 (1889) .. .. ..

(c) P 12½ (1888–89)

14 1d. rose (Die 3) (1889) .. .. £160 95·00
a. Mauve advert (2nd setting) (5.93)
x. Wmk reversed .. .. .. † —
15 2d. lilac (Die 2) .. .. .. £120 85·00
a. Die 3. *Deep lilac* (1889) .. .. 90·00 65·00
ab. Brn-red advert (3rd setting) (9.93) £160 85·00
16 2½d. blue (1891) .. .. .. £170 95·00

(d) *Mixed perfs* 12×11½ *and* 12½ (1891–93)

7a 14 1d. rose (Die 3) (brn-red advert. 3rd setting) .. .. † 50·00
7b 15 2d. lilac (Die 3) .. .. .. † —
ba. Brn-red advert (3rd setting) (9.93) † —
7c 18 4d. green .. .. .. † 55·00
7d 19 5d. olive-black .. .. .. † £100
7e 20 6d. brown (Die I) .. .. .. † £110
ea. Die 2 .. .. .. † £160

C. W **12***c*. *Paper with vert mesh* (1890). (*a*) *P* 12×11½

8 14 1d. rose (Die 3) .. .. .. 70·00 7·50
9 15 2d. purple (Die 3) .. .. .. 70·00 8·00
x. Wmk reversed .. .. ..
0 16 2½d. ultramarine (27.12) .. .. 55·00 9·00
x. Wmk reversed .. .. .. † 20·00
1 17 3d. yellow .. .. .. 70·00 17·00
a. Lemon-yellow .. .. .. 70·00 20·00
2 20 6d. brown (Die 1) .. .. .. £120 25·00
3 22 1s. deep red-brown .. .. .. £130 55·00

(b) P 12½

4 14 1d. rose (Die 3) £170 £100
5 15 2d. purple (Die 3) £150 £100
6 16 2½d. ultramarine £200 £100

(c) P 12×12½

6a 20 6d. brown (Die 1) £180 £140

). *Continuation of W* **12***b*. *Paper with vert mesh* (1891–1900)

(a) P 10×12½ (1891–94)

6b 14 1d. rose (Die 3) .. .. .. £180 90·00
ba. Perf 12½×10 .. .. .. £200 90·00
bb. Red-brn advert (1st setting) (2.93) £250 £120
bc. Brn-red advert (2nd setting) (4.93) £250 £100
bd. Mauve advert (2nd setting) (5.93) £250 £100
be. Green advert (2nd setting) (6.93) £250 £140
6c 15 2d. lilac (Die 3) .. .. .. £150 60·00
6d 16 2½d. blue (1893) .. .. .. £130 65·00
da. Perf 12½×10 .. .. .. £150
6e 17 3d. yellow .. .. .. £150 75·00
ea. Perf 12½×10 .. .. ..
6f 18 4d. green £170 £140
6g 19 5d. olive-black (1894) £180 £170
ga. Perf 12½×10 .. .. .. £200 £170
6h 20 6d. brown (Die 1) £190 £190
i. Die 2 (1892) £150 £150
ia. Brn-pur advert (3rd setting) (9.93) £200 £180
6j 22 1s. red-brown £170 £170
ja. Perf 12½×10 .. .. .. † —

(b) P 10 (1891–95)

17 13 ½d. black (1895) .. .. .. 4·50 75
18 14 1d. rose (Die 3) .. .. .. 5·50 30
a. Carmine .. .. 9·00 1·25
b. Imperf (pair) £325 £325
c. Imperf between (pair) £400
d. Imperf horiz (vert pair) £325
e. Mixed perfs 10 and 12½ .. £250 £120
f. Red-brn advert (1st setting) (2.93) 16·00 4·25
g. Red advert (1st setting) (3.93) .. 16·00 5·50

(218) h. Brown-red advert (2nd and 3rd settings) (4.93) .. .. .. 9·00 2·75
i. Blue advert (2nd setting) (4.93) .. 60·00 27·00
j. Mauve advert (2nd setting) (5.93) 9·00 2·75
k. Green advert (2nd setting) (6.93) 50·00 17·00
l. Brn-pur advert (3rd setting) (9.93) 9·00 3·00
w. Wmk inverted .. .. .. 30·00 6·00
x. Wmk reversed .. .. .. 18·00 8·00
219 15 2d. lilac (Die 3) .. .. .. 13·00 60
a. Purple .. .. 14·00 60
b. Imperf between (pair) £400
c. Mixed perfs 10 and 12½ .. .. — 95·00
d. Red-brn advert (1st setting) (2.93) 25·00 7·50
e. Red advert (1st setting) (3.93) .. 25·00 6·00
f. Brown-red advert (2nd and 3rd settings) (4.93) .. .. .. 14·00 3·00
g. Sepia advert (2nd setting) (5.93) 17·00 3·50
h. Green advert (2nd setting) (6.93) 38·00 9·50
i. Brn-pur advert (3rd setting) (9.93) 14·00 3·00
x. Wmk reversed .. .. .. 24·00 8·00
220 16 2½d. blue (1892) .. .. .. 50·00 3·50
a. Ultramarine .. .. .. 50·00 4·00
b. Mixed perfs 10 and 12½ .. £170 90·00
c. Mauve advert (2nd setting) (5.93) 65·00 9·00
d. Green advert (2nd setting) (6.93) 75·00 11·00
e. Brn-pur advert (3rd setting) (9.93) 65·00 8·00
ex. Wmk reversed .. .. .. † 25·00
221 17 3d. pale orange-yellow .. .. 45·00 8·50
a. Orange .. .. 45·00 10·00
b. Lemon-yellow .. .. .. 45·00 12·00
c. Mixed perfs 10 and 12½ .. £170 £120
d. Brown-red advert (2nd and 3rd settings) (4.93) .. .. .. 65·00 14·00
e. Sepia advert (2nd setting) (5.93) 75·00 27·00
f. Brn-pur advert (3rd setting) (9.93) 65·00 12·00
222 18 4d. green (1892) .. .. .. 50·00 3·00
a. Blue-green .. .. .. 50·00 3·75
b. Mixed perfs 10 and 12½ .. £200 85·00
c. Brn-red advert (2nd setting) (4.93) 65·00 4·00
d. Brn-pur advert (3rd setting) (9.93) 65·00 4·00
223 19 5d. olive-black (1893) .. .. 45·00 11·00
a. Brn-pur advert (3rd setting) (9.93) 65·00 17·00
ab. Mixed perfs 10 and 12½ .. £110 65·00
224 20 6d. brown (Die 1) .. .. .. 85·00 20·00
a. Mixed perfs 10 and 12½ .. ..
b. Die 2 (1892) .. .. .. 48·00 6·50
ba. Black-brown .. .. .. 50·00 7·00
bb. Imperf (pair) £400
bc. Mixed perfs 10 and 12½ .. 95·00 55·00
bd. Sepia advert (2nd setting) (4.93) 85·00 11·00
be. Brn-red advert (3rd setting) (9.93) 85·00 11·00
bf. Brn-pur advert (3rd setting) (9.93) 85·00 11·00
bx. Wmk reversed (with brown-purple advert) .. .. † 30·00
225 21 8d. blue (brown-purple advert. 3rd setting) (9.93) .. .. .. 65·00 45·00
226 22 1s. red-brown .. .. .. 75·00 5·50
a. Imperf between (pair) £650
b. Mixed perfs 10 and 12½ .. £160 £120
c. Sepia advert (2nd setting) (5.93) £100 17·00
d. Black advert (2nd setting) (5.93) £180 £110
e. Brn-red advert (3rd setting) (9.93) £100 17·00
f. Brn-pur advert (3rd setting) (9.93) £100 17·00

(c) P 10×11 (1895–97)

227 13 ½d. black (1896) .. .. .. 3·25 50
a. Mixed perfs 10 and 11 .. .. 90·00 35·00
b. Perf 11×10 .. .. .. 30·00 12·00
228 14 1d. rose (Die 3) .. .. .. 4·75 15
a. Mixed perfs 10 and 11 .. .. 90·00 50·00
b. Perf 11×10 .. .. .. 55·00 9·00
x. Wmk reversed .. .. .. £100 50·00
229 15 2d. purple (Die 3) .. .. .. 10·00 30
a. Mixed perfs 10 and 11 .. .. 65·00 50·00
230 16 2½d. blue (1896) .. .. .. 48·00 3·75
a. Ultramarine .. .. .. 48·00 4·50
b. Mixed perfs 10 and 11 .. .. — 70·00
231 17 3d. lemon-yellow (1896) .. .. 60·00 9·50
232 18 4d. pale green (1896) .. .. 70·00 12·00
a. Mixed perfs 10 and 11 .. .. — 90·00
233 19 5d. olive-black (1897) .. .. 48·00 10·00
234 20 6d. deep brown (Die 2) (1896) .. 65·00 6·50
a. Mixed perfs 10 and 11 .. ..
b. Perf 11×10 .. .. .. £160 50·00
235 22 1s. red-brown (1896) .. .. 75·00 9·00
a. Mixed perfs 10 and 11 .. .. £150 75·00

(d) P 11 (1895–1900)

236 13 ½d. black (1897) .. .. .. 3·75 15
aw. Wmk inverted .. .. .. 40·00 15·00
ax. Wmk reversed .. .. .. 50·00 20·00
b. Thin coarse toned paper (1898) .. 23·00 2·25
ba. Wmk sideways .. .. .. — £160
237 14 1d. rose (Die 3) .. .. .. 3·75 10
a. Deep carmine .. .. .. 5·50 1·50
b. Imperf between (pair) £425
c. Dp carm/thin coarse toned (1898) 8·50 1·50
ca. Wmk sideways .. .. .. — £225
w. Wmk inverted .. .. .. 15·00 15·00
x. Wmk reversed .. .. .. 15·00 15·00
y. Wmk inverted and reversed .. 25·00 25·00
238 15 2d. mauve (Die 3) .. .. .. 9·00 30
a. Purple .. .. 9·00 30
b. Dp purple/thin coarse toned (1898) 8·50 2·25
ba. Wmk sideways .. .. .. — £180
w. Wmk inverted .. .. .. 15·00 5·00
x. Wmk reversed .. .. .. 25·00 8·00
239 16 2½d. blue (1897) .. .. .. 45·00 3·75
a. Thin coarse toned paper (1898) .. 55·00 14·00
240 17 3d. pale yellow (1897) .. .. 50·00 4·75
a. Pale dull yellow/thin coarse toned (1898) .. .. 60·00 12·00
b. Orange (1899) .. .. .. 42·00 9·00
c. Dull orange-yellow (1900) .. 48·00 15·00
241 18 4d. yellowish green .. .. .. 48·00 3·50
a. Bluish green (1897) .. .. 48·00 3·25
w. Wmk inverted .. .. .. 75·00 10·00
242 19 5d. olive-black/*thin coarse toned* (1899) 50·00 22·00
243 20 6d. brown (Die 2) (1897) .. .. 65·00 3·25
a. Black-brown .. .. .. 65·00 3·25
b. Brown/thin coarse toned (1898) .. 80·00 6·50
x. Wmk reversed .. .. .. † 20·00
244 21 8d. blue (1898) .. .. .. 65·00 45·00
245 22 1s. red-brown (1897) .. .. 75·00 7·00

Only the more prominent shades have been included.

Stamps perf compound of 11 and 12½ exist but we do not list them as there is some doubt as to whether they are genuine.

For the ½d. and 2d. with double-lined watermark, see Nos. 271/2.

23 Mount Cook or Aorangi — 24 Lake Taupo and Mount Ruapehu — 25 Pembroke Peak, Milford Sound

26 Lake Wakatipu and Mount Earnslaw, inscribed "WAKITIPU" — 27 Lake Wakatipu and Mount Earnslaw, inscribed "WAKATIPU"

28 Sacred Huia Birds — 29 White Terrace, Rotomahana — 30 Otira Gorge and Mount Ruapehu

31 Brown Kiwi — 32 Maori War Canoe

33 Pink Terrace, Rotomahana — 34 Kea and Kaka

35 Milford Sound — 36 Mount Cook

(Des H. Young (½d.), J. Gaut (1d.), W. Bock (2d., 3d., 9d., 1s.), E. Howard (4d., 6d., 8d.), E. Luke (others). Eng A. Hill (2½d., 1s.), J. A. C. Harrison (5d.), Rapkin (others). Recess Waterlow)

1898 (5 Apr). *No wmk*. *P* 12 *to* 16.

246 23 ½d. purple-brown .. .. .. 5·00 85
a. Imperf between (pair) £650 £700
b. Purple-slate .. .. .. 5·00 85
c. Purple-black .. .. .. 7·00 2·50
247 24 1d. blue and yellow-brown .. .. 4·00 20
a. Imperf between (horiz pair) .. £700
b. Imperf vert (horiz pair) £500 £550
c. Imperf horiz (vert pair) £500 £550
d. Blue and brown .. .. .. 4·25 80
da. Imperf between (pair) £650
248 25 2d. lake .. .. 26·00 20
a. Imperf vert (horiz pair) £400
b. Rosy lake .. .. .. 26·00 20
ba. Imperf between (vert pair) .. £650
bb. Imperf vert (horiz pair) £400
249 26 2½d. sky-blue (inscr "WAKITIPU") .. 7·00 25·00
a. Blue .. .. 7·00 25·00
250 27 2½d. blue (inscr "WAKATIPU") .. 25·00 2·50
a. Deep blue .. .. .. 25·00 2·50
251 28 3d. yellow-brown .. .. .. 23·00 7·00
252 29 4d. bright rose .. .. .. 12·00 16·00
a. Lake-rose .. .. .. 15·00 17·00
b. Dull rose .. .. .. 12·00 16·00
253 30 5d. sepia .. .. 65·00 £160
a. Purple-brown .. .. .. 40·00 15·00
254 31 6d. green .. .. 50·00 26·00
a. Grass-green .. .. .. 65·00 65·00
255 32 8d. indigo .. .. 38·00 35·00
a. Prussian blue .. .. .. 38·00 28·00
256 33 9d. purple .. .. 40·00 24·00
257 34 1s. vermilion .. .. .. 55·00 19·00
a. Dull red .. .. .. 55·00 19·00
ab. Imperf between (pair) £2000
258 35 2s. grey-green £100 £100
a. Imperf between (vert pair) .. £2000 £2000
259 36 5s. vermilion £170 £275
246/59 .. .. *Set of* 13 £500 £475

For these designs with face values in cents and dollars see the centenary issue Nos. 2158/71.

37 Lake Taupo and Mount Ruapehu

(Recess Govt Printer, Wellington)

1899 (May)–**03.** *Thick, soft ("Pirie") paper. No wmk. P* 11.
260 **27** 2½d. blue (6.99) .. 13·00 3·50
a. Imperf between (horiz pair) .. £600
b. Imperf horiz (vert pair) .. £375
c. Deep blue .. 13·00 3·50
261 **28** 3d. yellow-brown (5.00) .. 27·00 2·00
a. Imperf between (pair) .. £850
b. Imperf vert (horiz pair) .. £425
c. Deep brown .. 27·00 2·00
ca. Imperf between (pair) .. £850
262 **37** 4d. indigo and brown (8.99) .. 5·50 2·75
a. Bright blue and chestnut .. 5·50 2·75
b. Deep blue and bistre-brown .. 5·50 2·75
263 **30** 5d. purple-brown (6.99) .. 25·00 3·25
a. Deep purple-brown .. 25·00 3·25
ab. Imperf between (pair) .. £1000
264 **31** 6d. deep green .. 55·00 60·00
a. Yellow-green .. 70·00 95·00
265 6d. pale rose (5.5.00) .. 35·00 4·00
a. Imperf vert (horiz pair) .. £375
b. Rose-red .. 35·00 4·00
ba. Printed double .. £425 £450
bb. Imperf between (vert pair) .. £650
bc. Imperf vert (horiz pair) .. £250
bd. Showing part of sheet wmk (7.02)* .. 75·00 50·00
c. Scarlet .. 55·00 12·00
ca. Imperf vert (horiz pair) .. £450
266 **32** 8d. indigo .. 28·00 12·00
a. Prussian blue .. 28·00 11·00
267 **33** 9d. deep purple (8.99) .. 45·00 25·00
a. Rosy purple .. 38·00 9·50
268 **34** 1s. red (5.00) .. 48·00 8·50
a. Dull orange-red .. 50·00 4·00
b. Dull brown-red .. 50·00 8·50
c. Bright red .. 60·00 27·00
269 **35** 2s. blue-green (7.99) .. 75·00 32·00
a. Laid paper (1.03) .. £180 £200
b. Grey-green .. 85·00 45·00
270 **36** 5s. vermilion (7.99) .. £170 £200
a. Carmine-red .. £275 £325
260/70 .. *Set of* 11 £425 £275

*No. 265bd is on paper without general watermark, but showing the words "LISBON SUPERFINE" wmkd once in the sheet; the paper was obtained from Parsons Bros, an American firm with a branch at Auckland.

38

1900. *Thick, soft ("Pirie") paper. Wmk double-lined "NZ" and Star,* W **38** *(sideways**). *P* 11.
271 **13** ½d. black .. 7·50 8·50
x. Wmk reversed .. 40·00 30·00
272 **15** 2d. bright purple .. 18·00 8·50
w. Wmk sideways inverted .. 28·00 11·00
y. Wmk sideways inverted and reversed .. — 22·00

*The normal sideways wmk on Nos. 271/2 shows the star to the right of NZ, *as seen from the back of the stamp.*

39 White Terrace, Rotomahana

41

40 Commemorative of the New Zealand Contingent in the South African War

(Des J. Nairn (1½d.). Recess Govt Printer, Wellington)

1900 (Mar–Dec). *Thick, soft ("Pirie") paper.* W **38**. *P* 11.
273 **23** ½d. pale yellow-green (7.3.00) .. 8·00 3·75
a. Yellow-green .. 6·00 1·00
b. Green .. 5·50 50
ba. Imperf between (pair) .. £300
c. Deep green .. 5·50 50
w. Wmk inverted .. 20·00 10·00
y. Wmk inverted and reversed .. 40·00 20·00
274 **39** 1d. crimson (7.3.00) .. 13·00 10
a. Rose-red .. 13·00 10
ab. Imperf between (pair) .. £650 £700
ac. Imperf vert (horiz pair) .. £375
b. Lake .. 26·00 3·75
w. Wmk inverted .. † —
x. Wmk reversed .. † —
275 **40** 1½d. khaki (7.12.00) .. £800 £550
a. Brown .. 50·00 50·00
ab. Imperf vert (horiz pair) .. £500
ac. Imperf (pair) .. £600
b. Chestnut .. 9·50 4·00
ba. Imperf vert (horiz pair) .. £500
bb. Imperf horiz (vert pair) .. £650
c. Pale chestnut .. 9·50 4·00
ca. Imperf (pair) .. £600
276 **41** 2d. dull violet (3.00) .. 8·00 65
a. Imperf between (pair) .. £700
b. Mauve .. 10·00 1·50
c. Purple .. 8·00 65
ca. Imperf between (pair) .. £600

The above ½d. stamps are slightly smaller than those of the previous printing. A new plate was made to print 240 stamps instead of 120 as previously, and to make these fit the watermarked paper the border design was redrawn and contracted, the centre vignette remaining as before. The 2d. stamp is also from a new plate providing smaller designs.

42

(Des G. Bach and G. Drummond. Eng J. A. C. Harrison. Recess Waterlow)

1901 (1 Jan). *Universal Penny Postage. No wmk. P* 12 *to* 16.
277 **42** 1d. carmine .. 3·50 3·75

All examples of No. 277 show a small dot above the upper left corner of the value tablet which is not present on later printings.

(Recess Govt Printer, Wellington)

1901 (Feb–Dec). *Thick, soft ("Pirie") paper.* W **38**. (*a*) *P* 11.
278 **42** 1d. carmine .. 6·00 15
a. Imperf vert (horiz pair) .. £250
b. Deep carmine .. 6·00 15
ba. Imperf vert (horiz pair) .. £250
c. Carmine-lake .. 20·00 8·00
x. Wmk reversed .. † —
y. Wmk inverted and reversed .. — 55·00

(*b*) *P* 14
279 **23** ½d. green (11.01) .. 13·00 4·75
280 **42** 1d. carmine .. 42·00 10·00
a. Imperf vert (horiz pair) .. £225
y. Wmk inverted and reversed .. 75·00 35·00

(*c*) *P* 14×11
281 **23** ½d. green .. 8·00 6·50
a. Deep green .. 8·00 6·50
b. Perf 11×14 .. 12·00 15·00
282 **42** 1d. carmine .. £200 75·00
a. Perf 11×14 .. £1200 £450

(*d*) *P* 11 *and* 14 *mixed**
283 **23** ½d. green .. 42·00 50·00
284 **42** 1d. carmine .. £200 75·00

*The term "mixed" is applied to stamps from sheets which were at first perforated 14, or 14×11, and either incompletely or defectively perforated. These sheets were patched on the back with strips of paper, and re-perforated 11 in those parts where the original perforation was defective.

Nos. 278/84 were printed from new plates supplied by Waterlow. These were subsequently used for Nos. 285/307 with later printings on Cowan paper showing considerable plate wear.

WATERMARK VARIETIES. The watermark on the Basted Mills version of the W **38** paper used for Nos. 285/92 occurs indiscriminately normal, reversed, inverted etc.

(Recess Govt Printer, Wellington)

1901 (Dec). *Thin, hard ("Basted Mills") paper.* W **38.** (*a*) *P* 11.
285 **23** ½d. green .. 50·00 60·00
286 **42** 1d. carmine .. 75·00 90·00

(*b*) *P* 14
287 **23** ½d. green .. 25·00 22·00
a. Imperf vert (horiz pair) .. £325
288 **42** 1d. carmine .. 14·00 3·75
a. Imperf vert (horiz pair) .. £250
b. Imperf horiz (vert pair) .. £250

(*c*) *P* 14×11
289 **23** ½d. green .. 22·00 50·00
a. Deep green .. 22·00 50·00
b. Perf 11×14 .. 22·00 55·00
290 **42** 1d. carmine .. 18·00 7·50
a. Perf 11×14 .. 12·00 3·25

(*d*) *Mixed perfs*
291 **23** ½d. green .. 50·00 60·00
292 **42** 1d. carmine .. 75·00 75·00

(Recess Govt Printer, Wellington)

1902 (Jan). *Thin, hard ("Cowan") paper. No wmk.* (*a*) *P* 11.
293 **23** ½d. green .. 95·00 £170

(*b*) *P* 14
294 **23** ½d. green .. 10·00 5·00
295 **42** 1d. carmine .. 12·00 2·75

(*c*) *P* 14×11
296 **23** ½d. green .. 65·00 £120
a. Perf 11×14 .. 75·00 £130
297 **42** 1d. carmine .. £110 £120
a. Perf 11×14 .. £110 £140

(*d*) *Mixed perfs*
298 **23** ½d. green .. 90·00 £130
299 **42** 1d. carmine .. £120 £130

43 "Single" Wmk

SIDEWAYS WATERMARKS. In its sideways format single NZ and Star watermark, W **43**, exists indiscrimin[ately] sideways, sideways inverted, sideways reversed and side[ways] inverted plus reversed.

(Recess Govt Printer, Wellington)

1902 (Apr). *Thin, hard ("Cowan") paper.* W **43**. (*a*) *P* 11.
300 **23** ½d. green .. 55·00 8
301 **42** 1d. carmine .. £650

(*b*) *P* 14
302 **23** ½d. green .. 5·50
a. Imperf vert (horiz pair) .. £180
b. Deep green .. 5·50
ba. Imperf vert (horiz pair) .. £180
c. Yellow-green .. 6·50
d. Pale yellow-green .. 14·00
w. Wmk inverted .. 20·00 1
x. Wmk reversed .. 30·00 2
y. Wmk inverted and reversed .. 40·00 2
303 **42** 1d. carmine .. 3·00
a. Imperf horiz (vert pair) .. £170
b. Booklet pane of 6 (21.8.02) .. £200
c. Pale carmine .. 3·00
ca. Imperf horiz (vert pair) .. £170
cb. Booklet pane of 6 .. £200
*d. Deep carmine** .. 32·00
w. Wmk inverted .. 60·00 3
x. Wmk reversed .. 60·00 3
y. Wmk inverted and reversed .. 35·00 1

(*c*) *P* 14×11
304 **23** ½d. green .. 19·00
a. Deep green .. 25·00
b. Perf 11×14 .. 18·00
305 **42** 1d. carmine .. £100 £
a. Perf 11×14 .. £120 £
*ab. Deep carmine** .. £425 £

(*d*) *Mixed perfs*
306 **23** ½d. green .. 24·00 4
a. Deep green .. 30·00
307 **42** 1d. carmine .. 24·00 3
a. Pale carmine .. 24·00 3
*b. Deep carmine** .. £275 £
y. Wmk inverted and reversed ..

*Nos. 303*d*, 305*a* and 307*b* were printed from a plate made [by] Waterlow & Sons, known as the "Reserve" plate. The stamps [do] not show evidence of wearing and the area surrounding [the] upper part of the figure is more deeply shaded. This plate [was] subsequently used to produce Nos. 362, 364, and 366/9.

A special plate, made by W. R. Royle & Sons, showing [a] minute dot between the horizontal rows, was introduced in 1[9..] to print the booklet pane, No. 303b. A special characteristic [of] the booklet pane was that the pearl in the top left-handed cor[ner] was large. Some panes exist with the outer edges imperfora[te].

(Recess Govt Printer, Wellington)

1902 (28 Aug)–**09.** *Thin, hard ("Cowan") paper.* W (*sideways on 3d., 5d., 6d., 8d., 1s. and 5s.*). (*a*) *P* 11
308 **27** 2½d. blue (5.03) .. 11·00 12
a. Deep blue .. 13·00 12
w. Wmk inverted .. 80·00 50
x. Wmk reversed .. 50·00 25
y. Wmk inverted and reversed .. 70·00 40
309 **28** 3d. yellow-brown .. 26·00 1
a. Bistre-brown .. 26·00 1
b. Pale bistre .. 35·00 3
310 **37** 4d. dp blue & dp brn/*bluish* (27.11.02) 6·00 55
a. Imperf vert (horiz pair) .. £450
311 **30** 5d. red-brown (4.03) .. 26·00 8
a. Deep brown .. 24·00 5
b. Sepia .. 38·00 16
312 **31** 6d. rose (9.02) .. 35·00 6
a. Rose-red .. 35·00 7
ab. Wmk upright .. £550 £3
b. Rose-carmine .. 40·00 7
ba. Imperf vert (horiz pair) .. £425
bb. Imperf horiz (vert pair) ..
c. Bright carmine-pink .. 50·00 8
d. Scarlet .. 60·00 16
313 **32** 8d. blue (2.03) .. 28·00 11
a. Steel-blue .. 28·00 11
ab. Imperf vert (horiz pair) .. £750
ac. Imperf horiz (vert pair) .. £750
314 **33** 9d. purple (5.03) .. 45·00 12
w. Wmk inverted .. 65·00 40
x. Wmk reversed .. 85·00 75
y. Wmk inverted and reversed .. 70·00 40
315 **34** 1s. brown-red (11.02) .. 48·00 9
a. Bright red .. 48·00 10
b. Orange-red .. 48·00 4
ba. Error. Wmk W **12***b* (inverted) .. † £14
c. Orange-brown .. 60·00 13
316 **35** 2s. green (4.03) .. 80·00 50
a. Blue-green .. 70·00 45
w. Wmk inverted .. £225 65
317 **36** 5s. deep red (6.03) .. £170 £22
a. Wmk upright .. £200 £27
b. Vermilion .. £170 £22
ba. Wmk upright .. £200 £27
w. Wmk inverted .. £475 £40

(*b*) *P* 14
318 **40** 1½d. chestnut (2.07) .. 16·00 48·0

2d. grey-purple (12.02) .. .. 5·50 1·50
a. Purple .. .. 5·50 1·50
ab. Imperf vert (horiz pair) £375
ac. Imperf horiz (vert pair) £375
b. Bright reddish purple .. .. 6·50 2·25
7 2½d. blue (1906) .. .. .. 13·00 3·25
a. Deep blue .. .. .. 13·00 3·25
x. Wmk reversed .. .. .. † —
3 3d. bistre-brown (1906) .. .. 27·00 3·75
a. Imperf vert (horiz pair) £550
b. Bistre .. .. 27·00 3·75
c. Pale yellow-bistre .. .. 48·00 11·00
7 4d. dp blue & dp brown/*bluish* (1903) 6·00 2·75
a. Imperf vert (horiz pair) £400
b. Imperf horiz (vert pair) £400
c. Centre inverted .. .. ..
d. Blue and chestnut/bluish .. 4·00 2·25
e. Blue and ochre-brown/bluish .. 4·00 2·25
w. Wmk inverted .. .. .. 20·00 8·00
x. Wmk reversed .. .. .. 15·00 6·00
y. Wmk inverted and reversed .. 40·00 14·00
0 5d. black-brown (1906) .. .. 50·00 18·00
a. Red-brown .. .. .. 27·00 8·00
1 6d. bright carmine-pink (1906) .. 55·00 9·50
a. Imperf vert (horiz pair) £500
b. Rose-carmine .. .. .. 55·00 9·50
2 8d. steel-blue (1907) .. .. .. 27·00 9·50
3 9d. purple (1906) .. .. .. 27·00 8·00
w. Wmk inverted .. .. .. 60·00 23·00
4 1s. orange-brown (1906) .. .. 60·00 7·00
a. Orange-red .. .. .. 55·00 7·00
b. Pale red .. .. 80·00 40·00
5 2s. green (1.06) .. .. .. 65·00 22·00
a. Blue-green .. .. .. 70·00 30·00
aw. Wmk inverted .. .. .. £200 65·00
ax. Wmk reversed .. .. .. † —
6 5s. deep red (1906) £170 £200
a. Wmk upright £200 £250
b. Dull red £170 £200
ba. Wmk upright £190 £250

(c) *Perf compound of* 11 *and* 14

0 1½d. chestnut (1907) £700
1 2d. purple (1903) £275
3 3d. bistre-brown (1906) £550 £450
7 4d. blue and yellow-brown (1903) .. £300 £300
0 5d. red-brown (1906) £600 £600
1 6d. rose-carmine (1907) £325 £200
2 8d. steel-blue (1907) £650
3 9d. purple (1906) £950 £950
6 5s. deep red (1906) £1800

(d) *Mixed perfs*

40 1½d. chestnut (1907) £700
41 2d. purple (1903) £170
28 3d. bistre-brown (1906) £550 £450
37 4d. blue and chestnut/*bluish* (1904) .. £250 £250
a. Blue and yellow-brown/bluish .. £250 £250
30 5d. red-brown (1906) £475 £475
31 6d. rose-carmine (1907) £275 £200
a. Bright carmine-pink £300 £200
32 8d. steel-blue (1907) £650
33 9d. purple (1906) £850 £850
35 2s. blue-green (1906) £1000 £1000
36 5s. vermilion (*wmk upright*) (1906) .. £1600
w. Wmk inverted .. .. ..

o sizes of paper were used for the above stamps:—
A sheet containing 240 wmks, with a space of 9 mm between

A sheet containing 120 wmks, with a space of 24 mm between vertical row.

e (1) was used for the ½d., 1d., 2d., and 4d., and size (2) for ., 5d., 9d., and 2s. The paper in each case exactly fitted the , and had the watermark in register, though in the case of the he plate of which contained only 80 stamps, the paper was cut print it. The 3d., 6d., 8d., and 1s. were printed on variety (1), vith watermark sideways: by reason of this, specimens from margins of the sheets show parts of the words "NEW LAND POSTAGE" in large letters, and some copies have no rmark at all. For the 1½d. and 5s. stamps variety (1) was also , but two watermarks appear on each stamp.

e only known example of No. 322c, postmarked at Picton on March 1904, was purchased for the New Zealand Post ive collection in 1998.

(Recess Govt Printer, Wellington)

4 (Feb). *Printed from new "dot" plates made by W.R. Royle Sons. Thin, hard ("Cowan") paper. W* 43. (*a*) *P* 14.

42 1d. rose-carmine .. .. .. 7·50 50
a. Pale carmine .. .. .. 7·50 50
w. Wmk inverted .. .. .. 75·00 26·00
y. Wmk inverted and reversed .. 85·00 35·00

(*b*) *P* 11×14

42 1d. rose-carmine £120 £120

(*c*) *Mixed perfs*

42 1d. rose-carmine .. .. .. 27·00 28·00
a. Pale carmine .. .. .. 27·00 28·00

hese plates have a minute dot in the horizontal margins veen the rows, centred under each stamp, but it is frequently out by the perforations. However, they can be further inguished by the notes below.

1906 fresh printings were made from four new plates, two of ch, marked in the margin "W1" and "W2", were supplied by terlow Bros and Layton, and the other two, marked "R1" and ", by W. R. Royle & Son. The intention was to note which pair lates wore the best and produced the best results. They can be inguished as follows:—

(*a*)

(*b*)

(*c*)

(*d*)

(*e*)

(*f*)

(*a*) Four o'clock flaw in rosette at top right corner. Occurs in all these plates but not in the original Waterlow plates.
(*b*) Pearl at right strong.
(*c*) Pearl at right weak.
(*d*) Dot at left and S-shaped ornament unshaded.
(*e*) S-shaped ornament with one line of shading within.
(*f*) As (*e*) but with line from left pearl to edge of stamp.
"Dot" plates comprise (*a*) and (*d*).
Waterlow plates comprise (*a*), (*b*) and (*e*).
Royle plates comprise (*a*), (*c*) and (*e*) and the line in (*f*) on many stamps but not all.

(Recess Govt Printer, Wellington)

1906. *Thin, hard ("Cowan") paper.* W 43.

(*a*) *Printed from new Waterlow plates.* (i) *P* 14

352 **42** 1d. deep rose-carmine .. .. .. 25·00 1·50
a. Imperf horiz (vert pair) £200
b. Aniline carmine .. .. .. 24·00 1·50
ba. Imperf vert (horiz pair) £200
c. Rose-carmine .. .. .. 24·00 1·50
y. Wmk inverted and reversed .. ..

(ii) *P* 11

353 **42** 1d. aniline carmine £600 £700

(iii) *P* 11×14

354 **42** 1d. rose-carmine £425 £475
a. Perf 14×11 .. .. .. £425 £750

(iv) *Mixed perfs*

355 **42** 1d. deep rose-carmine £400 £400

(*b*) *Printed from new Royle plates.* (i) *P* 14

356 **42** 1d. rose-carmine .. .. .. 10·00 1·25
a. Imperf horiz (vert pair) £225 £225
b. Bright rose-carmine .. .. 12·00 1·40
w. Wmk inverted .. .. ..
y. Wmk inverted and reversed .. — £150

(ii) *P* 11

357 **42** 1d. bright rose-carmine £100 £180

(iii) *P* 11×14

358 **42** 1d. rose-carmine £100
a. Perf 14×11 .. .. .. £100 £150

(iv) *Mixed perfs*

359 **42** 1d. rose-carmine £100 £130

(v) *P* 14×14½ (*comb*)

360 **42** 1d. bright rose-carmine .. .. 60·00 50·00
a. Rose-carmine .. .. .. 60·00 50·00

Nos. 360/*a* are known both with and without the small dot. See also No. 386.

1905 (15 June)–**06.** *Stamps supplied to penny-in-the-slot machines.*

(i) *"Dot" plates of* 1904. (ii) Waterlow *"reserve" plate of* 1902

(*a*) *Imperf top and bottom; zigzag roulette* 9½ *on one or both sides, two large holes at sides*

361 **42** 1d. rose-carmine (i) £140
362 1d. deep carmine (ii) £160

(*b*) *As last but rouletted* 14½ (8.7.05)

363 **42** 1d. rose-carmine (i) £150
364 1d. deep carmine (ii) £300

(*c*) *Imperf all round, two large holes each side* (6.3.06)

365 **42** 1d. rose-carmine (i) £120
366 1d. deep carmine (ii) £120

(*d*) *Imperf all round* (21.6.06)

367 **42** 1d. deep carmine (ii) £130

(*e*) *Imperf all round. Two small indentations on back of stamp* (1.06)

368 **42** 1d. deep carmine (ii) £160 £140

(*f*) *Imperf all round; two small pin-holes in stamp* (21.6.06)

369 **42** 1d. deep carmine (ii) £140 £140

No. 365 *only* exists from strips of Nos. 361 or 363 (resulting from the use of successive coins) which have been separated by scissors. Similarly strips of Nos. 362 and 364 can produce single copies of No. 366 but this also exists in singles from a different machine.

Most used copies of Nos. 361/7 are forgeries and they should only be collected on cover.

44 Maori Canoe, *Te Arawa*

(Des L. J. Steele. Eng W. R. Bock. Typo Govt Printer, Wellington)

1906 (1–17 Nov). *New Zealand Exhibition, Christchurch.* T **44** *and similar horiz designs.* W **43** (*sideways*). *P* 14.

370 ½d. emerald-green .. .. .. 20·00 28·00
371 1d. vermilion .. .. .. 16·00 16·00
a. Claret £6000 £9000
372 3d. brown and blue .. .. .. 48·00 75·00
373 6d. pink and olive-green (17.11) .. £170 £250
370/3 .. .. *Set of* 4 £225 £325

Designs:—1d. Maori art; 3d. Landing of Cook; 6d. Annexation of New Zealand.

The 1d. in claret was the original printing, which was considered unsatisfactory.

47 (T **28** reduced)

48 (T **31** reduced)

49 (T **34** reduced)

(New plates (except 4d.), supplied by Perkins Bacon. Recess Govt Printer, Wellington).

1907–8. *Thin, hard ("Cowan") paper.* W **43**. (*a*) *P* 14 (*line*).

374 **23** ½d. green (1907) .. .. .. 25·00 9·00
a. Imperf (pair) £130
b. Yellow-green .. .. .. 17·00 2·75
c. Deep yellow-green .. .. 17·00 2·75
375 **47** 3d. brown (6.07) .. .. .. 48·00 25·00
376 **48** 6d. carmine-pink (3.07) .. .. 45·00 8·00
a. Red .. .. 60·00 35·00

(*b*) *P* 14×13, 13½ (*comb*)

377 **23** ½d. green (1907) .. .. .. 17·00 9·50
a. Yellow-green .. .. .. 8·00 3·00
b. Imperf three sides (top stamp of vert pair) £200
378 **47** 3d. brown (2.08) .. .. .. 48·00 28·00
a. Yellow-brown .. .. .. 48·00 29·00
379 **37** 4d. blue and yellow-brown/*bluish* (6.08) 29·00 29·00
380 **48** 6d. pink (2.08) £275 £110
381 **49** 1s. orange-red (12.07) .. .. £130 48·00

(*c*) *P* 14×15 (*comb*)

382 **23** ½d. yellow-green (1907) .. .. 8·00 1·00
a. Imperf three sides (top stamp of vert pair) £200
y. Wmk inverted and reversed .. — £150
383 **47** 3d. brown (8.08) .. .. .. 35·00 15·00
a. Yellow-brown .. .. .. 35·00 15·00
384 **48** 6d. carmine-pink (8.08) .. .. 40·00 11·00
385 **49** 1s. orange-red (8.08) .. .. £120 24·00
a. Deep orange-brown £325 £500

The ½d. stamps of this 1907–8 issue have a minute dot in the margin between the stamps, where not removed by the perforation. (See note after No. 351*a*). Those perforated 14 can be distinguished from the earlier stamps, Nos. 302/*d*, by the absence of plate wear. This is most noticeable on the 1902 printings as a white patch at far left, level with the bottom of the "P" in "POSTAGE". Such damage is not present on the new plates used for Nos. 374/*c*.

Stamps of T **47**, **48** and **49** also have a small dot as described in note after No. 351*a*.

TYPOGRAPHY PAPERS. 1908–30. De La Rue paper is chalk-surfaced and has a smooth finish. The watermark is as illustrated. The gum is toned and strongly resistant to soaking. **Jones paper** is chalk-surfaced and has a coarser texture, is poorly surfaced and the ink tends to peel. The outline of the watermark commonly shows on the surface of the stamp. The gum is colourless or only slightly toned and washes off readily. **Cowan paper** is chalk-surfaced and is white and opaque. The watermark is usually smaller than in the "Jones" paper and is often barely visible
Wiggins Teape paper is chalk-surfaced and is thin and hard. It has a vertical mesh with a narrow watermark, whereas the other papers have a horizontal mesh and a wider watermark.

50

(Typo Govt Printer, Wellington, from Perkins Bacon plate).

1908 (1 Dec). *De La Rue chalk-surfaced paper.* W **43**. *P* 14×15 (*comb*).

386 **50** 1d. carmine .. .. .. 22·00 1·00
w. Wmk inverted .. .. .. — 50·00

The design of Type **50** differs from Type **42** by alterations in the corner rosettes and by the lines on the globe which are diagonal instead of vertical.

51

52

53

(Eng. P.B. Typo Govt Printer, Wellington)

1909 (8 Nov)–**12.** *De La Rue chalk-surfaced paper with toned gum.* W **43**. *P* 14×15 (*comb*).

387 **51** ½d. yellow-green .. .. .. 4·25 50
aa. Deep green .. .. .. 4·25 50
a. Imperf (pair) £170
b. Booklet pane. Five stamps plus label in position 1 (4.10) £500
c. Ditto, but label in position 6 (4.10) £500
d. Booklet pane of 6 (4.10) £160
e. Ditto, but with coloured bars on selvedge (5.12) £150
w. Wmk inverted .. .. .. † £300

Stamps with blurred and heavy appearance are from booklets.

(Eng W. R. Royle & Son, London. Recess Govt Printer, Wellington)

1909 (8 Nov)–**16.** T **52** *and similar portraits.*

(*a*) W **43**. *P* 14×14½ (*comb*)

388 2d. mauve .. .. 11·00 6·50
a. Deep mauve .. .. .. 18·00 6·50
w. Wmk inverted .. .. .. † —
389 3d. chestnut .. .. 23·00 1·25

390 4d. orange-red .. .. 26·00 27·00
 a. Orange-yellow (1912) .. .. .. 6·00 6·50
 aw. Wmk inverted .. .. £250 75·00
391 5d. brown (1910) .. .. 17·00 2·50
 a. Red-brown .. .. 15·00 2·50
 w. Wmk inverted .. .. † —
392 6d. carmine (1910) .. .. .. 40·00 1·25
 a. Deep carmine (29.10.13) .. .. 42·00 2·75
393 8d. indigo-blue .. .. 10·00 1·25
 a. Deep bright blue .. .. .. 13·00 1·25
 w. Wmk inverted .. .. 35·00 20·00
394 1s. vermilion (1910) .. .. .. 48·00 2·50
 w. Wmk inverted .. .. £150 50·00
388/94 .. .. *Set of* 8 £160 45·00

(*b*) *W* **43**. *P* 14 (*line*)*

395 3d. chestnut (1910) .. .. .. 42·00 8·00
396 4d. orange (1910) .. .. .. 20·00 14·00
397 5d. brown .. .. 24·00 4·50
 a. Red-brown (15.9.11) .. .. .. 26·00 5·00
 w. Wmk inverted .. ..
398 6d. carmine .. .. 48·00 10·00
399 1s. vermilion .. .. 48·00 13·00
395/9 .. .. *Set of* 5 £160 45·00

(*c*) *W* **43** (*sideways*) (*paper with widely spaced watermark as used for Nos.* 308 *and* 320 – *see note below No.* 348). *P* 14 (*line*)*

400 8d. indigo-blue (8.16) .. .. .. 19·00 50·00
 a. No wmk .. .. 60·00 £140

(*d*) *W* **43**. *P* 14×13½ (*comb*)†

401 3d. chestnut (1915) .. .. .. 60·00 75·00
 a. Vert pair. P 14×13½ and 14×14½ .. £225 £275
 w. Wmk inverted £120 £120
402 5d. red-brown (1916) .. .. .. 19·00 3·00
 a. Vert pair. P 14×13½ and 14×14½ .. 50·00 70·00
403 6d. carmine (1915) .. .. .. 70·00 75·00
 a. Vert pair. P 14×13½ and 14×14½ .. £225 £275
404 8d. indigo-blue (3.16) .. .. .. 24·00 3·00
 a. Vert pair. P 14×13½ and 14×14½ .. 50·00 70·00
 b. Deep bright blue .. .. .. 27·00 3·25
 ba. Vert pair. P 14×13½ and 14×14½ .. 50·00 70·00
 w. Wmk inverted .. .. 35·00 20·00
401/4 .. .. *Set of* 4 £150 £140

*In addition to showing the usual characteristics of a line perforation, these stamps may be distinguished by their vertical perforation which measures 13.8. Nos. 388/94 generally measure vertically 14 to 14.3. An exception is 13.8 one vertical side but 14 the other.

†The 3d. and 6d. come in full sheets perf 14×13½. The 3d., 5d. and 6d. values also exist in two combinations: (*a*) five top rows perf 14×13½ with five bottom rows perf 14×14½ and (*b*) four top rows perf 14×13½ with six bottom rows perf 14×14½. The 8d. perf 14×13½ only exists from combination (*b*).

(Eng P.B. Typo Govt Printer, Wellington)

1909 (8 Nov)–**26**. *P* 14×15 (*comb*).

(*a*) *W* **43**. *De La Rue chalk-surfaced paper with toned gum*

405 **53** 1d. carmine .. .. 1·75 10
 a. Imperf (pair) £275
 b. Booklet pane of 6 (4.10) £140
 c. Ditto, but with coloured bars on selvedge (5.12) £110
 w. Wmk inverted .. .. .. 25·00 22·00
 y. Wmk inverted and reversed .. ..

(*b*) *W* **43**. *Jones chalk-surfaced paper with white gum*

406 **53** 1d. deep carmine (6.24) .. .. 12·00 5·50
 a. On unsurfaced paper. *Pale carmine* £325
 b. Booklet pane of 6 with bars on selvedge (1.12.24) £100
 w. Wmk inverted .. .. .. 35·00 27·00

(*c*) *W* **43**. *De La Rue unsurfaced medium paper with toned gum*

407 **53** 1d. rose-carmine (4.25) .. .. 30·00 £100

(*d*) *W* **43** (*sideways*). *De La Rue chalk-surfaced paper with toned gum*

408 **53** 1d. bright carmine (4.25) .. .. 8·00 42·00
 a. No wmk .. .. 20·00 60·00
 b. Imperf (pair) .. .. .. 55·00

(*e*) *No wmk, but bluish "NZ" and Star lithographed on back. Art paper*

409 **53** 1d. rose-carmine (7.25) .. .. 2·50 3·25
 a. "NZ" and Star in black .. .. 13·00
 b. "NZ" and Star colourless .. .. 24·00

(*f*) *W* **43**. *Cowan thick, opaque, chalk-surfaced paper with white gum*

410 **53** 1d. deep carmine (8.25) .. .. 5·00 1·10
 a. Imperf (pair) .. .. .. 75·00 85·00
 b. Booklet pane of 6 with bars and adverts on selvedge £100
 w. Wmk inverted .. .. .. 30·00 22·00
 x. Wmk reversed (1926) .. .. 7·00 2·25
 y. Wmk inverted and reversed (1926) 30·00 24·00

(*g*) *W* **43**. *Wiggins Teape thin, hard, chalk-surfaced paper with white gum*

411 **53** 1d. rose-carmine (6.26) .. .. 25·00 15·00
 w. Wmk inverted .. .. .. 35·00 22·00

Examples of No. 405 with a blurred and heavy appearance are from booklets.

No. 406a comes from a sheet on which the paper coating was missing from the right-hand half.

Many stamps from the sheets of No. 408 were without watermark or showed portions of "NEW ZEALAND POSTAGE" in double-lined capitals.

AUCKLAND EXHIBITION, 1913.

(59)

60

1913 (1 Dec). *Auckland Industrial Exhibition. Nos.* 387*aa*, 389, 392 *and* 405 *optd with T* **59** *by Govt Printer, Wellington.*

412 **51** ½d. deep green .. .. .. 13·00 45·00
413 **53** 1d. carmine .. .. .. 19·00 40·00
414 **52** 3d. chestnut £130 £250
415 6d. carmine £150 £275
412/15 .. .. .. *Set of* 4 £275 £550

These overprinted stamps were only available for letters in New Zealand and to Australia.

(Des H. L. Richardson. Recess Govt Printer, Wellington, from plates made in London by P.B.)

1915 (30 July)–**30**. (*a*) *W* **43**, *Cowan unsurfaced paper. P* 14×13½ (*comb*) (*see notes below*).

416 **60** 1½d. grey-slate .. .. .. 3·00 1·75
 a. Perf 14×14½ (1915) .. .. 3·00 1·75
 aw. Wmk inverted .. .. .. 40·00 35·00
 b. Vert pair. Nos. 416/a .. .. 35·00 75·00
417 2d. bright violet .. .. .. 7·00 38·00
 a. Perf 14×14½ .. .. .. 7·00 32·00
 b. Vert pair. Nos. 417/a .. .. 24·00 £140
418 2d. yellow (15.1.16) .. .. 7·00 30·00
 a. Perf 14×14½ .. .. .. 7·00 30·00
 b. Vert pair. Nos. 418/a .. .. 18·00 £225
419 2½d. blue .. .. 3·25 4·75
 a. Perf 14×14½ (1916) .. .. 9·50 23·00
 b. Vert pair. Nos. 419/a .. .. 35·00 £100
420 3d. chocolate .. .. .. 12·00 1·25
 aw. Wmk inverted .. .. .. £110 65·00
 ax. Wmk reversed .. .. ..
 b. Perf 14×14½ .. .. .. 12·00 2·00
 bw. Wmk inverted .. .. .. £110 65·00
 bx. Wmk reversed £225
 c. Vert pair. Nos. 420 and 420b .. 40·00 £120
 cw. Wmk inverted .. .. ..
 cx. Wmk reversed .. .. ..
421 4d. yellow .. .. 4·25 50·00
 a. Re-entry (Pl 20 R. 1/6) .. .. 32·00
 b. Re-entry (Pl 20 R. 4/10) .. .. 38·00
 c. Perf 14×14½ .. .. .. 4·25 55·00
 d. Vert pair. Nos. 421 and 421c .. 26·00 £180
422 4d. bright violet (7.4.16) .. .. 9·00 50
 a. Imperf (horiz pair) £850
 b. Re-entry (Pl 20 R. 1/6) .. .. 38·00 20·00
 c. Re-entry (Pl 20 R. 4/10) .. .. 42·00 24·00
 dx. Wmk reversed .. .. ..
 e. Perf 14×14½ .. .. .. 7·00 50
 ew. Wmk inverted .. .. .. † —
 ex. Wmk reversed .. .. .. — £150
 f. Vert pair. Nos. 422 and 422e .. 55·00 £110
 fx. Wmk reversed .. .. ..
423 4½d. deep green .. .. .. 12·00 22·00
 a. Perf 14×14½ (1915) .. .. 12·00 38·00
 b. Vert pair. Nos. 423/a .. .. 50·00 £150
424 5d. light blue (4.22) .. .. 6·50 1·00
 a. Imperf (pair) £130 £160
 bw. Wmk inverted .. .. .. — £100
 c. Perf 14×14½ .. .. .. 14·00 38·00
 d. Pale ultramarine (5.30) .. .. 9·00 8·50
 da. Perf 14×14½ .. .. .. 12·00 19·00
 db. Vert pair. Nos. 424d/da .. .. 55·00 £150
425 6d. carmine .. .. 7·50 50
 a. Imperf three sides (top stamp of vert pair) £1300
 bw. Wmk inverted .. .. .. £120 65·00
 bx. Wmk reversed .. .. .. — £120
 by. Wmk inverted and reversed .. ..
 c. Carmine-lake (11.27) £500 £275
 d. Perf 14×14½ (1915) .. .. 7·00 60
 dw. Wmk inverted .. .. .. 50·00 40·00
 e. Vert pair. Nos. 425 and 425d .. 65·00 £120
426 7½d. red-brown .. .. .. 10·00 23·00
 a. Perf 14×14½ (10.20) .. .. 13·00 50·00
 b. Vert pair. Nos. 426/a .. .. 50·00 £180
427 8d. indigo-blue (19.4.21) .. .. 11·00 48·00
 a. Perf 14×14½ .. .. .. 11·00 48·00
 b. Vert pair. Nos. 427/a .. .. 38·00 £160
428 8d. red-brown (3.22) .. .. 18·00 1·50
429 9d. sage-green .. .. .. 17·00 2·75
 a. Imperf (pair) £850
 b. Imperf three sides (top stamp of vert pair) £1400
 c. Yellowish olive (12.25) .. .. 20·00 13·00
 d. Perf 14×14½ .. .. .. 21·00 14·00
 e. Vert pair. Nos. 429 and 429d .. 75·00 £180
430 1s. vermilion .. .. .. 13·00 2·25
 a. Imperf (pair) £2250
 bw. Wmk inverted £225 £130
 c. Perf 14×14½ (1915) .. .. 14·00 50
 ca. Pale orange-red (4.24) .. .. 30·00 18·00
 cb. Imperf (pair) £325
 cc. Orange-brown (1.2.28) £500 £250
 cw. Wmk inverted £225
 d. Vert pair. Nos. 430 and 430c .. 75·00 £200
 dw. Wmk inverted .. .. ..
416/30 .. .. .. *Set of* 15 £120 £190

(*b*) *W* **43** (*sideways on* 2d., 3d. *and* 6d.). *Thin paper with widely spaced watermark as used for Nos.* 308 *and* 320 (*see note below No.* 348). *P* 14×13½ (*comb*) (*see notes below*) (1½d.) *or* 14 (*line*) (*others*)

431 **60** 1½d. grey-slate (3.16) .. .. 2·25 6·50
 a. No wmk .. .. 3·25 13·00
 b. Perf 14×14½ .. .. .. 2·25 6·50
 ba. No wmk .. .. .. 3·25 13·00
 by. Wmk inverted and reversed .. ..
 c. Vert pair. Nos. 431 and 431b .. 20·00 75·00
 ca. Vert pair. Nos. 431a and 431ba .. 45·00 £100
432 2d. yellow (6.16) .. .. .. 4·75 50·00
 a. No wmk .. .. 38·00 £110
433 3d. chocolate (6.16) .. .. .. 7·00 28·00
 a. No wmk .. .. 38·00 80·00
434 6d. carmine (6.16) .. .. .. 8·00 60·00
 a. No wmk .. .. 65·00 £150
431/4 .. .. *Set of* 4 20·00 £130

The 1½d., 2½d., 4½d. and 7½d. have value tablets as shown in Type **60**. For the other values the tablets are shortened and the ornamental border each side of the crown correspondingly extended.

With the exception of Nos. 432/4 stamps in this issue were comb-perforated 14×13½, 14×14½ or a combination of the two.

The 1½d. (No. 416), 2½d., 4d. (both), 4½d., 5d., 6d., 7½d., 8d. red-brown, 9d. and 1s. are known to have been produced in sheets perforated 14×13½ throughout with the 4d. violet, 5d., 6d. and 1s. known perforated 14×14½ throug

On the sheets showing the two perforations combined four rows are usually perforated 14×13½ and the bott 14×14½. Combination sheets are known to have been pr in this form for the 1½d. (Nos. 416 and 431), 2d. (both), 3d., 4d. (both), 4½d., 6d., 7½d., 8d. indigo-blue, 9d. and 1 late printing of the 4d. bright violet and 5d. pale ultramar arrangement is different with the top five rows perf 14×14½ and the bottom five 14×13½.

With the exception of Nos. 432/4 any with perfor measuring 14×14 or nearly must be classed as 14×14 being an irregularity of the comb machine, and not a pro the 14-line machine.

During the laying-down of plate 20 for the 4d., from the die which also contained dies of other values, an impress the 4½d. value was placed on R. 1/6 and of the 2½d. on R These errors were subsequently corrected by re-entries 4d. impression, but on R. 1/6 traces of the original impre can be found in the right-hand value tablet and above th frame line, while on R. 4/10 the foot of the "2" is visible left-hand value tablet with traces of "½" to its right.

61

62

WAR STAM

(**63**)

Type **62** (from local plates) can be identified from Ty (prepared by Perkins Bacon) by the shading on the portrait is diagonal on Type **62** and horizontal on Type **61**.

(Die eng W. R. Bock. Typo Govt Printer, Wellington, from p made by P.B. (T **61**) or locally (T **62**))

1915 (30 July)–**33**. *P* 14×15.

(*a*) *W* **43**. *De La Rue chalk-surfaced paper with toned gu*

435 **61** ½d. green .. .. 1·25
 a. Booklet pane of 6 with bars on selvedge £110
 b. Yellow-green .. .. .. 3·75
 ba. Booklet pane of 6 with bars on selvedge .. .. 90·00
 c. Very thick, hard, highly surfaced paper with white gum (12.15) .. 12·00
 w. Wmk inverted .. .. .. 32·00
 x. Wmk reversed .. .. .. —
 y. Wmk inverted and reversed .. —
436 **62** 1½d. grey-black (4.16) .. .. .. 6·50
 a. Black .. .. 7·50
 y. Wmk inverted and reversed .. —
437 **61** 1½d. slate (5.9.16) .. .. .. 6·50
 w. Wmk inverted .. .. .. —
438 1½d. orange-brown (9.18) .. .. 2·25
 w. Wmk inverted .. .. .. 80·00
 x. Wmk reversed .. .. .. †
 y. Wmk inverted and reversed .. £110
439 2d. yellow (9.16) .. .. .. 2·25
 a. Pale yellow .. .. .. 3·75
 w. Wmk inverted .. .. .. 80·00
440 3d. chocolate (5.19) .. .. .. 7·00
435/40 .. .. *Set of* 6 23·00

(*b*) *W* **43**. *Jones chalk-surfaced paper with white gum*

441 **61** ½d. green (10.24) .. .. .. 7·00
 a. Booklet pane of 6 with bars on selvedge (1.12.24) £100
 w. Wmk inverted .. .. .. 42·00
442 2d. dull yellow (7.24) .. .. 7·00
 w. Wmk inverted .. .. .. 32·00
443 3d. deep chocolate (3.25) .. .. 19·00
441/3 .. .. *Set of* 3 30·00

(*c*) *No wmk, but bluish "NZ" and Star lithographed on bac Art paper*

444 **61** ½d. apple-green (4.25) .. .. 2·00
 a. "NZ" and Star almost colourless .. 4·50
445 2d. yellow (7.25) .. .. .. 6·50

(*d*) *W* **43**. *Cowan thick, opaque, chalk-surfaced paper with white gum*

446 **61** ½d. green (8.25) .. .. .. 1·00
 a. Booklet pane of 6 with bars and adverts on selvedge .. .. 90·00
 ab. Booklet pane of 6 with bars on selvedge (1928) £250
 bw. Wmk inverted .. .. .. 38·00
 bx. Wmk reversed (1926) .. .. 3·50
 by. Wmk inverted and reversed (1926) 38·00
 c. Perf 14 (1927) .. .. .. 1·00
 ca. Booklet pane of 6 with bars on selvedge (1928) .. .. .. 85·00
 cb. Booklet pane of 6 with bars and adverts on selvedge (1928) .. 85·00
 cc. Imperf three sides (horiz pair) .. £500
 cw. Wmk inverted .. .. .. 42·00
447 1½d. orange-brown (*p* 14) (8.29) .. 8·50
 a. Perf 14×15 (7.33) .. .. 35·00
448 2d. yellow (8.25) .. .. .. 6·00
 ax. Wmk reversed (1927) .. .. 10·00
 ay. Wmk inverted and reversed (1927) £110
 b. Perf 14 (1929) .. .. .. 2·75
 bw. Wmk inverted .. .. .. 38·00
449 3d. chocolate (8.25) .. .. .. 7·50
 aw. Wmk inverted .. .. .. 60·00
 b. Perf 14 (1929) .. .. .. 7·50
446/9 .. .. *Set of* 4 17·00

(*e*) *W* **43**. *Wiggins Teape thin, hard, chalk-surfaced paper*

450 **61** 1½d. orange-brown (*p* 14) (1930) .. 35·00
451 2d. yellow (5.26) .. .. .. 7·50
 aw. Wmk inverted .. .. .. 24·00
 b. Perf 14 (10.27) .. .. .. 6·50
 bw. Wmk inverted .. .. .. 32·00

The designs of these stamps also differ as described benea No. 434.

Stamps from booklet panes often have blurred, heav impressions. Different advertisements can be found on the liste booklet panes.

mples of No. 446cc, which occur in booklet panes, show the s perforated at top.

½d. and 2d. (Nos. 446c and 448b) are known showing ½d. . local surcharges from 1932 applied diagonally in blue to s previously stuck on to envelopes or cards at church (½d.) or Wellington (1d.).

24 Sept). *No.* 435 *optd with T* **63**.
61 ½d. green .. .. 1·75 50

64 "Peace" and Lion

65 "Peace" and Lion

and typo D.L.R. from plates by P.B., Waterlow and D.L.R.)

(27 Jan). *Victory. T* **64/5** *and similar designs. W* **43** *eways on ½d., 1½d., 3d. and 1s.). De La Rue lk-surfaced paper. P* 14.

½d. green ..	..	3·00	2·50
a. Pale yellow-green	..	25·00	26·00
1d. carmine-red ..	..	4·50	60
a. Bright carmine	..	6·00	70
w. Wmk inverted	..	15·00	7·50
x. Wmk reversed	..	48·00	16·00
1½d. brown-orange	..	3·50	50
3d. chocolate	..	13·00	14·00
6d. violet ..	..	15·00	17·00
a. Wmk sideways	..	†	£350
x. Wmk inverted	..	—	£120
1s. orange-red	..	24·00	48·00
..	*Set of* 6	55·00	75·00

signs: *Horiz* (*as T* **65**)—1½d. Maori chief. (*As T* **64**)—3d. 1s. King George V. *Vert* (*as T* **64**)—6d. "Peace" and gress".

e above stamps were placed on sale in London in November,

2d. 2d.

TWOPENCE

(68)

69

(Mar). *No.* 453 *surch with T* **68**.
64 2d. on ½d. green (R.) .. .. .. 3·50 1·40

es and eng W. R. Bock. Typo Govt Printer, Wellington)

(1 Oct)–**25**. *Restoration of Penny Postage. W* **43**. *P* 14 × 15.

(*a*) *De La Rue chalk-surfaced paper with toned gum*
69 1d. carmine .. .. 3·00 60

(*b*) *Jones chalk-surfaced paper with white gum*
69 1d. carmine (3.24) .. .. .. 6·00 4·50
a. Wmk sideways .. .. .. † —
w. Wmk inverted .. .. .. 55·00 42·00

(*c*) *Cowan unsurfaced paper with very shiny gum*
69 1d. carmine-pink (4.25) .. .. 27·00 27·00

ne paper used for No. 462 is similar to that of Nos. 416/30.

70 Exhibition Buildings

s H. L. Richardson. Eng and typo Govt Printer, Wellington)

25 (17 Nov). *Dunedin Exhibition. W* **43**. *Cowan chalk-surfaced paper. P* 14 × 15.

70	½d. yellow-green/*green*	..	3·00	11·00
	w. Wmk inverted	..	£225	£100
	1d. carmine/*rose*	..	3·50	5·50
	w. Wmk inverted	..	£225	£100
	4d. mauve/*pale mauve*	..	35·00	70·00
	a. "POSTAGF" at right (R. 1/2, R 10/1)		£110	£170
/5	..	*Set of* 3	38·00	80·00

71

72

es H. L. Richardson; plates by B.W. (1d. from sheets), P.B. (1d. from booklets), Royal Mint, London (others). Typo Govt Printer, Wellington)

26 (12 July)–**34**. *W* **43**. *P* 14. (*a*) *Jones chalk-surfaced paper with white gum.*

6 **72**	2s. deep blue ..	..	48·00	55·00
	w. Wmk inverted	..	48·00	55·00
7	3s. mauve ..	..	70·00	£150
	w. Wmk inverted	..	70·00	£150

(*b*) *Cowan thick, opaque, chalk-surfaced paper with white gum*

468 **71**	1d. rose-carmine (15.11.26)	..	75	20
	a. Imperf (pair)	..	£110	
	b. Booklet pane of 6 with bars on selvedge (1928)	..	75·00	
	c. Booklet pane of 6 with bars and adverts on selvedge (1928)	..	75·00	
	dw. Wmk inverted	..	20·00	11·00
	e. Perf 14×15 (3.27) ..	..	65	50
	ea. Booklet pane of 6 with bars and adverts on selvedge (1934)	..	85·00	
	ew. Wmk inverted	..	20·00	11·00
	ex. Wmk reversed	..	10·00	
469 **72**	2s. light blue (5.27)	..	48·00	21·00
470	3s. pale mauve (9.27) ..	..	80·00	£130
468/70	..	*Set of* 3	£120	£140

(*c*) *Wiggins Teape thin, hard, chalk-surfaced paper with white gum*

471 **71**	1d. rose-carmine (6.30)	..	15·00	9·00
	w. Wmk inverted	..	35·00	22·00

No. 468ex exists in a range of colours including scarlet and deep carmine to magenta but we have insufficient evidence to show that these were issued.

Following the reduction of the postage rate to ½d. on 1 June 1932 the firm of R. H. White & Co. Ltd. of Stratford returned a quantity of envelopes stamped with 1d. stamps (No. 468) to the New Plymouth post office who surcharged the stamps "HALFPENNY" in purple using a handstamp. The covers were then returned to the firm for nornal use. Similar local surcharges were applied diagonally to 1d. stamps stuck onto postcards or lettercards at Dunedin, Greymouth and Invercargill in blue or at Palmerston North in purple. With the exception of the Greymouth provisional, where forty mint examples were acquired by a stamp dealer, these local surcharges are only found unused, no gum, or used.

73 Nurse

74 Smiling Boy

(Typo Govt Printing Office, Wellington)

1929–30. *Anti-Tuberculosis Fund. T* **73** *and similar design. W* **43**. *P* 14.

(*a*) *Inscribed* "HELP STAMP OUT TUBERCULOSIS".
544 1d. + 1d. scarlet (11.12.29) .. .. 11·00 18·00
w. Wmk inverted £190 £190

(*b*) *Inscribed* "HELP PROMOTE HEALTH"
545 1d. + 1d. scarlet (29.10.30) .. .. 22·00 32·00

(Des L. C. Mitchell. Dies eng and plates made Royal Mint, London (1d.), Govt Ptg Office, Wellington from W. R. Bock die (2d.). Typo Govt Ptg Office, Wellington)

1931 (31 Oct). *Health Stamps. W* **43** (*sideways*). *P* 14½ × 14.
546 **74** 1d. + 1d. scarlet .. .. .. 75·00 75·00
547 2d. + 1d. blue .. .. .. 75·00 60·00

75 New Zealand Lake Scenery

FIVE PENCE

(76)

(Des L. C. Mitchell. Plates, Royal Mint, London. Typo Govt Ptg Office)

1931 (10 Nov)–**35**. *Air. W* **43**. *P* 14×14½.

548 **75**	3d. chocolate ..	..	24·00	15·00
	a. Perf 14×15 (4.35)	..	£130	£425
549	4d. blackish purple	..	24·00	19·00
550	7d. brown-orange	..	27·00	9·00
548/50	..	*Set of* 3	65·00	38·00

1931 (18 Dec). *Air. Surch with T* **76**. *W* **43**. *P* 14×14½.
551 **75** 5d. on 3d. green (R.) .. .. .. 12·00 8·00

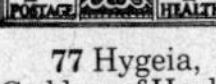

77 Hygeia, Goddess of Health

78 The Path to Health

(Des R. E. Tripe and W. J. Cooch. Eng H. T. Peat. Recess Govt Printing Office, Wellington)

1932 (18 Nov). *Health Stamp. W* **43**. *P* 14.
552 **77** 1d. + 1d. carmine .. .. .. 23·00 27·00
w. Wmk inverted £225 £120
x. Wmk reversed .. .. .. † £275

(Des J. Berry. Eng H. T. Peat. Recess Govt Printing Office, Wellington)

1933 (8 Nov). *Health Stamp. W* **43**. *P* 14.
553 **78** 1d. + 1d. carmine .. .. .. 13·00 17·00
w. Wmk inverted £150 £110

TRANS-TASMAN
AIR MAIL
"FAITH IN AUSTRALIA."

(79)

80 Crusader

1934 (17 Jan). *Air. T* **75** *in new colour optd with T* **79**. *W* **43**. *P* 14×14½.
554 **75** 7d. light blue (B.) .. .. .. 35·00 40·00

(Des J. Berry. Recess D.L.R.)

1934 (25 Oct). *Health Stamp. W* **43** (*sideways*). *P* 14×13½.
555 **80** 1d. + 1d. carmine .. .. .. 11·00 17·00

81 Collared Grey Fantail

82 Brown Kiwi

83 Maori Woman

84 Maori Carved House

85 Mt Cook

86 Maori Girl

87 Mitre Peak

88 Striped Marlin

89 Harvesting

90 Tuatara Lizard

91 Maori Panel

92 Tui

93 Capt. Cook at Poverty Bay

94 Mt Egmont

Die I Die II

"Captain Coqk"
(R. 1/4)

(Des J. Fitzgerald (½d., 4d.), C. H. and R. J. G. Collins (1d.), M. Matthews (1½d.), H. W. Young (2d.), L. C. Mitchell (2½d., 3d., 8d., 1s., 3s.), W. J. Cooch and R. E. Tripe (5d.), T. I. Archer (6d.), I. F. Calder (9d.) and I. H. Jenkins (2s.). Litho Waterlow (9d.). Recess D.L.R. (remainder))

1935 (1 May)–**36.** *W* **43** (*sideways on 8d.*).
556 **81** ½d. bright green, *p* 14×13½ .. 1·50 60
w. Wmk inverted .. 2·25 2·25
557 **82** 1d. scarlet (Die I), *p* 14×13½ .. 1·75 50
aw. Wmk inverted .. 2·25 2·00
b. Perf 13½×14 (1936) .. 75·00 45·00
c. Die II. Perf 14×13½ (1935) .. 5·50 2·75
ca. Booklet pane of 6 with adverts on selvedge .. 40·00
w. Wmk inverted .. 12·00 3·00
558 **83** 1½d. red-brown, *p* 14×13½ .. 6·50 9·50
a. Perf 13½×14 (1935) .. 4·75 6·00
ay. Wmk inverted and reversed (2.36) 18·00 23·00
559 **84** 2d. orange, *p* 14×13½ .. 3·25 60
w. Wmk inverted .. 75·00 22·00
560 **85** 2½d. chocolate and slate, *p* 13–14×13½ 5·50 24·00
aw. Wmk inverted .. 20·00 38·00
b. Perf 13½×14 (11.35) .. 4·00 19·00
bx. Wmk reversed .. † £450
561 **86** 3d. brown, *p* 14×13½ .. 12·00 2·00
w. Wmk inverted .. — £120
562 **87** 4d. black and sepia, *p* 14 .. 3·75 1·60
w. Wmk inverted .. £200 80·00
563 **88** 5d. ultramarine, *p* 13–14×13½ .. 23·00 24·00
aw. Wmk inverted .. † 90·00
b. Perf 13½×14 .. 24·00 35·00
564 **89** 6d. scarlet, *p* 13½×14 .. 6·50 5·50
w. Wmk inverted .. — 60·00
565 **90** 8d. chocolate, *p* 14×13½ .. 9·50 9·00
566 **91** 9d. scarlet and black, *p* 14×14½ .. 11·00 3·25
567 **92** 1s. deep green, *p* 14×13½ .. 20·00 12·00
w. Wmk inverted .. — 70·00
568 **93** 2s. olive-green, *p* 13–14½×13½ .. 38·00 35·00
a. "CAPTAIN COQK" .. 85·00
bw. Wmk inverted .. 80·00 45·00
c. Perf 13½×14 (1935) .. 48·00 45·00
ca. "CAPTAIN COQK" .. 95·00
569 **94** 3s. choc & yell-brn, *p* 13–14×13½ .. 15·00 45·00
a. Perf 13½×14 (11.35) .. 19·00 45·00
aw. Wmk inverted .. † £200
ay. Wmk inverted and reversed (1936) £325 £350
556/69 .. *Set of* 14 £130 £150

Some stamps from sheets perforated 14×13½ by De La Rue sometimes show the horizontal perforations nearer 13½.

In the 2½d., 5d., 2s. and 3s. perf 13–14×13½ the horizontal perforations of each stamp are in two sizes, one half of each horizontal side measuring 13 and the other 14.

See also Nos. 577/90 and 630/1.

95 Bell Block Aerodrome

96 King George V and Queen Mary

(Des J. Berry. Eng Stamp Printing Office, Melbourne. Recess Govt Printing Office, Wellington)

1935 (4 May). *Air. W* **43**. *P* 14.
570 **95** 1d. carmine .. 1·00 70
w. Wmk inverted .. 60·00 40·00
571 3d. violet .. 5·00 3·00
w. Wmk inverted .. 75·00 40·00
572 6d. blue .. 9·50 3·00
w. Wmk inverted .. 85·00 60·00
570/2 .. *Set of* 3 14·00 6·00

(Frame by J. Berry. Recess B.W.)

1935 (7 May). *Silver Jubilee. W* **43**. *P* 11×11½.
573 **96** ½d. green .. 75 1·00
574 1d. carmine .. 1·25 80
575 6d. red-orange .. 21·00 25·00
573/5 .. *Set of* 3 21·00 25·00

97 "The Key to Health"

98 "Multiple Wmk"

(Des S. Hall. Recess John Ash, Melbourne)

1935 (30 Sept). *Health Stamp. W* **43**. *P* 11.
576 **97** 1d. + 1d. scarlet .. 2·50 2·75

WATERMARKS. In W **43** the wmk units are in vertical columns widely spaced and the sheet margins are unwatermarked or wmkd "NEW ZEALAND POSTAGE" in large letters.

In W **98** the wmk units are arranged alternately in horizontal rows closely spaced and are continued into the sheet margins.

Stamps with W **98** sideways show the star to the left of NZ, *as seen from the back*. Sideways inverted varieties have the star to right *as seen from the back*.

(Litho Govt Ptg Office, Wellington (9d). Recess Waterlow or D.L.R. (others))

1936–42. *W* **98**.
577 **81** ½d. bright green, *p* 14×13½ .. 3·00 10
w. Wmk inverted .. 5·50 1·50
578 **82** 1d. scarlet (Die II), *p* 14×13½ (4.36) 2·50 10
w. Wmk inverted .. 7·00 2·50
579 **83** 1½d. red-brown, *p* 14×13½ (6.36) .. 11·00 5·50
580 **84** 2d. orange, *p* 14×13½ (3.36) .. 30 10
aw. Wmk inverted .. 80·00 27·00
b. Perf 12½*† (6.41) .. 3·75 10
bw. Wmk inverted ..
c. Perf 14 (6.41) .. 25·00 90
d. Perf 14×15 (6.41) .. 38·00 20·00
581 **85** 2½d. chocolate and slate, *p* 13–14×13½ 6·50 16·00
aw. Wmk inverted .. 22·00 32·00
b. Perf 14 (11.36) .. 5·00 1·50
bw. Wmk inverted .. 14·00 17·00
c. Perf 14×13½ (11.42) .. 50 4·00
582 **86** 3d. brown, *p* 14×13½ .. 35·00 55
w. Wmk inverted .. 60·00 27·00
583 **87** 4d. black and sepia, *p* 14×13½ .. 5·00 50
aw. Wmk inverted .. 15·00 8·00
b. Perf 12½* (1941) .. 27·00 10·00
bw. Wmk inverted .. † —
c. Perf 14, line (1941) .. 65·00 95·00
d. Perf 14×14½ comb (7.42) .. 1·00 10
dw. Wmk inverted .. 90·00
584 **88** 5d. ultramarine, *p* 13–14×13½ (8.36) 16·00 2·50
aw. Wmk inverted .. 32·00 14·00
b. Perf 12½*† (7.41) .. 20·00 3·00
c. Perf 14×13½ (11.42) .. 2·50 1·00
cw. Wmk inverted .. 90·00 70·00
585 **89** 6d. scarlet, *p* 13½×14 (8.36) .. 13·00 1·00
aw. Wmk inverted .. 38·00 5·50
b. Perf 12½* (10.41) .. 3·00 3·50
c. Perf 14½×14 (6.42) .. 1·25 10
cw. Wmk inverted .. £225 65·00
586 **90** 8d. choc, *p* 14×13½ (*wmk sideways*) 11·00 3·25
aw. Wmk sideways inverted .. 25·00 9·50
b. Wmk upright (7.39) .. 4·00 3·25
bw. Wmk inverted ..
c. Perf 12½* (*wmk sideways*) (7.41) 3·75 1·50
d. Perf 14×14½ (*wmk sideways*) (7.42) .. 3·75 70
dw. Wmk sideways inverted .. — 35·00
587 **91** 9d. red and grey, *p* 14×15 (*wmk sideways*) .. 42·00 3·25
ay. Wmk sideways inverted and reversed .. — 75·00
b. Wmk upright. *Red and grey-black*, *p* 13½×14 (1.3.38) .. 65·00 3·25
bw. Wmk inverted .. 95·00 24·00
588 **92** 1s. deep green, *p* 14×13½ .. 2·50 60
aw. Wmk inverted .. 55·00 10·00
b. Perf 12½* (11.41) .. 65·00 17·00
589 **93** 2s. olive-green, *p* 13–14×13½ (8.36) 35·00 6·00
a. "CAPTAIN COQK" .. 60·00
bw. Wmk inverted .. £100 28·00
c. Perf 13½×14 (3.39) .. £275 3·00
ca. "CAPTAIN COQK" .. £275
d. Perf 12½*† (7.41) .. 26·00 7·00
da. "CAPTAIN COQK" .. 60·00
e. Perf 14×13½ (10.42) .. 8·00 1·50
ea. "CAPTAIN COQK" .. 85·00
ew. Wmk inverted .. — 85·00
590 **94** 3s. chocolate & yell-brn, *p* 13–14×13½ 42·00 7·00
aw. Wmk inverted .. 65·00 16·00
b. Perf 12½* (1941) .. 80·00 48·00
c. Perf 14×13½ (1942) .. 4·50 2·25
577/90c .. *Set of* 14 £100 14·00

*†Stamps indicated with an asterisk were printed and perforated by Waterlow; those having a dagger were printed by D.L.R. and perforated by Waterlow. No. 580d was printed by D.L.R. and perforated by Harrison and No. 583c was printed by Waterlow and perforated by D.L.R. These are all known as "Blitz perfs" because De La Rue were unable to maintain supplies after their works were damaged by enemy action. All the rest, except the 9d., were printed and perforated by D.L.R.

On stamps printed and perforated by De La Rue the perf 14×13½ varies in the sheet and is sometimes nearer 13½. 2d. perf 14×15 is sometimes nearer 14×14½.

2½d., 5d., 2s. and 3s. In perf 13–14×13½ one half the length of each horizontal perforation measures 13 and the other 14. In perf 14×13½ the horizontal perforation is regular.

4d. No. 583c. is line-perf measuring 14 exactly and has a blackish sepia frame. No. 583d is a comb-perf measuring 14×14.3 or 14×14.2 and the frame is a warmer shade.

2s. No. 589c is comb-perf and measures 13.5×13.75.

For 9d. typographed, see Nos. 630/1.

99 N.Z. Soldier at Anzac Cove

100 Wool

(Des L. C. Mitchell. Recess John Ash, Melbourne)

1936 (27 Apr). *Charity. 21st Anniv of "Anzac" Landing at Gallipoli. W* **43**. *P* 11.
591 **99** ½d. + ½d. green .. 60 1·75
592 1d. + 1d. scarlet .. 60 1·40

(Des L. C. Mitchell. Recess John Ash, Melbourne)

1936 (1 Oct). *Congress of British Empire Chambers of Commerce, Wellington. Industries Issue. T* **100** *and similar horiz designs. W* **43** (*sideways*). *P* 11½.
593 ½d. emerald-green .. 30 30
594 1d. scarlet .. 30 20
595 2½d blue .. 1·00 8·00
596 4d. violet .. 80
597 6d. red-brown .. 2·00
593/7 .. *Set of* 5 4·00

Designs:—1d. Butter; 2½d. Sheep; 4d. Apples; 6d. Export

105 Health Camp

106 King George VI ar Queen Elizabeth

(Des J. Berry. Recess John Ash, Melbourne)

1936 (2 Nov). *Health Stamp. W* **43** (*sideways*). *P* 11.
598 **105** 1d. + 1d. scarlet .. 1·75

(Recess B.W.)

1937 (13 May). *Coronation. W* **98**. *P* 14 × 13½.
599 **106** 1d. carmine .. 30
600 2½d. Prussian blue .. 80
601 6d. red-orange .. 1·10
599/601 .. *Set of* 3 2·00

107 Rock climbing

108 King George VI

108

(Des G. Bull and J. Berry. Recess John Ash, Melbourne)

1937 (1 Oct). *Health Stamp. W* **43**. *P* 11.
602 **107** 1d. + 1d. scarlet .. 2·25

Broken ribbon flaw (R. 6/6 of Pl 8)

(Des W. J. Cooch. Recess B.W.)

1938–44. *W* **98**. *P* 14×13½.
603 **108** ½d. green (1.3.38) .. 6·50
w. Wmk inverted .. 14·00
604 ½d. orange-brown (10.7.41) .. 20
w. Wmk inverted ..
605 1d. scarlet (1.7.38) .. 5·00
a. Broken ribbon .. 60·00
w. Wmk inverted .. 14·00
606 1d. green (21.7.41) .. 20
w. Wmk inverted .. 30·00
607 **108a** 1½d purple-brown (26.7.38) .. 26·00
w. Wmk inverted .. 38·00
608 1½d. scarlet (1.2.44) .. 20
w. Wmk inverted .. —
609 3d. blue (26.9.41) .. 20
w. Wmk inverted .. —
603/9 .. *Set of* 7 35·00

For other values see Nos. 680/9.

109 Children playing

110 Beach Ball

(Des J. Berry. Recess B.W.)

1938 (1 Oct). *Health Stamp. W* **98**. *P* 14 × 13½.
610 **109** 1d. + 1d. scarlet .. 5·00

(Des S. Hall. Recess Note Printing Branch, Commonwealth Ba of Australia, Melbourne)

1939 (16 Oct). *Health Stamps. Surcharged with new value. W P* 11.
611 **110** 1d. on ½d. + ½d. green .. 3·75
612 2d. on 1d. + 1d. scarlet .. 3·75

MINIMUM PRICE

The minimum price quote is 10p which represen a handling charge rather than a basis for valuin common stamps. For further notes about price see introductory pages.

Arrival of the Maoris, 1350

115 Signing Treaty of Waitangi, 1840

. C. Mitchell (½d., 3d., 4d.); J. Berry (others). Recess B.W.)

2 Jan–8 Mar). *Centenary of Proclamation of British Sovereignty. T* **111, 115** *and similar designs. W* **98.** *P* 14 × 13½ (2½*d.*), × 14 (5*d.*) *or* 13½ (*others*).
½d. blue-green 30 10
1d. chocolate and scarlet .. .. .. 2·75 10
1½d. light blue and mauve 30 50
2d. blue-green and chocolate .. .. 1·50 10
2½d. blue-green and blue .. .. .. 2·00 90
3d. purple and carmine .. .. .. 3·75 90
4d. chocolate and lake .. .. .. 16·00 1·50
5d. pale blue and brown .. .. .. 7·00 3·50
6d. emerald-green and violet .. .. 13·00 1·00
7d. black and red .. .. 1·50 3·75
8d. black and red (8.3) .. .. .. 13·00 2·75
9d. olive-green and orange .. .. .. 7·50 1·75
1s. sage-green and deep green .. .. 17·00 3·50
.. .. *Set of* 13 75·00 17·00
igns: *Horiz* (*as T* **111**)—1d. *Endeavour*, Chart of N.Z., and Cook; 1½d. British Monarchs; 2d. Tasman with his ship hart; 3d. Landing of immigrants, 1840; 4d. Road, Rail, Sea ir Transport; 6d. *Dunedin* and "Frozen Mutton Route" to n; 7d., 8d. Maori council; 9d. Gold mining in 1861 and 1940. **115**)—5d. H.M.S. *Britomar* at Akaroa, 1840. *Vert* (*as T* -1s. Giant Kauri tree.

(1 Oct). *Health Stamps. As T* **110**, *but without extra charge. W* **43**. *P* 11.
110 1d. + ½d. blue-green .. .. .. 13·00 14·00
2d. + 1d. brown-orange .. .. 13·00 14·00

1ᴰ

2ᴰ

1941

(123) Inserted "2" (124)

Nos. 603 *and* 607 *surch as T* **123**.
108 1d. on ½d. green (1.5.41) .. .. 1·25 10
108*a* 2d. on 1½d. purple-brown (4.41) .. 1·25 10
a. Inserted "2" £550 £300
e surcharge on No. 629 has only one figure, at top left, and is only one square to obliterate the original value at bottom .

e variety "Inserted 2" occurs on the 10th stamp, 10th row. It is tified by the presence of remnants of the damaged "2", and by pacing of "2" and "D" which is variable and different from the al.

(Typo Govt Printing Office, Wellington)

. *As T* **91**, *but smaller* (17½×20½ *mm*). *Chalk-surfaced per. P* 14×15. (*a*) *W* **43**.
91 9d. scarlet and black (5.41) .. .. 95·00 25·00
w. Wmk inverted .. .. .. † £200

(*b*) *W* **98**
91 9d. scarlet and black (29.9.41) .. 3·25 2·50
w. Wmk inverted .. .. .. £120 75·00

(4 Oct). *Health Stamps. Nos.* 626/7 *optd with T* **124**.
110 1d. + ½d. blue-green .. .. .. 30 2·00
2d. + 1d. brown-orange .. .. 30 2·00

125 Boy and Girl on Swing

126 Princess Margaret

s S. Hall. Recess Note Printing Branch, Commonwealth Bank of Australia, Melbourne)

2 (1 Oct). *Health Stamps. W* **43**. *P* 11.
125 1d. + ½d. blue-green 30 90
5 2d. + 1d. orange-red 30 90

(Des J. Berry. Recess B.W.)

3 (1 Oct). *Health Stamps. T* **126** *and similar triangular design. W* **98.** *P* 12.
6 1d. + ½d. green .. .. 20 1·10
a. Imperf between (vert pair) £7000
7 2d. + 1d. red-brown 20 20
a. Imperf between (vert pair) £9000 £9000
Design:—2d. Queen Elizabeth II as Princess.

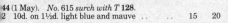

(128)

44 (1 May). *No.* 615 *surch with T* **128**.
2 10d. on 1½d. light blue and mauve 15 20

129 Queen Elizabeth II as Princess and Princess Margaret

130 Statue of Peter Pan, Kensington Gardens

(Recess B.W.)

1944 (9 Oct). *Health Stamps. W* **98.** *P* 13½.
663 **129** 1d. + ½d. green 25 40
664 2d. + 1d. blue 25 30

(Des J. Berry. Recess B.W.)

1945 (1 Oct). *Health Stamps. W* **98.** *P* 13½.
665 **130** 1d. + ½d. green and buff 15 20
w. Wmk inverted .. .. .. 50·00 35·00
666 2d. + 1d. carmine and buff 15 20
w. Wmk inverted .. .. .. 60·00 45·00

131 Lake Matheson

132 King George VI and Parliament House, Wellington

133 St. Paul's Cathedral

139 "St. George" (Wellington College War Memorial Window)

Printer's guide mark (R. 12/3)

Completed rudder (R. 2/4 of Pl 42883 and R. 3/2 of Pl 42796)

(Des J. Berry. Photo Harrison (1½d. and 1s.). Recess B.W. (1d. and 2d.) and Waterlow (others))

1946 (1 Apr). *Peace issue. T* **131/3, 139** *and similar designs. W* **98** (*sideways on* 1½*d.*). *P* 13 (1*d.*, 2*d.*), 14×14½ (1½*d.*, 1*s.*), 13½ (*others*).
667 ½d. green and brown 20 50
a. Printer's guide mark .. .. 8·00
w. Wmk inverted .. .. .. 55·00 40·00
668 1d. green 10 10
w. Wmk inverted .. .. .. 38·00 23·00
669 1½d. scarlet 10 30
w. Wmk sideways inverted 10 10
670 2d. purple 15 10
671 3d. ultramarine and grey 30 15
a. Completed rudder .. .. .. 7·00
672 4d. bronze-green and orange 20 20
w. Wmk inverted .. .. .. 90·00 42·00
673 5d. green and ultramarine 40 60
674 6d. chocolate and vermilion 15 30
675 8d. black and carmine 15 20
676 9d. blue and black 15 20
677 1s. grey-black 15 20
667/77 .. .. *Set of* 11 1·75 2·40
Designs: *Horiz* (*as T* **132**)—2d. The Royal Family. (*As T* **131**) —3d. R.N.Z.A.F. badge and airplanes; 4d. Army badge, tank and plough; 5d. Navy badge, H.M.N.Z.S. *Achilles* (cruiser) and *Dominion Monarch* (liner); 6d. N.Z. coat of arms, foundry and farm; 9d. Southern Alps and Franz Josef Glacier. *Vert* (*as T* **139**)—1s. National Memorial Campanile.

NEW INFORMATION

The editor is always interested to correspond with people who have new information that will improve or correct the Catalogue.

142 Soldier helping Child over Stile

(Des J. Berry. Recess Waterlow)

1946 (24 Oct). *Health Stamps. W* **98.** *P* 13½.
678 **142** 1d. + ½d. green and orange-brown .. 15 15
a. Yellow-green and orange-brown .. 4·50 5·00
w. Wmk inverted .. .. .. 14·00 14·00
679 2d. + 1d. chocolate and orange-brown 15 15

144 King George VI

145 Statue of Eros

Plate 1

Plate 2

(Des W. J. Cooch. Recess T **108*a***, B.W.; T **144**, D.L.R.)

1947–52. *W* **98** (*sideways on "shilling" values*). (*a*) *P* 14×13½.
680 **108*a*** 2d. orange 15 10
w. Wmk inverted .. .. .. 80·00
681 4d. bright purple 70 50
682 5d. slate 50 90
683 6d. carmine 50 10
w. Wmk inverted .. .. .. 80·00 16·00
684 8d. violet 65 50
685 9d. purple-brown .. .. .. 1·75 50
w. Wmk inverted .. .. .. 38·00 12·00

(*b*) *P* 14
686 **144** 1s. red-brown and carmine (Plate 1) 1·40 80
aw. Wmk sideways inverted .. 14·00 9·00
b. Wmk upright (Plate 1) 50 80
c. Wmk upright (Plate 2) .. .. 2·25 1·25
cw. Wmk inverted .. .. .. 60·00 23·00
687 1s. 3d. red-brown and blue (Plate 2) 1·25 1·25
aw. Wmk sideways inverted .. 9·00 6·00
b. Wmk upright (14.1.52) .. .. 2·25 4·50
bw. Wmk inverted .. .. .. † —
688 2s. brown-orange and green (Plate 1) 3·75 2·50
aw. Wmk sideways inverted .. 16·00 12·00
b. Wmk upright (Plate 1) .. .. 5·00 7·50
689 3s. red-brown and grey (Plate 2) .. 3·50 3·50
w. Wmk sideways inverted .. 30·00 16·00
680/9 .. .. *Set of* 10 12·00 9·50
In head-plate 2 the diagonal lines of the background have been strengthened and result in the upper corners and sides appearing more deeply shaded.

(Des J. Berry. Recess Waterlow)

1947 (1 Oct). *Health Stamps. W* **98** (*sideways*). *P* 13½.
690 **145** 1d. + ½d. green 15 15
w. Wmk sideways inverted .. .. 25·00 25·00
691 2d. + 1d. carmine 15 15
w. Wmk sideways inverted .. .. 38·00 38·00

146 Port Chalmers, 1848

148 First Church, Dunedin

(Des J. Berry. Recess B.W.)

1948 (23 Feb). *Centennial of Otago. T* **146, 148** *and similar designs. W* **98** (*sideways on* 3*d.*). *P* 13½.
692 1d. blue and green 20 20
w. Wmk inverted .. .. .. 50·00 50·00
693 2d. green and brown 20 20
694 3d. purple 20 40
695 6d. black and rose 20 40
w. Wmk inverted .. .. .. — £170
692/5 .. .. *Set of* 4 70 1·10
Designs: *Horiz*—2d. Cromwell, Otago; 6d. University of Otago.

150 Boy Sunbathing and Children Playing   151 Nurse and Child

(Des E. Linzell. Recess B.W.)

1948 (1 Oct). *Health Stamps. W* **98**. *P* 13½.
696 **150** 1d. + ½d. blue and green 15 15
w. Wmk inverted .. .. .. 20·00 20·00
697 2d. + 1d. purple and scarlet 15 15

1949 ROYAL VISIT ISSUE. Four stamps were prepared to commemorate this event: 2d. Treaty House, Waitangi; 3d. H.M.S. *Vanguard*; 5d. Royal portraits; 6d. Crown and sceptre. The visit did not take place and the stamps were destroyed, although a few examples of the 3d. later appeared on the market. A similar set was prepared in 1952, but was, likewise, not issued.

(Des J. Berry. Photo Harrison)

1949 (3 Oct). *Health Stamps. W* **98**. *P* 14 × 14½.
698 **151** 1d. + ½d. green 20 20
699 2d. + 1d. ultramarine 20 20
a. No stop below "D" of "1D." (R.1/2) 6·50 16·00

1½d.

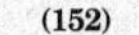

(152)

153 Queen Elizabeth II and Prince Charles

1950 (28 July). *As Type* F **6**, *but without value, surch with T* **152**. *W* **98** *(inverted). Chalk-surfaced paper. P* 14.
700 **F 6** 1½d. carmine 30 30
w. Wmk upright .. .. .. 2·50 3·25

(Des J. Berry and R. S. Phillips. Photo Harrison)

1950 (2 Oct). *Health Stamps. W* **98**. *P* 14×14½.
701 **153** 1d. +½d. green 15 15
w. Wmk inverted .. .. .. 4·75 4·75
702 2d. +1d. plum 15 15
w. Wmk inverted .. .. .. 16·00 16·00

154 Christchurch Cathedral   155 Cairn on Lyttleton Hills

(Des L. C. Mitchell (2d.), J. A. Johnstone (3d.) and J. Berry (others). Recess B.W.)

1950 (20 Nov). *Centennial of Canterbury, N.Z. T* **154/5** *and similar designs. W* **98** *(sideways on 1d. and 3d.). P* 13½.
703 1d. green and blue 25 40
704 2d. carmine and orange 25 40
705 3d. dark blue and blue 25 60
706 6d. brown and blue 30 60
707 1s. reddish purple and blue 30 80
703/7 .. .. *Set of* 5 1·25 2·50
Designs: *Vert (as T* **154**)—3d. John Robert Godley. *Horiz (as T* **155**)—6d. Canterbury University College; 1s. Aerial view of Timaru.

159 "Takapuna" class Yachts

(Des J. Berry and R. S. Phillips. Recess B.W.)

1951 (1 Nov). *Health Stamps. W* **98**. *P* 13½.
708 **159** 1½d. + ½d. scarlet and yellow .. 15 70
709 2d. + 1d. deep green and yellow .. 15 10
w. Wmk inverted .. .. .. 45·00 45·00

STAMP BOOKLETS

Nos. SB1 to SB19 are stapled.
Nos. SB1/5 were sold at ½d. above the face value of the stamps to cover the cost of manufacture.

1901 (1 Apr). *White card covers with postage rates.*
SB1 1s. ½d. booklet containing twelve 1d. (No. 278) in blocks of 6 .. .. £2250
SB2 2s. 6½d. booklet containing thirty 1d. (No. 278) in blocks of 6 .. .. £2750
Original printings of Nos. SB1/2 showed the face value on the cover in small figures. Subsequent printings show large figures of value on the covers and the prices quoted are for this type.

1902 (21 Aug)–**05.** *White card covers with postage rates.*
SB3 1s. ½d. booklet containing twelve 1d. in panes of 6 (Nos. 303b or 303cb) £1800
SB4 2s. ½d. booklet containing twenty-four 1d. in panes of 6 (Nos. 303b or 303cb) (21.3.05) .. £2000
SB5 2s. 6½d. booklet containing thirty 1d. in panes of 6 (Nos. 303b or 303cb) £2750

1910 (Apr). *White card cover with postage rates.*
SB6 2s. booklet containing eleven ½d. in pane of 5 with 1 label (Nos. 387b or 387c) and pane of 6 (No. 387d), and eighteen 1d. in three panes of 6 (No. 405b) £3750

1912 (May). *White card cover.*
SB7 2s. booklet containing twelve ½d. and eighteen 1d. in panes of 6 with bars on the selvedge (Nos. 387e, 405c) £2750

1915 (Feb). *Red card cover.*
SB8 2s. booklet containing twelve ½d. and eighteen 1d. in panes of 6 with bars on the selvedge (Nos. 435a or 435ba, 405c) £1300
a. Grey cover .. ..
b. Blue cover .. ..
c. Yellow-buff cover .. ..
d. Purple-buff cover .. ..

1924 (1 Dec)–**25.** *Cover inscription within frame.*
SB9 2s. booklet containing twelve ½d. and eighteen 1d. in panes of 6 with bars on the selvedge (Nos. 441a, 406b) (lilac cover) £1400
a. Grey cover .. ..
SB10 2s. booklet containing twelve ½d. and eighteen 1d. in panes of 6 with bars and advertisements on the selvedge (Nos. 446a, 410b) (yellow-buff cover) (1925) £1500
a. Grey-green cover £1500
b. Grey-buff cover .. ..
c. Grey-pink cover £1800

1928–34.
SB11 2s. booklet containing twelve ½d. (*p* 14×15) and eighteen 1d. in panes of 6 with bars on the selvedge (Nos. 446ab, 468b) £2000
a. As No. SB11, but ½d. (*p* 14) (Nos. 446ca, 468b) £1300
b. As No. SB11 but panes with bars and advertisements on the selvedge (Nos. 446cb, 468c) £1300
SB12 2s. booklet containing twenty-four 1d (*p* 14) in panes of 6 with bars and advertisements on the selvedge (No. 468c) (1930) £1300
a. As No. SB12, but 1d. (*p* 14×15) (No. 468ea) (1934) £1200

1935.
SB15 2s. booklet containing twenty-four 1d. in panes of 6 with advertisements on the selvedge (No. 557ca) £375

1936.
SB16 2s. booklet containing twenty-four 1d. (No. 578) in blocks of 6 .. .. £250

B 1

1938 (1 July). *Cream cover as Type* B **1**.
SB17 2s. booklet containing twenty-four 1d. (No. 605) in blocks of 6 .. .. £325

1938 (Nov). *Cream (No. SB18) or blue (No. SB19) covers as Type* B **1**.
SB18 2s. booklet containing twelve ½d. and eighteen 1d. (Nos. 603, 605) in blocks of 6 .. .. £425
SB19 2s. 3d. booklet containing eighteen 1½d. (No. 607) in blocks of 6 .. .. £375

EXPRESS DELIVERY STAMPS

E 1

(Typo Govt Printing Office, Wellington)

1903 (9 Feb). *Value in first colour. W* **43** *(sideways). P* 1
E1 E 1 6d. red and violet .. .. .. 35·00

1926–36. *Thick, white, opaque chalk-surfaced "Cowan" p W* **43**.
(a) P 14×14½
E2 E 1 6d. vermilion and bright violet .. 42·00
w. Wmk inverted £130
(b) P 14×15 (1936)
E3 E 1 6d. carmine and bright violet .. 55·00

1937–39. *Thin, hard, chalk-surfaced "Wiggins Teape" paper*
(a) P 14 × 14½
E4 E 1 6d. carmine and bright violet .. .. 85·00
(b) P 14 × 15 (1939)
E5 E 1 6d. vermilion and bright violet .. £150

E 2 Express Mail Delivery Van

(Des J. Berry. Eng Stamp Ptg Office, Melbourne Recess Govt Office, Wellington)

1939 (16 Aug). *W* **43**. *P* 14.
E6 E 2 6d. violet .. .. 1·50
w. Wmk inverted .. .. .. 75·00

POSTAGE DUE STAMPS

D 1   (I)   (II)

3D.   **5D.**

(a) Large "D"   *(b)* Small "D"

(Typo Govt Printing Office, Wellington)

1899 (1 Dec). *W* **12***b*. *Coarse paper. P* 11.

I. Type I. *Circle of* 14 *ornaments,* 17 *dots over* "N.Z.", "N.Z. *large. (a) Large* "D"
D1 D 1 ½d. carmine and green .. .. 14·00 25
a. No stop after "D" (Right pane R. 2/3) .. .. 85·00 £1
D2 8d. carmine and green .. .. 60·00 75
a. Carmine "8D." printed double ..
D3 1s. carmine and green .. .. 65·00 85
D4 2s. carmine and green £120 £1
D1/4 .. .. *Set of* 4 £225 £2
To avoid further subdivision the 1s. and 2s. are placed with *pence* values, although the two types of "D" do not apply to higher values.

(b) Small "D"
D6 D 1 5d. carmine and green .. .. .. 22·00 22
D7 6d. carmine and green .. .. .. 29·00 25
D8 10d. carmine and green .. .. .. 70·00 85
D6/8 .. .. *Set of* 3 £110 £1

II. Type II. *Circle of* 13 *ornaments,* 15 *dots over* "N.Z.", "N.Z." *sm*
(a) Large "D"
D 9 D 1 ½d. vermilion and green .. .. 3·00 16
a. No stop after "D" (Right pane R. 2/3) .. .. 55·00 95
D10 1d. vermilion and green .. .. 11·00 1
D11 2d. vermilion and green .. .. 48·00 9
D12 3d. vermilion and green .. .. 13·00 3
D9/12 .. .. *Set of* 4 65·00 26

(b) Small "D"
D14 D 1 1d. vermilion and green .. .. 15·00 1
D15 2d. vermilion and green .. .. 45·00 5·
D16 4d. vermilion and green .. .. 32·00 9·
D14/16 .. .. *Set of* 3 80·00 14·
Nos. D9/16 were printed from a common frame plate of 240 panes of 60) used in conjunction with centre plates of 120 panes of 60) for the ½d. and 4d. or 240 for the other valu Sheets of the 1d. and 2d. each contained two panes with lar "D" and two panes with small "D".

D 2   D 3

(Des W. R. Bock. Typo Govt Printing Office)

28 Feb). *No wmk. P* 11.
D 2 ½d. red and deep green .. .. 1·75 6·00

08. *"Cowan" unsurfaced paper. W* **43** *(sideways). (a) P* 11.
D 2 ½d. red and green (4.04) .. .. 1·75 1·50
a. Imperf between (horiz pair) .. £600
1d. red and green (5.12.05) .. .. 8·50 3·50
2d. red and green (5.4.06) .. .. 90·00 £100
0 .. .. *Set of* 3 90·00 £100

(b) P 14
D 2 1d. carmine and green (12.06) .. 14·00 1·50
a. Rose-pink and green (9.07) .. 13·00 1·50
. 2d. carmine and green (10.06) .. 9·00 5·50
a. Rose-pink and green (6.08) .. 5·50 1·50

(Jan)–**20**. *"De La Rue" chalky paper. Toned gum. W* **43**.
4 × 15.
D 2 ½d. carmine and green (6.19) .. 3·25 3·75
1d. carmine and green .. .. 7·00 50
w. Wmk inverted .. .. † —
2d. carmine and green (8.20) .. 11·00 2·50
.. .. *Set of* 3 19·00 6·00

(May). *"Jones" chalky paper. White gum. W* **43**. *P* 14 × 15.
D 2 ½d. carmine and green .. .. 35·00 42·00

(July). *No wmk, but bluish "N Z" and Star lithographed on k. P* 14 × 15.
D 2 ½d. carmine and green .. .. 2·00 23·00
2d. carmine and green .. .. 3·50 20·00

(Nov)–**35**. *"Cowan" thick, opaque chalky paper. W* **43**.

(a) P 14 × 15
D 2 ½d. carmine and green (12.26) .. 1·75 8·00
1d. carmine and green .. .. 3·75 80
2d. carmine and green (6.26).. .. 19·00 4·25
3d. carmine and green (6.35).. .. 48·00 55·00
32 .. .. *Set of* 4 65·00 60·00

(b) P 14
D 2 ½d. carmine and green (10.28).. .. 45·00 30·00
1d. rose and pale yellow-green (6.28) .. 4·00 1·25
2d. carmine and green (10.29).. .. 7·00 3·00
3d. carmine and green (5.28) .. .. 15·00 42·00
6.. .. .. .. *Set of* 4 65·00 70·00

–**38**. *"Wiggins Teape" thin, hard chalky paper. W* **43**.
14 × 15.
D 2 ½d. carmine and yellow-green (2.38).. 21·00 32·00
1d. carmine and yellow-green (1.37).. 11·00 3·75
2d. carmine and yellow-green (6.37).. 35·00 13·00
3d. carmine and yellow-green (11.37) 90·00 65·00
40 .. .. *Set of* 4 £140 £100

(Des J. Berry. Typo Govt Printing Office, Wellington)

–**49**. *P* 15×14. *(a) W* **43** *(sideways inverted)* (16.8.39).
D 3 ½d. turquoise-green .. .. 5·00 5·00
1d. carmine .. .. 2·75 50
w. Wmk sideways .. .. £150 1·50
2d. bright blue .. .. 6·00 2·75
3d. orange-brown .. .. 23·00 25·00
w. Wmk sideways
/4 .. .. *Set of* 4 32·00 30·00

) *W* **98** *(sideways (1d.), sideways inverted (2d.) or upright (3d.)*
D 3 1d. carmine (4.49) .. .. 16·00 5·50*
2d. bright blue (12.46) .. 8·00 1·40
w. Wmk sideways (4.49) .. 2·75 8·50
3d. orange-brown (1943) .. 45·00 32·00
a. Wmk sideways inverted (6.45) 18·00 5·00
aw. Wmk sideways (28.11.49) .. 9·00 9·00
5/7 .. .. *Set of* 3 25·00 10·00*

The use of Postage Due stamps ceased on 30 September 1, our used price for No. D45 being for stamps postmarked er this date (*price for examples clearly cancelled* 1949–51,).

OFFICIAL STAMPS

1 (Dec)–**1906**. *Contemporary issues handstamped* "O.P. S.O." *diagonally. (a) Stamps of* 1873 *type. W* **12***b*. *P* 12½.
1 **3** ½d. rose (V.) .. .. — £475

(b) Stamps of 1882–97 *optd in rose or magenta. W* **12***b*.
2 **13** ½d. black (*p* 10).. .. .. — £200
a. Violet opt .. .. .. — £250
3 ½d. black (*p* 10 × 11) .. .. — £200
4 **14** 1d. rose (*p* 12 × 11½) .. .. — £200
5 1d. rose (*p* 11) .. .. — £200
6 **15** 2d. purple (*p* 11) .. .. — £350
7 2d. mauve-lilac (*p* 10) .. .. — £350
a. Violet opt
8 **16** 2½d. blue (*p* 11) .. .. — £250
9 2½d. ultramarine (*p* 10) .. .. — £250
10 2½d. ultramarine (*p* 10 × 11) .. — £250
11 **19** 5d. olive-black (*p* 12 × 11½) .. — £400
12 **20** 6d. brown (*p* 12 × 11½) .. .. — £550

(c) Stamps of 1898–1903 *optd in violet. P* 11. (i) *No wmk*
13 **23** ½d. green (*p* 14) (No. 294) .. — £200
14 **26** 2½d. blue (*p* 12–16) (No. 249*a*).. .. — £425
15 **27** 2½d. blue (No. 260) .. .. — £350
16 **37** 4d. indigo and brown (No. 262) .. — £400
17 **30** 5d. purple-brown (No. 263) .. .. — £425
a. Green opt .. .. .. — £400
18 **32** 8d. indigo (No. 266) .. .. — £500

(ii) *W* **38**
19 **42** 1d. carmine (No. 278).. .. .. — £200

(iii) *W* **43** *(sideways on* 3d., 1s.)
20 **42** 1d. carmine (*p* 14) (No. 303) .. — £200
a. Green opt .. .. .. — £200
21 **27** 2½d. blue (No. 308) .. .. — £300
22 **28** 3d. yellow-brown (No. 309) .. .. — £425
23 **34** 1s. orange-red (No. 315*b*) .. .. — £850
24 **35** 2s. green (No. 316) .. .. — £1300

The letters signify "On Public Service Only", and stamps so overprinted were used by the Post Office Department at Wellington on official correspondence to foreign countries.

Unused examples with the "O.P.S.O." handstamp are generally considered to be reprints.

OFFICIAL.

(O 3)

1907. *Stamps of* 1902–6 *optd with Type* O 3 *(vertically upwards). W* **43** *(sideways on* 3d., 6d., 1s. *and* 5s.). *P* 14.
O59 **23** ½d. yellow-green .. .. .. 8·50 60
a. Perf 11×14 .. .. .. £110
b. Mixed perfs £110
O60 **42** 1d. carmine (No. 303) (1.7.07*) .. 7·00 10·00
a. Booklet pane of 6 .. .. 42·00
ab. Imperf horiz (booklet pane of 6) £1400
O60*b* 1d. rose-carmine (Waterlow) (No. 352) 9·00 50
ba. Perf 11×14 .. .. .. — £250
bb. Mixed perfs .. .. .. — £250
O60*c* 1d. carmine (Royle) .. .. 17·00 50
ca. Perf 11×14 .. .. .. £225
cb. Mixed perfs £225
O61 **41** 2d. purple .. .. .. 9·00 1·75
a. Bright reddish purple .. .. 8·50 1·60
ab. Mixed perfs £190 £200
O63 **28** 3d. bistre-brown .. .. .. 42·00 1·75
O64 **31** 6d. bright carmine-pink .. .. £130 18·00
a. Imperf vert (horiz pair) £800
b. Mixed perfs £500 £450
O65 **34** 1s. orange-red .. .. .. 85·00 15·00
O66 **35** 2s. blue-green .. .. .. 70·00 55·00
a. Imperf between (pair) £1500
b. Imperf vert (horiz pair) £1200
w. Wmk inverted £250
O67 **36** 5s. deep red £150 £170
a. Wmk upright £700 £750

*Though issued in 1907, a large quantity of booklets was mislaid and not utilized until they were found in 1930.

1908–09. *Optd as Type* O 3. *W* **43**.
O69 **23** ½d. green (*p* 14 × 15) .. .. 7·50 2·25
O70 **50** 1d. carmine (*p* 14 × 15) .. .. 65·00 2·50
O71 **48** 6d. pink (*p* 14 × 13, 13½) .. .. £140 45·00
O72 6d. pink (*p* 14 × 15) (1909) .. .. £110 35·00
O72*a* F 4 £1 rose-pink (*p* 14) (No. F89) £500 £400

1910. *No.* 387 *optd with Type* O 3.
O73 **51** ½d. yellow-green .. .. .. 4·25 30
a. Opt inverted (reading downwards) † £1400

1910–16. *Nos.* 389 *and* 392/4 *optd with Type* O 3. *P* 14×14½.
O74 **52** 3d. chestnut .. .. .. 14·00 80
a. Perf 14×13½ (1915) .. .. 60·00 70·00
ab. Vert pair. Nos. O74/a £300 £350
O75 – 6d. carmine .. .. .. 19·00 5·00
a. Perf 14 (line) (No. 398) .. .. † —
b. Deep carmine .. .. .. 25·00 5·50
w. Wmk inverted
O76 – 8d. indigo-blue (R.) (5.16) .. .. 12·00 18·00
aw. Wmk inverted .. .. .. 30·00 30·00
b. Perf 14×13½ .. .. .. 12·00 18·00
bw. Wmk inverted .. .. .. 30·00 30·00
c. Vert pair, Nos. O76 and O76b .. 45·00 70·00
cw. Wmk inverted .. .. .. 85·00 £120
O77 – 1s. vermilion .. .. .. 48·00 15·00
O74/7 .. .. *Set of* 4 85·00 35·00

1910–26. *Optd with Type* O 3. *(a) W* **43**. *De La Rue chalk-surfaced paper with toned gum.*
O78 **53** 1d. carmine (No. 405) .. .. .. 3·25 10
y. Wmk inverted and reversed

(b) W **43**. *Jones chalk-surfaced paper with white gum*
O79 **53** 1d. deep carmine (No. 406) (1925) .. 10·00 6·50

(c) No wmk, but bluish "NZ" and Star lithographed on back. Art paper
O80 **53** 1d. rose-carmine (No. 409) (1925) .. 6·00 16·00

(d) W **43**. *Cowan thick, opaque, chalk-surfaced paper with white gum*
O81 **53** 1d. deep carmine (No. 410) (1925) .. 8·00 1·25
x. Wmk reversed (1926) .. .. 25·00 20·00

1913–25. *Postal Fiscal stamps optd with Type* O 3.

(i) *Chalk-surfaced De La Rue paper. (a) P* 14 (1913–14)
O82 F 4 2s. blue (30.9.14) .. .. .. 48·00 42·00
O83 5s. yellow-green (13.6.13) .. .. 75·00 90·00
O84 £1 rose-carmine (1913) £550 £550
O82/4.. .. .. .. *Set of* 3 £600 £600

(b) P 14½ × 14, *comb* (1915)
O85 F 4 2s. deep blue (Aug) .. .. 55·00 42·00
a. No stop after "OFFICIAL" .. £120 £100
O86 5s. yellow-green (Jan).. .. .. 65·00 80·00
a. No stop after "OFFICIAL" .. £200 £250

(ii) *Thick, white, opaque chalk-surfaced Cowan paper. P* 14½ × 14 (1925)
O87 F 4 2s. blue .. .. .. 80·00 75·00
a. No stop after "OFFICIAL" .. £180 £180

The overprint on these last, and on Nos. O69 and O72*a*, is from a new set of type, giving a rather sharper impression than Type O 3, but otherwise resembling it closely.

1915 (12 Oct)–**34**. *Optd with Type* O 3. *P* 14 × 15. *(a) On Nos.* 435/40 *(De La Rue chalk-surfaced paper with toned gum).*
O88 **61** ½d. green .. .. .. 1·25 20
O89 **62** 1½d. grey-black (6.16) .. .. 7·00 2·50
O90 **61** 1½d. slate (12.16) .. .. .. 5·00 90
O91 1½d. orange-brown (4.19) .. .. 5·00 30
O92 2d. yellow (4.17) .. .. .. 5·00 20
O93 3d. chocolate (11.19) .. .. .. 11·00 90
O88/93 .. .. .. *Set of* 6 30·00 4·50

(b) On Nos. 441 *and* 443 *(Jones chalk-surfaced paper with white gum)*
O94 **61** ½d. green (1924) .. .. .. 4·50 3·50
O95 3d. deep chocolate (1924) .. .. 38·00 9·50

(c) On Nos. 446/7 *and* 448*a*/9 *(Cowan thick, opaque, chalk-surfaced paper with white gum)*
O96 **61** ½d. green (1925) .. .. .. 1·25 10
ax. Wmk reversed (1927) .. .. 8·50 11·00
ay. Wmk inverted and reversed (1927) .. .. .. 32·00 22·00
b. Perf 14 (1929) .. .. .. 3·50 35
ba. No stop after "OFFICIAL" .. 23·00 32·00
O97 1½d. orange-brown (*p* 14) (1929) .. 9·50 11·00
a. No stop after "OFFICIAL" .. 48·00 60·00
b. Perf 14×15 (1934) .. .. 22·00 28·00
O98 2d. yellow (*p* 14) (1931) .. .. 2·00 50
a. No stop after "OFFICIAL" .. 35·00 38·00
O99 3d. chocolate (1925) .. .. .. 4·25 50
a. No stop after "OFFICIAL" .. 65·00 45·00
b. Perf 14 (1930) .. .. .. 35·00 1·75
ba. No stop after "OFFICIAL" .. £120 50·00
O96/9 .. .. *Set of* 4 15·00 11·00

1915 (Dec)–**27**. *Optd with Type* O 3. *P* 14×13½. *(a) Nos.* 420, 422, 425, 428 *and* 429/30 *(Cowan unsurfaced paper).*
O100 **60** 3d. chocolate .. .. .. 4·50 1·50
aw. Wmk inverted .. .. .. 15·00 4·50
b. Perf 14×14½ .. .. .. 4·50 1·50
bw. Wmk inverted .. .. .. 15·00 4·50
c. Vert pair, Nos. O100 and O100b 35·00 85·00
cw. Wmk inverted .. .. .. 75·00 £110
O101 4d. bright violet (4.25) .. .. 14·00 3·50
a. Re-entry (Pl 20 R. 1/6) .. .. 45·00 22·00
b. Re-entry (Pl 20 R. 4/10) .. .. 50·00 30·00
c. Perf 14×14½ (4.27) .. .. 27·00 1·00
O102 6d. carmine (6.16) .. .. .. 5·00 75
aw. Wmk inverted .. .. .. 90·00
b. Perf 14×14½ .. .. .. 6·00 1·00
c. Vert pair, Nos. O102 and O102b 55·00 £120
O103 8d. red-brown (8.22) .. .. .. 65·00 £150
O104 9d. sage-green (4.25) .. .. .. 40·00 38·00
O105 1s. vermilion (9.16) .. .. .. 18·00 13·00
aw. Wmk inverted £180 £120
b. Perf 14×14½ .. .. .. 7·00 2·00
ba. Pale orange-red .. .. .. 20·00 20·00
bw. Wmk inverted £180 £180
c. Vert pair. Nos. O105 and O105b 65·00 £150
cw. Wmk inverted £450
O100/5 .. .. *Set of* 6 £120 £170

(b) No. 433 *(Thin paper with widely spaced sideways wmk)*
O106 **60** 3d. chocolate (*p* 14) (7.16) .. .. 3·00 12·00
a. No wmk .. .. .. 35·00 55·00

1927–33. *Optd with Type* O 3. *W* **43**. *P* 14.
O111 **71** 1d. rose-carmine (No. 468) .. .. 2·00 20
a. No stop after "OFFICIAL" .. 22·00 26·00
bw. Wmk inverted .. .. .. † 27·00
c. Perf 14×15 .. .. .. 2·00 20
O112 **72** 2s. light blue (No. 469) (2.28) .. 70·00 £100
O113 F 6 5s. green (1933) £250 £300
O111/13 .. .. *Set of* 3 £300 £350

Official (O 4) *Official* (O 5)

1936–61. *Pictorial issue optd horiz or vert* (2s.) *with Type* O 4.

(a) W **43** *(Single "N Z" and Star)*
O115 **82** 1d. scarlet (Die I) (*p* 14×13½) .. 3·00 1·25
a. Perf 13½×14 .. .. .. 75·00 65·00
O116 **83** 1½d. red-brown (*p* 13½×14) .. .. 23·00 25·00
a. Perf 14×13½ £5500
O118 **92** 1s. deep green (*p* 14×13½) .. .. 28·00 45·00
w. Wmk inverted .. .. .. † 80·00
O119 F 6 5s. green (*p* 14) (12.38) .. .. £130 42·00
O115/19 .. .. *Set of* 4 £160 £100

The watermark of No. O119 is almost invisible.

Only four examples of No. O116a exist. The error occurred when a sheet of No. 558a was found to have a block of four missing. This was replaced by a block of No. 558 and the sheet was then sent for overprinting.

(b) W **98** *(Mult "N Z" and Star)*
O120 **81** ½d. bright green, *p* 14×13½ (7.37) 7·50 4·50
O121 **82** 1d. scar (Die II), *p* 14×13½ (11.36) 4·50 50
w. Wmk inverted .. .. .. 9·00 6·00
O122 **83** 1½d. red-brown, *p* 14×13½ (7.36) .. 18·00 4·75
O123 **84** 2d. orange, *p* 14×13½ (1.38) .. 3·00 10
aw. Wmk inverted .. .. .. — £110
b. Perf 12½ (1942) .. .. .. £190 55·00
c. Perf 14 (1942) .. .. .. 50·00 15·00
O124 **85** 2½d. chocolate & slate, *p* 13–14×13½ (26.7.38) .. .. .. 55·00 80·00
a. Perf 14 (1938) .. .. .. 14·00 21·00
O125 **86** 3d. brown, *p* 14×13½ (1.3.38) .. 48·00 3·50
w. Wmk inverted .. .. .. — 28·00
O126 **87** 4d. black and sepia, *p* 14×13½ (8.36) 8·50 1·10
a. Perf 14 (8.41) .. .. .. 8·50 4·50
b. Perf 12½ (1941) .. .. .. 6·00 5·50
c. Perf 14×14½ (10.42) .. .. 3·75 85
cw. Wmk inverted .. .. .. — 45·00
O127 **89** 6d. scarlet, *p* 13½×14 (12.37) .. 16·00 80
aw. Wmk inverted .. .. .. † —
b. Perf 12½ (1941) .. .. .. 15·00 5·50
c. Perf 14½×14 (7.42) .. .. 9·50 30
O128 **90** 8d. chocolate, *p* 12½ (*wmk sideways*) (1942) .. .. .. 15·00 17·00
a. Perf 14×14½ (*wmk sideways*) (1945) .. .. .. 8·50 16·00
b. Perf 14×13½ .. .. .. † £1600
O129 **91** 9d. red & grey-black (G.) (No. 587*a*), *p* 13½×14 (1.3.38) .. .. 60·00 38·00
O130 9d. scar & blk (*chalk-surfaced paper*) (Blk.) (No. 631), *p* 14×15 (1943) 20·00 22·00
O131 **92** 1s. deep green, *p* 14×13½ (2.37) 48·00 1·50
aw. Wmk inverted .. .. .. — 90·00
b. Perf 12½ (1942) .. .. .. 23·00 1·50
O132 **93** 2s. olive-green, *p* 13–14×13½ (5.37) 80·00 30·00
a. "CAPTAIN COQK" .. .. .. 95·00
b. Perf 13½×14 (1939) .. .. £170 6·50
ba. "CAPTAIN COQK" £180
c. Perf 12½ (1942) .. .. .. 90·00 27·00
ca. "CAPTAIN COQK" £110
d. Perf 14×13½ (1944) .. .. 42·00 7·00
da. "CAPTAIN COQK" £250

O133 F 6 5s. green (*chalk-surfaced paper*), *p* 14 (3.43) .. .. .. 40·00 6·00
aw. Wmk inverted .. .. 40·00 6·00
b. Perf 14×13½. *Yellow-green (ordinary paper)* (10.61) .. 17·00 32·00
O120/33 .. .. *Set of* 14 £250 £110

The opt on No. O127a was sometimes applied at the top of the stamp, instead of always at the bottom, as on No. O127.

All examples of No. O128b were used by a government office in Whangerei.

The 5s. value on ordinary paper perforated 14×13½ does not exist without the "Official" overprint.

See notes on perforations after No. 590b.

1938–51. *Nos.* 603 *etc., optd with Type* O 4.
O134 **108** ½d. green (1.3.38) .. .. .. 18·00 2·25
O135 ½d. brown-orange (1946) .. .. 1·60 3·50
O136 1d. scarlet (1.7.38) .. .. .. 18·00 15
O137 1d. green (10.7.41) .. .. .. 2·50 10
O138 **108a** 1½d. purple-brown (26.7.38) .. .. 75·00 18·00
O139 1½d. scarlet (2.4.51) .. .. .. 9·00 5·50
O140 3d. blue (16.10.41) .. .. .. 2·50 10
O134/40 .. .. *Set of* 7 £110 26·00

1940 (2 Jan–8 Mar). *Centennial. Nos.* 613, *etc., optd with Type* O **5**.
O141 ½d. blue-green (R.) .. .. .. 2·00 35
a. "ff" joined, as Type O 4 .. .. 50·00 60·00
O142 1d. chocolate and scarlet .. .. 4·25 10
a. "ff" joined, as Type O 4 .. .. 50·00 60·00
O143 1½d. light blue and mauve .. .. 3·00 2·00
O144 2d. blue-green and chocolate .. .. 4·00 10
a. "ff" joined, as Type O 4 .. .. 60·00 60·00
O145 2½d. blue-green and ultramarine .. 4·25 2·75
a. "ff" joined, as Type O 4 .. .. 50·00 65·00
O146 3d. purple and carmine (R.) .. .. 8·00 1·00
a. "ff" joined, as Type O 4 .. .. 42·00 48·00
O147 4d. chocolate and lake .. .. 40·00 2·00
a. "ff" joined, as Type O 4 .. .. £120 80·00
O148 6d. emerald-green and violet .. .. 25·00 2·00
a. "ff" joined, as Type O 4 .. .. 70·00 70·00
O149 8d. black and red (8.3) .. .. 30·00 17·00
a. "ff" joined, as Type O 4 .. .. 70·00 £100
O150 9d. olive-green and vermilion .. .. 11·00 7·00
O151 1s. sage-green and deep green .. .. 48·00 4·00
O141/51 .. .. *Set of* 11 £160 35·00

For this issue the Type O 4 overprint occurs on R.4/3 of the 2½d. and on R.1/10 of the other values.

1947–49. *Nos.* 680, *etc., optd with Type* O 4.
O152 **108a** 2d. orange .. .. 1·75 10
O153 4d. bright purple .. .. .. 4·25 2·50
O154 6d. carmine .. .. 12·00 50
O155 8d. violet .. .. 8·00 6·50
O156 9d. purple-brown .. .. .. 9·00 6·50
O157 **144** 1s. red-brown and carmine (*wmk upright*) (Plate 1) .. .. 17·00 1·25
a. Wmk sideways (Plate 1) (1949) 8·50 9·00
aw. Wmk sideways inverted .. 35·00 15·00
b. Wmk upright (Plate 2) .. 24·00 7·00
bw. Wmk inverted .. .. .. 65·00 28·00
O158 2s. brown-orange and green (*wmk sideways*) (Plate 1) .. .. 25·00 16·00
a. Wmk upright (Plate 1) .. .. 32·00 45·00
O152/8 .. .. *Set of* 7 60·00 30·00

STAMP BOOKLET

1907 (1 July). *White card cover.*
OB1 10s. booklet containing one hundred and twenty 1d. in panes of 6 (No. O60a) £1000

PROVISIONALS ISSUED AT REEFTON AND USED BY THE POLICE DEPARTMENT

1907 (Jan). *Current stamps of* 1906, *optd* "Official", *in red manuscript, and handstamped with a circular* "Greymouth—PAID—3". *P* 14.
P1 **23** ½d. green £1000 £1200
P2 **40** 1d. carmine £1100 £1100
P3 **38a** 2d. purple £1300 £1500
P4 **28** 3d. bistre £1600
P5 **31** 6d. pink £1600
P6 **34** 1s. orange-red £2000
P7 **35** 2s. green £6000

Only the ½d., 1d. and 2d. are known postally used, cancelled with the Reefton squared circle postmark. The 3d. and 6d. were later cancelled by favour at Wanganui.

LIFE INSURANCE DEPARTMENT

L 1 Lighthouse L 2

(Des W. B. Hudson and J. F. Rogers; eng A. E. Cousins. Typo Govt Printing Office, Wellington)

1891 (2 Jan)–**98.** A. *W* **12c**. *P* 12×11½.
L 1 L 1 ½d. bright purple .. .. .. 60·00 6·00
a. Mixed perf 12×11 and 12½ .. † —
x. Wmk reversed .. .. .. † —
L 2 1d. blue .. .. 55·00 4·00
ax. Wmk reversed .. .. ..
ay. Wmk inverted and reversed .. † 35·00
b. Wmk **12b** .. .. .. 90·00 20·00
bx. Wmk reversed .. .. .. † —
L 3 2d. brown-red .. .. .. 85·00 7·00
ax. Wmk reversed .. .. .. † 85·00
b. Wmk **12b** .. .. .. 95·00 13·00
L 4 3d. deep brown .. .. .. £160 20·00
L 5 6d. green .. .. £275 60·00
L 6 1s. rose £500 £120
L1/6 .. .. *Set of* 6 £1000 £200

B. *W* **12b** (1893–98). (*a*) *P* 10 (1893)
L 7 L 1 ½d. bright purple .. .. .. 60·00 8·50
L 8 1d. blue .. .. 55·00 1·25
L 9 2d. brown-red .. .. .. 80·00 3·75
L7/9 .. .. *Set of* 3 £170 12·00

(*b*) *P* 11×10
L10 L 1 ½d. bright purple (1896) .. .. 90·00 26·00
a. Perf 10×11 .. .. .. £150 65·00
L11 1d. blue (1897) .. .. .. † —
a. Perf 10×11 .. .. .. 60·00 12·00

(*c*) *Mixed perfs* 10 *and* 11 (1897)
L12 L 1 2d. brown-red £650 £650

(*d*) *P* 11 (1897–98)
L13 L 1 ½d. bright purple .. .. .. 55·00 3·25
a. Thin coarse toned paper (1898) 80·00 5·50
L14 1d. blue .. .. 55·00 75
a. Thin coarse toned paper (1898) 75·00 2·00
x. Wmk reversed .. .. .. £120 13·00
y. Wmk inverted and reversed .. £120 24·00
L15 2d. brown-red .. .. .. 75·00 3·50
a. *Chocolate* .. .. .. £110 24·00
b. Thin coarse toned paper (1898) £130 3·50
L13/15 .. .. *Set of* 3 £170 6·50

1902–04. *W* **43** (*sideways*). (*a*) *P* 11.
L16 L 1 ½d. bright purple (1903) .. .. 55·00 5·50
L17 1d. blue (1902) .. .. .. 55·00 1·00
L18 2d. brown-red (1904) .. .. 90·00 8·00
L16/18 .. .. *Set of* 3 £180 13·00

(*b*) *P* 14×11
L19 L 1 ½d. bright purple (1903) £1400
L20 1d. blue (1904) .. .. .. 95·00 11·00

Nos. L16/17 and L20 are known without watermark from the margins of the sheet.

1905–6. *Redrawn, with* "V.R." *omitted. W* **43** (*sideways*). (*a*) *P* 11.
L21 L 2 2d. brown-red (12.05) .. .. £1000 80·00

(*b*) *P* 14
L22 L 2 1d. blue (7.06) .. .. .. £160 30·00

(*c*) *P* 14×11
L23 L 2 1d. blue (7.06) £475 £150
a. Mixed perfs .. .. .. † £400

Between January 1907 and the end of 1912 the Life Insurance Department used ordinary Official stamps.

1913 (2 Jan)–**37.** *New values and colours. W* **43**.
(*a*) *"De La Rue" paper. P* 14×15
L24 L 2 ½d. green .. .. 12·00 1·50
a. Yellow-green .. .. .. 12·00 1·50
L25 1d. carmine .. .. 8·00 1·00
a. Carmine-pink .. .. .. 15·00 1·40
L26 1½d. black (1917) .. .. .. 40·00 7·00
L27 1½d. chestnut-brown (1919) .. .. 1·50 2·25
L28 2d. bright purple .. .. .. 48·00 26·00
w. Wmk inverted .. .. .. † 80·00
L29 2d. yellow (1920) .. .. .. 5·50 2·00
L30 3d. yellow-brown .. .. .. 45·00 26·00
L31 6d. carmine-pink .. .. .. 35·00 23·00
L24/31 .. .. *Set of* 8 £170 75·00

(*b*) *"Cowan" paper.* (i) *P* 14×15
L31*a* L 2 ½d. yellow-green (1925) .. .. 30·00 4·50
L31*b* 1d. carmine-pink (1925) .. .. 30·00 3·50
bw. Wmk inverted .. .. .. 38·00 5·00

(ii) *P* 14
L32 L 2 ½d. yellow-green (1926) .. .. 10·00 2·25
w. Wmk inverted .. .. .. † 11·00
L33 1d. scarlet (1931) .. .. .. 7·50 1·50
w. Wmk inverted .. .. .. 13·00 2·75
L34 2d. yellow (1937) .. .. .. 7·00 5·50
w. Wmk inverted .. .. .. 32·00 26·00
L35 3d. brown-lake (1931) .. .. 18·00 22·00
L36 6d. pink (1925) .. .. .. 35·00 38·00
L32/6 .. .. *Set of* 5 70·00 60·00

(*c*) *"Wiggins Teape" paper. P* 14×15
L36*a* L 2 ½d. yellow-green (3.37) .. .. 8·00 10·00
L36*b* 1d. scarlet (3.37) .. .. .. 15·00 3·25
L36*c* 6d. pink (7.37) .. .. .. 35·00 40·00
L36*a/c* .. .. *Set of* 3 50·00 48·00

For descriptions of the various types of paper, see after No. 385.

In the 1½d. the word "POSTAGE" is in both the side-labels instead of at left only.

1944–47. *W* **98**. *P* 14×15.
L37 L 2 ½d. yellow-green (7.47) .. .. 5·00 9·00
L38 1d. scarlet (6.44) .. .. .. 3·25 2·00
L39 2d. yellow (1946) .. .. .. 11·00 15·00
L40 3d. brown-lake (10.46) .. .. 15·00 38·00
L41 6d. pink (7.47) .. .. .. 13·00 35·00
L37/41 .. .. *Set of* 5 42·00 90·00

L 3 Castlepoint Lighthouse

L 6 Cape Campbell Lighthouse

(Des J. Berry. Recess B.W.).

1947 (1 Aug)–**65.** *Type* L **3**, L **6** *and similar designs. W* **98** (*sideways on* 1d., 2d., 2½d.). *P* 13½.
L42 ½d. grey-green and orange-red .. 1·25 60
L43 1d. olive-green and pale blue .. 1·25 90
L44 2d. deep blue and grey-black .. 70 60
L45 2½d. black and bright blue (*white opaque paper*) (4.11.63) .. .. 9·50 13·00
L46 3d. mauve and pale blue .. .. 2·75 50
L47 4d. brown and yellow-orange .. .. 3·50
a. Wmk sideways (*white opaque paper*) (13.10.65) .. .. .. 4·00
L48 6d. chocolate and blue .. .. .. 3·50
L49 1s. red-brown and blue .. .. .. 3·50
L42/49 .. .. *Set of* 8 23·00

Designs: *Horiz* (*as Type* L **3**)–1d Taiaroa lighthouse; 2d. Palliser lighthouse; 6d. The Brothers lighthouse. *Vert* (*as* L **6**)–3d. Eddystone lighthouse; 4d. Stephens Island lighthous Cape Brett lighthouse.

POSTAL FISCAL STAMPS

As from 1 April 1882 fiscal stamps were authorised for posta and conversely postage stamps became valid for fiscal use. St in the designs of 1867 with "STAMP DUTY" above the Qu head were withdrawn and although some passed through the quite legitimately they were mainly "philatelic" and we no lo list them. The issue which was specifically authorised in 1882 the one which had originally been put on sale for fiscal use in

Although all fiscal stamps were legally valid for postage values between 2s. and £1 were stocked at ordinary post of Other values could only be obtained by request from the G. Wellington or from offices of the Stamp Duties Department. I the Arms types above £1 could also be obtained from the head offices in Auckland, Christchurch, Dunedin and also a branch office at Christchurch North where there was a local deman them.

It seems sensible to list under Postal Fiscals the Queen Vic stamps up to the £1 value and the Arms types up to the £5 bec by 1931 the higher values were genuinely needed for p purposes. Even the £10 was occasionally used on insured air parcels.

Although 2s. and 5s. values were included in the 1898 pict issue, it was the general practice for the Postal Department to the postage issues to 1s. until 1926 when the 2s. and 3s. appea These were then dropped from the fiscal issues and when in the 5s. and 10s. were introduced in 1953 and the £1 in 196 further printings of these values occurred in the fiscal series.

FORGED POSTMARKS. Our prices are for stamps with gen postal cancellations. Beware of forged postmarks on stamps f which fiscal cancellations have been cleaned off.

Many small post offices acted as agents for government dep ments and it was the practice to use ordinary postal date-stamp stamps used fiscally, so that when they are removed from d ments they are indistinguishable from postally used specim unless impressed with the embossed seal of the Stamp Du Department.

Date-stamps very similar to postal date-stamps were someti supplied to offices of the Stamp Duties Department and it is clear when this practice ceased. Prior to the Arms types the c sure proof of the postal use of off-cover fiscal stamps is when t bear a distinctive duplex, registered or parcel post cancellation, beware of forgeries of the first two.

F 1 F 2 F 3

(Die eng W. R. Bock. Typo Govt Ptg Office)

1882 (Feb). *W* **12a**. *P* 12×11½.
F1 F 1 1d. lilac .. .. £250 £
F2 1d. blue £120 25
w. Wmk inverted .. ..

The 1d. fiscal was specifically authorised for postal use February 1882 owing to a shortage of the 1d. Type **5** and pendi the introduction of the 1d. Type **14** on 1 April.

The 1d. lilac fiscal had been replaced by the 1d. blue in 1878 postally used copies with 1882 duplex postmarks are kno although most postally used examples are dated from 1890 a these must have been philatelic.

(Des and dies eng W. R. Bock. Typo Govt Ptg Office)

1882 (early). *W* **12a**. *P* 12×11½.
F3 F 2 1s. grey-green .. .. ..
F4 F 3 1s. grey-green and red .. .. ..
F4*a* 2s. rose and blue .. .. ..

Examples of these are known postally used in 1882 a although not specifically authorised for postal use it is believ that their use was permitted where there was a shortage of t appropriate postage value.

WMK TYPE F 5. The balance of the paper employed for the 18 issue was used for early printings of Type F 4 introduced in 18 before changing over to the "N Z" and Star watermark. The valu we list with this watermark are known with 1882–83 postal da stamps. Others have later dates and are considered to be philate but should they be found with 1882–83 postal dates we would prepared to add them to the list.

In the following list the 4d., 6d., 8d. and 1s. are known with ea 1882 postal date-stamps and, like Nos. F3/4, it is assumed that th were used to meet a temporary shortage of postage stamps.

F 4

F 5

The 12s. 6d. value has the head in an oval (as Type **10**), and th 15s. and £1 values have it in a broken circle (as Type **7**).

(Dies eng W.R. Bock. Typo Govt Ptg Office)

Apr). *Type* **F 4** *and similar types. "De La Rue" paper.*

A. *W* **12***a* (6 *mm*). (*a*) *P* 12 (1882)

No.	Description	Unused	Used
	4d. orange-red (*Wmk* **F 5**)	—	£170
	6d. lake-brown	—	£170
	8d. green (*Wmk* **F 5**)		
	1s. pink		
	a. Wmk **F 5**		
	2s. blue	50·00	4·50
	2s. 6d. grey-brown	85·00	4·50
	a. Wmk **F 5**		
	3s. mauve	£110	6·00
	4s. brown-rose	£110	11·00
	a. Wmk **F 5**		
	5s. green	£140	12·00
	a. Yellow-green	£140	12·00
	6s. rose	£150	29·00
	7s. ultramarine	£160	50·00
	7s. 6d. bronze-grey	£250	85·00
	8s. deep blue	£170	60·00
	9s. orange	£190	55·00
	10s. brown-red	£140	20·00
	a. Wmk **F 5**		
	15s. green	£250	85·00
	£1 rose-pink	£190	50·00

(*b*) *P* 12½ (1886)

No.	Description	Unused	Used
	2s. blue	50·00	4·50
	2s. 6d. grey-brown	85·00	4·50
	3s. mauve	£110	6·00
	4s. purple-claret	£110	11·00
	a. Brown-rose	£110	11·00
	5s. green	£140	12·00
	a. Yellow-green	£140	12·00
	6s. rose	£150	29·00
	7s. ultramarine	£160	50·00
	8s. deep blue	£170	60·00
	9s. orange	£190	55·00
	10s. brown-red	£140	20·00
	15s. green	£250	85·00
	£1 rose-pink	£190	50·00

B. *W* **12***b* (7 *mm*). *P* 12½ (1888)

No.	Description	Unused	Used
	2s. blue	45·00	4·50
	2s. 6d. grey-brown	80·00	4·50
	3s. mauve	£100	6·00
	4s. brown-rose	£100	11·00
	a. Brown-red	£100	11·00
	5s. green	£130	12·00
	a. Yellow-green	£130	12·00
	6s. rose	£150	29·00
	7s. ultramarine	£160	50·00
	7s. 6d. bronze-grey	£250	85·00
	8s. deep blue	£170	60·00
	9s. orange	£190	55·00
	10s. brown-red	£140	18·00
	a. Maroon	£140	18·00
	£1 pink	£190	50·00

C. *W* **12***c* (4 *mm*). *P* 12½ (1890)

No.	Description	Unused	Used
	2s. blue	75·00	11·00
	2s. 6d. grey-brown	£110	13·00
	3s. mauve	£150	27·00
	4s. brown-red	£120	15·00
	5s. green	£140	13·00
	6s. rose	£160	29·00
	7s. ultramarine	£170	50·00
	8s. deep blue	£180	60·00
	9s. orange	£200	65·00
	10s. brown-red	£150	20·00
	15s. green	£275	£100

D. *Continuation of W* **12***b*. *P* 11 (1895–1901)

No.	Description	Unused	Used
	2s. blue	27·00	5·50
	2s. 6d. grey-brown	80·00	4·50
	a. Inscr "COUNTERPART" (1901)*	£160	£180
	3s. mauve	£100	6·00
	4s. brown-red	£100	10·00
	5s. yellow-green	£130	13·00
	6s. rose	£140	29·00
	7s. pale blue	£160	50·00
	7s. 6d. bronze-grey	£250	85·00
	8s. deep blue	£170	60·00
	9s. orange	£190	55·00
	a. Imperf between (horiz pair)	£900	
	10s. brown-red	£140	18·00
	a. Maroon	£140	18·00
	15s. green	£250	85·00
	£1 rose-pink	£190	50·00

The plate normally printed in yellow and inscribed)UNTERPART" just above the bottom value panel, was for use :he counterparts of documents but was issued in error in the ur of the normal fiscal stamp and accepted for use.

E. *W* **43** (*sideways*)

(i) *Unsurfaced "Cowan" paper.* (*a*) *P* 11 (1903)

No.	Description	Unused	Used
	2s. 6d. grey-brown	80·00	4·50
	3s. mauve	£100	6·00
	4s. orange-red	£100	10·00
	6s. rose	£140	29·00
3	7s. pale blue	£160	50·00
	8s. deep blue	£170	60·00
5	10s. brown-red	£130	20·00
	a. Maroon	£130	20·00
6	15s. green	£250	85·00
7	£1 rose-pink	£170	50·00

(*b*) *P* 14 (1906)

No.	Description	Unused	Used
8	2s. 6d. grey-brown	80·00	4·50
9	3s. mauve	£100	6·00
0	4s. orange-red	£100	7·50
1	5s. yellow-green	90·00	8·50
2	6s. rose	£140	29·00
3	7s. pale blue	£150	50·00
4	7s. 6d. bronze-grey	£250	85·00
5	8s. deep blue	£170	60·00
6	9s. orange	£180	55·00
7	10s. maroon	£130	18·00
8	15s. green	£250	85·00
9	£1 rose-pink	£170	50·00

(*c*) *P* 14½ × 14, *comb* (*clean-cut*) (1907)

No.	Description	Unused	Used
0	2s. blue	25·00	4·00
1	2s. 6d. grey-brown	80·00	4·50
2	3s. mauve	£100	6·00
F93	4s. orange-red	90·00	7·50
F94	6s. rose	£140	29·00
F95	10s. maroon	£130	18·00
F96	15s. green	£250	85·00
F97	£1 rose-pink	£170	50·00

(ii) *Chalk-surfaced "De La Rue" paper.* (*a*) *P* 14 (1913)

No.	Description	Unused	Used
F 98	2s. blue	25·00	4·00
F 99	2s. 6d. grey-brown	27·00	4·50
F100	3s. purple	70·00	6·00
F101	4s. orange-red	70·00	7·00
F102	5s. yellow-green	70·00	8·50
F103	6s. rose	£110	15·00
F104	7s. pale blue	£120	25·00
F105	7s. 6d. bronze-grey	£250	85·00
F106	8s. deep blue	£150	30·00
F107	9s. orange	£180	55·00
F108	10s. maroon	£130	16·00
F109	15s. green	£250	85·00
F110	£1 rose-carmine	£170	50·00

(*b*) *P* 14½ × 14, *comb* (1913–21)

No.	Description	Unused	Used
F111	2s. deep blue	25·00	4·00
F112	2s. 6d. grey-brown	27·00	4·50
F113	3s. purple	70·00	6·00
F114	4s. orange-red	70·00	7·00
F115	5s. yellow-green	70·00	8·50
F116	6s. rose	£110	15·00
F117	7s. pale blue	£120	25·00
F118	8s. deep blue	£150	30·00
F119	9s. orange	£170	55·00
F120	10s. maroon	£130	16·00
F121	12s. 6d. deep plum (1921)	£3750	£1500
F122	15s. green	£250	85·00
F123	£1 rose-carmine	£170	50·00

The "De La Rue" paper has a smooth finish and has toned gum which is strongly resistant to soaking.

(iii) *Chalk-surfaced "Jones" paper. P* 14½ × 14, *comb* (1924)

No.	Description	Unused	Used
F124	2s. deep blue	30·00	5·00
F125	2s. 6d. deep grey-brown	32·00	5·50
F126	3s. purple	80·00	6·50
F127	5s. yellow-green	80·00	9·00
F128	10s. brown-red	£140	16·00
F129	12s. 6d deep purple	£3750	£1500
F130	15s. green	£275	95·00

The "Jones" paper has a coarser texture, is poorly surfaced and the ink tends to peel. The outline of the watermark commonly shows on the surface of the stamp. The gum is colourless or only slightly toned and washes off readily.

(iv) *Thick, opaque, chalk-surfaced "Cowan" paper. P* 14½×14, *comb* (1925–30)

No.	Description	Unused	Used
F131	2s. blue	27·00	5·00
F132	2s. 6d. deep grey-brown	30·00	5·50
F133	3s. mauve	£100	10·00
F134	4s. orange-red	70·00	10·00
F135	5s. yellow-green	70·00	12·00
	x. Wmk reversed (1927)	£100	20·00
F136	6s. rose	£110	18·00
F137	7s. pale blue	£120	25·00
F138	8s. deep blue	£150	30·00
	a. Error. Blue (as 2s.) (1930)	£500	
F139	10s. brown-red	£130	16·00
	x. Wmk reversed (1927)	£200	£150
F140	12s. 6d. blackish purple	£3750	£1500
F141	15s. green	£275	95·00
F142	£1 rose-pink	£170	50·00

The "Cowan" paper is white and opaque and the watermark, which is usually smaller than in the "Jones" paper, is often barely visible.

(v) *Thin, hard, chalk-surfaced "Wiggins Teape" paper. P* 14½ × 14, *comb* (1926)

No.	Description	Unused	Used
F143	4s. orange-red	80·00	13·00
F144	£1 rose-pink	£180	95·00

The "Wiggins Teape" paper has a horizontal mesh, in relation to the design, with narrow watermark, whereas other chalk-surfaced papers with this perforation have a vertical mesh and wider watermark.

F 6

35/-

(**F 7**)

(Des H. L. Richardson. Typo Govt Ptg Office)

1931–40. *As Type* **F 6** (*various frames*). *W* **43**. *P* 14.

(i) *Thick, opaque, chalk-surfaced "Cowan" paper, with horizontal mesh* (1931–35)

No.	Description	Unused	Used
F145	1s. 3d. lemon (4.31)	6·00	38·00
F146	1s. 3d. orange-yellow	6·00	7·00
F147	2s. 6d. deep brown	13·00	4·50
F148	4s. red	14·00	5·50
F149	5s. green	17·00	10·00
F150	6s. carmine-rose	32·00	13·00
F151	7s. blue	27·00	20·00
F152	7s. 6d. olive-grey	60·00	80·00
F153	8s. slate-violet	28·00	32·00
F154	9s. brown-orange	30·00	28·00
F155	10s. carmine-lake	24·00	9·00
F156	12s. 6d. deep plum (9.35)	£140	£140
F157	15s. sage-green	60·00	38·00
F158	£1 pink	60·00	19·00
F159	25s. greenish blue	£275	£400
F160	30s. brown (1935)	£250	£140
F161	35s. orange-yellow	£2500	£2750
F162	£2 bright purple	£300	60·00
F163	£2 10s. red	£275	£325
F164	£3 green	£325	£170
F165	£3 10s. rose (1935)	£1300	£1100
F166	£4 light blue (1935)	£325	£140
F167	£4 10s. deep olive-grey (1935)	£1000	£1100
F168	£5 indigo-blue	£325	90·00

(ii) *Thin, hard "Wiggins Teape" paper with vertical mesh* (1936–40)

(*a*) *Chalk-surfaced* (1936–39)

No.	Description	Unused	Used
F169	1s. 3d. pale orange-yellow	15·00	3·25
F170	2s. 6d. dull brown	55·00	3·25
F171	4s. pale red-brown	70·00	6·00
F172	5s. green	70·00	7·00
	w. Wmk inverted		
F173	6s. carmine-rose	70·00	27·00
F174	7s. pale blue	90·00	28·00
F175	8s. slate-violet	£110	45·00
F176	9s. brown-orange	£120	65·00
F177	10s. pale carmine-lake	£130	6·50
F178	15s. sage-green	£180	50·00
F179	£1 pink	£140	25·00
F180	30s. brown (1.39)	£350	£140
F181	35s. orange-yellow	£3000	£3250
F182	£2 bright purple (1937)	£550	85·00
	w. Wmk inverted		
F183	£3 green (1937)	£600	£250
F184	£5 indigo-blue (1937)	£800	£180

(*b*) *Unsurfaced* (1940)

No.	Description	Unused	Used
F185	7s. 6d. olive-grey	£150	75·00

Not all values listed above were stocked at ordinary post offices as some of them were primarily required for fiscal purposes but all were valid for postage.

1939. *No.* F161 *surch with Type* F **7**.

No.	Description	Unused	Used
F186	35/- on 35s. orange-yellow	£400	£225

Because the 35s. orange-yellow could so easily be confused with the 1s. 3d. in the same colour it was surcharged.

1940 (June). *New values surch as Type* **F 7**. *W* **43**. *"Wiggins Teape" chalk-surfaced paper. P* 14.

No.	Description	Unused	Used
F187	3/6 on 3s. 6d. grey-green	50·00	17·00
F188	5/6 on 5s. 6d. lilac	85·00	50·00
F189	11/- on 11s. yellow	£150	£130
F190	22/- on 22s. scarlet	£375	£300
F187/90	*Set of* 4	£600	£450

These values were primarily needed for fiscal use.

1940–58. *As Type* **F 6** (*various frames*). *W* **98**.

(i) *P* 14. *"Wiggins Teape" chalk-surfaced paper with vertical mesh* (1940–56)

No.	Description	Unused	Used
F191	1s. 3d. orange-yellow	8·00	1·50
	w. Wmk inverted		
F192	1s. 3d. yellow and black (*wmk inverted*) (14.6.55)	1·50	1·00
	aw. Wmk upright (9.9.55)	27·00	27·00
	b. Error. Yellow and blue (*wmk inverted*) (7.56)	4·50	5·50
F193	2s. 6d. deep brown	8·00	60
	w. Wmk inverted (3.49)	8·00	50
F194	4s. red-brown	14·00	1·00
	w. Wmk inverted (3.49)	16·00	1·00
F195	5s. green	17·00	1·00
	w. Wmk inverted (1.5.50)	22·00	1·00
F196	6s. carmine-rose	32·00	3·25
	w. Wmk inverted (1948)	32·00	3·25
F197	7s. pale blue	32·00	5·50
F198	7s. 6d. ol-grey (*wmk inverted*) (21.12.50)	60·00	50·00
F199	8s. slate-violet	48·00	17·00
	w. Wmk inverted (6.12.50)	45·00	18·00
F200	9s. brown-orange (1.46)	22·00	40·00
	w. Wmk inverted (9.1.51)	50·00	40·00
F201	10s. carmine-lake	29·00	2·25
	w. Wmk inverted (4.50)	29·00	2·50
F202	15s. sage-green	42·00	18·00
	w. Wmk inverted (8.12.50)	60·00	25·00
F203	£1 pink	27·00	3·75
	w. Wmk inverted (1.2.50)	40·00	4·25
F204	25s. greenish blue (1946)	£350	£350
	w. Wmk inverted (7.53)	£425	£425
F205	30s. brown (1946)	£250	£100
	w. Wmk inverted (9.49)	£225	£100
F206	£2 bright purple (1946)	80·00	20·00
	w. Wmk inverted (17.6.52)	85·00	20·00
F207	£2 10s. red (*wmk inverted*) (9.8.51)	£250	£275
F208	£3 green (1946)	£120	48·00
	w. Wmk inverted (17.6.52)	£110	45·00
F209	£3 10s. rose (11.48)	£1500	£1100
	w. Wmk inverted (5.52)	£1600	£1100
F210	£4 light blue (*wmk inverted*) (12.2.52)	£130	£110
	w. Wmk upright	†	—
F211	£5 indigo-blue	£275	55·00
	w. Wmk inverted (11.9.50)	£160	45·00
F191/211	*Set of* 21	£2750	£1900

THREE SHILLINGS I.

THREE SHILLINGS II.

3s. 6d.

Type I. Broad serifed capitals

Type II. Taller capitals, without serifs

Surcharged as Type **F 7**

No.	Description	Unused	Used
F212	3/6 on 3s. 6d. grey-green (I) (1942)	20·00	7·00
	w. Wmk inverted (12.10.50)	35·00	9·00
F213	3/6 on 3s. 6d. grey-green (II) (6.53)	13·00	38·00
	w. Wmk inverted (6.53)	42·00	42·00
F214	5/6 on 5s. 6d. lilac (1944)	48·00	18·00
	w. Wmk inverted (13.9.50)	55·00	18·00
F215	11/- on 11s. yellow (1942)	75·00	48·00
F216	22/- on 22s. scarlet (1945)	£250	£130
	w. Wmk inverted (1.3.50)	£275	£140
F212/16	*Set of* 5	£350	£200

(ii) *P* 14×13½. *"Wiggins Teape" unsurfaced paper with horizontal mesh* (1956–58)

No.	Description	Unused	Used
F217	1s. 3d. yellow and black (11.56)	2·00	2·50
	w. Wmk inverted	20·00	20·00
F218	£1 pink (20.10.58)	32·00	12·00

No. F192b had the inscription printed in blue in error but as many as 378,000 were printed.

From 1949–53 inferior paper had to be used and for technical reasons it was necessary to feed the paper into the machine in a certain way which resulted in whole printings with the watermark inverted for most values.

ANTARCTIC EXPEDITIONS

VICTORIA LAND

These issues were made under authority of the New Zealand Postal Department and, while not strictly necessary, they actually franked correspondence to New Zealand. They were sold to the public at a premium.

1908 (15 Jan). *Shackleton Expedition. T* **42** *of New Zealand (p 14), optd* "King Edward VII Land", *in two lines, reading up, by Coulls, Culling and Co., Wellington.*

A1 1d. rose-carmine (No. 356 Royle) (G.) .. £400 35·00
a. Opt double .. .. † £1500
A1*b* 1d. rose-carmine (No. 352*c* Waterlow) (G.) .. £1300 £800

Nos. A1/1*b* were used on board the expedition ship, *Nimrod*, and at the Cape Royds base in McMurdo Sound. Due to adverse conditions Shackleton landed in Victoria Land rather than King Edward VII Land the intended destination.

1911 (9 Feb)–**13.** *Scott Expedition. Stamps of New Zealand optd* "VICTORIA LAND.", *in two lines by Govt Printer, Wellington.*

A2 **51** ½d. deep green (No. 387*aa*) (18.1.13) £550 £650
A3 **53** 1d. carmine (No. 405) .. .. 45·00 85·00
a. No stop after "LAND" (R. 7/5) .. £275 £600

Nos. A2/3 were used at the Cape Evans base on McMurdo Sound or on the *Terra Nova*.

AITUTAKI

The island of Aitutaki, under British protection from 1888, was annexed by New Zealand on 11 June 1901.

NEW ZEALAND DEPENDENCY

Stamps of COOK ISLANDS were used in Aitutaki from 1892 until 1903.

PRICES FOR STAMPS ON COVER TO 1945

Nos. 1/7	*from* × 4
Nos. 9/14	*from* × 3
Nos. 15/29	*from* × 4
Nos. 30/2	*from* × 6

Stamps of New Zealand overprinted or surcharged. For illustrations of New Zealand watermarks and definitive types see the beginning of Cook Islands.

AITUTAKI.
(1)

Ava Pene.
(2) ½d.

Tai Pene.
(3) 1d.

Rua Pene Ma Te Ava.
(4) 2½d.

Toru Pene.
(5) 3d.

Ono Pene.
(6) 6d.

Tai Tiringi.
(7) 1s.

1903 (29 June)–**11.** *T* **23, 27/8, 31, 34** *and* **42** *surch with T* **1** *at top and T* **2** *to* **7** *at foot. Thin, hard Cowan paper. W* **43.**

(*a*) *P* 14

1 ½d. green (No. 302) (R.) .. .. .. 4·50 6·50
2 1d. carmine (No. 303) (B.) .. .. .. 4·75 5·50
3 2½d. deep blue (No. 320*a*) (R.) (9.11) .. 8·00 18·00
a. "Ava" without stop £140 £180
1/3 .. .. *Set of* 3 15·00 27·00

(*b*) *P* 11

4 2½d. blue (No. 308) (R.) .. .. .. 11·00 12·00
5 3d. yellow-brown (No. 309) (B.) .. .. 18·00 15·00
6 6d. rose-red (No. 312*a*) (B.) .. .. 30·00 25·00
7 1s. bright red (No. 315*a*) (B.) .. .. 55·00 85·00
a. "Tiringi" without stop (R. 7/12) .. £475 £650
b. Orange-red .. .. 65·00 95·00
ba. "Tiringi" without stop (R. 7/12) .. £600 £750
4/7 .. .. *Set of* 4 £100 £120

Nos. 1/2 and 4/7 were placed on sale in Auckland on 12 June 1903.

There were four states of the overprint used for No. 3. On the first the "no stop" variety (No. 3a) occurs on R. 6/8, on the second it appears on R. 1/4, 2/4 and 6/8, on the third on R. 5/8 and 6/8, and on the fourth all stops are present.

AITUTAKI.

Ono Pene.

(8)

1911–16. *T* **51** *and* **53** *surch with T* **1** *at top and T* **2** *or* **3** *at foot and T* **52** *surch as T* **8.** *P* 14×15 (½d., 1d.) *or* 14×14½ (*others*).

9 ½d. green (No. 387) (R.) (9.11) .. .. 1·00 3·00
10 1d. carmine (No. 405) (B.) (2.13) .. .. 3·00 9·50
11 6d. carmine (No. 392) (B.) (23.5.16) .. 45·00 95·00
12 1s. vermilion (No. 394) (B.) (9.14) .. 55·00 £140
9/12 .. .. *Set of* 4 90·00 £225

1916–17. *T* **60** (*recess*) *surch as T* **8.** *W* **43.** *P* 14×13½.

13 6d. carmine (No. 425) (B.) (6.6.16) .. .. 14·00 50·00
a. Perf 14×14½ .. .. 7·50 27·00
b. Vert pair. Nos. 13/13a .. .. .. 50·00 £150
14 1s. vermilion (No. 430) (B.) (3.17) .. .. 24·00 90·00
a. Perf 14×14½ .. .. 28·00 90·00
ab. "Tai" without dot (R. 8/9, 9/12, 10/12) .. £225 £425
ac. "Tiringi" without dot on second "i" (R. 8/12, 10/7) £275 £475
ad. "Tiringi" without dot on third "i" (R. 8/11) £350 £550
b. Vert pair. Nos. 14/14a £120 £350

1917–18. *T* **60** (*recess*) *optd* "AITUTAKI" *only, as in T* **8.** *W* **43.** *P* 14×13½.

15 2½d. blue (No. 419) (R.) (12.18) .. .. 2·00 15·00
a. Perf 14×14½ .. .. 1·75 15·00
b. Vert pair. Nos. 15/15a .. .. .. 40·00 £130
16 3d. chocolate (No. 420) (B.) (1.18) .. .. 1·75 23·00
a. Perf 14×14½ .. .. 1·50 23·00
b. Vert pair. Nos. 16/16a .. .. .. 38·00 £140
17 6d. carmine (No. 425) (B.) (11.17) .. .. 7·50 21·00
a. Perf 14×14½ .. .. 4·75 21·00
b. Vert pair. Nos. 17/17a .. .. .. 50·00 £140
18 1s. vermilion (No. 430) (B.) (11.17) .. .. 17·00 38·00
a. Perf 14×14½ .. .. 12·00 32·00
b. Vert pair. Nos. 18/18a .. .. .. 75·00 £180
15/18 .. .. *Set of* 4 18·00 80·00

1917–20. *T* **53** *and* **61** (*typo*) *optd* "AITUTAKI" *only, as in T* **8.** *W* **43.** *P* 14×15.

19 ½d. green (No. 435) (R.) (2.20) .. .. 1·00 5·50
20 1d. carmine (No. 405) (B.) (5.20) .. .. 3·50 25·00
21 1½d. slate (No. 437) (R.) (11.17) .. .. 3·75
22 1½d. orange-brown (No. 438) (R.) (2.19) .. 80
23 3d. chocolate (No. 440) (B.) (6.19) .. .. 3·50
19/23 .. .. *Set of* 5 11·00

(Des and recess Perkins, Bacon & Co)

1920 (23 Aug). *T* **9/14** *of Cook Islands, but inscr* "AITUT *No wmk. P* 14.

24 ½d. black and green .. .. .. 3·50
25 1d. black and dull carmine .. .. 3·50
a. Double derrick flaw (R.2/8, 3/6 or 5/2) 11·00
26 1½d. black and sepia .. .. .. 6·00
27 3d. black and deep blue .. .. .. 2·50
28 6d. red-brown and slate .. .. .. 5·50
29 1s. black and purple .. .. .. 9·50
24/9 .. .. *Set of* 6 27·00

(Recess Govt Printing Office, Wellington)

1924–27. *T* **9/10** *and* **16** *of Cook Islands, but* "AITUTAKI". *W* **43** *of New Zealand. P* 14.

30 ½d. black and green (5.27) .. .. 2·00
31 1d. black and deep carmine (10.24) .. 6·00
a. Double derrick flaw (R.2/8, 3/6 or 5/2) 15·00
32 2½d. black and dull blue (10.27) .. .. 7·50
30/2 .. .. *Set of* 3 14·00

Cook Islands stamps superseded those of Aitutak 15 March 1932. Separate issues were resumed in 1972.

COOK ISLANDS

This group of fifteen islands was originally also known a Hervey Islands. A British Protectorate was declared ove group by the local Vice-Consul on 20 September 1888.

Before the introduction of the Cook Islands Post Office was forwarded via Auckland, New Zealand.

PRICES FOR STAMPS ON COVER TO 1945

Nos. 1/4	*from* × 5
Nos. 5/74	*from* × 4
Nos. 75/145	*from* × 3

Watermarks of New Zealand used for Cook Island (including Aitutaki and Penrhyn Island)

W 12*b*

W 38

W 43

W 98

Types of New Zealand Definitives overprinted or surcharged for Cook Islands (including Aitutaki and Penrhyn Island)

23

27

28

31

34

42

51 52 53

60 61 72

F 4

F 6

BRITISH PROTECTORATE

1

2 Queen Makea Takau

3 White Tern or Torea

(Des F. Moss. Typo Govt Printing Office, Wellington)

(19 Apr). *No wmk. Toned paper. P* 12½.

1d. black .. .. 27·00 26·00
b. White paper .. .. 26·00 26·00
ba. Imperf between (vert pair) £8500
1½d. mauve .. .. 40·00 38·00
a. Imperf (pair) £9000
b. White paper .. .. 40·00 38·00
2½d. blue .. .. 40·00 38·00
a. White paper .. .. 40·00 38·00
10d. carmine £140 £130
a. White paper £160 £130
.. .. *Set of* 4 £200 £200

s. 1/4 were printed in sheets of 60 (6×10) from plates
tructed from a matrix of 6 slightly different types.

Eng A. E. Cousins. Typo Govt Printing Office, Wellington)

(28 July)–**1900.** *W* **12***b of New Zealand* (N Z *and Star wide
art*) (*sideways on T* **3**). (*a*) *P* 12 × 11½.

2 1d. brown .. .. 35·00 45·00
1d. blue (3.4.94) .. .. .. 8·00 2·00
a. Perf 12×11½ and 12½ mixed .. † £1000
1½d. mauve .. .. 8·00 6·00
2½d. rose .. .. 38·00 23·00
a. Rose-carmine .. .. .. 60·00 48·00
ab. Perf 12×11½ and 12½ mixed .. £1700
5d. olive-black .. .. 15·00 13·00
10d. green .. .. 70·00 48·00
.. .. *Set of* 6 £150 £110

(*b*) *P* 11 (July 1896–1900)

3 ½d. steel blue (1st setting) (11.99) .. 30·00 45·00
a. Upper right "d" omitted £1500
b. Second setting .. .. .. 19·00 22·00
ba. Deep blue (1900) .. .. .. 4·00 5·00
2 1d. blue .. .. 5·00 4·50
1d. deep brown/*cream* (4.99) .. .. 14·00 14·00
a. Wmk sideways .. .. ..
b. Bistre-brown (1900) .. .. .. 17·00 18·00
1½d. deep lilac .. .. 9·00 6·50
a. Deep mauve (1900) .. .. .. 9·00 6·50
3 2d. brown/*thin toned* (7.98) .. .. 11·00 6·50
a. Deep brown (1900) .. .. .. 8·50 6·50
2 2½d. pale rose .. .. 48·00 38·00
a. Deep rose (1900) .. .. .. 15·00 9·00
5d. olive-black .. .. 24·00 17·00
3 6d. purple/*thin toned* (7.98) .. .. 24·00 28·00
a. Bright purple (1900) .. .. .. 19·00 21·00
2 10d. green .. .. 18·00 48·00
3 1s. red/*thin toned* (7.98) .. .. .. 60·00 70·00
a. Deep carmine (1900) .. .. .. 48·00 48·00
20*a* .. .. *Set of* 10 £140 £160

Examples of the 1d., 1½d., 2½d. and 5d. perforated 11 and on
paper are perforation trials.

On the 1st setting of the ½d. the face values are misplaced in
h corner. As corrected in the second setting the face values
correctly positioned in each corner.

ONE
HALF
PENNY

(4)

(5)

1899 (24 Apr). *No.* 12 *surch with T* **4** *by Govt Printer, Rarotonga.*

21 **2** ½d. on 1d. blue .. .. 32·00 42·00
a. Surch inverted £850 £900
b. Surch double £1000 £850

NEW ZEALAND TERRITORY

On 8 and 9 October 1900 the chiefs of all the main islands, except Aitutaki, ceded their territory to the British Crown. On 11 June 1901 all the islands, including Aitutaki, were transferred by Great Britain to New Zealand control.

1901 (8 Oct). *No.* 13 *optd with T* **5** *by Govt Printer, Rarotonga.*

22 **2** 1d. brown £180 £140
a. Crown inverted £1800 £1400
c. Optd with crown twice £1500 £1500

1902. *No wmk. P* 11.

(*a*) *Medium white Cowan paper* (Feb)

23 **3** ½d. blue-green .. .. 6·50 7·00
a. Imperf horiz (vert pair) £1100
24 **2** 1d. dull rose .. .. 9·00 12·00

(*b*) *Thick white Pirie paper* (May)

25 **3** ½d. yellow-green .. .. 4·25 4·25
26 **2** 1d. rose-red .. .. 12·00 11·00
a. Rose-lake .. .. 11·00 6·50
27 2½d. dull blue .. .. 13·00 21·00

NEW ZEALAND WATERMARKS. In W **43** the wmk units are in vertical columns widely spaced and the sheet margins are unwatermarked or wmkd "NEW ZEALAND POSTAGE" in large letters.

In W **98** the wmk units are arranged alternately in horizontal rows closely spaced and are continued into the sheet margins.

Stamps with W **98** sideways show the star to the left of NZ, *as seen from the back*. Sideways inverted varieties have the star to the right, *as seen from the back*.

1902 (Sept). *W* **43** *of New Zealand* (*single-lined* NZ *and Star, close together; sideways on T* **2**). *P* 11.

28 **3** ½d. yellow-green .. .. 2·75 3·25
a. Grey-green .. .. 18·00 40·00
29 **2** 1d. rose-pink .. .. 4·00 3·00
30 1½d. deep mauve .. .. 4·00 8·50
31 **3** 2d. deep brown .. .. 4·75 10·00
a. No figures of value £1900 £2750
b. Perf 11 × 14 .. .. £1300
32 **2** 2½d. deep blue .. .. 3·75 7·00
33 5d. olive-black .. .. 35·00 48·00
34 **3** 6d. purple .. .. 32·00 28·00
35 **2** 10d. green .. .. 48·00 90·00
36 **3** 1s. carmine .. .. 48·00 70·00
a. Perf 11 × 14 .. .. £1500
28/36 .. .. *Set of* 9 £150 £225

Stamps in Type **3** were printed from a master plate with the value added by a series of separate duty plates. One sheet of the 2d. missed this second pass through the press and was issued without value.

1909–11. *W* **43** *of New Zealand.*

37 **3** ½d. green (*p* 14½×14) (1911) .. .. 6·00 8·00
38 **2** 1d. deep red (*p* 14) .. .. .. 35·00 26·00
a. Wmk sideways (24.12.09) .. .. 14·00 9·00
w. Wmk inverted .. .. .. † —

1913–19. *W* **43** *of New Zealand* (*sideways on T* **3**). *Chalk-surfaced paper.*

39 **3** ½d. deep green (*p* 14) (1915) .. .. 4·00 15·00
a. Wmk upright .. .. .. 5·00 10·00
40 **2** 1d. red (*p* 14) (7.13) .. .. .. 4·50 4·00
41 1d. red (*p* 14 × 14½) (1914) .. .. 5·50 5·50
42 1½d. deep mauve (*p* 14) (1915) .. .. 75·00 45·00
43 1½d. deep mauve (*p* 14 × 15) (1916) .. 7·50 4·00
44 **3** 2d. deep brown (*p* 15 × 14) (1919) .. 5·00 45·00
45 **2** 10d. green (*p* 14 × 15) (1918) .. .. 15·00 85·00
46 **3** 1s. carmine (*p* 15 × 14) (1919) .. .. 27·00 85·00
39/46 .. .. *Set of* 6 55·00 £200

RAROTONGA

APA PENE

(8)

1919 (Apr–July). *Stamps of New Zealand surch as T* **8**.

(*a*) *T* **53**. *W* **43**. *De La Rue chalk-surfaced paper. P* 14×15

47 1d. carmine (No. 405) (B.) (June) .. .. 1·00 3·00

(*b*) *T* **60** (*recess*). *W* **43**. *Cowan unsurfaced paper. P* 14×13½.

48 2½d. blue (No. 419) (R.) (June) .. .. 2·25 6·50
a. Perf 14×14½ .. .. 2·00 2·25
b. Vert pair. Nos. 48/a .. .. .. 20·00 45·00
49 3d. chocolate (No. 420) (B.) .. .. 2·00 7·50
a. Perf 14×14½ .. .. 2·25 2·00
b. Vert pair. Nos. 49/a .. .. .. 22·00 50·00
50 4d. bright violet (No. 422) (B.) .. .. 2·00 5·50
a. Re-entry (Pl 20 R. 1/6) .. .. .. 60·00
b. Re-entry (Pl 20 R. 4/10) .. .. .. 60·00
c. Perf 14×14½ .. .. 1·75 4·25
d. Vert pair. Nos. 50 and 50c .. .. 20·00 55·00
51 4½d. deep green (No. 423) (B.) .. .. 2·00 7·00
a. Perf 14×14½ .. .. 1·75 8·00
b. Vert pair. Nos. 51/a .. .. .. 20·00 65·00
52 6d. carmine (No. 425) (B.) (June) .. .. 3·00 8·50
a. Perf 14×14½ .. .. 1·75 5·50
b. Vert pair. Nos. 52/a .. .. .. 38·00 80·00
53 7½d. red-brown (No. 426a) (B.) .. .. 1·50 5·50
54 9d. sage-green (No. 429) (R.) .. .. 3·25 15·00
a. Perf 14×14½ .. .. 2·00 15·00
b. Vert pair. Nos. 54/a .. .. .. 38·00 £100
55 1s. vermilion (No. 430) (B.) (June) .. .. 11·00 30·00
a. Perf 14×14½ .. .. 2·75 18·00
b. Vert pair. Nos. 55/a .. .. .. 48·00 £110

(*c*) *T* **61** (*typo*). *W* **43**. *De La Rue chalk-surfaced paper. P* 14×15

56 ½d. green (No. 435) (R.) (June) .. .. 40 1·00
57 1½d. orange-brown (No. 438) (R.) (June) .. 50 75
58 2d. yellow (No. 439) (R.) .. .. .. 1·50 1·75
59 3d. chocolate (No. 440) (B.) (July) .. .. 2·75 13·00
47/59 .. .. *Set of* 13 19·00 70·00

9 Capt. Cook landing

10 Wharf at Avarua

11 "Capt. Cook" (Dance)

12 Palm Tree

13 Huts at Arorangi

14 Avarua Harbour

R.2/8

R.3/6

R.5/2

Double derrick flaws

(Des, eng and recess Perkins, Bacon & Co)

1920 (23 Aug). *No wmk. P* 14.

70 **9** ½d. black and green .. .. .. 4·00 18·00
71 **10** 1d. black and carmine-red .. .. 4·75 18·00
a. Double derrick flaw (R.2/8, 3/6 or 5/2) 12·00
72 **11** 1½d. black and dull blue .. .. .. 8·50 8·50
73 **12** 3d. black and chocolate .. .. .. 2·25 5·50
74 **13** 6d. brown and yellow-orange .. .. 3·00 8·50
75 **14** 1s. black and violet .. .. .. 5·00 17·00
70/5 .. .. *Set of* 6 24·00 65·00

Examples of the 1d. and 1s. with centre inverted were not supplied to the Post Office.

RAROTONGA

(15)

RAROTONGA

Trimmed overprint (R. 1/6 and R. 3/7)

1921 (Oct)–**23**. *Postal Fiscal stamps as Type* F **4** *of New Zealand optd with T* **15**. *W* **43** (*sideways*). *Chalk-surfaced "De La Rue" paper. P* 14½×14.

76 2s. deep blue (No. F111) (R.) .. .. 27·00 55·00
a. Trimmed opt .. .. 95·00
b. Carmine opt (1923) £150 £170
ba. Trimmed opt £425
77 2s. 6d. grey-brown (No. F112) (B.) .. .. 18·00 50·00
a. Trimmed opt .. .. 75·00
78 5s. yellow-green (No. F115) (R.) .. .. 27·00 65·00
a. Trimmed opt .. .. 95·00
79 10s. maroon (No. F120) (B.) .. .. 55·00 95·00
a. Trimmed opt £160
80 £1 rose-carmine (No. F123) (B.) .. .. 90·00 £160
a. Trimmed opt £275
76/80 .. .. *Set of* 5 £200 £375

See also Nos. 85/9.

16 Te Po, Rarotongan Chief

17 Harbour, Rarotonga and Mt Ikurangi

(2½d. from a print; 4d. des A. H. Messenger. Plates by P.B. Recess Govt Ptg Office, Wellington)

1924–27. *W* **43** *of New Zealand. P* 14.
81 **9** ½d. black and green (13.5.26) .. .. 4·50 8·50
82 **10** 1d. black and deep carmine (10.11.24) 6·00 2·25
a. Double derrick flaw (R. 2/8, 3/6 or 5/2) .. .. 16·00
x. Wmk reversed £150
83 **16** 2½d. red-brown and steel blue (15.10.27) 5·00 24·00
84 **17** 4d. green and violet (15.10.27) .. 8·00 16·00
81/4 .. .. *Set of* 4 21·00 45·00

1926 (Feb–May). *As Nos. 76/80, but on thick, opaque white chalk-surfaced "Cowan" paper.*
85 2s. blue (No. F131) (C.) £120 £170
a. Trimmed opt £350
86 2s. 6d. deep grey-brown (No. F132) (B.) 65·00 £100
87 5s. yellow-green (No. F135) (R.) (May) .. 65·00 90·00
a. Trimmed opt £160
88 10s. brown-red (No. F139) (B.) (May) .. 70·00 £110
89 £1 rose-pink (No. F142) (B.) (May) .. 95·00 £160
a. Trimmed opt £300
85/9 .. .. *Set of* 5 £375 £550

1926 (Oct)–**28.** *T* **72** *of New Zealand, overprinted with T* **15.**

(*a*) *Jones chalk-surfaced paper*
90 2s. deep blue (No. 466) (R.) .. .. 10·00 40·00
w. Wmk inverted .. .. ..

(*b*) *Cowan thick, opaque chalk-surfaced paper*
91 2s. light blue (No. 469) (R.) (18.6.27) .. 15·00 40·00
92 3s. pale mauve (No. 470) (R.) (30.1.28) .. 16·00 42·00
90/2 .. .. *Set of* 3 38·00 £110

TWO PENCE (18) **COOK ISLANDS.** (19)

1931 (Mar). *Surch with T* **18.** *P* 14. (*a*) *No wmk.*
93 **11** 2d. on 1½d. black and blue (R.) .. 9·50 2·75

(*b*) *W* **43** *of New Zealand*
94 **11** 2d. on 1½d. black and blue (R.) .. 4·75 11·00

1931 (12 Nov)–**32.** *Postal Fiscal stamps as Type* **F 6** *of New Zealand. W* **43.** *Thick, opaque, white chalk-surfaced Cowan paper. P* 14.

(*a*) *Optd with T* **15**
95 2s. 6d. deep brown (No. F147) (B.) .. 10·00 22·00
96 5s. green (No. F149) (R.) .. .. .. 17·00 50·00
97 10s. carmine-lake (No. F155) (B.) .. .. 35·00 90·00
98 £1 pink (No. F158) (B.) .. .. .. 85·00 £140

(*b*) *Optd with T* **19** (3.32)
98*a* £3 green (No. F164) (R.) £200 £375
98*b* £5 indigo-blue (No. F168) (R.) £170 £325
The £3 and £5 values were mainly used for fiscal purposes.

20 Capt. Cook landing

21 Capt. Cook

22 Double Maori Canoe

23 Natives working Cargo

24 Port of Avarua

25 R.M.S. *Monowai*

26 King George V

(Des L. C. Mitchell. Recess P.B.)

1932 (15 Mar–2 May). *No wmk. P* 13.
99 **20** ½d. black and deep green .. .. 3·50 16·00
a. Perf 14 .. .. 28·00 90·00
100 **21** 1d. black and lake .. .. 6·50 4·50
a. Centre inverted £2750 £2750
b. Perf compound of 13 and 14 .. £180 £200
c. Perf 14 .. .. 15·00 20·00
101 **22** 2d. black and brown .. .. 3·00 5·50
a. Perf 14 .. .. 9·00 20·00
102 **23** 2½d. black and deep blue .. 8·50 50·00
a. Perf 14 .. .. 14·00 50·00
103 **24** 4d. black and bright blue .. .. 20·00 60·00
a. Perf 14 .. .. 10·00 48·00
b. Perf 14×13 .. .. .. 30·00 95·00
c. Perf compound of 14 and 13 .. 50·00 £100
104 **25** 6d. black and orange .. .. .. 24·00 48·00
a. Perf 14 .. .. 4·25 15·00
105 **26** 1s. black and violet (*p* 14) (2 May) .. 8·50 22·00
99/105 .. .. *Set of* 7 38·00 £140

Nos. 100b and 103c come from sheets reperforated 14 on arrival at Wellington. No. 100b comes from the first vertical column of a sheet and has 14 at left and No. 103c from the third or fourth vertical column with 13 at left or right.

Other major errors exist on this issue, but these are not listed as they originated from printer's waste which appeared on the market in 1935.

(Recess from P.B. plates at Govt Printing Office, Wellington)

1933–36. *W* **43** *of New Zealand* (*Single N Z and Star*). *P* 14.
106 **20** ½d. black and deep green .. .. 1·00 4·50
w. Wmk inverted .. .. — 75·00
107 **21** 1d. black and scarlet (1935) .. 1·25 2·00
w. Wmk inverted and reversed ..
108 **22** 2d. black and brown (1936) .. 1·50 50
w. Wmk inverted .. ..
109 **23** 2½d. black and deep blue .. .. 1·50 2·25
110 **24** 4d. black and bright blue .. .. 1·50 50
111 **25** 6d. black and orange-yellow (1936) .. 1·75 2·25
112 **26** 1s. black and violet (1936) .. 27·00 35·00
106/12 .. .. *Set of* 7 32·00 42·00

SILVER JUBILEE OF KING GEORGE V. 1910-1935. (27)

Normal letters **B K E N**
B K E N Narrow letters

1935 (7 May). *Silver Jubilee. Optd with T* **27** (*wider vertical spacing on* 6d.). *Colours changed. W* **43** *of New Zealand. P* 14.
113 **21** 1d. red-brown and lake .. .. 60 1·40
a. Narrow "K" in "KING" .. .. 2·75 4·75
b. Narrow "B" in "JUBILEE" .. 6·00 10·00
114 **23** 2½d. dull and deep blue (R.) .. .. 1·00 2·50
a. Narrow first "E" in "GEORGE" .. 3·50 6·00
115 **25** 6d. green and orange .. .. 3·50 6·00
a. Narrow "N" in "KING" .. .. 13·00 20·00
113/15 .. .. *Set of* 3 4·50 9·00

1936 (15 July)–**44.** *Stamps of New Zealand optd with T* **19.** *W* **43.** *P* 14.

(*a*) *T* **72.** *Cowan thick, opaque chalk-surfaced paper*
116 2s. light blue (No. 469) .. .. .. 13·00 45·00
117 3s. pale mauve (No. 470) .. .. 13·00 70·00

(*b*) *Type* **F 6.** *Cowan thick, opaque chalk-surfaced paper*
118 2s. 6d. deep brown (No. F147) .. .. 17·00 65·00
119 5s. green (No. F149) (R.) .. .. 21·00 85·00
120 10s. carmine-lake (No. F155) .. .. 42·00 £160
121 £1 pink (No. F158) .. .. .. 65·00 £180
118/21 .. .. *Set of* 4 £130 £450

(*c*) *Type* **F 6.** *Thin, hard, chalk-surfaced Wiggins, Teape paper*
122 2s. 6d. dull brown (No. F170) (12.40) .. 85·00 £100
123 5s. green (No. F172) (R.) (10.40) .. £325 £350
123*a* 10s. pale carmine-lake (No. F177) (11.44) £120 £180
123*b* £3 green (No. F183) (R.) (date?) .. £325 £550
122/3*b* .. .. *Set of* 4 £750 £1100

COOK IS'DS. (28) **IS'DS.** Small second "S" (R. 1/2)

1937 (1 June). *Coronation. Nos.* 599/601 *of New Zealand* (*inscr* "12th MAY 1937") *optd with T* **28.**
124 1d. carmine 40 35
a. Small second "S" .. .. .. 12·00
125 2½d. Prussian blue 80 40
a. Small second "S" .. .. .. 20·00
126 6d. red-orange 80 35
a. Small second "S" .. .. .. 20·00
124/6 .. .. *Set of* 3 1·75 1·00

29 King George VI

30 Native Village

31 Native Canoe

32 Tropical Landscape

(Des J. Berry (2s., 3s., and frame of 1s.). Eng B.W. Recess Govt Ptg. Office, Wellington)

1938 (2 May). *W* **43** *of New Zealand. P* 14.
127 **29** 1s. black and violet .. .. .. 8·50 12·00
128 **30** 2s. black and red-brown .. .. 18·00 13·00
w. Wmk inverted .. .. ..
129 **31** 3s. light blue and emerald-green .. 45·00 35·00
127/9 .. .. *Set of* 3 65·00 55·00

(Recess B.W.)

1940 (2 Sept). *Surch as in T* **32.** *W* **98** *of New Ze*
P 13½ × 14.
130 **32** 3d. on 1½d. black and purple 50
Type **32** was not issued without surcharge.

1943–54. *Postal Fiscal stamps as Type* **F 6** *of New Ze*
optd with T **19**. *W* **98**. *Wiggins, Teape chalk-surfaced*
P 14.
131 2s. 6d. dull brown (No. F193) (3.46) .. 42·00
w. Wmk inverted (2.4.51) .. .. 18·00
132 5s. green (No. F195) (R.) (11.43) .. 8·50
w. Wmk inverted (5.54) .. .. .. 21·00
133 10s. pale carmine-lake (No. F201) (10.48) 55·00
w. Wmk inverted (10.51) .. .. 48·00
134 £1 pink (No. F203) (11.47) .. .. 50·00
w. Wmk inverted (19.5.54) .. .. 55·00
135 £3 green (No. F208) (R.) (1946?) .. £500
w. Wmk inverted (28.5.53) .. .. 55·00
136 £5 indigo-blue (No. F211) (R.) (25.10.50) £225
w. Wmk inverted (19.5.54) £250
131/6 .. .. *Set of* 6 £350
The £3 and £5 were mainly used for fiscal purposes.

(Recess Govt Ptg Office, Wellington)

1944–46. *W* **98** *of New Zealand* (*sideways on* ½*d.* 1*d.*, 1*s.*, *an*
P 14.
137 **20** ½d. black and deep green (11.44) .. 1·75
w. Wmk sideways inverted .. .. 7·00
138 **21** 1d. black and scarlet (3.45) .. .. 2·00
w. Wmk sideways inverted .. .. 10·00
x. Wmk sideways reversed ..
139 **22** 2d. black and brown (2.46) .. .. 1·75
140 **23** 2½d. black and deep blue (5.45) .. 75
141 **24** 4d. black and blue (4.44) .. .. 4·00
y. Wmk inverted and reversed .. 40·00
142 **25** 6d. black and orange (6.44) .. .. 2·00
143 **29** 1s. black and violet (9.44) .. .. 2·25
144 **30** 2s. black and red-brown (8.45) .. 35·00
145 **31** 3s. light blue & emerald-green (6.45) 32·00
w. Wmk inverted .. .. .. 90·00
137/45 .. .. *Set of* 9 70·00

COOK ISLANDS (33)

1946 (4 June). *Peace. Nos.* 668, 670, 674/5 *of New Zealand*
with T **33** (*reading up and down at sides on* 2*d.*).
146 1d. green (Parliament House) 30
147 2d. purple (Royal family) (B.) 30
148 6d. chocolate and vermilion (Coat of arms, foundry and farm) 30
149 8d. black and carmine ("St. George") (B.) 30
146/9 .. .. *Set of* 4 1·10

34 Ngatangiia Channel, Rarotonga

41 Map and Statue of Capt. Cook

(Des J. Berry. Recess Waterlow)

1949 (1 Aug)–**61.** *T* **34, 41** *and similar designs. W* **98** *of N*
Zealand (*sideways on shilling values*). *P* 13½ × 13 (*horiz*
13 × 13½ (*vert*).
150 ½d. violet and brown 10 1
151 1d. chestnut and green .. .. .. 3·50 2
152 2d. reddish brown and scarlet .. .. 1·75 2
153 3d. green and ultramarine .. .. 1·50 2
aw. Wmk inverted £100
b. Wmk sideways (white opaque paper) (22.5.61) .. .. 3·50 2
154 5d. emerald-green and violet .. .. 4·75 1
155 6d. black and carmine .. .. .. 4·75 2
156 8d. olive-green and orange 55 3
w. Wmk inverted .. .. .. 90·00 50
157 1s. light blue and chocolate .. .. 4·25 3
158 2s. yellow-brown and carmine .. .. 3·00 13
w. Wmk sideways inverted .. ..
159 3s. light blue and bluish green .. .. 9·00 24
150/9 .. .. *Set of* 10 29·00 50

Designs: *Horiz*—1d. Capt. Cook and map of Hervey Islan 2d. Rarotonga and Revd. John Williams; 3d. Aitutaki and pa trees; 5d. Rarotonga Airfield; 6d. Penrhyn village; 8d. Nati hut. *Vert*—2s. Native hut and palms; 3s. *Matua* (inter-isla freighter).

See note on white opaque paper below No. 736 of N Zealand.

PRICES OF SETS

Set prices are given for many issues, generall those containing three stamps or more. Definitiv sets include one of each value or major colo change, but do not cover different perforation die types or minor shades. Where a choice i possible the set prices are based on the cheape versions of the stamps included in the listings.

NIUE

e became a British Protectorate on 20 April 1900 and was ferred to New Zealand control on 11 June 1901. There was derable local resentment at attempts to incorporate Niue the Cook Islands and, in consequence, the island was nised as a separate New Zealand dependency from 1902.

PRICES FOR STAMPS ON COVER TO 1945	
No. 1	*from* × 3
Nos. 2/5	*from* × 8
Nos. 6/7	—
Nos. 8/9	*from* × 30
Nos. 10/12	—
Nos. 13/31	*from* × 3
Nos. 32/7c	—
Nos. 38/47	*from* × 5
Nos. 48/9	—
No. 50	*from* × 15
Nos. 51/4	—
Nos. 55/61	*from* × 8
Nos. 62/8	*from* × 12
Nos. 69/71	*from* × 3
Nos. 72/4	*from* × 10
Nos. 75/8	*from* × 8
Nos. 79/88	—
Nos. 89/97	*from* × 2

NEW ZEALAND DEPENDENCY

Stamps of New Zealand overprinted

NIUE

(1)

(4 Jan). *Handstamped with T* **1**, *in green or bluish green. rie paper. Wmk double-lined "N Z" and Star, W* **38** *of New aland. P* 11.
42 1d. carmine £300 £300

few overprints were made with a *greenish violet* ink. These rred only in the first vertical row and part of the second row of first sheet overprinted owing to violet ink having been applied e pad (*Price* £1400 *un*).

UE. PENI. (2) — **NIUE. TAHA PENI.** (3) 1d. — **NIUE. 2½ PENI.** (4)

2 (4 Apr). *Type-set surcharges. T* **2**, **3**, *and* **4**.

(*i*) *Pirie paper. No wmk. P* 11.
27 2½d. blue (R.) .. .. 1·25 4·00
a. No stop after "PENI" .. .. 25·00 48·00
b. Surch double £2000

i) *Basted Mills paper. Wmk double-lined "N Z" and Star, W* **38** *of New Zealand.*

(*a*) *P* 14
3 ½d. green (R.) .. .. 2·50 4·50
a. Spaced "U" and "E" (R. 3/3, 3/6, 8/3, 8/6) .. .. 11·00 18·00
b. Surch inverted £300 £500
c. Surch double £850
2 1d. carmine (B.) .. .. 20·00 22·00
a. Spaced "U" and "E" (R. 3/3, 3/6, 8/6) .. £100 £110
b. No stop after "PENI" (R. 9/3) £250 £275
c. Varieties a. and b. on same stamp (R. 8/3) £250 £275

(*b*) *P* 11×14
42 1d. carmine (B.) .. .. 1·75 2·50
b. Spaced "U" and "E" (R. 3/3, 3/6, 8/6) .. 12·00 15·00
c. No stop after "PENI" (R. 9/3) .. 32·00 45·00
d. Varieties b. and c. on same stamp (R. 8/3) .. .. 32·00 45·00

(*c*) *Mixed perfs*
23 ½d. green (R.) £1100
42 1d. carmine (B.) £700

02 (2 May). *Type-set surcharges, T* **2**, **3**. *Cowan paper. Wmk single-lined "N Z" and Star, W* **43** *of New Zealand.* (*a*) *P* 14.
23 ½d. green (R.) .. .. 1·00 1·00
a. Spaced "U" and "E" (R. 3/3, 3/6, 8/3, 8/6) .. .. 6·50 8·00
42 1d. carmine (B.) .. .. .. 60 1·00
a. Surch double £1100 £1200
b. Spaced "U" and "E" (R. 3/3, 3/6, 8/6) 9·00 14·00
c. No stop after "PENI" (R. 5/3, 7/3, 9/3, 10/3, 10/6) .. .. 9·00 14·00
d. Varieties b. and c. on same stamp (R. 8/3) .. .. 30·00 45·00
e. "I" of "NIUE" omitted (R. 6/5 from end of last ptg) .. ..

(*b*) *P* 14×11
23 ½d. green (R.) .. ..

(*c*) *Mixed perfs*
23 ½d. green (R.) £1000
42 1d. carmine (B.) £180
a. Spaced "U" and "E" (R. 3/3, 3/6, 8/3, 8/6) £475
b. No stop after "PENI" (R. 5/3, 7/3, 9/3, 10/3, 10/6) £475

NIUE. (5) — **Tolu e Pene.** (6) 3d.

Ono e Pene. (7) 6d. — **Taha e Sileni.** (8) 1s.

1903 (2 July). *Optd with name at top, T* **5**, *and values at foot, T* **6/8**, *in blue. W* **43** *of New Zealand* (*sideways*). *P* 11.
13 **28** 3d. yellow-brown .. .. .. 9·50 5·00
14 **31** 6d. rose-red .. .. 12·00 11·00
15 **34** 1s. brown-red ("Tahae" joined) £650
a. Surch double, one albino £850
16 1s. bright red .. .. 35·00 35·00
a. Orange-red .. .. 45·00 48·00
13/16 .. .. *Set of* 3 50·00 45·00

NIUE. ½ PENI. (9) — **NIUE. 2½ PENI.** (9*a*) — **NIUE.** (10)

1911 (30 Nov). *½d. surch with T* **9**, *others optd at top as T* **5** *and values at foot as T* **7**, **8**. *W* **43** *of New Zealand. P* 14×15 (*½d.*) *or* 14×14½ (*others*).
17 **51** ½d. green (C.) 50 50
18 **52** 6d. carmine (B.) .. .. 2·00 7·00
19 1s. vermilion (B.) .. .. .. 6·50 45·00
17/19 .. .. *Set of* 3 8·00 48·00

1915 (Sept). *Surch with T* **9***a*. *W* **43** *of New Zealand. P* 14.
20 **27** 2½d. deep blue (C.) .. .. .. 15·00 30·00

1917 (Aug). 1*d. surch as T* **3**, 3*d. optd as T* **5** *with value as T* **6**. *W* **43** *of New Zealand.*
21 **53** 1d. carmine (*p* 14×15) (Br.) .. .. 9·50 5·50
a. No stop after "PENI" (R. 10/16) .. £300
22 **60** 3d. chocolate (*p* 14×14½) (B.) .. .. 42·00 80·00
a. No stop after "Pene" (R. 10/4) .. £700
b. Perf 14×13½ .. .. .. 55·00 90·00
c. Vert pair, Nos. 22/b £160

1917–21. *Optd with T* **10**. *W* **43** *of New Zealand.* (*a*) *P* 14×15.
23 **61** ½d. green (R.) (2.20) .. .. .. 70 2·50
24 **53** 1d. carmine (B.) (10.17) .. .. 10·00 8·50
25 **61** 1½d. slate (R.) (11.17) .. .. .. 1·00 2·25
26 1½d. orange-brown (R.) (2.19) .. .. 70 4·00
27 3d. chocolate (B.) (6.19) .. .. 1·40 25·00

(*b*) *P* 14×13½
28 **60** 2½d. blue (R.) (10.20) .. .. .. 2·50 6·50
a. Perf 14×14½ .. .. .. 1·25 4·50
ab. Opt double, one albino .. ..
b. Vert pair, Nos. 28/a .. .. 18·00 48·00
29 3d. chocolate (B.) (10.17) .. .. 1·60 2·00
a. Perf 14×14½ .. .. .. 1·25 1·50
b. Vert pair, Nos. 29/a .. .. 22·00 45·00
30 6d. carmine (B.) (8.21) .. .. 6·00 23·00
a. Perf 14×14½ .. .. .. 4·75 23·00
b. Vert pair, Nos. 30/a .. .. 32·00 90·00
31 1s. vermilion (B.) (10.18) .. .. 8·50 23·00
a. Perf 14×14½ .. .. .. 5·50 23·00
b. Vert pair, Nos. 31/a .. .. 35·00 90·00
23/31 .. .. *Set of* 9 24·00 85·00

1918–29. *Postal Fiscal stamps as Type* F **4** *of New Zealand optd with T* **10**. *W* **43** *of New Zealand* (*sideways*).

(i) *Chalk-surfaced "De La Rue" paper.* (*a*) *P* 14
32 5s. yellow-green (R.) (7.18) £100 £110

(*b*) *P* 14½ × 14, *comb*
33 2s. deep blue (R.) (9.18) .. .. .. 15·00 32·00
34 2s. 6d. grey-brown (B.) (2.23) .. .. 21·00 48·00
35 5s. yellow-green (R.) (10.18) .. .. 25·00 50·00
36 10s. maroon (B.) (2.23) .. .. .. 90·00 £120
37 £1 rose-carmine (B.) (2.23) £130 £180
33/7 .. .. *Set of* 5 £250 £400

(ii) *Thick, opaque, white chalk-surfaced "Cowan" paper. P* 14½ × 14
37*a* 5s. yellow-green (R.) (10.29) .. .. 27·00 55·00
37*b* 10s. brown-red (B.) (2.27) .. .. .. 80·00 £110
37*c* £1 rose-pink (B.) (2.28) £130 £180
37*a*/*c* .. .. *Set of* 3 £200 £300

11 Landing of Captain Cook

12 Landing of Captain Cook

R.2/8

R.3/6

R.5/2

Double derrick flaws

(Des, eng and recess P.B.)

1920 (23 Aug). *T* **11** *and similar designs. No wmk. P* 14.
38 ½d. black and green .. .. .. 3·75 3·75
39 1d. black and dull carmine .. .. 2·00 1·25
a. Double derrick flaw (R.2/8, 3/6 or 5/2) 6·50
40 1½d. black and red .. .. .. 2·50 7·50
41 3d. black and blue .. .. .. 75 14·00
42 6d. red-brown and green .. .. 1·75 18·00
43 1s. black and sepia .. .. .. 1·75 18·00
38/43 .. .. *Set of* 6 11·00 55·00

Designs: *Vert*—1d. Wharf at Avarua; 1½d. "Capt Cook (Dance)"; 3d. Palm tree. *Horiz*—6d. Huts at Arorangi; 1s. Avarua Harbour.

Examples of the 6d. with inverted centre were not supplied to the Post Office.

1925–27. *As Nos.* 38/9 *and new values. W* **43** *of New Zealand. P* 14.
44 ½d. black and green (1927) .. .. 1·50 8·00
45 1d. black and deep carmine (1925) .. 1·75 1·00
a. Double derrick flaw (R.2/8, 3/6 or 5/2) 5·50
46 2½d. black and blue (10.27) .. .. 4·25 11·00
47 4d. black and violet (10.27) .. .. 7·00 19·00
44/7 .. .. *Set of* 4 13·00 35·00

Designs: *Vert*—2½d. Te Po, Rarotongan chief. *Horiz*—4d. Harbour, Rarotonga, and Mount Ikurangi.

1927–28. *Admiral type of New Zealand optd as T* **10**. *W* **43** *of New Zealand. P* 14.

(*a*) *"Jones" paper* (*wmk inverted*)
48 **72** 2s. deep blue (2.27) (R.) .. .. 15·00 48·00

(*b*) *"Cowan" paper*
49 **72** 2s. light blue (R.) (2.28) .. .. 18·00 32·00

1931 (Apr). *No.* 40 *surch as T* **18** *of Cook Is.*
50 2d. on 1½d. black and red .. .. .. 2·25 1·00

1931 (12 Nov). *Postal Fiscal stamps as Type* F **6** *of New Zealand optd as T* **10**. *W* **43** *of New Zealand. Thick, opaque, chalk-surfaced "Cowan" paper. P* 14.
51 2s. 6d. deep brown (B.) .. .. .. 4·00 11·00
52 5s. green (R.) .. .. 32·00 65·00
53 10s. carmine-lake (B.) .. .. .. 35·00 95·00
54 £1 pink (B.) .. .. 55·00 £130
51/4 .. .. *Set of* 4 £110 £275

See also Nos. 79/82 for different type of overprint.

(Des L. C. Mitchell. Recess P.B.)

1932 (16 Mar). *T* **12** *and similar designs inscr* "NIUE" *and* "COOK ISLANDS". *No wmk. P* 13.
55 ½d. black and emerald .. .. .. 9·50 22·00
a. Perf 13×14×13×13 .. .. .. £250
56 1d. black and deep lake .. .. .. 1·00 40
57 2d. black and red-brown .. .. .. 2·50 4·00
a. Perf 14×13×13×13 .. .. .. £100 £160
58 2½d. black and slate-blue .. .. .. 8·00 70·00
59 4d. black and greenish blue .. .. 14·00 55·00
a. Perf 14 .. .. 16·00 50·00
60 6d. black and orange-vermilion .. .. 2·50 2·00
61 1s. black and purple (*p* 14) .. .. 2·25 5·00
55/61 .. .. *Set of* 7 35·00 £140

Designs: *Vert*—1d. Capt. Cook; 1s. King George V. *Horiz*—2d. Double Maori canoe; 2½d. Islanders working cargo; 4d. Port of Avarua; 6d. R.M.S. *Monowai*.

Examples of the 2½d. with inverted centre were not supplied to the Post Office.

Nos. 55a and 57a are mixed perforations, each having one side perforated 14 where the original perforation, 13, was inadequate.

(Recess from Perkins, Bacon's plates at Govt Ptg Office, Wellington, N.Z.)

1932–36. *As Nos.* 55/61, *but W* **43** *of New Zealand. P* 14.
62 ½d. black and emerald .. .. .. 50 2·75
63 1d. black and deep lake .. .. .. 50 1·25
w. Wmk inverted .. .. .. 45·00
64 2d. black and yellow-brown (1.4.36) .. 50 1·25
w. Wmk inverted .. .. .. 25·00 45·00
65 2½d. black and slate-blue .. .. .. 50 4·25
w. Wmk inverted .. .. .. 45·00
66 4d. black and greenish blue .. .. 1·75 3·00
w. Wmk inverted .. .. ..
67 6d. black and red-orange (1.4.36) 70 75
68 1s. black and purple (1.4.36) .. .. 8·50 24·00
62/8 .. .. *Set of* 7 11·50 32·00

Imperforate proofs of No. 65 are known used on registered mail from Niue postmarked 30 August 1945 or 29 October 1945.

See also Nos. 89/97.

SILVER JUBILEE OF KING GEORGE V. 1910-1935.

(13)

Normal letters: **B K E N**
Narrow letters: **B K E N**

1935 (7 May). *Silver Jubilee. Designs as Nos.* 63, 65 *and* 67 (*colours changed*) *optd with T* **13** (*wider vertical spacing on 6d.*). *W* **43** *of New Zealand. P* 14.
69 1d. red-brown and lake .. .. .. 60 3·50
a. Narrow "K" in "KING" .. .. 2·75 9·00
b. Narrow "B" in "JUBILEE" .. .. 2·75 9·00
70 2½d. dull and deep blue (R.) .. .. 3·25 6·50
a. Narrow first "E" in "GEORGE" .. 4·00 13·00
71 6d. green and orange .. .. .. 3·25 6·00
a. Narrow "N" in "KING" .. .. 15·00 35·00
69/71 .. .. *Set of* 3 6·50 14·00

Examples of No. 70 imperforate horizontally are from proof sheets not issued through the Post and Telegraph Department (*Price* £250 *for vert pair*).

NIUE

(14)

15 King George VI

16 Tropical Landscape

1937 (13 May). *Coronation. Nos.* 599/601 *of New Zealand optd with T* **14**.
72 1d. carmine 30 10
73 2½d. Prussian blue 40 50
74 6d. red-orange 40 20
72/4 .. .. *Set of* 3 1·00 70

1938 (2 May). *T* **15** *and similar designs inscr* "NIUE COOK ISLANDS". *W* **43** *of New Zealand. P* 14.
75 1s. black and violet .. .. .. 9·00 7·00
76 2s. black and red-brown .. .. .. 12·00 16·00
77 3s. light blue and emerald-green .. .. 32·00 16·00
75/7 .. .. *Set of* 3 48·00 35·00
Designs: *Vert*—2s. Island village. *Horiz*—3s. Cook Islands canoe.

1940 (2 Sept). *Unissued stamp surch as in T* **16**. *W* **98** *of New Zealand. P* 13½×14.
78 3d. on 1½d. black and purple 50 20

NIUE.

(17)

1941–67. *Postal Fiscal stamps as Type* **F 6** *of New Zealand with thin opt, T* **17**. *P* 14.

(i) *Thin, hard, chalk-surfaced "Wiggins Teape" paper with vertical mesh* (1941–43). (a) *W* **43** *of New Zealand*
79 2s. 6d. deep brown (B.) (4.41) .. .. 65·00 75·00
80 5s. green (R.) (4.41) £250 £190
81 10s. pale carmine-lake (B.) (6.42) £120 £190
82 £1 pink (B.) (2.43?) £180 £275
79/82 .. .. *Set of* 4 £550 £650

(b) *W* **98** *of New Zealand* (1944–54)
83 2s. 6d. deep brown (B.) (3.45) .. .. 3·50 9·00
w. Wmk inverted (11.51) .. .. 10·00 14·00
84 5s. green (R.) (11.44) .. .. 7·50 11·00
w. Wmk inverted (19.5.54) .. .. 7·50 13·00
85 10s. carmine-lake (B.) (11.45) .. .. 55·00 £100
w. Wmk inverted .. .. .. 55·00 £100
86 £1 pink (B.) (6.42) .. .. .. 42·00 55·00
83/6 .. .. *Set of* 4 95·00 £160

(ii) *Unsurfaced "Wiggins Teape" paper with horizontal mesh. W* **98** *of New Zealand* (1957–67)
87 2s. 6d. deep brown (*p* 14 × 13½) (1.11.57) .. 8·00 10·00
88 5s. pale yellowish green (*wmk sideways*) (6.67) .. .. 24·00 75·00

No. 88 came from a late printing made to fill demands from Wellington, but no supplies were sent to Niue. It exists in both line and comb perf.

1944–46. *As Nos. 62/7 and 75/7, but W* **98** *of New Zealand* (*sideways on* ½*d.,* 1*d.,* 1*s. and* 2*s.*).
89 **12** ½d. black and emerald .. .. 50 2·00
90 – 1d. black and deep lake .. .. 50 1·00
91 – 2d. black and red-brown .. .. 5·50 6·50
92 – 2½d. black and slate-blue (1946) .. 60 1·25
93 – 4d. black and greenish blue .. 4·25 90
w. Wmk inverted and reversed .. 16·00
94 – 6d. black and red-orange .. .. 2·25 1·40
95 **15** 1s. black and violet .. .. .. 1·25 85
96 – 2s. black and red-brown (1945) .. 8·50 3·00
97 – 3s. light blue and emerald-green (1945) 15·00 7·00
89/97 .. .. *Set of* 9 35·00 22·00

1946 (4 June). *Peace. Nos.* 668, 670, 674/5 *of New Zealand optd as T* **17** *without stop* (*twice, reading up and down on* 2*d.*).
98 1d. green (Blk.) 20 10
99 2d. purple (B.) 20 10
100 6d. chocolate and vermilion (Blk.) .. 20 40
a. Opt double, one albino £200
101 8d. black and carmine (B.) 30 40
98/101 .. .. .. *Set of* 4 80 80
Nos. 102/112 are no longer used.

18 Map of Niue

19 H.M.S. *Resolution*

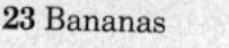

23 Bananas

24 Matapa Chasm

(Des J. Berry. Recess B.W.)

1950 (3 July). *T* **18/19, 23/24** *and similar designs. W* **98** *of New Zealand* (*sideways inverted on* 1*d.,* 2*d.,* 3*d.,* 4*d.,* 6*d. and* 1*s.*). *P* 13½×14 (*horiz*) *or* 14×13½ (*vert*).
113 ½d. orange and blue 10 50
114 1d. brown and blue-green .. .. 2·25 1·75
115 2d. black and carmine .. .. 1·00 90
116 3d. blue and violet-blue 10 15
117 4d. olive-green and purple-brown .. 10 15
118 6d. green and brown-orange .. .. 60 1·00
119 9d. orange and brown 10 90
120 1s. purple and black 10 15
121 2s. brown-orange and dull green .. 1·00 4·00
122 3s. blue and black .. .. .. 4·50 4·00
113/22 .. .. .. *Set of* 10 8·00 12·00
Designs: *Horiz* (*as T* **19**)—2d. Alofi landing; 3d. Native hut; 4d. Arch at Hikutavake; 6d. Alofi bay; 1s. Cave, Makefu. *Vert* (*as T* **18**)—9d. Spearing fish.

MINIMUM PRICE

The minimum price quote is 10p which represents a handling charge rather than a basis for valuing common stamps. For further notes about prices see introductory pages.

PENRHYN ISLAND

Stamps of COOK ISLANDS were used on Penrhyn Island from late 1901 until the issue of the surcharged stamps in May 1902.

PRICES FOR STAMPS ON COVER TO 1945
No. 1 *from* ×25
No. 3 —
Nos. 4/5 *from* ×25
Nos. 6/8 —
Nos. 9/10 *from* ×50
Nos. 11/13 —
Nos. 14/18 *from* × 3
Nos. 19/23 *from* × 2
Nos. 24/37 *from* × 3
Nos. 38/40 *from* × 5

NEW ZEALAND DEPENDENCY

The island of Penrhyn, under British protection from 20 September 1888, was annexed by New Zealand on 11 June 1901.

Stamps of New Zealand overprinted or surcharged. For illustrations of New Zealand watermarks and definitive types see the beginning of Cook Islands.

PENRHYN ISLAND. ½ PENI. (1)

PENRHYN ISLAND. TAI PENI. (2) 1d.

PENRHYN ISLAND. 2½ PENI. (3)

1902 (5 May). *T* **23, 27** *and* **42** *surch with T* **1, 2** *and* **3**.

(a) *Thick, soft Pirie paper. No wmk. P* 11
1 2½d. blue (No. 260) (R.) .. .. .. 2·50 8·00
a. "½" and "P" spaced (all stamps in 8th vert row) .. .. .. 14·00 32·00

(b) *Thin, hard Basted Mills paper. W* **38** *of New Zealand.*

(i) *P* 11
3 1d. carmine (No. 286) (Br.) £850 £900

(ii) *P* 14
4 ½d. green (No. 287) (R.) .. .. 80 5·00
a. No stop after "ISLAND" £150 £200
5 1d. carmine (No. 288) (Br.) .. .. 3·25 14·00

(iii) *Perf compound of* 11 *and* 14
6 1d. carmine (No. 290) (Br.) £850 £900

(iv) *Mixed perfs*
7 ½d. green (No. 291) (R.) £1100
8 1d. carmine (No. 292) (Br.) £1300

(c) *Thin, hard Cowan paper. W* **43** *of New Zealand.* (i) *P* 14
9 ½d. green (No. 302) (R.) .. .. 2·00 5·00
a. No stop after "ISLAND" (R. 10/6) .. £140 £180
10 1d. carmine (No. 303) (B.) .. .. 1·25 3·50
a. No stop after "ISLAND" (R. 10/6) .. 48·00 80·00

(ii) *Perf compound of* 11 *and* 14
11 1d. carmine (No. 305) (B.) £7000

(iii) *Mixed perfs*
12 ½d. green (No. 306) (R.) £1200 £1300
13 1d. carmine (No. 307) (B.) £600 £650

PENRHYN ISLAND. (4)

Toru Pene. (5) 3d.

Ono Pene. (6) 6d.

Tahi Silingi. (7) 1s.

1903 (28 Feb). *T* **28, 31** *and* **34** *surch with name at top, T* **4**, *and values at foot, T* **5/7**. *Thin, hard Cowan paper. W* **43** (*sideways*) *of New Zealand. P* 11.
14 3d. yellow-brown (No. 309) (B.) .. .. 10·00 20·00
15 6d. rose-red (No. 312*a*) (B.) .. .. 15·00 32·00
16 1s. brown-red (No. 315) (B.) .. .. 55·00 55·00
a. Bright red .. .. .. 48·00 48·00
b. Orange-red .. .. .. 55·00 55·00
14/16 .. .. *Set of* 3 65·00 90·00

1914 (May)–**15.** *T* **51/2** *surch with T* **1** (½*d.*) *or optd with T* **4** *at top and surch with T* **6/7** *at foot.*
19 ½d. yellow-green (No. 387) (C.) (5.14) .. 80 8·00
a. No stop after "ISLAND" .. .. 30·00 75·00
b. No stop after "PENI" (R. 3/17) .. 90·00 £160
c. Vermilion opt (1.15) .. .. .. 80 8·00
ca. No stop after "ISLAND" .. .. 10·00 45·00
cb. No stop after "PENI" (R. 3/5, 3/17) .. 40·00 £100
22 6d. carmine (No. 393) (B.) (8.14) .. 27·00 70·00
23 1s. vermilion (No. 394) (B.) (8.14) .. 48·00 95·00
19/23 .. .. *Set of* 3 65·00 £150

The "no stop after ISLAND" variety occurs on R. 1/4, 1/10, 1/16, 1/22, 6/4, 6/10, 6/16 and 6/22 of the carmine surcharge, No. 19, and on these positions plus R. 1/12, 1/24, 6/12 and 6/24 for the vermilion, No. 19c.

1917 (Nov)–**20.** *Optd as T* **4**.

(a) *T* **60** (*recess*). *W* **43** *of New Zealand. P* 14×13½.
24 2½d. blue (No. 419) (R.) (10.20) .. .. 3·00
a. Perf 14×14½ .. .. 2·00
ab. No stop after "ISLAND" (R. 10/8) .. £170
b. Vert pair. Nos. 24/4a .. .. .. 45·00
25 3d. chocolate (No. 420) (B.) (6.18) .. 12·00
a. Perf 14×14½ .. .. 9·50
b. Vert pair. Nos. 25/5a .. .. .. 70·00
26 6d. carmine (No. 425) (B.) (1.18) .. 8·00
a. Perf 14×14½ .. .. 5·00
ab. No stop after "ISLAND" (R. 10/8) .. £375
b. Vert pair. Nos. 26/6a .. .. .. 55·00
27 1s. vermilion (No. 430) (B.) (12.17) .. 15·00
a. Perf 14×14½ .. .. 12·00
ab. No stop after "ISLAND" (R. 10/8) .. £400
b. Vert pair. Nos. 27/7a £100
24/7 .. .. *Set of* 4 25·00

(b) *T* **61** (*typo*). *W* **43** *of New Zealand. P* 14×15
28 ½d. green (No. 435) (R.) (2.20) .. .. 1·00
a. No stop after "ISLAND" (R. 2/24) .. £110
b. Narrow spacing .. .. 6·00
29 1½d. slate (No. 437) (R.) .. .. .. 6·50
a. Narrow spacing .. .. 18·00
30 1½d. orange-brown (No. 438) (R.) (2.19) .. 60
a. Narrow spacing .. .. 5·00
31 3d. chocolate (No. 440) (B.) (6.19) .. 3·50
a. Narrow spacing .. .. 15·00
28/31 .. .. *Set of* 4 10·50

The narrow spacing variety occurs on R. 1/5–8, 4/21–4, 7 and 9/21–4.

(Recess P.B.)

1920 (23 Aug). *As T* **9/14** *of Cook Islands, but i* "PENRHYN". *No wmk. P* 14.
32 ½d. black and emerald .. .. .. 1·00
a. Part imperf block of 4 .. .. £1200
33 1d. black and deep red .. .. .. 1·50
a. Double derrick flaw (R.2/8, 3/6 or 5/2) 5·50
34 1½d. black and deep violet .. .. .. 6·50
35 3d. black and red .. .. 2·50
36 6d. red-brown and sepia .. .. .. 3·25
37 1s. black and slate-blue .. .. .. 10·00
32/7 .. .. *Set of* 6 22·00

No. 32a comes from sheets on which two rows w imperforate between horizontally and the second additionally imperforate vertically.

Examples of the ½d. and 1d. with centre inverted were supplied to the Post Office.

(Recess Govt Printing Office, Wellington)

1927–29. *As T* **9/10** *and* **16** *of Cook Islands, but in* "PENRHYN". *W* **43**. *P* 14.
38 ½d. black and green (5.29) .. .. 5·50 21
39 1d. black and deep carmine (14.3.28) .. 5·50 18
a. Double derrick flaw (R.2/8, 3/6 or 5/2) 16·00
40 2½d. red-brown and dull blue (10.27) .. 3·50 26
38/40 .. .. *Set of* 3 13·00 60

Cook Islands stamps superseded those of Penrhyn Island 15 March 1932.

TOKELAU ISLANDS

Formerly known as the Union Islands, and administered part of the Gilbert & Ellice Islands Colony, Tokelau w transferred to New Zealand on 4 November 1925 a administered with Western Samoa. The islands were final incorporated in New Zealand on 1 January 1949 and became dependency. The name Tokelau was officially adopted on 7 M 1946.

Stamps of GILBERT AND ELLICE ISLANDS were used in Tokelau from February 1911 until June 1926 when they were replaced by those of SAMOA. These were current until 1948.

The post office on Atafu opened in 1911, but the cancellations for the other two islands, Fakaofo and Nukunono, did not appear until 1926.

NEW ZEALAND ADMINISTRATION

1 Atafu Village and Map

(Des J. Berry from photographs by T. T. C. Humphrey. Recess B.W

1948 (22 June). *T* **1** *and similar horiz designs. Wmk T* **98** *of Ne Zealand* (*Mult N Z and Star*). *P* 13½.
1 ½d. red-brown and purple 15 5
2 1d. chestnut and green 15 3
w. Wmk inverted £275
3 2d. green and ultramarine 15 3
1/3 .. .. *Set of* 3 40 1·0

Designs:—1d. Nukunono hut and map; 2d. Fakaofo village and map.

Covers are known postmarked 16 June 1948, but this was in error for 16 July.

WESTERN SAMOA

PRICES FOR STAMPS ON COVER TO 1945

Nos. 1/20 are very rare used on cover.

Nos. 21/40	*from* × 20
Nos. 41/8	*from* × 100
Nos. 49/56	*from* × 4
Nos. 57/64	*from* × 12
Nos. 65/8	*from* × 2
Nos. 69/97	*from* × 20
Nos. 101/9	*from* × 3
Nos. 110/14	—
Nos. 115/21	*from* × 3
Nos. 122/32	—
Nos. 134/64	*from* × 3
Nos. 165/76	—
Nos. 177/214	*from* × 2

INDEPENDENT KINGDOM OF SAMOA

e first postal service in Samoa was organised by C. L. ths, who had earlier run the *Fiji Times* Express post in . In both instances the principal purpose of the service was listribution of newspapers of which Griffiths was the ietor. The first issue of the *Samoa Times* (later the *Samoa s and South Sea Gazette*) appeared on 6 October 1877 and ewspaper continued in weekly publication until 27 August

il from the Samoa Express post to addresses overseas was d via New South Wales, New Zealand or U.S.A. and ved additional franking with stamps of the receiving ry on landing.

ncellations, inscribed "APIA SAMOA", did not arrive until h 1878 so that examples of Nos. 1/9 used before that date cancelled in manuscript.

1

A
2nd State (Nos. 4/9)

B
3rd State (Nos. 10/19)

(Des H. H. Glover. Litho S. T. Leigh & Co, Sydney, N.S.W.)

377 (1 Oct)–**80**.

A. 1*st state: white line above* "X" *in* "EXPRESS" *not broken.* *P* 12½

	1	1d. ultramarine	£250	£120
		3d. deep scarlet	£300	£130
		6d. bright violet	£300	£110
		a. Pale lilac	£325	£110

2*nd state: white line above* "X" *broken by a spot of colour, and* *ot between top of* "M" *and* "O" *of* "SAMOA". *P* 12½ (1878–79)

	1	1d. ultramarine	90·00	95·00
		3d. bright scarlet	£325	£130
		6d. bright violet	£190	90·00
		1s. dull yellow	£150	90·00
		a. Line above "X" not broken	£180	£120
		b. Perf 12 (1879)	80·00	95·00
		c. Orange-yellow	95·00	£100
		2s. red-brown	£275	£200
		a. Chocolate	£300	£350
		5s. green	£800	£1000
		a. Line above "X" not broken	£1000	£1200

C. 3*rd state: line above* "X" *repaired, dot merged with upper right serif of* "M" (1879). (*a*) *P* 12½

10	1	1d. ultramarine	90·00	90·00
11		3d. vermilion	£120	£120
12		6d. lilac	£120	85·00
13		2s. brown	£250	£250
		a. Chocolate	£250	£250
14		5s. green	£500	£500
		a. Line above "X" not repaired (R.2/3)	£650	

(*b*) *P* 12

15	1	1d. blue	24·00	40·00
		a. Deep blue	32·00	70·00
		b. Ultramarine	28·00	40·00
16		3d. vermilion	48·00	75·00
		a. Carmine-vermilion	48·00	85·00
17		6d. bright violet	40·00	48·00
		a. Deep violet	40·00	80·00
18		2s. deep brown	£150	£250
19		5s. yellow-green	£400	£600
		a. Deep green	£375	£550
		b. Line above "X" not repaired (R.2/3)	£500	

D. 4*th state: spot of colour under middle stroke of* "M". *P* 12 (1880)

20	1	9d. orange-brown	60·00	£120

Originals exist imperf, but are not known used in this state.

On sheets of the 1d., 1st state, at least eight stamps have a stop after "PENNY". In the 2nd state, three stamps have the stop, and in the 3rd state, only one.

In the 1st state, all the stamps, 1d., 3d. and 6d., were in sheets of 20 (5 × 4) and also the 1d. in the 3rd state.

All values in the 2nd state, all values except the 1d. in the 3rd state and No. 20 were in sheets of 10 (5 × 2).

As all sheets of all printings of the originals were imperf at the outer edges, the only stamps which can have perforations on all four sides are Nos. 1 to 3*a*, 10 and 15 to 15*b*, all other originals being imperf on one or two sides.

The perf 12 stamps, which gauge 11.8, are generally very rough but later the machine was repaired and the 1d., 3d. and 6d. are known with clean-cut perforations.

Remainders of the 1d., unissued 2d. rose, 6d. (in sheets of 21 (7 × 3), 3d., 9d., 1s. (in sheets of 12 (4 × 3)) and of the 2s. and 5s. (sheet format unknown) were found in the Samoan post office when the service closed down in 1881. The remainders are rare in complete sheets, but of very little value as singles, compared with the originals.

Reprints of all values, in sheets of 40 (8 × 5), were made after the originals had been withdrawn from sale. These are practically worthless.

The majority of both reprints and remainders are in the 4th state as the 9d. with the spot of colour under the middle stroke of the "M", but a few stamps (both remainders and reprints) do not show this, while on some it is very faint.

There are three known types of forgery, one of which is rather dangerous, the others being crude.

The last mail despatch organised by the proprietors of the Samoa Express took place on 31 August 1881, although one cover is recorded postmarked 24 September 1881.

After the withdrawal of the Samoa Express service it would appear that the Apia municipality appointed a postmaster to continue the overseas post. Covers are known franked with U.S.A. or New Zealand stamps in Samoa, or routed via Fiji.

In December 1886 the municipal postmaster, John Davis, was appointed Postmaster of the Kingdom of Samoa by King Malietoa. Overseas mail sent via New Zealand was subsequently accepted without the addition of New Zealand stamps, although letters to the U.S.A. continued to require such franking until August 1891.

2 Palm Trees

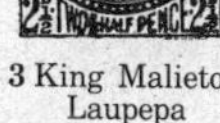

3 King Malietoa Laupepa

4*a* 6 mm

4*b* 7 mm

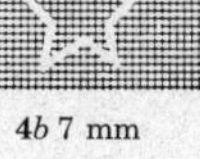

4*c* 4 mm

Description of Watermarks

(These are the same as W **12***a*/*c* of New Zealand)

W 4*a*. 6 mm between "N Z" and star; broad irregular star; comparatively wide "N"; "N Z" 11½ mm wide.

W 4*b*. 7 mm between "N Z" and star; narrower star; narrow "N"; "N Z" 10 mm wide.

W 4*c*. 4 mm between "N Z" and star; narrow star; wide "N"; "N Z" 11 mm wide.

(Des A. E. Cousins (T **3**). Dies eng W. R. Bock and A. E. Cousins (T **2**) or A. E. Cousins (T **3**). Typo Govt Ptg Office, Wellington)

1886–1900. (i) *W* **4***a*. (*a*) *P* 12½ (Oct–Nov 1886).

21	2	½d. purple-brown	21·00	48·00
22		1d. yellow-green	8·50	12·00
23		2d. dull orange	26·00	10·00
24		4d. blue	42·00	10·00
25		1s. rose-carmine	65·00	10·00
		a. Bisected (2½d.) (on cover)*	†	£325
26		2s. 6d. reddish lilac	55·00	70·00

(*b*) *P* 12×11½ (July–Nov 1887)

27	2	½d. purple-brown	70·00	80·00
28		1d. yellow-green	£100	25·00
29		2d. yellow	95·00	£140
30		4d. blue	£250	£200
31		6d. brown-lake	26·00	12·00
32		1s. rose-carmine	—	£190
33		2s. 6d. reddish lilac	£350	

(ii) *W* 4*c*. *P* 12×11½ (May 1890)

34	2	½d. purple-brown	75·00	28·00
35		1d. green	55·00	38·00
36		2d. brown-orange	80·00	38·00
37		4d. blue	£140	5·00
38		6d. brown-lake	£300	11·00
39		1s. rose-carmine	£350	13·00
		x. Wmk reversed	†	30·00
40		2s. 6d. reddish lilac	£400	8·50

(iii) *W* 4*b*. (*a*) *P* 12 × 11½ (1890–92)

41	2	½d. pale purple-brown	4·25	4·25
		a. Blackish purple	4·25	4·25
42		1d. myrtle-green (5.90)	24·00	1·40
		a. Green	24·00	1·40
		b. Yellow-green	24·00	1·40
43		2d. dull orange (5.90)	30·00	1·75
44	3	2½d. rose (11.92)	75·00	3·50
		a. Pale rose	75·00	3·50
45	2	4d. blue	£225	17·00
46		6d. brown-lake	£110	8·50
47		1s. rose-carmine	£225	5·00
48		2s. 6d. slate-lilac	—	7·50

(*b*) *P* 12½ (Mar 1891–92)

49	2	½d. purple-brown		
50		1d. green		
51		2d. orange-yellow	—	£160
52	3	2½d. rose (1.92)	24·00	4·50
53	2	4d. blue	—	£450
54		6d. brown-purple	£2500	£1100
55		1s. rose-carmine	—	£450
56		2s. 6d. slate-lilac		

(*c*) *P* 11 (May 1895–1900)

57	2	½d. purple-brown	2·50	1·75
		a. Deep purple-brown	2·00	1·75
		b. Blackish purple (1900)	1·75	35·00
58		1d. green	6·50	1·75
		a. Bluish green (1897)	6·50	1·75
		b. Deep green (1900)	2·25	22·00
59		2d. pale yellow	40·00	40·00
		a. Orange (1896)	40·00	40·00
		b. Bright yellow (1.97)	11·00	4·75
		c. Pale ochre (10.97)	5·00	1·25
		d. Dull orange (1900)	7·50	
60	3	2½d. rose	2·50	4·50
		a. Deep rose-carmine (1900)	1·75	42·00
61	2	4d. blue	9·00	2·00
		a. Deep blue (1900)	1·25	50·00
62		6d. brown-lake	9·00	3·00
		a. Brown-purple (1900)	1·75	60·00
63		1s. rose	9·00	3·75
		a. Dull rose-carmine/toned (5.98)	2·75	35·00
		b. Carmine (1900)	1·25	
64		2s. 6d. purple	55·00	10·00
		a. Reddish lilac (wmk inverted) (1897)	11·00	7·50
		b. Deep purple/toned (wmk reversed) (5.98)	4·75	9·50
		ba. Imperf between (vert pair)	£350	
		c. Slate-violet	£120	

*Following a fire on 1 April 1895 which destroyed stocks of all stamps except the 1s. value perf 12½, this was bisected diagonally and used as a 2½d. stamp for overseas letters between 24 April and May 1895, and was cancelled in blue. Fresh supplies of the 2½d. did not arrive until July 1895, although other values were available from 23 May.

Examples of the 1s. rose perforated 11, No. 63, were subsequently bisected and supplied cancelled-to-order by the post office to collectors, often with backdated cancellations. Most of these examples were bisected vertically and all were cancelled in black (*Price* £7).

The dates given relate to the earliest dates of printing in the various watermarks and perforations and not to issue dates.

The perf 11 issues (including those later surcharged or overprinted), are very unevenly perforated owing to the large size of the pins. Evenly perforated copies are extremely hard to find.

For the 2½d. black, see Nos. 81/2 and for the ½d. green and 1d. red-brown, see Nos. 88/9.

FIVE PENCE
(5)

FIVE PENCE
(6)

5d
(7)

1893 (Nov–Dec). *Handstamped singly, at Apia.*

(*a*) *In two operations*

65	5	5d. on 4d. blue (37)	50·00	45·00
		a. Bars omitted	£500	£400
66		5d. on 4d. blue (45)	65·00	£100
67	6	5d. on 4d. blue (37)	95·00	£110
68		5d. on 4d. blue (45)	95·00	

(*b*) *In three operations* (Dec)

69	7	5d. on 4d. blue (37) (R.)	24·00	30·00
		a. Stop after "d"	£250	60·00
		b. Bars omitted	—	£400
70		5d. on 4d. blue (45) (R.)	27·00	50·00

In Types **5** and **6** the bars obliterating the original value vary in length from 13½ to 16½ mm and can occur with either the thick bar over the thin one or vice versa.

Double handstamps exist but we do not list them.

No. 69a came from a separate handstamp which applied the "5d." at one operation. Where the "d" was applied separately its position in relation to the "5" naturally varies.

8

Surcharged 1½d. (9)

R 3d. (10)

The "R" in Type **10** indicates use for registration fee.

(Des and die eng A. E. Cousins. Typo New Zealand Govt Ptg Office)

1894–1900. *W* **4***b* *(sideways). (a) P* 11½ × 12.
71 **8** 5d. dull vermilion (3.94) .. .. 32·00 2·75
a. Dull red .. .. 32·00 3·75
(b) P 11
72 **8** 5d. dull red (1895) .. .. .. 19·00 7·00
a. Deep red (1900) .. .. .. 2·50 15·00

1895–1900. *W* **4***b*.
(i) *Handstamped with T* **9** *or* **10.** *(a) P* 12 × 11½ (26.1.95)
73 **2** 1½d. on 2d. dull orange (B.) .. .. 14·00 7·50
74 3d. on 2d. dull orange .. .. .. 42·00 11·00
(b) P 11 (6.95)
75 **2** 1½d. on 2d. orange (B.) .. .. .. 3·00 7·00
a. Pair, one without handstamp ..
b. On 2d. yellow .. .. .. 75·00 60·00
76 3d. on 2d. orange .. .. .. 8·00 9·50
a. On 2d. yellow .. .. .. 75·00 60·00
(ii) *Surch printed*. P* 11
77 **2** 1½d. on 2d. orange-yellow (B.) £100
(iii) *Handstamped as T* **9** *or* **10**.† *P* 11 (1896)
78 **2** 1½d. on 2d. orange-yellow (B.) .. .. 3·00 22·00
79 3d. on 2d. orange-yellow .. .. 3·75 45·00
a. Imperf between (vert pair) .. £425
b. Pair, one without handstamp ..
(iv) *Surch typo as T* **10**. *P* 11 (Feb 1900)
80 **2** 3d. on 2d. deep red-orange (G.) .. 1·50 £130

*It is believed that this was type-set from which clichés were made and set up in a forme and then printed on a hand press. This would account for the clear indentation on the back of the stamp and the variation in the position on the stamps which probably resulted from the clichés becoming loose in the forme.

†In No. 78 the "2" has a serif and the handstamp is in pale greenish blue instead of deep blue. In No. 79 the "R" is slightly narrower. In both instances the stamp is in a different shade.

A special printing in a distinctly different colour was made for No. 80 and the surcharge is in green.

Most of the handstamps exist double.

1896 (Aug). *Printed in the wrong colour. W* **4***b*. *(a) P* 10 × 11.
81 **3** 2½d. black .. .. 1·50 3·00
(b) P 11
82 **3** 2½d. black .. .. 50·00 65·00
a. Mixed perfs 10 and 11 .. .. £350

Surcharged 2½d. (11)

PROVISIONAL GOVT. (12)

1898–99. *W* **4***b*. *P* 11. *(a) Handstamped as T* **11** (10.98).
83 **2** 2½d. on 1s. dull rose-carmine/*toned* .. 42·00 50·00
(b) Surch as T **11** (1899)
84 **2** 2½d. on 1d. bluish green (R.) .. .. 75 3·00
a. Surch inverted .. .. .. — £350
85 2½d. on 1s. dull rose-carmine/*toned* (R.) 7·50 13·00
a. Surch double £350
86 2½d. on 1s. dull rose-carmine/*toned* (Blk.) 7·50 13·00
a. Surch double £450
87 2½d. on 2s. 6d. deep purple/*toned* .. 8·50 15·00

The typographed surcharge was applied in a setting of nine, giving seven types differing in the angle and length of the fractional line, the type of stop, etc.

1899. *Colours changed. W* **4***b*. *P* 11.
88 **2** ½d. dull blue-green .. .. .. 1·60 2·25
a. Deep green .. .. .. 1·60 2·25
89 1d. deep red-brown .. .. .. 2·25 2·25

1899–1900. *Provisional Government. New printings optd with T* **12** *(longer words and shorter letters on 5d.). W* **4***b*. *P* 11.
90 **2** ½d. dull blue-green (R.) .. .. .. 1·75 3·50
a. Yellowish green (1900) .. .. 1·75 4·50
91 1d. chestnut (B.) .. .. .. 2·50 7·00
92 2d. dull orange (R.) .. .. .. 2·50 7·50
a. Orange-yellow (1900) .. .. 2·00 7·50
93 4d. deep dull blue (R.) .. .. .. 70 8·50
94 **8** 5d. dull vermilion (B.) .. .. .. 2·75 8·00
a. Red (1900) .. .. .. 2·75 8·00
95 **2** 6d. brown-lake (B.) .. .. .. 1·50 8·00
96 1s. rose-carmine (B.) .. .. .. 1·50 24·00
97 2s. 6d. reddish purple (R.) .. .. 4·75 21·00
90/7 .. .. *Set of* 8 16·00 80·00

The Samoan group of islands was partitioned on 1 March 1900: Western Samoa (Upolu, Savaii, Apolima and Manono) to Germany and Eastern Samoa (Tutuila, the Manu'a Is and Rose Is) to the United States. German issues of 1900–14 will be found listed in Part 7 (*Germany*) of this catalogue, there were no U.S. issues.

The Samoan Kingdom post office run by John Davis was suspended in March 1900.

WESTERN SAMOA

NEW ZEALAND OCCUPATION

The German Islands of Samoa surrendered to the New Zealand Expeditionary Force on 30 August 1914 and were administered by New Zealand until 1962.

G.R.I. 1d. (13)

G.R.I. 1 Shillings. (14)

SETTINGS. Nos. 101/9 were surcharged by a vertical setting of ten, repeated ten times across the sheet. Nos. 110/14 were from a horizontal setting of four repeated five times in the sheet.

Nos. 101b, 102a and 104a occurred on position 6. The error was corrected during the printing of No. 102.

Nos. 101c, 102c, 104d and 105b are from position 10.

Nos. 101d, 102e and 104b are from position 1.

No. 108b is from position 9.

(Surch by *Samoanische Zeitung*, Apia)

1914 (3 Sept). *German Colonial issue (ship) (no wmk) inscr "SAMOA" surch as T* **13** *or* **14** *(mark values).*
101 ½d. on 3 pf. brown .. .. 30·00 9·00
a. Surch double £650 £500
b. No fraction bar .. .. .. 55·00 30·00
c. Comma after "I" £600 £400
d. "1" to left of "2" in "½" .. .. 55·00 30·00
102 ½d. on 5 pf. green .. .. .. 50·00 11·00
a. No fraction bar .. .. .. £120 55·00
c. Comma after "I" £350 £170
d. Surch double £650 £500
e. "1" to left of "2" in "½" .. .. £100 40·00
103 1d. on 10 pf. carmine .. .. .. 95·00 40·00
a. Surch double £650 £500
104 2½d. on 20 pf. ultramarine .. .. 35·00 10·00
a. No fraction bar .. .. .. 75·00 38·00
b. "1" to left of "2" in "½" .. .. 75·00 38·00
c. Surch inverted £800 £750
d. Comma after "I" £450 £325
e. Surch double £650 £550
105 3d. on 25 pf. black and red/*yellow* .. 55·00 40·00
a. Surch double £750 £600
b. Comma after "I" £4750 £1000
106 4d. on 30 pf. black and orange/*buff* .. £110 60·00
107 5d. on 40 pf. black and carmine .. .. £110 70·00
108 6d. on 50 pf. black and purple/*buff* .. 60·00 35·00
a. Surch double £850 £800
b. Inverted "9" for "6" £170 £100
109 9d. on 80 pf. black and carmine/*rose* .. £200 £100
110 "1 shillings" on 1 m. carmine £3250 £3500
111 "1 shilling" on 1 m. carmine £9500 £7000
112 2s. on 2 m. blue £3000 £2750
113 3s. on 3 m. violet-black £1400 £1200
a. Surch double £8000 £9000
114 5s. on 5 m. carmine and black £1100 £1000
a. Surch double £11000 £11000

No. 108b is distinguishable from 108, as the "d" and the "9" are not in a line, and the upper loop of the "9" turns downwards to the left.

UNAUTHORISED SURCHARGES. Examples of the 2d. on 20 pf., 3d. on 30 pf., 3d. on 40 pf., 4d. on 40 pf., 6d. on 80 pf., 2s. on 3 m. and 2s. on Marshall Islands 2 m., together with a number of errors not listed above, were produced by the printer on stamps supplied by local collectors. These were not authorised by the New Zealand Military Administration.

SAMOA. (15)

1914 (29 Sept)–**15**. *Stamps of New Zealand. T* **50, 51, 52** *and* **27**, *optd as T* **15**, *but opt only 14 mm long on all except 2½d. Wmk "N Z" and Star, W* **43** *of New Zealand.*
115 ½d. yellow-green (R.) (*p* 14×15) 80 30
116 1d. carmine (B.) (*p* 14×15) 80 10
117 2d. mauve (R.) (*p* 14×14½) (10.14) .. 80 1·00
118 2½d. deep blue (R.) (*p* 14) (10.14) .. .. 1·75 1·75
w. Wmk inverted .. .. ..
119 6d. carmine (B.) (*p* 14×14½) (10.14) .. 1·75 1·75
a. Perf 14×13½ .. .. .. 17·00 21·00
b. Vert pair. Nos. 119/a (1915) .. 45·00 75·00
120 6d. pale carmine (B.) (*p* 14×14½) (10.14) 10·00 10·00
121 1s. vermilion (B.) (*p* 14×14½) (10.14) .. 5·00 17·00
115/21 .. .. *Set of* 6 9·50 20·00

1914–24. *Postal Fiscal stamps as Type* F **4** *of New Zealand optd with T* **15**. *W* **43** *of New Zealand (sideways). Chalk-surfaced "De La Rue" paper.*
(a) P 14 (Nov 1914–17)
122 2s. blue (R.) (9.17) .. .. 90·00 £100
123 2s. 6d. grey-brown (B.) (9.17) .. .. 5·50 9·00
124 5s. yellow-green (R.) .. .. .. 12·00 11·00
125 10s. maroon (B.) .. .. 24·00 28·00
126 £1 rose-carmine (B.) .. .. .. 60·00 45·00
(b) P 14½×14, *comb* (1917–24)
127 2s. deep blue (R.) (3.18) .. .. .. 5·50 5·50
128 2s. 6d. grey-brown (B.) (10.24) £225 £140
129 3s. purple (R.) (6.23) .. .. .. 16·00 48·00
130 5s. yellow-green (R.) (9.17) .. .. 15·00 15·00
131 10s. maroon (B.) (11.17) .. .. .. 55·00 45·00
132 £1 rose-carmine (B.) (3.18) .. .. 65·00 70·00

We no longer list the £2 value as it is doubtful if this was used for postal purposes.

See also Nos. 165/6*e*.

1916–19. *King George V stamps of New Zealand optd as T* **15**, *but 14 mm long. (a) Typo. P* 14×15.
134 **61** ½d. yellow-green (R.) 60
135 1½d. slate (R.) (1917) 50
136 1½d. orange-brown (R.) (1919) 30
137 2d. yellow (R.) (14.2.18) .. .. .. 1·50
138 3d. chocolate (B.) (1919) .. .. .. 1·75
(b) Recess. P 14×13½
139 **60** 2½d. blue (R.) 60
a. Perf 14×14½ .. .. 1·25
b. Vert pair. Nos. 139/a .. .. .. 15·00
140 3d. chocolate (B.) (1917) 50
a. Perf 14×14½ 50
b. Vert pair. Nos. 140/a .. .. .. 15·00
141 6d. carmine (B.) (5.5.17) .. .. .. 1·50
a. Perf 14×14½ .. .. 1·50
b. Vert pair. Nos. 141/a .. .. .. 17·00
142 1s. vermilion (B.) .. .. 2·00
a. Perf 14×14½ .. .. 4·75
b. Vert pair. Nos. 142/a .. .. .. 22·00
134/42 .. .. *Set of* 9 8·25

LEAGUE OF NATIONS MANDATE

Administered by New Zealand.

1920 (July). *Victory. Nos. 453/8 of New Zealand optd as T* **15**, *but 14 mm long.*
143 ½d. green (R.) .. .. 3·75
144 1d. carmine (B.) .. .. 2·75
145 1½d. brown-orange (R.) .. .. .. 1·50
146 3d. chocolate (B.) .. .. 8·00
147 6d. violet (R.) .. .. 4·50
148 1s. orange-red (B.) .. .. 13·00 11
143/8 .. .. *Set of* 6 30·00 45

16 Native Hut

SILVER JUBILEE OF KING GEORGE V 1910 - 1935. (17)

(Eng B.W. Recess-printed at Wellington, N.Z.)

1921 (23 Dec). *W* **43** *of New Zealand. (a) P* 14×14½.
149 **16** ½d. green .. .. 2·00
150 1d. lake .. .. 3·25
151 1½d. chestnut 80 1
152 2d. yellow .. .. 2·25
149/52 .. .. *Set of* 4 7·50 1
(b) P 14 × 13½
153 **16** ½d. green .. .. 4·50 1
154 1d. lake .. .. 5·00
155 1½d. chestnut .. .. 10·00 9
156 2d. yellow .. .. 13·00
157 2½d. grey-blue .. .. 1·75 8
158 3d. sepia .. .. 1·75 4
159 4d. violet .. .. 1·75 3
160 5d. light blue .. .. 1·75 7
161 6d. bright carmine .. .. 1·75 6
162 8d. red-brown .. .. 1·75 10
163 9d. olive-green .. .. 2·00 26
164 1s. vermilion .. .. 1·75 24
153/64 .. .. *Set of* 12 42·00 90

1925–28. *Postal Fiscal stamps as Type* F **4** *of New Zealand optd with T* **15**. *W* **43** *of New Zealand (sideways). P* 14½×
(a) Thick, opaque, white chalk-surfaced "Cowan" paper
165 2s. blue (R.) (12.25) £140 £1
166 2s. 6d. deep grey-brown (B.) (10.28) .. 75·00 95·
166*a* 3s. mauve (R.) (9.25) .. .. .. 60·00 75·
166*b* 5s. yellow-green (R.) (11.26) .. .. 16·00 40·
ba. Opt at top of stamp £1100
166*c* 10s. brown-red (B.) (12.25) .. .. .. £140 95·
166*d* £1 rose-pink (B.) (11.26) .. .. .. 65·00 85·
165/6*d* .. .. *Set of* 6 £450 £5
(b) Thin, hard, chalk-surfaced "Wiggins Teape" paper
166*e* £1 rose-pink (B.) (1928) .. .. .. — £9

1926–27. *T* **72** *of New Zealand, optd with T* **15**, *in red.*
(a) "Jones" paper
167 2s. deep blue (11.26) .. .. 5·00 18·
168 3s. mauve (10.26) .. .. 14·00 45·
w. Wmk inverted .. .. 14·00 45·
(b) "Cowan" paper
169 2s. light blue (10.11.27) .. .. .. 6·00 45·
170 3s. pale mauve (10.11.27) .. .. .. 48·00 95·

1932 (Aug). *Postal Fiscal stamps as Type* F **6** *of New Zealand opt with T* **15**. *W* **43** *of New Zealand. Thick, opaque, whi chalk-surfaced "Cowan" paper. P* 14.
171 2s. 6d. deep brown (B.) .. .. .. 16·00 45·
172 5s. green (R.) .. .. 26·00 48·
173 10s. carmine-lake (B.) .. .. .. 45·00 95·
174 £1 pink (B.) .. .. 65·00 £13
175 £2 bright purple (R.) £650
176 £5 indigo-blue (R.) £1700

The £2 and £5 values were primarily for fiscal use.

1935 (7 May). *Silver Jubilee. Optd with T* **17**. *P* 14 × 13½.
177 **16** 1d. lake 30
a. Perf 14 × 14½ .. .. 85·00 £15
178 2½d. grey-blue 60
179 6d. bright carmine .. .. 2·75 2·5
177/9 .. .. *Set of* 3 3·25 3·0

18 Samoan Girl

19 Apia

21 Chief and Wife

25 Lake Lanuto'o

(Recess D.L.R.)

(7 Aug). *T* **18/19, 21, 25** *and similar designs. W* **43** *of New* *aland* ("N Z" *and Star*). *P* 14×13½ (*½d., 2½d., 2s., 3s.*), 14 *l.*) *or* 13½×14 (*others*).

½d. green		10	35
1d. black and carmine		10	10
2d. black and orange		3·50	3·25
aw. Wmk inverted			
b. Perf 13½×14		4·00	4·25
2½d. black and blue		10	10
4d. slate and sepia		70	15
6d. bright magenta		50	10
1s. violet and brown		30	10
2s. green and purple-brown		80	50
3s. blue and brown-orange		1·50	3·50
8	*Set of* 9	6·50	7·00

esigns: *Horiz*—2d. River scene; 4d. Canoe and house; 6d. . Stevenson's home "Vailima"; 1s. Stevenson's Tomb. *Vert T* **25**)—3s. Falefa Falls.

ee also Nos. 200/3.

WESTERN SAMOA.

(27)

5–42. *Postal Fiscal stamps as Type* F **6** *of New Zealand optd ith T* **27**. *W* **43** *of New Zealand. P* 14.

(*a*) *Thick, opaque chalk-surfaced "Cowan" paper* (7.8.35)

2s. 6d. deep brown (B.)	6·00	16·00
5s. green (B.)	12·00	21·00
10s. carmine-lake (B.)	50·00	75·00
£1 pink (B.)	60·00	95·00
£2 bright purple (R.)	£140	£300
£5 indigo-blue (R.)	£250	£475

) *Thin, hard chalk-surfaced "Wiggins, Teape" paper* (1941–42)

4a	5s. green (B.) (6.42)	80·00	£100
4b	10s. pale carmine-lake (B.) (6.41)	£130	£140
4c	£2 bright purple (R.) (2.42)	£450	£700
4d	£5 indigo-blue (R.) (2.42)	£900	£1100

The £2 and £5 values were primarily for fiscal use.

See also Nos. 207/14.

28 Coastal Scene

31 Robert Louis Stevenson

(Des J. Berry (1d. and 1½d.). L. C. Mitchell (2½d. and 7d.). Recess B.W.)

939 (29 Aug). *25th Anniv of New Zealand Control. T* **28, 31** *and similar horiz designs. W* **98** *of New Zealand. P* 13½ × 14 *or* 14 × 13½ (*7d.*).

95	1d. olive-green and scarlet	30	15
96	1½d. light blue and red-brown	45	40
97	2½d. red-brown and blue	90	65
98	7d. violet and slate-green	6·50	3·00
95/8	*Set of* 4	7·50	3·75

Designs:—1½d. Map of Western Samoa; 2½d. Samoan ancing party.

32 Samoan Chief

33 Apia Post Office

(Recess B.W.)

1940 (2 Sept). *W* **98** *of New Zealand* (*Mult* "N Z" *and Star*). *P* 14 × 13½.

199	**32**	3d. on 1½d. brown	30	10

T **32** was not issued without surcharge.

(T **33**. Des L. C. Mitchell. Recess B.W.)

1944–49. *As Nos.* 180, 182/3 *and T* **33**. *W* **98** *of New Zealand* (*Mult* "N Z" *and Star*) (*sideways on 2½d.*). *P* 14 *or* 13½ × 14 (*5d.*).

200	½d. green	30	16·00
202	2d. black and orange	3·00	5·50
203	2½d. black and blue (1948)	4·75	26·00
205	5d. sepia and blue (8.6.49)	1·25	50
200/5	*Set of* 4	8·50	42·00

1945–53. *Postal Fiscal stamps as Type* **F 6** *of New Zealand optd with T* **27**. *W* **98** *of New Zealand. Thin hard, chalk-surfaced "Wiggins Teape" paper. P* 14.

207	2s. 6d. deep brown (B.) (6.45)	7·00	13·00
	w. Wmk inverted	8·00	10·00
208	5s. green (B.) (5.45)	13·00	12·00
	w. Wmk inverted	14·00	13·00
209	10s. carmine-lake (B.) (4.46)	20·00	17·00
	w. Wmk inverted	26·00	28·00
210	£1 pink (B.) (6.48)	90·00	£170
	w. Wmk inverted		
211	30s. brown (8.48)	£150	£300
	w. Wmk inverted	£325	£450
212	£2 bright purple (R.) (11.47)	£160	£275
	w. Wmk inverted	£250	£350
213	£3 green (8.48)	£190	£375
	w. Wmk inverted	£350	£550
214	£5 indigo-blue (R.) (1946)	£325	£450
	w. Wmk inverted (5.53)	£325	£450
207/10	*Set of* 4	£110	£190

The £2 to £5 values were mainly used for fiscal purposes.

See also Nos. 232/5.

WESTERN SAMOA

(34)

1946 (4 June). *Peace Issue. Nos.* 668, 670 *and* 674/5 *of New Zealand optd with T* **34** (*reading up and down at sides on 2d.*).

215	1d. green	10	10
	w. Wmk inverted	£140	
216	2d. purple (B.)	10	10
217	6d. chocolate and vermilion	20	10
218	8d. black and carmine (B.)	20	10
215/18	*Set of* 4	50	30

Nigeria

LAGOS

A British Consul was established at Lagos during 1853 as part of the anti-slavery policy, but the territory was not placed under British administration until occupied by the Royal Navy in August 1861. From 19 February 1866 Lagos was administered with Sierra Leone and from July 1874 as part of Gold Coast. It became a separate colony on 13 January 1886.

Although a postal service had been established by the British G.P.O. in April 1852 no postal markings were supplied to Lagos until 1859. The British G.P.O. retained control of the postal service until June 1863, when it became the responsibility of the colonial authorities.

CROWNED-CIRCLE HANDSTAMPS

CC 1

CC1 CC 1 LAGOS (19.12.1859) .. .. *Price on cover* £1600

First recorded use of No. CC1 is 12 December 1871. It is later known used as a cancellation.

PRICES FOR STAMPS ON COVER

Nos. 1/9	*from* × 10
Nos. 10/26	*from* × 8
Nos. 27/9	—
Nos. 30/8	*from* × 10
Nos. 39/41	—
No. 42	*from* × 20
Nos. 44/50	*from* × 8
Nos. 51/3	—
Nos. 54/60	*from* × 8
Nos. 61/3	—

PRINTERS. All the stamps of Lagos were typographed by D.L.R.

1

1874 (10 June)–**75.** *Wmk Crown CC. P* 12½.

1	1	1d. lilac-mauve	55·00	30·00
2		2d. blue	55·00	27·00
3		3d. red-brown (2.75)	95·00	42·00
4		3d. red-brown and chestnut	85·00	50·00
5		4d. carmine	75·00	40·00
6		6d. blue-green	90·00	11·00
8		1s. orange (value 15½ mm) (2.75)	£400	£140
9		1s. orange (value 16½ mm) (7.75)	£275	60·00
1/9		*Set of* 6	£550	£180

1876–79. *Wmk Crown CC. P* 14.

10	1	1d. lilac-mauve	38·00	18·00
11		2d. blue	38·00	13·00
12		3d. red-brown	£100	18·00
13		3d. chestnut	£110	35·00
14		4d. carmine	£180	11·00
		a. Wmk sideways	£1000	£130
15		6d. green	90·00	6·00
16		1s. orange (value 16½ mm long) (1879)	£600	85·00
10/16		*Set of* 6	£950	£130

1882 (June). *Wmk Crown CA. P* 14.

17	1	1d. lilac-mauve	18·00	10·00
18		2d. blue	£140	4·75
19		3d. chestnut	14·00	5·00
20		4d. carmine	£130	12·00
17/20		*Set of* 4	£275	29·00

1884 (Dec)–**86.** *New values and colours. Wmk Crown CA. P* 14.

21	1	½d. dull green (1885)	2·00	80
22		1d. rose-carmine	2·00	80
		w. Wmk inverted	—	85·00
23		2d. grey	55·00	5·50
24		4d. pale violet	£100	8·50
25		6d. olive-green	8·00	38·00
26		1s. orange (3.85)	7·00	20·00
27		2s. 6d. olive-black (1886)	£275	£250
28		5s. blue (1886)	£500	£425
29		10s. purple-brown (1886)	£1300	£900
21/9		*Set of* 9	£2000	£1500
27s/9s		Optd "Specimen" *Set of* 3	£425	

We would warn collectors against clever forgeries of Nos. 27 to 29 on genuinely watermarked paper.

1887 (Mar)–**1902**. *Wmk Crown CA. P* 14.
30 1 2d. dull mauve and blue .. .. 3·00 2·00
31 2½d. ultramarine (A) (1891) .. .. 3·50 1·75
a. Larger letters of value (B) . .. 22·00 17·00
b. Blue (A) .. .. 80·00 50·00
32 3d. dull mauve and chestnut (4.91) .. 2·50 3·25
33 4d. dull mauve and black .. .. 2·25 1·75
34 5d. dull mauve and green (2.94) .. 2·00 11·00
35 6d. dull mauve and mauve .. .. 4·75 3·00
a. Dull mauve and carmine (10.02) .. 5·00 12·00
36 7½d. dull mauve and carmine (2.94) .. 2·00 27·00
37 10d. dull mauve and yellow (2.94) .. 3·25 13·00
38 1s. yellow-green and black .. .. 5·50 24·00
a. Blue-green and black .. .. 5·00 25·00
39 2s. 6d. green and carmine .. .. 23·00 80·00
40 5s. green and blue .. .. 40·00 £150
41 10s. green and brown .. .. 75·00 £200
30/41 .. .. *Set of* 12 £140 £475
30s/41s Optd "Specimen" .. *Set of* 12 £250

HALF PENNY

(2)

3

1893 (2 Aug). *No. 33 surch with T* **2** *locally.*
42 1 ½d. on 4d. dull mauve and black .. 4·00 2·50
a. Surch double .. .. .. 55·00 55·00
b. Surch treble £120
c. Error. ½d. on 2d. (No. 30) .. .. — £15000

There were two separate settings of No. 42. The most common, of which there were five separate printings, shows "HALF PENNY" 16 mm long and was applied as a horizontal pair or triplet. The scarcer setting, also applied as a triplet, shows "HALF PENNY" 16½ mm long.

Three examples of No. 42c are known, two unused and one used. Only the latter is in private hands.

1904 (22 Jan–Nov). *Wmk Crown CA. P* 14.
44 3 ½d. dull green and green .. .. 1·50 5·50
45 1d. purple and black/*red* .. .. 1·00 15
46 2d. dull purple and blue .. .. 6·00 7·00
47 2½d. dull purple and blue/*blue* (B) .. 1·00 1·50
aw. Wmk inverted .. .. — 65·00
b. Smaller letters of value as A .. 4·50 8·50
bw. Wmk inverted £110 £110
48 3d. dull purple and brown .. .. 2·25 1·75
49 6d. dull purple and mauve .. .. 35·00 10·00
50 1s. green and black .. .. .. 35·00 42·00
51 2s. 6d. green and carmine .. .. 85·00 £190
52 5s. green and blue £150 £275
53 10s. green and brown (Nov) £275 £750
44/53 .. .. *Set of* 10 £500 £1100
44s/53s Optd "Specimen" .. *Set of* 10 £180

1904–06. *Wmk Mult Crown CA. Ordinary paper. P* 14.
54 3 ½d. dull green and green (30.10.04) .. 7·50 2·50
a. Chalk-surfaced paper (12.3.06) .. 10·00 1·75
w. Wmk inverted .. .. ..
55 1d. purple and black/*red* (22.10.04) .. 7·00 10
a. Chalk-surfaced paper (21.9.05) .. 1·50 10
aw. Wmk inverted .. .. .. — 65·00
56 2d. dull purple and blue (2.05) .. .. 2·25 2·00
a. Chalk-surfaced paper (25.9.06) .. 13·00 8·50
aw. Wmk inverted .. .. .. 90·00
57 2½d. dull purple and blue/*blue* (B) (*chalk-surfaced paper*) (13.10.05) .. .. 1·75 16·00
a. Smaller letters of value as A .. 55·00 £120
58 3d. dull purple and brown (27.4.05) .. 3·50 1·25
a. Chalk-surfaced paper (2.8.06) .. 15·00 1·75
w. Wmk inverted .. .. ..
59 6d. dull purple and mauve (31.10.04) .. 6·50 2·25
a. Chalk-surfaced paper (1.3.06) .. 4·25 1·25
60 1s. green and black (15.10.04) .. .. 13·00 17·00
a. Chalk-surfaced paper (4.06) .. 23·00 2·25
w. Wmk inverted .. .. ..
61 2s. 6d. green and carmine (3.12.04) .. 16·00 48·00
a. Chalk-surfaced paper (21.10.06) .. 35·00 48·00
62 5s. green and blue (1.05) .. .. 22·00 95·00
a. Chalk-surfaced paper (21.10.06) .. 60·00 £150
63 10s. green and brown (3.12.04) .. .. 60·00 £200
a. Chalk-surfaced paper (12.3.06) .. 75·00 £190
54/63 .. .. *Set of* 10 £120 £325

Lagos was incorporated into the Colony and Protectorate of Southern Nigeria, previously formed from Niger Coast Protectorate and part of the Niger Company territories, on 16 February 1906. Stamps of Lagos were then authorised for use throughout Southern Nigeria.

NIGER COAST PROTECTORATE

OIL RIVERS PROTECTORATE

A British consulate for the Bights of Benin and Biafra was established in 1849 on the off-shore Spanish island of Fernando Po. In 1853 the appointment was divided with a consul for the Bight of Benin at Lagos. The consulate for the Bight of Biafra was transferred to Old Calabar in 1882.

A British protectorate was proclaimed over the coastal area, with the exceptions of the colony of Lagos and the centre of the Niger delta, on 5 June 1885. It was not, however, until July 1891 that steps were taken to set up an administration with a consul-general at Old Calabar and vice-consuls at some of the river ports.

The consulate-general at Old Calabar and the vice-consulates at Benin, Bonny, Brass, Forcados and Opobo acted as collection and distribution centres for mail from November 1891, but were not recognised as post offices until 20 July 1892.

For a few months from July 1892 local administrative handstamps, as Type Z 1, were in use either as obliterators or in conjunction with the c.d.s.

Z 1

These oval handstamps are usually found on the 1892 overprinted issue, but the following are known on unoverprinted stamps of Great Britain:

1892

BENIN

Stamps of GREAT BRITAIN *cancelled with oval postmark, Type* Z 1, *inscribed* "BENIN".
Z1 2½d. purple/*blue* (V.) £1000

BONNY

Stamps of GREAT BRITAIN *cancelled with oval postmark, Type* Z 1, *inscribed* "BONNY".
Z2 2½d. purple/*blue* (V.) £1000

BRASS RIVER

Stamps of GREAT BRITAIN *cancelled with oval postmark, Type* Z 1, *inscribed* "BRASS".
Z3 2½d. purple/*blue* (Blk.) £750

OLD CALABAR RIVER

Stamps of GREAT BRITAIN *cancelled with oval postmark, Type* Z 1, *inscribed* "OLD CALABAR".
Z4 2½d. purple/*blue* (Blk.) £750

Stamps of GREAT BRITAIN *cancelled* "BRITISH VICE-CONSULATE OLD CALABAR" *within double-lined circle.*
Z5 2½d. purple/*blue* (V.) £450
Z6 5d. dull purple and blue (V.) .. ..

For later use of Type Z 1 and the circular Vice-Consulate marks see note beneath No. 6.

Z 2.

Unoverprinted stamps of Great Britain remained officially valid for postage in the Protectorate until 30 September 1892, but were available from post offices in the Niger Company Territories up to the end of 1899. The two areas were so closely linked geographically that offices in the Protectorate continued to accept letters franked with Great Britain stamps until the reorganisation of 1900. The listing below covers confirmed examples, known on cover or piece, the prices quoted being for the latter.

1892 *to* **1899**

Stamps of GREAT BRITAIN *cancelled with circular postmarks as Type* Z **2**.

BENIN RIVER

Z 7 2d. green and carmine .. ..
Z 8 2½d. purple/*blue* £550
Z 9 3d. purple/*yellow* £550
Z10 5d. dull purple and blue .. .. ..
Z11 1s. green .. ..

BONNY RIVER

Z12 ½d. vermilion £375
Z12*a* 1d. lilac £325
Z13 2½d. purple/*blue* £275
Z14 5d. dull purple and blue £375
Z15 6d. deep purple/*red* £375

BRASS RIVER

Z16 1½d. dull purple and green £800
Z17 2½d. purple/*blue* £700
Z17*a* 2½d. purple/*blue* (squared-circle cancellation) £850
Z18 6d. purple/*red* £750

FORCADOS RIVER

Z19 1d. lilac £600
Z20 2½d. purple/*blue* .. ..
Z21 5d. dull purple and blue (m/s cancellation)
Z22 10d. dull purple and carmine .. ..

OLD CALABAR RIVER

Z23 ½d. vermilion £325
Z24 1d. lilac £275
Z25 1½d. dull purple and green £375
Z26 2d. green and vermilion £375
Z27 2½d. purple/*blue* £275
Z28 5d. dull purple and blue £375
Z29 6d. purple/*red* £375
Z30 1s. green £475

OPOBO RIVER

Z31 2½d. purple/*blue* .. ..
Z32 10d. dull purple and carmine .. ..

Some later covers are known franked with G.B. stamps, b origin of the stamps involved is uncertain.

PRICES FOR STAMPS ON COVER

Nos. 1/6	*from* × 12
Nos. 7/36	*from* × 4
Nos. 37/44	—
Nos. 45/50	*from* × 10
Nos. 51/6	*from* × 12
Nos. 57/65	*from* × 3
Nos. 66/73	*from* × 12

BRITISH PROTECTORATE

OIL RIVERS

(1)

(2)

1892 (20 July)–**94.** *Nos.* 172, 197, 200/1, 207*a and* 211 *of G Britain optd by D.L.R. with T* **1**.
1 ½d. vermilion .. .. 9·50
2 1d. lilac .. .. 5·50
a. Opt reversed "OIL RIVERS" at top .. £4250
b. Bisected (½d.) (on cover) .. .. † £2
3 2d. grey-green and carmine .. .. 20·00
a. Bisected (1d.) (on cover) .. .. † £2
4 2½d. purple/*blue* .. .. 6·50
5 5d. dull purple and blue (Die II (No. 207*a*)) 8·00
a. On Die I (No. 207) .. .. ..
6 1s. dull green .. .. 55·00 7
1/6 .. .. *Set of* 6 90·00 9
1s/6s H/S "Specimen" .. .. *Set of* 6 £250

Nos. 2b and 3a were used at Bonny River during August September 1894.

Die II of the 5d. shows thin vertical lines to the right of "5 On Die I there are square dots in this position.

OVAL HANDSTAMPS. In addition to Nos. Z1/4 postmark Type Z 1 are also known used on the 1892–94 overprinted is from the following offices:

Bakana (Nos. 2, 4/6)
Benin (Nos. 1/6)
Bonny (No. 2)
Brass (Nos. 3/5)
Buguma (Nos. 4 and 6)
Old Calabar (No. 4)
Opobo (Nos. 1/3)
Sombreiro River (Nos. 1/6)

The Vice-Consulate marks, as Nos. Z5/6, are also known str on examples of No. 4 from Bonny, Forcados or Old Calabar.

Nos. 2 to 6 surcharged locally

1893 (3 Sept). *Issued at Old Calabar. Surch with T* **2** *and th bisected.*
7 ½d. on half of 1d. (R.) £150 £1
a. Unsevered pair £450 £4
ab. Surch inverted and dividing line reversed (unsevered pair) .. .. — £95
b. Surch reversed (dividing line running from left to right) (unsevered pair) .. — £95
c. Straight top to "1" in ½ £350 £3
d. "½" omitted .. .. ..
e. Surch double (unsevered pair with normal) .. .. — £16
f. Vert *se-tenant* pair. Nos. 7a/8a .. — £120
8 ½d. on half of 1d. (V.) £4000 £37
a. Unsevered pair £9500 £90
b. Surch double (pair) £15000

The surcharge was applied in a setting covering one horizont row at a time. Violet ink was used for the top row in the first she but was then replaced with red.

HALF PENNY. (3) **HALF PENNY.** (4)

In T **3** "HALF" measures 9½ mm and "PENNY" 12½ mm wi space 1½ mm between the words. Bar 14½ mm ending below th stop. The "F" is nearly always defective.

In T **4** "HALF" is 8½ mm, "PENNY" 12½ mm, spacing 2½ mr and bar 16 mm, extending beyond the stop.

HALF PENN.Y **5** (Stop after "N") **HALF PENNY** **6** (No stop after "N")

In T **5** the "P" and "Y" are raised, and the space between th words is about 4 mm. Bar is short, approx 13½ mm. T **6** is simila but without the stop after "N".

Half Penny (7)   Half Penny (8)

7 the "a" and "e" are narrow and have a short upward al hook. The "l" has a very small hook. The letters "nny" urved serifs, and the distance between the words is 5½ mm. 8 the "a" and "e" are wider. The "l" has a wider hook. The "nny" have straight serifs, and the distance between the is 4¼ mm.

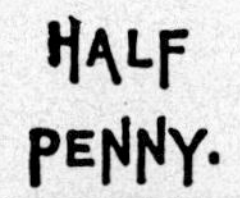

(9)

HALF PENNY (10)

(Dec). *Issued at Old Calabar. Nos. 3/4 handstamped.*

(*a*) *With T* **3**

½d. on 2d. (V.) £500 £300
a. Surch inverted £4250
b. Surch diagonal (up or down) .. £2250
c. Surch vertical (up or down) .. £2750
½d. on 2½d. (Verm.) £8500
½d. on 2½d. (C.) £20000

(*b*) *With T* **4**

½d. on 2½d. (G.) £250 £250
a. Surch double £2000 £2000
b. Surch diagonally inverted £2750
½d. on 2½d. (Verm.) £700 £300
½d. on 2½d. (C.) £350 £350
a. Surch omitted (in pair) .. ..
½d. on 2½d. (B.) £325 £400
½d. on 2½d. (Blk.) £3500
a. Surch inverted £5500
b. Surch diagonal inverted (up or down) £4000
½d. on 2½d. (B.-Blk.) £3250

(*c*) *With T* **5**

½d. on 2½d. (Verm.) £650 £200
a. Surch double .. .. .. — £1300
b. Surch vertical (up) .. .. — £2750

(*d*) *With T* **6**

½d. on 2d. (V.) £600 £350
½d. on 2½d. (Verm.) £275 £300
a. Surch inverted £2250
b. Surch double .. .. .. — £1600
c. Surch diagonal (up or down) .. £1400
d. Surch omitted (in strip of 3) .. £11000
e. Surch vertical (up or down) .. £1800
f. Surch diagonal, inverted (up or down) £1800

(*e*) *With T* **7**

½d. on 2d. (V.) £300 £225
a. Surch double .. .. .. — £5500
b. Surch vertical (up or down) .. £2500
c. Surch diagonal (up or down) .. £2000
d. Surch diagonal (inverted) .. £3250
e. Surch inverted .. .. ..
½d. on 2½d. (Verm.) £275 £180
a. Surch double £4000
b. Surch vertical (up or down) .. £1800
c. Surch inverted £2250
d. Surch diagonal (up or down) .. £1300
e. Surch diagonal, inverted (up) .. £3250
½d. on 2½d. (B.) £9000 £9000
½d. on 2½d. (C.) £8500
½d. on 2½d. (V.) £4250

(*f*) *With T* **8**

½d. on 2½d. (Verm.) £425 £550
a. Surch diagonal (up) £1900
½d. on 2½d. (B.) £20000
½d. on 2½d. (G.) £375 £450
a. Surch double £5000
½d. on 2½d. (C.) £15000 £15000

(*g*) *With T* **9**

½d. on 2d. (V.) £300 £325
½d. on 2d. (B.) £1300 £600
a. Surch double .. .. ..
½d. on 2½d. (Verm.) £450 £500
a. Surch double .. .. ..
½d. on 2½d. (B.) £300 £300
½d. on 2½d. (G.) £325 £375
a. Surch double (G.) £1600
b. Surch double (G. + Verm.) .. ..
½d. on 2½d. (V.) £4000

(*h*) *With T* **10**

½d. on 2½d. (G.) £400 £450
½d. on 2½d. (Verm.) £5500

Various types of surcharges on Nos. 9 to 36 were printed on e same sheet, and different types in different colours may be und *se-tenant* (*Prices, from £1700 per pair, unused*).

One Shilling (11)   5/- (12)

893 (Dec). *Issued at Old Calabar. Nos. 3 and 5/6 handstamped.*

(*a*) *With T* **11**

7 1s. on 2d. (V.) £400 £350
a. Surch inverted £4250
b. Surch vertical (up or down) .. £3500
c. Surch diagonal (up or down) .. £2500
d. Surch diagonal, inverted (up or down) £4000
e. Pair, Nos. 37 and 38 .. .. £2000
8 1s. on 2d. (Verm.) £550 £3750
a. Surch inverted £6000
b. Surch diagonal (up or down) .. £4000
c. Surch vertical (up or down) .. £6000

39 1s. on 2d. (Blk.) £5500
a. Surch inverted £10000
b. Surch vertical (up or down) .. £8500
c. Surch diagonal (up) £6500

(*b*) *As T* **12**

40 5s. on 2d. (V.) £9000 £10000
a. Surch inverted £15000
b. Surch vertical (up or down) .. £15000 £15000
c. Surch diagonal (down) £15000
41 10s. on 5d. (Verm.) £6000 £8000
a. Surch inverted £14000
b. Surch vertical (up or down) .. £14000
c. Surch diagonal (down) .. ..
42 20s. on 1s. (V.) £70000
a. Surch inverted £90000
43 20s. on 1s. (Verm.) £70000
44 20s. on 1s. (Blk.) £70000

There are two main settings of the "One Shilling" surcharge:—

Type A. The "O" is over the "hi" of "Shilling" and the downstrokes on the "n" in "One", if extended, would meet the "ll" of "Shilling". The "g" is always raised. Type A is known in all three colours from one sheet of 120.

Type B. The "O" is over the first "i" of "Shilling" and the downstrokes of the "n" would meet the "li" of "Shilling". Type B is known in violet (two sheets) and vermilion (one sheet).

NIGER COAST PROTECTORATE

The protectorate was extended into the interior and the name changed to Niger Coast Protectorate on 12 May 1893.

PERFORATION. There are a number of small variations in the perforation of the Waterlow issues of 1893 to 1898 which were due to irregularity of the pins rather than different perforators.

In the following lists, stamps perf 12, 12½, 13 or compound are described as perf 12–13, stamps perf 13½, 14 or compound are described as perf 13½–14 and those perf 14½, 15 or compound are listed as perf 14½–15. In addition the 13½–14 perforation exists compound with 14½–15 and with 12–13, whilst perf 15½–16 comes from a separate perforator.

13

14

(Des G. D. Drummond. Recess Waterlow)

1894 (1 Jan). *T* **13** (*with* "OIL RIVERS" *obliterated and* "NIGER COAST" *in top margin*). *Various frames. No wmk. Thick and thin papers. P* 14½–15.

45 ½d. vermilion .. .. .. 4·00 3·75
a. Perf 13½–14 .. .. .. 7·00 7·50
46 1d. pale blue .. .. .. 6·00 3·25
a. Bisected (½d.) (on cover) .. † £550
b. Dull blue .. .. .. 3·75 3·25
ba. Bisected (½d.) (on cover) .. † £450
c. Perf 13½–14 .. .. .. 4·00
d. Perf 13½–14, comp 12–13 ..
e. Perf 12–13 .. .. .. — 32·00
47 2d. green .. .. .. 27·00 23·00
a. Imperf between (horiz pair) .. † £4500
b. Bisected (1d.) (on cover) .. † £700
c. Perf 14½–15, comp 12–13 ..
d. Perf 13½–14 .. .. .. 19·00 13·00
e. Perf 13½–14, comp 12–13 .. 35·00 29·00
f. Perf 12–13 .. .. ..
48 2½d. carmine-lake .. .. .. 8·50 3·50
a. Perf 13½–14 .. .. .. 12·00 9·00
b. Perf 13½–14, comp 12–13 ..
c. Perf 12–13 .. .. ..
49 5d. grey-lilac .. .. .. 16·00 12·00
a. Lilac (1894) .. .. .. 14·00 18·00
b. Perf 13½–14 .. .. .. 14·00 13·00
50 1s. black .. .. .. 14·00 12·00
a. Perf 14½–15, comp 12–13 ..
b. Perf 13½–14 .. .. .. 26·00 22·00
c. Perf 13½–14, comp 12–13 .. 27·00
d. Perf 14½–15, comp 13½–14 .. — 38·00
45/50 .. .. .. *Set of* 6 55·00 42·00

There were three printings of each value, in November 1893, Jan 1894 and March 1894.

Nos. 46a, 46ba and 47b were used at Bonny River during August and September 1894.

(Recess Waterlow)

1894 (May). *T* **14** (*various frames*). *No wmk. P* 14½–15.

51 ½d. yellow-green .. .. .. 4·75 4·50
a. Deep green .. .. .. 5·50 5·50
b. Perf 14½–15, comp 13½–14 ..
c. Perf 13½–14 .. .. .. 7·00 7·00
d. Perf 13½–14, comp 12–13 .. 18·00
52 1d. orange-vermilion .. .. .. 16·00 10·00
a. Vermilion .. .. .. 13·00 7·50
b. Bisected diagonally (½d.) (on cover) † £500
c. Perf 15½–16 .. .. ..
d. Perf 13½–14 .. .. .. 18·00
e. Perf 13½–14, comp 12–13 .. — 14·00
53 2d. lake .. .. .. 29·00 6·50
a. Bisected diagonally (1d.) (on cover)
b. Perf 13½–14 .. .. .. 30·00 7·00
c. Perf 13½–14, comp 12–13 .. 40·00
54 2½d. blue .. .. .. 14·00 3·75
a. Pale blue .. .. .. 8·50 7·50
b. Perf 13½–14 .. .. .. 19·00
55 5d. purple .. .. .. 6·00 5·50
a. Deep violet .. .. .. 6·00 5·50
56 1s. black .. .. .. 35·00 15·00
a. Perf 13½–14 .. .. .. 35·00 7·00
b. Perf 13½–14, comp 12–13 .. 42·00
51/6 .. .. .. *Set of* 6 85·00 30·00

Nos. 52b and 53a were used at Bonny River during August and September 1894.

½ (15)   1 (16)   ONE HALF PENNY (17)

1894. *Provisionals. Issued at Opobo.*

(*a*) *Nos.* 46*b and* 46 *bisected vertically and surch with T* **15** (May–June)

57 "½" on half of 1d dull blue (R.) (May) .. £1000 £375
a. Surch inverted (in strip of 3 with normals) £9500
58 "½" on half of 1d. pale blue (R.) (June) .. £700 £275
a. Surch *tête-bêche* (pair) .. ..
b. Surcharge inverted £3750

(*b*) *No.* 3 *bisected vertically and surch*

(i) *With T* **16** (12 *mm high*) (June–Oct)

59 "1" on half of 2d. (Verm.) £1400 £300
a. Surch double £2500 £1200
b. Surch inverted .. .. .. — £1500
c. Unsevered pair .. .. .. † —

(ii) *Smaller* "1" (4¾ *mm high*)

60 "1" on half of 2d. (C.) .. .. .. — £4250

(iii) *Smaller* "1" (3¾ *mm high*)

61 "1" on half of 2d. (C.) .. ..

Nos. 60 and 61 exist *se-tenant*. (*Price* £20000 *used*)

(*c*) *No.* 52*a bisected, surch with T* **15** (Aug–Sept)

62 ½ on half of 1d. vermilion (Blk.) .. £3250 £850
63 ½ on half of 1d. vermilion (V.) .. £2250 £550
64 ½ on half of 1d. vermilion (B.) .. £1800 £375
a. "½" double .. .. .. — £2500

The stamp is found divided down the middle and also diagonally.

1894 (10 Aug). *Issued at Old Calabar. No.* 54 *surch with T* **17** *and two bars through value at foot.*

65 ½d. on 2½d. blue £350 £225
a. Surch double £2750 £1500
b. "OIE" for "ONE" £1500 £1000
c. Ditto. Surch double .. .. — £4250

There are eight types in the setting of Type **17**, arranged as a horizontal row. No. 65b occurred on No. 8 in the setting at some point during surcharging.

(Recess Waterlow)

1897 (Mar)–**98**. *As T* **14** (*various frames*). *Wmk Crown CA. P* 14½–15.

66 ½d. green (7.97) .. .. .. 3·50 1·50
a. Sage-green .. .. .. 4·25 2·25
b. Perf 13½–14 .. .. .. 3·25 3·00
c. Perf 15½–16 .. .. .. 12·00 6·50
d. Perf 13½–14, comp 12–13 .. 18·00
x. Wmk reversed .. .. .. 75·00
67 1d. orange-vermilion .. .. .. 4·50 1·50
a. Vermilion .. .. .. 4·50 1·50
b. Imperf vert (horiz pair) .. £4250
c. Perf 15½–16 .. .. .. 8·00 6·50
d. Perf 13½–14 .. .. .. 2·50 2·75
e. Perf 13½–14, comp 12–13 .. — 10·00
68 2d. lake (7.97) .. .. .. 1·75 1·75
a. Perf 15½–16 .. .. .. 4·00 2·25
b. Perf 13½–14 .. .. .. 4·00 3·75
c. Perf 13½–14, comp 12–13 .. 23·00
x. Wmk reversed .. .. .. 75·00 75·00
69 2½d. slate-blue (8.97) .. .. .. 7·50 2·00
a. Deep bright blue .. .. .. 8·50 1·75
b. Perf 13½–14 .. .. .. 6·00 4·00
c. Perf 15½–16 .. .. .. — 30·00
w. Wmk inverted .. .. ..
70 5d. red-violet (*p* 13½–14) (1898) .. 9·00 60·00
a. Purple .. .. .. 9·00 65·00
b. Perf 13½–14, comp 12–13 .. 19·00
71 6d. yellow-brown (6.98) .. .. 7·00 6·50
a. Perf 13½–14 .. .. .. 8·50
b. Perf 15½–16 .. .. .. — 17·00
x. Wmk reversed .. .. ..
72 1s. black (1898) .. .. .. 15·00 29·00
a. Perf 13½–14 .. .. .. 14·00 29·00
b. Perf 13½–14, comp 12–13 .. 38·00
73 2s. 6d. olive-bistre (6.98) .. .. 50·00
a. Perf 15½–16 .. .. .. 50·00
b. Perf 13½–14 .. .. .. 22·00 75·00
74 10s. deep violet (6.98) .. .. 95·00 £170
a. Bright violet .. .. .. 95·00 £170
b. Perf 13½–14 .. .. .. 80·00 £160
ba. Bright violet .. .. .. 80·00 £160
c. Perf 13½–14, comp 12–13 .. £150
66/74 .. .. .. *Set of* 9 £130 £300
71s, 73s/4s Optd "Specimen" .. *Set of* 3 £225

Owing to temporary shortages in Southern Nigeria, the above issue was again in use at various times from 1902 until 1907.

On 1 January 1900 the Niger Coast Protectorate together with the southern portion of the Niger Company Territories became the protectorate of Southern Nigeria.

NIGER COMPANY TERRITORIES

Following the development of trade along the Niger, British commercial interests formed the United African Company in 1879 which became the National African Company in 1882 and the Royal Niger Company in 1886. A charter was granted to the Company in the same year to administer territory along the Rivers Niger and Benue over which a British protectorate had been proclaimed in June 1885. The Company's territories extended to the Niger delta to provide access to the interior.

Post Offices were opened at Akassa (1887), Burutu (1896), Lokoja (1899) and Abutshi (1899). The stamps of Great Britain were used from 1888.

On the establishment of postal services in 1887 the Company arranged with the British G.P.O. that unstamped mail marked with their handstamps would be delivered in Great Britain, the recipients only being charged the normal rate of postage from West Africa. This system was difficult to administer, however, so the British authorities agreed in 1888 to the supply of G.B. stamps for use at the Company post offices.

Initially the stamps on such covers were left uncancelled until the mail arrived in the United Kingdom, the Company handstamp being struck elsewhere on the address side. This method continued to be used until early 1896, although a number of covers from the twelve months prior to that date do show the Company handstamp cancelling the stamps. Some of these covers were later recancelled on arrival in Great Britain. From May 1896 the postage stamps were cancelled in the Niger Territories.

In the following listings no attempt has been made to cover the use of the Company marks on the reverse of envelopes.

Dates given are those of earliest known postmarks. Colour of postmarks in brackets. Where two or more colours are given, price is for cheapest. Illustrations are reduced to two-thirds linear of the actual size.

Stamps of GREAT BRITAIN *cancelled as indicated below.*

ABUTSHI

1899. *Cancelled as T* **8**, *but inscribed* "THE ROYAL NIGER CO. C. & L. ABUTSHI" *with* "CUSTOMS (date) OFFICE" *in central oval.*

Z1		½d. vermilion (V.)	£550
Z2		1d. lilac (V.)	£400
Z3		2½d. purple/*blue* (V.)	£550
Z4		5d. dull purple and blue (V.)	£600
Z5		10d. dull purple and carmine (V.)	£700
Z6		2s. 6d. deep lilac (V.)	£800

AKASSA

The listings for Nos. Z7/15*a* are for *covers* on which the Akassa handstamp appears on the front, but is *not* used as a cancellation for the G.B. stamps. Examples of Nos. Z16/26 occur, from 1895–96, with the handstamp struck on the front of the cover away from the stamps, or, from 1896, used as a cancellation. The prices quoted are for *single stamps* showing the cancellation; covers from either period being worth considerably more. On Nos. Z29/42*b* the handstamp was used as a cancellation and the prices quoted are for *single stamps.*

1

2

1888–90. *Cancelled as T* **3**, *but with Maltese cross each side of* "AKASSA". *Size* 36×22 *mm.*

Z7		6d. deep purple/*red* (V.)	£1100

1889–94. *Size* 39×24 *mm.*

Z 8	1	2½d. purple/*blue* (V.)	£600
Z 9		3d. purple/*yellow* (V.)	
Z10		5d. dull purple and blue (V.)	
Z11		6d. deep purple/*red* (V.)	£400
Z12		10d. dull purple and carmine (V.)	
Z12*a*		1s. green (V.)	
Z13		2s. 6d. lilac (V.)	

1894–95.

Z14	2	1d. lilac (V.)	£400
Z15		2½d. purple/*lilac* (V.)	
Z15*a*		2s. 6d. lilac (V.)	

3

THE ROYAL NIGER COMPANY
CHARTERED & LIMITED.
7 - AUG. 98
POST OFFICE
AKASSA.

4

1895. *Size* 39×25 *mm.*

Z16	3	2½d. purple/*blue* (V.)	

1895–99.

Z17	4	½d. vermilion (V.)	75·00
Z18		1d. lilac (V.)	70·00
Z19		2d. green and vermilion (V.)	£400
Z20		2½d. purple/*blue* (V.)	38·00
Z21		3d. purple/*yellow* (V.)	£275
Z22		5d. dull purple and blue (V.)	55·00
Z23		6d. deep purple/*red* (V.)	£275
Z24		9d. dull purple and blue (V.)	£350
Z25		10d. dull purple and carmine (V.)	90·00
Z26		2s. 6d. deep lilac (V.)	£225

THE ROYAL NIGER COMPANY,
CHARTERED & LIMITED.
4 NOV. 1889
POST OFFICE,
AKASSA.

5

1897–99.

Z29	5	½d. vermilion (V.)	55·00
Z30		1d. lilac (V.)	48·00
		a. "RECD" for year in postmark	£550
Z31		2d. green and vermilion (V.)	£200
Z32		2½d. purple/*blue* (V.)	55·00
		a. "RECD" for year in postmark (1898)	£1000
Z33		3d. purple/*yellow* (V.)	£190
Z34		4d. green and brown (V.)	£225
Z35		4½d. green and carmine (V.)	£800
Z36		5d. dull purple and blue (V.)	70·00
Z37		6d. deep purple/*red* (V.)	£225
Z38		9d. dull purple and blue (V.)	£375
Z39		10d. dull purple and carmine (V.)	£170
Z40		1s. green (V.)	£700
Z41		2s. 6d. deep lilac (V.)	£325

1899. *Cancelled as T* **7**, *but inscribed* "AKASSA".

Z42		5d. dull purple and blue (V.)	£1000

1899. *Cancelled as T* **4**, *but* "CUSTOMS DEPT" *in place of* "POST OFFICE".

Z42*a*		1d. lilac (V.)	£600
Z42*b*		2½d. purple/*blue* (V.)	£600

BURUTU

6

1896–99. *Cancelled as T* **6**, "BURUTU" *in sans-serif caps. Size* 44×24 *mm.*

Z43	6	½d. vermilion (V., Blk.)	95·00
Z44		1d. lilac (V.)	85·00
Z45		1½d. dull purple and green (V.)	£350
Z46		2d. green and carmine (V.)	£200
Z47		2½d. purple/*blue* (V., Blk.)	38·00
Z48		3d. purple/*yellow* (V., Blk.)	£200
Z49		4d. green and brown (V.)	£200
Z50		5d. dull purple and blue (V., Blk.)	75·00
Z51		6d. deep purple/*red* (V.)	£250
Z52		9d. dull purple and blue (V.)	£375
Z53		10d. dull purple and carmine (V., Blk.)	£130
Z54		1s. green (V.)	£650
Z55		2s. 6d. lilac (V.)	£275

1898–99. *Cancelled as T* **4**, *but inscribed* "BURUTU" *in serifed caps. Size* 44×27 *mm.*

Z56		½d. vermilion (V., Blk.)	65·00
Z57		1d. lilac (V., Blk.)	48·00
Z58		2d. green and vermilion (V.)	£300
Z59		2½d. purple/*blue* (V., Blk.)	48·00
Z60		3d. purple/*yellow* (V.)	£250
Z61		4d. green and brown (V.)	£250
Z62		4½d. green and carmine (V.)	£800
Z63		5d. dull purple and blue (V.)	75·00
Z64		6d. deep purple/*red* (V.)	£275
Z65		9d. dull purple and blue (V.)	£400
Z66		10d. dull purple and carmine (V., Blk.)	£120
Z67		2s. 6d. lilac (V., Blk.)	£325

7

1898–99.

Z68	7	1d. lilac (V.)	
Z69		2½d. purple/*blue* (V.)	£325

1899. *Cancelled as T* **4**, *but inscribed* "CUSTOM DEPT. BURUTU".

Z70		1d. lilac (V.)	

LOKOJA

LOKOJA
-8 OCT 1899
POST OFFICE.

8

1899.

Z71	8	½d. vermilion (V.)	£110
Z72		1d. lilac (V.)	80·00
Z73		2½d. purple/*blue* (V.)	£250
Z74		5d. dull purple and blue (V.)	£375
Z75		10d. dull purple and carmine (V.)	£425
Z76		2s. 6d. deep lilac (V.)	£500

AGENT GENERAL NIGER TERRITORIES

The listings for Nos. Z78/9 are for covers showing a handstamp struck on the address side, but *not* used as a cancellation for the G.B. stamp.

1894–99. *Cancelled as T* **8**, *but inscribed* "AGENT GENERAL NIGER TERRITORIES".

Z77		1d. lilac (V.)	
Z78		2½d. purple/*blue* (V.)	£1100

1895–96. *Cancelled as T* **7**, *but inscribed as Nos.* Z77/8.

Z79		2½d. purple/*blue* (V.)	£1100
Z80		5d. dull purple and blue (V.)	
Z81		10d. dull purple and carmine (V.)	
Z82		2s. 6d. deep lilac (V.)	

It is now believed that these cancellations may have been used at Asaba. They all occur on covers with Akassa handstamps, often of different dates.

The British Government purchased the Royal Niger Company territories and from 1 January 1900 they were incorporated into the protectorates of Northern and Southern Nigeria. Of the post offices listed above only Lokoja was then situated in Northern Nigeria, the remainder joining Niger Coast in forming Southern Nigeria.

Issues for Northern Nigeria did not reach Lokoja until sometime in March 1900 and the post office there continued to use unoverprinted stamps of Great Britain until these supplies arrived.

NORTHERN NIGERIA

The protectorate of Northern Nigeria was formec January 1900 from the northern part of the Niger Cc Territories. Only one post office existed in this area, at and this continued to use unoverprinted stamps of C BRITAIN until the arrival of Nos. 1/9 during April 1900

PRICES FOR STAMPS ON COVER	
Nos. 1/7	*from* × 6
Nos. 8/9	—
Nos. 10/16	*from* × 5
Nos. 17/19	—
Nos. 20/6	*from* × 5
No. 27	—
Nos. 28/37	*from* × 5
Nos. 38/9	—
Nos. 40/9	*from* × 5
Nos. 50/2	—

PRINTERS. All issues were typographed by De La Rue & C

1

2

1900 (Apr). *Wmk Crown CA. P* 14.

1	1	½d. dull mauve and green	2·75
2		1d. dull mauve and carmine	3·50
3		2d. dull mauve and yellow	12·00
4		2½d. dull mauve and ultramarine	9·00
5	2	5d. dull mauve and chestnut	20·00
6		6d. dull mauve and violet	18·00
7	1	1s. green and black	24·00
8		2s. 6d. green and ultramarine	90·00
9		10s. green and brown	£200
1/9		*Set of* 9	£325
1s/9s Optd "Specimen"		*Set of* 9	£180

Examples of all values are known showing a forged Nor Nigeria postmark dated "AU 14 1900".

3

4

1902 (1 July). *Wmk Crown CA. P* 14.

10	3	½d. dull purple and green	2·00	
11		1d. dull purple and carmine	2·25	
12		2d. dull purple and yellow	2·00	
13		2½d. dull purple and ultramarine	1·50	
14	4	5d. dull purple and chestnut	2·50	
15		6d. dull purple and violet	6·00	
16	3	1s. green and black	3·50	
17		2s. 6d. green and ultramarine	8·00	4
18		10s. green and brown	48·00	5
10/18		*Set of* 9	65·00	
10s/18s Optd "Specimen"		*Set of* 9	£150	

1904 (Apr). *Wmk Mult Crown CA. P* 14.

19	4	£25 green and carmine	£38000

No. 19, although utilising the "POSTAGE & REVENUE" type, was intended to pay the fiscal fee for liquor licences.

1905 (Aug)–**07.** *Wmk Mult Crown CA. Ordinary paper. P*

20	3	½d. dull purple and green (10.05)	16·00	
		a. Chalk-surfaced paper (1906)	5·50	
21		1d. dull purple and carmine	16·00	
		a. Chalk-surfaced paper (1906)	5·00	
22		2d. dull purple and yellow (10.05)	13·00	32
		a. Chalk-surfaced paper (1907)	19·00	23
23		2½d. dull purple and ultramarine (10.05)	6·50	7
24	4	5d. dull purple and chestnut (10.05)	24·00	60
		a. Chalk-surfaced paper (1907)	35·00	60
25		6d. dull purple and violet (10.05)	27·00	45
		a. Chalk-surfaced paper (1906)	32·00	32
26	3	1s. green and black (10.05)	55·00	90
		a. Chalk-surfaced paper (1906)	22·00	48
27		2s. 6d. green and ultramarine (10.05)	48·00	50
		a. Chalk-surfaced paper (1906)	30·00	48
20/7		*Set of* 8	£120	£2

1910 (30 Jan)–**11.** *Wmk Mult Crown CA. Ordinary paper* (½ *to* 2½*d.*) *or chalk-surfaced paper* (*others*). *P* 14.

28	3	½d. green (15.4.10)	2·00	1
29		1d. carmine	2·00	1
30		2d. grey (26.10.11)	4·25	2
31		2½d. blue (10.10.)	2·25	7·
32	4	3d. purple/*yellow* (10.9.11)	3·50	
34		5d. dull purple and olive-green (26.2.11)	4·00	10·
35		6d. dull purple and purple (10.11.10)	6·00	14·
		a. Dull and bright purple (1911)	5·00	6·
36	3	1s. black/*green* (10.11.10)	2·25	
37		2s. 6d. black and red/*blue* (15.3.11)	10·00	27·
38	4	5s. green and red/*yellow* (10.9.11)	23·00	75·
39	3	10s. green and red/*green* (15.3.11)	42·00	48·
28/39		*Set of* 11	90·00	£1
28s/39s Optd "Specimen"		*Set of* 11	£225	

5

6

Wmk Mult Crown CA. Ordinary paper (½d., 1d., 2d.) *or k-surfaced paper* (*others*). *P* 14.

½d. deep green .. 1·25 60
1d. red .. 1·25 60
2d. grey .. 3·00 6·50
3d. purple/*yellow* .. 2·25 1·25
4d. black and red/*yellow* .. 1·25 2·25
5d. dull purple and olive-green .. 4·00 8·00
6d. dull and bright purple .. 4·00 4·25
9d. dull purple and carmine .. 2·00 12·00
1s. black/*green* .. 4·50 2·25
2s. 6d. black and red/*blue* .. 7·00 35·00
5s. green and red/*yellow* .. 20·00 80·00
10s. green and red/*green* .. 38·00 48·00
£1 purple and black/*red* .. £170 £110
.. *Set of* 13 £225 £275
s Optd "Specimen" .. *Set of* 13 £200

amples of most values are known showing forged arks of Lokoja dated "MR 22 12" or Minna dated "JN 16 . These forged postmarks have also been seen on examples lier issues.

1 January 1914 Northern Nigeria became part of Nigeria.

SOUTHERN NIGERIA

Colony and Protectorate of Southern Nigeria was formed January 1900 by the amalgamation of Niger Coast ctorate with the southern part of the Niger Territories. was incorporated into the territory on 1 May 1906.

The stamps of NIGER COAST PROTECTORATE were used Southern Nigeria until the introduction of Nos. 1/9, and also ring a shortage of these values in mid-1902. The issues of GOS were utilized throughout Southern Nigeria after 1 ay 1906 until supplies were exhausted.

PRICES FOR STAMPS ON COVER

Nos. 1/7	*from* × 8
Nos. 8/9	—
Nos. 10/18	*from* × 4
Nos. 19/20	—
Nos. 21/30	*from* × 4
Nos. 31/2	—
Nos. 33/42	*from* × 4
Nos. 43/4	—
Nos. 45/53	*from* × 4
Nos. 55/6	—

NTERS. All issues of Southern Nigeria were typographed by a Rue & Co, Ltd, London.

1

2

3

1 (Mar)–02. *Wmk Crown CA. P* 14.

½d. black and pale green .. 1·75 2·25
a. Sepia and green (1902) .. 2·25 2·50
1d. black and carmine .. 1·40 1·50
a. Sepia and carmine (1902) .. 2·25 1·75
2d. black and red-brown .. 3·25 3·75
4d. black and sage-green .. 2·75 15·00
6d. black and purple .. 2·75 6·50
1s. green and black .. 8·00 25·00
2s. 6d. black and brown .. 45·00 80·00
5s. black and orange-yellow .. 48·00 95·00
10s. black and purple/*yellow* .. 85·00 £160
.. *Set of* 9 £180 £350
9s Optd "Specimen" .. *Set of* 9 £140

03 (Mar)–04. *Wmk Crown CA. P* 14.

2 ½d. grey-black and pale green .. 1·00 30
w. Wmk inverted
1d. grey-black and carmine .. 1·25 70
2d. grey-black and chestnut .. 6·50 1·50
2½d. grey-black and blue (1904) .. 2·00 75
4d. grey-black and olive-green .. 2·75 5·50
6d. grey-black and purple .. 4·00 8·00
1s. green and black .. 29·00 19·00
2s. 6d. grey-black and brown .. 26·00 55·00
5s. grey-black and yellow .. 55·00 £130
10s. grey-black and purple/*yellow* .. 28·00 90·00
£1 green and violet .. £300 £600
/20 .. *Set of* 11 £400 £800
s/20s Optd "Specimen" .. *Set of* 11 £180

Two Dies of Head Plate:

A

B

In Head A the fifth line of shading on the king's cheek shows as line of dots and the lines of shading up to the king's hair are roken in places. In Head B the lines of shading are more regular, specially the fifth line.

1904 (June)–**09.** *Head Die A. Wmk Mult Crown CA. Ordinary paper. P* 14.

21 2 ½d. grey-black and pale green .. 50 10
a. Chalk-surfaced paper (1905) .. 1·25 90
22 1d. grey-black and carmine .. 12·00 20
a. Chalk-surfaced paper (1905) .. 12·00 10
23 2d. grey-black and chestnut (1905) .. 2·50 45
a. Pale grey and chestnut (Head Die B) (1907) .. 4·50 40
24 2½d. grey-black and bright blue (9.09) .. 1·00 1·00
25 3d. orange-brown & bright purple (*chalk-surfaced paper*) (Head Die B) (18.8.07) 9·50 1·25
s. Optd "Specimen" .. 20·00
26 4d. grey-black and olive-green (12.05) .. 14·00 25·00
a. Chalk-surfaced paper (1906) .. 26·00 30·00
ab. Grey-black and pale olive-green (Head Die B) (1907) .. 38·00 29·00
27 6d. grey-black and bright purple (12.05) 12·00 3·50
a. Chalk-surfaced paper (1906) .. 13·00 5·00
ab. Head Die B (1907) .. 18·00 2·25
28 1s. grey-green and black (19.9.07) .. 3·25 3·50
a. Chalk-surfaced paper (Head Die B) (1907) .. 35·00 3·25
29 2s. 6d. grey-black and brown (30.4.06) 24·00 17·00
a. Chalk-surfaced paper (1906) .. 38·00 13·00
ab. Head Die B (1907) .. 32·00 14·00
30 5s. grey-black and yellow (10.12.07) .. 40·00 70·00
a. Chalk-surfaced paper (Head Die B) (1908) .. 55·00 70·00
31 10s. grey-black and purple/*yellow* (*chalk-surfaced paper*) (Head Die B) (9.08) £100 £160
32 £1 green and violet (19.3.06) .. £180 £225
a. Chalk-surfaced paper (1906) .. £190 £225
ab. Head Die B (1907) .. £140 £180
21/32 .. *Set of* 12 £325 £400

I

II

Die I. Thick "1", small "d". (double working plate).
Die II. Thinner "1", larger "d" (single working plate).

1907–11. *Colours changed. Head Die B. Ordinary paper* (½d. *to* 2½d.) *or chalk-surfaced paper* (*others*). *Wmk Mult Crown CA. P* 14.

33 2 ½d. pale green (1907) .. 1·50 20
a. Head Die A .. 6·00 65
b. Blue-green (1910) .. 2·25 20
34 1d. carmine (I) (12.8.07) .. 3·25 60
a. Head Die A .. 9·00 1·00
ab. Die II. *Carmine-red* (1910) .. 75 10
35 2d. greyish slate (9.09) .. 2·50 70
36 2½d. blue (9.09) .. 2·00 3·75
37 3d. purple/*yellow* (7.09) .. 2·00 30
38 4d. black and red/*yellow* (9.09) .. 2·25 80
39 6d. dull purple and purple (9.09) .. 25·00 3·25
a. Dull purple and bright purple (1911) 26·00 3·25
aw. Wmk inverted
40 1s. black/*green* (7.09) .. 7·00 40
41 2s. 6d. black and red/*blue* (9.09) .. 5·00 1·00
42 5s. green and red/*yellow* (9.09) .. 38·00 48·00
43 10s. green and red/*green* (9.09) .. 60·00 90·00
44 £1 purple and black/*red* (9.09) .. £180 £200
33/44 .. *Set of* 12 £300 £300
33s/44s Optd "Specimen" .. *Set of* 12 £225

1912. *Wmk Mult Crown CA. P* 14.

45 3 ½d. green .. 1·75 10
46 1d. red .. 1·50 10
w. Wmk inverted .. — £110
47 2d. grey .. 75 85
48 2½d. bright blue .. 2·75 2·75
49 3d. purple/*yellow* .. 1·00 30
50 4d. black and red/*yellow* .. 1·25 2·00
51 6d. dull and bright purple .. 1·25 1·25
52 1s. black/*green* .. 2·75 75
53 2s. 6d. black and red/*blue* .. 8·00 28·00
54 5s. green and red/*yellow* .. 20·00 75·00
55 10s. green and red/*green* .. 45·00 90·00
56 £1 purple and black/*red* .. £170 £200
45/56 .. *Set of* 12 £225 £350
45s/56s Optd "Specimen" .. *Set of* 12 £200

STAMP BOOKLETS

1904. *Black on red cover. Stapled.*
SB1 2s. 1d. booklet containing twenty-four 1d (No. 11) in blocks of 6 ..

1905 (1 June)–**06.** *Black on red cover. Stapled.*
SB2 2s. 1d. booklet containing twenty-four 1d. (No. 22) in blocks of 6 .. £1500
a. As No. SB2 but containing No. 22a (1906) .. £1500

1907 (7 Oct). *Black on red cover. Stapled.*
SB3 2s. 1d. booklet containing twenty-four 1d (No. 34) in blocks of 6 .. £2000

1910 (19 Sept). *Black on red cover. Stapled.*
SB4 2s. booklet containing eleven ½d. and eighteen 1d. (Nos. 33*b*, 34ab) in blocks of 6 or 5 ..

1912 (Oct). *Black on red cover. Stapled.*
SB5 2s. booklet containing twelve ½d. and eighteen 1d. (Nos. 45/6) in blocks of 6 .. £1500

On 1 January 1914 Southern Nigeria became part of Nigeria.

COVER PRICES

Cover factors are quoted at the beginning of each country for most issues to 1945. An explanation of the system can be found on page x. The factors quoted do not, however, apply to philatelic covers.

NIGERIA

Nigeria was formed on 1 January 1914 from the former protectorates of Northern and Southern Nigeria.

PRICES FOR STAMPS ON COVER TO 1945

Nos. 1/10	*from* × 3
Nos. 11/12	—
Nos. 15/28	*from* × 3
Nos. 29/a	—
Nos. 30/3	*from* × 3
Nos. 34/59	*from* × 2

CROWN COLONY

1

2

(Typo D.L.R.)

1914 (1 June)–**29.** *Die I. Wmk Mult Crown CA. Ordinary paper* (½d. *to* 2½d.) *or chalk-surfaced paper* (*others*). *P* 14.

1 1 ½d. green .. 4·50 70
2 1d. carmine-red .. 4·75 10
a. Scarlet (1916) .. 7·00 20
w. Wmk inverted .. 80·00 £100
3 2d. grey .. 8·00 1·75
a. Slate-grey (1918) .. 9·00 75
4 2½d. bright blue .. 6·00 2·75
a. Dull blue (1915) .. 10·00 3·75
5 2 3d. purple/*yellow* (*white back*) .. 3·25 10·00
a. Lemon back (19.8.15) .. 1·50 2·75
b. On deep yellow (*yellow back*) (*thick paper*) (1915) .. 27·00 7·50
bs. Optd "Specimen" .. 38·00
c. On orange-buff (1920) .. 9·00 22·00
d. On buff (1920) .. 11·00
e. On pale yellow (1921) .. 11·00 15·00
6 4d. black and red/*yellow* (*white back*) .. 1·40 10·00
a. Lemon back (19.8.15) .. 1·00 4·25
b. On deep yellow (*yellow back*) (*thick paper*) (1915) .. 27·00 8·00
bs. Optd "Specimen" .. 38·00
c. On orange-buff (1920) .. 11·00 10·00
d. On buff (1920) .. 11·00
e. On pale yellow (1921) .. 10·00 17·00
7 6d. dull purple and bright purple .. 9·00 9·50
8 1 1s. black/*blue-green* (*white back*) .. 1·50 20·00
a. On yellow-green (*white back*) (1915) £150
b. Yellow-green back (19.8.15) .. 35·00 35·00
c. Blue-green back (1915) .. 1·00 9·50
cs. Optd "Specimen" .. 38·00
d. Pale olive back (1917) .. 24·00 24·00
dw. Wmk inverted
e. On emerald (*pale olive back*) (1920) 8·00 28·00
f. On emerald (*emerald back*) (1920) 1·25 15·00
9 2s. 6d. black and red/*blue* .. 16·00 6·50
10 2 5s. green and red/*yellow* (*white back*) .. 12·00 48·00
a. Lemon back (19.8.15) .. 21·00 50·00
b. On deep yellow (*yellow back*) (*thick paper*) (1915) .. 50·00 65·00
bs. Optd "Specimen" .. 42·00
c. On orange-buff (1920) .. 40·00 80·00
d. On buff (1920) .. 50·00
e. On pale yellow (1921) .. 60·00 £120
11 1 10s. green and red/*blue-green* (*white back*) 45·00 £140
a. Blue-green back (19.8.15) .. 48·00 85·00
as. Optd "Specimen" .. 48·00
b. Pale olive back (1917) .. £700 £1200
c. On emerald (*pale olive back*) (1920) 95·00 £140
d. On emerald (*emerald back*) (1921) 35·00 95·00
12 2 £1 deep purple and black/*red* .. £160 £200
a. Purple and black/red (1917) .. £160 £190
b. Die II. *Dp purple & blk/red* (19.1.27) £170 £275
ba. Purple and black/red (1929) .. £180 £275
1/12 .. *Set of* 12 £225 £300
1s/12s Optd "Specimen" .. *Set of* 12 £300

The ½d. and 1d. were printed in sheets of 240 using two plates one above the other.

1921–32. *Wmk Mult Script CA. Ordinary paper* (½d. *to* 3d.) *or chalk-surfaced paper* (*others*). *P* 14.

15 1 ½d. green (Die I) (1921) .. 1·25 40
aw. Wmk inverted .. 70·00 70·00
b. Die II (1925) .. 3·75 85
c. Vert gutter pair. Die I and Die II. Nos. 15/b (1925) .. £160
16 1d. rose-carmine (Die I) (1921) .. 3·25 30
aw. Wmk inverted .. 65·00 65·00
b. Die II (1925) .. 1·75 55
c. Vert gutter pair. Die I and Die II. Nos. 16/b (1925) .. £160
17 2 1½d. orange (Die II) (1.4.31) .. 4·25 15
18 1 2d. grey (Die I) (1921) .. 1·50 4·75
a. Die II (1924) .. 7·50 40
19 2d. chestnut (Die II) (1.10.27) .. 4·50 1·00
20 2d. chocolate (Die II) (1.7.28) .. 1·25 15
a. Die I (1932) .. 5·50 75
21 2½d. bright blue (Die I) (1921) .. 1·00 6·00
22 2 3d. bright violet (Die I) (1924) .. 5·00 3·25
a. Die II (1925) .. 10·00 1·50
23 3d. bright blue (Die II) (1.4.31) .. 6·00 1·50
24 4d. black & red/*pale yellow* (Die II) (1923) 65 55
a. Die I (1932) .. 5·50 7·00
25 6d. dull purple & brt purple (Die I) (1921) 12·00 17·00
a. Die II (1923) .. 7·00 8·00
aw. Wmk inverted .. 80·00
26 1 1s. black/*emerald* (Die II) (1924) .. 1·25 2·00
27 2s. 6d. black and red/*blue* (Die II) (1925) 6·50 24·00
a. Die I (1932) .. 40·00 65·00
28 2 5s. green & red/*pale yellow* (Die II) (1926) 15·00 65·00
a. Die I (1932) .. 65·00 £170

29 1 10s. green and red/*green* (Die II) (1925) 55·00 £180
a. Die I (1932) .. £100 £375
15/29 .. *Set of* 15 £100 £250
15s/29s (*ex* 5s.) Optd or Perf (1½d., 3d. blue) "Specimen" .. *Set of* 14 £350

The ½d. and 1d., together with the 1½d. from 1932, were printed in sheets of 240 using two plates one above the other. Nos. 15c and 16c come from printings in November 1924 which combined Key Plate No. 7 (Die I) above Key Plate No. 12 (Die II).

1935 (6 May). *Silver Jubilee. As Nos.* 91/4 *of Antigua, but ptd by Waterlow. P* 11×12.
30 1½d. ultramarine and grey .. 80 1·00
31 2d. green and indigo .. 1·50 1·00
k. Kite and vertical log .. 70·00
32 3d. brown and deep blue .. 3·00 10·00
33 1s. slate and purple .. 3·00 26·00
30/3 .. *Set of* 4 7·50 35·00
30s/3s Perf "Specimen" .. *Set of* 4 75·00

For illustration of plate variety see Omnibus section following Zanzibar.

3 Apapa Wharf

4 Fishing Village

5 Victoria-Buea Road

(Recess D.L.R.)

1936 (1 Feb). *Designs as T* **3/5**. *Wmk Mult Script CA*.

(*a*) *P* 11½ × 13

34 ½d. green .. 1·50 1·40
35 1d. carmine .. 50 40
36 1½d. brown .. 2·00 40
a. Perf 12½ × 13½ .. 48·00 4·00
37 2d. black .. 50 80
38 3d. blue .. 2·00 1·50
a. Perf 12½ × 13½ .. 90·00 24·00
39 4d. red-brown .. 2·00 2·00
40 6d. dull violet .. 50 60
41 1s. sage-green .. 1·75 4·75

(*b*) *P* 14

42 2s. 6d. black and ultramarine .. 3·50 21·00
43 5s. black and olive-green .. 6·00 26·00
44 10s. black and grey .. 45·00 70·00
45 £1 black and orange .. 75·00 £150
34/45 .. *Set of* 12 £120 £250
34s/45s Perf "Specimen" .. *Set of* 12 £225

Designs: *Vert as T* **3/4**—1d. Cocoa; 1½d. Tin dredger; 2d. Timber industry; 4d. Cotton ginnery; 6d. Habe minaret; 1s. Fulani Cattle. *Horiz as T* **5**—5s. Oil Palms; 10s. River Niger at Jebba; £1, Canoe pulling.

1937 (12 May). *Coronation. As Nos.* 95/7 *of Antigua. P* 11×11½.
46 1d. carmine .. 30 2·00
47 1½d. brown .. 1·25 2·25
48 3d. blue .. 1·40 2·25
46/8 .. *Set of* 3 2·75 6·00
46s/8s Perf "Specimen" .. *Set of* 3 55·00

15 King George VI

16 Victoria-Buea Road

(Recess B.W. (T **15**), D.L.R. (others))

1938 (1 May)–**51**. *Designs as T* **15/16**. *Wmk Mult Script CA. P* 12 (*T* **15**) *or* 13×11½ (*others*).
49 **15** ½d. green .. 10 10
a. Perf 11½ (15.2.50) .. 90 20
50 1d. carmine .. 19·00 2·50
a. Rose-red (*shades*) (1940) .. 75 30
ab. "A" of "CA" missing from wmk ..
50*b* 1d. bright purple (1.12.44) .. 10 20
ba. Perf 11½ (15.2.50) .. 30 50
bw. Wmk inverted (*p* 12) ..
51 1½d. brown .. 20 10
a. Perf 11½ (15.11.50) .. 10 10
52 2d. black .. 10 1·00
52*a* 2d. rose-red (1.12.44) .. 10 80
ab. Perf 11½ (15.2.50) .. 10 50
52*b* 2½d. orange (4.41) .. 10 70
53 3d. blue .. 10 10
a. Wmk sideways .. † £3000
53*b* 3d. black (1.12.44) .. 15 50
54 4d. orange .. 48·00 2·75
54*a* 4d. blue (1.12.44) .. 15 1·75
55 6d. blackish purple .. 40 10
a. Perf 11½ (17.4.51) .. 90 60
56 1s. sage-green .. 60 10
a. Perf 11½ (15.2.50) .. 15 10
57 **15** 1s. 3d. light blue (1940) .. 90 30
a. Perf 11½ (14.6.50) .. 80 70
ab. Wmk sideways .. † £2750
58 **16** 2s. 6d. black and blue .. 60·00 13·00
a. Perf 13½ (6.42) .. 3·75 4·25
ab. Black and deep blue (1947) .. 55·00 55·00
b. Perf 14 (1942) .. 2·25 3·50
c. Perf 12 (15.8.51) .. 1·75 3·75
59 – 5s. black and orange .. £110 12·00
a. Perf 13½ (8.42) .. 5·50 4·50
b. Perf 14 (1948) .. 6·00 3·00
c. Perf 12 (19.5.49) .. 5·50 4·00
49/59c .. *Set of* 16 50·00 12·00
49s/59s (*ex* 2½d.) Perf "Specimen" *Set of* 15 £200

Design: *Horiz as T* **16**—5s. R. Niger at Jebba.

The 1d., No. 50ba, exists in coils constructed from normal sheets.

1946 (21 Oct). *Victory. As Nos.* 110/11 *of Antigua*.
60 1½d. chocolate .. 25 10
61 4d. blue .. 25 1·25
60s/1s Perf "Specimen" .. *Set of* 2 55·00

1948 (20 Dec). *Royal Silver Wedding. As Nos.* 112/13 *of Antigua*.
62 1d. bright purple .. 35 30
63 5s. brown-orange .. 5·00 8·50

1949 (10 Oct). *75th Anniv of U.P.U. As Nos.* 114/17 *of Antigua*.
64 1d. bright reddish purple .. 15 10
65 3d. deep blue .. 1·00 2·50
66 6d. purple .. 30 2·25
67 1s. olive .. 50 1·75
64/7 .. *Set of* 4 1·75 6·00

STAMP BOOKLETS

1915. *Crimson cover.*
SB1 2s. booklet containing twelve ½d. and eighteen 1d. (Nos. 1/2) in blocks of 6 ..

1921–26. *Black on scarlet cover. Stapled.*
SB2 4s. booklet containing twelve 1d. and eighteen 2d. grey (both Die I) (Nos. 16, 18) in blocks of 6
a. Containing Nos. 16 and 18a (Die II) (1924) .. £1500
b. Containing Nos. 16b and 18a (both Die II) (1926) ..

1928. *Scarlet cover.*
SB5 4s. booklet containing twelve 1d. (Die II) and eighteen 2d. chestnut (Nos. 16b, 19) in blocks of 6 ..

1929.
SB6 4s. booklet containing twelve 1d. (Die II) and eighteen 2d. chocolate (Nos. 16b, 20) in blocks of 6 ..

1931 (Jan).
SB7 4s. booklet containing twelve 1d. and twenty-four 1½d. (Nos. 16a, 17) in blocks of 6 ..

Niue
see after New Zealand

Norfolk Island
see after Australia

North Borneo

PRICES FOR STAMPS ON COVER TO 1945

No. 1	*from* × 100
Nos. 2/3	*from* × 10
Nos. 4/5	—
Nos. 6/19	*from* × 10
Nos. 19*b*/21*b*	—
Nos. 22/8	*from* × 50
Nos. 29/35	—
Nos. 36/44	*from* × 100
Nos. 45/50	—
Nos. 51/2	*from* × 10
No. 54	—
Nos. 55/65	*from* × 10
Nos. 66/79	*from* × 4
Nos. 81/6	—
Nos. 87/91	*from* × 12
Nos. 92/111	*from* × 4
Nos. 112/26	*from* × 10
Nos. 127/40	*from* × 6
Nos. 141/5	—
Nos. 146/57	*from* × 5
Nos. 158/79	*from* × 8
Nos. 181/5	—
Nos. 186/8	*from* × 10
Nos. 189/230	*from* × 4
Nos. 231/4	—
Nos. 235/49	*from* × 3
Nos. 250/2	—
Nos. 253/75	*from* × 12
Nos. 276/92	*from* × 7
Nos. 293/4	—
Nos. 295/300	*from* × 6
Nos. 301/2	—
Nos. 303/17	*from* × 3
Nos. 318/19	*from* × 20
Nos. 320/34	*from* × 3
Nos. D1/30	*from* × 25
Nos. D31/6	*from* × 12
No. D37	—
Nos. D38/84	*from* × 40
Nos. D85/9	*from* × 8

BRITISH NORTH BORNEO COMPANY ADMINISTRATION

PRINTERS. The stamps of this country up to 1894 were design by T. Macdonald and printed in lithography by Blades, East a. Blades, London.

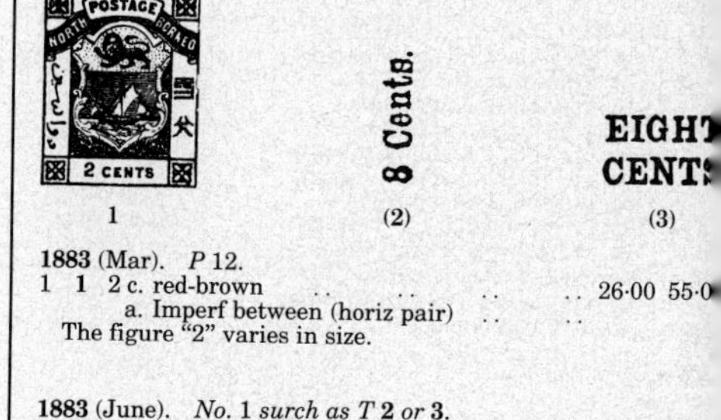
1 (2) (3)

1883 (Mar). *P* 12.
1 1 2 c. red-brown .. 26·00 55·0
a. Imperf between (horiz pair) ..

The figure "2" varies in size.

1883 (June). *No.* 1 *surch as T* **2** *or* **3**.
2 2 8 c. on 2 c. red-brown .. £950 £65
3 3 8 c. on 2 c. red-brown .. £450 £19
a. Surch double .. † £400

Type **2** was handstamped and stamps without stop are generall forgeries. Type **3** was a setting of 50 (10 × 5) providing ten varietie it normally has a stop which sometimes failed to print.

CANCELLED-TO-ORDER—Prices are separately indicated in a third price column, for stamps showing the recognisable black bars remainder cancellation. The issues since 1916 have not been thus cancelled.

It should be noted, however, that a postmark of this form was in use for postal purposes up to this period, and was used at one or two of the smaller post-offices until 1949. A small oval with five bars was used to mark railway mail during 1945/55 and also as a paquebot mark at Jesselton *c.* 1950.

4

5

and
Revenue
(6)

P 14.
50 c. violet .. .. £110 — 23·00
a. Inverted "L" for first "F" in "FIFTY" (R.5/2) .. .. £800 — £160
$1 scarlet .. .. £100 — 10·00

(July). *P* 12.
4 c. pink .. .. 42·00 50·00
a. Imperf (horiz pair) .. .. .. † —
8 c. green .. .. 75·00 55·00

P 14.
½ c. magenta .. .. 90·00 £180
1 c. orange £180 £325
a. Imperf (pair) £275 £275
b. Imperf horiz (vert pair) £900
2 c. brown .. .. 24·00 23·00
a. Imperf between (horiz pair) £550
4 c. pink .. .. 17·00 50·00
8 c. green .. .. 19·00 50·00
a. Imperf between (horiz pair) £750
10 c. blue .. .. 27·00 50·00
a. Imperf (pair) £300
.. .. *Set of* 6 £325 £600
perforate examples of the 4 c. pink are listed under No. 6a.

(Sept). *Nos.* 8 *and* 13 *optd with T* **6**.
½ c. magenta £100 £180
10 c. blue £150 £180

3 ENTS (7)   5 CENTS (8)   3 CENTS Small "3" variety (R.3/1, 3/4, 3/7)

(Surchd by *North Borneo Herald*, Sandakan)

6 (Sept). *T* **1** *surch as T* **7/8**. (*a*) *P* 12.
7 3 c. on 4 c. pink £160 £225
a. Small "3" .. .. — £5000
8 5 c. on 8 c. green £180 £225

(*b*) *P* 14
7 3 c. on 4 c. pink .. .. 85·00 £110
a. Small "3" £1600
8 5 c. on 8 c. green .. .. 90·00 £110
a. Surch inverted £2000

9

10

11

12

13

86–87. (*a*) *P* 14.
b **9** ½ c. magenta .. .. 15·00 50·00
½ c. rose .. .. 2·75 13·00
a. Imperf (pair) .. .. .. 28·00
1 c. orange-yellow .. .. .. 8·50 26·00
a. Imperf between (vert pair) .. £300
b. Imperf (pair) .. .. .. 35·00
1 c. orange .. .. 2·00 8·00
a. Imperf (pair) .. .. .. 27·00
2 c. brown .. .. 2·00 8·50
a. Imperf (pair) .. .. .. 27·00
4 c. pink .. .. 2·75 9·50
a. Imperf (pair) .. .. .. 28·00
b. Imperf between (horiz or vert pair) £250
c. Imperf vert (horiz pair) £250
d. Error. 1 c. pink (R. 2/3) (centre stamp of strip of 3) £190 £475
da. Imperf between (pair) .. ..
db. Imperf (pair) £3500

27 **9** 8 c. green .. .. 9·00 18·00
a. Imperf (pair) .. .. .. 27·00
28 10 c. blue .. .. 7·00 25·00
a. Imperf between (vert pair) .. £325
b. Imperf (pair) .. .. .. 27·00
29 **10** 25 c. indigo .. .. £160 11·00
a. Imperf between (vert pair) ..
b. Imperf (pair) .. .. .. £250 25·00
30 **11** 50 c. violet .. .. £225 13·00
a. Imperf (pair) .. .. .. £325 25·00
31 **12** $1 scarlet .. .. £250 11·00
a. Imperf (pair) .. .. .. £325 25·00
32 **13** $2 sage-green .. .. £325 17·00
a. Imperf (pair) .. .. .. £225 27·00
22/32 .. .. *Set of* 10 £900 £120

(*b*) *P* 12
34 **9** ½ c. magenta £160 £325
35 1 c. orange £130 £170

Nos. 21*b*/32 are known to have been sold as cancelled remainders, but these are difficult to distinguish from postally used. Values above 10 c. are infrequently found postally used so that the used prices quoted are for the remainders.

14

15

16

17

18

1888–92. *T* **14** (*as T* **9** *but inscr* "POSTAGE & REVENUE") *and T* **15/18** (*T* **10/13** *redrawn*). *P* 14.
36 **14** ½ c. magenta (1889) .. .. 4·00 24·00 2·00
a. Imperf vert (horiz pair) .. † † £200
b. Rose .. .. 1·25 4·00 60
ba. Imperf between (horiz pair) £350
c. Imperf (pair) .. .. 27·00 — 8·50
37 1 c. orange (1892) .. .. 1·75 3·75 50
a. Imperf vert (horiz pair) .. £300
b. Imperf (pair) .. .. 27·00 — 7·50
38 2 c. brown (1889) .. .. 7·50 12·00 90
a. Imperf between (horiz pair) † † £350
b. Lake-brown .. .. 3·25 12·00 50
c. Imperf (pair) .. .. 27·00 — 7·00
39 3 c. violet (1889) .. .. 2·50 11·00 50
b. Imperf (pair) .. .. 21·00 — 7·00
40 4 c. rose-pink (1889) .. .. 5·00 28·00 50
a. Imperf between (pair) .. — £150 —
b. Imperf (pair) .. .. 27·00 — 7·50
41 5 c. slate (1889) .. .. 2·75 19·00 50
a. Imperf between (pair) ..
b. Imperf (pair) .. .. 27·00 — 7·50
42 6 c. lake (1892) .. .. 7·50 19·00 50
a. Imperf (pair) .. .. 27·00 — 9·00
43 8 c. blue-green (1891) .. 22·00 27·00 1·00
a. Yellow-green .. .. 17·00 23·00 50
c. Imperf (pair) .. .. 27·00 — 9·00
44 10 c. blue (1891) .. .. 8·00 25·00 1·00
a. Imperf between (vert pair) .. † † £200
b. Dull blue .. .. 6·50 19·00 50
ba. Imperf between (horiz pair)
d. Imperf (pair) .. .. 27·00 — 8·50
45 **15** 25 c. indigo .. .. .. 50·00 80·00 75
a. Imperf (pair) .. .. £180 † 14·00
b. Imperf vert (horiz pair) .. † † £275
46 **16** 50 c. violet .. .. .. 80·00 £130 75
a. Imperf (pair) .. .. £250 † 14·00
b. Chalky blue .. .. † £120 †
47 **17** $1 scarlet .. .. .. 27·00 £110 75
a. Imperf (pair) .. .. £180 † 14·00
48 **18** $2 dull green .. .. £120 £170 1·50
a. Imperf (pair) .. .. £300 † 16·00
36*b*/48 .. .. *Set of* 13 £275 £550 7·50

Nos. 39, 43 and 44 showing stamps printed double or triple, one inverted, are from waste sheets subsequently sold by the British North Borneo Company to collectors.

These stamps to the 10 c. value were forged on several occasions. Most forgeries of the ½ c. value can be identified by the presence of a diagonal line joining the top two horizontal strokes of the uppermost Chinese character.

The new 25 c. has the inscription "BRITISH NORTH BORNEO" in taller capitals. In the 50 c. the "0" of the numerals "50" in the two upper corners is square-shaped at the top and bottom instead of being oval. The 1 dollar has 14 pearls instead of 13 at each side, and on the 2 dollars the word "BRITISH" measures 10½ to 11 mm in length in place of 12 mm.

19

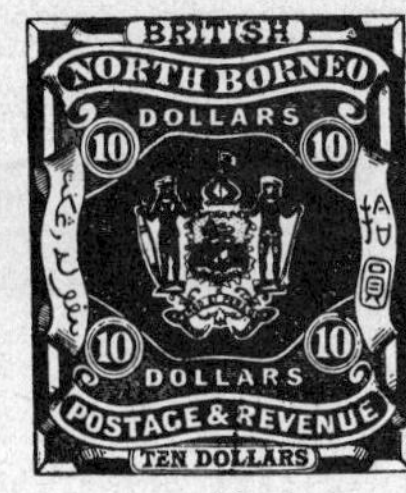

20

1889. *P* 14.
49 **19** $5 bright purple .. .. .. £160 £170 8·50
a. Imperf (pair) .. .. .. £400 † 30·00
50 **20** $10 brown .. .. £200 £300 12·00
a. Imperf (pair) .. .. .. £500 † 35·00
b. "DOLLAPS" for "DOLLARS" (R.2/1) £1100 £1400 £325
ba. Ditto. Imperf (pair) .. .. £2000 † £700

Two Cents. (21)   6 cents. (22)   1 cent. (23)

1890 (Dec). *Surch as T* **21**, *in red*.
51 **15** 2 c. on 25 c. indigo .. .. .. 65·00 85·00
a. Surch inverted £400 £400
52 8 c. on 25 c. indigo .. .. .. 90·00 £100

The first printing of Nos. 51/2 had the two lines of the surcharge 3.5 mm apart. On a second printing of both values this gap widened to 5 mm.

1891–92. *Surch with T* **22**.
54 **9** 6 c. on 8 c. green (1892) £7000 £3750
a. Large "s" in "cents" £13000
55 **14** 6 c. on 8 c. yellow-green .. .. 18·00 9·50
a. Surch inverted £350 £400
b. Inverted "c" in "cents" (R.5/4) .. £400 £450
c. "cetns." for "cents" (R.3/7) .. £400 £450
d. Large "s" in "cents" (R.2/9 or 3/7) .. £170 £170
56 **9** 6 c. on 10 c. blue .. .. .. 55·00 19·00
a. Surch inverted £200 £200
b. Surch double .. .. ..
c. Surch treble £400
d. Large "s" in "cents" £225 £150
57 **14** 6 c. on 10 c. blue .. .. .. £130 26·00
a. Large "s" in "cents" £475 £180

Unused examples of Nos. 55 and 57 are normally without gum.

There were three settings of the surcharge for No. 55. On the first two the large "s" in "cents" occurred on R.2/9 with the other two listed varieties also included. Nos. 55b/c were corrected on the third setting and the large "s" in cents occurred on R.3/7.

1892 (Mar–Nov). *Surch as T* **23** ("Cents." *with capital* "C" *as in T* **21** *on No.* 65), *in red*.
63 **14** 1 c. on 4 c. rose-pink .. .. 22·00 14·00
a. Surch double £1000
b. Surch on back and on front .. — £600
ba. As b, but with surch double on front
64 1 c. on 5 c. slate (Nov) .. .. 7·00 6·00
65 **15** 8 c. on 25 c. indigo (date?) £130 £150

Unused examples of Nos. 63/5 are normally without gum.

24 Dyak Chief

25 Sambar Stag (*Cervus unicolor*)

26 Sago Palm

27 Great Argus Pheasant

28 Arms of the Company

29 Malay Dhow

30 Estuarine Crocodile

31 Mount Kinabalu

32 Arms of the Company with Supporters

ORATION. There are a number of small variations in the tion of the Waterlow issues of 1894 to 1922 which we were due to irregularity of the pins rather than different tors.

e following lists, stamps perf 12, 12½, 13 or compound are ed as perf 12–13, stamps perf 13½, 14 or compound are ed as perf 13½–14 and those perf 14½, 15 or compound are s perf 14½–15. In addition the 13½–14 perforation exists nd with 14½–15 and with 12–13, whilst perf 15½–16 from a separate perforator.

(Recess Waterlow)

Feb). *P* 14½–15.

1 c. black and olive-bistre .. .. 1·25 9·00 50
a. Imperf between (horiz or vert pair) .. £600
b. Perf 13½–14 .. 1·50 9·50 50
c. Perf 13½–14, comp 14½–15 .. 38·00 55·00 —
d. Perf 13½–14, comp 12–13 .. 21·00 45·00 —
e. Perf 12–13 ..
1 c. black and bistre-brown .. 1·75 11·00 50
a. Perf 13½–14 .. 2·25 11·00 50
b. Perf 13½–14, comp 12–13 .. 24·00 55·00 —
c. Perf 12–13 ..
2 c. black and rose-lake .. 5·50 4·75 50
a. Imperf between (horiz or vert pair) .. £550 £550 †
b. Perf 13½–14 .. 32·00 40·00 —
2 c. black and lake .. 5·50 4·75 50
a. Perf 13½–14 .. 35·00 35·00 1·50
b. Perf 13½–14, comp 12–13 .. 27·00 28·00 —
c. Imperf between (horiz pair) ..
3 c. olive-green and dull purple .. 2·75 8·00 50
a. Imperf between (horiz pair) .. — £475 †
b. *Bronze-green and dull purple* .. 4·75 — 50
c. Perf 13½–14
3 c. olive-green & violet (*p* 13½–14) 15·00 48·00 —
a. Imperf between (horiz pair)
7 5 c. black and vermilion .. 13·00 11·00 60
a. Imperf between (horiz or vert pair) .. £475
b. Perf 13½–14 .. 45·00 60·00 1·25
c. Perf 13½–14, comp 12–13 .. — 65·00 5·50
d. Perf 13½–14, comp 14½–15 ..
e. Perf 12–13 ..
8 6 c. black and bistre-brown .. 60·00 80·00 60
a. Perf 13½–14 .. 4·25 17·00 60
b. Perf 13½–14, comp 12–13 .. — 65·00 5·50
c. Perf 13½–14, comp 14½–15 .. 60·00
d. Imperf between (horiz pair) ..
9 8 c. black and dull purple .. 6·00 10·00 60
a. Imperf between (vert pair) .. £475
b. Perf 13½–14 .. 8·50 32·00 80
ba. Imperf between (vert pair) .. £400 † £300
d. Perf 13½–14, comp 12–13 ..
0 12 c. black and blue .. 28·00 85·00 2·50
a. Perf 13½–14 .. 28·00 80·00 2·50
b. Imperf between (horiz pair) .. £800 † £500
12 c. black and ultramarine .. 42·00 85·00 3·00
a. Perf 13½–14 .. 40·00 85·00 3·00
b. Imperf between (pair) ..
1 18 c. black and deep green .. 26·00 50·00 2·00
a. Perf 13½–14 .. 27·00 50·00 2·00
2 24 c. blue and rose-lake .. 22·00 75·00 2·00
a. Imperf between (vert pair) .. — — £350
b. Imperf between (vert strip of 3) † † £425
c. Perf 13½–14 .. 22·00 75·00 2·00
d. Perf 13½–14, comp 14½–15
9 .. *Set of* 9 90·00 £225 9·00

32*a*

32*b*

32*c*

32*d*

(Litho Blades, East & Blades, London)

94 (Feb). *T* **32a** *to* **32d** *and T* **19/20**, *but inscribed* "THE STATE OF NORTH BORNEO". *P* 14.

25 c. indigo .. 8·50 28·00 1·00
a. Imperf (pair) .. 32·00 † 8·00
b. Imperf between (horiz or vert pair) .. £650 — 90·00
50 c. deep slate-purple .. 18·00 55·00 1·50
a. Imperf (pair) .. — † 8·00
b. Imperf between (horiz pair) ..
d. *Chalky blue* .. — 55·00 —
$1 scarlet .. 12·00 24·00 1·25
a. Perf 14×11 .. £200
b. Imperf (pair) .. 32·00 † 8·00
$2 dull green .. 18·00 75·00 2·00
a. Imperf (pair) .. — † 11·00
$5 bright purple .. £200 £250 14·00
a. Imperf (pair) .. £325 † 35·00
b. *Dull purple* .. £170 £225 7·00
$10 brown .. £200 £275 13·00
a. Imperf (pair) .. £325 † 35·00
/6 .. *Set of* 6 £400 £600 23·00
s/6s Optd "Specimen" .. *Set of* 6 £150

For Nos. 81 to 83 in other colours, see Labuan 80*a*, 81*a* and 82*a*.

Nos. 81/4 showing stamps printed double, double, one inverted, or on both sides are from waste sheets subsequently sold by the British North Borneo Company to collectors.

4

CENTS

(**33** (3½ mm between lines of surcharge))

(Surcharged by Waterlow)

1895 (June). *No.* 83 *surch as T* **33**.

87 **32c** 4 cents on $1 scarlet .. 5·50 1·50 50
a. Surch double, one diagonal £850
88 10 cents on $1 scarlet .. 17·00 1·75 50
89 20 cents on $1 scarlet .. 40·00 16·00 50
90 30 cents on $1 scarlet .. 27·00 25·00 50
91 40 cents on $1 scarlet .. 27·00 48·00 50
87/91 .. *Set of* 5 £100 85·00 2·25
87s/91s Optd "Specimen" .. *Set of* 5 85·00

For 4 c. on $1 with wider spacing see No. 121.

No. 88 exists with the figures of the surcharge 2½ mm away from "CENTS". The normal setting has a space of 3½ mm. Examples of the narrow setting have, so far, only been seen on cancelled-to-order stamps.

34

35

36

37 Orang-Utan

38

39

40

41 Sun Bear

42

43 Borneo Railway Train

44

45

(Recess Waterlow)

1897 (Mar)–**1902**. *T* **34** *to* **45**. *New frames. P* 13½–14.

92 1 c. black and bistre-brown .. 11·00 3·50 40
aa. Perf 16 ..
a. Perf 14½–15 .. 9·50 2·50 40
b. Perf 13½–14, comp 12–13 .. 60·00 45·00 —
c. Imperf between (horiz pair) .. † † £425
93 1 c. black and ochre .. 45·00 14·00 50
a. Perf 14½–15 .. 27·00 11·00 50
ab. Imperf between (horiz pair) .. † † £425
b. Perf 13½–14, comp 12–13 ..
94 2 c. black and lake .. 29·00 3·50 40
a. Perf 14½–15 .. 19·00 3·00 40
ab. Imperf between (horiz pair) .. † † £450
b. Perf 13½–14, comp 12-13 .. — 16·00 1·25
c. Perf 12–13 ..
d. Imperf between (vert pair) .. † † £450
95 2 c. black and green (1900) .. 45·00 1·50 50
a. Perf 14½–15 .. 80·00 13·00 —
b. Perf 13½–14, comp 12–13 .. £100 24·00 —
c. Perf 12–13 ..
d. Imperf between (horiz pair) .. — £700 †
96 3 c. green and rosy mauve .. 42·00 9·50 40
a. Perf 14½–15 .. 55·00 50·00 1·00
b. Perf 13½–14, comp 12–13 .. 75·00 75·00 —
97 3 c. green & dull mauve (*p* 14½–15) 14·00 3·00 50
98 4 c. black and green (1900) .. 9·00 — 1·50
a. Perf 13½–14, comp 12–13 ..
99 4 c. black and carmine (1900) .. 32·00 7·00 50
a. Perf 16 .. 65·00 40·00 50
b. Perf 14½–15 .. 50·00 2·00 50
c. Perf 13½–14, comp 12–13 .. 35·00 40·00 —
d. Perf 12–13 ..
100 5 c. black and orange-vermilion .. 85·00 3·50 50
a. Perf 14½–15 .. 85·00 3·00 50
ab. Imperf between (horiz pair) .. † £1100 †
b. Perf 13½–14, comp 12–13 .. 85·00 14·00 60
c. Perf 12–13 ..
101 6 c. black and bistre-brown .. 42·00 19·00 50
a. Perf 14½–15 .. 24·00 3·25 50
102 8 c. black and brown-purple .. 75·00 50·00 —
a. Perf 16 .. £110 15·00 70
ab. Imperf between (vert pair) .. £375 £375 —
b. Perf 14½–15 .. 35·00 2·75 60
103 8 c. black and brown .. 11·00 26·00 75
a. Perf 14½–15 .. 60·00 75·00 —
b. Perf 16 ..
104 10 c. brown and slate-lilac (1902) .. 80·00 38·00 2·75
a. Imperf between (vert pair) ..
105 10 c. brown and slate-blue (1902) .. £180 75·00 1·50
106 12 c. black and dull blue .. £120 48·00 1·75
a. Imperf between (vert pair) .. † † £475
b. Perf 14½–15 .. 80·00 32·00 1·50
c. Perf 13½–14, comp 12–13 .. £150 55·00 —
d. Perf 12–13 ..
107 16 c. green and chestnut (1902) .. £130 90·00 3·25
a. Perf 14½–15 .. £140 £130 10·00
108 18 c. black and green (*p* 16) .. 19·00 70·00 1·50
a. Imperf vert (horiz pair) .. † † 80·00
b. Imperf between (vert pair) .. † † £300
c. Imperf (pair) .. † † £170
109 24 c. blue and lake .. 17·00 85·00 1·75
a. Perf 13½–14, comp 12–13 .. 35·00 £100 1·75
b. Perf 12–13 .. £100
92/109 (*one of each value*) .. *Set of* 12 £450 £300 11·00
92s/109s (*excl* 93, 97, 103, 105) Optd "Specimen" .. *Set of* 14 £275

No. 98 was printed in an incorrect frame colour and it is doubtful if it was issued for postal purposes in North Borneo. Used examples come from dealers' stock sent to the territory for cancellation.

In the above the 18 c. has "POSTAL REVENUE" instead of "POSTAGE AND REVENUE" and the 24 c. has those words omitted. These stamps were replaced by others with corrected inscriptions; see Nos. 110 and 111.

46

47

1897. *Corrected inscriptions. P* 13½–14.

110 **46** 18 c. black and green .. 80·00 24·00 1·50
a. Imperf between (horiz pair) † † £425
b. Perf 14½–15 .. 65·00 12·00 1·50
c. Perf 13½–14, comp 12–13 ..
111 **47** 24 c. blue and lake .. 65·00 35·00 2·00
a. Perf 16 .. £110 £100 2·00
b. Perf 14½–15 .. 42·00 55·00 2·50
c. Perf 13½–14, comp 12–13 ..
d. Perf 12–13 ..
110s/11s Optd "Specimen" .. *Set of* 2 50·00

4 CENTS — BRITISH PROTECTORATE. — 4 cents

(**48**) (4½ mm between lines of surcharge) (**49**) (**50**)

1899 (22 July–Oct). *Surch with T* **48**. (*a*) *4½ mm between lines of surch. P* 14½–15 (*Nos.* 112/17) *or* 14 (*Nos.* 118/24).

112 4 c. on 5 c. (No. 100a) .. 42·00 48·00
a. Perf 13½–14 .. 22·00 10·00
b. Perf 13½–14, comp 12–13 .. 30·00 30·00
113 4 c. on 6 c. (No. 101a) (date?) .. 19·00 23·00
a. Perf 13½–14 .. 15·00 45·00
114 4 c. on 8 c. (No. 102b) (Oct) .. 15·00 10·00
115 4 c. on 12 c. (No. 106b) (Oct) .. 18·00 13·00
a. Imperf between (horiz pair) .. £550
b. Imperf between (vert pair) .. — £550
c. Perf 13½–14 .. 35·00
d. Perf 12–13 ..
e. Perf 13½–14, comp 12–13 .. 29·00
116 4 c. on 18 c. (No. 110a) (Oct) .. 9·50 13·00
a. Perf 13½–14 .. 25·00 30·00
117 4 c. on 24 c. (No. 111b) (Oct) .. 21·00 17·00
a. Perf 16 .. 50·00 50·00
b. Perf 13½–14 .. 17·00 38·00
c. Perf 13½–14, comp 12–13 .. 32·00 38·00
d. Perf 12–13 .. 45·00 60·00
118 4 c. on 25 c. indigo (No. 81) .. 5·50 8·50
a. Imperf between (horiz strip of 3) .. £850
119 4 c. on 50 c. deep slate-purple (No. 82) .. 7·50 16·00
a. *Chalky blue* .. 28·00 38·00
121 4 c. on $1 scarlet (No. 83) .. 5·50 11·00
122 4 c. on $2 dull green (No. 84) .. 5·50 12·00
123 4 c. on $5 bright purple (No. 85) .. £150 £225
a. *Dull purple* .. £190 £225
124 4 c. on $10 brown (No. 86) .. £110 £200
112/24 .. *Set of* 12 £325 £500
112s/24s Optd "Specimen" .. *Set of* 12 £190

(*b*) *8½ mm between lines of surch. P* 14

125 4 c. on $5 (No. 85) .. 6·00 13·00
126 4 c. on $10 (No. 86) .. 6·00 13·00

No. 121 differs only from No. 87 in having the "4" and "cents" wider apart.

Examples of the Kudat postmark dated "AU 15 1899" struck on Nos. 112/24 are generally considered to be faked.

A new setting of the surcharge, with 2½ mm between "4" and "CENTS" for values to $2 and 3½ mm on the $5 and $10, was used for the Specimen overprints, including unissued surcharges on the 1 c., 2 c. and 3 c. values (*price* £100 *the set of three*).

(Optd by Waterlow)

1901 (8 Oct)–**05.** *Optd as T* **49**. (*a*) *P* 13½–14.

No.	Description			
127	1 c. (No. 92) (R.)	3·50	1·50	30
	a. Perf 14½–15	2·50	1·75	30
128	2 c. (No. 95) (R.)	3·50	1·25	30
	a. Perf 16	3·50	9·50	30
	b. Perf 14½–15	10·00	10·00	30
129	3 c. (No. 96)	1·60	4·50	30
	a. Imperf between (vert pair)			
	b. Perf 14½–15	8·00	2·25	30
	c. Perf 13½–14, comp 14½–15	50·00		
130	4 c. (No. 99) (G.)	8·00	1·50	30
	a. Perf 14½–15	19·00	1·50	30
131	5 c. (No. 100) (G.)	40·00	3·50	30
	a. Perf 14½–15	12·00	2·50	30
132	6 c. (No. 101) (R.)	45·00	60·00	1·25
	a. No stop after "Protectorate"	70·00	70·00	1·25
	b. Perf 16	3·50	13·00	70
133	8 c. (No. 103) (B.)	3·50	3·50	50
	a. No stop after "Protectorate"	3·00	23·00	1·50
	b. Perf 13½–14, comp 12–13	55·00	21·00	—
	c. Imperf horiz (vert pair)	†	†	£325
134	10 c. (No. 104) (R.) (7.02)	45·00	5·00	80
	a. Perf 14½–15	85·00	28·00	1·75
	c. Perf 13½–14. No stop after "Protectorate"	£150	—	8·50
	d. Opt double	£550	†	£250
	e. On 10 c. (No. 105)	£160	—	1·00
	f. Imperf vert (horiz pair)	†	†	£425
135	12 c. (No. 106) (R.)	45·00	12·00	1·50
136	16 c. (No. 107) (7.02)	£110	22·00	2·25
	a. Perf 14½–15	£120	40·00	2·25
	b. Perf 13½–14, comp 12–13	£160	60·00	—
137	18 c. (No. 110) (R.)	11·00	25·00	1·25
	a. No stop after "Protectorate"			
	b. Perf 13½–14, comp 12–13	—	—	1·50
138	24 c. (No. 111)	16·00	40·00	1·50
	a. Perf 14½–15	60·00	80·00	1·75
	b. Imperf between (horiz pair)			
	(*b*) *P* 14			
139	25 c. (No. 81) (R.)	2·00	10·00	50
	a. No stop after "Protectorate"	£140	£160	22·00
	b. Overprints *tête-bêche* (horiz pair)			
	c. Overprint inverted	£375		
140	50 c. (No. 82) (R.)	2·75	11·00	55
	a. No stop after "Protectorate"	75·00	£130	—
	b. Chalky blue			
141	$1 (No. 83) (R.) (1.04)	10·00	65·00	—
142	$1 (No. 83)	6·50	38·00	2·50
	a. Imperf horiz (vert pair)	£500		
	b. Opt double	†	†	£300
	c. Opt treble			
143	$2 (No. 84) (R.) (1903)	30·00	95·00	3·50
	a. Opt double	£1000	†	£325
144	$5 (No. 85*b*) (R.) (2.05)	£190	£425	8·00
145	$10 (No. 86) (R.) (2.05)	£350	£600	11·00
	a. Opt inverted	£1400	†	£375
127/45	*Set of* 18	£750	£1200	30·00
127s/40s	Optd "Specimen" *Set of* 14	£275		

There was more than one setting of the overprint for some of the values. Full sheets of the 6 c. and 8 c. are known, without stop throughout.

1904–5. *Surch locally with T* **50.** (*a*) *P* 14½–15.

No.	Description			
146	4 c. on 5 c. (No. 100a)	30·00	42·00	10·00
	a. Surch omitted (in pair with normal)			
147	4 c. on 6 c. (No. 101a)	7·00	20·00	9·00
	a. Surch inverted	£200		
148	4 c. on 8 c. (No. 102b)	12·00	26·00	9·50
	a. Surch inverted	£275		
149	4 c. on 12 c. (No. 106b)	24·00	40·00	10·00
	a. Perf 13½–14	45·00	60·00	10·00
	b. Perf 13½–14, comp 12–13	24·00	60·00	—
	c. Surch omitted (in pair with normal)			
150	4 c. on 18 c. (No. 110b)	14·00	38·00	10·00
	a. Perf 13½–14			
151	4 c. on 24 c. (No. 111b)	19·00	48·00	10·00
	a. Perf 16	16·00	48·00	10·00
	b. Perf 13½–14	20·00	48·00	10·00
	c. Perf 12–13			
	(*b*) *P* 14			
152	4 c. on 25 c. (No. 81)	3·50	25·00	10·00
153	4 c. on 50 c. (No. 82)	4·00	38·00	10·00
154	4 c. on $1 (No. 83)	5·50	48·00	10·00
155	4 c. on $2 (No. 84)	5·50	48·00	10·00
156	4 c. on $5 (No. 85)	11·00	48·00	10·00
	a. Surch on No. 85*b*	30·00	48·00	—
157	4 c. on $10 (No. 86)	11·00	48·00	10·00
	a. Surch inverted	£1300		
	b. Surch omitted (in pair with normal)			
146/57	*Set of* 12	£110	£425	£110

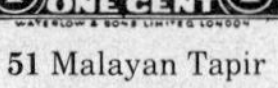

51 Malayan Tapir

52 Travellers' Tree

53 Jesselton Railway Station

54 The Sultan of Sulu, his staff and W. C. Cowie, Managing Director of the Company

55 Indian Elephant

56 Sumatran Rhinoceros

57 Ploughing with Buffalo

58 Wild Boar

59 Palm Cockatoo

60 Rhinoceros Hornbill

61 Banteng

62 Dwarf Cassowary

(Recess Waterlow)

1909 (1 July)–**23.** *Centres in black. P* 13½–14.

No.	Type	Description			
158	**51**	1 c. chocolate-brown	6·00	1·00	30
		a. Perf 14½–15	35·00	12·00	40
159		1 c. brown	13·00	1·60	30
		a. Perf 14½–15	27·00	3·25	30
		b. Imperf between (vert pair)	£1100		
160	**52**	2 c. green	1·00	70	30
		a. Imperf between (pair)			
		b. Perf 14½–15	2·25	70	30
161	**53**	3 c. lake	3·25	2·25	30
162		3 c. rose-lake	2·75	2·25	40
		a. Perf 14½–15	28·00	—	55
163		3 c. green (1923)	15·00	1·50	—
164	**54**	4 c. scarlet	2·75	30	30
		a. Imperf between (vert pair)			
		b. Perf 14½–15	13·00	1·75	35
165	**55**	5 c. yellow-brown	9·50	6·00	40
		a. Perf 14½–15			
166		5 c. dark brown	17·00	5·50	—
167	**56**	6 c. olive-green	8·00	1·75	30
		a. Perf 14½–15	65·00	6·50	60
168		6 c. apple-green	28·00	3·25	60
169	**57**	8 c. lake	3·50	1·75	60
		a. Perf 14½–15			
170	**58**	10 c. greyish blue	45·00	8·00	1·25
		a. Perf 14½–15	80·00	28·00	—
171		10 c. blue	50·00	3·75	—
172		10 c. turquoise-blue	27·00	2·00	1·25
		a. Perf 14½–15	55·00	5·50	—
173	**59**	12 c. deep blue	25·00	3·25	1·00
		a. Perf 14½–15			
		b. Imperf between (horiz pair)	†	†	£475
173*c*		12 c. deep bright blue			
174	**60**	16 c. brown-lake	25·00	7·00	1·00
175	**61**	18 c. blue-green	90·00	32·00	1·00
176	**62**	24 c. deep rose-lilac	28·00	3·50	1·25
		a. Deep lilac	—	6·00	—
158/76		*Set of* 13	£225	55·00	—
158s/76s		Optd "Specimen" *Set of* 13	£275		

For this issue perf 12½ see Nos. 277, etc.

20

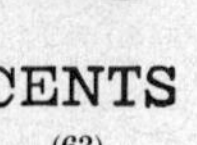

(63)

64

65

1909 (7 Sept). *No.* 175 *surch with T* **63** *by Wat*
P 13½–14.

No.	Description		
177	20 c. on 18 c. blue-green (R.)	7·00	1·00
	a. Perf 14½–15	£180	60·00
	s. Optd "Specimen"	40·00	

(Recess Waterlow)

1911 (7 Mar). *P* 13½–14.

No.	Type	Description		
178	**64**	25 c. black and yellow-green	8·50	4·50
		a. Perf 14½–15	11·00	35·00
		b. Imperf (pair)	48·00	
178*c*		25 c. black and blue-green	38·00	
179		50 c. black and steel-blue	8·50	4·00
		a. Perf 14½–15	17·00	19·00
		ab. Imperf between (horiz pair)	£1900	
		c. Imperf (pair)	75·00	
180		$1 black and chestnut	16·00	4·00
		a. Perf 14½–15	42·00	15·00
		b. Imperf (pair)	£120	
181		$2 black and lilac	55·00	17·00
182	**65**	$5 black and lake	95·00	£110
		a. Imperf (pair)	£180	
183		$10 black and brick-red	£300	£350
		a. Imperf (pair)	£325	
178/83		*Set of* 6	£425	£450
178s/83s		Optd "Specimen" *Set of* 6	£250	

BRITISH

PROTECTORATE

(66)

2

cents

(67)

1912 (July). *Nos.* 85*b and* 86 *optd with T* **66**.

No.	Description		
184	$5 dull purple (R.)	£950	£1100
185	$10 brown (R.)	£1300	—
	a. Opt inverted	†	†

1916 (Feb). *Nos.* 162, 167 *and* 173 *surch as T* **67** *by*
Printing Office, Sandakan. P 13½–14.

No.	Type	Description		
186	**53**	2 c. on 3 c. black and rose-lake	23·00	1
		a. "s" inverted (R. 2/5)	£100	9
		b. Surch double		
187	**56**	4 c. on 6 c. black and olive-green (R.)	18·00	1
		a. "s" inverted (R. 2/5)	95·00	9
		b. "s" inserted by hand	—	£
		c. Perf 14½–15	£140	£
		ca. "s" inverted		
188	**59**	10 c. on 12 c. black and deep blue (R.)	50·00	6
		a. "s" inverted (R. 2/5)	£150	£
		b. "s" inserted by hand	£950	
186/8		*Set of* 3	80·00	8
186s/8s		Optd "Specimen" *Set of* 3	£110	

Nos. 186/8 were surcharged from a setting of 25 (5×5)
which the required face values were inserted.

1916 (May). *Stamps of* 1909–11 *optd with T* **68** *by Waterl*
P 13½–14. *Centres in black.* (*a*) *Cross in vermilion* (*th*
shiny ink).

No.	Type	Description		
189	**51**	1 c. brown	7·50	35
190	**52**	2 c. green	40·00	75
		a. Perf 14½–15	32·00	80
		ab. Opt double, one albino	£225	
191	**53**	3 c. rose-lake	27·00	48
		a. Nos. 191 and 204 *se-tenant* (vert pair)	£1800	
192	**54**	4 c. scarlet	5·50	32
		a. Perf 14½–15	£180	£1
193	**55**	5 c. yellow-brown	30·00	55
		a. Perf 14½–15		
194	**56**	6 c. apple-green	50·00	60·
		a. Perf 14½–15	£180	£1
195	**57**	8 c. lake	23·00	60·
196	**58**	10 c. blue	40·00	70·
197	**59**	12 c. deep blue	85·00	90·
198	**60**	16 c. brown-lake	85·00	90·
199	**61**	20 c. on 18 c. blue-green	32·00	85·
200	**62**	24 c. dull mauve	90·00	£1
		a. Imperf between (vert pair)		
201	**64**	25 c. green (*p* 14½–15)	£300	£3
189/201		*Set of* 13	£700	£10
		(*b*) *Cross in shades of carmine* (*matt ink*)		
202	**51**	1 c. brown	26·00	65·
		a. Perf 14½–15	£180	
203	**52**	2 c. green	27·00	48·
		b. Perf 14½–15	£160	
		ba. Opt double	†	
204	**53**	3 c. rose-lake	38·00	65·
204*a*	**54**	4 c. scarlet	£600	
205	**55**	5 c. yellow-brown	50·00	70·
206	**56**	6 c. apple-green	45·00	65·
		a. Perf 14½–15	£160	£1
207	**57**	8 c. lake	25·00	55·
208	**58**	10 c. blue	48·00	70·
209	**59**	12 c. deep blue	80·00	£1
210	**60**	16 c. brown-lake	85·00	£1
211	**61**	20 c. on 18 c. blue-green	75·00	£1
212	**62**	24 c. dull mauve	85·00	£1
213	**64**	25 c. green	£750	
		a. Perf 14½–15	£425	£4
202/13 (*ex* 4 *c.*)		*Set of* 12	£900	£12

The British North Borneo Company donated a proportion
the above issue to be sold by the National Philatelic War Fu
for the benefit of the Red Cross and St. John's Ambulan
Brigade.

RED CROSS

TWO CENTS

(69)

FOUR CENTS

(70)

Aug). *Stamps of* 1909–11 *surch as T* **69**. *P* 13½–14.

(*a*) *Lines of surcharge* 9 *mm apart*

51 1 c. + 2 c. brown .. .. .. 3·50 12·00
a. Imperf between (horiz pair) .. £1700
52 2 c. + 2 c. green .. .. 1·00 8·50
a. Imperf between (horiz or vert pair) £1900
b. Imperf (pair) .. .. ..
c. Perf 14½–15 .. .. ..
53 3 c. + 2 c. rose-red .. .. .. 12·00 17·00
a. Imperf between (horiz pair) .. £1900
b. Perf 14½–15 .. .. .. 25·00 65·00
3 c. + 2 c. dull rose-carmine £150
a. Perf 14½–15 .. .. .. £180
54 4 c. + 2 c. scarlet .. .. .. 70 4·50
a. Surch inverted £375
55 5 c. + 2 c. deep brown .. .. .. 8·00 22·00
5 c. + 2 c. pale brown .. .. .. 8·50 27·00
56 6 c. + 2 c. olive-green .. .. .. 5·00 22·00
a. Perf 14½–15 .. .. .. £170 £190
6 c. + 2 c. apple-green .. .. ..
c. Perf 14½–15 .. .. .. £275
57 8 c. + 2 c. lake .. .. .. 5·50 11·00
a. Inverted figure "3" for "C" in "CENTS" .. ..
58 10 c. + 2 c. blue .. .. .. 7·50 24·00
59 12 c. + 2 c. deep bright blue .. .. 20·00 45·00
a. Surch inverted £600
60 16 c. + 2 c. brown-lake .. .. .. 21·00 45·00
62 24 c. + 2 c. mauve .. .. .. 21·00 45·00

(*b*) *Lines of surch* 13–14 *mm apart*

52 2 c. + 2 c. green .. .. 80·00 £150
56 6 c. + 2 c. olive-green £400 £700
64 25 c. + 2 c. green .. .. 10·00 38·00
50 c. + 2 c. steel-blue .. .. .. 12·00 38·00
$1 + 2 c. chestnut .. .. .. 45·00 50·00
$2 + 2 c. lilac .. .. 70·00 95·00
65 $5 + 2 c. lake £325 £475
$10 + 2 c. brick-red £325 £475
4 .. .. *Set of* 17 £800 £1300

e above stamps were dispatched from London in three gnments, of which two were lost through enemy action at sea. ly one sheet was found of No. 228.

ese stamps were sold at a premium of 2 c. per stamp, which to the Red Cross Society.

(Oct). *Stamps of* 1909–11 *surch with T* **70**, *in red*. 13½–14.

51 1 c. + 4 c. chocolate .. .. .. 60 5·00
a. Imperf between (horiz pair) .. £1600
52 2 c. + 4 c. green .. .. 65 8·00
53 3 c. + 4 c. rose-lake .. .. .. 1·00 3·75
54 4 c. + 4 c. scarlet .. .. .. 40 4·75
55 5 c. + 4 c. brown .. .. .. 2·00 21·00
56 6 c. + 4 c. apple-green .. .. .. 1·90 12·00
a. Imperf between (vert pair) £1500
57 8 c. + 4 c. lake .. .. .. 1·25 9·50
58 10 c. + 4 c. turquoise-blue .. .. 3·75 12·00
10 c. + 4 c. greenish blue .. .. 8·50 40·00
59 12 c. + 4 c. deep blue .. .. .. 13·00 14·00
a. Surch double £900
60 16 c. + 4 c. brown-lake .. .. .. 7·50 16·00
62 24 c. + 4 c. mauve .. .. .. 10·00 20·00
64 25 c. + 4 c. yellow-green .. .. .. 6·00 50·00
25 c. + 4 c. blue-green .. .. .. 24·00 75·00
50 c. + 4 c. steel-blue .. .. .. 15·00 42·00
a. Perf 14½–15 .. .. .. 60·00
$1 + 4 c. chestnut .. .. .. 15·00 60·00
a. Perf 14½–15 .. .. .. 95·00
$2 + 4 c. lilac .. .. 48·00 80·00
65 $5 + 4 c. lake £275 £400
$10 + 4 c. brick-red £275 £400
52 .. .. *Set of* 17 £600 £1000

os. 235/52 were sold at face, plus 4 c. on each stamp for Red s Funds.

xamples of a double-ring "SANDAKAN N. BORNEO" mark dated "1 NOV 1918" on these stamps are generally sidered to be faked.

THREE

MALAYA-BORNEO
EXHIBITION
1922.
(71)

CENTS
(72)

2 (31 Mar). *Malaya-Borneo Exhibition, Singapore. Stamps f* 1909–22, *some in different shades, optd as T* **71** *by Govt rinting Office, Sandakan. P* 13½–14.

3 51 1 c. brown (R.) .. .. .. 10·00 55·00
a. "BORHEO" £300 £375
b. "BORNEQ" £450 £550
c. Stop after "EXHIBITION." .. 65·00
d. Raised stop after "1922" £450
e. "EXHIBITICN." with stop .. £500
f. Perf 14½–15 .. .. .. 25·00 70·00
fa. "BORHEO" £425
fb. "BORNEQ" £700
fc. Raised stop after "1922" £650
fd. "EXHIBITICN." with stop .. £750
fe. "MHLAYA" and stop after "EXHIBITION" £2250
ff. Stop after "EXHIBITION." .. £100
3g 1 c. brown (B.) (*p* 14½–15) £1000
ga. Vert pair, with and without opt .. £4000
gb. Raised stop after "1922." .. £2750
gc. "BORHEO" £2250
gd. "BORNEQ" £3000
gf. "EXHIBITICN." with stop .. £3000
gg. "MHLAYA" and stop after "EXHIBITION" .. .. ..
4 1 c. orange-brown (R.) .. .. 25·00 60·00
5 52 2 c. green (R.) .. .. .. 1·75 19·00
a. Stop after "EXHIBITION." .. 27·00
6 53 3 c. rose-lake (B.) .. .. .. 12·00 48·00
a. Stop after "EXHIBITION." .. 65·00
b. "EXHIBITICN." with stop £2250
c. Raised stop after "1922" £1600

257 **54** 4 c. scarlet (B.) .. .. .. 1·75 32·00
a. Stop after "EXHIBITION." .. 27·00
b. Perf 14½–15 .. .. .. 65·00
ba. Stop after "EXHIBITION." .. £275
258 **55** 5 c. orange-brown (B.) .. .. 9·00 50·00
a. Imperf between (vert pair) £1200 £1200
b. Stop after "EXHIBITION." .. 55·00
c. Opt double £1800
d. Opt double (with stop) £4250
259 5 c. chestnut (B.) .. .. .. 19·00 60·00
a. Stop after "EXHIBITION." .. 85·00
260 **56** 6 c. apple-green (R.) .. .. 7·00 55·00
a. Stop after "EXHIBITION." .. 48·00
b. Opt double £1800
c. Opt double (with stop) £4250
261 **57** 8 c. dull rose (B.) .. .. .. 5·00 42·00
a. Stop after "EXHIBITION." .. 55·00
262 8 c. deep rose-lake (B.) .. .. .. 5·50 45·00
a. Stop after "EXHIBITION." .. 60·00
263 **58** 10 c. turquoise-blue (R.) .. .. 9·00 50·00
a. Stop after "EXHIBITION." .. 60·00
b. Perf 14½–15 .. .. .. 30·00
ba. Stop after "EXHIBITION." .. £150
264 10 c. greenish blue (R.) .. .. 9·00 65·00
a. Stop after "EXHIBITION." .. 60·00
265 **59** 12 c. deep blue (R.) .. .. .. 5·50 21·00
a. Stop after "EXHIBITION." .. 60·00 £130
266 12 c. deep bright blue (R.) .. .. 32·00
a. Stop after "EXHIBITION." .. £170
267 **60** 16 c. brown-lake (B.) .. .. .. 16·00 55·00
a. Stop after "EXHIBITION." .. 85·00
b. Opt in red £5000
268 **61** 20 c. on 18 c. blue-green (B.) .. 17·00 70·00
a. Stop after "EXHIBITION." .. £140
269 20 c. on 18 c. blue-green (R.) .. 20·00 £130
a. Stop after "EXHIBITION." .. £200 £325
270 **62** 24 c. mauve (R.) .. .. .. 30·00 55·00
a. Stop after "EXHIBITION." .. £140 £275
271 24 c. lilac (R.) .. .. .. 30·00 55·00
a. Stop after "EXHIBITION." .. £140
272 24 c. reddish lilac (R.) .. .. 40·00 70·00
a. Stop after "EXHIBITION." .. £170
273 **64** 25 c. blue-green (R.) .. .. .. 16·00 60·00
a. Stop after "EXHIBITION." .. 75·00
274 25 c. yellow-green (R.) .. .. 5·00 50·00
a. Stop after "EXHIBITION." .. 55·00
b. Opt double £2500
c. Perf 14½–15 .. .. .. 13·00 60·00
ca. Stop after "EXHIBITION." .. £200
cb. Opt double £2750
275 50 c. steel-blue (R.) .. .. .. 8·00 48·00
a. Stop after "EXHIBITION." .. 75·00
b. Perf 14½–15 .. .. .. 20·00 70·00
ba. Stop after "EXHIBITION." .. £150
253/75 .. .. *Set of* 14 £120 £600
253s/75s Optd "Specimen" .. *Set of* 14 £450

These overprints were applied from a number of settings covering 10, 20, 25 or 30 stamps at a time.

Of the ten settings known for the horizontal stamps the earliest were only used for the 1 c. on which most of the varieties occur. Of the others the vast majority come from settings of 20 (10 × 2) with the stop after "EXHIBITION" variety on R. 2/7, or 25 (5 × 5) on which the same variety can be found on R. 5/4. In addition the 3 c. comes from a different setting of 20 (10 × 2) on which there is a raised stop after "1922" on R. 2/8 and "EXHIBITICN." on R. 2/9.

The 1 c. sequence is complicated, but additionally includes a setting of 10 with "BORHEO" on stamps 3 and 10, "BORNEQ" on stamp 4, raised stop on stamp 8 and "EXHIBITICN." on stamp 9. A setting of 20 repeats this sequence on its bottom line as does one of 30, although in this instance "MHLAYA" replaces "EXHIBITICN" as the variety on stamp 9.

For the vertical stamps (2, 6, 10, 12, 16 and 20 c. on 18 c.) the settings were of 20 (10 × 2) or 25 (5 × 5). The stop after "EXHIBITION" occurs on R. 2/7 of the former and R. 5/4 of the latter.

The 25 c. and 50 c. high values were overprinted from a setting of 20 (10 × 2), with the stop after "EXHIBITION" on R. 2/7, or 25 (5 × 5).

1923 (Oct). *T* **54** *surch with T* **72**.

276 3 c. on 4 c. black and scarlet .. .. 1·25 5·50
a. Surch double £800
s. Optd "Specimen" .. .. .. 50·00

1925–28. *Designs as* 1909–22 *issue with centres in black and some frame colours changed. P* 12½.

277 **51** 1 c. chocolate-brown .. .. .. 1·00 70
a. Imperf between (horiz pair) .. £900
278 **52** 2 c. claret 70 60
a. Imperf between (vert pair) .. — £750
b. Imperf between (horiz pair) ..
279 **53** 3 c. green .. .. 2·75 75
a. Imperf between (horiz pair) ..
280 **54** 4 c. scarlet 50 10
a. Imperf between (vert pair) .. £275 £375
b. Imperf between (horiz pair) .. £750
c. Imperf between (vert strip of three)
281 **55** 5 c. yellow-brown .. .. .. 4·75 2·75
a. Imperf between (vert pair) .. £850
282 **56** 6 c. olive-green .. .. .. 5·50 90
283 **57** 8 c. carmine .. .. 3·25 50
a. Imperf between (vert pair) .. £450
b. Imperf between (horiz pair) ..
c. Imperf between (vert strip of four) £1200
284 **58** 10 c. turquoise-blue .. .. .. 3·75 90
a. Imperf between (horiz pair) .. £750 £1000
b. Imperf between (vert pair) ..
285 **59** 12 c. deep blue .. .. .. 21·00 80
286 **60** 16 c. red-brown .. .. .. 28·00 £130
287 **61** 20 c. on 18 c. blue-green (R.) .. 7·50 3·00
288 **62** 24 c. violet .. .. 48·00 £100
289 **64** 25 c. green .. .. 7·50 4·25
290 50 c. steel-blue .. .. .. 10·00 13·00
291 $1 chestnut .. .. 16·00 £225
292 $2 mauve .. .. 50·00 £275
293 **65** $5 lake (1928) £150 £650
294 $10 orange-red (1928) £300 £750
277/94 .. .. *Set of* 18 £600 £2000

Examples of No. 278 were supplied for U.P.U. distribution punched with a 3½ mm diameter hole.

Examples of the 16 c., 24 c., $1, $2, $5 and $10 in this perforation were not supplied to the territory for postal purposes. Used examples exist from covers prepared by stamp dealers.

73 Head of a Murut

76 Mount Kinabalu

(Eng J. A. C. Harrison. Recess Waterlow)

1931 (1 Jan). *50th Anniv of British North Borneo Company. T* **73**, **76** *and similar designs. P* 12½.

295 3 c. black and blue-green .. .. .. 1·25 80
296 6 c. black and orange .. .. .. 16·00 3·25
297 10 c. black and scarlet .. .. .. 4·25 12·00
298 12 c. black and ultramarine .. .. 4·75 8·00
299 25 c. black and violet .. .. .. 38·00 35·00
300 $1 black and yellow-green .. .. 27·00 £100
301 $2 black and chestnut .. .. .. 48·00 £110
302 $5 black and purple £140 £375
295/302 .. .. *Set of* 8 £250 £600
295s/302s Optd "Specimen" .. *Set of* 8 £275

Designs: *Vert*—6 c. Orang-Utan; 10 c. Dyak warrior; $1 Badge of the Company; $5 Arms of the Company. *Horiz*—25 c. Clouded Leopard; $2 Arms of the Company.

Examples of all values are known showing a forged Jesselton postmark dated "22 AUG 1931".

81 Buffalo Transport

82 Palm Cockatoo

(Eng J. A. C. Harrison. Recess Waterlow)

1939 (1 Jan). *T* **81/2** *and similar designs. P* 12½.

303 1 c. green and red-brown .. .. .. 2·25 1·25
304 2 c. purple and greenish blue .. .. 5·00 1·25
305 3 c. slate-blue and green .. .. .. 3·00 2·00
306 4 c. bronze-green and violet .. .. 5·00 50
307 6 c. deep blue and claret .. .. .. 4·50 6·00
308 8 c. scarlet .. .. 8·00 1·50
309 10 c. violet and bronze-green .. .. 38·00 6·00
310 12 c. green and royal blue .. .. 24·00 5·00
a. Green and blue .. .. .. 42·00 6·50
311 15 c. blue-green and brown .. .. 20·00 7·50
312 20 c. violet and slate-blue .. .. 12·00 3·25
313 25 c. green and chocolate .. .. .. 16·00 9·50
314 50 c. chocolate and violet .. .. 18·00 7·50
315 $1 brown and carmine .. .. .. 70·00 19·00
316 $2 violet and olive-green .. .. £100 95·00
317 $5 indigo and pale blue £300 £200
303/17 .. .. *Set of* 15 £550 £325
303s/17s Perf "Specimen" .. *Set of* 15 £275

Designs: *Vert*—3 c. Native; 4 c. Proboscis Monkey; 6 c. Mounted Bajaus; 10 c. Orang-Utan; 15 c. Dyak; $1, $2 Badge of the Company. *Horiz*—8 c. Eastern Archipelago; 12 c. Murut with blow-pipe; 20 c. River scene; 25 c. Native boat; 50 c. Mt Kinabalu; $5 Arms of the Company.

WAR TAX
(96)

WAR TAX
(97)

1941 (24 Feb). *Nos.* 303/4 *optd at Sandakan with T* **96/7**.

318 1 c. green and red-brown .. .. .. 1·25 3·00
a. Optd front and back £350
319 2 c. purple and greenish blue .. .. 5·50 3·50

The 1 c. was for compulsory use on internal mail and the 2 c. on overseas mail, both in addition to normal postage.

BRITISH MILITARY ADMINISTRATION

North Borneo, including Labuan, was occupied by the Japanese in January 1942. Australian forces landed on Labuan on 10 June 1945 and by the end of the war against Japan on 14 August had liberated much of western North Borneo. The territory was placed under British Military Administration on 5 January 1946.

BMA
(98)

(99)

1945 (17 Dec). *Nos.* 303/17 *optd with T* **98**.

320 1 c. green and red-brown .. .. .. 5·00 1·75
321 2 c. purple and greenish blue .. .. 14·00 1·75
a. Opt double £5500
322 3 c. slate-blue and green .. .. .. 1·25 1·25
323 4 c. bronze-green and violet .. .. 16·00 15·00
324 6 c. deep blue and claret .. .. .. 1·25 75
325 8 c. scarlet .. .. 3·00 75
326 10 c. violet and bronze-green .. .. 3·00 40
327 12 c. green and blue .. .. .. 6·00 2·75
a. Green and royal blue .. .. .. 9·00 1·00
328 15 c. blue-green and brown .. .. 1·50 1·00

329 20 c. violet and slate-blue .. .. .. 4·25 1·25
330 25 c. green and chocolate .. .. .. 6·50 1·50
331 50 c. chocolate and violet .. .. .. 3·00 1·50
332 $1 brown and carmine .. .. .. 48·00 35·00
333 $2 violet and olive-green .. .. .. 40·00 28·00
a. Opt double £3000
334 $5 indigo and pale blue .. .. .. 17·00 13·00
320/34 .. .. .. *Set of* 15 £140 90·00

These stamps and the similarly overprinted stamps of Sarawak were obtainable at all post offices throughout British Borneo (Brunei, Labuan, North Borneo and Sarawak), for use on local and overseas mail.

CROWN COLONY

North Borneo became a Crown Colony on 15 July 1946.

Lower bar broken at right (R. 8/3)

Lower bar broken at left (R. 8/4)

1947 (1 Sept–22 Dec). *Nos.* 303 *to* 317 *optd with T* **99** *and bars obliterating words* "THE STATE OF" *and* "BRITISH PROTECTORATE".
335 1 c. green and red-brown (15.12) .. .. 15 1·00
b. Lower bar broken at right .. .. 17·00
c. Lower bar broken at left .. .. 17·00
336 2 c. purple and greenish blue (22.12) .. 1·75 90
337 3 c. slate-blue and green (R.) (22.12) .. 15 90
338 4 c. bronze-green and violet 70 65
339 6 c. deep blue and claret (R.) (22.12) .. 25 20
340 8 c. scarlet 30 20
b. Lower bar broken at right .. .. 20·00
341 10 c. violet and bronze-green (15.12) .. 1·25 40
342 12 c. green and royal blue (22.12) .. .. 2·00 2·50
a. Green and blue .. .. 5·50 5·00
343 15 c. blue-green and brown (22.12) .. 2·25 30
344 20 c. violet and slate-blue (22.12) .. .. 2·00 85
b. Lower bar broken at right .. .. 32·00
345 25 c. green and chocolate (22.12) .. .. 2·50 50
b. Lower bar broken at right .. .. 48·00
346 50 c. chocolate and violet (22.12) .. .. 2·00 85
b. Lower bar broken at right .. .. 50·00
c. Lower bar broken at left .. .. 50·00
347 $1 brown and carmine (22.12) .. .. 4·25 1·50
348 $2 violet and olive-green (22.12) .. .. 11·00 15·00
349 $5 indigo and pale blue (R.) (22.12) .. 20·00 15·00
b. Lower bar broken at right £130
335/49 .. .. .. *Set of* 15 45·00 35·00
335/49 Perf "Specimen" .. .. *Set of* 15 £250

1948 (1 Nov). *Royal Silver Wedding. As Nos.* 112/13 *of Antigua.*
350 8 c. scarlet 30 80
351 $10 mauve .. .. 20·00 35·00

1949 (10 Oct). *75th Anniv of U.P.U. As Nos.* 114/17 *of Antigua.*
352 8 c. carmine 40 30
353 10 c. brown .. .. 2·75 1·00
354 30 c. orange-brown .. .. 90 1·75
355 55 c. blue .. .. 90 2·25
352/5 .. .. .. *Set of* 4 4·50 4·75

100 Mount Kinabalu

102 Coconut Grove

(Photo Harrison)

1950 (1 July)–**52.** *T* **100, 102** *and similar designs. Wmk Mult Script CA. Chalk-surfaced paper. P* 13½ × 14½ *(horiz),* 14½ × 13½ *(vert).*
356 1 c. red-brown 15 80
357 2 c. blue 15 50
358 3 c. green 15 15
359 4 c. bright purple 15 10
360 5 c. violet 15 10
361 8 c. scarlet 75 85
362 10 c. maroon .. .. 1·00 15
363 15 c. ultramarine .. .. 2·00 65
364 20 c. brown .. .. 1·00 10
365 30 c. olive-brown .. .. 3·25 20
366 50 c. rose-carmine ("JESSLETON") .. 85 3·00
366*a* 50 c. rose-carmine ("JESSELTON") (1.5.52) .. 6·50 2·00
367 $1 red-orange .. .. 3·25 1·00
368 $2 grey-green .. .. 3·75 12·00
369 $5 emerald-green .. .. 14·00 18·00
370 $10 dull blue .. .. 38·00 48·00
356/70 .. .. .. *Set of* 16 65·00 75·00

Designs: *Horiz*—2 c. Native musical instrument; 8 c. Map; 10 c. Log pond; 15 c. Malay prau, Sandakan; 20 c. Bajau Chief; $2 Murut with blowpipe; $5 Net-fishing; $10 Arms of North Borneo. *Vert*—4 c. Hemp drying; 5 c. Cattle at Kota Belud; 30 c. Suluk river canoe, Lahad Datu; 50 c. Clock tower, Jesselton; $1 Bajau horsemen.

POSTAL FISCALS

Three Cents. Revenue
(F 1)
(Raised stop)

Ten Cents. Revenue
(F 2)

1886. *Regular issues surch as Type* F 1 *or* F 2.
F1 1 3 c. on 4 c. pink (No. 6) £100 £150
a. Raised stop after "Cents" .. .. 90·00 £140
F2 5 c. on 8 c. green (No. 7) £100 £150
a. Raised stop after "Cents" .. .. 90·00 £140
F3 4 10 c. on 50 c. violet (No. 4) £140 £160
a. Surch double .. .. .. — £1000
b. No stop after "Cents" and stop after "Revenue." £400 £450
c. Inverted "L" for first "F" in "FIFTY" (R.5/2) .. .. .. — £700

It is believed that Nos. F1/2 were each surcharged from a horizontal setting of five so that the raised stop variety occurs on every stamp in the first, second, third, sixth, seventh and eighth vertical columns in the sheets of 50 (10×5).

POSTAGE DUE STAMPS

POSTAGE DUE
(D 1)

1895 (1 Aug)–**97.** *Nos.* 68/79 *optd with Type* D **1** *horizontally* (8, 12, 18 *and* 24 *c.*) *or vertically, reading upwards (others). P* 14½–15.
D 1 25 2 c. black and rose-lake .. .. 18·00 35·00 2·75
a. Opt double* .. .. † † £250
b. Opt vertical, reading downwards* .. .. † † £300
D 2 2 c. black and lake .. .. 15·00 23·00 1·75
a. Perf 13½–14 .. ..
b. Perf 13½–14, comp 12–13* .. † † 10·00
c. Opt omitted (in vert pair with normal)* .. † † £1200
D 3 26 3 c. olive-green and dull purple 5·50 16·00 1·00
a. Bronze-green and dull purple
b. Opt vertical, reading downwards* .. .. † † —
D 4 3 c. olive-green and violet .. ..
a. Perf 13½–14 .. ..
b. Opt double* .. .. † † £375
D 5 27 5 c. black and vermilion .. 50·00 25·00 3·00
a. Printed double .. .. † — —
b. With stop after "DUE" in opt (1897) £150
c. Opt double £550
d. Perf 13½–14 .. .. — 50·00 2·50
e. Perf 13½–14, comp 12–13 .. — 55·00 —
D 6 28 6 c. black and bistre-brown .. 50·00 65·00 2·50
a. Perf 13½–14 .. .. 12·00 42·00 2·50
b. Perf 12–13* .. .. † † —
c. Perf 13½–14, comp 12–13 ..
d. Opt vertical, reading downwards* .. .. † † —
D 7 29 8 c. black and dull purple .. 42·00 45·00 2·75
a. Opt double* .. .. † † £325
b. Perf 13½–14 .. ..
ba. Opt inverted* .. .. † † £180
c. Perf 13½–14, comp 12–13 .. 60·00
D 8 30 12 c. black and blue .. .. — 50·00 2·50
a. Opt double* .. .. † † £325
b. Perf 13½–14 .. .. 65·00 48·00 2·50
D 9 12 c. black & ultram (*p* 13½–14) 75·00 60·00 —
D10 31 18 c. black and deep green .. 65·00 60·00 4·00
a. Opt inverted .. .. £275 £350 †
b. Perf 13½–14 .. .. 70·00 80·00 4·00
ba. Opt double* .. .. † † £250
c. Opt vertical, reading upwards (1897) .. 70·00 90·00 4·25
ca. Opt vertical, reading downwards .. .. £350 £250 †
D11 32 24 c. blue and rose-lake .. .. 65·00 80·00 4·00
a. Opt double* .. .. † † £275
b. Perf 13½–14 .. .. 25·00 50·00 4·00
c. Perf 13½–14, comp 14½–15
D3s, D5s, D8s, D10cs, D11s Optd "Specimen" .. .. *Set of* 5 £150

There were two local overprintings of these stamps which show variations in the distance between the two words. Further overprints were produced in London for sale to dealers by the British North Borneo Company. Those listings marked with an *only exist from the London overprinting and are usually only known cancelled-to-order.

No. D5b comes from at least one sheet which was included in a later overprinting.

1897–99. *Nos.* 94/7, 99/103, 106, 108/11 *optd with Type* D **1** *horizontally* (8 *c.*) *or vertically reading upwards (others). P* 14½–15.
D12 35 2 c. black and lake (1898) .. 8·50 9·00 1·50
a. Perf 13½–14 .. .. 27·00
b. Opt horizontal* £100
s. Optd "Specimen" .. .. 27·00
D13 2 c. black and green (*p* 13½–14)* 42·00 † 70
a. Perf 13½–14, comp 12–13* — † 90
b. Perf 16* .. ..
c. Perf 12–13* .. ..
d. Opt vertical, reading downwards* .. ..
e. Opt horizontal* £100
D14 36 3 c. green and rosy mauve* .. 15·00 † 50
a. Perf 13½–14* .. .. 26·00 † 1·00
b. Perf 13½–14, comp 14½–15*
c. Opt double* .. ..
D15 3 c. green and dull mauve .. 15·00 30·00 †
D16 37 4 c. black and carmine* .. — † 85
a. Perf 13½–14 .. .. 35·00 † 50
D17 38 5 c. black & orange-verm (1899) 60·00 60·00 90
a. Perf 13½–14 .. .. 20·00 38·00 1·75
D18 39 6 c. black and bistre-brown .. 5·00 27·00
a. Perf 13½–14 .. .. — 30·00
b. Perf 13½–14, comp 12–13* — †
s. Optd "Specimen" .. .. 27·00
D19 40 8 c. black & brown-purple (1898) 55·00 70·00
a. Opt vertical, reading upwards (*p* 16)* .. .. † †
s. Optd "Specimen" .. .. 27·00
D20 8 c. black and brown (opt vertical, reading upwards)* .. .. 5·50 †
a. Opt vertical, reading downwards* .. .. † †
b. Perf 13½–14* ..
D21 42 12 c. black and dull blue* .. — †
a. Perf 13½–14* .. .. 85·00 †
D22 44 18 c. black and green (*p* 16)* .. † †
D23 46 18 c. black and green (*p* 13½–14)* 45·00 †
a. Perf 13½–14, comp 12–13* 85·00 †
D24 45 24 c. blue and lake* .. .. — †
D25 47 24 c. blue and lake* .. .. 20·00 †
a. Perf 13½–14* ..

In addition to local overprints stamps from the 1897- series were also overprinted by Waterlow on two occasio sale by the British North Borneo Company to dealers London. These Waterlow overprints were not supplied to N Borneo for postal purposes and are indicated by an * i above listing.

1901–02. *Nos.* 96/7, 100 *and* 102/3 *optd locally as Type but with stop after* "DUE", *horizontally* (8 *c.*) *or vert reading upwards (others). P* 13½–14.
D26 36 3 c. green and rosy mauve (1902) .. 50·00
a. Opt double £200
D27 3 c. green & dull mve (*p* 14½–15) (1902) 50·00
a. Opt double £225
D28 38 5 c. black & orange-verm (*p* 14½–15) .. 50·00
D29 40 8 c. black and brown-purple .. .. 22·00
D30 8 c. black and brown (*p* 14½–15) .. £130

1902 (10 Oct)–**12.** *Stamps of* 1901–05 (*optd* "BRIT PROTECTORATE") *further optd with Type* D **1** *locally* D31) *or by Waterlow (others). P* 13½–14. (*a*) *Optd horizon showing stop after* "DUE"
D31 34 1 c. black and bistre-brown .. .. 4·50 5
a. With raised stop after "DUE" .. 4·75 6

(*b*) *Optd vertically reading upwards*
D32 35 2 c. black and green (*p* 16) .. £275
D33 36 3 c. green and rosy mauve .. .. 85·00 9
D34 38 5 c. black & orange-verm (*p* 14½–15) £140 9
D35 40 8 c. black and brown £120 8
D36 47 24 c. blue and lake £150 8

(*c*) *Optd horizontally at centre of stamp*
D37 34 1 c. black and bistre-brown* .. — † 2
a. Perf 14½–15* .. .. £200 † 2
D38 35 2 c. black and green (1909) .. 10·00 3·75
a. Perf 14½–15 (1903) .. 45·00 45·00
D39 36 3 c. green and rosy mauve (1912) 4·75 3·25
a. Perf 14½–15 (1904) .. 45·00 32·00
ab. Type D 1 opt double ..
D40 37 4 c. black and carmine (1912) .. 9·00 6·50
a. Type D 1 opt double* .. — †
b. Perf 14½–15 (1.3.03) .. 6·00 13·00
D41 38 5 c. black & orange-verm (1905) 20·00 4·50
a. Perf 14½–15 (1905) .. 60·00 24·00
D42 39 6 c. black & bistre-brown (1912) 13·00 11·00
a. Type D 1 opt inverted* .. £375 † 9
b. Type D 1 opt double .. † —
c. No stop after "PROTECTORATE" (1912) .. ..
d. Perf 16 (1906) .. .. 60·00 32·00
D43 40 8 c. black and brown (1912) .. 20·00 4·25
a. No stop after "PROTECTORATE" (1903) .. .. 45·00 55·00
D44 41 10 c. brown and slate-lilac (1906) £160 55·00
a. No stop after "PROTECTORATE" (1906) .. .. — —
D45 10 c. brown and slate-blue (1912) 70·00 16·00
D46 42 12 c. black and dull blue (2.12.10) 20·00 13·00 1
D47 43 16 c. green and chestnut (2.12.10) 35·00 18·00 1
D48 46 18 c. black and green (2.12.10) .. 8·00 18·00 1
a. Type D 1 opt double* .. £425 † 50
b. Imperf between (vert pair) — † £4
D49 47 24 c. blue and lake (1906) .. 11·00 22·00 1
a. Perf 14½–15 (1909) .. — —
b. Type D 1 opt double* .. £225 † 75

(*d*) *Optd horizontally at top of stamp*
D50 35 2 c. black and green (*p* 16) (1907) .. 80·00 40
a. Perf 14½–15 (1908) .. .. 65·00 45
D51 37 4 c. black and carmine (1906) .. 65·00 20

Items marked * only occur in stocks obtained from the Brit North Borneo Company in London.

POSTAGE DUE
(D 2)

POSTAGE DUE
(D 3)

Type D 2. Thick letters. Ends of "S" and top of "G" straig Pointed beard to "G".
Type D 3. Thinner letters. Ends of "S" and top of "G" slant Square beard to "G".

1918–30. *Optd with Type* D **2** *locally.* (*a*) *On stamps* 1909–23. *P* 13½–14
D52 52 2 c. black and green (opt at foot) (1.24) 11·00 75
a. Perf 14½–15 .. .. .. 18·00 80
s. Optd "Specimen" .. .. .. 28·00
D53 53 3 c. black and green (opt at foot) (1.9.23) 4·50 40
D54 54 4 c. black and scarlet (opt at top) (10.18) 85·00 17
D55 4 c. black and scarlet (opt at foot) (1.22) 1·00 1
D56 4 c. black & scarlet (opt in centre) (5.23) — 10
D57 55 5 c. black & yell-brn (opt at foot) (1.22) 8·50 18
D58 5 c. blk & yell-brn (opt in centre) (1.23) 8·50 18
D59 56 6 c. black & ol-grn (opt at foot) (1.9.23) 8·00 7
D60 6 c. black & ol-grn (opt in centre) (6.23) 10·00 7
D61 6 c. blk & apple-grn (opt at foot) (1.9.23) 10·00 15
D62 57 8 c. blk & rose-lake (opt at foot) (1.9.23) 1·50 1
a. Opt double £700
D63 58 10 c. black & turq-bl (opt at foot) (1.8.24) 13·00 19
a. Perf 14½–15 .. .. .. 65·00 £1

9 12 c. black and deep blue (1.8.24) .. 48·00 42·00
a. Horiz pair, one without opt .. £8000
0 16 c. black and brown-lake (2.29)
a. Black and red-brown .. .. 17·00 50·00
s. Optd "Specimen" .. .. 28·00

n stamps of 1925–28 *with opt at foot. P* 12½ (1928–30)
2 2 c. black and claret (3.30) .. .. 75 1·75
3 3 c. black and green (1926) .. .. 5·50 22·00
4 4 c. black and scarlet (1926) .. .. 1·50 1·75
5 5 c. black and yellow-brown (1926) .. 7·50 85·00
6 6 c. black and olive-green (3.28) .. 4·50 2·75
7 8 c. black and carmine (2.28) .. .. 3·25 14·00
8 10 c. black and turquoise-blue (1926) .. 8·50 85·00
9 12 c. black and deep blue (1926) .. 29·00 £150
es given as month and year only indicate first known
ark where recorded

38. *Optd with Type* D 3, *locally, at foot of stamp.* (a) *On*
ps of 1909–23. *P* 13½–14
7 8 c. black and carmine (1931) .. — 1·50
0 16 c. black and brown-lake (11.31) .. 17·00 75·00
a. Black and red-brown .. .. 6·50

(b) *On stamps of* 1925–28. *P* 12½
2 2 c. black and claret (5.31) .. .. 50 2·00
3 3 c. black and green (11.38) .. .. 5·50 22·00
4 4 c. black and scarlet (6.36) .. .. — 1·75
5 5 c. black and yellow-brown .. .. 10·00
6 6 c. black and olive-green (12.30) .. 4·00 2·50
7 8 c. black and carmine (9.31) .. .. 2·75 14·00
8 10 c. black and turquoise-blue (12.32) .. 10·00 85·00
9 12 c. black and deep blue .. .. 29·00
0 16 c. black and red-brown .. .. 48·00 £180
es given are those of earliest postmark where recorded.

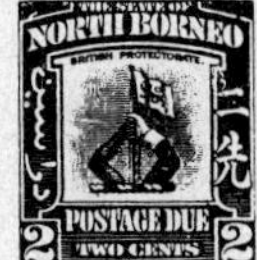

D 4 Crest of the Company

(Recess Waterlow)

(1 Jan). *P* 12½.
D 4 2 c. brown .. .. 6·50 70·00
4 c. scarlet .. .. 6·50 95·00
6 c. violet .. .. 22·00 £120
8 c. green .. .. 23·00 £200
10 c. blue .. .. 48·00 £350
9 .. .. *Set of* 5 95·00 £750
/9s Perf "Specimen" .. .. *Set of* 5 £140

LABUAN

CROWN COLONY

e island of Labuan, off the northern coast of Borneo, was
1 to Great Britain by the Sultan of Brunei in December
.

Stamps of STRAITS SETTLEMENTS were used from
367 until 1879. Covers of 1864 and 1865 are known from
abuan franked with stamps of INDIA or HONG KONG.

PRICES FOR STAMPS ON COVER

Nos. 1/4	—
Nos. 5/10	*from* × 40
Nos. 11/13	—
Nos. 14/21	*from* × 30
Nos. 22/5	—
Nos. 26/35	*from* × 40
Nos. 36/8	—
Nos. 39/47	*from* × 100
Nos. 49/50	*from* × 12
Nos. 51/7	*from* × 60
Nos. 62/74	*from* × 15
Nos. 75/9	*from* × 40
Nos. 80/8	*from* × 20
Nos. 89/97	*from* × 15
Nos. 98/116	*from* × 10
Nos. 117/28	*from* × 30
Nos. 129/37	*from* × 10
Nos. 138/42	—
Nos. D1/9	*from* × 30

1

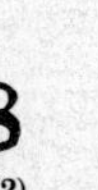

(2)

(3)

(Recess D.L.R.)

9 (May). *Wmk CA over Crown, sideways. P* 14.
1 2 c. blue-green £850 £600
6 c. orange-brown £180 £170
a. No dot at upper left (R. 2/4) .. £400 £375
12 c. carmine £1500 £600
a. No right foot to second Chinese character (R. 2/3) £2500 £1000
16 c. blue .. .. 55·00 £110
This watermark is always found sideways, and extends over two
mps, a single specimen showing only a portion of the Crown or
letters CA, these being tall and far apart. This paper was chiefly
ed for long fiscal stamps.

1880 (Jan)–**82**. *Wmk Crown CC (reversed on 8 c.). P* 14.
5 1 2 c. yellow-green .. .. 19·00 27·00
x. Wmk reversed .. .. 38·00 48·00
y. Wmk inverted and reversed .. .. 60·00 60·00
6 6 c. orange-brown .. .. 90·00 95·00
a. No dot at upper left £190 £200
w. Wmk inverted £160
7 8 c. carmine (4.82) .. .. .. 90·00 90·00
a. No dot at lower left (R. 2/5) £180 £180
x. Wmk normal (not reversed) £190 £190
8 10 c. brown .. .. £130 80·00
w. Wmk inverted .. .. £100 85·00
9 12 c. carmine £225 £300
a. No right foot to second Chinese character £425 £475
w. Wmk inverted £300
x. Wmk reversed £225 £300
10 16 c. blue (1881) .. .. 80·00 80·00
w. Wmk inverted £140 £140
x. Wmk reversed £110 £120
y. Wmk inverted and reversed £170
5/10 .. .. *Set of* 6 £550 £600

1880 (Aug). (a) *No.* 9 *surch with T* 2 *in black and with the original value obliterated by manuscript bar in red or black.*
11 8 c. on 12 c. carmine £1000 £700
a. Type 2 inverted £1200 £750
b. "12" not obliterated £1700 £1100
c. As b. with Type 2 inverted .. ..
d. No right foot to second Chinese character £1700 £1100
x. Wmk reversed £950 £650

(b) *No.* 4 *surch with two upright figures and No.* 9 *surch with two at right angles as T* 3.
12 6 c. on 16 c. blue (R.) £1800 £750
a. With one "6" only .. .. ..
13 8 c. on 12 c. carmine £1200 £850
a. Both "8's" upright .. .. ..
b. Upright "8" inverted £1300 £900
c. No right foot to second Chinese character £1800 £1300
w. Wmk inverted .. .. † £1200
x. Wmk reversed £1200 £850

EIGHT CENTS (4) Eight Cents (5) one Dollar A.S.H. (6)

1881 (Mar). *No.* 9 *handstamped with T* 4.
14 8 c. on 12 c. carmine £275 £325
a. No right foot to second Chinese character £500 £600
w. Wmk inverted £350
x. Wmk reversed £275 £325

1881 (June). *No.* 9 *surch with T* 5.
15 8 c. on 12 c. carmine £110 £120
a. Surch double £1600 £1600
b. Surch inverted £9000
c. "Eighr" £14000
d. No right foot to second Chinese character £190 £225
w. Wmk inverted £190
x. Wmk reversed £100 £110
The error "Eighr" occurred on R. 2/1 of the first printing, but was soon corrected.
Only one sheet of 10 has been reported of No. 15b, which also shows wmk inverted and reversed.

1883. *Wmk Crown CA (reversed on 8 c.). P* 14.
17 1 2 c. yellow-green .. .. 16·00 25·00
a. Imperf between (horiz pair) £8000
w. Wmk inverted .. .. 45·00
x. Wmk reversed .. .. 17·00 35·00
18 8 c. carmine .. .. £225 90·00
a. No dot at lower left £425 £170
19 10 c. yellow-brown .. .. 27·00 38·00
w. Wmk inverted .. .. 60·00 70·00
x. Wmk reversed .. .. 60·00 70·00
20 16 c. blue .. .. 90·00 £170
21 40 c. amber .. .. 14·00 90·00
x. Wmk reversed .. .. 22·00 90·00
17/21 .. .. *Set of* 5 £325 £375

1883 (May). *No.* 10 *surch "One Dollar A.S.H." by hand as T* 6.
22 1 $1 on 16 c. blue (R.) £2750
The initials are those of the postmaster, Mr. A. S. Hamilton.

2 CENTS (7) 2 Cents (8)

(9)

1885 (June). *Nos.* 18 *and* 10 *handstamped as T* 7.
23 1 2 c. on 8 c. carmine £180 £375
a. No dot at lower left £375
24 2 c. on 16 c. blue £950 £850
w. Wmk inverted £1000
x. Wmk reversed .. .. † £850

1885 (July). *No.* 20 *surch as T* 8.
25 1 2 c. on 16 c. blue £110 £160
a. Surch double .. .. † £3750
b. "2" inserted £1400
w. Wmk inverted
No. 25b shows a second "2" applied by a separate handstamp to correct indistinct impressions of Type 8.

1885 (Sept). *No.* 18 *handstamped diag as T* 9.
26 1 2 c. on 8 c. carmine .. .. .. 65·00 £100
a. No dot at lower left £130 £225
x. Wmk normal (not reversed) £100

1885 (Sept)–**86**. *Wmk Crown CA. P* 14.
30 1 2 c. rose-red .. .. 2·00 9·00
a. Pale rose-red (1886) .. .. .. 2·00 8·00
x. Wmk reversed .. .. 5·50
31 8 c. deep violet .. .. 19·00 7·00
a. No dot at lower left .. .. .. 45·00 20·00
b. Mauve (1886) .. .. 22·00 8·00
ba. No dot at lower left .. .. .. 50·00 22·00
bw. Wmk inverted .. .. 60·00
32 10 c. sepia (1886) .. .. 9·00 32·00
w. Wmk inverted .. .. 35·00
x. Wmk reversed .. .. 22·00
33 16 c. grey (1886) £100
x. Wmk reversed .. .. 90·00 £150
30/3 .. .. *Set of* 4 £110 £170
30s/3s Optd "Specimen" .. .. *Set of* 4 £400

ISSUES OF BRITISH NORTH BORNEO COMPANY

From 1 January 1890 while remaining a Crown Colony, the administration of Labuan was transferred to the British North Borneo Co, which issued the following stamps.

6 Cents (10) Two CENTS (11) Six CENTS (12)

1891 (July)–**92**. *Handstamped with T* 10.
34 1 6 c. on 8 c. deep violet (No. 31) .. .. £100 90·00
a. Surch inverted £170 £160
b. Surch double £450
c. Surch double, one inverted £750
d. "Cents" omitted £400 £400
f. Pair, one without surch, one surch inverted £1200
g. No dot at lower left £200 £190
35 6 c. on 8 c. mauve (No. 31*b*) .. .. 7·50 7·50
a. Surch inverted .. .. 55·00 55·00
b. Surch double, one inverted £650
c. Surch double, both inverted £650
d. "6" omitted £425
e. Pair, one without surcharge £1000 £1000
f. Surch inverted with "Cents" omitted £425
g. Pair, one without surch, one surch inverted £1200
h. Surch double £325
i. No dot at lower left .. .. .. 18·00 18·00
j. Imperf between (horiz pair) .. ..
w. Wmk inverted .. .. 40·00 40·00
x. Wmk reversed .. .. 27·00
36 6 c. on 8 c. mauve (R.) (No. 31*b*) (2.92) .. £750 £375
a. Surch inverted £1000 £500
37 6 c. on 16 c. blue (No. 4) (3.92) £1800 £1600
a. Surch inverted £6500 £4750
38 6 c. on 40 c. amber (No. 21) £7000 £3750
a. Surch inverted £6000 £5500
There are two different versions of Type 10 with the lines of the surcharge either 1 mm or 2 mm apart.

(Recess D.L.R.)

1892–93. *No wmk. P* 14.
39 1 2 c. rose-lake .. .. 3·75 3·50
40 6 c. bright green .. .. 8·00 4·50
a. No dot at upper left .. .. .. 19·00 15·00
41 8 c. violet .. .. 3·25 8·00
a. Pale violet (1893) .. .. .. 4·25 8·00
43 10 c. brown .. .. 9·00 8·00
a. Sepia-brown (1893) .. .. .. 9·00 13·00
45 12 c. bright blue .. .. 4·75 6·50
a. No right foot to second Chinese character .. .. 13·00 18·00
46 16 c. grey .. .. 5·00 9·00
47 40 c. ochre .. .. 20·00 32·00
a. Brown-buff (1893) .. .. .. 40·00 25·00
39/47 .. .. *Set of* 7 48·00 55·00
The 6 c., 12 c., 16 c. and 40 c. are in sheets of 10, as are all the earlier issues. The other values are in sheets of 30.

1892 (Dec). *Nos.* 47 *and* 46 *surch locally as T* 11 *or* 12.
49 1 2 c. on 40 c. ochre (13 December) .. £150 90·00
a. Surch inverted £350 £475
50 6 c. on 16 c. grey (20 December) .. £300 £140
a. Surch inverted £425 £250
b. Surch sideways £425 £250
c. Surch "Six Cents" £1400
There are 10 slightly different versions of each of these surcharges which were applied in settings of 5×2, although instances of single handstamps are known.
A "SIX CENTS" handstamp with Roman "I" in "SIX" (without dot) is a clandestine surcharge, although it can be found with genuine postmarks. It also exists sideways or inverted.
The "Six Cents" surcharge of No. 50c was handstamped onto examples where the Type 12 surcharge had failed to print or where it was partially or completely albino.

CANCELLED-TO-ORDER. Prices are separately indicated, in a third price column, for stamps showing the recognisable black bars remainder cancellation. Earlier issues of the Company administration were also so treated, but, as postal cancellations were used, these cannot be identified.

(Litho D.L.R.)

1894 (Apr). *No wmk. P* 14.
51 1 2 c. carmine-pink .. .. .. 1·40 12·00 50
52 6 c. bright green .. .. .. 11·00 26·00 50
a. Imperf between (horiz pair) .. £5000
b. No dot at upper left .. .. 24·00 55·00 1·25
53 8 c. bright mauve .. .. .. 9·50 26·00 50
54 10 c. brown .. .. 38·00 40·00 50
55 12 c. pale blue .. .. 18·00 55·00 60
a. No right foot to second Chinese character .. .. 40·00 90·00 1·25

56 1 16 c. grey .. .. 23·00 90·00 50
57 40 c. orange-buff .. .. .. 45·00 £100 50
51/7 .. .. .. *Set of* 7 £130 £300 3·25
51s/7s H/S "Specimen" .. .. *Set of* 7 £110
Collectors are warned against forgeries of this issue.

PERFORATION. There are a number of small variations in the perforation of the Waterlow issues of 1894 to 1905 which we believe to be due to irregularity of the pins rather than different perforators.

In the following lists, stamps perf 12, 12½, 13 or compound are described as perf 12–13, stamps perf 13½, 14 or compound are described as perf 13½–14 and those perf 14½, 15 or compound are listed as perf 14½–15. In addition the 13½–14 perforation exists compound with 14½–15 and with 12–13, whilst perf 16 comes from a separate perforator.

13

LABUAN
40
CENTS
(14)

1894 (May)–**96**. *T* 24/32 *of North Borneo (colours changed), with* "LABUAN" *engraved on vignette plate as T* 13 (8, 12, 24 c.) *or horizontally (others). P* 14½–15.

(a) Name and central part of design in black

62 **24** 1 c. grey-mauve .. .. .. 1·50 7·50 50
b. Perf 13½–14 .. .. .. 8·50 9·00 —
ba. Imperf between (vert pair) .. £700 — £375
c. Perf 13½–14, comp 14½–15 22·00
d. Perf 13½–14, comp 12–13 .. 21·00 10·00 90
e. Perf 12–13 .. .. ..
63 **25** 2 c. blue .. .. .. 2·50 7·50 50
a. Imperf (pair) £600
b. Perf 13½–14 .. .. 4·00 7·50 —
c. Perf 13½–14, comp 14½–15 25·00
d. Perf 13½–14, comp 12–13
e. Perf 12–13 .. .. 75·00
64 **26** 3 c. ochre .. .. .. 3·75 15·00 50
a. Perf 13½–14 .. .. 7·50 9·00 —
b. Perf 13½–14, comp 14½–15 ..
c. Perf 13½–14, comp 12–13 .. 35·00
d. Perf 12–13 .. ..
65 **27** 5 c. green .. .. .. 32·00 23·00 65
a. Perf 13½–14 .. .. 35·00 12·00 —
ab. Imperf between (horiz pair) .. £1100
b. Perf 13½–14, comp 12–13 .. 48·00
c. Perf 12–13 .. .. 85·00
67 **28** 6 c. brown-lake .. .. .. 2·50 13·00 50
a. Imperf (pair) .. .. £550 † £300
b. Perf 13½–14 .. .. — — 1·50
c. Perf 13½–14, comp 14½–15 .. — — 90
d. Perf 13½–14, comp 12–13 ..
e. Perf 12–13 ..
68 **29** 8 c. rose-red .. .. .. 20·00 24·00 50
a. Perf 13½–14 .. .. 24·00 38·00 —
69 8 c. pink (1896) .. .. 7·00 23·00 50
a. Perf 13½–14 .. .. 25·00 32·00 50
70 **30** 12 c. orange-vermilion .. .. 23·00 48·00 50
a. Perf 13½–14 .. .. 65·00 70·00 2·00
b. Perf 12–13 .. ..
c. Perf 13½–14, comp 12–13 .. — 85·00 —
71 **31** 18 c. olive-brown .. .. 22·00 55·00 50
a. Perf 13½–14 .. .. 60·00
72 18 c. olive-bistre (1896) .. .. 55·00 70·00 50
a. Perf 13½–14 .. .. 27·00 65·00 —
b. Perf 13½–14, comp 12–13 ..
c. Imperf between (vert pair) .. † † £900

(b) Name and central part in blue

73 **32** 24 c. pale mauve .. .. 21·00 55·00 50
a. Perf 13½–14 .. .. 19·00 50·00 —
74 24 c. dull lilac (1896) .. .. 15·00 45·00 50
a. Perf 13½–14 .. .. 13·00 42·00 50
62/74 .. .. *Set of* 9 95·00 £190 4·00
62s/74s Optd "Specimen" .. .. *Set of* 9 £140

1895 (June). *No.* 83 *of North Borneo* ($1 *inscr* "STATE OF NORTH BORNEO") *surch as T* 14.

75 **32*c*** 4 c. on $1 scarlet .. .. .. 1·00 2·00 40
76 10 c. on $1 scarlet .. .. .. 3·00 1·40 40
77 20 c. on $1 scarlet .. .. .. 26·00 10·00 40
78 30 c. on $1 scarlet .. .. .. 29·00 35·00 40
79 40 c. on $1 scarlet .. .. .. 26·00 27·00 40
75/9 .. .. *Set of* 5 75·00 65·00 1·75
75s/9s Optd "Specimen" .. *Set of* 5 80·00

No. 76 exists with the figures of the surcharge 2½ mm away from "CENTS". The normal setting has a space of 4 mm. Examples of the narrow setting have, so far, only been seen on cancelled-to-order stamps (*Price* £18 *c.t.o.*).

LABUAN (15) — 1846 JUBILEE 1896 (16) — 4 CENTS (17)

1896. *T* **32*a*** *to* **32*c*** *of North Borneo (as Nos.* 81 *to* 83, *but colours changed) optd with T* **15**.

80 25 c. green .. .. .. 23·00 27·00 60
a. Opt omitted .. .. 20·00 — 1·25
b. Imperf (pair) .. .. — — 60·00
ba. Opt omitted .. .. 38·00
81 50 c. maroon .. .. .. 23·00 27·00 60
a. Opt omitted .. .. 18·00 — 1·25
b. Imperf (pair) .. .. — — 60·00
ba. Opt omitted .. .. 38·00
82 $1 blue .. .. .. 55·00 50·00 60
a. Opt omitted .. .. 27·00 — 1·25
b. Imperf (pair) .. .. — — 60·00
ba. Opt omitted .. .. 40·00
80s/2s Optd "Specimen" .. .. *Set of* 3 60·00

Nos. 80/1 showing stamps either printed double or double, one inverted, are from waste sheets subsequently sold by the British North Borneo Company to collectors.

1896 (24 Sept). *Jubilee of Cession of Labuan to Gt Britain. Nos.* 62 *to* 68 *optd with T* **16**. *P* 14½–15.

83 1 c. black and grey-mauve .. .. 18·00 21·00 80
b. Opt in orange .. .. £180 £180 20·00
c. "JEBILEE" (R. 8/7) £950 £500 £275
d. "JUBILE" (R. 3/10) £1400
e. Perf 13½–14 .. .. 22·00 22·00 —
ea. Opt double .. .. £275 £300 —
eb. Opt in orange .. .. £225 £190 †
f. Perf 13½–14, comp 12–13 .. 27·00 18·00 —
fa. Opt in orange .. .. — £190 †
g. Perf 12–13 .. ..
84 2 c. black and blue .. .. 35·00 20·00 80
a. Imperf horiz (vert pair) .. £650 £750 †
b. "JEBILEE" (R. 8/7) .. .. £1000 £1000 —
c. "JUBILE" (R. 3/10) £1700
d. Perf 13½–14 .. .. 35·00 14·00 —
e. Perf 13½–14, comp 14½–15 .. — 38·00 —
f. Perf 13½–14, comp 12–13 .. 45·00
85 3 c. black and ochre .. .. 32·00 22·00 80
a. "JEBILEE" (R. 8/7) .. .. — £1200 £700
b. "JUBILE" (R. 3/10) .. ..
d. Perf 13½–14 .. .. 40·00 28·00 90
db. Opt treble £650
e. Perf 13½–14, comp 14½–15 ..
f. Perf 13½–14, comp 12–13 ..
fa. Opt double £350 £350 £150
fb. Opt treble £650
86 5 c. black and green .. .. 50·00 16·00 90
a. Opt double .. .. £475 £450 —
b. Perf 13½–14 .. .. 55·00 22·00 90
c. Perf 13½–14, comp 12–13 ..
87 6 c. black and brown-lake .. .. 25·00 20·00 80
a. Opt double .. .. £600 £450 †
b. "JUBILE" (R. 3/10) £1700
c. Perf 13½–14, comp 14½–15 ..
d. Perf 13½–14 .. .. — 65·00 —
88 8 c. black and pink .. .. 42·00 13·00 80
a. Opt double .. .. † £2000 †
b. Perf 13½–14 .. .. 38·00 11·00 80
c. Perf 13½–14, comp 14½–15 .. 50·00 18·00 —
83/8 .. .. *Set of* 6 £180 90·00 4·50
83s/8s Optd "Specimen" .. .. *Set of* 6 £150

The normal overprint on the 1 c. varies in appearance from pure black to brownish black due to a mixing of the inks. The orange overprint on this value is in a clear, bright, unadulterated ink.

No. 84b is known in a vertical strip of 3 imperf horizontally except at the base of the bottom stamp (*Price* £5000 *unused*).

1897 (Apr)–**1901**. *T* 34/45 *of North Borneo (colours changed), with* "LABUAN" *engraved on vignette plate as T* **13** (8, 10, 12, 24 c.) *or horizontally (others). Name and central part in black* (24 c. *in blue*). *P* 13½–14.

89 **34** 1 c. dull claret (*p* 14½–15) .. 4·00 4·75 50
a. Perf 13½–14, comp 14½–15
b. Brown (1901) .. .. 13·00 16·00 65
ba. Perf 14½–15 .. .. 3·00
bb. Perf 16 .. .. 13·00 13·00 —
90 **35** 2 c. blue .. .. .. 13·00 4·25 65
a. Imperf between (vert pair) .. † † £550
b. Imperf between (horiz pair) .. † † £600
c. Perf 14½–15 .. .. 20·00 — 75
d. Perf 13½–14, comp 12–13 .. 32·00 18·00 —
e. Perf 16 .. .. — — 7·00
91 **36** 3 c. ochre .. .. .. 12·00 22·00 50
a. Imperf between (vert pair) .. £700 † £475
b. Perf 14½–15 .. .. 8·50 6·50 50
c. Perf 13½–14, comp 12–13 .. 24·00 28·00
92 **38** 5 c. green .. .. .. 50·00 50·00 70
a. Perf 14½–15 .. .. 40·00 48·00 —
b. Perf 13½–14, comp 12–13 ..
93 **39** 6 c. brown-lake .. .. 8·50 28·00 50
b. Perf 14½–15 .. .. 6·00 21·00 50
ba. Imperf between (vert pair) .. † † £500
c. Perf 13½–14, comp 12–13 .. — — 5·50
94 **40** 8 c. rose-red .. .. .. 45·00 — 50
a. Perf 14½–15 .. .. 18·00 12·00 —
b. Perf 13½–14, comp 12–13 .. 29·00 — 2·75
c. Vermilion .. .. 14·00 — 50
ca. Perf 16 .. .. — — 4·50
95 **42** 12 c. vermilion .. .. .. 70·00 80·00 80
a. Perf 14½–15 .. .. 35·00 48·00 80
96 **44** 18 c. olive-bistre .. .. 60·00 60·00 50
a. Imperf between (vert pair) .. † † —
b. Perf 16 .. .. 16·00 45·00 50
97 **45** 24 c. grey-lilac .. .. 35·00 65·00 60
a. Perf 14½–15 .. .. 12·00 45·00 50
89/97 .. .. *Set of* 9 £130 £200 4·75
89s/97s Optd "Specimen" .. .. *Set of* 9 £160

The 12, 18 and 24 c. above were errors; in the 12 c., "LABUAN" is over the value at the top; the 18 c. has "POSTAL REVENUE" instead of "POSTAGE AND REVENUE", and the 24 c. is without "POSTAGE AND REVENUE".

1897 (Nov)–**98**. *(a) Types of North Borneo (colours changed), with* "LABUAN" *engraved on the vignette plate as in T* **13**. *P* 13½–14.

98 **42** 12 c. black and vermilion (3.98) .. † — 3·00
a. Perf 14½–15 .. .. 42·00 48·00 —
b. Perf 13½–14, comp 14½–15 ..
c. Perf 16 .. .. .. 55·00 60·00 —
99 **46** 18 c. black and olive-bistre ..
a. Perf 14½–15 .. .. 80·00 60·00 2·00
b. Perf 16 .. .. † — 8·00
100 **47** 24 c. blue and lilac-brown .. 27·00 55·00 2·00
a. Perf 14½–15 .. .. 27·00 55·00 —
b. Perf 13½–14, comp 12–13 .. — 65·00 —
c. Perf 16 .. .. 29·00
d. Blue and ochre (*p* 14½–15) .. — — 2·50

In the 12 c. "LABUAN" is now correctly placed at foot of stamp. The 18 c. and 24 c. have the inscriptions on the stamps corrected, but the 18 c. still has "LABUAN" *over* the value at foot, and was further corrected as follows.

(b) As No. 99, *but* "LABUAN" *at top*

101 **46** 18 c. black and olive-bistre (3.98) 60·00 60·00
a. Perf 14½–15 .. .. 25·00 65·00
b. Perf 13½–14, comp 12–13 32·00 55·00
c. Perf 12–13
98s, 100s/1as Optd "Specimen" .. *Set of* 3 70·00

1899 (July). *Surch with T* **17** *(a) P* 14½–15.

102 **38** 4 c. on 5 c. (No. 92a) .. .. 35·00
103 **39** 4 c. on 6 c. (No. 93b) .. .. 21·00
a. Perf 13½–14 .. .. 29·00
b. Perf 13½–14, comp 12–13 .. 50·00
104 **40** 4 c. on 8 c. (No. 94a) .. .. 55·00
a. Perf 13½–14 .. .. 27·00
b. Perf 13½–14, comp 12–13 .. 29·00
c. Perf 12–13 .. ..
105 **42** 4 c. on 12 c. (No. 98a) .. .. 38·00
a. Perf 13½–14 .. .. 38·00
b. Perf 16 .. .. 38·00
c. Perf 13½–14, comp 12–13 .. 55·00
106 **46** 4 c. on 18 c (No. 101a) .. .. 24·00
a. Surch double £375
107 **47** 4 c. on 24 c. (No. 100a) .. .. 23·00
a. Perf 13½–14 .. .. 19·00
b. Perf 13½–14, comp 12–13 .. 28·00
c. Perf 16 .. .. 42·00

(b) P 14

108 **32*a*** 4 c. on 25 c. (No. 80) .. .. 6·00
109 **32*b*** 4 c. on 50 c. (No. 81) .. .. 6·50
110 **32*c*** 4 c. on $1 (No. 82) .. .. 6·50
102/10 .. .. *Set of* 9 £160
102s/10s Optd "Specimen" .. *Set of* 9 £150

A new setting of the surcharge with closer spacing (2½ … between "4" and "CENTS" was used for the Speci… overprints, including unissued surcharges on the 1 c., 2 c. 3 c. values (*price* £140 *for the set of three*).

1900–02. *Types of North Borneo with* "LABUAN" *engrav… the vignette plate as in T* **13**, *in green on* 16 c. *P* 13½–14

111 **35** 2 c. black and green .. 3·75 2·50
a. Imperf between (horiz pair) £2000
b. Perf 13½–14, comp 12–13 ..
112 **37** 4 c. black and yellow-brown .. 7·00 38·00
a. Imperf between (vert pair) .. £850
b. Perf 13½–14, comp12–13 .. 28·00
113 4 c. black and carmine (8.1900) .. 12·00 2·75
a. Perf 14½–15 .. .. 6·50 8·50
b. Perf 13½–14, comp 12–13 .. 29·00 8·00
c. Perf 16 .. ..
114 **38** 5 c. black and pale blue .. 28·00 18·00
a. Perf 13½–14, comp 12–13 .. — 80·00
115 **41** 10 c. brown & slate-lilac (*p* 14½–15) (1902) .. .. 50·00 80·00
116 **43** 16 c. green and chestnut (1902) .. 50·00 £110
a. Perf 13½–14, comp 12–13 .. 80·00 £110
b. Perf 12–13 .. .. £170
c. Perf 14½–15 .. .. 95·00
111/16 .. .. *Set of* 6 £130 £225
111s/16s Optd "Specimen" .. *Set of* 6 £150

No. 112 was printed in an incorrect frame colour and was issued for postal purposes in Labuan. Used examples come f… dealers' stock sent to the island for cancellation.

18

Line through "B" (R.5/10)

(Recess Waterlow)

1902 (Sept)–**03**. *P* 13½–14.

117 **18** 1 c. black and purple (10.03) .. 3·50 7·00
a. Perf 14½–15 .. .. 75·00 7·50
b. Perf 13½–14, comp 12–13 .. 70·00
c. Line through "B" .. .. 45·00 75·00 6…
118 2 c. black and green .. .. 3·50 4·25
a. Perf 14½–15 .. .. — 5·00
b. Line through "B" .. .. 45·00 60·00 6…
119 3 c. black and sepia (10.03) .. 3·25 10·00
a. Line through "B" .. .. 45·00 75·00 6…
120 4 c. black and carmine .. .. 3·25 3·50
a. Perf 14½–15 .. .. 6·00 7·00
b. Perf 13½–14, comp 12–13 .. 60·00 48·00
c. Line through "B" .. .. 45·00 50·00 6…
121 8 c. black and vermilion .. .. 9·00 9·00
a. Perf 14½–15 .. .. 7·00
b. Line through "B" .. .. 65·00 85·00 6…
122 10 c. brown and slate-blue .. 3·25 10·00
b. Perf 14½–15 .. .. 4·50
ba. Imperf between (vert pair) .. † † £6…
c. Line through "B" .. .. 45·00 90·00 6…
123 12 c. black and yellow .. .. 5·00 12·00
a. Imperf between (vert strip of 3) .. .. .. † £2…
b. Perf 16 .. .. 5·00 16·00
c. Line through "B" .. .. 55·00 £100 6…
124 16 c. green and brown .. .. 4·75 16·00
a. Imperf between (vert pair) .. † —
b. Line through "B" .. .. 60·00 £120 6…
125 18 c. black and pale brown .. 3·25 20·00
a. Line through "B" .. .. 50·00 £140 6…
126 25 c. green and greenish blue .. 7·00 18·00
a. Perf 14½–15 .. .. 15·00 28·00
b. Error. Black and greenish blue — † £4…
c. Line through "B" .. .. 75·00 £150 6…
127 50 c. dull purple and lilac .. 10·00 42·00
a. Perf 13½–14, comp 12–13 .. 16·00 48·00
b. Line through "B" .. .. £150 £325 9…
128 $1 claret and orange .. .. 8·50 48·00
a. Perf 14½–15 .. .. 10·00 —
b. Line through "B" .. .. £100 £325 10…
117/28 .. .. *Set of* 12 55·00 £180 4…
117s/28s Optd "Specimen" .. *Set of* 12 £180

4
cents

(19)

(Dec). *Issues of* 1895 *and* 1897–8 *surch with T* **19**.

(*a*) *P* 14½–15

38	4 c. on 5 c. (No. 92a)	40·00	40·00	14·00
39	4 c. on 6 c. (No. 93b)	12·00	38·00	14·00
40	4 c. on 8 c. (No. 94a)	25·00	42·00	14·00
42	4 c. on 12 c. (No. 98a)	19·00	42·00	14·00
	a. Perf 16	25·00	45·00	—
46	4 c. on 18 c. (No. 101) (*p* 13½–14)	23·00	45·00	14·00
	a. Perf 13½–14, comp 12–13 ..	27·00	45·00	—
	b. Perf 12–13			
47	4 c. on 24 c. (No. 100a)	16·00	50·00	14·00
	a. Perf 13½–14	24·00	38·00	—
	b. Perf 13½–14, comp 12–13 ..	30·00	48·00	—
	c. Perf 16	26·00	40·00	14·00

(*b*) *P* 14

32*a*	4 c. on 25 c. (No. 80)	8·50	23·00	14·00
32*b*	4 c. on 50 c. (No. 81)	8·50	23·00	14·00
	a. Surch double	£275		
32*c*	4 c. on $1 (No. 82)	8·50	23·00	14·00
7	.. .. .. *Set of* 9	£140	£275	£110

. 136a usually shows one complete surcharge and parts of further examples due to the position of the second ession.

e barred cancels can be found used on "philatelic" covers of ssue.

LABUAN **LABUAN**

(20) (21)

(12 Oct)–**05.** *Nos.* 81, 83 (*in Labuan colour*), *and* 84/6 *of* rth Borneo optd locally with T **20** (25 c., $2) *or* **21** (*others*).

32*a*	25 c. indigo (2.05)	£1000	†	—
32*c*	$1 blue (2.05)	†	†	£650
32*d*	$2 dull green	£2500	£2750	—
14	$5 bright purple (2.05) ..	£5000	£5500	£1000
15	$10 brown (11.05)	£17000	†	£6500

ngerous forgeries exist.

e overprint on No. 140 is 12 mm long.

POSTAGE DUE STAMPS

POSTAGE DUE

(D 1)

1. *Optd with Type* D **1**, *reading vertically upwards.* 13½–14.

35	2 c. black and green (111) ..	13·00	21·00	50
	a. Opt double	£325		
	b. Perf 13½–14, comp 12–13 ..	60·00	65·00	10·00
36	3 c. black and ochre (91) ..	16·00	75·00	70
	a. Perf 13½–14, comp 12–13 ..	60·00	—	2·00
37	4 c. black and carmine (113) ..	29·00	—	1·00
	a. Opt double	†	†	£475
	b. Perf 14½–15	29·00	75·00	50
38	5 c. black and pale blue (114) ..	45·00	90·00	75
	a. Perf 14½–15	—	—	1·00
	b. Perf 13½–14, comp 12–13 ..	60·00	£120	—
39	6 c. black and brown-lake (93) ..	23·00	85·00	75
	a. Perf 14½–15	35·00	75·00	—
	b. Perf 16	42·00	—	65
40	8 c. black and vermilion (94c) ..	50·00	80·00	1·00
	b. Perf 14½–15	60·00	£100	85
	ba. Frame inverted	†	†	£7500
	c. Perf 16	60·00	80·00	—
	d. Black and rose-red (94) ..	60·00	95·00	—
	da. Perf 14½–15	—	—	7·00
	db. Perf 13½–14, comp 12–13 ..			
42	12 c. black and vermilion (98) ..	80·00	—	3·25
	a. Opt reading downwards ..	†	†	£475
	b. Perf 14½–15	75·00	95·00	12·00
46	18 c. black and olive-bistre (101) (*p* 14½–15)	19·00	90·00	1·25
47	24 c. blue and lilac-brown (100) ..	38·00	95·00	5·00
	a. Perf 13½–14, comp 12–13 ..	60·00		
	b. Perf 14½–15	28·00		
	ba. Blue and ochre	55·00	—	1·25
	c. Perf 16	40·00	75·00	—
/9	.. .. .. *Set of* 9	£250	£600	8·75

No. D6ba only comes cancelled-to-order. About 20 examples ist, many having been found in 6d. stamp packets sold to lectors.

The administration of Labuan reverted to Colonial Office ntrol, as part of an agreement with Brunei, on 1 January 06. By Letters Patent dated 30 October 1906 Labuan was corporated with Straits Settlements and ceased issuing its n stamps. In 1946 it became part of the Colony of North rneo.

JAPANESE OCCUPATION OF NORTH BORNEO

Japanese forces landed in Northern Borneo on 15 December 941 and the whole of North Borneo had been occupied by 19 anuary 1942.

Brunei, North Borneo, Sarawak and, after a short period, abuan, were administered as a single territory by the apanese. Until September–October 1942, previous stamp sues, without overprint, continued to be used in conjunction ith existing postmarks. From October 1942 onwards noverprinted stamps of Japan were made available and kamples can be found used from the area for much of the emainder of the War. Japanese Occupation issues for Brunei, orth Borneo and Sarawak were equally valid throughout the mbined territory but not, in practice, equally available.

PRICES FOR STAMPS ON COVER

Nos. J1/17	*from* × 5
Nos. J18/19	*from* × 6
Nos. J20/32	*from* × 25
Nos. J33/4	*from* × 2
Nos. J35/48	*from* × 12

(1) **2** Mt Kinabalu **3** Borneo Scene

1942 (30 Sept). *Stamps of North Borneo handstamped with T* **1**.

(*a*) *In violet on Nos.* 303/17

J 1	1 c. green and red-brown	£150	£225
	a. Black opt	£225	£200
	ab. Pair, one without opt ..	£2250	
J 2	2 c. purple and greenish blue ..	£160	£225
	a. Black opt	£250	£225
J 3	3 c. slate-blue and green	£130	£225
	a. Black opt	£275	£250
J 4	4 c. bronze-green and violet ..	£140	£225
	a. Black opt	50·00	£120
J 5	6 c. deep blue and claret	£130	£225
	a. Black opt	£275	£250
J 6	8 c. scarlet	£160	£190
	a. Pair, one without opt ..	£2250	
	b. Black opt	£225	£190
J 7	10 c. violet and bronze-green ..	£150	£225
	a. Black opt	£250	£225
J 8	12 c. green and bright blue ..	£170	£375
	a. Black opt	£425	£375
J 9	15 c. blue-green and brown ..	£160	£375
	a. Pair, one without opt ..	£2250	
	b. Black opt	£450	£375
J10	20 c. violet and slate-blue	£190	£425
	a. Black opt	£500	£425
J11	25 c. green and chocolate	£190	£425
	a. Black opt	£500	£425
J12	50 c. chocolate and violet	£275	£475
	a. Black opt	£600	£475
J13	$1 brown and carmine	£275	£600
	a. Black opt	£700	£600
J14	$2 violet and olive-green ..	£425	£800
	a. Pair, one without opt ..	£3250	
	b. Black opt	£900	£800
J15	$5 indigo and pale blue	£500	£900
	a. Black opt	£1100	£900

(*b*) *In black on Nos.* 318/19 ("WAR TAX")

J16	1 c. green and red-brown	£475	£275
	a. Pair, one without opt	†	£3000
	b. Violet opt	—	£500
J17	2 c. purple and greenish blue ..	£1100	£400
	a. Violet opt	—	£650

(Litho Kolff & Co., Batavia)

1943 (29 Apr). *P* 12½.

J18	**2**	4 c. red	15·00	35·00
J19	**3**	8 c. blue	14·00	35·00

(4) (5)

("Imperial Japanese Postal Service North Borneo")

1944 (30 Sept). *Nos.* 303/15 *of North Borneo optd as T* **4**.

J20	1 c. green and red-brown	5·00	12·00
J21	2 c. purple and greenish blue ..	7·50	9·00
	a. Optd on No. J2	£425	
J22	3 c. slate-blue and green	4·50	8·50
	a. Optd on No. J3	£425	
J23	4 c. bronze-green and violet ..	6·50	13·00
J24	6 c. deep blue and claret	4·50	6·50
J25	8 c. scarlet	6·00	17·00
	a. Optd on No. J6	£425	
J26	10 c. violet and bronze-green ..	8·50	13·00
	a. Optd on No. J7	£425	
	b. Optd on No. J7a	£190	£375
J27	12 c. green and bright blue ..	8·00	13·00
	a. Optd on No. J8	£425	
J28	15 c. blue-green and brown ..	8·00	16·00
	a. Optd on No. J9	£425	
J29	20 c. violet and slate-blue	19·00	42·00
	a. Optd on No. J10	£1200	
J30	25 c. green and chocolate	19·00	42·00
	a. Optd on No. J11	£1200	
J31	50 c. chocolate and violet	60·00	£110
	a. Optd on No. J12	£1700	
J32	$1 brown and carmine	85·00	£150
J20/32	.. .. .. *Set of* 13	£225	£400

The spacing between the second and third lines of the overprint is 12 mm on the horizontal stamps, and 15 mm on the upright.

1944 (11 May). *No.* J1 *surch with T* **5**.

J33	**81**	$2 on 1 c. green and red-brown ..	£4500	£3750

(6) **7** Girl War-worker (8) ("North Borneo")

1944 (11 May). *North Borneo No.* 315 *surch with T* **6**.

J34	$5 on $1 brown and carmine	£4000	£2750
	a. Surch on No. J13	—	£5500

1944 (2 Oct)–**45.** *Contemporary stamps of Japan as T* **7** (*various subjects*) *optd with T* **8** *at Chinese Press, Kuching.*

J35	1 s. red-brown (No. 391) (2.45)	7·00	18·00
J36	2 s. scarlet (No. 318) (10.44)	6·50	15·00
J37	3 s. emerald-green (No. 319) (8.45) ..	5·50	18·00
J38	4 s. yellow-green (No. 395) (12.44) ..	8·00	16·00
J39	5 s. claret (No. 396) (1.45)	9·00	19·00
J40	6 s. orange (No. 322) (8.45)	8·50	20·00
	a. Opt double, one inverted	£375	£375
J41	8 s. violet (No. 324) (2.45)	6·00	20·00
J42	10 s. carmine and pink (No. 399) (11.44) ..	6·00	19·00
J43	15 s. blue (No. 401) (11.44)	8·00	19·00
J44	20 s. blue-slate (No. 328) (11.44)	90·00	85·00
J45	25 s. brown and chocolate (No. 329) (2.45)	55·00	70·00
J46	30 s. turquoise-blue (No. 330)	£160	95·00
J47	50 s. olive and bistre (No. 331) (8.45) ..	60·00	65·00
J48	1 y. red-brown & chocolate (No. 332) (5.45)	60·00	90·00
J35/48	.. .. *Set of* 14	£425	£500

Designs:—2 s. General Nogi; 3 s. Hydro-electric Works; 4 s. Hyuga Monument and Mt Fuji; 5 s. Admiral Togo; 6 s. Garambi Lighthouse, Formosa; 8 s. Meiji Shrine; 10 s. Palms and map of S.E. Asia; 15 s. Airman; 20 s. Mt Fuji and cherry blossoms; 25 s. Horyu Temple; 30 s. Torii, Itsukushima Shrine at Miyajima; 50 s. Kinkaku Temple; 1 y. Great Buddha, Kamakura.

Examples of some values have been found with hand-painted forged overprints.

POSTAGE DUE STAMPS

1942 (30 Sept). *Nos.* D66/7 *and* D69 *of North Borneo handstamped with T* **1** *in black.*

JD1	D **2**	2 c. brown	—	£2500
JD2		4 c. scarlet	—	£2500
JD3		8 c. green	—	£2500

Northern Nigeria *see* Nigeria

Northern Rhodesia

The north-eastern and north-western provinces of Rhodesia, previously administered by the British South Africa Company, became a Crown Colony on 1 April 1924.

The current stamps of Rhodesia (the "Admiral design" first issued in 1913) remained in use until 31 March 1925 and continued to be valid for postal purposes until 30 September of that year.

PRICES FOR STAMPS ON COVER TO 1945	
Nos. 1/21	*from* × 2
Nos. 22/4	*from* × 5
Nos. 25/45	*from* × 2
Nos. D1/4	*from* × 15

1

2

(Eng W. G. Fairweather. Recess Waterlow)

1925 (1 April)–**29.** *Wmk Mult Script CA. P* 12½.

No.	Type	Description	Unused	Used
1	**1**	½d. green	1·75	80
2		1d. brown	1·75	10
3		1½d. carmine-red	1·75	30
4		2d. yellow-brown	2·00	10
5		3d. ultramarine	2·00	1·25
6		4d. violet	4·00	50
7		6d. slate-grey	4·25	40
8		8d. rose-purple	3·75	40·00
9		10d. olive-green	4·25	38·00
10	**2**	1s. yellow-brown and black	3·75	1·75
11		2s. brown and ultramarine	14·00	22·00
12		2s. 6d. black and green	15·00	7·00
13		3s. violet and blue (1929)	23·00	19·00
14		5s. slate-grey and violet	29·00	17·00
15		7s. 6d. rose-purple and black	95·00	£150
16		10s. green and black	70·00	70·00
17		20s. carmine-red and rose-purple	£150	£170
1/17		*Set of* 17	£375	£475
1s/17s		Optd or Perf (3s.) "Specimen" *Set of* 17	£750	

A used example of the 4d. exists imperforate between the stamp and a fragment of another below it.

1935 (6 May). *Silver Jubilee. As Nos.* 91/4 *of Antigua. P* 13½×14.

No.	Description	Unused	Used
18	1d. light blue and olive-green	80	1·50
	f. Diagonal line by turret	45·00	65·00
	h. Dot by flagstaff	80·00	£100
	i. Dash by turret	80·00	£100
19	2d. green and indigo	80	1·50
	f. Diagonal line by turret	60·00	80·00
	g. Dot to left of chapel	95·00	£120
20	3d. brown and deep blue	2·50	5·50
	f. Diagonal line by turret	90·00	£130
	g. Dot to left of chapel	£170	£225
21	6d. slate and purple	3·75	1·50
	a. Frame printed double, one albino	£1800	
	h. Dot by flagstaff	£190	£150
18/21	*Set of* 4	7·00	9·00
18s/21s	Perf "Specimen" *Set of* 4	£100	

For illustrations of plate varieties see Omnibus section following Zanzibar.

THERN_RHODE

Hyphen between "NORTHERN" AND "RHODESIA" (R. 9/6)

1937 (12 May). *Coronation. As Nos.* 95/7 *of Antigua. P* 11×11½.

No.	Description	Unused	Used
22	1½d. carmine	30	35
23	2d. buff	40	35
24	3d. blue	60	1·25
	a. Hyphen flaw	£160	
22/4	*Set of* 3	1·10	1·75
22s/4s	Perf "Specimen" *Set of* 3	75·00	

3

4

"Tick bird" flaw (Pl 1 R. 7/1 of ptgs from Sept 1938 onwards)

(Recess Waterlow)

1938 (1 Mar)–**52.** *Wmk Mult Script CA. P* 12½.

No.	Type	Description	Unused	Used
25	**3**	½d. green	10	10
		a. "C" of "CA" missing from wmk		
26		½d. chocolate (15.11.51)	10	80
		a. Perf 12½×14 (22.10.52)	1·40	5·00
27		1d. brown	10	10
		a. Chocolate (1948)	1·60	60
28		1d. green (15.11.51)	60	1·00
29		1½d. carmine-red	45·00	40
		a. Imperf between (horiz pair)	£13000	
		b. "Tick bird" flaw	£2500	£225
30		1½d. yellow-brown (10.1.41)	30	10
		b. "Tick bird" flaw	65·00	30·00
31		2d. yellow-brown	45·00	1·25
32		2d. carmine-red (10.1.41)	30	30
33		2d. purple (1.12.51)	45	1·00
34		3d. ultramarine	30	10
35		3d. scarlet (1.12.51)	50	2·25
36		4d. dull violet	30	40
37		4½d. blue (5.5.52)	40	5·00
38		6d. grey	30	10
39		9d. violet (5.5.52)	40	3·00
40	**4**	1s. yellow-brown and black	2·50	40
41		2s. 6d. black and green	7·00	2·50
42		3s. violet and blue	13·00	6·00
43		5s. grey and dull violet	10·00	6·50
44		10s. green and black	13·00	12·00
45		20s. carmine-red and rose-purple	38·00	45·00
25/45		*Set of* 21	£160	75·00
25s/45s		Perf "Specimen" *Set of* 15	£275	

Nos. 26a and 28 exist in coils, constructed from normal sheets.

1946 (26 Nov). *Victory. As Nos.* 110/11 *of Antigua. P* 13½×14.

No.	Description	Unused	Used
46	1½d. red-orange	10	10
	a. Perf 13½	14·00	12·00
47	2d. carmine	10	40
46s/7s	Perf "Specimen" *Set of* 2	60·00	

The decimal perforation gauge for Nos. 46/7 is 13.7×14.1 and for No. 46a 13.7×13.4.

1948 (1 Dec). *Royal Silver Wedding. As Nos.* 112/13 *of Antigua, but 20s. ptd in recess.*

No.	Description	Unused	Used
48	1½d. orange	30	10
49	20s. brown-lake	42·00	45·00

1949 (10 Oct). *75th Anniv of U.P.U. As Nos.* 114/17 *of Antigua.*

No.	Description	Unused	Used
50	2d. carmine	20	30
51	3d. deep blue	1·50	1·25
52	6d. grey	55	1·25
53	1s. red-orange	55	1·00
50/3	*Set of* 4	2·50	3·50

POSTAGE DUE STAMPS

D 1

1929 (June)–**52.** *Wmk Mult Script CA. Ordinary paper. P* 14.

No.	Type	Description	Unused	Used
D1	**D 1**	1d. grey-black	2·50	2·50
		a. Chalk-surfaced paper. *Blk* (22.1.52)	20·00	75·00
		ab. Error. St. Edward's Crown, W9*b*	£1700	
D2		2d. grey-black	3·00	3·00
D3		3d. grey-black	3·00	26·00
		a. Chalk-surfaced paper. *Blk* (22.1.52)	7·00	65·00
		ab. Error. Crown missing, W9*a*	£275	
		ac. Error. St. Edward's Crown, W9*b*	£160	
D4		4d. grey-black	9·50	30·00
D1/4		*Set of* 4	16·00	55·00
D1s/4s		Perf "Specimen" *Set of* 4	95·00	

The 2d. is known bisected and used as a 1d. at Luanshya or Nkana on various dates between 1937 and 1951 and on understamped letters from South Africa at Chingola in May 1950 (*Price on cover* £450).

North-West Pacific Islands *see* New Guinea *after* Australia

Nova Scotia *see* Canada

Nyasaland

PRICES FOR STAMPS ON COVER TO 1945	
Nos. 1/9*a*	*from* × 15
Nos. 10/19	—
No. 20	*from* × 10
Nos. 21/6	*from* × 5
Nos. 27/31	—
Nos. 32/7	*from* × 6
Nos. 38/42	—
Nos. 43/7	*from* × 12
Nos. 48/52	—
No. 53	*from* × 15
No. 54	*from* × 2
No. 55	*from* × 4
Nos. 55*b*/7*a*	*from* × 7
Nos. 57*d*/63	*from* × 6
Nos. 64/71	—
Nos. 72/9	*from* × 5
Nos. 80/2	—
Nos. 83/95	*from* × 4
Nos. 96/9	—
Nos. 100/57	*from* × 2

By 1891 the territory west of Lake Nyasa was recognis being under British protection and the southern, eastern northern borders had been delineated with the Portuguese German governments.

BRITISH CENTRAL AFRICA

A protectorate under the name "Nyassaland Districts" declared on 14 May 1891, the title being changed to the "Br Central Africa Protectorate" on 22 February 1893. Such a des tion had been in use for some time previously and the handwr notice of 20 July 1891, announcing the introduction of p services, described the area as "British Central Africa".

Until 1895 the British South Africa Company contribut the revenues of the protectorate administration which, in re governed North-eastern Rhodesia. Stamps of the British S Africa Company overprinted "B.C.A.", in addition to us British Central Africa, were issued to post offices at Fife, Rosebery, Katwe, Johnston Falls, Rhodesia (later Kalung and Tanganyika (later Abercorn) in North-eastern Rhod from 1893 until 1899.

B.C.A. (1)

B.C.A. FOUR SHILLINGS. (2)

ONE PENN (3)

1891 (20 July)–**95.** *Stamps of Rhodesia optd as T* **1**. *P* 14, 1

No.	Type	Description	Unused	Used
1	**1**	1d. black	4·00	
2	**4**	2d. sea-green and vermilion	4·00	
		a. Bisected (1d.) (on cover) (1895)	†	£2
3		4d. reddish chestnut and black	4·25	
4	**1**	6d. ultramarine	48·00	2
5		6d. deep blue	6·50	
6	**4**	8d. rose-lake and ultramarine	14·00	2
6*a*		8d. red and ultramarine	25·00	4
7	**1**	1s. grey-brown	15·00	1
8		2s. vermilion	26·00	5
9		2s. 6d. grey-purple	65·00	8
9*a*		2s. 6d. lilac	65·00	8
10	**4**	3s. brown and green (1895)	60·00	6
11		4s. grey-black and vermilion (2.93)	60·00	8
12	**1**	5s. orange-yellow	70·00	7
13		10s. deep green	£140	£
14	**2**	£1 deep blue	£600	£
15		£2 rose-red	£800	
16		£5 sage-green	£1400	
17		£10 brown	£3250	
1/14		*Set of* 13	£950	£1

The overprint varies on values up to 10s. Sets may be made w *thin* or *thick* letters.

The bisected 2d, No. 2a, was authorised for use at Blanty Chiromo and Zomba in July and October 1895.

1892 (Aug)–**93.** *Stamps of Rhodesia surch as T* **2**.

No.	Type	Description	Unused	Used
18	**4**	3s. on 4s. grey-black and vermilion (10.93)	£325	£
19	**1**	4s. on 5s. orange-yellow	70·00	85

1895. *No. 2 surch at Cape Town with T* **3**.

No.	Type	Description	Unused	Used
20	**4**	1d. on 2d. sea-green and vermilion	7·50	28
		a. Surch double	£3500	£25

Specimens are known with double surcharge, without st after "PENNY". These are from a trial printing made Blantyre, but it is believed that they were not issued to t public (*Price* £550 *un.*).

5 Arms of the Protectorate **6**

(Des Sir Harry Johnston. Litho D.L.R.)

1895. *No wmk. P* 14.

No.	Type	Description	Unused	Used
21	**5**	1d. black	14·00	9·
22		2d. black and green	22·00	12·
23		4d. black and reddish buff	42·00	35·
24		6d. black and blue	55·00	7·5
25		1s. black and rose	65·00	27·

2s. 6d. black and bright magenta .. £180 £300
3s. black and yellow .. .. .. £110 50·00
5s. black and olive £140 £170
£1 black and yellow-orange £900 £375
£10 black and orange-vermilion .. £4250 £3750
£25 black and blue-green .. £7500
.. .. Set of 8 £550 £550
ptd "Specimen" .. .. Set of 9 £375

ellations inscribed "BRITISH CENTRAL AFRICA" a double-circle and with the name of a town across the or at foot were intended for use on stamps presented for ment of the hut tax. Such marks can be found in black, r blue and are without date. Stamps with such fiscal ations are of little value. Prices quoted are for postally

eb). *Wmk Crown CA* (**T 5**) *or CC* (*sideways*) (**T 6**). *P* 14.
1d. black .. .. 3·25 4·75
y. Wmk inverted and reversed .. † £275
2d. black and green .. .. .. 15·00 5·00
4d. black and orange-brown .. .. 22·00 17·00
6d. black and blue .. .. .. 24·00 13·00
1s. black and rose .. .. .. 24·00 14·00
2s. 6d. black and magenta £120 £120
3s. black and yellow .. .. .. 90·00 50·00
5s. black and olive £140 £170
£1 black and blue £800 £475
£10 black and orange £5000 £3500
s. Optd "Specimen" £175
£25 black and green £9000
s. Optd "Specimen" £325
.. .. Set of 8 £400 £350
s Optd "Specimen" .. Set of 9 £375

7

8

(Typo D.L.R.)

Aug)–1900. **T 7** (*wmk Crown CA*) *and* **8** (*wmk Crown* *P* 14.
7 1d. black and ultramarine .. .. 3·25 1·25
w. Wmk inverted £140 £200
2d. black and yellow .. .. .. 2·00 2·00
4d. black and carmine .. .. .. 6·50 1·50
6d. black and green .. .. .. 45·00 4·25
1s. black and dull purple .. .. 11·00 7·00
8 2s. 6d. black and ultramarine .. .. 48·00 42·00
3s. black and sea-green £190 £225
4s. black and carmine .. .. .. 70·00 80·00
10s. black and olive-green (1900) .. £120 £130
£1 black and dull purple £275 £160
£10 black and yellow £4500 £1700
s. Optd "Specimen" £200
.. .. Set of 10 £700 £600
1s Optd "Specimen" .. Set of 10 £250

ONE

PENNY

(9)

10

(31 Dec). *No.* 49 *surch with T* **9**, *in red.*
1d. on 3s. black and sea-green .. .. 6·00 9·50
a. "PNNEY" (R. 4/2) £2250 £2250
b. "PENN" £1500 £1200
c. Surch double £450
. 53b shows an albino impression of the "Y".

(11 Mar). *Imperf.*

etting I. The vertical frame lines of the stamps cross the space between the two rows of the sheet

) With the initials "J.G." or "J.T.G." on the back in black ink
10 1d. vermilion and grey-blue .. .. — £700
a. Without the initials £2500
b. Without the initials and centre inverted £10000

Vith a control number and letter or letters, printed in plain relief at the back
10 1d. vermilion and grey-blue .. .. — £450

Setting II. The vertical frame lines do not cross the space etween the rows except at the extreme ends of the sheet. ontrol as No. 55.
10 1d. vermilion and pale ultramarine — 90·00
c. Control on face .. .. .. — £3250
d. Centre omitted (vert pair with normal) £12000
1d. vermilion and deep ultramarine — 90·00
a. Without Control at back .. £2000 £140
b. Control doubly impressed .. — £425

8 (June). *Setting II. Control as No.* 55. *P* 12.
10 1d. vermilion and pale ultramarine .. £2250 18·00
1d. vermilion and deep ultramarine .. — 32·00
ab. Without Control at back .. .. £2250 85·00
ac. Two different Controls on back .. — £600
ad. Control printed in black £3000
he two different settings of these stamps are each in 30 types, ed without gum.

1901. *Wmk Crown CA. P* 14.
57*d* **7** 1d. dull purple and carmine-rose .. 2·50 50
57*e* 4d. dull purple and olive-green .. 8·50 11·00
58 6d. dull purple and brown .. .. 3·75 3·00
57*d*/8 .. .. Set of 3 13·00 13·00
57ds/8s Optd "Specimen" .. Set of 3 60·00

11

12

(Typo D.L.R.)

1903–4. *T* **11** (*Wmk Crown CA*) *and* **12** (*Wmk Crown CC*). *P* 14.
59 **11** 1d. grey and carmine .. .. .. 6·50 1·75
60 2d. dull and bright purple .. .. 3·50 1·00
61 4d. grey-green and black .. .. 2·50 9·00
62 6d. grey and reddish buff .. .. 3·25 2·00
aw. Wmk inverted £100
62*b* 1s. grey and blue .. .. .. 3·50 10·00
63 **12** 2s. 6d grey-green and green .. .. 45·00 70·00
64 4s. dull and bright purple .. .. 60·00 75·00
w. Wmk inverted £550
65 10s. grey-green and black £100 £180
66 £1 grey and carmine £225 £170
67 £10 grey and blue £4250 £3250
s. Optd "Specimen" £300
59/66 .. .. Set of 9 £400 £450
59s/66s Optd "Specimen" .. Set of 9 £275

1907. *Wmk Mult Crown CA. Chalk-surfaced paper. P* 14.
68 **11** 1d. grey and carmine .. .. .. 4·50 2·75
69 2d. dull and bright purple £9000
70 4d. grey-green and black £9000
71 6d. grey and reddish buff .. .. 27·00 45·00
Nos. 69/70 were prepared, but not issued in Nyasaland due to the Protectorate's name being changed. It is estimated that no more than a dozen examples of each remain in collectors' hands.

NYASALAND PROTECTORATE

The title of the Protectorate was changed again from 6 July 1907.

13

14

POSTAGE

Serif on "G" (R. 4/5. All ptgs of £1 Duty plate)

(Typo D.L.R.)

1908 (22 July)–**11.** *P* 14. (*a*) *Wmk Crown CA. Chalk-surfaced paper.*
72 **13** 1s. black/*green* .. .. 2·75 9·00

(*b*) *Wmk Mult Crown CA. Ordinary paper* (½*d.*, 1*d.*) *or chalk-surfaced paper* (*others*)
73 **13** ½d. green .. .. 1·75 2·00
74 1d. carmine .. .. 4·00 1·00
75 3d. purple/*yellow* .. .. .. 1·50 4·25
w. Wmk inverted £160
76 4d. black and red/*yellow* .. .. 1·50 1·50
w. Wmk inverted £100 £100
77 6d. dull purple and bright purple .. 3·75 11·00
78 **14** 2s. 6d. brownish black & carm-red/*blue* 48·00 85·00
a. Brownish black and deep rose-red/pale blue (1911) £180 £225
79 4s. carmine and black .. .. .. 80·00 £120
80 10s. green and red/*green* £110 £200
81 £1 purple and black/*red* £450 £550
c. Serif on "G" £1700 £1900
82 £10 purple and ultramarine £7000 £4750
s. Optd "Specimen" £550
72/81 .. .. Set of 10 £650 £850
72s/81s Optd "Specimen" .. Set of 10 £475

15

16

Nick in top right scroll (R. 3/12)

"Bullet holes" flaw (R. 5/2. March 1919 ptgs)

Triangle flaw (R. 3/5. March 1919 ptg of 4s.)

1913 (1 Apr)–**19.** *Wmk Mult Crown CA. Ordinary paper* (½*d. to* 2½*d.*) *or chalk-surfaced paper* (*others*). *P* 14.
83 **15** ½d. green .. .. 1·25 1·50
84 ½d. blue-green (1918) .. .. .. 1·50 1·75
85 1d. carmine-red .. .. 1·50 2·00
86 1d. scarlet (1916) .. .. .. 2·75 90
87 2d. grey (1916) .. .. 2·25 1·00
88 2d. slate .. .. 5·50 2·50
89 2½d. bright blue .. .. 2·25 7·00
90 3d. purple/*yellow* (1914) .. .. 4·50 4·50
a. On pale yellow .. .. .. 4·25 9·50
w. Wmk inverted .. .. ..
91 4d. black and red/*yellow* (*shades*) .. 2·00 2·50
a. On pale yellow .. .. .. 6·00 8·00
92 6d. dull and bright purple .. .. 3·50 9·50
92*a* 6d. dull purple and bright violet .. 9·50 10·00
93 1s. black/*green* .. .. 1·75 8·50
a. On blue-green, olive back .. 5·50 1·50
aw. Wmk inverted .. .. .. 90·00 £130
b. On emerald back .. .. .. 3·75 6·50
bs. Optd "Specimen" .. .. 42·00
94 **16** 2s. 6d. black and red/*blue* .. .. 11·00 11·00
a. Break in scroll £140
b. Broken crown and scroll £180
d. Nick in top right scroll £150
e. "Bullet-holes" flaw £225
x. Wmk reversed .. .. .. † £1100
95 4s. carmine and black .. .. .. 13·00 50·00
a. Break in scroll £150
b. Broken crown and scroll £190
d. Nick in top right scroll £160
e. "Bullet-holes" flaw £250
f. Triangle flaw £250
96 10s. pale green and deep scarlet/*green* 75·00 95·00
d. Nick in top right scroll £375
e. Green and deep scarlet/green (1919) 70·00 90·00
ea. Break in scroll £350
eb. Broken crown and scroll £350
ee. "Bullet holes" flaw £425
98 £1 purple and black/*red* £160 £140
a. Break in scroll £550
b. Broken crown and scroll £550
c. Serif on "G" £600 £500
d. Nick in top right scroll £600
e. "Bullet holes" flaw £900

99 16 £10 purple and dull ultramarine .. £4250
d. Nick in top right scroll .. ..
e. Purple and royal blue (1919) .. £2750 £1700
eb. Break in scroll £4500 £3000
ec. Broken crown and scroll .. ..
ee. "Bullet holes" flaw .. ..
s. Optd "Specimen" £375
83/98 .. .. *Set of* 12 £250 £275
83s/98s Optd "Specimen" .. *Set of* 12 £375

For illustrations of the other varieties on Nos. 94/9 see above Leeward Islands No. 58.

For stamps overprinted "N.F." see TANZANIA.

Break through scroll (R. 1/9. Ptgs from June 1929)

Damaged crown (R. 4/1. Ptgs from June 1924)

1921–30. *Wmk Mult Script CA. Ordinary paper* (½d. *to* 2d.) *or chalk-surfaced paper* (*others*). *P* 14.
100 15 ½d. green .. .. 1·50 50
w. Wmk inverted .. .. .. — £120
101 1d. carmine .. .. 2·25 50
102 1½d. orange .. .. 3·25 17·00
103 2d. grey .. .. 1·00 50
105 3d. purple/*pale yellow* .. .. 10·00 3·25
106 4d. black and red/*yellow* .. .. 3·00 11·00
107 6d. dull and bright purple .. .. 3·00 3·25
108 1s. black/*emerald* (1930) .. .. 9·00 4·50
109 16 2s. purple and blue/*blue* (1926) .. 15·00 12·00
a. Break in scroll £110 £110
b. Broken crown and scroll £110 £110
c. Break through scroll £170 £170
110 2s. 6d. black and red/*blue* (1924) .. 20·00 16·00
a. Break in scroll £130 £130
b. Broken crown and scroll £130 £130
c. Break through scroll £190 £190
d. Damaged crown £225 £200
111 4s. carmine and black (1927) .. 19·00 25·00
a. Break in scroll £130
b. Broken crown and scroll £130
112 5s. green and red/*yellow* (1929) .. 38·00 75·00
a. Break in scroll £190
b. Broken crown and scroll £190
113 10s. green and red/*pale emerald* (1926) 80·00 95·00
a. Break in scroll £325 £400
b. Broken crown and scroll £325 £400
c. Green and scarlet/emerald (1927) .. £350 £500
ca. Break in scroll £1000
cb. Broken crown and scroll £1000
100/13 .. .. *Set of* 13 £180 £225
100s/13s Optd or Perf (1s., 5s.) "Specimen" *Set of* 13 £350

For illustrations of tbe other varieties on Nos. 109/13 see above Leeward Islands No. 58.

17 King George V and Symbol of the Protectorate

(Des Major H. E. Green. Recess Waterlow)

1934 (June)–**35.** *Wmk Mult Script CA. P* 12½.
114 17 ½d. green .. .. 75 1·25
115 1d. brown 75 75
116 1½d. carmine .. .. 75 3·00
117 2d. pale grey .. .. 80 1·25
118 3d. blue .. .. 2·50 1·75
119 4d. bright magenta (20.5.35) .. 2·50 3·50
120 6d. violet .. .. 2·50 50
121 9d. olive-bistre (20.5.35) .. .. 6·00 9·00
122 1s. black and orange .. .. .. 8·50 14·00
114/22 .. .. *Set of* 9 23·00 32·00
114s/22s Perf "Specimen" .. *Set of* 9 £190

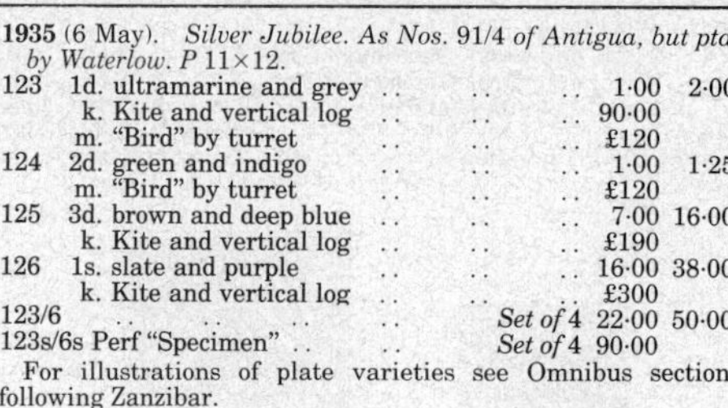

1935 (6 May). *Silver Jubilee. As Nos. 91/4 of Antigua, but ptd by Waterlow. P* 11×12.
123 1d. ultramarine and grey .. .. .. 1·00 2·00
k. Kite and vertical log .. .. .. 90·00
m. "Bird" by turret £120
124 2d. green and indigo .. .. .. 1·00 1·25
m. "Bird" by turret £120
125 3d. brown and deep blue .. .. .. 7·00 16·00
k. Kite and vertical log £190
126 1s. slate and purple .. .. .. 16·00 38·00
k. Kite and vertical log £300
123/6 .. .. *Set of* 4 22·00 50·00
123s/6s Perf "Specimen" .. *Set of* 4 90·00

For illustrations of plate varieties see Omnibus section following Zanzibar.

1937 (12 May). *Coronation. As Nos.* 95/7 *of Antigua. P* 11×11½.
127 ½d. green 30 60
128 1d. brown 50 40
129 2d. grey-black .. .. 50 1·50
127/9 .. .. *Set of* 3 1·10 2·25
127s/9s Perf "Specimen" .. .. *Set of* 3 65·00

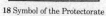

18 Symbol of the Protectorate 19

(T 18 recess Waterlow; T 19 typo D.L.R.)

1938 (1 Jan)–**44.** *Chalk-surfaced paper* (2s. *to* £1). *P* 12½ (T **18**) *or* 14 (T **19**). (*a*) *Wmk Mult Script CA*
130 18 ½d. green .. .. 30 1·50
130*a* ½d. brown (12.12.42) .. .. .. 10 1·75
131 1d. brown .. .. 1·75 30
131*a* 1d. green (12.12.42) 30 75
132 1½d. carmine .. .. 3·50 4·50
132*a* 1½d. grey (12.12.42) .. .. .. 30 4·50
133 2d. grey .. .. 6·00 1·00
133*a* 2d. carmine (12.12.42) .. .. .. 30 1·75
134 3d. blue 60 50
135 4d. bright magenta .. .. .. 2·50 1·25
136 6d. violet .. .. 2·50 1·25
137 9d. olive-bistre .. .. 2·50 2·50
138 1s. black and orange .. .. .. 3·25 1·50
139 19 2s. purple and blue/*blue* .. .. 10·00 9·50
140 2s. 6d. black and red/*blue* .. .. 12·00 11·00
141 5s. pale green and red/*yellow* .. 40·00 18·00
a. Ordinary paper. *Green and red/ pale yellow* (3.44) .. .. 80·00 90·00
142 10s. emerald and deep red/*pale green* 50·00 35·00
a. Ordinary paper. *Bluish green and brown-red/pale green* (1.38) .. £325 £275
(*b*) *Wmk Mult Crown CA*
143 19 £1 purple and black/*red* .. .. 30·00 26·00
c. Serif on "G" £600 £450
130/43 .. .. *Set of* 18 £150 £110
130s/43s Perf "Specimen" .. *Set of* 18 £600

No. 141a has a yellow surfacing often applied in horizontal lines giving the appearance of laid paper.

The printer's archives record the despatch of No. 142a to Nyasaland in January 1938, but no examples have been reported used before 1945. The paper coating on this printing varied considerably across the sheet. It is reported that some examples show a faint reaction to the silver test.

20 Lake Nyasa 21 King's African Rifles

(Recess B.W.)

1945 (1 Sept). *T* **20/1** *and similar designs. Wmk Mult Script CA* (*sideways on horiz designs*). *P* 12.
144 ½d. black and chocolate 30 10
145 1d. black and emerald 20 70
146 1½d. black and grey-green 20 50
147 2d. black and scarlet 75 60
148 3d. black and light blue 20 30
149 4d. black and claret .. .. .. 1·25 50
150 6d. black and violet .. .. .. 1·25 50
151 9d. black and olive .. .. .. 1·50 2·50
152 1s. indigo and deep green .. .. .. 1·25 20
153 2s. emerald and maroon .. .. .. 3·75 4·25
154 2s. 6d. emerald and blue .. .. .. 7·50 4·25
155 5s. purple and blue .. .. .. 4·50 6·00
156 10s. claret and emerald .. .. .. 12·00 13·00
157 20s. scarlet and black .. .. .. 17·00 25·00
144/57 .. .. *Set of* 14 45·00 50·00
144s/57s Perf "Specimen" .. *Set of* 14 £275

Designs: *Horiz*—1½d., 6d. Tea estate; 2d., 1s., 10s. Map of Nyasaland; 4d., 2s. 6d. Tobacco; 9d. Type **20**; 5s., 20s. Badge of Nyasaland. *Vert*—3d., 2s. Fishing Village.

1946 (16 Dec). *Victory. As Nos.* 110/11 *of Antigua.*
158 1d. green 10 10
159 2d. red-orange 30 10
158s/9s Perf "Specimen" .. .. *Set of* 2 55·00

26 Symbol of the Protectorate 27 Arms in 1891 and 1951

(Recess B.W.)

1947 (20 Oct). *Wmk Mult Script CA. P* 12.
160 26 1d. red-brown and yellow-green .. 50
a. Perf "Specimen" .. .. .. 45·00

1948 (15 Dec). *Royal Silver Wedding. As Nos.* 112 *Antigua.*
161 1d. green 15
162 10s. mauve .. .. 15·00

1949 (21 Nov). *75th Anniv of U.P.U. As Nos.* 114 *Antigua.*
163 1d. blue-green 30
164 3d. greenish blue .. .. 1·75
165 6d. purple 50
166 1s. ultramarine 30
163/6 .. .. *Set of* 4 2·50

(Des C. Twynam. Recess B.W.)

1951 (15 May). *Diamond Jubilee of Protectorate. Wmk Mult CA. P* 11 × 12.
167 27 2d. black and scarlet .. .. .. 1·00
168 3d. black and turquoise-blue .. .. 1·00
169 6d. black and violet .. .. .. 1·00
170 5s. black and indigo .. .. .. 3·50
167/70 .. .. *Set of* 4 6·00

POSTAGE DUE STAMPS

D 1

(Typo D.L.R.)

1950 (1 July). *Wmk Mult Script CA. P* 14.
D1 D 1 1d. scarlet .. .. 3·75
D2 2d. ultramarine .. .. 9·00
D3 3d. green .. .. 9·50
D4 4d. purple .. .. 17·00
D5 6d. yellow-orange .. .. 23·00
D1/5 .. .. *Set of* 5 55·00

Orange Free State *see* South Africa

Pakistan

(Currency. 12 pies = 1 anna; 16 annas = 1 rupee)

DOMINION

PAKISTAN (1) PAKISTAN (2)

(1 Oct). *Nos. 259/68 and 269a/77 (King George VI) of* *lia optd by litho at Nasik, as T* **1** *(3 p. to 12 a.) or* **2** *(14 a. and* *ee values).*

Value	Description	Unused	Used
3 p.	slate	10	10
1/2 a.	purple	10	10
9 p.	green	10	10
1 a.	carmine	10	10
11/2 a.	dull violet	10	10
w.	Wmk inverted		
2 a.	vermilion	10	20
3 a.	bright violet	10	20
31/2 a.	bright blue	65	2·25
4 a.	brown	20	10
6 a.	turquoise-green	1·00	75
8 a.	slate-violet	30	60
12 a.	lake	1·00	20
14 a.	purple	2·50	1·50
1 r.	grey and red-brown	1·75	80
2 r.	purple and brown	3·25	1·50
5 r.	green and blue	4·00	3·75
10 r.	purple and claret	4·00	2·50
15 r.	brown and green	48·00	80·00
25 r.	slate-violet and purple	55·00	45·00
	Set of 19	£110	£120

umerous provisional "PAKISTAN" overprints, both hand-iped and machine-printed, in various sizes and colours, on age and Official stamps, also exist.

nese were made under authority of Provincial Governments, rict Head Postmasters or Local Postmasters and are of iderable philatelic interest.

ne 1 a. 3 p. (India No. 269) exists only as a local issue (*Price,* achi opt 90*p. unused*; £1.75 *used*).

ne 12 a., as No. 12 but overprinted at Karachi, exists with print inverted (*Price* £60 *unused*).

ne 1 r. value with Karachi local overprint exists with print inverted (*Price* £150 *unused*) or as a vertical pair with stamp without overprint (*Price* £600 *unused*).

3 Constituent Assembly Building, Karachi

6 Crescent and Stars

(Des A. Chughtai (1 r.). Recess D.L.R.)

48 (9 July). *Independence. T* **3**, **6** *and similar horiz designs.* *P* 13½ × 14 *or* 11½ (1 *r*.).

Value	Description	Unused	Used
1½ a.	ultramarine	70	50
2½ a.	green	70	10
3 a.	purple-brown	70	20
1 r.	scarlet	70	50
a.	Perf 14 × 13½	4·50	14·00
3	*Set of* 4	2·50	1·10

Designs:—2½ a. Karachi Airport entrance; 3 a. Gateway to hore Fort.

cales of Justice

8 Star and Crescent

9 Lloyds Barrage

10 Karachi Airport

13 Khyber Pass

(Des M. Suharwardi (T **8**). Recess Pakistan Security Ptg Corp Ltd, Karachi (P 13 and 13½), D.L.R. (others))

1948 (14 Aug)–**56?** *T* **7/10**, **13** *and similar designs. P* 13½×14 *or* 11½ (1 *r*.).

No.	Type	Value	Description	Unused	Used
24	**7**	3 p.	red (*p* 12½)	10	10
		a.	Perf 13½ (1954?)	20	1·00
25		6 p.	violet (*p* 12½)	80	10
		a.	Perf 13½ (1954?)	2·50	2·25
26		9 p.	green (*p* 12½)	50	10
		a.	Perf 13½ (1954?)	1·00	1·50
27	**8**	1 a.	blue (*p* 12½)	10	50
28		1½ a.	grey-green (*p* 12½)	10	10
29		2 a.	red (*p* 12½)	70	50
30	**9**	2½ a.	green (*p* 14×13½)	2·75	6·50
31	**10**	3 a.	green (*p* 14)	7·50	1·00
32	**9**	3½ a.	bright blue (*p* 14×13½)	3·50	5·50
33		4 a.	reddish brown (*p* 12½)	50	10
34	–	6 a.	blue (*p* 14×13½)	50	50
35	–	8 a.	black (*p* 12½)	50	60
36	**10**	10 a.	scarlet (*p* 14)	4·50	7·00
37	–	12 a.	scarlet (*p* 14×13½)	6·50	1·00
38	–	1 r.	ultramarine (*p* 14)	5·50	10
		a.	Perf 13½ (1954?)	15·00	4·00
39	–	2 r.	chocolate (*p* 14)	20·00	50
		a.	Perf 13½ (1954?)	25·00	2·00
40	–	5 r.	carmine (*p* 14)	15·00	60
		a.	Perf 13½ (7.53)	10·00	20
41	**13**	10 r.	magenta (*p* 14)	10·00	17·00
		a.	Perf 12	75·00	5·00
		b.	Perf 13 (1951)	18·00	70
42		15 r.	blue-green (*p* 12)	18·00	12·00
		a.	Perf 14	16·00	38·00
		b.	Perf 13 (1956?)	18·00	12·00
43		25 r.	violet (*p* 14)	55·00	80·00
		a.	Perf 12	28·00	30·00
		b.	Perf 13 (1954)	40·00	24·00
24/43			*Set of* 20	£100	55·00

Designs: *Vert* (*as T* **7**)—6 a., 8 a., 12 a. Karachi Port Trust. (*As T* **10**)—1 r., 2 r., 5 r. Salimullah Hostel, Dacca.

For 25 r. with W **98**, see No. 210.

14 Star and Crescent

15 Karachi Airport

(Recess Pakistan Security Ptg Corp (P 13½), D.L.R. (others).

1949 (Feb)–**53?** *Redrawn. Crescent moon with points to left as T* **14/15**.

No.	Type	Value	Description	Unused	Used
44	**14**	1 a.	blue (*p* 12½)	4·00	70
		a.	Perf 13½ (1953?)	3·50	10
45		1½ a.	grey-green (*p* 12½)	3·75	70
		a.	Perf 13½ (1952?)	3·00	10
		ab.	Printed on the gummed side	55·00	
46		2 a.	red (*p* 12½)	4·00	10
		a.	Perf 13½ (1953?)	3·50	10
47	**15**	3 a.	green (*p* 14)	9·50	65
48	–	6 a.	blue (as No. 34) (*p* 14×13½)	8·50	75
49	–	8 a.	black (as No. 35) (*p* 12½)	5·00	1·00
50	**15**	10 a.	scarlet (*p* 14)	16·00	1·50
51	–	12 a.	scarlet (as No. 37) (*p* 14×13½)	18·00	30
44/51			*Set of* 8	55·00	3·50

16

(Recess D.L.R.)

1949 (11 Sept). *First Death Anniv of Mohammed Ali Jinnah. T* **16** *and similar design. P* 14.

No.	Type	Value	Description	Unused	Used
52	**16**	1½ a.	brown	1·50	90
53		3 a.	green	1·50	90
54	–	10 a.	black	5·00	6·50
52/4			*Set of* 3	7·00	7·50

Design:—10 a. Similar inscription reading "QUAID-I-AZAM/ MOHAMMAD ALI JINNAH" etc.

17 Pottery

18 Aeroplane and Hour-glass

Two Types of 3½ a.:

I 

 II

19 Saracenic Leaf Pattern

20 Archway and Lamp

(Des A. Chughtai. Recess D.L.R., later printings, Pakistan Security Ptg Corp)

1951 (14 Aug)–**56.** *Fourth Anniv of Independence. P* 13.

No.	Type	Value	Description	Unused	Used
55	**17**	2½ a.	carmine	1·25	70
56	**18**	3 a.	purple	50	10
57	**17**	3½ a.	blue (I)	75	3·25
57*a*		3½ a.	blue (II)(12.56)	3·25	4·00
58	**19**	4 a.	green	50	10
59		6 a.	brown-orange	50	10
60	**20**	8 a.	sepia	4·25	10
61		10 a.	violet	1·50	80
62	**18**	12 a.	slate	1·50	10
55/62			*Set of* 9	12·50	8·00

The above and the stamps issued on the 14 August 1954, 1955 and 1956, are basically definitive issues, although issued on the Anniversary date of Independence.

OFFICIAL STAMPS

PAKISTAN (O 1)

1947. *Nos.* O138/41 *and* O143/50 (*King George VI*) *of India, optd as Type* O **1** (*Nos.* O1/9) *or as T* **2** (*Nos.* O10/13) *both in litho by Nasik.*

No.	Value	Description	Unused	Used
O 1	3 p.	slate	1·25	30
O 2	½ a.	purple	30	10
O 3	9 p.	green	4·50	2·50
O 4	1 a.	carmine	30	10
O 5	1½ a.	dull violet	30	10
	w.	Wmk inverted	20·00	
O 6	2 a.	vermilion	30	10
O 7	2½ a.	bright violet	7·00	8·00
O 8	4 a.	brown	1·25	50
O 9	8 a.	slate-violet	1·75	1·25
O10	1 r.	grey and red-brown	80	1·00
O11	2 r.	purple and brown	4·00	3·25
O12	5 r.	green and blue	16·00	28·00
O13	10 r.	purple and claret	45·00	85·00
O1/13		*Set of* 13	75·00	£110

See note after No. 19. The 1 a. 3 p. (India No. O146*a*) exists as a local issue (*Price*, Karachi opt, £6 *mint*, £19 *used*).

SERVICE (O 2) SERVICE (O 3)

NOTE. Apart from a slight difference in size, Types O **2** and O **3** can easily be distinguished by the difference in the shape of the "c".

PRINTERS. Type O **2** was overprinted by De La Rue and Type O **3** by the Pakistan Security Ptg Corp.

1948 (14 Aug)–**54?** *Optd with Type* O **2**.

No.	Type	Value	Description	Unused	Used
O14	**7**	3 p.	red (No. 24)	10	10
O15		6 p.	violet (No. 25) (R.)	10	10
O16		9 p.	green (No. 26) (R.)	10	10
O17	**8**	1 a.	blue (No. 27) (R.)	3·75	10
O18		1½ a.	grey-green (No. 28) (R.)	3·50	10
O19		2 a.	red (No. 29)	1·50	10
O20	**10**	3 a.	green (No. 31)	26·00	7·50
O21	**9**	4 a.	reddish brown (No. 33)	1·00	10
O22	–	8 a.	black (No. 35) (R.)	2·00	8·50
O23	–	1 r.	ultramarine (No. 38)	1·00	10
O24	–	2 r.	chocolate (No. 39)	14·00	8·00
O25	–	5 r.	carmine (No. 40)	30·00	8·00
O26	**13**	10 r.	magenta (No. 41)	14·00	40·00
		a.	Perf 12 (10.10.51)	17·00	45·00
		b.	Perf 13 (1954?)	13·00	48·00
O14/26			*Set of* 13	85·00	65·00

1949. *Optd with Type* O **2**.

No.	Value	Description	Unused	Used
O27	1 a.	blue (No. 44) (R.)	1·50	10
O28	1½ a.	grey-green (No. 45) (R.)	50	10
	a.	Opt inverted	£250	40·00
O29	2 a.	red (No. 46)	1·25	10
	a.	Opt omitted (in pair with normal)	—	£130
O30	3 a.	green (No. 47)	23·00	5·00
O31	8 a.	black (No. 49) (R.)	35·00	15·00
O27/31		*Set of* 5	55·00	18·00

1951 (14 Aug). *4th Anniv of Independence. As Nos. 56, 58 and 60, but inscr* "SERVICE" *instead of* "PAKISTAN POSTAGE".

No.	Type	Value	Description	Unused	Used
O32	**18**	3 a.	purple	6·50	9·00
O33	**19**	4 a.	green	1·75	10
O34	**20**	8 a.	sepia	7·50	3·50
O32/4			*Set of* 3	14·00	11·50

1953. *Optd with Type* O **3**.

No.	Value	Description	Unused	Used
O35	3 p.	red (No. 24a)	10	10
O36	6 p.	violet (No. 25a) (R.)	10	10
O37	9 p.	green (No. 26a) (R.)	10	10
O38	1 a.	blue (No. 44a) (R.)	10	10
O39	1½ a.	grey-green (No. 45a) (R.)	10	10
O40	2 a.	red (No. 46a) (1953?)	15	10
O41	1 r.	ultramarine (No. 38a)	10·00	3·00
O42	2 r.	chocolate (No. 39a)	4·25	20
O43	5 r.	carmine (No. 40a)	30·00	14·00
O44	10 r.	magenta (No. 41b) (date?)	22·00	48·00
O35/44		*Set of* 10	60·00	60·00

BAHAWALPUR

Bahawalpur, a former feudatory state situated to the west of the Punjab, was briefly independent following the partition of India on 15 August 1947 before acceding to Pakistan on 3 October of the same year.

East India Company and later Indian Empire post offices operated in Bahawalpur from 1854. By a postal agreement of 1879 internal mail from the state administration was carried unstamped, but this arrangement was superseded by the issue of Official stamps in 1945.

These had been preceded by a series of pictorial stamps prepared in 1933–34 on unwatermarked paper. It was intended that these would be used as state postage stamps, but permission for such use was withheld by the Indian Government so they were used for revenue purposes. The same designs were utilised for the 1945 Official series, Nos. O1/6, on paper watermarked Star and Crescent. Residual stocks of the unwatermarked 1 a., 8 a., 1 r. and 2 r. were used for the provisional Officials, Nos. O7 and O11/13.

A commemorative 1 a. Receipt stamp was produced to mark the centenary of the alliance with Great Britain. This may not have been ready until 1935, but an example of this stamp is known used on cover from Deh Rawal to Sadiq Garh and postmarked 14 August 1933. Both this 1 a. and the same value from the unwatermarked set also exist with Official Arabic overprint in black. These were not issued for postal purposes although one used example of the latter has been recorded postmarked 22 February 1933 also from Deh Rawal.

Stamps of India were overprinted in the interim period between 15 August and 3 October 1947. After the state joined Pakistan postage stamps were issued for internal use until 1953.

PRICES FOR STAMPS ON COVER

The postage and Official stamps of Bahawalpur are rare used on cover.

Nawab (from 1947 Amir) Sadiq Mohammad Khan Abbasi V, 1907–1966

(1)

1947 (15 Aug). *Nos. 265/8, 269a/77 and 259/62 (King George VI) of India optd locally with T* **1**.

No.	Description	Price
1	3 p. slate (R.)	17·00
2	½ a. purple	17·00
3	9 p. green (R.)	17·00
4	1 a. carmine	17·00
5	1½ a. dull violet (R.)	17·00
6	2 a. vermilion	17·00
	a. Opt double	£1000
7	3 a. bright violet (R.)	17·00
8	3½ a. bright blue (R.)	17·00
9	4 a. brown	17·00
10	6 a. turquoise-green (R.)	17·00
	a. Opt double	£1000
11	8 a. slate-violet (R.)	17·00
12	12 a. lake	17·00
13	14 a. purple	55·00
14	1 r. grey and red-brown	22·00
	a. Opt double, one albino	£300
15	2 r. purple and brown (R.)	£1100
16	5 r. green and blue (R.)	£1100
17	10 r. purple and claret	£1100
1/17	*Set of* 17	£3250

Nos. 1/17 were issued during the interim period, following the implementation of the Indian Independence Act, during which time Bahawalpur was part of neither of the two Dominions created. The Amir acceded to the Dominion of Pakistan on 3 October 1947 and these overprinted stamps of India were then withdrawn.

The stamps of Bahawalpur only had validity for use within the state. For external mail Pakistan stamps were used.

PRINTERS. All the following issues were recess-printed by De La Rue & Co, Ltd, London.

2 Amir Muhammad Bahawal Khan I Abbasi

3

1947 (1 Dec). *Bicentenary Commemoration. W* **3** *(sideways). P* 12½×11½.

No.	Type	Description	Unused	Used
18	**2**	½ a. black and carmine	1·75	2·00

4 H.H. the Amir of Bahawalpur

5 The Tombs of the Amirs

6 Mosque in Sadiq-Garh

7 Fort Derawar from the Lake

8 Nur-Mahal Palace

9 The Palace, Sadiq-Garh

10 H.H. the Amir of Bahawalpur

11 Three Generations of Rulers; H.H. the Amir in centre

1948 (1 Apr). *W* **3** *(sideways on vert designs). P* 12½ *(T* **4**), 11½ × 12½ *(T* **5**, **7**, **8** *and* **9**), 12½ × 11½ *(T* **6** *and* **10**) *or* 13½ × 14 *(T* **11**).

No.	Type	Description	Unused	Used
19	**4**	3 p. black and blue	1·25	17·00
20		½ a. black and claret	1·25	17·00
21		9 p. black and green	1·25	17·00
22		1 a. black and carmine	1·25	17·00
23		1½ a. black and violet	1·25	14·00
24	**5**	2 a. green and carmine	1·50	18·00
25	**6**	4 a. orange and brown	1·75	18·00
26	**7**	6 a. violet and blue	1·75	18·00
27	**8**	8 a. carmine and violet	1·75	18·00
28	**9**	12 a. green and carmine	2·00	26·00
29	**10**	1 r. violet and brown	19·00	38·00
30		2 r. green and claret	38·00	60·00
31		5 r. black and violet	38·00	75·00
32	**11**	10 r. scarlet and black	32·00	90·00
19/32		*Set of* 14	£130	£400

12 H.H. The Amir of Bahawalpur and Mohammed Ali Jinnah

13 Soldiers of 1848 and 1948

1948 (3 Oct). *First Anniv of Union of Bahawalpur with Pakistan. W* **3**. *P* 13.

No.	Type	Description	Unused	Used
33	**12**	1½ a. carmine and blue-green	85	2·00

1948 (15 Oct). *Multan Campaign Centenary. W* **3**. *P* 11½.

No.	Type	Description	Unused	Used
34	**13**	1½ a. black and lake	70	8·00

1948. *As Nos. 29/32, but colours changed.*

No.	Type	Description	Unused	Used
35	**10**	1 r. deep green and orange	1·25	16·00
36		2 r. black and carmine	1·50	19·00
37		5 r. chocolate and ultramarine	1·60	35·00
38	**11**	10 r. red-brown and green	1·75	40·00
35/8		*Set of* 4	5·50	£100

14 Irrigation

17 U.P.U. Monument, Berne

1949 (3 Mar). *Silver Jubilee of Accession of H.H. the A*[r…]
Bahawalpur. T **14** *and similar horiz designs. W* **3**. *P* 14.

No.	Description	Unused
39	3 p. black and ultramarine	10
40	½ a. black and brown-orange	10
41	9 p. black and green	10
42	1 a. black and carmine	10
39/42	*Set of* 4	30

Designs:—½ a. Wheat; 9 p. Cotton; 1 a. Sahiwal bull.

Nos. 39/42 exist imperforate (*Prices,* £15 *per pair, unuse*

1949 (10 Oct). *75th Anniv of Universal Postal Union. W* **3**. *P*

No.	Type	Description	Unused
43	**17**	9 p. black and green	20
		a. Perf 17½ × 17	1·25
44		1 a. black and magenta	20
		a. Perf 17½ × 17	1·25
45		1½ a. black and orange	20
		a. Perf 17½ × 17	1·25
46		2½ a. black and blue	20
		a. Perf 17½ × 17	1·25
43/6		*Set of* 4	70
43a/6a		*Set of* 4	4·50

Nos. 43/6 exist imperforate (*Prices,* £10 *per pair, unused*)

OFFICIAL STAMPS

O 1 Panjnad Weir

O 2 Dromedary and Calf

O 3 Blackbuck

O 4 Eastern White Pelican

O 5 Friday Mosque, Fort Derawar

O 6 Temple at Pattan Munara

1945 (1 Mar). *Various horizontal pictorial designs, with Arabic opt. W* **3**. *P* 14.

No.	Type	Description	Unused	Used
O1	O **1**	½ a. black and green	2·75	12
O2	O **2**	1 a. black and carmine	3·75	6
		a. Opt omitted	†	£
O3	O **3**	2 a. black and violet	3·25	9
O4	O **4**	4 a. black and olive-green	9·00	23
O5	O **5**	8 a. black and brown	21·00	13
O6	O **6**	1 r. black and orange	21·00	12
O1/6		*Set of* 6	55·00	65

Permission for the introduction of Nos. O1/6 was granted the Imperial Government as from 1 January 1945, but stamps were not used until 1 March. First Day covers e[x…] showing the January date.

Examples of No. O2a come from a sheet used at Rahim Khan.

It is believed that examples of Nos. O1/2 in different sha[des] and with white gum appeared in 1949 and were included in [the] Silver Jubilee Presentation Booklet.

O 7 Baggage Camels

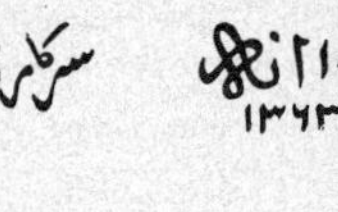

(O 8)

1945 (10 Mar). *Revenue stamp with red Arabic opt. No w*[mk].
P 14.

No.	Type	Description	Unused	Used
O7	O **7**	1 a. black and brown	32·00	48

1945 (Mar–June). *Surch as Type* O **8** *(at Security Printing Pre*[ss,] *Nasik) instead of red Arabic opt. No wmk. P* 14.

No.	Type	Description	Unused	Used
O11	O **5**	½ a. on 8 a. black and purple	4·25	3
O12	O **6**	1½ a. on 1 r. black and orange	35·00	9
O13	O **1**	1½ a. on 2 r. black and blue (1 June)	£120	7
O11/13		*Set of* 3	£140	18

The stamps used as a basis for Nos. O7 and O11/13 were pa[rt] of the Revenue series issued in 1933–34.

SERVICE

(O 9)

O 10 H.H. the Amir of Bahawalpur

Optd with Type O **9** (*by D.L.R.*) *instead of red Arabic opt. No*
k. P 14.

O 1 ½ a. black and carmine . . . . . . 1·25 11·00
O 2 1 a. black and carmine . . . . . . 2·00 13·00
O 3 2 a. black and orange . . . . . . 3·25 42·00
6 . . . . *Set of* 3 6·00 60·00

P 14.

O 10 3 p. black and blue . . . . . . 3·00 7·00
1½ a. black and violet . . . . . . 17·00 7·00

O 11 Allied Banners

(Des E. Meronti. Recess, background litho)

(1 May). *Victory. P* 14.

O 11 1½ a. green and grey . . . . . . 2·00 3·00

Nos. 19, 22, 24/5 *and* 35/8 *optd as Nos.* O1/6.

4 3 p. black and blue (R.) . . . . 70 10·00
1 a. black and carmine (Blk.) . . . . 70 9·00
5 2 a. green and carmine (Blk.) . . . . 70 10·00
6 4 a. orange and brown (Blk.) . . . . 70 14·00
10 1 r. deep green and orange (R.) . . 70 16·00
2 r. black and carmine (R.) . . . . 70 22·00
5 r. chocolate and ultramarine (R.) . . 70 35·00
11 10 r. red-brown and green (R.) . . 70 35·00
7 . . . . *Set of* 8 5·00 £130

(10 Oct). *75th Anniv of Universal Postal Union. Nos.* 43/6
td as Nos. O1/6.

17 9 p. black and green . . . . . . 15 4·50
aw. Wmk inverted . . . . . . † £120
b. Perf 17½×17 . . . . . . 2·00 26·00
1 a. black and magenta . . . . 15 4·50
b. Perf 17½×17 . . . . . . 2·00 26·00
1½ a. black and orange . . . . 15 4·50
b. Perf 17½×17 . . . . . . 2·00 26·00
2½ a. black and blue . . . . . . 15 4·50
b. Perf 17½×17 . . . . . . 2·00 26·00
/31 . . . . *Set of* 4 55 16·00
b/31b . . . . *Set of* 4 7·50 95·00
os. O28/31 exist imperforate (*Prices, £10 per pair, unused*)

rom 1947 stamps of Pakistan were used on all external mail. awalpur issues continued to be used on internal mail until 3.

Palestine

The stamps of TURKEY were used in Palestine from 1865.

In addition various European Powers, and Egypt, maintained post offices at Jerusalem (Austria, France, Germany, Italy, Russia), Jaffa (Austria, Egypt, France, Germany, Russia) and Haifa (Austria, France) using their own stamps or issues specially prepared for Levant post offices. All foreign post offices had closed by the time of the British Occupation.

PRICES FOR STAMPS ON COVER TO 1945	
No. 1	*from* × 6
No. 2	*from* × 4
Nos. 3/4	*from* × 5
Nos. 5/15	*from* × 4
Nos. 16/29	*from* × 3
Nos. 30/42	*from* × 2
No. 43	—
Nos. 44/57	*from* × 2
Nos. 58/9	—
Nos. 60/8	*from* × 3
Nos. 69/70	—
Nos. 71/89	*from* × 3
Nos. 90/103	*from* × 4
Nos. 104/11	*from* × 8
Nos. D1/5	*from* × 30
Nos. D6/20	*from* × 10

BRITISH MILITARY OCCUPATION

British and allied forces invaded Palestine in November 1917 capturing Gaza (7 November), Jaffa (16 November) and Jerusalem (9 December). The front line then stabilised until the second British offensive of September 1918.

Nos. 1/15 were issued by the British military authorities for use by the civilian population in areas they controlled previously part of the Ottoman Empire. Before the issue of Nos. 1/2 in February 1918 civilian mail was carried free. In addition to Palestine the stamps were available from E.E.F. post offices in Syria (including what subsequently became Transjordan) from 23 September 1918 to 23 February 1922, Lebanon from 21 October 1918 to September 1920 and Cilicia from 2 September 1919 to 16 July 1920. Use in the following post offices outside Palestine is recorded in *British Empire Campaigns and Occupations in the Near East, 1914–1924* by John Firebrace:

Adana, Cilicia
Akkari ("Akkar"), Syria
Aleppo ("Alep, Halep"), Syria
Aleih ("Alie"), Lebanon
Alexandretta, Syria
Antakie, Syria
Ba'abda, Lebanon
Baalbek, Lebanon
Bab, Syria
Babitoma, Syria
Behamdoun, Lebanon
Beit ed Dine, Lebanon
Bekaa, Lebanon
Beyrouth, Lebanon
Beit Mery, Beyrouth Lebanon
Bouzanti, Syria
Broumana, Lebanon
Damascus ("Damas"), Syria
Damour ("Damor"), Lebanon
Der'a ("Deraa"), Syria
Deurt-Yol, Syria
Djey Han, Syria
Djezzin ("Djezzine"), Lebanon
Djon, Lebanon
Djounie, Lebanon
Djubeil, Lebanon
Douma, Syria
Edleb, Syria
Feke, Turkey
Habib Souk, Syria
Hajjin ("Hadjin"), Cilicia
Hama, Syria
Hasbaya, Lebanon
Hasine, Cilicia
Hommana, Lebanon
Homs, Syria
Kozan, Cilicia
Lattakia ("Laskie, Lattaquie"), Syria
Massel el Chouf ("Moussalc"), Lebanon
Merdjajoun, Lebanon
Mersina ("Mersine"), Cilicia
Mounboudje, Syria
Nabatti, Lebanon
Nebk ("Nebik"), Syria
Payass, Syria
Racheya, Lebanon
Safita, Syria
Savour, Tyre, Lebanon
Selimie, Syria
Sidan ("Saida (Echelle)"), Lebanon
Suweidiya ("Suvedie"), Syria
Talia, Syria
Tarsous, Cilicia
Tartous, Syria
Tibnin, Lebanon
Tripoli, Syria
Zahle, Lebanon
Zebdani, Syria

This information is reproduced here by permission of the publishers, Robson Lowe Publications.

(Currency. 10 milliemes = 1 piastre)

1

(2)

3

"E.E.F." = Egyptian Expeditionary Force

W 100 of Great Britain

(Des G. Rowntree. Litho Typographical Dept, Survey of Egypt, Giza, Cairo)

1918 (10 Feb). *Wmk Royal Cypher in column* (*W* **100** *of Great Britain*). *Ungummed. Roul* 20.

1 **1** 1 p. indigo £180 £100
a. Deep blue . . . . £150 90·00
b. Blue . . . . £150 90·00
s. Optd "Specimen" £300

Control: A 18 (*Prices, corner block of* 4; No. 1 £850. No. 1*a*, £750. No. 1*b*, £850).

1918 (16 Feb). *As last* (*ungummed*) *surch with T* **2**.

2 **1** 5 m. on 1 p. cobalt-blue . . . . . . 90·00 £475
a. "MILLILMES" (R. 1/10) £3250 £9000
s. Optd "Specimen" £300
w. Wmk inverted . . . . . .

Control: B 18 A (*Corner block*, £1100).

1985 (5 Mar). *As No.* 1 *but colour changed. With gum.*

3 **1** 1 p. ultramarine (*shades*) . . . . . . 2·00 2·00
a. Crown missing from wmk . . . . 40·00
b. Printed on the gummed side . . . .
w. Wmk inverted £180 £225

Control: C 18. (*Corner block*, £70).

1918 (5 Mar *and* 13 May). *No.* 3 *surch with T* **2**.

4 **1** 5 m. on 1 p. ultramarine . . . . . . 3·50 2·75
a. Arabic surch wholly or partly missing (R. 1/11) £300 £400
b. Crown missing from wmk . . . . 60·00
w. Wmk inverted £250

Controls: C 18 B (Mar). (*Corner block*, £700).
D 18 C (May). (*Corner block*, £200).

(Typo Stamping Dept, Board of Inland Revenue, Somerset House, London)

1918 (16 July–27 Dec). *Wmk Royal Cypher in column* (*W* **100** *of Great Britain*). *P* 15×14.

5 **3** 1 m. sepia 30 40
a. Deep brown 40 40
6 2 m. blue-green 30 45
a. Deep green . . . . 1·00 80
7 3 m. yellow-brown (17 Dec) 35 35
a. Chestnut . . . . 12·00 6·00
8 4 m. scarlet 35 40
9 5 m. yellow-orange (25 Sept) . . . . 1·25 30
a. Orange 65 45
b. Crown missing from wmk £140
w. Wmk inverted . . . . . . — £1500
10 1 p. deep indigo (9 Nov) 35 25
a. Crown missing from wmk £120
w. Wmk inverted £150 £160
11 2 p. pale olive 85 60
a. Olive . . . . 1·75 1·10
12 5 p. purple . . . . 1·75 2·25
13 9 p. ochre (17 Dec) . . . . . . 3·25 4·50
14 10 p. ultramarine (17 Dec) . . . . 2·50 3·00
w. Wmk inverted £400
15 20 p. pale grey (27 Dec) . . . . . . 11·00 16·00
a. Slate-grey . . . . 16·00 22·00
5/15 . . . . *Set of* 11 19·00 25·00

There are two sizes of the design of this issue:
19 × 23 mm. 1, 2, and 4 m., and 2 and 5 p.
18 × 21½ mm. 3 and 5 m., and 1, 9, 10 and 20 p.

There are numerous minor plate varieties in this issue, such as stops omitted in "E.E.F.", malformed Arabic characters, etc.

CIVIL ADMINISTRATION UNDER BRITISH HIGH COMMISSIONER

Palestine was placed under civil administration by a British High Commissioner on 1 July 1920.

فلسطين	فلسطين	فلسطين
PALESTINE	PALESTINE	PALESTINE
פלשתינה איי	פלשתינה א״י	פלשתינה א״י
(4)	(5)	(6)

Differences:—
T **5**. 20 mm vert and 7 mm between English and Hebrew.
T **6**. 19 mm and 6 mm respectively.

Two settings of Type **4**:

Setting I (used for Nos. 16/26). This consisted of two horizontal rows of 12 of which the first setting row appeared on Rows 1, 3/7, 15, 17/18 and 20 of the sheet and the second on Rows 2, 8/14, 16 and 19.

On the first position in the top setting row the Arabic "t" (third character from the left) is incorrectly shown as an Arabic "z" by the addition of a dot to its right. On the eleventh position in the same row the first two letters in the Hebrew overprint were transposed so that " character appears first. On row 12 stamp 1 the final "E" of "PALESTINE" appears as a "B" on certain values. Once the errors were noticed vertical columns one and eleven were removed from the remaining sheets.

Setting II (used for Nos. 16/29). This consisted of a single horizontal row of 12 reproduced to overprint the complete sheet of 240. The order in which the horizontal rows were used was changed several times during overprinting. During one such re-arrangement a damaged impression was replaced by one from Setting I showing the Arabic "z" error. (R. 14/8 for 1, 2, 3, 4, 5 (p 14) 20p.). The "B" error also occurs in the second setting, once in each sheet on either R. 17/8, 18/8 or 19/8.

(Optd at Greek Orthodox Convent, Jerusalem)

1920 (1 Sept). *Optd with T* **4** (*Arabic* 8 *mm long*). (*a*) *P* 15×14

16 **3** 1 m. sepia . . . . 1·90 2·75
b. Arabic "z" (Settings I and II) . . £1000
c. Hebrew characters transposed (I) . . £1000
d. "PALESTINB" (II) . . . . . . 75·00
17 2 m. blue-green . . . . 6·00 4·50
b. "Arabic "z" (Settings I and II) . . £850
c. Hebrew characters transposed (I) . . £850
d. "PALESTINB" (II) . . . . . . 85·00

18 3 3 m. chestnut .. 4·75 6·00
a. Opt inverted .. £450 £600
b. Arabic "z" (Settings I and II) .. £1500
c. Hebrew characters transposed (I) .. £1500
d. "PALESTINB" (II) .. 45·00
19 4 m. scarlet .. 1·25 1·25
b. Arabic "z" (Settings I and II) .. £1500
c. Hebrew characters transposed (I) .. £1500
d. PALESTINB" (II) .. 45·00
20 5 m. yellow-orange .. 4·25 12·00
c. Hebrew characters transposed (I) .. † £2500
d. "PALESTINB" (II) .. 85·00
21 1 p. deep indigo (Sil.) .. 2·00 80
d. "PALESTINB" (II) .. 20·00
w. Wmk inverted .. £120 £130
22 2 p. deep olive .. 2·00 1·90
a. Crown missing from wmk .. £500
b. Arabic "z" (I) .. £180
c. Hebrew characters transposed (I) .. £180
d. "PALESTINB" (Settings I and II) .. 90·00
23 5 p. deep purple .. 13·00 20·00
b. Arabic "z" (I) .. £900
c. Hebrew characters transposed (I) .. £500
d. "PALESTINB" (Setting I and II) .. £140
24 9 p. ochre .. 8·00 20·00
b. Arabic "z" (I) .. £400
c. Hebrew characters transposed (I) .. £450
d. "PALESTINB" (Settings I and II) .. £160
25 10 p. ultramarine .. 10·00 17·00
b. Arabic "z" (I) .. £300
c. Hebrew characters transposed (I) .. £400
d. "PALESTINB" (Settings I and II) .. £200
26 20 p. pale grey .. 22·00 42·00
b. Arabic "z" (Settings I and II) .. £800
c. Hebrew characters transposed (I) .. £900
d. "PALESTINB" (Settings I and II) .. £1800

(*b*) *P* 14

27 3 2 m. blue-green .. 1·40 1·40
d. "PALESTINB" (II) .. 30·00
28 3 m. chestnut .. 55·00 55·00
29 5 m. orange .. 1·60 90
d. "PALESTINB" (II) .. 70·00
16/29 .. *Set of* 14 £130 £150

Faulty registration of the overprint in this issue has resulted in numerous misplaced overprints, either vertically or horizontally, which are not of great importance with the exception of Nos. 21 and 29 which exist with the overprint out of sequence, i.e. Hebrew/Arabic/English or English/Arabic/Hebrew or English/Hebrew only. Also all values are known with Arabic/English only.

1920 (Dec)–**21.** *Optd with T* **5*** (*Arabic* 10 *mm long*).

(*a*) *P* 15×14

30 3 1 m. sepia (27.12.20) .. 1·25 1·00
a. Opt inverted .. £400 †
31 2 m. blue-green (27.12.20) .. 6·00 4·00
a. Opt double ..
32 3 m. yellow-brown (27.12.20) .. 2·00 1·00
33 4 m. scarlet (27.12.20) .. 2·00 1·25
34 5 m. yellow-orange .. 2·25 75
35 1 p. deep indigo (Silver) (21.6.21) .. £425 25·00
36 2 p. olive (21.6.21) .. 60·00 25·00
37 5 p. deep purple (21.6.21) .. 32·00 9·50

(*b*) *P* 14

38 3 1 m. sepia .. £500 £700
39 2 m. blue-green .. 2·50 4·00
40 4 m. scarlet .. 55·00 75·00
41 5 m. orange .. 85·00 9·00
a. Yellow-orange .. 4·75 1·10
42 1 p. deep indigo (Silver) .. 40·00 1·25
43 5 p. purple .. £200 £450

*In this setting the Arabic and Hebrew characters are badly worn and blunted, the Arabic "S" and "T" are joined (i.e. there is no break in the position indicated by the arrow in our illustration); the letters of "PALESTINE" are often irregular or broken; and the space between the two groups of Hebrew characters varies from 1 mm to over 1¾ mm. The " character in the left-hand Hebrew word extends above the remainder of the line (*For clear, sharp overprint, see Nos.* 47/59.)

The dates of issue given are irrespective of the perforations, i.e. one or both perfs could have been issued on the dates shown.

Nos. 31 and 39 exist with any one line of the overprint partly missing.

1920 (6 Dec). *Optd with T* **6**. (*a*) *P* 15 × 14.

44 3 3 m. yellow-brown .. 40·00 32·00
44*a* 5 m. yellow-orange .. £14000 £12000

(*b*) *P* 14

45 3 1 m. sepia .. 40·00 32·00
46 5 m. orange .. £350 30·00

فلسطين | فلسطين | فلسطين
PALESTINE | PALESTINE | PALESTINE
פלשתינה א״י | פלשתינה א״י | פלשתינה א״י
(6*a*) | (7) | (8)

1921 (29 May–4 Aug). *Optd as T* **6a**. (*a*) *P* 15×14.

47 3 1 m. sepia (23.6) .. 9·00 3·50
48 2 m. blue-green (18.6) .. 15·00 5·50
49 3 m. yellow-brown (23.6) .. 24·00 3·00
50 4 m. scarlet (23.6) .. 26·00 3·50
51 5 m. yellow-orange .. 42·00 1·00
52 1 p. deep indigo (Silver) (1.7) .. 18·00 75
53 2 p. olive (4.8) .. 22·00 6·00
54 5 p. purple (4.8) .. 25·00 8·00
55 9 p. ochre (4.8) .. 50·00 90·00
56 10 p. ultramarine (4.8) .. 50·00 14·00
57 20 p. pale grey (4.8) .. 85·00 50·00
47/57 .. *Set of* 11 £300 £160

(*b*) *P* 14

58 3 1 m. sepia .. — £2000
59 20 p. pale grey .. £12000 £2500

In this setting the Arabic and Hebrew characters are sharp and pointed and there is usually a break between the Arabic "S" and "T", though this is sometimes filled with ink. The space between the two groups of Hebrew characters is always 1¾ mm. The top of the " character in the Hebrew aligns with the remainder of the word.

The 3 m. with "PALESTINE" omitted is an essay (*Price* £2500 *unused*).

1921 (26 Sept)–**22.** *Optd with T* **7** ("PALESTINE" *in sans-serif letters*) *by Stamping Dept, Board of Inland Revenue, Somerset House, London. Wmk Royal Cypher in column* (*W* **100** *of Great Britain*). *P* 15×14.

60 3 1 m. sepia (5.10.21) .. 1·25 30
61 2 m. blue-green (11.10.21) .. 1·25 30
62 3 m. yellow-brown (17.10.21) .. 1·50 30
63 4 m. scarlet (15.10.21) .. 1·50 60
64 5 m. yellow-orange .. 1·50 30
65 1 p. bright turquoise-blue (14.11.21) .. 1·50 35
66 2 p. olive (7.12.21) .. 2·25 40
67 5 p. deep purple (11.12.21) .. 6·00 5·00
68 9 p. ochre (10.3.22) .. 14·00 14·00
69 10 p. ultramarine (10.3.22) .. 19·00 £500
w. Wmk inverted .. † —
70 20 p. pale grey (10.3.22) .. 50·00 £1200
60/70 .. *Set of* 11 90·00

Dates quoted are of earliest known postmarks.

(Printed and optd by Waterlow & Sons from new plates)

1922 (Sept–Nov). *T* **3** (*redrawn*), *optd with T* **8**. *Wmk Mult Script CA.* (*a*) *P* 14.

71 3 1 m. sepia .. 60 30
a. Deep brown .. 70 30
b. Opt inverted .. — £12000
c. Opt double .. £225 £425
w. Wmk inverted .. 35·00 25·00
72 2 m. yellow .. 1·00 30
a. Orange-yellow .. 2·75 50
b. Wmk sideways .. † £1500
w. Wmk inverted .. 30·00 30·00
73 3 m. greenish blue .. 1·00 15
w. Wmk inverted .. 30·00 30·00
74 4 m. carmine-pink .. 1·00 20
w. Wmk inverted .. 38·00 38·00
75 5 m. orange .. 1·25 50
w. Wmk inverted .. 50·00 38·00
76 6 m. blue-green .. 1·50 30
w. Wmk inverted .. 40·00 40·00
77 7 m. yellow-brown .. 1·50 30
w. Wmk inverted .. £200 £200
78 8 m. scarlet .. 1·50 30
w. Wmk inverted .. 45·00 50·00
79 1 p. grey .. 1·50 30
w. Wmk inverted .. 50·00 50·00
80 13 m. ultramarine .. 1·50 15
w. Wmk inverted .. 30·00 20·00
81 2 p. olive .. 2·50 35
a. Opt inverted .. £300 £500
b. Ochre .. £120 6·50
w. Wmk inverted .. £180 £140
82 5 p. deep purple .. 4·75 1·25
aw. Wmk inverted .. † £550
82*b* 9 p. ochre .. £900 £200
83 10 p. light blue .. 45·00 10·00
a. "E.F.F." for "E.E.F." in bottom panel (R. 10/3) .. £600 £400
84 20 p. bright violet .. £120 90·00

(*b*) *P* 15×14

86 3 5 p. deep purple .. 45·00 4·00
87 9 p. ochre .. 9·00 9·00
88 10 p. light blue .. 7·50 2·50
a. "E.F.F." for "E.E.F." in bottom panel (R. 10/3) .. £375 £275
w. Wmk inverted .. £425 £225
89 20 p. bright violet .. 9·00 5·50
71s/89s Optd "Specimen" .. *Set of* 15 £400

Most values can be found on thin paper.

In this issue the design of all denominations is the same size, 18 mm × 21½ mm. Varieties may be found with one or other of the stops between "E.E.F." missing.

BRITISH MANDATE TO THE LEAGUE OF NATIONS

The League of Nations granted a mandate to Great Britain for the administration of Palestine on 29 September 1923.

(New Currency. 1,000 mils = 1 Palestine pound)

9 Rachel's Tomb

10 Dome of the Rock

11 Citadel, Jerusalem

12 Sea of Galilee

(Des F. Taylor. Typo Harrison)

1927 (1 June)–**45.** *Wmk Mult Script CA. P* 13½×14½ (2 *m. to* 20 *m.*) *or* 14.

90 9 2 m. greenish blue (14.8.27) .. 65 10
w. Wmk inverted .. † £500
91 3 m. yellow-green .. 75 10
w. Wmk inverted .. † £225
92 10 4 m. rose-pink (14.8.27) .. 3·75 1·25
93 11 5 m. orange (14.8.27) .. 1·25 10
a. From coils. Perf 14½×14 (1936) 14·00 18·00
ac. Yellow. From coils. Perf 14½×14 (1945) .. 30·00 27·00
aw. Wmk inverted .. 16·00 25·00
b. Yellow (12.44) .. 1·00 15
w. Wmk inverted .. 25·00 27·00
94 10 6 m. pale green (14.8.27) .. 3·00
a. Deep green .. 75
95 11 7 m. scarlet (14.8.27) .. 4·25
96 10 8 m. yellow-brown (14.8.27) .. 12·00
97 9 10 m. slate (14.8.27) .. 65
a. Grey. From coils. Perf 14½×14 (11.38) .. 20·00
aw. Wmk inverted ..
b. Grey (1944) .. 1·25
98 10 13 m. ultramarine .. 4·50
99 11 20 m. dull olive-green (14.8.27) .. 1·25
a. Bright olive-green (12.44) .. 1·25
w. Wmk inverted .. —
100 12 50 m. deep dull purple (14.8.27) .. 1·50
a. Bright purple (12.44) .. 1·75
x. Wmk reversed .. —
101 90 m. bistre (14.8.27) .. 55·00
102 100 m. turquoise-blue (14.8.27) .. 2·25
103 200 m. deep violet (14.8.27) .. 8·00
a. Bright violet (1928) .. 27·00
b. Blackish violet (12.44) .. 6·50
90/103*b* .. *Set of* 14 85·00
90s/103s Handstamped "Specimen" *Set of* 14 £325

Three sets may be made of the above issue; one on thin pape on thicker paper with a ribbed appearance, and another on white paper without ribbing.

2 m. stamps in the grey colour of the 10 m., includi example postmarked in 1935, exist as do 50 m. stamps in but it has not been established whether they were issued.

Nos. 90/1 and 93 exist in coils, constructed from no sheets.

1932 (1 June)–**44.** *New values and colours. Wmk Mult Scri P* 13½ × 14½ (4 *m. to* 15 *m.*) *or* 14.

104 10 4 m. purple (1.11.32) .. 1·00
w. Wmk inverted .. †
105 11 7 m. deep violet .. 60
106 10 8 m. scarlet .. 1·25
w. Wmk inverted .. †
107 13 m. bistre (1.8.32) .. 1·00
108 15 m. ultramarine (1.8.32) .. 2·50
a. Grey-blue (12.44) .. 1·75
b. Greenish blue .. 1·75
w. Wmk inverted .. †
109 12 250 m. brown (15.1.42) .. 4·00
110 500 m. scarlet (15.1.42) .. 4·50
111 £P1 black (15.1.42) .. 6·00
104/11 .. *Set of* 8 18·00
104s/11s Perf "Specimen" *Set of* 8 £375

No. 108 exists in coils, constructed from normal sheets.

STAMP BOOKLETS

1929. *Blue cover inscr* "PALESTINE POSTAGE ST BOOKLET" *and contents in English. Without advertisem on front. Stitched.*

SB1 150 m. booklet containing twelve 2 m., 3 m. and eighteen 5 m. (Nos. 90/1, 93) in blocks of 6 .. £
a. As No. SB1, but stapled .. £

1933. *Blue cover inscr* "PALESTINE POSTS TELEGRAPHS POSTAGE STAMP BOOKLET" *and con all in English, Arabic and Hebrew. Without advertisemen front. Stapled.*

SB2 150 m. booklet. Contents as No. SB1 ..

1937–38. *Red cover inscr* "POSTAGE STAMP BOOKL *and contents in English, Hebrew and Arabic. advertisements on front. Stapled.*

SB3 150 m. booklet containing 2 m., 3 m., 5 m. and 15 m. (Nos. 90/1, 93, 108) in blocks of 6 £
a. Blue cover (1938) .. £

1939. *Pink cover inscr* "POSTAGE STAMP BOOKLET" *contents in English, Hebrew and Arabic. With advertisem on front. Stapled.*

SB4 120 m. booklet containing six 10 m. and twelve 5 m. (Nos. 93, 97) in blocks of 6 .. £1

POSTAL FISCALS

Type-set stamps inscribed "O.P.D.A." (= Ottoman Public D Administration) or "H.J.Z." (Hejaz Railway); British 1d. star of 1912–24 and Palestine stamps overprinted with one or ot of the above groups of letters, or with the word "Devair", wit without surcharge of new value, are fiscal stamps. They known used as postage stamps, alone, or with other stamp make up the correct rates, and were passed by the po authorities, although they were not definitely authorised postal use.

POSTAGE DUE STAMPS

D 1

D 2 (MILLIEME)

D 3 (MIL)

(Typo Greek Orthodox Convent Press, Jerusalem)

1923 (1 Apr). *P* 11.

D1 D 1 1 m. yellow-brown .. 15·00 2
a. Imperf (pair) .. £300
b. Imperf between (horiz pair) .. £1100
D2 2 m. blue-green .. 10·00 1
a. Imperf (pair) .. £400
D3 4 m. scarlet .. 10·00 1
D4 8 m. mauve .. 7·00 7
a. Imperf (pair) .. £120
b. Imperf between (horiz pair) .. † £1
D5 13 m. steel blue .. 6·00 6
a. Imperf between (horiz pair) .. £850
D1/5 .. *Set of* 5 42·00 50

Perfectly centred and perforated stamps of this issue are wo considerably more than the above prices, which are for aver specimens.

(Types D 2/3. Typo D.L.R.)

Oct). *Wmk Mult Script CA. P* 14.

D 2	1 m. deep brown	90	2·00
	2 m. yellow	2·25	1·75
	w. Wmk inverted	†	£400
	4 m. green	2·00	1·25
	8 m. scarlet	3·00	90
	13 m. ultramarine	2·75	2·50
	5 p. violet	8·50	1·75
	.. .. *Set of* 6	17·00	9·00
	s Optd "Specimen" .. *Set of* 6	£275	

Feb)–**45.** *Wmk Mult Script CA. P* 14.

D 3	1 m. brown	50	85
	a. Perf 15×14 (1944)	32·00	65·00
	2 m. yellow	65	60
	w. Wmk inverted	†	£400
	4 m. green	1·00	1·60
	a. Perf 15×14 (1945)	55·00	80·00
	6 m. orange-brown (10.33)	15·00	5·00
	8 m. carmine	1·75	90
	10 m. pale grey	1·25	60
	13 m. ultramarine	1·50	1·75
	20 m. pale olive-green	1·60	1·25
	50 m. violet	2·50	1·25
	.. .. *Set of* 9	23·00	14·00
	20s Optd or Perf (6 m.) "Specimen" *Set of* 9	£300	

D12a and D14a were printed and perforated by Harrison ons following bomb damage to the De La Rue works on cember 1940.

British Mandate terminated on 14 May 1948. Later issues of s and occupation issues will be found listed under Gaza, and Jordan in Part 19 (*Middle East*) of this catalogue.

Papua
see after Australia

Penrhyn Island
see after New Zealand

Pitcairn Islands

CROWN COLONY

The settlement of Pitcairn Island by the *Bounty* mutineers in 1790 was not discovered until the American whaler *Topaz*, Capt. Mayhew Folger, called there in 1808. A visit by two Royal Navy frigates followed in 1814 and reports from their captains resulted in considerable interest being taken in the inhabitants' welfare by religious and philanthrophic circles in Great Britain.

Due to overcrowding the population was resettled on Tahiti in 1831, but many soon returned to Pitcairn which was taken under British protection in 1838. The island was again evacuated in 1856, when the inhabitants were moved to Norfolk Island, but a number of families sailed back to their original home in 1859 and 1864.

The earliest surviving letter from the island is dated 1849. Before 1921 the mail service was irregular, as it depended on passing ships, and mail for the island was often sent via Tahiti. Some covers, purportedly sent from Pitcairn between 1883 and 1890 are known handstamped "Pitcairn Island" or "PITCAIRN ISLAND", but these are now believed to be forgeries.

In 1920 a regular mail service was introduced. As there were no stamps available letters were allowed free postage as long as they carried a cachet, or manuscript endorsement, indicating their origin. Illustrations of Cachets I/VI, VIII, VIIIa, X and XIII are taken from *Pitcairn Islands Postal Markings 1883–1991*, published by the Pitcairn Islands Study Group, and are reproduced by permission of the author, Mr. Cy Kitching. Cachets I to XIII are shown three-quarter size.

POSTED IN PITCAIRN
NO STAMPS AVAILABLE

Cachet I

Cat No.		*Value on cover*
C1	**1920–25** Cachet I (62×8 *mm*) (*violet or black*) ..	£3000

POSTED AT PITCAIRN ISLAND
NO STAMPS AVAILABLE.

Cachet II

C2 **1921–25.** Cachet II (*violet or red*) £2500

POSTED AT PITCAIRN ISLAND
NO STAMPS AVAILABLE.

Cachet III

C3 **1922–28.** Cachet III (49×8½*mm*) (*vio, pur or blk*) £1800

POSTED IN PITCAIRN ISLAND
1923 NO STAMPS AVAILABLE

Cachet IV

C4 **1923.** Cachet IV (*black*) £2500

Posted at Pitcairn
Island no Stamps
Available

Cachet IVa

C4*a* **1923** Cachet IVa (73½×22 *mm*) (*red*) £2500

POSTED AT PITCAIRN ISLAND
NO STAMPS AVAILABLE

Cachet V

C5 **1923–28** (Aug). Cachet V (47×9 *mm*) (*red, violet or black*) £1700
C5*a* **1925–26.** As Cachet V, but second line shown as "No Stamps Available" (*black*) .. .. ..

POSTED AT PITCAIRN ISLAND.
NO STAMPS AVAILABLE.
NOT TO BE SURCHARGED.

Cachet VI

C6 **1923.** Cachet VI (*blue-green or red*) .. ..
C7 **1923.** As Cachet V, but in three lines (*red*) ..

POSTED AT PITCAIRN ISLAND
NO STAMPS AVAILABLE.

Cachet VII

C8 **1923–27.** Cachet VII (*violet*) £1700
C9 **1924.** As Cachet IV, but dated "1924" (*black*) .. £2250

POSTED AT PITCAIRN ISLAND.
NO STAMPS AVAILABLE.

Cachet VIII

C10 **1924–26** Cachet VIII (36×8 *mm*) (*vio, blk or red*) £2250

POSTED AT PITCAIRN
NO STAMPS AVAILABLE

Cachet VIIIa

C10*a* **1924–26.** Cachet VIIIa (36×8¾ *mm*) (*vio or blk*) £1800

POSTED AT PITCAIRN ISLAND
NO STAMPS AVAILABLE.

Cachet IX

C11 **1924** (Feb)–**25.** Cachet IX (63×7 *mm*) (*vio or blk*) £2500

POSTED·IN·PITCAIRN·
NO·STAMPS·AVAILABLE

Cachet IXa

C11*a* **1924–26.** Cachet IXa (58×8½ *mm*) (*vio or blk*)
C12 **1925** (Sept). As Cachet IV, but dated "1925" (*blk*) £2250

POSTED IN PITCAIRN
NO STAMPS AVAILABLE.

Cachet X

C13 **1925.** Cachet X (48×5 *mm*) £1900

POSTED AT PITCAIRN ISLAND,
NO STAMPS AVAILABLE.

Cachet XI

C14 **1925–26.** Cachet XI (50×10 *mm*) (*violet or blk*) £2250

Posted at PITCAIRN ISLAND
No Stamps Available

Cachet XII

C15 **1925** Cachet XII (55×7½ *mm*) (*violet*) .. ..

POSTED IN PITCAIRN
NO STAMPS AVAILABLE.

Cachet XIII

C16 **1926** (Jan). Cachet XIII (64×8 *mm*) (*pur or blk*)

The New Zealand Government withdrew the free postage concession on 12 May 1926, but after representations from the islanders opened a postal agency on Pitcairn using New Zealand stamps cancelled with Type Z 1. Some impressions of this postmark appear to show a double ring, but this is the result of heavy or uneven use of the handstamp. The postal agency operated from 7 June 1927 until 14 October 1940.

PRICES. Those quoted for Nos. Z1/72 and ZF1 are for examples showing a virtually complete strike of Type Z 1. Due to the size of the cancellation such examples will usually be on piece.

Z 1

Stamps of New Zealand cancelled with Type Z 1.

1915–29. *King George V (Nos.* 419, 422/6, 428/31 *and* 446/9).

Z 1	½d. green	24·00
Z 2	1½d. grey-slate	50·00
Z 3	1½d. orange-brown	42·00
Z 4	2d. yellow	38·00
Z 5	2½d. blue	70·00
Z 6	3d. chocolate	75·00
Z 7	4d. bright violet	70·00
Z 8	4½d. deep green	85·00
Z 9	5d. light blue	70·00
Z10	6d. carmine	85·00
Z11	7½d. red-brown	90·00
Z12	8d. red-brown	£120

Z13 9d. yellowish olive £120
Z14 1s. vermilion £120

1926–27. *King George V in Admiral's uniform (Nos. 468/9).*
Z15 1d. rose-carmine 24·00
Z16 2s. light blue £170

1929. *Anti-Tuberculosis Fund* (*No.* 544).
Z17 1d. + 1d. scarlet £110

1931. *Air* (*No.* 548).
Z18 3d. chocolate £190

1932. *Health* (*No.* 552).
Z21 1d. + 1d. carmine £110

1935. *Pictorials* (*Nos.* 556/8 *and* 560/9). *W* **43**.
Z22 ½d. bright green 55·00
Z23 1d. scarlet 35·00
Z24 1½d. red-brown 80·00
Z26 2½d. chocolate and slate 70·00
Z27 3d. brown 80·00
Z28 4d. black and sepia 90·00
Z29 5d. ultramarine 95·00
Z30 6d. scarlet 90·00
Z31 8d. chocolate 95·00
Z32 9d. scarlet and black 95·00
Z33 1s. deep green 85·00
Z34 2s. olive-green £170
Z35 3s. chocolate and yellow-brown £200

1935. *Silver Jubilee* (*Nos.* 573/5).
Z36 ½d. green 38·00
Z37 1d. carmine 38·00
Z38 6d. red-orange 70·00

1935. *Health* (*No.* 576).
Z39 1d. + 1d. scarlet 60·00

1936. *Pictorials* (*Nos.* 577/82). *W* **98**.
Z40 ½d. bright green 42·00
Z41 1d. scarlet 14·00
Z42 1½d. red-brown 70·00
Z43 2d. orange 55·00
Z44 2½d. chocolate and slate 60·00
Z45 3d. brown 65·00

1936. *21st Anniv of "Anzac" Landing at Gallipoli* (*Nos.* 591/2).
Z46 ½d. + ½d. green 40·00
Z47 1d. + 1d. scarlet 40·00

1936. *Congress of British Empire Chambers of Commerce* (*Nos.* 593/7).
Z48 ½d. emerald-green 38·00
Z49 1d. scarlet 38·00
Z50 2½d. blue 42·00
Z51 4d. violet 65·00
Z52 6d. red-brown 65·00

1936. *Health* (*No.* 598).
Z53 1d. + 1d. scarlet 60·00

1937. *Coronation* (*Nos.* 599/601).
Z54 1d. carmine 28·00
Z55 2½d. Prussian blue 30·00
Z56 6d. red-orange 30·00

1937. *Health* (*No.* 602).
Z57 1d. + 1d. scarlet 60·00

1938. *King George VI* (*Nos.* 603, 605, 607).
Z58 ½d. green 60·00
Z59 1d. scarlet 60·00
Z60 1½d. purple-brown 70·00

1940. *Centenary of British Sovereignty* (*Nos.* 613/22, 624/5).
Z61 ½d. blue-green 30·00
Z62 1d. chocolate and scarlet 35·00
Z63 1½d. light blue and mauve 38·00
Z64 2d. blue-green and chocolate 38·00
Z65 2½d. blue-green and blue 40·00
Z66 3d. purple and carmine 40·00
Z67 4d. chocolate and lake 60·00
Z68 5d. pale blue and brown 65·00
Z69 6d. emerald-green and violet 65·00
Z70 7d. black and red 85·00
Z71 9d. olive-green and orange 85·00
Z72 1s. sage-green and deep green 85·00

POSTAL FISCAL STAMPS

1932. *Arms* (*No.* F147).
ZF1 2s. 6d. deep brown £200

PRICES FOR STAMPS ON COVER TO 1945
Nos. 1/8 *from* × 10

1 Cluster of Oranges

2 Christian on *Bounty* and Pitcairn Island

(Recess B.W. (1d., 3d., 4d., 8d. and 2s. 6d.), and Waterlow (others))

1940 (15 Oct)–**51.** *T* **1/2** *and similar horiz designs. Wmk Mult Script CA. P* 11½×11 (1d., 3d., 4d., 8d. *and* 2s. 6d.) *or* 12½ (*others*).

1	½d. orange and green	40	60
2	1d. mauve and magenta	55	70
3	1½d. grey and carmine	55	50
4	2d. green and brown	1·75	1·40
5	3d. yellow-green and blue	1·25	1·40
	aw. Wmk inverted	£3250	
5*b*	4d. black and emerald-green (1.9.51)	15·00	10·00
6	6d. brown and grey-blue	5·00	1·50
6*a*	8d. olive-green and magenta (1.9.51)	16·00	7·00
7	1s. violet and grey	3·00	1·50
8	2s. 6d. green and brown	8·00	3·75
1/8	*Set of* 10	45·00	25·00
1s/8s (*ex* 4d., 8d.) Perf "Specimen"	*Set of* 8	£800	

Designs:—1½d. John Adams and his house; 2d. Lt. Bligh and H.M.S. *Bounty*; 3d. Pitcairn Islands and Pacific Ocean; 4d. *Bounty* Bible; 6d. H.M.S. *Bounty*; 8d. School, 1949; 1s. Fletcher Christian and Pitcairn Island; 2s. 6d. Christian on H.M.S. *Bounty* and Pitcairn Coast.

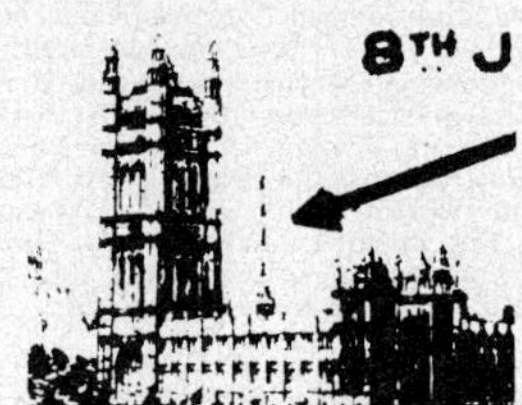

Flagstaff flaw
(R. 8/2)

1946 (2 Dec). *Victory. As Nos.* 110/11 *of Antigua.*

9	2d. brown	60	15
10	3d. blue	60	15
	a. Flagstaff flaw	27·00	
9s/10s Perf "Specimen"	*Set of* 2	£140	

1949 (1 Aug). *Royal Silver Wedding. As Nos.* 112/13 *of Antigua.*

11	1½d. scarlet	2·00	1·00
12	10s. mauve	35·00	50·00

1949 (10 Oct). *75th Anniv of U.P.U. As Nos.* 114/17 *of Antigua.*

13	2½d. red-brown	1·00	3·50
14	3d. deep blue	8·00	4·00
15	6d. deep blue-green	4·00	4·00
16	1s. purple	4·00	4·00
13/16	*Set of* 4	15·00	14·00

STAMP BOOKLETS

1940 (15 Oct). *Black on deep green cover. Stapled.*
SB1 4s. 8d. booklet containing one each ½d., 1d., 1½d., 2d., 3d., 6d., 1s. and 2s. 6d. (Nos. 1/5, 6, 7/8) £2750

Genuine examples of No. SB1 are interleaved with ordinary kitchen wax-paper, which frequently tones the stamps, and are secured with staples 17 mm long.

The status of other booklets using different size staples or paper fasteners is uncertain although it is believed that some empty booklet covers were available on the island.

Prince Edward Island *see* Canada

Queensland *see* Australia

Rhodesia

Stamps of BECHUANALAND (see BOTSWANA) w used in Matabeleland on the runner post betwe Gubulawayo and Mafeking (Bechuanaland) from 9 Aug 1888 until 5 May 1894. Such stamps were cancel "GUBULAWAYO" or by the barred oval "678" obliterati

Between 27 June 1890 and 13 May 1892 external m from Mashonaland sent via Bechuanaland was frank with that territory's stamps. A similar arrangement, usi the stamps of MOZAMBIQUE existed for the route v Beira inaugurated on 29 August 1891. In both instanc the stamps were cancelled by the post offices receiving t mail from Mashonaland. From 14 May until 31 July 18 letters via Bechuanaland were franked with a combinati of B.S.A Company and Bechuanaland issues.

Rhodesia joined the South African Postal Union on August 1892 when its stamps became valid f international mail. Combination frankings wi Mozambique stamps continued to be required until Ap 1894.

For the use of British Central Africa overprints in Nort eastern Rhodesia from 1893 to 1899 see MALAV (NYASALAND).

PRICES FOR STAMPS ON COVER TO 1945

Nos. 1/7	*from* × 5
Nos. 8/13	—
Nos. 14/17	*from* × 2
Nos. 18/24	*from* × 10
Nos. 25/6	—
Nos. 27/8	*from* × 7
Nos. 29/35	*from* × 10
Nos. 36/7	—
Nos. 41/6	*from* × 6
Nos. 47/50	—
Nos. 51/3	*from* × 2
Nos. 58/64	*from* × 3
Nos. 66/72	*from* × 8
Nos. 73/4	—
Nos. 75/87	*from* × 6
Nos. 88/93*a*	—
Nos. 94/9	*from* × 3
Nos. 100/10	*from* × 5
Nos. 111/13*e*	—
Nos. 114/18	*from* × 7
Nos. 119/60*a*	*from* × 8
Nos. 160*b*/6*b*	—
Nos. 167/78	*from* × 5
Nos. 179/81*a*	—
Nos. 182/5*a*	*from* × 4
Nos. 186/208	*from* × 6
Nos. 209/41	*from* × 5
Nos. 242/54*a*	—
Nos. 255/77	*from* × 5
Nos. 278/9*c*	—
Nos. 280/1	*from* × 10
Nos. 282/310	*from* × 5
Nos. 311/22	—

A. ISSUES FOR THE BRITISH SOUTH AFRICA COMPANY TERRITORY

1

2

(3)

(Recess B.W.)

1892 (2 Jan)*–**93**. *Thin wove paper. P* 14, 14½.

1	1	1d. black	10·00	2·7
2		6d. ultramarine	50·00	22·
3		6d. deep blue (1893)	25·00	3·
4		1s. grey-brown	32·00	7·5
5		2s. vermilion	40·00	25·
6		2s. 6d. grey-purple	29·00	32·(
7		2s. 6d. lilac (1893)	45·00	38·(
8		5s. orange-yellow	65·00	50·(
9		10s. deep green	80·00	£1(

£1 deep blue £180 £130
£2 rose-red** £400 £150
£5 sage-green £1600 £450
£10 brown £2750 £700
.. .. *Set of* 8 £400 £300

t caution is needed in buying the high values in either r unused condition, many stamps offered being revenue cleaned and re-gummed or with forged postmarks.

nting of stamps in Types **1**, **2** and **4** commenced in 1890, gh none were used for postal purposes before 2 January vhen the route to the East Coast was inaugurated.

r later printings of the £2 see No. 74.

following sheet watermarks are known on Nos. 1/26: (1) m Collins, Sons & Co's paper watermarked with the firm's gram, and "PURE LINEN WOVE BANK" in double-lined ls (1890 and 1891 ptgs). (2) As (1) with "EXTRA NG" and "139" added (1892 ptgs). (3) Paper by Wiggins, & Co, watermarked "W T & Co" in script letters in e-lined wavy border (1893 ptgs). (4) The same firm's paper, marked "1011" in double-lined figures (1894 ptgs except (5) "WIGGINS TEAPE & CO LONDON" in double-lined capitals (1894 ptg of No. 18). Many values can also be on a slightly thicker paper without wmk, but single nens are not easily distinguishable.

2 Jan). *Nos.* 2 *and* 4 *surch as T* **3**.
½d. on 6d. ultramarine .. .. .. 90·00 £250
2d. on 6d. ultramarine .. .. .. 95·00 £375
4d. on 6d. ultramarine £120 £450
8d. on 1s. grey-brown £120 £475

tion is needed in buying these surcharges as both forged arges and forged postmarks exist.

4

5 (ends of scrolls behind legs of springboks)

(T **4**. Centre recess; value B.W.)

(2 Jan)–**94**. *Thin wove paper* (*wmks as note after No.* 13). 4, 14½.
½d. dull blue and vermilion .. .. 2·50 3·00
½d. deep blue and vermilion (1893) .. 2·75 4·50
2d. deep dull green and vermilion .. 19·00 2·00
3d. grey-black and green (8.92) .. .. 9·50 3·25
4d. chestnut and black .. .. .. 19·00 2·25
8d. rose-lake and ultramarine .. .. 10·00 9·50
8d. red and ultramarine (1892) .. .. 10·00 8·50
3s. brown and green (1894) .. .. £140 75·00
4s. grey-black and vermilion (1893) .. 32·00 50·00
6 .. .. *Set of* 7 £200 £130

(Recess P.B. from the Bradbury, Wilkinson plates)

. *Thick soft wove paper. P* 12½.
4 2d. green and red .. .. .. 20·00 10·00
4d. yellow-brown and black .. .. 22·00 12·00
a. Imperf (pair) £1800

(Centre recess; value typo P.B.)

6–97. *Wove paper. P* 14.

(*a*) *Die I. Plates* 1 *and* 2.

mall dot to the right of the tail of the right-hand supporter in coat of arms. Body of lion only partly shaded.

5 1d. scarlet and emerald .. .. 12·00 4·50
a. Carmine-red and emerald .. ..
2d. brown and mauve .. .. .. 19·00 2·00
3d. chocolate and ultramarine .. .. 3·75 1·75
4d. ultramarine and mauve .. .. 50·00
a. Imperf between (pair) .. ..
b. Blue and mauve .. .. .. 23·00 14·00
6d. mauve and pink .. .. .. 80·00 16·00
8d. green and mauve/*buff* .. .. 4·50 60
a. Imperf between (pair) .. ..
b. Imperf (pair) £2000
1s. green and blue .. .. .. 15·00 2·75
3s. green and mauve/*blue* .. .. 65·00 32·00
a. Imperf (pair) £5500
4s. orange-red and blue/*green* .. .. 48·00 2·75
37 .. .. *Set of* 9 £225 65·00

(*b*) *Die II. Plates* 3 *and* 4

No dot. Body of lion heavily shaded all over.

5 ½d. slate and violet .. .. .. 2·50 3·25
1d. scarlet and emerald .. .. 3·00 3·75
2d. brown and mauve .. .. .. 6·50 4·50
4d. ultramarine and mauve .. .. 70·00 12·00
a. Blue and mauve .. .. .. 8·00 50
6d. mauve and rose .. .. .. 6·00 75
2s. indigo and green/*buff* .. .. 20·00 8·50
2s. 6d. brown and purple/*yellow* .. 70·00 45·00
5s. chestnut and emerald .. .. 42·00 9·00
10s. slate and vermilion/*rose* .. .. 90·00 60·00
/50 .. .. *Set of* 9 £225 £120

One Penny

(6)

THREE
PENCE.

(7)

(Surchd by *Bulawayo Chronicle*)

1896 (April). *Matabele Rebellion provisionals. Surch with T* **6** *and* **7**.
51 **6** 1d. on 3d. (No. 21) £450 £450
a. "P" in "Penny" inverted £22000
b. "y" in "Penny" inverted .. ..
c. Surch double .. .. ..
52 1d. on 4s. (No. 26) £250 £275
a. "P" in "Penny" inverted £18000
b. "y" in "Penny" inverted £18000
c. Single bar through original value £950 £1100
53 **7** 3d. on 5s. (No. 8) £170 £225
a. "R" in "THREE" inverted .. . £19000
b. "T" in "THREE" inverted .. . £22000

Nos. 51 and 52 occur in two settings, one with 9¾ mm between value and upper bar, the other with 11 mm between value and upper bar.

BRITISH
SOUTH AFRICA
COMPANY.

(8)

9 (Ends of scrolls between legs of springboks)

1896 (22 May–Aug). *Cape of Good Hope stamps optd by Argus Printing Co, Cape Town, with T* **8**. *Wmk Anchor* (*3d. wmk Crown CA*). *P* 14.
58 **6** ½d. grey-black (No. 48*a*) .. .. 9·50 15·00
59 **17** 1d. rose-red (No. 58) .. .. .. 10·00 17·00
60 **6** 2d. deep bistre (No. 50*a*) .. .. 14·00 9·00
61 3d. pale claret (No. 40) .. .. .. 50·00 70·00
62 4d. blue (No. 51) .. .. .. 16·00 16·00
a. "COMPANY," omitted £8000
63 **4** 6d. deep purple (No. 52*a*) .. .. 50·00 65·00
64 **6** 1s. yellow-ochre (No. 65) (Aug) .. £140 £140
58/64 .. .. *Set of* 7 £250 £300

No. 62 also exists with "COMPANY" partially omitted. Examples with the word completely omitted, as No. 62a, occur on positions 1 to 6 of the setting.

Forgeries of this overprint show a narrow final "A" in "AFRICA" and have a rectangular full stop. On the genuine overprint both "As" are the same and the stop is oval.

(Eng J. A. C. Harrison (vignette), Bain or Rapkin (£1) (frames). Recess Waterlow)

1897. *P* 13½ *to* 16.
66 **9** ½d. grey-black and purple .. .. 1·75 4·25
67 1d. scarlet and emerald .. .. .. 3·00 4·00
68 2d. brown and mauve .. .. .. 5·50 1·25
69 3d. brown-red and slate-blue .. .. 2·50 40
a. Imperf between (vert pair) £2000
70 4d. ultramarine and claret .. .. 8·00 1·50
a. Imperf between (horiz pair) £7500 £7500
71 6d. dull purple and pink .. .. .. 6·50 3·50
72 8d. green and mauve/*buff* .. .. 11·00 40
a. Imperf between (vert pair) .. .. — £2250
73 £1 black and red-brown/*green* £350 £225

(Recess Waterlow, from the Bradbury plate)

1897 (Jan). *P* 15.
74 **2** £2 rosy red £1700 £400

10

11

12

(Recess Waterlow)

1898–1908. *P* 13½ *to* 15½.
75 **10** ½d. dull bluish green .. .. 3·00 65
a. Yellow-green (1904) .. .. 2·00 65
aa. Imperf vert (horiz pair) £650
ab. Imperf (pair) £700
76 ½d. deep green (*shades*) (1908) .. 24·00 1·00
77 1d. rose (*shades*) .. .. .. 2·50 50
a. Imperf (pair) £600 £650
b. Imperf between (vert pair) .. £500
78 1d. red (*shades*) (1905) .. .. 3·75 50
a. Imperf vert (horiz pair) £350 £400
ab. Imperf horiz (vert pair) £650
b. Imperf (pair) £500 £550
c. Imperf between (horiz pair) .. † £425
79 2d. brown .. .. 2·50 60
80 2½d. dull blue (*shades*) .. .. 4·50 80
a. Imperf vert (horiz pair) £800 £850
b. Grey-blue (*shades*) (1903) .. 12·00 1·00
81 3d. claret .. .. 4·00 80
a. Imperf between (vert pair) .. £700
82 4d. olive .. .. 4·25 30
a. Imperf between (vert pair) .. £700
83 6d. reddish purple .. .. .. 10·00 1·75
a. Reddish mauve (1902) .. .. 15·00 5·50
84 **11** 1s. bistre .. .. 13·00 2·25
a. Imperf between (vert pair) .. £2500
ab. Imperf between (horiz pair) .. £2750
b. Deep olive-bistre (1907) £275
bc. Imperf (pair) £2500
bd. Imperf between (horiz pair) .. £3250
c. Bistre-brown (1908) .. .. 50·00 13·00
d. Brownish yellow (1908) .. .. 15·00 6·50
85 2s. 6d. bluish grey (11.06) .. .. 45·00 75
a. Imperf between (vert pair) .. £1000 £500
b. Imperf (vert pair) .. .. — £5000

86 **11** 3s. deep violet (1902) .. .. 12·00 1·25
a. Deep bluish violet (1908) .. 55·00 9·50
87 5s. brown-orange .. .. .. 38·00 9·00
88 7s. 6d. black (11.01) .. .. 65·00 15·00
89 10s. grey-green .. .. .. 22·00 1·00
90 **12** £1 greyish red-purple (*p* 15½) (7.01) £200 75·00
a. Perf 14. *Blackish purple* (1902) .. £350 75·00
91 £2 brown (5.08) .. .. .. 75·00 6·50
92 £5 deep blue (7.01) £3000 £2250
93 £10 lilac (7.01) £3250 £2250
93*a* £20 yellow-bistre (1901?) £14000
75/90 .. .. *Set of* 14 £375 95·00
80s/1s, 85s/6s, 88s/93s Perf "Specimen" *Set of* 10 £900

A £100 cherry-red, perf 13½, was ordered in June 1901, a number of mint, together with several examples showing fiscal cancellations being known.

13 Victoria Falls

RHODESIA.

(14)

(Recess Waterlow)

1905 (13 July). *Visit of British Association and Opening of Victoria Falls Bridge. P* 13½ *to* 15.
94 **13** 1d. red .. .. 3·00 4·25
95 2½d. deep blue .. .. 8·00 5·50
96 5d. claret .. .. 22·00 48·00
sa. Optd "Specimen" £150
97 1s. blue-green .. .. .. 22·00 35·00
a. Imperf (pair) £17000
b. Imperf between (horiz pair) .. £23000
c. Imperf between (vert pair) .. £23000
d. Imperf vert (horiz pair) £18000
98 2s. 6d. black £100 £150
99 5s. violet .. .. 85·00 40·00
94/9 .. .. *Set of* 6 £200 £250
94s/9s Optd or Perf (5d.) "Specimen" .. *Set of* 6 £350

1909 (15 Apr)–**12.** *Optd as T* **14**. *P* 13½ *to* 15.
100 **10** ½d. green *to* deep green .. .. 1·75 1·25
a. No stop .. .. 45·00 28·00
b. Yellow-green (1911) .. .. 35·00 27·00
101 1d. carmine-rose .. .. .. 2·25 75
a. No stop .. .. 60·00 25·00
b. Imperf between (horiz pair) .. £400
c. Deep carmine-rose .. .. 2·25 75
cd. Imperf between (horiz pair) .. £400
102 2d. brown .. .. 1·60 3·25
a. No stop .. .. 80·00 55·00
103 2½d. pale dull blue .. .. .. 1·25 70
a. No stop .. .. 35·00 24·00
104 3d. claret .. .. 1·60 30
a. No stop .. .. £100 55·00
b. Opt inverted .. .. .. † 15·00
105 4d. olive .. .. 2·75 1·00
a. No stop .. .. 60·00 55·00
b. Opt inverted .. .. .. † 15·00
106 6d. reddish purple .. .. .. 5·00 3·75
a. No stop .. ..
b. Reddish mauve .. .. ..
c. Dull purple .. .. .. 16·00 4·00
ca. No stop .. .. 80·00 45·00
107 **11** 1s. bistre .. .. 18·00
a. No stop £150
b. Bistre-brown .. .. ..
ba. No stop .. ..
c. Deep brownish bistre .. .. 8·50 2·75
ca. No stop .. .. 80·00 38·00
108 2s. 6d. bluish grey .. .. .. 16·00 8·00
a. No stop .. .. 80·00 55·00
b. Opt inverted .. .. .. † 20·00
109 3s. deep violet .. .. .. 15·00 8·00
110 5s. orange .. .. 25·00 28·00
a. No stop .. .. 90·00 80·00
111 7s. 6d. black .. .. 80·00 16·00
112 10s. dull green .. .. .. 30·00 10·00
a. No stop £225 £180
113 **12** £1 grey-purple .. .. .. £130 70·00
a. Vert pair, lower stamp without opt £25000
b. Opt in violet £350 £180
113*c* £2 brown £4000 £300
113*d* £2 rosy brown (*bluish paper*) (*p* 14½×15) (1912) £3250 £275
113*e* £5 deep blue (*bluish paper*) £6500 £3000
100/13 .. .. *Set of* 14 £275 £140
100s/13s Perf "Specimen" .. *Set of* 14 £325

In some values the no stop variety occurs on every stamp in a vertical row of a sheet, in other values only once in a sheet. Other varieties, such as no serif to the right of apex of "A", no serif to top of "E", etc., exist in some values.

No. 113a comes from a sheet with the overprint omitted from the bottom row.

RHODESIA.
5d

(15)

RHODESIA.
TWO SHILLINGS.

(16)

1909 (April)–**11**. *Surch as T* **15** *and* **16** (2*s.*), *in black.*
114 **10** 5d. on 6d. reddish purple .. .. 6·50 12·00
a. Surcharge in violet .. .. 90·00
b. Reddish mauve .. .. ..
c. Dull purple .. .. .. 14·00 12·00

116 11 7½d. on 2s. 6d. bluish grey .. .. .. 3·50 3·75
a. Surcharge in violet .. .. .. 17·00 9·00
ab. Surch double .. .. .. † £6500
117 10d. on 3s. deep violet .. .. .. 13·00 16·00
a. Surcharge in violet .. .. .. 4·00 3·75
118 2s. on 5s. orange .. .. .. 12·00 7·50
114s/18s Perf "Specimen" .. *Set of* 4 £180

In the 7½d. and 10d. surcharges the bars are spaced as in **T 16**.

17

18

(Recess Waterlow)

1910 (11 Nov)–**13**. (*a*) *P* 14.
119 17 ½d. yellow-green .. .. .. 9·00 1·75
a. Imperf between (horiz pair) .. £18000
120 ½d. bluish green .. .. .. 18·00 2·25
a. Imperf (pair) £10000 £4250
121 ½d. olive-green .. .. .. 25·00 2·25
122 ½d. dull green .. .. .. 60·00 50·00
123 1d. bright carmine .. .. .. 15·00 1·75
a. Imperf between (vert pair) .. £15000 £10000
b. Imperf between (horiz pair) ..
124 1d. carmine-lake .. .. .. 38·00 1·75
125 1d. rose-red .. .. .. 17·00 1·75
126 2d. black and grey .. .. .. 45·00 8·00
127 2d. black-purple and slate-grey .. £160 £650
128 2d. black and slate-grey .. .. 48·00 5·50
129 2d. black and slate .. .. .. 55·00 6·50
130 2d. black and grey-black .. .. 65·00 11·00
131 2½d. ultramarine .. .. .. 19·00 5·50
131*a* 2½d. bright ultramarine .. .. 18·00 5·50
132 2½d. dull blue .. .. .. 22·00 6·00
133 2½d. chalky blue .. .. .. 16·00 12·00
134 3d. purple and ochre .. .. 25·00 26·00
135 3d. purple and yellow-ochre .. .. 30·00 11·00
136 3d. magenta and yellow-ochre .. £120 11·00
137 3d. violet and ochre .. .. .. 95·00 75·00
138 4d. greenish black and orange .. 80·00 85·00
139 4d. brown-purple and orange .. .. 60·00 50·00
140 4d. black and orange .. .. .. 29·00 11·00
141 5d. purple-brown and olive-green .. 23·00 38·00
141*a* 5d. purple-brown and olive-yellow .. 23·00 48·00
ab. Error. Purple-brown and ochre .. £550 £150
143 5d. lake-brown and olive .. .. £225 60·00
143*a* 5d. lake-brown and green (10.12) .. £19000 £1600
144 6d. red-brown and mauve .. .. 28·00 28·00
145 6d. brown and purple .. .. .. 26·00 11·00
145*a* 6d. bright chestnut and mauve .. £650 60·00
146 8d. black and purple £4500
147 8d. dull purple and purple .. .. £150 90·00
148 8d. greenish black and purple .. £120 85·00
149 10d. scarlet and reddish mauve .. .. 28·00 48·00
150 10d. carmine and deep purple. .. £600 60·00
151 1s. grey-black and deep blue-green 32·00 16·00
151*a* 1s. black and deep blue-green .. £130 24·00
152 1s. black and pale blue-green .. .. 38·00 10·00
152*a* 1s. purple-black and blue-green .. £225 40·00
153 2s. black and ultramarine .. .. 70·00 50·00
154 2s. black and dull blue .. .. £1000 60·00
154*a* 2s. purple-black and ultramarine .. £2750 £225
155 2s. 6d. black and lake £300 £300
155*a* 2s. 6d. black and crimson £300 £275
156 2s. 6d. sepia and deep crimson .. £400 £325
156*a* 2s. 6d. bistre-brown and crimson .. £1000 £550
157 2s. 6d. black and rose-carmine .. £275 £300
158 3s. green and violet (*shades*) .. £150 £140
158*a* 3s. bright green and magenta .. £1100 £600
159 5s. vermilion and deep green .. £250 £300
160 5s. scarlet and pale yellow-green .. £275 £180
160*a* 5s. crimson and yellow-green .. £225 £180
160*b* 7s. 6d. carmine and pale blue .. £600 £425
161 7s. 6d. carmine and light blue .. £650 £700
162 7s. 6d. carmine and bright blue .. £1900 £900
163 10s. deep myrtle and orange £600 £250
164 10s. blue-green and orange £375 £350
165 £1 carmine-red and bluish black .. £1000 £450
166 £1 rose-scarlet and bluish black .. £1100 £350
166*a* £1 crimson and slate-black .. £1300 £800
b. Error. Scarlet and reddish mauve £9000

(*b*) *P* 15
167 17 ½d. blue-green .. .. .. £250 13·00
168 ½d. yellow-green .. .. .. £325 11·00
169 ½d. apple-green .. .. .. £550 27·00
170 1d. carmine .. .. .. £250 8·50
170*a* 1d. carmine-lake .. .. .. £400 14·00
170*b* 1d. rose-carmine .. .. .. £275 11·00
171 2d. black and grey-black .. .. £850 30·00
171*a* 2d. black and grey .. .. .. £850 30·00
171*b* 2d. black and slate .. .. .. £900 30·00
172 2½d. ultramarine (*shades*) .. .. 70·00 35·00
173 3d. purple and yellow-ochre .. .. £4750 65·00
173*a* 3d. claret and pale yellow-ochre .. £2250 50·00
174 4d. black and orange (*shades*) .. 40·00 60·00
175 5d. lake-brown and olive .. .. £700 75·00
176 6d. brown and mauve .. .. £800 60·00
177 1s. black and blue-green (*shades*) .. £900 55·00
178 2s. black and dull blue £1800 £325
179 £1 red and black £14000 £3000

(*c*) *P* 14×15 (½d., 3d., 1s.) *or* 15×14 (1d., 4d.)
179*a* 17 ½d. yellow-green .. .. .. † £2750
179*b* 1d. carmine .. .. .. † £5000
180 3d. purple and ochre £5000 £225
181 4d. black and orange £425
181*a* 1s. black and blue-green £20000 £2500

(*d*) *P* 13½
182 17 ½d. yellow-green .. .. .. £250 40·00
182*a* ½d. green .. .. .. £325 40·00
183 1d. bright carmine .. .. £1800 48·00
184 2½d. ultramarine (*shades*) .. .. 35·00 60·00
185 8d. black and purple (*shades*) .. 60·00 £250
185*a* 17 8d. grey-purple and dull purple .. £375 £450
119s/85s Optd "Specimen" (all perf 14 except 2½d. and 8d. perf 13½) .. .. *Set of* 18 £3250

Plate varieties in T 17 are:—½d., double dot below "D" in right-hand value tablet (R. 3/9) (*from* £500 *un.* £350 *used*); 2d. to £1 excluding 2½d., straight stroke in Queen's right ear known as the "gash in ear" variety (R. 1/2) (*from* 3 *to* 5 *times normal*).

Stamps from the above and the next issue are known compound perf with 14 or 15 on one side only or on adjoining sides but we no longer list them.

Examples of some values are known with a forged registered Bulawayo postmark dated "JA 10 11".

(Recess Waterlow)

1913 (1 Sept)–**22**. *No wmk.* (i) *From single working plates.*

(*a*) *P* 14.
186 18 ½d. blue-green .. .. .. 5·00 1·50
187 ½d. deep green .. .. .. 4·25 1·50
a. Imperf horiz (vert pair) £700
188 ½d. yellow-green .. .. .. 9·00 1·50
188*b* ½d. dull green .. .. .. 7·00 1·50
ba. Imperf vert (horiz pair) £750 £750
189 ½d. bright green .. .. .. 15·00 1·50
a. Imperf between (vert pair) .. £1200
190 1d. rose-carmine .. .. .. 4·50 1·00
a. Imperf between (horiz pair) .. £700 £600
191 1d. carmine-red (*shades*) .. .. 9·00 1·00
a. Imperf between (pair) £1000
192 1d. brown-red .. .. .. 3·50 1·00
193 1d. red .. .. .. 4·50 1·00
a. Imperf between (horiz pair) .. £700
194 1d. scarlet .. .. .. 13·00 1·25
a. Imperf between (horiz pair) .. £850
195 1d. rose-red .. .. .. 7·50 1·00
a. Imperf between (horiz pair) .. £550
b. Imperf between (vert pair) .. £1600
196 1d. rosine .. .. .. £500 19·00
197 1½d. brown-ochre (1919) .. .. 3·00 1·25
a. Imperf between (horiz pair) .. £600 £600
198 1½d. bistre-brown (1917) .. .. 3·00 1·25
a. Imperf between (horiz pair) .. £650 £650
199 1½d. drab-brown (1917) .. .. 3·50 1·25
a. Imperf between (horiz pair) .. £550
b. Imperf between (vert pair) .. £1500
200 2½d. deep blue .. .. .. 4·00 22·00
201 2½d. bright blue .. .. .. 4·00 22·00

(*b*) *P* 15
202 18 ½d. blue-green .. .. .. 8·50 13·00
203 ½d. green .. .. .. 13·00 12·00
204 1d. rose-red .. .. .. £550 22·00
a. Imperf between (horiz pair) .. £11000
205 1d. brown-red .. .. .. 2·50 4·50
206 1½d. bistre-brown (1919) .. .. 24·00 7·00
a. Imperf between (horiz pair) .. £13000
206*b* 1½d. brown-ochre (1917) .. .. 32·00 10·00
207 2½d. deep blue .. .. .. 19·00 38·00
208 2½d. bright blue .. .. .. 16·00 35·00

(*c*) *P* 14 × 15
208*a* 18 ½d. green £4750 £170

(*d*) *P* 15×14
208*b* 18 ½d. green £4750 £300
208*c* 1½d. drab-brown .. .. ..

(*e*) *P* 13½
208*d* 18 1d. red (1914) .. .. .. † £450

Die I

Die II

Die III

The remaining values were printed from double, i.e. head and duty, plates. There are at least four different head plates made from three different dies, which may be distinguished as follows:—

Die I. The King's left ear is neither shaded nor outlined; no outline to top of cap. Shank of anchor in cap badge is complete.

Die II. The ear is shaded all over, but has no outline. The top of the cap has a faint outline. Anchor as Die I.

Die III. The ear is shaded and outlined; a heavy continuous outline round the cap. Shank of anchor is broken just below the lowest line which crosses it.

(ii) *Printed from double plates. Head Die* I (*a*) *P* 14
209 18 2d. black and grey .. .. .. 9·50 6·50
210 3d. black and yellow .. .. .. 70·00 6·50
211 4d. black and orange-red .. .. 6·00 25·00
212 5d. black and green .. .. .. 3·75 9·50
213 6d. black and mauve .. .. .. £190 23·00
213*a* 8d. violet and green £4750
214 2s. black and brown .. .. .. 85·00 75·00

(*b*) *P* 15
215 18 3d. black and yellow .. .. .. 4·50 15·00
216 4d. black and orange-red .. .. £130 15·00
217 6d. black and mauve .. .. .. 4·50 5·00
217*a* 8d. violet and green £16000 £16000
218 2s. black and brown .. .. .. 10·00 28·00

(iii) *Head Die* II. (*a*) *P* 14
219 18 2d. black and grey .. .. .. 13·00 2·25
220 2d. black and brownish grey .. .. 38·00 4·50
221 3d. black and deep yellow .. .. 26·00 4·25
222 3d. black and yellow .. .. .. 60·00 4·25
223 3d. black and buff .. .. .. 7·00 4·25
224 4d. black and orange-red .. .. 17·00 6·00
225 4d. black and deep orange-red .. 9·00 6·00
226 5d. black and grey-green .. .. 13·00 27·00
227 5d. black and bright green .. .. 11·00 27·00
228 6d. black and mauve .. .. .. 25·00 2·50
229 6d. black and purple .. .. .. 70·00 3·50
230 8d. violet and green .. .. .. 9·50 48·00
231 10d. blue and carmine-red .. .. 16·00 38·00
232 1s. black and greenish blue .. .. 45·00 38·00
233 1s. black and turquoise-blue .. .. 8·50 8·50
234 2s. black and brown .. .. .. 70·00 8·00
235 18 2s. black and yellow-brown £275
236 2s. 6d. indigo and grey-brown .. 45·00
236*a* 2s. 6d. pale blue and brown £275
236*b* 3s. brown and blue .. .. .. 75·00
237 3s. chestnut and bright blue .. .. 70·00
238 5s. blue and yellow-green £110
239 5s. blue and blue-green .. .. 45·00
240 7s. 6d. blackish purple and slate-black £225
241 10s. crimson and yellow-green £170
242 £1 black and purple £375
243 £1 black and violet £325

(*b*) *P* 15
244 18 2d. black and grey .. .. .. 5·00
245 4d. black and deep orange-vermilion .. £1100
246 8d. violet and green £170
247 10d. blue and red .. .. .. 5·50
248 1s. black and greenish blue .. .. 42·00
249 2s. 6d. indigo and grey-brown .. 35·00
250 3s. chocolate and blue £600
251 5s. blue and yellow-green £100
251*a* 5s. blue and blue-green £1500
252 7s. 6d. blackish purple and slate-black £110
253 10s. red and green £160
254 £1 black and purple .. .. .. £1200 £
254*a* £1 black and deep purple .. .. £2750 £
186s, 190s, 198s, 208s, 209s, 211s/12s, 215s, 217s/18s, 230s, 232s, 237s/8s, 240s/2s, 247s, 249s Optd "Specimen" .. .. *Set of* 19 £2000

(iv) *Head Die III. Toned paper, yellowish gum.* (*a*) *P* 14
255 18 2d. black and brownish grey .. .. 7·50
256 2d. black and grey-black .. .. 5·50
a. Imperf between (horiz pair) .. £4250
b. Imperf between (horiz strip of 3) .£7500
c. Imperf vert (horiz pair) .. .. £3750 £
257 2d. black and grey .. .. .. 7·00
258 2d. black and sepia .. .. .. 32·00
259 3d. black and yellow .. .. .. 7·50
260 3d. black and ochre .. .. .. 7·50
261 4d. black and orange-red .. .. 11·00
262 4d. black and dull red .. .. 9·00
263 5d. black and pale green .. .. 6·00 2
a. Imperf between (horiz strip of 3) £13000
264 5d. black and green .. .. .. 6·00 2
265 6d. black and reddish mauve .. .. 5·00
a. Imperf between (horiz pair) .. £10000
266 6d. black and dull mauve .. .. 5·00
267 8d. mauve and dull blue-green .. 18·00 5
268 8d. mauve and greenish blue .. .. 17·00 4
a. Imperf vert (horiz pair) £9000
269 10d. indigo and carmine .. .. 13·00 4
270 10d. blue and red .. .. .. 12·00 4
271 1s. black and greenish blue .. .. 8·00
272 1s. black and pale blue-green .. .. 5·50
272*a* 1s. black and light blue .. .. 9·50 1
272*b* 1s. black and green .. .. .. 70·00 2
273 2s. black and brown .. .. .. 12·00 1
aa. Imperf between (vert pair) .. † £21
273*a* 2s. black and yellow-brown .. .. £2000 £
274 2s. 6d. dp ultramarine & grey-brn 29·00 5
274*a* 2s. 6d. pale blue and pale bistre-brown (*shades*) .. .. .. 80·00 5
274*b* 3s. chestnut and light blue .. .. £190 £
275 5s. deep blue and blue-green (*shades*) 65·00 5
276 5s. blue & pale yell-grn (*shades*) 85·00 5
276*a* 7s. 6d. maroon and slate-black .. £750 £1
277 10s. carmine-lake and yellow-green .. £300 £
278 £1 black and bright purple .. .. £400 £
279 £1 black and deep purple .. .. £425 £
279*a* £1 black and violet-indigo .. .. £475 £
279*b* £1 black and deep violet .. .. £500 £

(*b*) *P* 15
279*c* 18 2d. black and brownish grey .. .. £5500 £

Half Penny
(19)

Half- Penny.
(20)

1917 (15 Aug). *No.* 190 *surch at the Northern Rhodesian Adm- istrative Press, Livingstone, with* **T 19**, *in violet or violet-black.*
280 18 ½d. on 1d. rose-carmine (*shades*) .. 2·50 7·
a. Surch inverted £1400 £14
b. Letters "n n" spaced wider .. 11·00 25·
c. Letters "n y" spaced wider .. .. 7·50 20·

The setting was in two rows of 10 repeated three times in t sheet.

The two colours of the surcharge occur on the same sheet.

1917 (22 Sept). *No.* 190 *surch as* **T 20** (*new setting with hyphe and full stop after* "Penny"), *in deep violet.*
281 18 ½d. on 1d. rose-carmine (*shades*) .. 1·75 6·

1922–24. *New printings on white paper with clear white gum.*

(i) *Single working plates.* (*a*) *P* 14
282 18 ½d. dull green (1922) .. .. .. 5·50 4·
a. Imperf between (vert pair) .. £1800 £13
283 ½d. deep blue-green (1922) .. .. 5·50 4·
284 1d. bright rose (1922) .. .. .. 7·00 5·
285 1d. bright rose-scarlet (1923) .. .. 7·00 4·
a. Imperf between (horiz pair) .. £1500
286 1d. aniline red (8.24) .. .. .. 20·00 5·
287 1½d. brown-ochre (1923) .. .. 7·00 5·
a. Imperf between (vert pair) .. £1900 £13

(*b*) *P* 15
288 18 ½d. dull green (1923) .. .. .. 40·00
289 1d. bright rose-scarlet (1923) .. .. 48·00
290 1½d. brown-ochre (1923) .. .. 48·00

(ii) *Double plates. Head Die* III. (*a*) *P* 14
291 18 2d. black and grey-purple (1922) .. 4·50 3·0
292 2d. black and slate-purple (1923) .. 4·50 3·7
293 3d. black and yellow (1922) .. .. 10·00 22·0
294 4d. black & orange-vermilion (1922–3) 9·00 26·0
295 6d. jet-black and lilac (1922–3) .. 4·75 3·7
296 8d. mauve and pale blue-green (1922) 30·00 70·0

18 8d. violet and grey-green (1923) .. 32·00 70·00
10d. bright ultramarine and red (1922) 10·00 50·00
10d. brt ultramarine & carm-red (1923) 14·00 50·00
1s. black and dull blue (1922–3) .. 6·00 8·00
a. Imperf between (horiz pair) .. £8500
b. Imperf between (vert pair) .. £10000
2s. black and brown (1922–3).. .. 19·00 38·00
2s. 6d. ultramarine and sepia (1922) .. 38·00 70·00
2s. 6d. violet-blue & grey-brown (1923) 45·00 65·00
3s. red-brown & turquoise-bl (1922) .. 75·00 90·00
3s. red-brown and grey-blue (1923) .. 95·00 £110
5s. brt ultramarine and emerald (1922) 90·00 £100
5s. deep blue and bright green (1923) 90·00 £100
7s. 6d. brown-purple and slate (1922) £170 £225
10s. crimson and brt yellow-green (1922) £160 £190
10s. carmine and yellow-green (1923) .. £170 £250
£1 black and deep magenta (1922) .. £550 £750
£1 black and magenta (1923).. .. £500 £750

(*b*) *P* 15 (1923)

18 2d. black and slate-purple .. .. 38·00
4d. black and orange-vermilion .. 40·00
6d. jet-black and lilac .. .. .. 50·00
8d. violet and grey-green .. .. 55·00
10d. bright ultramarine & carmine-red 60·00
1s. black and dull blue .. .. 70·00
2s. black and brown .. .. .. 95·00
2s. 6d. violet-blue and grey-brown .. £100
3s. red-brown and grey-blue £130
5s. deep blue and bright green .. £170
£1 black and magenta £750

e 1922 printing shows the mesh of the paper very clearly gh the gum. In the 1923 printing the gum is very smooth he mesh of the paper is not so clearly seen. Where date is 1 as "(1922–23)" two printings were made, which do not r sufficiently in colour to be listed separately.

s. 288/90 and 312/22 were never sent out to Rhodesia, but issued in London. Any used copies could, therefore, only been obtained by favour.

uthern Rhodesia, that part of the Company's territory h of the River Zambesi, became a self-governing colony on 1 ber 1923. British South Africa Company rule continued in hern Rhodesia until the administration was transferred to Colonial Office on 1 April 1924.

e current stamps of Rhodesia, the Admiral series first ed in 1913, continued to be used in Southern Rhodesia until ril 1924 (invalidated 1 May 1924) and in Northern Rhodesia 1 April 1925 (invalidated 30 September 1925).

St. Christopher
see St. Kitts-Nevis

St. Helena

CROWN COLONY

PRICES FOR STAMPS ON COVER TO 1945

Nos. 1/5	*from* × 12
Nos. 6/30	*from* × 10
Nos. 34/45	*from* × 15
Nos. 46/52	*from* × 6
Nos. 53/67	*from* × 5
No. 71	—
Nos. 72/86	*from* × 5
Nos. 87/8	*from* × 12
Nos. 89/95	*from* × 5
No. 96	—
Nos. 97/110	*from* × 5
Nos. 111/13	—
Nos. 114/40	*from* × 4

PERKINS BACON "CANCELLED". For notes on these handstamps, showing "CANCELLED" between horizontal bars forming an oval, see Catalogue Introduction.

1

ONE PENNY
(2)

FOUR PENCE
(3)

(Recess P.B.)

1856 (1 Jan). *Wmk Large Star, W* w **1**. *Imperf.*

1 **1** 6d. bl (H/S "CANCELLED" in oval £5000) £500 £180

1861 (April (?)). *Wmk Large Star, W* w **1**. (*a*) *Clean-cut perf* 14 *to* 16

2 **1** 6d. blue £1700 £275

(*b*) *Rough perf* 14 *to* 16

2*a* **1** 6d. blue £400 £130

NOTE: The issues which follow consist of 6d. stamps, T **1**, printed in various colours and (except in the case of the 6d. values) surcharged with a new value, as T **2** to **10**, *e.g.* stamps described as "1d." are, in fact, 1d. on 6d stamps, and so on.
The numbers in the Type column below refer to the *types of the lettering* of the surcharged value.

(Printed by D.L.R. from P.B. plate)

Two Types of Bar on 1d. value:
A. Bar 16–17 mm long.
B. Bar 18½–19 mm long.

1863 (July). *Wmk Crown CC. Surch as T* **2/3** *with thin bar approximately the same length as the words. Imperf.*

3 **2** 1d. lake (Type A) £110 £160
a. Surch double £4750 £2750
b. Surch omitted £15000
w. Wmk inverted £225
4 1d. lake (Type B) £120 £170
a. Vert pair. Nos. 3/4 .. .. .. £8000
5 **3** 4d. carmine (*bar* 15½–16½ *mm*) .. £500 £250
a. Surch double £12000 £9000

ONE PENNY (4 (A)) ONE PENNY (4 (B)) ONE PENNY (4 (C))

TWO PENCE (5) THREE PENCE (6) FOUR PENCE (7)

ONE SHILLING (8) FIVE SHILLINGS (9)

Three Types of Bar:
A. Thin bar (16½ to 17 mm) nearly the same length as the words.
B. Thick bar (14 to 14½ mm) much shorter than the words, except on the 2d. (Nos. 9, 22, 28) where it is nearly the same length.
C. Long bar (17 to 18 mm) same length as the words.

1864–80. *Wmk Crown CC. 6d. as T* **1**, *without surcharge.*

(*a*) *P* 12½ (1864–73)

6 **4** 1d. lake (Type A) (1864) .. .. 40·00 24·00
a. Surch double £6500
7 1d. lake (Type B) (1868) .. .. £140 50·00
a. Surch double .. .. ..
b. Imperf £2250
w. Wmk inverted .. .. .. — £100
8 **4** 1d. lake (Type C) (1871) .. .. 80·00 17·00
a. Surch in blue-black £1000 £550
x. Wmk reversed £120
y. Wmk inverted and reversed .. £170
9 **5** 2d. yellow (Type B) (1868) .. .. £160 60·00
a. Imperf £9500
x. Wmk reversed £200
10 2d. yellow (Type C) (1873) .. .. 80·00 38·00
a. Surch in blue-black £4000 £2250
b. Surch double, one albino .. ..
x. Wmk reversed £110
11 **6** 3d. deep dull purple (Type B) (1868) .. 75·00 50·00
a. Surch double .. .. .. — £6000
b. Imperf £800
c. *Light purple* £2750 £750
x. Wmk reversed £120
12 3d. deep dull purple (Type A) (1873) .. 85·00 50·00
13 **7** 4d. carmine (Type A) (*words* 17 *mm long*) (1864) .. .. .. £130 48·00
a. Surch double .. .. .. † £5500
14 4d. carmine (Type B) (*words* 18 *mm long*) (1868) .. .. .. 90·00 48·00
a. Surch double .. .. .. † £4500
b. Surch double (18 + 19 *mm widths*) £18000 £9000
c. Imperf £9500
x. Wmk reversed £130
15 4d. carmine-rose (Type B) (*words* 19 *mm long*) (1868) £200 £120
a. Surch omitted .. .. .. † —
16 – 6d. dull blue (1871) £650 £100
a. Ultramarine (1873) .. .. £375 80·00
17 **8** 1s. deep yellow-green (Type A) (1864) £250 26·00
a. Surch double .. .. .. † £18000
w. Wmk inverted .. .. .. — 45·00
18 1s. deep yellow-green (Type B) (1868) £550 £130
a. Surch double £13000
b. Imperf £13000
c. Surch omitted* £13000
19 1s. deep green (Type C) (1871) .. £400 16·00
a. Surch in blue-black .. ..
x. Wmk reversed .. .. .. — 50·00
20 **9** 5s. orange (Type B) (1868) .. .. 42·00 60·00
a. Yellow £450 £375
x. Wmk reversed £120

(*b*) *P* 14×12½ (1876)

21 **4** 1d. lake (Type B) .. .. .. 65·00 15·00
w. Wmk inverted £100
22 **5** 2d. yellow (Type B) .. .. .. 85·00 50·00
23 3d. purple (Type B) .. .. .. £190 70·00
24 4d. carmine (Type B) (*words* 16½ *mm long*) .. .. £100 60·00
y. Wmk inverted and reversed .. £100 60·00
25 – 6d. milky blue .. .. £350 45·00
26 **8** 1s. deep green (Type C) .. .. £500 20·00

(*c*) *P* 14 (1880)

27 **4** 1d. lake (Type B) .. .. .. 80·00 16·00
28 **5** 2d. yellow (Type B) .. .. .. 95·00 26·00
29 – 6d. milky blue .. .. £375 48·00
30 **8** 1s. yellow-green (Type B) .. .. 20·00 12·00
y. Wmk inverted and reversed .. — 65·00

Two used examples of No. 15a are known, one being in the Royal Collection and the other damaged at bottom right.

*No. 18c is from a sheet of the 1s. with surcharge misplaced, the fifth row of 12 stamps being thus doubly surcharged and the tenth row without surcharge.

$2\frac{1}{2}$d
(10)

11

12

1884–94. *Wmk Crown CA. T* **1** *surch. Bars similar to Type* B *above (except* 2½*d., T* **10**, *and the* 1*s., in which the bar is nearly the same length as the words). The* 6*d. as before without surcharge. P* 14.

34 – ½d. emerald (*words* 17 *mm*) (1884) .. 9·00 12·00
a. "N" and "Y" spaced £800
b. Surch double £1200 £1300
ba. Ditto. "N" and "Y" spaced .. £11000
35 – ½d. green (*words* 17 *mm*) (1885) .. 5·50 12·00
a. "N" and "Y" spaced £350 £500
x. Wmk reversed .. .. .. 6·50 13·00
36 – ½d. green (*words* 14½ *mm*) (1893) .. 1·25 1·50
a. "N" and "Y" spaced £1500
37 **4** 1d. red (1887) .. .. .. 2·75 2·50
x. Wmk reversed .. .. .. 3·25 3·00
38 1d. pale red (1890) .. .. .. 3·50 2·00
x. Wmk reversed .. .. .. 4·50 2·75
39 **5** 2d. yellow (1894) .. .. .. 1·50 4·00
40 **10** 2½d. ultramarine (1893) .. .. 2·00 5·00
a. Surch double £15000
b. Stamp doubly printed £7500
w. Wmk inverted .. .. .. 17·00
41 **6** 3d. deep mauve (1887) .. .. 5·50 8·50
a. Surch double .. .. .. — £9000
42 3d. deep reddish lilac (1887) .. 3·25 3·75
a. Surch double £8500 £6000
w. Wmk reversed .. .. .. 4·25 3·25
43 **7** 4d. pale brn (*words* 16½ *mm*) (1890) 16·00 20·00
a. Additional thin bar in surch (R. 7/4) £550
by. Wmk inverted and reversed .. 23·00
43*c* 4d. sepia (*words* 17 *mm*) (1894) .. 18·00 12·00
cx. Wmk reversed .. .. .. 22·00
44 – 6d. grey (1887) .. .. .. 14·00 4·00
x. Wmk reversed .. .. .. 20·00 3·50
45 **8** 1s. yellow-green (1894) .. .. 40·00 21·00
a. Surch double £4250
40s/1s, 43bys, 44s Optd "Specimen" .. *Set of* 4 £180

Examples of the above are sometimes found showing no watermark; these are from the bottom row of the sheet, which had escaped the watermark, the paper being intended for stamps of a different size to Type **1**.

Some are found without bar and others with bar at top of stamp, due to careless overprinting.

Nos. 34a and 35a occur on R. 18/12 and show a minimum space between the letters of 0.8 mm. Normal examples are spaced 0.5 mm, but some stamps show intermediate measurements due to loose type. On No. 34ba only one impression of the surcharge shows "N" and "Y" spaced. On the reset surcharge, No. 36, a similar variety occurs on R. 5/9.

Of the 2½d. with double surcharge only six copies exist, and of the 2½d. double printed, one row of 12 stamps existed on one sheet only.

CANCELLATIONS. Nos. 40/5 and No. 20 were sold as remainders in 1904 cancelled with a violet diamond-shaped grill with four interior bars extending over two stamps. These cannot be considered as *used* stamps, and they are consequently not priced in the list.

This violet obliteration is easily removed and many of these remainders have been cleaned and offered as unused; some are repostmarked with a date and name in thin type rather larger than the original, a usual date being "Ap.4.01."

(Typo D.L.R.)

1890–97. *Wmk Crown CA. Plate I for the 1½d. Plate II for the other values (for differences see Seychelles). P 14.*

46 **11** ½d. green (1897) .. .. .. 2·75 4·50
47 1d. carmine (1896) .. .. .. 13·00 1·00
48 1½d. red-brown and green (1890) .. 4·50 7·00
49 2d. orange-yellow (1896) .. .. 5·00 12·00
50 2½d. ultramarine (1896) .. .. 9·50 12·00
51 5d. mauve (1896) .. .. .. 11·00 27·00
52 10d. brown (1896) .. .. .. 22·00 55·00
46/52 .. .. *Set of* 7 60·00 £110
46s/52s Optd "Specimen" .. *Set of* 7 £275

The note below No. 45a *re* violet diamond-shaped grill cancellation also applies to Nos. 48/52.

1902. *Wmk Crown CA. P 14.*

53 **12** ½d. green (Mar) .. .. .. 1·50 2·00
54 1d. carmine (24 Feb) .. .. .. 4·75 70
53s/4s Optd "Specimen" .. .. *Set of* 2 70·00

13 Government House

14 The Wharf

(Typo D.L.R.)

1903 (May). *Wmk Crown CC. P 14.*

55 **13** ½d. brown and grey-green .. .. 2·00 3·25
w. Wmk inverted .. .. 95·00 £120
56 **14** 1d. black and carmine .. .. 1·50 35
57 **13** 2d. black and sage-green .. .. 6·00 1·25
58 **14** 8d. black and brown .. .. 22·00 32·00
59 **13** 1s. brown and brown-orange .. 22·00 40·00
60 **14** 2s. black and violet .. .. 48·00 85·00
55/60 .. .. *Set of* 6 90·00 £150
55s/60s Optd "Specimen" .. *Set of* 6 £200

A printing of the 1d. value in Type **14** in red only on Mult Crown CA paper was made in 1911, but not sold to the public. Examples are known overprinted "SPECIMEN" (*Price* £300).

15

(Typo D.L.R.)

1908 (May)–**11.** *P 14. (a) Wmk Mult Crown CA. Ordinary paper (2½d.) or chalk-surfaced paper (4d., 6d.).*

64 **15** 2½d. blue .. .. .. 1·50 1·50
66 4d. black and red/*yellow* .. .. 5·50 17·00
a. Ordinary paper (1911) .. .. 3·00 15·00
67 6d. dull and deep purple .. .. 9·00 24·00
a. Ordinary paper (1911) .. .. 3·25 14·00

(b) Wmk Crown CA. Chalk-surfaced paper.

71 **15** 10s. green and red/*green* £180 £250
64/71 .. .. *Set of* 4 £180 £250
64s/71s Optd "Specimen" .. *Set of* 4 £225

Examples of Nos. 58/60 and 66/71 are known showing a forged St. Helena postmark dated "JY 28 1".

16

17

(Typo D.L.R.)

1912–16. *Wmk Mult Crown CA. P 14.*

72 **16** ½d. black and green .. .. 2·25 10·00
73 **17** 1d. black and carmine-red .. .. 3·75 1·75
a. Black and scarlet (1916) .. .. 12·00 20·00
74 1½d. black and dull orange (1913) .. 3·50 5·50
75 **16** 2d. black and greyish slate .. .. 4·00 1·75
76 **17** 2½d. black and bright blue .. .. 3·50 5·50
77 **16** 3d. black and purple/*yellow* (1913) .. 3·50 5·00
78 **17** 8d. black and dull purple .. .. 7·00 50·00
79 **16** 1s. black/*green* .. .. .. 9·00 35·00
80 **17** 2s. black and blue/*blue* .. .. 40·00 80·00
81 3s. black and violet (1913) .. .. 50·00 £130
72/81 .. .. *Set of* 10 £110 £275
72s/81s Optd "Specimen" .. *Set of* 10 £250

No. 73*a* is on thicker paper than 73.

18

19

Split "A" (R. 8/3 of left pane) (ptgs to 1918)

(Typo D.L.R.)

1912. *Wmk Mult Crown CA. Chalk-surfaced paper. P 14.*

83 **18** 4d. black and red/*yellow* .. .. 11·00 23·00
84 6d. dull and deep purple .. .. 4·00 5·00
83s/4s Optd "Specimen" .. .. *Set of* 2 75·00

1913. *Wmk Mult Crown CA. P 14.*

85 **19** 4d. black and red/*yellow* .. .. 8·00 2·75
a. Split "A" £190
86 6d. dull and deep purple .. .. 14·00 25·00
a. Split "A" £350
85s/6s Optd "Specimen" .. *Set of* 2 80·00

WAR TAX

ONE PENNY

(20)

WAR TAX

1d.

(21)

1916 (Sept). *As No. 73a, on thin paper, surch with T* **20**.

87 **17** 1d. + 1d. black and scarlet .. .. 1·75 3·00
a. Surch double .. .. .. † £6000
s. Optd "Specimen" .. .. 50·00

1919. *No. 73 on thicker paper, surch with T* **21**.

88 **17** 1d. + 1d. black and carmine-red (*shades*) 1·50 4·25
s. Optd "Specimen" .. .. .. 50·00

1922 (Jan). *Printed in one colour. Wmk Mult Script CA. P 14.*

89 **17** 1d. green .. .. .. 1·75 26·00
w. Wmk inverted £130
y. Wmk inverted and reversed .. £130
90 1½d. rose-scarlet .. .. .. 10·00 26·00
91 **16** 3d. bright blue .. .. .. 18·00 55·00
y. Wmk inverted and reversed .. £140
89/91 .. .. *Set of* 3 27·00 95·00
89s/91s Optd "Specimen" .. *Set of* 3 85·00

22 Badge of St. Helena

PLATE FLAWS ON THE 1922–37 ISSUE. Many constant plate varieties exist on both the vignette and duty plates of this issue. The three major varieties are illustrated and listed below.

a. Broken mainmast. Occurs on R.2/1 of all sheets from the second printing onwards. It does not appear on Nos. 93/6 and 112/13 as these stamps only exist from the initial printing invoiced in May 1922.

b. Torn flag. Occurs on R.4/6 of all sheets from printings up to and including that invoiced in December 1922. The flaw was retouched for the printing invoiced in December 1926 and so does not occur on Nos. 99*e*, 103 and 107/10.

c. Cleft rock. Occurs on R.5/1 of all sheets from the second pri onwards. It does not appear on Nos. 93/6 and 112/13 as stamps only exist from the initial printing invoiced in May

(Des T. Bruce. Typo D.L.R.)

1922 (June)–**37.** *P 14 (a) Wmk Mult Crown CA. C surfaced paper.*

92 **22** 4d. grey and black/*yellow* (2.23) .. 11·00
a. Broken mainmast £130
b. Torn flag £130
c. Cleft rock £110
93 1s. 6d. grey and green/*blue-green* .. 22·00
b. Torn flag £350
94 2s. 6d. grey and red/*yellow* .. .. 25·00
b. Torn flag £400
95 5s. grey and green/*yellow* .. .. 38·00
b. Torn flag £500
96 £1 grey and purple/*red* £350
b. Torn flag £1800
92/6 .. .. *Set of* 5 £400
92s/6s Optd "Specimen" .. .. *Set of* 5 £500

The paper of No. 93 is bluish on the surface with a full g back.

(b) Wmk Mult Script CA. Ordinary paper (1s. 6d., 2s. 6d., or chalk-surfaced paper (others)

97 **22** ½d. grey and black (2.23) .. .. 1·75
a. Broken mainmast .. .. 42·00
b. Torn flag £130
c. Cleft rock .. .. .. 38·00
w. Wmk inverted £250
98 1d. grey and green .. .. 2·25
a. Broken mainmast .. .. 48·00
b. Torn flag £110
c. Cleft rock .. .. .. 42·00
99 1½d. rose-red (*shades*) (2.23) .. .. 2·75
a. Broken mainmast .. .. 75·00
b. Torn flag .. .. .. 75·00
c. Cleft rock .. .. .. 70·00
dw. Wmk inverted £650
e. Deep carmine-red (1937) .. .. 80·00
ea. Broken mainmast £650
ec. Cleft rock £650
100 2d. grey and slate (2.23) .. .. 3·50
a. Broken mainmast .. .. 85·00
b. Torn flag £150
c. Cleft rock .. .. .. 80·00
101 3d. bright blue (2.23) .. .. 2·00
a. Broken mainmast .. .. 80·00
b. Torn flag .. .. .. 85·00
c. Cleft rock .. .. .. 65·00
x. Wmk reversed £325
103 5d. green and carmine/*green* (1927) .. 3·00
a. Broken mainmast £130
c. Cleft rock £120
104 6d. grey and bright purple .. .. 4·50
a. Broken mainmast £160
b. Torn flag £180
c. Cleft rock £140
105 8d. grey and bright violet (2.23) .. 3·50
a. Broken mainmast £140
b. Torn flag £140
c. Cleft rock £120
106 1s. grey and brown .. .. 6·50
a. Broken mainmast £180
b. Torn flag £225
c. Cleft rock £160
107 1s. 6d. grey and green/*green* (1927) .. 15·00 45
a. Broken mainmast £225
c. Cleft rock £200
108 2s. purple and blue/*blue* (1927) .. 17·00 40·
a. Broken mainmast £225
c. Cleft rock £200
109 2s. 6d. grey and red/*yellow* (1927) .. 14·00 55·
a. Broken mainmast £225
c. Cleft rock £200
110 5s. grey and green/*yellow* (1927) .. 38·00 75·
a. Broken mainmast £375
c. Cleft rock £350
111 7s. 6d. grey and yellow-orange .. 75·00
a. Broken mainmast £3000
b. Torn flag £650
c. Cleft rock £3000
112 10s. grey and olive-green £110
b. Torn flag £1000
113 15s. grey and purple/*blue* £800
b. Torn flag £3250
97/112 .. .. *Set of* 15 £250
97s/113s Optd "Specimen" .. *Set of* 16 £1000

Examples of all values are known showing a forged St. Hele postmark dated "DE 18 27".

23 Lot and Lot's Wife

24 The "Plantation"

30 St. Helena

32 Badge of St. Helena

(Recess B.W.)

23 April). *Centenary of British Colonisation. T* **23/4, 30, 32**
similar horiz designs. Wmk Mult Script CA. P 12.

½d. black and purple .. .. 1·00 80
1d. black and green 65 85
1½d. black and scarlet .. .. 2·50 3·25
2d. black and orange .. .. 2·25 1·25
3d. black and blue .. .. 1·40 4·50
6d. black and light blue .. .. 3·25 3·00
1s. black and chocolate .. .. 6·50 18·00
2s. 6d. black and lake .. .. 35·00 48·00
5s. black and chocolate .. .. 75·00 85·00
10s. black and purple £200 £250
3 .. .. .. *Set of* 10 £300 £375
23s Perf "Specimen" .. *Set of* 10 £350

sign:—1½d. Map of St. Helena; 2d. Quay at Jamestown; 3d. s Valley; 6d. Jamestown; 1s. Munden's Promontory; 5s. High .

amples of all values are known showing a forged St. Helena nark dated "MY 12 34".

(6 May). *Silver Jubilee. As Nos.* 91/4 *of Antigua.* 3½×14.

1½d. deep blue and carmine .. .. 75 5·50
f. Diagonal line by turret .. .. 65·00
2d. ultramarine and grey .. .. 1·25 90
f. Diagonal line by turret .. .. 85·00
g. Dot to left of chapel £110
6d. green and indigo .. .. .. 6·50 3·25
a. Frame printed double, one albino .. £1500
f. Diagonal line by turret £150
h. Dot by flagstaff £225
1s. slate and purple .. .. .. 10·00 13·00
h. Dot by flagstaff £300
i. Dash by turret £300
7 .. .. .. *Set of* 4 17·00 20·00
7s Perf "Specimen" .. .. *Set of* 4 £100

r illustrations of plate varieties see Omnibus section wing Zanzibar.

7 (19 May). *Coronation. As Nos.* 95/7 *of Antigua, but ptd by L.R. P* 14.

1d. green 40 30
2d. orange 55 30
3d. bright blue 80 30
30 .. .. *Set of* 3 1·60 80
s/30s Perf "Specimen" .. *Set of* 3 60·00

33 Badge of St. Helena

(Recess Waterlow)

8 (12 May)–**44.** *Wmk Mult Script CA. P* 12½.

33 ½d. violet 10 50
1d. green .. .. 9·00 2·25
a 1d. yellow-orange (8.7.40) 20 30
1½d. scarlet 20 40
2d. red-orange 20 15
3d. ultramarine .. .. 80·00 18·00
a 3d. grey (8.7.40) 30 30
b 4d. ultramarine (8.7.40) .. .. .. 2·00 65
6d. light blue .. .. 2·00 60
a 8d. sage-green (8.7.40) .. .. .. 3·25 90
b. Olive-green (24.5.44) .. .. .. 4·50 4·00
1s. sepia .. .. 1·00 30
2s. 6d. maroon .. .. 17·00 6·50
5s. chocolate .. .. 18·00 12·00
10s. purple .. .. 18·00 18·00
/40 .. .. *Set of* 14 £130 50·00
s/40s Perf "Specimen" .. *Set of* 14 £300

See also Nos. 149/51.

46 (21 Oct). *Victory. As Nos.* 110/11 *of Antigua.*

1 2d. red-orange 15 10
2 4d. blue 15 10
1s/2s Perf "Specimen" .. .. *Set of* 2 60·00

48 (20 Oct). *Royal Silver Wedding. As Nos.* 112/13 *of Antigua.*

3 3d. black 30 20
4 10s. violet-blue .. .. 23·00 28·00

49 (10 Oct). *75th Anniv of U.P.U. As Nos.* 114/17 *of Antigua.*

5 3d. carmine 25 30
6 4d. deep blue .. .. 3·00 90
7 6d. olive 45 90
8 1s. blue-black .. .. 35 1·10
5/8 .. .. *Set of* 4 3·50 3·00

49 (1 Nov). *Wmk Mult Script CA. P* 12½.

9 33 1d. black and green 70 90
0 1½d. black and carmine 70 90
1 2d. black and scarlet .. .. .. 70 1·25
9/51 .. .. *Set of* 3 1·90 2·75

St. Kitts-Nevis

ST. CHRISTOPHER

From 1760 the postal service for St. Christopher was organised by the Deputy Postmaster General on Antigua. It was not until May 1779 that the first postmaster was appointed to the island and the use of postmarks on outgoing mail commenced.

Stamps of Great Britain were used between May 1858 and the end of March 1860 when control of the postal services passed to the local authorities. In the years which followed, prior to the introduction of St. Christopher stamps in April 1870, a circular "PAID" handstamp was used on overseas mail.

BASSETERRE

Stamps of GREAT BRITAIN *cancelled "A 12" as Type* Z 1 *of Jamaica.*

1858 *to* **1860.**

Z1 1d. rose-red (1857), *perf* 14 .. .. £600
Z2 2d. blue (1858) (Plate No. 7) £900
Z3 4d. rose (1857) £325
Z4 6d. lilac (1856) £190
Z5 1s. green (1856) £1300

PRICES FOR STAMPS ON COVER

Nos. 1/9	*from* × 25
Nos. 11/21	*from* × 30
Nos. 22/6	*from* × 25
No. 27	—
No. 28	*from* × 30
Nos. R1/6	—

1

Distorted "E" (R. 2/1)

1870 (1 Apr)–**79.** *Wmk Crown CC.* (*a*) *P* 12½.

1 1 1d. dull rose .. .. 75·00 45·00
a. Wmk sideways £225 £160
w. Wmk inverted .. ..
2 1d. magenta (*shades*) (1871) .. .. 60·00 28·00
a. Wmk sideways .. .. † £450
w. Wmk inverted .. .. 90·00 60·00
x. Wmk reversed .. ..
4 6d. yellow-green .. .. £110 19·00
w. Wmk inverted .. ..
5 6d. green (1871) .. .. £100 7·50

(*b*) *P* 14

6 1 1d. magenta (*shades*) (1875) .. .. 65·00 7·00
a. Bisected diag or vert (½d.) (on cover) (3.82) .. .. † £1500
w. Wmk inverted .. ..
7 2½d. red-brown (11.79) £180 £250
8 4d. blue (11.79) .. .. £160 15·00
a. Wmk sideways £700 £120
w. Wmk inverted .. .. £300 42·00
9 6d. green (1876) .. .. 55·00 5·00
a. Imperf between (pair) .. .. ..
b. Wmk sideways £450 £100
x. Wmk reversed £150

The magenta used for the 1d. was a fugitive colour which reacts to both light and water.

No. 6a was authorised for use between March and June 1882 to make up the 2½d. letter rate and for ½d. book post.

1882 (June)–**90.** *Wmk Crown CA. P* 14.

11 1 ½d. dull green .. .. 1·25 1·50
a. Wmk sideways £250
x. Wmk reversed .. ..
12 1d. dull magenta .. .. £500 70·00
a. Bisected diagonally (½d.) (on cover)
13 1d. carmine-rose (2.84) .. .. .. 1·00 2·25
a. Bisected (½d.) (on cover) .. ..
b. Distorted "E" .. .. 15·00
x. Wmk reversed .. ..
14 2½d. pale red-brown .. .. .. £180 60·00
15 2½d. deep red-brown .. .. .. £190 65·00
16 2½d. ultramarine (2.84) .. .. .. 1·50 1·50
17 4d. blue .. .. £400 20·00
w. Wmk inverted .. ..
18 4d. grey (10.84) .. .. 1·25 1·00
19 6d. olive-brown (3.90) .. .. .. 80·00 £300
w. Wmk inverted .. ..
20 1s. mauve (6.86) .. .. 90·00 65·00
w. Wmk inverted .. .. — £130
21 1s. bright mauve (1890) .. .. .. 80·00 £150
19s/20s Optd "Specimen" .. .. *Set of* 2 £120

FOUR PENCE

(2)

Halfpenny

(3)

1884 (Dec). *No.* 9 *surch with T* **2** *by* The Advertiser Press.

22 1 4d. on 6d. green .. .. 65·00 50·00
a. Full stop after "PENCE" .. .. .. 65·00 50·00
b. Surch double .. .. — £2000

No. 22a occurred on alternate stamps.

1885 (Mar). *No.* 13 *bisected and each half diagonally surch with T* **3**.

23 1 ½d. on half of 1d. carmine-rose .. .. 24·00 40·00
a. Unsevered pair £110 £120
ab. Ditto, one surch inverted £400 £275
b. Surch inverted £225 £110
ba. Ditto, unsevered pair £1000
c. Surch double .. ..

ONE PENNY.

(4)

4d.

(5)

1886 (June). *No.* 9 *surch with T* **4** *or* **5** *each showing a manuscript line through the original value.*

24 1 1d. on 6d. green .. .. 18·00 29·00
a. Surch inverted £6000
b. Surch double .. .. — £1300
25 4d. on 6d. green.. .. .. .. 48·00 90·00
a. No stop after "d" £180 £250
b. Surch double £1600 £1700

No. 24b is only known penmarked with dates between 21 July and 3 August 1886, or with violet handstamp.

1887 (May). *No.* 11 *surch with T* **4** *showing a manuscript line through the original value.*

26 1 1d. on ½d. dull green .. .. .. 30·00 42·00

ONE PENNY.

(7)

1888 (May). *No.* 16 *surch.*

(*a*) *With T* **4**. *Original value unobliterated*

27 1 1d. on 2½d. ultramarine £13000 £8500

(*b*) *With T* **7** *showing a manuscript line through the original value*

28 1 1d. on 2½d. ultramarine .. .. .. 55·00 55·00
a. Surch inverted £8500 £5500

The 1d. of Antigua was used provisionally in St. Christopher between February and March 1890 during a shortage of 1d. stamps. Such use can be distinguished by the postmark, which is "A 12" in place of "A02" (*price from* £120 *used*).

REVENUE STAMPS USED FOR POSTAGE

Saint Christopher

(R 1)

SAINT KITTS NEVIS REVENUE

(R 2)

1883. *Nos.* F6 *and* F8 *of Nevis optd with Type* R **1**, *in violet. Wmk Crown CA. P* 14.

R1 1d. lilac-mauve £250
R2 6d. green .. .. 70·00 £120

1885. *Optd with Type* R **2**. *Wmk Crown CA. P* 14.

R3 1 1d. rose .. .. 2·25 12·00
R4 3d. mauve .. .. 14·00 65·00
R5 6d. orange-brown .. .. 8·00 50·00
R6 1s. olive .. .. 2·25 40·00

Other fiscal stamps with overprints as above also exist, but none of these was ever available for postal purposes.

The stamps for St. Christopher was superseded by the general issue for Leeward Islands on 31 October 1890.

Stamps for St. Kitts, issued from 1980 onwards will be found listed after those for the combined colony.

NEVIS

Little is known concerning the early postal affairs of Nevis, although several covers exist from the island in the 1660s. It is recorded that the British G.P.O. was to establish a branch office on the island under an Act of Parliament of 1710, although arrangements may not have been finalised for a number of years afterwards. Nevis appears as "a new office" in the P.O. Accounts of 1787.

Stamps of Great Britain were used on the island from May 1858 until the colonial authorities assumed control of the postal service on 1 May 1860. Between this date and the introduction of Nevis stamps in 1861 No. CC1 was again used on overseas mail.

CHARLESTOWN

CROWNED-CIRCLE HANDSTAMPS

CC 1

CC1 CC 1 NEVIS (R.) (9.1852) .. *Price on cover* £3250

No. CC1, struck in black or red (1882) was later used on several occasions up to 1882 when there were shortages of adhesive stamps.

Stamps of GREAT BRITAIN *cancelled* "A 09" *as Type* Z **1** *of Jamaica.*

1858 *to* **1860.**

Z1 1d. rose-red (1857), *perf* 14 .. .. £425
Z2 2d. blue (1858) (Plate Nos. 7, 8) £1600
Z3 4d. rose (1857) £325
Z4 6d. lilac (1856) £275
Z5 1s. green (1856) .. ..

PRICES FOR STAMPS ON COVER

Nos. 5/22	*from* × 20
Nos. 23/4	*from* × 10
Nos. 25/34	*from* × 20
Nos. 35/6	*from* × 10
Nos. F1/8	*from* × 30

1

2

3

4

The designs on the stamps refer to a medicinal spring on the island

(Recess Nissen & Parker, London)

1861. *Greyish paper. P* 13.

5 **1** 1d. dull lake .. .. 65·00 42·00
a. On blued paper £200 £100
6 **2** 4d. rose .. .. 90·00 55·00
a. On blued paper £650 £150
7 **3** 6d. grey-lilac .. .. 90·00 45·00
a. On blued paper £500 £190
8 **4** 1s. green .. .. £200 60·00
a. On blued paper £750 £170

Nos. 5/8 and later printings of Types **1/4** were in sheets of 12 (3×4).

1866–76. *White paper. P* 15.

9 **1** 1d. pale red .. .. 38·00 38·00
10 1d. deep red .. .. 38·00 38·00
11 **2** 4d. orange .. .. 95·00 19·00
12 4d. deep orange .. .. 95·00 19·00
13 **4** 1s. blue-green .. .. £200 27·00
14 1s. yellow-green (1876) £850 £110
a. Vertically laid paper £12000 £3750
b. No. 9 on sheet with crossed lines on hill £3500 £500
c. Ditto. On laid paper .. .. .. † £8500

Examples of the 4d. exist showing part of a papermakers watermark reading "A. COWAN & SONS EXTRA SUPERFINE".

(Lithographed by transfer from the engraved plates Nissen and Parker, London)

1876–78. (*a*) *P* 15.

15 **1** 1d. pale rose-red .. .. 18·00 13·00
a. Imperf (pair) £550
16 1d. deep rose-red .. .. 28·00 23·00
17 1d. vermilion-red .. .. 24·00 23·00
a. Bisected (½d.) (on cover) .. .. † £1800
18 **2** 4d. orange-yellow (1878) .. .. .. £160 28·00
a. Imperf between (vert pair) £3500
19 **3** 6d. grey (1878) £200 £180
20 **4** 1s. pale green (1878) .. .. .. 80·00 95·00
a. Imperf
b. Imperf between (horiz strip of three) £4500
c. No. 9 on sheet with crossed lines on hill £225
21 1s. deep green .. .. 85·00 £120
c. No. 9 on sheet with crossed lines on hill

(*b*) *P* 11½

22 **1** 1d. vermilion-red (1878) .. .. .. 42·00 50·00
a. Bisected (½d.) (on cover) .. .. † £1800
b. Imperf (pair) £350
c. Imperf between (horiz pair) .. ..

No. 21c occurs on a small part of the deep green printing only.

RETOUCHES. 1d. Lithograph.

i. No. 1 on sheet. Top of hill over kneeling figure redrawn by five thick lines and eight small slanting lines £140 £150
ii. No. 1 on sheet. Another retouch. Three series of short vertical strokes behind the kneeling figure £140 £150
iii. No. 3 on sheet. Right upper corner star and border below star retouched £140 £150
iv. No. 9 on sheet. Retouch in same position as on No. 3 but differing in detail £160 £170
v. No. 12 on sheet. Dress of standing figure retouched by a number of horizontal and vertical lines £140 £150

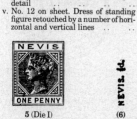

5 (Die I)

NEVIS. ½d.
(6)

(Typo D.L.R.)

1879–80. *Wmk Crown CC. P* 14.

23 **5** 1d. lilac-mauve (1880) .. .. .. 60·00 29·00
a. Bisected (½d.) (on cover) .. .. † £950
w. Wmk inverted .. .. ..
24 2½d. red-brown .. .. £100 85·00

1882–90. *Wmk Crown CA. P* 14.

25 **5** ½d. dull green (11.83) .. .. .. 3·75 11·00
a. Top left triangle detached £110
26 1d. lilac-mauve .. .. 85·00 26·00
a. Bisected (½d.) on cover (1883) .. † £700
27 1d. dull rose (11.83) .. .. .. 22·00 14·00
a. Carmine (1884) .. .. .. 7·00 7·00
ab. Top left triangle detached £180
28 2½d. red-brown .. .. £100 45·00
29 2½d. ultramarine (11.83) .. .. .. 15·00 13·00
a. Top left triangle detached £350
30 4d. blue .. .. £275 45·00
31 4d. grey (1884) .. .. 7·50 3·00
a. Top left triangle detached £275 £275
32 6d. green (11.83) £350 £350
33 6d. chestnut (10.88) .. .. .. 19·00 50·00
a. Top left triangle detached £375
34 1s. pale violet (3.90) .. .. .. 95·00 £170
a. Top left triangle detached £850
33s/4s Optd "Specimen" .. .. *Set of* 2 £110

For illustration of the "top left triangle detached" variety, which occurs on Plate 2 R. 3/3 of the right pane, see below Montserrat No. 5.

1883 (4 Sept). *No.* 26 *bisected vertically and surch with T* **6**, *reading upwards or downwards.*

35 ½d. on half 1d. lilac-mauve (V.) .. .. £800 40·00
a. Surch double .. .. — £300
b. Surch on half "REVENUE" stamp No. F6 .. .. — £550
36 ½d. on half 1d. lilac-mauve .. .. £950 38·00
a. Surch double .. .. — £300
b. Unsevered pair £3000 £475
c. Surch on half "REVENUE" stamp No. F6 .. .. — £550

FISCALS USED FOR POSTAGE

Revenue (F 1)

REVENUE (F 2)

1882. (*a*) *Stamps of* 1876–78 *optd with Type* F **1**.

F1 **1** 1d. bright red .. .. 50·00
F2 **2** 1d. rose .. .. 50·00 19·00
F3 4d. orange .. .. 85·00
F4 **3** 6d. grey £140
F5 **4** 1s. green £160
a. No. 9 on sheet with crossed lines on hill

(*b*) *Nos.* 26, 30 *and* 32 *optd with Type* F **2**

F6 **5** 1d. lilac-mauve .. .. 50·00 50·00
a. Bisected (½d.) (on cover) .. ..
F7 4d. blue .. .. 27·00 55·00
F8 6d. green .. .. 18·00 60·00

Nos. F1/5 were produced from fresh transfers. Similar "REVENUE" handstamps, both with and without stop, were also applied to postage issues.

The stamps of Nevis were superseded by the general issue for Leeward Islands on 31 October 1890.

ST. KITTS-NEVIS

CROWN COLONY

Stamps for the combined colony were introduced in 1903, and were used concurrently with the general issues of Leeward Islands until the latter were withdrawn on 1 July 1956.

PRICES FOR STAMPS ON COVER TO 1945

Nos. 1/9	*from* × 3
No. 10	—
Nos. 11/20	*from* × 3
No. 21	—
Nos. 22/3	*from* × 15
Nos. 24/34	*from* × 3
Nos. 35/6	—
Nos. 37/47	*from* × 2
Nos. 47*a*/*b*	—
Nos. 48/57	*from* × 2
Nos. 58/60	—
Nos. 61/4	*from* × 2
Nos. 65/7	*from* × 5
Nos. 68/77	*from* × 2

1 Christopher Columbus

2 Medicinal Spring

(Typo D.L.R.)

1903. *Wmk Crown CA. P* 14.

1 **1** ½d. dull purple and deep green .. .. 1·75 70
2 **2** 1d. grey-black and carmine .. .. 4·75 20
3 **1** 2d. dull purple and brown .. .. 2·25 11·00
4 2½d. grey-black and blue .. .. 17·00 4·25
5 **2** 3d. deep green and orange .. .. 11·00 26·00
6 **1** 6d. grey-black and bright purple .. 4·25 35·00
7 1s. grey-green and orange .. .. 6·00 11·00
8 **2** 2s. deep green and grey-black .. .. 12·00 20·00
9 **1** 2s. 6d. grey-black and violet .. .. 18·00 42·00
10 **2** 5s. dull purple and sage-green .. .. 55·00 55·00
1/10 .. .. *Set of* 10 £120 £180
1s/10s Optd "Specimen" .. .. *Set of* 10 £130

1905–18. *Wmk Mult Crown CA. Chalk-surfaced pape*
(No. 13), 5*s.) or ordinary paper (others). P* 14.

11 **1** ½d. dull purple and deep green .. .. 5·00
12 ½d. grey-green (1907) .. .. .. 1·00
a. Dull blue-green (1916) 50
13 **2** 1d. grey-black and carmine (1906) .. 1·50
14 1d. carmine (1907) .. .. .. 2·25
a. Scarlet (1916) 70
15 **1** 2d. dull purple and brown .. .. 8·50
a. Chalk-surfaced paper (1906) .. 6·50
16 2½d. grey-black and blue (1907) .. .. 14·00
17 2½d. bright blue (1907) .. .. .. 2·50
18 **2** 3d. deep green and orange .. .. 5·50
a. Chalk-surfaced paper (1906) .. 2·75
19 **1** 6d. grey-black and deep violet .. .. 22·00
a. Chalk-surfaced paper. *Grey-black and deep purple* (1908) .. .. .. 13·00
ab. Grey-black and bright purple (1916) 5·50
20 1s. grey-green and orange (1909) .. 19·00
a. Chalk-surfaced paper .. .. 3·50
21 **2** 5s. dull purple and sage-green (11.18) 32·00
11/21 .. .. *Set of* 11 65·00
12s, 14s, 17s Optd "Specimen" .. *Set of* 3 60·00

WAR TAX
(3)

WAR STAMP
(3a)

1916 (Oct). *Optd with T* **3**. *Wmk Mult Crown CA. P* 14.

22 **1** ½d. dull blue-green (No. 12*a*) 90
a. Deep green 90
s. Optd "Specimen" .. .. .. 40·00
x. Wmk reversed .. .. .. 35·00

No. 22*a* was a special printing produced for this overprin

1918 (Aug). *Optd with T* **3***a*. *Wmk Mult Crown CA. P* 14.

23 **1** 1½d. orange 80
a. Short opt (right pane R. 10/1) .. 17·00
s. Optd "Specimen" .. .. .. 45·00

No. 23 was a special printing produced for this overprint
No. 23a shows the overprint 2 mm high instead of 2½ m

4

5

(Typo D.L.R.)

1920–22. *Wmk Mult Crown CA (sideways*). Ordinary p*
(½d. to 2½d.) or chalk-surfaced paper (others). P 14.

24 **4** ½d. blue-green .. .. 3·75
25 **5** 1d. scarlet .. .. 2·25
26 **4** 1½d. orange-yellow .. .. .. 1·25
x. Wmk sideways reversed .. .. 65·00
y. Wmk sideways inverted and reversed .. ..
27 **5** 2d. slate-grey .. .. 3·00
28 **4** 2½d. ultramarine .. .. 2·00
a. "A" of "CA" missing from wmk .. £300
29 **5** 3d. purple/*yellow* .. .. .. 1·75 1
30 **4** 6d. dull purple and bright mauve .. 3·50 1
31 **5** 1s. grey and black/*green* .. .. 3·50 4
32 **4** 2s. dull purple and blue/*blue* .. .. 15·00 20
x. Wmk sideways reversed £130
33 **5** 2s. 6d. grey and red/*blue* .. .. 5·00 28
y. Wmk sideways inverted and reversed £130
34 **4** 5s. green and red/*pale yellow* .. .. 5·00 40
x. Wmk sideways reversed .. .. 90·00
35 **5** 10s. green and red/*green* .. .. 12·00 48
36 **4** £1 purple and black/*red* (1922) .. £225 £
24/36 .. .. *Set of* 13 £250 £4
24s/36s Optd "Specimen" .. *Set of* 13 £275

*The normal sideways watermark shows Crown to left of
as seen from the back of the stamp.

Examples of most values are known showing a forged St. K
postmark dated "8 DE 23".

1921–9. *Wmk Mult Script CA (sideways*). Chalk-surfa*
paper (2½*d. (No.* 44), 3*d. (No.* 45*a) and* 6*d. to* 5*s.) or ordin*

37 **4** ½d. blue-green .. .. 2·25 1
a. Yellow-green (1922) .. .. .. 1·50
38 **5** 1d. rose-carmine 65
sa. Perf "Specimen" (1929) .. .. 70·00
39 1d. deep violet (1922) .. .. .. 3·75
a. Pale violet (1929) .. .. .. 7·00 1
40 **4** 1½d. red (1925) .. .. 2·50 2
40*a* 1½d. red-brown (1929) .. .. .. 1·00
41 **5** 2d. slate-grey (1922) 40
42 **4** 2½d. pale bright blue (1922) .. .. 3·00 2
43 2½d. brown (1922) .. .. .. 2·25 9·
44 2½d. ultramarine (1927) .. .. .. 1·50 3·
45 **5** 3d. dull ultramarine (1922) .. .. 1·00 4·
45*a* 3d. purple/*yellow* (1927) .. .. 75 4·
46 **4** 6d. dull and bright purple (1924) .. 5·00 5·
aw. Wmk Crown to right of CA .. 4·00 5·
46*b* **5** 1s. black/*green* (1929) .. .. .. 3·75 6·
47 **4** 2s. purple and blue/*blue* (1922) .. 8·00 23·
47*a* **5** 2s. 6d. black and red/*blue* (1927) .. 15·00 29·
47*b* **4** 5s. green and red/*yellow* (1929) .. 40·00 65·
37/47*b* .. .. *Set of* 16 75·00 £1
37s/47*b*s Optd or Perf (1½d. red-brown, 1s., 5s.) "Specimen" .. .. *Set of* 16 £325

*The normal watermark shows Crown to left of CA, *as se*
from the back of the stamp.

NEW INFORMATION

The editor is always interested to correspond wi
people who have new information that w
improve or correct the Catalogue.

6 Old Road Bay and Mount Misery

(Typo D.L.R.)

Tercentenary of Colony. Chalk-surfaced paper. P 14.

(*a*) *Wmk Mult Script CA* (*sideways*)

6 ½d. black and green .. .. .. 2·25 7·00
1d. black and bright violet .. .. 4·50 1·50
1½d. black and scarlet .. .. .. 4·50 10·00
2d. black and slate-grey .. .. 3·75 1·50
2½d. black and brown .. .. .. 6·00 32·00
3d. black and ultramarine .. .. 3·75 15·00
6d. black and bright purple .. .. 9·50 32·00
1s. black and sage-green .. .. 14·00 32·00
2s. black and blue/*blue* .. .. 40·00 50·00
2s. 6d. black and red/*blue* .. .. 48·00 70·00
10s. black and red/*emerald* £250 £375

(*b*) *Wmk Mult Crown CA* (*sideways*)

6 5s. black and red/*pale yellow* .. .. 65·00 £160
£1 black and purple/*red* £700 £1300
.. .. *Set of* 13 £1000 £1800
0s Optd "Specimen" .. *Set of* 13 £650
amples of all values are known showing a forged St. Kitts
nark dated "8 DE 23."

(6 May). *Silver Jubilee. As Nos.* 91/4 *of Antigua, but ptd Waterlow. P* 11×12.

1d. deep blue and scarlet .. .. .. 1·00 70
k. Kite and vertical log .. .. .. 60·00
l. Kite and horizontal log .. .. 90·00
1½d. ultramarine and grey 75 75
k. Kite and vertical log .. .. .. 55·00 65·00
2½d. brown and deep blue .. .. .. 1·00 80
1s. slate and purple .. .. .. 5·50 15·00
k. Kite and vertical log £170
l. Kite and horizontal log £190
.. .. *Set of* 4 7·50 15·00
4s Perf "Specimen" .. .. *Set of* 4 75·00
r illustrations of plate varieties see Omnibus section
wing Zanzibar.

(12 May). *Coronation. As Nos.* 95/7 *of Antigua, but ptd by L.R. P* 14.

1d. scarlet 30 20
1½d. buff 40 10
2½d. bright blue 60 45
.. .. *Set of* 3 1·10 65
7s Perf "Specimen" .. .. *Set of* 3 55·00
os. 61/7 are inscribed "ST. CHRISTOPHER AND NEVIS".

7 King George VI

8 King George VI and Medicinal Spring

9 King George VI and Christopher Columbus

10 King George VI and Anguilla Island

Break in value tablet (R. 12/5) (1947 ptg only)

Break in oval (R. 12/1) (1938 ptg only)

Break in value tablet frame (R.3/2)

Break in value tablet frame (R. 12/3) (ptgs between 1941 and 1945)

Break in frame above ornament (R. 2/4) (ptgs between 1941 and 1950)

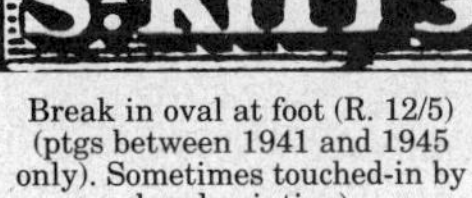

Break in oval at foot (R. 12/5) (ptgs between 1941 and 1945 only). Sometimes touched-in by hand painting)

Break in oval at left (R. 7/1) (ptgs between 1941 and 1945 only)

(Typo; centre litho (T **10**). D.L.R.)

1938 (15 Aug)–**50.** *Wmk Mult Script CA* (*sideways on T* **8** *and* **9**). *Chalk-surfaced paper* (10*s*., £1). *P* 14 (*T* **7** *and* **10**) *or* 13×12 (*T* **8/9**).

68 **7** ½d. green .. .. 3·50 20
a. Blue-green (5.4.43) 10 10
69 1d. scarlet .. .. 5·50 70
a. Carmine (5.43) .. .. .. 1·25 50
b. Carmine-pink (4.47) .. .. 60·00 16·00
c. Rose-red (7.47) .. .. .. 1·25 80
70 1½d. orange 20 30
71 **8** 2d. scarlet and grey .. .. .. 19·00 2·50
a. Chalk-surfaced paper. *Carmine and deep grey* (5.41*) .. .. .. 55·00 10·00
b. Perf 14. *Scarlet & pale grey* (6.43*) 80 1·25
ba. Scarlet and deep grey (6.42*) .. 22·00 5·00
c. Perf 14. Chalk-surfaced paper. *Scarlet and pale grey* (2.50*) .. 2·00 3·00
72 **7** 2½d. ultramarine .. .. .. 3·50 30
a. Bright ultramarine (5.4.43) .. 50 30
73 **8** 3d. dull reddish purple and scarlet .. 15·00 4·00
a. Chalk-surfaced paper. *Brown-purple and carmine-red* (1940) .. 19·00 5·00
b. Perf 14. Chalk-surfaced paper. *Dull reddish purple & carm-red* (6.43*) 32·00 3·75
c. Perf 14. Ordinary paper. *Reddish lilac and scarlet* (8.46*) .. .. 3·25 12·00
d. Perf 14. Ordinary paper. *Purple and bright scarlet* (1.46*) .. .. 8·00 7·50
da. Break in value tablet £110
e. Perf 14. Chalk-surfaced paper. *Deep purple and scarlet* (12.47*) .. 75·00 19·00
f. Perf 14. Ordinary paper. *Rose-lilac and bright scarlet* (1.49*) .. 7·00 8·00
g. Perf 14. Chalk-surfaced paper. *Deep reddish purple & brt scarlet* (8.50*) 4·50 5·00
74 **9** 6d. green and bright purple .. .. 6·50 2·25
a. Break in oval £110
b. Perf 14. Chalk-surfaced paper. *Green and deep claret* (17.5.43*) .. 55·00 11·00
c. Perf 14. Ordinary paper. *Green and purple* (10.44*) .. .. .. 4·75 1·50
d. Perf 14. Chalk-surfaced paper. *Green and purple* (11.48*) .. 4·75 3·00
75 **8** 1s. black and green .. .. .. 12·00 1·25
a. Break in value tablet frame .. £170
b. Perf 14 (8.43*) .. .. .. 3·75 85
ba. Break in value tablet frame .. 90·00
c. Perf 14. Chalk-surfaced paper (7.50*) .. .. 4·00 4·50
ca. Break in value tablet frame .. 90·00
76 2s. 6d. black and scarlet .. .. 32·00 9·00
a. Perf 14. Chalk-surfaced paper (12.43*) .. .. 15·00 6·00
ab. Ordinary paper (5.45*) .. .. 12·00 3·75
77 **9** 5s. grey-green and scarlet .. .. 65·00 18·00
a. Perf 14. Chalk-surfaced paper (25.10.43*) .. .. .. £130 28·00
ab. Break in value tablet frame .. £550
ac. Break in frame above ornament .. £550
ad. Break in oval at foot £550
ae. Break in oval at left £550
b. Perf 14. Ordinary paper. *Bluish green and scarlet* (7.11.45*) .. 24·00 12·00
ba. Break in value tablet frame .. £225
bb. Break in frame above ornament .. £250
bc. Break in oval at foot £200
bd. Break in oval at left £225
c. Perf 14. Chalk-surfaced paper. *Green & scarlet-vermilion* (10.50*) 40·00 45·00
cb. Break in frame above ornament .. £275
77*e* **10** 10s. black and ultramarine (1.9.48) .. 10·00 19·00
77*f* £1 black and brown (1.9.48) .. .. 10·00 23·00
68/77*f* .. .. *Set of* 12 65·00 60·00
68s/77s Perf "Specimen" .. .. *Set of* 10 £180

*Earliest postmark date, Many printings were supplied to St. Kitts-Nevis considerably earlier. Details of many of the dates are taken, with permission, from *A Study of the King George VI Stamps of St. Kitts-Nevis* by P. L. Baldwin (2nd edition 1997).

1946 (1 Nov). *Victory. As Nos.* 110/11 *of Antigua.*

78 1½d. red-orange 10 10
79 3d. carmine 10 10
78s/9s Perf "Specimen" .. .. *Set of* 2 60·00

1949 (3 Jan). *Royal Silver Wedding. As Nos.* 112/13 *of Antigua.*

80 2½d. ultramarine 10 50
81 5s. carmine .. .. 6·50 2·75

1949 (10 Oct). *75th Anniv of U.P.U. As Nos.* 114/17 *of Antigua.*

82 2½d. ultramarine 15 20
83 3d. carmine-red .. .. 1·00 70
84 6d. magenta 20 50
85 1s. blue-green 20 30
a. "A" of "CA" missing from wmk .. — £500
82/5 .. .. *Set of* 4 1·40 1·50

ANGUILLA ANGUILLA

TERCENTENARY 1650-1950 (11)

TERCENTENARY 1650—1950 (12)

1950 (10 Nov). *Tercentenary of British Settlement in Anguilla. Nos.* 69*c*, 70 *and* 72*a* (*perf* 14) *optd as T* **11** *and new ptgs of T* **8/9** *on chalk-surfaced paper perf* 13×12½ *optd as T* **12**.

86 **7** 1d. rose-red 10 20
87 1½d. orange 10 20
a. Error. Crown missing, W **9***a* .. £1600
b. Error. St. Edward's Crown, W **9***b* .. £850
88 2½d. bright ultramarine 10 20
89 **8** 3d. dull purple and scarlet 10 40
90 **9** 6d. green and bright purple 10 20
91 **8** 1s. black and green (R.) 30 20
a. Break in value tablet frame .. 10·00
86/91 .. .. *Set of* 6 60 1·25

Nos. 87a/b occur on a row in the watermark, in which the crowns and letters "CA" alternate.

(New Currency. 100 cents = 1 West Indian dollar)

1951 (16 Feb). *Inauguration of B.W.I. University College. As Nos.* 118/19 *of Antigua.*

92 3 c. black and yellow-orange 30 15
93 12 c. turquoise-green and magenta .. 30 85

ST. CHRISTOPHER, NEVIS AND ANGUILLA

LEGISLATIVE COUNCIL

13 Bath House and Spa, Nevis

14 Map of the Islands

(Recess Waterlow)

1952 (14 June). *Vert designs as T* **14** (3, 12 *c*.) *or horiz as* **13** (*others*). *Wmk Mult Script CA. P* 12½.

94 1 c. deep green and ochre .. .. .. 15 1·00
95 2 c. green .. .. 1·00 1·00
96 3 c. carmine-red and violet .. .. .. 30 1·00
97 4 c. scarlet 20 20
98 5 c. bright blue and grey 30 10
99 6 c. ultramarine 30 15
100 12 c. deep blue and reddish brown 85 10
101 24 c. black and carmine-red 30 10
102 48 c. olive and chocolate .. .. .. 1·75 2·00
103 60 c. ochre and deep green .. .. .. 1·50 2·50
104 $1.20, deep green and ultramarine .. .. 5·50 2·25
105 $4.80, green and carmine .. .. .. 13·00 18·00
94/105 .. .. *Set of* 12 23·00 26·00

Designs:—2 c. Warner Park; 4 c. Brimstone Hill; 5 c. Nevis from the sea, North; 6 c. Pinney's Beach, Nevis; 12 c. Sir Thomas Warner's Tomb; 24 c. Old Road Bay; 48 c. Sea Island cotton, Nevis; 60 c. The Treasury; $1.20, Salt pond, Anguilla; $4.80, Sugar factory.

St. Lucia

Although a branch office of the British G.P.O. was not opened at Castries, the island capital, until 1844 some form of postal arrangements for overseas mails existed from at least 1841 when the issue of a Ship Letter handstamp is recorded.

The stamps of Great Britain were used on the island from May 1858 until the end of April 1860 when the local authorities assumed responsibility for the postal service. No. CC1 was again used on overseas mail between 1 May and the introduction of St. Lucia stamps in December 1860.

CASTRIES

CROWN-CIRCLE HANDSTAMPS

CC1

CC1 CC1 ST. LUCIA (R.) (1.5.1844) *Price on cover* £750

No. CC1 was utilised, struck in black, during a shortage of 1d. stamps in late April and early May 1904. *Price on cover* £325.

Stamps of GREAT BRITAIN *cancelled* "A 11" *as Type* Z **1** *of Jamaica.*

1858 *to* **1860**
Z1 1d. rose-red (1857), *perf* 14 .. £1000
Z2 2d. blue (1855)
Z3 4d. rose (1857) .. £400
Z4 6d. lilac (1856) .. £225
Z5 1s. green (1856) .. £1100

PRICES FOR STAMPS ON COVER TO 1945

Nos. 1/3	*from* × 60
Nos. 5/8	*from* × 30
Nos. 9/10	†
Nos. 11/24	*from* × 15
Nos. 25/30	*from* × 10
Nos. 31/6	*from* × 6
Nos. 39/42	*from* × 10
Nos. 43/50	*from* × 15
Nos. 51/2	—
Nos. 53/62	*from* × 6
No. 63	*from* × 15
Nos. 64/75	*from* × 4
Nos. 76/7	—
Nos. 78/88	*from* × 3
No. 89	*from* × 4
No. 90	*from* × 20
Nos. 91/112	*from* × 3
Nos. 113/24	*from* × 2
Nos. 125/7	*from* × 10
Nos. 128/41	*from* × 2
Nos. D1/6	*from* × 10
Nos. F1/28	—

CROWN COLONY

PERKINS BACON "CANCELLED". For notes on these handstamps, showing "CANCELLED" between horizontal bars forming an oval, see Catalogue Introduction.

1

Half
penny

(2)

(Recess P.B.)

1860 (18 Dec). *Wmk Small Star, W* w **2**. *P* 14 *to* 16.
1 **1** (1d.) rose-red (H/S "CANCELLED" in oval £4000) .. 85·00 60·00
a. Imperf vert (horiz pair)
b. Double impression .. £1800
2 (4d.) blue (H/S "CANCELLED" in oval £5000) .. £200 £150
a. Deep blue
b. Imperf vert (horiz pair)
3 (6d.) green (H/S "CANCELLED" in oval £5000) .. £275 £200
a. Imperf vert (horiz pair)
b. Deep green .. £325 £225

(Recess D.L.R.)

1863. *Wmk Crown CC. P* 12½.
5 **1** (1d.) lake .. 60·00 80·00
ax. Wmk reversed .. 60·00 80·00
b. Brownish lake .. 75·00 75·00
bx. Wmk reversed
7 (4d.) indigo .. £100 £110
x. Wmk reversed
8 (6d.) emerald-green .. £150 £150
w. Wmk inverted
x. Wmk reversed .. £170 £150

Prepared for use, but not issued. Surch as T **2**
9 **1** ½d. on (6d.) emerald-green .. 65·00
x. Wmk reversed
10 6d. on (4d.) indigo .. £1000
All three values exist imperforate from proof sheets.

1864 (19 Nov)–**76.** *Wmk Crown CC.* (a) *P* 12½.
11 **1** (1d.) black .. 18·00 12·00
a. Intense black .. 17·00 11·00
ax. Wmk reversed .. — 15·00
12 (4d.) yellow .. £160 30·00
b. Lemon-yellow .. £1500
c. Chrome-yellow .. £170 30·00
d. Olive-yellow .. £325 80·00
w. Wmk inverted
x. Wmk reversed .. £200
y. Wmk inverted and reversed
13 (6d.) violet .. £100 28·00
a. Mauve .. £170 28·00
b. Deep lilac .. £120 32·00
x. Wmk reversed .. £120
14 (1s.) brown-orange .. £300 25·00
b. Orange .. £225 25·00
c. Pale orange .. £180 25·00
ca. Imperf between (horiz pair)
x. Wmk reversed

(b) *P* 14
15 **1** (1d.) black (6.76) .. 22·00 15·00
a. Imperf between (horiz pair)
x. Wmk reversed .. — 15·00
16 (4d.) yellow (6.76) .. 85·00 18·00
a. Olive-yellow .. £250 85·00
w. Wmk inverted
x. Wmk reversed
17 (6d.) mauve (6.76) .. 85·00 30·00
a. Pale lilac .. 85·00 18·00
b. Violet .. £225 65·00
x. Wmk reversed
18 (1s.) orange (10.76) .. £200 22·00
a. Deep orange .. £130 16·00
w. Wmk inverted
x. Wmk reversed .. — 22·00
All four values exist imperforate from proof sheets.

HALFPENNY (3)

2½ PENCE (4)

5

1881 (Sept). *Surch with T* **3** *or* **4**. *Wmk Crown CC. P* 14.
23 **1** ½d. green .. 60·00 80·00
x. Wmk reversed
24 2½d. brown-red .. 27·00 20·00
The 1d. black is known surcharged "1d." in violet ink by hand, but there is no evidence that this was done officially.

1882–84. *Surch as T* **3**. *Wmk Crown CA.* (a) *P* 14
25 **1** ½d. green (1882) .. 16·00 24·00
26 1d. black (C.) .. 24·00 8·50
a. Bisected (on cover) .. † —
27 4d. yellow .. £225 17·00
28 6d. violet .. 26·00 26·00
29 1s. orange .. £250 £160

(b) *P* 12
30 **1** 4d. yellow .. £250 28·00
Deep blue stamps, wmk Crown CA, perf 14 or 12, are fiscals from which the overprint "THREE PENCE—REVENUE", or "REVENUE", has been fraudulently removed.

(Typo D.L.R.)

1883 (6 July)–**86.** *Wmk Crown CA. Die* I. *P* 14.
31 **5** ½d. dull green .. 7·00 3·75
a. Top left triangle detached .. £140
32 1d. carmine-rose .. 32·00 8·50
33 2½d. blue .. 32·00 2·00
a. Top left triangle detached .. £450 90·00
34 4d. brown (1885) .. 27·00 1·00
a. Top left triangle detached .. £450 75·00
35 6d. lilac (1886) .. £250 £200
36 1s. orange-brown (1885) .. £375 £140
The 4d. and 6d. exist imperforate from proof sheets.
For illustration of "top left triangle detached" variety on this and the following issue see above No. 6 of Montserrat.

1886–87. *Wmk Crown CA. Die* I. *P* 14.
39 **5** 1d. dull mauve .. 4·75 6·00
a. Top left triangle detached .. £100
40 3d. dull mauve and green .. £100 17·00
a. Top left triangle detached .. — £350
41 6d. dull mauve and blue (1887) .. 3·75 8·00
a. Top left triangle detached .. £110
42 1s. dull mauve and red (1887) .. 95·00 22·00
a. Top left triangle detached .. £650
39/42 .. *Set of* 4 £180 48·00
39s/42s Optd "Specimen" .. *Set of* 4 £180
The 1d. exists imperforate from proof sheets.

1891–98. *Wmk Crown CA. Die* II. *P* 14.
43 **5** ½d. dull green .. 1·75 1·00
44 1d. dull mauve .. 2·50 30
45 2d. ultramarine and orange (1898) .. 2·00 1·00
46 2½d. ultramarine .. 3·00 1·00
47 3d. dull mauve and green .. 4·00 5·50
48 4d. brown .. 2·00 2·25
49 6d. dull mauve and blue .. 23·00 22·00
50 1s. dull mauve and red .. 4·25 5·00
51 5s. dull mauve and orange .. 45·00 £120
52 10s. dull mauve and black .. 80·00 £130
43/52 .. *Set of* 10 £150 £250
43s, 51s/2s Optd "Specimen" .. *Set of* 3 £120
For description and illustration of differences between Die I and Die II see Introduction.

ONE HALF PENNY (6)

½d (7)

ON PEN (8)

N — Normal "N"

N — Thick "N"

Three types of T **8**

I. All letters "N" normal.
II. Thick diagonal stroke in first "N".
III. Thick diagonal stroke in second "N".

1891–92. (a) *Stamps of Die* I *surch.*
53 **6** ½d. on 3d. dull mauve and green .. £120 7
a. Small "A" in "HALF" .. £300
b. Small "O" in "ONE" .. £300
c. Top left triangle detached .. £700
54 **7** ½d. on half 6d. dull mauve and blue .. 18·00
a. No fraction bar .. £180
b. Surch sideways .. £850
c. Surch double .. £500
d. "2" in fraction omitted .. £400
e. Thick "1" with sloping serif .. £180
f. Surch triple .. £850
g. Figure "1" used as fraction bar .. £475
55 **8** 1d. on 4d. brown (I) (12.91) .. 3·75
a. Surch double .. £180
b. Surch inverted .. £700 £
c. Type II .. 23·00 2
ca. Surch double .. £325
cb. Surch inverted .. — £
d. Type III .. 22·00 2
e. Top left triangle detached .. £120 £

(b) *Stamp of Die* II *surch*
56 **6** ½d. on 3d. dull mauve and green .. 65·00 2
a. Surch double .. £700 £
b. Surch inverted .. £1700 £
c. Surch both sides .. — £
d. Small "O" in "ONE" .. £160 90
e. Small "A" in "HALF" .. £160 90
f. "ONE" misplaced ("O" over "H") .. £160 90

9

10

(Typo D.L.R.)

1902–3. *Wmk Crown CA. P* 14.
58 **9** ½d. dull purple and green .. 2·75 1
59 1d. dull purple and carmine .. 5·00
60 2½d. dull purple and ultramarine .. 17·00 5
61 **10** 3d. dull purple and yellow .. 6·00 8
62 1s. green and black .. 10·00 25
58/62 .. *Set of* 5 38·00 38
58s/62s Optd "Specimen" .. *Set of* 5 £100

11 The Pitons

(Recess D.L.R.)

1902 (15 Dec). *400th Anniv of Discovery by Columbus. Wm Crown CC (sideways). P* 14.
63 **11** 2d. green and brown .. 8·50 1·
s. Optd "Specimen" .. 60·00
This stamp was formerly thought to have been issued on December but it has been seen on a postcard clearly postmarked December.

1904–10. *Wmk Mult Crown CA. Chalk-surfaced paper (No 71, 73/5 and 77) or ordinary paper (others). P* 14.
64 **9** ½d. dull purple and green .. 4·25 6
a. Chalk-surfaced paper .. 4·00 1·2
65 ½d. green (1907) .. 1·75 1·0
66 1d. dull purple and carmine .. 6·00 1·0
a. Chalk-surfaced paper .. 2·50 1·0
67 1d. carmine (1907) .. 4·25 3
68 2½d. dull purple and ultramarine .. 13·00 1·2
a. Chalk-surfaced paper .. 10·00 4·5
69 2½d. blue (1907) .. 3·75 1·7
70 **10** 3d. dull purple and yellow .. 4·25 3·0
71 3d. purple/*yellow* (1909) .. 2·75 12·0
72 6d. dull purple and violet (1905) .. 13·00 19·0
a. Chalk-surfaced paper .. 20·00 25·0
ab. Dull purple and bright purple (1907) 8·50 25·0
73 6d. dull purple (1910) .. 38·00 60·0
74 1s. green and black (1905) .. 30·00 24·0
75 1s. black/*green* (1909) .. 4·75 8·0
76 5s. green and carmine (1905) .. 65·00 £16
77 5s. green and red/*yellow* (1907) .. 60·00 70·0
64/77 .. *Set of* 14 £200 £32
65s, 67s, 69s, 71s/2s, 72abs and 75s/7s Optd "Specimen" .. *Set of* 9 £190
Examples of Nos. 71/7 are known with a forged Castries postmark dated "JA 21 09".

12

13

14

15

16

(Typo D.L.R.)

2–21. *Die I. Wmk Mult Crown CA. Chalk-surfaced paper* d. *to* 5s.). *P* 14.
12 ½d. deep green 70 50
a. Yellow-green (1916) 75 30
1d. carmine-red .. .. .. 1·90 10
a. Scarlet (1916) .. .. .. 3·25 10
b. Rose-red .. .. 7·00 1·00
13 2d. grey .. .. 1·50 4·25
a. Slate-grey (1916) .. .. .. 15·00 12·00
12 2½d. ultramarine .. .. .. 3·75 2·75
a. Bright blue .. .. .. 2·00 2·75
b. Deep bright blue (1916) .. .. 10·00 10·00
15 3d. purple/*yellow* .. .. .. 1·25 2·25
b. Die II. *On pale yellow* (1921) .. 8·50 32·00
bw. Wmk inverted .. .. ..
14 4d. black and red/*yellow* .. .. 1·00 2·00
a. White back .. .. .. 70 1·50
as. Optd "Specimen" .. .. 25·00
15 6d. dull and bright purple .. .. 2·00 9·50
a. Grey-purple and purple (1918) .. 16·00 16·00
1s. black/*green* .. .. .. 3·25 5·00
a. On blue-green (*olive back*) (1918) 7·00 7·00
1s. orange-brown (1920) .. .. 9·00 45·00
16 2s. 6d. black and red/*blue* .. .. 22·00 32·00
15 5s. green and red/*yellow* .. .. 24·00 75·00
88 .. .. *Set of* 11 60·00 £160
s/88s Optd "Specimen" .. *Set of* 11 £190

(17)

WAR TAX
(18)

16 (1 June). *No.* 79a *optd locally with T* 17.
12 1d. scarlet .. .. 8·50 8·50
a. Opt double £400 £400
b. Carmine-red .. .. .. 55·00 35·00

For overprinting with Type 17 the sheets were vertically vided to the left of the centre margin and the top margin of the eet was folded beneath the top row of stamps so that the arginal examples from this row show an inverted albino npression of the overprint in the top margin.

Examples are also recorded of similar albino overprints in the ght-hand and bottom margins but it is unclear if some sheets ad all margins folded under before overprinting.

916 (Sept). *No.* 79a *optd in London with T* 18.
12 1d. scarlet 75 30
s. Optd "Specimen" .. .. .. 40·00

921–30. *Die II. Wmk Mult Script CA. Chalk-surfaced paper* (3d. (*No.* 100) *to* 5s.). *P* 14.
91 12 ½d. green 75 50
92 1d. rose-carmine .. .. .. 8·50 13·00
93 1d. deep brown (1922) .. .. 1·40 15
94 14 1½d. dull carmine (1922) .. .. 75 2·50
95 13 2d. slate-grey 75 15
96 12 2½d. bright blue .. .. .. 3·75 2·75
97 2½d. orange (1925) .. .. 11·00 50·00
98 2½d. dull blue (1926) .. .. 3·25 2·50
99 15 3d. bright blue (1922) .. .. 5·00 16·00
a. Dull blue (1924) .. .. 2·50 11·00
00 3d. purple/*pale yellow* (1926) .. 1·00 12·00
a. Deep purple/pale yellow (1930) .. 12·00 12·00
01 14 4d. black and red/*yellow* (1924) .. 1·25 2·50
02 15 6d. grey-purple and purple .. .. 2·00 4·75
03 1s. orange-brown .. .. .. 2·25 3·25
04 16 2s. 6d. black and red/*blue* (1924) .. 18·00 27·00
05 15 5s. green and red/*pale yellow* (1923) 42·00 75·00
91/105 .. .. *Set of* 15 85·00 £190
91s/105s Optd "Specimen" .. *Set of* 15 £250

1935 (6 May). *Silver Jubilee. As Nos.* 91/4 *of Antigua. P* 13½×14.
109 ½d. black and green 15 75
f. Diagonal line by turret .. .. 24·00
110 2d. ultramarine and grey 45 90
f. Diagonal line by turret .. .. 38·00
111 2½d. brown and deep blue .. .. 90 1·25
f. Diagonal line by turret .. .. 50·00
g. Dot to left of chapel .. .. 80·00
112 1s. slate and purple .. .. .. 5·00 8·00
h. Dot by flagstaff £200
109/12 .. .. *Set of* 4 6·00 9·75
109s/12s Perf "Specimen" .. *Set of* 4 75·00

For illustrations of plate varieties see Omnibus section following Zanzibar.

19 Port Castries

20 Columbus Square, Castries (inscr "COLOMBUS SQUARE" in error)

21 Ventine Falls

25 The Badge of the Colony

(Recess D.L.R.)

1936 (1 Mar-Apr). *T* 19/21, 25 *and similar designs. Wmk Mult Script CA. P* 14 *or* 13 × 12 (1s. *and* 10s.).
113 19 ½d. black and bright green 30 50
a. Perf 13 × 12 (8.4.36) .. .. 1·75 9·00
114 20 1d. black and brown 40 10
a. Perf 13 × 12 (8.4.36) .. .. 2·50 2·50
115 21 1½d. black and scarlet 55 30
a. Perf 12 × 13 .. .. .. 6·00 2·25
116 19 2d. black and grey 50 20
117 20 2½d. black and blue 50 15
118 21 3d. black and dull green .. .. 1·25 70
119 19 4d. black and red-brown .. .. 50 1·00
120 20 6d. black and orange .. .. .. 1·00 1·00
121 – 1s. black and light blue .. .. 1·25 2·50
122 – 2s. 6d. black and ultramarine .. 8·50 14·00
123 – 5s. black and violet .. .. .. 8·50 20·00
124 25 10s. black and carmine.. .. .. 45·00 70·00
113/24 .. .. *Set of* 12 60·00 £100
113s/24s Perf "Specimen" .. *Set of* 12 £180

Designs: *Vert* (*as T* 21)—2s. 6d. Inniskilling monument. *Horiz* (*as T* 19)—1s. Fort Rodney, Pigeon Island; 5s. Government House.

Examples of most values are known with a forged Castries postmark dated "1 MR 36".

1937 (12 May). *Coronation. As Nos.* 95/7 *of Antigua. P* 11×11½.
125 1d. violet 30 30
126 1½d. carmine 55 20
127 2½d. blue 55 60
125/7 .. .. *Set of* 3 1·25 1·00
125s/7s Perf "Specimen" .. .. *Set of* 3 55·00

26 King George VI

27 Columbus Square

28 Government House

31 Device of St. Lucia

(Des E. Crafer (T 26), H. Fleury (5s.). Recess Waterlow (½d. to 3½d., 8d., 3s., 5s., £1), D.L.R. (6d., 1s.) and B.W. (2s., 10s.))

1938 (22 Sept)–48. *T* 26/8, 31 *and similar designs. Wmk Mult Script CA* (*sideways on* 2s.).
128 26 ½d. green (*p* 14½ × 14) .. .. 1·00 10
a. Perf 12½ (1943) 10 10
129 1d. violet (*p* 14½ × 14) .. .. 1·25 75
a. Perf 12½ (1938) 10 15
129*b* 1d. scarlet (*p* 12½) (1947) 20 10
c. Perf 14½ × 14 (1948) 10 10
130 1½d. scarlet (*p* 14½ × 14) .. .. 1·25 40
a. Perf 12½ (1943) .. .. .. 70 1·00
131 2d. grey (*p* 14½ × 14) .. .. 1·75 1·50
a. Perf 12½ (1943) 10 10
132 2½d. ultramarine (*p* 14½ × 14) .. 2·75 15
a. Perf 12½ (1943) 10 10
132*b* 2½d. violet (*p* 12½) (1947) 30 10
133 3d. orange (*p* 14½ × 14) 50 10
a. Perf 12½ (1943) 10 10
133*b* 3½d. ultramarine (*p* 12½) (1947) .. 30 15
134 27 6d. claret (*p* 13½) .. .. .. 3·75 50
a. Carmine-lake (*p* 13½) (1945) .. 1·75 35
b. Perf 12. *Claret* (1948) .. .. 1·00 1·50
134*c* 26 8d. brown (*p* 12½) (1946) .. .. 3·25 30
135 28 1s. brown (*p* 13½) 55 30
a. Perf 12 (1948) 50 20
136 – 2s. blue and purple (*p* 12) .. .. 3·50 1·25
136*a* 26 3s. bright purple (*p* 12½) (1946) .. 8·00 1·75
137 – 5s. black and mauve (*p* 12½) .. 14·00 6·00
138 31 10s. black/*yellow* (*p* 12) .. .. 6·50 9·00
141 26 £1 sepia (*p* 12½) (1946) .. .. 11·00 8·00
128a/41 .. .. *Set of* 17 42·00 26·00
128s/41s Perf "Specimen" .. *Set of* 17 £300

Designs: *Horiz* (*as T* 28)—2s. The Pitons; 5s. *Lady Hawkins* loading bananas.

1946 (8 Oct). *Victory. As Nos.* 110/11 *of Antigua.*
142 1d. lilac 10 10
143 3½d. blue 10 10
142s/3s Perf "Specimen" .. .. *Set of* 2 50·00

1948 (26 Nov). *Royal Silver Wedding. As Nos.* 112/13 *of Antigua.*
144 1d. scarlet 15 10
145 £1 purple-brown .. .. .. 13·00 35·00

(New Currency. 100 cents = 1 West Indian dollar)

32 King George VI

33 Device of St. Lucia

(Recess Waterlow (32), B.W. (33))

1949 (1 Oct)–**50**. *Value in cents or dollars. Wmk Mult Script CA. P* 12½ (1 c. *to* 16 c.), 11 × 11½ (*others*).
146 32 1 c. green 10 10
a. Perf 14 (1949) .. .. .. 2·00 40
147 2 c. magenta 50 10
a. Perf 14½ × 14 (1949) .. .. 2·00 1·00
148 3 c. scarlet .. .. 50 1·50
149 4 c. grey 50 10
a. Perf 14½ × 14 .. .. .. † £6500
150 5 c. violet 50 10
151 6 c. orange .. .. 50 1·50
152 7 c. ultramarine .. .. .. 2·00 2·00
153 12 c. claret .. .. 5·00 1·75
a. Perf 14½ × 14 (1950) £475 £350
154 16 c. brown .. .. 2·50 30
155 33 24 c. light blue 30 10
156 48 c. olive-green.. .. .. .. 1·50 1·00
157 $1.20, purple .. .. 2·25 7·50
158 $2.40, blue-green .. .. .. 3·00 17·00
159 $4.80, rose-carmine .. .. .. 7·00 18·00
146/159 .. .. *Set of* 14 23·00 45·00

Most examples of Nos. 146a and 147a were produced as coils, but a few sheets in these perforations were distributed and blocks of four are scarce.

No genuine mint example of No. 149a is known. Photographic forgeries do, however, exist.

1949 (10 Oct). *75th Anniv of U.P.U. As Nos.* 114/17 *of Antigua.*
160 5 c. violet 15 25
161 6 c. orange .. .. 1·10 1·25
162 12 c. magenta 20 20
163 24 c. blue-green 30 20
160/3 .. .. *Set of* 4 1·60 1·75

1951 (16 Feb). *Inauguration of B.W.I. University College. As Nos.* 118/19 *of Antigua.*
164 3 c. black and scarlet.. .. .. 45 50
165 12 c. black and deep carmine 55 50

34 Phoenix rising from Burning Buildings

N 1
E 9
W 5
1
CONSTITUTION
(35)

(Flames typo, rest recess B.W.)

1951 (19 June). *Reconstruction of Castries. Wmk Mult Script CA. P* 13½ × 13.
166 34 12 c. red and blue 15 70

1951 (25 Sept). *New Constitution. Nos.* 147, 149/50 *and* 153 *optd with T* 35 *by Waterlow. P* 12½.
167 32 2 c. magenta 15 60
168 4 c. grey 15 60
169 5 c. violet 15 40
170 12 c. claret 40 50
167/70 .. .. *Set of* 4 75 1·90

ALTERED CATALOGUE NUMBERS

Any Catalogue numbers altered from the last edition are shown as a list in the introductory pages.

POSTAGE DUE STAMPS

D 1

No. **No.**

Normal Wide fount

(Type-set Government Printing Office)

1930. *Each stamp individually handstamped with different number. No wmk. No gum. Rough perf* 12. (a) *Horizontally laid paper.*

D1 D 1 1d. black/*blue* .. .. 4·00 15·00
b. Wide, wrong fount "No." .. .. 14·00 38·00
c. Missing stop after "ST" .. .. 80·00 £140
d. Missing stop after "LUCIA" .. 80·00 £140
e. Handstamped number double .. £325
f. Handstamped number triple
g. Incorrect number with correction above .. ..
h. Two different numbers on same stamp £425
i. Number omitted £1500

(b) *Wove paper*

D2 D 1 2d. black/*yellow* .. .. .. 12·00 40·00
a. Imperf between (vert pair) .. £4250
b. Wide, wrong fount "No." .. .. 32·00 95·00
c. Missing stop after "ST" £170 £325
d. Missing stop after "LUCIA" .. £250
g. Incorrect number with correction above £550
h. Two different numbers on same stamp £650

Nos. D1/2 were produced in sheets of 60 (6×10) usually with imperforate outer edges at the top, at right and at foot. It would appear that the sheets were bound into books from which they could be detached using the line of perforations along the left-hand side.

There were three printings of each value, utilising the same basic type. The paper for the first two printings of the 1d. and the first printing of the 2d. showed papermaker's watermarks, that for the 1d. being "KINGSCLERE" in double-lined capitals below a crown with parts occurring on between ten and fourteen stamps in each sheet.

Details of the printings are as follows:

1d.

First printing. On paper with sheet watermark. Shows wide fount "No." on R. 10/3–6 and missing stop after "ST" on R. 5/3

Second printing. On paper with sheet watermark. Shows wide fount "No." on R. 10/2–6 and missing stop after "ST" on R. 5/3. The first two printings of the 1d. were numbered together as 1 to 12000.

Third printing. On paper without watermark. Shows wide fount "No." on all stamps in Row 10. Missing stop after "ST" on R. 5/3 corrected, but missing stop after "LUCIA" occurs on R. 9/2. Numbered 12001 to 24000.

2d.

First printing. On paper with sheet watermark. Shows wide fount "No." on R. 10/2–6 and missing stop after "ST" on R. 5/3 (as 1d. second printing). Numbered 1 to 4800.

Second printing. On paper without watermark. Shows wide fount "No." on all stamps in Row 10. Missing stop after "ST" corrected (printed *before* 1d. third printing). Numbered 4801 to 14820.

Third printing. On paper without watermark. Shows wide fount "No." on all stamps in Row 10. Missing stop after "ST" corrected, but missing stop after "LUCIA" occurs on R. 4/4 and 9/2 (printed *after* 1d. third printing). Numbered 14821 to 16800.

The handstamped numbers were applied at the Post Office using a numbering machine. Mistakes in the numbering on the 1d. were sometimes partially erased and then corrected with a second strike, either of the complete number or of incorrect digits, using a machine with a smaller font.

D 2

D 3

(Typo D.L.R.)

1933–47. *Wmk Mult Script CA. P* 14.

D3 D 2 1d. black .. .. 4·50 6·00
D4 2d. black .. .. 18·00 8·00
D5 4d. black (28.6.47) .. .. .. 5·50 38·00
D6 8d. black (28.6.47) .. .. .. 5·50 48·00
D3/6 .. .. *Set of* 4 30·00 90·00
D3s/6s Perf "Specimen" .. *Set of* 4 £130

1949 (1 Oct)–**52.** *Value in cents. Wmk Mult Script CA. Typo. P* 14.

D 7 D 3 2 c. black .. .. 1·75 26·00
a. Chalk-surfaced paper (27.11.52) 10 8·00
ab. Error. Crown missing, W **9***a* .. £100
ac. Error. St. Edward's Crown, W **9***b* 30·00
D 8 4 c. black .. .. 3·50 19·00
a. Chalk-surfaced paper (27.11.52) .. 40 10·00
ab. Error. Crown missing, W **9***a* .. £150
ac. Error. St. Edward's Crown, W **9***b* 42·00
D 9 D 3 8 c. black .. .. 3·25 23·00
a. Chalk-surfaced paper (27.11.52) .. 3·00 32·00
ac. Error. St. Edward's Crown, W **9***b* £275
D10 16 c. black .. .. 15·00 65·00
a. Chalk-surfaced paper (27.11.52) .. 4·50 50·00
ac. Error. St. Edward's Crown, W **9***b* £375
D7/10 .. .. *Set of* 4 21·00 £120
D7a/10a .. .. *Set of* 4 7·25 90·00

The 2 c. and 4 c. watermarked Block CA were issued in 1965.

POSTAL FISCAL STAMPS

Nos. F1/28 were authorised for postal use from 14 April 1885.

CANCELLATIONS. Many used examples of the Postal Fiscal stamps have had previous pen cancellations removed before being used postally.

SHILLING STAMP (F 1) One Penny Stamp (F 2) HALFPENNY Stamp (F 3)

1881. *Wmk Crown CC. P* 14. (a) *Surch as Type* **F 1**.

F1 1 ONE PENNY STAMP, black (C.) .. 50·00 48·00
a. Surch inverted £700 £700
b. Surch double £650 £700
F2 FOUR PENNY STAMP, yellow .. .. 85·00 70·00
a. Bisected (2d.) (on cover) .. ..
F3 SIX PENCE STAMP, mauve £140 £130
F4 SHILLING STAMP, orange .. .. 80·00 65·00
a. "SHILEING" £650
b. "SHILDING" £650 £600

(b) *Surch as Type* **F 2**

F 7 1 One Penny Stamp, black (R.) .. 50·00 48·00
a. Surch double £700
w. Wmk inverted .. ..
F 8 Four Pence Stamp, yellow .. .. 85·00 65·00
x. Wmk reversed .. ..
F 9 Six Pence Stamp, mauve .. .. 85·00 65·00
F10 Shilling Stamp, orange .. .. 90·00 85·00

(c) *Surch as Type* **F 3**

F11 1 Halfpenny Stamp, green .. .. 60·00 55·00
a. "Stamp" double £450 £450
F12 One Shilling Stamp, orange (*wmk Crown CA*) .. .. 95·00 75·00
a. "Stamp" double £450 £500

A fiscally used example of No. F1b is known showing one red and one black surcharge.

FOUR PENCE REVENUE (F 4) Revenue (F 5) REVENUE (F 6)

1882. *Wmk Crown CA. Surch as Type* **F 4**. (a) *P* 14.

F13 1 1d. black (C.) .. .. 35·00 22·00
F14 2d. pale blue .. .. 23·00 9·50
F15 3d. deep blue (C.) .. .. .. 70·00 45·00
F16 4d. yellow .. .. 27·00 4·00
F17 6d. mauve .. .. 45·00 25·00

(b) *P* 12

F18 1 1d. black (C.) .. .. 35·00 23·00
F19 3d. deep blue (C.) .. .. .. 50·00 20·00
F20 1s. orange .. .. 55·00 13·00

The 1d. and 2d. exist as imperforate proofs.

1883. *Nos.* 25, 26, 30 *and* 32 *optd locally as Type* **F 5**.

(a) *Word* 11 *mm long*

F21 1d. black (C.) .. .. 28·00 40·00
a. Opt inverted .. ..
b. Opt double £275 £350

(b) *Word* 13 *mm*

F22 1d. black (C.) .. .. — 65·00

(c) *Word* 15½ *mm*

F23 ½d. green .. .. — 55·00
a. "Revenue" double .. .. .. — £250
F24 1d. black (C.) .. .. 28·00 10·00
a. "Revenue" double £140
b. "Revenue" triple £275
c. "Revenue" double, one inverted .. £250 £300
F25 1d. rose (No. 32) .. .. .. — 60·00
F26 4d. yellow .. .. — 65·00

1884–85. *Optd with Type* **F 6**. *Wmk Crown CA. P* 14.

F27 5 1d. slate (C.) .. .. 20·00 12·00
F28 1d. dull mauve (Die I) (1885) .. .. 20·00 7·50

No. F27 exists as an imperforate proof.

St. Vincent

Although postal markings for St. Vincent are recorded as early as 1793 it was not until 1852 that the British G.P.O. oper[ned a] branch office at Kingstown, the island's capital.

The stamps of Great Britain were used between May 185[8 and] the end of April 1860. From 1 May in that year the local autho[rities] assumed responsibility for the postal services and fell back o[n the] use of No. CC1 until the introduction of St. Vincent stamps in [1861].

KINGSTOWN

CROWNED-CIRCLE HANDSTAMPS

CC 1

CC1 CC 1 ST. VINCENT (R.) (30.1.1852) *Price on cover* £

Stamps of GREAT BRITAIN *cancelled* "A 10" *as Type* Z [1 of] *Jamaica.*

1858 *to* **1860.**

Z1 1d. rose-red (1857), *perf* 14 .. .. .. £
Z2 2d. blue (1855) .. ..
Z3 4d. rose (1857) .. .. £
Z4 6d. lilac (1856) .. .. £
Z5 1s. green (1856) £1

PRICES FOR STAMPS ON COVER TO 1945

Nos. 1/7	*from* × 15
No. 8	—
No. 9	*from* × 15
No. 10	—
Nos. 11/19	*from* × 10
Nos. 20/1	*from* × 6
Nos. 22/5	*from* × 10
Nos. 26/8	—
Nos. 29/31	*from* × 12
No. 32	—
Nos. 33/4	*from* × 10
No. 35	—
Nos. 36/8	*from* × 8
Nos. 39/41	*from* × 15
Nos. 42/5	*from* × 8
No. 46	*from* × 15
Nos. 47/54	*from* × 4
Nos. 55/8	*from* × 8
No. 59	*from* × 10
No. 60	*from* × 6
Nos. 61/3	*from* × 8
Nos. 67/75	*from* × 3
Nos. 76/84	*from* × 2
Nos. 85/92	*from* × 3
No. 93	—
Nos. 94/8	*from* × 3
Nos. 99/107	*from* × 2
Nos. 108/19	*from* × 3
No. 120	—
No. 121	*from* × 3
No. 122	*from* × 5
No. 123	—
No. 124	*from* × 5
Nos. 126/9	*from* × 10
Nos. 131/45	*from* × 3
Nos. 146/8	*from* × 6
Nos. 149/59	*from* × 2

CROWN COLONY

1

(2)

3

(T 1, 3 and 7 recess P.B.)

1861 (8 May). *No wmk. Rough to intermediate perf* 14 *to* 16.

1 1 1d. rose-red .. .. 45·00 14·0[0]
a. Imperf vert (horiz pair) £300
b. Imperf (pair) £250
2 6d. deep yellow-green .. .. .. £6500 £20[0]

The perforations on the 1d. are usually rough, but individual examples can be found on which some, or all, of the holes have the appearance of the intermediate perforations. All examples of the 6d. show imtermediate perforations.

Imperforate examples, possibly proofs, exist of the 1d. rose-red and 6d. deep green handstamped "CANCELLED" in oval of bars (see note on Perkins Bacon "CANCELLED" in Catalogue Introduction). (*Price* 1d. £4000 6d. £5000)

1862 (Sept). *No wmk. Rough perf* 14 *to* 16.

4 1 6d. deep green .. .. 55·00 18·00
a. Imperf between (horiz pair) £3750 £4750
b. Imperf (pair) £850

-8. *No wmk. (a) P 11 to 12½.*
1d. rose-red (3.63) .. .. .. 35·00 15·00
4d. deep blue (*shades*) (1866) £275 £110
a. Imperf between (horiz pair) .. .. † —
6d. deep green (7.68) .. .. .. £200 75·00
1s. slate-grey (8.66) £1900 £900

(b) P 14 to 16
1s. slate-grey (*shades*) (8.66) £300 £140

(c) P 11 to 12½×14 to 16
1d. rose-red (1866) £3250 £1100
1s. slate-grey (*shades*) (8.66) £225 £120

Apr–Sep). *Colours changed. No wmk. P 11 to 12½.*
4d. yellow (9.69) £350 £160
1s. indigo .. .. £325 90·00
1s. brown (9.69) £450 £160

(Apr). *Wmk Small Star, W w* **2**. *Rough perf 14 to 16.*
1 1d. black .. .. 50·00 10·00
a. Imperf between (vert pair) .. £6000
6d. deep green .. .. .. £250 70·00
a. Wmk sideways .. .. .. — 85·00

(June). *Colour changed. W w* **2** *(sideways). P 11 to 12½.*
1s. deep rose-red £750 £140

-75. *W w* **2** *(sideways). (a) Perf about 15.*
1d. black (*shades*) (11.72) .. .. 45·00 7·50
a. Wmk upright .. .. .. 50·00 8·50
6d. dull blue-green (*shades*) (1873) .. £900 48·00
b. Deep blue-green (1875) .. .. £600 45·00
c. Wmk upright .. .. ..

(b) P 11 to 12½×15
1 1s. lilac-rose (1873) £5000 £350

Colour changed. W w **2** *(sideways). P 11 to 12½.*
1 1s. claret £600 £250

-78. *W w* **2** *(sideways). (a) P 11 to 12½×15.*
1 1d. black (*shades*) (4.75) .. .. 65·00 9·50
a. Imperf between (horiz pair) .. .. † £5500
b. Wmk upright .. .. .. — 50·00
6d. pale green (1877) .. .. £550 50·00
1s. vermilion (2.77) .. .. £900 85·00
a. Imperf vert (horiz pair) .. ..

(b) P 11 to 12½
1 4d. deep blue (7.77) .. .. .. £475 90·00

(c) Perf about 15
1 6d. pale green (3.77) £1500 £450
a. Wmk upright. *Lt yellow-green* (1878) £650 25·00
1s. vermilion (1878?) .. .. .. † £12000
a. Imperf .. .. † £6500

(May). *No. 19b divided vertically by a line of perforation gauging 12, and surch locally with T* **2** *in red.*
1 1d. on half 6d. deep blue-green £425 £325
a. Unsevered pair £1500 £1100

(June). *W w* **2** *(sideways). P 11 to 12½.*
1 1d. olive-green .. .. £130 3·75
6d. bright green .. .. .. £375 70·00
1s. bright vermilion .. .. .. £650 55·00
a. Imperf between (horiz pair) .. £7000
3 5s. rose-red £1000 £1200
a. Imperf £3750

d
1/2
(4)

ONE PENNY
(5)

4d
(6)

-81. *Nos. 30/1 surch locally. No. 33 is divided vertically as No. 28.*
4 ½d. on half 6d. bright green (R.) (1.9) .. £160 £160
a. Unsevered pair £400 £400
b. Fraction bar omitted (pair with and without bar) £3750 £4250
5 1d. on 6d. bright green (30.11) £450 £325
6 4d. on 1s. bright vermilion (28.11) .. £1400 £750

No. 33 exists showing the "1" of "½" with a straight serif. Some examples come from a constant variety on R. 6/20, but others are the result of faulty type.

It is believed that Type **4** was applied as a setting of 36 (6×6) surcharges repeated three times on each sheet across rows 1 to 9. The missing fraction bar occurs on R. 6/3 of the setting.

The tenth vertical row of stamps appears to have been surcharged from a separate setting of 12 (2×6) on which the constant "straight serif" flaw occurs on the bottom right half-stamp.

Three unused single copies of No. 33 are known with the surcharge omitted.

It is believed that Nos. 34 and 35 were surcharged in settings of 30 (10×3).

No. 34 was only on sale between the 30 November and 3 December when supplies of No. 37 became available.

7

2½ PENCE
(8)

1d
~~2½ PENCE~~
(9)

1881 (Dec). *W w* **2**. *P 11 to 12½.*
36 7 ½d. orange (*shades*) .. .. .. 7·00 3·50
37 1 1d. drab (*shades*) .. .. .. £500 8·50
38 4d. bright blue £1200 £110
a. Imperf between (horiz pair) .. ..

(Recess D.L.R. from Perkins, Bacon plates)

1882 (Nov)–**83**. *No. 40 is surch with T* **8**. *Wmk Crown CA. P 14.*
39 1 1d. drab .. .. 45·00 1·75
x. Wmk reversed .. .. .. 80·00 10·00
40 2½d. on 1d. lake (1883) .. .. .. 13·00 55
w. Wmk inverted .. .. ..
x. Wmk reversed .. .. .. 25·00 5·00
y. Wmk inverted and reversed ..
41 4d. ultramarine .. .. .. £425 35·00
a. Dull ultramarine £950 £350
w. Wmk inverted .. .. ..
x. Wmk reversed .. .. .. £425 35·00
y. Wmk inverted and reversed ..

1883–84. *Wmk Crown CA. P 12.*
42 7 ½d. green (1884) .. .. .. 80·00 26·00
x. Wmk reversed .. .. ..
43 1 4d. ultramarine-blue .. .. .. £400 22·00
a. Grey-blue £1000 £250
w. Wmk inverted .. .. ..
x. Wmk reversed .. .. .. £400 20·00
y. Wmk inverted and reversed ..
44 6d. bright green £150 £300
x. Wmk reversed .. .. ..
45 1s. orange-vermilion .. .. .. £120 60·00
x. Wmk reversed .. .. ..

The ½d. orange, 1d. rose-red, 1d. milky blue (without surcharge) and 5s. carmine-lake which were formerly listed are now considered to be colour trials. They are, however, of great interest (*Prices un.* ½d. £900, 1d. red £900, 1d. blue £1200, 5s. £1700).

1885 (Mar). *No. 40 further surch locally as in T* **9**.
46 1 1d. on 2½d. on 1d. lake .. .. .. 22·00 16·00
w. Wmk inverted .. .. ..
x. Wmk reversed .. .. .. 22·00 16·00

Stamps with three cancelling bars instead of two are considered to be proofs.

1885–93. *No. 49 is surch with T* **8**. *Wmk Crown CA. P 14.*
47 7 ½d. green .. .. 1·00 60
a. Deep green .. .. .. 2·50 60
w. Wmk inverted .. .. ..
x. Wmk reversed .. .. ..
48 1 1d. rose-red .. .. 3·00 1·00
a. Rose (1886) .. .. .. 4·75 1·75
b. Red (1887) .. .. .. 1·60 85
c. Carmine-red (1889) .. .. .. 24·00 3·75
w. Wmk inverted .. .. ..
x. Wmk reversed .. .. .. 5·00 1·50
49 2½d. on 1d. milky blue (1889) .. .. 23·00 5·50
x. Wmk reversed .. .. ..
50 4d. red-brown .. .. .. £850 22·00
x. Wmk reversed .. .. ..
51 4d. purple-brown (1886) .. .. 50·00 75
a. Chocolate (1887) .. .. .. 50·00 1·40
w. Wmk inverted .. .. ..
x. Wmk reversed .. .. ..
y. Wmk inverted and reversed ..
52 6d. violet (1888) £140 £160
w. Wmk inverted £150 £180
ws. Optd "Specimen" .. .. .. 75·00
x. Wmk reversed .. .. ..
53 3 5s. lake (1888) .. .. .. 27·00 50·00
a. Printed both sides £4250
b. Brown-lake (1893) .. .. .. 30·00 50·00
w. Wmk inverted .. .. ..
49s, 51s/2s Optd "Specimen" .. *Set of* 3 £180

2½d.
(10)

5
PENCE
(11)

1890 (Aug). *No. 51a surch locally with T* **10**.
54 1 2½d. on 4d. chocolate .. .. .. 75·00 £100
a. No fraction bar (R. 1/7, 2/4) £350 £400

1890–93. *No. 55 is surch with T* **8**. *Colours changed. Wmk Crown CA. P 14.*
55 1 2½d. on 1d. grey-blue (1890) .. .. 18·00 55
a. Blue (1893) .. .. .. 1·50 35
w. Wmk inverted .. .. ..
56 4d. yellow (1893) .. .. .. 1·60 7·50
s. Optd "Specimen" .. .. .. 30·00
57 6d. dull purple (1891) .. .. .. 2·25 11·00
58 1s. orange (1891) .. .. .. 5·50 11·00
a. Red-orange (1892) .. .. .. 11·00 17·00

1892 (Nov). *No. 51a surch locally with T* **11**, *in purple.*
59 1 5d. on 4d. chocolate .. .. .. 17·00 28·00
s. Optd "Specimen" .. .. .. 30·00
sa. Error. "Spicemen" £500

Some letters are known double due to loose type, the best known being the first "E", but they are not constant.

FIVE PENCE
(12)

13

14

1893–94. *Surch with T* **12**. *Wmk Crown CA. P 14.*
60 1 5d. on 6d. carmine-lake .. .. .. 20·00 30·00
a. Deep lake (1893) .. .. .. 1·00 1·75
b. Lake (1894) .. .. .. 1·75 4·25
c. Surch double £4000 £2500
s. Optd "Specimen" .. .. .. 45·00

(Recess D.L.R.)

1897 (13 July). *New values. Wmk Crown CA. P 14.*
61 1 2½d. blue .. .. 3·25 1·75
62 5d. sepia .. .. 5·50 19·00
61s/2s Optd "Specimen" .. .. *Set of* 2 60·00

1897 (6 Oct). *Surch as T* **12**. *Wmk Crown CA. P 14.*
63 1 3d. on 1d. mauve .. .. .. 5·00 17·00
a. Red-mauve .. .. .. 10·00 28·00
s. Optd "Specimen" .. .. .. 40·00

(Typo D.L.R.)

1899 (1 Jan). *Wmk Crown CA. P 14.*
67 13 ½d. dull mauve and green .. .. 2·75 2·50
68 1d. dull mauve and carmine .. .. 4·50 1·00
w. Wmk inverted £250
69 2½d. dull mauve and blue .. .. 4·00 2·00
70 3d. dull mauve and olive .. .. 4·00 13·00
71 4d. dull mauve and orange .. .. 4·00 17·00
72 5d. dull mauve and black .. .. 7·00 13·00
73 6d. dull mauve and brown .. .. 13·00 35·00
74 14 1s. green and carmine .. .. 13·00 48·00
75 5s. green and blue .. .. .. 75·00 £140
67/75 .. .. *Set of* 9 £110 £225
67s/75s Optd "Specimen" .. .. *Set of* 9 £170

15

16

(Typo D.L.R.)

1902. *Wmk Crown CA. P 14.*
76 15 ½d. dull purple and green .. .. 2·25 70
77 1d. dull purple and carmine .. .. 4·00 30
78 16 2d. dull purple and black .. .. 2·50 2·25
79 15 2½d. dull purple and blue .. .. 5·00 3·50
80 3d. dull purple and olive .. .. 5·00 2·75
81 6d. dull purple and brown .. .. 11·00 30·00
82 16 1s. green and carmine .. .. 24·00 55·00
83 15 2s. green and violet .. .. 25·00 55·00
84 16 5s. green and blue .. .. 70·00 £120
76/84 .. .. *Set of* 9 £130 £225
76s/84s Optd "Specimen" .. .. *Set of* 9 £120

1904–11. *Wmk Mult Crown CA. Ordinary paper (½d., 1d., 1s.) or chalk-surfaced paper (others). P 14.*
85 15 ½d. dull purple and green (1905) .. 7·00 2·50
a. Chalk-surfaced paper .. .. 1·25 1·25
86 1d. dull purple and carmine .. .. 24·00 1·50
a. Chalk-surfaced paper .. .. 20·00 1·50
88 2½d. dull purple and blue (1906) .. 16·00 42·00
89 6d. dull purple and brown (1905) .. 16·00 42·00
90 16 1s. green and carmine (1906) .. .. 18·00 48·00
a. Chalk-surfaced paper .. .. 11·00 55·00
91 15 2s. purple and bright blue/*blue* (3.09?) 22·00 42·00
92 16 5s. green and red/*yellow* (3.09?) .. 17·00 50·00
93 £1 purple and black/*red* (22.7.11) .. £275 £325
85/93 .. .. *Set of* 8 £350 £475
91s/3s Optd "Specimen" .. .. *Set of* 3 £190

Examples of most values are known showing a forged Kingstown postmark, code letter "O", dated "JA 7 10" or a forged Calliaqua postmark dated "SP 20 09". Both have also been seen on some values of the 1899 and 1902 issues.

17

18

(Recess D.L.R.)

1907–08. *Wmk Mult Crown CA. P 14.*
94 17 ½d. green (2.7.07) .. .. .. 3·25 2·25
95 1d. carmine (26.4.07) .. .. .. 3·50 15
96 2d. orange (5.08) .. .. .. 1·50 6·50
97 2½d. blue (8.07) .. .. .. 28·00 8·50
98 3d. violet (1.6.07) .. .. .. 8·00 15·00
94/8 .. .. *Set of* 5 40·00 29·00
94s/8s Optd "Specimen" .. .. *Set of* 5 £110

1909. *No dot below "d". Wmk Mult Crown CA. P 14.*
99 18 1d. carmine (3.09) .. .. .. 1·25 30
100 6d. dull purple (16.1.09) .. .. 5·50 32·00
101 1s. black/*green* (16.1.09) .. .. 4·25 8·50
99/101 .. .. *Set of* 3 10·00 38·00
99s/101s Optd "Specimen" .. .. *Set of* 3 70·00

1909 (Nov)–**11.** *T* **18**, *redrawn* (*dot below "d", as in T* **17**). *Wmk Mult Crown CA. P* 14.

102 ½d. green (31.10.10) 1·50 60
w. Wmk inverted 85·00
103 1d. carmine 1·50 20
104 2d. grey (3.8.11) 4·00 8·50
105 2½d. ultramarine (25.7.10) 8·00 3·50
106 3d. purple/*yellow* 2·50 7·00
107 6d. dull purple 10·00 5·00
102/7 *Set of* 6 25·00 22·00
102s, 104s/6s Optd "Specimen" *Set of* 4 85·00

19

ONE

PENNY.

(**20**)

(Recess D.L.R.)

1913 (1 Jan)–**17.** *Wmk Mult Crown CA. P* 14.

108 **19** ½d. green 75 20
109 1d. red 80 75
a. Rose-red 1·00 75
b. Scarlet (1.17) 14·00 5·00
w. Wmk inverted
y. Wmk inverted and reversed 75·00
110 2d. grey 7·00 28·00
a. Slate 3·00 28·00
111 2½d. ultramarine 50 75
x. Wmk reversed £100
112 3d. purple/*yellow* 80 5·00
a. On lemon 2·75 12·00
aw. Wmk inverted
ax. Wmk reversed
b. On pale yellow 2·50 9·00
113 4d. red/*yellow* 80 2·00
114 5d. olive-green (7.11.13) 2·25 14·00
x. Wmk reversed
115 6d. claret 2·00 4·50
116 1s. black/*green* 1·50 3·75
117 1s. bistre (1.5.14) 4·00 23·00
118 **18** 2s. blue and purple 4·75 25·00
119 5s. carmine and myrtle 13·00 48·00
x. Wmk reversed £170
120 £1 mauve and black 85·00 £160
108/20 *Set of* 13 £110 £275
108s/20s Optd "Specimen" *Set of* 13 £250

Nos. 118/20 are from new centre and frame dies, the motto "PAX ET JUSTITIA" being slightly over 7 mm long, as against just over 8 mm in Nos. 99 to 107. Nos. 139/41 are also from the new dies.

Examples of several values are known showing part strikes of the forged postmarks mentioned below Nos. 85/93.

1915. *No.* 116 *surch with T* **20**.

121 **19** 1d. on 1s. black/*green* (R.) 7·50 26·00
a. "ONE" omitted £900 £800
b. "ONE" double £650
c. "PENNY" and bar double £650 £650

The spacing between the two words varies from 7¾ mm to 10 mm.

WAR STAMP. (**21**) WAR STAMP. (**22**) WAR STAMP (**24**)

1916 (June). *No.* 109 *optd locally with T* **21**. (*a*) *First and second settings; words 2 to 2½ mm apart.*

122 **19** 1d. red 4·50 8·00
a. Opt double £160 £160
b. Comma for stop 8·00 15·00
w. Wmk inverted

In the first printing every second stamp has the comma for stop. The second printing of this setting has full stops only. These two printings can therefore only be distinguished in blocks or pairs.

(*b*) *Third setting; words only 1½ mm apart*

123 **19** 1d. red 80·00
a. Opt double £1100

Stamps of the first setting are offered as this rare one. Care must be taken to see that the distance between the lines is not over 1½ mm.

(*c*) *Fourth setting; optd with T* **22**. *Words 3½ mm apart*

124 **19** 1d. carmine-red 3·00 11·00
a. Opt double £225
w. Wmk inverted
y. Wmk inverted and reversed

1916 (Aug)–**18.** *T* **19**, *from new printings, optd with T* **24**.

126 1d. carmine-red 30 80
s. Optd "Specimen" 60·00
w. Wmk inverted
x. Wmk reversed
127 1d. pale rose-red 80 80
w. Wmk inverted 60·00
x. Wmk reversed
128 1d. deep rose-red 65 80
129 1d. pale scarlet (1918) 30 80

1921–32. *Wmk Mult Script CA. P* 14.

131 **19** ½d. green (3.21) 1·75 30
132 1d. carmine (6.21) 1·00 80
a. Red 2·50 15
132*b* 1½d. brown (1.12.32) 3·00 15
133 2d. grey (3.22) 2·50 80
133*a* 2½d. bright blue (12.25) 1·25 75
134 3d. bright blue (3.22) 1·00 6·00
135 3d. purple/*yellow* (1.12.26) 1·00 1·50
135*a* 4d. red/*yellow* (9.30) 1·75 6·00
136 5d. sage-green (8.3.24) 1·00 6·50
137 6d. claret (1.11.27) 1·50 3·50
138 1s. bistre-brown (9.21) 6·00 25·00
a. Ochre (1927) 3·25 17·00
139 **18** 2s. blue and purple (8.3.24) 7·50 13·00
140 5s. carmine and myrtle (8.3.24) 18·00 32·00
141 £1 mauve and black (9.28) 80·00 £120
131/41 *Set of* 14 £110 £180
131s/41s Optd or Perf (1½d., 4d., £1) "Specimen" *Set of* 14 £250

Examples of Nos. 140/1 are known with forged postmarks, including part strikes of those mentioned above, and others from Kingstown dated "6 MY 35" and "16 MY 41".

1935 (6 May). *Silver Jubilee. As Nos.* 91/4 *of Antigua, but ptd by Waterlow. P* 11×12.

142 1d. deep blue and scarlet 40 2·00
143 1½d. ultramarine and grey 1·00 3·50
144 2½d. brown and deep blue 1·90 3·50
145 1s. slate and purple 2·00 3·50
l. Kite and horizontal log £275
142/5 *Set of* 4 4·75 11·00
142s/5s Perf "Specimen" *Set of* 4 75·00

For illustration of plate variety see Omnibus section following Zanzibar.

1937 (12 May). *Coronation. As Nos.* 95/7 *of Antigua. P* 11×11½.

146 1d. violet 35 40
147 1½d. carmine 40 30
148 2½d. blue 45 1·50
146/8 *Set of* 3 1·10 2·00
146s/8s Perf "Specimen" *Set of* 3 50·00

25

26 Young's Island and Fort Duvernette

27 Kingstown and Fort Charlotte

28 Bathing Beach at Villa

29 Victoria Park, Kingstown

NEW CONSTITUTION 1951

(**29*a***)

(Recess B.W.)

1938 (11 Mar)–**47.** *Wmk Mult Script CA. P* 12.

149 **25** ½d. blue and green 20 10
150 **26** 1d. blue and lake-brown 20 10
151 **27** 1½d. green and scarlet 20 10
152 **25** 2d. green and black 40 35
153 **28** 2½d. blue-black and blue-green 20 40
153*a* **29** 2½d. green and purple-brown (1947) 40 20
154 **25** 3d. orange and purple 20 10
154*a* **28** 3½d. blue-black and blue-green (1947) 40 2·25
155 **25** 6d. black and lake 1·00 40
156 **29** 1s. purple and green 1·00 80
157 **25** 2s. blue and purple 6·00 75
157*a* 2s. 6d. red-brown and blue (1947) 1·25 3·50
158 5s. scarlet and deep green 10·00 2·50
158*a* 10s. violet and brown (1947) 3·75 8·50
aw. Wmk inverted £3500 £1300
159 £1 purple and black 16·00 15·00
149/59 *Set of* 15 35·00 30·00
149s/59s Perf "Specimen" *Set of* 15 £250

1946 (15 Oct). *Victory. As Nos.* 110/11 *of Antigua.*

160 1½d. carmine 10 10
161 3½d. blue 10 10
160s/1s Perf "Specimen" *Set of* 2 50·00

1948 (30 Nov). *Royal Silver Wedding. As Nos.* 112/13 *of Antigua.*

162 1½d. scarlet 10 10
163 £1 bright purple 15·00 18·00

No. 163 was originally printed in black, but the supply of these was stolen in transit. A few archive examples exist, some perforated "Specimen".

(New Currency. 100 cents = 1 West Indian dollar)

1949 (26 Mar)–**52.** *Value in cents and dollars. Wmk Mult Script CA. P* 12.

164 **25** 1 c. blue and green 20 1·50
164*a* 1 c. green and black (10.6.52) 30 2·25
165 **26** 2 c. blue and lake-brown 15 50
166 **27** 3 c. green and scarlet 50 90
166*a* **25** 3 c. orange and purple (10.6.52) 30 2·25
167 4 c. green and black 35 20
167*a* 4 c. blue and green (10.6.52) 30 20
168 **29** 5 c. green and purple-brown 15 10
169 **25** 6 c. orange and purple 50 1·25
169*a* **27** 6 c. green and scarlet (10.6.52) 30 2·25
170 **28** 7 c. blue-black and blue-green 4·50
170*a* 10 c. blue-black and blue-green (10.6.52) 50
171 **25** 12 c. black and lake 35
172 **29** 24 c. purple and green 35
173 **25** 48 c. blue and purple 2·50
174 60 c. red-brown and blue 1·75
175 $1.20, scarlet and deep green 4·25
176 $2.40, violet and brown 6·00
177 $4.80, purple and black 11·00
164/77 *Set of* 19 30·00

1949 (10 Oct). *75th Anniv of U.P.U. As Nos.* 114/17 *of An*

178 5 c. blue 20
179 6 c. purple 1·00
180 12 c. magenta 20
181 24 c. blue-green 20
178/81 *Set of* 4 1·40

1951 (16 Feb). *Inauguration of B.W.I. University Colle*
Nos. 118/19 *of Antigua.*

182 3 c. deep green and scarlet 30
183 12 c. black and purple 30

1951 (21 Sept). *New Constitution. Optd with T* **29*a*** *by B.*

184 **27** 3 c. green and scarlet 15
185 **25** 4 c. green and black 15
186 **29** 5 c. green and purple-brown 15
187 **25** 12 c. black and lake 65
184/7 *Set of* 4 1·00

Sarawak

ıwak was placed under British protection in 1888. It was to Great Britain on 1 July 1946 and was administered as a Colony until 16 September 1963 when it became a state of ederation of Malaysia.

'rom 1859 letters from Sarawak to overseas addresses, er than to other British possessions in Borneo and gapore, were franked by stamps of INDIA and, after 57, STRAITS SETTLEMENTS, a stock of which was ɔt by the Sarawak Post Office. The stamps of Sarawak tinued to have this limited validity until 1 July 1897 en the country joined the U.P.U.

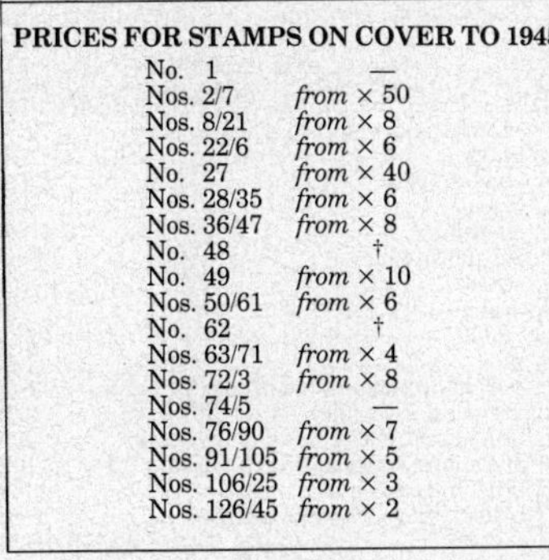

PRICES FOR STAMPS ON COVER TO 1945

No. 1	—
Nos. 2/7	*from* × 50
Nos. 8/21	*from* × 8
Nos. 22/6	*from* × 6
No. 27	*from* × 40
Nos. 28/35	*from* × 6
Nos. 36/47	*from* × 8
No. 48	†
No. 49	*from* × 10
Nos. 50/61	*from* × 6
No. 62	†
Nos. 63/71	*from* × 4
Nos. 72/3	*from* × 8
Nos. 74/5	—
Nos. 76/90	*from* × 7
Nos. 91/105	*from* × 5
Nos. 106/25	*from* × 3
Nos. 126/45	*from* × 2

BROOKE FAMILY ADMINISTRATION

Sir James Brooke. 1842–11 June 1868
Sir Charles Brooke. 11 June 1868–17 May 1917

USED PRICES. Nos. 1/7, 27 and 32/5 in unused condition are nally found to be without gum. Prices in the unused column are tamps in this state. Examples of these issues with original gum worth considerably more.

1 Sir James Brooke

2 Sir Charles Brooke

'he initials in the corners of T **1** and **2** stand for "James (Charles) oke, Rajah (of) Sarawak".

and **2**. Die eng Wm. Ridgway. Litho Maclure, Macdonald & Co, Glasgow)

9 (1 Mar). *P* 11.

1		3 c. brown/*yellow*	45·00	£225

imilar stamps are known printed from the engraved die in nge-brown on orange surface-coloured paper, and perf 12. ese are specimens submitted to the Sarawak authorities and st both with and without obliterations.

71 (1 Jan). *P* 11 (*irregular*).

2		3 c. brown/*yellow*	1·75	3·50
		a. Stop after "THREE"	42·00	55·00
		b. Imperf between (vert pair)	£475	
		c. Imperf between (horiz pair)	£750	

The "stop" variety, No. 2a, which occurs on R. 10/7 is of no ɔre philatelic importance than any of the numerous other riations, such as narrow first "A" in "SARAWAK" (R. 2/7) and " with long tail in left lower corner (R. 9/10), but it has been epted by collectors for many years, and we therefore retain it. e papermaker's wmk "L N L" appears once or twice in sheets No. 2.

Specimens are known, recess-printed, similar to those entioned in the note after No. 1.

TWO CENTS

Copies of No. 2 surcharged as above were first reported in 376 but following the discovery of dies for forgeries and faked ɔstmarks in 1891 it was concluded that the issue was bogus, pecially as the availability of the 2 c. of 1875 made it nnecessary to issue a provisional. It has now been established at a 2 c. postal rate was introduced from 1 August 1874 for the arriage of newspapers. Moreover four examples are known ith a stop after "CENTS." and showing other minor differences om the forgery illustrated. This version could be genuine and if hers come to light we will reconsider listing it.

875 (1 Jan). *P* 11½–12.

2		2 c. mauve/*lilac* (*shades*)	4·25	17·00
		4 c. red-brown/*yellow*	3·25	3·00
		a. Imperf between (vert pair)	£650	
		6 c. green/*green*	3·25	3·50
		8 c. bright blue/*blue*	3·25	3·50
		12 c. red/*pale rose*	6·50	6·50
/7		*Set of* 5	18·00	30·00

Nos. 3, 4, 6 and 7 have the watermark "L N L" in the sheet, as No. 2. No. 5 is watermarked "L N T".

All values exist imperf and can be distinguished from the proofs by shade and impression. Stamps rouletted, pin-perf, or roughly perf 6½ to 7 are proofs clandestinely perforated.

The 12 c. "laid" paper, formerly listed, is not on a true laid paper, the "laid" effect being accidental and not consistent.

The lithographic stones for Nos. 3 to 7 were made up from strips of five distinct impressions hence there are five types of each value differing mainly in the lettering of the tablets of value. There are flaws on nearly every individual stamp, from which they can be plated.

4 Sir Charles Brooke

(Typo D.L.R.)

1888 (10 Nov)–**1897.** *No wmk. P* 14.

8	**4**	1 c. purple and black (6.6.92)	1·75	50
9		2 c. purple and carmine (11.11.88)	1·75	1·25
		a. Purple and rosine (1897)	9·00	3·75
10		3 c. purple and blue (11.11.88)	2·50	2·00
11		4 c. purple and yellow	14·00	48·00
12		5 c. purple and green (12.6.91)	10·00	2·25
13		6 c. purple and brown (11.11.88)	12·00	55·00
14		8 c. green and carmine (11.11.88)	8·00	2·75
		a. Green and rosine (1897)	20·00	15·00
15		10 c. green and purple (12.6.91)	38·00	14·00
16		12 c. green and blue (11.11.88)	7·00	8·00
17		16 c. green and orange (28.12.97)	42·00	70·00
18		25 c. green and brown (19.11.88)	38·00	35·00
19		32 c. green and black (28.12.97)	27·00	50·00
20		50 c. green (26.7.97)	32·00	80·00
21		$1 green and black (2.11.97)	65·00	75·00
8/21		*Set of* 14	£275	£400

Prepared for use but not issued

21*a*	$2 green and blue	£600	
21*b*	$5 green and violet	£600	
21*c*	$10 green and carmine	£600	

On No. 21 the value is in black on an uncoloured ground.

The tablet of value in this and later similar issues is in the second colour given.

One Cent. (5)

one cent. (6)

2c (7)

5c (8)

5c. (9)

1889 (3 Aug)–**92.** *T* **4** *surch. P* 14.

22	**5**	1 c. on 3 c. purple and blue (12.1.92)	38·00	27·00
		a. Surch double	£550	£450
23	**6**	1 c. on 3 c. purple and blue (2.92)	2·75	2·75
		a. No stop after "cent" (R. 2/6)	£130	
24	**7**	2 c. on 8 c. green and carmine (3.8.89)	3·00	5·00
		a. Surch double	£400	
		b. Surch inverted	£2000	
		c. Surch omitted (in pair with normal)	£3750	
25	**8**	5 c. on 12 c. green and blue (with stop after "C") (17.2.91)	24·00	45·00
		a. No stop after "C"	24·00	42·00
		b. "C" omitted	£350	£350
		c. Surch double	£950	
		d. Surch double, one vertical	£2500	
		e. Surch omitted (in pair with normal)	£6500	
26	**9**	5 c. on 12 c. green and blue (17.2.91)	95·00	£150
		a. No stop after "C"	80·00	95·00
		b. "C" omitted	£475	£500
		c. Surch double	£1200	

ONE
CENT

(10)

1892 (23 May). *No.* 2 *surch with T* **10**.

27	**2**	1 c. on 3 c. brown/*yellow*	1·40	2·00
		a. Stop after "THREE."	32·00	38·00
		b. Imperf between (vert pair)	£600	
		c. Imperf horiz (vert pair)	£550	
		d. Bar omitted (1st ptg)	£180	
		e. Bar at top and bottom (1st ptg)	£225	
		f. Surch double (2nd ptg)	£350	£375

No. 27 was surcharged with a setting of 100 (10 × 10). It was originally intended that there should be no bar at foot, but this was then added at a second operation before the stamps were issued. Subsequent supplies were surcharged with "ONE CENT" and bar at one operation.

Varieties with part of the surcharge missing are due to gum on the face of the unsurcharged stamps receiving part of the surcharge, which was afterwards washed off.

11

12

13 Sir Charles Brooke

14

(Die eng Wm. Ridgeway. Recess P.B.)

1895 (12 Feb–Sept). *No wmk. P* 11½–12.

28	**11**	2 c. brown-red	7·00	9·00
		a. Imperf between (vert pair)	£400	
		b. Imperf between (horiz pair)	£325	
		c. Second ptg. Perf 12½ (Sept.)	9·00	4·50
		ca. Perf 12½. Imperf between (horiz pair)	£425	
29	**12**	4 c. black	6·50	3·50
		a. Imperf between (horiz pair)	£500	
30	**13**	6 c. violet	7·50	9·00
31	**14**	8 c. green	25·00	6·00
28/31		*Set of* 4	40·00	21·00

Stamps of these types, printed in wrong colours, are trials and these, when surcharged with values in "pence", are from waste sheets that were used by Perkins, Bacon & Co as trial paper when preparing an issue of stamps for British South Africa.

4
CENTS.

(15)

16

1899 (29 June–16 Nov). *Surch as T* **15**.

32	**2**	2 c. on 3 c. brown/*yellow* (19 Sept)	1·40	1·75
		a. Stop after "THREE"	48·00	50·00
		b. Imperf between (vert pair)	£850	
33		2 c. on 12 c. red/*pale rose*	2·75	3·00
		a. Surch inverted	£750	£1100
34		4 c. on 6 c. green/*green* (R.) (16 Nov)	25·00	55·00
35		4 c. on 8 c. bright blue/*blue* (R.)	3·50	6·50
32/5		*Set of* 4	29·00	60·00

A variety of surcharge with small "S" in "CENTS" may be found in the 2 c. on 12 c. and 4 c. on 8 c. and a raised stop after "CENTS" on the 4 c. on 6 c.

The omission of parts of the surcharge is due to gum on the surface of the stamps (see note after No. 27).

A block of 50 of No. 35 from the right of the pane is known line perforated 12.7 between the stamps and the margins at top and right.

(Typo D.L.R.)

1899 (10 Nov)–**1908.** *Inscribed* "POSTAGE POSTAGE." *No wmk. P* 14.

36	**4**	1 c. grey-blue and rosine (1.1.01)	1·25	1·25
		a. Grey-blue and red	4·50	1·75
		b. Ultramarine and rosine	7·00	2·50
		c. Dull blue and carmine	14·00	4·50
37		2 c. green (16.12.99)	2·00	90
38		3 c. dull purple (1.2.08)	6·50	65
39		4 c. rose-carmine (10.11.99)	7·50	2·50
		a. Aniline carmine	2·50	15
40		8 c. yellow and black (6.12.99)	1·75	80
41		10 c. ultramarine (10.11.99)	2·50	1·00
42		12 c. mauve (16.12.99)	4·50	4·50
		a. Bright mauve (1905)	22·00	8·00
43		16 c. chestnut and green (16.12.99)	2·50	1·75
44		20 c. bistre and bright mauve (4.00)	5·50	3·50
45		25 c. brown and blue (16.12.99)	4·25	5·00
46		50 c. sage-green and carmine (16.12.99)	20·00	23·00
47		$1 rose-carmine and green (16.12.99)	50·00	£110
		a. Rosine and pale green	70·00	£110
36/47		*Set of* 12	90·00	£130

Prepared for use but not issued

48	**4**	5 c. olive-grey and green	12·00	

The figures of value in the $1 are in colour on an uncoloured ground.

1902. *Inscribed* "POSTAGE POSTAGE". *W* **16**. *P* 14.

49	**4**	2 c. green	20·00	14·00

Sir Charles Vyner Brooke. 17 May 1917–1 June 1946

17 Sir Charles Vyner Brooke

ONE
cent

(18)

(Typo D.L.R.)

1918 (24 Mar–Apr). *No wmk. Chalk-surfaced paper. P* 14.

50	**17**	1 c. slate-blue and red	2·25	2·50
		a. Dull blue and carmine	2·25	2·50
51		2 c. green	2·50	1·50
52		3 c. brown-purple (Apr)	3·25	2·75
53		4 c. rose-carmine (Apr)	4·00	3·00
		a. Rose-red	4·50	3·00
54		8 c. yellow and black (Apr)	12·00	60·00
55		10 c. blue (*shades*) (Apr)	3·00	3·00
56		12 c. purple (Apr)	11·00	25·00
57		16 c. chestnut and green (Apr)	5·50	7·50

No.	Type	Description	Mint	Used
58	17	20 c. olive and violet (*shades*) (Apr)	7·00	6·50
59		25 c. brown and bright blue (Apr)	4·00	11·00
60		50 c. olive-green and carmine (Apr)	10·00	15·00
61		$1 bright rose and green (Apr)	16·00	28·00
50/61		*Set of* 12	70·00	£150
50s/61s Optd "Specimen"		*Set of* 12	£200	

Prepared for use but not issued

No.	Type	Description	Mint	Used
62	17	1 c. slate-blue and slate	22·00	

On the $1 the figures of value are in colour on an uncoloured ground.

Most values are known with part strikes of a forged Kuching postmark dated "12 MAR 90".

1922 (Jan)–**23.** *New colours and values. No wmk. Chalk-surfaced paper. P* 14.

No.	Type	Description	Mint	Used
63	17	2 c. purple (5.3.23)	2·00	2·50
64		3 c. dull green (23.3.22)	1·50	1·25
65		4 c. brown-purple (10.4.23)	1·50	85
66		5 c. yellow-orange	1·75	90
67		6 c. claret	1·50	1·40
68		8 c. bright rose-red (1922)	4·50	32·00
69		10 c. black (1923)	2·00	3·75
70		12 c. bright blue (12.22)	10·00	18·00
		a. Pale dull blue	9·50	17·00
71		30 c. ochre-brown and slate	3·75	4·25
63/71		*Set of* 9	25·00	55·00

1923 (Jan). *Surch as T* **18**. (*a*) *First printing. Bars* $1^1/_4$ *mm apart.*

No.	Type	Description	Mint	Used
72	17	1 c. on 10 c. dull blue	10·00	55·00
		a. "cnet" for "cent" (R. 9/5)	£325	£750
73		2 c. on 12 c. purple	6·50	40·00
		a. Thick, narrower "W" in "TWO"	18·00	85·00

(*b*) *Second printing. Bars* $^3/_4$ *mm apart*

No.	Type	Description	Mint	Used
74	17	1 c. on 10 c. dull blue	£275	
		b. "cnet" for "cent" (R. 9/5)	£10000	
		c. Bright blue	£110	£325
		ca. "en" of "cent" scratched out and "ne" overprinted (R. 9/5)	£4000	
75		2 c. on 12 c. purple	65·00	£190
		a. Thick, narrower "W" in "TWO"	£140	

In the 2 c. on 12 c. the words of the surcharge are about $7^1/_2$ mm from the bars.

The "cnet" error occurred on R.9/5 of all sheets from the first printing of the 1 c. on 10 c. A single example of the error, No. 74b, is known from the second printing, but the error was then corrected, as shown by the evidence of a surviving plate block, only to have the correct spelling scratched out, by a local employee, and "ne" substituted (No. 74ca).

The thick "W" variety occurs on all stamps of the last two horizontal rows of the first printing (12 stamps per sheet), and in the last two vertical rows of the second (20 stamps per sheet).

1928 (7 Apr)–**29.** *W* **16** (*Multiple*). *Chalk-surfaced paper. P* 14.

No.	Type	Description	Mint	Used
76	17	1 c. slate-blue and carmine	1·25	35
77		2 c. bright purple	1·25	1·25
78		3 c. green	1·50	5·00
79		4 c. brown-purple	1·50	10
80		5 c. yellow-orange (7.8.29)	10·00	5·00
81		6 c. claret	1·25	30
82		8 c. bright rose-red	3·25	14·00
83		10 c. black	1·75	1·25
84		12 c. bright blue	3·25	20·00
85		16 c. chestnut and green	3·25	4·00
86		20 c. olive-bistre and violet	3·25	5·50
87		25 c. brown and bright blue	5·50	8·50
88		30 c. bistre-brown and slate	4·50	10·00
89		50 c. olive-green and carmine	5·50	12·00
90		$1 bright rose and carmine	15·00	24·00
76/90		*Set of* 15	55·00	£100
76s/90s Optd or Perf (5 c.) "Specimen"		*Set of* 15	£250	

In the $1 the value is as before.

19 Sir Charles Vyner Brooke

20

(Recess Waterlow)

1932 (1 Jan). *W* **20.** *P* $12^1/_2$.

No.	Type	Description	Mint	Used
91	19	1 c. indigo	80	1·00
92		2 c. green	80	1·25
93		3 c. violet	3·25	1·00
94		4 c. red-orange	1·75	75
95		5 c. deep lake	7·00	1·25
96		6 c. scarlet	8·50	9·00
97		8 c. orange-yellow	4·50	8·50
98		10 c. black	2·25	3·25
99		12 c. deep ultramarine	4·00	9·00
100		15 c. chestnut	7·00	8·00
101		20 c. red-orange and violet	5·50	7·50
102		25 c. orange-yellow and chestnut	12·00	21·00
103		30 c. sepia and vermilion	9·00	21·00
104		50 c. carmine-red and olive-green	10·00	13·00
105		$1 green and carmine	18·00	32·00
91/105		*Set of* 15	85·00	£120
91s/105s Perf "Specimen"		*Set of* 15	£275	

21 Sir Charles Vyner Brooke

BMA

(22)

(Recess B.W.)

1934 (1 May)–**41.** *No wmk. P* 12.

No.	Type	Description	Mint	Used
106	21	1 c. purple	60	10
107		2 c. green	80	10
107*a*		2 c. black (1.3.41)	2·75	1·60
108		3 c. black	70	10
108*a*		3 c. green (1.3.41)	5·00	4·50
109		4 c. bright purple	70	15
110		5 c. violet	1·25	10
111		6 c. carmine	2·00	60
111*a*		6 c. lake-brown (1.3.41)	6·00	8·00
112		8 c. red-brown	2·00	10
112*a*		8 c. carmine (1.3.41)	6·50	10
113		10 c. scarlet	1·75	40
114		12 c. blue	2·50	25
114*a*		12 c. orange (1.3.41)	4·00	4·75
115		15 c. orange	2·75	8·00
115*a*		15 c. blue (1.3.41)	6·50	15·00
116		20 c. olive-green and carmine	3·00	80
117		25 c. violet and orange	3·00	1·50
118		30 c. red-brown and violet	3·00	2·50
119		50 c. violet and scarlet	3·00	75
120		$1 scarlet and sepia	1·00	75
121		$2 bright purple and violet	10·00	8·50
122		$3 carmine and green	27·00	28·00
123		$4 blue and scarlet	27·00	40·00
124		$5 scarlet and red-brown	27·00	38·00
125		$10 black and yellow	21·00	48·00
106/25		*Set of* 26	£150	£190
106s/25s Perf "Specimen"		*Set of* 26	£450	

For the 3 c. green, wmkd Mult Script CA, see No. 152a.

BRITISH MILITARY ADMINISTRATION

Following the Japanese surrender elements of the British Military Administration reached Kuching on 11 September 1945. From 5 November 1945 current Australian 1d., 3d., 6d. and 1s. stamps were made available for civilian use until replaced by Nos. 126/45. Other Australian stamps were also accepted as valid for postage during this period.

1945 (17 Dec). *Optd with T* **22**.

No.	Type	Description	Mint	Used
126	21	1 c. purple	75	60
127		2 c. black (R.)	75	70
		a. Opt double	†	£4500
128		3 c. green	75	70
129		4 c. bright purple	75	30
		a. Opt double, one albino	£1500	
130		5 c. violet (R.)	1·50	90
131		6 c. lake-brown	2·00	75
132		8 c. carmine	13·00	11·00
133		10 c. scarlet	1·00	70
134		12 c. orange	1·50	3·75
135		15 c. blue	2·75	40
136		20 c. olive-green and carmine	2·50	1·75
137		25 c. violet and orange (R.)	2·50	2·75
138		30 c. red-brown and violet	6·00	2·75
139		50 c. violet and scarlet	1·25	35
140		$1 scarlet and sepia	2·50	1·25
141		$2 bright purple and violet	9·00	9·00
142		$3 carmine and green	17·00	45·00
143		$4 blue and scarlet	25·00	35·00
144		$5 scarlet and red-brown	£130	£160
145		$10 black and yellow (R.)	£130	£180
126/45		*Set of* 20	£300	£400

These stamps, and the similarly overprinted stamps of North Borneo, were obtainable at all post offices throughout British Borneo (Brunei, Labuan, North Borneo and Sarawak), for use on local and overseas mail.

The administration of Sarawak was returned to the Brooke family on 15 April 1946, but the Rajah, after consulting the inhabitants, ceded the territory to Great Britain on 1 June 1946. Values from the 1934–41 issue were used until replaced by Nos. 150/64.

23 Sir James Brooke, Sir Charles Vyner Brooke and Sir Charles Brooke

(24)

(Recess B.W.)

1946 (18 May). *Centenary Issue. P* 12.

No.	Type	Description	Mint	Used
146	23	8 c. lake	1·10	60
147		15 c. blue	1·10	1·75
148		50 c. black and scarlet	1·25	2·00
149		$1 black and sepia	1·50	16·00
146/9		*Set of* 4	4·50	18·00
146s/9s Perf "Specimen"		*Set of* 4	95·00	

CROWN COLONY

1947 (16 Apr). *Optd with T* **24**, *typo by B.W. in blue-black or red. Wmk Mult Script CA. P* 12.

No.	Type	Description	Mint	Used
150	21	1 c. purple	15	30
151		2 c. black (R.)	15	15
152		3 c. green (R.)	15	15
		a. Albino opt	£4250	
153		4 c. bright purple	15	15
154		6 c. lake-brown	20	90
155		8 c. carmine	60	10
156		10 c. scarlet	20	20
157		12 c. orange	20	90
158		15 c. blue (R.)	20	40
159		20 c. olive-green and carmine (R.)	1·50	50
160		25 c. violet and orange (R.)	40	30
161		50 c. violet and scarlet (R.)	40	40
162		$1 scarlet and sepia	75	90
163		$2 bright purple and violet	1·40	3·25
164		$5 scarlet and red-brown	3·00	3·25
150/64		*Set of* 15	8·00	10·50
150s/64s Perf "Specimen"		*Set of* 15	£300	

No. 152a shows an uninked impression of T **24**.

1948 (25 Oct). *Royal Silver Wedding. As Nos.* 112 *Antigua.*

No.	Type	Description	Mint	Used
165		8 c. scarlet	30	
166		$5 brown	30·00	

1949 (10 Oct). *75th Anniv of U.P.U. As Nos.* 114/17 *of An*

No.	Type	Description	Mint	Used
167		8 c. carmine	1·25	
168		15 c. deep blue	2·50	
169		25 c. deep blue-green	2·00	
170		50 c. violet	2·00	
167/70		*Set of* 4	7·00	

25 *Trogonoptera brookiana* **26** Western Tarsier

(Recess; Arms typo B.W.)

1950 (3 Jan). *T* **25/6** *and similar designs. Wmk Mult Scrip P* $11^1/_2 \times 11$ (*horiz*) *or* $11 \times 11^1/_2$ (*vert*).

No.	Type	Description	Mint	Used
171		1 c. black	30	
172		2 c. red-orange	20	
173		3 c. green	20	
174		4 c. chocolate	20	
175		6 c. turquoise-blue	20	
176		8 c. scarlet	20	
177		10 c. orange	65	
178		12 c. violet	3·00	
179		15 c. blue	1·50	
180		20 c. purple-brown and red-orange	1·00	
181		25 c. green and scarlet	2·25	
182		50 c. brown and violet	2·50	
183		$1 green and chocolate	17·00	
184		$2 blue and carmine	25·00	
185		$5 black, yellow, red and purple	19·00	
171/85		*Set of* 15	60·00	

Designs: *Horiz*—8 c. Dayak dancer; 10 c. Malayan Pang 12 c. Kenyah boys; 15 c. Fire-making; 20 c. Kelemantan barn; 25 c. Pepper vines; $1 Kelabit smithy; $2 Map of Sara $5 Arms of Sarawak. *Vert*—3 c. Kayan tomb; 4 c. Kayan gir boy; 6 c. Bead work; 50 c. Iban woman.

40 Map of Sarawak

(Recess B.W.)

1952 (1 Feb). *Wmk Mult Script CA. P* $11^1/_2 \times 11$.

No.	Type	Description	Mint	Used
186	40	10 c. orange	1·50	

JAPANESE OCCUPATION OF SARAWAK

Japanese forces landed in North Borneo on 16 December 1 and Sarawak was attacked on 23 December 1941.

Brunei, North Borneo, Sarawak and after a short pe Labuan, were administered as a single territory by Japanese. Until September–October 1942, previous sta issues, without overprint, continued to be used in conjunct with existing postmarks. From 1 October 1942 onwa unoverprinted stamps of Japan were made available examples can be found used from the area for much of remainder of the War. Japanese Occupation issues for Bru North Borneo and Sarawak were equally valid throughout combined territory but not, in practice, equally available.

PRICES FOR STAMPS ON COVER	
Nos. J1/21	*from* × 8
Nos. J22/6	—

府政國帝本日大

(1)

("Imperial Japanese Government")

1942 (Oct). *Stamps of Sarawak handstamped with T* **1** *violet.*

No.	Type	Description	Mint	Used
J 1	21	1 c. purple	32·00	70·
		a. Pair, one without opt	£1500	
J 2		2 c. green	85·00	£1
		a. Black opt	85·00	
J 3		2 c. black	80·00	95·
		a. Black opt	£110	£1
J 4		3 c. black	£300	£3
J 5		3 c. green	45·00	80·
		a. Black opt	90·00	
J 6		4 c. bright purple	60·00	80·
		a. Black opt	90·00	
J 7		5 c. violet	70·00	80·
		a. Black opt	90·00	
J 8		6 c. carmine	£100	£11
J 9		6 c. lake-brown	70·00	80·
		a. Black opt	90·00	£10
J10		8 c. red-brown	£300	£30
		a. Black opt	£425	
J11		8 c. carmine	75·00	£12
		a. Black opt	£180	£20
J12		10 c. scarlet	65·00	85·0
		a. Black opt	90·00	

12 c. blue	£130	£150
a. Black opt	£180	
12 c. orange	£130	£160
15 c. orange	£300	£300
a. Black opt	£350	
15 c. blue	85·00	95·00
20 c. olive-green and carmine	50·00	85·00
a. Black opt	90·00	
25 c. violet and orange	80·00	85·00
a. Black opt	£100	
30 c. red-brown and violet	60·00	85·00
a. Black opt	90·00	
50 c. violet and scarlet	65·00	85·00
a. Black opt	£180	
b. Blue opt	£350	
$1 scarlet and sepia	85·00	£110
a. Blue opt	£225	
$2 bright purple and violet	£170	£225
a. Blue opt	£275	
$3 carmine and green	£1200	£1300
a. Black opt	£1700	
$4 blue and scarlet	£190	£300
$5 scarlet and red-brown	£200	£300
$10 black and yellow	£200	£300

overprint, being handstamped, exists inverted or double ne values. Those on Nos. J20b, J21a and J22a are al. The remainder are horizontal.

nps of T **21** optd with Japanese symbols within an oval are revenue stamps, while the same stamps overprinted three Japanese characters between two vertical double were used as seals.

Seychelles

Seychelles was administered as a dependency of Mauritius from 1810 until 1903, although separate stamp issues were provided from April 1890 onwards.

The first post office was opened, at Victoria on Mahé, on 11 December 1861 and the stamps of Mauritius were used there until 1890. No further post offices were opened until 1901.

Z 1

Stamps of MAURITIUS *cancelled with Type* Z **1**.

1848–59

Z1	2d. blue (intermediate impression) (No. 14)	£9000

1859–61.

Z2	6d. blue (No. 32)	£800
Z3	6d. dull purple-slate (No. 33)	£1700
Z4	1s. vermilion (No. 34)	£1300

1860–63. (*Nos.* 45/53).

Z 5	1d. purple-brown	£180
Z 6	2d. blue	£225
Z 7	4d. rose	£190
Z 8	6d. green	£700
Z 9	6d. slate	£500
Z10	9d. dull purple	£100
Z11	1s. buff	£300
Z12	1s. green	£550

1862.

Z13	6d. slate (No. 54)	£800

1863–72. (*Nos.* 56/72).

Z14	1d. purple-brown	£110
Z14*a*	1d. brown	90·00
Z15	1d. bistre	95·00
Z16	2d. pale blue	£110
Z17	2d. bright blue	£110
Z18	3d. deep red	£140
Z19	3d. dull red	85·00
Z20	4d. rose	48·00
Z21	6d. dull violet	£225
Z22	6d. yellow-green	£110
Z23	6d. blue-green	75·00
Z24	9d. yellow-green	£1200
Z25	10d. maroon	£325
Z26	1s. yellow	£100
Z27	1s. blue	£275
Z28	1s. orange	£110
Z29	5s. rosy mauve	£750
Z30	5s. bright mauve	£750

1876. (*Nos.* 76/7).

Z31	½d. on 9d. dull purple	£250
Z32	½d. on 10d. maroon	£250

1877. (*Nos.* 79/82).

Z33	½d. on 10d. rose	£475
Z34	1d. on 4d. rose-carmine	
Z35	1s. on 5s. rosy mauve	
Z36	1s. on 5s. bright mauve	

1878. (*Nos.* 83/91).

Z37	2 c. dull rose (lower label blank)	85·00
Z38	4 c. on 1d. bistre	£375
Z39	8 c. on 2d. blue	40·00
Z40	13 c. on 3d. orange-red	£120
Z41	17 c. on 4d. rose	40·00
Z42	25 c. on 6d. slate-blue	£100
Z43	38 c. on 9d. pale violet	£450
Z44	50 c. on 1s. green	£110
Z45	2 r. 50 on 5s. bright mauve	£450

1879–80. (*Nos.* 92/100).

Z46	2 c. Venetian red	£130
Z47	4 c. orange	£130
Z48	8 c. blue	40·00
Z49	13 c. slate	£1000
Z50	17 c. rose	90·00
Z51	25 c. olive-yellow	£190
Z52	38 c. bright purple	£1500
Z53	50 c. green	£800
Z54	2 r. 50, brown-purple	£750

1883–90.

Z55	2 c. Venetian red (No. 102)	95·00
Z56	2 c. green (No. 103)	£160
Z57	4 c. orange (No. 104)	65·00
Z58	4 c. carmine (No. 105)	95·00
Z59	16 c. chestnut (No. 109)	50·00
Z60	25 c. olive-yellow (No. 110)	£110
Z61	50 c. orange (No. 111)	£900

1883.

Z62	16 c. on 17 c. rose (No. 112)	£120

1883.

Z63	16 c. on 17 c. rose (No. 115)	42·00

1885.

Z64	2 c. on 38 c. bright purple (No. 116)	

1887.

Z65	2 c. on 13 c. slate (No. 117)	

POSTAL FISCAL

1889.

ZR1	4 c. lilac (No. R2)	£800

Mauritius stamps are occasionally found cancelled with the "SEYCHELLES" cds. Examples are known dated between 25 and 29 February 1884 when it seems that Type Z **1** may have been mislaid (*Price from* £275).

We no longer list the G.B. 1862 6d. lilac with this obliteration as there is no evidence that the stamps of Great Britain were sold by the Victoria post office.

PRICES FOR STAMPS ON COVER TO 1945

Nos. 1/8	*from* × 20
Nos. 9/24	*from* × 30
No. 25	*from* × 10
No. 26	*from* × 20
No. 27	*from* × 10
Nos. 28/32	*from* × 20
No. 33	*from* × 5
No. 34	*from* × 30
Nos. 35/6	—
Nos. 37/40	*from* × 40
Nos. 41/2	*from* × 25
Nos. 43/5	*from* × 10
Nos. 46/50	*from* × 30
Nos. 51/4	*from* × 10
Nos. 55/6	—
Nos. 57/9	*from* × 10
Nos. 60/7	*from* × 20
Nos. 68/70	—
Nos. 71/81	*from* × 10
Nos. 82/131	*from* × 5
Nos. 132/4	*from* × 10
Nos. 135/49	*from* × 3

(Currency: 100 cents = 1 Mauritius, later Seychelles rupee)

DEPENDENCY OF MAURITIUS

PRINTERS. Nos. 1 to 123 were typographed by De La Rue & Co.

1

Die I

Die II

In Die I there are lines of shading in the middle compartment of the diadem which are absent from Die II.

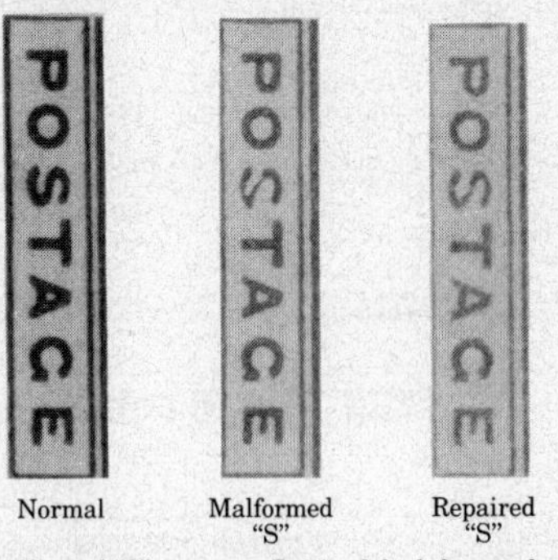

Normal — Malformed "S" — Repaired "S"

The malformed "S" occurs on R. 7/3 of the left pane from Key Plate 2. It is believed that the repair to it took place in mid-1898. Both states may occur on other stamps in Types **1** and **4**. Stamps subsequently printed from Key Plate 3 showed the "S" normal.

1890 (5 April)–**92.** *Wmk Crown CA. P* 14. (i) *Die* I.

1	**1**	2 c. green and carmine	3·00	9·00
2		4 c. carmine and green	24·00	11·00
3		8 c. brown-purple and blue	7·50	3·50
4		10 c. ultramarine and brown	6·50	16·00
5		13 c. grey and black	6·00	11·00
6		16 c. chestnut and blue	5·00	4·25
7		48 c. ochre and green	20·00	12·00
8		96 c. mauve and carmine	50·00	48·00
1/8		*Set of* 8	£110	£100
1s/8s		Optd "Specimen" *Set of* 8	£190	

(ii) *Die* II (1892)
9 **1** 2 c. green and rosine .. .. .. 2·50 90
10 4 c. carmine and green .. .. 2·50 1·00
11 8 c. brown-purple and ultramarine .. 6·50 1·75
12 10 c. bright ultramarine and brown .. 7·00 3·25
13 13 c. grey and black .. .. .. 3·25 1·75
14 16 c. chestnut and ultramarine .. 42·00 11·00
a. Malformed "S" .. ..
9/14 .. .. .. *Set of* 6 55·00 17·00

The 10 c. Die I also exists in ultramarine and chestnut, but has so far only been found with "SPECIMEN" overprint (*Price* £425).

3 cents (2)   **18 CENTS** (3)   4

1893 (1 Jan). *Surch locally as T* 2.
15 3 c. on 4 c. (No. 10) .. .. .. 1·10 1·50
a. Surch inverted £300 £375
b. Surch double £475
c. Surch omitted (in horiz pair with normal) £8000
16 12 c. on 16 c. (No. 6) .. .. .. 1·50 3·75
a. Surch inverted £450
b. Surch double .. .. — £9000
17 12 c. on 16 c. (No. 14) .. .. .. 9·50 2·50
a. Surch double £4500 £4500
b. Surch omitted (in pair with normal) ..
18 15 c. on 16 c. (No. 6) .. .. .. 8·50 13·00
a. Surch inverted £325 £300
b. Surch double £1100 £1100
19 15 c. on 16 c. (No. 14) .. .. .. 11·00 3·00
a. Surch inverted £850 £900
b. Surch double £650 £700
c. Surch triple £4250
20 45 c. on 48 c. (No. 7) .. .. .. 21·00 5·50
21 90 c. on 96 c. (No. 8) .. .. .. 48·00 32·00
a. Wide "O" (3½ mm wide instead of 3 mm) (R. 1/1, 2/1) £200
15/21 .. .. .. *Set of* 7 90·00 55·00

Nos. 15, 16, 18, 19 and 20 exist with "cents" omitted and with "cents" above value due to misplacement of the surcharge.

Some examples of No. 15b occur in the same sheet as No. 15c with the double surcharge on stamps from the last vertical row of the left pane and the surcharge omitted on stamps from the last vertical row of the right pane.

Most examples of the inverted surcharge error No. 16a were officially defaced with a red vertical ink line (*Price* £200, *unused*). Similarly examples of No. 19a exist defaced with a horizontal ink line (*Price* £400, *unused*).

1893 (Nov). *New values. Die* II. *Wmk Crown CA. P* 14.
22 **1** 3 c. dull purple and orange .. .. 1·50 50
23 12 c. sepia and green .. .. .. 2·50 60
24 15 c. sage-green and lilac .. .. .. 4·50 2·00
25 45 c. brown and carmine .. .. .. 23·00 35·00
22/5 .. .. *Set of* 4 28·00 35·00
22s/5s Optd "Specimen" .. *Set of* 4 95·00

1896 (1 Aug). *No. 25 surch as T* 3.
26 **1** 18 c. on 45 c. brown and carmine .. 7·00 2·75
a. Surch double £1300 £1300
b. Surch triple £1900
27 36 c. on 45 c. brown and carmine .. 8·00 48·00
a. Surch double £1500
26s/7s Optd "Specimen" .. *Set of* 2 70·00

1897–1900. *Colours changed and new values. Die* II. *Wmk Crown CA. P* 14.
28 **1** 2 c. orange-brown and green (1900) .. 2·00 1·25
a. Repaired "S" £150
29 6 c. carmine (1900) .. .. .. 3·50 50
a. Repaired "S" £225
30 15 c. ultramarine (1900) .. .. .. 4·50 3·25
a. Repaired "S" £250 £225
31 18 c. ultramarine .. .. .. 4·25 1·00
32 36 c. brown and carmine .. .. 23·00 4·50
33 **4** 75 c. yellow and violet (1900) .. .. 55·00 70·00
a. Repaired "S" £375
34 1 r. bright mauve and deep red .. 13·00 4·25
35 1 r. 50, grey and carmine (1900) .. 65·00 85·00
a. Repaired "S" £400
36 2 r. 25, bright mauve and green (1900) .. 95·00 85·00
a. Repaired "S" £550
28/36 .. .. .. *Set of* 9 £225 £225
28s/36s Optd "Specimen" .. *Set of* 9 £225

3 cents (5)   **6 cents** (5*a*)

1901 (21 June–Oct). *Surch locally with T* 5 *or* 5*a*.
37 3 c. on 10 c. bright ultramarine and brown (No. 12) (10.01) .. .. .. 1·25 60
a. Surch double £650
b. Surch triple .. ..
c. Malformed "S" £140
38 3 c. on 16 c. chestnut and ultramarine (No. 14) (8.01) .. .. .. 2·25 4·00
a. Surch inverted £650 £650
b. Surch double £500
c. "3 cents" omitted £550 £550
d. Malformed "S" £160
39 3 c. on 36 c. brown and carmine (No. 32) .. 50 80
a. Surch double £700 £800
b. "3 cents" omitted £650 £700
40 6 c. on 8 c. brn-pur & ultram (No. 11) (8.01) 1·00 3·00
a. Surch inverted £650 £750
37/40 .. .. .. *Set of* 4 4·50 7·50
37s/40s H/S "Specimen" .. .. *Set of* 4 £100

1902 (June). *Surch locally as T* 5.
41 **1** 2 c. on 4 c. carmine and green (No. 10) .. 1·60 2·75
42 **4** 30 c. on 75 c. yellow and violet (No. 33) .. 1·50 4·00
a. Narrow "0" in "30" (R. 3/6, 5/2-4) .. 10·00 45·00
b. Repaired "S" £180
43 30 c. on 1 r. bright mauve & dp red (No. 34) 4·50 26·00
a. Narrow "0" in "30" (R. 3/6, 5/2-4) .. 22·00 90·00
b. Surch double £1400
44 45 c. on 1 r. bright mauve & dp red (No. 34) 3·50 26·00
45 45 c. on 2 r. 25, brt mauve & grn (No. 36) 42·00 80·00
a. Narrow "5" in "45" (R. 4/1) £180 £350
b. Repaired "S" £375
41/5 .. .. .. *Set of* 5 48·00 £120
41s/5s Optd "Specimen" .. .. *Set of* 5 £120

6   7   **3 cents** (8)

Dented frame (R. 1/6 of left pane)

1903 (26 May). *Wmk Crown CA. P* 14.
46 **6** 2 c. chestnut and green .. .. .. 1·75 2·00
a. Dented frame .. .. .. 70·00 85·00
47 3 c. dull green .. .. .. 1·00 1·25
a. Dented frame .. .. .. 60·00 70·00
48 6 c. carmine .. .. .. 2·75 1·25
a. Dented frame .. .. .. 90·00 75·00
49 12 c. olive-sepia and dull green .. .. 2·50 2·50
a. Dented frame .. .. .. 90·00 £100
50 15 c. ultramarine .. .. .. 4·00 2·50
a. Dented frame £130 £110
51 18 c. sage-green and carmine .. .. 4·25 6·50
a. Dented frame £130 £180
52 30 c. violet and dull green .. .. 7·00 11·00
a. Dented frame £160 £225
53 45 c. brown and carmine .. .. .. 7·00 11·00
a. Dented frame £200 £225
w. Wmk inverted £250
54 **7** 75 c. yellow and violet .. .. .. 10·00 27·00
a. Dented frame £200
55 1 r. 50, black and carmine .. .. 42·00 70·00
a. Dented frame £375
56 2 r. 25, purple and green .. .. 29·00 85·00
a. Dented frame £325
46/56 .. .. .. *Set of* 11 95·00 £190
46s/56s Optd "Specimen" .. *Set of* 11 £190

1903. *Surch locally with T* 8.
57 **6** 3 c. on 15 c. ultramarine (3.7) .. .. 1·00 3·25
a. Dented frame £120
58 3 c. on 18 c. sage-green and carmine (2.9) 2·75 35·00
a. Dented frame £170
59 3 c. on 45 c. brown and carmine (21.7) .. 3·00 3·25
a. Dented frame £170
57/9 .. .. .. *Set of* 3 6·00 38·00
57s/9s H/S "Specimen" .. .. *Set of* 3 80·00

CROWN COLONY

The Seychelles became a Separate Crown Colony by Letters Patent dated 31 August 1903.

1906. *Wmk Mult Crown CA. P* 14.
60 **6** 2 c. chestnut and green .. .. .. 1·50 4·25
a. Dented frame .. .. .. 60·00 £100
61 3 c. dull green .. .. .. 1·50 1·50
a. Dented frame .. .. .. 70·00 75·00
62 6 c. carmine .. .. .. 1·75 80
a. Dented frame .. .. .. 75·00 60·00
63 12 c. olive-sepia and dull green .. .. 3·00 3·25
a. Dented frame £110 £120
64 15 c. ultramarine .. .. .. 3·00 2·00
a. Dented frame £100 £100
65 18 c. sage-green and carmine .. .. 3·00 6·50
a. Dented frame £100 £150
66 30 c. violet and dull green .. .. 6·00 8·00
a. Dented frame £180 £200
67 45 c. brown and carmine .. .. .. 3·00 6·50
a. Dented frame £160 £190
68 **7** 75 c. yellow and violet .. .. .. 8·50 55·00
a. Dented frame £225
69 1 r. 50, black and carmine .. .. 50·00 60·00
a. Dented frame £400
70 2 r. 25, purple and green .. .. 32·00 60·00
a. Dented frame £350
60/70 .. .. .. *Set of* 11 £100 £180

9   10

1912 (Apr)–**13.** *Wmk Mult Crown CA. P* 14.
71 **9** 2 c. chestnut and green .. .. .. 70 4·50
a. Split "A" .. .. .. 55·00
72 3 c. green .. .. 2·00 60
a. Split "A" .. .. .. 80·00 60·00
73 **9** 6 c. aniline carmine (6.13) .. .. 13·00
a. *Carmine-red* .. .. .. 4·25
b. Split "A" £120
74 12 c. olive-sepia and dull green (1.13) .. 1·25
a. Split "A" .. .. .. 85·00
75 15 c. ultramarine .. .. .. 3·75
a. Split "A" £120
76 18 c. sage-green and carmine (1.13) .. 3·25
a. Split "A" £110
77 30 c. violet and green (1.13) .. .. 5·00
a. Split "A" £150
78 45 c. brown and carmine (1.13) .. 2·75
a. Split "A" £130
79 **10** 75 c. yellow and violet (1.13) .. .. 2·75
a. Split "A" £130
80 1 r. 50, black and carmine (1.13) .. 7·50
a. Split "A" £225
81 2 r. 25, dp magenta & grn (*shades*) (1.13) 45·00
a. Split "A" £425
71/81 .. .. .. *Set of* 11 70·00
71s/81s Optd "Specimen" .. *Set of* 11 £225

For illustration of "Split A" flaw see above St. Helena No

11   12   13

1917–22. *Die I. Wmk Mult Crown CA. Chalk-surfaced p* (18 *c. to* 5 *r.*). *P* 14.
82 **11** 2 c. chestnut and green 50
83 3 c. gréen .. .. 2·00
84 **12** 5 c. deep brown (1920) .. .. .. 2·25
85 **11** 6 c. carmine .. .. 1·75
a. Rose (1919) .. .. .. 4·50
86 12 c. grey (1919) .. .. .. 1·00
87 15 c. ultramarine .. .. .. 1·75
88 18 c. purple/*yellow* (1919) .. .. 3·50 2
a. On orange-buff (1920) .. .. 14·00 5
b. On buff (1920) .. .. ..
c. Die II. *On pale yellow* (1922) .. 1·25 1
89 **13** 25 c. black and red/*buff* (1920) .. .. 1·75 3
a. On orange buff (1920) .. .. 40·00 7
b. Die II. *On pale yellow* (1922) .. 1·75
90 **11** 30 c. dull purple and olive (1918) .. 1·50
91 45 c. dull purple and orange (1919) .. 3·00 3
92 **13** 50 c. dull purple and black (1920) .. 5·50 2
93 75 c. black/*blue-green* (*olive back*) (1918) 1·60 1
a. Die II. *On emerald back* (1922) .. 1·40 2
94 1 r. dull purple and red (1920) .. .. 11·00 4
95 1 r. 50, reddish purple & blue/*blue* (1918) 9·00 5
a. Die II. *Blue-pur & blue/blue* (1922) 12·00 3
96 2 r. 25, yellow-green and violet (1918) 45·00 £
97 5 r. green and blue (1920) .. .. 75·00 £
82/97 .. .. *Set of* 16 £140 £
82s/97s Optd "Specimen" .. *Set of* 16 £300

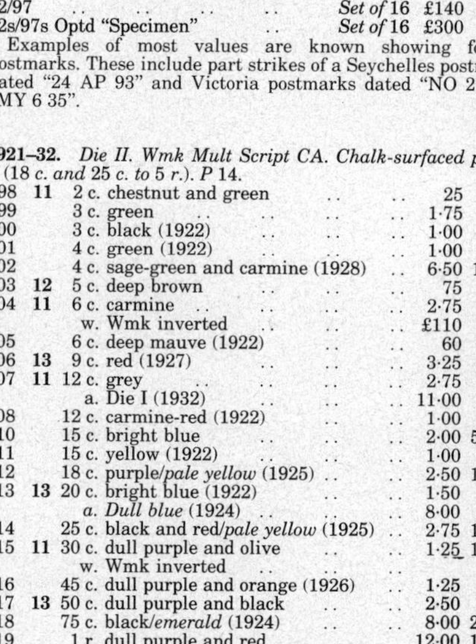

Examples of most values are known showing for postmarks. These include part strikes of a Seychelles postm dated "24 AP 93" and Victoria postmarks dated "NO 27" "MY 6 35".

1921–32. *Die II. Wmk Mult Script CA. Chalk-surfaced pa* (18 *c. and* 25 *c. to* 5 *r.*). *P* 14.
98 **11** 2 c. chestnut and green 25
99 3 c. green .. .. 1·75
100 3 c. black (1922) .. .. .. 1·00
101 4 c. green (1922) .. .. .. 1·00 2
102 4 c. sage-green and carmine (1928) .. 6·50 17
103 **12** 5 c. deep brown 75 5
104 **11** 6 c. carmine .. .. 2·75 9
w. Wmk inverted £110
105 6 c. deep mauve (1922) 60
106 **13** 9 c. red (1927) .. .. .. 3·25 4
107 **11** 12 c. grey .. .. 2·75
a. Die I (1932) .. .. .. 11·00
108 12 c. carmine-red (1922) .. .. 1·00
110 15 c. bright blue .. .. .. 2·00 55
111 15 c. yellow (1922) .. .. .. 1·00 2·
112 18 c. purple/*pale yellow* (1925) .. .. 2·50 12
113 **13** 20 c. bright blue (1922) .. .. 1·50
a. Dull blue (1924) .. .. .. 8·00
114 25 c. black and red/*pale yellow* (1925) .. 2·75 13·
115 **11** 30 c. dull purple and olive .. .. 1·25 15·
w. Wmk inverted .. .. ..
116 45 c. dull purple and orange (1926) .. 1·25 5·
117 **13** 50 c. dull purple and black .. .. 2·50 2·
118 75 c. black/*emerald* (1924) .. .. 8·00 21·
119 1 r. dull purple and red .. .. 12·00 18·
a. Die I (1932) .. .. .. 12·00 35·
121 1 r. 50, purple and blue/*blue* (1924) .. 14·00 22·
122 2 r. 25, yellow-green and violet .. 9·50 14·
123 5 r. yellow-green and blue .. .. 65·00 £1
98/123 .. .. *Set of* 24 £130 £3
98s/123s Optd "Specimen" .. *Set of* 24 £400

The 3 c. green and 12 c. grey (Die II) were reissued in 192 "Specimen" overprints on these printings are 15.5×1.75 m instead of the 14.5×2.5 mm of the original issue. (*Price*, 3 £130, 12 c. £110).

Examples of most values are known showing the forge postmarks mentioned above.

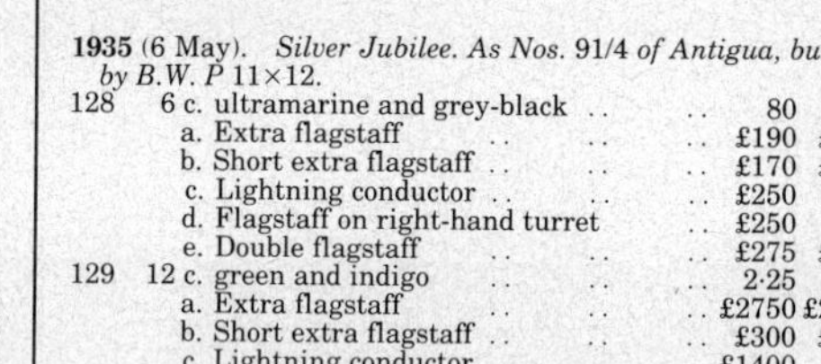

1935 (6 May). *Silver Jubilee. As Nos. 91/4 of Antigua, but p by B.W. P* 11×12.
128 6 c. ultramarine and grey-black .. .. 80 2·0
a. Extra flagstaff £190 £25
b. Short extra flagstaff £170 £19
c. Lightning conductor £250
d. Flagstaff on right-hand turret .. £250
e. Double flagstaff £275 £19
129 12 c. green and indigo .. .. .. 2·25 1·5
a. Extra flagstaff £2750 £250
b. Short extra flagstaff £300 £19
c. Lightning conductor £1400
d. Flagstaff on right-hand turret .. £375
e. Double flagstaff £375

20 c. brown and deep blue	2·00	1·50
a. Extra flagstaff	£300	£300
b. Short extra flagstaff	£200	
c. Lightning conductor	£325	
d. Flagstaff on right-hand turret ..	£325	
e. Double flagstaff	£325	
1 r. slate and purple	5·50	13·00
a. Extra flagstaff	£160	£190
b. Short extra flagstaff	£275	
c. Lightning conductor	£170	
d. Flagstaff on right-hand turret ..	£375	
1 .. .. *Set of* 4	9·50	16·00
31s Perf "Specimen" .. *Set of* 4	£100	

illustrations of plate varieties see Omnibus section ving Zanzibar.

(12 May). *Coronation. As Nos.* 95/7 *of Antigua.* 1×11½.

6 c. sage-green	35	15
12 c. orange	50	30
20 c. blue	70	65
.. .. *Set of* 3	1·40	1·00
4s Perf "Specimen" .. .. *Set of* 3	60·00	

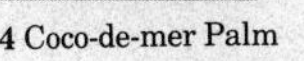
14 Coco-de-mer Palm

15 Giant Tortoise

16 Fishing Pirogue

"Handkerchief" on oar flaw (R. 6/2)

(Photo Harrison)

38 (1 Jan)–**49.** *Wmk Mult Script CA. Chalk-surfaced paper. P* 14½×13½ *(vert) or* 13½×14½ *(horiz).*

5	**14**	2 c. purple-brown (10.2.38)	1·50	40
		a. Ordinary paper (18.11.42) ..	30	1·40
6	**15**	3 c. green	8·00	1·25
6*a*		3 c. orange (8.8.41)	1·25	50
		ab. Ordinary paper (18.11.42) ..	55	1·50
7	**16**	6 c. orange	8·00	2·50
7*a*		6 c. greyish green (8.8.41)	3·50	70
		aw. Wmk inverted	£500	
		b. Ordinary paper. *Green* (18.11.42)	55	1·50
		c. Green (5.4.49)	5·00	75
8	**14**	9 c. scarlet (10.2.38)	10·00	2·00
8*a*		9 c. grey-blue (8.8.41)	8·50	40
		ab. Ordinary paper (18.11.42) ..	11·00	1·25
		ac. Ordinary paper. *Dull bl* (19.11.45)	4·50	1·75
		ad. Dull blue (5.4.49)	13·00	6·00
		aw. Wmk inverted		
9	**15**	12 c. reddish violet	38·00	1·25
9*a*		15 c. brown-carmine (8.8.41)	8·00	30
		ab. Ordinary paper. *Brn-red* (18.11.42)	5·00	1·75
9*c*	**14**	18 c. carmine-lake (8.8.41)	6·50	60
		ca. Ordinary paper (18.11.42) ..	4·50	2·00
		cb. Rose-carmine (5.4.49)	14·00	10·00
0	**16**	20 c. blue	42·00	5·00
0*a*		20 c. brown-ochre (8.8.41)	6·50	50
		ab. Ordinary paper (18.11.42) ..	2·50	2·25
		ac. "Handkerchief" flaw	£100	
1	**14**	25 c. brown-ochre	50·00	14·00
2	**15**	30 c. carmine (10.2.38)	50·00	9·00
2*a*		30 c. blue (8.8.41)	6·50	50
		ab. Ordinary paper (18.11.42) ..	2·00	3·00
3	**16**	45 c. chocolate (10.2.38)	15·00	1·50
		a. Ordinary paper. *Pur-brn* (18.11.42)	2·50	1·75
		b. Purple-brown (5.4.49)	16·00	10·00
4	**14**	50 c. deep reddish violet (10.2.38) ..	7·50	60
		a. Ordinary paper (18.11.42) ..	1·25	3·25
4*b*		50 c. bright lilac (13.6.49)	1·75	1·50
5	**15**	75 c. slate-blue (10.2.38)	85·00	38·00
5*a*		75 c. deep slate-lilac (8.8.41)	8·50	1·50
		ab. Ordinary paper (18.11.42) ..	2·00	2·50
46	**16**	1 r. yellow-green (10.2.38)	£100	48·00
46*a*		1 r. grey-black (8.8.41)	14·00	1·25
		ab. Ordinary paper (18.11.42) ..	1·50	2·50
47	**14**	1 r. 50, ultramarine (10.2.38) ..	21·00	2·00
		a. Ordinary paper (18.11.42) ..	4·50	6·00
		aw. Wmk inverted	£1400	
48	**15**	2 r. 25, olive (10.2.38)	25·00	4·75
		a. Ordinary paper (18.11.42) ..	14·00	16·00
149	**16**	5 r. red (10.2.38)	10·00	5·00
		a. Ordinary paper (18.11.42) ..	15·00	21·00
135/49		.. .. *Set of* 25	£400	£120
135s/49s (*ex* 50 c. bright lilac) Perf "Specimen"		*Set of* 24	£400	

Examples of most values are known showing forged Victoria postmarks dated "DE 12 41", "SP 14 42 ", "DE 21 42" or "NO 16 43".

Lamp on mast flaw (R. 1/5)

1946 (23 Sept). *Victory. As Nos.* 110/11 *of Antigua.*

150	9 c. light blue	10	10
151	30 c. deep blue	10	10
	a. Lamp on mast flaw	20·00	
150s/1s Perf "Specimen" .. .. *Set of* 2		50·00	

Line by crown (R. 1/3)

1948 (5 Nov). *Royal Silver Wedding. As Nos.* 112/13 *of Antigua.*

152	9 c. ultramarine	15	25
	a. Line by crown	20·00	
153	5 r. carmine	11·00	26·00

1949 (10 Oct). *75th Anniv of U.P.U. As Nos.* 114/17 *of Antigua, but inscribed* "SEYCHELLES" *in recess.*

154	18 c. bright reddish purple	15	15
155	50 c. purple	1·25	50
156	1 r. grey	25	15
157	2 r. 25, olive	30	60
154/7	.. .. *Set of* 4	1·75	1·25

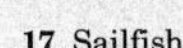
17 Sailfish

18 Map of Indian Ocean

(Photo Harrison)

1952 (3 Mar). *Various designs as T* **14/16** *but with new portrait and crown as in T* **17/18.** *Chalk-surfaced paper. Wmk Mult Script CA. P* 14½ × 13½ *(vert) or* 13½ × 14½ *(horiz).*

158	**17**	2 c. lilac	60	70
		a. Error. Crown missing, W **9***a* ..	£450	
		b. Error. St. Edward's Crown, W **9***b* ..	£110	
159	**15**	3 c. orange	60	30
		a. Error. Crown missing, W **9***a* ..	£375	
		b. Error. St. Edward's Crown, W **9***b* ..	£110	90·00
160	**14**	9 c. chalky blue	60	1·25
		a. Error. Crown missing, W **9***a* ..	£650	
		b. Error. St. Edward's Crown, W **9***b* ..	£225	
161	**16**	15 c. deep yellow-green	50	75
		a. Error. Crown missing, W **9***a* ..	£475	
		b. Error. St. Edward's Crown, W **9***b* ..	£200	
162	**18**	18 c. carmine-lake	1·25	20
		a. Error. Crown missing, W **9***a* ..	£600	
		b. Error. St. Edward's Crown, W **9***b* ..	£300	£250
163	**16**	20 c. orange-yellow	1·00	85
		a. Error. Crown missing, W **9***a* ..	£650	
		b. Error. St. Edward's Crown, W **9***b* ..	£350	
164	**15**	25 c. vermilion	70	1·00
		a. Error. Crown missing, W **9***a* ..	£800	
		b. Error. St. Edward's Crown, W **9***b* ..	£325	
165	**17**	40 c. ultramarine	90	90
		a. Error. Crown missing, W **9***a* ..	£800	
		b. Error. St. Edward's Crown, W **9***b* ..	£425	
166	**16**	45 c. purple-brown	70	30
		a. Error. Crown missing, W **9***a* ..	£900	
		b. Error. St. Edward's Crown, W **9***b* ..	£425	
167	**14**	50 c. reddish violet	1·25	1·00
		a. Error. Crown missing, W **9***a* ..	£950	
		b. Error. St. Edward's Crown, W **9***b* ..	£425	
168	**18**	1 r. grey-black	3·00	2·25
		b. Error. St. Edward's Crown, W **9***b* ..	£750	
169	**14**	1 r. 50, blue	5·50	10·00
		b. Error. St. Edward's Crown, W **9***b* ..	£1100	
170	**15**	2 r. 25, brown-olive	9·00	10·00
		b. Error. St. Edward's Crown, W **9***b* ..	£850	
171	**18**	5 r. red	9·00	12·00
		b. Error. St. Edward's Crown, W **9***b* ..	£750	
172	**17**	10 r. green	16·00	27·00
158/72		.. .. *Set of* 15	45·00	60·00

See *Introduction* re the watermark errors.

POSTAGE DUE STAMPS

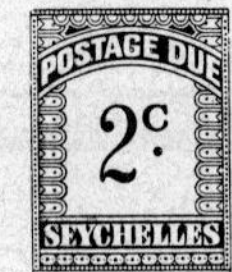

D 1

(Frame recess, value typo B.W.)

1951 (1 Mar). *Wmk Mult Script CA. P* 11½.

D1	**D 1**	2 c. scarlet and carmine	80	1·50
D2		3 c. scarlet and green	2·00	1·50
D3		6 c. scarlet and bistre	2·00	1·25
D4		9 c. scarlet and orange	2·00	1·25
D5		15 c. scarlet and violet	1·75	11·00
D6		18 c. scarlet and blue	1·75	11·00
D7		20 c. scarlet and brown	1·75	11·00
D8		30 c. scarlet and claret	1·75	7·50
D1/8		.. .. *Set of* 8	12·50	42·00

The 2 c. and 3 c. were issued on Block CA watermark in 1964–65.

Sierra Leone

PRICES FOR STAMPS ON COVER TO 1945

Nos. 1/15	*from* × 10
Nos. 16/26	*from* × 15
Nos. 27/34	*from* × 20
Nos. 35/7	*from* × 10
No. 38	—
No. 39	*from* × 15
Nos. 41/52	*from* × 8
No. 53	—
No. 54	*from* × 40
Nos. 55/63	*from* × 5
Nos. 64/71	—
Nos. 73/84	*from* × 4
No. 85	—
Nos. 86/97	*from* × 4
No. 98	—
Nos. 99/110	*from* × 4
No. 111	—
Nos. 112/26	*from* × 2
Nos. 127/30	—
Nos. 131/45	*from* × 2
Nos. 146/8	—
Nos. 155/66	*from* × 2
No. 167	—
Nos. 168/78	*from* × 2
Nos. 179/80	—
Nos. 181/4	*from* × 6
Nos. 185/7	*from* × 5
Nos. 188/200	*from* × 2

CROWN COLONY AND PROTECTORATE

The first settlement in Sierra Leone intended as a home for repatriated Africans, and subsequently those released by the Royal Navy from slave ships, was established in 1787. The Sierra Leone Company was created by Act of Parliment in 1791, but its charter was surrendered in 1808 and the coastal settlements then became a Crown Colony. The inland region was proclaimed a British protectorate on 21 August 1896.

A post office was established in 1843 but, until the inclusion of Freetown in the British Post Office packet system in 1850, overseas mail was carried at irregular intervals by passing merchant or naval vessels.

The stamps of GREAT BRITAIN were not sold at Sierra Leone post offices, although examples from ships of the West African Squadron do exist with local cancellations.

PRINTERS. All issues of Sierra Leone until 1932 were typographed by De La Rue & Co. Ltd, London.

1

2

HALF
PENNY

(3)

Dot after "SIX" and break in octagonal frame (R. 19/11)

1859 (21 Sept)–**74.** *No wmk. P* 14.
1 **1** 6d. dull purple .. .. £200 50·00
2 6d. grey-lilac (1865) .. .. .. £250 40·00
a. Dot after "SIX" .. .. — £300
3 6d. reddish violet (*p* 12½) (1872) .. .. £375 60·00
a. Dot after "SIX" .. .. — £400
4 6d. reddish lilac (1874) .. .. .. 50·00 27·00
a. Dot after "SIX" £275 £160

Imperforate proofs exist.

The paper used for the 6d. value often shows varying degrees of blueing, caused by a chemical reaction.

The 6d. plate contained 240 stamps arranged in panes of 20 (4×5) with the sheets containing 12 such panes in four horizontal rows of three.

1872–73. *Wmk Crown CC. P* 12½. (*a*) *Wmk sideways* (April 1872).
7 **2** 1d. rose-red .. .. 75·00 32·00
8 3d. buff .. .. £130 35·00
9 4d. blue .. .. £170 38·00
10 1s. green .. .. £400 55·00

(*b*) *Wmk upright* (Sept 1873)
11 **2** 1d. rose-red .. .. £110 30·00
w. Wmk inverted .. .. .. £160 80·00
12 2d. magenta .. .. £120 48·00
13 3d. saffron-yellow .. .. .. £500 85·00
14 4d. blue .. .. £250 50·00
15 1s. green .. .. £400 90·00

1876. *Wmk Crown CC. P* 14.
16 **2** ½d. brown .. .. 2·25 7·00
w. Wmk inverted £100
17 1d. rose-red .. .. 48·00 12·00
18 1½d. lilac (Nov) .. .. .. 48·00 7·50
19 2d. magenta .. .. 60·00 4·00
20 3d. buff .. .. 50·00 4·25
w. Wmk inverted .. .. ..
21 4d. blue .. .. £150 6·50
w. Wmk inverted .. .. ..
22 1s. green .. .. 55·00 6·50
16/22 .. .. *Set of* 7 £375 42·00

1883 (June–19 Sept). *Wmk Crown CA. P* 14.
23 **2** ½d. brown .. .. 21·00 48·00
24 1d. rose-red (19.9.83*) .. .. .. £200 35·00
25 2d. magenta .. .. 50·00 8·50
26 4d. blue .. .. £900 28·00

*Earliest known postmark date.

1884 SIERRA 5s. LEONE SURCHARGE. From 2 June 1884 the administration decided that, as a temporary measure, revenue and fiscal duties were to be paid with ordinary postage stamps. At that time there was no postage value higher than 1s., so a local surcharge, reading "SIERRA 5s. LEONE", was applied to No. 22 (*Price* £200 *unused*). Until withdrawal on 1 March 1885 this surcharge was valid for both fiscal and postal purposes, although no genuine postal cover or piece has yet been found. One mint example is known with overprint inverted (*Price* £750).

Remainders of the surcharge were cancelled by a horizontal red brush stroke (*Price* £32 *with upright surcharge*, £160 *with inverted surcharge*).

1884 (July)–**91.** *Wmk Crown CA. P* 14.
27 **2** ½d. dull green .. .. 2·00 1·50
w. Wmk inverted £160 £100
28 1d. carmine .. .. 3·50 1·00
a. Rose-carmine (1885?) .. .. 28·00 8·50
aw. Wmk inverted .. .. .. † £100
29 1½d. pale violet (1889) .. .. .. 2·75 6·50
30 2d. grey .. .. 29·00 2·50
31 2½d. ultramarine (1891) .. .. .. 7·50 1·00
32 3d. yellow (1889) .. .. .. 2·75 10·00
33 4d. brown .. .. 1·75 1·50
w. Wmk inverted £170
34 1s. red-brown (1888) .. .. .. 17·00 11·00
27/34 .. .. *Set of* 8 60·00 32·00
27s/34s (*ex* 1½d., 3d.) Optd "Specimen" .. *Set of* 6 £550
27sa/8sa, 30sa, 33sa Optd "Specimen" (*perf* 12) *Set of* 4 £850

1885–96. *Wmk Crown CC. P* 14.
35 **1** 6d. dull violet (1885) .. .. .. 60·00 23·00
a. Bisected (3d.) (on cover) .. .. † £2500
b. Dot after "SIX" .. .. .. — £140
36 6d. brown-purple (1890) .. .. .. 15·00 14·00
a. Dot after "SIX" .. .. .. 95·00 95·00
s. Optd "Specimen" .. .. .. 70·00
w. Wmk inverted .. .. ..
37 6d. purple-lake (1896) .. .. .. 2·25 6·50
a. Dot after "SIX" .. .. .. 40·00 70·00

Proofs of the 6d. brown-purple exist from 1889 on Crown CA watermark and perforated 12 (*Price* £1500, *unused*).

1893 (8 Jan). *Surch with T* **3** *by Govt Printer, Freetown.* (*a*) *On No.* 18. *Wmk Crown CC.*
38 **2** ½d. on 1½d. lilac £475 £700
a. "PFNNY" (R. 3/1) £2750 £3750

(*b*) *On No.* 29. *Wmk Crown CA*
39 **2** ½d. on 1½d. pale violet .. .. .. 3·00 3·00
a. Surch inverted £100 £100
b. "PFNNY" (R. 3/1) .. .. .. 70·00 70·00
ba. Ditto. Surch inverted £2250 £5000

On Nos. 38/9 the surcharge and the cancelling bars were applied separately so that No. 39a exists with the bars either normal or inverted with the rest of the surcharge.

Forged surcharges with "HALF PENNY" shown on one line were prepared by employees of the printer. It is believed that only a single example of this forgery still exists.

The 6d. fiscal, inscribed "STAMP DUTY" as Type **6** surcharged "ONE-PENNY" is known used for postage between June and August 1894, but no official sanction for such usage has been found.

4

5

1896–97. *Wmk Crown CA. P* 14.
41 **4** ½d. dull mauve and green (1897) .. 1·75 2·75
42 1d. dull mauve and carmine .. .. 2·25 1·75
43 1½d. dull mauve and black (1897) .. 4·00 17·00
44 2d. dull mauve and orange .. .. 2·50 5·00
45 2½d. dull mauve and ultramarine .. 2·25 1·25
46 **5** 3d. dull mauve and slate .. .. 8·00 7·00
47 4d. dull mauve and carmine (1897) .. 9·50 13·00
48 5d. dull mauve and black (1897) .. 12·00 12·00
49 6d. dull mauve (1897) .. .. .. 8·00 20·00
50 1s. green and black .. .. .. 6·00 18·00
51 2s. green and ultramarine .. .. 25·00 50·00
52 5s. green and carmine .. .. .. 60·00 £160
53 £1 purple/*red* £150 £425
41/53 .. .. *Set of* 13 £250 £650
41s/53s Optd "Specimen" .. .. *Set of* 13 £225

Examples of most values are known showing forged oval registered postmarks dated "16 JUL 11" or "4 SP 11".

6

POSTAGE
AND
REVENUE
(7)

2½d. (8) 2½d. (9) 2½ (10)
2½d. (11) 2½d. (12) 2½ (13)

POSTAGE AND
REVENUE
(14)

REVENU
Italic "N" (R. 3/4 of the setti

1897. *Fiscal stamps as T* **6**. *Wmk CA over Crown,* w **7**. *P*

(*a*) *Optd with T* **7** (26 Feb*)
54 1d. dull purple and green .. .. 3·75
a. Opt double .. .. £1400 £

(*b*) *Optd with T* **7** *and surch T* **8**, **10**, **11** (*with square stop*), **12** *with six thin bars across the original face value* (1 Ma
55 **8** 2½d. on 3d. dull purple and green .. 11·00 1
a. Surch double £17000
b. Surch double (Types **8** + **10**) .. £14000
c. Surch double (Types **8** + **11**) .. £24000
56 **10** 2½d. on 3d. dull purple and green .. 55·00 6
57 **11** 2½d. on 3d. dull purple and green .. £160
58 **12** 2½d. on 3d. dull purple and green .. £325
59 **8** 2½d. on 6d. dull purple and green .. 8·50 1
60 **10** 2½d. on 6d. dull purple and green .. 42·00 5
61 **11** 2½d. on 6d. dull purple and green .. £110
62 **12** 2½d. on 6d. dull purple and green .. £250

Nos. 55/8 and 59/62 were surcharged from a setting o (10×3) which contained twenty-two examples of Typ (including three with square stops), five of Type **10**, two of T **11** and one of Type **12.**

Two examples are known of No. 55a, five of No. 55b (of w two are in the Royal Collection) and two of No. 55c (one in Royal Collection). A unique example of a double surcharg No. 55 showing Types **8** + **12** is also in the Royal Collectior

(*c*) *Optd with T* **14** *and surch T* **8**, **9**, **10**, **11** (*with round st or* **13** *with five thin bars across the original face value* (1 M
63 **8** 2½d. on 1s. dull lilac .. .. 85·00 6
64 **9** 2½d. on 1s. dull lilac £1300 £1
65 **10** 2½d. on 1s. dull lilac £750
66 **11** 2½d. on 1s. dull lilac £400
a. Italic "N" £1100 £1
66*b* **13** 2½d. on 1s. dull lilac £1300 £1
67 **8** 2½d. on 2s. dull lilac £1600 £1
68 **9** 2½d. on 2s. dull lilac £32000 £38
69 **10** 2½d. on 2s. dull lilac £14000
70 **11** 2½d. on 2s. dull lilac £8000 £9
a. Italic "N" £16000 £16
71 **13** 2½d. on 2s. dull lilac £32000 £38

*Earliest known postmark date.

The setting of 30 (10×3) used for both Nos. 63/6*b* and 67 contained twenty-two examples of Type **8** (including one w square stop), one of Type **9**, two of Type **10**, four of Type (including one with italic "N") and one of Type **13**.

Most examples of Nos. 63/6*b* are water-stained. Stamps in t condition are worth about 30% of the price quoted.

15

16

1903. *Wmk Crown CA. P* 14.
73 **15** ½d. dull purple and green .. .. 3·00 4
74 1d. dull purple and rosine .. .. 2·00 1
75 1½d. dull purple and black .. .. 1·25 10
76 2d. dull purple and brown-orange .. 3·75 16
77 2½d. dull purple and ultramarine .. 4·50 8
78 **16** 3d. dull purple and grey .. .. 9·50 13
79 4d. dull purple and rosine .. .. 7·00 14
80 5d. dull purple and black .. .. 8·00 32
81 6d. dull purple .. .. .. 11·00 15·
82 1s. green and black .. .. .. 16·00 50·
83 2s. green and ultramarine .. .. 42·00 60·
84 5s. green and carmine .. .. .. 70·00 £1
85 £1 purple/*red* £200 £2
73/85 .. .. *Set of* 13 £350 £5
73s/85s Optd "Specimen" .. *Set of* 13 £180

1904–5. *Wmk Mult Crown CA. Ordinary paper* (1*d.*) *chalk-surfaced paper* (*others*). *P* 14.
86 **15** ½d. dull purple and green (1905) .. 5·00 4·
87 1d. dull purple and rosine .. .. 1·50 1·
a. Chalk-surfaced paper (1905) .. 4·00 1·
88 1½d. dull purple and black (1905) .. 3·00 13·
89 2d. dull purple and brown-orange (1905) 4·25 4·
90 2½d. dull purple and ultramarine (1905) 4·50 2·
91 **16** 3d. dull purple and grey (1905) .. 35·00 3·
w. Wmk inverted .. .. .. 42·00 30·
92 4d. dull purple and rosine (1905) .. 7·00 7·
w. Wmk inverted .. .. .. 90·00
93 5d. dull purple and black (1905) .. 12·00 26·
94 6d. dull purple (1905) .. .. .. 4·00 3·
95 1s. green and black (1905) .. .. 7·50 9·
96 2s. green and ultramarine (1905) .. 20·00 27·
97 5s. green and carmine (1905) .. .. 30·00 50·
98 £1 purple/*red* (1905) £200 £2
86/98 .. .. *Set of* 13 £275 £3

1907–12. *Wmk Mult Crown CA. Ordinary paper* (½*d. to* 2½*d or chalk-surfaced paper* (*others*). *P* 14.
99 **15** ½d. green 90 5
100 1d. carmine .. .. 11·00 7
a. Red .. .. 4·75 6
101 1½d. orange (1910) .. .. .. 1·25 2·0
102 2d. greyish slate (1909) .. .. .. 1·25 1·5
103 2½d. blue .. .. 3·75 3·0

		3d. purple/*yellow* (1909)	7·50	2·75
		a. Ordinary paper (1912)	9·50	11·00
		4d. black and red/*yellow* (1908)	2·25	1·60
		5d. purple and olive-green (1908)	7·00	5·00
		6d. dull and bright purple (1908)	7·50	8·00
		1s. black/*green* (1908)	5·50	5·00
		2s. purple and bright blue/*blue* (1908)	15·00	19·00
		5s. green and red/*yellow* (1908)	38·00	55·00
		£1 purple and black/*red* (1911)	£250	£190
		Set of 13	£300	£250
1s Optd "Specimen"		*Set of* 13	£300	

t values from the 1903, 1904–05 and 1907–12 issues are with forged postmarks. These include oval registered les dated "16 JUL 11" or "4 SP 11".

HIGH VALUES. The £2 and £5 values of the King V series were intended for fiscal use only. Before the uction of the airmail service at the end of 1926 there was tal rate for which they could be used. Under the airmail used between 1926 and 1932 it is just possible that a very letter may have required a £2 value. Postmarks on the £5 the £2 before December 1926 can only have been applied vour" or, in the case of the cds type, are on stamps removed telegraph forms. Used prices quoted for Nos. 129/30 and are for "by favour" cancellations.

17

18

19

20

-21. *Die I. Wmk Mult Crown CA. Chalk-surfaced paper . and 6d. to £5). P 14.*

	17	½d. blue-green	3·00	2·50
		a. Yellow-green (1914)	3·00	2·50
		b. Deep green (1919)	4·75	2·75
		1d. carmine-red	1·50	30
		a. Scarlet (1916)	3·50	1·00
		b. Rose-red (1918)	3·75	80
		bw. Wmk inverted	†	£120
		bx. Wmk reversed	£110	
		1½d. orange (1913)	2·00	2·50
		a. Orange-yellow (1919)	5·00	1·00
		2d. greyish slate	1·25	20
		w. Wmk inverted	35·00	35·00
		2½d. deep blue	9·50	2·50
		a. Ultramarine (1917)	1·00	80
	20	3d. purple/*yellow*	3·00	3·25
		ba. *On pale yellow* (1921)	3·25	3·25
	18	4d. black and red/*yellow*	2·75	8·50
		a. On lemon (1915)	4·00	6·50
		b. Die II. *On pale yellow* (1921)	4·25	5·50
		5d. purple and olive-green	1·25	6·00
		6d. dull and bright purple	3·25	6·00
	19	7d. purple and orange	3·00	8·50
		9d. purple and black	5·00	12·00
	18	10d. purple and red	3·00	18·00
	20	1s. black/*green*	4·25	4·50
		a. On blue-green, green back	4·50	3·25
		w. Wmk inverted	48·00	48·00
		2s. blue and purple/*blue*	13·00	5·50
		5s. red and green/*yellow*	13·00	26·00
		10s. red and green/*green*	65·00	£110
		a. Carmine and blue-green/green	85·00	£130
		b. Carmine and yellow-green/green	95·00	£150
		£1 black and purple/*red*	£150	£225
		£2 blue and dull purple	£475	£650
		s. Optd "Specimen"	£100	
		£5 orange and green	£1200	£1700
		s. Optd "Specimen"	£225	
/28		*Set of* 17	£250	£375
s/28s Optd "Specimen"		*Set of* 17	£300	

xamples of Nos. 127/8 are known with part strikes of the ged postmarks mentioned after Nos. 99/111.

1–27. *Die II. Wmk Mult Script CA. Chalk-surfaced paper 6d. to £5). P 14.*

	17	½d. dull green	1·25	80
		a. Bright green	3·50	1·50
		1d. bright violet (Die I) (1924)	1·50	2·25
		a. Die II (1925)	3·00	20
3		1½d. scarlet (1925)	1·75	1·25
4		2d. grey (1922)	1·00	20
5		2½d. ultramarine	1·00	7·00
6	**18**	3d. bright blue (1922)	1·25	1·25
7		4d. black and red/*pale yellow* (1925)	1·75	3·25
8		5d. purple and olive-green	1·25	1·25
9		6d. grey-purple and bright purple	1·25	2·50
		y. Wmk inverted and reversed		
0	**19**	7d. purple and orange (1927)	2·75	19·00
1		9d. purple and black (1922)	2·75	14·00
2	**18**	10d. purple and red (1925)	3·25	24·00
3	**20**	1s. black/*emerald* (1925)	7·00	7·00
4		2s. blue and dull purple/*blue*	9·50	10·00
		w. Wmk inverted	£100	£110
5		5s. red and green/*yellow* (1927)	9·50	50·00
6		10s. red and green/*green* (1927)	85·00	£170
7		£2 blue and dull purple (1923)	£425	£650
		s. Optd "Specimen"	£100	
8		£5 orange and green (1923)	£1100	£1700
		s. Optd "Specimen"	£225	
1/46		*Set of* 16	£120	£275
1s/46s Optd "Specimen"		*Set of* 16	£275	

21 Rice Field

22 Palms and Cola Tree

(Eng J.A.C. Harrison (T **21**))

1932 (1 Mar). *Wmk Mult Script CA. (a) Recess Waterlow. P* 12½.

155	**21**	½d. green	20	30
156		1d. violet	30	30
157		1½d. carmine	30	1·25
		a. Imperf between (horiz pair)		
158		2d. brown	30	30
159		3d. blue	60	1·75
160		4d. orange	60	6·50
161		5d. bronze-green	85	3·00
162		6d. light blue	60	3·00
163		1s. lake	2·25	5·50
		(b) Recess B.W. P 12.		
164	**22**	2s. chocolate	5·00	5·50
165		5s. deep blue	12·00	19·00
166		10s. green	60·00	£120
167		£1 purple	90·00	£190
155/67		*Set of* 13	£150	£325
155s/67s Perf "Specimen"		*Set of* 13	£180	

23 Arms of Sierra Leone

24 Old Slave Market, Freetown

27 African Elephant

28 King George V

(Des Father F. Welsh. Recess B.W.)

1933 (2 Oct). *Centenary of Abolition of Slavery and of Death of William Wilberforce. T* **23**/4, **27**/8 *and similar designs. Wmk Mult Script CA (sideways on horiz designs). P* 12.

168	½d. green	70	1·25
169	1d. black and brown	50	10
170	1½d. chestnut	4·50	4·50
171	2d. purple	2·75	20
172	3d. blue	2·75	1·75
173	4d. brown	6·50	10·00
174	5d. green and chestnut	7·00	13·00
175	6d. black and brown-orange	8·00	8·00
176	1s. violet	4·75	17·00
177	2s. brown and light blue	22·00	40·00
178	5s. black and purple	£140	£160
179	10s. black and sage-green	£170	£250
180	£1 violet and orange	£300	£400
168/80	*Set of* 13	£600	£800
168s/80s Perf "Specimen"	*Set of* 13	£500	

Designs: *Vert*—1d. "Freedom"; 1½d. Map of Sierra Leone; 4d. Government sanatorium. *Horiz*—3d. Native fruit seller; 5d. Bullom canoe; 6d. Punting near Banana; 1s. Government buildings; 2s. Bunce Island; £1 Freetown harbour.

1935 (6 May). *Silver Jubilee. As Nos.* 91/4 *of Antigua, but ptd by B.W. P* 11×12.

181	1d. ultramarine and grey-black	1·00	2·50
	a. Extra flagstaff	48·00	70·00
	b. Short extra flagstaff	£120	
	c. Lightning conductor	38·00	
182	3d. brown and deep blue	1·00	8·50
	a. Extra flagstaff	65·00	85·00
	b. Short extra flagstaff	£275	
	c. Lightning conductor	70·00	
183	5d. green and indigo	1·40	11·00
	a. Extra flagstaff	95·00	£150
	b. Short extra flagstaff	£350	
	c. Lightning conductor	£100	
184	1s. slate and purple	6·00	5·00
	a. Extra flagstaff	£300	£225
	b. Short extra flagstaff	£300	
	c. Lightning conductor	£300	£225
181/4	*Set of* 4	8·50	24·00
181s/4s Perf "Specimen"	*Set of* 4	80·00	

For illustrations of plate varieties see Omnibus section following Zanzibar.

1937 (12 May). *Coronation. As Nos.* 95/7 *of Antigua. P* 11×11½.

185	1d. orange	70	50
186	2d. purple	90	50
187	3d. blue	1·50	3·25
185/7	*Set of* 3	2·75	3·75
185s/7s Perf "Specimen"	*Set of* 3	55·00	

30 Freetown from the Harbour

31 Rice Harvesting

(Recess Waterlow)

1938 (1 May)–**44.** *Wmk Mult Script CA (sideways). P* 12½.

188	**30**	½d. black and blue-green	15	30
189		1d. black and lake	40	50
		a. Imperf between (vert pair)	†	—
190	**31**	1½d. scarlet	20·00	70
190*a*		1½d. mauve (1.2.41)	30	60
191		2d. mauve	40·00	1·75
191*a*		2d. scarlet (1.2.41)	30	1·50
192	**30**	3d. black and ultramarine	40	40
193		4d. black and red-brown (20.6.38)	80	3·50
194	**31**	5d. olive-green (20.6.38)	5·00	3·50
195		6d. grey (20.6.38)	75	40
196	**30**	1s. black and olive-green (20.6.38)	1·75	60
196*a*	**31**	1s. 3d. yellow-orange (1.7.44)	40	40
197	**30**	2s. black and sepia (20.6.38)	4·50	2·25
198	**31**	5s. red-brown (20.6.38)	10·00	6·50
199		10s. emerald-green (20.6.38)	17·00	8·00
200	**30**	£1 deep blue (20.6.38)	17·00	19·00
188/200		*Set of* 16	£100	42·00
188s/200s Perf "Specimen"		*Set of* 16	£250	

1946 (1 Oct). *Victory. As Nos.* 110/11 *of Antigua.*

201	1½d. lilac	20	10
202	3d. ultramarine	20	10
201s/2s Perf "Specimen"	*Set of* 2	55·00	

1948 (1 Dec). *Royal Silver Wedding. As Nos.* 112/13 *of Antigua.*

203	1½d. bright purple	15	15
204	£1 indigo	16·00	17·00

1949 (10 Oct). *75th Anniv of U.P.U. As Nos.* 114/17 *of Antigua.*

205	1½d. purple	20	50
206	3d. deep blue	1·25	3·00
207	6d. grey	35	3·25
208	1s. olive	35	1·00
205/8	*Set of* 4	1·90	7·00

STAMP BOOKLETS

1929.

SB1 1s. booklet containing twelve 1d. (No. 132a)

SB2 2s. booklet containing twelve 2d. (No. 134)

Singapore

A Crown Colony until the end of 1957. From 1 August 1958, an internally self-governing territory designated the State of Singapore. From 16 September 1963, part of the Malaysian Federation until 9 August 1965, when it became an independent republic within the Commonwealth.

Stamps in the Crown Colony Victory design with face values of 8 c. and 15 c. were prepared for Singapore in 1946, but were not issued.

(Currency. 100 cents = 1 Malayan dollar)

CROWN COLONY

(Typo D.L.R.)

1948 (1 Sept)–**52.** *As T* **58** *of Malaysia (Straits Settlements), but inscribed* "SINGAPORE" *at foot. Wmk Mult Script CA. Chalk-surfaced paper.* (*a*) *P* 14.

No.	Description	Unused	Used
1	1 c. black	15	80
2	2 c. orange	15	40
3	3 c. green	50	60
4	4 c. brown	20	1·00
5	6 c. grey	40	60
6	8 c. scarlet (1.10.48)	30	60
7	10 c. purple	20	10
8	15 c. ultramarine (1.10.48)	10·00	10
9	20 c. black and green (1.10.48)	3·50	20
10	25 c. purple and orange (1.10.48)	4·75	15
11	40 c. red and purple (1.10.48)	8·00	5·00
12	50 c. black and blue (1.10.48)	3·25	10
13	$1 blue and purple (1.10.48)	10·00	2·50
14	$2 green and scarlet (25.10.48)	48·00	3·75
15	$5 green and brown (1.10.48)	£120	5·00
1/15	*Set of* 15	£180	18·00
	(*b*) *P* 17½×18		
16	1 c. black (21.5.52)	75	3·25
17	2 c. orange (31.10.49)	70	80
19	4 c. brown (1.7.49)	1·00	10
19*a*	5 c. bright purple (1.9.52)	2·50	1·25
21	6 c. grey (10.12.52)	1·50	85
21*a*	8 c. green (1.9.52)	4·00	3·00
22	10 c. purple (9.2.50)	50	10
22*a*	12 c. scarlet (1.9.52)	6·00	7·50
23	15 c. ultramarine (9.2.50)	14·00	10
24	20 c. black and green (31.10.49)	4·50	3·50
24*a*	20 c. bright blue (1.9.52)	4·00	10
25	25 c. purple and orange (9.2.50)	1·00	10
25*a*	35 c. scarlet and purple (1.9.52)	4·00	1·00
26	40 c. red and purple (4.5.51*)	35·00	14·00
27	50 c. black and blue (9.2.50)	8·00	10
28	$1 blue and purple (31.10.49)	15·00	20
	a. Error. St. Edward's Crown, W **9***b*	£5000	
29	$2 green and scarlet (24.5.51)	90·00	1·25
	a. Error. St. Edward's Crown. W **9***b*	£5000	
	w. Wmk inverted		
30	$5 green and brown (19.12.51)	£180	1·25
	w. Wmk inverted		
16/30	*Set of* 18	£325	35·00

*Earliest known postmark date.

Single-colour values were from single plate printings (Die II) and all bi-colour, except the 25 c., from separate head and duty plates (Die I). For differences between the Dies see after Nos. 278/98 of Malaysia (Straits Settlements). The 25 c. is unique in this series in that it combines a Die II frame with a separate head plate.

Nos. 28a and 29a occur on rows in the watermark in which the crowns and letters "CA" alternate.

Postal forgeries of the 50 c., $1 and $2 exist on unwatermarked paper and perforated 14×14½.

1948 (25 Oct). *Royal Silver Wedding. As Nos.* 112/13 *of Antigua.*

No.	Description	Unused	Used
31	10 c. violet	75	50
32	$5 brown	£110	32·00

1949 (10 Oct). *75th Anniv of U.P.U. As Nos.* 114/17 *of Antigua.*

No.	Description	Unused	Used
33	10 c. purple	75	30
34	15 c. deep blue	6·00	2·25
35	25 c. orange	6·00	2·25
36	50 c. blue-black	6·00	3·00
33/6	*Set of* 4	17·00	7·00

Somaliland Protectorate

Egyptian post offices were opened in Somaliland during 1876 and the stamps of Egypt were used there until the garrisons were withdrawn in 1884.

Cancellations for these offices have been identified as follows (for illustrations of postmark types see SUDAN).

BARBARA (Berbera). Open 1876 to 1 November 1884. Circular datestamp as Sudan Type I.

ZEILA. Open 1876 to 1 November 1884. Circular datestamp as Sudan Types G and I, sometimes inscr ZEJLA. One example with seal type cancellation as Sudan Type B is also known.

Stamps of India were used at the two post offices from 1 January 1887 until 1903 usually cancelled with circular datestamps or the "B" obliterator used by all offices controlled from Bombay.

The Protectorate Post Office was established on 1 June 1903, when control of British Somaliland was transferred from the Indian Government to the British Foreign Office.

PRICES FOR STAMPS ON COVER TO 1945

Nos. 1/11	*from* × 25
Nos. 12/13	—
Nos. 18/22	*from* × 12
Nos. 23/4	—
Nos. 25/30	*from* × 30
Nos. 32/59	*from* × 12
Nos. 60/92	*from* × 6
Nos. 93/104	*from* × 3
Nos. 105/16	*from* × 4
Nos. O1/13	*from* × 8
Nos. O14/15	—

(Currency. 12 pies = 1 anna; 16 annas = 1 rupee)

BRITISH
SOMALILAND

(1)

2

3

SETTINGS OF TYPE 1

In all printings the ½, 1, 2, 2½, 3, 4, 8, 12 a. and 1 r. values were overprinted from a setting of 240 (2 panes 12 × 10, one above the other), covering the entire sheet at one operation.

The 6 a., which was in sheets of 320 (4 panes, each 8 × 10), had a modified setting of 160, applied twice to each sheet.

The high values were overprinted in sheets of 96 (8 panes, each 4 × 3).

The settings for the low value stamps contained two slightly different styles of overprint, identified by the position of "B" of "BRITISH". Type A shows this letter over the "M" of "SOMALILAND" and Type B over the "OM".

For the first printing with the overprint at the top of the design the 240 position setting showed all the stamps in the upper pane and 63 in the lower as Type A, with the remaining 57 as Type B. When the setting was used for the printing with overprint at foot it was amended slightly so that one of the Type A examples in the upper pane became a Type B.

The 6 a. value with overprint at top shows 250 examples of Type A and 70 as Type B in each sheet. This proportion altered in the printing with overprint at foot to 256 as Type A and 64 as Type B.

OVERPRINT VARIETIES

Missing second "I" in "BRITISH"—Occurs on the stamps with overprint at top from R.2/6 of the upper pane and R.5/1 of the lower, although it is believed that the example on the 2½ a. (No. 4a) only occurs from the second position. On the later printing with overprint at foot a similar error can be found on R.7/12 of the upper pane. Some examples of both these errors show traces of the letter remaining, but the prices quoted are for stamps with it completely omitted.

Figure "1" for first "I" in "BRITISH"—Occurs on R.6/4 of the upper pane for all printings of the 240 impression setting. In addition it has been reported from R.7/12 of the Queen Victoria 2½, 12 a. and 1 r. with overprint at foot. Both versions of the 6 a. show the variety on R.6/4 of the upper left and upper right panes.

Curved overprint—Occurs on R.3/4 of the top right-hand pane of the high values.

"SUMALILAND"—Occurs on R.2/9 of the upper pane for all low values with the overprint at foot, except the 6 a. A similar variety occurs on the high values from the same series on R.1/3 of the top left pane.

"SOMAL.LAND"—Occurs on R.7/5 of the lower pane from the 240 impression setting with the overprint at foot. In addition the Edwardian values of this series also have an example on R.6/7. The 6 a. has examples of the flaw on R.6/9 and R.7/5 of both the lower right and left panes. A similar variety occurs on the high values from the same series at R.3/4 of the third pane in the left-hand column.

1903 (1 June). *Nos.* 80, 94, 96, 98, 100, 106/9, 114/16 *and* 118 *of India (Queen Victoria) optd with T* **1,** *at top of stamp, in Calcutta. Wmk Elephant Head* (6 *a.*) *or Star* (*others*).

No.	Description	Unused	Used
1	½ a. yellow-green	2·75	4·00
	a. "BRIT SH"	£160	
2	1 a. carmine	2·75	3·75
	a. "BRIT SH"	£180	£250
	b. "BR1TISH"	£130	
3	2 a. pale violet	2·25	1·50
	a. "BRIT SH"	£275	£350
	b. "BR1TISH"	£250	
	c. Opt double	£650	
4	2½ a. ultramarine	2·00	1·75
	a. "BRIT SH"	£450	
	b. "BR1TISH"	£275	
5	3 a. brown-orange	3·25	3·00
	a. "BRIT SH"	£500	
	b. "BR1TISH"	£300	
6	4 a. slate-green	3·50	2·75
	a. "BR1TISH"	£300	£325
7	6 a. olive-bistre	4·75	4·50
	a. "BR1TISH"	£200	£225
8	8 a. dull mauve	3·75	5·00
	a. "BR1TISH"	£300	
9	12 a. purple/*red*	3·25	7·00
	a. "BR1TISH"	£300	£400
10	1 r. green and aniline carmine	7·00	10·00
	a. "BR1TISH"	£350	
11	2 r. carmine and yellow-brown	24·00	42·00
	a. Curved opt	£250	
12	3 r. brown and green	20·00	48·00
	a. Curved opt	£250	
13	5 r. ultramarine and violet	35·00	55·00
	a. Curved opt	£300	
1/13	*Set of* 13	£100	£170

1903 (1 Sept–2 Nov). *Stamps of India optd with T* **1,** *at b of stamp, in Calcutta.* (*a*) *On Nos.* 80, 100, 106/9 *an (Queen Victoria).*

No.	Description	Unused	Used
18	2½ a. ultramarine (2.11)	2·75	
	a. "BR1TISH"	£170	
	b. "SUMALILAND"	£200	
	c. "SOMAL.LAND"	£200	
19	6 a. olive-bistre (2.11)	6·00	
	a. "BR1TISH"	£225	
	b. "SOMAL.LAND"	£140	
20	12 a. purple/*red* (2.11)	5·50	
	a. "BR1TISH"	£200	
	b. "SUMALILAND"	£275	
	c. "SOMAL.LAND"	£275	
21	1 r. green and aniline carmine (2.11)	2·75	
	a. "BR1TISH"	£250	
	b. "SUMALILAND"	£350	
	c. "SOMAL.LAND"	£350	
22	2 r. carmine and yellow-brown (2.11)	70·00	
	a. Curved opt	£400	
	b. "SUMALILAND"	£400	
	c. "SOMAL.LAND"	£400	
23	3 r. brown and green (2.11)	75·00	
	a. Opt double, both inverted with one albino	£550	
	b. Curved opt	£475	
	c. "SUMALILAND"	£475	
	d. "SOMAL.LAND"	£475	
24	5 r. ultramarine and violet (2.11)	70·00	
	a. Curved opt	£400	
	b. "SUMALILAND"	£400	
	c. "SOMAL.LAND"	£400	
	(*b*) *On Nos.* 122/4, 127/8 *and* 133 (*King Edward VII*)		
25	½ a. green	2·25	
	a. "BRIT SH"	£350	
	b. "BR1TISH"	75·00	
	c. "SUMALILAND"	75·00	
	d. "SOMAL.LAND"	40·00	
26	1 a. carmine (8.10)	1·25	
	a. "BRIT SH"	£225	
	b. "BR1TISH"	80·00	
	c. "SUMALILAND"	80·00	
	d. "SOMAL.LAND"	40·00	
27	2 a. violet (2.11)	1·75	
	a. "BRIT SH"	£900	
	b. "BR1TISH"	£160	
	c. "SUMALILAND"	£160	
	d. "SOMAL.LAND"	70·00	
28	3 a. orange-brown (2.11)	2·50	
	a. "BR1TISH"	£170	
	b. "SUMALILAND"	£170	
	c. "SOMAL.LAND"	75·00	
29	4 a. olive (2.11)	1·50	
	a. "BR1TISH"	£170	
	b. "SUMALILAND"	£170	
	c. "SOMAL.LAND"	80·00	
30	8 a. purple (2.11)	1·75	
	a. "BR1TISH"	£200	
	b. "SUMALILAND"	£200	
	c. "SOMAL.LAND"	£100	
18/30	*Set of* 13	£200	

(Typo D.L.R.)

1904 (15 Feb–3 Sept). (*a*) *Wmk Crown CA. P* 14.

No.	Type	Description	Unused	Used
32	**2**	½ a. dull green and green	1·25	
33		1 a. grey-black and red (3.9)	8·00	
34		2 a. dull and bright purple (3.9)	1·50	
35		2½ a. bright blue (3.9)	2·50	
36		3 a. chocolate and grey-green (3.9)	1·50	
37		4 a. green and black (3.9)	1·75	
38		6 a. green and violet (3.9)	4·25	
39		8 a. grey-black and pale blue (3.9)	3·50	
40		12 a. grey-black and orange-buff (3.9)	6·50	
		(*b*) *Wmk Crown CC. P* 14		
41	**3**	1 r. green (3.9)	12·00	4
42		2 r. dull and bright purple (3.9)	40·00	7
43		3 r. green and black (3.9)	40·00	8
44		5 r. grey-black and red (3.9)	40·00	8
32/44		*Set of* 13	£140	
32s/44s		Optd "Specimen" *Set of* 13	£180	

1905 (July)–**11**. *Wmk Mult Crown CA. Ordinary paper. P*

No.	Type	Description	Unused	Used
45	**2**	½ a. dull green and green	1·25	7
46		1 a. grey-black and red (10.7.05)	12·00	4
		a. Chalk-surfaced paper (1906)	10·00	1
47		2 a. dull and bright purple	7·50	8
		a. Chalk-surfaced paper (1909)	8·00	11
48		2½ a. bright blue	3·00	10
49		3 a. chocolate and grey-green	2·00	14
		a. Chalk-surfaced paper (1911)	9·50	22
50		4 a. green and black	4·00	14
		a. Chalk-surfaced paper (1911)	12·00	30
51		6 a. green and violet	3·00	24
		a. Chalk-surfaced paper (1911)	22·00	38
52		8 a. grey-black and pale blue	5·50	8
		a. Chalk-surfaced paper. *Black and blue* (27.1.11)	32·00	70
53		12 a. grey-black and orange-buff	6·50	10
		a. Chalk-surfaced paper. *Black and orange-brown* (9.11.11)	17·00	55

1909 (30 Apr–May). *Wmk Mult Crown CA. P* 14.

No.	Type	Description	Unused	Used
58	**2**	½ a. bluish green (May)	22·00	26
59		1 a. red	2·50	2
		s. Optd "Specimen"	27·00	
45/59		*Set of* 11	60·00	£1

4

5

(Typo D.L.R.)

Sept)–**19.** *Wmk Mult Crown CA. Chalk-surfaced paper and 3 a. to 5 r.). P 14.*
½ a. green (11.13) .. 65 8·00
w. Wmk inverted .. 15·00 60·00
1 a. red .. 2·50 50
a. *Scarlet* (1917) .. 3·00 1·25
2 a. dull and bright purple (12.13) .. 3·50 13·00
a. *Dull purple and violet-purple* (4.19) 21·00 29·00
2½ a. bright blue (10.13) .. 1·00 8·50
3 a. chocolate and grey-green (10.13) .. 2·25 6·50
w. Wmk inverted .. 80·00
4 a. green and black (12.12) .. 2·50 10·00
6 a. green and violet (4.13) .. 2·50 5·00
8 a. grey-black and pale blue (10.13) .. 3·50 15·00
12 a. grey-black and orange-buff (10.13) 3·25 20·00
1 r. green (11.12) .. 11·00 16·00
2 r. dull purple and purple (4.19) .. 18·00 65·00
3 r. green and black (4.19) .. 50·00 £110
5 r. black and scarlet (4.19) .. 50·00 £150
.. *Set of* 13 £130 £350
2s Optd "Specimen" .. *Set of* 13 £170

Wmk Mult Script CA. Chalk-surfaced paper (2 *a. and to* 5 *r.*). *P* 14.
½ a. blue-green .. 2·75 9·00
1 a. carmine-red .. 3·50 70
2 a. dull and bright purple .. 4·25 1·00
2½ a. bright blue .. 1·00 4·50
3 a. chocolate and green .. 2·50 7·50
4 a. green and black .. 2·50 7·50
6 a. green and violet .. 1·50 13·00
8 a. grey-black and pale blue .. 2·00 5·50
12 a. grey-black and orange-buff .. 8·50 15·00
1 r. dull green .. 8·00 48·00
2 r. dull purple and purple .. 23·00 48·00
3 r. dull green and black .. 35·00 £100
5 r. black and scarlet .. 65·00 £160
.. *Set of* 13 £130 £350
5s Optd "Specimen" .. *Set of* 13 £170
amples of most values are known showing a forged Berbera mark dated "21 OC 1932".

(6 May). *Silver Jubilee. As Nos. 91/4 of Antigua, but ptd Waterlow. P 11×12.*
1 a. deep blue and scarlet .. 2·25 2·75
m. "Bird" by turret .. 80·00
2 a. ultramarine and grey .. 2·75 2·50
k. Kite and vertical log .. 60·00
3 a. brown and deep blue .. 2·25 11·00
k. Kite and vertical log .. 90·00
l. Kite and horizontal log .. 80·00
1 r. slate and purple .. 7·00 11·00
k. Kite and vertical log .. £140
l. Kite and horizontal log .. £120
.. *Set of* 4 13·00 24·00
9s Perf "Specimen" .. *Set of* 4 75·00
or illustrations of plate varieties see Omnibus section wing Zanzibar.

7 (13 May). *Coronation. As Nos. 95/7 of Antigua, but ptd by L.R. P 14.*
1 a. scarlet .. 15 20
2 a. grey-black .. 55 1·25
3 a. bright blue .. 70 55
.. *Set of* 3 1·25 1·75
2s Perf "Specimen" .. *Set of* 3 55·00

6 Berbera Blackhead Sheep

7 Lesser Kudu

8 Somaliland Protectorate

(Des H. W. Claxton. Recess Waterlow)

38 (10 May). *Portrait to left. Wmk Mult Script CA. P 12½.*
3 **6** ½ a. green .. 40 4·50
4 1 a. scarlet .. 40 1·25
5 2 a. maroon .. 1·25 1·25
6 3 a. bright blue .. 7·50 9·50
7 **7** 4 a. sepia .. 4·25 7·00
8 6 a. violet .. 6·00 12·00
9 8 a. grey .. 1·25 12·00
0 12 a. red-orange .. 5·50 14·00
1 **8** 1 r. green .. 8·50 45·00
2 2 r. purple .. 15·00 45·00
3 3 r. bright blue .. 18·00 27·00
4 5 r. black .. 20·00 27·00
a. Imperf between (horiz pair) £15000
/104 .. *Set of* 12 75·00 £180
s/104s Perf "Specimen" .. *Set of* 12 £150
Examples of most values are known showing a forged Berbera stmark dated "15 AU 38".

Following the Italian Occupation, from 19 August 1940 until 16 March 1941, the stamps of ADEN were used at Berbera from 1 July 1941 until 26 April 1942.

9 Berbera Blackhead Sheep

5 Cents
(10)

1 Shilling
(11)

(Recess Waterlow)

1942 (27 Apr). *As T* **6/8** *but with full-face portrait of King George VI, as in T* **9**. *Wmk Mult Script CA. P 12½.*
105 **9** ½ a. green .. 20 30
106 1 a. scarlet .. 20 10
107 2 a. maroon .. 50 20
108 3 a. bright blue .. 1·75 20
109 **7** 4 a. sepia .. 2·50 20
110 6 a. violet .. 2·50 20
111 8 a. grey .. 2·50 20
112 12 a. red-orange .. 3·00 40
113 **8** 1 r. green .. 1·25 40
114 2 r. purple .. 1·25 4·00
115 3 r. bright blue .. 2·00 7·00
116 5 r. black .. 6·50 5·50
105/16 .. *Set of* 12 22·00 17·00
105s/16s Perf "Specimen" .. *Set of* 12 £150

1946 (15 Oct). *Victory. As Nos. 110/11 of Antigua.*
117 1 a. carmine .. 10 10
a. Perf 13½ .. 11·00 45·00
118 3 a. blue .. 10 10
117s/18s Perf "Specimen" .. *Set of* 2 48·00

1949 (28 Jan). *Royal Silver Wedding. As Nos. 112/13 of Antigua.*
119 1 a. scarlet .. 10 10
120 5 r. black .. 3·50 3·25

1949 (24 Oct*). *75th Anniv of U.P.U. As Nos. 114/17 of Antigua. Surch with face values in annas.*
121 1 a. on 10 c. carmine .. 20 15
122 3 a. on 30 c. deep blue (R.) .. 1·00 50
123 6 a. on 50 c. purple .. 35 75
124 12 a. on 1s. red-orange .. 35 50
121/4 .. *Set of* 4 1·75 1·75
*This is the local date of issue. The Crown Agents released these stamps in London on 10 October.

(New Currency. 100 cents = 1 shilling)

1951 (1 Apr). *1942 issue surch as T* **10/11**.
125 5 c. on ½ a. green .. 30 75
126 10 c. on 2 a. maroon .. 30 30
127 15 c. on 3 a. bright blue .. 1·00 60
128 20 c. on 4 a. sepia .. 1·50 20
129 30 c. on 6 a. violet .. 1·50 30
130 50 c. on 8 a. grey .. 1·75 20
131 70 c. on 12 a. red-orange .. 2·50 3·00
132 1 s. on 1 r. green .. 85 30
133 2 s. on 2 r. purple .. 4·25 11·00
134 2 s. on 3 r. bright blue .. 4·75 3·50
135 5 s. on 5 r. black (R.) .. 5·50 6·00
125/35 .. *Set of* 11 22·00 24·00

OFFICIAL STAMPS

SERVICE

BRITISH SOMALILAND
(O 1)

BRITISH SOMALILAND
(O 2)

O. H. M. S.
(O 3)

SETTING OF TYPE O 1

The 240 impression setting used for the Official stamps differs considerably from that on the contemporary postage issue with overprint at foot, although the "BR1TISH" error can still be found on R.6/4 of the upper pane. The Official setting is recorded as consisting of 217 overprints as Type A and 23 as Type B.

OVERPRINT VARIETIES

Figure "1" for first "I" in "BRITISH". Occurs on R.6/4 of the upper pane as for the postage issue.
"BRITIS H"—Occurs on R.8, stamps 4 and 10 of the lower pane.

1903 (1 June). *Nos. O45, O48, O49a and O50/1 of India (Queen Victoria optd "O.H.M.S.") additionally optd with Type O 1 in Calcutta.*
O1 ½ a. yellow-green .. 6·50 48·00
a. "BR1TISH" .. £275
b. "BRITIS H" .. £120
O2 1 a. carmine .. 15·00 8·00
a. "BR1TISH" .. £300 £275
b. "BRITIS H" .. £140
O3 2 a. pale violet .. 8·00 48·00
a. "BR1TISH" .. £350
b. "BRITIS H" .. £160
O4 8 a. dull mauve .. 10·00 £375
a. "BR1TISH" .. £750
b. "BRITIS H" .. £350
c. Stop omitted after "M" of "O.H.M.S." (lower pane R. 12/10) .. £1600
O5 1 r. green and carmine .. 10·00 £550
a. "BR1TISH" .. £750
b. "BRITIS H" .. £350
O1/5 .. *Set of* 5 45·00 £900
No. O4c was caused by an attempt to correct a minor spacing error of the "O.H.M.S." overprint which is known on the equivalent India Official stamp.

SETTING OF TYPE O 2

This 240 impression setting of "BRITISH SOMALILAND" also differs from that used to prepare the postage issue with overprint at foot, although many of the errors from the latter still occur in the same positions for the Official stamps. The setting used for Nos. O6/9*f* contained 180 overprints as Type A and 60 as Type B.

OVERPRINT VARIETIES

Missing second "I" in "BRITISH"—Occurs R.7/12 of upper pane as for the postage issue.
Figure "1" for first "I" in "BRITISH"—Occurs R.6/4 of upper pane as for the postage issue.
"SUMALILAND"—Occurs R.2/9 of the upper pane as for the postage issue.
"SOMAL.LAND"—Occurs R.6/7 of the lower pane as for the postage issue.

SERVICE
(O 2*a*)

"SERVICE" in wrong fount (Type O **2***a*)—Occurs R.1/7 of lower pane.

1903. *Prepared for use but not issued. Nos. 106, 122/4 and 133 of India (1 r. Queen Victoria, rest King Edward VII), optd with Type O 2 in Calcutta.*
O6 ½ a. green .. 40
a. "BRIT SH" .. 65·00
b. "BR1TISH" .. 45·00
c. "SUMALILAND" .. 45·00
d. "SOMAL.LAND" .. 35·00
e. "SERVICE" as Type O **2***a* .. 40·00
O7 1 a. carmine .. 40
a. "BRIT SH" .. 65·00
b. "BR1TISH" .. 45·00
c. "SUMALILAND" .. 45·00
d. "SOMAL.LAND" .. 35·00
e. "SERVICE" as Type O **2***a* .. 40·00
O8 2 a. violet .. 70
a. "BRIT SH" .. 95·00
b. "BR1TISH" .. 70·00
c. "SUMALILAND" .. 70·00
d. "SERVICE" as Type O **2***a* .. 48·00
O9 8 a. purple .. 4·00
a. "BRIT SH" .. £1400
b. "BR1TISH" .. £500
c. "SUMALILAND" .. £500
d. "SERVICE" as Type O **2***a* .. £500
O9*f* 1 r. green and aniline carmine .. 17·00
fa. "BRIT SH" .. £1400
fb. "BR1TISH" .. £500
fc. "SUMALILAND" .. £500
fd. "SOMAL.LAND" .. £500
fe. "SERVICE" as Type O **2***a* .. £500
O6/9*f* .. *Set of* 5 20·00
Used examples of Nos. O6/9*f* are known, but there is no evidence that such stamps did postal duty.

SETTING OF TYPE O 3

The anna values were overprinted in sheets of 120 (2 panes 6 × 10) from a setting matching the pane size. The full stop after the "M" on the fifth vertical column was either very faint or completely omitted. The prices quoted are for stamps with the stop missing; examples with a partial stop are worth much less.

The 1 r. value was overprinted from a separate setting of 60 which did not show the "missing stop" varieties.

1904 (1 Sept)–**05.** *Stamps of Somaliland Protectorate optd with Type O 3. P 14. (a) Wmk Crown CA.*
O10 **2** ½ a. dull green and green .. 3·25 48·00
a. No stop after "M" .. £275
O11 1 a. grey-black and carmine .. 3·25 7·00
a. No stop after "M" .. £200 £275
O12 2 a. dull and bright purple .. £160 55·00
a. No stop after "M" .. £1800 £650
O13 8 a. grey-black and pale blue .. 60·00 £130
a. No stop after "M" .. £450 £600

(*b*) *Wmk Mult Crown CA*
O14 **2** 2 a. dull and bright purple, **O** (7.05?) 75·00 £750
a. No stop after "M" .. £1800

(*c*) *Wmk Crown CC*
O15 **3** 1 r. green .. £160 £550
O10s/13s, O15s Optd "Specimen" .. *Set of* 5 £120

South Africa

South Africa as a nation, rather than a geographical term, came into being with the creation of the Union of South Africa on 31 May 1910.

The development, both political and philatelic, of the area is very complex and the method adopted by the catalogue is to first list, in alphabetical order, the various colonies and republics which formed this federation, followed by stamps for the Union of South Africa.

The section is divided as follows:

I. CAPE OF GOOD HOPE. British Kaffraria. Mafeking Siege Stamps. Vryburg
II. GRIQUALAND WEST
III. NATAL.
IV. NEW REPUBLIC.
V. ORANGE FREE STATE. Orange River Colony
VI. TRANSVAAL. Pietersburg. Local British Occupation Issues
VII. ZULULAND
VIII. BRITISH ARMY FIELD OFFICES DURING SOUTH AFRICAN WAR
IX. UNION OF SOUTH AFRICA

I. CAPE OF GOOD HOPE

PRICES FOR STAMPS ON COVER

Nos. 1/4	*from* × 4
Nos. 5/14	*from* × 3
Nos. 18/21	*from* × 5
No. 22	—
Nos. 23/6	*from* × 5
Nos. 27/31	*from* × 8
Nos. 32/3	*from* × 10
No. 34	*from* × 25
No. 35	*from* × 20
No. 36	*from* × 10
Nos. 37/8	*from* × 25
Nos. 39/45	*from* × 10
Nos. 46/7	*from* × 12
Nos. 48/54	*from* × 10
Nos. 55/6	*from* × 25
No. 57	*from* × 50
Nos. 58/69	*from* × 10
Nos. 70/8	*from* × 6

PRICES. Our prices for early Cape of Good Hope are for stamps in very fine condition. Exceptional copies are worth more, poorer copies considerably less.

1 Hope

2

(Des Charles Bell, Surveyor-General. Eng W. Humphrys. Recess P.B.)

1853 (1 Sept). *W* **2**. *Imperf*. (*a*) *Paper deeply blued*.
1 1 1d. pale brick-red £3500 £275
a. Deep brick-red £5000 £300
b. Wmk sideways .. .. .. † £400
2 4d. deep blue £2000 £160
a. Wmk sideways £3000 £250

Plate proofs of the 4d. in a shade similar to the issued stamp exist on ungummed watermarked paper. The blueing on the reverse of these proofs is uneven giving a blotchy appearance.

(*b*) *Paper slightly blued* (*blueing not pronounced at back*)
3 1 1d. brick-red £3000 £200
a. Brown-red £3250 £225
b. Wmk sideways .. .. .. † £325
4 4d. deep blue £1300 £110
a. Blue £1400 £150
b. Wmk sideways .. .. .. † £275

PERKINS BACON "CANCELLED". For notes on these handstamps showing "CANCELLED" between horizontal bars forming an oval, see Catalogue Introduction.

1855–63. *W* **2**. (*a*) *Imperf*.
5 1 1d. brick-red/*cream toned paper* (1857) .. £5000 £900
a. Rose (1858) (H/S "CANCELLED" in oval £10000) .. £450 £200
ab. Wmk sideways .. .. — £375
b. Deep rose-red £650 £250
ba. Wmk sideways .. .. — £375
6 1 4d. deep blue/*white paper* (1855) .. £600 45·00
a. Blue (H/S "CANCELLED" in oval £10000) .. £400 45·00
b. Bisected (on cover) .. .. † £35000
c. Wmk sideways .. .. † £160
7 6d. pale rose-lilac/*white paper* (18.2.58) (H/S "CANCELLED" in oval £8000) £750 £200
a. Wmk sideways .. .. † £750
b. Deep rose-lilac/white paper .. £1700 £300
c. Slate-lilac/blued paper (1862) .. £4250 £450
d. Slate-purple/blued paper (1863) .. £3500 £1000
e. Bisected (on cover) .. .. † —
8 1s. bright yellow-green/*white paper* (18.2.58) (H/S "CANCELLED" in oval £10000) £2500 £180
a. Wmk sideways .. .. † £750
b. Deep dark green (1859) .. £225 £500

The method adopted for producing the plate of the 4d., 6d and 1s. stamps involved the use of two dies, so that there are two types of each of these values differing slightly in detail, but produced in equal numbers.

The 1d. value in dull rose on ungummed watermarked paper with the watermark sideways is a plate proof.

The 4d. is known bisected in 1858 and used with two other 4d. values to pay the inland registered fee. The 6d. is known bisected and used with 1d. for 4d. rate.

The paper of No. 5 is similar to that of Nos. 1/4, but is without the blueing. It is much thicker than the white paper used for later printings of the 1d. The evolution of the paper on these Cape of Good Hope stamps is similar to that on the line-engraved issues of Great Britain. Examples of the 6d. slate-lilac apparently on white paper have had the blueing washed out.

The 4d. value is known printed in black on white watermarked paper. Twelve authenticated examples have been recorded, the majority of which show cancellations or, at least, some indication that they have been used.

It was, at one time, believed that these stamps came from a small supply printed in black to mark the death of Prince Consort, but references to examples can be found in the philatelic press before news of this event reached Cape Town.

It is now thought that these stamps represent proof sheets, possibly pressed into service during a shortage of stamps in 1861.

There is, however, no official confirmation of this theory. (*Price* £35000 *un*, £30000 *with obliteration*).

(*b*) *Unofficially rouletted*
9 1 1d. brick-red .. .. .. † £3000
10 4d. blue .. .. .. † £2250
11 6d. rose-lilac .. .. .. † £1500
12 1s. bright yellow-green .. .. † £3250
a. Deep dark green .. .. † £3500

These rouletted stamps are best collected on cover.

3 Hope

(Local provisional (so-called "wood-block") issue. Engraved on steel by C. J. Roberts. Printed from stereotyped plates by Saul Solomon & Co, Cape Town)

1861 (Feb–April). *Laid paper. Imperf*.
13 3 1d. vermilion (27 February) £14000 £2250
a. Carmine (7 March) £24000 £3000
b. Brick-red (10 April) £35000 £4250
c. Error. Pale milky blue .. .. — £28000
ca. Pale bright blue .. .. — £30000
14 4d. pale milky blue (23 February) £10000 £1600
aa. Retouch or repair to rt-hand corner — £5500
a. Pale grey-blue (March?) .. £11000 £1600
b. Pale bright blue (March?) .. £11000 £1900
ba. Retouch or repair to rt-hand corner — £5500
c. Deep bright blue (12 April) .. £95000 £4500
d. Blue £15000 £3000
e. Error. Vermilion £150000 £40000
ea. Carmine .. .. — £95000
f. Sideways *tête-bêche* (pair) .. † £100000

Nos. 13/14 were each issued in *tête-bêche* pairs normally joined at edges bearing the same inscription ("POSTAGE" against "POSTAGE", etc). No. 14f, of which only one used example is known, comes from the first printing and shows the right-hand stamp misplaced so that "FOUR PENCE" adjoins "POSTAGE".

Nos. 13*c*/*ca* and 14*e*/*ea* were caused by the inclusion of incorrect clichés in the plates of the 1d. or 4d. values.

Both values were officially reprinted in March 1883, on wove paper. The 1d. is in deep red, and the 4d. in a deeper blue than that of the deepest shade of the issued stamp.

Specimens of the reprints have done postal duty, but their use thus was not intended. There are no reprints of the errors or of the retouched 4d.

Further reprints were made privately but with official permission, in 1940/41, in colours much deeper than those of any of the original printings, and on thick carton paper.

Examples of the 4d. are known unofficially rouletted.

Early in 1863, Perkins Bacon Ltd handed over the four plates used for printing the triangular Cape of Good Hope stamps to De La Rue & Co, Ltd, who made all the subsequent printings.

(Printed from the P.B. plates by D.L.R.)

1863–4. *Imperf*. (*a*) *W* **2**.
18 1 1d. deep carmine-red (1864) £120 £225
a. Wmk sideways £300 £300
b. Deep brown-red £375 £250
ba. Wmk sideways £500 £300
c. Brownish red £375 £225
ca. Wmk sideways £500 £275
19 4d. deep blue (1864) .. .. £120 48·00
a. Blue .. .. .. £130 60·00
b. Slate-blue £2000 £500
c. Steel-blue £2000 £250
d. Wmk sideways £400 £160
20 6d. bright mauve (1864) £160 £450
a. Wmk sideways .. .. † £900
21 1s. bright emerald-green £350 £450
a. Pale emerald-green £1000

(*b*) *Wmk Crown CC* (*sideways*)
22 1 1d. deep carmine-red .. .. £1500(

No. 22 was a trial printing, and is only known unused.

Our prices for the 4d. blue are for stamps which are b[illegible] comparison with the other listed shades. An exceptional[illegible] shade is recognised by specialists and is rare.

With the exception of the 4d., these stamps may be distinguished from those printed by Perkins Bacon by their [illegible] which are quite distinct.

The De La Rue stamps of all values are less clearly prin[illegible] figure of Hope and the lettering of the inscriptions standing [illegible] boldly, while the fine lines of the background appear blur[illegible] broken when examined under a glass. The background as [illegible] often shows irregularity in the apparent depth of colour, [illegible] wear of the plates.

For note regarding the two dies of the 4d., 6d., and 1s. valu[illegible] after No. 8.

All the triangular stamps were demonetised as from 1 ([illegible] 1900.

4 "Hope" seated, with vine and ram. (With outer frame-line)

Four Pence.

(5)

(Des Charles Bell. Die engraved on steel and stamps ty[illegible] D.L.R.)

1864–77. *With outer frame-line surrounding the design. Crown CC. P* 14.
23 4 1d. carmine-red (5.65) .. .. 85·00
a. Rose-red .. .. 80·00
w. Wmk inverted .. .. —
24 4d. pale blue (8.65) .. .. 95·00
a. Blue £100
b. Ultramarine £250
c. Deep blue (1872) £140
w. Wmk inverted £375
25 6d. pale lilac (before 21.3.64) £100
a. Deep lilac £200
b. Violet (*to bright*) (1877) .. £120
w. Wmk inverted .. .. †
26 1s. deep green (1.64) £500
a. Green £100
ax. Wmk reversed .. ..
b. Blue-green £110
w. Wmk inverted £550

The 1d. rose-red, 6d. lilac, and 1s. blue-green are known in[illegible] probably from proof sheets.

The 1d. and 4d. stamps of this issue may be found with[illegible] and/or top outer frame-lines missing, due to wear of the p[illegible]

See also Nos. 44 and 52/3.

(Surch by Saul Solomon & Co, Cape Town)

1868 (17 Nov). *No. 25a surch with T* **5**.
27 4 4d. on 6d. deep lilac (R.) £200
a. "Peuce" for "Pence" £1800
b. "Fonr" for "Four" .. .. —
w. Wmk inverted .. .. —

Specimens may also be found with bars omitted or at the t[illegible] the stamp, due to misplacement of the sheet.

The space between the words and bars varies from 12½ [illegible] mm, stamps with spacing 15½ and 16 mm being rare. There [illegible] two printings, one of 120,000 in November 1868 and anoth[illegible] 1,000,000 in December. Stamps showing widest spacings are [illegible] ably from the earlier printing.

6 (No outer frame-line)

(Die re-engraved. Typo D.L.R.)

1871–6. *Outer frame-line removed. Wmk Crown CC. P* 14.
28 6 ½d. grey-black (*shades*) (12.75) .. .. 14·00 [illegible]
w. Wmk inverted .. .. — 7[illegible]
29 1d. carmine-red (*shades*) (2.72) .. .. 28·00
w. Wmk inverted .. .. — £[illegible]
30 4d. dull blue (*shades*) (12.76) .. .. 95·00
b. Ultramarine .. .. £200 5[illegible]
w. Wmk inverted .. .. £300 7[illegible]
31 5s. yellow-orange (25.8.71) .. .. £300 1[illegible]

The ½d., 1d. and 5s. are known imperf, probably from p[illegible] sheets.

See also Nos. 36, 39, 40/3, 48/51, 54, 61/2 and 64/8.

ONE PENNY **THREE PENCE**

(7) (8)

(Surch by Saul Solomon & Co, Cape Town)

1874–6. *Nos. 25a and 26a surch with T* **7**.
32 4 1d. on 6d. deep lilac (R.) (1.9.74) .. £450 85
a. "E" of "PENNY" omitted .. .. — £1(
33 1d. on 1s. green (11.76) .. .. 60·00 40

These provisionals are found with the bar only, either across [illegible] centre of the stamp or at top, with value only; or with value a[illegible] bar close together, either at top or foot. Such varieties are due [illegible] misplacement of sheets during surcharging.

Nov). *No. 30 surch with T* **8**.
3d. on 4d. blue (R.) .. .. .. 90·00 1·75
a. "PENCB" for "PENCE" £1500 £225
b. "THE.EE" for "THREE" £1800 £275
c. Surch double £7500 £2750
d. Variety b. double ..

ouble surcharge must also have existed showing variety a.
variety b. is known.
are numerous minor varieties, including letters broken or
ignment, due to defective printing and use of poor type.
pacing between the bar and the words varies from 16½ to

THREEPENCE (9) **3** (10) **3** (11)

(Surch by D.L.R.)

eb). *Special printing of the 4d. in new colour, surch, T* **9**. *Wmk Crown CC.*
3d. on 4d. pale dull rose .. .. .. 60·00 1·75
w. Wmk inverted .. .. .. — £120

nor constant variety exists with foot of "P" in "PENCE" off, making the letter appear shorter.

July). *Wmk Crown CC. P* 14.
3d. pale dull rose .. .. .. £170 21·00
w. Wmk inverted .. .. .. — £225

(Surch by Saul Solomon & Co, Cape Town)

Aug). *No. 36 surch.*
"3" on 3d. pale dull rose .. .. 65·00 1·50
a. Surch inverted .. .. £800 40·00
b. Vert pair. Nos. 37/8 .. .. £850 £350
w. Wmk inverted .. .. — £100
"3" on 3d. pale dull rose .. .. £160 5·00
a. Surch inverted £7000 £900
w. Wmk inverted .. .. — £250

"3" (T **10**) is sometimes found broken. Vert pairs are
showing the two types of surcharge *se-tenant*, and
al strips of three exist, the top stamp having surcharge
he middle stamp being without surcharge, and the lower
having surcharge T **11** (*Price for strip of* 3 £3750 *un.*).

Jan). *Wmk Crown CC. P* 14.
3d. pale claret .. .. .. £110 2·50
a. Deep claret .. .. .. £100 2·25
w. Wmk inverted .. ..

s was a definite colour change made at the request of the Post-er-General owing to the similarity between the colours of the amp and the 3d. in pale dull rose. Imperf copies are probably proof sheets.
ofs of this value were printed in brown, on unwatermarked paper and imperf, but the colour was rejected as unsuitable.

(July)–**83**. *Wmk Crown CA. P* 14.
½d. black (1.9.82) .. .. 20·00 1·25
a. Grey-black .. .. 17·00 1·25
w. Wmk inverted .. .. — £120
1d. rose-red .. .. 42·00 80
a. Deep rose-red .. .. 48·00 80
w. Wmk inverted .. .. — £120
2d. pale bistre (1.9.82) .. .. 80·00 40
a. Deep bistre .. .. 85·00 40
w. Wmk inverted .. .. — £120
3d. pale claret .. .. 6·50 90
a. Deep claret .. .. 10·00 75
aw. Wmk inverted .. .. — 85·00
4 6d. mauve (to bright) (8.82) .. 85·00 70
5 5s. orange (8.83) £800 £200

perf pairs of the ½d., 1d. and 2d. are known, probably from sheets.

One Half-penny.

(12)

13 "Cabled Anchor"

(Surch by Saul Solomon & Co, Cape Town)

2 (July). *Nos. 39a and 43a surch with T* **12**.
6 ½d. on 3d. deep claret (Wmk CC) .. £2750 £130
a. Hyphen omitted .. .. — £3250
½d. on 3d. deep claret (Wmk CA) .. 22·00 3·00
a. "p" in "penny" omitted .. £2000 £700
b. "y" in "penny" omitted .. £1000 £600
c. Hyphen omitted £550 £350
w. Wmk inverted .. .. — £225

arieties also exist with broken and defective letters, and the obliterating bar omitted or at the top of the stamp.

4–**90**. W **13**. *P* 14.
6 ½d. black (1.86) .. .. 3·00 10
a. Grey-black .. .. 3·00 10
w. Wmk inverted .. ..
1d. rose-red (12.85) .. .. 3·00 10
a. Carmine-red .. .. 3·00 10
w. Wmk inverted .. .. — 75·00
2d. pale bistre (12.84) .. .. 22·00 70
a. Deep bistre .. .. 6·00 10
w. Wmk inverted .. .. — £100
4d. blue (6.90) .. .. 9·00 50
a. Deep blue .. .. 9·00 50
4 6d. reddish purple (12.84) .. .. 60·00 1·60
a. Purple (shades) .. .. 7·00 20
b. Bright mauve .. .. 10·00 50
w. Wmk inverted .. .. — £180
1s. green (12.85) .. .. £120 4·75
a. Blue-green (1889) .. .. 70·00 40
w. Wmk inverted .. .. — £275
6 5s. orange (7.87) .. .. 75·00 4·75
54 .. *Set of* 7 £150 5·50

All the above stamps are known in imperf pairs, probably m proof sheets.
For later shade and colour changes, etc., see Nos. 61, etc.

2½d (14)

15

ONE PENNY. (16)

(Surch by D.L.R.)

1891 (Mar). *Special printing of the 3d. in new colour, surch with T* **14**.
55 **6** 2½d. on 3d. pale magenta .. .. 4·50 1·00
a. Deep magenta .. .. 3·00 20
b. "1" with horiz serif .. .. 50·00 32·00

No. 55b occurs on two stamps (Nos. 8 and 49) of the pane of 60.
Two types of "d" are found in the surcharge, one with square end to serif at top, and the other with pointed serif.

1892 (June). W **13**. *P* 14.
56 **15** 2½d. sage-green .. .. 6·00 10
a. Olive-green .. .. 8·50 55
See also No. 63.

(Surch by W. A. Richards & Sons, Cape Town)

1893 (Mar). *Nos. 50/a surch with T* **16**.
57 **6** 1d. on 2d. pale bistre .. .. 3·25 60
a. Deep bistre .. .. 1·75 50
b. No stop after "PENNY" .. .. 50·00 11·00
c. Surch double .. .. — £400

No. 57b occurs on stamp No. 42 of the upper left-hand pane, and on No. 6 of the lower right-hand pane.
Minor varieties exist showing broken letters and letters out of alignment or widely spaced. Also with obliterating bar omitted, due to misplacement of the sheet during surcharging.

17 "Hope" standing. Table Bay in background

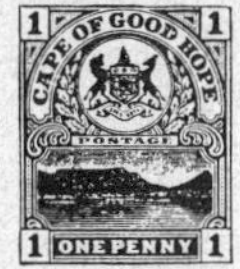

18 Table Mountain and Bay with Arms of the Colony

(Des Mr. Mountford. Typo D.L.R.)

1893 (Oct)–**1902**. W **13**. *P* 14.
58 **17** ½d. green (9.98) .. .. 1·50 10
59 1d. rose-red .. .. 2·50 65
a. Carmine .. .. 1·25 10
60 3d. magenta (3.02) .. .. 4·00 1·50
The 1d. is known in imperf pairs, probably from proof sheets.

1893–98. *New colours, etc.* W **13**. *P* 14.
61 **6** ½d. yellow-green (12.96) .. .. 1·50 50
a. Green .. .. 2·75 50
62 2d. chocolate-brown (3.97) .. .. 2·00 30
63 **15** 2½d. pale ultramarine (3.96) .. .. 3·50 15
a. Ultramarine .. .. 3·50 10
64 **6** 3d. bright magenta (9.98) .. .. 5·50 85
65 4d. sage-green (3.97) .. .. 4·00 1·00
66 1s. blue-green (12.93) .. .. 55·00 3·00
a. Deep blue-green .. .. 70·00 7·50
67 1s. yellow-ochre (5.96) .. .. 7·50 1·00
68 5s. brown-orange (6.96) .. .. 60·00 3·50
61/8 .. *Set of* 8 £120 9·00

(Des E. Sturman. Typo D.L.R.)

1900 (Jan). W **13**. *P* 14.
69 **18** 1d. carmine .. .. 2·25 10
w. Wmk inverted .. ..

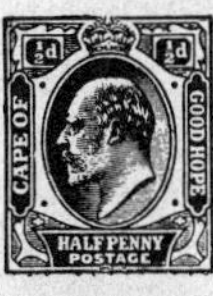

19

20

21

22 23

24

25 26

27

(Typo D.L.R.)

1902 (Dec)–**04**. W **13**. *P* 14.
70 **19** ½d. green .. .. 2·00 10
71 **20** 1d. carmine .. .. 2·00 10
w. Wmk inverted .. ..
y. Wmk inverted and reversed .. ..
72 **21** 2d. brown (10.04) .. .. 8·50 80
w. Wmk inverted .. ..
73 **22** 2½d. ultramarine (3.04) .. .. 2·75 6·50
74 **23** 3d. magenta (4.03) .. .. 7·00 75
75 **24** 4d. olive-green (2.03) .. .. 7·50 65
76 **25** 6d. bright mauve (3.03) .. .. 15·00 30
77 **26** 1s. yellow-ochre .. .. 12·00 80
78 **27** 5s. brown-orange (2.03) .. .. 65·00 10·00
70/8 .. *Set of* 9 £110 18·00
All values exist in imperf pairs, from proof sheets.

STAMP BOOKLETS

1902. *Black on red cover. Stapled.*
SB1 1s. ½d. booklet containing twelve 1d. (No. 71) in blocks of 6 .. ..

1905 (Dec). *Black on red cover. Stapled.*
SB2 2s. 7d. booklet containing thirty 1d. (No. 71) in blocks of 6 .. .. £2000

OFFICIAL STAMPS

The following stamps, punctured with a double triangle device, were used by the Stationery and Printed Forms Branch of the Cape of Good Hope Colonial Secretary's Department between 1904 and 1906. Later South Africa issues may have been similarly treated, but this has not been confirmed.

(O 1)

1904. *Various issues punctured as Type* O **1**. (*a*) *Nos. 50 and 52a.*
O 1 **6** 2d. pale bistre .. .. 13·00
O 2 **4** 6d. purple .. .. 15·00
(*b*) *Nos. 58 and 60*
O 3 **17** ½d. green .. .. 16·00
O 4 3d. magenta .. .. 13·00
(*c*) *Nos. 62 and 64/5*
O 5 **6** 2d. chocolate-brown .. .. 13·00
O 6 3d. bright magenta .. .. 17·00
O 7 4d. sage-green .. .. 16·00
(*d*) *No. 69*
O 8 **18** 1d. carmine .. .. 13·00
(*e*) *Nos. 70/2 and 74/8*
O 9 **19** ½d. green .. .. 15·00
O10 **20** 1d. carmine .. .. 10·00
O11 **21** 2d. brown .. .. 18·00
O12 **23** 3d. magenta .. .. 13·00
O13 **24** 4d. olive-green .. .. 14·00
O14 **25** 6d. bright mauve .. .. 14·00
O15 **26** 1s. yellow-ochre .. .. 17·00
O16 **27** 5s. brown-orange .. .. 45·00
Nos. O1/16 are only known used.

Cape of Good Hope became a province of the Union of South Africa on 31 May 1910.

BRITISH KAFFRARIA

The history of the Cape eastern frontier was punctuated by a series of armed conflicts with the native population, known as the Kaffir Wars. After a particularly violent outbreak in 1846 the Governor, Sir Harry Smith, advanced the line of the Cape frontier to the Keikama and Tyumie Rivers. In the area between the new frontier and the Kei River a buffer state, British Kaffraria, was established on 17 December 1847. This area was not annexed to the Cape, but was administered as a separate Crown dependency by the Governor of Cape Colony in his capacity as High Commissioner for South Africa.

The territory, with its administration based on King William's Town, used the stamps of the Cape of Good Hope from 1853 onwards, the mail being sent via Port Elizabeth or overland from the Cape. Covers from British Kaffraria franked with the triangular issues are rare.

The first postal marking known from British Kaffraria is the 1849 type octagonal numeral No. 47 from Port Beaufort. Oval postmarks of the 1853 type were used at Alice, Aliwal North, Bedford, Fort Beaufort, King William's Town and Queenstown. In 1864 numeral cancellations were issued to all post offices within the Cape system and it is known that the following numbers were initially assigned to post towns in Kaffraria: 4 (King William's Town), 7 (Bedford), 11 (Queenstown), 29 (East London), 32 (Fort Beaufort), 38 (Aliwal North) and 104 (Cathcart).

It is believed that post offices may have also existed at Adelaide, Barkly East, Sterkstoom and Stutterheim, but, to date, no examples of handstamps or cancellations are known from them during the British Kaffraria period.

Following the decimation by famine of the Xhosa tribes in 1857 British Kaffraria was annexed to Cape Colony in 1865. The area eventually formed the basis of the Ciskei independent "homeland".

MAFEKING SIEGE STAMPS

PRICES FOR STAMPS ON COVER	
Nos. 1/16	*from* × 12
Nos. 17/18	*from* × 20
Nos. 19/20	*from* × 15
Nos. 21/2	*from* × 10

23 MARCH to 17 MAY 1900

There are numerous forgeries of the Mafeking overprints, many of which were brought home by soldiers returning from the Boer War.

MAFEKING, 3d. BESIEGED. (1)
MAFEKING 3d. BESIEGED. (2)

(Surcharged by Townsend & Co, Mafeking)

1900 (23 Mar–28 Apr). *Various stamps surch as T* **1** *and* **2**.

(*a*) *Cape of Good Hope stamps surch as T* **1** (23 Mar)

1 **6** 1d. on ½d. green .. .. .. £180 60·00
2 **17** 1d. on ½d. green (24.3) .. .. .. £225 70·00
3 3d. on 1d. carmine .. .. .. £200 50·00
4 **6** 6d. on 3d. magenta (24.3) £26000 £250
5 1s. on 4d. sage-green (24.3) £6000 £325

A variety in the setting of each value exists without comma after "MAFEKING".

(*b*) *Nos.* 59 *and* 61/3 *of Bechuanaland Protectorate* (*previously optd on Great Britain*) *surch as T* **1**

6 1d. on ½d. vermilion (28.3) .. .. £180 55·00
a. Surch inverted .. .. .. † £4250
b. Vert pair, surch *tête-bêche* .. .. † £20000
7 3d. on 1d. lilac (4.4) .. .. .. £850 85·00
a. Surch double .. .. .. † £15000
8 6d. on 2d. green and carmine (6.4) .. £1700 70·00
9 6d. on 3d. purple/*yellow* (30.3) £4000 £250
a. Surch inverted .. .. .. † £20000
b. Surch double .. .. ..

(*c*) *Nos.* 12 *and* 35 *of British Bechuanaland* (4*d. previously optd on Great Britain*) *surch as T* **1**

10 6d. on 3d. lilac and black (27.3) .. .. £350 60·00
11 1s. on 4d. green and purple-brown (29.3) £1200 75·00
a. Surch double (both Type 1) .. .. † £16000
ab. Surch double (Type 1 and Type 2) .. £6500 £4250
b. Surch treble .. .. .. † £16000
c. Surch double, one inverted .. .. † £16000

(*d*) *Nos.* 61/2 *and* 65 *of Bechuanaland Protectorate* (*previously optd on Great Britain*) *surch as T* **2**

12 3d. on 1d. lilac (1 Apr) .. .. .. £900 70·00
a. Surch double .. .. .. † £6500
13 6d. on 2d. green and carmine (25 Apr) .. £1100 70·00
14 1s. on 6d. purple/*rose-red* (12 Apr) .. £4000 85·00

(*e*) *Nos.* 36/7 *of British Bechuanaland* (*previously optd on Great Britain*) *surch as T* **2**

15 1s. on 6d. purple/*rose-red* (28 Apr) .. £14000 £650
16 2s. on 1s. green (13 Apr) £7500 £325

On the stamps overprinted "BECHUANALAND PROTECTORATE" and "BRITISH BECHUANALAND" the local surcharge is so adjusted as not to overlap the original overprint.

3 Cadet Sergt.-major Goodyear

4 General Baden-Powell

(Des Dr. W. A. Hayes (T 3), Capt. H. Greener (T 4))

1900 (6–11 Apr). *Produced photographically by Dr. D. Taylor. Horiz laid paper with sheet wmk* "OCEANA FINE". *P* 12.

(*a*) 18½ *mm wide.* (*b*) 21 *mm wide*

17 **3** 1d. pale blue/*blue* (7.4) £800 £275
18 1d. deep blue/*blue* £800 £275
19 **4** 3d. pale blue/*blue* (*a*) £1200 £400
a. Reversed design £45000 £35000
20 3d. deep blue/*blue* (*a*) £1200 £350
a. Imperf between (horiz pair) .. .. † £48000
b. Double print .. .. .. † £16000
21 3d. pale blue/*blue* (*b*) (11.4) £6500 £750
a. Vert laid paper £7500
22 3d. deep blue/*blue* (*b*) (11.4) £7000 £950

These stamps vary a great deal in colour from deep blue to pale grey.

No. 18 imperforate and without gum is believed to be a proof (*Price for unused pair* £16000).

No. 19a comes from a sheet of 12 printed in reverse of which nine, three mint and six used, are known to have survived.

VRYBURG

PRICES FOR STAMPS ON COVER
Nos. 1/4 *from* × 5
Nos. 11/12 *from* × 2

BOER OCCUPATION

Vryburg was occupied by Boer forces on 15 October 1899. Unoverprinted stamps of Transvaal were used initially. Nos. 1/4 were only available from 24 to 29 November. The Boers evacuated the town on 7 May 1900.

½ PENCE Z.A.R. (1)

1899 (24 Nov). *Cape stamps surch as T* **1**. *Surch* 12 *mm high on No.* 3 *and* 10 *mm on all other values.*

1 **6** ½ PENCE green .. .. .. £200 80·00
a. Italic "Z" £1700 £700
b. Surch 12 mm high £1700 £700
2 **17** 1 PENCE rose £225 £100
a. Italic "Z" £1900 £800
b. Surch 12 mm high £1900 £800
c. "I" for "1" £1200 £500
3 **4** 2 PENCE on 6d. mauve £2000 £500
a. Italic "Z" £10000 £4250
4 **15** 2½ PENCE on 2½d. blue £1700 £425
a. Italic "Z" £10000 £4250
b. Surch 12 mm high £10000 £4250

The "2 PENCE" on 6d. shows the surcharge 12 mm high. It is possible that this was the first value surcharged as the remaining three show the height reduced to 10 mm with the exception of one position in the second vertical row of the setting. The italic "Z" occurs on one position in the sixth vertical row. It is believed that the setting was of 60 (6×10).

BRITISH REOCCUPATION

V. R. SPECIAL POST (2)

1900 (16 May). *Provisionals issued by the Military Authorities. Stamps of Transvaal handstamped with T* **2**.

11 **30** ½d. green .. .. — £2000
11*a* 1d. rose-red (No. 206) .. ..
12 1d. rose-red and green (No. 217) .. £8500 £4000
13 2d. brown and green .. ..
14 2½d. dull blue and green .. ..

No. 11 is known used with double handstamp and Nos. 11/12 with the overprint reading downwards

II. GRIQUALAND WEST

Griqualand West was situated to the North of Cape Colony, bounded on the north by what became British Bechuanaland and on the east by the Orange Free State.

The area was settled in the early nineteenth century by the Griqua tribal group, although many members of the tribe, including the paramount chief, migrated to Griqualand East (between Basutoland and the east coast of South Africa) in 1861–63. There was little European involvement in Griqualand West before 1866, but in that year the diamond fields along the Vaal River were discovered. Sovereignty was subsequently claimed by the Griqua Chief, the Orange Free State and the South African Republic (Transvaal). In 1871 the British authorities arbitrated in favour of the Griqua Chief who promptly ceded his territory to Great Britain. Griqualand West became a separate Crown Colony in January 1873.

During the initial stages of the prospecting boom mail was passed via the Orange Free State, but a post office connected to the Cape Colony postal system was opened at Klip Drift (subsequently Barkly) in late 1870. Further offices at De Beer's New Rush (subsequently Kimberley), Douglas and Du Toit's Pan (subsequently Beaconsfield) were open by September 1873.

Cape of Good Hope stamps to the 5s. value were in use from October 1871, but those originating in Griqualand West can only be identified after the introduction of Barred Oval Diamond Numeral cancellations in 1873. Numbers known to have been issued in the territory are:

1 De Beers N.R. (New Rush) (subsequently Kimberley)
3 Junction R. & M. (Riet and Modder Rivers)
4 Barkly
6 or 9 Du Toit's Pan (subsequently Beaconsfield)
8 Langford (transferred to Douglas)
10 Thornhill

PRICES FOR STAMPS ON COVER

The stamps of Griqualand West are worth from ×10 the price quoted for used stamps, when on cover from the territory.

FORGED OVERPRINTS. Many stamps show forged overprints. Great care should be taken when purchasing the scarcer items.

Stamps of the Cape of Good Hope, Crown CC, perf 14, overprinted.

1874 (Sept). *No.* 24*a of Cape of Good Hope surch* "1d." *in red manuscript by the Kimberley postmaster.*

1 1d. on 4d. blue £950 £1600

G. W. (1)

1877 (Mar). *Nos.* 29/30 *of Cape of Good Hope optd with T* **1**.

2 1d. carmine-red .. .. £450 80·00
a. Opt double .. .. † £1700
3 4d. dull blue (R.) .. .. £350 70·00

G (1*a*) G (2) G (3) G (4) G (5) G (6)
G (7) G (8) G (9) G (10) G (11)
G (12) G (13) G (14)

1877 (Mar)–**78.** *Nos.* 24*a*, 25*a*, 26*a and* 28/31 *Cape o[f Good] Hope optd with capital* "G".

(*a*) *First printing. Optd with T* **1*a*/6** *and* **8** *in black* (1*d.*) *o[r …]* (*others*)

4 ½d. grey-black
a. Opt Type **1*a*** .. .. 17·00
b. Opt Type **2** .. .. 40·00
c. Opt Type **3** .. .. 23·00
d. Opt Type **4** .. .. 40·00
e. Opt Type **5** .. .. 45·00
f. Opt Type **6** .. .. 21·00
g. Opt Type **8** £350
5 1d. carmine-red
a. Opt Type **1*a*** .. .. 18·00
b. Opt Type **2** .. .. 42·00
c. Opt Type **3** .. .. 23·00
d. Opt Type **4** .. .. 42·00
e. Opt Type **5** .. .. 48·00
f. Opt Type **6** .. .. 18·00
g. Opt Type **8** .. .. *
6 4d. blue (with frame-line) (No. 24*a*)
a. Opt Type **1*a*** £160
b. Opt Type **2** £400
c. Opt Type **3** £300
d. Opt Type **4** £400
e. Opt Type **5** £450
f. Opt Type **6** £225
g. Opt Type **8** £1600
7 4d. dull blue (without frame-line) (No. 30)
a. Opt Type **1*a*** £120
b. Opt Type **2** £300
c. Opt Type **3** £190
d. Opt Type **4** £300
e. Opt Type **5** £350
f. Opt Type **6** £180
g. Opt Type **8** £1300
8 6d. deep lilac
a. Opt Type **1*a*** .. .. 90·00
b. Opt Type **2** £190
c. Opt Type **3** £130
d. Opt Type **4** £190
e. Opt Type **5** £250
f. Opt Type **6** £120
g. Opt Type **8** £1100
9 1s. green
a. Opt Type **1*a*** £110
ab. Opt inverted .. .. —
b. Opt Type **2** £250
ba. Opt inverted .. .. —
c. Opt Type **3** £170
d. Opt Type **4** £250
da. Opt inverted .. .. —
e. Opt Type **5** £300
f. Opt Type **6** £160
fa. Opt inverted .. .. —
g. Opt Type **8** £2000
10 5s. yellow-orange
a. Opt Type **1*a*** £450
b. Opt Type **2** £750
c. Opt Type **3** £600
d. Opt Type **4** £750
e. Opt Type **5** £1000
f. Opt Type **6** £550
g. Opt Type **8** £2000

*The 1d. with overprint Type **8** from this setting can onl[y be] distinguished from that of the second printing when *se-te[nant]* with overprint Type **3.**

Nos. 4/10 were overprinted by a setting of 120 covering [both] panes of 60 (6×10). This setting contained 41 examples of T[ype] **1*a*,** 10 of Type **2,** 23 of Type **3,** 10 of Type **4,** 8 of Type **5,** 2[…] Type **6** and 1 of Type **8.** Sub-types of Types **1*a*** and **2** exist. […] single example of Type **8** occurs on R. 7/4 of the right-hand p[ane].

It is believed that there may have been an additional sett[ing] used for the 5s. which was in considerable demand to cover postage and registration on diamond consignments. It is […] possible that single panes of this value and of the 1s. w[ere] overprinted using the right-hand half of the normal 120 sett[ing].

(*b*) *Second printing. Optd with T* **6/14** *in black* (1878)

11 1d. carmine-red
a. Opt Type **6** .. .. *
b. Opt Type **7** .. .. 20·00
c. Opt Type **8** .. .. 40·00
d. Opt Type **9** .. .. 21·00
e. Opt Type **10** .. .. 60·00
f. Opt Type **11** .. .. 45·00
g. Opt Type **12** .. .. 55·00
h. Opt Type **13** .. .. 90·00
i. Opt Type **14** £300
12 4d. dull blue (without frame-line) (No. 30)
a. Opt Type **6** £250
b. Opt Type **7** .. .. 95·00
c. Opt Type **8** £225
d. Opt Type **9** £110
e. Opt Type **10** £300
f. Opt Type **11** £250
g. Opt Type **12** £275
h. Opt Type **13** £450
i. Opt Type **14** £1500
13 6d. deep lilac
a. Opt Type **6** .. .. £375 75[…]
b. Opt Type **7** .. .. £180 40[…]
ba. Opt double .. ..
c. Opt Type **8** .. .. £350 70[…]
d. Opt Type **9** .. .. £200 45[…]
da. Opt double .. .. —
e. Opt Type **10** £425
ea. Opt double .. .. †
f. Opt Type **11** .. .. £375 80[…]
g. Opt Type **12** £375
h. Opt Type **13** £600
i. Opt Type **14** £1500

*The 1d. with overprint Type **6** from this setting can only [be] distinguished from that of the first printing when *se-tenant* w[ith] Types **11, 12** or **13.**

Nos. 11/13 were overprinted by another double-pane setting [of] 120 in which only Types **6** and **8** were repeated from that us[ed] for the first printing. The second printing setting contained […] examples of Type **6,** 30 of Type **7,** 13 of Type **8,** 27 of Type **9,** 9 [of] Type **10,** 11 of Type **11,** 11 of Type **12,** 6 of Type **13** and 1 of Ty[pe] **14.** Sub-types of Types **7** and **12** exist.

G (15) G (16) G (17)

June). *Nos. 24a, 25a and 28/30 of Cape of Good Hope with small capital "G", T* **15/16**.
½d. grey-black (R.) .. .. 7·00 8·50
a. Opt inverted .. .. .. 8·50 8·50
b. Opt double .. .. 35·00 45·00
c. Opt double, both inverted .. .. 65·00 85·00
d. Black opt .. .. £150 80·00
da. Opt inverted £150
db. Opt double, one inverted in red .. £300
dc. Opt double, one inverted (Type **16**) in red .. .. 85·00
½d. grey-black (R.) .. .. .. 8·50 8·50
a. Opt inverted .. .. .. 8·50 10·00
b. Opt double .. .. 60·00 60·00
c. Opt double, both inverted .. ..
d. Black opt .. .. 35·00 35·00
da. Opt inverted .. .. .. 35·00 35·00
db. Opt double, one inverted (Type **15**) in red £120
1d. carmine-red .. .. .. 8·00 5·50
a. Opt inverted .. .. .. 8·00 8·00
b. Opt double .. .. £140 35·00
c. Opt double, both inverted .. .. £140 50·00
d. Opt double, both inverted with one in red .. .. 29·00 29·00
e. Opt double, both inverted with one (Type **16**) in red .. .. ..
6 1d. carmine-red .. .. .. 8·00 8·00
a. Opt inverted .. .. .. 65·00 23·00
b. Opt double .. .. — 70·00
c. Opt double, both inverted .. .. — 85·00
d. Opt double, both inverted with one in red .. .. 65·00 65·00
5 4d. blue (with frame-line) (No. 24*a*) .. — £110
6 4d. blue (with frame-line) (No. 24a) .. — £110
5 4d. dull blue (without frame-line) (No. 30) £100 21·00
a. Opt inverted .. .. .. £160 65·00
b. Opt double .. .. — £150
c. Opt double, both inverted .. .. — £200
d. Red opt .. .. £250 80·00
da. Opt inverted .. .. .. £750 60·00
6 4d. dull blue (without frame-line) (No. 30) £120 9·00
a. Opt inverted .. .. .. £170 23·00
b. Opt double .. .. — £160
c. Opt double, both inverted .. .. — £200
d. Red opt .. .. — 65·00
da. Opt inverted .. .. .. £250 65·00
5 6d. deep lilac .. .. £100 20·00
6 6d. deep lilac .. .. — 20·00

s. 14/23 were also overprinted using a double-pane setting 0. Based on evidence from surviving ½d. and 1d. sheets all prints in the left-hand pane were roman, Type **15**, and all in the right-hand pane italic, Type **16**, except for R. 1/6, 6/6, 7/6, 8/6, 9/6 and 10/6 which were Type **15**. There is derable evidence to suggest that after the ½d. value had overprinted the setting was amended to show a Type **15**, ad of a Type **16**, on R. 10/5 of the right-hand pane. Two es of the setting were required to overprint the sheets of and it would appear that on many sheets the bottom two s had the overprints inverted.

. *Nos. 25b, 26b and 28/31 of Cape of Good Hope optd with all capital "G", T* **17**.
½d. grey-black .. .. 11·00 6·00
a. Opt double £325 £225
1d. carmine-red .. .. 12·00 3·75
a. Opt inverted .. .. — 75·00
b. Opt double .. .. — £120
c. Opt treble .. .. — £170
4d. dull blue .. .. 23·00 3·75
a. Opt double .. .. — 95·00
6d. violet .. .. £110 6·50
a. Opt inverted .. .. — 26·00
b. Opt double £475 £140
1s. green .. .. 90·00 4·00
a. Opt double .. .. £275 80·00
5s. yellow-orange .. .. £325 7·50
a. Opt double .. .. £375 65·00
b. Opt treble .. .. — £250

os. 24/9 were also overprinted using a setting of 120 which tained a number of minor type varieties.

riqualand West was merged with Cape Colony in October 0. The remaining stock of the overprinted stamps was rned from Kimberley to Cape Town and redistributed ong various post offices in Cape Colony where they were used rdinary Cape stamps.

III. NATAL

PRICES FOR STAMPS ON COVER

Nos. 1/7	*from* × 2
Nos. 9/25	*from* × 3
Nos. 26/56	*from* × 4
Nos. 57/8	—
Nos. 59/73	*from* × 5
Nos. 76/84	*from* × 4
Nos. 85/93	*from* × 3
Nos. 96/103	*from* × 6
Nos. 104/5	*from* × 5
Nos. 106/25	*from* × 6
Nos. 127/42	*from* × 4
Nos. 143/5a	—
Nos. 146/57	*from* × 4
No. 162	—
Nos. 165/71	*from* × 3
No. F1	—
Nos. O1/6	*from* × 10

1 2 3 4 5

(Embossed in plain relief on coloured wove paper)

1857 (26 May)–**61**. *Imperf.*
1 **1** 1d. rose (1858) .. .. — £1700
2 1d. buff (1861) .. .. — £1000
3 1d. blue (8.59) .. .. — £1100
4 **2** 3d. rose .. .. — £400
a. *Tête-bêche* (pair) .. .. .. — £32000
5 **3** 6d. green .. .. — £1100
6 **4** 9d. blue .. .. — £7000
7 **5** 1s. buff .. .. — £5500

All the above have been reprinted more than once, and the early reprints of some values cannot always be distinguished with certainty from originals.

Stamps on surface-coloured paper with higher face values and perforated 12½ are fiscals.

NOTE. The value of the above stamps depends on their dimensions, and the clearness of the embossing, but our prices are for fine used.

PERKINS BACON "CANCELLED". For notes on these handstamps showing "CANCELLED" between horizontal bars forming an oval, see Catalogue Introduction.

6

7

(Eng C. H. Jeens. Recess P.B.)

1859–60. *No wmk. P* 14.
9 **6** 1d. rose-red (1860) (H/S "CANCELLED" in oval £6000) .. .. £120 70·00
10 3d. blue .. .. £150 42·00
a. Imperf between (vert pair) .. .. † £6500

No. 10a is only known from a cover of 1867 franked with two such pairs.

The 3d. also exists with "CANCELLED" in oval, but no examples are believed to be in private hands.

1861. *No wmk. Intermediate perf* 14 *to* 16.
11 **6** 3d. blue .. .. £200 65·00

1861–62. *No wmk. Rough perf* 14 *to* 16.
12 **6** 3d. blue .. .. £100 32·00
a. Imperf between (pair) £3250
b. Imperf (pair) .. .. — £2750
13 6d. grey (1862) .. .. £160 50·00

1862. *Wmk Small Star. Rough perf* 14 *to* 16.
15 **6** 1d. rose-red .. .. £130 65·00

The 1d. without watermark and the 3d. watermark Small Star, both imperforate, are proofs.

(Recess D.L.R.)

1863. *Thick paper. No wmk. P* 13.
18 **6** 1d. lake .. .. 85·00 27·00
19 1d. carmine-red .. .. 85·00 27·00

1863–65. *Wmk Crown CC. P* 12½.
20 **6** 1d. brown-red .. .. £130 35·00
21 1d. rose .. .. 85·00 32·00
x. Wmk reversed .. .. .. 85·00 32·00
22 1d. bright red .. .. 85·00 32·00
x. Wmk reversed .. .. .. 85·00 32·00
23 6d. lilac .. .. 55·00 17·00
24 6d. violet .. .. 45·00 28·00
x. Wmk reversed .. .. .. 45·00 28·00

(Typo D.L.R.)

1867 (Apr). *Wmk Crown CC. P* 14.
25 **7** 1s. green .. .. £130 28·00
w. Wmk inverted .. .. .. — £250

POSTAGE (7*a*) Postage. (7*b*) Postage. (7*c*)
Postage. (7*d*) POSTAGE. (7*e*)

1869 (23 Aug). *Optd horiz in Natal. No wmk* (*3d.*), *wmk Crown CC* (*others*). *P* 14 *or* 14–16 (*3d.*), 12½ (*1d., 6d*) *or* 14 (*1s.*).

(*a*) *With T* **7***a* (*tall capitals without stop*)
26 **6** 1d. rose .. .. £350 75·00
x. Wmk reversed .. .. .. £350 75·00
27 1d. bright red .. .. £300 65·00
x. Wmk reversed .. .. .. — 65·00
28 3d. blue (No. 10) £1400 £550
28*a* 3d. blue (No. 11) £500 £225
28*b* 3d. blue (No. 12) .. .. £425 85·00
29 6d. lilac .. .. £450 65·00
30 6d. violet .. .. £400 75·00
x. Wmk reversed .. .. .. — 75·00
31 **7** 1s. green £6000 £1100

(*b*) *With T* **7***b* (12¾ *mm long*)
32 **6** 1d. rose .. .. £325 70·00
33 1d. bright red .. .. £275 60·00
a. Opt double .. .. † £1200
x. Wmk reversed .. .. .. — 60·00
34 3d. blue (No. 10) .. .. — £250
34*a* 3d. blue (No. 11) £450 £180
34*b* 3d. blue (No. 12) .. .. £400 75·00
35 6d. lilac .. .. £425 60·00
36 6d. violet .. .. £350 70·00
x. Wmk reversed .. .. .. — 70·00
37 **7** 1s. green £4500 £800

(*c*) *With T* **7***c* (13¾ *mm long*)
38 **6** 1d. rose £550 £190
39 1d. bright red £650 £170
x. Wmk reversed .. .. .. — £170
40 3d. blue (No. 10) .. ..
40*a* 3d. blue (No. 11) .. .. — £650
40*b* 3d. blue (No. 12) £1000 £300
41 6d. lilac £1100 £140
42 6d. violet £950 £130
x. Wmk reversed .. .. .. — £150
43 **7** 1s. green .. .. — £1700

(*d*) *With T* **7***d* (14½ *to* 15½ *mm long*)
44 **6** 1d. rose £475 £160
45 1d. bright red £475 £140
46 3d. blue (No. 10) .. ..
46*a* 3d. blue (No. 11) .. .. — £325
46*b* 3d. blue (No. 12) .. .. — £225
47 6d. lilac .. .. — 95·00
48 6d. violet .. .. £850 90·00
49 **7** 1s. green £8500 £1500

(*e*) *With T* **7***e* (*small capitals with stop*)
50 **6** 1d. rose .. .. 85·00 35·00
x. Wmk reversed .. .. .. 85·00 35·00
51 1d. bright red .. .. £140 35·00
x. Wmk reversed .. .. .. £140 35·00
52 3d. blue (No. 10) .. .. £250 65·00
53 3d. blue (No. 11) .. .. £140 42·00
54 3d. blue (No. 12) .. .. £170 38·00
a. Opt double .. .. † £850
54*b* 6d. lilac .. .. £170 55·00
55 6d. violet .. .. £130 45·00
56 **7** 1s. green .. .. £190 60·00

It is believed that there were two settings of these overprints. The first setting, probably of 240, contained 60 examples of Type **7***a*, 72 of Type **7***b*, 20 of Type **7***c*, 28 of Type **7***d* and 60 of Type **7***e*. The second, probably of 60 (6×10), contained Type **7***e* only.

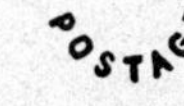

(8)

1870. *No.* 25 *optd with T* **8** *by De La Rue.*
57 **7** 1s. green (C.) .. .. — £3250
58 1s. green (Blk.) £2250 £1200
a. Opt double .. .. — £2250
59 1s. green (G.) .. .. 70·00 10·00

For 1s. orange, see No. 108.

POSTAGE POSTAGE (9)
POSTAGE POSTAGE (10)
POSTAGE (11)

1870–73. *Optd with T* **9** *by De La Rue. Wmk Crown CC. P* 12½.
60 **6** 1d. bright red .. .. 70·00 13·00
x. Wmk reversed .. .. .. 70·00 13·00
61 3d. bright blue (R.) (1872) .. .. 75·00 13·00
x. Wmk reversed .. .. .. 75·00 13·00
62 6d. mauve (1873) .. .. £150 25·00

1873 (July). *Fiscal stamp optd locally with T* **10**. *Wmk Crown CC. P* 14.
63 **7** 1s. purple-brown .. .. £170 18·00

1874 (July). *No.* 21 *optd locally with T* **11**.
65 **6** 1d. rose .. .. £200 65·00
a. Opt double .. ..
x. Wmk reversed .. .. .. — 65·00

12

13

14

15

16

(Typo D.L.R.)

1874 (Jan)–**99.** *Wmk Crown CC (sideways on 5s.). P* 14.
66 **12** 1d. dull rose 21·00 2·25
67 1d. bright rose 21·00 2·25
68 **13** 3d. blue 95·00 17·00
a. Perf 14×12½ £1500 £850
69 **14** 4d. brown (1878) £100 11·00
aw. Wmk inverted £350 £100
b. Perf 12½ £325 65·00
70 **15** 6d. bright reddish violet 42·00 6·00
71 **16** 5s. maroon (1882) £160 42·00
a. Perf 15½×15 (1874) £275 80·00
72 5s. rose 70·00 28·00
73 5s. carmine (H/S S. £160) 65·00 27·00
a. Wmk upright (1899)

POSTAGE (17) POSTAGE (18) ½ HALF (19)

1875–76. *Wmk Crown CC. P* 14 (1s.) *or* 12½ (*others*). (*a*) *Optd locally with T* **17**.
76 **6** 1d. rose £100 48·00
a. Opt double £850 £425
x. Wmk reversed £100 48·00
77 1d. bright red 95·00 60·00
x. Wmk reversed 95·00 60·00

(*b*) *Optd locally with T* **18** (14½ *mm long, without stop*)
81 **6** 1d. rose (1876) 85·00 50·00
a. Opt inverted £950 £425
x. Wmk reversed 85·00 50·00
82 1d. yellow (1876) 70·00 70·00
a. Opt double, one albino £200
x. Wmk reversed 80·00 80·00
83 6d. violet (1876) 55·00 6·00
a. Opt double — £550
b. Opt inverted £650 £150
w. Wmk inverted — £100
x. Wmk reversed 55·00 6·00
84 **7** 1s. green (1876) 80·00 5·50
a. Opt double — £325

TYPE 19. There are several varieties of this surcharge, of which T **19** is an example. They may be divided as follows:

(*a*) "½" 4½ mm high, "2" has straight foot.
(*b*) As last but "½" is 4 mm high.
(*c*) As last but "2" has curled foot.
(*d*) "½" 3½ mm. high, "2" has straight foot.
(*e*) As last but "2" has curled foot.
(*f*) As last but "2" smaller.

As the "½" and "HALF" were overprinted separately, they vary in relative position, and are frequently overlapping.

1877 (13 Feb). *No.* 66 *surch locally as T* **19**.
85 **12** ½d. on 1d. rose (*a*) 24·00 65·00
a. "½" double
86 ½d. on 1d. rose (*b*) £110
87 ½d. on 1d. rose (*c*) 95·00
88 ½d. on 1d. rose (*d*) 55·00 90·00
89 ½d. on 1d. rose (*e*) 55·00
90 ½d. on 1d. rose (*f*) 65·00

POSTAGE Half-penny (21)

23

ONE HALF- PENNY. (24)

1877 (7 Oct)–**79.** T **6** (*wmk Crown CC. P* 12½) *surch locally as T* **21**.
91 ½d. on 1d. yellow 8·00 12·00
a. Surch inverted £275 £190
b. Surch double £250 £180
c. Surch omitted (lower stamp, vertical pair) £1500 £1100
d. "POSTAGE" omitted (in pair with normal) £1500
e. "S" of "POSTAGE" omitted (R. 8/3) £250 £190
f. "T" of "POSTAGE" omitted £250 £250
x. Wmk reversed 8·00 12·00
92 1d. on 6d. violet (10.10.77) 50·00 8·50
a. "S" of "POSTAGE" omitted (R. 8/3) £375 £150
x. Wmk reversed — 8·50
93 1d. on 6d. rose (12.2.79) 95·00 35·00
a. Surch inverted £550 £300
b. Surch double — £250
c. Surch double, one inverted £250 £200
d. Surch four times £375 £200
e. "S" of "POSTAGE" omitted (R. 8/3) £450 £300
x. Wmk reversed — 35·00

No. 93c. is known with one surcharge showing variety "S" of "POSTAGE" omitted.
Other minor varieties exist in these surcharges.

(Typo D.L.R.)

1880 (13 Oct). *Wmk Crown CC. P* 14.
96 **23** ½d. blue-green 10·00 16·00
a. Imperf between (vert pair)

1882 (20 Apr)–**89.** *Wmk Crown CA. P* 14.
97 **23** ½d. blue-green (23.4.84) 90·00 16·00
a. Dull green (10.4.85) 2·00 50
99 **12** 1d. rose (*shades*) (1.84) 2·50 10
a. Carmine 2·75 20
w. Wmk inverted † £150
100 **13** 3d. blue (23.4.84) £100 17·00
101 3d. grey (11.89) 3·00 1·00
102 **14** 4d. brown 3·75 75
103 **15** 6d. mauve 3·25 80
w. Wmk inverted † £100
97*a*/103 *Set of* 6 £100 18·00
97as, 99as, 101s/3s H/S "Specimen" *Set of* 5 £250

1885 (26 Jan). *No.* 99 *surch locally with T* **24**.
104 **12** ½d. on 1d. rose 16·00 11·00
a. No hyphen after "HALF" 60·00 42·00

TWO PENCE (25)

NATAL POSTAGE TWO PENCE 26

TWOPENCE HALFPENNY (27)

1886 (7 Jan). *No.* 101 *surch with T* **25** *by D.L.R.*
105 **13** 2d. on 3d. grey 18·00 5·50

(Typo D.L.R.)

1887 (Sept)–**89.** *Wmk Crown CA. P* 14.
106 **26** 2d. olive-green (Die I*) 27·00 1·60
a. Top left triangle detached — £140
s. Optd "Specimen" 70·00
107 2d. olive-green (Die II) (1889) 2·25 1·40
s. Handstamped "Specimen" 60·00

The differences between Dies I and II are shown in the introduction.

1888 (16 Mar). *As No.* 25, *but colour changed and wmk Crown CA, optd with T* **8** *by D.L.R.*
108 **7** 1s. orange (C.) 3·50 85
a. Opt double — £1500
s. Handstamped "Specimen" 90·00

1891 (22 Apr). *Surch locally with T* **27**.
109 **14** 2½d. on 4d. brown 10·00 8·50
a. "TWOPENGE" 50·00
b. "HALFPENN" £225 £180
c. Surch double £250 £180
d. Surch inverted £350 £275
s. Handstamped "Specimen" 50·00

POSTAGE.

28

Half-Penny (29)

POSTAGE. Varieties of long-tailed letters

(Typo D.L.R.)

1891 (June). *Wmk Crown CA. P* 14.
113 **28** 2½d. bright blue 4·25 50
s. Handstamped "Specimen" 60·00

1895 (12 Mar). *No.* 24 *surch locally with T* **29** *in carmine.*
114 ½d. on 6d. violet 1·25 3·00
a. "Ealf-Penny" 20·00 26·00
b. "Half-Penny" and long "P" 18·00 26·00
ba. "Half Penny" and long "T" and "A" 18·00 26·00
c. No stop after "POSTAGE" and long "P", "T" and "A" 18·00 26·00
d. Long "P" 2·25 4·00
e. Long "T" 2·25 4·00
f. Long "A" 3·25 5·00
g. Long "P" and "T" 2·25 4·00
h. Long "P" and "A" 2·25 4·00
i. Long "T" and "A" 3·00 4·75
k. Long "P", "T" and "A" 3·00 4·75
ka. Long "P", "T" and "A" with comma after "POSTAGE" 6·50 10·00
l. Surch double £250
la. Surch double, one vertical £250
m. "POSTAGE" omitted £1000
s. Handstamped "Specimen" 50·00
x. Wmk reversed 1·25 3·00

The surcharge was applied as a setting of 60 (12×5) which contained seventeen normals, one each of Nos. 114a, 114b, 114ba, 114c, six of No. 114d, six of 114e, three of 114f, six of 114g, seven of 114h, five of No. 114i, four of No. 114k and two of No. 114ka.

HALF (30)

31

32

1895 (18 Mar). *No.* 99 *surch locally with T* **30**.
125 HALF on 1d. rose (*shades*) 1·25
a. Surch double £325
b. "H" with longer left limb 20·00
c. Pair, one without surcharge
s. Handstamped "Specimen" 50·00

No. 125b occurs on the second, fourth, sixth etc., stamps first vertical row of the righthand pane. It was very soon cor

In some printings what appears to be a broken "E" (with limb removed) was used instead of "L" in "HALF" on the last in the sheet (*Price* £30)

(Typo D.L.R.)

1902–03. *Inscr* "POSTAGE REVENUE". *Wmk Crown P* 14.
127 **31** ½d. blue-green 2·00
128 1d. carmine 5·00
129 1½d. green and black 2·50
130 2d. red and olive-green 1·50
131 2½d. bright blue 1·25
132 3d. purple and grey 1·00
133 4d. carmine and cinnamon 3·25
134 5d. black and orange 1·50
w. Wmk inverted £120
135 6d. green and brown-purple 1·50
136 1s. carmine and pale blue 2·75
137 2s. green and bright violet 48·00
138 2s. 6d. purple 40·00
139 4s. deep rose and maize 65·00
a. Imperf between (horiz pair)
127/39 *Set of* 13 £160
127s/39s Optd "Specimen" *Set of* 13 £160

No. 139a is also imperforate between stamp and left margin.

(Typo D.L.R.)

1902–3. *Wmk Crown CC. P* 14.
140 **32** 5s. dull blue and rose 23·00
141 10s. deep rose and chocolate 65·00
142 £1 black and bright blue £160
143 £1 10s. green and violet £325
s. Optd "Specimen" 65·00
144 £5 mauve and black £2000
s. Optd "Specimen" £100
145 £10 green and orange £6500
as. Optd "Specimen" £200
145*b* £20 red and green £13000
bs. Optd "Specimen" £325
140s/2s Optd "Specimen" *Set of* 3 £100

USED HIGH VALUES. Collectors are warned against fis used high value Natal stamps with penmarks cleaned of forged postmarks added.

1904–8. *Wmk Mult Crown CA. Chalk-surfaced paper* (£1 1 *P* 14.
146 **31** ½d. blue-green 3·75
147 1d. rose-carmine 4·25
a. Booklet pane of 6, one stamp optd "NOT FOR USE" (1907) £275
148 1d. deep carmine 6·50
w. Wmk inverted † 8
149 2d. red and olive-green 6·00
152 4d. carmine and cinnamon 2·75
153 5d. black and orange (1908) 4·00
155 1s. carmine and pale blue 70·00
156 2s. dull green and bright violet 55·00 3
157 2s. 6d. purple 45·00 3
162 **32** £1 10s. brown-orange & dp pur (1908) £1000 £
s. Optd "Specimen" £170
146/57 *Set of* 9 £170 7

1908–9. *Inscr* "POSTAGE POSTAGE". *Wmk Mult Crown P* 14.
165 **31** 6d. dull and bright purple 4·50
166 1s. black/*green* 6·00
167 2s. purple and bright blue/*blue* 15·00
168 2s. 6d. black and red/*blue* 25·00
169 **32** 5s. green and red/*yellow* 18·00 2
170 10s. green and red/*green* 60·00 6
171 £1 purple and black/*red* £225 £
165/71 *Set of* 7 £325 £
165s/71s Optd "Specimen" *Set of* 7 £180

STAMP BOOKLETS

1906. *Black on red cover. Stapled.*
SB1 2s. 7d. booklet containing thirty 1d. (No. 147) in blocks of 6

1907. *Black on red cover. Stapled.*
SB2 2s. 6d. booklet containing thirty 1d. (No. 147) in blocks of 6 £1

The first stamp of the first block in No. SB2 was cance "NOT FOR USE", the additional penny being used to defray cost of production.

FISCALS USED FOR POSTAGE

1869. *Embossed on coloured wove, surfaced paper. P* 12½.
F1 **1** 1d. yellow 50·00 80

Examples of 1d. yellow and 6d. rose values as Type **6**, 1s. pur brown as Type **7** and various values between 5s. and £10 in design illustrated above are believed to exist postally used, but, such use was not authorised, they are not now listed.

OFFICIAL STAMPS

OFFICIAL

(O 1)

T 31, *wmk Mult Crown CA, optd with Type* O 1. *P* 14.

Stamp		Un.	Us.
½d. blue-green		3·00	35
1d. carmine		2·75	70
2d. red and olive-green		18·00	9·50
3d. purple and grey		10·00	4·00
6d. green and brown-purple		38·00	50·00
1s. carmine and pale blue		£110	£170
	Set of 6	£160	£200

e use of stamps overprinted as above was discontinued after ay 1907. Stamps perforated with the letters "N.G.R." were for n Government Railways.

tal became a province of the Union of South Africa on 31 1910.

IV. NEW REPUBLIC

ring the unrest following the death of Cetshwayo, the Zulu , in 1884, a group of Boers from the Transvaal offered their ort to his son, Dinizulu. The price for this support was the on of a sizeable portion of Zulu territory to an independent republic. The New Republic, centred on Vryheid, was aimed on 16 August 1884 with the remaining Zulu tory becoming a protectorate of the new administration. first reference to an organised postal service occurs in mber 1884.

armed by these developments the British authorities xed the southernmost part of the land grant, around St. a Bay, to prevent access to the Indian Ocean. The remainder e New Republic was, however, recognised as independent on ctober 1886. Zululand was annexed by the British on 22 1887.

fficulties beset the New Republic, however, and its Volks- voted for union with the South African Republic (Trans-). The two republics united on 21 July 1888. In 1903 the tory of the former New Republic was transferred to Natal. ail from Vryheid in 1884–85 was franked with issues of nsvaal (for dispatches made via Utrecht) or Natal (for those via Dundee from August 1885 onwards). Issues of the New ublic were never accepted as internationally valid by these inistrations so that all external mail continued to show nsvaal or Natal stamps used in combination with those of republic.

PRICES FOR STAMPS ON COVER

Nos.	
No. 1	—
Nos. 2/5	*from* × 50
Nos. 6/25	—
Nos. 26/9	*from* × 50
Nos. 30/47	—
Nos. 48/50	*from* × 50
No. 51	—
Nos. 52/3	*from* × 50
Nos. 72/5	*from* × 50
Nos. 76/7*b*	—
Nos. 78/80	*from* × 50
Nos. 81/95	—

NIEUWE REPUBLIEK 1d 8 NOV 86 ZUID-AFRIKA.

1

inted with a rubber handstamp on paper bought in Europe and sent out ready gummed and perforated.

86 (7 Jan)–87. *Various dates indicating date of printing.* ? 11½.

A. *Without Arms.* (i) *Yellow paper*

No.	Type	Description	Un.	Us.
	1	1d. black (9.1.86)	†	£3000
		1d. violet (9.1.86)	10·00	12·00
		a. "1d." omitted (in pair with normal) (24.4.86)	£1500	
		2d. violet (9.1.86)	10·00	15·00
		a. "d" omitted (13.10.86)	£3000	
		3d. violet (13.1.86)	23·00	
		a. "d" omitted (13.10.86)	£3000	
		b. *Tête-bêche* (pair) (13.10.86)		
		4d. violet (30.8.86)	35·00	
		6d. violet (20.2.86)	30·00	
		a. "6d." omitted (in pair with normal) (2.7.86)		
		9d. violet (13.1.86)	30·00	
		1s. violet (30.8.86)	65·00	
		a. "1s." omitted (in pair with normal) (6.9.86)		
		1/s. violet (13.10.86)	£500	
		1/6 violet (30.8.86)	65·00	
		1s. 6d. violet (13.1.86)	£400	
		a. *Tête-bêche* (pair) (6.9.86)		
		b. "d" omitted (13.10.86)	85·00	
		2s. violet (30.8.86)	38·00	
		a. *Tête-bêche* (pair) (6.9.86)	£475	
		2/6 violet (13.1.86)	£150	
		2s. 6d. violet (1.86)	95·00	
		4/s. violet (17.1.87)	£400	
		5s. violet (1.86)	28·00	30·00
		a. "s" omitted (in pair with normal) (7.3.86)	£2000	
		5/6 violet (20.2.86)	35·00	
		5s. 6d. violet (13.1.86)	£160	
19	1	7/6 violet (13.1.86)	£170	
20		7s. 6d. violet (24.5.86)	95·00	
21		10s. violet (13.1.86)	95·00	
		a. *Tête-bêche* (pair) (2.7.86)		
22		10s. 6d. violet (1.86)	£170	
		a. "d" omitted (1.86)	48·00	
23		13s. violet (24.11.86)	£400	
24		£1 violet (13.1.86)	£120	
		a. *Tête-bêche* (pair) (13.10.86)		
25		30s. violet (13.1.86)	95·00	
		a. *Tête-bêche* (pair) (24.11.86)	£500	

(ii) *Blue granite paper*

No.	Type	Description	Un.	Us.
26	1	1d. violet (20.1.86)	13·00	14·00
		a. "d" omitted (24.11.86)	£375	
		b. "1" omitted (in pair with normal) (24.11.86)		
27		2d. violet (24.1.86)	13·00	14·00
		a. "d" omitted (24.4.86)	£750	
		b. "2d." omitted (in pair with normal) (24.4.86)		
28		3d. violet (13.10.86)	16·00	18·00
		a. *Tête-bêche* (pair) (13.10.86)	£300	
29		4d. violet (24.5.86)	13·00	16·00
30		6d. violet (7.3.86)	25·00	21·00
		a. "6" omitted (in pair with normal) (24.5.86)	£1500	
31		9d. violet (6.9.86)	24·00	
32		1s. violet (1.86)	28·00	30·00
		a. *Tête-bêche* (pair) (21.5.86)	£325	
		b. "1s." omitted (in pair with normal) (29.4.86)	£1500	
33		1s. 6d. violet (2.7.86)	35·00	
		a. *Tête-bêche* (pair) (6.9.86)	£475	
34		1/6 violet (6.9.86)	£150	
35		2s. violet (21.5.86)	£120	
		a. "2s." omitted (in pair with normal) (24.5.86)	£1500	
36		2s. 6d. violet (19.8.86)	£140	
37		2/6 violet (19.8.86)	£180	
38		4/s. violet (17.1.87)	£200	
39		5/6 violet (13.1.86)	£200	
		a. "/" omitted (13.1.87)		
40		5s. 6d. violet (13.1.86)	£170	
41		7/6 violet (13.1.86)	£200	
41*a*		7s. 6d. violet (13.1.86)		
42		10s. violet (1.86)	£200	£200
		a. *Tête-bêche* (pair) (2.7.86)	£425	
		b. "s" omitted (13.1.86)		
43		10s. 6d. violet (1.86)	£200	
		a. *Tête-bêche* (pair) (13.1.86)		
		b. "d" omitted (1.86)	£450	
44		12s. violet (13.1.86)	£300	
45		13s. violet (17.1.87)	£475	
46		£1 violet (13.1.86)	£250	
47		30s. violet (13.1.86)	£250	

B. *With embossed Arms of New Republic.* (i) *Yellow paper*

No.	Type	Description	Un.	Us.
48	1	1d. violet (20.1.86)	13·00	15·00
		a. Arms inverted (20.1.86)	25·00	25·00
		b. Arms *tête-bêche* (pair) (14.4.86)	£100	£120
		c. *Tête-bêche* (pair) (3.11.86)	£800	
49		2d. violet (30.8.86)	13·00	15·00
		a. Arms inverted (24.11.86)	23·00	28·00
50		4d. violet (2.12.86)	18·00	22·00
		a. Arms inverted (12.86)	95·00	60·00
		b. Arms *tête-bêche* (pair) (12.86)	£250	
51		6d. violet (2.12.86)	45·00	

(ii) *Blue granite paper*

No.	Type	Description	Un.	Us.
52	1	1d. violet (20.1.86)	14·00	16·00
		a. Arms inverted (10.2.86)	35·00	40·00
		b. Arms *tête-bêche* (pair) (3.11.86)		
53		2d. violet (24.5.86)	14·00	16·00
		a. Arms inverted (30.8.86)	48·00	
		b. Arms *tête-bêche* (pair) (2.12.86)	£500	£500

Stamps as Type 1 were produced as and when stocks were required, each printing including in its design the date on which it was prepared. The dates quoted above for Nos. 1/53 are those on which the various stamps first appeared. Details of the various printing dates are given below. From these dates it can be seen that some values share common printing dates, and, it is believed, that the different values were produced *se-tenant* within the same sheet, at least in some instances. A reported proof sheet in the Pretoria Postal Museum, on yellow paper and embossed, contains 4 examples of the 6d. value and 3 each of the 3d., 4d., 9d., 1s., 1/6, 2/-, 2/6, 3s., 4s., 5s., 5/6, 7/6, 10/-, 10/6, £1 and 30/-.

The significance, if any, of the two coloured papers and the use of the embossing machine have never been satisfactorily explained. Both the different papers and the embossing machine were introduced in January 1886, and occur throughout the period that the stamps with dates were used.

PRINTINGS

Date	*Paper*	*Face value*	*Cat. No.*	*Un.*	*Us.*
Jan 86	*Yellow*	5s.	16	28·00	30·00
		10s. 6d.	22	£170	
		10s. 6d.	22a	80·00	
	Blue	1s.	32		
		10s.	42	£200	£200
		10s. 6d.	43	£200	
		10s. 6d.	43b	£450	
7 Jan 86	*Yellow*	10s. 6d.	22	£160	
	Blue	10s.	42		
		10s. 6d.	43	£450	
9 Jan 86	*Yellow*	1d. blk	1	†	£3000
		1d. vio	2	10·00	12·00
		2d.	3	10·00	15·00
13 Jan 86	*Yellow*	1d.	2	35·00	
		2d.	3	14·00	15·00
		3d.	4	40·00	
		9d	7	£200	
		1s. 6d.	11	£400	
		2/6	13	£160	
		2s. 6d.	14	95·00	
		5s. 6d.	18		
		7/6	19	£170	
		10s.	21		
		£1	24	£130	
		30s.	25	95·00	
	Blue	5/6	39	£200	
		5s. 6d.	40	£170	
		7/6	41	£200	
		7s. 6d.	41*a*		
		10s.	42	£400	
		10s.	42b		
		10s. 6d.	43	£200	
		10s. 6d.	43a		
		12s.	44	£300	
		£1	46	£250	
		30s.	47	£250	
20 Jan 86	*Yellow*	1d.	2		
	Blue	1d.	26	£250	
	Yellow, embossed	1d.	48	32·00	
		1d.	48a	48·00	
	Blue, embossed	1d.	52	95·00	
Jan 20 86	*Blue*	1d.	26	23·00	
	Yellow, embossed	1d.	48a		
	Blue, embossed	1d.	52	£100	
24 Jan 86	*Blue*	1d.	26	18·00	
		2d.	27	30·00	
10 Feb 86	*Yellow*	1d.	2		
	Yellow, embossed	1d.	48		
		1d.	48a	48·00	
	Blue, embossed	1d.	52	£130	
		1d.	52a	35·00	
20 Feb 86	*Yellow*	6d.	6		
		1s. 6d.	11		
		2s. 6d.	14	£130	
		5/6	17	£120	
		5s. 6d.	18		
7 Mar 86	*Yellow*	1d.	2	£110	
		2/6	13		
		2s. 6d.	14	95·00	
		5s.	16	£200	85·00
		5s.	16a		
		5/6	17	35·00	
		5s. 6d.	18	£160	
	Blue	2d.	27	95·00	
		6d.	30		
		1s.	32		
17 Mar 86	*Yellow*	1d.	2	95·00	
	Yellow, embossed	1d.	48	48·00	
	Blue, embossed	1d.	52	95·00	
		1d.	52a	80·00	
26 Mar 86	*Blue, embossed*	1d.	52a	£130	
14 Apr 86	*Yellow*	1d.	2		
	Yellow, embossed	1d.	48	23·00	
		1d.	48a	£120	
		1d.	48b	£100	£120
	Blue, embossed	1d.	52	45·00	
		1d.	52a		
24 Apr 86	*Yellow*	1d.	2	£100	
		1d.	2a	£1500	
		5s.	16		
	Blue	2d.	27	28·00	
		2d.	27a	£750	
		2d.	27b		
29 Apr 86	*Blue*	1s.	32	£110	
		1s.	32b		
21 May 86	*Yellow*	6d.	6	£130	
	Blue	1d.	26	85·00	
		1s.	32	28·00	30·00
		1s.	32a	£325	
		1s.	32b	£1500	
		2s.	35	£275	
23 May 86	*Blue, embossed*	1d.	52a	95·00	
24 May 86	*Yellow*	1d.	2	95·00	
		2d.	3	£120	
		5s.	16	70·00	
		7/6	19	£170	
		7s. 6d.	20	95·00	
	Blue	1d.	26	13·00	14·00
		2d.	27	£300	£300
		4d.	29	85·00	
		6d.	30	£120	
		6d.	30a		
		1s.	32	£200	
		1s.	32b		
		2s.	35	£120	
		2s.	35a	£1500	
	Blue, embossed	2d.	53		
26 May 86	*Yellow*	1d.	2		
	Blue	1d.	26	£110	
	Yellow, embossed	1d.	48	£250	
		1d.	48a	95·00	
	Blue, embossed	1d.	52	£130	
		1d.	52a	48·00	50·00
28 May 86	*Yellow, embossed*	1d.	48	32·00	
Jun 30 86	*Blue*	1d.	26	15·00	16·00
	Yellow, embossed	1d.	48	14·00	16·00
		1d.	48a	25·00	28·00
		1d.	48b	£200	£225
	Blue, embossed	1d.	52	45·00	40·00
2 Jul 86	*Yellow*	6d.	6	£200	
		6d.	6a		
		9d	7	95·00	95·00
		10s.	21		
		10s.	21a		
	Blue	1s. 6d.	33	35·00	
		10s.	42	£200	
		10s.	42a	£425	
		10s. 6d.	43		
		10s. 6d.	43b		
3 Jul 86	*Blue*	10s.	42		
Jul 7 86	*Yellow*	1d.	2		
	Blue	1d.	26		
	Yellow, embossed	1d.	48	25·00	
		1d.	48a	95·00	95·00
	Blue, embossed	1d.	52	14·00	16·00
		1d.	52a	55·00	40·00
4 Aug 86	*Yellow*	1d.	2		
	Yellow, embossed	1d.	48	55·00	
	Blue, embossed	1d.	52	35·00	
		1d.	52a		
19 Aug 86	*Yellow*	2/6	13		
		2s. 6d.	14	£140	
	Blue	2s. 6d.	36	£140	
		2/6	37	£180	
30 Aug 86	*Yellow*	1d.	2	10·00	12·00
		2d.	3	11·00	
		3d.	4	23·00	
		4d.	5	48·00	
		6d.	6	32·00	
		9d.	7	48·00	
		1s.	8	65·00	
		1/6	10	65·00	
		2s.	12	95·00	

…te	*Paper*	*Face value*	*Cat. No.*	*Un.*	*Us.*
		2/6	13	£150	
	Blue	2d.	27	13·00	14·00
	Yellow, embossed	2d.	49		
	Blue, embossed	2d.	53	42·00	
		2d.	53a	£110	
…ep 86	*Yellow*	1d.	2	12·00	
		2d.	3	8·50	9·00
		3d.	4	38·00	
		4d.	5	40·00	
		6d.	6	30·00	
		9d.	7	30·00	
		1s.	8	95·00	
		1s.	8a		
		1/6	10	70·00	
		1s. 6d.	11	£400	
		1s. 6d.	11a		
		2s.	12	£100	
		2s.	12a	£475	
		2/6	13	£150	
		2s. 6d.	14		
		5s.	16	£140	
		7s. 6d.	20	£200	
		10s.	21	95·00	
		£1	24	£120	
	Blue	6d.	30	20·00	21·00
		9d.	31	£110	
		1s.	32	65·00	
		1s. 6d.	33	£140	
		1s. 6d.	33a	£475	
		1/6	34		
		2s. 6d.	36		
		2/6	37	£400	
		10s. 6d.	43		
…p 86	*Yellow*	1d.	2		
	Yellow, embossed	1d.	48	48·00	
		1d.	48a	48·00	
	Blue, embossed	1d.	52	85·00	
…t 86	*Yellow*	1d.	2		
	Blue	1d.	26	85·00	
	Yellow, embossed	1d.	48	23·00	18·00
		1d.	48a		
	Blue, embossed	1d.	52	45·00	18·00
		1d.	52a	85·00	
…ct 86	*Yellow*	1d.	2	12·00	12·00
		2d.	3	10·00	11·00
		2d.	3a	£3000	
		3d.	4	23·00	25·00
		3d.	4a	£3000	
		3d.	4b		
		4d.	5	35·00	
		6d.	6	30·00	32·00
		9d.	7	35·00	
		1s.	8	70·00	
		1/s	9	£500	
		1/6	10	£150	
		1s. 6d.	11b	85·00	
		2s.	12	38·00	
		2/6	13	£160	
		5s.	16	42·00	
		10s.	21	95·00	£100
		10s. 6d.	22a	48·00	
		£1	24	£120	
		£1	24a		
	Blue	2d.	27	13·00	14·00
		3d.	28	16·00	18·00
		3d.	28a	£300	
		4d.	29	28·00	28·00
		1s.	32	28·00	
		1/6	34	£150	
		2s.	35	£120	
…ov 86	*Yellow*	1d.	2	28·00	
	Blue	1d.	26		
	Yellow, embossed	1d.	48	13·00	15·00
		1d.	48a	25·00	28·00
		1d.	48b	£100	£120
		1d.	48c	£800	
	Blue, embossed	1d.	52	14·00	
		1d.	52a	35·00	40·00
		1d.	52b		
…ov 86	*Yellow*	1d.	2	35·00	
…ov 86	*Yellow*	1d.	2	14·00	
		2d.	3	10·00	11·00
		3d.	4	30·00	32·00
		1/6	10		
		10s.	21	£200	
		13s.	23	£400	
		30s.	25	95·00	
		30s.	25a	£500	
	Blue	1d.	26	38·00	17·00
		1d.	26a	£375	
		1d.	26b		
		2d.	27	18·00	
		2d.	27a		
		4d.	29	13·00	16·00
		6d.	30	20·00	21·00
		9d.	31	24·00	
		1s.	32	45·00	48·00
		1/6	34	£160	
		2s.	35	£140	
		2s.	35a	£3000	
	Yellow, embossed	2d.	49	£160	
		2d.	49a		
Nov 86	*Yellow*	1/6	10	£140	
Dec 86	*Yellow*	1d.	2		
		2d.	3		
	Blue	2d.	27		
	Yellow, embossed	1d.	48	13·00	15·00
		1d.	48a	£160	
		2d.	49	13·00	15·00
		2d.	49a	23·00	28·00
		4d.	50	80·00	
		6d.	51	45·00	
	Blue, embossed	1d.	52	28·00	
		1d.	52a	£160	
		2d.	53	14·00	16·00
		2d.	53a	48·00	
		2d.	53b	£500	£500
Dec 86	*Yellow, embossed*	6d.	51		
Dec 86	*Yellow*	6d.	6		
	Blue	4d.	29		
	Yellow, embossed	4d.	50	18·00	22·00
		4d.	50a	95·00	60·00
		4d.	50b	£250	
		6d.	51	42·00	

Date	*Paper*	*Face value*	*Cat. No.*	*Un.*	*Us.*
4 Jan 87	*Yellow*	1d.	2	35·00	
		2d.	3	32·00	
		13s.	23	£400	
	Blue	1d.	26	13·00	14·00
		2d.	27	16·00	14·00
	Blue, embossed	2d.	53	42·00	
13 Jan 87	*Blue*	5/6	39	£425	
		5/6	39a		
		7/6	41	£475	
17 Jan 87	*Yellow*	1d.	2	38·00	
		2d.	3	30·00	
		3d.	4	45·00	
		4/s.	15	£200	
	Blue	1d.	26	75·00	
		4/s.	38	£200	
		13s.	45	£475	
		30s.	47	£250	
20 Jan 87	*Blue*	2d.	27	32·00	
	Yellow, embossed	2d.	49	50·00	
		2d.	49a	£140	
	Blue, embossed	2d.	53	42·00	
		2d.	53a	95·00	
Jan 20 87	*Yellow, embossed*	1d.	48a	£400	

1887 (Jan–Mar). *As T* **1**, *but without date. With embossed Arms.*

(*a*) *Blue granite paper*

72	1d. violet	14·00	14·00
	a. Imperf between (pair)		
	b. Stamps *tête-bêche* (pair)	£375	
	c. Arms *tête-bêche* (pair)		
	d. Arms inverted	23·00	23·00
	e. Arms omitted	£110	£110
	f. Arms sideways		
73	2d. violet	8·50	8·50
	a. Stamps *tête-bêche* (pair)	£325	
	b. Arms inverted	23·00	23·00
	c. Arms omitted	£110	95·00
	d. Arms *tête-bêche* (pair)		
74	3d. violet	13·00	13·00
	a. Stamps *tête-bêche* (pair)	£375	
	b. Arms *tête-bêche* (pair)		
	c. Arms inverted	48·00	48·00
75	4d. violet	13·00	13·00
	a. Stamps *tête-bêche* (pair)	£325	
	b. Arms *tête-bêche* (pair)	£275	
	c. Arms inverted	85·00	
76	6d. violet	13·00	13·00
	a. Arms inverted	85·00	
77	1/6 violet	14·00	14·00
	a. Arms inverted	80·00	
	b. Arms *têtê-bêche* (pair)	£350	
77*c*	2/6 violet	†	£750

(*b*) *Yellow paper* (March 1887)

78	2d. violet (*arms omitted*)	13·00	
79	3d. violet	13·00	13·00
	a. Imperf between (pair)		
	b. Stamps *tête-bêche* (pair)	£325	£375
	c. Arms *tête-bêche* (pair)	£200	
	d. Arms inverted	23·00	23·00
	da. Double impression		
80	4d. violet	13·00	13·00
	a. Arms inverted	14·00	14·00
81	6d. violet	8·00	8·00
	a. Arms *tête-bêche* (pair)	£350	
	b. Arms inverted	42·00	42·00
	c. Arms omitted	80·00	
	ca. Double impression		
82	9d. violet	8·50	8·50
	a. Arms inverted	£200	
	b. Arms *tête-bêche* (pair)	£350	
83	1s. violet	8·50	8·50
	a. Arms inverted	70·00	
84	1/6 violet	17·00	14·0
85	2s. violet	18·00	16·00
	a. Arms inverted	55·00	50·00
	b. Arms omitted	70·00	
86	2/6 violet	23·00	23·00
	a. Arms inverted	28·00	28·00
87	3s. violet	42·00	42·00
	a. Arms inverted	45·00	45·00
	b. Stamps *tête-bêche* (pair)	£450	
88	4s. violet	11·00	11·00
	a. Arms omitted	£180	
88*b*	4/s violet	90·00	
	ba. Arms omitted	£130	
89	5s. violet	13·00	13·00
	a. Imperf between (pair)		
	b. Arms inverted	—	80·00
90	5/6 violet	12·00	12·00
91	7/6 violet	14·00	17·00
	a. Arms *tête-bêche* (pair)		
	a. Arms inverted	45·00	
92	10s. violet	12·00	12·00
	a. Imperf between (pair)		
	b. Arms *tête-bêche* (pair)	£120	
	c. Arms inverted	23·00	
	d. Arms omitted	£110	45·00
93	10/6 violet	16·00	16·00
	a. Imperf between (pair)		
	b. Arms inverted		
94	£1 violet	45·00	45·00
	a. Stamps *tête-bêche* (pair)	£300	£350
	b. Arms inverted	55·00	
95	30s. violet	£110	

A £15 value as Nos. 78/95 exists, but is only known fiscally used (*Price* £4000).

New Republic united with the South African Republic (Transvaal) on 21 July 1888. In 1903 the territory of the former New Republic was transferred to Natal.

MINIMUM PRICE

The minimum price quote is 10p which represents a handling charge rather than a basis for valuing common stamps. For further notes about prices see introductory pages.

V. ORANGE FREE STATE

PRICES FOR STAMPS ON COVER

Nos. 1/9	*from* × 20
Nos. 10/13	*from* × 25
Nos. 18/19	*from* × 20
No. 20	—
Nos. 21/42	*from* × 20
Nos. 48/51	*from* × 25
Nos. 52/138	*from* × 10
Nos. 139/51	*from* × 7
Nos. F1/17	—
Nos. PF1/3	*from* × 20
No. M1	—

Supplies of Cape of Good Hope stamps were available at Bloemfontein and probably elsewhere in the Orange Free State, from mid-1856 onwards for use on mail to Cape Colony and beyond. Such arrangements continued after the introduction of Orange Free State stamps in 1868. It is not known if the dumb cancellations used on the few surviving covers were applied in the Free State or at Cape Town.

1

(Typo D.L.R.)

1868 (1 Jan)–**94.** *P* 14.

1	**1**	1d. pale brown	10·00	1·00
2		1d. red-brown	10·00	45
3		1d. deep brown	11·00	45
4		6d. pale rose (1868)	42·00	8·00
5		6d. rose (1871)	15·00	5·50
6		6d. rose-carmine (1891)	15·00	12·00
7		6d. bright carmine (1894)	9·00	2·00
8		1s. orange-buff	70·00	5·50
9		1s. orange-yellow	28·00	1·50
		a. Double print	—	£3000

4 4 4 4

(**2**) (*a*) (*b*) (*c*) (*d*)

1877. *No.* 5 *surcharged T* **2** (*a*) *to* (*d*).

10	**1**	4d. on 6d. rose (*a*)	£325	55·00
		a. Surch inverted	—	£550
		b. Surch double (*a* + *c*)		
		c. Surch double. one inverted (*a* + *c* inverted)	—	£2750
		d. Surch double, one inverted (*a* inverted + *c*)	—	£4500
11		4d. on 6d. rose (*b*)	£1200	£160
		a. Surch inverted	—	£1100
		b. Surch double (*b* + *d*)		
12		4d. on 6d. rose (*c*)	£180	25·00
		a. Surch inverted	—	£350
		b. Surch double		
13		4d. on 6d. rose (*d*)	£225	35·00
		a. Surch inverted	£1100	£375

1878 (July). *P* 14.

18	**1**	4d. pale blue	17·00	2·75
19		4d. ultramarine	4·00	2·50
20		5s. green	9·00	11·00

1d. 1d. 1d. 1d. 1d. 1d.

(**3**) (*a*) (*b*) (*c*) (*d*) (*e*) (*f*)

Type **3**: (*a*) Small "1" and "d." (*b*) Sloping serif. (*c*) Same size as (*b*), but "1" with straighter horizontal serif. (*d*) Taller "1" with horizontal serif and antique "d". (*e*) Same size as (*d*) but with sloping serif and thin line at foot. (*f*) as (*d*) but with Roman "d".

1881 (19 May). *No.* 20 *surch T* **3** (*a*) *to* (*f*) *with heavy black bar cancelling the old value.*

21	**1**	1d. on 5s. green (*a*)	85·00	17·00
22		1d. on 5s. green (*b*)	50·00	17·00
		a. Surch inverted	—	£750
		b. Surch double	—	£1000
23		1d. on 5s. green (*c*)	£170	70·00
		a. Surch inverted	—	£1100
		b. Surch double	—	£1300
24		1d. on 5s. green (*d*)	70·00	17·00
		a. Surch inverted	£1500	£750
		b. Surch double	—	£1000
25		1d. on 5s. green (*e*)	£400	£225
		a. Surch inverted	—	£2000
		b. Surch double	—	£2000
26		1d. on 5s. green (*f*)	70·00	17·00
		a. Surch inverted	—	£700
		b. Surch double	—	£800

No. 21 was the first printing in one type only. Nos. 22 to 25 constitute the second printing about a year later, and are all found on the same sheet; and No. 26 the third printing of which about half have the stop raised.

Owing to defective printing examples of Nos. 22 and 24/5 may be found with the obliterating bar at the top of the stamps or, from the top row, without the bar.

½d

(**4**)

1882 (Aug). *No. 20 surch with T* **4** *and with a thin black line cancelling old value.*
36 1 ½d. on 5s. green 12·00 3·75
a. Surch double £400 £325
b. Surch inverted £1200 £800

3d 3d 3d 3d 3d
(**5**) (*a*) (*b*) (*c*) (*d*) (*e*)

1882. *No.* 19 *surch with T* **5** (*a*) *to* (*e*) *with thin black line cancelling value.*
38 1 3d. on 4d. ultramarine (*a*) 70·00 23·00
a. Surch double — £750
39 3d. on 4d. ultramarine (*b*) 70·00 18·00
a. Surch double — £700
40 3d. on 4d. ultramarine (*c*) 27·00 16·00
a. Surch double — £700
41 3d. on 4d. ultramarine (*d*) 70·00 19·00
a. Surch double — £700
42 3d. on 4d. ultramarine (*e*) £180 60·00
a. Surch double — £1400

Examples of Nos. 39 and 41/2 exist without the cancelling bar due to the misplacement of the surcharge.

1883–84. *P* 14.
48 1 ½d. chestnut 1·50 50
49 2d. pale mauve 10·00 40
50 2d. bright mauve 10·00 30
51 3d. ultramarine 2·25 2·00

For 1d. purple, see No. 68.

2d 2d 2d
(**6**) (*a*) (*b*) (*c*)

1888 (Sept–Oct). *No.* 51 *surch with T* **6**(*a*), (*b*) *or* (*c*).
(*a*) *Wide* "2". (*b*) *Narrow* "2"
52 1 2d. on 3d. ultramarine (*a*) (Sept) 50·00 9·00
a. Surch inverted — £700
53 2d. on 3d. ultramarine (*b*) 27·00 2·00
a. Surch inverted — £300
b. "2" with curved foot (*c*) £1200 £500

1d 1d 1d
(**7**) (*a*) (*b*) (*c*)

1890 (Dec)–**91.** *Nos.* 51 *and* 19 *surch with T* **7** (*a*) *to* (*c*).
54 1 1d. on 3d. ultramarine (*a*) 3·75 60
a. Surch double 80·00 70·00
c. "1" and "d" wide apart £140 £110
d. Dropped "d" (Right pane R. 5/6)
55 1d. on 3d. ultramarine (*b*) 17·00 2·75
a. Surch double £225 £250
57 1d. on 4d. ultramarine (*a*) 22·00 4·00
a. Surch double £130 £110
b. Surch double (*a* + *b*) £375
c. Surch triple — £1500
d. Raised "1" (Left pane R. 3/1)
58 1d. on 4d. ultramarine (*b*) 75·00 50·00
a. Surch double £375 £300
59 1d. on 4d. ultramarine (*c*) £1300 £475
a. Surch double

The settings of the 1d. on 3d. and on 4d. are not identical. The variety (*c*) does not exist on the 3d.

2½d. 2½d.
(**8**) Printers leads after surcharge (Lower right pane No. 43)

1892 (Oct). *No.* 51 *surch with T* **8**.
67 1 2½d. on 3d. ultramarine 9·50 70
a. No stop after "d" 70·00
b. Printers leads after surcharge — 50·00

1894 (Sept). *Colour changed. P* 14.
68 1 1d. purple 2·75 30

½d ½d ½d
(**9**) (*a*) (*b*) (*c*)

½d ½d ½d ½d
(*d*) (*e*) (*f*) (*g*)

Types (*a*) and (*e*) differ from types (*b*) and (*f*) respectively, in the serifs of the "1", but owing to faulty overprinting this distinction is not always clearly to be seen.

1896 (Sept). *No.* 51 *surch with T* **9** (*a*) *to* (*g*).
69 1 ½d. on 3d. ultramarine (*a*) 3·25 9·00
70 ½d. on 3d. ultramarine (*b*) 7·50 7·50
71 ½d. on 3d. ultramarine (*c*) 6·50 2·50
72 ½d. on 3d. ultramarine (*d*) 6·50 2·25
73 ½d. on 3d. ultramarine (*e*) 6·50 2·25
74 ½d. on 3d. ultramarine (*f*) 8·00 9·50
75 ½d. on 3d. ultramarine (*g*) 5·00 2·75
a. Surch double 13·00 10·00
b. Surch triple 60·00 60·00

The double and triple surcharges are often different types, but are always type (*g*), or in combination with type (*g*).

Double surcharges in the same type, but without the "d" and bar, also exist, probably from a trial sheet prepared by the printer. Both mint and used examples are known.

Halve Penny.
(**10**)

2½
(**11**)

1896. *No.* 51 *surch with T* **10**.
77 1 ½d. on 3d. ultramarine 65 50
(i) *Errors in setting*
78 1 ½d. on 3d. (no stop) 12·00 25·00
79 ½d. on 3d. ("Peuny") 12·00 25·00
(ii) *Surch inverted*
81 1 ½d. on 3d. 55·00 60·00
81*a* ½d. on 3d. (no stop)
81*b* ½d. on 3d. ("Peuny") £1500
(iii) *Surch double, one inverted*
81*c* 1 ½d. on 3d. (Nos. 77 and 81) £180 £200
81*d* ½d. on 3d. (Nos. 77 and 81*a*) £750 £750
81*e* ½d. on 3d. (Nos. 77 and 81*b*) £850 £850
81*f* ½d. on 3d. (Nos. 81 and 78) — £850
82 ½d. on 3d. (Nos. 81 and 79) — £850

Examples from the top horizontal row can be found without the bar due to the surcharge being misplaced.

Nos. 69 to 75 also exist surcharged as last but they are considered not to have been issued with authority (*Prices from £30 each, unused*).

1897 (1 Jan). *No.* 51 *surch with T* **11**. (*a*) *As in illustration.* (*b*) *With Roman* "1" *and antique* "2" *in fraction.*
83 1 2½d. on 3d. ultramarine (*a*) 4·50 80
83*a* 2½d. on 3d. ultramarine (*b*) £140 90·00

1897. *P* 14.
84 1 ½d. yellow (March) 2·00 35
85 ½d. orange 2·00 35
87 1s. brown (Aug) 16·00 1·50

The 6d. blue was prepared for use in the Orange Free State, but had not been brought into use when the stamps were seized in Bloemfontein. A few have been seen without the "V.R.I." overprint but they were not authorized or available for postage (*Price* £60).

BRITISH OCCUPATION

V. R. I. V. R. I. V. R. I.

4d ½d ½d
31 (Level stops) (**32**) Thin "V" (Raised stops) (**33**) Thick "V"

V. R I.
Inserted "R"

(Surch by Curling & Co, Bloemfontein)

1900. *T* **1** *surch as T* **31/33** (2½*d. on* 3*d. optd* "V.R.I." *only*).
(*a*) *First printings surch as T* **31** *with stops level* (March)
101 ½d. on ½d. orange 2·25 2·50
a. No stop after "V" 17·00 19·00
b. No stop after "I" £160 £160
c. "½" omitted £170 £170
d. "I" omitted £180 £180
e. "V.R.I." omitted £160
f. Value omitted £100
g. Small "½" 50·00 50·00
h. Surch double £160
102 1d. on 1d. purple 2·50 1·25
a. Surch on 1d. deep brown (No. 3) £600 £400
b. No stop after "V" 12·00 10·00
c. No stop after "R" £150 £160
d. No stop after "I"
e. "1" omitted £170 £180
f. "I" omitted £300 £300
g. "I" and stop after "R" omitted £300 £300
h. "V.R.I." omitted £140 £150
i. "d" omitted £300 £300
j. Value omitted 80·00 85·00
k. Inverted stop after "R" £200
l. Wider space between "1" and "d" £100 £100
m. "V" and "R" close £150
n. Pair, one without surch £425
o. "V" omitted £800
103 2d. on 2d. bright mauve 1·50 80
a. No stop after "V" 11·00 14·00
b. No stop after "R" £250
c. No stop after "I" £250
d. "V.R.I." omitted £300
e. Value omitted £300
104 2½d. on 3d. ultramarine (*a*) 11·00 8·50
a. No stop after "V" 75·00 75·00
105 2½d. on 3d. ultramarine (*b*) £180 £180
106 3d. on 3d. ultramarine 1·75 1·00
a. No stop after "V" 15·00 14·00
b. Pair, one without surch £400
c. "V.R.I." omitted £250
d. Value omitted £250
107 4d. on 4d. ultramarine 5·50 11·00
a. No stop after "V" 50·00 55·00
108 6d. on 6d. bright carmine 35·00 35·00
a. No stop after "V" £250 £275
b. "6" omitted £300 £300
109 6d. on 6d. blue 5·00 2·75
a. No stop after "V" 32·00 35·00
b. "6" omitted 65·00 70·00
c. "V.R.I." omitted — £300
110 1s. on 1s. brown 7·00
a. Surch on 1s. orange-yellow (No. 9) £3250
b. No stop after "V" 35·00
c. "1" omitted £110
ca. "1" inserted by hand †
d. "1" omitted and spaced stop after "s" £130
e. "V.R.I." omitted £150
f. Value omitted £150
g. Raised stop after "s" 13·00
h. Wider space between "1" and "s" £150
111 5s. on 5s. green 17·00
a. No stop after "V" £200
b. "5" omitted £900
c. Inverted stop after "R" £650
d. Wider space between "5" and "s" £120
e. Value omitted £350

All values are found with a rectangular, instead of an stop after "R". Misplaced surcharges (upwards or sidev occur.

No. 110ca shows the missing "1" replaced by a handstam different type face.

(*b*) *Subsequent printings.* (i) *Surch as T* **32**
112 ½d. on ½d. orange 30
a. Raised and level stops mixed 1·75
b. Pair, one with level stops 10·00
c. No stop after "V" 2·50
d. No stop after "I" 26·00
e. "V" omitted £550
f. Small "½" 14·00
g. As a, and small "½" 14·00
i. Space between "V" and "R"
j. Value omitted £120
113 1d. on 1d. purple 30
a. Raised and level stops mixed 1·40
b. Pair, one with level stops 19·00
c. No stop after "V" 3·25
d. No stop after "R" 15·00
e. No stop after "I" 15·00
f. No stops after "V" and "I" £300
g. Surch inverted £300
h. Surch double £100
i. Pair, one without surch £200
j. Short figure "1" £100
k. Space between "V" and "R" 50·00
l. Space between "R" and "I" £100
m. Space between "1" and "d" £180
n. Inserted "R" £325
o. Inserted "V" £700
114 2d. on 2d. bright mauve 85
a. Raised and level stops mixed 4·50
b. Pair, one with level stops 8·00
c. Surch inverted £300
d. "1" raised 75·00
e. Pair, one without surch £275
f. No stop after "V" £1000
g. No stop after "I"
115 2½d. on 3d. ultramarine (*a*) £200
a. Raised and level stops mixed £550
116 2½d. on 3d. ultramarine (*b*) £1200
117 3d. on 3d. ultramarine 50
a. Raised and level stops mixed 6·50
b. Pair, one with level stops 17·00
c. No stop after "V" £140
d. No stop after "R" £350
e. "I" omitted £400
f. Surch double £400
g. Surch double, one diagonal £375
h. Ditto, diagonal surch with mixed stops £6500
n. Inserted "R"
o. Space between "3" and "d" £140
118 4d. on 4d. ultramarine 1·50
a. Raised and level stops mixed 8·00
b. Pair, one with level stops 19·00
119 6d. on 6d. bright carmine 35·00
a. Raised and level stops mixed £140
b. Pair, one with level stops £200
120 6d. on 6d. blue 70
a. Raised and level stops mixed 7·50
b. Pair, one with level stops 19·00
c. No stop after "V" £500
d. No stop after "R" £300
e. Value omitted £450
121 1s. on 1s. brown 3·25
a. Surch on 1s. orange-yellow (No. 9) £1300
b. Raised and level stops mixed 16·00
c. Pair, one with level stops 30·00
f. "s" omitted £250
g. "V.R.I." omitted £400
122 5s. on 5s. green 6·50
a. Raised and level stops mixed £300
b. Pair, one with level stops £950
c. Short top to "5" 60·00
s. Handstamped "Specimen" 50·00

(ii) *Surch as T* **33**
123 ½d. on ½d. orange 2·75
124 1d. on 1d. purple 3·00
a. Inverted "1" for "I" 17·00
b. No stops after "R" and "I" 85·00
c. No stop after "R" 38·00
d. Surch double £300
n. Inserted "R" £400
125 2d. on 2d. bright mauve 5·50
a. Inverted "1" for "I" 24·00
126 2½d. on 3d. ultramarine (*a*) £600
127 2½d. on 3d. ultramarine (*b*) £3500
128 3d. on 3d. ultramarine 4·75
a. Inverted "1" for "I" 65·00
b. Surch double £550
ba. Surch double, one diagonal £550
129 6d. on 6d. bright carmine £425
130 6d. on 6d. blue 8·00
131 1s. on 1s. brown 16·00
132 5s. on 5s. green 45·00
s. Handstamped "Specimen" £150

Stamps with thick "V" occur in certain positions in *later* settir of the type with stops above the line (T **32**). *Earlier* settings w stops above the line have all stamps with thin "V".

Some confusion has previously been caused by the listing certain varieties as though they occurred on stamps with thick "V in fact they occur on stamps showing the normal thin "V", includ in the settings which also contained the thick "V".

For a short period small blocks of unsurcharged Free Sta

could be handed in for surcharging so that varieties which are not found in the complete settings. Nos. 102a, nd 121a also occur from such stocks.

inserted "R" variety occurs on positions 6 (T **32**) and 12 of the forme. The "R" of the original surcharge failed to nd the "R", but not the full stop, was added by the use of a amp. Traces of the original letter are often visible. The "V" flaw, also shown in the illustration, does not appear 124n.

ORANGE RIVER COLONY

CROWN COLONY

NGE
VER
ONY.
(34)

4d
(35)

E. R. I.
6d
(36)

10 Aug)–**02.** *Nos. 58a, 61a and 67 of Cape of Good Hope k Cabled Anchor. P 14) optd with T* **34** *by W. A. Richards Sons, Cape Town.*

½d. green (13.10.00) 30 10
a. No stop .. .. 7·00 14·00
b. Opt double £600 £650
1d. carmine (May 1902) 60 10
a. No stop .. .. 12·00 20·00
2½d. ultramarine 85 35
a. No stop .. .. 60·00 70·00
.. .. *Set of* 3 1·60 50

he ½d. and 2½d., the "no stop" after "COLONY" variety was rst stamp in the left lower pane. In the 1d. it is the twelfth in the right lower pane on which the stop was present at the ning of the printing but became damaged and soon failed to

(14 Feb). *Surch with T* **35** *by "Bloemfontein Express".*
4d. on 6d. on 6d. blue (No. 120) (R.) .. 1·50 75
a. No stop after "R" .. .. .. 32·00 38·00
b. No stop after "I" £1200
c. Surch on No. 130 (Thick "V") .. .. 2·00 5·00
ca. Inverted "1" for "I" .. .. .. 6·00 13·00

(Aug). *Surch with T* **36.**
1 6d. on 6d. blue .. .. 3·00 8·50
a. Surch double, one inverted ..
b. Wide space between "6" and "d" (R.4/2) .. .. 60·00 90·00

One
Shilling
*
(37)

38 King Edward VII, Springbok and Gnu

(Sept). *Surch with T* **37.**
1 1s. on 5s. green (O.) .. .. .. 7·00 10·00
a. Thick "V" .. .. 15·00 29·00
b. Short top to "5" .. .. .. 70·00 80·00
c. Surch double .. ..

(Typo D.L.R.)

3 (3 Feb)–**04.** *Wmk Crown CA. P 14.*
38 ½d. yellow-green (6.7.03) .. .. 8·00 1·25
w. Wmk inverted .. .. .. — 85·00
1d. scarlet .. .. 4·25 10
w. Wmk inverted .. .. .. — 75·00
2d. brown (6.7.03) .. .. .. 4·50 80
2½d. bright blue (6.7.03) .. .. .. 1·60 50
3d. mauve (6.7.03) .. .. .. 7·00 90
4d. scarlet and sage-green (6.7.03) .. 32·00 2·00
a. "IOSTAGE" for "POSTAGE" .. £800 £450
6d. scarlet and mauve (6.7.03) .. 7·00 1·00
1s. scarlet and bistre (6.7.03) .. 25·00 1·75
5s. blue and brown (31.10.04) .. 75·00 22·00
/47 .. .. .. *Set of* 9 £140 27·00
s/47s Optd "Specimen" .. *Set of* 9 £150

o. 144a occurs on R. 10/2 of the upper left pane.
everal of the above values are found with the overprint S.A.R.", in black, for use by the Central South African ways. Examples also exist perforated "CSAR" or "NGR".

5 (Nov)–**09.** *Wmk Mult Crown CA. P 14.*
38 ½d. yellow-green (28.7.07) .. .. 9·00 50
1d. scarlet .. .. 8·50 30
4d. scarlet and sage-green (8.11.07) .. 4·50 2·00
a. "IOSTAGE" for "POSTAGE" .. £180 £150
1s. scarlet and bistre (2.09) .. .. 38·00 12·00
/51 .. .. *Set of* 4 55·00 13·00

POSTCARD STAMPS

rom 1889 onwards the Orange Free State Post Office sold tcards franked with adhesives as Type 1, some subsequently charged, over which the State Arms had been overprinted.

There are five known dies of the Arms overprint which can be identified as follows:

(a) Shield without flags. Three cows (two lying down, one standing) at left. Point of shield complete.
(b) Shield with flags. Four cows (two lying down, two standing) at left (*illustrated*).
(c) Shield with flags. Three cows (one lying down, two standing) at left.
(d) Shield without flags. Three cows (one lying down, two standing) at left.
(e) Shield without flags. Three cows (two lying down, one standing) at left. Point of shield broken.

There are also other differences between the dies.

PRICES. Those in the left-hand column are for unused examples on complete postcard; those on the right for used examples off card. Examples used on postcard are worth more.

1889 (Feb). *No. 2 (placed sideways on card) optd Shield Type* (a).
P1 1 1d. red-brown .. .. 75·00 35·00
a. Optd Shield Type (b) .. .. .. 26·00 6·50

1891 (Aug). *No. 48 optd Shield Type* (b).
P2 1 ½d. chestnut .. .. 4·00 1·50
a. Optd Shield Type (c) .. .. .. 9·00 4·00
b. Optd Shield Type (d) .. .. .. 4·50 2·00
c. Optd Shield Type (e) .. .. .. 11·00 4·75

1892 (June). *No. 54 optd Shield Type* (b).
P3 1 1d. on 3d. ultramarine .. .. .. 75·00 42·00
a. Optd Shield Type (c) .. .. .. 12·00 2·75

1½d. (P 1)   1½d. (P 2)   1½d. (P 3)

1892 (Sept)–**95.** *Nos. 50/1 optd Shield Type* (b) *or* (d) *(No. P6) and surch with Types* P **1/3.**
P4 1 1½d. on 2d. bright mauve (Type P 1) (11.92) 6·50 3·50
P5 1½d. on 2d. bright mauve (Type P 2) (9.93) 4·00 1·50
a. Surch inverted
P6 1½d. on 2d. brt mauve (Type P 3) (R.) (6.95) 10·00 4·00
P7 1½d. on 3d. ultramarine (Type P 1) .. 6·00 2·00

No. P5a shows the stamp affixed to the card upside down with the surcharge correctly positioned in relation to the card.

½d.
(P 4)

1895 (Aug). *No. 48 optd Shield Type* (e) *and surch with Type* P **4.**
P8 1 ½d. on ½d. chestnut .. .. 10·00 2·50

1½d. (P 5)   1½d. (P 6)

1895 (Dec)–**97.** *No. 50 optd Shield Type* (e) *and surch with Types* P **5/6.**
P 9 1 1½d. on 2d. bright mauve (Type P 5) .. 5·00 2·50
P10 1½d. on 2d. brt mauve (Type P 6) (12.97) 5·50 3·00
P11 1½d. on 2d. bright mauve (as Type P 6, but without stop) (12.97) .. .. 5·50 3·00

1897 (Mar). *No. 85 optd Shield Type* (d).
P12 1 ½d. orange .. .. 10·00 1·50
a. Optd Shield Type (e) .. .. 11·00 2·50

V.R.I.
(P 7)

1900. *Nos. P10/11 optd as T* **31/2** *or with Type* P **7.**
P13 1 1½d. on 2d. bright mauve (No. P10) (T 31) 22·00 5·00
P14 1½d. on 2d. bright mauve (No. P11) (T 31) 22·00 5·00
P15 1½d. on 2d. bright mauve (No. P10) (T 32) 22·00 5·00
P16 1½d. on 2d. bright mauve (No. P11) (T 32) 22·00 5·00
P17 1½d. on 2d. brt mve (No. P10) (Type P 7) 32·00 9·00
P18 1½d. on 2d. brt mve (No. P11) (Type P 7) 32·00 9·00

POLICE FRANK STAMPS

The following frank stamps were issued to members of the Orange Free State Mounted Police ("Rijdende Dienst Macht") for use on official correspondence.

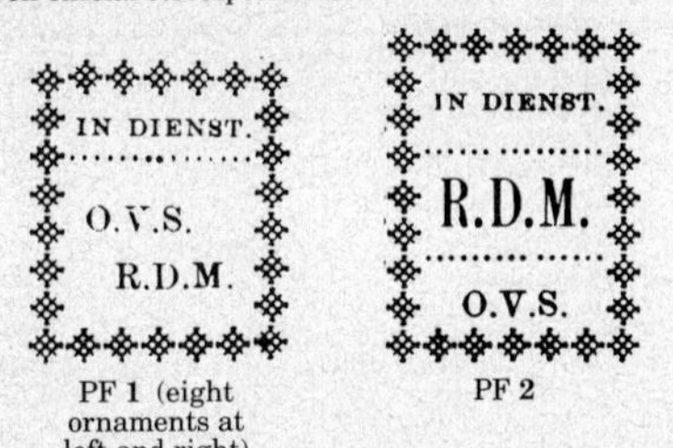

PF 1 (eight ornaments at left and right)   PF 2

1896. *P 12.*
PF1 PF 1 (–) Black £190

No. PF1 was printed in horizontal strips of 5 surrounded by wide margins.

1898. *As Type* PF **1,** *but with nine ornaments at left and right. P 12.*
PF2 (–) Black £130 £160

No. PF2 was printed in blocks of 4 (2×2) surrounded by wide margins.

1899. *P 12.*
PF3 PF 2 (–) Black/*yellow* £120 £120
a. No stop after "V" £500

No. PF3 was printed in sheets of 24 (6×4) with the edges of the sheet imperforate. It is believed that they were produced from a setting of 8 (2×4) repeated three times. No. PF3a occurs on R. 1/1 of the setting.

Examples of No. PF3 are known postmarked as late as 28 April 1900. The O.F.S. Mounted Police were disbanded by the British authorities at the end of the following month.

MILITARY FRANK STAMP

M 1

(Typeset Curling & Co, Bloemfontein)

1899 (15 Oct). *P 12.*
M1 M 1 (–) Black/*bistre-yellow* .. .. .. 12·00 45·00

Supplies of No. M1 were issued to members of the Orange Free State army on active service during the Second Boer War. To pass free through the O.F.S. fieldpost system letters had to be franked with No. M1 or initialled by the appropriate unit commander. The franks were in use between October 1899 and February 1900.

No. M1 was printed in sheets of 20 (5×4) using a setting of five different types in a horizontal row. The colour in the paper runs in water.

Typeset forgeries can be identified by the appearance of 17 pearls, instead of the 16 of the originals, in the top and bottom frames. Forgeries produced by lithography omit the stops after "BRIEF" and "FRANKO".

FISCAL STAMPS USED FOR POSTAGE

The following were issued in December 1877 (Nos. F1 and F3 in 1882) and were authorised for postal use between 1882 and 1886.

F 1

F 2

F 3

(Typo D.L.R.)

1882–86. *P 14.*
F 1 F 1 6d. pearl-grey .. .. .. 7·00 12·00
F 2 6d. purple-brown .. .. .. 25·00 18·00
F 3 F 2 1s. purple-brown .. .. .. 8·00 14·00
F 4 1s. pearl-grey .. .. .. 40·00 48·00
F 5 1s. 6d. blue .. .. .. 16·00 12·00
F 6 2s. magenta .. .. .. 16·00 12·00
F 7 3s. chestnut .. .. .. 19·00 48·00
F 8 4s. grey .. ..
F 9 5s. rose .. .. .. 20·00 20·00
F10 6s. green .. .. .. — 50·00
F11 7s. violet .. .. ..
F12 10s. orange .. .. .. 45·00 32·00
F13 F 3 £1 purple .. .. .. 50·00 35·00
a. "VRY-STAAT" (R. 1/5) ..
F14 £2 red-brown .. .. .. 60·00
a. "VRY-STAAT" (R. 1/5) ..
F14*b* £4 carmine .. .. ..
ba. "VRY-STAAT" (R. 1/5) ..
F15 £5 green .. .. .. 85·00 42·00
a. "VRY-STAAT" (R. 1/5) ..

Die proofs of Type F 3 showed a hyphen in error between "VRY" and "STAAT". This was removed from each impression on the plate before printing, but was missed on R. 1/5.

A fiscally used example of No. F2 exists showing "ZES PENCE" double, one inverted.

The 8s. yellow was prepared but we have no evidence of its use postally without surcharge Type F 3.

ZES PENCE.
(F 4)

1886. *Surch with Type* F **4.**
F16 F 2 6d. on 4s. grey .. .. ..
F17 6d. on 8s. yellow £180

Postage stamps overprinted for use as Telegraph stamps and used postally are omitted as it is impossible to say with certainty which stamps were genuinely used for postal purposes.

Orange Free State became a province of the Union of South Africa on 31 May 1910.

VI. TRANSVAAL

(*formerly* South African Republic)

From 1852 mail from the Transvaal was forwarded to the Cape of Good Hope, via the Orange Free State, by a post office at Potchefstroom. In 1859 the Volksraad voted to set up a regular postal service and arrangements were made for letters sent to the Cape and for overseas to be franked with Cape of Good Hope stamps.

The Potchefstroom postmaster placed his first order for these on 23 August 1859 and examples of all four triangular values are known postmarked there. From 1868 mail via the Orange Free State required franking with their issues also.

A similar arrangement covering mail sent overseas via Natal was in operation from 9 July 1873 until the first British Occupation. Such letters carried combinations of Transvaal stamps, paying the rate to Natal, and Natal issues for the overseas postage. Such Natal stamps were sold, but not postmarked, by Transvaal post offices.

PRICES FOR STAMPS ON COVER

Nos. 1/6 are rare used on cover.

Nos. 7/80	*from* × 20
Nos. 86/155	*from* × 3
Nos. 156/62	*from* × 6
Nos. 163/9	*from* × 5
Nos. 170/225	*from* × 10
Nos. 226/34	*from* × 20
Nos. 235/7	—
Nos. 238/43	*from* × 12
Nos. 244/55	*from* × 4
Nos. 256/7	*from* × 6
Nos. 258/9	—
Nos. 260/76	*from* × 20
Nos. F1/5	*from* × 5
Nos. D1/7	*from* × 20

The issues for Pietersburg, Lydenburg, Rustenburg, Schweizer Renecke and Wolmaransstad are very rare when on cover.

1 (Eagle with spread wings)

2

3

(Typo Adolph Otto, Gustrow, Mecklenburg-Schwerin)

1870 (1 May). *Thin paper, clear and distinct impressions.*

(*a*) *Imperf*

1	1	1d. brown-lake	£350	
		a. Orange-red	£350	£350
2		6d. bright ultramarine	£130	£130
		a. Pale ultramarine	£150	£160
3		1s. deep green	£550	£550
		a. *Tête-bêche* (pair)		

(*b*) *Fine roulette, 15½ to 16*

4	1	1d. brown-lake	85·00	
		a. Brick-red	65·00	
		b. Orange-red	65·00	
		c. Vermilion	65·00	
5		6d. bright ultramarine	60·00	60·00
		a. Pale ultramarine	70·00	
6		1s. deep green	£130	£130
		a. Yellow-green	£100	95·00
		b. Emerald-green	80·00	80·00

Examples of Nos. 1/6 may have been sold to dealers at some stage between their arrival in Transvaal during August 1869 and the sale of stamps to the public for postal purposes on 1 May 1870.

PLATES. The German printings of the 1d., 6d. and 1s. in Type **1** were from two pairs of plates, each pair printing sheets of 80 in two panes of five horizontal rows of eight.

One pair of plates, used for Nos. 4*a*, 4*c*, 5*a* and 6/*a*, produced stamps spaced 1¼ to 1½ mm apart with the rouletting close to the design on all four sides. The 1d. from these "narrow" plates shows a gap in the outer frame line at the bottom right-hand corner. The second pair, used for Nos. 1/3, 4, 4*b*, 5/*a* and 6*b*, had 2½ to 3½ mm between the stamps. These "wide" plates were sent to the Transvaal in 1869 and were used there to produce either single or double pane printings until 1883.

The 6d. and 1s. "wide" plates each had an inverted *cliché*. When printed these occurred on right-hand pane R. 4/1 of the 6d. and right-hand pane R.1/1 of the 1s. These were never corrected and resulted in *tête-bêche* pairs of these values as late as 1883.

REPRINTS AND IMITATIONS. A number of unauthorised printings were made of these stamps by the German printer. Many of these can be identified by differences in the central arms, unusual colours or, in the case of the 1d., by an extra frame around the numeral tablets at top.

Genuine stamps always show the "D" of "EENDRAGT" higher than the remainder of the word, have no break in the border above "DR" and depict the flagstaff at bottom right, behind "MAGT", stopping short of the central shield. They also show the eagle's eye as a clear white circle. On the forgeries the eye is often blurred.

The most difficult of the reprints to detect is the 1s. yellow-green which was once regarded as genuine, but was subsequently identified, by J. N. Luff in *The Philatelic Record* 1911–12, as coming from an unauthorised plate of four. Stamps from this plate show either a white dot between "EEN" and "SHILLING" or a white flaw below the wagon pole.

(Typo M. J. Viljoen, Pretoria)

1870 (1 May–4 July).

I. *Thin gummed paper from Germany. Impressions coarse and defective.* (*a*) *Imperf*

8	1	1d. dull rose-red	70·00	
		a. Reddish pink	60·00	
		b. Carmine-red	55·00	65·00
9		6d. dull ultramarine	£250	60·00
		a. *Tête-bêche* (pair)		

(*b*) *Fine roulette, 15½ to 16*

10	1	1d. carmine-red	£700	£250
11		6d. dull ultramarine	£180	90·00
		a. Imperf between (vert pair)	£600	

(*c*) *Wide roulette, 6½*

12	1	1d. carmine-red	—	£850

II. *Thick, hard paper with thin yellow smooth gum* (*No.* 15) *or yellow streaky gum* (*others*). (*a*) *Imperf*

13	1	1d. pale rose-red	60·00	
		a. Carmine-red	60·00	70·00
14		1s. yellow-green	85·00	75·00
		a. *Tête-bêche* (pair)	£14000	
		b. Bisected (6d.) (on cover)	†	£1300

(*b*) *Fine roulette, 15½ to 16*

15	1	1d. carmine-red (24 May)	80·00	
16		6d. ultramarine (10 May)	80·00	80·00
		a. *Tête-bêche* (pair)	£22000	£17000
17		1s. yellow-green	£550	£550

III. *Medium paper, blotchy heavy printing and whitish gum. Fine roulette 15½ to 16* (4 July)

18	1	1d. rose-red	60·00	75·00
		a. Carmine-red	40·00	45·00
		b. Crimson. From over-inked plate	£130	
19		6d. ultramarine	75·00	65·00
		a. *Tête-bêche* (pair)		
		b. Deep ultram. From over-inked plate	£400	£150
20		1s. deep green	£100	65·00
		a. From over-inked plate	£450	£150

The rouletting machine producing the wide 6½ gauge was not introduced until 1875.

Nos. 18*b*, 19*b* and 20a were printed from badly over-inked plates giving heavy blobby impressions.

(Typo J. P. Borrius, Potchefstroom)

1870 (Sept)–**71**. *Stout paper, but with colour often showing through, whitish gum.* (*a*) *Imperf*

21	1	1d. black	£120	£100

(*b*) *Fine roulette, 15½ to 16*

22	1	1d. black	17·00	25·00
		a. Grey-black	17·00	25·00
23		6d. blackish blue (7.71)	£120	60·00
		a. Dull blue	90·00	75·00

(Typo Adolph Otto, Gustrow, Mecklenburg-Schwerin)

1871 (July). *Thin paper, clear and distinct impressions. Fine roulette, 15½ to 16.*

24	2	3d. pale reddish lilac	80·00	90·00
		a. Deep lilac	85·00	95·00
		b. Vert laid paper		

No. 24 and later printings in the Transvaal were produced from a pair of plates in the same format as the 1869 issue. All genuine stamps have a small dot on the left leg of the eagle.

Imperforate examples in the issued shade, without the dot on eagle's leg, had been previously supplied by the printer, probably as essays, but were not issued for postal purposes. (*Price £750 unused*). They also exist *tête-bêche* (*Price for un pair* £3250).

Imperforate and rouletted stamps in other colours are reprints.

(Typo J. P. Borrius, Potchefstroom)

1872–74. *Fine roulette, 15½ to 16.* (*a*) *Thin transparent paper*

25	1	1d. black	£170	£550
26		1d. bright carmine	£140	50·00
27		6d. ultramarine	£100	40·00
28		1s. green	£120	55·00

(*b*) *Thinnish opaque paper, clear printing* (Dec 1872)

29	1	1d. reddish pink	55·00	38·00
		a. Carmine-red	55·00	38·00
30	2	3d. grey-lilac	85·00	45·00
31	1	6d. ultramarine	55·00	27·00
		a. Pale ultramarine	65·00	29·00
32		1s. yellow-green	70·00	38·00
		a. Green	70·00	38·00
		aa. Bisected (6d.) (on cover)	†	£1500

(*c*) *Thickish wove paper* (1873–74)

33	1	1d. dull rose	£400	70·00
		a. Brownish rose	£475	£110
		b. Printed on both sides		
34		6d. milky blue	£140	45·00
		a. Deep dull blue	85·00	40·00
		aa. Imperf (pair)	£600	
		ab. Imperf between (horiz pair)	£650	
		ac. Wide roulette 6½		

(*d*) *Very thick dense paper* (1873–74)

35		1d. dull rose	£500	£120
		a. Brownish rose	£375	95·00
36		6d. dull ultramarine	£170	65·00
		a. Bright ultramarine	£180	60·00
37		1s. yellow-green	£750	£550

(Typo P. Davis & Son, Pietermaritzburg)

1874 (Sept). *P* 12½. (*a*) *Thin transparent paper.*

38	1	1d. pale brick-red	80·00	35·00
		a. Brownish red	75·00	35·00
39		6d. deep blue	£120	50·00

(*b*) *Thicker opaque paper*

40	1	1d. pale red	£130	65·00
41		6d. blue	£100	45·00
		a. Imperf between (pair)		
		b. Deep blue	£100	45·00

(Typo Adolph Otto, Gustrow, Mecklenburg-Schweri

1874 (Oct). *Thin smooth paper, clearly printed. Fine r* 15½ *to* 16.

42	3	6d. bright ultramarine	60·0
		a. Bisected (3d.) (on cover)	

Stamps in other shades of blue, brown or red, often o types of paper, are reprints.

(Typo J. F. Celliers on behalf of Stamp Commission, Pre

1875 (29 Apr)–**77.**

I. *Very thin, soft opaque* (*semi-pelure*) *paper.* (*a*) *Impe*

43	1	1d. orange-red	£120
		a. Pin-perf	£500
44	2	3d. lilac	80·00
45	1	6d. blue	75·00
		a. Milky blue	£120
		aa. *Tête-bêche* (pair)	£9500
		ab. Pin-perf	—

(*b*) *Fine roulette, 15½ to 16*

46	1	1d. orange-red	£400
47	2	3d. lilac	£425
48	1	6d. blue	£400

(*c*) *Wide roulette, 6½*

49	1	1d. orange-red	—
50	2	3d. lilac	£550
51	1	6d. blue	—
		a. Bright blue	—
		b. Milky blue	—

II. *Very thin, hard transparent* (*pelure*) *paper* (1875–7
(*a*) *Imperf*

52	1	1d. brownish red	48·00
		a. Orange-red	38·00
		b. Dull red	42·00
		ba. Pin-perf	£425
53	2	3d. lilac	45·00
		a. Pin-perf	—
		b. *Deep lilac*	55·00
54	1	6d. pale blue	45·00
		a. Blue	45·00
		ab. *Tête-bêche* (pair)	
		ac. Pin-perf	—
		b. *Deep blue*	50·00

(*b*) *Fine roulette 15½ to 16*

55	1	1d. orange-red	£250
		a. Brown-red	£250
56	2	3d. lilac	£325
57	1	6d. blue	£150
		a. Deep blue	£150

(*c*) *Wide roulette, 6½*

58	1	1d. orange-red	£700
		a. Bright red	—
59	2	3d. lilac	£600
60	1	6d. deep blue	£700

III. *Stout hard-surfaced paper with smooth, nearly white,*
(1876). (*a*) *Imperf*

61	1	1d. bright red	22·00
62	2	3d. lilac	£300
63	1	6d. bright blue	90·00
		a. *Tête-bêche* (pair)	
		b. Pale blue	90·00
		c. Deep blue (deep brown gum)	55·00
		ca. *Tête-bêche* (pair)	— £1

(*b*) *Fine roulette, 15½ to 16*

64	1	1d. bright red	£400
65	2	3d. lilac	£275
66	1	6d. bright blue	—
		a. Deep blue (deep brown gum)	£600

(*c*) *Wide roulette, 6½*

67	1	1d. bright red	£450
68		6d. pale blue	—
		a. Deep blue (deep brown gum)	£500

IV. *Coarse, soft white paper* (1876–77). (*a*) *Imperf*

69	1	1d. brick-red	£100
70		6d. deep blue	£160
		a. Milky blue	£275
71		1s. yellow-green	£275
		a. Bisected (6d.) (on cover)	† £1

(*b*) *Fine roulette, 15½ to 16*

72	1	1d. brick-red	— £
73		6d. deep blue	— £
74		1s. yellow-green	£550 £

(*c*) *Wide roulette, 6½*

75	1	1d. brick-red	— £
76		6d. deep blue	— £
77		1s. yellow-green	— £

(*d*) *Fine × wide roulette*

78	1	1d. brick-red	£550 £

V. *Hard, thick, coarse yellowish paper* (1876–77)

79	1	1d. brick-red (*imperf*)	— £
80		1d. brick-red (*wide roulette*)	— £

The pin-perforated stamps have various gauges and w probably produced privately or by one or more post offices ot than Pretoria.

On Nos. 63*c*/ca, 66*a* and 68*a* the brown gum used was intense that it caused staining of the paper which is still visi on used examples.

See also Nos. 171/4.

FIRST BRITISH OCCUPATION

By 1876 conditions in the Transvaal had deteriorated and t country was faced by economic collapse, native wars a internal dissension. In early 1877 Sir Theophilus Shepsto appointed Special Commissioner to the South African Repub by the British Government, arrived in Pretoria and on 12 Ap annexed the Transvaal with the acquiesence of at least part the European population.

V. R.

TRANSVAAL.
(4)

V. R.

TRANSVAAL.
(5)

is the normal overprint, but Setting I No. 11 (R. 2/3) has a spaced overprint as T **5**.

Apr). *Optd with T* **4** *in red. (a) Imperf.*
3d. lilac (*semi-pelure*) (No. 44) £1100 £250
a. Opt Type **5** .. ..
3d. lilac (*pelure*) (No. 53) £1100 £170
a. Opt Type **5** £3500 £1400
b. Opt on back £3000 £3000
c. Opt double, in red and in black .. £4750
6d. milky blue (No. 70) £1300 £170
a. Opt inverted .. .. — £4250
b. Opt double £3500 £750
c. Opt Type **5** £4250
d. Deep blue .. .. — £225
1s. yellow-green (No. 71) £475 £170
a. Bisected (6d.) (on cover) .. † £1400
b. Opt inverted .. .. — £3250
c. Opt Type **5** £3000 £750
d. *Tête-bêche* (pair) .. ..

(b) Fine roulette, 15½ to 16
3d. lilac (*pelure*) (No. 56) .. .. — £1100
6d. deep blue (No. 73) .. .. — £1100
1s. yellow-green (No. 74) £1100 £500
a. Opt Type **5** .. ..

(c) Wide roulette, 6½
3d. lilac (*pelure*) (No. 59) .. .. — £1100
a. Opt Type **5** .. ..
6d. deep blue (No. 76) .. .. — £1100
a. Opt Type **5** .. ..
1s. yellow-green (No. 77) £2750 £1000
a. Opt inverted .. .. — £3500
s. 88a, 89b and 95a occurred on the inverted *cliché* of the stamps.

(June). *Optd with T* **4** *in black.*
I. *Very thin, hard transparent (pelure) paper*
1 1d. orange-red (*imperf*) (No. 52*a*) .. £170 95·00
1d. orange-red (*fine roulette*) (No. 55) .. — £1000
Stout hard-surfaced paper with smooth, nearly white, gum
1 1d. bright red (*imperf*) (No. 61) .. .. 21·00 21·00
a. Opt inverted £475 £400
b. Opt Type **5** £550 £600
1d. bright red (*fine roulette*) (No. 64) .. £140 45·00
a. Opt inverted .. ..
b. Opt double .. .. — £750
c. Imperf between (horiz pair) .. £650
1d. bright red (*wide roulette*) (No. 67) .. £475 £140
1d. bright red (*fine×wide roulette*) (No. 78)
III. *New ptgs on coarse, soft white paper. (a) Imperf*
1 1d. brick-red (5.77) .. .. 21·00 21·00
a. Opt double .. .. — £900
b. Opt Type **5** £600
2 3d. lilac .. .. 70·00 38·00
a. Opt inverted .. ..
b. Deep lilac .. .. £140 80·00
1 6d. dull blue .. .. 85·00 32·00
a. Opt double £2750
b. Opt inverted £1200 £150
d. Opt Type **5** .. .. — £750
da. Opt Type **5** inverted .. ..
e. Blue (bright to deep) .. .. £150 27·00
ea. Bright blue, opt inverted .. — £475
f. Pin-perf .. .. — £450
1s. yellow-green .. .. 90·00 45·00
a. Opt inverted £950 £180
b. *Tête-bêche* (pair) £15000 £15000
c. Opt Type **5** £2750 £900
d. Bisected (6d.) (on cover) .. † £1100

(b) Fine roulette, 15½ to 16
1 1d. brick-red .. .. 65·00 65·00
a. Imperf horiz (vert strip of 3) ..
b. Imperf between (horiz pair) .. † £600
2 3d. lilac .. .. £140 55·00
1 6d. dull blue .. .. £160 45·00
a. Opt inverted .. .. — £550
b. Opt Type **5** £3500
1s. yellow-green .. .. £160 85·00
a. Opt inverted £850 £375
b. Opt Type **5** .. .. — £2500

(c) Wide roulette, 6½
1 1d. brick-red £550 £140
a. Opt Type **5** .. .. — £650
2 3d. lilac .. .. — £550
1 6d. dull blue .. .. — £1100
a. Opt inverted .. .. — £3000
1s. yellow-green £350 £120
a. Opt inverted £1100 £475

7 (31 Aug). *Optd with T* **4** *in black.*
1 6d. blue/*rose* (*imperf*) .. .. 70·00 45·00
a. Bisected (3d.) (on cover) ..
b. Opt inverted .. .. 85·00 45·00
c. *Tête-bêche* (pair) .. ..
d. Opt omitted £2750 £2000
1 6d. blue/*rose* (*fine roulette*) .. .. £150 60·00
a. Opt inverted .. .. £425 60·00
b. *Tête-bêche* (pair) .. ..
c. Opt omitted .. ..
d. Bisected (3d.) (on cover) ..
6d. blue/*rose* (*wide roulette*) .. ..
a. Opt inverted .. ..
b. Opt omitted .. ..
Nos. 113/15 were overprinted from a setting of 40 which was plied upright to one pane in each sheet and inverted on the ner.

V. R.

Transvaal
(6)

V. R.

Transvaal
(7)

1877 (28 Sept)–**79**. *Optd with T* **6** *in black. (a) Imperf*
116 1 1d. red/*blue* .. .. 48·00 26·00
a. "Transvral" (Right pane R. 2/3) .. £4000 £2000
b. Opt double £3000
c. Opt inverted £600 £300
d. Opt omitted .. ..
117 1d. red/*orange* (6.12.77) .. .. 17·00 16·00
a. Pin-perf .. ..
b. Printed both sides .. ..
c. Opt double £2500
d. Optd with Type **7** (15.4.78) .. 45·00 38·00
e. Pair. Nos. 117 and 117d .. £100
118 2 3d. mauve/*buff* (24.10.77) .. .. 38·00 24·00
a. Opt inverted .. .. — £550
b. Pin-perf .. ..
c. Bisected (1½d) (on cover) .. † —
d. Optd with Type **7** (15.4.78) .. 55·00 32·00
da. Pin-perf £550 £550
e. Pair. Nos. 118 and 118d .. £130
119 3d. mauve/*green* (18.4.79) .. .. £140 42·00
a. Pin-perf .. ..
b. Opt inverted .. .. — £1500
c. Opt double .. ..
d. Printed both sides .. .. † —
e. Optd with Type **7** .. .. 95·00 35·00
ea. Opt inverted .. .. — £1500
eb. Printed both sides .. ..
f. Opt omitted .. .. — £2750
g. Pair. Nos. 119 and 119e .. £300
120 1 6d. blue/*green* (27.11.77) .. .. 75·00 35·00
a. Deep blue/green .. .. 90·00 38·00
b. Broken "Y" for "V" in "V.R." (Left pane R. 3/7) .. .. — £550
c. Small "v" in "Transvaal" (Left pane R. 5/2) .. .. — £550
d. "V..R." (Right pane R. 3/4) .. — £550
e. *Tête-bêche* (pair) .. .. — £14000
f. Opt inverted .. .. — £700
g. Pin-perf .. ..
h. Bisected (3d.) (on cover) .. † —
121 6d. blue/*blue* (20.3.78) .. .. 48·00 24·00
a. *Tête-bêche* (pair) .. ..
b. Opt inverted .. .. — £700
c. Opt omitted .. .. — £1600
d. Opt double .. .. — £2500
e. Pin-perf .. ..
f. Bisected (3d.) (on cover) .. † £700
g. Optd with Type **7** .. .. 95·00 27·00
ga. *Tête-bêche* (pair) £11000
gb. Opt inverted .. .. — £400
gc. Bisected (3d.) (on cover) .. † —
h. Pair. Nos. 121 and 121g .. £200

(b) Fine roulette, 15½ to 16
122 1 1d. red/*blue* .. .. 75·00 35·00
a. "Transvral" (Right pane R. 2/3) .. — £2250
123 1d. red/*orange* (6.12.77) .. .. 30·00 24·00
a. Imperf between (pair) .. £500
b. Optd with Type **7** (15.4.78) .. £130 £110
c. Pair. Nos. 123 and 123b .. £225
124 2 3d. mauve/*buff* (24.10.77) .. .. 85·00 25·00
a. Imperf horiz (vert pair) .. £600
b. Opt inverted .. .. — £2500
c. Optd with Type **7** (15.4.78) .. £130 95·00
ca. Imperf between (pair) ..
d. Pair. Nos. 124 and 124c .. £325
125 3d. mauve/*green* (18.4.79) £550 £150
a. Optd with Type **7** £500 £150
b. Pair. Nos. 125 and 125a ..
126 1 6d. blue/*green* (27.11.77) .. .. 70·00 25·00
a. "V..R" (Right pane R. 3/4) .. — £1000
b. *Tête-bêche* (pair) ..
c. Opt inverted .. .. — £500
d. Opt omitted .. .. — £3000
e. Bisected (3d.) (on cover) .. † £550
127 6d. blue/*blue* (20.3.78) .. .. £180 48·00
a. Opt inverted .. .. — £900
b. Opt omitted .. .. — £2500
c. Imperf between (pair) ..
d. Bisected (3d.) (on cover) .. † £600
e. Optd with Type **7** £300 £100
ea. Opt inverted .. .. — £800

(c) Wide roulette, 6¼
128 1 1d. red/*orange* (15.4.78) £250 £100
a. Optd with Type **7** .. .. — £250
129 2 3d. mauve/*buff* (24.10.77) .. .. — £100
a. Optd with Type **7** (15.4.78) .. — £300
130 3d. mauve/*green* (18.4.79) £375 £275
a. Optd with Type **7** .. .. — £300
131 1 6d. blue/*green* (27.11.77) .. .. — £850
132 6d. blue/*blue* (20.3.78) .. .. — £250
a. Opt inverted .. ..
b. Optd with Type **7** .. .. — £300
ba. Opt inverted .. ..

Nos. 116/32 were overprinted from various settings covering sheets of 80 or panes of 40 (8×5). Initially these settings contained Type **6** only, but from March 1878 settings also contained examples of Type **7**. Details of these mixed settings are as follows:
1d. red/*orange* (sheets of 80): all Type **6** except for 16 Type **7**.
3d. mauve/*buff* (panes of 40): 16 Type **7**.
3d. mauve/*green* (panes of 40): uncertain, some panes at least contained 27 Type **7**.
6d. blue/*blue* (sheets of 80): either 24 or 27 Type **7**.

9

(Recess B.W.)

1878 (26 Aug)–**80**. *P* 14, 14½.
133 9 ½d. vermilion (1880) .. .. 18·00 70·00
134 1d. pale red-brown .. .. 9·00 3·25
a. Brown-red .. .. 8·50 2·75
135 3d. dull rose .. .. 11·00 3·50
a. Claret .. .. 16·00 4·75
136 4d. sage-green .. .. 16·00 4·25
137 6d. olive-black .. .. 8·00 3·25
a. Black-brown .. .. 9·50 2·75
138 1s. green .. .. £100 32·00
139 2s. blue .. .. £140 65·00

The above prices are for specimens perforated on all four sides. Stamps from margins of sheets, with perforations absent on one or two sides, can be supplied for about 30% less.

1 Penny (10) 1 Penny (11) 1 Penny (12)

1 Penny (13) 1 Penny (14)

1 PENNY (15) 1 Penny (16)

1879 (22 Apr). *No.* 137*a surch with T* **10** *to* **16** *in black.*
140 **10** 1d. on 6d. .. .. 70·00 40·00
a. Surch in red £190 £130
141 **11** 1d. on 6d. .. .. £170 75·00
a. Surch in red £475 £275
142 **12** 1d. on 6d. .. .. £170 75·00
a. Surch in red £475 £275
143 **13** 1d. on 6d. .. .. 75·00 45·00
a. Surch double .. ..
b. Surch in red £225 £150
144 **14** 1d. on 6d. £450 £140
a. Surch in red .. .. — £1500
145 **15** 1d. on 6d. .. .. 38·00 22·00
a. Surch in red .. .. £120 65·00
146 **16** 1d. on 6d. .. .. £160 70·00
a. Surch in red £425 £250

Nos. 140/6 were surcharged from a setting of 60 containing eleven examples of Type **10**, four of Type **11**, four of Type **12**, nine of Type **13**, two of Type **14** (although there may have been only one in the first two ptgs), twenty-five of Type **15** and five of Type **16**.

The red surcharges may have been produced first.

V. R.

Transvaal
(16*a*)

V. R.

Transvaal

Small "T" (R. 2/8, 3/8, 4/8, 5/8 on right pane of 1d. and left pane of 3d.)

1879 (Aug–Sept). *Optd with T* **16***a in black. (a) Imperf.*
147 1 1d. red/*yellow* .. .. 40·00 35·00
a. Small "T" £225 £150
b. Red/orange .. .. 35·00 25·00
ba. Small "T" £160 £150
148 2 3d. mauve/*green* (Sept) .. .. 35·00 20·00
a. Small "T" .. .. £160 85·00
149 3d. mauve/*blue* (Sept) .. .. 42·00 25·00
a. Small "T" .. .. £170 85·00

(b) Fine roulette 15½ to 16
150 1 1d. red/*yellow* £350 £200
a. Small "T" £800 £550
b. Red/orange £750 £375
ba. Small "T" .. ..
151 2 3d. mauve/*green* £700 £225
a. Small "T" .. ..
152 3d. mauve/*blue* .. .. — £160
a. Small "T" .. .. — £600

(c) Wide roulette 6½
153 1 1d. red/*yellow* £600 £600
a. Small "T" .. ..
b. Red/orange .. ..
154 2 3d. mauve/*green* .. ..
a. Small "T" .. ..
155 3d. mauve/*blue* .. ..

(d) Pin-perf about 17
156 1 1d. red/*yellow* .. .. — £450
a. Small "T" .. ..
157 2 3d. mauve/*blue* .. .. — £600

SECOND REPUBLIC

Following the first Boer War the independence of the South African Republic was recognised by the Convention of Pretoria from 8 August 1881.

Nos. 133/9 remained valid and some values were available for postage until 1885.

EEN PENNY
(17)

1882 (11 Aug). *No.* 136 *surch with T* **17**.
170 **9** 1d. on 4d. sage-green .. .. 9·50 4·00
a. Surch inverted £300 £200

Used examples of a similar, but larger, surcharge (width 20 mm) are known. These were previously considered to be forgeries, but it is now believed that some, at least, may represent a trial printing of the "EEN PENNY" surcharge.

(Typo J. F. Celliers)

1883 (20 Feb). *Re-issue of T* **1** *and* **2**. *P* 12.
171 **1** 1d. grey (*to black*) (Apr) .. .. .. 4·00 1·25
a. Imperf vert (horiz pair) £250
b. Imperf horiz (vert pair) .. .. .. † £325
172 **2** 3d. grey-black (*to black*)/*rose* .. .. 20·00 3·75
a. Bisected (1d.) (on cover) .. .. .. † £550
173 3d. pale red (Mar) .. .. .. 7·50 1·75
a. Bisected (1d.) (on cover) .. .. .. † £550
b. *Chestnut* .. .. 22·00 3·50
ba. Imperf between (horiz pair) .. .. † —
c. *Vermilion* .. .. 22·00 4·50
174 **1** 1s. green (*to deep*) (July) .. .. .. 42·00 3·00
a. Bisected (6d.) (on cover) .. .. .. † £425
b. *Tête-bêche* (pair) £650 £120

Reprints are known of Nos. 172, 173, 173*b* and 173*c*. The paper of the first is *bright rose* in place of *dull rose*, and the impression is brownish black in place of grey-black to deep black. The reprints on white paper have the paper thinner than the originals, and the gum yellowish instead of white. The colour is a dull deep orange-red.

18

PERFORATIONS. Stamps perforated 11½×12 come from the first vertical row of sheets of the initial printing otherwise perforated 12½×12 .

REPRINTS. Reprints of the general issues 1885–93, 1894–95, 1895–96 and 1896–97 exist in large quantities produced using the original plates from 1911 onwards. They cannot readily be distinguished from genuine originals except by comparison with used stamps, but the following general characteristics may be noted. The reprints are all perf 12½, large holes; the paper is whiter and thinner than that usually employed for the originals and their colours lack the lustre of those of the genuine stamps. Forged surcharges have been made on these reprints.

(Des J. Vurtheim. Typo Enschedé)

1885 (13 Mar)–**1893**. *P* 12½.
175 **18** ½d. grey (30.3.85) 30 10
a. Perf 13½ .. .. 4·75 90
b. Perf 12½×12 .. .. 1·75 10
ba. Perf 11½×12 .. .. 20·00 6·00
176 1d. carmine 30 10
a. Perf 12½×12 .. .. 70 10
aa. Perf 11½×12 .. .. 12·00 2·75
b. *Rose* 30 10
ba. Perf 12½×12 .. .. 65 10
177 2d. brown-purple (*p* 12½×12) (9.85) .. 1·75 1·75
178 2d. olive-bistre (14.4.87) 50 10
a. Perf 12½×12 .. .. 3·75 10
179 2½d. mauve (*to bright*) (8.93) .. .. 1·25 50
180 3d. mauve (*to bright*) .. .. .. 1·50 70
a. Perf 12½×12 .. .. 6·00 75
aa. Perf 11½×12 .. .. 27·00 17·00
181 4d. bronze-green .. .. 2·25 50
a. Perf 13½ .. .. 6·00 85
b. Perf 12½×12 .. .. 13·00 65
ba. Perf 11½×12 .. .. £160 60·00
182 **18** 6d. pale dull blue .. .. 3·75 2·25
a. Perf 13½ .. .. 4·50 70
b. Perf 12½×12 .. .. 5·50 20
ba. Perf 11½×12 .. ..
183 1s. yellow-green .. .. 2·50 35
a. Perf 13½ .. .. 22·00 5·50
b. Perf 12½×12 .. .. 7·50 45
184 2s. 6d. orange-buff (*to buff*) (2.12.85) .. 3·75 1·60
a. Perf 12½×12 .. .. 14·00 4·00
185 5s. slate (2.12.85) .. .. 6·00 2·75
a. Perf 12½×12 .. .. 30·00 4·50
186 10s. fawn (2.12.85) .. .. 30·00 6·00
187 £5 dp grn (3.92)* (Optd "Monster" £150) £3250 £180

Singles of the 6d. pale dull blue imperforate have been reported used in 1893.

*Most examples of No. 187 on the market are either forgeries or reprints.

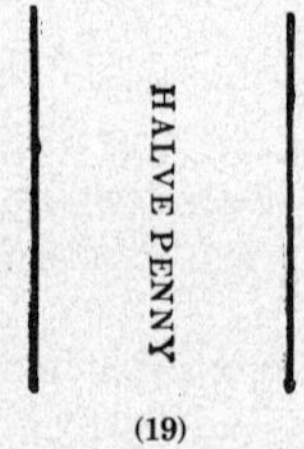

(19)

1885 (22 May–Aug). *Surch with T* **19**. *Reading up or down*.
188 **2** ½d. on 3d. (No. 173) .. .. .. 3·50 8·00
189 **1** ½d. on 1s. (No. 174) (Aug) .. .. 17·00 42·00
a. *Tête-bêche* (pair) £650 £300

Nos. 188/9 were surcharged by a setting of 40. After the left pane had been surcharged reading down the sheets were turned so that the right pane had the surcharges reading up.

HALVE PENNY Z.A.R (20) TWEE PENCE Z. A. R. (21) HALVE PENNY (22)

1885 (1 Sept). *No.* 137*a surch with T* **20/1** *in red.*
190 **9** ½d. on 6d. black-brown .. .. .. 42·00 70·00
191 2d. on 6d. black-brown .. .. .. 3·75 8·50

1885 (28 Sept). *No.* 180*a surch with T* **22**.
192 **18** ½d. on 3d. mauve .. .. .. 3·00 3·00
a. "PRNNY" (R. 6/6) .. .. .. 32·00 48·00
b. 2nd "N" inverted (R. 3/8) .. .. 75·00 90·00
c. Perf 11½×12 .. .. .. 9·50 9·00

2d (23) 2d (24)

1887 (15 Jan). *No.* 180*a surch with T* **23/4**.
193 **18** 2d. on 3d. mauve (Type **23**) .. .. 5·50 5·50
a. Surch double .. .. .. — £225
b. Perf 11½×12 .. .. .. 20·00 10·00
194 2d. on 3d. mauve (Type **24**) .. .. 1·00 2·25
a. Surch double .. .. .. — £160
b. Perf 11½×12 .. .. .. 5·00 7·00

Nos. 193/4 were surcharged from the same setting of 60 (10 × 6) which showed Type **24** on the top five horizontal rows and Type **23** on the sixth horizontal row.

Halve Penny (25) 1 Penny (26)

2½ Pence (27) 2½ Pence (28)

Two types of surcharge:
A. Vertical distance between bars 12½ mm.
B. Distance 13½ mm.

1893. *T* **18** *surch. P* 12½. (*a*) *In red.*
195 **25** ½d. on 2d. olive-bistre (A) (27 May) .. 80 80
a. Surch inverted .. .. .. 2·00 1·50
b. Surch Type B .. .. .. 1·50 1·50
ba. Surch inverted .. .. .. 4·75 8·00

(*b*) *In black*
196 **25** ½d. on 2d. olive-bistre (A) (2 July) .. 85 60
a. Surch inverted .. .. .. 4·00 4·50
b. Extra surch on back inverted .. £150
c. Surch Type B .. .. .. 1·10 1·10
ca. Surch inverted .. .. .. 17·00 14·00
cb. Extra surch on back inverted .. £250
197 **26** 1d. on 6d. blue (A) (26 Jan) 50 30
a. Surch double .. .. .. 50·00 40·00
b. Surch inverted .. .. .. 1·40 1·60
c. Surch treble .. .. ..
d. Surch Type B 70 55
da. Surch inverted .. .. .. 4·50 3·25
db. Surch double .. .. .. — 70·00
e. Pair, one without surch £200
198 **27** 2½d. on 1s. green (A) (2 Jan) .. .. 90 2·25
a. "2/½" for "2½" (R. 1/10) .. .. 30·00 40·00
b. Surch inverted .. .. .. 6·50 7·50
ba. Surch inverted and "2/½" for "2½" £325 £275
c. Extra surch on back inverted .. £400 £400
d. Surch double, one inverted .. £600
e. Surch Type B .. .. .. 1·50 2·75
ea. Surch inverted .. .. .. 7·50 16·00
199 **28** 2½d. on 1s. green (A) (24 June) .. 3·25 3·25
a. Surch double .. .. .. 45·00 40·00
b. Surch inverted .. .. .. 7·00 7·00
c. Surch Type B .. .. .. 7·00 7·50
ca. Surch double .. .. .. 70·00 80·00
cb. Surch inverted .. .. .. 16·00 16·00

Surcharge Types **25/8** all show a similar setting of the horizontal bars at top and bottom. On horizontal rows 1 to 4 and 6 the bars are 12½ mm apart and on row 5 the distance is 13½ mm.

29 (Wagon with shafts)

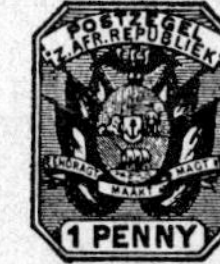

30 (Wagon with pole)

1894 (July). *P* 12½.
200 **29** ½d. grey 60
201 1d. carmine 60
202 2d. olive-bistre 60
203 6d. pale dull blue .. .. 1·25
204 1s. yellow-green .. .. 8·00

For note *re* reprints, see below T **18**.

1895 (16 Mar)–**96**. *P* 12½.
205 **30** ½d. pearl-grey (1895) 50
a. *Lilac-grey* 50
206 1d. rose-red 50
207 2d. olive-bistre (1895) 50
208 3d. mauve (1895) .. .. .. 1·00
209 4d. olive-black (1895) .. .. .. 1·50
210 6d. pale dull blue (1895) .. .. .. 1·50
211 1s. yellow-green (18.3.95) .. .. .. 2·00
212 5s. slate (1896) .. .. .. 11·00
212*a* 10s. pale chestnut (1896) .. .. 11·00
205s/8s, 211s Optd "Monster" .. *Set of* 5 £150

For note re reprints, see below T **18**.

Halve Penny (31)

1d. (32—Round dot) 1d. (32*a*—Square dot)

1895 (July–August). *Nos.* 211 *and* 179 *surch with T* **31/2**
213 **30** ½d. on 1s. green (R.) 50
a. Surch spaced .. .. .. 1·10
b. "Pennij" for "Penny" (R. 6/6) .. 42·00
c. Surch inverted .. .. .. 3·50
d. Surch double .. .. .. 60·00
214 **18** 1d. on 2½d. bright mauve (G.) 50
a. Surch inverted .. .. .. 17·00
b. Surch double .. .. .. 60·00
c. Surch on back only .. .. .. 70·00
d. Surch Type **32***a* .. .. .. 1·50
da. Surch inverted .. .. .. 60·00
e. Surch treble £500

The normal space between "Penny" and the bars is 3 mm. No. 213a, which comes from the fifth horizontal row of setting, this is increased to 4 mm. Copies may be found in w one or both of the bars have failed to print.

Type **32***a* with square stop occurred on R. 3/3-4, 3/6-8, 4/ 4/7-8, 4/10, 6/3, 6/7-8 and 6/10 of the setting of 60.

33

34

1895 (July). *Fiscal stamp optd* "POSTZEGEL". *P* 11½.
215 **33** 6d. bright rose (G.) 75
a. Imperf between (pair) .. ..
b. Opt inverted .. ..

(Litho The Press Printing and Publishing Works, Pretoria

1895 (6 Sept). *Introduction of Penny Postage*. *P* 11.
215*c* **34** 1d. red (*pale to deep*) .. .. .. 1·50
ca. Imperf between (pair) .. .. 60·00 65
cb. Imperf vert (horiz pair) .. ..
cc. Imperf (pair) .. ..

1896–97. *P* 12½.
216 **30** ½d. green (1896) 30
217 1d. rose-red and green (1896) 30
218 2d. brown and green (2.97) 30
219 2½d. dull blue and green (6.96) 50
220 3d. purple and green (3.97) .. .. 1·00
221 4d. sage-green and green (3.97) .. .. 1·00
222 6d. lilac and green (11.96) 60
223 1s. ochre and green (3.96) 75
224 2s. 6d. dull violet and green (6.96) .. 1·50

For note *re* reprints, see below T **18**.

SECOND BRITISH OCCUPATION

The Second Boer War began on 11 October 1899 and w concluded by the Peace of Vereeniging on 31 May 1902. Preto was occupied by the British on 5 June 1900 and a civilian pos service began operating thirteen days later.

FORGERIES. The forgeries of the "V.R.I." and "E.R.I." overprin most often met with can be recognised by the fact that the type us is perfect and the three stops are always in alignment with t bottom of the letters. In the genuine overprints, which were ma from old type, it is impossible to find all three letters perfect and three stops perfect and in exact alignment with the bottom of t letters.

V. R. I. (35) E. R. I. (36) E. R. I. Half Penny (37)

18 June). *Optd with T* **35**.
0 ½d. green 30 15
a. No stop after "V" .. .. .. 10·00 10·00
b. No stop after "R" .. .. .. 8·00 8·00
c. No stop after "I" .. .. .. 6·50 6·50
d. Opt inverted .. .. .. 8·50 10·00
e. Opt double .. .. ..
f. "V.I.R." (R. 4/4) £500
1d. rose-red and green 30 15
a. No stop after "V" .. .. .. 10·00 10·00
b. No stop after "R" .. .. .. 8·00 8·00
c. No stop after "I" .. .. .. 5·00 5·00
d. Opt inverted .. .. .. 8·50 15·00
e. Opt double .. .. .. 60·00 75·00
f. No stops after "R" and "I" .. 65·00 65·00
g. Opt omitted (in pair with normal) £250
2d. brown and green .. .. .. 2·00 90
a. No stop after "V" .. .. .. 23·00 23·00
c. No stop after "I" .. .. .. 27·00 27·00
d. Opt inverted .. .. .. 15·00 17·00
e. Opt double .. .. ..
f. "V.I.R." (R. 4/4) £500
g. Opt albino .. .. ..
2½d. dull blue and green 90 90
a. No stop after "V" .. .. .. 17·00 19·00
b. No stop after "R" .. .. .. 40·00 45·00
c. No stop after "I" .. .. .. 13·00 15·00
d. Opt inverted .. .. .. 9·00 10·00
3d. purple and green 90 90
a. No stop after "V" .. .. .. 20·00 22·00
b. No stop after "R" .. .. .. 40·00 45·00
c. No stop after "I" .. .. .. 26·00 29·00
d. Opt inverted .. .. .. 60·00 70·00
4d. sage-green and green .. .. 1·75 50
a. No stop after "V" .. .. .. 35·00 35·00
b. No stop after "R" .. .. .. 45·00 45·00
c. No stop after "I" .. .. .. 30·00 30·00
d. Opt inverted .. .. .. 22·00 25·00
f. "V.I.R." (R. 4/4) £500
6d. lilac and green .. .. .. 1·75 80
a. No stop after "V" .. .. .. 16·00 16·00
b. No stop after "R" .. .. .. 22·00 22·00
c. No stop after "I" .. .. .. 22·00 22·00
d. Opt inverted .. .. .. 24·00 28·00
1s. ochre and green .. .. .. 1·75 2·00
a. No stop after "V" .. .. .. 17·00 20·00
b. No stop after "R" .. .. .. 17·00 20·00
c. No stop after "I" .. .. .. 29·00 35·00
d. Opt inverted .. .. .. 28·00 35·00
e. Opt double .. .. .. 65·00 75·00
2s. 6d. dull violet and green .. .. 3·00 6·50
a. No stop after "V" .. .. .. 30·00
b. No stop after "R" .. .. .. 65·00
5s. slate .. .. 4·75 8·50
a. No stop after "V" .. .. .. 90·00
10s. pale chestnut .. .. .. 7·00 10·00
a. No stop after "V" .. .. .. 75·00
c. No stop after "I" .. .. .. 75·00
18 £5 deep green* £1800 £750
a. No stop after "V" .. .. ..
7s Optd "Specimen" .. *Set of* 4 £200
any examples of No. 237 on the market are forgeries and tamps should only be purchased if accompanied by a recent rt committee certificate.
e error "V.I.R." occurred on R.4/4 in the first batch of ps to be overprinted—a few sheets of the ½d., 2d. and 4d. error was then corrected and stamps showing it are very

number of different settings were used to apply the print to Nos. 226/37. The missing stop varieties listed above loped during overprinting and occur on different positions e various settings.

(Jan)–**02.** *Optd with T* **36**.
30 ½d. green 50 50
a. Opt double .. .. ..
1d. rose-red and green (20.3.01) .. 50 10
a. "E" of opt omitted .. .. 70·00
3d. purple and green (6.02) .. .. 2·25 2·50
4d. sage-green and green (6.02) .. 2·25 2·50
2s. 6d. dull violet and green (10.02) .. 6·50 12·00

(July). *Surch with T* **37**.
30 ½d. on 2d. brown and green 65 65
a. No stop after "E" (R.4/6) .. .. 45·00

38 (POSTAGE REVENUE) **39** (POSTAGE POSTAGE)

(Typo D.L.R.)

2 (1 Apr)–**03.** *Wmk Crown CA. P* 14.
38 ½d. black and bluish green .. .. 1·50 20
w. Wmk inverted .. .. .. 80·00 55·00
1d. black and carmine .. .. 1·25 15
w. Wmk inverted .. .. .. 60·00 45·00
2d. black and purple .. .. .. 3·00 50
2½d. black and blue .. .. .. 4·50 1·25
w. Wmk inverted .. .. .. 55·00 30·00
3d. black and sage-green (1903) .. 5·00 50
4d. black and brown (1903) .. .. 4·00 75
6d. black and orange-brown .. .. 3·75 60
1s. black and sage-green .. .. 9·50 7·00
2s. black and brown .. .. .. 29·00 32·00
39 2s. 6d. magenta and black .. .. 14·00 8·00
5s. black and purple/*yellow* .. .. 22·00 22·00
10s. black and purple/*red* .. .. 45·00 24·00
55 .. .. *Set of* 12 £130 85·00
s/55s (*inc* 247ws) Optd "Specimen" *Set of* 12 £130
he colour of the "black" centres varies from brownish grey or to black.

1903. *Wmk Crown CA. P* 14.
256 **39** 1s. grey-black and red-brown .. .. 11·00 2·00
257 2s. grey-black and yellow .. .. 15·00 9·50
258 £1 green and violet £170 £100
259 £5 orange-brown and violet £1200 £475
256s/9s Optd "Specimen" .. *Set of* 4 £180

1904–09. *Wmk Mult Crown CA. Ordinary paper. P* 14.
260 **38** ½d. black and bluish green .. .. 6·00 2·00
w. Wmk inverted .. .. .. 85·00 55·00
y. Wmk inverted and reversed .. 85·00 30·00
261 1d. black and carmine .. .. 3·25 20
262 2d. black and purple (*chalk-surfaced paper*) (1906) .. .. .. 7·00 50
263 2½d. black and blue (1905) .. .. 9·00 4·25
a. Chalk-surfaced paper .. .. 9·00 1·75
264 3d. black & sage-green (*chalk-surfaced paper*) (1906) .. .. .. 3·50 30
265 4d. black and brown (*chalk-surfaced paper*) (1906) .. .. .. 4·75 70
w. Wmk inverted .. .. .. 75·00 55·00
266 6d. black and orange (1905) .. .. 6·00 90
a. Chalk-surfaced paper. *Black and brown-orange* (1906) .. .. 2·50 50
w. Wmk inverted .. .. .. 85·00 65·00
267 **39** 1s. black and red-brown (1905) .. 6·00 50
268 2s. black and yellow (1906) .. .. 20·00 4·50
269 2s. 6d. magenta and black (1909) .. 35·00 3·50
270 5s. black and purple/*yellow* .. .. 16·00 1·50
271 10s. black and purple/*red* (1907) .. 40·00 2·75
272 £1 green and violet (1908) .. .. £170 24·00
a. Chalk-surfaced paper .. .. £160 16·00
260/72 .. .. *Set of* 13 £275 30·00
There is considerable variation in the "black" centres as in the previous issue.

1905–09. *Wmk Mult Crown CA. P* 14.
273 **38** ½d. yellow-green .. .. .. 1·75 10
a. Deep green (1908) .. .. .. 2·50 20
w. Wmk inverted .. .. .. £110 65·00
274 1d. scarlet .. .. 1·25 10
aw. Wmk inverted .. .. .. — £250
b. Wmk Cabled Anchor, T **13** of Cape of Good Hope .. .. .. — £325
275 2d. purple (1909) .. .. .. 3·50 50
276 2½d. bright blue (1909) .. .. 12·00 3·75
273/6 .. .. *Set of* 4 17·00 3·75
273s/6s Optd "Specimen" .. *Set of* 4 50·00
A 2d. grey, T **38**, was prepared for use but not issued. It exists overprinted "Specimen", *price* £120.
The monocoloured ½d. and 1d. are printed from new combined plates. These show a slight alteration in that the frame does not touch the crown.
Many of the King's Head stamps are found overprinted or perforated "C.S.A.R.", for use by the Central South African Railways.

STAMP BOOKLETS

1905 (July). *Black on red cover showing arms. Stapled.*
SB1 2s. 7d. booklet containing thirty 1d. (No. 261) in blocks of 6 .. .. £2000

1905. *Black on red cover. Stapled.*
SB2 2s. 7d. booklet containing thirty 1d. (No. 274) in blocks of 6 .. .. £2250

1909. *Black on red cover. Stapled.*
SB3 2s. 6d. booklet containing ten ½d. (No. 273) in block of 6 and block of 4, and twenty-four 1d. (No. 274) in blocks of 6 .. .. .. £2750
Stocks of No. SB3 were supplied containing twelve examples of the ½d., it being intended that the postal clerks would remove two stamps before the booklets were sold. In some instances this did not occur.

POSTAL FISCAL STAMPS

1900–02. *Fiscal stamps as in T* **33**, *but optd with T* **35**. *P* 11½.
F1 1d. pale blue .. .. — 45·00
F2 6d. dull carmine .. .. — 60·00
F3 1s. olive-bistre .. .. — 75·00
F4 1s. 6d. brown .. .. — 90·00
F5 2s. 6d. dull purple .. .. — £100
Nos. F1/5, previously listed as Nos. 1/5 of Volksrust, are fiscal issues which are known postally used from various Transvaal post offices between June 1900 and June 1902.

Other fiscal stamps are found apparently postally used, but these were used on telegrams not on postal matter.

POSTAGE DUE STAMPS

D 1

(Typo D.L.R.)

1907. *Wmk Mult Crown CA. P* 14.
D1 D 1 ½d. black and blue-green .. .. 3·25 1·25
D2 1d. black and scarlet .. .. .. 4·00 85
D3 2d. brown-orange .. .. .. 4·00 1·25
D4 3d. black and blue .. .. .. 7·50 4·00
D5 5d. black and violet .. .. .. 2·00 12·00
D6 6d. black and red-brown .. .. 4·25 12·00
D7 1s. scarlet and black .. .. .. 8·50 8·00
D1/7 .. .. *Set of* 7 30·00 35·00

Transvaal became a province of the Union of South Africa on 31 May 1910.

PIETERSBURG

After the fall of Pretoria to the British in June 1900 the Transvaal government withdrew to the north of the country. Those post offices in areas not occupied by the British continued to function, but by early the following year supplies of stamps were exhausted. The following stamps were then authorised by the State Secretary and remained in use in some towns to early May 1901. Pietersburg itself was taken by British forces on 9 April.

PRICES. Genuinely used examples are very rare. Stamps cancelled by favour exist and are worth the same as the unused prices quoted.
The issued stamps are initialled by the Controller J. T. de V. Smit. All values exist without his signature and these are believed to come from remainders abandoned when the Boers evacuated Pietersburg.

P 1

P 2

P 3

TYPES P 1/3. Each value was printed in sheets of 24 (6×4) of which the first two horizontal rows were as Type P **1**, the third row as Type P **2** and the fourth as Type P **3**. The stamps were issued to post offices in blocks of 12.

(Type-set *De Zoutpansberg Wachter* Press, Pietersburg)

1901 (20 Mar (*1d.*)–3 Apr (*others*)). A. *Imperf.*

(*a*) *Controller's initials in black*
1 P 1 ½d. black/*green* .. .. 15·00
e. Controller's initials omitted .. 95·00
2 P 2 ½d. black/*green* .. .. 45·00
d. Controller's initials omitted .. 95·00
3 P 3 ½d. black/*green* .. .. 45·00
d. Controller's initials omitted .. 95·00
4 P 1 1d. black/*red* .. .. 3·50
5 P 2 1d. black/*red* .. .. 5·50
6 P 3 1d. black/*red* .. .. 7·00
7 P 1 2d. black/*orange* .. .. 6·00
8 P 2 2d. black/*orange* .. .. 14·00
9 P 3 2d. black/*orange* .. .. 22·00
10 P 1 4d. black/*blue* .. .. 5·50
11 P 2 4d. black/*blue* .. .. 9·50
12 P 3 4d. black/*blue* .. .. 32·00
13 P 1 6d. black/*green* .. .. 9·50
14 P 2 6d. black/*green* .. .. 15·00
15 P 3 6d. black/*green* .. .. 40·00
16 P 1 1s. black/*yellow* .. .. 8·00
17 P 2 1s. black/*yellow* .. .. 14·00
18 P 3 1s. black/*yellow* .. .. 25·00

(*b*) *Controller's initials in red*
19 P 1 ½d. black/*green* .. .. 15·00
20 P 2 ½d. black/*green* .. .. 35·00
21 P 3 ½d. black/*green* .. .. 40·00

B. *P* 11½. (*a*) *Controller's initials in red*
22 P 1 ½d. black/*green* .. .. 5·50
c. Imperf vert (horiz pair) .. .. 95·00
23 P 2 ½d. black/*green* .. .. 17·00
c. Imperf vert (horiz pair) £120
24 P 3 ½d. black/*green* .. .. 12·00
b. Imperf vert (horiz pair) £120

(*b*) *Controller's initials in black*
25 P 1 1d. black/*red* .. .. 2·00
m. Imperf vert (horiz pair) .. .. 55·00
n. Imperf between (vert pair: No. 25 + No. 26) .. ..
o. Imperf horiz (vert pair) .. ..
26 P 2 1d. black/*red* .. .. 2·75
f. Imperf vert (horiz pair) .. .. 80·00
g. Imperf horiz (vert pair: No. 26 + No. 27) .. ..
27 P 3 1d. black/*red* .. .. 4·00
f. Imperf vert (horiz pair) .. .. 80·00
28 P 1 2d. black/*orange* .. .. 5·50
29 P 2 2d. black/*orange* .. .. 8·00
30 P 3 2d. black/*orange* .. .. 14·00
For the ½d. the First printing had initials in either black or red, those of the Second printing had them in black and all of the Third were in red.

CONSTANT VARIETIES

Rows 1 *and* 2 *are as Type* P **1**, *Row* 3 *as Type* P **2** *and Row* 4 *as Type* P **3**.

½d. value
First printing—Imperf
R.1/1 & 4 Top left "½" inverted, no stop after right "AFR" .. .. .. (No. 19c) 70·00
R.1/2 Top right "½" inverted .. .. (No. 19d) 90·00
R.1/3 "⅓" at lower right .. .. .. (No. 19e) 90·00
R.1/5 "POSTZFGEL" .. .. .. (No. 19f) 90·00
R.1/6 Left spray inverted, "AFB" at right (No. 19g) 90·00
R.2/1 "REB" at left. left side of inner frame 3 mm too high .. .. .. (No. 19h) 90·00
R.2/2 "BEP" at left .. .. .. (No. 19i) 90·00

"POSTZEOEL" .. .. (No. 19j) 90·00
"AER" at right, left side of inner frame 2 mm too high .. .. (No. 19k) 90·00
No stop after date .. .. .. (No. 19l) 90·00
No stop after "PENNY" .. .. (No. 19m)
"$^1/_3$" at top left, "PE" of "PENNY" spaced .. .. (No. 20c) 90·00
Right spray inverted .. .. (No. 20d) 90·00
Top left "$^1/_2$" inverted .. .. (No. 20e) 90·00
No stop after "2" at left .. .. (No. 20f)
Centre figures "$^1/_2$" level .. .. (No. 20g)
"POSTZEGFL", no stop after right "AFR" .. .. .. (No. 20h)
"$^1/_3$" at top right .. .. .. (No. 21b) 90·00
Lower left "$^1/_2$" inverted .. .. (No. 21c) 90·00
"$^1/_4$" at top left .. .. .. (No. 21d) 90·00
Left spray inverted, "901" for "1901" (No. 21e)
s printing was produced first and was then adapted for the r values.

d printing
No stop after left "AFR" .. *Imperf* (No. 1a) 60·00
"$^1/_3$" at top left, no bar over lower right "$^1/_2$" .. .. *Imperf* (No. 1b) 60·00
No stop after date .. *Imperf* (No. 1c) 60·00
"BEP" at left, no stop after date .. .. .. *Imperf* (No. 1d) 60·00
"AFB" at left .. .. *Imperf* (No. 2a) 60·00
Perf (No. 23a)
"POSTZEGEI" .. .. *Imperf* (No. 2b) 60·00
Perf (No. 23b)
No bar over lower right "$^1/_2$" *Imperf* (No. 2c) 60·00
No stop after right "AFR" .. *Imperf* (No. 3a) 60·00
No stop after left "Z", no bar under top right "$^1/_2$" .. .. .. *Imperf* (No. 3b) 60·00
Perf (No. 23c)
"POSTZECEL AER" at left *Imperf* (No. 3c) 60·00

l printing
No stop after right "AFR" .. *Imperf* (No. 19a) 70·00
Perf (No. 22a) 40·00
Left side of inner frame too high .. .. .. *Imperf* (No. 19b) 70·00
Perf (No. 22b) 40·00
Centre figures "$^1/_2$" level .. *Imperf* (No. 20a) 70·00
Perf (No. 23d) 40·00
No stop after right "AFR" .. *Imperf* (No. 20b) 70·00
Perf (No. 23e) 40·00
Hyphen between right "AFR" and "REP" .. .. .. *Imperf* (No. 21a) 70·00
Perf (No. 24a) 40·00

alue
printing
Inverted "1" at lower left, first "1" of date dropped .. .. .. *Imperf* (No. 4a) 35·00
Perf (No. 25a) 22·00
No bar under top left "1" .. *Imperf* (No. 4b) 35·00
Perf (No. 25b) 22·00
No bar over lower right "1" .. *Imperf* (No. 4c) 35·00
Perf (No. 25c) 22·00
"POSTZFGEL" .. .. *Imperf* (No. 4d) 35·00
Perf (No. 25d) 22·00
5 "AFB" at right .. .. *Imperf* (No. 4e) 35·00
Perf (No. 25e) 22·00
"REB" at left .. .. *Imperf* (No. 4f) 35·00
Perf (No. 25f) 22·00
2 "BEP" at left .. .. *Imperf* (No. 4g) 35·00
Perf (No. 25g) 22·00
"POSTZEOEL" .. .. *Imperf* (No. 4h) 35·00
Perf (No. 25h) 22·00
4 "AER" at right .. .. *Imperf* (No. 4i) 35·00
Perf (No. 25i) 22·00
5 No stop after date .. .. *Imperf* (No. 4j) 35·00
Perf (No. 25j) 22·00
6 No stop after "PENNY" .. *Imperf* (No. 4k) 35·00
Perf (No. 25k) 22·00
2 Right spray inverted .. .. *Imperf* (No. 5a) 35·00
Perf (No. 26a) 22·00
3 No bar over lower left "1" .. *Imperf* (No. 5b) 35·00
Perf (No. 26b) 22·00
4 No stop after left "Z" .. .. *Imperf* (No. 5c) 35·00
Perf (No. 26c) 22·00
6 "POSTZEGFL", no stop after right "AFR" .. .. .. *Imperf* (No. 5d) 35·00
Perf (No. 26d) 22·00
1 No stop after right "AFR" .. *Imperf* (No. 6a) 35·00
Perf (No. 27a) 22·00
2 & 6 Left spray inverted .. .. *Imperf* (No. 6b) 22·00
Perf (No. 27b) 13·00
3 "POSTZEGEI" .. .. .. *Imperf* (No. 6c) 35·00
Perf (No. 27c) 22·00
4 No bar under top right "1" .. *Imperf* (No. 6d) 35·00
Perf (No. 27d) 22·00

ond printing
2 First "1" in date dropped .. *Imperf* (No. 4l) 35·00
Perf (No. 25l) 22·00
6 No stop after right "AFR" .. *Imperf* (No. 5e) 35·00
Perf (No. 26e) 22·00
5 Dropped "P" in "PENNY" .. *Imperf* (No. 6e) 35·00
Perf (No. 27e) 22·00
t has been suggested that there may have been a third nting.

value
st printing—Imperf
1 "1" at lower right .. .. .. (No. 7a) 45·00
2 No stop after left "AFR" (*on small part of printing*) .. .. (No. 7b) 90·00
3 No bar over lower right "2" (*on small part of printing*) .. .. (No. 7c) 90·00
3 "PENNY" for "PENCE" .. .. .. (No. 7d) 45·00
5 "POSTZFGEL" .. .. (No. 7e) 45·00
6 "AFB" at right .. .. (No. 7f) 45·00
2/1 "REB" at left .. .. (No. 7g) 45·00
2/2 "AFB" at left .. .. (No. 7h) 45·00
2/3 "POSTZEOEL" .. .. (No. 7i) 45·00
2/4 "AER" at right .. .. (No. 7j) 45·00
2/5 No stop after date .. .. .. (No. 7k) 45·00
2/6 No stop after date, vertical line after "POSTZEGEL" .. .. (No. 7l) 45·00

R.3/2 Right spray inverted .. .. .. (No. 8a) 45·00
R.3/3 No bar over lower left "2" .. .. (No. 8b) 45·00
R.3/4 Centre "2" inverted, no stop after left "Z" (No. 8c) 45·00
R.3/6 "POSTZEGFL", no stop after right "AFR" .. .. (No. 8d) 45·00
R.4/1 Centre "2" wider, no stop after right "AFR" (*occurs on second printing also*) (No. 9a) 38·00
R.4/2 Centre "2" wider, left spray inverted .. (No. 9b) 45·00
R.4/3 "POSTZEGEI" .. .. (No. 9c) 45·00
R.4/4 No bar under top right "2" .. .. (No. 9d) 45·00
R.4/5 "1" at lower left, "P" in "PENCE" dropped .. .. (No. 9e) 45·00
R.4/6 Left spray inverted .. .. .. (No. 9f) 45·00

Second printing
R.1/2 First "1" in date dropped .. *Imperf* (No. 7m) 45·00
Perf (No. 28a) 30·00
R.2/1 No stop after left "REP" .. *Imperf* (No. 7n) 45·00
Perf (No. 28b) 30·00
R.3/4 No stop after left "Z" .. .. *Imperf* (No. 8e) 45·00
R.3/6 No stop after right "AFR" .. *Imperf* (No. 8f) 45·00
Perf (No. 29a) 30·00
R.4/1 Centre 2 wider, no stop after right "AFR" (*occurs on first printing also*) .. .. *Imperf* (No. 9a) 38·00
Perf (No. 30a) 30·00
R.4/2 Centre "2" wider .. .. *Imperf* (No. 9g) 45·00
Perf (No. 30b) 30·00
R.4/5 "P" in "PENCE" dropped .. *Imperf* (No. 9h) 45·00
Perf (No. 30c) 30·00

It has been suggested that there was a third printing of this value.

4d. value
First printing
R.1/2 No stop after left "AFR' .. .. (No. 10a) 45·00
R.1/3 No bar over lower right "4" .. .. (No. 10b) 45·00
R.1/3 "PENNY" for "PENCE" (*on small part of printing*) .. .. (No. 10c) 90·00
R.1/5 "POSTZFGEL" .. .. (No. 10d) 45·00
R.1/6 "AFB" at right .. .. (No. 10e) 45·00
R.2/1 "REB" at left .. .. (No. 10f) 45·00
R.2/2 "AFB" at left .. .. (No. 10g) 45·00
R.2/3 "POSTZEOEL" .. .. (No. 10h) 45·00
R.2/4 "AER" at right .. .. (No. 10i) 45·00
R.2/5 No stop after date .. .. .. (No. 10j) 45·00
R.3/2 Right spray inverted .. .. .. (No. 11a) 45·00
R.3/3 No bar over lower left "4" (*on small part of printing*) .. .. (No. 11b) 90·00
R.3/4 No stop after left "Z" .. .. .. (No. 11c) 45·00
R.3/6 "POSTZEGFL" .. .. (No. 11d) 45·00
R.4/1 Centre "4" wider, no stop after right "AFR" .. .. (No. 12a) 45·00
R.4/2 Centre "4" wider, left spray inverted .. (No. 12b) 45·00
R.4/3 "POSTZEGEI" .. .. (No. 12c) 45·00
R.4/4 No bar under top right "4" .. .. (No. 12d) 45·00
R.4/5 "AER" at left, "P" in "PENCE" dropped (No. 12e) 45·00
R.4/6 Left spray inverted .. .. .. (No. 12f) 45·00

Second printing
R.2/1 Left inner frame too high .. .. (No. 10k) 45·00
R.4/1–2 Centre "4" wider .. .. .. (No. 12g) 35·00
R.4/5 "P" in "PENCE" dropped .. .. (No. 12h) 45·00

6d. value
First printing
R.1/2 No stop after left "AFR" .. .. (No. 13a) 55·00
R.1/3 No bar over lower right "6" .. .. (No. 13b) 55·00
R.1/3 "PENNY" for "PENCE" (*on small part of printing*) .. .. (No. 13c) £100
R.1/5 "POSTZFGEL" .. .. (No. 13d) 55·00
R.1/6 "AFB" at right .. .. (No. 13e) 55·00
R.2/1 "REB" at left .. .. (No. 13f) 55·00
R.2/2 "AFB" at left .. .. (No. 13g) 55·00
R.2/3 "POSTZEOEL" .. .. (No. 13h) 55·00
R.2/4 "AER" at right .. .. (No. 13i) 55·00
R.2/5 No stop after date .. .. .. (No. 13j) 55·00
R.3/2 Right spray inverted .. .. .. (No. 14a) 55·00
R.3/4 Centre "6" inverted, no stop after left "Z" (*on small part of printing*) .. .. (No. 14b) £100
R.3/4 No stop after left "Z" .. .. .. (No. 14c) 55·00
R.3/6 "POSTZEGFL" .. .. (No. 14d) 55·00
R.4/1 Centre "6" wider, no stop after right "AFR" .. .. (No. 15a) 55·00
R.4/2 Centre "6" wider, left spray inverted .. (No. 15b) 55·00
R.4/3 "POSTZEGEI" .. .. (No. 15c) 55·00
R.4/4 No bar under top right "6" .. .. (No. 15d) 55·00
R.4/5 "AER" at left, "P" in "PENCE" dropped (No. 15e) 55·00
R.4/6 Left spray inverted .. .. .. (No. 15f) 55·00
Second printing
R.2/1 Left inner frame too high, no stop after left "REP" .. .. (No. 13k) 55·00
R.4/1–2 Centre "6" wider .. .. .. (No. 15g) 40·00
R.4/5 "P" in "PENCE" dropped .. .. (No. 15h) 55·00

1s. value
R.1/2 No stop after left "AFR" .. .. (No. 16a) 40·00
R.1/3 No bar over lower right "1" .. .. (No. 16b) 40·00
R.2/5 No stop after date .. .. .. (No. 16c) 40·00
R.3/3 Centre "1" inverted (*on small part of printing*) .. .. (No. 17a)
R.3/4 "POSTZEGEI", no stop after left "Z" (No. 17b) 40·00
R.4/1 No stop after right "AFR" .. .. (No. 18a) 40·00
R.4/4 No bar under top right "1" .. .. (No. 18b) 40·00
R.4/5 "AER" at left .. .. (No. 18c) 40·00

LOCAL BRITISH OCCUPATION ISSUES DURING THE SOUTH AFRICAN WAR 1900–2

Stamps of the Transvaal Republic, unless otherwise stated, variously overprinted or surcharged.

LYDENBURG

Lydenburg fell to the British on 6 September 1900.

V.R.I.
3d.
(L 1)

1900 (Sept). *Nos. 215b and 217 surch as Type* L **1**, *others optd "V.R.I" only.*
1 **30** $^1/_2$d. green £110 £110
2 1d. rose-red and green .. .. .. £100 90·00
2a **34** 1d. on 1d. red .. ..
3 **30** 2d. brown and green £1000 £700
4 $2^1/_2$d. blue and green £1900 £800
5 3d. on 1d. rose-red and green .. .. 85·00 75·00
6 3d. purple and green .. .. ..
7 4d. sage-green and green £2500 £650
8 6d. lilac and green £2000 £600
9 1s. ochre and green £3500 £2250

The above were cancelled by British Army postal service postmarks. These overprints with Transvaal cancellations are believed to be forgeries.

RUSTENBURG

The British forces in Rustenburg, west of Pretoria, were besieged by the Boers during June 1900. When relieved on the 22 June 1900 no "V.R.I" stamps were available so a local handstamp was applied.

V.R.
(R 1)

1900 (23 June). *Handstamped with Type* R **1** *in violet.*
1 **30** $^1/_2$d. green .. .. £130 90·00
2 1d. rose-red and green .. .. .. 95·00 70·00
3 2d. brown and green £275 £100
4 $2^1/_2$d. blue and green .. .. .. £160 90·00
5 3d. purple and green £200 £110
6 6d. lilac and green £1000 £300
7 1s. ochre and green £1500 £700
8 2s. 6d. dull violet and green £8500 £4250
a. Handstamp in black .. .. .. † £7500

Nos. 2 and 5 exist with the handstamp inverted.

SCHWEIZER RENECKE

BESIEGED
(SR 1)

1900 (Sept). *Handstamped with Type* SR **1** *in black, reading vert up or down. (a) On stamps of Transvaal.*
1 **30** $^1/_2$d. green .. .. † £225
2 1d. rose-red and green .. .. .. † £225
3 2d. brown and green .. .. .. † £300
4 6d. lilac and green .. .. .. † £850

(*b*) *On stamps of Cape of Good Hope*
5 **17** $^1/_2$d. green .. .. † £400
6 1d. carmine .. .. † £400

Schweizer Renecke, near the Bechuanaland border, was under siege from 1 August 1900 to 9 January 1901. The British commander authorised the above stamps shortly after 19 August. All stamps were cancelled with the dated circular town postmark ("Schweizer Renecke, Z.A.R."), usually after having been stuck on paper before use. Unused, without the postmark, do not exist.

No. 4 exists with double handstamp.

WOLMARANSSTAD

A British party occupied this town in the south-west of the Transvaal from 15 June to 27 July 1900. Transvaal stamps, to a face value of £5 2s. 6d., were found at the local firm of Thos. Leask and Co. and surcharged as below. The first mail left on 24 June and the last on 21 July.

Cancelled V-R-I. (L 3)   Cancelled V-R-I. (L 4)

1900 (24 June). *Optd with Type* L **3**.
1 **30** $^1/_2$d. green (B.) £225 £350
a. Opt inverted £700
b. Opt in black .. ..
1c $^1/_2$d. on 1s. green (B.) .. .. ..
2 1d. rose-red and green (B.) £150 £250
a. Opt in green £1800
b. Opt in black .. .. ..
3 2d. brown and green (B.) £1700 £1700
a. Opt in black £3000
4 $2^1/_2$d. blue and green (R.) £1600
a. Opt in blue £2750 £2750
b. Opt in black .. .. ..
5 3d. purple and green (B.) £2750 £3000
6 4d. sage-green and green (B.) .. £3500 £4000
7 6d. lilac and green (B.) £3750 £4000
8 1s. ochre and green (B.) .. .. — £7500

The two lines of the overprint were handstamped separately. The $^1/_2$d. exists with two impressions of the "Cancelled" handstamp, the $2^1/_2$d. with two impressions of "V-R-I", one in red and one in blue and the 3d. with "Cancelled" in green and "V.R.I." in blue.

1900 (24 June). *Optd with Type* L **4**.
9 **34** 1d. red (B.) £150 £275

The $^1/_2$d., 1d. and 3d. in Type **30** are also known with this overprint.

PRICES OF SETS

Set prices are given for many issues, generally those containing three stamps or more. Definitive sets include one of each value or major colour change, but do not cover different perforations, die types or minor shades. Where a choice is possible the set prices are based on the cheapest versions of the stamps included in the listings.

VII. ZULULAND

Zululand remained an independent kingdom until annexed by Great Britain on 19 May 1887 when it was declared a Crown Colony.

The first European postal service was operated by a Natal postal agency at Eshowe opened in 1876 which cancelled Natal stamps with a "No. 56 P.O. Natal" postmark. The agency closed during the Zulu War of 1879 and did not re-open until 1885 when a Eshowe postmark was provided. "ZULULAND" was added to the cancellation in 1887 and stamps of Natal continued to be used until replaced by the overprinted series on 1 May 1888.

PRICES FOR STAMPS ON COVER

Nos. 1/2	*from* × 100
Nos. 3/10	*from* × 20
No. 11	—
Nos. 12/16	*from* × 20
Nos. 20/3	*from* × 30
No. 24	*from* × 20
Nos. 25/6	*from* × 12
Nos. 27/9	—
No. F1	*from* × 100

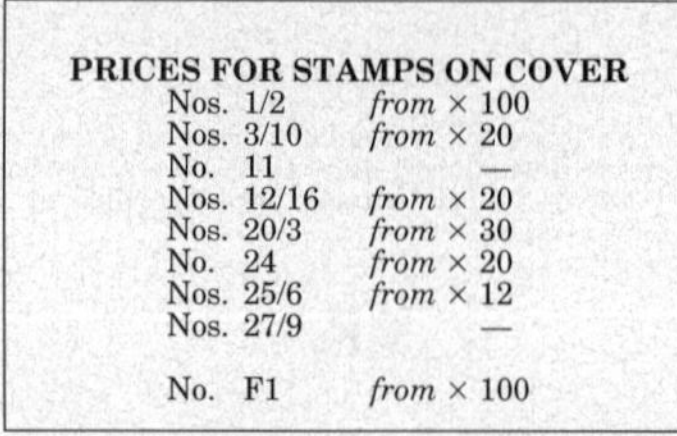

(1) (2)

1888 (1 May)–**93.** (*a*) *Nos.* 173, 180, 197, 200/2, 205*a*, 207*a*/8, 209 *and* 211 *of Great Britain* (*Queen Victoria*) *optd with T* **1** *by D.L.R.*

1	½d. vermilion (11.88)	3·00	2·50
2	1d. deep purple	25·00	3·75
3	2d. grey-green and carmine	11·00	24·00
4	2½d. purple/*blue* (9.91)	19·00	20·00
5	3d. purple/*yellow*	25·00	22·00
6	4d. green and deep brown	40·00	55·00
7	5d. dull purple and blue (3.93)	90·00	£120
	w. Wmk inverted	†	—
8	6d. purple/*rose-red*	12·00	17·00
9	9d. dull purple and blue (4.92)	85·00	90·00
10	1s. dull green (4.92)	£110	£130
11	5s. rose (4.92)	£500	£600
1/11	*Set of* 11	£800	£950
1s/11s (*ex* 1d.) H/S "Specimen"	*Set of* 10	£600	

(*b*) *No.* 97*a of Natal optd with T* **2** *at Pietermaritzburg*

12	½d. dull green (with stop) (7.88)	55·00	75·00
	a. Opt double	£1000	£1100
	b. Opt inverted	£1200	
	d. Opt omitted (vert pair with normal)	£5500	
13	½d. dull green (without stop)	23·00	38·00
	a. Opt double	£1400	£1500

1893 (29 Nov*). *T* **15** *of Natal* (*Wmk Crown CA. P* 14) *optd with T* **1** *by D.L.R.*

16 6d. dull purple .. 55·00 55·00

*Earliest known date of use. No. 16 was, apparently, originally supplied in 1889 for fiscal purposes.

3

4

(Typo D.L.R.)

1894 (18 Apr)–**96.** *Wmk Crown CA. P* 14.

20 **3**	½d. dull mauve and green	3·25	4·25
	w. Wmk inverted	£120	£130
21	1d. dull mauve and carmine	5·00	1·75
22	2½d. dull mauve and ultramarine	14·00	8·50
23	3d. dull mauve and olive-brown	8·00	3·00
24 **4**	6d. dull mauve and black	20·00	20·00
25	1s. green	38·00	38·00
26	2s. 6d. green and black (2.96)	75·00	85·00
27	4s. green and carmine	£110	£150
28	£1 purple/*red*	£450	£550
29	£5 purple and black/*red*	£4500	£1500
	s. Optd "Specimen"	£400	
20/8	*Set of* 9	£650	£750
20s/8s Optd "Specimen"	*Set of* 9	£350	

Dangerous forgeries exist of the £1 and £5.

FISCAL STAMP USED FOR POSTAGE

1891 (5 May*). *Fiscal stamp of Natal* (*Wmk Crown CA. P* 14) *optd with T* **1**.

F1	1d. dull mauve	3·00	3·00
	a. Top left triangle detached	£110	£110
	s. Handstamped "Specimen"	60·00	

*Earliest known date of postal use. A proclamation published in the *Natal Government Gazette* on 27 June 1891 authorised the use of this stamp for postal purposes, but it is clear from the wording that such use had already commenced.

Other values, 1s. to £20 as No. F1 exist apparently with postmarks, but, as these were never authorised for postal use, they are no longer listed.

Zululand was annexed to Natal on 31 December 1897 and its stamps were withdrawn from sale on 30 June 1898.

ALTERED CATALOGUE NUMBERS

Any Catalogue numbers altered from the last edition are shown as a list in the introductory pages.

VIII. BRITISH ARMY FIELD OFFICES DURING SOUTH AFRICAN WAR, 1899 –1902

Z 1

Z 2

Stamps of GREAT BRITAIN *used by British Army Field Offices in South Africa cancelled as Types* Z **1**, Z **2** *or similar postmarks.*

1881. *Stamp of Queen Victoria.*

Z1 1d. lilac (16 *dots*) .. 5·00

1883–84. *Stamps of Queen Victoria.*

Z1*a*	2s. 6d lilac	£200
Z2	5s. rose	£200
Z2*a*	10s. ultramarine	£400

1887–92. *Stamps of Queen Victoria.*

Z 3	½d. vermilion	6·00
Z 4	1½d. dull purple and green	20·00
Z 5	2d. grey-green and carmine	14·00
Z 6	2½d. purple/*blue*	6·00
Z 7	3d. purple/*yellow*	12·00
Z 8	4d. green and brown	16·00
Z 9	4½d. green and carmine	48·00
Z10	5d. dull purple and blue (Die II)	14·00
Z11	6d. purple/*rose-red*	11·00
Z12	9d. dull purple and blue	50·00
Z13	10d. dull purple and carmine	48·00
Z14	1s. dull green	70·00
Z15	£1 green	£750

1900. *Stamps of Queen Victoria.*

Z16	½d. blue-green	6·00
Z17	1s. green and carmine	£130

1902. *Stamps of King Edward VII.*

Z18	½d. blue-green	7·00
Z19	1d. scarlet	5·00
Z20	1½d. purple and green	
Z21	2d. yellowish green and carmine-red	
Z22	2½d. ultramarine	10·00
Z23	3d. purple/*orange-yellow*	
Z24	4d. green and grey-brown	
Z25	5d. dull purple and ultramarine	
Z26	6d. pale dull purple	15·00
Z27	9d. dull purple and ultramarine	
Z28	10d. dull purple and carmine	
Z29	1s. dull green and carmine	

ARMY OFFICIAL STAMPS

1896–1901. *Stamps of Queen Victoria optd* "ARMY OFFICIAL".

ZO1	½d. vermilion	£100
ZO2	½d. blue-green	£100
ZO3	1d. lilac (16 *dots*)	85·00
ZO4	6d. purple/*rose-red*	

IX. UNION OF SOUTH AFRICA

The province continued to use their existing issues until the introduction of Nos. 3/17. From 19 August 1910 the issues of any province were valid for use throughout the Union until they were demonetised on 31 December 1937.

PRICES FOR STAMPS ON COVER TO 1945

Nos. 1/15	*from* × 4
Nos. 16/17	—
Nos. 18/21	*from* × 6
Nos. 26/32	*from* × 2
No. 33	*from* × 4
Nos. 34/110	*from* × 1
Nos. D1/7	*from* × 4
Nos. D8/33	*from* × 6
Nos. O1/33	*from* × 4

1

(Des H. S. Wilkinson. Recess D.L.R.)

1910 (4 Nov). *Opening of Union Parliament. Inscribed bilingually. Wmk Multiple Rosettes. P* 14.

1 **1**	2½d. deep blue	3·00	3·00
	s. Handstamped "Specimen"	£325	
2	2½d. blue	1·75	1·40

The deep blue shade is generally accompanied by a blueing of the paper.

No. 1s. has the overprint in italic capital and lower case letters which measure 12½ mm in length.

2

3

4 Springbok's

(Typo D.L.R.)

1913 (1 Sept)–**24.** *Inscribed bilingually. W* **4**. (*a*) *P* 14.

3 **2**	½d. green	1·25	
	a. Stamp doubly printed	£10000	
	b. Blue-green	2·00	
	c. Yellow-green	2·50	
	d. Printed on the gummed side	£600	
	w. Wmk inverted	2·00	
4	1d. rose-red (*shades*)	1·25	
	a. Carmine-red	2·25	
	b. Scarlet (*shades*)	2·00	
	c. Printed on the gummed side	£600	
	w. Wmk inverted	2·50	
5	1½d. chestnut (*shades*) (23.8.20)	80	
	a. *Tête-bêche* (pair)	1·75	
	b. Printed on the gummed side	£650	
	c. Wmk sideways	†	
	w. Wmk inverted	80	
6 **3**	2d. dull purple	1·75	
	a. Deep purple	2·50	
	b. Printed on the gummed side	£650	
	w. Wmk inverted	3·25	
7	2½d. bright blue	3·75	
	a. Deep blue	5·50	
	w. Wmk inverted	65·00	
8	3d. black and orange-red	9·50	
	a. Black and dull orange-red	10·00	
	w. Wmk inverted	16·00	
9	3d. ultramarine (*shades*) (4.10.22)	3·50	
	w. Wmk inverted	8·50	
10	4d. orange-yellow and olive-green	8·50	
	a. Orange-yellow and sage-green	6·50	
	w. Wmk inverted	8·00	
11	6d. black and violet	5·50	
	a. Black and bright violet	8·00	
	aw Wmk inverted	16·00	
12	1s. orange	16·00	
	a. Orange-yellow	25·00	
	w. Wmk inverted	18·00	
13	1s. 3d. violet (*shades*) (1.9.20)	13·00	
	w. Wmk inverted	90·00	
14	2s. 6d. purple and green	55·00	
15	5s. purple and blue	£110	
	a. Reddish purple and light blue	£110	
	w. Wmk inverted	£2750	
16	10s. deep blue and olive-green	£180	
	w. Wmk inverted	£4000	
17	£1 green and red (7.16)	£600	
	a. Pale olive-green and red (1924)	£800	
3/17	*Set of* 15	£900	
3s/8s, 10s/17s Optd or H/S (1½d. and 1s. 3d. in violet, £1 in green) "Specimen"	*Set of* 14	£1300	

(*b*) *Coil stamps. P* 14×*imperf*

18 **2**	½d. green	6·00	
	w. Wmk inverted	£450	
19	1d. rose-red (13.2.14)	8·00	
	a. Scarlet	12·00	
	w. Wmk inverted	£450	
20	1½d. chestnut (15.11.20)	10·00	1
	w. Wmk inverted	†	
21 **3**	2d. dull purple (7.10.21)	12·00	
18/21	*Set of* 4	32·00	2

The 6d. exists with "Z" of "ZUID" wholly or partly missing to wear of plate (*Price wholly missing, £80 un, £38 us*).

5 De Havilland D.H.9 Biplane

(Eng A. J. Cooper. Litho *Cape Times* Ltd)

1925 (26 Feb). *Air. Inscr bilingually. P* 12.

26 **5**	1d. carmine	3·75	
27	3d. ultramarine	7·00	
28	6d. magenta	9·00	1
29	9d. green	23·00	4
26/9	*Set of* 4	38·00	7

Beware of forgeries of all values perforated 11, 11½ or 1

INSCRIPTIONS. From 1926 until 1951 most issues w inscribed in English and Afrikaans alternately throughout sheets.

PRICES for Nos. 30/135 are for unused horizontal pairs used horizontal pairs and used singles (either inscription *unless otherwise indicated.* Vertical pairs are wort between 25% and 40% of the prices quoted for horizonta pairs.

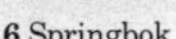

6 Springbok

7 *Dromedaris* (Van Riebeeck's ship)

8 Orange Tree

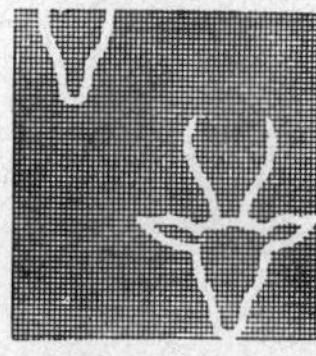

9

o Waterlow until 1927, thereafter Govt Printer, Pretoria)

(2 Jan)–**27.** *W* **9.** *P* 14½×14.

No.	Description	*Un pair*	*Used pair*	*Used single*
6	½d. black and green	3·00	4·00	10
	a. Missing "1" in "½"	£2000		
	b. Centre omitted (in pair with normal)	£1400		
	cw. Wmk inverted	3·75	4·00	
	d. Frame printed double ..	£2000		
	e. Perf 13½×14 (1927)	55·00	55·00	4·00
	ea. *Tête-bêche* (pair)	£850		
	ew. Wmk inverted	55·00	55·00	
7	1d. black and carmine	2·00	50	10
	a. Imperf (vert pair)*	£650		
	b. Imperf 3 sides (vert pair)* ..	£650	£700	
	cw. Wmk inverted	4·50	1·50	
	d. Perf 13½×14 (1927)	75·00	65·00	4·00
	da. *Tête-bêche* (pair)	£950		
	dw. Wmk inverted	75·00	65·00	
	e. Wmk sideways	£2000	£2000	
8	6d. green and orange (1.5.26) ..	38·00	38·00	1·50
	w. Wmk inverted	65·00	70·00	
2	.. .. .. *Set of* 3	38·00	38·00	1·50

o. 30a exists in Afrikaans only. Nos. 30e and 31d were only ed in booklets.

o. 30d occurred on the bottom left-hand corner of one sheet included the bottom four stamps in the first vertical row and bottom two in the second. As listed No. 30d shows the -hand stamp with the frame completely double and the nt-hand stamp with two-thirds of the frame double.

Both Nos. 31a and 31b occur in blocks of four with the other tical pair imperforate at left.

'or ½d. with pale grey centre, see No. 126.

'or rotogravure printing see Nos. 42, etc.

10 "Hope"

(Recess B.W.)

26 (2 Jan). *T* **10**. *Inscribed in English or Afrikaans. W* **9** *upright or inverted in equal quantities*).

Description	*Single stamps*	
4d. grey-blue (English inscr) (*shades*) ..	1·75	1·25
a. Inscr in Afrikaans	1·75	1·25

n this value the English and Afrikaans inscriptions are on parate sheets.

This stamp is known with private perforations or roulettes.

11 Union Buildings, Pretoria

12 Groot Schuur

12*a* A Native Kraal

13 Black and Blue Wildebeest

14 Ox-wagon inspanned

15 Ox-wagon outspanned

16 Cape Town and Table Bay

(Recess B.W.)

1927 (1 Mar)–**30.** *W* **9.** *P* 14.

No.	Type	Description	*Un pair*	*Used pair*	*Used single*
34	**11**	2d. grey and maroon	10·00	20·00	60
		aw. Wmk inverted	£350	£400	
		b. Perf 14×13½ (2.30) ..	20·00	20·00	70
35	**12**	3d. black and red	15·00	25·00	60
		a. Perf 14×13½ (1930) ..	48·00	50·00	80
35*b*	**12*a***	4d. brown (23.3.28)	22·00	50·00	1·00
		bw. Wmk inverted	£500	£450	
		c. Perf 14×13½ (1930) ..	42·00	55·00	1·25
36	**13**	1s. brown and deep blue ..	28·00	50·00	1·00
		a. Perf 14×13½ (1930) ..	48·00	60·00	1·25
37	**14**	2s. 6d. green and brown ..	£110	£325	17·00
		a. Perf 14×13½ (1930) ..	£250	£400	22·00
38	**15**	5s. black and green	£225	£650	35·00
		a. Perf 14×13½ (1930) ..	£350	£750	40·00
39	**16**	10s. bright blue and brown ..	£150	£130	10·00
		a. Centre inverted (*single stamp*)	£9500		
		b. Perf 14×13½ (1930) ..	£170	£150	11·00
34/9		.. .. .. *Set of* 7	£500	£1100	55·00
34s/9s		H/S "Specimen" .. *Set of* 7	£850		

17 De Havilland D.H.60 Cirrus Moth

(Typo Govt Ptg Wks, Pretoria)

1929 (16 Aug). *Air. Inscribed bilingually. No wmk. P* 14 × 13½.

No.	Type	Description	*Un single*	*Us single*
40	**17**	4d. green	5·50	2·50
41		1s. orange	16·00	13·00

PRINTER. All the following issues, except *where stated otherwise*, are printed by rotogravure (the design having either plain lines or a dotted screen) by the Government Printer, Pretoria.

I

II

The two types of the 1d. differ in the spacing of the horizontal lines in the side panels:—Type I close; Type II wide. The Afrikaans had the spacing of the words POSSEEL-INKOMSTE close in Type I and more widely spaced in Type II.

Window flaw (R. 20/4 on all ptgs before 1937)

Spear flaw (R. 9/2)

Twisted horn (Cyl 7020 R.1/5)

1930–45. *T* **6** *to* **8** *and* **11** *to* **14** *redrawn*, "SUIDAFRIKA" (*in one word*) *on Afrikaans stamps. W* **9.** *P* 15 × 14 (*½d., 1d., and 6d.*) *or* 14.

No.	Description	*Un pair*	*Used pair*	*Used single*
42	½d. black and green (5.30)	2·50	2·50	10
	a. Two English or two Afrikaans stamps *se-tenant* (vert strip of 4)	40·00		
	b. *Tête-bêche*	£850		
	w. Wmk inverted	2·50	1·75	10
43	1d. black and carmine (I) (4.30) ..	3·25	2·25	10
	a. *Tête-bêche*	£1000		
	b. Frame omitted (*single stamp*) ..	£450		
	cw. Wmk inverted	3·25	1·75	10
43*d*	1d. black and carmine (II) (8.32) ..	35·00	3·50	10
	dw. Wmk inverted	30·00	3·25	10
44	2d. slate-grey and lilac (4.31) ..	18·00	11·00	20
	a. *Tête-bêche*	£3000		
	b. Frame omitted (*single stamp*) ..	£1500		
	cw. Wmk inverted	16·00	8·50	20
44*d*	2d. blue and violet (3.38)	£275	65·00	2·50
45	3d. black and red (11.31)	50·00	70·00	2·00
	aw. Wmk inverted	32·00	60·00	1·25
	b. Window flaw	£100		
45*c*	3d. blue (10.33)	16·00	7·00	20
	cw. Wmk inverted	6·00	4·75	10
	d. Window flaw	35·00		
	e. Centre omitted			
	f. Frame omitted (*single stamp*) ..			
46	4d. brown (19.11.32)	£130	95·00	6·00
	aw. Wmk inverted	30·00	30·00	40
	b. Spear flaw	£100		
46*c*	4d. brown (*shades*) (*again redrawn*) (1936)	3·00	2·25	10
	cw. Wmk inverted	11·00	6·00	10
47	6d. green and orange (*wmk inverted*) (13.5.31)	13·00	3·25	10
	w. Wmk upright (8.32)	28·00	5·50	10
48	1s. brown and deep blue (14.9.32)	75·00	35·00	40
	aw. Wmk inverted	32·00	25·00	25
	b. Twisted horn flaw	£160		
49	2s. 6d. grn & brn (*shades*) (24.12.32)	95·00	£100	3·25
	aw. Wmk inverted	£110	£120	3·25
49*b*	2s. 6d. blue and brown (1945) ..	24·00	9·00	20
42/9*b*	.. .. .. *Set of* 13	£500	£275	6·50

For similar designs with "SUID-AFRIKA" hyphenated, see Nos. 54 etc. and Nos. 114 etc.

Nos. 42/3, 43*d*/4 exist in coils.

No. 42a comes from the coil printing on the cylinder for which two horizontal rows were incorrectly etched so that two Afrikaans-inscribed stamps were followed by two English. This variety is normally without a coil join, although some examples do occur showing a repair join.

The 1d. (Type I) exists without watermark from a trial printing (*Price* £25 *un*).

Although it appears to be printed in one colour No. 45c was produced from vignette and frame cylinders in the same way as the bicoloured version. The clouds in the background, which are present on No. 45e, were printed from the frame cylinder.

Nos. 45b, 45d, 46b and 48b all occur on printings with either upright or inverted watermark. The price quoted is for the cheapest version in each instance.

The Rotogravure printings may be distinguished from the preceding Typographed and Recess printed issues by the following tests:—

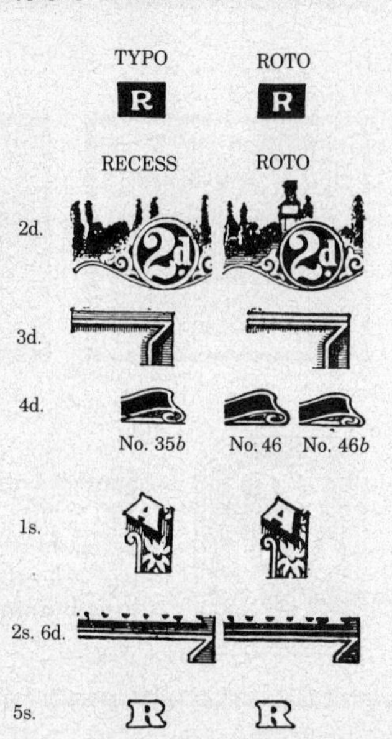

)GRAVURE:

1d. and 6d. Leg of "R" in "AFR" ends squarely on the bottom
e.

The newly built War Memorial appears to the left of the value.

Two fine lines have been removed from the top part of the
me.

No. 46. The scroll is in solid colour.
No. 46c. The scroll is white with a crooked line running through it. (No. 35b. The scroll is shaded by the diagonal lines.)

The shading of the last "A" partly covers the flower beneath.

d. The top line of the centre frame is thick and leaves only
e white line between it and the name.

Nos. 64/b). The leg of the "R" is straight.

gravure impressions are generally coarser.

18 Church of the Vow

19 "The Great Trek" (C. Michell)

20 A Voortrekker

21 Voortrekker Woman

Blurred "SOUTH AFRICA" and red "comet" flaw (Cyls 6917/6922 R. 2/7)

(Des J. Prentice (½d., 2d., 3d.)

33 (3 May)–36. *Voortrekker Memorial Fund. W* **9** *(sideways).*
P 14.
18 ½d. + ½d. black and green (16.1.36) 3·50 4·50 50
19 1d. + ½d. grey-black and pink .. 2·75 1·50 25
a. Blurred "SOUTH AFRICA" and red "comet" flaw .. .. 40·00
20 2d. + 1d. grey-green and purple .. 3·50 4·00 55
21 3d. + 1½d. grey-green and blue .. 5·50 5·00 70
/3 .. .. .. *Set of* 4 14·00 13·50 1·75

22 Gold Mine

22a Groot Schuur

Dies of 6d.

I

II

III

23 Groot Constantia

"Falling ladder" flaw (R. 5/10)

1933–48. "SUID-AFRIKA" *(hyphenated) on Afrikaans stamps. W* **9**. *P* 15×14 *(½d., 1d. and 6d.) or* 14 *(others).*

54	**6**	½d.	grey and green (*wmk inverted*) (9.35)	3·50	1·50	10
		aw.	Wmk upright (1936) ..	7·50	1·75	10
		b.	Coil stamp. Perf 13½×14 (1935)	32·00	50·00	1·00
		bw.	Wmk upright	32·00	50·00	1·00
		c.	Booklet pane of 6 (with adverts on margins) (*wmk upright*)	22·00		
56	**7**	1d.	grey & car (*shades*) (19.4.34)	1·00	1·00	10
		a.	Imperf (pair) (*wmk inverted*)	£140		
		b.	Frame omitted (*single stamp*)	£250		
		cw.	Wmk inverted	1·00	1·00	10
		d.	Coil stamp. Perf 13½×14 (1935)	35·00	55·00	1·40
		dw.	Wmk inverted	35·00	55·00	1·40
		e.	Booklet pane of 6 (with adverts on margins) (1935)	12·00		
		f.	Booklet pane of 6 (with blank margins) (1937) ..	13·00		
		h.	Booklet pane of 6 (with postal slogans on margins) (1948)	4·00		
		i.	*Grey & brt rose-carm* (7.48)	70	1·50	10
57	**22**	1½d.	green & brt gold (12.11.36)	2·75	2·00	10
		a.	Shading omitted from mine dump (in pair with normal)	£170	£140	
		bw.	Wmk inverted	1·50	1·50	10
		c.	*Blue-grn & dull gold* (8.40)	6·50	3·00	10
58	**11**	2d.	blue and violet (11.38) ..	65·00	32·00	75
58*a*		2d.	grey and dull purple (5.41)	42·00	70·00	1·25
59	**22*a***	3d.	ultramarine (2.40) ..	7·00	2·00	10
61	**8**	6d.	green & vermilion (I) (10.37)	70·00	23·00	70
		a.	"Falling ladder" flaw ..	£180	£225	
61*b*		6d.	green & vermilion (II) (6.38)	32·00	1·00	10
61*c*		6d.	grn & red-orge (III) (11.46)	15·00	75	10
62	**13**	1s.	brown & chalky blue (2.39)	45·00	9·00	10
		a.	Frame omitted (*single stamp*)	£2000		
64	**15**	5s.	black and green (10.33) ..	55·00	60·00	1·75
		aw.	Wmk inverted	£110	£110	3·00
		b.	*Black and blue-green* (9.44)	35·00	15·00	35
64*c*	**23**	10s.	blue and sepia (8.39) ..	65·00	14·00	70
		ca.	*Blue & blackish brn* (8.39)	42·00	5·50	30
54/9, 61*c*/64*ca*			.. .. *Set of* 10	£225	£120	2·50

The ½d. and 1d. coil stamps may be found in blocks emanating from the residue of the large rolls which were cut into sheets and distributed to Post Offices.

Nos. 54 and 56 also exist in coils.

1d. Is printed from Type II. Frames of different sizes exist due to reductions made from time to time for the purpose of providing more space for the perforations.

3d. In No. 59 the frame is unscreened and composed of solid lines. Centre is diagonally screened. Scrolls above "3d." are clear lined, light in the middle and dark at sides.

6d. Die I. Green background lines faint. "SUID-AFRIKA" 16¼ mm long.

Die II. Green background lines heavy. "SUID-AFRIKA" 17 mm long. "S" near end of tablet. Scroll open.

Die III. Scroll closed up and design smaller (18 × 22 mm).

Single specimens of the 1933–48 issue inscribed in English may be distinguished from those of 1930–45 as follows:—

½d. and 1d. Centres in grey instead of varying intensities of black.

2d. The letters of "SOUTH AFRICA" are narrower and thinner.

3d. The trees are taller and the sky is without lines.

6d. The frame is vermilion.

1s. The frame is chalky blue.

For similar designs, but printed in screened rotogravure, see Nos. 114 to 122a.

BOOKLET PANES. Booklets issued in 1935 contained ½d. and 1d. stamps in panes with advertisements in the top and bottom margins and no margin at right (Nos. 54b and 56d). These were replaced in 1937 by editions showing blank margins on all four sides (Nos. 56e and 75ba). Following a period when the booklet panes were without margins, a further 3s. booklet was issued in 1948 which had four margins on the panes and postal slogans at top and bottom (Nos. 56h, 87b and 114a).

24

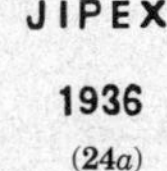

(24a)

"Cleft skull" flaw (R. 14/2)

(Des J. Booysen)

1935 (1 May). *Silver Jubilee. Inscr bilingually. W* **9**. *P* 15 × 14.

65	**24**	½d.	black and blue-green ..	2·25	12·00	10
		a.	"Cleft skull" flaw	6·00		
66		1d.	black and carmine	2·25	4·25	10
		a.	"Cleft skull" flaw	6·00		
67		3d.	blue	13·00	55·00	2·25
		a.	"Cleft skull" flaw	35·00		
68		6d.	green and orange	23·00	70·00	3·25
		a.	"Cleft skull" flaw	55·00		
65/8			.. .. .. *Set of* 4	35·00	£130	5·00

In stamps with English at top the ½d., 3d. and 6d. have "SILWER JUBILEUM" to left of portrait, and "POSTAGE REVENUE" or "POSTAGE" (3d. and 6d.) in left value tablet. In the 1d., "SILVER JUBILEE" is to the left of portrait. In alternate stamps the positions of English and Afrikaans inscriptions are reversed.

1936 (2 Nov). *Johannesburg International Philatelic Exhibition. Optd with T* **24*a***.

			Un sheet	*Us sheet*
MS69	**6**	½d. grey and green (No. 54)	3·50	10·00
MS70	**7**	1d. grey and carmine (No. 56)	2·75	7·00

Issued each in miniature sheet of six stamps with marginal advertisements.

25

"Mouse" flaw (R. 4/1)

(Des J. Prentice)

1937 (12 May). *Coronation. W* **9** *(sideways*). P* 14.

71	**25**	½d.	grey-black and blue-green ..	50	80	10
		w.	Wmk horns pointing to left	50	80	10
72		1d.	grey-black and carmine ..	50	50	10
		w.	Wmk horns pointing to left	50	50	10
73		1½d.	orange and greenish blue ..	50	50	10
		a.	"Mouse" flaw	5·00		
		w.	Wmk horns pointing to left	50	50	10
74		3d.	ultramarine	1·50	2·50	10
		w.	Wmk horns pointing to left	1·50	2·50	10
75		1s.	red-brown and turquoise-blue	2·25	4·50	15
		a.	Hyphen on Afrikaans stamp omitted (R. 2/13)	45·00		
		w.	Wmk horns pointing to left	2·25	4·50	15
71/5			.. .. .. *Set of* 5	4·75	8·00	40

*The normal sideways watermark shows the horns of the springbok pointing to the right, *as seen from the back of the stamp.*

No. 75a shows the hyphen completely omitted and the top of the "K" damaged. A less distinct flaw, on which part of the hyphen is still visible and with no damage to the "K", occurs on R. 4/17.

25a

"Tick" flaw on ear and spot on nose (multipositive flaw (occurring in 1947) (R. 3/4, or 3/1 on some ptgs of No. 114)

1937–40. *W* **9**. *P* 15×14.

75*b*	**25*a***	½d.	grey and green	7·50	1·25	10
		ba.	Booklet pane of 6 (with blank margins) (1937)	45·00		
		bd.	*Grey and blue-green* (1940)	5·50	90	10
		be.	"Tick" flaw and spot on nose	50·00		

The lines of shading in T **25*a*** are all horizontal and thicker than in T **6**. In Nos. 75*b* and 75*bd* the design is composed of solid lines. For stamps with designs composed of dotted lines, see No. 114. Later printings of No. 75*bd* have a smaller design.

26 Voortrekker Ploughing

27 Wagon crossing Drakensberg

28 Signing of Dingaan–Retief Treaty

29 Voortrekker Monument

(Des W. Coetzer and J. Prentice)

1938 (14 Dec). *Voortrekker Centenary Memorial Fund.* W **9**. *P* 14 (*Nos.* 76/7) *or* 15 × 14 (*others*).

76	**26**	½d. + ½d. blue and green ..	10·00	4·00	30
77	**27**	1d. + 1d. blue and carmine ..	11·00	5·00	40
78	**28**	1½d. + 1½d. chocolate & blue-grn	15·00	8·00	80
79	**29**	3d. + 3d. bright blue	17·00	9·00	1·00
76/9		.. .. .. *Set of* 4	48·00	23·00	2·25

30 Wagon Wheel

31 Voortrekker Family

Three bolts in wheel rim (R. 15/5)

(Des W. Coetzer and J. Prentice)

1938 (14 Dec). *Voortrekker Commemoration.* W **9**. *P* 15×14.

80	**30**	1d. blue and carmine	5·00	3·25	30
		a. Three bolts in wheel rim ..	29·00		
81	**31**	1½d. greenish blue and brown ..	7·00	3·25	30

32 Old Vicarage, Paarl, now a museum

33 Symbol of the Reformation

34 Huguenot Dwelling, Drakenstein Mountain Valley

(Des J. Prentice)

1939 (17 July). *250th Anniv of Huguenot Landing in South Africa and Huguenot Commemoration Fund.* W **9**. *P* 14 (*Nos.* 82/3) *or* 15 × 14 (*No.* 84).

82	**32**	½d. + ½d. brown and green ..	4·75	5·00	30
83	**33**	1d. + 1d. green and carmine ..	11·00	5·50	30
84	**34**	1½d. + 1½d. blue-green and purple	26·00	11·00	1·00
82/4		.. .. .. *Set of* 3	38·00	19·00	1·40

34a Gold Mine

1941 (Aug)–**48**. W **9** (*sideways*). *P* 14 × 15.

87	**34a**	1½d. blue-grn and yellow-buff (*shades*)	1·00	50	10
		a. Yellow-buff (centre) omitted	£2000	£1300	
		b. Booklet pane of 6 (with postal slogans on margins) (1948)	6·00		

35 Infantry

36 Nurse and Ambulance

37 Airman

38 Sailor, Destroyer and Lifebelts

39 Women's Auxiliary Services

40 Artillery

41 Electric Welding

42 Tank Corps

42a Signaller

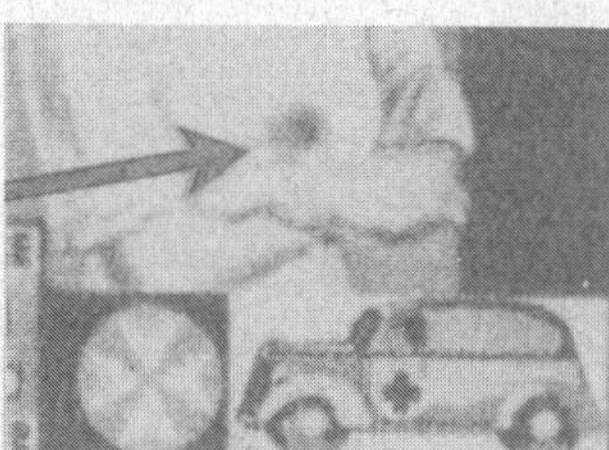

"Stain" on uniform (R. 14/11)

"Cigarette" flaw (R. 18/2)

1941–46. *War Effort.* W **9** (*sideways on 2d., 4d., 6d.*). *P* 14 (*2d., 4d., 6d.*) *or* 15 × 14 (*others*). (*a*) *Inscr alternately.*

88	**35**	½d. green (19.11.41)	1·50	1·75	10
		a. Blue-green (7.42)	3·50	2·25	10
89	**36**	1d. carmine (3.10.41)	2·00	1·75	10
		a. "Stain" on uniform flaw ..	20·00		
90	**37**	1½d. myrtle-green (12.1.42) ..	1·50	1·25	10
91	**39**	3d. blue (1.8.41)	21·00	26·00	50
		a. "Cigarette" flaw	70·00		
92	**40**	4d. orange-brown (20.8.41) ..	20·00	16·00	15
		a. Red-brown (6.42)	35·00	32·00	1·25
93	**41**	6d. red-orange (3.9.41)	12·00	11·00	15
94	**42a**	1s. 3d. olive-brown (2.1.43) ..	12·00	6·50	20
		a. Blackish brown (5.46) ..	4·00	6·50	20

(*b*) *Inscr bilingually*

			Un single	*Us single*
95	**38**	2d. violet (15.9.41)	90	30
96	**42**	1s. brown (27.10.41)	3·25	50
88/96		.. .. .. *Set of 7 pairs and 2 singles*	55·00	55·00

ALTERED CATALOGUE NUMBERS

Any Catalogue numbers altered from the last edition are shown as a list in the introductory pages.

43 Infantry

44 Nurse

45 Airman

46 Sa[ilor]

47 Women's Auxiliary Services

48 Electric Welding

49 Heavy Gu[n] Concrete Tu[rret]

50 Tank Corps

Unit (*pair*)

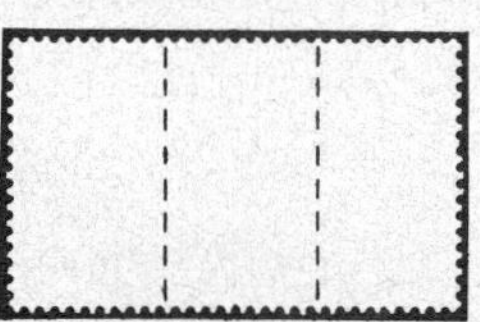

Unit (*triplet*)

Ear Flap flaw (Cyl 43 R. 13/3)

Apostrophe flaw (Cyl 6931 R. 19/1) (later corrected)

Line on Cap (Cyl 39 R. 12/11)

"Bursting Shell" (Cyl 46 R. 11/20)

Smoking "L" (Cyl 46 R. 8/2)

…44. *War Effort. Reduced sizes. In pairs perf* 14 (P) *or* …*s of three, perf* 15×14 (T), *subdivided by roulette* 6½. *W* **9** …*ways* on* 3d., 4d. *and* 1s.). (a) *Inscr alternately.*

		Un unit	Us unit	Us single
43	½d. blue-green (T) (10.42)	1·25	1·50	10
	a. Green (3.43)	2·75	2·00	10
	b. Greenish blue (7.44)	2·00	1·50	10
	c. Roulette omitted	£650		
44	1d. carmine-red (T) (5.1.43)	1·50	1·25	10
	a. Bright carmine (3.44)	1·00	1·00	10
	b. Both roulettes omitted	£500	£550	
	ba. Left-hand roulette omitted	£650		
45	1½d. red-brown (P) (9.42)	65	1·50	10
	a. Roulette 13 (8.42)	1·50	4·00	15
	b. Roulette omitted	£225	£250	
	c. Ear flap flaw	15·00		
46	2d. violet (P) (2.43)	90	1·75	10
	a. Reddish violet (6.43)	1·50	65	10
	b. Roulette omitted	£450		
	c. Apostrophe flaw	50·00		
	d. Line on cap	50·00		
47	3d. blue (T) (10.42)	7·00	15·00	10
48	6d. red-orange (P) (10.42)	2·00	1·60	10
	(*b*) *Inscr bilingually*			
49	4d. slate-green (T) (10.42)	18·00	6·50	10
50	1s. brown (P) (11.42)	15·00	3·25	10
	a. "Bursting shell"	60·00		
	b. Smoking "L"	60·00		
…4	*Set of* 8	40·00	27·00	65

…he sideways watermark shows springbok horns pointing to …n the 3d. and 1s., and to right on the 4d., *all as seen from …ack of the stamp.*

52

53

. *Coil stamps. Redrawn. In single colours with plain back-…ound. W* **9**. *P* 15 × 14.

		Un pair	Used pair	Used single
52	½d. blue-green (18.2.43)	1·75	4·00	20
53	1d. carmine (9.43)	2·50	3·25	15

…uoted prices are for *vertical* pairs.

54 Union Buildings, Pretoria

…5–46. *Redrawn. W* **9**. *P* 14.

54	2d. slate and violet (3.45)	10·00	2·50	10
	a. Slate & brt vio (shades) (10.46)	2·75	8·00	15

…n Nos. 107 and 107*a* the Union Buildings are shown at a …erent angle from Nos. 58 and 58*a*. Only the centre is screened … composed of very small square dots of colour arranged in …ight diagonal lines. For whole design screened and colours …nged, see No. 116. No. 107*a* also shows "2" of "2d." clear of white …le at top.

55 "Victory"

56 "Peace"

57 "Hope"

…45 (3 Dec). *Victory. W* **9**. *P* 14.

…8	55	1d. brown and carmine	20	80	10
…9	56	2d. slate-blue and violet	20	85	10
…0	57	3d. deep blue and blue	20	1·25	10
…8/10		*Set of* 3	55	2·75	25

58 King George VI

59 King George VI and Queen Elizabeth

60 Queen Elizabeth II as Princess, and Princess Margaret

"Bird" on "2" (Cyl 6912 R. 10/6)

(Des J. Prentice)

1947 (17 Feb). *Royal Visit. W* **9**. *P* 15 × 14.

111	**58**	1d. black and carmine	10	10	10
112	**59**	2d. violet	15	30	10
		a. "Bird" on "2" flaw	2·50		
113	**60**	3d. blue	15	30	10
111/13		*Set of* 3	35	60	20

"Flying saucer" flaw (Cyl 17 R. 17/2)

5s.

1947–54. "SUID-AFRIKA" *hyphenated on Afrikaans stamps. Printed from new cylinders with design in screened rotogravure. W* **9**. *P* 15×14 (½d., 1d. *and* 6d.) *or* 14 (*others*).

114	**25a**	½d. grey and green (frame only screened) (1947)	1·75	2·50	10
		a. Booklet pane of 6 (with postal slogans on margins) (1948)	3·00		
		b. "Tick" flaw and spot on nose	35·00		
		c. Entire design screened (2.49)	1·75	2·75	10
		ca. Booklet pane of 6 (with margin at right) (1951)	3·50		
115	**7**	1d. grey and carmine (1.9.50)	1·50	2·75	10
		a. Booklet pane of 6 (with margin at right) (1951)	4·00		
116	**54**	2d. slate-blue & purple (3.50)	1·75	6·00	10
117	**22a**	3d. dull blue (4.49)	2·00	4·50	10
117*a*		3d. blue (3.51)	2·75	3·50	10
		ab. "Flying saucer" flaw	40·00		
		b. Deep blue (1954)	60·00	65·00	4·00
118	**12a**	4d. brown (22.8.52)	2·50	6·00	10
119	**8**	6d. grn & red-orge (III) (1.50)	2·50	80	10
		a. Grn & brn-orge (III) (1951)	2·00	50	10
120	**13**	1s. brown & chalky blue (1.50)	10·00	6·50	10
		a. Blackish brown & ultram (4.52)	18·00	9·00	15
121	**14**	2s. 6d. green and brown (8.49)	10·00	27·00	1·00
122	**15**	5s. blk & pale bl-grn (I) (9.49)	45·00	55·00	1·25
122*a*		5s. blk & dp yell-grn (II) (1.54)	55·00	80·00	3·00
114/22		*Set of* 9	65·00	95·00	2·00

In screened rotogravure the design is composed of very small squares of colour arranged in straight diagonal lines.

½d. Size 17¾ × 21¾ mm. Early printings have only the frame screened.

1d. Size 18 × 22 mm. For smaller, redrawn design, see No. 135.

2d. For earlier issue with centre only screened, and in different colours, see Nos. 107/*a*.

3d. No. 117. Whole stamp screened with irregular grain. Scrolls above "3d." solid and toneless. Printed from two cylinders.

No. 117*a*/*b*. Whole stamp diagonally screened. Printed from one cylinder. Clouds more pronounced.

4d. Two groups of white leaves below name tablet and a clear white line down left and right sides of stamp.

61 Gold Mine

62 King George VI and Queen Elizabeth

1948 (1 Apr). *W* **9** (*sideways*). *In pair, perf* 14, *sub-divided by roulette* 6½.

			Un unit of 4	Us unit	Used single
124	**61**	1½d. blue-green and yellow-buff	1·75	3·25	10

(Des J. Booysen and J. Prentice)

1948 (26 Apr). *Silver Wedding. W* **9**. *P* 14.

			Un pair	Used pair	Used single
125	**62**	3d. blue and silver	50	60	10

(Typo Government Printer, Pretoria)

1948 (July). *W* **9**. *P* 14½ × 14.

126	**6**	½d. pale grey and blue-green	1·00	8·00	65

This was an economy printing made from the old plates of the 1926 issue for the purpose of using up a stock of cut paper. For the original printing in black and green, see No. 30.

63 *Wanderer* (emigrant ship) entering Durban

Extended rigging on mainmast (R. 14/2)

(Des J. Prentice)

1949 (2 May). *Centenary of Arrival of British Settlers in Natal. W* **9**. *P* 15 × 14.

127	**63**	1½d. claret	50	50	10
		a. Extended rigging	6·00		

64 Hermes

65 Wagons approaching Bingham's Berg

Serif on "C" (R. 1/1)

"Lake" in East Africa (R. 2/19)

(Des J. Booysen and J. Prentice)

1949 (1 Oct). *75th Anniv of Universal Postal Union. As T* **64** *inscr* "UNIVERSAL POSTAL UNION" *and* "WERELDPOSUNIE" *alternately. W* **9** (*sideways*). *P* 14 × 15.

128	**64**	½d. blue-green	50	75	10
129		1½d. brown-red	50	75	10
130		3d. bright blue	60	1·00	10
		a. Serif on "C"	25·00		
		b. "Lake" in East Africa	26·00		
128/30		*Set of* 3	1·40	2·25	25

(Des W. Coetzer and J. Prentice)

1949 (1 Dec). *Inauguration of Voortrekker Monument, Pretoria. T* **65** *and similar horiz designs. W* **9**. *P* 15 × 14.

		Un single	Us single
131	1d. magenta	10	10
132	1½d. blue-green	10	10
133	3d. blue	15	15
131/3	*Set of* 3	30	30

Designs:—1½d. Voortrekker Monument, Pretoria; 3d. Bible, candle and Voortrekkers.

68 Union Buildings, Pretoria

1950 (Apr)–**51**. *W* **9** (*sideways*). *P* 14 × 15.

			Un pair	Used pair	Used single
134	**68**	2d. blue and violet	30	65	10
		a. Booklet panes of 6 (with margin at right) (1951)	4·00		

1951 (22 Feb). *As No. 115, but redrawn with the horizon clearly defined. Size reduced to 17¼ × 21¼ mm.*
135 7 1d. grey and carmine .. .. 1·25 2·00 10

STAMP BOOKLETS

1913. *Black on red cover. With* "UNION OF SOUTH AFRICA" *at top and* "UNIE VAN ZUID AFRIKA" *at foot. Stapled.*
SB1 2s. 6d. booklet containing twelve ½d. and twenty-four 1d. (Nos. 3/4) in blocks of 6 .. .. £4500

1913–20. *Black on red cover with* "UNION OF SOUTH AFRICA" *and* "UNIE VAN ZUID AFRIKA" *both at top. Stapled.*
SB2 2s. 6d. booklet containing twelve ½d. and twenty-four 1d. (Nos. 3/4) in blocks of 6 .. .. £4500
a. Black on pink cover (1920) £4500

1921. *Black on salmon-pink cover with* "UNION OF SOUTH AFRICA" *and* "UNIE VAN ZUID AFRIKA" *either side of arms and telegraph rates beneath. Stapled.*
SB3 3s. booklet containing twelve ½d., 1d. and 1½d. (Nos. 3/5) in blocks of 6 .. .. .. £450

1922. *Black on salmon-pink cover as No. SB3 surch. Stapled.*
SB4 3s. 6d. on 3s. booklet containing twelve ½d., 1d. and 2d. (Nos. 3/4, 6) in blocks of 6 .. .. £750

1926. *Black on salmon-pink cover as No. SB3. Stitched.*
SB5 2s. 6d. booklet containing twelve ½d. and twenty-four 1d. (Nos. 30/1) £1200

1927. *Black on salmon-pink cover as No. SB3, but inscr* "Union of South Africa" *and* "Unie van Suidafrika". *Stitched.*
SB6 2s. 6d. booklet containing twelve ½d. and twenty-four 1d. (Nos. 30e, 31d) £3500

1930. *Black on pink cover as No. SB6, but with advertisement at foot instead of telegraph rates. Stitched.*
SB7 2s. 6d. booklet containing twelve ½d. and twenty-four 1d. (Nos. 42/3) in blocks of 6 .. .. £1000

1931. *Black on pink cover. Smaller inscr and advertisement on front cover. Stitched.*
SB8 3s. booklet containing twelve 1d. (No. 43) in blocks of 6 and twelve 2d. (No. 44) in blocks of 4 .. £1000

1935. *Black on lemon cover. Advertisement on front cover. Stitched.*
SB9 2s. 6d. booklet containing two panes of six ½d. (No. 54c) and four panes of six 1d. (No. 56e), all with adverts on margins £200

1937. *Black on lemon cover. Advertisement on front cover. Stitched.*
SB10 2s. 6d. booklet containing two panes of six ½d. (No. 75ba) and four panes of six 1d. (No. 56f), all with blank margins £400

1937. *Machine vended booklets. Red cover. Stitched.*
SB11 6d. booklet containing four ½d. and 1d. (Nos. 75*b*, 56) in pairs .. .. 7·00

1938. *Machine vended booklets. Blue cover. Stitched.*
SB12 3d. booklet containing ½d. and 1d. (Nos. 75*b*, 56), each in pair .. .. 40·00

1938. *Black on buff cover. Union arms at top left with advertisement at foot. Stitched.*
SB13 2s. 6d. booklet containing twelve ½d. and twenty-four 1d. (Nos. 75*b*, 56) in blocks of 6 £350

1939. *Black on buff cover. Union arms centred at top with advertisement at foot. Stitched.*
SB14 2s. 6d. booklet containing twelve ½d. and twenty-four 1d. (Nos. 75*b*, 56) in blocks of 6 £300

1939–40. *Green on buff cover. Union arms centred at top with large advertisement at bottom left. Stitched.*
SB15 2s. 6d. booklet containing twelve ½d. and twenty-four 1d. (Nos. 75*b*, 56) in blocks of 6 £1800
a. Blue on buff cover (1940) .. .. .. 80·00

1941. *Blue on buff cover as No. SB15. Stitched.*
SB17 2s. 6d. booklet containing twelve ½d. and 1d. (Nos. 75*b*, 56) in blocks of 6 and 1½d. (No. 57) in block of 4 .. .. .. £130

1948. *Black on buff cover. With advertisement. Stitched.*
SB18 3s. booklet containing two panes of six ½d., 1d. and 1½d. (Nos. 114a, 56h, 87b), all with postal slogans on margins, and pane of air mail labels .. .. 30·00

1951. *Black on buff cover. Stitched.*
SB19 3s. 6d. booklet containing two panes of six ½d., 1d. and 2d. (Nos. 114ca, 115a, 134a), each with margins at right .. .. .. 13·00

NEW INFORMATION

The editor is always interested to correspond with people who have new information that will improve or correct the Catalogue.

POSTAGE DUE STAMPS

D 1

UNION OF SOUTH AFRICA (A) UNION OF SOUTH AFRICA (B)

(Typo D.L.R.)

1914–22. *Inscribed bilingually. Lettering as A. W* **4**. *P* 14.

			Un single	*Used single*
D1	D 1	½d. black and green (19.3.15) ..	2·00	3·75
D2		1d. black and scarlet (19.3.15) ..	2·25	15
		a. Black ptd double	£1500	
		w. Wmk inverted	80·00	
D3		2d. black and reddish violet (12.12.14)	6·50	50
		a. Black and bright violet (1922) ..	7·00	60
		w. Wmk inverted	£120	
D4		3d. black and bright blue (2.2.15) ..	2·25	60
		w. Wmk inverted	25·00	
D5		5d. black and sepia (19.3.15) ..	4·00	21·00
D6		6d. black and slate (19.3.15) ..	7·00	27·00
D7		1s. red and black (19.3.15) ..	60·00	£140
D1/7		.. .. *Set of* 7	75·00	£170

There are interesting minor varieties in some of the above values, e.g. ½d. to 3d., thick downstroke to "d"; 1d., short serif to "1"; raised "d"; 2d., forward point of "2" blunted; 3d., raised "d"; very thick "d".

(Litho Govt Printer, Pretoria)

1922. *Lettering as A. No wmk. Rouletted.*

D 8	D 1	½d. black and bright green (6.6.22) ..	1·50	11·00
D 9		1d. black and rose-red (3.10.22) ..	1·00	1·00
D10		1½d. black and yellow-brown (3.6.22) ..	1·25	1·75
D8/10		.. .. *Set of* 3	3·25	12·00

(Litho Govt Printer, Pretoria)

1922–26. *Type* D 1 *redrawn. Lettering as B. No wmk. P* 14.

D11	½d. black and green (1.8.22)	80	1·75
D12	1d. black and rose (16.5.23)	90	15
D13	1½d. black and yellow-brown (12.1.24) ..	90	1·25
D14	2d. black and pale violet (16.5.23) ..	1·00	70
	a. Imperf (pair)	£225	£300
	b. Black and deep violet	11·00	2·00
D15	3d. black and blue (3.7.26)	8·00	18·00
D16	6d. black and slate (9.23)	12·00	4·50
D11/16	.. .. *Set of* 6	21·00	24·00

The locally printed stamps, perf 14, differ both in border design and in figures of value from the rouletted stamps. All values except the 3d. and 6d. are known with closed "G" in "POSTAGE" usually referred to as the "POSTADE" variety. This was corrected in later printings.

D 2 D 3 D 4

Blunt "2" (R. 3/6, 8/6)

(Typo Pretoria)

1927–28. *Inscribed bilingually. No wmk. P* 13½×14.

D17	D 2	½d. black and green	80	3·25
		a. Blunt "2"	10·00	
D18		1d. black and carmine	1·25	30
D19		2d. black and mauve	1·25	30
		a. Black and purple	14·00	80
D20		3d. black and blue	8·50	22·00
D21		6d. black and slate	21·00	4·50
D17/21		.. .. *Set of* 5	29·00	27·00

1932–42. *Type* D 2 *redrawn. W* **9**. *P* 15×14.

(a) Frame roto, value typo

D22	½d. black and blue-green (1934) ..	2·75	1·75
	w. Wmk inverted	2·25	1·60
D23	2d. black and deep purple (10.4.33) ..	9·00	2·25
	w. Wmk inverted	9·00	2·25

(b) Whole stamp roto

D25	1d. black & carmine (*wmk inverted*) (3.34)	2·25	10
D26	2d. black and deep purple (1940) ..	22·00	10
	a. Thick (double) "2d." (R. 5/6, R. 18/2)	£225	20·00
	w. Wmk inverted	22·00	10
D27	3d. black and Prussian blue (3.8.32) ..	23·00	14·00
D28	3d. dp blue & blue (*wmk inverted*) (1935)	7·00	30
	a. Indigo and milky blue (*wmk inverted*) (1942)	60·00	2·75
	w. Wmk upright	35·00	1·00
D29	6d. green and brown-ochre (*wmk inverted*) (7.6.33)	25·00	5·00
	a. Green & brt orge (*wmk inverted*) (1938)	11·00	3·00
D22/9a	.. .. *Set of* 7	70·00	19·00

In No. D26 the value is screened, whereas in No. D23 the black of the value is solid.

1943–44. *Inscr bilingually. Roto. W* **9**. *In units of* *perf* 15 × 14 *subdivided by roulette* 6½.

			Un unit	*Us unit*
D30	D 3	½d. blue-green (1944)	10·00	40·00
D31		1d. carmine	10·00	5·50
D32		2d. dull violet	6·50	11·00
		a. Bright violet	16·00	45·00
D33		3d. indigo (1943)	48·00	60·00
D30/3		.. .. *Set of* 4	65·00	£120

Split "D" (R. 7/5 on every fourth sheet)

1948–49. *New figure of value and capital* "D". *Whole stam* *W* **9**. *P* 15 × 14.

D34	D 4	½d. black and blue-green	6·00
D35		1d. black and carmine	11·00
D36		2d. black and violet (1949)	11·00
		a. Thick (double) "2D." (R. 15/5–6, R. 16/5–6)	50·00
D37		3d. deep blue and blue	15·00
		a. Split "D"	£150
D38		6d. green and bright orange (1949)	25·00
D34/8		.. .. *Set of* 5	60·00

1950–58. *As Type* D 4, *but* "SUID-AFRIKA" *hyphenated.* *stamp roto. W* **9**. *P* 15 × 14.

D39	1d. black and carmine (5.50)		70
D40	2d. black and violet (4.51)		50
	a. Thick (double) "2D." (R. 15/5–6, R. 16/5–6)		8·00
	b. Black and reddish violet (12.52) ..		70
	ba. Thick (double) "2D."		8·00
	bb. Black (value) omitted		£1800
D41	3d. deep blue and blue (5.50)		4·50
	a. Split "D"		80·00
D42	4d. deep myrtle-green and emerald (2.58)		12·00
D43	6d. green and bright orange (3.50) ..		7·00
D44	1s. black-brown and purple-brown (2.58)		12·00
D39/44	.. .. *Set of* 6		32·00

No. D40bb occurs in horizontal pair with a normal.

OFFICIAL STAMPS

OFFICIAL. OFFISIEEL. OFFISIEEL OFFICIAL

(O 1) (O 2)

(Approximate measurements of the space between the two of overprint are quoted in millimetres, either in the headings or after individual listings)

1926 (1 Dec). *Optd with Type* O 1 *(reading upwards with s and* 12½ *mm between lines of opt).*

(a) On 1913 issue (No. 6)

O1 3 2d. purple .. .. .. 18·00

(b) On 1926 issue (Nos. 30/2)

			Un pair	*Us pair si*
O2	6	½d. black and green	6·00	15·00
O3	7	1d. black and carmine	3·25	5·00
O4	8	6d. green and orange	£550	75·00 1(
		w. Wmk inverted	£900	£350 3(

The overprint occurs on both the London and Pret printings of Nos. 30/2. For the lower two values the overprin London printings are scarcer than the Pretoria, but for the the ratio is reversed.

1928–30. *Nos.* 32 *and* 34 *optd as Type* O 1 *(reading upwa without stops).*

O5	11	2d. grey & maroon (*p* 14) (17½ *mm*)	5·00	19·00 2
		a. Lines of opt 19 mm apart (1929)	4·00	13·00
		ab. On No. 34a (*p* 14×13½) (1930)	25·00	38·00 5
O6	8	6d. green and orange (11½–12 *mm*)	18·00	32·00 2

1929–31. *Optd with Type* O **2**. *(a) On 1926 (Typo) issue (N* 30/2) *(13½–15 mm between lines of opt).*

O7	6	½d. black and green ..	2·25	3·50
		a. Stop after "OFFISIEEL" on English inscr stamp (1930)	32·00	32·00 3
		b. Ditto, but on Afrikaans inscr stamp (1930)	40·00	40·00 3
O8	7	1d. black and carmine ..	3·00	4·50
O9	8	6d. green and orange ..	9·50	32·00 3
		a. Stop after "OFFISIEEL" on English inscr stamp (1930)	65·00	£110 10
		b. Ditto, but on Afrikaans inscr stamp (1930)	75·00	£120 12

(b) On 1927 (Recess) issue (Nos. 36a/7) (17½–19 mm betwee lines of opt)

O10	13	1s. brown and deep blue (1931)	32·00	90·00 9
		a. Stop after "OFFICIAL" on Afrikaans inscr stamp (R. 10/1, 10/7)	£100	£225
		b. Lines of opt 22 mm apart	£250	

14 2s. 6d. green and brown (1931) 60·00 £150 19·00
a. Stop after "OFFICIAL" on Afrikaans inscr stamp (R. 10/1) £275 £475
.. .. .. Set of 5 95·00 £250 29·00

"stop" varieties for the ½d., and 6d. occur on R. 5/3, 5/11, .5/3, 15/11, 18/12 with English inscriptions and R. 9/10, 9/10, 19/12 with Afrikaans on the 1930 overprinting only nly the lefthand panes of the 2s. 6d. were overprinted in he stop variety only occurs once. A further overprinting in vas on both panes, but did not include No. O11a.

47. *Nos.* 42/4 *and* 47/9 ("SUIDAFRIKA" *in one word*) *with Type* O **2**.

6 ½d. black and green (9½–12½ *mm*) (1931) .. .. 2·25 4·25 40
a. Stop after "OFFISIEEL" on English inscr stamp .. 38·00 45·00 4·00
b. Ditto, but on Afrikaans inscr stamp .. .. .. 32·00 40·00 3·50
w. Wmk inverted (1934) .. 5·00 8·00 60
7 1d. black & carm (I) (12½ *mm*) 4·50 4·50 55
a. Stop after "OFFISIEEL" on English inscr stamp .. 45·00 48·00 4·00
b. Ditto, but on Afrikaans inscr stamp .. .. .. 35·00 40·00 3·50
cw. Wmk inverted (1931) .. 4·50 4·50 55
d. On Type II (No. 43*d*) (12½–13½ *mm*) (1933) .. .. 13·00 9·00 90
da. Opt double £275 £300
11 2d. slate-grey and lilac (20½–22½ *mm*) (1931) .. .. 6·00 11·00 1·50
w. Wmk inverted (1934) .. 50·00 85·00 8·00
2d. blue and violet (20½–22½ *mm*) (1938) .. .. £110 £100 9·00
8 6d. green & orange (12½–13½ *mm*) (*wmk inverted*) (1931) 7·00 8·50 85
a. Stop after "OFFISIEEL" on English inscr stamp .. 70·00 75·00 6·50
b. Ditto, but on Afrikaans inscr stamp .. .. .. 60·00 65·00 5·50
c. "OFFISIEEL" reading upwards (R. 17/12, 18/12, 19/12, 20/12) (1933) .. £500
w. Wmk upright (1935) .. 50·00 75·00 7·00
13 1s. brown and deep blue (19 *mm*) (*wmk inverted*) (1932) 45·00 80·00 8·50
a. Twisted horn flaw .. £225
b. Lines of opt 21 mm apart (*wmk inverted*) (1933) .. 48·00 70·00 7·50
ba. Twisted horn flaw .. £225
bw. Wmk upright (1936) .. 60·00 £100 10·00
14 2s. 6d. green and brown (17½–18½ *mm*) (1933) .. .. 75·00 £140 15·00
a. Lines of opt 21 mm apart (1934) .. .. .. 48·00 75·00 8·50
aw. Wmk inverted (1937) .. £200 £275
2s. 6d. blue and brown (19½–20 *mm*) (11.47) .. .. 32·00 70·00 6·50
a. Diaeresis over second "E" of "OFFISIEEL" on Afrikaans inscr stamp (R. 6/2) .. £850 £950
b. Ditto, but on English inscr stamp (R. 6/3) £850 £950

he stop varieties for the ½d., 1d. and 6d. occur on R. 9/10, , 19/10, 19/12 with English inscriptions and R. 5/3, 5/11, , 15/3, 15/11, 18/12 with Afrikaans on the 1930 and 1931 printings only.

OFFICIAL OFFISIEEL — (O 3)

OFFISIEEL OFFICIAL — (O 4)

5–49. *Nos.* 54, 56/8, 61/2 *and* 64*a*/*b* ("SUID-AFRIKA" *hyphenated*) *optd*.

) *With Type* O **2** (*reading downwards with* "OFFICIAL" *at right*)

) 6 ½d. grey and green (12½ *mm*) (*wmk inverted*) (1936) .. 4·50 22·00 1·75
w. Wmk upright (1937) .. 4·50 22·00 1·25
7 1d. grey and carmine (11½–13 *mm*) (*wmk inverted*) .. 3·00 3·00 35
aw. Wmk upright (1937) .. 1·75 2·00 20
b. Grey & bright rose-carmine (No. 56*i*) (1949) .. .. 2·50 3·25 30
2 22 1½d. green and bright gold (20 *mm*) (*wmk inverted*) (1937) 35·00 24·00 1·75
aw. Wmk upright (1939) .. 24·00 17·00 80
b. Blue-green and dull gold (No. 57*c*) (1941) .. .. 45·00 11·00 1·10
3 11 2d. blue & violet (20 *mm*) (1939) £110 23·00 2·25
4 8 6d. green and vermilion (I) (11½–13 *mm*) (1937) .. 80·00 45·00 3·75
a. "Falling ladder" flaw .. £350
b. Die II (No. 61*b*) (1938) .. 10·00 12·00 1·25
c. Die III. *Green & red-orange* (No. 61*c*) (11.47) .. .. 4·00 8·50 85
5 13 1s. brown and chalky blue (20 *mm*) (1939) .. .. 75·00 30·00 2·25
a. Diaeresis over second "E" of "OFFISIEEL" on both English and Afrikaans inscr stamps (1941) £1400 £950
b. Ditto, but on English inscr stamp only (11.47) .. £1200 £850
26 15 5s. black and blue-green (20 *mm*) (6.48) .. .. 55·00 £140 13·00
27 23 10s. blue and blackish brown (No. 64*ba*) (20 *mm*) (6.48) .. 90·00 £250 23·00

b) *With Type* O **3** (*reading downwards with* "OFFICIAL" *at left and* 18–19 *mm between lines of opt*)

28 15 5s. black and blue-green (1940) 85·00 £110 12·00
29 23 10s. blue and sepia (1940) .. £375 £400 38·00

(*c*) *With Type* O **4** (*reading upwards with* "OFFICIAL" *at right and* 18½ *mm between lines of opt*

O30 **11** 2d. grey and dull purple (No. 58*a*) (1941) .. .. 10·00 24·00 2·25

No. O25a first appeared in the 1941 overprinting where the variety occurs on stamps 5 and 6 of an unidentified row. The variety reappears in the November 1947 overprinting where the stamps involved are R. 6/1 and 2. No. O25b occurs on R. 6/3 of the same overprinting.

Horizontal rows of 6 of the 1s. exist with "OFFICIAL" twice on the first stamp and "OFFISIEEL" twice on the last stamp. Such rows are believed to come from two half sheets which were overprinted in 1947, but not placed into normal stock (*Price for row of* 6, £2250, *unused*).

OFFICIAL OFFISIEËL — (O 5)

OFFICIAL OFFISIEEL — (O 6)

1937–44. *No.* 75*b* (*redrawn design*) *optd.* (*a*) *With Type* O **2** (*reading downwards with* "OFFICIAL" *at right and* 11–12½ *mm between lines of opt*)

O31 **25***a* ½d. grey and green .. .. 13·00 14·00 1·25
a. Grey and blue-green (No. 75*bd*) (1944) .. .. 1·75 8·00 60

(*b*) *With Type* O **5** (*reading up and down with* "OFFICIAL" *at left and diaeresis over the second* "E" *of* "OFFISIEEL". 10 *mm between lines of opt*)

O32 **25***a* ½d. grey and blue-green (No. 75*bd*) (1944) .. .. 24·00 23·00 2·00

1944–50. *Nos.* 87 *and* 134 *optd.* (*a*) *With Type* O **2** (*reading downwards with* "OFFICIAL" *at right*)

O33 **34***a* 1½d. blue-green and yellow-buff (14½ *mm*) .. .. 2·50 9·00 80
a. With diaeresis over second "E" of "OFFISIEEL" .. £450 £225 20·00
b. Lines of opt 16½ mm apart (6.48) .. .. .. 2·25 8·50 50

(*b*) *With Type* O **6** (*reading upwards with* "OFFICIAL" *at left and* 16 *mm between lines of opt*)

O34 **34***a* 1½d. bl-green & yell-buff (1949) 45·00 45·00 4·00
O35 **68** 2d. blue and violet (1950) .. £1800 £2500 £170

Two different formes were used to overprint Type **34***a* between 1944 and 1946. The first, applied to the left halves of sheets only, had a diaeresis over the second "E" of "OFFISIEEL" on all positions of the setting, except for R. 1/2, 2/2 and 3/2. The second form, from which the majority of the stamps came, was applied twice to overprint complete sheets, had no diaeresis.

1947 (Nov)–**49.** *No.* 107 *optd with Type* O **2** (*reading downwards with* "OFFICIAL" *at right and* 20 *mm between lines of opt*).

O36 **54** 2d. slate and violet .. .. 4·25 20·00 1·75
a. With diaeresis over second "E" of "OFFISIEEL" (R. 1/5-6, 11/5-6) £400 £600
b. Slate-purple and bright violet (No. 107*a*) (1949) .. .. 5·50 15·00 1·60

1949–50. *Nos.* 114 *and* 120 *optd with Type* O **2** (*reading downwards with* "OFFICIAL" *at right*).

O37 **25***a* ½d. grey and green (11 *mm*) .. 2·00 7·50 70
O38 **13** 1s. brown and chalky blue (17½–18½ *mm*) (1950) .. 9·00 28·00 2·50

OFFISIEEL OFFICIAL — (O 7)

1950 (June)–**54.** *Optd as Type* O **7** *using stereo blocks measuring either* 10 (½*d.*, 1*d.*, 6*d.*), 14½ (1½*d.*, 2*d.*) *or* 19 *mm* (*others*) *between the lines of opt.*

O39 **25***a* ½d. grey and green (No. 114c) (6.51) .. .. 70 1·50 15
O41 **7** 1d. grey & bright rose-carmine (No. 56*i*) .. .. .. 1·00 5·50 50
O42 1d. grey & car (No. 115) (3.51) 1·00 3·00 20
O43 1d. grey & car (No. 135) (6.52) 90 2·00 20
O44 **34***a* 1½d. blue-green and yellow-buff (No. 87) (3.51) .. .. 1·40 4·00 30
O45 **68** 2d. blue and violet (No. 134) 1·00 2·00 20
a. Opt inverted £1000
O46 **8** 6d. green & red-orge (No. 119) 1·00 3·50 35
a. Green and brown-orange (No. 119*a*) (6.51) .. 1·50 3·50 35
O47 **13** 1s. brn & chalky bl (No. 120) 5·50 18·00 2·00
a. Blackish brown and ultram (No. 120*a*) (2.53) .. £150 £160 18·00
O48 **14** 2s. 6d. green & brn (No. 121) 8·50 35·00 3·50
O49 **15** 5s. black and blue-green (No. 64*a*) (3.51) .. .. £180 90·00 9·00
O50 5s. black and pale blue-green (I) (No. 122) (2.53) .. 60·00 75·00 6·50
a. Black & deep yellow-green (II) (No. 122*a*) (1.54) .. 75·00 90·00 9·00
O51 **23** 10s. blue and blackish brown (No. 64*ca*) .. .. 70·00 £225 22·00

The use of official stamps ceased in January 1955.

South Australia
see Australia

Southern Nigeria
see Nigeria

Southern Rhodesia

PRICES FOR STAMPS ON COVER TO 1945
Nos. 1/61 *from* × 2

SELF-GOVERNMENT

The southern part of Rhodesia, previously administered by the British South Africa Company, was annexed by the British Government and granted the status of a self-governing colony from 1 October 1923.

The existing stamps of Rhodesia (the "Admiral" design first issued in 1913) remained in use until 31 March 1924 and continued to be valid for postal purposes until 30 April of that year.

1

2 King George V

3 Victoria Falls

(Recess Waterlow)

1924 (1 Apr)–**29.** *P* 14.

1 **1** ½d. blue-green .. .. 1·75 10
a. Imperf between (horiz pair) .. £700 £800
b. Imperf between (vert pair) .. £700 £800
c. Imperf vert (horiz pair) £750
2 1d. bright rose .. .. .. 1·60 10
a. Imperf between (horiz pair) .. £600 £700
b. Imperf between (vert pair) .. £1000
c. Perf 12½ (coil) (1929) .. .. 2·75 80·00
3 1½d. bistre-brown .. .. .. 1·75 80
a. Imperf between (horiz pair) .. £7500
b. Imperf between (vert pair) .. £4500
c. Printed double, once albino .. £325
4 2d. black and purple-grey .. .. 2·25 70
a. Imperf between (horiz pair) .. £9500
5 3d. blue .. .. 2·25 2·50
6 4d. black and orange-red .. .. 2·50 2·75
7 6d. black and mauve .. .. .. 2·00 3·50
a. Imperf between (horiz pair) .. £30000
8 8d. purple and pale green .. .. 11·00 42·00
a. Frame double, once albino ..
9 10d. blue and rose .. .. .. 11·00 45·00
10 1s. black and light blue .. .. 5·00 5·00
11 1s. 6d. black and yellow .. .. 19·00 32·00
12 2s. black and brown .. .. .. 17·00 17·00
13 2s. 6d. blue and sepia .. .. .. 30·00 60·00
14 5s. blue and blue-green .. .. 60·00 £120
1/14 .. .. .. *Set of* 14 £150 £300

Prices for "imperf between" varieties are for adjacent stamps from the same pane and not for those separated by wide gutter margins between vertical or horizontal pairs, which come from the junction of two panes.

(T **2** recess by B.W.; T **3** typo by Waterlow)

1931 (1 April)–**37.** *T* **2** (*line perf* 12 *unless otherwise stated*) *and* **3** (*comb perf* 15 × 14). (*The* 11½ *perf is comb.*).

15 **2** ½d. green .. .. 85 1·00
a. Perf 11½ (1933) 65 20
b. Perf 14 (1935) .. .. .. 1·60 30
16 1d. scarlet .. .. 1·00 70
a. Perf 11½ (1933) .. .. .. 1·75 20
b. Perf 14 (1935) 50 20
16*c* 1½d. chocolate (3.3.33) .. .. .. 55·00 42·00
d. Perf 11½ (1.4.32) .. .. .. 2·50 80
17 **3** 2d. black and sepia .. .. .. 4·00 1·40
18 3d. deep ultramarine .. .. .. 10·00 11·00
19 **2** 4d. black and vermilion .. .. 1·25 1·50
a. Perf 11½ (1935) .. .. .. 17·00 5·00
b. Perf 14 (10.37) .. .. .. 32·00 48·00
20 6d. black and magenta .. .. 2·25 3·00
a. Perf 11½ (1933) .. .. .. 15·00 1·50
b. Perf 14 (1936) .. .. .. 7·00 85
21 8d. violet and olive-green .. .. 1·75 3·25
a. Perf 11½ (1934) .. .. .. 17·00 32·00
21*b* 9d. vermilion and olive-green (1.9.34) 6·00 9·00
22 10d. blue and scarlet .. .. .. 7·00 2·25
a. Perf 11½ (1933) .. .. .. 6·00 13·00
23 1s. black and greenish blue .. .. 2·00 2·50
a. Perf 11½ (1935) .. .. .. £100 60·00
b. Perf 14 (10.37) £200 £140
24 1s. 6d. black and orange-yellow .. 10·00 16·00
a. Perf 11½ (1936) .. .. .. 50·00 £100
25 2s. black and brown .. .. .. 21·00 6·50
a. Perf 11½ (1933) .. .. .. 35·00 30·00

26 2 2s. 6d. blue and drab .. .. .. 32·00 35·00
a. Perf 11½ (1933) .. .. .. 28·00 30·00
27 5s. blue and blue-green .. .. 48·00 48·00
a. Printed on gummed side £3750
15/27 .. .. *Set of* 15 £130 £110
No. 16*c* was only issued in booklets.

PRINTERS. All stamps from Types **4** to **29** were recess-printed by Waterlow and Sons, Ltd, London, except where otherwise stated.

4

1932 (1 May). *P* 12½.
29 **4** 2d. green and chocolate .. .. .. 3·75 1·00
30 3d. deep ultramarine .. .. .. 4·00 1·75
a. Imperf horiz (vert pair) £6000 £8000
b. Imperf between (vert pair) £15000

5 Victoria Falls

1935 (6 May). *Silver Jubilee. P* 11×12.
31 **5** 1d. olive and rose-carmine .. .. 3·25 1·75
32 2d. emerald and sepia .. .. .. 5·50 5·00
33 3d. violet and deep blue .. .. .. 5·50 10·00
34 6d. black and purple .. .. .. 8·00 14·00
31/4 .. .. *Set of* 4 20·00 28·00

1935–41. *Inscr* "POSTAGE AND REVENUE".
35 **4** 2d. green and chocolate (*p* 12½) .. .. 2·50 9·00
a. Perf 14 (1941) .. .. .. 1·50 10
35*b* 3d. deep blue (*p* 14) (1938) .. .. 3·00 10

6 Victoria Falls and Railway Bridge

7 King George VI

1937 (12 May). *Coronation. P* 12½.
36 **6** 1d. olive and rose-carmine 60 60
37 2d. emerald and sepia .. .. .. 60 1·50
38 3d. violet and blue .. .. .. 3·25 7·00
39 6d. black and purple .. .. .. 1·75 3·25
36/9 .. .. *Set of* 4 5·50 11·00

1937 (25 Nov). *P* 14.
40 **7** ½d. green 50 10
41 1d. scarlet 50 10
42 1½d. red-brown .. .. 1·00 30
43 4d. red-orange .. .. 1·50 10
44 6d. grey-black .. .. 1·50 50
45 8d. emerald-green .. .. 2·00 2·00
46 9d. pale blue .. .. 1·50 70
47 10d. purple .. .. 2·25 2·50
48 1s. black and blue-green .. .. .. 1·75 10
a. Frame double, one albino £1200
49 1s. 6d. black and orange-yellow .. .. 10·00 2·25
50 2s. black and brown .. .. .. 14·00 55
51 2s. 6d. ultramarine and purple .. .. 9·00 4·75
52 5s. blue and blue-green .. .. .. 18·00 2·25
40/52 .. .. *Set of* 13 55·00 14·00
Nos. 40/1 exist in coils, constructed from normal sheets.
On No. 48a the frame appears blurred and over-inked.

8 British South Africa Co's Arms

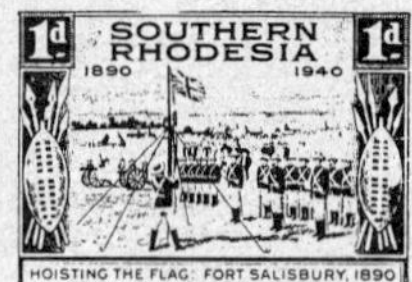

9 Fort Salisbury, 1890

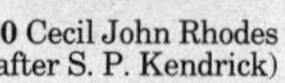

10 Cecil John Rhodes (after S. P. Kendrick)

15 Lobengula's Kraal and Govt House, Salisbury

Recut shirt collar (R. 6/1)

"Cave" flaw (R. 6/6)

(Des Mrs. L. E. Curtis (½d., 1d., 1½d., 3d.), Mrs I. Mount (others))

1940 (3 June). *British South Africa Company's Golden Jubilee. T* **8/10**, **15** *and similar designs. P* 14.
53 ½d. slate-violet and green 10 55
54 1d. violet-blue and scarlet 10 10
55 1½d. black and red-brown 15 80
a. Recut shirt collar .. .. .. 20·00
56 2d. green and bright violet 30 70
57 3d. black and blue .. .. .. 30 1·50
a. Cave flaw .. .. .. 35·00
58 4d. green and brown .. .. .. 2·00 2·50
59 6d. chocolate and green .. .. .. 50 2·00
60 1s. blue and green .. .. .. 50 2·00
53/60 .. .. *Set of* 8 3·50 9·00
Designs: *Horiz* (*as T* **8**)—2d. Fort Victoria; 3d. Rhodes makes peace. *Vert* (*as T* **10**)—4d. Victoria Falls Bridge; 6d. Statue of Sir Charles Coghlan.

16 Mounted Pioneer

Hat brim retouch (P1 1B R. 1/8)

(Roto South African Govt Printer, Pretoria)

1943 (1 Nov). *50th Anniv of Occupation of Matabeleland. W* **9** *of South Africa* (*Mult Springbok*) *sideways. P* 14.
61 **16** 2d. brown and green 20 75
a. Hat brim retouch .. .. .. 17·00

17 Queen Elizabeth II when Princess and Princess Margaret

1947 (1 Apr). *Royal Visit. T* **17** *and similar horiz design. P* 14.
62 ½d. black and green 15 60
63 1d. black and scarlet 15 60
Design:—1d. King George VI and Queen Elizabeth.

19 Queen Elizabeth

20 King George VI

21 Queen Elizabeth II when Princess

22 Princess Margaret

Damage to right-hand frame (R.1/10)

1947 (8 May). *Victory. P* 14.
64 **19** 1d. carmine 10
65 **20** 2d. slate 10
a. Double print £1000
b. Damaged frame .. .. .. 27·00
66 **21** 3d. blue 65
67 **22** 6d. orange 30
64/7 .. .. *Set of* 4 1·00

(Recess B.W.)

1949 (10 Oct). *75th Anniv of U.P.U. As Nos.* 115/16 *of An*
68 2d. slate-green 70
69 3d. blue 80

23 Queen Victoria, Arms and King George VI

1950 (12 Sept). *Diamond Jubilee of Southern Rhodesia. P* 1
70 **23** 2d. green and brown 50

STAMP BOOKLETS

1928 (1 Jan). *Black on blue cover. Stitched.*
SB1 2s. 6d. booklet containing twelve ½d. and twenty-four 1d. (Nos. 1/2) in blocks of 6 .. .. £

1931. *Black on blue cover. Stitched.*
SB2 2s. 6d. booklet containing twelve ½d. and twenty-four 1d. (Nos. 15/16) in blocks of 6 .. .. £

1933 (3 Mar). *Black on red cover, size* 69×53 *mm. Stitched*
SB3 3s. booklet containing twelve ½d., 1d. and 1½d. (Nos. 15, 16, 16c) in blocks of 6 .. .. £2
The 1½d. postage rate was reduced to 1d. eight weeks a No. SB3 was issued. Postal officials were instructed to de the 1½d. panes and use them for other purposes. The remair stocks of the booklet were then sold for 1s. 6d.

1938 (Oct)–**45.** *Black on yellow cover. Stitched.*
SB4 2s. 6d. booklet containing twenty-four ½d. and eighteen 1d. (Nos. 40/1) in blocks of 6 with postage rates on inside front cover .. .. £
a. Label with new rates affixed to inside front cover (1945) .. ..
b. Inside front cover blank .. .. ..
No. SB4b was issued sometime between 1945 and 1949.

POSTAGE DUE STAMPS

SOUTHERN

RHODESIA

(D 1)

1951 (1 Oct). *Postage Due stamps of Great Britain optd u Type* D 1.
D1 D 1 ½d. emerald (No. D27) .. .. 3·25 15
D2 1d. violet-blue (No. D36) .. .. 3·00 2
D3 2d. agate (No. D29) .. .. 2·50 1
D4 3d. violet (No. D30) .. .. 2·75 2
D5 4d. blue (No. D38) .. .. 1·75 3
D6 4d. dull grey-green (No. D31) £180 £5
D7 1s. deep blue (No. D33) .. .. 2·50 3
D1/5, 7 .. .. .. *Set of* 6 14·00 27
No. D6 is reported to have been issued to Fort Victoria a Gwelo main post offices only.

ALTERED CATALOGUE NUMBERS

Any Catalogue numbers altered from the la edition are shown as a list in the introducto pages.

South West Africa

he stamps of Germany were used in the colony from July 86 until the introduction of issues for GERMAN SOUTH-EST AFRICA in May 1897. Following occupation by South rican forces in 1914–15 the issues of SOUTH AFRICA were ed, being replaced by the overprinted issues in 1923.

alvis (or Walfish) Bay, the major anchorage on the South West a coast, was claimed by Great Britain as early as 1796. In 1878 30 sq mile area around the port, together with a number of ore islands, was annexed to Cape Province, passing to the n of South Africa in 1910.

amps of the Cape of Good Hope and South Africa were used at ish Bay, often cancelled with numeral obliterator 300, until enclave was transferred to the South West Africa adminis-on on 1 October 1922.

e Walfish Bay territory reverted to South Africa on 30 August and from that date the stamps of South Africa were, once n, in use.

PRICES FOR STAMPS ON COVER TO 1945	
Nos. 1/40*a*	*from* × 6
Nos. 41/133	*from* × 2
Nos. D1/5	*from* × 10
Nos. D6/51	*from* × 20
Nos. O1/4	*from* × 3
Nos. O5/20	*from* × 15
No. O21	*from* × 2
No. O22	*from* × 15

CRIPTIONS. Most of the postage stamps up to No. 140 are ribed alternately in English and Afrikaans throughout the ts and the same applies to all the Official stamps and to Nos. /33.

RICES for Nos. 1/140 are for unused horizontal pairs, sed horizontal pairs or used singles (either inscr), *unless therwise indicated.*

ERPRINT SETTINGS. Between 1923 and 1928 the King rge V definitives of South Africa, Types **2** and **3**, and the ious postage due stamps were issued overprinted for use in th West Africa. A number of overprint settings were used:

- etting I – Overprint Types **1** and **2** ("Zuid-West Afrika"). 14 mm between lines of overprint. See Nos. 1/12 and D1/9
- etting II – As Setting I, but 10 mm between lines of overprint. See Nos. 13/15 and D10/13
- etting III – Overprint Types **3** ("Zuidwest Afrika") and **4**. "South West" 14 mm long. "Zuidwest" 11 mm long. 14 mm between lines of overprint. See Nos. 16/27 and D14/17
- etting IV – As Setting III, but "South West" 16 mm long, "Zuidwest" 12 mm long and 14 mm between lines of overprint. See Nos. 28 and D17*a*/20
- etting V – As Setting IV, but 12 mm between lines of overprint. See Nos. D21/4
- etting VI – As Setting IV, but 9½ mm between lines of overprint. See Nos. 29/40 and D25/32.

South West — Africa. (1)   Zuid-West — Afrika. (2)

23 (1 Jan–17 June). *Nos. 3/4, 6 and 9/17 of South Africa optd alternately with T* **1** *and* **2** *by typography.*

		Un pair	Us pair	Us single
	(a) Setting I (14 mm between lines of opt)			
	½d. green	2·50	9·00	1·00
	a. "Wes" for "West" (R. 20/8)	80·00	£120	
	b. "Afr ica" (R. 20/2)	£120		
	c. Litho opt in shiny ink (17 June)	9·00	50·00	4·75
	1d. rose-red	3·25	9·00	1·00
	a. Opt inverted	£475		
	b. "Wes" for "West" (R. 12/2)	£150		
	c. "Af.rica" for "Africa" (R. 20/6)	£150	£180	
	d. Opt double	£850		
	e. "Afr ica" (R. 20/2)	£120		
	f. "Afrika" without stop (R. 17/8)	£250		
3	2d. dull purple	4·25	12·00	1·50
	a. Opt inverted	£550	£600	
	b. "Wes" for "West" (R. 20/8)	£250		
	c. Litho opt in shiny ink (30 Mar)	38·00	£100	10·00
4	3d. ultramarine	7·50	16·00	2·75
5	4d. orange-yellow and sage-green	13·00	45·00	4·00
	a. Litho opt in shiny ink (19 Apr)	35·00	70·00	8·00
6	6d. black and violet	8·00	40·00	4·00
	a. Litho opt in shiny ink (19 Apr)	35·00	75·00	7·50
7	1s. orange-yellow	23·00	48·00	5·00
	a. Litho opt in shiny ink (19 Apr)	60·00	£110	11·00
	b. "Afrika" without stop (R. 17/8)			
8	1s. 3d. pale violet	30·00	55·00	5·50
	a. Opt inverted	£325		
	b. Litho opt in shiny ink (19 Apr)	75·00	£140	14·00
9	2s. 6d. purple and green	60·00	£130	18·00
	a. Litho opt in shiny ink (19 Apr)	£130	£275	35·00
10	5s. purple and blue	£140	£325	50·00
11	10s. blue and olive-green	£1300	£2500	£400
12	£1 green and red	£700	£1700	£250
1/12	*Set of* 12	£2000	£4250	£650
1s/12s	Optd "Specimen" *Set of 12 singles*	£1300		

Nos. 1/12 were overprinted in complete sheets of 240 (4 panes 6×10).

No. 3b shows traces of a type spacer to the right of where the "t" should have been. This spacer is not visible on Nos. 1a and 2b.

Minor varieties, such as broken "t" in "West", were caused by worn type. Stamps showing one line of overprint only or with the lower line above the upper line due to overprint misplacement may also be found. All values exist showing a faint stop after "Afrika" on R. 17/8, but only examples of the 1d. and 1s. have been seen with it completely omitted.

	(b) Setting II (10 mm between lines of opt) (31 Mar)			
13	5s. purple and blue	£140	£250	45·00
	a. "Afrika" without stop (R.6/1)	£1000	£1100	£225
14	10s. blue and olive-green	£500	£850	£140
	a. "Afrika" without stop (R.6/1)	£2250	£2750	£550
15	£1 green and red	£1000	£1400	£200
	a. "Afrika" without stop (R.6/1)	£4000	£5000	£1000
13/15	*Set of* 3	£1500	£2250	£350

Nos. 13/15 were overprinted in separate panes of 60 (6×10).

Examples of most values are known showing a forged Windhoek postmark dated "30 SEP 24".

Zuidwest — Afrika. (3)   South West — Africa. (4)

1923 (15 July)–**26**. *Nos. 3/4, 6 and 9/17 of South Africa optd as T* **3** *("Zuidwest" in one word, without hyphen) and* **4** *alternately.*

	(a) Setting III ("South West" 14 mm long, "Zuidwest" 11 mm long, 14 mm between lines of opt)			
16	½d. green (5.9.24)	6·00	35·00	3·75
	a. "outh" for "South" (R. 1/1)	£1500		
17	1d. rose-red (28.9.23)	5·50	9·00	1·40
	a. "outh" for "South" (R. 1/1)	£1500		
18	2d. dull purple (28.9.23)	5·50	9·00	1·25
	a. Opt double	£950		
19	3d. ultramarine	5·00	10·00	1·25
20	4d. orange-yellow and sage-green	6·00	21·00	2·75
	w. Wmk inverted	†	†	—
21	6d. black and violet (28.9.23)	14·00	45·00	5·00
22	1s. orange-yellow	14·00	45·00	5·00
23	1s. 3d. pale violet	29·00	45·00	5·50
24	2s. 6d. purple and green	45·00	80·00	10·00
25	5s. purple and blue	60·00	£130	18·00
26	10s. blue and olive-green	£160	£250	40·00
27	£1 green and red (28.9.23)	£300	£400	60·00
16/27	*Set of* 12	£600	£1000	£140

Nos. 16/27 were overprinted in complete sheets of 240 (4 panes 6×10).

Two sets may be made with this overprint, one with bold lettering, and the other from September 1924, with thinner lettering and smaller stops.

	(b) Setting IV ("South West" 16 mm long, "Zuidwest" 12 mm long, 14 mm between lines of opt)			
28	2s. 6d purple and green (29.6.24)	80·00	£150	28·00

No. 28 was overprinted on two panes of 60 horizontally side by side.

	(c) Setting VI ("South West" 16 mm long, "Zuidwest" 12 mm long, 9½ mm between lines of opt)			
29	½d. green (16.12.25)	7·00	40·00	5·00
30	1d. rose-red (9.12.24)	3·25	10·00	1·40
	a. Opt omitted (in pair with normal)	£1300		
31	2d. dull purple (9.12.24)	5·00	22·00	1·75
32	3d. ultramarine (31.1.26)	4·50	29·00	2·75
	a. Deep bright blue (20.4.26)	42·00	95·00	12·00
33	4d. orge-yellow & sage-grn (9.12.24)	6·50	42·00	4·00
34	6d. black and violet (9.12.24)	9·00	48·00	5·00
35	1s. orange-yellow (9.12.24)	11·00	48·00	5·00
36	1s. 3d. pale violet (9.12.24)	15·00	48·00	5·00
37	2s. 6d. purple and green (9.12.24)	28·00	70·00	10·00
38	5s. purple and blue (31.1.26)	42·00	£100	14·00
39	10s. blue and olive-green (9.12.24)	65·00	£130	20·00
40	£1 green and red (9.1.26)	£225	£400	55·00
	a. Pale olive-green and red (8.11.26)	£225	£400	65·00
29/40*a*	*Set of* 12	£375	£850	£120
35s, 39s/40s	H/S "Specimen" *Set of* 3	£500		

Nos. 29/40 were overprinted in complete sheets of 240 (4 panes of 6×10) with, initially, "South West Africa" 16½ mm long on the upper two panes and 16 mm long on the lower two. This order was subsequently reversed. For printings from 8 November 1926 all four panes showed the 16½ mm measurement. No. 40*a* only comes from this printing.

Examples of most values are known showing a forged Windhoek postmark dated "30 SEP 24".

Suidwes — Afrika. (5)   South West — Africa. (6)

1926 (1 Jan–1 May). *Nos. 30/2 of South Africa optd with T* **5** *(on stamps inscr in Afrikaans) and* **6** *(on stamps inscr in English) sideways, alternately in black.*

41	½d. black and green	3·75	9·00	1·00
42	1d. black and carmine	3·00	8·00	80
43	6d. green and orange (1 May)	25·00	48·00	7·00
41/3	*Set of* 3	28·00	60·00	8·00

SOUTH WEST AFRICA (7)   SUIDWES-AFRIKA (8)

1926. *No. 33 of South Africa, imperf, optd. (a) With T* **7** *(English)*

		Single stamps	
44A	4d. grey-blue	75	3·00
	(b) With T **8** *(Afrikaans)*		
44B	4d. grey-blue	75	3·00

1927. *As Nos. 41/3, but Afrikaans opt on stamp inscr in English and vice versa.*

45	½d. black and green	1·60	6·00	80
	a. "Africa" without stop (R.13/8)	£150		
46	1d. black and carmine	1·60	2·50	50
	a. "Africa" without stop (R.13/8)	£275		
47	6d. green and orange	11·00	26·00	3·00
	a. "Africa" without stop (R.13/8)	£170		
45/7	*Set of* 3	13·00	30·00	3·75

SOUTH WEST AFRICA (9)   S.W.A. (10)   S.W.A. (11)

1927. *As No. 44A, but overprint T* **9**.

		Single stamps	
48	4d. grey-blue	6·00	19·00
	s. Handstamped "Specimen"	70·00	

1927 (Apr). *Nos. 34/9 of South Africa optd alternately as T* **5** *and* **6**, *in blue, but with lines of overprint spaced 16 mm.*

49	2d. grey and purple	4·75	15·00	1·75
50	3d. black and red	4·75	26·00	2·50
51	1s. brown and blue	15·00	32·00	4·00
52	2s. 6d. green and brown	35·00	85·00	13·00
53	5s. black and green	75·00	£160	20·00
54	10s. blue and bistre-brown	65·00	£130	20·00
49/54	*Set of* 6	£180	£400	50·00
49s/51s, 54s	H/S "Specimen" *Set of* 4	£350		

A variety of Nos. 49, 50, 51 and 54, with spacing 16½ mm between lines of overprint, occurs in the third vertical row of each sheet.

1927. *As No. 44, but perf 11½ by John Meinert Ltd, Windhoek.*

		Single stamps	
	(a) Optd with T **7** *(English)*		
55A	4d. grey-blue	80	4·25
	a. Imperf between (pair)	32·00	70·00
	s. Handstamped "Specimen"	70·00	
	(b) Optd with T **8** *(Afrikaans)*		
55B	4d. grey-blue	80	4·25
	a. Imperf between (pair)	32·00	70·00
	s. Handstamped "Specimen"	70·00	

1927 (Aug)–**30**. *Optd with T* **10**. *(a) On Nos. 13 and 17a of South Africa.*

		Single stamps	
56	1s. 3d. pale violet	1·25	6·50
	a. Without stop after "A" (R. 3/4)	£100	
	s. Handstamped "Specimen"	75·00	
57	£1 pale olive-green and red	90·00	£160
	a. Without stop after "A" (R. 3/4)	£1400	£2250

	(b) On Nos. 30/2 and 34/9 of South Africa	Un pair	Us pair	Us single
58	½d. black and green	2·00	6·50	80
	a. Without stop after "A"	40·00	75·00	
	b. "S.W.A." opt above value	2·75	15·00	2·25
	c. As b, in vert pair, top stamp without opt	£500		
59	1d. black and carmine	1·25	3·25	55
	a. Without stop after "A"	40·00	75·00	
	b. "S.W.A." opt at top (30.4.30)	1·75	14·00	1·60
	c. As b, in vert pair, top stamp without opt	£450		
60	2d. grey and maroon	9·00	23·00	1·50
	c. Perf 14×13½	15·00	30·00	
	ca. Without stop after "A"	75·00	£110	
	cb. Opt double, one inverted	£700	£900	
61	3d. black and red	6·00	23·00	3·25
	a. Without stop after "A"	75·00	£120	
	b. Perf 14×13½	11·00	38·00	
	ba. Without stop after "A"	75·00	£120	
	bb. Without stop after "W"	£150		
62	4d. brown (4.28)	15·00	40·00	7·00
	a. Without stop after "A"	85·00	£130	
	b. Perf 14×13½	20·00	48·00	
63	6d. green and orange	11·00	22·00	2·75
	a. Without stop after "A"	£110		
64	1s. brown and deep blue	20·00	48·00	5·00
	b. Perf 14×13½	40·00	80·00	
	ba. Without stop after "A"	£1300	—	£350
65	2s. 6d. green and brown	40·00	85·00	12·00
	a. Without stop after "A"	£160	£275	
	b. Perf 14×13½	65·00	£110	
	ba. Without stop after "A"	£180	£300	
66	5s. black and green	60·00	£120	18·00
	a. Without stop after "A"	£225	£375	
	b. Perf 14×13½	90·00	£150	
	ba. Without stop after "A"	£225	£375	
67	10s. bright blue and brown	£100	£190	28·00
	a. Without stop after "A"	£325	£550	
58/67	*Set of* 10	£225	£500	70·00
58s/61s, 63s/7s	H/S "Specimen" *Set of* 9	£550		

On the ½d., 1d. and 6d. the missing stop variety occurs three times on each sheet, R.1/7, 13/4 and one position not yet identified. For the other values it comes on R.2/3 of the right pane and, for the 2s. 6d., 5s. and 10s., on R.8/1 of the left pane.

The missing stop after "W" on the 3d. occurs on R. 10/5 of the right pane.

The overprint is normally found at the base of the ½d., 1d., 6d., 1s. 3d. and £1 values and at the top of the remainder.

Examples of all values are known showing a forged Windhoek postmark dated "20 MAR 31".

1930–31. *Nos. 42 and 43 of South Africa (rotogravure printing) optd with T* **10**.

68	½d. black and green (1931)	8·00	26·00	2·75
69	1d. black and carmine	6·00	25·00	2·75

1930 (27 Nov–Dec). *Air. Nos.* 40/1 *of South Africa optd.*

(*a*) *As T* **10**.

No.	Description	Un single	Us single
70	4d. green (*first printing*)	10·00	28·00
	a. No stop after "A" of "S.W.A."	65·00	£130
	b. Later printings	7·00	28·00
71	1s. orange (*first printing*)	70·00	£120
	a. No stop after "A" of "S.W.A."	£425	£550
	b. Later printings	11·00	50·00

First printing: Thick letters, blurred impression. Stops with rounded corners.

Later printings: Thinner letters, clear impression. Clean cut, square stops.

(*b*) *As T* **11** (12.30)

No.	Description		
72	4d. green	1·25	6·00
	a. Opt double	£170	
	b. Opt inverted	£170	
73	1s. orange	3·75	15·00
	a. Opt double	£500	

12 Kori Bustard

13 Cape Cross

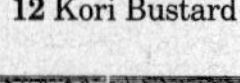

14 Bogenfels

15 Windhoek

16 Waterberg

17 Luderitz Bay

18 Bush Scene

19 Elands

20 Mountain Zebra and Blue Wildebeests

21 Herero Huts

22 Welwitschia Plant

23 Okuwahaken Falls

24 Monoplane over Windhoek

25 Biplane over Windhoek

(Recess B.W.)

1931 (5 Mar). *T* **12** *to* **25** (*inscr alternately in English and Afrikaans*). *W* **9** *of South Africa. P* 14 × 13½. (*a*) *Postage.*

No.	Description			
74	½d. black and emerald	2·25	2·50	10
75	1d. indigo and scarlet	2·25	2·50	10
76	2d. blue and brown	70	3·50	15
	w. Wmk inverted	£375		
77	3d. grey-blue and blue	70	4·25	15
78	4d. green and purple	1·75	7·00	20
79	6d. blue and brown	1·50	9·00	20
80	1s. chocolate and blue	1·50	9·00	25
81	1s. 3d. violet and yellow	7·50	11·00	50
82	2s. 6d. carmine and grey	20·00	24·00	1·75
83	5s. sage-green and red-brown	16·00	40·00	2·75
84	10s. red-brown and emerald	45·00	50·00	6·00
85	20s. lake and blue-green	80·00	90·00	10·00
	(*b*) *Air*			
86	3d. brown and blue	25·00	30·00	2·50
87	10d. black and purple-brown	35·00	65·00	5·00
74/87	*Set of* 14	£200	£300	27·00

Examples of most values are known showing a forged Windhoek postmark dated "20 MAR 31".

26

(Recess B.W.)

1935 (1 May). *Silver Jubilee. Inscr bilingually. W* **9** *of South Africa. P* 14 × 13½.

No.	Type	Description	Un single	Us single
88	**26**	1d. black and scarlet	1·00	25
89		2d. black and sepia	1·00	25
90		3d. black and blue	10·00	18·00
91		6d. black and purple	4·50	10·00
88/91		*Set of* 4	15·00	26·00

1935–36. *Voortrekker Memorial Fund. Nos.* 50/3 *of South Africa optd with T* **10**.

No.	Description			
92	½d. + ½d. black and green	1·50	5·50	75
	a. Opt inverted	£275		
93	1d. + ½d. grey-black and pink	1·50	3·25	40
94	2d. + 1d. grey-green and purple	5·50	6·00	80
	a. Without stop after "A"	£200	£225	
	b. Opt double	£225		
95	3d. + 1½d. grey-green and blue	16·00	32·00	4·00
	a. Without stop after "A"	£250	£300	
92/5	*Set of* 4	22·00	42·00	5·50

27 Mail Train

28

(Recess B.W.)

1937 (1 Mar). *W* **9** *of South Africa. P* 14 × 13½.

No.	Type	Description			
96	**27**	1½d. purple-brown	20·00	3·00	25

(Recess B.W.)

1937 (12 May). *Coronation. W* **9** *of South Africa* (*sideways*). *P* 13½×14.

No.	Type	Description			
97	**28**	½d. black and emerald	40	15	10
98		1d. black and scarlet	40	15	10
99		1½d. black and orange	40	15	10
100		2d. black and brown	40	15	10
101		3d. black and blue	50	15	10
102		4d. black and purple	50	20	10
103		6d. black and yellow	50	2·00	20
104		1s. black and grey-black	55	2·50	25
97/104		*Set of* 8	3·25	5·00	65

1938 (14 Dec). *Voortrekker Centenary Memorial. Nos.* 76/9 *of South Africa optd as T* **11**.

No.	Description			
105	½d. + ½d. blue and green	8·00	17·00	1·75
106	1d. + 1d. blue and carmine	18·00	10·00	1·00
107	1½d. + 1½d. chocolate & blue-green	22·00	22·00	2·75
108	3d. + 3d. bright blue	42·00	50·00	6·50
105/8	*Set of* 4	80·00	90·00	11·00

1938 (14 Dec). *Voortrekker Commemoration. Nos.* 80/1 *of South Africa optd as T* **11**.

No.	Description			
109	1d. blue and carmine	10·00	16·00	1·50
	a. Three bolts in wheel rim	42·00		
110	1½d. greenish blue and brown	12·00	18·00	1·75

1939 (17 July). *250th Anniv of Landing of Huguenots in South Africa and Huguenot Commemoration Fund. Nos.* 82/4 *of South Africa optd as T* **11**.

No.	Description			
111	½d. + ½d. brown and green	12·00	12·00	1·10
112	1d. + 1d. green and carmine	15·00	12·00	1·25
113	1½d. + 1½d. blue-green and purple	22·00	12·00	1·25
111/13	*Set of* 3	45·00	32·00	3·25

SWA	SWA	SWA	S W A
(29)	(30)	(31)	(32)

1941 (1 Oct)–**43**. *War Effort. Nos.* 88/96 *of South Africa optd with T* **29** *or* **30** (*3d. and 1s.*). (*a*) *Inscr alternately.*

No.	Description			
114	½d. green (1.12.41)	75	3·50	20
	a. Blue-green (1942)	65	2·00	15
115	1d. carmine (1.11.41)	55	2·25	15
	a. "Stain" on uniform	7·00		
116	1½d. myrtle-green (21.1.42)	55	2·50	15
117	3d. blue	22·00	18·00	1·00
	a. Cigarette flaw	60·00		
118	4d. orange-brown	6·50	12·00	1·00
	a. Red-brown	18·00	24·00	3·00
119	6d. red-orange	2·50	3·25	50
120	1s. 3d. olive-brown (15.1.43)	11·00	16·00	1·25

(*b*) *Inscr bilingually*

No.	Description	Un single	Us single
121	2d. violet	50	60
122	1s. brown (17.11.41)	60	60
114/22	*Set of* 7 *pairs and* 2 *singles*	40·00	50·00

1943–44. *War Effort (reduced sizes). Nos.* 97/104 *of* Africa, optd with T **29** (1½d. *and* 1s., *No.* 130), *or T* **31** (*ot*

(*a*) *Inscr alternately*

No.	Description	Un unit	Us unit	s
123	½d. blue-green (T)	50	3·25	
	a. Green	4·00	4·50	
	b. Greenish blue	4·00	4·50	
124	1d. carmine-red (T)	1·75	3·50	
	a. Bright carmine	2·50	4·00	
125	1½d. red-brown (P)	50	75	
126	2d. violet (P)	5·50	3·75	
	a. Reddish violet	8·00	4·00	
	b. Apostrophe flaw	20·00		
127	3d. blue (T)	3·25	15·00	
128	6d. red-orange (P)	5·50	2·75	
	a. Opt inverted	£450		
	(*b*) *Inscr bilingually*			
129	4d. slate-green (T)	2·00	16·00	
	a. Opt inverted	£550	£350	5
130	1s. brown (opt T **29**) (P)	11·00	23·00	
	a. Opt inverted	£450	£325	
	b. Opt T **31** (1944)	4·00	5·00	
	c. Opt T **31** inverted	£400	£300	4
	d. "Bursting shell"	30·00		
123/30*b*	*Set of* 8	20·00	45·00	

The "units" referred to above consist of pairs (P) or triplets (

No. 128 exists with another type of opt as Type **31**, but broader "s", narrower "w" and more space between the letters.

1945. *Victory. Nos.* 108/10 *of South Africa optd with T* **30**.

No.	Description		
131	1d. brown and carmine	25	50
	a. Opt inverted	£250	£275
132	2d. slate-blue and violet	30	55
133	3d. deep blue and blue	1·25	90
131/3	*Set of* 3	1·60	1·75

1947 (17 Feb). *Royal Visit. Nos.* 111/13 *of South Africa opt* *T* **31**, *but* 8½ × 2 *mm.*

No.	Description		
134	1d. black and carmine	10	10
135	2d. violet	10	25
	a. "Bird" on "2"	6·00	
136	3d. blue	15	25
134/6	*Set of* 3	30	50

1948 (26 Apr). *Royal Silver Wedding. No.* 125 *of South Af* *optd as T* **31**, *but* 4 × 2 *mm.*

No.	Description		
137	3d. blue and silver	1·00	35

1949 (1 Oct). *75th Anniv of U.P.U. Nos.* 128/30 *of South Af* *optd as T* **30**, *but* 13 × 4 *mm.*

No.	Description		
138	½d. blue-green	75	1·50
139	1½d. brown-red	75	1·00
140	3d. bright blue	1·00	1·00
	a. Serif on "C"	22·00	
	b. "Lake" in East Africa	27·00	
138/40	*Set of* 3	2·50	3·25

1949 (1 Dec). *Inauguration of Voortrekker Monument, Preto* *Nos.* 131/3 *of South Africa optd with T* **32**.

No.	Description	Un single	si
141	1d. magenta	10	
142	1½d. blue-green	10	
143	3d. blue	15	
141/3	*Set of* 3	30	

POSTAGE DUE STAMPS

PRICES for Nos. D1/39 are for unused horizontal pairs, us horizontal pairs and used singles.

1923 (1 Jan–July). *Optd with T* **1** *and* **2** *alternately.*

(*a*) *Setting* I (*14 mm between lines of overprint*) (i) *On Nos.* D5/6 *of Transvaal*

No.	Description			
D1	5d. black and violet	4·00	50·00	11
	a. "Wes" for "West" (R. 8/6, 10/2 left pane)	£140		
	b. "Afrika" without stop (R. 6/1)	85·00		
D2	6d. black and red-brown	17·00	50·00	11·
	a. "Wes" for "West" (R. 10/2)	£275		
	b. "Afrika" without stop (R. 6/1, 7/2)	£160		
	(ii) *On Nos.* D3/4 *and* D6 *of South Africa* (*De La Rue printing*			
D3	2d. black and violet	25·00	48·00	10·(
	a. "Wes" for "West" (R. 10/2)	£180	£250	
	b. "Afrika" without stop (R. 6/1, 7/2)	£180		
D4	3d. black and blue	13·00	48·00	10·
	a. "Wes" for "West" (R. 10/2)	£130		
D5	6d. black and slate (20 Apr)	26·00	55·00	13·(
	a. "Wes" for "West" (R. 8/6)	£160		
	(iii) *On Nos.* D9/10, D11 *and* D14 *of South Africa* (*Pretoria printings*)			
D6	½d. black and green (*p* 14)	6·00	28·00	5·5
	a. Opt inverted	£425		
	b. Opt double	£800	£850	
	c. "Wes" for "West" (R. 10/2)	80·00		
	d. "Afrika" without stop (R. 6/1, 7/2)	80·00		
D7	1d. black and rose (*roul*)	7·00	30·00	6·
	a. "Wes" for "West" (R. 10/2)	90·00		
	b. "Afrika" without stop (R. 6/1)	90·00		
	c. Imperf between (horiz pair)	£1100		
D8	1½d. black and yellow-brown (*roul*)	1·25	14·00	2·7
	a. "Wes" for "West" (R. 8/6, 10/2)	75·00		
	b. "Afrika" without stop (R. 6/1)	75·00		
D9	2d. black and violet (*p* 14) (21 June)	3·50	25·00	5·0
	a. "Wes" for "West" (R. 8/6)	85·00		
	b. "Afrika" without stop (R. 6/1)	£100		

Nos. D1/9 were initially overprinted as separate panes of 6 but some values were later done as double panes of 120.

A variety of Nos. D1, D4/5 and D9 with 15 mm between the lines of overprint occurs on four positions in each pane fro some printings.

etting II (10 *mm between lines of overprint*). (i) *On No.* D5 *of Transvaal*
5d. black and violet (20 Apr) .. 55·00 £150

ii) *On Nos.* D3/4 *of South Africa* (*De La Rue printing*)
2d. black and violet (20 Apr) .. 17·00 45·00 9·00
a. "Afrika" without stop (R.6/1) £160
3d. black and blue (20 Apr) .. 7·50 27·00 5·50
a. "Afrika" without stop (R.6/1) 85·00

ii) *On No.* D9 *of South Africa* (*Pretoria printing*). *Roul*
1d. black and rose (July) .. £8500 —£1500

(30 July)–**26**. *Optd as T* **3** ("Zuidwest" *in one word* *thout hyphen*) *and* **4**.

Setting III ("South West" 14 *mm long*, "Zuidwest" 11 *mm long and* 14 *mm between lines of overprint*).

(i) *On No.* D6 *of Transvaal*
6d. black and red-brown .. .. 21·00 85·00 20·00

n Nos. D9 *and* D11/12 *of South Africa* (*Pretoria printing*)
½d. black and green (*p* 14) .. 11·00 28·00 5·50
1d. black and rose (*roul*) .. 3·75 28·00 5·50
1d. black and rose (*p* 14) (2.8.23) 14·00 28·00 5·50

Setting IV ("South West" 16 *mm long*, "Zuidwest" 12 *mm long and* 14 *mm between lines of overprint*).

(i) *On No.* D5 *of Transvaal*
ı 5d. black and violet (1.7.24) .. £450 £900

(ii) *On Nos.* D11/12 *and* D16 *of South Africa* (*Pretoria printing*). *P* 14
½d. black and green (1.7.24) .. 7·50 28·00 5·50
1d. black and rose (1.7.24) .. 5·50 28·00 5·50
6d. black and slate (1.7.24) .. 2·25 42·00 9·00
a. "Africa" without stop (R.9/5) £120

(*c*) *Setting* V (12 *mm between lines of overprint*).

(i) *On No.* D5 *of Transvaal*
5d. black and violet (6.8.24) .. 4·00 48·00 9·00

(ii) *On No.* D4 *of South Africa* (*De La Rue printing*)
3d. black and blue (6.8.24) .. 16·00 50·00 11·00

On Nos. D11 *and* D13 *of South Africa* (*Pretoria printing*). *P* 14
½d. black and green (6.8.24) .. 3·00 29·00 6·50
1½d. black & yellow-brown (6.8.24) 5·00 40·00 7·50

(*d*) *Setting* VI (9½ *mm between lines of overprint*).

(i) *On No.* D5 *of Transvaal*
5d. black and violet (7.9.24) .. 2·75 18·00 3·50
a. "Africa" without stop (R. 9/5) 70·00

(ii) *On No.* D4 *of South Africa* (*De La Rue printing*)
3d. black and blue (3.2.26) .. 7·00 55·00 11·00

i) *On Nos.* D11/16 *of South Africa* (*Pretoria printing*). *P* 14
½d. black and green (1.3.26) .. 9·50 35·00 7·50
1d. black and rose (16.3.25) .. 2·00 11·00 1·60
a. "Africa" without stop (R. 9/5 right pane) .. .. .. 75·00
1½d. black & yellow-brown (1.10.26) 4·50 32·00 6·50
a. "Africa" without stop (R. 9/5 right pane) .. .. .. 80·00
2d. black and violet (7.9.24) .. 2·50 18·00 3·50
a. "Africa" without stop (R. 9/5) right pane) .. .. .. 65·00
3d. black and blue (6.5.26) .. 4·50 19·00 3·75
a. "Africa" without stop (R. 9/5) right pane) .. .. .. 70·00
6d. black and slate (1.10.26) .. 9·00 50·00 14·00
a. "Africa" without stop (R. 9/5 right pane) £130
7/32 .. .. .. *Set of* 6 29·00 £150 32·00

For Setting VI the overprint was applied to sheets of 120 (2 nes of 60) of the 1d., 3d. and 6d., and to individual panes of 60 the other values. The two measurements of "South West", as tailed under No. 40, also occur on the postage dues. Nos. D25 d D31/2 show it 16 mm long, No. 27 16½ mm long and the ner stamps can be found with either measurement. In addition the complete panes the 16½ mm long "South West" also curs on R.2/4 in the 16 mm left pane for Nos. D28 and D30/2.

Suidwes **Afrika.** (D 1)

South West **Africa.** (D 2)

27 (14 May–27 Sept). *Optd as Types* D **1** *and* D **2**, *alternately*, 12 *mm between lines of overprint*. (*a*) *On No.* D5 *of Transvaal*.
33 5d. black and violet (27 Sept) .. 19·00 85·00 23·00

b) *On Nos.* D13/16 *of South Africa* (*Pretoria printing*). *P* 14
34 1½d. black and yellow-brown .. 1·00 18·00 3·50
35 2d. black and pale violet (27 Sept) 4·75 14·00 3·25
a. Black and deep violet .. 7·50 15·00 3·50
37 3d. black and blue (27 Sept) .. 13·00 45·00 11·00
38 6d. black and slate (27 Sept) .. 7·50 35·00 8·50

(*c*) *On No.* D18 *of South Africa* (*Pretoria printing*). *P* 14
39 1d. black and carmine .. .. 1·00 10·00 2·25
33/9 .. .. .. *Set of* 6 42·00 £190 45·00

No. D33 was overprinted in panes of 60 and the remainder as mplete sheets of 120.

Examples of all values can be found with very small or very int stops from various positions in the sheet.

928–29. *Optd with T* **10**. (*a*) *On Nos.* D15/16 *of South Africa*

		Un Single	*Us Single*
40	3d. black and blue	1·50	14·00
	a. Without stop after "A" (R.3/6) ..	30·00	
41	6d. black and slate	6·00	27·00
	a. Without stop after "A" (R.3/6) ..	£120	
	(*b*) *On Nos.* D17/21 *of South Africa*		
42	½d. black and green	50	8·00
43	1d. black and carmine	50	3·25
	a. Without stop after "A" (R.3/6) ..	40·00	
44	2d. black and mauve	50	4·50
	a. Without stop after "A" (R.3/6) ..	55·00	
D45	3d. black and blue	2·25	26·00
D46	6d. black and slate	1·50	20·00
	a. Without stop after "A" (R.3/6) ..	45·00	
D42/6	.. .. .. *Set of* 5	4·75	55·00

D 3

(Litho B.W.)

1931 (23 Feb). *Inscribed bilingually*. W **9** *of South Africa*. *P* 12.

D47	D **3** ½d. black and green	1·00	9·00
D48	1d. black and scarlet	1·00	1·25
D49	2d. black and violet	1·00	2·75
D50	3d. black and blue	4·25	17·00
D51	6d. black and slate	13·00	27·00
D47/51	.. .. .. *Set of* 5	18·00	50·00

OFFICIAL STAMPS

OFFICIAL South West Africa. (O 1)

OFFISIEEL Suidwes Afrika. (O 2)

1926 (Dec). *Nos.* 30, 31, 6 *and* 32 *of South Africa optd with Type* O **1** *on English stamp and* O **2** *on Afrikaans stamp alternately*.

		Un pair	*Us pair*	*Us single*
O1	½d. black and green	70·00	£170	30·00
O2	1d. black and carmine	70·00	£170	30·00
O3	2d. dull purple	£160	£275	45·00
O4	6d. green and orange	90·00	£160	30·00
O1/4	.. .. .. *Set of* 4	£350	£700	£120

OFFICIAL S.W.A. (O 3)

OFFISIEEL S.W.A. (O 4)

1929 (May). *Nos.* 30, 31, 32 *and* 34 *of South Africa optd with Type* O **3** *on English stamp and* O **4** *on Afrikaans stamp*.

O5	½d. black and green	1·00	14·00	2·75
O6	1d. black and carmine	1·00	14·00	2·75
	w. Wmk inverted	£200		
O7	2d. grey and purple	1·50	19·00	3·50
	a. Pair, stamp without stop after "OFFICIAL" ..	5·50	42·00	
	b. Pair, stamp without stop after "OFFISIEEL"	5·50	42·00	
	c. Pair, comprising a and b ..	16·00	80·00	
O8	6d. green and orange	2·00	19·00	3·75
O5/8	.. .. *Set of* 4	5·00	60·00	11·50

Types O 3 and O 4 are normally spaced 17 mm between lines on all except the 2d. value, which is spaced 13 mm.

Except on No. O7, the words "OFFICIAL" or "OFFISIEEL" normally have no stops after them.

OFFICIAL S.W.A. (O 5)

OFFISIEEL S.W.A. (O 6)

OFFICIAL. S.W.A. (O 7)

OFFISIEEL. S.W.A. (O 8)

1929 (Aug). *Nos.* 30, 31 *and* 32 *of South Africa optd with Types* O **5** *and* O **6**, *and No.* 34 *with Types* O **7** *and* O **8**, *languages to correspond*.

O 9	½d. black and green	75	14·00	2·75
O10	1d. black and carmine	1·00	14·00	2·75
O11	2d. grey and purple	1·00	14·00	3·25
	a. Pair, one stamp without stop after "OFFICIAL" ..	3·75	40·00	
	b. Pair, one stamp without stop after "OFFISIEEL"	3·75	40·00	
	c. Pair, comprising a and b ..	18·00	90·00	
O12	6d. green and orange	2·50	27·00	6·50
O9/12	.. .. *Set of* 4	4·75	60·00	13·50

Examples of Nos. O1/12 are known showing forged Windhoek postmarks dated "30 SEP 24" or "20 MAR 31".

OFFICIAL (O 9)

OFFISIEEL (O 10)

1931. *English stamp optd with Type* O **9** *and Afrikaans stamp with Type* O **10** *in red*.

O13	**12**	½d. black and emerald	10·00	17·00	3·50
O14	**13**	1d. indigo and scarlet	75	17·00	3·50
O15	**14**	2d. blue and brown	2·00	10·00	2·25
O16	**17**	6d. blue and brown	2·75	14·00	3·25
O13/16		.. .. .. *Set of* 4	14·00	50·00	11·50

OFFICIAL (O 11)

OFFISIEEL (O 12)

1938 (1 July). *English stamp optd with Type* O **11** *and Afrikaans with Type* O **12** *in red*.

O17	**27**	1½d. purple-brown	25·00	45·00	6·00

OFFICIAL (O 13)

OFFISIEEL (O 14)

1945–50. *English stamp optd with Type* O **13**, *and Afrikaans stamp with Type* O **14** *in red*.

O18	**12**	½d. black and emerald	13·00	27·00	5·00
O19	**13**	1d. indigo and scarlet (1950) ..	5·00	16·00	3·25
		a. Opt double	£425		
O20	**27**	1½d. purple-brown	45·00	45·00	6·50
O21	**14**	2d. blue and brown (1947?) ..	£475	£600	£100
O22	**17**	6d. blue and brown	14·00	48·00	7·00
O18/20, O22		.. .. *Set of* 4	70·00	£120	20·00

OFFICIAL (O 15)

OFFISIEEL (O 16)

1951 (16 Nov)–**52**. *English stamp optd with Type* O **15** *and Afrikaans stamp with Type* O **16**, *in red*.

O23	**12**	½d. black and emerald (1952) ..	13·00	20·00	4·50
O24	**13**	1d. indigo and scarlet	4·00	14·00	1·75
		a. Opts transposed	80·00	£140	
O25	**27**	1½d. purple-brown	24·00	24·00	5·00
		a. Opts transposed	70·00	80·00	
O26	**14**	2d. blue and brown	1·50	16·00	3·50
		a. Opts transposed	50·00	£140	
O27	**17**	6d. blue and brown	2·75	38·00	7·50
		a. Opts transposed	22·00	£110	
O23/7		.. .. *Set of* 5	40·00	£100	20·00

The above errors refer to stamps with the English overprint on Afrikaans stamp and *vice versa*.

The use of official stamps ceased in January 1955.

Sudan

ANGLO-EGYPTIAN CONDOMINIUM

An Egyptian post office was opened at Suakin in 1867 and the stamps of Egypt, including postage dues and the official (No. O64), were used in the Sudan until replaced by the overprinted "SOUDAN" issue of 1897.

Cancellations have been identified from eleven post offices, using the following postmark types:

A

B

C

D

E

F

G

H

I

J

K

L

BERBER (*spelt* BARBAR). *Open* 1 October 1873 *to* 20 May 1884. *Postmark type* G.
DABROUSSA. *Open* 1891 *onwards. Postmark as type* J *but with* 11 *bars in arcs.*
DONGOLA. *Open* 1 October 1873 *to* 13 June 1885 *and* 1896 *onwards. Postmark types* F, G, K, L.
GEDAREF. *Open* August 1878 *to* April 1884. *Postmark type* H.
KASSALA. *Open* 15 May 1875 *to* 30 July 1885. *Postmark type* G.
KHARTOUM. *Open* 1 October 1873 *to* 14 December 1885. *Postmark types* E (*spelt* KARTUM), G (*spelt* HARTUM), I (*with or without line of Arabic above date*).
KORTI. *Open* January *to* March 1885 *and* 1897. *Postmark type* K.
SUAKIN. *Open* November 1867 *onwards. Postmark types* A, B, C (*spelt* SUAKIM), D (*spelt* SUAKIM *and also with year replaced by concentric arcs*), I (*spelt* SOUAKIN), J (*spelt* SAWAKIN, *number of bars differs*).
TANI. *Open* 1885. *Postmark type* K.
TOKAR. *Open* 1891 *onwards. Postmark type* J (7 *bars in arcs*).
WADI HALFA. *Open* 1 October 1873 *onwards. Postmark types* F (*spelt* WADI HALFE), G (*spelt* WADI HALFE), I, J (*number of bars differs*).
WADI HALFA CAMP. *Open* 1896 *onwards. Postmark type* I.

Official records also list post offices at the following locations, but no genuine postal markings from them have yet been reported: Chaka, Dara, Debeira, El Abiad, El Fasher, El Kalabat, Faras, Fashoda, Fazogl, Ishkeit, Kalkal, Karkok, Mesellemia, Sara, Sennar and Taoufikia (not to be confused with the town of the same name in Egypt).

M

The post office at Kassala was operated by Italy from 1894 until 1896, using stamps of Eritrea cancelled with postmark type M.

From the last years of the nineteenth century that part of Sudan lying south of the 5 degree North latitude line was administered by Uganda (the area to the east of the Nile) (until 1912) or by Belgium (the area to the west of the Nile, known as the Lado Enclave) (until 1910).

Stamps of Uganda or East Africa and Uganda were used at Gondokoro and Nimuli between 1901 and 1911, usually cancelled with circular date stamps or, probably in transit at Khartoum, by a lozenge-shaped grid of 18 × 17 dots.

Stamps of Belgian Congo were used from the Lado Enclave between 1897 and 1910, as were those of Uganda (1901–10) and Sudan (1902–10), although no local postmarks were supplied, examples being initially cancelled in manuscript.

Stamps of Sudan were used at Gambeila (Ethiopia) between 1910 and 10 June 1940 and from 22 March 1941 until 15 October 1956. Sudan stamps were also used at Sabderat (Eritrea) between March 1910 and 1940.

PRICES FOR STAMPS ON COVER TO 1945	
Nos. 1/9	*from* × 20
Nos. 10/17	*from* × 6
Nos. 18/29	*from* × 5
Nos. 30/95	*from* × 2
Nos. D1/11	*from* × 30
Nos. O1/3	*from* × 10
Nos. O4/22	*from* × 15
Nos. A1/16	*from* × 6

(Currency. 10 milliemes = 1 piastre. 100 piastres = £1 Sudanese)

السودان
SOUDAN

(1)

1897 (1 Mar). *Nos. 54b, 55a, 57/a, 58a, 59, 60, 62a and 63 of Egypt optd as T* 1 *by Govt Ptg Wks, Būlāq, Cairo.*

No.	Description	Unused	Used
1	1 m. pale brown	2·00	2·00
	a. Opt inverted	£200	
	b. Opt omitted (in vert pair with normal)	£1000	
	c. Deep brown	2·00	2·25
	w. Wmk inverted		
3	2 m. green	1·25	1·75
	a. Opt omitted (in vert pair with normal)	£3000	
4	3 m. orange-yellow	1·40	1·50
	a. Opt omitted (in vert pair with normal)	£3000	
5	5 m. rose-carmine	2·00	70
	a. Opt inverted	£200	£225
	b. Opt omitted (in vert pair with normal)	£1100	
6	1 p. ultramarine	7·00	2·00
7	2 p. orange-brown	45·00	16·00
	w. Wmk inverted	75·00	
8	5 p. slate	45·00	
	a. Opt double	£3000	
	b. Opt omitted (in vert pair with normal)	£3000	
9	10 p. mauve	30·00	
1/9	*Set of* 8	£120	

Numerous forgeries exist including some which sho[…] characteristics of the varieties mentioned below.

There are six varieties of the overprint on each value. Ve[…] strips of 6 showing them are worth a premium.

In some printings the large dot is omitted from the lef[…] Arabic character on one stamp in the pane of 60.

Only two examples, one unused and the other used ([…] Royal Collection), are known of No. 8a. In both instance[…] impression is partially albino.

PRINTERS. All stamps of Sudan were printed by De La Rue Ltd, London, *except where otherwise stated.*

2 Arab Postman

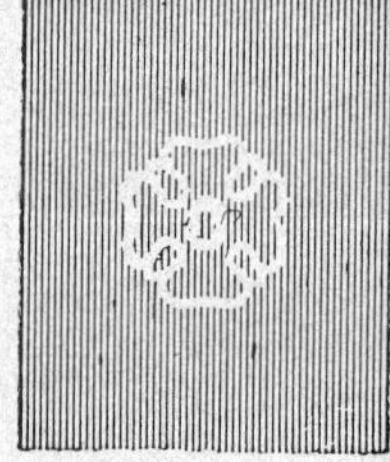
3

(Des E. A. Stanton. Typo)

1898 (1 Mar). *W* **3**. *P* 14.

No.	Type	Description	Unused	Used
10	**2**	1 m. brown and pink	65	
11		2 m. green and brown	2·00	
12		3 m. mauve and green	2·00	
13		5 m. carmine and black	1·75	
14		1 p. blue and brown	5·50	
15		2 p. black and blue	22·00	
16		5 p. brown and green	28·00	
17		10 p. black and mauve	25·00	
10/17		*Set of* 8	75·00	

4

5 Milliemes

(5)

1902–21. *W* 4. *Ordinary paper. P* 14.

No.	Type	Description	Unused	Used
18	**2**	1 m. brown and carmine (5.05)	1·25	
19		2 m. green and brown (11.02)	1·75	
20		3 m. mauve and green (3.03)	2·25	
21		4 m. blue and bistre (20.1.07)	1·50	
22		4 m. vermilion and brown (10.07)	1·50	
23		5 m. scarlet and black (12.03)	2·00	
		w. Wmk inverted	†	£
24		1 p. blue and brown (12.03)	2·25	
25		2 p. black and blue (2.08)	24·00	
26		2 p. purple & orge-yellow (*chalk-surfaced paper*) (22.12.21)	3·75	1[…]
27		5 p. brown and green (2.08)	22·00	
		a. Chalk-surfaced paper	28·00	
28		10 p. black and mauve (2.11)	22·00	
		a. Chalk-surfaced paper	25·00	
18/28		*Set of* 11	75·00	1[…]

1903 (Sept). *No.* 16 *surch at Khartoum with T* **5**, *in block[…]* 30.

No.	Type	Description	Unused	Used
29	**2**	5 m. on 5 pi. brown and green	6·50	9[…]
		a. Surch inverted	£250	£[…]

6

7

1921–23. *Chalk-surfaced paper. Typo. W* **4**. *P* 14.

No.	Type	Description	Unused	Used
30	**6**	1 m. black and orange (4.2.22)	80	4[…]
31		2 m. yellow-orange and chocolate (1922)	9·00	11[…]
		a. Yellow and chocolate (1923)	11·00	11[…]
32		3 m. mauve and green (25.1.22)	2·50	8[…]
33		4 m. green and chocolate (21.3.22)	6·00	3[…]
34		5 m. olive-brown and black (4.2.22)	2·25	
35		10 m. carmine and black (1922)	3·00	
36		15 m. bright blue and chestnut (14.12.21)	2·75	1[…]
30/36		*Set of* 7	24·00	25[…]

1927–41. *W* **7**. *Chalk-surfaced paper. P* 14.

No.	Type	Description	Unused	Used
37	**6**	1 m. black and orange	70	
		a. Ordinary paper (1941)	70	
38		2 m. orange and chocolate	60	
		a. Ordinary paper (1941)	1·50	
39		3 m. mauve and green	70	
		a. Ordinary paper (1941)	2·75	
40	**6**	4 m. green and chocolate	60	
		a. Ordinary paper (1941)	3·50	
		aw. Wmk inverted	75·00	75·[…]
41		5 m. olive-brown and black	60	
		a. Ordinary paper (1941)	2·50	

10 m. carmine and black	.. ..	1·50	10
a. Ordinary paper (1941)	.. ..	3·00	10
15 m. bright blue and chestnut	.. ..	1·50	10
a. Ordinary paper (1941)	.. ..	1·50	10
2 2 p. purple and orange-yellow	.. ..	1·50	10
a. Ordinary paper (1941)	.. ..	4·00	10
3 p. red-brown and blue (1.1.40)	..	2·75	10
ba. Ordinary paper (1941)	..	16·00	10
4 p. ultramarine and black (2.11.36)	..	3·50	10
5 p. chestnut and green	.. ..	1·25	10
a. Ordinary paper (1941)	.. ..	5·00	1·25
6 p. greenish blue and black (2.11.36)		6·00	1·25
ba. Ordinary paper (1941)	.. ..	29·00	1·25
8 p. emerald and black (2.11.36)	..	6·00	2·50
ca. Ordinary paper (1941)	.. ..	32·00	4·00
10 p. black and reddish purple	.. ..	3·00	10
a. Ordinary paper. *Black and bright mauve* (1941)	.. ..	8·50	70
20 p. pale blue and blue (17.10.35)	..	3·00	10
ba. Ordinary paper (1941)	.. ..	5·00	10
b	*Set of* 15	29·00	3·75

e ordinary paper of this issue is thick, smooth and opaque was a wartime substitute for chalk-surfaced paper.

similar stamps, but with different Arabic inscriptions, see 96/111.

MAIL (8) AIR MAIL (9) AIR — Extended foot to "R" (R.5/12)

(15 Feb–Mar). *Air. Nos.* 41/2 *and* 44 *optd with T* **8** *or* **9** p.).

5 m. olive-brown and black (Mar)	..	35	70
10 m. carmine and black ..	..	85	9·50
2 p. purple and orange-yellow	.. ..	85	7·50
a. Extended foot to "R"	.. ..	24·00	
.. ..	*Set of* 3	1·90	16·00

2½ 2½

10 Statue of Gen. Gordon

AIR MAIL (11)

(1 Sept)–37. *Air. Recess. W* **7** *(sideways*). P* 14.

10 3 m. green and sepia (1.1.33)	.. ..	2·50	6·00
5 m. black and green ..	.. ..	1·00	10
10 m. black and carmine	.. ..	1·00	20
15 m. red-brown and sepia	.. ..	40	10
aw. Wmk top of G to right	.. ..		
b. Perf $11^1/_2\times12^1/_2$ (1937)	.. ..	4·50	10
2 p. black and orange	.. ..	30	10
ax. Wmk reversed	.. ..		
b. Perf $11^1/_2\times12^1/_2$ (1937)	.. ..	4·50	15·00
$2^1/_2$ p. magenta and blue (1.1.33)	..	3·50	10
d. Perf $11^1/_2\times12^1/_2$ (1936)	.. ..	3·00	10
da. Aniline magenta and blue	.. ..	7·50	3·50
dx. Wmk reversed	.. ..		
dy. Wmk sideways inverted (top of G to right) and reversed	.. ..		
3 p. black and grey	.. ..	60	15
a. Perf $11^1/_2\times12^1/_2$ (1937)	.. ..	85	35
$3^1/_2$ p. black and violet ..	.. ..	1·50	80
a. Perf $11^1/_2\times12^1/_2$ (1937)	.. ..	2·50	11·00
ay. Wmk sideways inverted (top of G to right) and reversed	.. ..	†	—
$4^1/_2$ p. red-brown and grey	.. ..	10·00	15·00
5 p. black and ultramarine	.. ..	1·00	30
a. Perf $11^1/_2\times12^1/_2$ (1937)	.. ..	3·75	35
$7^1/_2$ p. green and emerald (17.10.35)	..	9·50	4·75
by. Wmk sideways inverted (top of G to right) and reversed	.. ..		
c. Perf $11^1/_2\times12^1/_2$ (1937)	.. ..	4·00	10·00
10 p. brown and greenish blue (17.10.35)		9·00	1·75
e. Perf $11^1/_2\times12^1/_2$ (1937)	.. ..	4·00	18·00
ey. Wmk sideways inverted (top of G to right) and reversed	.. ..		
/57d	*Set of* 12 (*p* 14)	35·00	25·00
/7e	*Set of* 8 (*p* $11^1/_2\times12^1/_2$)	24·00	48·00

The normal sideways watermark shows the top of the G nting left *as seen from the back of the stamp.*

32 (18 July). *Air. No.* 44 *surch with T* **11**.

2 $2^1/_2$ p. on 2 p. purple and orange-yellow	..	1·40	3·50

12 Gen. Gordon (after C. Ouless)

13 Gordon Memorial College, Khartoum

14 Gordon Memorial Service, Khartoum (after R. C. Woodville)

1935 (1 Jan). *50th Death Anniv of General Gordon. Recess. W* **7**. *P* 14.

59	**12**	5 m. green	35	10
60		10 m. yellow-brown	85	25
61		13 m. ultramarine	85	9·50
62		15 m. scarlet	1·75	25
63	**13**	2 p. blue	1·25	20
64		5 p. orange-vermilion	1·25	40
65		10 p. purple	7·50	8·50
66	**14**	20 p. black	22·00	48·00
67		50 p. red-brown	80·00	£110
59/67		.. .. .. *Set of* 9	£100	£160

7½ PIASTRES (15) 5 MILLIEMES (16)

1935. *Air. Nos.* 49*b*/51 *and* 56 *surch as T* **15**.

68	**10**	15 m. on 10 m. black and carmine (Apr) ..	40	10
		a. Surch double	£600	£700
69		$2^1/_2$ p. on 3 m. green and sepia (Apr) ..	85	5·50
		a. Second arabic letter from left missing	50·00	£100
		b. Small "½"	2·25	20·00
70		$2^1/_2$ p. on 5 m. black and green (Apr)	50	1·50
		a. Second Arabic letter from left missing	25·00	55·00
		b. Small "½"	1·25	8·00
		c. Surch inverted	£650	£750
		d. Ditto with variety a. ..	£3250	
		e. Ditto with variety b. ..	£1300	£1400
71		3 p. on $4^1/_2$ p. red-brown and grey (Apr)	1·75	15·00
72		$7^1/_2$ p. on $4^1/_2$ p. red-brown and grey (Mar)	6·50	48·00
73		10 p. on $4^1/_2$ p. red-brown and grey (Mar)	6·50	48·00
68/73		.. .. .. *Set of* 6	15·00	£110

Nos. 69a and 70a occur in position 49 of the sheet of 50; the small "½" variety occurs in positions 17, 27, 32, 36, 41, 42 and 46.

The 15 m. on 10 m. surcharged in red and the $2^1/_2$ p. on 3 m. and $2^1/_2$ p., on 5 m. in green are from proof sheets; the latter two items being known cancelled (*Price, £200 each, unused*).

There were four proof sheets of the $7^1/_2$ p. on $4^1/_2$ p., two in red and two in black. The setting on these proof sheets showed three errors subsequently corrected before No. 72 was surcharged. Twelve positions showed an Arabic "⅓" instead of "½", one an English "¼" for "½" and another one of the Arabic letters inverted.

1938 (1 July). *Air. Nos.* 53*d*, 55, 57*b and* 57*d surch as T* **16**.

74	**10**	5 m. on $2^1/_2$ p. mag & bl (*p* $11^1/_2\times12^1/_2$)	3·50	10
		w. Wmk top of G to right ..		
		x. Wmk reversed		
75		3 p. on $3^1/_2$ p. black and violet (*p* 14)	35·00	48·00
		a. Perf $11^1/_2\times12^1/_2$	£425	£550
76		3 p. on $7^1/_2$ p, green and emerald (*p* 14)	7·00	6·50
		ax. Wmk reversed		
		ay. Wmk sideways inverted (top of G to right) and reversed	50·00	
		b. Perf $11^1/_2\times12^1/_2$	£425	£550
77		5 p. on 10 p. brown & greenish bl (*p* 14)	1·75	4·75
		a. Perf $11^1/_2\times12^1/_2$	£425	£550
74/7		.. .. .. *Set of* 4	42·00	55·00

A 5 p. on $2^1/_2$ p., perf $11^1/_2\times12^1/_2$, exists either mint or cancelled from a trial printing (*Price £350 unused*).

5 Mills. (17) Normal ("Malime")

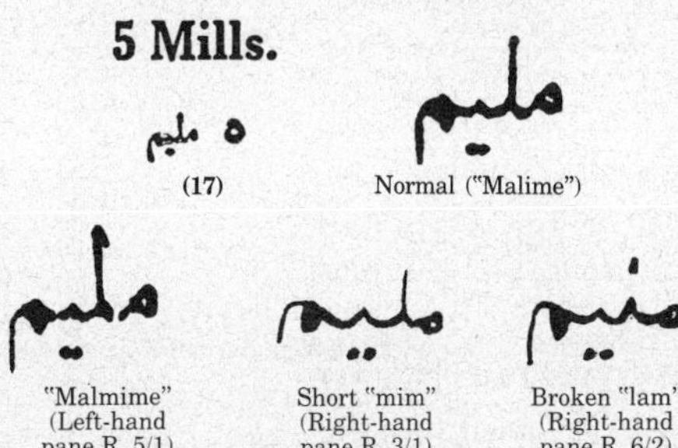

"Malmime" (Left-hand pane R. 5/1) Short "mim" (Right-hand pane R. 3/1) Broken "lam" (Right-hand pane R. 6/2)

5 M

Inserted "5" (Bottom right-hand pane R. 4/5)

1940 (25 Feb). *No.* 42 *surch with T* **17** *by McCorquodale (Sudan) Ltd, Khartoum.*

78	**6**	5 m. on 10 m. carmine and black	50	30
		a. "Malmime"	55·00	65·00
		b. Two dots omitted (Right-hand pane R. 8/6)	55·00	65·00
		c. Short "mim"	55·00	65·00
		d. Broken "lam"	55·00	65·00
		e. Inserted "5"	£150	

4½ PIASTRES (18) 4½ Piastres (19)

1940–1. *Nos.* 41 *and* 45*c surch as T* **18** *or* **19** *at Khartoum.*

79	**6**	$4^1/_2$ p. on 5 m. olive-brown & blk (9.2.41) ..	48·00	5·00
80	**2**	$4^1/_2$ p. on 8 p. emerald and black (12.12.40)	40·00	9·00

20 Tuti Island, R. Nile, near Khartoum

21 Tuti Island, R. Nile near Khartoum

(Des Miss H. M. Hebbert. Litho Security Printing Press, Nasik, India)

1941 (25 Mar–10 Aug). *P* 14 × 13½ (*T* **20**) *or P* 13½ × 14 (*T* **21**).

81	**20**	1 m. slate and orange (10.8)	1·25	3·50
82		2 m. orange and chocolate (10.8)	1·25	3·50
83		3 m. mauve and green (10.8)	1·25	20
84		4 m. green and chocolate (10.8)	80	60
85		5 m. olive-brown and black (10.8)	30	10
86		10 m. carmine and black (10.8)	7·00	1·75
87		15 m. bright blue and chestnut ..	80	10
88	**21**	2 p. purple and orange-yellow (10.8) ..	4·50	60
89		3 p. red-brown and blue	80	10
90		4 p. ultramarine and black	1·00	10
91		5 p. chestnut and green (10.8) ..	5·00	8·50
92		6 p. greenish blue and black (10.8) ..	18·00	40
93		8 p. emerald and black (10.8)	14·00	45
94		10 p. slate and purple (10.8)	50·00	75
95		20 p. pale blue and blue (10.8)	50·00	30·00
81/95		.. .. .. *Set of* 15	£140	45·00

22

23

1948 (1 Jan–June). *Arabic inscriptions below camel altered. Typo. W* **7**. *Ordinary paper* (8, 10, 20 *p.*) *or chalk-surfaced paper (others). P* 14.

96	**22**	1 m. black and orange	35	3·25
97		2 m. orange and chocolate	80	4·25
98		3 m. mauve and green	30	3·75
99		4 m. deep green and chocolate ..	30	30
100		5 m. olive-brown and black	5·00	1·75
		w. Wmk inverted	75·00	
101		10 m. rose-red and black	5·00	10
		a. Centre inverted	†	—
102		15 m. ultramarine and chestnut ..	4·50	10
103	**23**	2 p. purple and orange-yellow ..	7·00	2·00
104		3 p. red-brown and deep blue ..	6·00	30
105		4 p. ultramarine and black	4·00	1·75
106		5 p. brown-orange and deep green	4·00	2·00
107		6 p. greenish blue and black ..	4·50	3·00
108		8 p. bluish green and black ..	4·50	3·00
109		10 p. black and mauve	11·00	4·00
		a. Chalk-surfaced paper (June) ..	30·00	4·75
110		20 p. pale blue and deep blue ..	4·50	30
		a. Perf 13. Chalk-surfaced paper (June)	50·00	£170
111		50 p. carmine and ultramarine ..	6·50	2·00
96/111		.. .. .. *Set of* 16	60·00	28·00

A single used example is known of No. 101a.

For similar stamps, but with different Arabic inscriptions, see Nos. 37/46*b*.

24

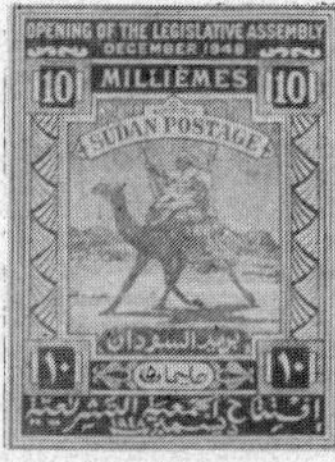

25

1948 (1 Oct). *Golden Jubilee of "Camel Postman" design. Chalk-surfaced paper. Typo. W* **7**. *P* 13.

112	**24**	2 p. black and light blue	20	10

1948 (23 Dec). *Opening of Legislative Assembly. Chalk-surfaced paper. Typo. W* **7**. *P* 13.

113	**25**	10 m. rose-red and black	30	10
114		5 p. brown-orange and deep green	70	1·25

26 Blue Nile Bridge, Khartoum

(Des Col. W. L. Atkinson ($2^1/_2$ p., 6 p.), G. R. Wilson (3 p.), others from photographs. Recess)

1950 (1 July). *Air. T* **26** *and similar horiz designs. W* **7**. *P* 12.

115	2 p. black and blue-green	4·50	1·25
116	$2^1/_2$ p. light blue and red-orange ..	75	1·00
117	3 p. reddish purple and blue ..	3·00	1·00
118	$3^1/_2$ p. purple-brown and yellow-brown	2·00	2·75

119 4 p. brown and light blue .. .. .. 1·25 2·50
120 4½ p. black and ultramarine .. .. .. 2·50 3·50
a. *Black and steel-blue* .. .. .. 8·50 6·50
121 6 p. black and carmine .. .. .. 2·00 3·00
122 20 p. black and purple .. .. .. 2·25 5·00
115/122 .. .. *Set of* 8 16·00 18·00

Designs:—2½ p. Kassala Jebel; 3 p. Sagia (water wheel); 3½ p. Port Sudan; 4 p. Gordon Memorial College; 4½ p. *Gordon Pasha* (Nile mail boat); 6 p. Suakin; 20 p. G.P.O., Khartoum.

34 Ibex

35 Cotton Picking

(Des Col. W. L. Atkinson (1 m., 2 m., 4 m., 5 m., 10 m., 3 p., 3½ p., 20 p.), Col. E. A. Stanton (50 p.) others from photographs. Typo)

1951 (1 Sept)–**62?**. *Designs as T* **34/5**. *Chalk-surfaced paper. W* **7**. *P* 14 (*millieme values*) *or* 13 (*piastre values*).

123 1 m. black and orange .. .. .. 1·25 1·25
124 2 m. black and bright blue .. .. .. 1·75 80
125 3 m. black and green .. .. .. 6·50 3·00
126 4 m. black and yellow-green .. .. .. 1·50 3·00
127 5 m. black and purple .. .. .. 2·25 10
a. *Black and reddish purple* (11.61*) .. 6·00 50
128 10 m. black and pale blue 30 10
129 15 m. black and chestnut .. .. .. 3·50 10
a. *Black and brown-orange* (1961*) .. 4·50 10
130 2 p. deep blue and pale blue 30 10
a. *Deep blue and very pale blue* (1960*) 4·00 10
131 3 p. brown and dull ultramarine .. .. 6·50 10
a. *Brown and deep blue* (9.60*) .. 9·00 1·25
132 3½ p. bright green and red-brown .. .. 2·00 10
a. *Light emerald and red-brown* (11.61*) 4·00 10
133 4 p. ultramarine and black .. .. 1·25 10
a. *Deep blue and black* (7.59*) .. 7·00 10
134 5 p. orange-brown and yellow-green .. 50 10
135 6 p. blue and black .. .. .. 8·00 2·50
a. *Deep blue and black* (1962?) .. 16·00 6·50
136 8 p. blue and brown .. .. .. 13·00 2·75
a. *Deep blue and brown* (1962?) .. 16·00 2·50
137 10 p. black and green .. .. .. 1·50 10
138 20 p. blue-green and black .. .. .. 5·00 1·75
139 50 p. carmine and black .. .. .. 13·00 1·75
123/39 .. .. *Set of* 17 60·00 15·00

Designs: *Vert as T* **34**—2 m. Whale-headed Stork; 3 m. Giraffe; 4 m. Baggara girl; 5 m. Shilluk warrior; 10 m. Hadendowa; 15 m. Policeman. *Horiz as T* **35**—3 p. Ambatch reed canoe; 3½ p. Nuba wrestlers; 4 p. Weaving; 5 p. Saluka farming; 6 p. Gum tapping; 8 p. Darfur chief; 10 p. Stack Laboratory; 20 p. Nile Lechwe. *Vert as T* **35**—50 p. Camel postman.

*Earliest known postmark date.

STAMP BOOKLETS

Nos. SB1/4 have one cover inscribed in English and one in Arabic.

1912 (Dec). *Black on pink cover, size* 74×29 *mm. Stapled.*
SB1 100 m. booklet containing twenty 5 m. (No. 23) in pairs £650

1924. *Black on pink cover, size* 45×50 *mm. Stapled.*
SB2 105 m. booklet containing twenty 5 m. (No. 34) in blocks of 4 .. ..

1926. *Black on pink cover, size* 45×50 *mm. Stapled.*
SB3 105 m. booklet containing twenty 5 m. (No. 41) in blocks of 4 .. ..

No examples of No. SB3 are known to have survived.

1930. *Black on pink cover, size* 45×50 *mm. Stapled.*
SB4 100 m. booklet containing twenty 5 m. (No. 41) in blocks of 4 .. .. £950

Some supplies of No. SB4 included a page of air mail labels.

POSTAGE DUE STAMPS

1897 (1 Mar). *Type* D **24** *of Egypt, optd with T* **1** *at Bûlâq.*
D1 2 m. green .. .. 1·75 5·00
a. Opt omitted (in horiz pair with normal) £2250
D2 4 m. maroon .. .. 1·75 5·00
a. Bisected (2 m.) (on cover) .. .. † —
D3 1 p. ultramarine .. .. 10·00 3·50
D4 2 p. orange .. .. 10·00 7·00
a. Bisected (1 p.) (on cover) .. .. † £1200
D1/4 .. .. .. *Set of* 4 21·00 18·00

In some printings the large dot is omitted from the left-hand Arabic character on one stamp in the pane.

No. D1 has been recorded used as a bisect.

D 1 Gunboat *Zafir* D 2

1901 (1 Jan)–**26**. *Typo. W* **4** (*sideways*). *Ordinary paper. P* 14.
D5 D **1** 2 m. black and brown 55 60
a. Wmk upright (1912) .. .. £150 60·00
b. Chalk-surfaced paper (6.24*) .. 75 5·00
D6 4 m. brown and green .. .. 2·00 90
a. Chalk-surfaced paper (9.26*) .. 5·00 1·75
D7 10 m. green and mauve .. .. 3·75 3·75
a. Wmk upright (1912) .. .. £100 50·00
b. Chalk-surfaced paper (6.24*) .. 10·00 9·00
D8 20 m. ultramarine and carmine .. 3·25 3·25
D5/8 .. .. .. *Set of* 4 8·00 7·50

*Dates quoted for the chalk-surfaced paper printings are those of the earliest recorded postal use. These printings were despatched to the Sudan in March 1922 (10 m.) or September 1922 (others)).

The 4 m is known bisected at Khartoum or Omdurman in November/December 1901 and the 20 m. at El Obeid in 1904–05.

1927–30. *W* **7**. *Chalk-surfaced paper. P* 14.
D 9 D **1** 2 m. black and brown (1930) .. 2·50 2·50
D10 4 m. brown and green .. .. 1·00 80
D11 10 m. green and mauve .. .. 1·25 1·60
a. Ordinary paper .. .. .. 18·00
D9/11 .. .. .. *Set of* 3 4·25 4·50

1948 (1 Jan). *Arabic inscriptions at foot altered. Chalk-surfaced paper. Typo. W* **7**. *P* 14.
D12 D **2** 2 m. black and brown-orange .. 1·00 32·00
D13 4 m. brown and green .. .. 2·00 32·00
D14 10 m. green and mauve .. .. 18·00 18·00
D15 20 m. ultramarine and carmine .. 18·00 32·00
D12/15 .. .. .. *Set of* 4 35·00 £100

The 10 and 20 m. were reissued in 1980 on Sudan arms watermarked paper.

OFFICIAL STAMPS

1900 (8 Feb). *5 mils of* 1897 *punctured* "S G" *by hand. The* "S" *has* 14 *and the* "G" 12 *holes.*
O1 5 m. rose-carmine .. .. .. 45·00 16·00

1901 (Jan). *1 m. wmk Quatrefoil, punctured as No.* O1.
O2 1 m. brown and pink .. .. .. 42·00 30·00

Nos. O1/2 are found with the punctured "SG" inverted, reversed or inverted and reversed.

O.S.G.S. O.S.G.S.

(O 1) ("On Sudan Government Service") (O 2)

1902. *No.* 10 *optd at Khartoum as Type* O **1** *in groups of* 30 *stamps.*
O3 **2** 1 m. brown and pink .. .. 2·00 8·50
a. Oval "O" (No. 19) .. .. 40·00 £110
b. Round stops. (Nos. 25 to 30) .. 7·50 40·00
c. Opt inverted £250 £350
d. Ditto and oval "O" £2500
e. Ditto and round stops £600 £750
f. Opt double £350
g. Ditto and round stops £800
h. Ditto and oval "O" .. ..

1903–12. *T* **2** *optd as Type* O **2**, *by D.L.R. in sheets of* 120 *stamps.*

(i) *Wmk Quatrefoil* (3.06)

O 4 10 p. black and mauve .. .. 13·00 24·00
a. Malformed "O" £120

(ii) *Wmk Mult Star and Crescent*

O 5 1 m. brown and carmine (9.04) .. 50 10
a. Opt double .. .. ..
b. Malformed "O" .. .. .. 19·00
O 6 3 m. mauve and green (2.04) .. 2·50 15
a. Opt double £850 £850
b. Malformed "O" .. .. .. 42·00
O 7 5 m. scarlet and black (1.1.03) .. 2·50 10
a. Malformed "O" .. .. .. 42·00
O 8 1 p. blue and brown (1.1.03) .. 2·50 10
a. Malformed "O" .. .. .. 42·00
O 9 2 p. black and blue (1.1.03) .. 22·00 20
a. Malformed "O" £150
O10 5 p. brown and green (1.1.03) .. 2·00 30
a. Malformed "O" .. .. .. 45·00
O11 10 p. black and mauve (9.12) .. 4·00 50·00
a. Malformed "O" .. .. .. 65·00
O4/11 .. .. .. *Set of* 8 45·00 65·00

The malformed "O" is slightly flattened on the left-hand side and occurs on position 7 of the lower pane.

1913 (Jan)–**22**. *Nos.* 18/20 *and* 23/8 *punctured* "SG" *by machine. The* "S" *has* 12 *holes and the* "G" 13.
O12 **2** 1 m. brown and carmine .. .. 7·00 25
O13 2 m. green and brown (1915) .. 8·00 7·50
O14 3 m. mauve and green .. .. 11·00 70
O15 5 m. scarlet and black .. .. 4·50 15
O16 1 p. blue and brown .. .. 6·50 35
O17 2 p. black and blue .. .. 14·00 65
O18 2 p. purple and orange-yellow (*chalk-surfaced paper*) (1922) .. 5·50 8·00
O19 5 p. brown and green .. .. 25·00 1·50
a. Chalk-surfaced paper .. .. 25·00 3·75
O20 10 p. black and mauve (1914) .. 32·00 32·00
a. Chalk-surfaced paper .. .. 32·00 32·00
O12/20 .. .. .. *Set of* 9 £100 45·00

1922. *Nos.* 32/5 *punctured* "SG" *by machine. The* "S" *has* 9 *holes and the* "G" 10.
O21 **6** 3 m. mauve and green .. .. 16·00 14·00
O22 4 m. green and chocolate .. .. 17·00 9·00
O23 5 m. olive-brown and black .. .. 2·00 1·50
O24 10 m. carmine and black .. .. 2·25 1·50
O21/4 .. .. .. *Set of* 4 32·00 23·00

1927–30. *Nos.* 39/42, 44, 45 *and* 46 *punctured* "SG" *by machine. Nos.* O25/8 *have* 9 *holes in the* "S" *and* 10 *in the* "G"; *Nos.* O29/31 12 *holes in the* "S" *and* 13 *in the* "G".
O25 **6** 3 m. mauve and green (1928) .. 11·00 3·25
O26 4 m. green and chocolate (1930) .. 70·00 48·00
O27 5 m. olive-green and black .. .. 4·75 10
O28 10 m. carmine and black .. .. 12·00 35
O29 **2** 2 p. purple and orange-yellow .. 15·00 1·00
O30 5 p. chestnut and green .. .. 18·00 3·50
O31 10 p. black and reddish purple .. 35·00 10·00
O25/31 .. .. .. *Set of* 7 £150 60·00

The use of Nos. O25/31 on internal official mail ceased in 1932, but they continued to be required for official mail to foreign destinations until replaced by Nos. O32/46 in 1936.

S.G. S.G. S.G.

(O 3) (O 4) (O 4*a*)

1936 (19 Sept)–**46**. *Nos.* 37a, 38a, 39/43 *optd with Type and* 44, 44ba, 44*c*, 45, 45ba, 45ca, 46 *and* 46ba *with Typ W* **7**. *P* 14.
O32 **6** 1 m. black and orange (22.11.46) .. 2·25
a. Opt double .. .. .. †
O33 2 m. orange and chocolate (*ordinary paper*) (4.45) 80
a. Chalk-surfaced paper .. .. —
O34 3 m. mauve and green (*chalk-surfaced paper*) (1.37) .. .. .. 2·75
O35 4 m. green and chocolate (*chalk-surfaced paper*) .. .. .. 3·25
O36 5 m. olive-brown and black (*chalk-surfaced paper*) (3.40) .. .. 2·25
a. Ordinary paper .. .. .. 18·00
O37 10 m. carmine and black (*chalk-surfaced paper*) (6.46) 90
O38 15 m. bright blue and chestnut (*chalk-surfaced paper*) (21.6.37) .. 7·00
a. Ordinary paper .. .. .. 40·00
O39 **2** 2 p. purple and orange-yellow (*chalk-surfaced paper*) (4.37) .. .. 13·00
a. Ordinary paper .. .. .. 32·00
O39*b* 3 p. red-brown and blue (4.46) .. 5·50
O39*c* 4 p. ultramarine and black (*chalk-surfaced paper*) (4.46) .. .. 26·00
ca. Ordinary paper .. .. .. 50·00
O40 5 p. chestnut and green (*chalk-surfaced paper*) .. .. .. 16·00
a. Ordinary paper .. .. .. 55·00
O40*b* 6 p. greenish blue and black (4.46) .. 7·50
O40*c* 8 p. emerald and black (4.46) .. 5·50 2
O41 10 p. black and reddish purple (*chalk-surfaced paper*) (10.37) .. .. 30·00
a. Ordinary paper. *Black and bright mauve* (1941) .. .. .. 48·00
O42 20 p. pale blue and blue (6.46) .. 27·00 2
O32/42 .. .. .. *Set of* 15 £130 7

1948 (1 Jan). *Nos.* 96/102 *optd with Type* O **3**, *and* 103/111 *Type* O **4**.
O43 **22** 1 m. black and orange 30
O44 2 m. orange and chocolate .. .. 1·25
O45 3 m. mauve and green .. .. .. 3·00
O46 4 m. deep green and chocolate .. .. 3·00
O47 5 m. olive-brown and black .. .. 3·00
O48 10 m. rose-red and black .. .. .. 3·00
O49 15 m. ultramarine and chestnut .. .. 3·00
O50 **23** 2 p. purple and orange-yellow .. .. 3·00
O51 3 p. red-brown and deep blue .. .. 3·00
O52 4 p. ultramarine and black .. .. 3·00
a. Perf 13 (optd Type O **4***a*) .. .. 13·00 1
O53 5 p. brown-orange and deep green .. 3·50
O54 6 p. greenish blue and black .. .. 3·00
O55 8 p. bluish green and black .. .. 3·00
O56 10 p. black and mauve .. .. .. 4·50
O57 20 p. pale blue and deep blue .. .. 4·50
O58 50 p. carmine and ultramarine .. .. 60·00
O43/58 .. .. .. *Set of* 16 90·00

1950 (1 July). *Air. Optd with Type* O **4***a*.
O59 2 p. black and blue-green (R.) .. .. 15·00
O60 2½ p. light blue and red-orange .. .. 1·50
O61 3 p. reddish purple and blue 80
O62 3½ p. purple-brown and yellow-brown .. 80
O63 4 p. brown and light blue 80
O64 4½ p. black and ultramarine (R.) .. .. 3·75
a. *Black and steel-blue* .. .. .. 8·00
O65 6 p. black and carmine (R.) .. .. 1·00
O66 20 p. black and purple (R.) .. .. .. 4·00
O59/66 .. .. .. *Set of* 8 25·00

1951 (1 Sept)–**62**? *Nos.* 123/9 *optd with Type* O **3**, *and* 13 *with Type* O **4***a*.
O67 1 m. black and orange (R.) 40
O68 2 m. black and bright blue (R.) 50
O69 3 m. black and green (R.) .. .. 3·25 15
O70 4 m. black and yellow-green (R.) 10 5
O71 5 m. black and purple (R.) 10
O72 10 m. black and pale blue (R.) 10
O73 15 m. black and chestnut (R.) 30
O74 2 p. deep blue and pale blue 10
a. Opt inverted £500
b. *Deep blue and very pale blue* (1962?) 1·25
O75 3 p. brown and dull ultramarine .. 6·50
a. *Brown and deep blue* (1962?) .. 7·00 1
O76 3½ p. bright green and red-brown .. 25
a. *Light emerald & red-brown* (1962?) 3·25 1
O77 4 p. ultramarine and black 30
a. *Deep blue and black* (1962?) .. 2·25
O78 5 p. orange-brown and yellow-green .. 25
O79 6 p. blue and black 30 2
a. *Deep blue and black* (1962?) .. 8·00 6
O80 8 p. blue and brown 55
a. *Deep blue and brown* (1962?) .. 4·00 2
O81 10 p. black and green (R.) 50
O81*a* 10 p. black and green (Blk.) (1958) .. 13·00 2
O82 20 p. blue-green and black .. .. 1·25
a. Opt inverted .. .. .. —
O83 50 p. carmine and black .. .. 3·50 1
O67/83 .. .. .. *Set of* 18 27·00 27

The 5, 10 and 15 m. values were later reissued with a thin overprint.

ARMY SERVICE STAMPS

ARMY OFFICIAL ARMY OFFICIAL Arm Servic

(A 1) (A 2) (A 3)

(1 Jan). *T* **2** *optd at Khartoum as Types* A **1** *or* A **2**. *Wmk lt Star and Crescent.* (i) "ARMY" *reading up.*
1 m. brown and carmine (A **1**) . . . . 2·50 2·00
a. "!" for "1" . . . . 50·00 30·00
b. Opt Type A **2** . . . . 38·00 23·00
c. Pair. Types A **1** and A **2** *se-tenant* . . 75·00

(ii) *Overprint horizontal*
1 m. brown and carmine (A **1**) £325
a. "!" for "1" £3500
b. Opt Type A **2** £2000
e horizontal overprint exists with either "ARMY" or 'ICIAL" reading the right way up. It did not fit the stamps, ting in misplacements where more than one whole overprint ars, or when the two words are transposed.

(iii) "ARMY" *reading down*
1 m. brown and carmine (A **1**) . . . . 75·00 65·00
a. "!" for "1" £750 £750
b. Opt Type A **2** £650 £450

(Nov). *As No.* A1, *but wmk Quatrefoil, W* **3**.
1 m. brown and pink (A **1**) £130 £140
a. "!" for "1" £3000 £1700
b. Opt Type A **2** £1400 £1400
c. Pair. Types A **1** and A **2** *se-tenant* . . £2500
e setting used for overprinting Nos. A1/4 was 30 (6×5). The or "1" variety occurs on R. 5/4 and overprint Type A **2** on 6 and 2/6 of the setting.

Two varieties of the 1 millieme
st Ptg. 14 mm between lines of opt.
ater Ptgs. 12 mm between lines.
l other values are Type B.

(Jan)–**11.** *T* **2** *optd as Type* A **3**.
(i) *Wmk Mult Star and Crescent, W* **4**
1 m. brown and carmine (Type A) . . £300 £250
a. Opt double, one albino £300
1 m. brown and carmine (Type B) . . . . 1·50 20
a. Opt double, one diagonal . . . . † £750
b. Opt inverted £400 £425
c. Pair, one without opt . . . .
d. "Service" omitted . . . . † £3500
e. "A" for "A" in "Army" £150 £150
2 m. green and brown . . . . . . 9·50 1·00
a. Pair, one without opt £2500
b. "Army" omitted £3000
3 m. mauve and green . . . . . . 17·00 40
a. Opt inverted £1900
5 m. scarlet and black . . . . . . 1·50 10
a. Opt. double £190 £190
ab. Opt double, one diagonal £200
b. Opt inverted . . . . . . † £220
c. "Amry" . . . . . . † £2250
d. "A" for "A" in "Army" . . . . — £250
e. Opt double, one inverted £800 £375
1 p. blue and brown . . . . . . 13·00 15
a. "Army" omitted . . . . . . † £2000
2 p. black and blue (1.09) . . . . 55·00 13·00
a. Opt double . . . . . . † £3000
5 p. brown and green (5.08) . . . . £110 60·00
10 p. black and mauve (5.11) £450 £550
/10s Optd "Specimen" . . . . *Set of* 5 £110
here were a number of printings of these Army Service stamps; earlier are as Type A **3**; the 1908 printing has a narrower "A" Army" and the 1910–11 printings have the tail of the "y" in my" much shorter.

(ii) *Wmk Quatrefoil, W* **3**
2 p. black and blue . . . . . . 65·00 10·00
5 p. brown and green . . . . . . 90·00 £160
10 p. black and mauve £130 £325
/16 . . . . . . *Set of* 3 £250 £450
s/16s Optd "Specimen" . . . . *Set of* 3 £100

2 (1 Jan)–**22.** *Nos.* 18/20 *and* 23/8 *punctured* "AS" *by* *achine. The* "A" *has* 12 *holes and the* "S" 11.
7 **2** 1 m. brown and carmine . . . . 27·00 3·50
8 2 m. green and brown . . . . 6·50 70
9 3 m. mauve and green . . . . 42·00 3·00
0 5 m. scarlet and black . . . . 8·00 50
a. On No. 13 . . . .
1 1 p. blue and brown . . . . 20·00 75
2 2 p. black and blue . . . . 45·00 4·00
3 2 p. purple and orange-yellow (*chalk-surfaced paper*) (1922) . . . . 55·00 55·00
4 5 p. brown and green . . . . 55·00 25·00
a. Chalk-surfaced paper . . . . 55·00 25·00
5 10 p. black and mauve (1914) £400 £225
7/25 . . . . . . *Set of* 9 £600 £275

22–24. *Nos.* 31*a and* 34/5 *punctured* "AS" *by machine. The* "A" *has* 8 *holes and the* "S" 9.
6 **6** 2 m. yellow and chocolate (1924) . . 65·00 42·00
7 5 m. olive-brown and black (4.2.22) . . 9·50 3·75
8 10 m. carmine and black . . . . 15·00 4·25
6/8 . . . . . . *Set of* 3 80·00 45·00
The use of Nos. A17/28 on internal Army mail ceased when the yptian units were withdrawn at the end of 1924, but existing ocks continued to be used on Army mail to foreign destinations til supplies were exhausted.

Swaziland

PRICES FOR STAMPS ON COVER TO 1945

Nos. 1/10	*from* × 40
Nos. 11/20	*from* × 4
Nos. 21/4	*from* × 5
Nos. 25/7	*from* × 10
Nos. 28/38	*from* × 4
Nos. 39/41	*from* × 5
Nos. D1/2	*from* × 30

TRIPARTITE GOVERNMENT

Following internal unrest and problems caused by the multitude of commercial concessions granted by the Swazi king the British and Transvaal governments intervened during 1889 to establish a tripartite administration under which the country was controlled by their representatives, acting with the agent of the Swazi king.

The Pretoria government had previously purchased the concession to run the postal service and, on the establishment of the tripartite administration, provided overprinted Transvaal stamps for use from a post office at Embekelweni and later at Bremersdorp and Darkton.

Swazieland
(1)

1889 (18 Oct)–**90.** *Stamps of Transvaal (South African Republic) optd with T* 1, *in black.* (a) *P* 12½×12
1 **18** 1d. carmine . . . . . . 17·00 16·00
a. Opt inverted £700 £650
2 2d. olive-bistre . . . . . . 85·00 21·00
a. Opt inverted . . . . . . — £1100
b. "Swazielan" £1000 £650
3 1s. green . . . . . . 10·00 13·00
a. Opt inverted £600 £450

(*b*) *P* 12½
4 **18** ½d. grey . . . . . . 9·00 18·00
a. Opt inverted £800 £650
b. "Swazielan" £1100 £700
c. "Swazielan" inverted . . . . — £3750
5 2d. olive-bistre . . . . . . 17·00 15·00
a. Opt inverted £700 £450
b. "Swazielan" £475 £400
c. "Swazielan" inverted £3500 £3250
d. Opt double £2250
6 6d. blue . . . . . . 20·00 38·00
7 2s. 6d. buff (20.10.90) £225 £250
8 5s. slate-blue (20.10.90) £140 £180
a. Opt inverted £1600 £1800
b. "Swazielan" £4000
c. "Swazielan" inverted . . . .
9 10s. fawn (20.10.90) £4500 £3000

The variety without "d" occurs on the left-hand bottom corner stamp in each sheet of certain printings.

A printing of the ½d, 1d., 2d. and 10s. with stop after "Swazieland" was made in July 1894, but such stamps were not issued.

It is possible that the dates quoted above were those on which the overprinting took place in Pretoria and that the stamps were issued slightly later in Swaziland itself.

1892 (Aug). *Optd in carmine. P* 12½.
10 **18** ½d. grey . . . . . . 7·50 16·00
a. Opt inverted £500
b. Opt double £450 £450
c. Pair, one without opt . . . . — £1600

No. 10 was overprinted in Pretoria during August 1892 when Swaziland was under quarantine due to smallpox. It is unlikely that it saw much postal use before all the overprints were withdrawn, although cancelled-to-order examples are plentiful.

It appears likely that no further supplies of stamps overprinted "Swazieland" were provided by Pretoria after December 1892, although stocks held at post offices were used up. The overprinted stamps were declared to be invalid from 7 November 1894. They were replaced by unoverprinted issues of the Transvaal (South African Republic).

Stamps of TRANSVAAL (SOUTH AFRICAN REPUBLIC) *used in Swaziland between* December 1892 *and* January 1900.

1885–93. (*Nos.* 175/87).
Z1 ½d. grey . . . . . . 24·00
Z2 1d. carmine . . . . . . 24·00
Z3 2d. olive-bistre . . . . . . 12·00
Z4 2½d. mauve . . . . . . 24·00
Z5 3d. mauve . . . . . . 24·00
Z6 4d. bronze-green . . . . . . 24·00
Z9 2s. 6d. orange-buff . . . .

1893. (*Nos.* 195/9).
Z10 ½d. on 2d. olive-bistre (Type A surch in red) . .
Z11 ½d. on 2d. olive-bistre (Type A surch in black)
Z12 1d. on 6d. blue (Type A surch) . . . . 26·00
a. Surch Type B . . . . . . 26·00
Z13 2½d. on 1s. green ("2½ Pence" in one line) (Type A surch) . . . . 26·00
a. Surch Type B . . . . . . 26·00

1894 (*Nos.* 200/4).
Z16 1d. carmine . . . . . . 24·00
Z17 2d. olive-bistre . . . . . . 24·00

1895–96. (*Nos.* 205/12*a*)
Z20 ½d. pearl-grey . . . . . . 24·00
Z21 1d. rose-red . . . . . . 12·00
Z22 2d. olive-bistre . . . . . . 12·00
Z25 6d. pale dull blue . . . . . . 24·00

1895. (*Nos.* 213/14).
Z27 ½d. on 1s. green . . . .

1895. *Introduction of Penny Postage* (*No.* 215*b*)
Z29 1d. red . . . .

1896–97. (*Nos.* 216/24).
Z30 ½d. green . . . . . . 24·00
Z31 1d. rose-red and green . . . . 12·00
Z35 4d. sage-green and green . . . . 24·00
Z36 6d. lilac and green . . . . 24·00
Z37 1s. ochre and green . . . .

Prices are for clear and fairly complete postmarks. Examples dated in 1892 and 1893 are worth a premium. For list of post offices open during this period see boxed note below. Most known examples are from Bremersdorp (squared circle inscr "SWAZIEL" later replaced by "Z.A.R." or c.d.s.) or Darkton (c.d.s.).

Shortly after the outbreak of the Boer War in 1899 the Transvaal administration withdrew from Swaziland, although the post office at Darkton, which was on the border, was still operating in early 1900. There was, however, no further organised postal service in Swaziland until the country became a British Protectorate in March 1902. From that date, until the introduction of the 1933 definitives, the stamps of Transvaal and subsequently South Africa were in use.

The following post offices or postal agencies existed in Swaziland before 1933. Dates given are those on which it is generally accepted that the offices were first opened. Some were subsequently closed before the end of the period.

Bremersdorp (1890)	Mankaiana (1913)
Darkton (1891)	Mbabane (*previously* Embabaan) (1905)
Dwaleni (1918)	M'dimba (1898)
Embabaan (1895)	Mhlotsheni (1910)
Embekelweni (1889)	Mooihoek (1918)
Ezulweni (1910)	Motshane (1929)
Forbes Reef (1906)	Nomahasha (1904)
Goedgegun (1925)	Nsoko (1927)
Hlatikulu (1903)	Piggs Peak (1899)
Hluti (1912)	Sandhlan (1903)
Ivy (1912)	Sicunusa (1913)
Kubuta (1926)	Stegi (1910)
Mahamba (1899)	Umkwakweni (1898)
Malkerns (1914)	White Umbuluzi (1925)
Malomba (1928)	

BRITISH PROTECTORATE

2 King George V

3 King George VI

(Des Rev. C. C. Tugman. Recess D.L.R.)

1933 (2 Jan). *Wmk Mult Script CA. P* 14.
11 **2** ½d. green 30 30
12 1d. carmine 30 20
13 2d. brown 30 45
14 3d. blue . . . . . . 45 2·25
15 4d. orange . . . . . . 2·75 3·00
16 6d. bright purple . . . . . . 1·25 1·00
17 1s. olive . . . . . . 1·50 2·75
18 2s. 6d. bright violet . . . . 15·00 22·00
19 5s. grey . . . . . . 30·00 48·00
20 10s. sepia . . . . . . 80·00 £100
11/20 . . . . . . *Set of* 10 £120 £150
11s/20s Perf "Specimen" . . . . *Set of* 10 £225

The ½d, 1d., 2d. and 6d. values exist overprinted "OFFICIAL", but authority for their use was withdrawn before any were actually used. However, some stamps had already been issued to the Secretariat staff before instructions were received to invalidate their use (*Price* £12000 *per set un*).

1935 (4 May). *Silver Jubilee. As Nos.* 91/4 *of Antigua, but ptd by* B.W. *P* 11×12.
21 1d. deep blue and scarlet . . . . 50 1·50
a. Extra flagstaff £225
b. Short extra flagstaff £275
c. Lightning conductor £275
d. Flagstaff on right-hand turret . . . . 90·00
e. Double flagstaff . . . . 90·00
22 2d. ultramarine and grey-black . . . . 50 1·25
a. Extra flagstaff . . . . 95·00
b. Short extra flagstaff . . . . 90·00
c. Lightning conductor . . . . 80·00
23 3d. brown and deep blue . . . . 55 5·00
a. Extra flagstaff . . . . 75·00
b. Short extra flagstaff . . . . 80·00
c. Lightning conductor . . . . 80·00
24 6d. slate and purple . . . . 65 1·50
a. Extra flagstaff . . . . 85·00
b. Short extra flagstaff . . . . 85·00
c. Lightning conductor . . . . 90·00
21/4 . . . . *Set of* 4 2·00 8·50
21s/4s Perf "Specimen" . . . . *Set of* 4 85·00

For illustrations of plate varieties see Omnibus section following Zanzibar.

1937 (12 May). *Coronation. As Nos.* 95/7 *of Antigua. P* 11×11½.
25 1d. carmine . . . . . . 50 1·25
26 2d. yellow-brown 50 20
27 3d. blue 50 50
25/7 . . . . . . *Set of* 3 1·40 1·75
25s/7s Perf "Specimen" . . . . *Set of* 3 65·00

(Recess D.L.R.)

. Apr)–54. *Wmk Mult Script CA. P* 13½×13.

½d. green 2·00 1·00
 a. Perf 13½×14 (1.43) 30 2·50
 b. Perf 13½×14. *Bronze-green* (2.50) 1·50 5·00
1d. rose-red 2·00 1·00
 a. Perf 13½×14 (1.43) 1·00 1·75
1½d. light blue 4·00 65
 a. Perf 14 (1941) 2·50 1·00
 b. Perf 13½×14 (1.43) 30 75
 ba. Printed on the gummed side £2500
2d. yellow-brown 2·50 1·00
 a. Perf 13½×14 (1.43) 30 50
3d. ultramarine 10·00 1·75
 a. Deep blue (10.38) 15·00 1·75
 b. Perf 13½×14. *Ultramarine* (1.43) 3·00 4·50
 c. Perf 13½×14. *Light ultram* (10.46) 19·00 12·00
 d. Perf 13½×14. *Deep blue* (10.47) 10·00 11·00
4d. orange 4·50 1·50
 a. Perf 13½×14 (1.43) 50 1·40
6d. deep magenta 11·00 2·50
 a. Perf 13½×14 (1.43) 4·00 4·00
 b. Perf 13½×14. *Reddish purple (shades)* (7.44) 4·00 1·25
 c. Perf 13½×14. *Claret* (13.10.54) 6·00 4·50
1s. brown-olive 11·00 1·75
 a. Perf 13½×14 (1.43) 1·25 65
2s. 6d. bright violet 24·00 4·00
 a. Perf 13½×14. *Violet* (1.43) 12·00 2·50
 b. Perf 13½×14. *Reddish violet* (10.47) 12·00 8·00
5s. grey 50·00 12·00
 a. Perf 13½×14. *Slate* (1.43) 55·00 50·00
 b. Perf 13½×14. *Grey* (5.44) 25·00 13·00
10s. sepia 50·00 5·50
 a. Perf 13½×14 (1.43) 6·50 6·00
a *Set of* 11 48·00 25·00
3s Perf "Specimen" *Set of* 11 £225

e above perforations vary slightly from stamp to stamp, but verage measurements are respectively: 13.3 × 13.2 comb × 13), 14.2 line (14) and 13.3 × 13.8 comb (13½ × 14).

Swaziland

(4)

3 Dec). *Victory. Nos.* 108/10 *of South Africa optd with T* 4.

	Un pair	Us pair	Us single
1d. brown and carmine	55	50	10
2d. slate-blue and violet	55	50	10
3d. deep blue and blue	55	2·00	20
Set of 3	1·50	2·75	30

(17 Feb). *Royal Visit. As Nos.* 32/5 *of Basutoland.*

	Un	Us
1d. scarlet	10	10
2d. green	10	10
3d. ultramarine	10	10
1s. mauve	10	10
Set of 4	30	30
s Perf "Specimen" *Set of* 4	80·00	

(1 Dec). *Royal Silver Wedding. As Nos.* 112/13 *of tigua.*

1½d. ultramarine 50 10
10s. purple-brown 23·00 26·00

(10 Oct). *75th Anniv of U.P.U. As Nos.* 114/17 *of Antigua.*

1½d. blue 15 10
3d. deep blue 1·75 2·00
6d. magenta 30 60
1s. olive 30 70
1 *Set of* 4 2·25 3·00

POSTAGE DUE STAMPS

D 1

(Typo D.L.R.)

3 (2 Jan)–57. *Wmk Mult Script CA. P* 14.

D 1 1d. carmine 30 8·50
 a. Chalk-surfaced paper. *Dp carmine* (24.10.51) 20 13·00
 ac. Error. St Edward's Crown, W 9*b* £200
2d. pale violet 2·00 23·00
 a. Chalk-surfaced paper (22.2.57) 4·75 30·00
 ab. Large "d" 50·00
2 Perf "Specimen" *Set of* 2 42·00

or illustrations of No. D2ab see above No. D1 of Basutoland.

Tanganyika

The stamps of GERMANY were used in the colony between October 1890 and July 1893 when issues for GERMAN EAST AFRICA were provided.

PRICES FOR STAMPS ON COVER TO 1945

The Mafia Island provisionals (No. M1/52) are very rare used on cover.

Nos. N1/5	*from* ×8
Nos. 45/59	*from* ×6
Nos. 60/2	—
Nos. 63/73	*from* ×6
Nos. 74/86	*from* ×8
Nos. 87/8	—
Nos. 89/92	*from* ×6
Nos. 93/106	*from* ×3
No. 107	—

MAFIA ISLAND

BRITISH OCCUPATION

Mafia Island was captured by the British from the Germans in January 1915. Letters were first sent out unstamped, then with stamps handstamped with Type M 1. Later the military were supplied with handstamps by the post office in Zanzibar. These were used to produce Nos. M11/52.

(Currency. 100 heller = 1 rupee)

G.R.
MAFIA

(M 1)

(M 3)

1915 (Jan). *German East Africa Yacht types, handstamped with Type* M 1. *Wmk Lozenges, or no wmk* (1 *r.,* 2 *r.*). A. *In black* (2½ *h. in blackish lilac*). B. *In deep purple.* C. *In reddish violet.*

No.		A	B	C
M 1	2½ h. brown	£475	†	£200
	a. Pair, one without handstamp	†		£2000
M 2	4 h. green	£550	£650	£250
	a. Pair, one without handstamp	†		£1900
M 3	7½ h. carmine	£400	£450	£100
	a. Pair, one without handstamp	£3500	†	£1600
M 4	15 h. ultramarine	£450	£550	£160
	a. Pair, one without handstamp	†		£1700
M 5	20 h. black and red/*yellow*	£550	£600	£325
	a. Pair, one without handstamp		† £3500	£2000
M 6	30 h. black and carmine	£650	£850	£350
	a. Pair, one without handstamp	£3750	†	£2000
M 7	45 h. black and mauve	£700	£800	£400
	a. Pair, one without handstamp	£3750	†	£2500
M 8	1 r. carmine	£5000	†	£3250
M 9	2 r. green	£5500	†	£3750
M10	3 r. blue-black and red	£6500	†	£4000

Prices are for unused examples.

A few contemporary Zanzibar stamps (1, 3, 6 and 15 c.) are known with the above handstamp.

(Currency. 100 cents = 1 rupee)

1915 (May). *German East Africa Yacht types with handstamped four-line surcharge* "G.R.—POST—6 CENTS—MAFIA" *in black, green or violet. Wmk Lozenges or no wmk* (1 *r.,* 2 *r.*).

M11	6 c. on 2½ h. brown	£950	£1100
	a. Pair, one without handstamp	†	£3750
M12	6 c. on 4 h. green	£950	£1100
	a. Pair, one without handstamp	£3750	
M13	6 c. on 7½ h. carmine	£1000	£1200
	a. Pair, one without handstamp		
M14	6 c. on 15 h. ultramarine	£1000	£1200
M15	6 c. on 20 h. black and red/*yellow*	£1200	£1400
M16	6 c. on 30 h. black and carmine	£1600	£1700
M17	6 c. on 45 h. black and mauve	£1600	£1700
	a. Pair, one without handstamp		
M18	6 c. on 1 r. carmine	£8000	
M19	6 c. on 2 r. green	£9000	
M20	6 c. on 3 r. blue-black and red	£10000	

The 5, 20 and 40 pesa values of the 1901 Yacht issue are also known with the above surcharge as are the contemporary 1 c. and 6 c. Zanzibar stamps.

1915 (Sept). (*a*) *German East African fiscal stamps.* "Statistik des Waaren-Verkehrs" (*Trade Statistical Charge*) *handstamped in bluish green or violet,* "O.H.B.M.S. Mafia" *in a circle, as Type* M 3.

M21	24 pesa, vermilion/*buff*	£650	£800
M22	12½ heller, drab	£650	£850
	a. Pair, one without handstamp	£3000	
M23	25 heller, dull green	£650	£850
M24	50 heller, slate	£650	£850
	a. Pair, one without handstamp	£3000	
M25	1 rupee, lilac	£650	£850

(*b*) *German East African* "Ubersetzungs- Gebühren" *Fee) stamp, overprinted as before*

M26	25 heller, grey	£650	£850

G. R
POST
MAFIA

(M 4)

G. R.
Post
MAFIA.

(M 5)

(*c*) *Stamps as above, but with further opt as Type* M 4, *in bluish green or violet*

M27	24 pesa, vermilion/*buff*	£850
M28	12½ heller, drab	£850
M29	25 heller, dull green	£850
M30	50 heller, slate	£850
M31	1 rupee, lilac	£850
M32	25 heller, grey (No. M26)	£850
	a. Pair, one without handstamp Type M 4	£3000

Type M 3 is also known handstamped on the 7½ h., 20 h. and 30 h. values of German East Africa 1905 Yacht issue and also on contemporary 1, 3, 6 and 25 c. Zanzibar stamps.

(Currency. 12 pies = 1 anna. 16 annas = 1 rupee)

1915 (Sept). *Nos.* E1/2, E4/9, E11 *and* E13 *of Indian Expeditionary Forces* (*India King George V optd* "I.E.F.") *with a further opt Type* M 4 *handstruck in green, greenish black or dull blue.*

M33	3 p. slate-grey	28·00	70·00
	a. Pair, one stamp without opt	—	£800
M34	½ a. yellow-green	48·00	75·00
	a. Pair, one stamp without opt	—	£850
M35	1 a. carmine	50·00	75·00
M36	2 a. mauve	75·00	£120
M37	2½ a. ultramarine	£100	£150
M38	3 a. orange-brown	£100	£160
	a. Pair, one stamp without opt	—	£1000
M39	4 a. olive-green	£120	£180
M40	8 a. purple	£200	£300
	a. Pair, one stamp without opt	—	£1300
M41	12 a. dull claret	£275	£400
M42	1 r. red-brown and blue-green	£325	£425
M33/42	*Set of* 10	£1200	£1800

All values exist with the overprint inverted, and several are known with overprint double or sideways.

1916 (Oct). *Nos.* E1/2, E4/9, E11 *and* E13 *of Indian Expeditionary Forces* (*India King George V optd* "I.E.F.") *with further opt Type* M 5 *handstruck in green, greenish black, dull blue or violet.*

M43	3 p. slate-grey	£110	£130
M44	½ a. yellow-green	£110	£120
M45	1 a. carmine	90·00	£100
M46	2 a. mauve	£150	£150
M47	2½ a. ultramarine	£160	£170
M48	3 a. orange-brown	£160	£170
M49	4 a. olive-green	£225	£250
M50	8 a. purple	£300	£375
M51	12 a. dull claret	£325	£450
M52	1 r. red-brown and blue-green	£375	£425
M43/52	*Set of* 10	£1800	£2000

Stamps with handstamp inverted are known.

Used examples of Nos. M43/52 with black double-ring backdated postmarks of "JA 23 1915" are worth about 50% of the prices quoted.

NYASALAND-RHODESIAN FORCE

This issue was sanctioned for use by the Nyasaland-Rhodesian Force during operations in German East Africa, Mozambique and Nyasaland. Unoverprinted Nyasaland stamps were used by the Force prior to the introduction of Nos. N1/5 and, again, in 1918.

N. F.

(N 1)

1916 (7 Aug–18 Sept*). *Nos.* 83, 86, 90/1 *and* 93 *of Malawi* (*Nyasaland*) *optd with Type* N 1 *by Govt Printer, Zomba.*

N1	½d. green	1·50	7·50
N2	1d. scarlet	1·50	3·25
N3	3d. purple/*yellow* (15 Sept*)	7·00	17·00
	a. Opt double		† £8000
N4	4d. black and red/*yellow* (13 Sept*)	29·00	40·00
N5	1s. black/*green* (18 Sept*)	29·00	42·00
N1/5	*Set of* 5	60·00	£100
N1s/5s Optd "Specimen"	*Set of* 5	£200	

* Earliest known dates of use.

Of No. N3a only six copies were printed, these being the bottom row on one pane issued at M'bamba Bay F.P.O., German East Africa in March 1918.

This overprint was applied in a setting of 60 (10 rows of 6) and the following minor varieties occur on all values: small stop after "N" (R. 1/1); broken "F" (R. 4/3); very small stop after "F" (R. 6/5); no serifs at top left and bottom of "N" (R. 10/1).

TANGANYIKA

BRITISH OCCUPATION OF GERMAN EAST AFRICA

Following the invasion of German East Africa by Allied forces civilian mail was accepted by the Indian Army postal service, using Indian stamps overprinted "I.E.F.". Some offices reverted to civilian control on 1 June 1917 and these used stamps of East Africa and Uganda until the "G.E.A." overprints were ready. The last field post offices, in the southern part of the country, did not come under civilian control until 15 March 1919.

(Currency. 100 cents = 1 rupee)

G.E.A. (1) G.E.A. (2) G.E.A. (3)

1917 (Oct)–**21.** *Nos.* 44/5, 46*a*/51, 52*b*, 53/9 *and* 61 *of Kenya, Uganda and Tanganyika optd with T* **1** *and* **2.** *Wmk Mult Crown CA. Ordinary paper* (1 c. *to* 15 c.) *or chalk-surfaced paper* (*others*).

No.	Description	Unused	Used
45	1 c. black (R.)	15	80
	aw. Wmk inverted	£150	
	ay. Wmk inverted and reversed	90·00	
	b. Vermilion opt	20·00	16·00
47	3 c. green	15	15
48	6 c. scarlet	15	10
	a. Wmk sideways	£1800	£1800
	w. Wmk inverted	†	£160
49	10 c. yellow-orange	50	60
	y. Wmk inverted and reversed	£120	
50	12 c. slate-grey	50	2·25
	y. Wmk inverted and reversed	95·00	
51	15 c. bright blue	70	2·00
	w. Wmk inverted	£110	
52	25 c. black and red/*yellow*	80	3·50
	a. On pale yellow (1921)	1·40	14·00
	as. Optd "Specimen"	40·00	
53	50 c. black and lilac	80	3·25
54	75 c. black/*blue-green, olive back* (R.)	1·00	4·50
	a. On emerald back (1921)	3·25	45·00
	as. Optd "Specimen"	50·00	
55	1 r. black/*green* (R.)	2·75	7·00
	a. On emerald back (1919)	5·00	48·00
56	2 r. red and black/*blue*	8·50	42·00
	x. Wmk reversed		
57	3 r. violet and green	13·00	75·00
58	4 r. red and green/*yellow*	17·00	90·00
59	5 r. blue and dull purple	38·00	90·00
60	10 r. red and green/*green*	70·00	£300
	a. On emerald back	75·00	£300
61	20 r. black and purple/*red*	£190	£350
62	50 r. carmine and green	£475	£750
	s. Optd "Specimen"	£160	
45/61	*Set of* 16	£300	£850
45s/61s Optd "Specimen"	*Set of* 16	£400	

Early printings of the rupee values exist with very large stop after the "E" in "G.E.A." (R. 5/3). There are round stops after "E" varieties, which in one position of later printings became a small stop.

The only known used example of No. 48a is cancelled at Tanga in August 1918.

1921. *Nos.* 69/74 *of Kenya, Uganda and Tanganyika optd with T* **1** *or* **2.** *Wmk Mult Script CA. Chalk-surfaced paper* (50 c. *to* 5 *r.*).

No.	Description	Unused	Used
63	12 c. slate-grey	6·50	90·00
64	15 c. bright blue	1·75	3·75
65	50 c. black and dull purple	9·00	85·00
66	2 r. red and black/*blue*	32·00	£120
67	3 r. violet and green	50·00	£150
68	5 r. blue and dull purple	75·00	£180
63/8	*Set of* 6	£160	£550
63s/8s Optd "Specimen"	*Set of* 6	£200	

1922. *Nos.* 65 *and* 68 *of Kenya, Uganda and Tanganyika optd by the Government Printer at Dar-es-Salaam with T* **3.** *Wmk Mult Script CA.*

No.	Description	Unused	Used
72	1 c. black (R.)	70	15·00
73	10 c. orange	70	14·00
	y. Wmk inverted and reversed	£100	

BRITISH MANDATED TERRITORY

(New Currency. 100 cents = 1 shilling)

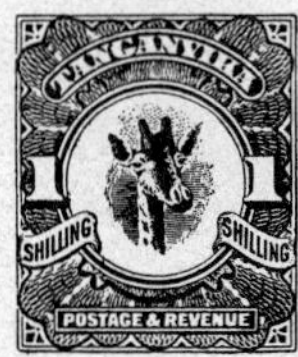

4 Giraffe 5

(Recess B.W.)

1922. *Head in black.* (*a*) *Wmk Mult Script CA. P* 15×14.

No.	Type	Description	Unused	Used
74	4	5 c. slate-purple	2·25	20
75		10 c. green	2·25	85
76		15 c. carmine-red	2·00	10
77		20 c. orange	1·75	10
78		25 c. black	5·50	6·50
79		30 c. blue	5·00	5·00
80		40 c. yellow-brown	2·75	4·50
81		50 c. slate-grey	2·00	1·50
82		75 c. yellow-bistre	3·25	17·00
		(*b*) *Wmk Mult Script CA* (*sideways*). *P* 14.		
83	5	1 s. green	3·25	13·00
		a. Wmk upright	2·50	11·00
84		2 s. purple	5·50	14·00
		a. Wmk upright	4·50	20·00
85		3 s. black	12·00	28·00
86		5 s. scarlet	24·00	85·00
		a. Wmk upright	13·00	75·00
87		10 s. deep blue	95·00	£180
		a. Wmk upright	50·00	95·00
88		£1 yellow-orange	£150	£300
		a. Wmk upright	£140	£275
74/88		*Set of* 15	£225	£475
74s/88s Optd "Specimen"		*Set of* 15	£450	

On the £1 stamp the words of value are on a curved scroll running across the stamp above the words "POSTAGE AND REVENUE".

Nos. 83/8 are known showing a forged Dodoma postmark, dated "16 JA 22".

1925. *As* 1922. *Frame colours changed.*

No.	Type	Description	Unused	Used
89	4	5 c. green	2·00	1·50
90		10 c. orange-yellow	3·75	1·50
91		25 c. blue	4·00	17·00
92		30 c. purple	4·00	12·00
89/92		*Set of* 4	12·00	29·00
89s/92s Optd "Specimen"		*Set of* 4	70·00	

6 7

(Typo D.L.R.)

1927–31. *Head in black. Wmk Mult Script CA. Chalk-surfaced paper* (5 *s.*, 10 *s.*, £1). *P* 14.

No.	Type	Description	Unused	Used
93	6	5 c. green	1·25	10
94		10 c. yellow	2·00	10
95		15 c. carmine-red	1·25	10
96		20 c. orange-buff	2·50	10
97		25 c. bright blue	3·50	2·00
98		30 c. dull purple	2·75	2·50
98*a*		30 c. bright blue (1931)	24·00	30
99		40 c. yellow-brown	2·00	4·50
100		50 c. grey	2·25	1·00
101		75 c. olive-green	2·00	11·00
102	7	1 s. green	3·75	2·75
103		2 s. deep purple	14·00	4·50
104		3 s. black	14·00	48·00
105		5 s. carmine-red	14·00	16·00
106		10 s. deep blue	55·00	95·00
107		£1 brown-orange	£140	£225
93/107		*Set of* 16	£250	£375
93s/107s Optd or Perf (No. 98as) "Specimen"		*Set of* 16	£250	

Examples of Nos. 104/7 are known showing a forged Dar-es-salaam postmark dated "20 NO 1928".

Tanganyika became part of the joint East African postal administration on 1 January 1933 and subsequently used the stamps of KENYA, UGANDA AND TANGANYIKA.

STAMP BOOKLETS

1922–25. *Black on red cover.*

No.	Description	Price
SB1	3 s. booklet containing 5 c., 10 c., 15 c. and 20 c. (Nos. 74/7), each in block of 6	
	a. As No. SB1, but contents changed (Nos. 89/90, 76/7) (1925)	

1922–26. *Black on red cover. Stapled.*

No.	Description	Price
SB2	3 s. booklet containing six 10 c., and twelve 5 c. and 15 c. (Nos. 74/6) in blocks of 6	
	a. As No. SB2, but contents changed (Nos. 74, 90, 76) (1925)	
	b. As No. SB2, but contents changed (Nos. 89/90, 76) (1926)	£1100

1927. *Black on red covers. Stapled.*

No.	Description	Price
SB3	3 s. booklet containing six 10 c., and twelve 5 c. and 15 c. (Nos. 93/5) in blocks of 6	£800
SB4	3 s. booklet containing 5 c., 10 c. and 15 c. (Nos. 93/5), each in block of 10	

Tasmania
see Australia

Tobago
see Trinidad and Toba

Togo

The stamps of GERMANY were used in the colony March 1888 until June 1897 when issues for TOGO provided.

PRICES FOR STAMPS ON COVER

Nos.	Price
Nos. H1/7	*from* × 6
No. H8	—
No. H9	*from* × 6
No. H10	*from* × 2
No. H11	—
Nos. H12/13	*from* × 6
Nos. H14/16	—
Nos. H17/19	*from* × 12
Nos. H20/6	—
Nos. H27/8	*from* × 20
No. H29	—
Nos. H30/1	*from* × 6
Nos. H32/3	—
Nos. H34/58	*from* × 6

ANGLO-FRENCH OCCUPATION

French forces invaded southern Togo on 8 August 191 the British landed at Lomé on 12 August. The Ge administration surrendered on 26 August 1914.

The territory was jointly administered under martial lav was formally divided between Great Britain and Fr effective 1 October 1920. League of Nations mandates issued for both areas from 20 July 1922.

(Currency. 100 pfennig = 1 mark)

Stamps of German Colonial issue Yacht Types 1900 1909–14 (5 pf. and 10 pf.)

TOGO
Anglo-French
Occupation

(1)

Half penny

(2)

SETTINGS. Nos. H1/33 were all overprinted or surcharg the Catholic Mission, Lome.

The initial setting for the 3 pf. to 80 pf. was of 50 (10 repeated twice on each sheet of 100. Overprints from this set used for Nos. H1/9, had the lines of type 3 mm apart.

Nos. H1/2 were subsequently surcharged, also from a se of 50, to form Nos. H12/13. The surcharge setting showed a dropped "y" with small serifs on R. 1/1–2, 2/1, 3/1, 4/1 and 5

The type from the overprint and surcharge was then am mated in a new setting of 50 on which the lines of the over were only 2 mm apart. On this amalgamated setting, use Nos. H27/8, the thin "y" varieties were still present and F showed the second "O" of "TOGO" omitted.

The surcharge was subsequently removed from this "2 setting which was then used to produce Nos. H17/19. missing "O" was spotted and corrected before any of the 3 stamps were overprinted.

The remaining low values of the second issue, Nos. H14/1 H20/2, were overprinted from settings of 25 (5×5), either t from the last setting of 50 or from an amended version on w there was no space either side of the hyphen. This sli narrower overprint was subsequently used for Nos. H29/3 shows the top of the second "O" broken so that it resembles a on R. 1/5.

The mark values were overprinted from settings of 20 (5 showing the same differences in the spacing of the lines as o low values.

It is believed that odd examples of some German col values were overprinted from individual settings in e spacing.

1914 (17 Sept*). *Optd with T* **1** *by Catholic Mission, L Wide setting. Lines 3 mm apart.*

No.	Description	Unused	Used
H 1	3 pf. brown	£110	
H 2	5 pf. green	£100	
H 3	10 pf. carmine (Wmk Lozenges)	£120	
	a. Opt inverted	£7500	£
	b. Opt *tête-bêche* in vert pair	†	£
	c. No wmk	†	£
H 4	20 pf. ultramarine	28·00	3
H 5	25 pf. black and red/*yellow*	28·00	2
H 6	30 pf. black and orange/*buff*	30·00	4
H 7	40 pf. black and carmine	£225	
H 8	50 pf. black and purple/*buff*	£9000	£7
H 9	80 pf. black and carmine/*rose*	£225	

1 m. carmine £5000 £2500
2 m. blue.. .. .. £8000 £8500
a. "Occupation" double £13000 £11000
b. Opt inverted £10000

...post office at Lome was open for four hours on ...ember, before closing again on instructions from Accra. ...ly reopened on 24 September.

...ête-bêche overprint on the 10 pf. is due to the sheet being ...round after the upper 50 stamps had been overprinted so ...rtical pairs from the two middle rows have the overprint ...che.

...Oct). *Nos.* H1 *and* H2 *surch as T* 2.
½d. on 3 pf. brown £160 £140
a. Thin "y" in "penny".. .. .. £400 £350
1d. on 5 pf. green £160 £140
a. Thin "y" in "penny".. .. .. £400 £350

TOGO
Anglo-French
Occupation
(3)

TOGO
Anglo-French
Occupation
Half penny
(4)

...Oct). (a) *Optd with T* 3. *Narrow Setting. Lines* 2 *mm* ...t. "Anglo-French" *measures* 16 *mm.*
3 pf. brown £4500 £900
5 pf. green £1100 £700
10 pf. carmine .. .. † £2750
20 pf. ultramarine .. .. 16·00 12·00
a. "TOG" £4000 £4000
b. Nos. H4 and H17 *se-tenant* (vert pair) £6500
25 pf. black and red/*yellow* .. .. 22·00 30·00
a. "TOG" £12000
30 pf. black and orange/*buff* .. .. 19·00 29·00
40 pf. black and carmine £4500 £1500
50 pf. black and purple/*buff* .. .. † £6000
80 pf. black and carmine/*rose* £1800 £1800
1 m. carmine £7000 £4000
2 m. blue.. .. .. † £8500
3 m. violet-black .. .. † £38000
5 m. lake and black .. .. .. † £38000

(b) *Narrow setting, but including value, as T* 4
½d. on 3 pf. brown .. .. .. 35·00 26·00
a. "TOG" £425 £300
b. Thin "y" in "penny" .. .. 60·00 60·00
1d. on 5 pf. green .. .. .. 4·25 4·25
a. "TOG" £130 £110
b. Thin "y" in "penny" .. .. 12·00 15·00

...he 20 pf. one half of a sheet was overprinted with the wide ...g (3 mm), and the other half with the narrow setting (2 mm), ...t vertical pairs from the middle of the sheet show the two ...ies of the overprint.

...OGO
...o-French
...upation
(6)

TOGO
ANGLO-FRENCH
OCCUPATION
(7)

TOGO
ANGLO-FRENCH
OCCUPATION
(8)

...7 Jan). *Optd as T* 6. *The words* "Anglo-French" *measure* 15 ...*n instead of* 16 *mm as in T* 3.
3 pf. brown £7500 £2500
5 pf. green £200 £130
a. "Occupation" omitted £7000
10 pf. carmine £200 £130
a. No wmk .. .. † £7000
20 pf. ultramarine £1400 £475
40 pf. black and carmine .. .. .. † £7500
50 pf. black and purple/*buff* £12000 £9500

...is printing was made on another batch of German Togo ...ps, found at Sansane-Mangu.

Stamps of Gold Coast overprinted

...(May). *Nos.* 70/81, 82*a and* 83/4 *of Gold Coast* (*King* ...*orge V*) *optd at Govt Press, Accra, with T* 7 ...OCCUPATION" 14½ *mm long*).
½d. green 30 70
a. Small "F" in "FRENCH" .. .. 1·50 3·00
b. Thin "G" in "TOGO" .. .. 3·00 6·00
c. No hyphen after "ANGLO" .. .. 3·00 6·00
e. "CUPATION" for "OCCUPATION" .. 85·00
f. "CCUPATION" for "OCCUPATION" .. 48·00
1d. red 30 50
a. Small "F" in "FRENCH" .. .. 1·75 3·00
b. Thin "G" in "TOGO" .. .. 4·50 7·00
c. No hyphen after "ANGLO" .. .. 4·50 7·00
f. "CCUPATION" for "OCCUPATION" .. £130
g. Opt double £325 £450
h. Opt inverted £160 £250
ha. Ditto. "TOGO" omitted £5500
2d. grey .. .. 30 1·25
a. Small "F" in "FRENCH" .. .. 1·75 4·00
b. Thin "G" in "TOGO" .. .. 5·50 10·00
c. No hyphen after "ANGLO" .. .. 70·00
d. Two hyphens after "ANGLO" .. 42·00
f. "CCUPATION" for "OCCUPATION" .. £130
2½d. bright blue .. .. 75 3·00
a. Small "F" in "FRENCH" .. .. 2·50 8·50
b. Thin "G" in "TOGO" .. .. 9·00 23·00
c. No hyphen after "ANGLO" .. .. 38·00
d. Two hyphens after "ANGLO" .. 45·00
f. "CCUPATION" for "OCCUPATION" .. £110
3d. purple/*yellow* 65 90
a. Small "F" in "FRENCH" .. .. 2·75 4·50
b. Thin "G" in "TOGO" .. .. 9·50 15·00
c. No hyphen after "ANGLO" .. .. 38·00
f. "CCUPATION" for "OCCUPATION" .. £130
g. White back .. .. 4·00 15·00
ga. Small "F" in "FRENCH" .. .. 19·00 40·00
gb. Thin "G" in "TOGO" .. .. 55·00 85·00

H40 6d. dull and bright purple .. .. 65 1·75
a. Small "F" in "FRENCH" .. .. 4·25 11·00
b. Thin "G" in "TOGO" .. .. 10·00 23·00
f. "CCUPATION" for "OCCUPATION" £180
H41 1s. black/*green* .. .. .. 1·25 4·00
a. Small "F" in "FRENCH" .. .. 4·25 13·00
b. Thin "G" in "TOGO" .. .. 11·00 32·00
f. "CCUPATION" for "OCCUPATION" £100
g. Opt double £950
H42 2s. purple and blue/*blue* .. .. 8·50 12·00
a. Small "F" in "FRENCH" .. .. 26·00 42·00
b. Thin "G" in "TOGO" .. .. 55·00 80·00
c. No hyphen after "ANGLO" £140
f. "CCUPATION" for "OCCUPATION" £300
H43 2s. 6d. black and red/*blue* .. .. 4·50 19·00
a. Small "F" in "FRENCH" .. .. 18·00 60·00
b. Thin "G" in "TOGO" .. .. 42·00 £100
c. No hyphen after "ANGLO" £130
f. "CCUPATION" for "OCCUPATION" £450
H44 5s. green and red/*yellow* (*white back*) .. 8·00 15·00
a. Small "F" in "FRENCH" .. .. 38·00 60·00
b. Thin "G" in "TOGO" .. .. 60·00 £120
c. No hyphen after "ANGLO" £170
f. "CCUPATION" for "OCCUPATION" £300
H45 10s. green and red/*green* .. .. 35·00 60·00
a. Small "F" in "FRENCH" .. .. 80·00
b. Thin "G" in "TOGO" £170
f. "CCUPATION" for "OCCUPATION" £425
H46 20 s. purple and black/*red* £120 £140
a. Small "F" in "FRENCH" £275
b. Thin "G" in "TOGO" £475
f. "CCUPATION" for "OCCUPATION" £650
H34/46 .. .. *Set of* 12 £150 £225

Varieties (*Nos. indicate positions in pane*).
a. Small "F" in "FRENCH" (25, 58 and 59).
b. Thin "G" in "TOGO" (24).
c. No hyphen after "ANGLO" (5).
d. Two hyphens after "ANGLO" (5).
e. "CUPATION" for "OCCUPATION" (33).
f. "CCUPATION" for "OCCUPATION" (57).

Varieties c and e also occur together on position 28 of the ½d. value only.

The 1d. opt inverted (No. H35h) exists with small "F" (*Price* £1200 *unused*), thin "G" (*Price* £3250 *unused*) and "No hyphen" (*Price* £3250 *unused*).

Examples of all values, and especially the varieties, are known showing a forged Lome postmark dated "22 1 15".

1916 (Apr)–**20.** *Nos.* 70/84 *of Gold Coast* (*King George V*) *optd in London with T* 8 ("OCCUPATION" 15 *mm long*). *Heavy type and thicker letters showing through on back.*
H47 ½d. green .. .. 30 2·50
H48 1d. red 30 85
H49 2d. grey 50 60
H50 2½d. bright blue .. .. .. 50 1·50
H51 3d. purple/*yellow* .. .. .. 1·25 70
H52 6d. dull and bright purple .. .. 1·25 1·00
w. Wmk inverted .. .. .. 85·00
H53 1s. black/*green* .. .. .. 1·75 4·00
a. On blue-green (*olive back*) (1918) .. 4·50 12·00
b. On emerald-green (*olive back*) (1920) £425
c. On emer-grn (*emer-grn back*) (1920) £250 £500
H54 2s. purple and blue/*blue* .. .. 4·50 8·50
a. Wmk sideways £2000 £2000
H55 2s. 6d. black and red/*blue* .. .. 4·50 7·00
H56 5s. green and red/*yellow* .. .. 10·00 26·00
a. On orange-buff (1919) .. .. 10·00 38·00
b. On buff (1920) .. .. ..
H57 10s. green and red/*green* .. .. 24·00 60·00
a. On blue-green (*olive back*) (1920) 16·00 50·00
H58 20s. purple and black/*red* £130 £150
H47/58 .. .. *Set of* 12 £150 £225
H47s/58s Optd "Specimen" .. *Set of* 12 £300

Nos. H47/58 were withdrawn in October 1920 when Gold Coast stamps were introduced.

The mandates were transferred to the United Nations in January 1946. The inhabitants of the British mandate voted to join Ghana in 1957.

Tokelau
see after **New Zealand**

Tonga

The Tongan Post Office was established in 1885 and FIJI 2d. and 6d. stamps are recorded in use until the arrival of Nos. 1/4.

PRICES FOR STAMPS ON COVER TO 1945	
Nos. 1/4	*from* × 60
Nos. 5/9	*from* × 20
Nos. 10/28	*from* × 8
Nos. 29/31	*from* × 7
Nos. 32/7	*from* × 6
Nos. 38/54	*from* × 5
Nos. 55/63	*from* × 6
Nos. 64/70	*from* × 3
Nos. 71/87	*from* × 2
Nos. O1/10	*from* × 25

PROTECTORATE KINGDOM

King George I, 1845–93

1 King George I

2

(Eng Bock and Cousins. Plates made and typo Govt Ptg Office, Wellington)

1886–88. *W* 2. *P* 12½ (*line*) *or* 12 × 11½ (*comb*)*.
1 1 1d. carmine (*p* 12½) (27.8.86) .. .. £375 6·00
a. Perf 12½ × 10 .. .. ..
b. Perf 12 × 11½ (15.7.87) .. .. 10·00 3·25
ba. Pale carmine (*p* 12 × 11½) .. .. 16·00 8·50
2 2d. pale violet (*p* 12½) (27.8.86) .. 50·00 10·00
a. Bright violet .. .. .. 70·00 3·50
b. Perf 12 × 11½ (15.7.87) .. .. 28·00 2·75
ba. Bright violet (*p* 12 × 11½) .. .. 40·00 3·00
3 6d. blue (*p* 12½) (9.10.86) .. .. 60·00 2·25
a. Perf 12 × 11½ (15.10.88) .. .. 50·00 2·25
ab. Dull blue (*p* 12 × 11½) .. .. 27·00 2·25
4 1s. pale green (*p* 12½) (9.10.86) .. 85·00 4·50
a. Deep green (*p* 12½) .. .. .. 95·00 2·25
b. Perf 12 × 11½ (15.10.88) .. .. 55·00 6·00
ba. Deep green (*p* 12 × 11½) .. .. 55·00 3·25

*See note after New Zealand, No. 186.

FOUR
PENCE.
(3)

EIGHT
PENCE.
(4)

(Surch Messrs Wilson & Horton, Auckland, N.Z.)

1891 (10 Nov). *Nos.* 1b *and* 2b *surch.*
5 3 4d. on 1d. carmine .. .. .. 3·00 11·00
a. No stop after "PENCE" .. .. 50·00 £110
6 4 8d. on 2d. violet .. .. .. 35·00 90·00
a. Short "T" in "EIGHT" £160 £275

No. 5a occurred on R. 6/8 and 9, R. 10/11, all from the righthand pane.

1891 (23 Nov). *Optd with stars in upper right and lower left corners. P* 12½.
7 1 1d. carmine .. .. 42·00 50·00
a. Three stars £300
b. Four stars £400
c. Five stars £600
d. Perf 12 × 11½ £300
da. Three stars £475
db. Four stars £600
dc. Five stars £850
8 2d. violet.. .. .. 70·00 38·00
a. Perf 12 × 11½ £375

1892 (15 Aug). *W* 2. *P* 12 × 11½.
9 1 6d. yellow-orange .. .. .. 16·00 26·00

5 Arms of Tonga

6 King George I

Damaged "O" in "TONGA" (R. 1/1, later corrected)

(Dies eng A. E. Cousins. Typo at Govt Printing Office, Wellington, N.Z.)

1892 (10 Nov). *W* 2. *P* 12 × 11½.
10 5 1d. pale rose .. .. 12·00 17·00
a. Bright rose .. .. 12·00 17·00
b. Bisected diag (½d.) (1893) (on cover) † £850
c. Damaged "O" £100
11 6 2d. olive .. .. 15·00 16·00
12 5 4d. chestnut .. .. 48·00 70·00
13 6 8d. bright mauve .. .. .. 55·00 £170
14 1s. brown .. .. 80·00 £110
10/14 .. .. *Set of* 5 £190 £350

No. 10b was used from 31 May 1893 to provide a 2½d. rate before the arrival of No. 15, and on subsequent occasions up to 1895.

½d.
(7)

2½d.
(8)

FIVE
PENCE.
(9)

7½d.
(10)

1893. *Printed in new colours and surch with T* 7/10 *by Govt Printing Office, Wellington.* (a) *In carmine. P* 12½ (21 Aug).
15 5 ½d. on 1d. bright ultramarine .. .. 23·00 27·00
a. Surch omitted .. .. ..
16 6 2½d. on 2d. green.. .. .. .. 14·00 12·00
17 5 5d. on 4d. orange .. .. .. 4·00 6·50
18 6 7½d. on 8d. carmine .. .. .. 24·00 75·00

(*b*) *In black. P* 12×11½ (Nov)

No.	Type	Description	Unused	Used
19	5	½d. on 1d. dull blue	45·00	48·00
20	6	2½d. on 2d. green	17·00	17·00
		a. Surch double	—	£1700
		b. Fraction bar completely omitted (R. 3/3)		

King George II, 1893–1918

SURCHARGE. HALF-PENNY (11)

SURCHARGE, 2½d. (12)

HALF-PEI — Small "F" in "HALF"

(Surch at the *Star* Office, Auckland, N.Z.)

1894 (June–Nov). *Surch with T* **11** *or* **12**.

No.	Type	Description	Unused	Used
21	5	½d. on 4d. chestnut (B.) (Nov)	2·00	7·00
		a. "SURCHARCE"	9·00	20·00
		b. Small "F"	9·00	20·00
22	6	½d. on 1s. brown	2·50	11·00
		a. "SURCHARCE"	10·00	38·00
		b. Small "F"	10·00	38·00
		c. Surch double	£275	
		d. Surch double with "SURCHARCE"	£900	
		e. Surch double with small "F"	£750	
23		2½d. on 8d. mauve	5·00	8·00
		a. No stop after "SURCHARGE"	32·00	55·00
24		2½d. on 1s. deep green (No. 4*a*) (Nov)	55·00	24·00
		a. No stop after "SURCHARGE"	£170	
		b. Perf 12×11½	15·00	42·00
		ba. No stop after "SURCHARGE"	55·00	

Nos. 21/4 were surcharged in panes of 60 (6×10) with No. 21a occurring on R. 2/6, 4/6, 5/6, 8/6 and 10/6, No. 21b on R. 1/4, 3/4, 6/4, 7/4 and 9/4, No. 22a on R. 1/6, 3/6, 5/6, 8/6 and 10/6, No. 22b on R. 2/4, 4/4, 6/4, 7/4 and 9/4 (both after the setting had been rearranged), No. 23a on R. 3/1–3 and Nos. 24a and 24ba on R. 6/3 and R. 7/3 or R. 7/1–2.

Sheets used for these provisionals were surcharged with the remains of the tissue interleaving still in place. This sometimes subsequently fell away taking parts of the surcharge with it.

Deformed "E" in "PENI" (R. 2/2)

(Design resembling No. 11 litho and surch at *Star* Office Auckland, N.Z.)

1895 (22 May*). *As T* **6** *surch as T* **11** *and* **12**. *No wmk. P* 12.

No.	Type	Description	Unused	Used
25	11	1d. on 2d. pale blue (C.)	45·00	22·00
		a. Deformed "E"	£110	
26	12	1½d. on 2d. pale blue (C.)	60·00	27·00
		a. Deformed "E"	£150	
		b. Perf 12×11	45·00	27·00
		ba. Deformed "E"	£110	
27		2½d. on 2d. pale blue (C.)†	40·00	45·00
		a. No stop after "SURCHARGE"	£225	£225
		b. Deformed "E"	£110	
28		7½d. on 2d. pale blue (C.)	£400	
		a. Deformed "E"		
		b. Perf 12×11	60·00	45·00
		ba. Deformed "E"	£150	

* Earliest known date of use.

†The 2½d. on 2d. is the only value which normally has a stop after the word "SURCHARGE".

No. 27a occurs on R.1/3 of the right-hand pane.

12*a* King George II

13 King George II

Half- Penny- VAEUA OE PENI

(14)

"BU" joined (R. 1/1)

Missing eyebrow (R.2/4)

"7" for "1" in "½d." (R. 2/1)

1895 (20 June*). *Unissued stamp surch as in T* **12***a*. *No wmk. P* 12.

No.	Type	Description	Unused	Used
29	11	½d. on 2½d. vermilion	30·00	32·00
		a. "BU" joined	75·00	
		b. "SURCHARCE"	70·00	
		c. Missing eyebrow	75·00	
		d. Stop after "POSTAGE" (R. 2/5)	75·00	
		e. "7" for "1" in "½d."	75·00	
30		1d. on 2½d. vermilion	60·00	40·00
		a. "BU" joined	£110	
		c. Missing eyebrow	£110	
		d. Stop after "POSTAGE" (R. 2/5)	£110	
		e. "7" for "1" in "½d."	£110	
31	12	7½d. on 2½d. vermilion	55·00	60·00
		a. "BU" joined	£100	
		c. Missing eyebrow	£100	
		d. Stop after "POSTAGE" (R. 2/5)	£100	
		e. "7" for "1" in "½d."	£100	

*Earliest known date of use.

No. 29b occurs on R. 1/6 and 3/6 of both the right and the left pane.

In the ½d. surcharge there is a stop after "SURCHARGE" and not after "PENNY". In the 1d. and 7½d. the stop is after the value only.

"Black Eye" flaw (Rt pane R. 2/4)

(Litho *Star* Office, Auckland, N.Z.)

1895 (9 July–Sept). *No wmk. P* 12.

No.	Type	Description	Unused	Used
32	13	1d. olive-green	19·00	26·00
		a. Bisected diagonally (½d.) (on cover) (9.95)	†	£750
		b. Imperf between (horiz pair)	—	£6000
33		2½d. rose	20·00	16·00
		a. Stop (flaw) after "POSTAGE" (R. 4/5)	60·00	60·00
34		5d. blue	22·00	50·00
		a. "Black eye" flaw	60·00	
		b. Perf 12×11	23·00	50·00
		ba. "Black eye" flaw	65·00	
		c. Perf 11	£350	
		ca. "Black eye" flaw		
35		7½d. orange-yellow	30·00	48·00
		a. Yellow	30·00	48·00

1896 (May). *Nos.* 26b *and* 28b *with typewritten surcharge* "Half-Penny-", *in violet, and Tongan surcharge, in black, as T* **14**.

A. *Tongan surch reading downwards (right panes)*

No.	Type	Description	Unused	Used
36A	6	½d. on 1½d. on 2d.	£450	
		a. Perf 12	£425	£425
		e. "Halef"	£4750	
		f. "H" over "G"		
37A		½d. on 7½d. on 2d.	85·00	£110
		a. "Hafl" for "Half"	£1500	£1600
		b. "Hafl" ("Penny" omitted)	£3250	
		c. "PPenny"	£600	
		d. Stops instead of hyphens	£900	
		e. "Halyf"		
		f. "Half-Penny-" inverted	£1900	
		g. No hyphen after "Penny"		
		l. Capital "P" over small "p"		
		p. Perf 12	£800	
		pa. No hyphen after "Half"		

B. *Tongan surch reading upwards (left panes)*

No.	Type	Description	Unused	Used
36B	6	½d. on 1½d. on 2d.	£425	£425
		a. Perf 12	£450	£450
		ab. "Haalf"	£1900	
		c. "H" double		
		d. Tongan surch omitted	£4250	
		e. "Penyny"	£2000	
37B		½d. on 7½d. on 2d.	85·00	£110
		d. Stops instead of hyphens	£950	
		f. "Half-Penny-" inverted	£2750	
		h. "Hwlf"		
		i. No hyphen after "Half"	£800	
		j. "Penny" double		
		k. "Penny" twice, with "Half" on top of upper "Penny"	£3500	
		m. "Half H"	£750	
		n. Tongan surch double	£1200	
		o. Two hyphens between "Half" and "Penny"		
		p. Perf 12	£800	

Nos. 26b and 28b were in sheets of 48 (2 panes 6×4). The panes were separated before the surcharges were applied.

There are variations in the relative positions of the words "Half" and "Penny", both vertically and horizontally.

15 Arms

16 Ovava Tree, Kana-Kub

17 King George II

18 Prehistoric Trilith at Haamonga

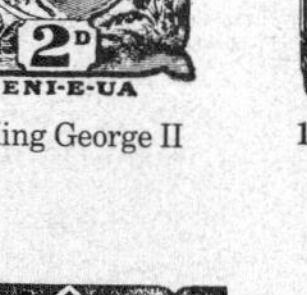

19 Bread Fruit

20 Coral

21 View of Haapai

22 Red Shining Parro

23 View of Vavau Harbour

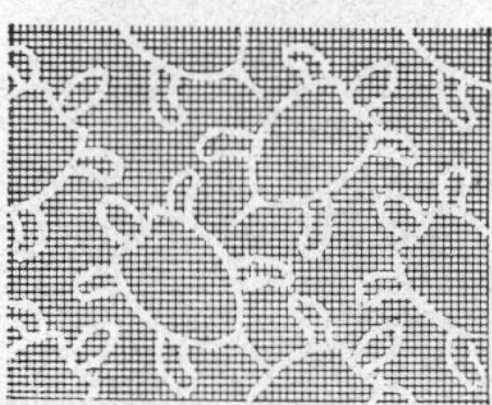

24 Tortoises (*upright*)

Types of Type **17**:

Type I. Top of hilt showing

Type II. No sword hilt

Normal

Lopped branch (R. 8/5) (ptgs from 1934 onwards)

Normal

Small "2" (R. 1/2, 1/4–5, 2/8, 4/4, 5/4 and 6/1)

Normal

Both "O"'s small in "HOGOFULU" (R. 1/7)

Small second "O" in "HOGOFULU" (R. 2/7)

ERMARKS. Stamps with W **24** upright show all the se heads pointing upwards, or downwards if inverted. On ps with sideways watermark the heads point upwards or wards alternately.

(Recess D.L.R.)

(1 June). *W* **24**. *P* 14.

15	½d.	indigo	4·25	2·75
		a. Wmk sideways	70	3·00
16	1d.	black and scarlet	80	80
		a. Wmk sideways	6·50	3·50
		b. Lopped branch	42·00	
17	2d.	sepia and bistre (I)	16·00	5·50
		a. Wmk sideways	13·00	3·50
		b. Small "2"	35·00	15·00
	2d.	sepia and bistre (II)	32·00	9·00
		a. Wmk sideways	22·00	9·00
		b. Small "2"	55·00	25·00
	2d.	grey and bistre (II)	32·00	3·25
		a. Wmk sideways	16·00	3·00
		b. Small "2"	38·00	5·50
	2½d.	black and blue	6·00	1·40
		a. No fraction bar in "½" (R. 2/10)	95·00	60·00
		b. Wmk sideways	3·50	1·60
		ba. No fraction bar in "½" (R. 2/10)	60·00	60·00
18	3d.	black and yellow-green	3·50	8·00
		a. Wmk sideways	2·50	6·50
19	4d.	green and purple	3·75	4·00
		a. Wmk sideways	4·00	4·50
17	5d.	black with orange (II)	32·00	14·00
		a. Wmk sideways		
20	6d.	red	13·00	6·00
		a. Wmk sideways	8·50	4·50
17	7½d.	black and green (II)	16·00	23·00
		a. Centre inverted	£3750	
	10d.	black and lake (II)	45·00	48·00
		a. Wmk sideways		
		b. Both "O"'s small	£225	£225
		c. Small second "O"	£225	£225
	1s.	black and red-brown (II)	14·00	7·50
		a. No hyphen before "TAHA" (R. 3/5)	£140	£140
		b. Wmk sideways		
21	2s.	black and ultramarine	60·00	65·00
		a. Wmk sideways	20·00	28·00
22	2s.	6d. deep purple	48·00	30·00
		a. Wmk sideways	65·00	50·00
23	5s.	black and brown-red	48·00	45·00
		a. Wmk sideways	26·00	32·00
53a		*Set of* 14	£200	£180

ıe 1d., 3d. and 4d. are known bisected and used for half their ıe.

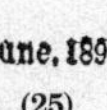

(25)

26 Queen Salote

9 (1 June). *Royal Wedding. No.* 39a *optd with T* **25** *at* "Star" *ffice, Auckland, N.Z.*

16	1d.	black and scarlet (hyphen 2 mm long)	28·00	55·00
		a. "1889" for "1899" (R. 8/1, 8/4)	£200	£350
		b. Hyphen 3 mm long	45·00	80·00
		c. Wmk upright	50·00	85·00
		ca. "1889" for "1899" (R. 8/1, 8/4)	£375	£550
		cb. Hyphen 3 mm long	75·00	£130

he letters "T L" stand for Taufa'ahau, the King's family ıe, and Lavinia, the bride.

lo. 54 was overprinted from a setting of 30 (3×10) applied ce to the sheets of 60. The setting contains twenty-one mples of the 2 mm hyphen and nine of the 3 mm.

PRICES OF SETS

t prices are given for many issues, generally ose containing three stamps or more. Definitive ts include one of each value or major colour ange, but do not cover different perforations, e types or minor shades. Where a choice is ssible the set prices are based on the cheapest ersions of the stamps included in the listings.

Queen Salote, 1918–65

Dies of the 2d.:

Die I (As used for 1897 issue)

Die II

Normal

"2½" recut (note lines on "2" and different "½") (R. 1/1)

Retouched (small) hyphen (R. 3/5)

(Recess D.L.R.)

1920 (Apr)–**35.** *W* **24** (*sideways*). *P* 14.

55	**15**	½d.	yellow-green (1934)	1·00	1·25
			a. Wmk upright	18·00	26·00
56	**26**	1½d.	grey-black (1935)	50	3·00
57		2d.	agate and aniline violet (Die I)	8·50	13·00
			a. Wmk upright	18·00	40·00
			b. Small "2"	60·00	85·00
			c. *Black and slate-violet* (1924)	8·00	2·25
			ca. Wmk upright		
			cb. Small "2"	55·00	20·00
			d. *Black and deep purple* (1925)	10·00	3·00
			db. Small "2"	65·00	25·00
57*e*		2d.	black & blackish lilac (Die II) (1932)	4·50	6·00
58		2½d.	black and blue (3.21)	4·75	40·00
59		2½d.	bright ultramarine (1934)	2·00	1·00
			a. Recut "2½"	20·00	9·50
60		5d.	black and orange-vermilion (1922)	3·25	4·75
61		7½d.	black and yellow-green (1922)	1·75	1·75
62		10d.	black and lake (1922)	2·50	4·75
			a. Both "O"'s small	28·00	45·00
			b. Small second "O"	28·00	45·00
			c. *Black and aniline carmine* (9.25)	7·00	
			ca. Both "O"'s small	75·00	
			cb. Small second "O"	75·00	
63		1s.	black and red-brown (1922)	1·25	2·50
			a. Retouched (small) hyphen	15·00	24·00
			b. Wmk upright	26·00	26·00
			ba. Retouched (small) hyphen	£130	£130
55/63			*Set of* 10	26·00	55·00
55s/63s			Optd or Perf (Nos. 55s/6s and 59s) "Specimen" *Set of* 9	£180	

In Die II the ball of the "2" is larger and the word "PENI-E-UA" is re-engraved and slightly shorter; the "U" has a spur on the left side.

For illustration of No. 62a see above No. 38.

TWO PENCE

TWO PENCE

PENI-E-UA (27)

PENI-E-UA (28)

1923 (20 Oct)–**24.** *Nos.* 46, 48/9, 50, 51/2 *and* 53a *surch as T* **27** (*vert stamps*) *or* **28** (*horiz stamps*).

64	**17**	2d. on 5d. black and orange (II) (B.)	1·00	85
		a. Wmk sideways	8·00	6·00
65		2d. on 7½d. black and green (II) (B.)	17·00	28·00
		a. Wmk sideways	55·00	65·00
66		2d. on 10d. black and lake (II) (B.)	10·00	50·00
		a. Wmk sideways	38·00	70·00
		b. Both "O"'s small	75·00	
		c. Small second "O"	75·00	
67		2d. on 1s. black and red-brown (II) (B.)	48·00	22·00
		a. No hyphen before "TAHA" (R. 3/5)	£300	£200
		b. Wmk sideways	65·00	55·00
68	**21**	2d. on 2s. black and ultramarine (R.)	19·00	20·00
		a. Wmk sideways	11·00	5·00
69	**22**	2d. on 2s. 6d. deep purple (R.)	32·00	6·50
		a. Wmk sideways	£100	55·00
70	**23**	2d. on 5s. black and brown-red (R.)	13·00	13·00
		a. Wmk sideways	3·25	2·50
64/70a		*Set of* 7	£110	£100

29 Queen Salote

(Recess D.L.R.)

1938 (12 Oct). *20th Anniv of Queen Salote's Accession. Tablet at foot dated* "1918–1938". *W* **24** (*sideways*). *P* 13½.

71	**29**	1d. black and scarlet	60	3·00
72		2d. black and purple	7·50	2·25
73		2½d. black and ultramarine	7·50	3·00
71/3		*Set of* 3	14·00	7·50
71s/3s		Perf "Specimen" *Set of* 3	70·00	

For Silver Jubilee issue in a similar design, see Nos. 83/7.

Further die of 2d.:

Die III

(Recess D.L.R.)

1942–49. *Wmk Mult Script CA* (*sideways on* 5s.). *P* 14.

74	**15**	½d.	yellow-green	30	2·25
75	**16**	1d.	black and scarlet	2·00	2·25
			a. Lopped branch	42·00	
76	**26**	2d.	black and purple (Die II)	5·00	2·75
			a. Die III (4.49)	4·00	7·00
77		2½d.	bright ultramarine	1·50	1·50
			a. Recut "2½"	30·00	
78	**18**	3d.	black and yellow-green	50	3·25
79	**20**	6d.	red	3·00	2·00
80	**26**	1s.	black and red-brown	3·00	3·25
			a. Retouched (small) hyphen	35·00	38·00
81	**22**	2s.	6d. deep purple (1943)	28·00	21·00
82	**23**	5s.	black and brown-red (1943)	16·00	45·00
74/82			*Set of* 9	50·00	75·00
74s/82s			Perf "Specimen" *Set of* 9	£170	

In Die III the foot of the "2" is longer than in Die II and extends towards the right beyond the curve of the loop; the letters of "PENI-E-UA" are taller and differently shaped.

Damage to the "2" on R. 4/9 of No. 77 was frequently corrected by hand-painting.

For illustration of No. 75a see above No. 38 and of No. 77a see above No. 55.

The ½d., 1d., 3d. and 1s. exist perforated from either line or comb machines. The other values only come line perforated.

UANIMA TA'U 'OE PULE 'A 'ENE 'AFIO 1918–1943

30

(Recess D.L.R.)

1944 (25 Jan). *Silver Jubilee of Queen Salote's Accession. As T* **29**, *but inscr* "1918–1943" *at foot, as T* **30**. *Wmk Mult Script CA. P* 14.

83	1d. black and carmine	15	80
84	2d. black and purple	15	80
85	3d. black and green	15	80
86	6d. black and orange	65	1·60
87	1s. black and brown	55	1·60
83/7	*Set of* 5	1·50	5·00
83s/7s	Perf "Specimen" *Set of* 5	75·00	

1949 (10 Oct). *75th Anniv of U.P.U. As Nos.* 114/17 *of Antigua.*

88	2½d. ultramarine	20	60
89	3d. olive	1·60	2·75
90	6d. carmine-red	20	50
91	1s. red-brown	25	50
88/91	*Set of* 4	2·00	4·00

31 Queen Salote **33**

32 Queen Salote

(Photo Waterlow)

1950 (1 Nov). *Queen Salote's Fiftieth Birthday. Wmk Mult Script CA. P* 12½.

92	**31**	1d. carmine	50	1·75
93	**32**	5d. green	50	2·00
94	**33**	1s. violet	50	2·25
92/4		*Set of* 3	1·40	5·50

34 Map

35 Palace, Nuku'alofa

(Recess Waterlow)

1951 (2 July). *50th Anniv of Treaty of Friendship between Great Britain and Tonga. T* **34/5** *and similar designs. Wmk Mult Script CA. P* 12½ (3*d.*), 13 × 13½ (½*d.*), 13½ × 13 (*others*).

95	½d. green	20	2·50
96	1d. black and carmine	15	2·50
97	2½d. green and brown	30	2·50
98	3d. yellow and bright blue	2·00	2·50
99	5d. carmine and green	1·25	80
100	1s. yellow-orange and violet	1·00	80
95/100	*Set of* 6	4·50	10·50

Designs: *Horiz*—2½d. Beach scene; 5d. Flag; 1s. Arms of Tonga and G.B. *Vert*—3d. H.M.N.Z.S. *Bellona*.

OFFICIAL STAMPS

G.F.B.

(O 1)

(O 2)

(G.F.B. = Gaue Faka Buleaga = On Government Service)

1893 (13 Feb). *Optd with Type* O 1 *by Govt Printing Office, Wellington, N.Z. W* **2.** *P* 12 × 11½.

O1	**5**	1d. ultramarine (C.)	10·00	45·00
		a. Bisected diagonally (½d.) (on cover)		
O2	**6**	2d. ultramarine (C.)	27·00	50·00
O3	**5**	4d. ultramarine (C.)	45·00	90·00
O4	**6**	8d. ultramarine (C.)	85·00	£160
O5		1s. ultramarine (C.)	95·00	£180
O1/5		*Set of* 5	£225	£475

Above prices are for stamps in good condition and colour. Faded and stained stamps from the remainders are worth much less.

1893 (Dec). *Nos* O1 *to* O5 *variously surch with new value, sideways as Type* O **2.**

O 6	**5**	½d. on 1d. ultramarine	17·00	48·00
O 7	**6**	2½d. on 2d. ultramarine	23·00	42·00
O 8	**5**	5d. on 4d. ultramarine	23·00	42·00
O 9	**6**	7½d. on 8d. ultramarine	23·00	75·00
		a. "D" of "7½D." omitted	£1200	
		b. Surch double	£1900	
O10		10d. on 1s. ultramarine	27·00	80·00
O6/10		*Set of* 5	£100	£250

Transjordan

PRICES FOR STAMPS ON COVER

Nos. 1/88*a*	*from* × 10
Nos. 89/142	*from* × 5
Nos. 143/243	*from* × 3
Nos. D112/24	*from* × 5
Nos. D159/248	*from* × 3
No. O117	*from* × 5

Transjordan was part of the Turkish Empire from 1516 to 1918.

Turkish post offices are known to have existed at Ajlun ("Adjiloun"), Amman ("Omman"), Amman Station, Kerak ("Kerek"), Ma'an ("Mohan" or "Maan"), Qatrana, Salt and Tafila ("Tafile"). Stamps cancelled "Ibin" may have been used at Ibbin.

The area was overrun by British and Arab forces, organised by Colonel T. E. Lawrence, in September 1918, and as Occupied Enemy Territory (East), became part of the Syrian state under the Emir Faisal, who was king of Syria from 11 March to 24 July 1920. During 1920 the stamps of the Arab Kingdom of Syria were in use. On 25 April 1920 the Supreme Council of the Allies assigned to the United Kingdom a mandate to administer both Palestine and Transjordan, as the area to the east of the Jordan was called. The mandate came into operation on 29 September 1923.

E.E.F. post offices, using the stamps of Palestine, operated in the area from September 1918.

BRITISH MANDATED TERRITORY

(Currency. 1000 milliemes = 100 piastres = £1 Egyptian)

"EAST". Where the word "East" appears in the Arabic overprints it is not used in its widest sense but as implying the land or government "East of Jordan".

شرقي الاردن

("East of Jordan")
(1)

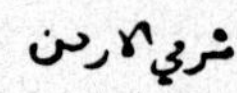

(1*a*)

(Optd at Greek Orthodox Convent, Jerusalem)

1920 (Nov). *T* 3 *of Palestine optd with T* **1.** (*a*) *P* 15 × 14.

1	**1**	1 m. sepia	50	1·25
		a. Opt inverted	£120	£250
2		2 m. blue-green	8·00	9·50
		a. Silver opt		
3		3 m. yellow-brown	1·00	1·25
		a. Opt Type 1*a*	£1100	
4		4 m. scarlet	1·00	1·25
5		5 m. yellow-orange	2·00	1·25
5*a*		1 p. deep indigo (Silver)	£2000	
6		2 p. olive	3·75	6·00
		a. Opt Type 1*a*	£850	
7		5 p. deep purple	25·00	32·00
		a. Opt Type 1*a*	£1400	
8		9 p. ochre	£800	£1400
1/7 (*ex* 5*a*)		*Set of* 7	38·00	48·00
		(*b*) *P* 14		
9	**1**	1 m. sepia	1·25	1·40
		a. Opt inverted	£150	
10		2 m. blue-green	50	70
		a. Silver opt	£550	£600
11		3 m. yellow-brown	16·00	16·00
12		4 m. scarlet	15·00	19·00
13		5 m. orange	2·00	80
14		1 p. deep indigo (Silver)	1·50	1·75
15		2 p. deep olive	3·50	3·00
16		5 p. purple	2·50	6·00
17		9 p. ochre	3·50	22·00
18		10 p. ultramarine	4·75	22·00
19		20 p. pale grey	8·00	38·00
9/19		*Set of* 11	50·00	£120

Nos. 1/9 were surcharged from five different settings of 120 (12×10) which produced eight sub-types of Type **1**. Type 1*a* occurred on R. 8/12 from one setting. The 9 p. also exists with this overprint, but no example appears to have survived without further overprint or surcharge.

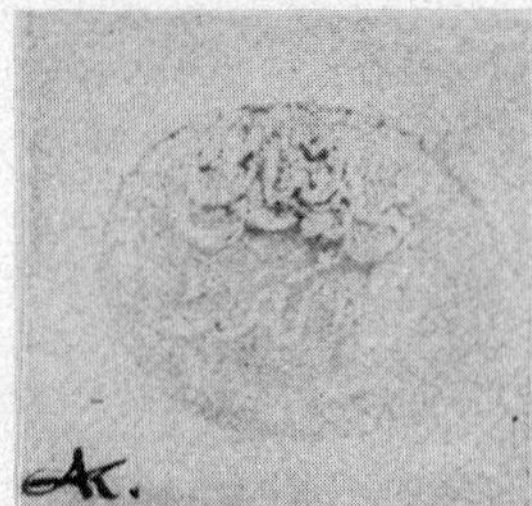

1*b* Moab District Seal (*full size*)

1920 (Nov). *Issued at Kerak. Handstamped. Manuscript initials "AK" in violet. Imperf.*

19*a*	1*b*	(1 p.) pale blue	£3500	£4000

No. 19*a* was issued in November 1920 by the political officer for Moab District, Captain (later Sir) Alex Kirkbride, and was used until supplies of Nos. 1/19 reached the area in March 1921. The local Turkish canceller was used as a postmark.

Emir Abdullah, 1 April 1921–22 May 1946

Abdullah, a son of the King of the Hejaz, was made Em Transjordan in 1921. On 26 May 1923 Transjordan was recog as an autonomous state and on 20 February 1928 it was accor degree of independence.

عشر القرش

("Tenth of a piastre")
(2)

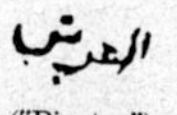

("Piastre")
(3)

("Arab Governm of the East April 1921")
(4)

1922 (Nov). *Nos.* 1/19 *additionally handstamped with steel d Amman as T* **2** *or* **3**. (*a*) *P* 15 × 14.

20	**2**	¹⁄₁₀ p. on 1 m. sepia	25·00	4
		a. Red surch	70·00	7
		b. Violet surch	70·00	7
21		²⁄₁₀ p. on 2 m. blue-green	28·00	2
		a. Error. Surch "³⁄₁₀" for "²⁄₁₀"	£110	
		b. Red surch	80·00	8
		c. Violet surch	£100	
		ca. Error. "³⁄₁₀" for "²⁄₁₀"		
22		³⁄₁₀ p. on 3 m. yellow-brown	10·00	
		a. Pair, one without surch	£750	
		b. Opt Type 1*a*	£1200	£1
		c. Error. "²⁄₁₀" for "³⁄₁₀"		
		d. Violet surch	£150	
		da. Opt Type 1*a*	£2750	
23		⁴⁄₁₀ p. on 4 m. scarlet	50·00	5
		a. Violet surch		
24		⁵⁄₁₀ p. on 5 m. yellow-orange	£180	
		a. Pair, one without surch		
		b. Violet surch	£250	£
25	**3**	2 p. on 2 p. olive	£250	7
		a. Opt Type 1*a*	£1300	
		b. Red surch	£325	8
		ba. Opt Type 1*a*		
		c. Violet surch	£300	9
26		5 p. on 5 p. deep purple	50·00	7
		a. Opt Type 1*a*	£1500	
		b. Violet surch		
27		9 p. on 9 p. ochre	£300	£
		a. Red surch	£130	£
		b. Violet surch		
		(*b*) *P* 14		
28	**2**	¹⁄₁₀ p. on 1 m. sepia	20·00	2
		a. Pair, one without surch		
		b. Red surch	60·00	6
		c. Violet surch	£250	£
29		²⁄₁₀ p. on 2 m. blue-green	25·00	25
		a. Pair, one without surch	£1500	
		b. Error. Surch "³⁄₁₀" for "²⁄₁₀"	£100	£
		c. Red surch	80·00	8(
		ca. Error. Surch "³⁄₁₀" for "²⁄₁₀"		
		d. Violet surch	80·00	8(
30		⁵⁄₁₀ p. on 5 m. orange	£225	£
		a. Pair, one without surch	†	£2
		b. Violet surch	£275	
31	**3**	1 p. on 1 p. deep indigo (R.)	£200	6(
		a. Pair, one without surch	£1800	
		b. Violet surch	£400	
32		9 p. on 9 p. ochre (R.)	£500	£
		a. Violet surch		
33		10 p. on 10 p. ultramarine	£850	£1
		a. Violet surch inverted		
34		20 p. on 20 p. pale grey	£650	£
		a. Violet surch	£900	£
		T 3 *of Palestine* (*perf* 15×14) *similarly surch*		
35	**3**	10 p. on 10 p. ultramarine	£1800	£2
36		20 p. on 20 p. pale grey	£2500	£3
		a. Violet surch		

T **2** reads "tenths of a piastre" and T **3** "the piastre", both w Arabic figures below. These surcharges were applied in order translate the Egyptian face values of the stamps into currency of the Arab Kingdom of Syria, but the actual face va of the stamps remained unchanged.

Being handstamped the surcharge may be found either at t top or bottom of the stamp, and exists double on most values.

1922 (Dec). *Stamps of* 1920, *handstamped with a steel die as T in red-purple, violet or black.** (*a*) *P* 15 × 14.

37	**4**	1 m. sepia (R.P.)	25·00	25
		a. Violet opt	28·00	28
		b. Black opt	22·00	22
38		2 m. blue-green (R.P.)	22·00	22
		a. Violet opt	20·00	20
		b. Black opt	18·00	18
39		3 m. yellow-brown (R.P.)	40·00	40
		a. Opt Type 1*a*	£1600	
		b. Violet opt	7·00	7
		ba. Pair, one without opt	£1200	
		bb. Opt Type 1*a*	£1500	£2(
		c. Black opt	8·00	8
		ca. Opt Type 1*a*		
40		4 m. scarlet (R.P.)	45·00	50·
		b. Violet opt	45·00	50·
		c. Black opt	45·00	50·
41		5 m. yellow-orange (R.P.)	35·00	10·
		a. Violet opt	15·00	10·
42		2 p. olive (R.P.)	55·00	40·
		a. Opt Type 1*a*	£1500	
		b. Violet opt	20·00	15·
		ba. Opt Type 1*a*	£1500	£13
		c. Black opt	12·00	10·
43		5 p. deep purple (R.P.)	£100	£1
		a. Pair, one without opt	£1500	
		b. Violet opt	60·00	80·
		c. Black opt		
44		9 p. ochre (R.P.)	£400	£4
		a. Violet opt	£200	£2
		ab. Opt Type 1*a*	£2250	
		b. Black opt	65·00	80·

(b) P 14

4 1 m. sepia (R.P.) .. 12·00 15·00
a. Pair, one without opt .. £1200
b. Violet opt .. 22·00 20·00
c. Black opt .. 18·00 18·00
2 m. blue-green (R.P.) .. 25·00 25·00
a. Violet opt .. 8·00 8·00
b. Black opt .. 10·00 10·00
3 m. yellow-brown (V.) .. £800 £350
5 m. orange (R.P.) .. £300 75·00
a. Violet opt .. 25·00 20·00
1 p. deep indigo (R.P.) .. 25·00 15·00
a. Violet opt .. 15·00 9·00
2 p. deep olive (V.) .. 75·00 80·00
5 p. purple (R.P.) .. 90·00 £100
a. Violet opt .. £100 £110
b. Black opt
9 p. ochre (V.) .. £900 £1000
10 p. ultramarine (R.P.) .. £1800 £1900
a. Violet opt .. £1100 £1600
b. Black opt
20 p. pale grey (R.P.) .. £1600 £2000
a. Violet opt .. £1100 £1800
b. Black opt

he ink of the "black" overprint is not a true black, but is ed by a mixture of inks from different ink-pads. The colour owever, very distinct from either of the others.
ost values are known with inverted and/or double prints.

حكومة الشرق
العربية
نيسان سنة ٩٢١

("Arab Government of the East, April 1921")
(5)

3 (1 Mar). *Stamps of* 1920, *with typographed overprint*, T **5** *pplied by Govt Printing Press, Amman.*

(a) P 15×14

5 1 m. sepia (Gold) .. £1400 £1800
2 m. blue-green (Gold) .. 20·00 22·00
3 m. yellow-brown (Gold) .. 12·00 15·00
a. Opt double .. £500
b. Opt inverted .. £550
c. Black opt .. 75·00 85·00
4 m. scarlet .. 10·00 12·00
5 m. yellow-orange .. 50·00 45·00
a. Opt Type 1 albino .. £1200 £1400
2 p. olive (Gold) .. 15·00 15·00
a. Opt Type 1*a* .. £1200 £1000
b. Black opt .. £250 £250
ba. Opt Type 1*a*
5 p. deep purple (Gold) .. 60·00 80·00
a. Opt inverted .. £225
b. Opt Type 1*a* .. £2000
ba. Opt inverted .. £2500
c. Black opt inverted .. £1500

(b) P 14

5 1 m. sepia (Gold) .. 16·00 24·00
a. Opt inverted .. £600
2 m. blue-green (Gold) .. 14·00 18·00
a. Opt inverted .. £350 £350
b. Opt double .. £275
c. Black opt .. £300
ca. Opt double .. £1500
5 m. orange .. 10·00 12·00
1 p. deep indigo (Gold) .. 10·00 14·00
a. Opt double .. £450 £475
b. Black opt .. £800 £850
9 p. ochre .. 75·00 £100
a. Gold opt .. £3000
10 p. ultramarine (Gold) .. 70·00 £100
20 p. pale grey (Gold) .. 70·00 £100
a. Opt inverted .. £350
b. Opt double .. £425
c. Opt double, one inverted .. £425
e. Opt double, one gold, one black, latter inverted .. £700
f. Opt treble, one inverted .. £1000
g. Black opt .. £800
ga. Opt inverted .. £1000
gb. Opt double, one inverted .. £1200

The gold overprints were created by sprinkling gold dust on t black ink.
There are numerous constant minor varieties in this overprint all values.
The 9 p. perforated 15×14 was also prepared with this erprint, but the entire stock was used for No. 85.
The 20 p. exists with top line of overprint only or with the lines ansposed, both due to misplacement.

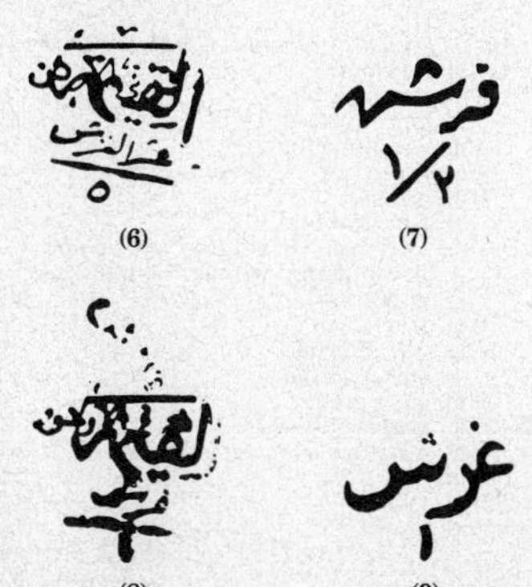

(6) (7) (8) (9)

1923 (Apr–Oct). *Stamps of the preceding issues further surch by means of handstamps.* (a) *Issue of Nov* 1920.

70 – 2½/10ths p. on 5 m. (13) (B.–Blk.) .. £160 £160
a. Black surch .. £160 £160
b. Violet surch .. £160 £160
70*c* 6 5/10 p. on 3 m. (3) .. † £5000
70*d* 5/10 p. on 5 m. (13)
70*e* 9 2 p. on 20 p. (19)

(b) *Stamp of Palestine*

71 6 5/10 p. on 3 m. (*p* 15×14) .. £3000

(c) *Issue of Nov* 1922

72 6 5/10 p. on 3 m. (22) .. £7000
a. Pair, one without surch .. £7500
73 5/10 p. on 5 p. (26) (V.) .. 70·00 80·00
a. Black surch
ab. Opt Type 3 omitted .. £1200
73*b* 5/10 p. on 9 p. (27a) .. £1200
74 7 ½ p. on 5 p. (26) .. 70·00 80·00
a. Pair, one without surch .. £750
75 ½ p. on 9 p. (27) .. £3500
a. On No. 27a .. £350 £400
ab. Opt Type 1*a* .. £3500
76 ½ p. on 9 p. (32) .. — £8000
77 8 1 p. on 5 p. (26) .. 80·00 £100

(d) *Issue of Dec* 1922

78 6 5/10 p. on 3 m. (39) (V.) .. 85·00 £100
a. Black surch .. £750
ab. Opt Type 1*a*
b. On No. 39b .. 40·00 50·00
ba. Pair, one without surch .. £1400
bb. Without numeral of value
bc. Black surch
79 5/10 p. on 5 p. (43b) (Blk.) .. 8·00 14·00
a. Opt Type 1*a* .. £2000
b. Pair, one without surch .. £500
c. Violet surch
79*d* 5/10 p. on 9 p. (44b) .. — £1200
da. On No. 44a. Violet surch .. — £1300
80 7 ½ p. on 2 p. (42) .. £100 £120
a. Opt Type 1*a* .. £2000
b. On No. 42b .. 80·00 £110
c. On No. 42c .. 60·00 £110
ca. Pair, one without surch .. £1000
w. Wmk inverted
81 ½ p. on 5 p. (43) .. £3000
a. On No. 43b .. £1000
82 ½ p. on 5 p. (50) .. £2000
a. On No. 50a .. £2500
83 8 1 p. on 5 p. (43) .. £3750
b. On No. 43b .. £2000 £2250
83*c* 1 p. on 5 p. (50) .. £2500

(e) *Issue of* 1 *March* 1923

84 6 5/10 p. on 3 m. (56) .. 25·00 30·00
a. On No. 56c .. £700
85 7 ½ p. on 9 p. (*p* 15×14) .. 90·00 £150
a. Pair, one without surch .. £5000
86 ½ p. on 9 p. (66) .. £150
87 9 1 p. on 10 p. (67) .. £2250 £2500
a. Violet surch .. £2750
88 2 p. on 20 p. (68) .. 60·00 80·00
88*a* 2 p. on 20 p. (68g) .. £2000

The handstamp on Nos. 70*c*, 88 and 88*a* has an Arabic "2" in place of the "1" shown in the illustration of Type **9**.
Being handstamped many of the above exist inverted or double.

TYPES OF SAUDI ARABIA. The following illustrations are repeated here for convenience from Saudi Arabia.

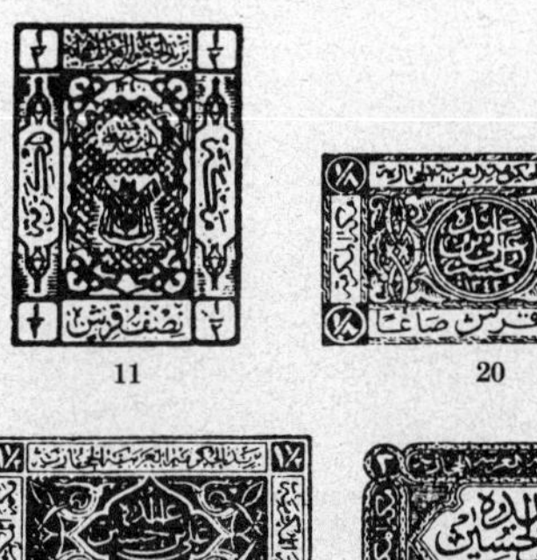

11 20

21

22

حكومة
الشرق العربية
٩ شعبان ١٣٤١

("Arab Government of the East, 9 Sha'ban 1341")
(10)

("Arab Government of the East. Commemoration of Independence, 25 May 1923")
(11)

It should be noted that as Arabic is read from right to left, the overprint described as reading downwards appears to the English reader as though reading upwards. Our illustration of Type **11** shows the overprint reading downwards.

1923 (April). *Stamps of Saudi Arabia.* T **11**, *with typographed opt*, T **10**.

89 10 1/8 p. chestnut .. 2·00 1·75
a. Opt double .. £200
b. Opt inverted .. £110
90 ½ p. scarlet .. 2·00 1·75
a. Opt inverted
91 1 p. blue .. 1·50 1·00
a. Opt inverted .. £120 £140
92 1½ p. lilac .. 1·50 1·75
a. Opt double .. £150
b. Top line omitted .. — £250
c. Pair, one without opt .. £250
d. Imperf between (horiz pair) .. £150
93 2 p. orange .. 2·00 5·50
94 3 p. brown .. 3·00 8·00
a. Opt inverted .. £225
b. Opt double .. £225 £250
c. Pair, one without opt .. £375
95 5 p. olive .. 5·00 9·00
89/95 .. *Set of* 7 15·00 26·00

On same stamps, surcharged with new values (*Saudi Arabia, Nos.* 47 *and* 49)

96 10 ¼ p. on 1/8 p. chestnut .. 4·00 5·50
a. Opt and surch inverted .. £150
b. Ditto, but 2nd and 3rd lines of opt omitted .. £200
c. Opt double .. † £200
97 10 p. on 5 p. olive .. 15·00 22·00
a. Top line omitted .. £350

In this setting the third line of the overprint measures 19–21 mm. On 35 stamps out of the setting of 36 the Arabic "9" (right-hand character in bottom line) is widely spaced from the rest of the inscription. Minor varieties of this setting exist on all values.
For later setting, varying from the above, see Nos. 121/4.

Normal. "923" Error. "933"

An error reading "933" instead of "923" occurs as No. 3 in the setting of 24 on all values. Only 24 stamps are believed to have been overprinted for each of Nos. 103A, 108A, 105B and 107B so that for these stamps only one example of the error can exist. No example has yet been confirmed for Nos. 103A or 105B.

1923 (25 May). T **3** *of Palestine optd with* T **11**, *reading up or down, in black or gold by Govt Press, Amman, in a setting of* 24 (12×2).

A. *Reading downwards*

98A 1 m. (Blk) .. 17·00 17·00
a. Opt double, one inverted (Blk.) .. £650 £650
b. Arabic "933" .. 85·00
c. Gold opt .. £150 £160
ca. Opt double, one inverted (Gold) .. £900
cb. Opt double (Blk. + Gold) .. £900 £900
cc. Arabic "933" .. £300
99A 2 m. (Blk) .. 28·00 35·00
a. Arabic "933" .. £160
100A 3 m. (Blk.) .. 10·00 12·00
a. Arabic "933" .. 70·00
101A 4 m. (Blk.) .. 10·00 12·00
a. Arabic "933" .. 70·00
102A 5 m. (Blk.) .. 50·00 60·00
a. Arabic "933" .. £300
103A 1 p. (Gold) .. £650 £750
a. Opt double .. £750 £850
104A 2 p. (Blk.) .. 50·00 70·00
a. Arabic "933" .. £275
105A 5 p. (Gold) .. 60·00 70·00
a. Opt double (Gold) .. £650
b. Arabic "933" .. £300
c. Opt double (Blk.) .. £1500
106A 9 p. (Blk.) .. 70·00 90·00
a. Arabic "933" .. £325
107A 10 p. (Blk.) .. 60·00 80·00
a. Arabic "933" .. £300
108A 20 p. (Blk.) .. £700
a. Arabic "933" .. £2500

B. *Reading upwards*

98B 1 m. (Blk.) .. 90·00 £110
b. Arabic "933" .. £250
c. Gold opt .. £150 £160
cc. Arabic "933" .. £350
99B 2 m. (Blk.) .. 45·00 50·00
a. Arabic "933" .. £250
100B 3 m. (Blk.) .. 90·00 £110
a. Arabic "933" .. £250
101B 4 m. (Blk.) .. 25·00 32·00
a. Arabic "933" .. £130
103B 1 p. (Gold) .. 50·00 60·00
a. Opt double .. £600
b. Black opt
c. Arabic "933" .. £300
105B 5 p. (Gold) .. £750 £550
a. Opt double
106B 9 p. (Blk.) .. 50·00 60·00
a. Arabic "933" .. £275
107B 10 p. (Blk.) .. £600
a. Arabic "933" .. £2500
108B 20 p. (Blk.) .. 70·00 90·00
a. Arabic "933" .. £325

The 9 and 10 p. are perf 14, all the other values being perf 15×14.

No. 107A *surch with* T **9**

109 1 p. on 10 p. ultramarine .. £6000

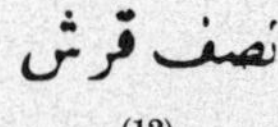

(12)

1923 (Sept). *No.* 92 *surch with T* **12**. (*a*) *Handstamped.*
110 **12** ½ p. on 1½ p. lilac .. .. .. 6·50 7·00
a. Surch and opt inverted .. .. 55·00
b. Opt double .. .. 75·00
c. Opt double, one inverted .. .. 90·00 £100
d. Pair, one without opt £150

This handstamp is known inverted, double and double, one inverted.

(*b*) *Typographed*
111 **12** ½ p. on 1½ p. lilac .. .. .. 50·00 50·00
a. Surch inverted £150
b. Surch double £180
c. Pair, one without surch £500

حكومة حكومة

الشرق العربية الشرق العربية

٩ شبان ١٣٤١ ٩ شعبان ١٣٤١

(**13*a***) (**13*b***)
("Arab Government of the East, 9 Sha'ban, 1341")

These two types differ in the spacing of the characters and in the position of the bottom line which is to the left of the middle line in T **13*a*** and centrally placed in T **13*b***.

1923 (Oct). *T* **11** *of Saudi Arabia handstamped as T* **13*a*** *or* **13*b***.
112 **13*a*** ½ p. scarlet .. .. 6·50 8·00
113 **13*b*** ½ p. scarlet .. .. 6·50 8·00

No. 112 exists with handstamp inverted.

د ٠ ق ٠ ج

ملك العرب

١ ج ٠ ث ٣٤٢

(**15** "Arab Government of the East") ("Commemorating the coming of His Majesty the King of the Arabs" and date) (**16**)

1924 (Jan). *T* **11** *of Saudi Arabia with typographed opt T* **15**.
114 **15** ½ p. scarlet .. .. 6·00 8·00
a. Opt inverted £180
115 1 p. blue £300 £200
116 1½ p. lilac £350
a. Pair, one without opt £1500

The ½ p. exists with thick, brown gum, which tints the paper, and with white gum and paper.

The 2 p. in the same design was also overprinted, but was not issued without the subsequent Type **16** overprint.

1924 (18 Jan). *Visit of King Hussein of Hejaz. Nos.* 114/16 *and unissued* 2 p. *with further typographed opt T* **16** *in black.*
117 **16** ½ p. scarlet .. .. 1·00 1·25
a. Type **15** omitted £150
b. Type **16** inverted £150
c. Imperf between (pair) £110
d. Type **16** in gold .. .. 2·00 2·25
dc. Imperf between (pair) £250
118 1 p. blue .. .. 1·25 1·50
a. Type **15** omitted £150
b. Both opts inverted £200
c. Imperf between (pair) .. ..
d. Type **16** in gold .. .. 2·00 2·25
db. Both opts inverted £300
dc. Imperf between (pair) £225
119 1½ p. lilac .. .. 2·00 2·25
a. Type **15** omitted .. ..
b. Type **15** inverted £130
d. Type **16** in gold .. .. 3·00 3·25
da. Type **15** inverted £150
120 2 p. orange .. .. 4·00 4·25
d. Type **16** in gold .. .. 6·00 6·50

The spacing of the lines of the overprint varies considerably, and a variety dated "432" for "342" occurs on the twelfth stamp in each sheet (*Price* £75 *un*).

حكومة

الشرق العربية

٩ شعبان ١٣٤١

(**16*a***)

شعبان شعبال شعبن

"Shaban" (normal) "Shabal" (R.4/6) "Shabn" (R.5/3)

1924 (Mar–May). *T* **11** *of Saudi Arabia optd with T* **16*a*** (*new setting of Type* **10**).
121 ⅛ p. chestnut .. .. 12·00 9·00
a. Opt inverted £100
122 ½ p. scarlet .. .. 3·50 3·50
a. "Shabal" .. .. 50·00
b. "Shabn" .. .. 50·00
c. Opt inverted £120
123 1 p. blue .. .. 6·00 2·00
a. "Shabal" .. .. 75·00
b. "Shabn" .. .. 75·00
c. Opt double £120
d. Imperf between (horiz pair) with opt double £500
124 1½ p. lilac .. .. 9·00 11·00
a. "Shabal" .. .. 90·00
b. "Shabn" .. .. 90·00

This setting is from fresh type with the third line measuring 18¼ mm.

On all stamps in this setting (except Nos. 1, 9, 32 and 33) the Arabic "9" is close to the rest of the inscription.

The dots on the character "Y" (the second character from the left in the second line) are on many stamps vertical (:) instead of horizontal (..).

On some sheets of the ⅛ p. and ½ p. the right-hand character, "H", in the first line, was omitted from the second stamp in the first row of the sheet.

حكومة الشرق العربي ١٣٤٢ حكومة الشرق العربي سنة ١٣٤٣

("Government of the Arab East, 1342") (**17**) ("Government of the Arab East, 1343") (**18**)

حكومة جكرمة

"Hukumat" (normal) "Jakramat" (R. 2/1)

١٣٤٢ ١٣٤٣ ١٢٤٢

"1342" (normal) "1343" (R. 4/2) "1242" (R. 6/1)

1924 (Sept–Nov). *T* **11** *of Saudi Arabia with type-set opt as T* **17** *by Govt Press, Amman.*
125 **17** ⅛ p. chestnut 35 35
a. Opt inverted £130
b. "Jakramat" .. .. .. 25·00
c. "1242" .. .. 25·00
126 ¼ p. green 30 30
a. *Tête-bêche* (pair, both opts normal) 7·50 10·00
b. Opt inverted .. .. .. 85·00
c. *Tête-bêche* (pair, one with opt inverted) £300
d. "Jakramat" .. .. .. 25·00
e. "1242" .. .. 25·00
127 ½ p. bright scarlet 30 30
a. Deep rose-red .. .. ..
b. "1343" .. .. 25·00
129 1 p. blue .. .. 2·50 1·50
a. Imperf between (horiz pair) .. £130
b. Opt inverted .. .. ..
c. "Jakramat" .. .. .. 35·00
d. "1242" .. .. 35·00
130 1½ p. lilac .. .. 2·50 2·75
a. "1343" .. .. 50·00
131 2 p. orange .. .. 2·00 2·25
a. Opt double .. .. ..
b. "1343" .. .. 50·00
132 3 p. brown-red .. .. 1·50 1·75
a. Opt inverted £100
b. Opt double £100
c. "1343" .. .. 75·00
133 5 p. olive .. .. 2·00 2·75
a. "Jakramat" .. .. .. 60·00
b. "1242" .. .. 60·00
134 10 p. brown-purple and mauve (R.) .. 4·00 5·50
a. Centre inverted £2000
b. Black opt £200
c. "Jakramat" .. .. .. 90·00
d. "1242" .. .. 90·00
125/34 .. .. *Set of* 9 14·00 16·00

Type **11** of Saudi Arabia was printed in sheets of 36 (6×6). The ¼ p. value had the bottom three rows inverted, giving six vertical *tête-bêche* pairs. A few sheets were overprinted with the normal setting of Type **17**, with the result that the overprints on the bottom rows were inverted in relation to the stamp, including on one of the stamps in the *tête-bêche* pair (No. 126c). A corrected setting with the overprint inverted on the lower rows was used for the majority of the printing giving *tête-bêche* pairs with the overprints both normal in relation to the stamps (No. 126a).

1925 (2 Aug). *T* **20/2** *of Saudi Arabia with lithographed opt T* **18** *applied in Cairo.*
135 **18** ⅛ p. chocolate 30 90
a. Imperf between (horiz pair) .. £120 £140
b. Opt inverted .. .. .. 60·00
136 ¼ p. ultramarine 30 90
a. Opt inverted .. .. .. 60·00
137 ½ p. carmine 50 40
a. Opt inverted .. .. .. 60·00
138 1 p. green 40 40
139 1½ p. orange .. .. 90 2·00
a. Opt inverted .. .. .. 60·00
140 2 p. blue .. .. 1·25 2·25
a. Opt treble £150 £200
141 **18** 3 p. sage-green (R.) .. .. .. 1·75
a. Imperf between (horiz pair) .. £120
b. Opt inverted .. .. .. 80·00
c. Black opt £120
142 5 p. chestnut .. .. 2·00
a. Opt inverted .. .. .. 80·00
135/42 .. .. *Set of* 8 6·75

All values exist imperforate.

No. 141 imperforate with gold overprint comes fr presentation sheet for the Emir.

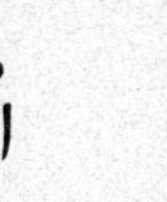

("East of the Jordan") (**19**)

22 Emir Abdullah

23 Emir Ab

(Opt typo by Waterlow)

1925 (1 Nov)–**26**. *Stamps of Palestine,* 1922 (*without the t line Palestine opt*), *optd with T* **19**. *Wmk Mult Script CA.*
143 **19** 1 m. deep brown 15
144 2 m. yellow 15
145 3 m. greenish blue 20
146 4 m. carmine-pink 30
147 5 m. orange 50
a. Yellow-orange .. .. .. 35·00
148 6 m. blue-green 50
149 7 m. yellow-brown 50
150 8 m. scarlet 50
151 1 p. grey 50
152 13 m. ultramarine 50
153 2 p. olive .. .. 1·50
a. Olive-green £100
154 5 p. deep purple .. .. 3·00
155 9 p. ochre .. .. 6·00
a. Perf 15×14 (1926) £850
156 10 p. light blue .. .. 12·00
a. Error. "E.F.F." in bottom panel (R. 10/3) £750
b. Perf 15×14 (1926) .. .. 75·00
157 20 p. light violet .. .. 20·00
a. Perf 15×14 (1926) £850
143/57 .. .. *Set of* 15 40·00
143s/57s Optd "Specimen" .. *Set of* 15 £160

(New Currency. 1000 milliemes = £1 Palestinian)

(Recess Perkins, Bacon & Co)

1927 (1 Nov)–**29**. *New Currency. Wmk Mult Script CA. P*
159 **22** 2 m. greenish blue 15
160 3 m. carmine-pink 90
161 4 m. green 90
162 5 m. orange 50
163 10 m. scarlet 60
164 15 m. ultramarine 70
165 20 m. olive-green 80
166 **23** 50 m. purple .. .. 2·50
167 90 m. bistre .. .. 6·00
168 100 m. blue .. .. 8·00
169 200 m. violet .. .. 17·00
170 500 m. brown (5.29) .. .. .. 60·00
171 1000 m. slate-grey (5.29) £100
159/71 .. .. *Set of* 13 £180
159s/71s Optd or Perf (500, 1000 m.) "Specimen" *Set of* 13 £180

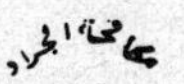

دستور

("Constitution") (**24**)

LOCUST CAMPAIGN

(**27**)

1928 (1 Sept). *New Constitution of* 20 *February* 1928. *with T* **24** *by Atwood, Morris & Co, Cairo.*
172 **22** 2 m. greenish blue .. .. .. 1·00
173 3 m. carmine-pink .. .. .. 1·00
174 4 m. green .. .. 1·25
175 5 m. orange .. .. 1·25
176 10 m. scarlet .. .. 1·50
177 15 m. ultramarine .. .. .. 1·50
178 20 m. olive-green .. .. .. 3·00
179 **23** 50 m. purple .. .. 5·00
180 90 m. bistre .. .. 14·00
181 100 m. blue .. .. 22·00
182 200 m. violet .. .. 65·00
172/82 .. .. *Set of* 11 £100

1930 (1 Apr). *Locust Campaign. Optd as T* **27** *by Whitehe Morris & Co, Alexandria.*
183 **22** 2 m. greenish blue .. .. .. 1·40
a. Opt inverted £200
184 3 m. carmine-pink .. .. .. 1·50
185 4 m. green .. .. 1·50
186 5 m. orange .. .. 16·00
a. Opt double £300
b. Vert pair, top stamp opt double. Lower stamp without bottom line of opt £1000
187 10 m. scarlet .. .. 1·50
188 15 m. ultramarine .. .. .. 1·50
a. Opt inverted £180
189 20 m. olive-green .. .. .. 1·50
190 **23** 50 m. purple .. .. 5·00 11
191 90 m. bistre .. .. 10·00 45
192 100 m. blue .. .. 12·00 45
193 200 m. violet .. .. 30·00 85
194 500 m. brown .. .. 75·00
a. "C" of "LOCUST" omitted (R. 5/3) £700
183/94 .. .. *Set of* 12 £140

No. 186a was sold at Kerak.

28

29

(…ngraved with figures of value at left only. Recess Perkins, Bacon)

…(1 June)–**39.** *Wmk Mult Script CA. P* 14.

	28	1 m. red-brown (6.2.34)	60	1·00
		c. Perf 13½×13 (1939)	4·00	3·50
		2 m. greenish blue	50	50
		a. Perf 13½×13. *Bluish grn* (1939)	8·50	2·00
		3 m. carmine-pink	50	70
		3 m. green (6.2.34)	2·50	85
		b. Perf 13½×13 (1939)	15·00	4·25
		4 m. green	60	2·00
		4 m. carmine-pink (6.2.34)	2·75	90
		b. Perf 13½×13 (1939)	55·00	20·00
		5 m. orange	50	40
		a. Coil stamp. Perf 13½×14 (29.2.36)	19·00	16·00
		b. Perf 13½×13 (1939)	55·00	3·00
		10 m. scarlet	1·25	15
		a. Perf 13½×13 (1939)	85·00	4·25
		15 m. ultramarine	85	20
		a. Coil stamp. Perf 13½×14 (29.2.36)	19·00	16·00
		b. Perf 13½×13 (1939)	35·00	3·75
		20 m. olive-green	1·25	35
		a. Perf 13½×13 (1939)	60·00	12·00
	29	50 m. purple	1·75	1·25
		90 m. bistre	2·50	4·25
		100 m. blue	3·75	4·25
		200 m. violet	9·00	14·00
		500 m. brown	20·00	38·00
		£P1 slate-grey	48·00	80·00
…/207		*Set of* 16	85·00	£130
…s/207s Perf "Specimen"		*Set of* 16	£170	

…r stamps perf 12 see Nos. 230/43, and for T **28** lithographed, … 13½, see Nos. 222/9.

30 Mushetta

31 Threshing Scene

32 The Khazneh at Petra

33 Emir Abdullah

(…gnettes from photographs; frames des Yacoub Sukker. Recess Bradbury, Wilkinson)

…**3** (1 Feb). *As T* **30** (*various designs*) *and T* **31/3**. *Wmk Mult Script CA. P* 12.

	1 m. black and maroon	50	1·40
	2 m. black and claret	75	1·00
	3 m. blue-green	1·00	1·60
	4 m. black and brown	1·50	2·25
	5 m. black and orange	1·75	1·25
	10 m. carmine	1·75	3·00
	15 m. blue	2·50	1·25
	20 m. black and sage-green	3·50	5·00
	50 m. black and purple	10·00	10·00
	90 m. black and yellow	14·00	27·00
	100 m. black and blue	14·00	27·00
	200 m. black and violet	45·00	60·00
	500 m. scarlet and red-brown	£130	£170
	£P1 black and yellow-green	£350	£550
…3/21	*Set of* 14	£500	£750
…3s/21s Perf "Specimen"	*Set of* 14	£500	

…Designs: *As T* **30**—2 m. Nymphaeum, Jerash; 3 m. Kasr …arana; 4 m. Kerak Castle; 5 m. Temple of Artemis, Jerash; 10 m. …un Castle; 20 m. Allenby Bridge over the Jordan.

…The 90 m., 100 m. and 200 m. are similar to the 3 m., 5 m. and …m. respectively, but are larger (33½ × 23½ mm). The 500 m. …similar to T **32**, but larger (23½ × 33½ mm).

34

(Litho Survey Dept, Cairo)

…**42** (18 May). *T* **28**, *but with Arabic characters above portrait and in top left circle modified as in T* **34**. *No wmk. P* 13½.

…2	**34**	1 m. red-brown	80	3·25
…3		2 m. green	1·50	1·50
…4		3 m. yellow-green	2·25	2·25
…5		4 m. carmine-pink	2·25	3·00
…6		5 m. yellow-orange	3·25	1·00
…7		10 m. scarlet	3·50	2·75
…8		15 m. blue	8·00	1·75
…9		20 m. olive-green	11·00	12·00
…22/9		*Set of* 8	29·00	24·00

Forgeries of the above exist on whiter paper with rough …rforations.

(Recess Bradbury, Wilkinson)

1943 (1 Jan)–**46.** *Wmk Mult Script CA. P* 12.

230	**28**	1 m. red-brown	20	75
231		2 m. bluish green	1·00	75
232		3 m. green	2·00	1·25
233		4 m. carmine-pink	1·75	1·25
234		5 m. orange	1·50	20
235		10 m. red	3·00	1·25
236		15 m. blue	3·00	30
237		20 m. olive-green (26.8.46)	3·00	1·00
238	**29**	50 m. purple (26.8.46)	3·00	1·00
239		90 m. bistre (26.8.46)	4·75	4·00
240		100 m. blue (26.8.46)	5·00	1·75
241		200 m. violet (26.8.46)	9·00	6·50
242		500 m. brown (26.8.46)	13·00	12·00
243		£P1 slate-grey (26.8.46)	24·00	22·00
230/43		*Set of* 14	65·00	48·00

Nos. 237/43 were released in London by the Crown Agents in May 1944, but were not put on sale in Transjordan until 26 August 1946.

Printings of the 3, 4, 10, 12, 15 and 20 m. in changed colours were released on 12 May 1947.

POSTAGE DUE STAMPS

مستحق

(D 12 "Due")

حكومة
مستحق
الشرق العربية
٩ شعبان ١٣٤١

(D 13)

1923 (Sept). *Issue of April, 1923, with opt T* **10**, *with further typographed opt Type* D **12** (*the 3 p. with handstamped surch as T* **12** *at top*).

D112	½ p. on 3 p. brown	15·00	18·00
	a. "Due" inverted	50·00	55·00
	b. "Due" double	50·00	60·00
	ba. "Due" double, one inverted	£150	
	c. Arabic "t" & "h" transposed (R. 1/2)	£100	
	ca. As c, inverted	£350	
	d. Surch at foot of stamp	26·00	
	da. Ditto, but with var. c	£120	
	e. Surch omitted	£200	
D113	1 p. blue	9·50	11·00
	a. Type **10** inverted	80·00	
	b. "Due" inverted	45·00	40·00
	c. "Due" double	50·00	
	d. "Due" double, one inverted	£150	
	e. Arabic "t" & "h" transposed (R. 1/2)	70·00	
	f. "Due" omitted (in vertical pair with normal)	£200	
D114	1½ p. lilac	10·00	11·00
	a. "Due" inverted	45·00	45·00
	b. "Due" double	50·00	
	ba. "Due" double, one diagonal	75·00	
	c. Arabic "t" & "h" transposed (R. 1/2)	70·00	
	ca. As c, inverted	£275	
	d. "Due" omitted (in pair with normal)	£200	
D115	2 p. orange	12·00	13·00
	a. "Due" inverted	60·00	60·00
	b. "Due" double	65·00	
	ba. "Due" double, one diagonal	£100	
	c. "Due" treble	£150	
	d. Arabic "t" & "h" transposed (R. 1/2)	70·00	
	e. Arabic "h" omitted	90·00	

The variety, Arabic "t" and "h" transposed, occurred on R. 1/2 of all values in the first batch of sheets printed. The variety, Arabic "h" omitted, occurred on every stamp in the first three rows of at least three sheets of the 2 p.

Handstamped in four lines as Type D **13** *and surch as on No.* D112

D116	½ p. on 3 p. brown	48·00	50·00
	a. Opt and surch inverted	£200	
	b. Opt double	£200	
	c. Surch omitted	£225	
	d. Opt inverted. Surch normal, but at foot of stamp	£150	
	e. Opt omitted and opt inverted (pair)	£300	
	f. "Due" double, one inverted	£160	
	h. Surch double	£250	

حكومة
الشرق العربية
مستحق
٩ شعبان ١٣٤١

(D 14)

مستحق
شرق الاردن

("Due. East of the Jordan")
(D **20**)

1923 (Oct). *T* **11** *of Saudi Arabia handstamped with Type* D **14**.

D117	½ p. scarlet	1·00	2·75
D118	1 p. blue	2·50	3·00
	a. Pair, one without handstamp		
D119	1½ p. lilac	2·50	3·75
D120	2 p. orange	3·50	4·25
D121	3 p. brown	5·00	8·50
	a. Pair, one without handstamp	£500	
D122	5 p. olive	8·00	13·00
D117/22	*Set of* 6	20·00	32·00

There are three types of this handstamp, differing in some of the Arabic characters. They occur inverted, double etc.

1923 (Nov). *T* **11** *of Saudi Arabia with opt similar to Type* D **14** *but first three lines typo and fourth handstruck.*

D123	1 p. blue	50·00	
D124	5 p. olive	8·00	
	a. Imperf between (vert pair)		

(Opt typo by Waterlow)

1925 (Nov). *Stamps of Palestine* 1922 (*without the three-line Palestine opt*), *optd with Type* D **20**. *P* 14.

D159	1 m. deep brown	1·40	5·50
D160	2 m. yellow	1·75	3·75
D161	4 m. carmine-pink	2·75	7·00
D162	8 m. scarlet	3·75	9·50
D163	13 m. ultramarine	4·50	9·50
D164	5 p. deep purple	5·00	13·00
	a. Perf 15 × 14	40·00	55·00
D159/64	*Set of* 6	17·00	42·00
D159s/64s Optd "Specimen"	*Set of* 6	65·00	

Stamps as No. D164, but with a different top line to overprint Type D **20**, were for revenue purposes.

مستحق

١ مليم (1 m.) (D **21**) — ٢ مليم (2 m.) — ٤ مليم (4 m.)

٨ مليم (8 m.) — ١٣ مليم (13 m.) — ٥ قروش (5 p.)

(Surch typo at Jerusalem)

1926 (Feb–May). *Postage stamps of 1 November 1925, surch "Due" and new value as Type* D **21** *by Greek Orthodox Printing Press, Jerusalem. Bottom line of surcharge differs for each value as illustrated.*

D165	1 m. on 1 m. deep brown	4·00	6·00
	a. Red opt	£100	
D166	2 m. on 1 m. deep brown	4·00	6·00
D167	4 m. on 3 m. greenish blue	4·25	7·00
D168	8 m. on 3 m. greenish blue	4·25	7·00
D169	13 m. on 13 m. ultramarine	5·50	8·00
D170	5 p. on 13 m. ultramarine	6·50	12·00
D165/70	*Set of* 6	26·00	42·00

١ مستحق ١

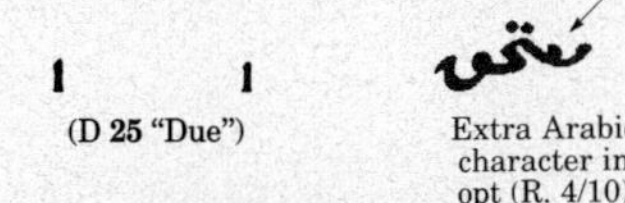
(D **25** "Due") — Extra Arabic character in opt (R. 4/10)

1929 (1 Jan). *Nos.* 159 *etc. optd only or surch in addition as Type* D **25** *by Whitehead, Morris & Co, Alexandria.*

D183	**22**	1 m. on 3 m. carmine-pink	70	4·50
		a. Extra Arabic character	25·00	
D184		2 m. greenish blue	80	4·50
		a. Pair, one without opt	£300	
D185		4 m. on 15 m. ultramarine	1·25	5·00
		a. Surch inverted	£120	£180
D186		10 m. scarlet	1·50	5·00
D187	**23**	20 m. on 100 m. blue	3·75	12·00
		a. Vert pair, one without surch	£375	
D188		50 m. purple	4·75	15·00
		a. Horiz pair, one without opt	£400	
D183/8		*Set of* 6	11·00	42·00

D 26

D 35

(Recess Perkins, Bacon)

1929 (1 Apr)–**39.** *Wmk Mult Script CA. P* 14.

D189	D **26**	1 m. red-brown	70	4·00
		a. Perf 13½×13 (1939)	80·00	50·00
D190		2 m. orange-yellow	1·00	4·50
D191		4 m. green	1·75	5·50
D192		10 m. scarlet	3·00	5·50
D193		20 m. olive-green	7·00	11·00
D194		50 m. blue	9·00	19·00
D189/94		*Set of* 6	20·00	45·00
D189s/94s Perf "Specimen"		*Set of* 6	65·00	

(Litho Survey Dept, Cairo)

1942 (22 Dec). *Redrawn. Top line of Arabic in taller lettering. No wmk. P* 13½.

D230	D **35**	1 m. red-brown	1·75	13·00
D231		2 m. orange-yellow	10·00	9·00
D232		10 m. scarlet	13·00	6·00
D230/2		*Set of* 3	22·00	25·00

Forgeries of the above exist on whiter paper with rough perforations.

(Recess Bradbury, Wilkinson)

1944–49. *Wmk Mult Script CA. P* 12.

D244	D **26**	1 m. red-brown	35	3·00
D245		2 m. orange-yellow	40	3·50
D246		4 m. green	55	4·50
D247		10 m. carmine	1·40	6·00
D248		20 m. olive-green (1949)	32·00	48·00
D244/8		*Set of* 5	32·00	60·00

OFFICIAL STAMP

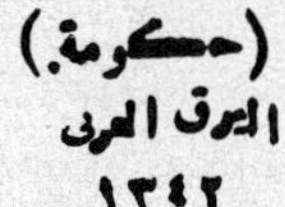

("Arab Government of the East, 1342" = 1924)
(O 16)

1924. *T* **11** *of Saudi Arabia with typographed opt, Type* O **16**.
O117 ½ p. scarlet .. .. 20·00 £100
a. Arabic "1242" (R. 2/2, 3/6, 4/5, 4/6) £150

By treaty of 22 March 1946 with the United Kingdom, Transjordan was proclaimed an independent kingdom on 25 May 1946.
Later issues are listed under JORDAN in Part 19 (*Middle East*) of this catalogue.

Transvaal

see South Africa

Trinidad and Tobago

TRINIDAD

CROWN COLONY

The first post office was established at Port of Spain in 1800 to deal with overseas mail. Before 1851 there was no post office inland service, although a privately-operated one along the coast did exist, for which rates were officially fixed (see No. 1). During 1851 the colonial authorities established an inland postal system which commenced operation on 14 August. Responsibility for the overseas mails passed to the local post authorities in 1858.

No. CC1 is recorded in the G.P.O. Record Book on 21 March 1852, but no examples have been recorded used on cover before February 1858. The prepayment of postage on mail to Great Britain was made compulsory from 9 October 1858. From March 1859 it was used with the early Britannia 1d. stamps to indicate prepayment of the additional overseas rate in cash or, later, to show that letters were fully franked with adhesive stamps. This is the normal usage of the handstamp and commands little, if any premium over the cover price quoted below for the stamps involved. The use of the handstamp without an adhesive is rare.

PORT OF SPAIN

CROWNED-CIRCLE HANDSTAMPS

CC 1

CC1 CC 1 TRINIDAD (R.) (*without additional adhesive stamp*) (21.3.52) *Price on cover* £2500

PRICES FOR STAMPS ON COVER

No. 1	*from* × 2
Nos. 2/12	*from* × 10
Nos. 13/20	*from* × 4
Nos. 25/9	*from* × 10
No. 30	—
Nos. 31/44	*from* × 4
No. 45	—
Nos. 46/59	*from* × 4
Nos. 60/3	*from* × 5
Nos. 64/8	*from* × 4
Nos. 69/74	*from* × 20
Nos. 75/8	*from* × 50
No. 79	—
No. 87	*from* × 20
Nos. 98/102	*from* × 6
No. 103	—
Nos. 104/5	*from* × 20
Nos. 106/12	*from* × 12
No. 113	—
Nos. 114/21	*from* × 4
Nos. 122/4	—
No. 125	*from* × 10
Nos. 126/30	*from* × 5
No. 131	—
Nos. 132/43	*from* × 3
Nos. 144/5	—
Nos. 146/8	*from* × 3
Nos. D1/17	*from* × 15

1

2 Britannia

1847 (16 Apr). *Litho. Imperf.*
1 **1** (5 c.) blue £25000 £10000

The "LADY McLEOD" stamps were issued in April 1847, by David Bryce, owner of the S.S. *Lady McLeod*, and sold at five cents each for the prepayment of the carriage of letters by his vessel between Port of Spain and San Fernando.

The price quoted for used examples of No. 1 is for pen-cancelled. Stamps cancelled by having a corner skimmed-off are worth less.

(Recess P.B.)

1851 (14 Aug)–**56.** *No value expressed. Imperf. Blued pa*
2 **2** (1d.) purple-brown (1851) .. .. .. 10·0
3 (1d.) blue *to* deep blue (12.51) .. .. 10·0
4 (1d.) deep blue (1852)* £15
5 (1d.) grey (11.52) .. .. 60·0
6 (1d.) brownish grey (1853) .. .. .. 38·0
7 (1d.) brownish red (1853) £30
8 (1d.) brick-red (1856) £14

*No. 4 shows the paper deeply and evenly blued, especially back. It has more the appearance of having been printed paper rather than on white paper that has become blued.

1854–57. *Imperf. White paper.*
9 **2** (1d.) deep purple (1854) .. .. .. 22·00
10 (1d.) dark grey (1854) .. .. .. 32·00
11 (1d.) blue (? date).. .. .. ..
12 (1d.) rose-red (1857) £1700

PRICES. Prices quoted for the unused of most of the above and Nos. 25 and 29 are for "remainders" with original gum in London. Old colours that have been out to Trinidad are o greater value.

3 Britannia 4

The following provisional issues were lithographed in the C (from die engraved by Charles Petit), and brought into use to shortages of the Perkins Bacon stamps during the foll periods:

(1) Sept 1852–May 1853; (2) March 1855–June 1855; (3 1856–Jan 1857; (4) Oct 1858–Jan 1859; (5) March 1860–June

1852–60. *No value expressed. Imperf.*

A. *First Issue* (Sept 1852). *Fine impression; lines of backg clear and distinct.* (i) *Yellowish paper*
13 **3** (1d.) blue .. .. £8500 £

(ii) *Bluish cartridge paper* (Feb 1853)
14 **3** (1d.) blue .. .. — £

B. *Second issue* (March 1855). *Thinner paper. Impressio distinct than before*
15 **3** (1d.) pale blue *to* greenish blue .. .. —

C. *Third issue* (*August* 1856). *Background often of soli colour, but with clear lines in places*
16 **3** (1d.) bright blue *to* deep blue .. .. £4500 £

D. *Fourth issue* (October 1858). *Impression less distinct, and r showing more than traces of background lines*
17 **3** (1d.) very deep greenish blue .. .. —
18 (1d.) slate-blue £4000

E. *Fifth issue* (March 1860). *Impression shows no* (*or hardly background lines*
19 **3** (1d.) grey *to* bluish grey £4000
20 (1d.) red (*shades*) .. .. .. 13·00

In the worn impression of the fourth and fifth issues impression varies according to the position on the stone. Gene speaking, stamps of the fifth issue have a flatter appearance cancellations are often less well defined. The paper of both issues is thin or very thin. In all issues except 1853 (Feb) the tends to give the paper a toned appearance.

Stamps in the slate-blue shade (No. 18) also occur in the issue, but are not readily distinguishable.

PERKINS BACON "CANCELLED". For notes on th handstamps, showing "CANCELLED" between horizontal forming an oval, see Catalogue Introduction.

(Recess P.B.)

1859 (9 May). *Imperf.*
25 **4** 4d. grey-lilac (H/S "CANCELLED" in oval £5000) .. .. 85·00 £
28 6d. deep green (H/S "CANCELLED" in oval £5000) .. .. — £
29 1s. indigo .. .. 85·00 £
30 1s. purple-slate .. ..

"CANCELLED" examples of No. 25 are in lilac rather t grey-lilac.

No. 30 may be of unissued status.

1859 (Sept). (*a*) *Pin-perf* 12½.
31 **2** (1d.) rose-red £1500 55
32 (1d.) carmine-lake £1800 50
33 **4** 4d. dull lilac .. .. — £
34 4d. dull purple .. .. £6000 £
35 6d. yellow-green .. .. .. £2750 £
36 6d. deep green .. .. £2750 £
37 1s. purple-slate.. .. .. .. £6000 £1

(*b*) *Pin-perf* 13½–14
38 **2** (1d.) rose-red £120 2
39 (1d.) carmine-lake £275 2
40 **4** 4d. dull lilac £1200 75
40*a* 4d. brownish purple .. .. .. £100 £
41 4d. dull purple .. .. £350 £
42 6d. yellow-green £500 70
43 6d. deep green £500 65
43*a* 6d. bright yellow-green .. .. £100 £
b. Imperf between (vert pair).. .. £4000
44 1s. purple-slate.. .. .. .. £6000 £

(*c*) *Compound pin-perf* 13½–14 × 12½
45 **2** (1d.) carmine-lake .. .. .. † £3
45*a* **4** 4d. dull purple .. .. †

PRICES. The Pin-perf stamps are very scarce with perforations all sides and the prices quoted above are for good aver specimens.

The note after No. 12 also applies to Nos. 38, 40*a*, 43*a*, 46, and 50.

Aug). *Clean-cut perf* 14–16½.
(1d.) rose-red .. .. £110 55·00
a. Imperf vert (horiz pair) £1100
4d. brownish lilac .. .. £110 80·00
4d. lilac .. .. — £300
6d. bright yellow-green .. .. .. £375 90·00
6d. deep green £225 £140

June). *Rough perf* 14–16½.
(1d.) rose-red (H/S "CANCELLED" in oval £5000) .. .. £100 25·00
(1d.) rose .. .. £100 22·00
4d. brownish lilac .. .. £200 70·00
4d. lilac .. .. £600 75·00
a. Imperf .. ..
6d. yellow-green .. .. £225 75·00
6d. deep green .. .. £400 65·00
1s. indigo £750 £250
1s. dp bluish purple (H/S "CANCELLED" in oval £5000) £1200 £400

(Recess D.L.R.)

63. *Thick paper.* (*a*) *P* 11½, 12.
2 (1d.) crimson-lake .. .. £100 16·00
4 4d. deep purple .. .. £140 55·00
6d. deep green .. .. £1000 80·00
1s. bluish slate .. .. £2000 85·00

(*b*) *P* 11½, 12, *compound with* 11
2 (1d.) crimson-lake £1600 £475
4 6d. deep green .. .. — £6500

(*c*) *P* 13 (1863)
2 (1d.) lake .. .. 32·00 16·00
4 6d. emerald-green .. .. £450 55·00
1s. bright mauve £4000 £275

(*d*) *P* 12½ (1863)
2 (1d.) lake .. .. 40·00 17·00

–80. *Wmk Crown CC.* (*a*) *P* 12½
2 (1d.) lake .. .. 42·00 4·50
a. Wmk sideways .. .. £120 12·00
b. Rose .. .. 42·00 1·60
ba. Imperf (pair) .. ..
c. Scarlet .. .. 42·00 1·50
d. Carmine .. .. 42·00 1·75
w. Wmk inverted .. .. † 50·00
x. Wmk reversed .. .. 45·00 2·00
y. Wmk inverted and reversed .. .. — 60·00
4 4d. bright violet .. .. 95·00 8·50
a. Pale mauve .. .. £170 12·00
b. Dull lilac .. .. £130 12·00
w. Wmk inverted .. .. £225 50·00
x. Wmk reversed .. .. £100 10·00
4d. grey (1872) .. .. £100 4·25
a. Bluish grey .. .. 95·00 4·50
ax. Wmk reversed .. .. 95·00 6·00
w. Wmk inverted .. .. — 60·00
6d. emerald-green .. .. 70·00 11·00
a. Deep green .. .. £350 7·50
b. Yellow-green .. .. 65·00 3·50
c. Apple-green .. .. 60·00 4·75
d. Blue-green .. .. £110 6·00
x. Wmk reversed .. .. 80·00 6·00
1s. bright deep mauve .. .. .. £120 6·50
a. Lilac-rose .. .. 95·00 6·50
b. Mauve (aniline) .. .. .. 85·00 4·25
bw. Wmk inverted .. ..
bx. Wmk reversed .. .. — 6·00
1s. chrome-yellow (1872) .. .. .. £120 1·25
x. Wmk reversed .. .. — 5·00

(*b*) *P* 14 (1876)
2 (1d.) lake .. .. 21·00 90
a. Bisected (½d.) (on cover) .. .. † £550
b. Rose-carmine .. .. 21·00 1·00
c. Scarlet .. .. 38·00 75
x. Wmk reversed .. .. 25·00 1·00
4 4d. bluish grey .. .. 90·00 70
y. Wmk inverted and reversed .. .. † 75·00
6d. bright yellow-green .. .. .. 80·00 1·25
a. Deep yellow-green .. .. .. £100 1·00
w. Wmk inverted .. .. † 65·00
x. Wmk reversed .. ..
1s. chrome-yellow .. .. 95·00 2·50

(*c*) *P* 14×12½ (1880)
4 6d. yellow-green .. .. — £5000

he 1s. perforated 12½ in purple-slate is a colour changeling.

5

(Typo D.L.R.)

69. *Wmk Crown CC. P* 12½.
5 5s. rose-lake .. .. £160 75·00

HALFPENNY (6) **ONE PENNY** (7)

79–82. *Surch with T* **6** *or* **7**. *P* 14.

(*a*) *Wmk Crown CC* (June 1879)
8 2 ½d. lilac .. .. 10·00 6·50
w. Wmk inverted .. .. £100 32·00
x. Wmk reversed .. .. 10·00 6·50
9 ½d. mauve .. .. 10·00 6·50
a. Wmk sideways .. .. 50·00 50·00
w. Wmk inverted .. .. † —

(*b*) *Wmk Crown CA* (1882)
100 2 ½d. lilac (*wmk reversed*) .. .. .. £180 65·00
101 1d. rosy carmine .. .. 25·00 70
a. Bisected (½d.) (on cover) .. .. † £550
x. Wmk reversed .. .. 25·00 1·00

1882. *Wmk Crown CA. P* 14.
102 4 4d. bluish grey .. .. £160 6·50
x. Wmk reversed .. ..

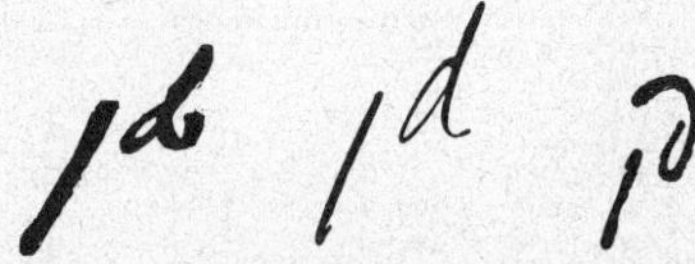

(8) Various styles

1882 (9 May). *Surch by hand in various styles as T* **8** *in red or black ink and the original value obliterated by a thick or thin bar or bars, of the same colour.*
103 1d. on 6d. (No. 77) (Bk.) .. .. .. — £1500
104 1d. on 6d. (No. 77) (R.) .. .. .. 6·50 4·25
x. Wmk reversed .. .. 10·00 7·50
105 1d. on 6d. (No. 77*a*) (R.) .. .. .. 6·50 4·25
a. Bisected (½d.) (on cover) .. .. † £300

10

11 Britannia

12 Britannia

(Typo D.L.R.)

1883–94. *P* 14. (*a*) *Wmk Crown CA.*
106 10 ½d. dull green .. .. 3·50 1·25
107 1d. carmine .. .. 10·00 50
a. Bisected (½d.) (on cover) .. .. † £650
w. Wmk inverted .. .. † £100
108 2½d. bright blue .. .. 11·00 60
110 4d. grey .. .. 2·50 60
w. Wmk inverted .. .. † £120
111 6d. olive-black (1884) .. .. .. 3·25 4·25
112 1s. orange-brown (1884) .. .. .. 3·50 2·25

(*b*) *Wmk Crown CC*
113 5 5s. maroon (1894) .. .. 50·00 80·00
106/13 .. .. *Set of* 7 75·00 80·00
106s/12s Optd "Specimen" .. .. *Set of* 6 £400

Two types of 1d. value:

ONE PENNY (I) (round "o") **ONE PENNY** (II) (oval "o")

(Typo D.L.R.)

1896 (17 Aug)–**1906.** *P* 14. (*a*) *Wmk Crown CA.*
114 11 ½d. dull purple and green .. .. 3·25 30
115 1d. dull purple and rose (I) .. .. 3·50 10
116 1d. dull purple and rose (II) (1900) .. £300 4·00
117 2½d. dull purple and blue .. .. 4·75 20
118 4d. dull purple and orange .. .. 6·50 16·00
119 5d. dull purple and mauve .. .. 6·50 14·00
120 6d. dull purple and black .. .. 7·50 5·50
121 1s. green and brown .. .. .. 7·00 6·50

(*b*) *Wmk CA over Crown. Ordinary paper*
122 12 5s. green and brown .. .. .. 40·00 70·00
123 10s. green and ultramarine £140 £250
124 £1 green and carmine £120 £180
a. Chalk-surfaced paper (1906) .. £180
114/24 .. .. *Set of* 10 £300 £500
114s/24s Optd "Specimen" .. .. *Set of* 10 £150

No. 119, surcharged "3d." was prepared for use in 1899 but not issued (*Price* £2750 *unused*). It also exists overprinted "Specimen" (*Price* £75).

Collectors are warned against apparently postally used copies of this issue which bear "REGISTRAR-GENERAL" obliterations and are of very little value.

13 Landing of Columbus

(Recess D.L.R.)

1898. 400*th Anniv of Discovery of Trinidad. Wmk Crown CC. P* 14.
125 13 2d. brown and dull violet .. .. 2·50 1·25
s. Optd "Specimen" .. .. .. 50·00

1901–06. *Colours changed. Wmk Crown CA or CA over Crown* (5*s.*). *Ordinary paper. P* 14.
126 11 ½d. grey-green (1902) .. .. .. 65 1·75
127 1d. black/*red* (II) .. .. .. 1·25 10
a. Value omitted £25000
w. Wmk inverted .. .. .. † £150
128 2½d. purple and blue/*blue* (1902) .. 15·00 25
129 4d. green and blue/*buff* (1902) .. 1·75 13·00
a. Chalk-surfaced paper .. .. 3·50 13·00
130 1s. black and blue/*yellow* (1903) .. 18·00 5·50
131 12 5s. lilac and mauve .. .. .. 40·00 65·00
a. Chalk-surfaced paper. *Deep purple and mauve* (1906) .. .. 65·00 80·00
126/31 .. .. *Set of* 6 70·00 75·00
126s/31s Optd "Specimen" .. *Set of* 6 £110

A pane of sixty of No. 127a was found at the San Fernando post office of which fifty-one were subsequently returned to London and destroyed. Only three mint examples, one of which is in the Royal Collection, are now thought to survive.

1904–09. *Wmk Mult Crown CA. Ordinary paper* (½*d.*, 1*d.*, 2½*d.* (*No.* 137)) *or chalk-surfaced paper* (*others*). *P* 14.
132 11 ½d. grey-green .. .. 2·50 1·00
a. Chalk-surfaced paper .. .. 4·75 2·25
133 ½d. blue-green (1906) .. .. .. 9·00 2·50
134 1d. black/*red* (II) .. .. .. 3·50 10
a. Chalk-surfaced paper .. .. 5·50 10
135 1d. rose-red (1907) .. .. .. 1·25 10
136 2½d. purple and blue/*blue* .. .. 22·00 90
137 2½d. blue (1906) .. .. 2·50 15
138 4d. grey and red/*yellow* (1906) .. 1·50 8·00
a. Black and red/yellow .. .. 9·00 21·00
139 6d. dull purple and black (1905) .. 15·00 15·00
140 6d. dull and bright purple (1906) .. 7·00 8·50
141 1s. black and blue/*yellow* .. .. 20·00 8·00
142 1s. purple and blue/*golden yellow* .. 10·00 12·00
143 1s. black/*green* (1906) .. .. .. 1·75 1·25
144 12 5s. deep purple and mauve (1907) .. 42·00 80·00
145 £1 green and carmine (1907) £120 £200
132/45 .. .. *Set of* 13 £225 £300
135s/43s (*ex* Nos. 136, 139, 141) Optd "Specimen" *Set of* 6 £110

No. 135 is from a new die, the letters of "ONE PENNY" being short and thick, while the point of Britannia's spear breaks the uppermost horizontal line of shading in the background.

14

15

16

(Typo D.L.R.)

1909. *Wmk Mult Crown CA. P* 14.
146 14 ½d. green .. .. 3·00 10
147 15 1d. rose-red .. .. 2·50 10
148 16 2½d. blue .. .. 9·50 3·25
146/8 .. .. *Set of* 3 13·50 3·25
146s/8s Optd "Specimen" .. .. *Set of* 3 60·00

TOBAGO

Although a Colonial Postmaster was appointed in January 1765 it was not until 1841 that the British G.P.O. established a branch office at Scarborough, the island capital, to handle the overseas mail.

The stamps of Great Britain were in use from May 1858 to the end of April 1860 when the control of the postal service passed to the local authorities.

From April 1860 Nos. CC1/2 were again used on overseas mail, pending the introduction of Tobago stamps in 1879.

SCARBOROUGH

CROWNED-CIRCLE HANDSTAMPS

CC 1

CC 2

CC1 CC 1 TOBAGO (R.) (31.10.1851) *Price on cover* £700
CC2 CC 2 TOBAGO (R.) (1875) *Price on cover* £2500

Stamps of GREAT BRITAIN *cancelled "*A 14*" as Type* Z **1** *of Jamaica.*

1858 *to* **1860.**
Z 1 1d. rose-red (1857), *perf* 14 .. .. .. £700
Z 2 4d. rose (1857) £275
Z 3 6d. lilac (1856) £225
Z 4 1s. green (1856) £1100

PRICES FOR STAMPS ON COVER

Nos. 1/4	*from* × 25
Nos. 5/7	—
Nos. 8/12	*from* × 10
Nos. 13/19	*from* × 6
Nos. 20/4	*from* × 40
Nos. 26/33	*from* × 25

CANCELLATIONS. Beware of early stamps of Tobago with fiscal endorsements removed and forged wide "A 14" postmarks added.

1

2

2½ PENCE
(3)

(T 1 and 2 Typo D.L.R.)

1879 (1 Aug). *Fiscal stamps issued provisionally pending the arrival of stamps inscr* "POSTAGE". *Wmk Crown CC. P* 14.
1 1 1d. rose .. .. 80·00 65·00
2 3d. blue .. .. 75·00 48·00
3 6d. orange .. .. 38·00 50·00
w. Wmk inverted .. .. 90·00 £100
4 1s. green .. .. £375 65·00
a. Bisected (6d.) (on cover) .. .. .. † —
5 5s. slate £650 £600
6 £1 mauve £4000
The stamps were introduced for fiscal purposes on 1 July 1879.
Stamps of T 1, watermark Crown CA, are fiscals which were never admitted to postal use.

1880 (Nov). *No. 3 bisected vertically and surch with pen and ink.*
7 1 1d. on half of 6d. orange £4500 £750
w. Wmk inverted .. .. ..

1880 (20 Dec). *Wmk Crown CC. P* 14.
8 2 ½d. purple-brown .. .. 35·00 55·00
9 1d. Venetian red .. .. 95·00 55·00
a. Bisected (½d.) (on cover) .. .. .. † £1800
10 4d. yellow-green .. .. £200 27·00
a. Bisected (2d.) (on cover) .. .. .. † £1800
b. Malformed "CE" in "PENCE" £1300 £400
w. Wmk inverted .. .. — £120
11 6d. stone £300 £100
12 1s. yellow-ochre .. .. 60·00 70·00
w. Wmk inverted £130
For illustration of Nos. 10b, 18a, 22b, 30a, 31a and 33b see above No. 4 of Dominica.

1883 (Apr). *No.* 11 *surch with T* 3.
13 2 2½d. on 6d. stone .. .. 45·00 45·00
a. Surch double £2750 £1300
b. Large "2" with long tail £110 £120

"SLASH" FLAW. Stamps as Type 2 were produced from Key and Duty plates. On the Key plate used for consignments between 2 October 1892 and 16 December 1896, damage in the form of a large cut or "slash" shows after the "E" of "POSTAGE" on R.1/4.
After 1896 an attempt was made to repair the "slash". This resulted in its disappearance, but left an incomplete edge to the circular frame at right.

1882–84. *Wmk Crown CA. P* 14.
14 2 ½d. purple-brown (1882) .. .. .. 1·00 12·00
15 1d. Venetian red (1882) .. .. .. 2·75 1·75
a. Bisected diag (½d.) (on cover) .. ..
16 2½d. dull blue (1883) .. .. .. 28·00 1·40
a. *Bright blue* .. .. 4·50 75
b. *Ultramarine* .. .. 4·50 75
c. "Slash" flaw .. .. 38·00 38·00
ca. "Slash" flaw repaired .. .. .. 85·00
18 4d. yellow-green (1882) .. .. .. £180 90·00
a. Malformed "CE" in "PENCE" £1200 £475
19 6d. stone (1884) £500 £475

1885–96. *Colours changed and new value. Wmk Crown CA. P* 14.
20 2 ½d. dull green (1886) .. .. .. 1·50 50
a. "Slash" flaw .. .. 23·00 28·00
ab. "Slash" flaw repaired .. .. .. 42·00
w. Wmk inverted .. ..
21 1d. carmine (1889) .. .. 2·25 60
a. "Slash" flaw .. .. 30·00 30·00
ab. "Slash" flaw repaired .. .. .. 55·00
22 4d. grey (1885) .. .. 2·25 1·00
a. Imperf (pair) £1700
b. Malformed "CE" in "PENCE" .. .. 50·00 80·00
c. "Slash" flaw .. .. 70·00 £100
ca. "Slash" flaw repaired £100
23 6d. orange-brown (1886) .. .. .. 2·00 4·00
a. "Slash" flaw .. .. 80·00 £130
ab. "Slash" flaw repaired £110
24 1s. olive-yellow (1894) .. .. .. 2·25 15·00
a. *Pale olive-yellow* .. .. .. 6·50
b. "Slash" flaw .. .. 90·00 £190
ba. "Slash" flaw repaired £120
24c 1s. orange-brown (1896) .. .. .. 7·50 60·00
ca. "Slash" flaw £130
20s/3s (*ex* 4d.) Optd "Specimen" .. .. *Set of* 3 £170
No. 24c was printed in the colour of the 6d. by mistake.

½ PENNY
(4)

2½ PENCE
(5)

½d
POSTAGE
(6)

1886–89. *Nos.* 16, 19 *and* 23 *surch as T* 4.
26 ½d. on 2½d. dull blue (4.86) .. .. .. 4·25 11·00
a. Figure further from word .. .. .. 18·00 50·00
b. Surch double £1600 £1300
c. Surch omitted. Vert pair with No. 26 .. £9000
d. Ditto with No. 26a £16000
27 ½d. on 6d. stone (1.86) .. .. .. 2·25 18·00
a. Figure further from word .. .. .. 25·00 £110
b. Surch inverted £1400
c. Surch double £1600
28 ½d. on 6d. orange-brown (8.87) £100 £130
a. Figure further from word £300 £325
b. Surch double .. .. — £1200
29 1d. on 2½d. dull blue (7.89) .. .. .. 55·00 16·00
a. Figure further from word .. .. .. £140 75·00
The surcharge is in a setting of 12 (two rows of 6) repeated five times in the pane. Nos. 7, 9 and 10 in the setting have a raised "P" in "PENNY", and No. 10 also shows the wider spacing between figure and word.

1891–92. *No.* 22 *surch with T* 4 *or* 5.
30 ½d. on 4d. grey (3.92) .. .. 12·00 45·00
a. Malformed "CE" in "PENCE" £200 £375
b. Surch double £1900
31 2½d. on 4d. grey (8.91) .. .. 5·00 6·50
a. Malformed "CE" in "PENCE" £130 £200
b. Surch double £1900 £1900

1896. *Fiscal stamp (T* 1*, value in second colour, wmk Crown CA, P* 14*), surch with T* 6.
33 ½d. on 4d. lilac and carmine .. .. .. 50·00 29·00
a. Space between "½" and "d" .. .. .. £110 65·00
b. Malformed "CE" in "PENCE" £475 £475

Tobago became a ward of Trinidad on 1 January 1899. Stamps of Trinidad were used until issues inscribed "TRINIDAD AND TOBAGO" appeared in 1913.

TRINIDAD AND TOBAGO

PRICES FOR STAMPS ON COVER	
Nos. 149/55	*from* × 3
Nos. 156/7	—
Nos. 174/89	*from* × 10
Nos. 206/56	*from* × 2
Nos. D18/25	*from* × 12

17

18

(Typo D.L.R.)

1913–23. *Wmk Mult Crown CA. Ordinary paper (½d. to 4d. and 1s.) or chalk-surfaced paper (others). P* 14.
149 17 ½d. green .. .. 3·00 10
a. *Yellow-green* (1915) .. .. .. 3·50 20
b. *Blue-green* (*thick paper*) (1917) .. 7·00 1·00
ba. Wmk sideways .. .. † £1300
c. *Blue-green/bluish* (3.18) .. .. 14·00 12·00
w. Wmk inverted .. ..
150 1d. bright red .. .. 1·50 10
a. *Red* (*thick paper*) (1916) .. .. 3·25 30
b. *Pink* (1918) .. .. 22·00 3·00
c. *Carmine-red* (5.18) .. .. .. 2·50 10
w. Wmk inverted .. ..
151 2½d. ultramarine .. .. 5·50 50
a. *Bright blue* (*thick paper*) (1916) .. 6·50 50
b. *Bright blue* (*thin paper*) (1918) .. 8·00 50
152 4d. black and red/*yellow* .. .. ..
a. Chalk-surfaced paper .. .. .. 70 6·00
b. *White back* (12.13) .. .. .. 1·75 10·00
bs. Optd "Specimen" .. .. .. 18·00
c. *On lemon* (1917) .. .. .. 10·00
d. *On pale yellow* (1923) .. .. .. 5·00 8·50
ds. Optd "Specimen" .. .. .. 22·00
153 6d. dull and reddish purple .. .. 8·50 6·50
a. *Dull and deep purple* (1918) .. .. 8·50 3·75
b. *Dull purple and mauve* (2.18) .. .. 10·00 8·00
154 1s. black/*green* .. .. 1·75 4·50
a. *White back* .. .. 1·00 5·00
as. Optd "Specimen" .. .. .. 18·00
b. *On blue-green, olive back* .. .. 7·50 9·00
c. *On emerald back* .. .. .. 1·50 3·00
cs. Optd "Specimen" .. .. .. 22·00
155 18 5s. dull purple and mauve (1914) .. 50·00 90·00
a. *Deep purple and mauve* (1918) .. 50·00 90·00
b. *Lilac and violet* .. .. .. 85·00 £120
c. *Dull purple and violet* .. .. 90·00 £130
d. *Brown-purple and violet* .. .. 45·00 90·00
156 £1 grey-green and carmine (1914) .. £120 £160
a. *Deep yellow-green & carmine* (1918) £120 £160
149/56 .. .. *Set of* 8 £150 £225
149s/56s Optd "Specimen" .. .. *Set of* 8 £160
No. 156a is from a plate showing background lines very worn.

18a

1914 (18 Sept). *Red Cross Label authorised for use as ½d. s Typo. P* 11–12.
157 18a (½d.) Red .. .. 10·00
The above was authorised for internal use on one day on raise funds for the Red Cross. The used price is for stamp on c

21. 10. 15.
(19)

19. 10. 16.

(19a)

1915 (21 Oct). *Optd with T* 19. *Cross in red with outline and in black.*
174 17 1d. red .. .. 1·50
a. Cross 2 mm to right .. .. .. 18·00
b. "1" of "15" forked foot .. .. .. 9·50
c. Broken "0" in "10" .. .. .. 12·00
The varieties occur in the following positions on the pane c a. No. 11. b. No. 42. c. No. 45. Variety a. is only found on the ri hand pane.

1916 (19 Oct). *Optd with T* 19a. *Cross in red with outline and in black.*
175 17 1d. scarlet 50
a. No stop after "16" .. .. .. 7·50 2
b. "19.10.16" omitted .. .. ..
c. Red shading on cross omitted .. ..
No. 175a appears on stamp No. 36 on the right-hand pane or

FORGERIES. Beware of forgeries of the "War Tax" errors l below. There are also other unlisted errors which are purely fa

WAR TAX
(19b)

WAR TAX
(20)

WAR TAX
(21)

WAR TAX
(22)

1917 (2 Apr). *Optd with T* 19b.
176 17 1d. red .. .. 2·25
a. Opt inverted .. .. £170 £
b. *Scarlet* .. .. 2·25
w. Wmk inverted .. ..

1917 (May). *Optd with T* 20.
177 17 ½d. green 10
a. Pair, one without opt £375
178 1d. red 75
a. Pair, one without opt .. .. .. £375 £
b. *Scarlet* .. .. 3·00
ba. Opt double £110
The varieties without overprint were caused by the type be shifted over towards the left so that one stamp in the lowest ro each pane escaped.

1917 (21 June). *Optd with T* 21.
179 17 ½d. yellow-green .. .. 1·40 6
a. *Pale green* 10 5
b. *Deep green* .. .. 1·25 6
180 1d. red 10
a. Pair, one without opt .. .. ..
No. 180a was caused by a shifting of the type to the left-ha side, but only a few stamps on the right-hand vertical row escap the overprint and such pairs are very rare.

1917 (21 July–Sept). *Optd with T* 22.
181 17 ½d. yellow-green .. .. 4·00 6
a. *Deep green* 10 2
aw. Wmk inverted £100
182 1d. red (Sept) .. .. 3·00 1

WAR TAX
(23)

WAR TAX
(24)

WAR TAX
(25)

1917 (1 Sept). *Optd with T* 23 *(closer spacing between lines of o*
183 17 ½d. deep green 10 2
a. *Pale yellow-green* .. .. ..
184 1d. red .. .. 28·00 24

1917 (31 Oct). *Optd with T* 24.
185 17 1d. scarlet 60 1
a. Opt inverted .. .. 95·00

1918 (7 Jan). *Optd with T* 25.
186 17 1d. scarlet .. .. 1·50
a. Opt double £170 £1
b. Opt inverted £100 £1

COVER PRICES

Cover factors are quoted at the beginning of eac country for most issues to 1945. An explanation c the system can be found on page x. The factor quoted do not, however, apply to philatelic covers

Var War
Tax Tax
(26) (26a)

27

13 Feb–May). *Optd with T* **26**.
7 ½d. bluish green .. .. .. 10 1·75
a. Pair, one without opt £550
1d. scarlet .. .. 85 1·25
a. Opt double £100
b. Rose-red (1.5.18) 10 60
½d. exists with "TAX" omitted caused by a paper fold.

(14 Sept). *New printing as T* **26**, *but 19 stamps on each sheet*
e the letters of the word "Tax" wider spaced, the "x" being to
right of "r" of "War" as T **26a**. *Thick bluish paper.*
17 1d. scarlet ("Tax" spaced) .. .. 35 4·50
a. Opt double £180

–22. *Wmk Mult Script CA. Chalk-surfaced paper (6d. to*
. P 14.
17 ½d. green .. .. 1·75 2·25
1d. scarlet 60 30
1d. brown (17.2.22) .. .. .. 60 1·50
2d. grey (17.2.22) .. .. .. 1·00 1·25
2½d. bright blue .. .. .. 80 12·00
3d. bright blue (17.2.22) .. .. 3·00 3·00
6d. dull and bright purple .. .. 2·00 16·00
18 5s. dull purple and purple (1921) .. 48·00 £120
5s. deep purple and purple (1922) .. 48·00 £120
£1 green and carmine .. .. 80·00 £200
5 .. .. *Set of* 9 £120 £300
15s Optd "Specimen" .. *Set of* 9 £200

(Typo D.L.R.)

–28. *P* 14. *Chalk-surfaced paper* (4d. *to* £1).
(*a*) *Wmk Mult Crown CA*
27 4d. black and red/*pale yellow* .. 3·25 6·50
1s. black/*emerald* .. .. .. 3·50 9·50
(*b*) *Wmk Mult Script CA*
27 ½d. green 50 10
1d. brown 50 10
w. Wmk inverted .. .. .. 30·00
1½d. bright rose .. .. .. 2·25 20
aw. Wmk inverted .. .. .. 65·00
b. Scarlet .. .. 1·75 30
bw. Wmk inverted .. .. ..
2d. grey .. .. 50 1·25
3d. blue .. .. 50 1·25
4d. black and red/*pale yellow* (1928) 3·25 3·25
6d. dull purple and bright magenta .. 2·25 25·00
6d. green and red/*emerald* (1924) .. 1·25 60
1s. black/*emerald* .. .. .. 5·50 1·75
5s. dull purple and mauve .. .. 22·00 38·00
£1 green and bright rose .. .. 90·00 £200
/29 .. .. .. *Set of* 13 £120 £250
s/29s Optd "Specimen" .. *Set of* 13 £225

(New Currency. 100 cents = 1 West Indian dollar)

28 First Boca **29** Imperial College of Tropical Agriculture

(Recess B.W.)

35 (1 Feb)–37. *T* **28/9** *and similar horiz designs. Wmk Mult Script CA (sideways). P* 12.
1 c. blue and green 40 85
a. Perf 13×12½ (1936) 30 10
1 2 c. ultramarine and yellow-brown .. 75 1·00
a. Perf 13×12½ (1936) .. .. 1·00 10
2 3 c. black and scarlet .. .. .. 1·00 30
a. Perf 13×12½ (1936) .. .. 2·50 30
3 6 c. sepia and blue .. .. .. 4·25 2·50
a. Perf 13×12½ (1937) .. .. 4·50 2·50
4 8 c. sage-green and vermilion .. .. 3·75 3·50
5 12 c. black and violet .. .. .. 3·25 1·75
a. Perf 13×12½ (1937) .. .. 5·00 4·25
6 24 c. black and olive-green .. .. 2·75 1·50
a. Perf 13×12½ (1937) .. .. 11·00 7·00
7 48 c. deep green .. .. .. 8·50 15·00
8 72 c. myrtle-green and carmine .. .. 28·00 30·00
0/8 .. .. *Set of* 9 45·00 48·00
0s/8s Perf "Specimen" .. *Set of* 9 £110
Designs:—3 c. Mt Irvine Bay, Tobago; 6 c. Discovery of Lake Asphalt; 8 c. Queen's Park, Savannah; 12 c. Town Hall, San Fernando; 24 c. Government House; 48 c. Memorial Park; 72 c. Blue Basin.

35 (6 May). *Silver Jubilee. As Nos.* 91/4 *of Antigua, but ptd by B.W. P* 11×12.
39 2 c. ultramarine and grey-black 30 75
a. Extra flagstaff .. .. .. 35·00
b. Short extra flagstaff .. .. 40·00
c. Lightning conductor .. .. 30·00
d. Flagstaff on right-hand turret .. 55·00
40 3 c. deep blue and scarlet .. .. 30 1·25
a. Extra flagstaff .. .. .. 55·00
c. Lightning conductor .. .. 42·00
41 6 c. brown and deep blue .. .. 1·50 2·50
a. Extra flagstaff .. .. .. 90·00
b. Short extra flagstaff .. .. 95·00
c. Lightning conductor .. .. 80·00

242 24 c. slate and purple .. .. .. 5·50 16·00
a. Extra flagstaff £130
c. Lightning conductor £120
d. Flagstaff on right-hand turret .. £160
e. Double flagstaff £170
239/42 .. .. *Set of* 4 7·00 18·00
239s/42s Perf "Specimen" .. *Set of* 4 75·00
For illustrations of plate varieties see Omnibus section following Zanzibar.

1937 (12 May). *Coronation. As Nos.* 95/7 *of Antigua, but ptd by D.L.R. P* 14.
243 1 c. green 15 10
244 2 c. yellow-brown 35 10
245 8 c. orange .. .. 90 1·50
243/5 .. .. *Set of* 3 1·25 1·50
243s/5s Perf "Specimen" .. *Set of* 3 65·00

37 First Boca **47** King George VI

(Recess B.W.)

1938 (2 May)–**44**. *T* **37** *and similar horiz designs, and T* **47**. *Wmk Mult Script CA (sideways on* 1 c. *to* 60 c.).
(*a*) *P* 11½×11
246 1 c. blue and green 80 30
247 2 c. blue and yellow-brown .. .. 1·00 20
248 3 c. black and scarlet .. .. .. 11·00 1·00
248*a* 3 c. green and purple-brown (1941) .. 30 20
ab. "A" of "CA" missing from wmk ..
249 4 c. chocolate .. .. 25·00 1·25
249*a* 4 c. scarlet (1941) .. .. .. 50 1·00
249*b* 5 c. magenta (1.5.41) 30 15
250 6 c. sepia and blue .. .. .. 2·75 80
251 8 c. sage-green and vermilion .. .. 2·25 1·00
252 12 c. black and purple .. .. .. 16·00 1·75
a. Black and slate-purple (1944) .. 2·50 10
253 24 c. black and olive-green .. .. 1·75 10
254 60 c. myrtle-green and carmine .. .. 8·50 1·50
(*b*) *T* **47**. *P* 12
255 $1.20, blue-green (1.40) .. .. .. 10·00 1·50
256 $4.80, rose-carmine (1.40) .. .. 20·00 28·00
246/56 .. .. *Set of* 14 75·00 32·00
246s/56s (*ex* 5 c.) Perf "Specimen" *Set of* 13 £200
Designs:—2 c. Imperial College of Tropical Agriculture; 3 c. Mt Irvine Bay, Tobago; 4 c. Memorial Park; 5 c. G.P.O. and Treasury; 6 c. Discovery of Lake Asphalt; 8 c. Queen's Park, Savannah; 12 c. Town Hall, San Fernando; 24 c. Government House; 60 c. Blue Basin.

1946 (1 Oct). *Victory. As Nos.* 110/11 *of Antigua.*
257 3 c. chocolate 10 10
258 6 c. blue .. .. 10 1·00
257s/8s Perf "Specimen" .. *Set of* 2 50·00

1948 (22 Nov). *Royal Silver Wedding. As Nos.* 112/13 *of Antigua, but* $4.80 *in recess.*
259 3 c. red-brown 10 10
260 $4.80, carmine .. .. 18·00 24·00

1949 (10 Oct). *75th Anniv of U.P.U. As Nos.* 114/17 *of Antigua.*
261 5 c. bright reddish purple 30 60
262 6 c. deep blue .. .. 1·25 65
263 12 c. violet 30 85
264 24 c. olive 40 75
261/4 .. .. *Set of* 4 2·00 2·50

1951 (16 Feb). *Inauguration of B.W.I. University College. As Nos.* 118/19 *of Antigua.*
265 3 c. green and red-brown 20 60
266 12 c. black and reddish violet 30 60

STAMP BOOKLETS

1925.
SB1 2s. booklet containing eight ½d., 1d. and 1½d. (Nos. 218/20) in blocks of 4 ..

1931–32. *Black on pink covers.*
SB2 1s. 8d. booklet containing eight ½d. and sixteen 1d. (Nos. 218/19) in blocks of 8 ..
SB3 2s. booklet containing eight ½d., 1d. and 1½d. (Nos. 218/20) in blocks of 8 (1932) ..

1935.
SB4 48 c. booklet containing eight 1, 2 and 3 c. (Nos. 230/2) in blocks of 4 ..

POSTAGE DUE STAMPS

D 1

1/- 1/-
Row 4 Row 5

The degree of inclination of the stroke on the 1s. value varies for each vertical row of the sheet: Rows 1, 2 and 6 104°, Row 3 108°, Row 4 107° and Row 5 (Nos. D9a, D17a, D25a) 100°.

(Typo D.L.R.)

1885 (1 Jan). *Wmk Crown CA. P* 14.
D1 D **1** ½d. slate-black .. .. .. 15·00 45·00
D2 1d. slate-black .. .. .. 4·50 20
D3 2d. slate-black .. .. .. 23·00 20
D4 3d. slate-black .. .. .. 48·00 40
D5 4d. slate-black .. .. .. 28·00 3·25
D6 5d. slate-black .. .. .. 23·00 60
D7 6d. slate-black .. .. .. 38·00 4·00
D8 8d. slate-black .. .. .. 55·00 3·00
D9 1s. slate-black .. .. .. 55·00 5·00
a. Upright stroke .. .. .. £110 15·00
D1/9 .. .. *Set of* 9 £250 55·00

1905–06. *Wmk Mult Crown CA. P* 14.
D10 D **1** 1d. slate-black .. .. .. 3·25 20
D11 2d. slate-black .. .. .. 19·00 20
w. Wmk inverted .. .. .. † £150
D12 3d. slate-black .. .. .. 9·00 2·75
w. Wmk inverted .. .. .. — £100
D13 4d. slate-black .. .. .. 11·00 10·00
w. Wmk inverted .. .. ..
D14 5d. slate-black .. .. .. 11·00 10·00
D15 6d. slate-black .. .. .. 6·00 9·50
D16 8d. slate-black .. .. .. 12·00 14·00
D17 1s. slate-black .. .. .. 12·00 32·00
a. Upright stroke .. .. .. 25·00 65·00
D10/17 .. .. *Set of* 8 75·00 70·00

1923–45. *Wmk Mult Script CA. P* 14.
D18 D **1** 1d. black .. .. .. 80 1·50
D19 2d. black .. .. .. 1·50 1·50
D20 3d. black (1925) .. .. .. 1·50 2·25
D21 4d. black (1929) .. .. .. 2·75 20·00
D22 5d. black (1944) .. .. .. 35·00 85·00
D23 6d. black (1945) .. .. .. 50·00 32·00
D24 8d. black (1945) .. .. .. 42·00 £140
D25 1s. black (1945) .. .. .. 65·00 £100
a. Upright stroke £130 £190
D18/25 .. .. *Set of* 8 £180 £350
D18s/25s Optd or Perf (5d. to 1s.) "Specimen" *Set of* 8 £140

1947 (1 Sept)–**61**. *Values in cents. Wmk Mult Script CA. Ordinary paper. P* 14.
D26 D **1** 2 c. black .. .. .. 1·75 2·75
a. Chalk-surfaced paper (20.1.53) .. 20 3·75
ab. Error. Crown missing. W **9***a* .. 75·00
ac. Error. St. Edward's Crown. W **9***b* 25·00
D27 4 c. black .. .. 85 3·00
a. Chalk-surfaced paper (10.8.55) .. 2·50 4·50
D28 6 c. black .. .. 1·40 6·00
a. Chalk-surfaced paper (20.1.53) .. 30 7·50
ab. Error. Crown missing. W **9***a* .. £200
ac. Error. St. Edward's Crown. W **9***b* 60·00
D29 8 c. black .. .. 1·10 22·00
a. Chalk-surfaced paper (10.9.58) .. 35 20·00
D30 10 c. black .. .. 1·10 3·50
a. Chalk-surfaced paper (10.8.55) .. 3·25 10·00
D31 12 c. black .. .. 1·10 18·00
a. Chalk-surfaced paper (20.1.53) .. 40 17·00
ab. Error. Crown missing. W **9***a* .. £275
ac. Error. St. Edward's Crown. W **9***b* £100
D32 16 c. black .. .. 2·00 40·00
a. Chalk-surfaced paper (22.8.61) .. 9·00 50·00
D33 24 c. black .. .. 7·00 7·50
a. Chalk-surfaced paper (10.8.55) .. 3·50 35·00
D26/33 .. .. *Set of* 8 14·50 90·00
D26a/33a .. .. *Set of* 8 17·00 £130
D26s/33s Perf "Specimen" .. *Set of* 8 £140

"TOO LATE" STAMPS

A handstamp with the words "TOO LATE" was used upon letters on which a too-late fee had been paid, and was sometimes used for cancelling the stamps on such letters.

OFFICIAL STAMPS

O S OFFICIAL OFFICIAL
(O 1) (O 2) (O 3)

1894. *Optd with Type* O **1**. (*a*) *On Nos.* 106/12. *Wmk Crown CA. P* 14.
O1 **10** ½d. dull green .. .. .. 32·00 50·00
O2 1d. carmine .. .. 35·00 55·00
O3 2½d. bright blue .. .. .. 45·00 85·00
O4 4d. grey .. .. 45·00 90·00
O5 6d. olive-black .. .. .. 45·00 90·00
O6 1s. orange-brown .. .. .. 60·00 £120
(*b*) *On No.* 87. *Wmk Crown CC. P* 12½.
O7 **5** 5s. rose-lake £150 £450

1909. *Nos.* 133 *and* 135 *optd with Type* O **2**. *Wmk Mult Crown CA. P* 14.
O8 **11** ½d. blue-green .. .. .. 90 5·50
O9 1d. rose-red .. .. 90 5·50
a. Opt double .. .. — £275
b. Opt vertical .. .. .. 90·00 £110
c. Opt inverted £750 £200

1910. *No.* 146 *optd with Type* O **2**. *Wmk Mult Crown CA. P* 14.
O10 **14** ½d. green .. .. 4·00 5·50

1913. *No.* 149 *optd with Type* O **3**.
O11 **17** ½d. green .. .. 80 5·50
a. Opt vertical .. .. ..

OFFICIAL OFFICIAL OFFICIAL
(O 4) (O 5) (O 6)

1914. *No.* 149 *optd with Type* O **4**.
O12 **17** ½d. green .. .. 1·60 11·00

1914–17. *No.* 149 *optd with Type* O **5** (*without stop*).

O13	17	½d. green	2·50	11·00
		a. Blue-green (thick paper) (1917)	50	6·00

1916. *No.* 149*a optd with Type* O **5** (*with stop*).

O14	17	½d. yellow-green	1·00	2·50
		a. Opt double	24·00	

1917 (22 Aug). *No.* 149 *optd with Type* O **6**.

O15	17	½d. green	2·50	14·00
		a. Yellow-green	3·25	17·00
		b. Blue-green (thick paper)	1·00	15·00

Tristan Da Cunha

Although first settled in 1817 no surviving mail is known from Tristan da Cunha until two whaler's letters written in 1836 and 1843, these being carried home in other whaling ships. Then there is a long gap until the late 1800's when other letters are known—surprisingly only some seven in number, up to 1908 when the first of the island cachet handstamps came into use.

The collecting of postal history material from 1908 to 1952, when Tristan's first stamps were issued, revolves around the numerous cachets of origin which were struck on mail from the island during these 44 years. The handstamps producing these cachets were supplied over the years by various people particularly interested in the island and the islanders, and were mostly used by the clergymen who volunteered to go and serve as the community's ministers.

The postal cachets are illustrated below. The use of the different cachets on mail frequently overlapped, at one period in 1930 there were five different types of handstamp in use. As there was no official source for providing them they appeared on the island from various donors; then disappeared without trace once they became worn out. Only one of these early rubber handstamps has apparently survived, Cachet Va.

Covers bearing the cachets are recognised collector's items, but are difficult to value in general terms. As elsewhere the value is discounted by poor condition of the cover, and may be increased by use on a scarce date or with additional postal markings.

Cachet Types V and VII on cover are the commonest, Type Va, used only for three months, and Type IVa are the scarcest, equalling the scarcest use of Type I examples. All cacheted covers, particularly if non-philatelic, are desirable forerunner items. Even a philatelic cover of Type V is, at present, worth in the region of £35.

Dates given are of the first recorded use.

Cachet I Cachet II

Cat. No.			*Value on cover*
C1	**1908** (May).	Cachet I	*from* £4000
C2	**1919** (31 July).	Cachet II	*from* £425

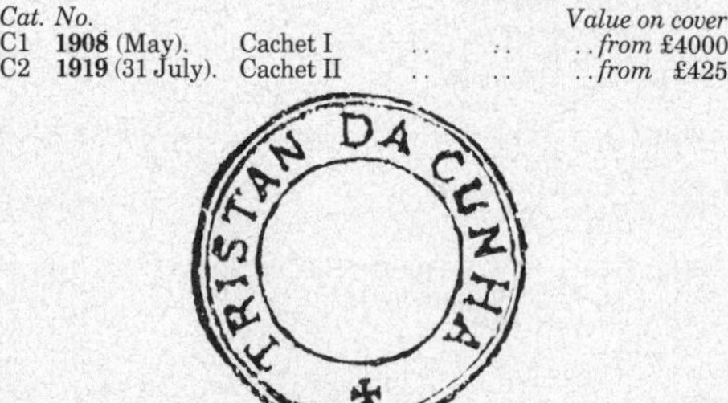

Cachet III

C3	**1921** (8 Feb).	Cachet III	*from* £275

Cachet IVa

C4	**1927** (1 Oct).	Cachet IV (*as* IVa, *but without centre label*)	*from* £800
C5	**1928** (28 Oct).	Cachet IVa	*from* £5500

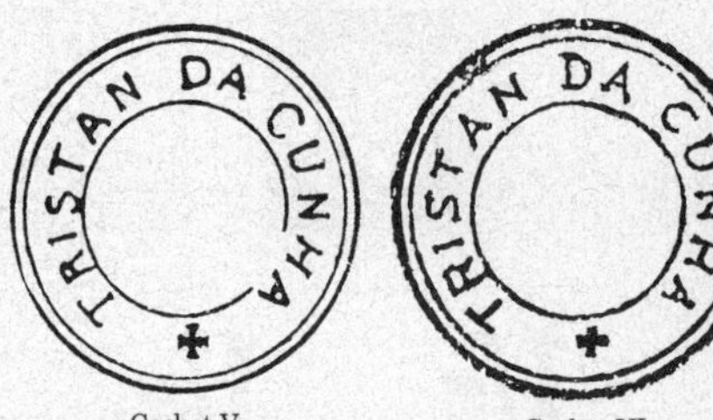

Cachet V Cachet VI

C6	**1929** (24 Feb).	Cachet V	*from* 35·00
C7	**1929** (15 May).	Cachet Va (*as* V, *but without break in inner ring. Shows* "T" "C" *and* "N" *damaged*)	*from* £6500
C8	**1936** (Aug).	Cachet VI	*from* 60·00

Cachet VII

C9	**1936** (1 Feb).	Cachet VII	*from*

During World War II there was little mail from the island function as a meteorological station was cloaked by security covers as are known are generally struck with the "tomb naval censor mark and postmarked "maritime mail" or have African postal markings. A few philatelic items from early war bearing cachets exist, but this usage was soon stopped military commander and the handstamps were put away peace returned. Covers from the period would be worth fro to, at least, £350.

Cachet VIII

C10	**1946** (8 May).	Cachet VIII	*from*

Cachet IX

C11	**1948** (2 Feb).	Cachet IX	*from*

This cachet with "A.B.C." below the date was in private between 1942 and 1946.

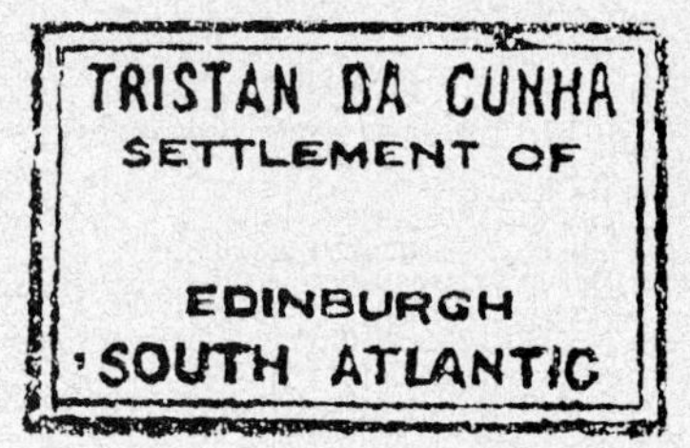

Cachet X

C12	**1948** (29 Feb).	Cachet X	*from* 5

TRISTAN
DA CUNHA

(1)

1952 (1 Jan). *Nos.* 131, 135a/40 *and* 149/51 *of St. Helena o with T* 1.

1	½d. violet	15	1
2	1d. black and green	70	1
3	1½d. black and carmine	70	1
4	2d. black and scarlet	70	1
5	3d. grey	1·00	1
6	4d. ultramarine	3·25	2
7	6d. light blue	4·25	2
8	8d. olive-green	3·50	4
9	1s. sepia	4·25	2
10	2s. 6d. maroon	17·00	13
11	5s. chocolate	21·00	20
12	10s. purple	35·00	30
1/12	*Set of* 12	80·00	70

urks and Caicos Islands

TURKS ISLANDS

DEPENDENCY OF JAMAICA

anch of the British Post Office opened at Grand Turk on cember 1854 replacing an earlier arrangement under mail for the islands was sorted by local R.M.S.P. agents. CC1 is known used between 22 October 1857 and 20 April

GRAND TURK

CROWNED-CIRCLE HANDSTAMPS

CC 1

CC 1 TURKS-ISLANDS (Oct 1857) *Price on cover* £5000

PRICES FOR STAMPS ON COVER TO 1945	
Nos. 1/5	*from* × 30
No. 6	—
Nos. 7/20	*from* × 50
Nos. 20*a*/48	—
Nos. 49/52	*from* × 12
Nos. 53/7	*from* × 10
Nos. 58/65	*from* × 20
Nos. 66/9	*from* × 5
Nos. 70/2	*from* × 10
Nos. 101/9	*from* × 8
Nos. 110/26	*from* × 6
Nos. 129/39	*from* × 4
Nos. 140/53	*from* × 12
Nos. 154/90	*from* × 3
Nos. 191/3	*from* × 10
Nos. 194/205	*from* × 2

1

Throat flaw (R.3/4)

(Recess P.B.)

7 (4 Apr). *No wmk. P* 11–12.

1d. dull rose .. .. 50·00 50·00
 a. Throat flaw £160 £180
6d. black .. .. 90·00 £120
1s. dull blue .. .. 90·00 60·00

73–79. *Wmk Small Star. W* w **2** (*sideways on Nos.* 5 *and* 6). P 11–12 × 14½–15½.

1 1d. dull rose-lake (7.73) .. .. .. 48·00 48·00
 a. Throat flaw £160 £180
 b. Wmk sideways .. .. .. 85·00 85·00
 ba. Throat flaw £275 £300
1d. dull red (1.79) .. .. 55·00 60·00
 a. Imperf between (horiz pair) £13000
 b. Throat flaw £180 £200
 c. Wmk upright .. ..
1s. lilac (1.79) £5000 £2000

81 (1 Jan). *Stamps of the preceding issues surcharged locally, in black.*

There are twelve different settings of the ½d., nine settings of e 2½d., and six settings of the 4d.

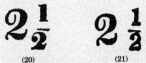

½ (2) ½ (3)

Setting 1. *T* **2**. *Long fraction bar. Two varieties repeated fifteen times in the sheet.*

7 ½ on 6d. black .. .. 75·00 £120

Setting 2. *T* **3**. *Short fraction bar. Three varieties in a vertical strip repeated ten times in sheet.*

Setting 3. *Similar to setting* 2, *but the middle stamp of the three varieties has a longer bar.*

8 ½ on 6d. black (*setting* 2 *only*) .. .. 70·00 £100
9 ½ on 1s. dull blue .. .. 95·00 £160
 a. Surch double £5000

½ (4) ½ (5) ½ (6)

Three varieties in a vertical strip repeated ten times in sheet.

Section 4. *Types* **4**, **5**, **6**.
Setting 5. *Types* **4** (*without bar*), **5**, **6**.
Setting 6. *Types* **4**, **5**, **6** (*without bar*).
Setting 7. *Types* **4** (*shorter thick bar*), **6**, **6**.

10 ½ on 1d. dull red (*setting* 7 *only*) (T **6**) ..
 a. Type **4** (shorter thick bar) £8000
11 ½ on 1s. dull blue (*setting* 6 *and* 7) (T **4**) .. £1200
 a. Type **4** (shorter thick bar) £1500
 b. Type **5** £950
 c. Type **6** £850
 d. Type **6** (without bar) £1300
 e. Surch double (T **6** without bar) .. ..
12 ½ on 1s. lilac (T **4**) £250 £375
 a. Without bar £500
 b. With short thick bar £475
 c. Surch double £3000
 cb. Surch double and short thick bar .. £6000
13 ½ on 1s. lilac (T **5**) £120 £200
 a. Surch double £2750
14 ½ on 1s. lilac (T **6**) £120 £200
 a. Without bar £550
 b. Surch double £4250
 ba. Surch double and without bar £6000

Care should be taken in the identification of Types **6** and **7** which are very similar. For the 1s. value some varieties of No. 9 are often confused with Nos. 11b/c.

½ (7) ½ (8) ½ (9) ½ (10)

Setting 8. *T* **7**. *Three varieties in a vertical strip. All have a very short bar.*

15 ½ on 1d. dull red .. .. 60·00 £100
 a. Throat flaw £225

Setting 9. *T* **8**. *Three varieties in a vertical strip. Bars long and thick and "1" leaning a little to left.*

16 ½ on 1d. dull red £180 £250
 a. Surch double £3500
 b. Throat flaw £500

Setting 10. *T* **9** *and* **10**. *Fifteen varieties repeated twice in a sheet. Ten are of T* **9** (*Rows* 1 *and* 2), *five of T* **10** (*Row* 3).

17 ½ on 1d. dull red (T **9**) .. .. .. 50·00 £110
 a. Surch double £3250
18 ½ on 1d. dull red (T **10**) .. .. .. 80·00 £160
 a. Surch double £5500
 b. Throat flaw £250
19 ½ on 1s. lilac (T **9**) .. .. .. 90·00 £170
20 ½ on 1s. lilac (T **10**) £160 £325
20*a* ½ on 1s. dull blue (T **9**) £7500
20*b* ½ on 1s. dull blue (T **10**) £12000

Types **9** and **11**. The difference is in the position of the "2" in relation to the "1". In setting 10 the "2" is to the left of the "1" except on No. 10 (where it is directly below the "1") and in setting 11 it is to the right except on No. 2 (where it is to the left, as in setting 10).

½ (11) ½ (12) ½ (13) ½ (14)

Setting 11. *T* **9** *and* **11** *to* **14**. *Fifteen varieties repeated twice in a sheet. Nine of T* **11**, *three of T* **12**, *and one each of T* **9**, **13** *and* **14**.

Setting 12. *Similar to last, but T* **13** *replaced by another T* **12**.

21 ½ on 1d. dull red (T **11**) £100 £170
22 ½ on 1d. dull red (T **12**) £225
 a. Throat flaw £1100
23 ½ on 1d. dull red (T **13**) £1000
 a. Throat flaw £1000
24 ½ on 1d. dull red (T **14**) £550
24*a* ½ on 1s. dull blue (T **11**) £12000

Type **9** from these settings, where it occurs on position 2, can only be distinguished from similar stamps from setting 10 when *se-tenant* with Type **11**.

2½ (15) 2½ (16)

Setting 1. *T* **15**. *Fraction in very small type.*

25 2½ on 6d. black £8000

Setting 2. *T* **16**. *Two varieties repeated fifteen times in a sheet. Large "2" on level with top of the "1", long thin bar.*

26 2½ on 6d. black £300 £400
 a. Imperf between (horiz pair) £12000
 b. Surch double £7000

2½ (17) 2½ (18) 2½ (19)

Setting 3. *T* **17**. *As T* **16**, *but large "2" not so high up.*

27 2½ on 1s. lilac £2000

Setting 4. *T* **18**. *Three varieties in a vertical strip repeated ten times in sheet. Large "2" placed lower and small bar.*

28 2½ on 6d. black £150 £275
 a. Surch double £7000

Setting 5. *T* **19**. *Three varieties in a vertical strip repeated ten times in sheet "2" further from "½", small fraction bar.*

29 2½ on 1s. lilac £550 £850

2½ (20) 2½ (21)

Setting 6. *T* **20** *and* **21**. *Fifteen varieties. Ten of T* **20** *and five of T* **21**, *repeated twice in a sheet.*

30 2½ on 1s. lilac (T **20**) £7500
31 2½ on 1s. lilac (T **21**) £11000

2½ (22) 2½ (23) 2½ (24)

Setting 7. *T* **22**. *Three varieties in a vertical strip, repeated ten times in a sheet.*

32 2½ on 6d. black £7500
33 2½ on 1s. dull blue £12000

Setting 8. *T* **23** *and* **24**. *Fifteen varieties. Ten of T* **23** *and five of T* **24**, *repeated twice in a sheet.*

34 2½ on 1d. dull red (T **23**) £600
35 2½ on 1d. dull red (T **24**) £1200
 a. Throat flaw £3000
36 2½ on 1s. lilac (T **23**) £550 £700
 a. Surch "½" double £2750
37 2½ on 1s. lilac (T **24**) £1200
 a. Surch "½" double £4750

2½ (25) 2½ (26) 2½ (27)

Setting 9. *T* **25**, **26**, *and* **27**. *Fifteen varieties. Ten of T* **25**, *three of T* **26**, *one of T* **26** *without bar, and one of T* **27**, *repeated twice in a sheet.*

38 2½ on 1s. dull blue (T **25**) £700
39 2½ on 1s. dull blue (T **26**) £1800
40 2½ on 1s. dull blue (T **26**) (without bar) .. £6500
41 2½ on 1s. dull blue (T **27**) £6500

4 (28) 4 (29) 4 (30)

Setting 1. *T* **28**. *"4" 8 mm high, pointed top.*

42 4 on 6d. black £375 £300

Settings 2–6. *T* **29** *and* **30**.

43 4 on 6d. black (T **29**) .. .. .. 70·00 £100
44 4 on 6d. black (T **30**) £325 £425
45 4 on 1s. lilac (T **29**) £400
 a. Surch double .. ..
46 4 on 1s. lilac (T **30**) £2250
 a. Surch double .. ..
47 4 on 1d. dull red (T **29**) £700 £475
48 4 on 1d. dull red (T **28**) £800 £550

The components of these settings can only be distinguished when in blocks. Details are given in the handbook by John J. Challis.

31

One Penny

(32)

(Typo D.L.R.)

1881. *Wmk Crown CC (sideways* on T* 1*). P* 14.
49 1 1d. brown-red (Oct) 60·00 80·00
a. Throat flaw £180 £225
50 31 4d. ultramarine (Die I) (Aug) £100 60·00
51 1 6d. olive-black (Oct) £100 £140
52 1s. slate-green (Oct) £130 £120

*The normal sideways watermark shows Crown to right of CC, *as seen from the back of the stamp.*

Nos. 49 and 51/2 also exist showing Crown to left of CC, but due to the position of the watermark such varieties are difficult to detect on single stamps.

1882–85. *Wmk Crown CA (reversed on 1d.). P* 14.
53 31 ½d. blue-green (Die I) (2.82) 8·00 20·00
a. *Pale green* (12.85) 2·25 3·50
b. Top left triangle detached £100
55 1 1d. orange-brown (10.83) 60·00 30·00
a. Bisected (½d.) (on cover) † £4250
b. Throat flaw £180 £110
x. Wmk normal (not reversed) 90·00
56 31 2½d. red-brown (Die I) (2.82) 17·00 10·00
57 4d. grey (Die I) (10.84) 15·00 2·00
a. Bisected (2d.) (on cover) † £4250

For illustration of "top left triangle detached" variety see above No. 6 of Montserrat.

1887 (July)–89. *Wmk Crown CA. (a) P* 12
58 1 1d. crimson-lake 15·00 3·50
a. Imperf between (horiz pair) £11000
b. Throat flaw 40·00 12·00
x. Wmk reversed 10·00 2·50

(*b*) *P* 14
59 1 6d. yellow-brown (2.89) 2·50 2·75
s. Optd "Specimen" 60·00
60 1s. sepia 4·00 2·75

> During a shortage of 1d. stamps a supply of JAMAICA No. 27 was sent to the Turks and Caicos Islands in April 1889 and used until replaced by No. 61. *Price from* £200 *used.*

1889 (May). *Surch at Grand Turk with T* **32**.
61 31 1d. on 2½d. red-brown 6·50 9·50
a. "One" omitted £1500
b. Bisected (½d.) (on cover) † £4750

No. 61a was caused by misplacement of the surcharge. Stamps from the same sheet can be found with the surcharge reading "Penny One".

Neck flaw (R.3/2)

1889–93. *Wmk Crown CA. P* 14.
62 1 1d. crimson-lake (7.89) 3·00 3·50
a. Bisected (½d.) (on cover) † £4250
b. Throat flaw 14·00 15·00
c. Neck flaw 18·00 20·00
x. Wmk reversed 38·00
63 1d. lake 2·25 2·25
a. Bisected (½d.) (on cover) † £4250
b. Throat flaw 9·00 9·00
c. Neck flaw 13·00 14·00
64 1d. pale rosy lake 2·00 4·00
b. Throat flaw 8·00 16·00
c. Neck flaw 11·00 19·00
65 31 2½d. ultramarine (Die II) (4.93) 2·25 1·50
s. Optd "Specimen" 55·00

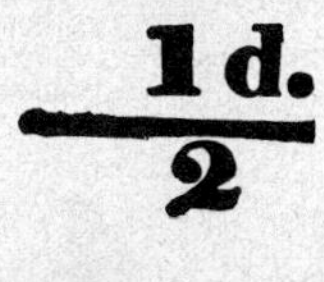

(33) 34

1893 (10 June). *No. 57 surch at Grand Turk with T* **33**.

Setting 1. Bars between "1d." and "2" separate, instead of continuous across the rows of stamps.
66 ½d. on 4d. grey £2000 £800

Setting 2. Continuous bars. Thin and thick bar 10¾ mm apart. "2" under the "1".
67 ½d. on 4d. grey £170 £130

Setting 3. As last, but bars 11¾ mm apart.
68 ½d. on 4d. grey £140 £150

Setting 4. Bars 11 mm apart. Five out of the six varieties in the strip have the "2" below the space between the "1" and "d".
69 ½d. on 4d. grey £170 £160

There is a fifth setting, but the variation is slight.

(Typo D.L.R.)

1893–95. *Wmk Crown CA. P* 14.
70 31 ½d. dull green (Die II) (12.93) 2·25 1·75
71 4d. dull purple & ultram (Die II) (5.95) 9·50 12·00
72 34 5d. olive-green and carmine (6.94) 3·75 11·00
a. Bisected (2½d.) (on cover) † £3750
70/2 *Set of* 3 14·00 22·00
71s/2s Optd "Specimen" *Set of* 2 £100

TURKS AND CAICOS ISLANDS

35 Badge of the Islands **36**

The dates on the stamps have reference to the political separation from Bahamas.

(Recess D.L.R.)

1900 (10 Nov)–04. *Wmk Crown CA* (½d. *to* 1s.) *or Wmk Crown CC* (2s., 3s.). *P* 14.
101 35 ½d. green 2·75 4·00
x. Wmk reversed
102 1d. red 3·50 75
w. Wmk inverted 65·00
103 2d. sepia 1·00 1·25
w. Wmk inverted
x. Wmk reversed 85·00
104 2½d. blue 7·50 16·00
a. *Greyish blue* (1904) 1·75 1·00
aw. Wmk inverted 65·00
ay. Wmk inverted and reversed
105 4d. orange 3·75 7·00
106 6d. dull mauve 2·50 6·50
107 1s. purple-brown 3·25 17·00
108 36 2s. purple 40·00 55·00
109 3s. lake 55·00 75·00
101/9 *Set of* 9 £100 £150
101s/9s Optd "Specimen" *Set of* 9 £225

1905–08. *Wmk Mult Crown CA. P* 14.
110 35 ½d. green 5·00 15
111 1d. red 15·00 50
w. Wmk inverted
112 3d. purple/*yellow* (1908) 2·25 6·00
s. Optd "Specimen" 50·00
w. Wmk inverted
110/12 *Set of* 3 20·00 6·00

37 Turk's-head Cactus **38**

(Recess D.L.R.)

1909 (2 Sept)–11. *Wmk Mult Crown CA. P* 14.
115 37 ¼d. rosy mauve (1910) 1·75 1·00
w. Wmk inverted
116 ¼d. red (1911) 60 40
w. Wmk inverted
117 38 ½d. yellow-green 75 40
w. Wmk inverted
x. Wmk reversed 45·00
y. Wmk inverted and reversed
118 1d. red 1·25 40
119 2d. greyish slate 2·25 1·40
120 2½d. blue 2·25 3·75
w. Wmk inverted
x. Wmk reversed 55·00
121 3d. purple/*yellow* 2·50 2·00
122 4d. red/*yellow* 3·25 7·00
123 6d. purple 7·00 7·00
124 1s. black/*green* 7·00 8·50
w. Wmk inverted
125 2s. red/*green* 30·00 48·00
126 3s. black/*red* 30·00 40·00
115/26 *Set of* 12 80·00 £110
115s/26s Optd "Specimen" *Set of* 12 £200

See also Nos. 154 and 162.

39

WAR TAX

(40)

1913 (1 Apr)–21. *Wmk Mult Crown CA. P* 14.
129 39 ½d. green 50 1·75
w. Wmk inverted
130 1d. red 1·00 2·25
a. *Bright rose-scarlet* 1·10 2·00
ax. Wmk reversed 42·00
b. *Rose-carmine* (1918) 3·75 5·50
131 2d. greyish slate 2·25 3·50
132 2½d. ultramarine 2·25 3·00
aw. Wmk inverted
b. *Bright blue* (1918) 4·00 2·75
133 3d. purple/*yellow* 2·25 11·00
a. *On lemon* 16·00
b. *On yellow-buff* 4·00 9·50
c. *On orange-buff* 1·75
cx. Wmk reversed 65·00
d. *On pale yellow* 2·25 8·50
134 4d. red/*yellow* 1·00 9·50
a. *On orange-buff* 1·60 7·50
ab. "A" of "CA" missing from wmk
as. Optd "Specimen" 48·00
b. *Carmine on pale yellow* 7·50 16·00
135 5d. pale olive-green (18.5.16) 6·50 22·00
136 6d. dull purple 2·50 3·50
w. Wmk inverted
x. Wmk reversed
137 39 1s. brown-orange 1·50
w. Wmk inverted
138 2s. red/*blue-green* 7·50
a. *On greenish white* (1919) 24·00
b. *On emerald* (3.21) 48·00
bs. Optd "Specimen" 48·00
bx. Wmk reversed £130
139 3s. black/*red* 15·00
129/39 *Set of* 11 35·00
129s/39s Optd "Specimen" *Set of* 11 £180

1917 (3 Jan). *Optd with T* **40** *at bottom of stamp.*
140 39 1d. red 10
a. Opt double £180
ab. Opt double (in horiz pair with normal)
b. "TAX" omitted
c. "WAR TAX" omitted in vert pair with normal £400
d. Opt inverted at top 65·00
e. Opt double, one inverted £110
f. Opt inverted only, in pair with No. 140e £475
141 3d. purple/*yellow-buff* 1·00
a. Opt double 85·00
b. *Purple/lemon* 2·00
ba. Opt double 85·00
bb. Opt double, one inverted £325

The overprint was in a setting of 60, applied twice t sheets of 120. One sheet of the 1d. exists with the right impression of the setting misplaced one row to the left so stamps in vertical row 6 show a double overprint (No. 140a appears that the righthand vertical row on this sheet ha overprint applied at a third operation.

In Nos. 140e/f the inverted overprint is at foot and reads " WAR" owing to displacement. No. 140e also exists with "W omitted from the inverted overprint.

In both values of the first printings the stamp in the botto hand corner of the sheet has a long "T" in "TAX", and on th stamp of the sixth row the "X" is damaged and looks like a rev "K".

1917 (Oct). *Second printing with overprint at top or in m of stamp.*
143 39 1d. red 10
a. Inverted opt at bottom or centre 45·00
c. Opt omitted (in pair with normal) £375
d. Opt double, one at top, one at bottom 55·00
e. As d., but additional opt in top margin £110
f. Horiz pair, one as d., the other normal £250
g. Pair, one opt inverted, one normal £400
h. Double opt at top (in pair with normal) £225
i. Opt double 40·00
144 3d. purple/*yellow* 60
a. Opt double 40·00
b. Opt double, one inverted £300
c. *Purple/lemon* 3·50

1918. *Overprinted with T* **40**.
145 39 3d. purple/*yellow* (R.) 8·50 2
a. Opt double £300

WAR TAX (41) — WAR TAX (42) — WAR TAX (43)

1918. *Optd with T* **41** *in London by D.L.R.*
146 39 1d. rose-carmine 20
a. *Bright rose-scarlet* 15
aw. Wmk inverted 65·00
147 3d. purple/*yellow* 1·75
146/7 Optd "Specimen" *Set of* 2 80·00

1919. *Optd with T* **41** *in London by D.L.R.*
148 39 3d. purple/*orange-buff* (R.) 10 2
s. Optd "Specimen" 40·00

1919. *Local overprint. T* **40**, *in violet.*
149 39 1d. bright rose-scarlet 30 3
a. "WAR" omitted £150
b. Opt double 21·00
c. Opt double in pair with normal £120
d. Opt double, one inverted
e. *Rose-carmine* 6·50 14
ea. Opt double
w. Wmk inverted 32·00

1919. *Optd with T* **42**.
150 39 1d. scarlet 10
a. Opt double £140 £
b. Opt double, one albino and reversed
151 3d. purple/*orange-buff* 30 2
w. Wmk inverted 32·00
x. Wmk reversed 32·00

1919 (17 Dec). *Optd with T* **43**.
152 39 1d. scarlet 20 2
a. Opt inverted
153 3d. purple/*orange-buff* 50 2
w. Wmk inverted 30·00
x. Wmk reversed 25·00
y. Wmk inverted and reversed 12·00

The two bottom rows of this setting have the words "WA and "TAX" about 1 mm further apart.

1921 (23 Apr). *Wmk Mult Script CA. P* 14.
154 37 ¼d. rose-red 2·50 13·
155 39 ½d. green 2·75 5·
156 1d. carmine-red 1·00 5·
157 2d. slate-grey 1·00 17·
y. Wmk inverted and reversed 48·00
158 2½d. bright blue 1·75 7·
159 5d. sage-green 8·00 42·

39 6d. purple .. .. 6·50 42·00
w. Wmk inverted .. .. ..
x. Wmk reversed .. .. .. 50·00
1s. brown-orange .. .. .. 6·50 24·00
1 .. .. Set of 8 26·00 £140
61s Optd "Specimen" .. Set of 8 £140

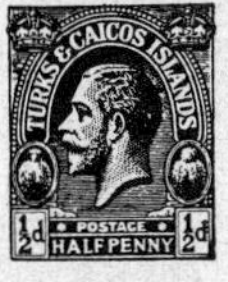

44

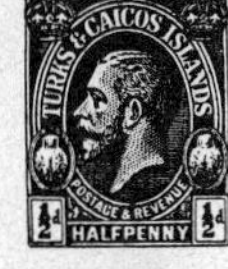

45

(Recess D.L.R.)

(20 Nov)–26. *P* 14. (*a*) *Wmk Mult Script CA*
37 ¼d. black (11.10.26) .. .. .. 80 1·00
44 ½d. yellow-green .. .. .. 2·00 3·00
a. Bright green .. .. .. 2·00 2·75
b. Apple-green .. .. .. 5·50 10·00
1d. brown .. .. .. 50 3·25
1½d. scarlet (24.11.25) .. .. .. 6·50 15·00
2d. slate .. .. .. 50 5·00
2½d. purple/*pale yellow* .. .. .. 50 1·75
44 3d. bright blue .. .. .. 50 5·00
4d. red/*pale yellow* .. .. .. 1·25 14·00
ax. Wmk reversed .. .. .. 48·00
b. Carmine/pale yellow .. .. .. 4·50 16·00
5d. sage-green .. .. .. 85 22·00
y. Wmk inverted and reversed .. 50·00
6d. purple .. .. .. 70 4·50
x. Wmk reversed .. .. .. 55·00
1s. brown-orange .. .. .. 80 17·00
2s. red/*emerald* .. .. .. 2·00 9·00

(*b*) *Wmk Mult Crown CA*
44 2s. red/*emerald* (24.11.25) .. .. 25·00 65·00
3s. black/*red* (24.11.25) .. .. 5·00 26·00
75 .. .. .. Set of 14 40·00 £170
/75s Optd "Specimen" .. Set of 14 £200

3 (1 Mar). *Inscr* "POSTAGE & REVENUE". *Wmk Mult Script A. P* 14.
45 ½d. green 75 50
1d. brown 75 70
1½d. scarlet .. .. 75 3·00
2d. grey 75 50
2½d. purple/*yellow* .. .. .. 75 5·00
3d. bright blue .. .. .. 75 6·00
6d. purple .. .. 75 7·50
1s. brown-orange .. .. .. 3·75 7·50
2s. red/*emerald* .. .. .. 6·00 35·00
5s. green/*yellow* .. .. .. 11·00 35·00
10s. purple/*blue* .. .. .. 48·00 £100
/86 .. .. .. Set of 11 65·00 £180
s/86s Optd "Specimen" .. Set of 11 £140

5 (6 May). *Silver Jubilee. As Nos.* 91/4 *of Antigua, but ptd y Waterlow. P* 11×12.
½d. black and green 30 75
k. Kite and vertical log .. .. .. 32·00
l. Kite and horizontal log .. .. 25·00
3d. brown and deep blue .. .. 2·75 4·50
k. Kite and vertical log .. .. .. 70·00
6d. light blue and olive-green .. .. 1·75 4·75
k. Kite and vertical log .. .. .. 70·00
1s. slate and purple .. .. .. 1·75 3·25
k. Kite and vertical log .. .. .. 70·00
/90 .. .. .. Set of 4 6·00 12·00
s/90s Perf "Specimen" .. Set of 4 75·00
For illustrations of plate varieties see Omnibus section owing Zanzibar.

37 (12 May). *Coronation. As Nos.* 95/7 *of Antigua, but ptd by D.L.R. P* 14.
1 ½d. myrtle-green 10 10
a. Deep green .. .. .. 40·00
2 2d. grey-black 50 40
3 3d. bright blue 60 40
1/3 .. .. .. Set of 3 1·00 75
1s/3s Perf "Specimen" .. Set of 3 55·00

46 Raking Salt

47 Salt Industry

(Recess Waterlow)

938 (18 June)–45. *Wmk Mult Script CA. P* 12½.
94 46 ¼d. black 20 10
95 ½d. yellowish green .. .. .. 4·00 15
a. Deep green (6.11.44) .. .. 1·25 70
96 1d. red-brown 75 10
97 1½d. scarlet 75 15
98 2d. grey .. .. 1·00 30
99 2½d. yellow-orange .. .. .. 4·25 80
a. Orange (6.11.44) .. .. .. 2·25 1·50
00 3d. bright blue 70 30
01 6d. mauve .. .. 9·50 1·25
01*a* 6d. sepia (9.2.45) 50 20
02 1s. yellow-bistre .. .. .. 3·75 7·50
02*a* 1s. grey-olive (9.2.45) 50 20
03 47 2s. deep rose-carmine .. .. .. 42·00 13·00
a. Bright rose-carmine (6.11.44) .. 17·00 16·00
04 5s. yellowish green .. .. .. 48·00 15·00
a. Deep green (6.11.44) .. .. 35·00 20·00
05 10s. bright violet .. .. .. 12·00 6·50
94/205 .. .. .. Set of 14 75·00 40·00
94s/205s Perf "Specimen" .. Set of 14 £200

1946 (4 Nov). *Victory. As Nos.* 110/11 *of Antigua.*
206 2d. black 10 10
207 3d. blue 15 10
206s/7s Perf "Specimen" .. .. Set of 2 55·00

1948 (13 Sept). *Royal Silver Wedding. As Nos.* 112/13 *of Antigua.*
208 1d. red-brown 15 10
209 10s. mauve .. .. 7·00 11·00

50 Badge of the Islands

53 Queen Victoria and King George VI

(Recess Waterlow)

1948 (14 Dec). *Centenary of Separation from Bahamas. T* 50, 53 *and similar designs. Wmk Mult Script CA. P* 12½.
210 50 ½d. blue-green 70 15
211 2d. carmine .. .. 1·25 15
212 – 3d. blue .. .. 1·50 15
213 – 6d. violet 50 30
214 53 2s. black and bright blue 75 65
215 5s. black and green .. .. .. 90 3·25
216 10s. black and brown .. .. .. 90 3·50
210/16 .. .. Set of 7 5·75 7·25
Designs: *Horiz*—3d. Flag of Turks and Caicos Islands; 6d. Map of islands.

1949 (10 Oct). *75th Anniv of U.P.U. As Nos.* 114/17 *of Antigua.*
217 2½d. red-orange 20 85
218 3d. deep blue .. .. 1·50 50
219 6d. brown 20 50
220 1s. olive 20 35
217/20 .. .. Set of 4 1·90 2·00

65 Bulk Salt Loading

66 Dependency's Badge

(Recess Waterlow)

1950 (1 Aug). *T* 65 *and similar horiz designs, and T* 66. *Wmk Mult Script CA. P* 12½.
221 ½d. green 60 40
222 1d. red-brown 50 75
223 1½d. deep carmine 90 55
224 2d. red-orange 30 40
225 2½d. grey-olive 70 50
226 3d. bright blue 30 40
227 4d. black and rose .. .. .. 2·50 70
228 6d. black and blue .. .. .. 2·00 50
229 1s. black and blue-green 80 40
230 1s. 6d. black and scarlet .. .. 7·00 3·25
231 2s. emerald and ultramarine .. .. 2·50 4·00
232 5s. blue and black .. .. .. 16·00 7·50
233 10s. black and violet .. .. .. 16·00 17·00
221/33 .. .. .. Set of 13 45·00 32·00
Designs:—1d. Salt Cay; 1½d. Caicos mail; 2d. Grand Turk; 2½d. Sponge diving; 3d. South Creek; 4d. Map; 6d. Grand Turk Light; 1s. Government House; 1s. 6d. Cockburn Harbour; 2s. Government Offices; 5s. Loading salt.

Uganda

PRICES FOR STAMPS ON COVER TO 1945

The type-written stamps of Uganda, Nos. 1/53, are very rare used on cover.

Nos. 54/60	*from* × 20
No. 61	—
Nos. 70/5	*from* × 12
No. 76	—
Nos. 84/90	*from* × 20
No. 91	—
Nos. 92/3	*from* × 40

PROTECTORATE

Following a period of conflict between Islamic, Protestant and Roman Catholic factions, Uganda was declared to be in the British sphere of influence by the Anglo-German Agreement of July 1890. The British East Africa Company exercised a variable degree of control until 27 August 1894 when the country was declared a British Protectorate.

Before the introduction of Nos. 84/91 the stamps of Uganda were only valid for internal postage. Letters for overseas were franked with British East Africa issues on arrival at Mombasa.

(Currency. 200 cowries = 1 rupee)

'U G' 50
1

'U G' 20
2

TYPE-WRITTEN STAMPS. Nos. 2/53 were type-written by the Revd. E. Millar at Mengo for the Uganda administration. For all "printings" a thin laid paper was used, and all issues were imperforate.

The original typewriter used had wide letters, but in late April, 1895 Millar obtained a new machine on which the type face was in a narrower fount.

Each sheet was made up of whatever values were required at the time, so that different values can be found *se-tenant* or *tête-bêche*. These last were caused by the paper being inverted in the machine so that space at the foot could be utilised.

For the first issue the sheets were of 117 (9 × 13), but with the introduction of the narrower width (Nos. 17 onwards) a larger number of stamps per sheet, 143 (11 × 13), was adopted.

The manuscript provisionals, Nos. 9*a*/16, come from the Mission at Ngogwe, most of the manuscript surcharges including the initials of the Revd. G. R. Blackledge stationed there.

1895 (20 Mar). *Wide letters. Wide stamps,* 20 *to* 26 *mm wide.*
2 1 10 (c.) black £2750 £1200
4 20 (c.) black £4000 £1200
a. "U A" for "U G" .. .. .. † £2750
6 30 (c.) black £1400 £1400
7 40 (c.) black £2500 £1200
8 50 (c.) black £1200 £1000
a. "U A" for "U G" .. .. .. † £4250
9 60 (c.) black £1600 £1600
It is now believed that the 5, 15 and 25 cowries values in this width, previously Nos. 1, 3 and 5, do not exist.
A strip of three of No. 2 is known on cover of which one stamp has the value "10" altered to "5" in manuscript and initialled "E.M.".

1895 (May). *Wide stamps with pen-written surcharges, in black.*
9*a* 1 10 on 30 (c.) black .. .. .. † £30000
10 10 on 50 (c.) black .. .. .. † £30000
11 15 on 10 (c.) black .. .. .. † £22000
12 15 on 20 (c.) black .. .. .. † £26000
13 15 on 40 (c.) black .. .. .. † £26000
14 15 on 50 (c.) black .. .. .. † £30000
15 25 on 50 (c.) black .. .. .. † £30000
16 50 on 60 (c.) black .. .. .. † £30000

1895 (April). *Wide letters. Narrow stamps,* 16 *to* 18 *mm wide.*
17 1 5 (c.) black £1500 £950
18 10 (c.) black £1500 £1000
19 15 (c.) black £1000 £1000
20 20 (c.) black £1300 £650
21 25 (c.) black £950 £950
22 30 (c.) black £7500 £7500
23 40 (c.) black £7000 £7000
24 50 (c.) black £3250
25 60 (c.) black £5500

1895 (May). *Narrow letters. Narrow stamps* 16 *to* 18 *mm wide.*
26 2 5 (c.) black £750
27 10 (c.) black £750
28 15 (c.) black £750
29 20 (c.) black £550
30 25 (c.) black £750
31 30 (c.) black £750
32 40 (c.) black £800
33 50 (c.) black £650
34 60 (c.) black £1400

1895 (Nov). *Narrow letters. Narrow stamps,* 16–18 *mm wide. Change of colour.*
35 2 5 (c.) violet £500 £500
36 10 (c.) violet £475 £475
37 15 (c.) violet £600 £425
38 20 (c.) violet £375 £275
a. "G U" for "U G" .. .. ..
39 25 (c.) violet £700 £700
40 30 (c.) violet £950 £700
41 40 (c.) violet £800 £800

50 (c.) violet £800 £850
100 (c.) violet £2500 £2500
ımps of 35 (c.) and 45 (c.) have been recorded in violet. They never prepared for postal use, and did not represent a l rate, but were type-written to oblige a local official. (*Price 0 each, unused*)

'V.96.R'

25

'Uganda'

3

(June).
3 5 (c.) violet £475 £500
10 (c.) violet £425 £400
15 (c.) violet £475 £500
20 (c.) violet £275 £200
25 (c.) violet £450
30 (c.) violet £500 £650
40 (c.) violet £550 £650
50 (c.) violet £600 £650
60 (c.) violet £1400
100 (c.) violet £1200 £1400

(New Currency. 16 annas = 1 rupee)

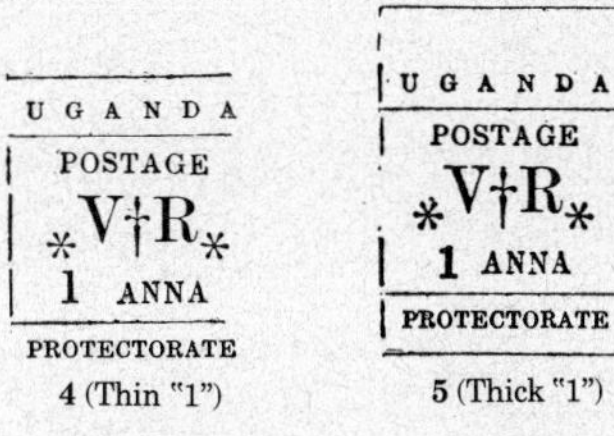

4 (Thin "1") 5 (Thick "1")

6

7

n the 2 a. and 3 a. the dagger points upwards; the stars in the . are level with the top of "VR". The 8 a. is as T **6** but with left r at top and right star at foot. The 1 r. has three stars at foot. The . has central star raised and the others at foot.

(Type-set by the Revd. F. Rowling at Lubwa's, in Usoga)

96 (7 Nov). *Thick white wove paper* (*Nos.* 54/8) *or thin ellowish paper ruled with vertical lines* 9 *mm apart* (*Nos.* 59/61). (*a*) *Types* **4/6**
4 1 a. black .. .. 95·00 85·00
a. Small "o" in "POSTAGE" £500 £475
5 1 a. black .. .. 16·00 21·00
a. Small "o" in "POSTAGE" .. .. 65·00 80·00
6 2 a. black .. .. 22·00 26·00
a. Small "o" in "POSTAGE" .. .. 85·00 95·00
3 a. black .. .. 24·00 28·00
a. Small "o" in "POSTAGE" .. .. 90·00 £110
4 a. black .. .. 23·00 27·00
a. Small "o" in "POSTAGE" .. .. 85·00 £100
8 a. black .. .. 26·00 28·00
a. Small "o" in "POSTAGE" £100 £120
1 r. black .. .. 75·00 95·00
a. Small "o" in "POSTAGE" £300 £400
5 r. black £190 £300
a. Small "o" in "POSTAGE" £650 £850

(*b*) *Optd* "L", *in black as in T* **7** *for local use, by a postal official, R. R. Racey, at Kampala*
4 1 a. black £170 £150
a. Small "o" in "POSTAGE" £900 £800
6 2 a. black .. .. 80·00 £100
a. Small "o" in "POSTAGE" £300 £375
3 a. black £190 £225
a. Small "o" in "POSTAGE" £950 £1100
4 a. black .. .. 90·00 £140
a. Small "o" in "POSTAGE" £425
8 a. black £160 £200
a. Small "o" in "POSTAGE" £850 £1000
1 r. black £325 £375
a. Small "o" in "POSTAGE" £1200
6 5 r. black £9500 £9500

Tête-bêche pairs of all values may be found owing to the ttings of 16 (4×4) being printed side by side or above one nother. They are worth a premium. The variety with small "O" ccurs on R. 3/1.

8

9

UGANDA
(10)

(Recess D.L.R.)

1898 (Nov)–**1902.** *P* 14. (*a*) *Wmk Crown CA.*
84 **8** 1 a. scarlet .. .. 1·75 2·00
a. Carmine-rose (1902).. .. .. 2·00 1·00
86 2 a. red-brown .. .. 2·00 7·00
87 3 a. pale grey .. .. 8·00 24·00
a. Bluish grey .. .. 8·50 13·00
88 4 a. deep green .. .. 3·50 6·50
89 8 a. pale olive .. .. 6·50 24·00
a. Grey-green .. .. 8·50 27·00

(*b*) *Wmk Crown CC*
90 **9** 1 r. dull blue .. .. 32·00 42·00
a. Bright blue .. .. 42·00 45·00
91 5 r. brown .. .. 70·00 £100
84/91 .. .. *Set of* 7 £110 £170
84s/91s Optd "Specimen" .. *Set of* 7 £150

On 1 April 1901 the postal administrations of British East Africa and Uganda were merged. Subsequent issues to 1962 are listed under KENYA, UGANDA and TANGANYIKA.

1902 (Feb). *T* **11** *of British East Africa* (*Kenya, Uganda, and Tanganyika*) *optd with T* **10**.
92 ½ a. yellow-green .. .. 2·00 1·40
a. Opt omitted (in pair with normal) .. £3750
b. Opt inverted (at foot) £1500
c. Opt double £1600
93 2½ a. deep blue (R.) .. .. 2·75 3·00
a. Opt double £600
b. Inverted "S" (R. 1/1) .. .. .. 55·00 80·00

The Eastern Province of Uganda was transferred to British East Africa on 1 April 1902.

Victoria
see Australia

Virgin Islands

CROWN COLONY

Apart from the 1951 Legislative Council issue, the word "BRITISH" did not appear regularly on the stamps until 1968 when it was introduced to avoid confusion with the nearby Virgin Islands of the United States (the former Danish West Indies).

Most mail from the early years of the islands' history was sent via the Danish island of St. Thomas.

It is not known exactly when the first post office, or agency, was established on Tortola, but an entry in a G.P.O. account book suggest that it was operating by 1787 and the earliest letter postmarked "TORTOLA" dates from June of that year. The stamps of Great Britain were used from 1858 to May 1860, when the colonial authorities assumed responsibility for the overseas mails from the British G.P.O.

For illustrations of the handstamp and postmark types see BRITISH POST OFFICES ABROAD notes, following GREAT BRITAIN.

TORTOLA

CROWNED-CIRCLE HANDSTAMPS

CC1 CC **1** TORTOLA (R.) (15.12.1842) *Price on cover* £4000
CC2 CC **5** TORTOLA (R.) (21.6.1854) *Price on cover* £7000

No. CC2 is known used as an Official Paid mark during the years 1900 to 1918. *Price on cover* £1200.

Stamps of GREAT BRITAIN *cancelled* "A 13" *as Type* **2**.

1858 *to* **1860.**
Z1 1d. rose-red (1857), *perf* 14 .. .. .. £3250
Z2 4d. rose (1857) £3000
Z3 6d. lilac (1856) £1200
Z4 1s. green (1856) .. ..

PRICES FOR STAMPS ON COVER TO 1945

Nos. 1/7	*from* × 15
Nos. 8/22	*from* × 12
Nos. 24/31	*from* × 8
Nos. 32/41	*from* × 10
No. 42	*from* × 20
Nos. 43/50	*from* × 6
Nos. 54/77	*from* × 5
Nos. 78/81	*from* × 6
Nos. 82/101	*from* × 3
Nos. 103/6	*from* × 4
Nos. 107/9	*from* × 6
Nos. 110/21	*from* × 2

1

St. Ursula

2

(Litho Nissen & Parker from original dies by Waterlow)

1866 (Dec). *No wmk. P* 12. (*a*) *White wove paper*
1 **1** 1d. green .. .. 45·00 60·00
2 1d. deep green .. .. 55·00 65·00
3 **2** 6d. rose .. .. 90·00 £110
4 6d. deep rose £130 £140
a. Large "V" in "VIRGIN" (R. 2/1) .. £375 £475

(*b*) *Toned paper*
5 **1** 1d. green .. .. 48·00 60·00
a. Perf 15×12 .. .. £4250 £5500
6 1d. deep green £100 £120
7 **2** 6d. rose-red .. .. 60·00 90·00
a. Large "V" in "VIRGIN" (R. 2/1) .. £275 £375

The above were printed in sheets of 25.

6d. stamps showing part of the papermaker's watermark ("A. Cowan & Sons Extra Superfine A. C. & S.") are worth 50% more.

Beware of fakes of No. 5a made from perf 12 stamps.

3

4

Normal Variety

1s. Long-tailed "S" in "ISLANDS" (R. 3/1)

(Litho and typo (figure of the Virgin) (1s.) or litho (others) Nissen and Parker from original dies by Waterlow)

1867–70. *No wmk. P* 15. 1*s. with double-lined frame.*

(*a*) *White wove paper*
8 **1** 1d. yellow-green (1868) .. .. 80·00 80·00
9 1d. blue-green (1870) .. .. .. 65·00 70·00
10 **2** 6d. pale rose £500 £500
11 **4** 1s. black and rose-carmine £225 £300
a. Long-tailed "S" £600 £700

(*b*) *Greyish* (*No.* 14) *or toned paper* (*others*)
12 **1** 1d. yellow-green (1868) .. .. 85·00 80·00
13 **2** 6d. dull rose (1868) £225 £275
14 **4** 1s. black & rose-carmine (*greyish paper*) £225 £300
a. Long-tailed "S" £600 £700
14*b* 1s. black and rose-carmine (*toned paper*) £300 £325
ba. Long-tailed "S" £650 £750

(*c*) *Pale rose paper*
15 **3** 4d. lake-red .. .. 50·00 70·00

(*d*) *Buff paper*
16 **3** 4d. lake-red .. .. 40·00 60·00
17 4d. lake-brown .. .. 40·00 60·00

The thin lines of the frame on the 1s. are close together and sometimes merge into one.

The 1d. from the 1868 printing was in sheets of 20 (5×4) with narrow margins between the stamps. Later printings were in sheets of 12 (3×4) with wider margins. The 4d. was in sheets of 25; and the remaining two values in sheets of 20 (5×4).

The greyish paper used for Nos. 14 and 20 often shows traces of blue.

1867. *Nos.* 11 *and* 14/*b with crimson frames superimposed extending into margins. P* 15.
18 **4** 1s. black and rose-carmine (*white paper*) 48·00 60·00
a. Long-tailed "S" £160 £180
b. Figure of Virgin omitted £60000
19 1s. black and rose-carmine (*toned paper*) 48·00 60·00
a. Long-tailed "S" £160 £180
20 1s. black and rose-carmine (*greyish paper* £700 £850
a. Long-tailed "S" £1600 £1600

1868. *Nos.* 11 *and* 14*b with frame lines retouched so as to make them single lines. Margins remain white. P* 15.
21 **4** 1s. black and rose-carmine (*white paper*) £130 £160
a. Long-tailed "S" £375 £450
21*b* 1s. black and rose-carmine (*toned paper*) £130 £160
ba. Long-tailed "S" £375 £450

(Litho D.L.R.)

1878. *Wmk Crown CC* (*sideways*). *P* 14.
22 **1** 1d. green .. .. 70·00 90·00
a. Yellow-green £170 £130
ab. Wmk upright .. .. 90·00 £120

6 (Die I)

4D
(7)

(Typo D.L.R.)

1879–80. *Wmk Crown CC. P* 14.
24 **6** 1d. emerald-green (1880) .. .. 65·00 85·00
25 2½d. red-brown .. .. 90·00 £120

1883 (June)–**84.** *Wmk Crown CA. P* 14.

No.	Type	Description	Unused	Used
26	6	½d. yellow-buff	85·00	80·00
27		½d. dull green (*shades*) (11.83) ..	4·25	8·00
		b. Top left triangle detached	£110	
29		1d. pale rose (15.9.83)	24·00	27·00
		a. Deep rose (1884)	55·00	60·00
31		2½d. ultramarine (9.84)	2·50	14·00
		b. Top left triangle detached	£110	
		w. Wmk inverted		

For illustration of "top left triangle detached" variety see above No. 21 of Antigua.

(Litho D.L.R.)

1887–89. *Wmk Crown CA. P* 14.

No.	Type	Description	Unused	Used
32	1	1d. red (5.89)	2·00	7·00
33		1d. rose-red	2·25	7·00
34		1d. rose	5·00	14·00
35	3	4d. chestnut	35·00	65·00
		x. Wmk reversed		
36		4d. pale chestnut	35·00	65·00
37		4d. brown-red	45·00	70·00
38	2	6d. dull violet	13·00	48·00
39		6d. deep violet	12·00	42·00
40	4	1s. sepia (2.89)	80·00	£100
41		1s. brown *to* deep brown	45·00	70·00
34s/40s		Optd "Specimen" .. *Set of* 4	£300	

The De La Rue transfers of T 1 to 4 are new transfers and differ from those of Messrs. Nissen and Parker, particularly T 4.

1888 (July). *Nos.* 18/19 *surch with T* 7, *in violet, in Antigua.*

No.	Type	Description	Unused	Used
42	4	4d. on 1s. black & rose-car (*toned paper*)	£110	£150
		a. Surch double	£6500	
		b. Surch inverted (in pair with normal)	£40000	
		c. Long-tailed "S"	£400	£500
42*d*		4d. on 1s. black & rose-car (*white paper*)	£150	£190
		dc. Long-tailed "S"	£475	£550

The special issues for Virgin Islands were superseded on 31 October 1890, by the general issue for Leeward Islands. In 1899, however, a new special issue, Nos. 43/50, appeared; it did not supersede the general issue for Leeward Islands, but was used concurrently, as were all subsequent issues, until 1 July 1956, when the general Leeward Islands stamps were withdrawn.

8

9

10

(Recess D.L.R.)

1899 (Jan). *Wmk Crown CA. P* 14.

No.	Type	Description	Unused	Used
43	8	½d. yellow-green	1·00	55
		a. Error. "HALFPFNNY" (R. 10/1) ..	80·00	£120
		b. Error. "HALΓPENNY" (R. 8/2) ..	80·00	£120
		c. Imperf between (horiz pair) ..	£7000	
44		1d. brick-red	2·75	3·00
45		2½d. ultramarine	12·00	4·00
46		4d. brown	4·00	18·00
		a. Error "FOURPENCF" (R.10/3) ..	£750	£1100
47		6d. dull violet	4·50	4·50
48		7d. deep green	7·50	8·00
49		1s. brown-yellow	22·00	35·00
50		5s. indigo	70·00	85·00
43/50		.. .. .. *Set of* 8	£110	£140
43s/50s		Optd "Specimen" .. *Set of* 8	£160	

Nos. 43a/b and 46a were corrected after the first printing.

(Typo D.L.R.)

1904 (1 June). *Wmk Mult Crown CA. P* 14.

No.	Type	Description	Unused	Used
54	9	½d. dull purple and green	75	40
55		1d. dull purple and scarlet	2·50	35
56	10	2d. dull purple and ochre	6·00	4·50
57	9	2½d. dull purple and ultramarine ..	2·00	2·00
58	10	3d. dull purple and black	3·50	3·00
59	9	6d. dull purple and brown	2·75	3·00
60	10	1s. green and scarlet	4·00	5·00
61		2s. 6d. green and black	23·00	55·00
62	9	5s. green and blue	48·00	65·00
54/62		.. .. *Set of* 9	80·00	£120
54s/62s		Optd "Specimen" .. *Set of* 9	£140	

11

12

(Typo D.L.R.)

1913 (Feb)–**19.** *Die I. Wmk Mult Crown CA. Chalk-surfaced paper* (3*d. to* 5*s.*). *P* 14.

No.	Type	Description	Unused	Used
69	11	½d. green	50	3·50
		a. Yellow-green (8.16)	2·75	11·00
		b. Blue-green and deep green (3.19) ..	1·25	5·50
70		1d. deep red	8·50	11·00
		a. Deep red and carmine (10.17) ..	2·25	14·00
		b. Scarlet (10.17)	2·25	14·00
		c. Carmine-red (3.19)	48·00	27·00
71	12	2d. grey	4·00	23·00
		a. Slate-grey (1919)	4·25	27·00
72	11	2½d. bright blue	5·50	9·00
73	12	3d. purple/*yellow*	2·75	6·50
74	11	6d. dull and bright purple	5·00	10·00
75	12	1s. black/*blue-green*	3·25	9·00
76		2s. 6d. black and red/*blue*	48·00	50·00
77	11	5s. green and red/*yellow*	35·00	£110
69/77		.. .. .. *Set of* 9	95·00	£200
69s/77s		Optd "Specimen" .. *Set of* 9	£180	

Stock of the original printing of the ½d., No. 69, was exhausted by January 1916 and Leeward Islands ½d. stamps were used until the yellow-green printing, No. 69*a*, arrived in August 1916.

WAR STAMP

(13)

14

1916 (20 Oct)–**19.** *Optd with T* **13**.

No.	Type	Description	Unused	Used
78	11	1d. carmine	1·75	18·00
		a. Watermark sideways	£1100	
		b. Pale red/bluish	50	7·00
		bw. Wmk inverted	55·00	
		by. Wmk inverted and reversed ..		
		c. Scarlet (11.3.19)	30	3·75
		d. Short opt (right pane R. 10/1) ..	20·00	
79	12	3d. purple/*yellow*	1·75	14·00
		a. Purple/lemon (12.3.17) ..	3·00	10·00
		b. Purple/buff-yellow (11.3.19) ..	2·50	18·00
		bw. Wmk inverted	10·00	45·00
		by. Wmk inverted and reversed ..		
		c. Short opt (right pane R. 10/1) ..	32·00	
78s/9s		Optd "Specimen" .. *Set of* 2	70·00	

Nos. 78d and 79c show the overprint 2 mm high instead of 2½ mm.

1921 (18 Nov). *As* 1913–19, *but Die II and wmk Mult Script CA.*

No.	Type	Description	Unused	Used
80	11	½d. green	3·00	26·00
		w. Wmk inverted		
81		1d. scarlet and deep carmine ..	2·00	21·00
80s/1s		Optd "Specimen" .. *Set of* 2	70·00	

(Typo D.L.R.)

1922 (Mar)–**28.** *P* 14. (*a*) *Wmk Mult Crown CA. Chalk-surfaced paper.*

No.	Type	Description	Unused	Used
82	14	3d. purple/*pale yellow* (15.6.22) ..	65	16·00
83		1s. black/*emerald* (15.6.22) ..	75	14·00
84		2s. 6d. black and red/*blue* (15.6.22) ..	5·50	11·00
85		5s. green and red/*pale yellow* (15.6.22)	30·00	95·00
82/5		.. .. *Set of* 4	32·00	£120
82s/5s		Optd "Specimen" .. *Set of* 4	90·00	

(*b*) *Wmk Mult Script CA. Chalk-surfaced paper* (5*d. to* 5*s.*)

No.	Type	Description	Unused	Used
86	14	½d. dull green	85	2·75
87		1d. rose-carmine	60	60
88		1d. bright violet (1.27)	1·00	3·50
89		1d. scarlet (12.28)	14·00	14·00
90		1½d. carmine-red (1.27)	1·50	2·50
91		1½d. Venetian red (11.28)	1·75	2·00
92		2d. grey	1·00	6·00
93		2½d. pale bright blue	1·50	16·00
94		2½d. dull orange (1.9.23)	1·25	1·50
95		2½d. bright blue (1.27)	2·50	3·50
96		3d. purple/*pale yellow* (2.28) ..	2·25	11·00
97		5d. dull purple and olive (6.22) ..	5·50	45·00
98		6d. dull and bright purple (6.22) ..	1·50	6·50
99		1s. black/*emerald* (2.28)	2·50	14·00
100		2s. 6d. black and red/*blue* (2.28) ..	19·00	48·00
101		5s. green and red/*yellow* (1.9.23) ..	19·00	70·00
86/101		.. .. *Set of* 16	65·00	£225
86s/101s		Optd or Perf (Nos. 89, 91) "Specimen" *Set of* 16	£275	

In the 1½d. stamps the value is in colour on a white ground.

1935 (6 May). *Silver Jubilee. As Nos.* 91/4 *of Antigua but printed by Waterlow. P* 11 × 12.

No.	Description	Unused	Used
103	1d. deep blue and scarlet	1·25	3·50
	k. Kite and vertical log	65·00	
	l. Kite and horizontal log	70·00	
104	1½d. ultramarine and grey	1·25	3·50
	k. Kite and vertical log	70·00	
	l. Kite and horizontal log	75·00	
	m. "Bird" by turret	£110	
105	2½d. brown and deep blue	1·25	3·50
	k. Kite and vertical log	75·00	
	l. Kite and horizontal log	80·00	
106	1s. slate and purple	6·50	16·00
	k. Kite and vertical log	£150	
	l. Kite and horizontal log	£150	
103/6	.. .. *Set of* 4	9·00	24·00
103s/6s	Perf "Specimen" .. *Set of* 4	85·00	

For illustrations of plate varieties see Omnibus section following Zanzibar.

1937 (12 May). *Coronation. As Nos.* 95/7 *of Antigua. P* 11×11½.

No.	Description	Unused	Used
107	1d. carmine	20	1·00
108	1½d. yellow-brown	50	2·50
109	2½d. blue	45	1·00
107/9	.. .. *Set of* 3	1·10	4·00
107s/9s	Perf "Specimen" .. *Set of* 3	55·00	

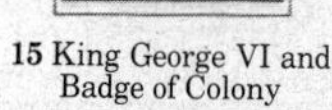

15 King George VI and Badge of Colony

16 Map

(Photo Harrison)

1938 (1 Aug)–**47.** *Wmk Mult Script CA. Chalk-surfaced paper. P* 14.

No.	Type	Description	Unused	Used
110	15	½d. green	2·50	
		a. Ordinary paper (10.43)	30	
111		1d. scarlet	3·25	
		a. Ordinary paper (10.43)	30	
112		1½d. red-brown	4·75	
		a. Ordinary paper (10.43)	1·00	
		w. Wmk inverted	†	
113		2d. grey	4·75	
		a. Ordinary paper (10.43)	1·00	
114		2½d. ultramarine	4·00	
		a. Ordinary paper (10.43)	70	
115		3d. orange	5·50	
		a. Ordinary paper (10.43)	70	
116		6d. mauve	4·25	
		a. Ordinary paper (10.43)	2·00	
117		1s. olive-brown	11·00	
		a. Ordinary paper (8.42)	1·50	
118		2s. 6d. sepia	26·00	
		a. Ordinary paper (8.42)	15·00	
119		5s. carmine	48·00	
		a. Ordinary paper (8.42)	13·00	
120		10s. blue (1.12 47)	6·00	
121		£1 black (1.12.47)	8·00	
110/21		.. .. .. *Set of* 12	45·00	
110s/21s		Perf "Specimen" .. *Set of* 12	£225	

The ordinary paper, used as a substitute for chalk-surfaced for printings between 1942 and 1945, is smooth and opaque.

1946 (1 Nov). *Victory. As Nos.* 110/11 *of Antigua.*

No.	Description	Unused	Used
122	1½d. lake-brown	10	
123	3d. orange	10	
122s/3s	Perf "Specimen" .. .. *Set of* 2	55·00	

1949 (3 Jan). *Royal Silver Wedding. As Nos.* 112/1 *Antigua.*

No.	Description	Unused	Used
124	2½d. ultramarine	10	
125	£1 black	13·00	

1949 (10 Oct). *75th Anniv of U.P.U. As Nos.* 114/17 *of Antig*

No.	Description	Unused	Used
126	2½d. ultramarine	30	
127	3d. orange	80	
128	6d. magenta	30	
129	1s. olive	30	
126/9	.. .. .. *Set of* 4	1·50	

(New Currency. 100 cents = 1 B.W.I. dollar)

1951 (16 Feb–10 Apr). *Inauguration of B.W.I. Unive College. As Nos.* 118/19 *of Antigua.*

No.	Description	Unused	Used
130	3 c. black and brown-red (10 Apr) ..	40	
131	12 c. black and reddish violet	60	

Issue of the 3 c. value was delayed when the supplies sent to Puerto Rico by mistake.

(Recess Waterlow)

1951 (2 Apr). *Restoration of Legislative Council. Wmk Mult S CA. P* 14½ x 14.

No.	Type	Description	Unused	Used
132	16	6 c. orange	30	
133		12 c. purple	30	
134		24 c. olive	30	
135		$1.20 carmine	80	
132/5		.. .. .. *Set of* 4	1·50	

17 Sombrero Lighthouse

18 Map of Jost Van Dyke

(Recess D.L.R.)

1952 (15 Apr). *T* **17/18** *and similar designs. Wmk Mult Script P* 12½ × 13 (*vert*) *or* 13 × 12½ (*horiz*).

No.	Description	Unused	Used
136	1 c. black	80	
137	2 c. deep green	70	
138	3 c. black and brown	80	
139	4 c. carmine-red	70	
140	5 c. claret and black	1·50	
141	8 c. bright blue	70	1
142	12 c. dull violet	80	1
143	24 c. deep brown	70	
144	60 c. yellow-green and blue	3·50	11
145	$1.20, black and bright blue	4·25	12
146	$2.40, yellowish green and red-brown ..	10·00	16
147	$4.80, bright blue and carmine	11·00	16
136/47	.. .. .. *Set of* 12	30·00	55

Designs: *Horiz*—3 c. Sheep industry; 4 c. Map of Anegada; Cattle industry; 8 c. Map of Virgin Gorda; 12 c. Map of Tortola; 6 Dead Man's Chest; $1.20, Sir Francis Drake Channel; $2.40, R Town; $4.80, Map of Virgin Islands. *Vert*—24 c. Badge of Presidency.

Western Australia *see* Australia

Western Samoa *see after* New Zealand

Zanzibar

n Indian post office opened in Zanzibar in November 1868, was closed for political reasons on 1 April of the following . Little has survived from this period. Subsequently mail forwarded via Seychelles or, later, Aden.

amps of INDIA were used in Zanzibar from 1 October 1875 l 10 November 1895, when the administration of the postal ice was transferred from India to British East Africa. arate cancellations for Zanzibar are known from 1 June 3.

Z 1

mps of INDIA *cancelled with Type* Z **1** (1878–79).

5. (*Nos.* 54/65).
1 a. deep brown £140
2 a. orange £140

6–78. (*Nos.* 69/72).
4 a. blue-green (Die II) £120

3. (*Nos.* 75/6).
½ a. blue (Die II) £120

urviving covers show that Type Z 1 was normally used as a estamp, struck clear of the stamps which were obliterated by omboid of bars, but examples of the c.d.s. used as a cancel known.

Z 2

mps of INDIA *cancelled with Type* Z **2** (1879–82).

65. (*Nos.* 54/65).
0 8 p. mauve £140
1 1 a. deep brown .. .. 17·00
2 2 a. orange .. .. 17·00

66–78. (*Nos.* 69/72).
3 4 a. green (Die I) £100
4 4 a. blue-green (Die II) .. .. 25·00

68. (*Nos.* 73/4).
5 8 a. rose (Die II) .. .. 65·00

73. (*Nos.* 75/6).
6 ½ a. blue (Die II) .. .. 17·00

74. (*Nos.* 77/9).
17 1 r. slate £150

76. (*Nos.* 80/2).
18 6 a. pale brown .. .. 65·00
19 12 a. Venetian red £100

OFFICIAL STAMPS

1874–82. (*Nos.* O31/7).
Z20 2 a. orange £140

Z 3

Stamps of INDIA *cancelled with Type* Z **3** (1882–84)

1865. (*Nos.* 54/65).
Z25 1 a. deep brown .. .. 30·00
Z26 2 a. brown-orange .. .. 25·00

1866–78. (*Nos.* 69/72).
Z27 4 a. blue-green (Die II) .. .. 30·00

1868. (*Nos.* 73/4).
Z28 8 a. rose (Die II) .. .. 42·00

1873. (*Nos.* 75/6).
Z29 ½ a. blue (Die II) .. .. 24·00

1876. (*Nos.* 80/2).
Z30 6 a. pale brown .. .. 38·00
Z31 12 a. Venetian red .. .. 75·00

1882–83. (*Nos.* 84/101).
Z32 1 a. brown-purple .. .. 24·00
Z33 1 a. 6 p. sepia .. .. 29·00
Z34 3 a. orange .. .. 30·00

Z 4

Z 5

Stamps of INDIA *cancelled with Type* Z **4** (June 1884–May 1887) (*between* January *and* September 1885 *the postmark was used without year numerals*).

1865. (*Nos.* 54/65).
Z39 1 a. deep brown .. .. 60·00
Z40 2 a. brown-orange .. .. 30·00

1866–78. (*Nos.* 69/72).
Z41 4 a. blue-green (Die II) .. .. 30·00

1868. (*Nos.* 73/4).
Z42 8 a. rose (Die II) .. .. 30·00

1873. (*Nos.* 75/6).
Z43 ½ a. blue (Die II) .. .. 29·00

1874. (*Nos.* 77/9).
Z44 1 r. slate £100

1876. (*Nos.* 80/2).
Z45 6 a. pale brown .. .. 50·00

1882–86. (*Nos.* 84/101).
Z46 ½ a. blue-green .. .. 13·00
Z47 1 a. brown-purple .. .. 24·00
Z48 1 a. 6 p. sepia .. .. 19·00
Z49 2 a. blue .. .. 38·00
Z50 3 a. orange .. .. 13·00
Z51 4 a. olive-green .. .. 38·00
Z52 4 a. 6 p. yellow-green .. .. 18·00
Z53 8 a. dull mauve .. .. 38·00
Z54 1 r. slate .. .. 38·00

OFFICIAL STAMPS

1867–73. (*Nos.* O20/30*a*)
Z55 2 a. orange £140

1874–82. (*Nos.* O31/7).
Z56 1 a. brown .. .. 80·00

1883–95. (*Nos.* O37*a*/48).
Z57 1 a. brown-purple .. .. 80·00

Stamps of INDIA *cancelled with Type* Z **5** (1887–94).

1876. (*Nos.* 80/2).
Z60 6 a. pale brown .. .. 16·00
Z61 12 a. Venetian red .. .. 42·00

1882–88. (*Nos.* 84/101).
Z62 ½ a. blue-green .. .. 5·50
Z63 9 p. aniline carmine .. .. 38·00
Z64 1 a. brown-purple .. .. 5·00
Z65 1 a. 6 p. sepia .. .. 7·50
Z66 2 a. blue .. .. 6·00
Z67 3 a. orange .. .. 8·00
Z68 3 a. brown-orange .. .. 6·50
Z69 4 a. olive-green .. .. 38·00
Z70 4 a. 6 p. yellow-green .. .. 10·00
Z71 8 a. dull mauve .. .. 18·00
Z72 12 a. purple/*red* .. .. 38·00
Z73 1 r. slate .. .. 14·00

1891. (*No.* 102).
Z74 2½ a. on 4 a. 6 p. yellow-green .. .. .. 7·00

1892–95. (*Nos.* 103/6).
Z75 2 a. 6 p. yellow-green .. .. 5·00

OFFICIAL STAMPS

1874. (*Nos.* O31/7).
Z76 ½ a. blue .. .. 70·00
Z77 1 a. brown .. .. 70·00

Z 6

Z 7

Stamps of INDIA *cancelled with Type* Z **6** (1888–95).

1876. (*Nos.* 80/2).
Z80 6 a. pale brown .. .. 17·00

1882–88. (*Nos.* 84/101).
Z81 ½ a. blue-green .. .. 28·00
Z82 9 p. aniline carmine .. .. 42·00
Z83 1 a. brown-purple .. .. 8·00
Z84 1 a. 6 p. sepia .. .. 7·50
Z85 2 a. blue .. .. 8·50
Z86 3 a. orange .. .. 18·00
Z87 3 a. brown-orange .. .. 14·00
Z88 4 a. olive-green .. .. 14·00
Z89 4 a. 6 p. yellow-green .. .. 13·00
Z90 8 a. dull mauve .. .. 18·00
Z91 12 a. purple/*red* .. .. 38·00
Z92 1 r. slate .. .. 16·00

1891. (*No.* 102).
Z93 2½ a. on 4 a. 6 p. yellow-green .. .. .. 18·00

1892–95. (*Nos.* 103/6).
Z94 2 a. 6 p. yellow-green .. .. 17·00

Stamps of INDIA *cancelled with Type* Z **7** (1894–95).

1876. (*Nos.* 80/2)
Z95 6 a. pale brown .. .. 48·00

1882–88. (*Nos.* 84/101).
Z100 ½ a. blue-green .. .. 17·00
Z101 9 p. aniline carmine .. .. 50·00
Z102 1 a. brown-purple .. .. 25·00
Z103 1 a. 6 p. sepia .. .. 38·00
Z104 2 a. blue .. .. 17·00
Z105 3 a. brown-orange .. .. 35·00
Z106 4 a. olive-green .. .. 35·00
Z107 8 a. dull mauve .. .. 48·00
Z108 12 a. purple/*red* .. .. 50·00
Z109 1 r. slate .. .. 45·00

1892–95. (*Nos.* 103/6).
Z110 2 a. 6 p. yellow-green .. .. 10·00

1895. (*Nos.* 107/9).
Z111 2 r. carmine and yellow-brown £200

A French post office was opened on the island in January 1889 and this service used the stamps of FRANCE until 1894 when specific stamps for this office were provided. The French postal service on the island closed on 31 July 1904 and it is known that French stamps were again utilised during the final month.

A German postal agency operated in Zanzibar between 27 August 1890 and 31 July 1891, using stamps of GERMANY.

MINIMUM PRICE

The minimum price quote is 10p which represents a handling charge rather than a basis for valuing common stamps. For further notes about prices see introductory pages.

PRICES FOR STAMPS ON COVER TO 1945

Nos.	1/2	—
Nos.	3/16	*from* × 30
No.	17	*from* × 8
No.	18	*from* × 25
Nos.	19/21	—
No.	22	*from* × 30
Nos.	23/5	—
No.	26	*from* × 40
Nos.	27/40	—
Nos.	41/6	*from* × 25
Nos.	156/68	*from* × 15
Nos.	169/77	—
Nos.	178/87	*from* × 20
Nos.	188/204	*from* × 15
Nos.	205/9	*from* × 20
Nos.	210/38	*from* × 15
Nos.	239/45	—
Nos.	246/59	*from* × 8
Nos.	260/*f*	—
Nos.	261/330	*from* × 4
Nos.	D1/3	*from* × 8
No.	D4	*from* × 1
No.	D5	*from* × 15
No.	D6	—
No.	D7	*from* × 1
Nos.	D8/12	*from* × 15
No.	D13	*from* × 1
No.	D14	—
Nos.	D15/16	*from* × 6
No.	D17	*from* × 4
Nos.	D18/24	*from* × 15
Nos.	D25/30	*from* × 30

PROTECTORATE

(Currency. 12 pies = 1 anna. 16 annas = 1 rupee)

Zanzibar
(1)

1895 (10 Nov)–**96.** *Nos.* 81, 85, 90/6, 98/101, 103 *and* 106/9 *of India* (*Queen Victoria*) *optd with T* 1 *by* Zanzibar Gazette.

(*a*) *In blue*
1 ½ a. blue-green £12000 £3500
2 1 a. plum £2250 £500
j. "Zanzidar" (R. 4/6, 8/5) .. .. † £13000

(*b*) *In black*
3 ½ a. blue-green .. .. 3·25 3·00
j. "Zanzidar" (R. 4/6, 8/5) £1000 £600
k. "Zanibar" (R. 7/2) £1100 £1500
l. Diaeresis over last "a" (R. 10/5) .. £1100 £1100
m. Opt double, one albino £225
4 1 a. plum .. .. 3·50 3·00
j. "Zanzidar" (R. 4/6, 8/5) .. .. — £2500
k. "Zanibar" (R. 7/2) £1400 £1600
l. Diaeresis over last "a" (R. 10/5) .. £1600
5 1 a. 6 p. sepia .. .. 4·00 3·00
j. "Zanzidar" (R. 4/6, 8/5) £3000 £900
k. "Zanibar" (R. 7/2) £1300 £1400
l. "Zanizbar" (R. 1/9)
m. Diaeresis over last "a" (R. 10/5) .. £1100
6 2 a. pale blue .. .. 4·25 4·00
7 2 a. blue .. .. 4·50 4·25
j. "Zanzidar" (R. 4/6, 8/5) £3250 £1600
k. "Zanibar" (R. 7/2) £3250 £1700
l. Diaeresis over last "a" (R. 10/5) .. £1500
m. Opt double £250
n. Opt double, one albino £250
8 2½ a. yellow-green .. .. .. 6·50 4·25
j. "Zanzidar" (R. 4/6, 8/5) £3000 £1500
k. "Zanibar" (R. 7/2) £550 £1000
l. "Zapzibar" .. .. ..
m. "Zanzipar" .. .. ..
n. Diaeresis over last "a" (R. 10/5) .. £1300 £1100
o. Second "z" italic (R. 10/1) £250 £375
p. Opt double, one albino £250
10 3 a. brown-orange .. .. .. 9·00 8·50
j. "Zanzidar" (R. 4/6, 8/5) £750 £1400
k. "Zanizbar" (R. 1/9) £3500 £3750
11 4 a. olive-green .. .. .. 16·00 13·00
j. "Zanzidar" ((R. 4/6, 8/5) £5000 £3250
12 4 a. slate-green .. .. .. 9·00 11·00
l. Diaeresis over last "a" (R. 10/5) .. £1700
13 6 a. pale brown .. .. .. 16·00 11·00
j. "Zanzidar" (R. 4/6, 8/5) £5500 £3500
k. "Zanibar" (R. 7/2) £650 £1200
l. "Zanzibarr" £3750 £3500
m. Opt double .. .. ..
n. Opt double, one albino £130
o. Opt triple, two albino £170
14 8 a. dull mauve .. .. .. 20·00 18·00
j. "Zanzidar" (R. 4/6, 8/5) £5000 £5000
15 8 a. magenta (7.96) .. .. .. 12·00 20·00
16 12 a. purple/*red* .. .. .. 14·00 10·00
j. "Zanzidar" (R. 4/6, 8/5) £4750 £3500
17 1 r. slate .. .. 70·00 70·00
j. "Zanzidar" (R. 4/6, 8/5) £4750 £4000
18 1 r. green and aniline carmine (7.96) .. 12·00 24·00
j. Opt vert downwards £425
19 2 r. carmine and yellow-brown .. .. 50·00 75·00
j. "r" omitted £6500
k. "r" inverted £3750 £3750
20 3 r. brown and green .. .. .. 45·00 60·00
j. "r" omitted £6500
k. "r" inverted £3500 £4000
l. Opt double, one albino £750
21 5 r. ultramarine and violet .. .. 50·00 75·00
j. "r" omitted £6500
k. "r" inverted £3000 £4000
l. Opt double, one inverted £850
3/21 .. .. *Set of* 15 £275 £350

There were a number of different settings for this overprint. Values to 1 r. were initially overprinted from settings of 120 (12×10) including one which showed "Zanzidar" on R.4/6 and R.8/5 (soon corrected) and "Zanizbar" on R.1/9 (also soon corrected). Later supplies of these values were overprinted from settings of 80 (8×10) for the 6 a. only or 60 (6×10) for the others. One of these settings included "Zanibar" on R.7/2. Another late setting, size unknown, showed a diaeresis over last "a" on R.10/5.

Many forgeries of this overprint exist and also bogus errors.

MINOR VARIETIES. The following minor varieties of type exist on Nos. 1/21:

A. First "Z" antique (all values)
B. Broken "p" for "n" (all values to 1 r.)
C. Tall second "z" (all values)
D. Small second "z" (all values)
E. Small second "z" and inverted "q" for "b" (all values)
F. Second "z" Gothic (½ a. to 12 a. and 1 r.) (No. 18) (black opts only)
G. No dot over "i" (all values to 1 r.)
H. Inverted "q" for "b" (all values to 1 r.)
I. Arabic "2" for "r" (all values to 1 r.) (black opts only)

Varieties D and E are worth the same as normal examples, A (2, 3, 5 r.) and C normal plus 50%, G and I from 3 times normal, A (values to 1 r.), F and H from 4 times normal and B from 5 times normal.

2½ (2) 2½ (3) 2½ (4) 2½ (5)

1895–98. *Provisionals.* I. *Stamps used for postal purposes.*

(*a*) *No.* 5 *surch in red* (30.11.95)
22 2 2½ on 1½ a. sepia .. .. 50·00 35·00
j. "Zanzidar" £1200 £1100
k. "Zanizbar" £3750 £1900
l. Inverted "1" in "½" £1100 £900

(*b*) *No.* 4 *surch in black* (11.5.96)
23 3 2½ on 1 a. plum £140 £100
24 4 2½ on 1 a. plum £400 £275
j. Inverted "1" in "½" £2250
25 5 2½ on 1 a. plum £150 £110

2½ (6) 2½ (7) 2½ (8)

(*c*) *No.* 6 *surch in red* (15.8.96)
26 6 2½ on 2 a. pale blue .. .. .. 50·00 26·00
j. Inverted "1" in "½" £375 £275
k. Roman "I" in "½" £225 £150
l. "Zanzibar" double, one albino .. £140
27 7 2½ on 2 a. pale blue .. .. .. £130 85·00
j. "2" of "½" omitted £4500
k. "2" for "2½" £6000
l. "1" of "½" omitted £4500 £3250
m. Inverted "1" in "½" £1700
n. "Zanzibar" double, one albino .. £300
28 8 2½ on 2 a. pale blue £4250 £1700

No. 28 only exists with small "z" and occurs on R. 2/2 in the setting of 60.

(*d*) *No.* 5 *surch in red* (15.11.96)
29 6 2½ on 1½ a. sepia £130 £100
j. Inverted "1" in "½" £1100 £950
k. Roman "I" in "½" £800 £750
l. Surch double, one albino £225
30 7 2½ on 1½ a. sepia £375 £325
l. Surch double, one albino £600
31 8 2½ on 1½ a. sepia £10000 £7000

No. 31 only exists with small "z" and occurs on R. 2/2 in the setting of 60.

II. *Stamps prepared for official purposes. Nos.* 4, 5 *and* 7 *surch as before in red* (1.98)
32 3 2½ on 1 a. plum £225 £550
33 4 2½ on 1 a. plum £425 £850
34 5 2½ on 1 a. plum £250 £550
35 3 2½ on 1½ a. sepia .. .. 75·00 £170
j. Diaeresis over last "a" £4000
36 4 2½ on 1½ a. sepia £170 £400
37 5 2½ on 1½ a. sepia £100 £225
38 3 2½ on 2 a. dull blue .. .. 90·00 £225
39 4 2½ on 2 a. dull blue £180 £425
40 5 2½ on 2 a. dull blue £100 £275

It is doubtful whether Nos. 32/40 were issued to the public.

1896. *Nos.* 65/6, 68 *and* 71/3 *of British East Africa* (*Queen Victoria*), *optd with T* 1.
41 ½ a. yellow-green (23 May) .. .. 29·00 16·00
42 1 a. carmine-rose (1 June) .. .. 25·00 15·00
j. Opt double £750 £850
k. Opt double, one albino £275
43 2½ a. deep blue (R.) (24 May) .. .. 75·00 42·00
44 4½ a. orange-yellow (12 Aug) .. .. 42·00 48·00
45 5 a. yellow-bistre (12 Aug) .. .. 48·00 30·00
j. "r" omitted .. .. — £2250
46 7½ a. mauve (12 Aug) .. .. .. 35·00 48·00
41/6 .. .. *Set of* 6 £225 £180

MINOR VARIETIES. The various minor varieties of type detailed in the note below No. 21 also occur on Nos. 22 to 46 as indicated below:

A. Nos. 23, 25, 27, 30, 35, 38, 41/6
B. Nos. 22/3, 26, 29/30, 32/3, 36, 39, 44/6
C. Nos. 22, 25/6, 32, 36, 38, 40/6
D. Nos. 22/46
E. Nos. 22/46
F. Nos. 22, 25/6, 29, 41/6
G. Nos. 25/6, 29, 35, 37/8, 40/6
H. Nos. 22, 41/6 (on the British East Africa stamps this variety occurs in the same position as variety C)
I. Nos. 26, 29, 35, 38, 41/6

The scarcity of these varieties on the surcharges (Nos. 22/40) is similar to those on the basic stamps, but examples on the British East Africa values (Nos. 41/6) are more common.

PRINTERS. All Zanzibar stamps up to Type **37** were printed by De La Rue & Co.

12

13

14 Sultan Seyyid Hamed-bin-Thwain

No right serif to left-hand "4" (R. 1/1)

1896 (Dec). *Recess. Flags in red on all values. W* **12**. *P* 14
156 13 ½ a. yellow-green .. .. .. 3·50
157 1 a. indigo .. .. 2·00
158 1 a. violet-blue .. .. .. 4·00
159 2 a. red-brown .. .. .. 2·75
160 2½ a. bright blue .. .. .. 10·00
161 2½ a. pale blue .. .. 11·00
162 3 a. grey .. .. 8·00
163 3 a. bluish grey .. .. .. 9·00
164 4 a. myrtle-green .. .. .. 5·50
165 4½ a. orange .. .. 4·00
a. No right serif to left-hand "4" .. 90·00
b. No fraction bar at right (R. 2/1) .. 90·00
166 5 a. bistre .. .. 3·50
a. Bisected (2½ a.) (on cover) .. † £
167 7½ a. mauve .. .. 3·50
168 8 a. grey-olive .. .. 9·50
169 14 1 r. blue .. .. 11·00
170 1 r. deep blue .. .. 17·00
171 2 r. green .. .. 23·00
172 3 r. dull purple .. .. .. 21·00
173 4 r. lake .. .. 17·00
174 5 r. sepia .. .. 22·00
156/74 .. .. *Set of* 15 £130
156s/74s Optd "Specimen" .. *Set of* 15 £190

The ½, 1, 2, 2½, 3 and 8 a. are known without wmk, t being from edges of the sheets.

1897 (5 Jan). *No.* 164 *surch as before, in red.*
175 3 2½ on 4 a. myrtle-green .. .. 55·00
176 4 2½ on 4 a. myrtle-green £190
177 5 2½ on 4 a. myrtle-green .. .. 75·00
175/7 .. .. *Set of* 3 £275

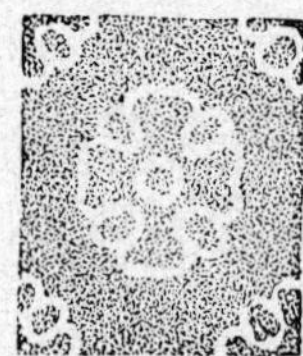
18

1898 (May). *Recess. W* **18**. *P* 14.
178 13 ½ a. yellow-green .. .. .. 1·50
179 1 a. indigo .. .. 2·00
a. Greenish black .. .. .. 4·25
180 2 a. red-brown .. .. .. 3·75
a. Deep brown .. .. .. 4·50
181 2½ a. bright blue .. .. .. 2·25
182 3 a. grey .. .. 5·50
183 4 a. myrtle-green .. .. .. 3·25
184 4½ a. orange .. .. 6·00
a. No right serif to left-hand "4" .. £130 45
b. No fraction bar at right (R. 2/1) £130 45
185 5 a. bistre .. .. 13·00
a. Pale bistre .. .. .. 13·00
186 7½ a. mauve .. .. 6·50
187 8 a. grey-olive .. .. .. 9·50
178/87 .. .. *Set of* 10 45·00 10

19

20 Sultan Seyyid Hamoud-bin-Mohammed bin Said

1899 (June)–**1901**. *Recess. Flags in red. W* **18** (*Nos.* 188/99) *W* **12** (others). *P* 14.
188 19 ½ a. yellow-green .. .. .. 2·00
a. Wmk sideways .. .. .. 10·00
189 1 a. indigo .. .. 4·50
a. Wmk sideways .. .. .. 22·00
190 1 a. carmine (1901) .. .. .. 2·00
191 2 a. red-brown .. .. 2·25
192 2½ a. bright blue .. .. .. 2·25
193 3 a. grey .. .. 2·25
194 4 a. myrtle-green .. .. .. 3·25
195 4½ a. orange .. .. 9·50

9 4½ a. blue-black (1901) .. .. .. 12·00 12·00
5 a. bistre .. .. 3·00 1·25
7½ a. mauve .. .. 3·25 3·75
8 a. grey-olive .. .. 3·25 4·50
20 1 r. blue .. .. 18·00 15·00
2 r. green .. .. 18·00 18·00
3 r. dull purple.. .. .. .. 30·00 35·00
4 r. lake .. .. 45·00 50·00
5 r. sepia .. .. 50·00 60·00
4 .. .. Set of 17 £190 £190
04s Optd "Specimen" .. Set of 17 £200

e

Two & Half (22)

Two & Half (22a) Thin open "w" (R. 2/2, 3/4)

Two & Half (22b) Serif to foot of "f" (R. 3/1)

Nos. 194/6 *and* 198/9 *surch as T* **21** *and* **22**, *in black or* (L.) *by* Zanzibar Gazette *in setting of* 30 (6×5).
19 1 on 4½ a. orange .. .. .. 4·00 4·00
1 on 4½ a. blue-black (L.) .. .. 4·50 18·00
2 on 4 a. myrtle-green (L.) .. .. 14·00 18·00
2½ on 7½ a. mauve .. .. .. 13·00 20·00
a. Opt Type **22***a* .. .. .. 75·00 95·00
b. Opt Type **22***b* £120 £160
c. "Hlaf" for "Half" £11000
2½ on 8 a. grey-olive .. .. . 15·00 29·00
a. Opt Type **22***a* £100 £150
b. Opt Type **22***b* £160 £250
c. "Hlaf" for "Half" £10000 £6000
.. .. Set of 5 45·00 80·00

23 **24**

Monogram of Sultan Seyyid Ali bin Hamoud bin Naherud

(8 June). *Typo. Background of centre in second colour. W* **18**. 14.
23 ½ a. green .. .. 1·25 90
1 a. rose-red .. .. 1·25 10
2 a. brown .. .. 1·50 45
2½ a. blue .. .. 2·50 35
3 a. grey .. .. 2·25 2·25
4 a. deep green .. .. 2·25 1·60
4½ a. black .. .. 3·00 2·50
5 a. yellow-brown .. .. .. 3·25 1·25
7½ a. purple .. .. 4·00 7·00
8 a. olive-green .. .. 3·75 2·75
24 1 r. blue and red .. .. .. 20·00 11·00
a. Wmk sideways .. .. .. 75·00 35·00
2 r. green and red .. .. .. 22·00 35·00
a. Wmk sideways £140 £180
3 r. violet and red .. .. .. 40·00 75·00
4 r. claret and red .. .. .. 45·00 90·00
5 r. olive-brown and red .. .. 48·00 95·00
24 .. .. Set of 15 £180 £275
/24s Optd "Specimen" .. Set of 15 £140

25 **26**

27 Sultan Ali bin Hamoud **28** View of Port

08 (May)–**09.** *Recess. W* **18** (*sideways on* 10 *r. to* 30 *r.*). *P* 14.
5 **25** 1 c. pearl-grey (10.09) .. .. 2·25 30
6 3 c. yellow-green .. .. .. 4·00 10
a. Wmk sideways .. .. .. 4·00 1·25
7 6 c. rose-carmine .. .. .. 8·00 10
a. Wmk sideways .. .. .. 8·00 2·25
8 10 c. brown (10.09) .. .. .. 2·25 2·00
9 12 c. violet .. .. 11·00 2·50
a. Wmk sideways .. .. .. 10·00 1·25
0 **26** 15 c. ultramarine .. .. .. 9·00 40
a. Wmk sideways .. .. .. 9·00 5·50
1 25 c. sepia .. .. 3·25 1·00
2 50 c. blue-green .. .. .. 5·00 3·75
3 75 c. grey-black (10.09) .. .. 9·00 12·00
4 **27** 1 r. yellow-green .. .. .. 24·00 12·00
a. Wmk sideways .. .. .. 50·00 9·00
5 2 r. violet .. .. 18·00 14·00
a. Wmk sideways .. .. .. £120 60·00
6 3 r. orange-bistre .. .. .. 25·00 48·00
7 4 r. vermilion .. .. .. 45·00 75·00
8 5 r. steel-blue .. .. .. 40·00 55·00

239 **28** 10 r. blue-green and brown £110 £225
s. Optd "Specimen" .. .. 32·00
240 20 r. black and yellow-green £225 £425
s. Optd "Specimen" .. .. 40·00
241 30 r. black and sepia £275 £550
s. Optd "Specimen" .. .. 50·00
242 40 r. black and orange-brown £425
s. Optd "Specimen" .. .. 60·00
243 50 r. black and mauve £375
s. Optd "Specimen" .. .. 70·00
244 100 r. black and steel-blue £650
s. Optd "Specimen" £110
245 200 r. brown and greenish black .. £1000
s. Optd "Specimen" £160
225/38 .. .. Set of 14 £180 £200
225s/38s Optd "Specimen" .. Set of 14 £170

29 Sultan Kalif bin Harub **30** Sailing Canoe

31 Dhow

1913. *Recess. W* **18** (*sideways on* 75 *c. and* 10 *r. to* 200 *r.*). *P* 14.
246 **29** 1 c. grey 40 20
247 3 c. yellow-green 50 20
248 6 c. rose-carmine .. .. .. 1·50 20
249 10 c. brown .. .. 1·10 1·75
250 12 c. violet .. .. 1·00 20
251 15 c. blue .. .. 1·25 30
252 25 c. sepia .. .. 1·00 75
253 50 c. blue-green .. .. .. 2·00 3·50
254 75 c. grey-black .. .. .. 2·00 2·75
a. Wmk upright £150
255 **30** 1 r. yellow-green .. .. .. 6·00 8·00
256 2 r. violet .. .. 11·00 22·00
257 3 r. orange-bistre .. .. .. 12·00 35·00
258 4 r. scarlet .. .. 25·00 60·00
259 5 r. steel-blue .. .. .. 32·00 35·00
260 **31** 10 r. green and brown .. .. 95·00 £170
260*b* 20 r. black and green £140 £300
bs. Optd "Specimen" .. .. 32·00
260*c* 30 r. black and brown £150 £375
cs. Optd "Specimen" .. .. 42·00
260*d* 40 r. black and vermilion £325 £500
ds. Optd "Specimen" .. .. 60·00
260*e* 50 r. black and purple £300 £500
es. Optd "Specimen" .. .. 65·00
260*f* 100 r. black and blue £375
fs. Optd "Specimen" .. .. 90·00
260*g* 200 r. brown and black £650
gs. Optd "Specimen" £120
246/60 .. .. Set of 15 £170 £300
246s/60as Optd "Specimen" .. Set of 15 £180

1914–22. *Wmk Mult Crown CA* (*sideways on* 10 *r.*). *P* 14.
261 **29** 1 c. grey 80 25
262 3 c. yellow-green .. .. .. 1·25 10
a. Dull green .. .. .. 4·00 15
263 6 c. deep carmine 85 10
a. Bright rose-carmine 85 10
aw. Wmk inverted .. .. .. † 95·00
264 8 c. purple/*pale yellow* (1922) .. 75 3·25
265 10 c. myrtle/*pale yellow* (1922) .. 75 30
266 15 c. deep ultramarine .. .. 1·10 4·50
268 50 c. blue-green .. .. .. 4·50 4·00
269 75 c. grey-black .. .. .. 3·00 20·00
270 **30** 1 r. yellow-green .. .. .. 4·00 3·50
271 2 r. violet .. .. 5·00 8·00
272 3 r. orange-bistre .. .. .. 16·00 29·00
273 4 r. scarlet .. .. 16·00 85·00
y. Wmk inverted and reversed .. 95·00
274 5 r. steel-blue .. .. .. 16·00 65·00
w. Wmk inverted .. .. .. 95·00
275 **31** 10 r. green and brown .. .. 95·00 £350
261/75 .. .. Set of 14 £150 £500
261s/75s Optd "Specimen" .. Set of 14 £190

1921–29. *Wmk Mult Script CA* (*sideways on* 10 *r. to* 30 *r.*). *P* 14.
276 **29** 1 c. slate-grey .. .. .. 20 7·00
277 3 c. yellow-green .. .. .. 50 3·25
278 3 c. yellow (1922) 30 10
w. Wmk inverted .. .. ..
279 4 c. green (1922) 50 60
280 6 c. carmine-red 30 50
281 6 c. purple/*blue* (1922) 35 10
w. Wmk inverted .. .. .. † £160
282 10 c. brown .. .. 70 8·00
283 12 c. violet 40 30
w. Wmk inverted .. .. ..
284 12 c. carmine-red (1922) 40 40
285 15 c. blue .. .. 55 8·00
286 20 c. indigo (1922) .. .. .. 1·00 30
287 25 c. sepia .. .. 75 9·50
288 50 c. myrtle-green .. .. .. 1·25 3·75
y. Wmk inverted and reversed .. 95·00
289 75 c. slate .. .. 2·50 48·00
290 **30** 1 r. yellow-green .. .. .. 4·25 3·50
291 2 r. deep violet .. .. .. 3·25 7·50
292 3 r. orange-bistre .. .. .. 4·25 7·50
293 4 r. scarlet .. .. 12·00 35·00

294 **30** 5 r. Prussian blue .. .. .. 19·00 65·00
w. Wmk inverted £140
295 **31** 10 r. green and brown .. .. .. 85·00 £225
296 20 r. black and green £170 £375
s. Optd "Specimen" .. .. 70·00
297 30 r. black and brown (1929) £170 £475
s. Perf "Specimen" .. .. 80·00
276/95 .. .. Set of 20 £120 £375
276s/95s Optd "Specimen" .. Set of 20 £250

32 Sultan Kalif bin Harub **33**

1926–27. *T* **32** ("CENTS" *in serifed capitals*). *Recess. Wmk Mult Script CA. P* 14.
299 **32** 1 c. brown 50 10
300 3 c. yellow-orange 20 15
301 4 c. deep dull green 20 30
302 6 c. violet 20 10
303 8 c. slate .. .. 1·00 4·50
304 10 c. olive-green .. .. .. 1·00 40
305 12 c. carmine-red .. .. .. 1·50 10
306 20 c. bright blue 50 30
307 25 c. purple/*yellow* (1927) .. .. 4·00 2·50
308 50 c. claret .. .. 1·75 35
309 75 c. sepia (1927) .. .. .. 16·00 19·00
299/309 .. .. Set of 11 24·00 25·00
299s/309s Optd "Specimen" .. Set of 11 £120

(New Currency. 100 cents = 1 shilling)

1936 (1 Jan). *T* **33** ("CENTS" *in sans-serif capitals*), *and T* **30/1**, *but values in shillings. Recess. Wmk Mult Script CA. P* 14×13½–14.
310 **33** 5 c. green 10 10
311 10 c. black 10 10
312 15 c. carmine-red .. .. .. 10 1·00
313 20 c. orange 10 10
314 25 c. purple/*yellow* 10 10
315 30 c. ultramarine 10 10
316 40 c. sepia 15 10
317 50 c. claret 30 10
318 **30** 1 s. yellow-green 50 10
319 2 s. slate-violet .. .. .. 75 1·25
320 5 s. scarlet .. .. 9·00 6·00
321 7 s. 50, light blue .. .. .. 20·00 23·00
322 **31** 10 s. green and brown .. .. 21·00 21·00
310/22 .. .. Set of 13 45·00 48·00
310s/22s Perf "Specimen" .. Set of 13 £130

36 Sultan Kalif bin Harub

1936 (9 Dec). *Silver Jubilee of Sultan. Recess. Wmk Mult Script CA. P* 14.
323 **36** 10 c. black and olive-green .. .. 1·00 30
324 20 c. black and bright purple .. .. 3·00 50
325 30 c. black and deep ultramarine .. 7·00 35
326 50 c. black and orange-vermilion .. 7·50 3·00
323/6 .. .. Set of 4 17·00 3·75
323s/6s Perf "Specimen" .. .. Set of 4 70·00

37 *Sham Alam* (Sultan's dhow)

VICTORY ISSUE 8TH JUNE 1946 (**38**)

1944 (20 Nov). *Bicentenary of Al Busaid Dynasty. Recess. Wmk Mult Script CA. P* 14.
327 **37** 10 c. ultramarine .. .. .. 60 2·00
a. "C" of "CA" missing from wmk .. £400
328 20 c. red .. .. 60 2·75
a. "C" of "CA" missing from wmk .. £400
329 50 c. blue-green 60 30
330 1 s. dull purple 60 50
a. "A" of "CA" missing from wmk ..
327/30 .. .. Set of 4 2·25 5·00
327s/30s Perf "Specimen" .. Set of 4 70·00

1946 (11 Nov). *Victory. Nos.* 311 *and* 315 *optd with T* **38**.
331 **33** 10 c. black (R.) 20 30
332 30 c. ultramarine (R.) 20 40
331s/2s Perf "Specimen" .. Set of 2 45·00

1949 (10 Jan). *Royal Silver Wedding. As Nos.* 112/13 *of Antigua*.
333 20 c. orange .. .. 30 1·50
334 10 s. brown .. .. 17·00 28·00

1949 (10 Oct). *75th Anniv of U.P.U. As Nos. 114/17 of Antigua.*

No.	Description	Unused	Used
335	20 c. red-orange	30	2·50
336	30 c. deep blue	1·40	80
	a. "C" of "CA" missing from wmk	£750	
337	50 c. magenta	1·00	2·25
338	1 s. blue-green	1·00	3·75
335/8	*Set of* 4	3·25	8·50

POSTAGE DUE STAMPS

Insufficiently prepaid.
Postage due.
1 cent.

D 1

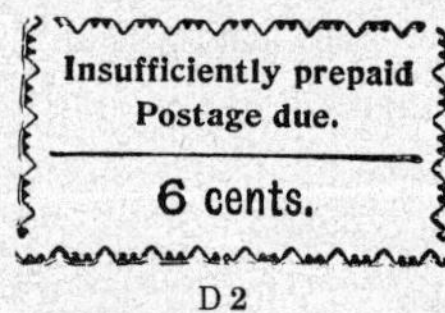

D 2

(Types D 1 and D 2 typo by the Government Printer)

1926–30. *Rouletted 10, with imperf sheet edges. No gum.*

No.	Type	Description	Unused	Used
D 1	D 1	1 c. black/*orange*	11·00	95·00
D 2		2 c. black/*orange*	4·50	48·00
D 3		3 c. black/*orange*	5·00	40·00
		a. "cent.s" for "cents."	£110	
D 4		6 c. black/*orange*	—	£7000
		a. "cent.s" for "cents."	—	£16000
D 5		9 c. black/*orange*	2·75	20·00
		a. "cent.s" for "cents."	20·00	75·00
D 6		12 c. black/*orange*	£9000	£8500
		a. "cent.s" for "cents."		
D 7		12 c. black/*green*	£1400	£600
		a. "cent.s" for "cents."	£3750	£1700
D 8		15 c. black/*orange*	2·75	22·00
		a. "cent.s" for "cents."	19·00	80·00
D 9		18 c. black/*salmon*	4·25	38·00
		a. "cent.s" for "cents."	35·00	£110
D10		18 c. black/*orange*	15·00	60·00
		a. "cent.s" for "cents."	60·00	£170
D11		20 c. black/*orange*	4·00	50·00
		a. "cent.s" for "cents."	38·00	£150
D12		21 c. black/*orange*	3·50	29·00
		a. "cent.s" for "cents."	30·00	£100
D13		25 c. black/*magenta*	£2750	£1300
		a. "cent.s" for "cents."	£6500	£3750
D14		25 c. black/*orange*	£10000	£10000
D15		31 c. black/*orange*	9·50	70·00
		a. "cent.s" for "cents."	50·00	
D16		50 c. black/*orange*	21·00	£140
		a. "cent.s" for "cents."	95·00	
D17		75 c. black/*orange*	65·00	£300
		a. "cent.s" for "cents."	£250	

Initial printings, except the 1 c. and 2 c., contained the error "cent.s" for "cents" on R. 4/1 in the sheets of 10 (2×5). The error was corrected on subsequent supplies of the 3 c., 9 c. and 15 c.

It is known that examples of these stamps used before early 1929 were left uncancelled on the covers. Unused examples of Nos. D4, D6/7 and D13/14 which are not in very fine condition, must be assumed to have been used.

1930–33. *Rouletted 5. No gum.*

No.	Type	Description	Unused	Used
D18	D 2	2 c. black/*salmon*	13·00	27·00
D19		3 c. black/*rose*	3·00	45·00
D21		6 c. black/*yellow*	3·00	30·00
D22		12 c. black/*blue*	4·00	24·00
D23		25 c. black/*rose*	9·00	65·00
D24		25 c. black/*lilac*	12·00	45·00
D18/24		*Set of* 6	40·00	£200

D 3

(Typo D.L.R.)

1936 (1 Jan)–**62**. *Wmk Mult Script CA. P* 14.

No.	Type	Description	Unused	Used
D25	D 3	5 c. violet	3·50	8·00
		a. Chalk-surfaced paper (18.7.56)	30	14·00
D26		10 c. scarlet	2·75	2·75
		a. Chalk-surfaced paper (6.3.62)	30	6·50
D27		20 c. green	2·00	4·25
		a. Chalk-surfaced paper (6.3.62)	30	15·00
D28		30 c. brown	6·50	17·00
		a. Chalk-surfaced paper (18.7.56)	30	12·00
D29		40 c. ultramarine	7·00	24·00
		a. Chalk-surfaced paper (18.7.56)	40	26·00
D30		1 s. grey	7·00	28·00
		a. Chalk-surfaced paper (18.7.56)	1·00	19·00
D25/30		*Set of* 6	26·00	75·00
D25a/30a		*Set of* 6	2·40	80·00
D25s/30s Perf "Specimen"		*Set of* 6	60·00	

See footnote after No. 413.

Zululand
see South Africa

Set Prices for British
mpire Omnibus Issues

composition of these sets is in accordance with the tables on
llowing pages. Only such items considered basic stamps are
ed; varieties such as shades, perforation changes and
nark changes are excluded.

1935 SILVER JUBILEE

Silver Jubilee. *Complete set of 250 stamps*	*Price Un* £900	*Used* £1200
try	*Catalogue Nos.*	*Stamps*
t Britain	453/6	4
gua	91/4	4
nsion	31/4	4
ralia	156/8	3
uru	40/3	4
w Guinea	206/7	2
pua	150/3	4
mas	141/4	4
ados	241/4	4
toland	11/14	4
uanaland	111/14	4
nuda	94/7	4
sh Guiana	301/4	4
sh Honduras	143/6	4
sh Solomon Islands	53/6	4
ada	335/40	6
ewfoundland	250/3	4
nan Islands	108/11	4
on	379/82	4
us	144/7	4
inica	92/5	4
ot–British Forces	A10	1
land Islands	139/42	4
	242/5	4
bia	143/6	4
altar	114/17	4
ert and Ellice Islands	36/9	4
l Coast	113/16	4
nada	145/8	4
g Kong	133/6	4
a	240/6	7
aica	114/17	4
ya, Uganda and Tanganyika	124/7	4
ward Islands	88/91	4
aya—Straits Settlements	256/9	4
a	210/13	4
ritius	245/8	4
tserrat	94/7	4
occo Agencies		
ritish Currency	62/5	4
panish Currency	149/52	4
rench Currency	212/15	4
angier	238/40	3
Zealand	573/5	3
ook Islands	113/15	3
iue	69/71	3
Vestern Samoa	177/9	3
eria	30/3	4
thern Rhodesia	18/21	4
saland	123/6	4
Helena	124/7	4
Kitts-Nevis	61/4	4
Lucia	109/12	4
Vincent	142/5	4
chelles	128/31	4
ra Leone	181/4	4
naliland Protectorate	86/9	4
th Africa	65/8	4×2
thern Rhodesia	31/4	4
th West Africa	88/91	4
aziland	21/4	4
nidad and Tobago	239/42	4
ks and Caicos Islands	187/9	4
gin Islands	103/6	4
al		250

The concept initiated by the 1935 Silver Jubilee omnibus issue s provided a pattern for a series of Royal commemoratives over e past 50 years which have introduced countless collectors to the bby.

The Crown Colony Windsor Castle design by Harold Fleury is, ely, one of the most impressive produced in the 20th-century d its reproduction in the recess process by three of the leading mp-printing firms of the era has provided a subject for philatelic earch which has yet to be exhausted.

Each of the three, Bradbury, Wilkinson & Co. and Waterlow d Sons, who both produced fifteen issues, together with De La e & Co. who printed fourteen, used a series of vignette (centre) ates coupled with individual frame plates for each value. All were ken from dies made by Waterlow. Several worthwhile varieties ist on the frame plates, but most interest has been concentrated the centre plates, each of which was used to print a considerable mber of different stamps.

Sheets printed by Bradbury, Wilkinson were without printed ate numbers, but research has now identified eleven centre plates ich were probably used in permanent pairings. A twelfth plate aits confirmation. Stamps from some of these centre plates have vealed a number of prominent plate flaws, the most famous of ich, the extra flagstaff, has been eagerly sought by collectors for any years.

Extra flagstaff (Plate "1" R.9/1)

Short extra flagstaff (Plate "2" R.2/1)

Lightning conductor (Plate "3" R.2/5)

Flagstaff on right-hand turret (Plate "5" R.7/1)

Double flagstaff (Plate "6" R.5/2)

De La Rue sheets were initially printed with plate numbers, but in many instances these were subsequently trimmed off. Surviving examples do, however, enable a positive identification of six centre plates, 2A, 2B, (2A), (2B), 4 and 4/ to be made. The evidence of sheet markings and plate flaws clearly demonstrates that there were two different pairs of plates numbered 2A 2B. The second pair is designated (2A) (2B) by specialist collectors to avoid further confusion. The number of major plate flaws is not so great as on the Bradbury, Wilkinson sheets, but four examples are included in the catalogue.

Diagonal line by turret (Plate 2A R.10/1 and 10/2)

Dot to left of chapel (Plate 2B R.8/3)

Dot by flagstaff (Plate 4 R.8/4)

Dash by turret (Plate 4/ R.3/6)

Much less is known concerning the Waterlow centre plate system as the sheets did not show plate numbers. Ten individual plates have, so far, been identified and it is believed that these were used in pairs. The two versions of the kite and log flaw from plate "2" show that this plate exists in two states.

Damaged turret (Plate "1" R.5/6)

Kite and vertical log (Plate "2A" R.10/6)

Kite and horizontal log (Plate "2B" R.10/6)

Bird by turret (Plate "7" R.1/5)

1937 CORONATION

1937. Coronation. *Complete set of 202 stamps*	£110	£130
Country	*Catalogue Nos.*	*Stamps*
Great Britain	461	1
Aden	13/15	3
Antigua	95/7	3
Ascension	35/7	3
Australia		
Nauru	44/7	4
New Guinea	208/11	4
Papua	154/7	4
Bahamas	146/8	3
Barbados	245/7	3
Basutoland	15/17	3
Bechuanaland	115/17	3
Bermuda	107/9	3
British Guiana	305/7	3
British Honduras	147/9	3
British Solomon Islands	57/9	3
Canada	356	1
Newfoundland	254/6, 257/67	14
Cayman Islands	112/14	3
Ceylon	383/5	3
Cyprus	148/50	3
Dominica	96/8	3
Falkland Islands	143/5	3
Fiji	246/8	3
Gambia	147/9	3
Gibraltar	118/20	3
Gilbert and Ellice Islands	40/2	3
Gold Coast	117/19	3
Grenada	149/51	3
Hong Kong	137/9	3
Jamaica	118/20	3
Kenya, Uganda and Tanganyika	128/30	3
Leeward Islands	92/4	3
Malaya—Straits Settlements	275/7	3
Malta	214/16	3
Mauritius	249/51	3
Montserrat	98/100	3
Morocco Agencies		
Spanish Currency	164	1
French Currency	229	1
Tangier	244	1
New Zealand	599/601	3
Cook Islands	124/6	3
Niue	72/4	3
Nigeria	46/8	3
Northern Rhodesia	22/4	3
Nyasaland	127/9	3
St. Helena	128/30	3
St. Kitts-Nevis	65/7	3
St. Lucia	125/7	3
St. Vincent	146/8	3
Seychelles	132/4	3
Sierra Leone	185/7	3
Somaliland Protectorate	90/2	3
South Africa	71/5	5×2
Southern Rhodesia	36/9	4

Country	*Catalogue Nos.*	*Stamps*
South West Africa	97/104	8×2
Swaziland	25/7	3
Trinidad and Tobago	243/5	3
Turks and Caicos Islands	191/3	3
Virgin Islands	107/9	3
Total		202

1945–46 VICTORY

1945–46. Victory. *Complete set of* 164 *stamps* 30·00 30·00

Country	*Catalogue Nos.*	*Stamps*
Great Britain	491/2	2
Aden	28/9	2
Seiyun	12/13	2
Shihr and Mukalla	12/13	2
Antigua	110/11	2
Ascension	48/9	2
Australia	213/15	3
Bahamas	176/7	2
Barbados	262/3	2
Basutoland	29/31	3×2
Bechuanaland	129/31	3×2
Bermuda	123/4	2
British Guiana	320/1	2
British Honduras	162/3	2
British Solomon Islands	73/4	2
Burma	64/7	4
Cayman Islands	127/8	2
Ceylon	400/1	2
Cyprus	164/5	2
Dominica	110/11	2
Falkland Islands	164/5	2
Falkland Islands Dependencies	G17/18	2
Fiji	268/9	2
Gambia	162/3	2
Gibraltar	132/3	2
Gilbert and Ellice Islands	55/6	2
Gold Coast	133/4	2
Grenada	164/5	2
Hong Kong	169/70	2
India	278/81	4
Hyderabad	53	1
Jamaica	141/2	2
Kenya, Uganda and Tanganyika	155/6	2
Leeward Islands	115/16	2
Malta	232/3	2
Mauritius	264/5	2
Montserrat	113/14	2
Morocco Agencies		
Tangier	253/4	2
New Zealand	667/77	11
Cook Islands	146/9	4
Niue	98/101	4
Western Samoa	215/18	4
Nigeria	60/1	2
Northern Rhodesia	46/7	2
Nyasaland	158/9	2
Pakistan		
Bahawalpur	O19	1
Pitcairn Islands	9/10	2
St. Helena	141/2	2
St. Kitts-Nevis	78/9	2
St. Lucia	142/3	2
St. Vincent	160/1	2
Seychelles	150/1	2
Sierra Leone	201/2	2
Somaliland Protectorate	117/18	2
South Africa	108/10	3×2
Southern Rhodesia	64/7	4
South West Africa	131/3	3×2
Swaziland	39/41	3×2
Trinidad and Tobago	257/8	2
Turks and Caicos Islands	206/7	2
Virgin Islands	122/3	2
Zanzibar	331/2	2
Total		164

1948 ROYAL SILVER WEDDING

1948–49. Royal Silver Wedding. *Complete set of* 138 *stamps* £1600 £1600

Country	*Catalogue Nos.*	*Stamps*
Great Britain	493/4	2
Aden	30/1	2
Seiyun	14/15	2
Shihr and Mukalla	14/15	2
Antigua	112/13	2
Ascension	50/1	2
Bahamas	194/5	2
Bahrain	61/2	2
Barbados	265/6	2
Basutoland	36/7	2
Bechuanaland	136/7	2
Bermuda	125/6	2
British Guiana	322/3	2
British Honduras	164/5	2
British Postal Agencies in		
Eastern Arabia	25/6	2
British Solomon Islands	75/6	2
Cayman Islands	129/30	2
Cyprus	166/7	2
Dominica	112/13	2
Falkland Islands	166/7	2
Falkland Islands Dependencies	G19/20	2
Fiji	270/1	2
Gambia	164/5	2
Gibraltar	134/5	2
Gilbert and Ellice Islands	57/8	2
Gold Coast	147/8	2
Grenada	166/7	2
Hong Kong	171/2	2
Jamaica	143/4	2
Kenya, Uganda and Tanganyika	157/8	2
Kuwait	74/5	2
Leeward Islands	117/18	2
Malaya		
Johore	131/2	2
Kedah	70/1	2
Kelantan	55/6	2
Malacca	1/2	2
Negri Sembilan	40/1	2
Pahang	47/8	2
Penang	1/2	2
Perak	122/3	2
Perlis	1/2	2
Selangor	88/9	2
Trengganu	61/2	2
Malta	249/50	2
Mauritius	270/1	2
Montserrat	115/16	2
Morocco Agencies		
Spanish Currency	176/7	2
Tangier	255/6	2
Nigeria	62/3	2
North Borneo	350/1	2
Northern Rhodesia	48/9	2
Nyasaland	161/2	2
Pitcairn Islands	11/12	2
St. Helena	143/4	2
St. Kitts-Nevis	80/1	2
St. Lucia	144/5	2
St. Vincent	162/3	2
Sarawak	165/6	2
Seychelles	152/3	2
Sierra Leone	203/4	2
Singapore	31/2	2
Somaliland Protectorate	119/20	2
South Africa	125	1×2
South West Africa	137	1×2
Swaziland	46/7	2
Trinidad and Tobago	259/60	2
Turks and Caicos Islands	208/9	2
Virgin Islands	124/5	2
Zanzibar	333/4	2
Total		138

1949 75th ANNIVERSARY OF U.P.U.

1949. U.P.U. 75th Anniversary *Complete set of* 310 *stamps* £275 £325

Country	*Catalogue Nos.*	*Stamps*
Great Britain	449/502	4
Aden	32/5	4
Seiyun	16/19	4
Shihr and Mukalla	16/19	4
Antigua	114/17	4
Ascension	52/5	4
Australia	232	1
Bahamas	196/9	4
Bahrain	67/70	4
Barbados	267/70	4
Basutoland	38/41	4
Bechuanaland	138/41	4
Bermuda	130/3	4
British Guiana	324/7	4
British Honduras	172/5	4
British Postal Agencies in		
Eastern Arabia	31/4	4
British Solomon Islands	77/80	4
Brunei	96/9	4
Cayman Islands	131/4	4
Ceylon	410/12	3
Cyprus	168/71	4
Dominica	114/17	4
Falkland Islands	168/71	4
Falkland Islands Dependencies	G21/4	4
Fiji	272/5	4
Gambia	166/9	4
Gibraltar	136/9	4
Gilbert and Ellice Islands	59/62	4
Gold Coast	149/52	4
Grenada	168/71	4
Hong Kong	173/6	
India	325/8	
Jamaica	145/8	
Kenya, Uganda and Tanganyika	159/62	
Kuwait	80/3	
Leeward Islands	119/22	
Malaya		
Johore	148/51	
Kedah	72/5	
Kelantan	57/60	
Malacca	18/21	
Negri Sembilan	63/6	
Pahang	49/52	
Penang	23/6	
Perak	124/7	
Perlis	3/6	
Selangor	111/14	
Trengganu	63/6	
Malta	251/4	
Mauritius	272/5	
Montserrat	117/20	
Morocco Agencies		
Tangier	276/9	
New Hebrides	64/7, F77/80	
Nigeria	64/7	
North Borneo	352/5	
Northern Rhodesia	50/3	
Nyasaland	163/6	
Pakistan		
Bahawalpur	43/6, O28/31	
Pitcairn Islands	13/16	
St. Helena	145/8	
St. Kitts-Nevis	82/5	
St. Lucia	160/3	
St. Vincent	178/81	
Sarawak	167/70	
Seychelles	154/7	
Sierra Leone	205/8	
Singapore	33/6	
Somaliland Protectorate	121/4	
South Africa	128/30	
Southern Rhodesia	68/9	
South West Africa	138/40	
Swaziland	48/51	
Tonga	88/91	
Trinidad and Tobago	261/4	
Turks and Caicos Islands	217/20	
Virgin Islands	126/9	
Zanzibar	335/8	
Total		

1951 INAUGURATION OF B.W.I. UNIVERSITY COLLEG

1951. B.W.I. University College *Complete set of* 28 *stamps* 10·00 1

Country	*Catalogue Nos.*	*Sta*
Antigua	118/19	
Barbados	283/4	
British Guiana	328/9	
British Honduras	176/7	
Dominica	118/19	
Grenada	185/6	
Jamaica	149/50	
Leeward Islands	123/4	
Montserrat	121/2	
St. Kitts-Nevis	92/3	
St. Lucia	164/5	
St. Vincent	182/3	
Trinidad and Tobago	265/6	
Virgin Islands	130/1	
Total		

Index

INDEX

Notes